Chilton's truck and van repair manual

from 1970 to 1976
gasoline and diesel engines

President	William A. Barbour
Executive Vice President	K. Robert Brink
Vice President & General Manager	William D. Byrne
Editorial Director	John D. Kelly
Managing Editor	John H. Weise, S.A.E.
Editorial Staff	Arthur I. Birney
	Stephen Davis
	Kerry Freeman
	Martin J. Gunther
	Martin W. Kane
	Peter Meyer
	Richard J. Rivele
Editorial Production	Dru Brown
	Donna Hoffman
	Milton Fox
Technical Consultants	Stan Stephenson
	Richard T. Moritz
	Edward K. Shea
Production Manager	Warren Owens
Assistant	Timothy Frelick

CHILTON BOOK COMPANY Chilton Way, Radnor, Pa. 19089

Copyright ©1976 by Chilton Book Company   All Rights Reserved
Published in Radnor, Pa. by Chilton Book Company and
simultaneously in Ontario, Canada by Thomas Nelson & Sons, Ltd.
ISBN 0-8019-6425-3 Library of Congress Catalog Card Number 75-42766
Manufactured in the United States of America

Contents

GENERAL REPAIR SECTIONS

TRANSMISSION SECTIONS

Index

TUNE-UP SPECIFICATIONS

CU. IN. DISPLACE-MENT (cu. in.)	YEAR	SPARK PLUG GAP (in.)	DISTRIBUTOR POINT DWELL (deg.)	POINT GAP (in.)	IGNITION TIMING (DEGREES)	CRANKCASE COMP. PRESSURE	VALVE CLEARANCE Int. Lot Exh.	GOV. RPM NO LOAD (rpm)	PUMP FUEL PRESS (psi)	IDLE SPEED* (rpm) STD.	AUTO.
SIX CYLINDER											
250	1970	0.035	31-34	0.019	TDC①	130	Hyd.		3.5-4.5	750⑥	600⑦
	1971	0.035	31-34	0.019	4B	130	Hyd.		3.5-4.5	550	500
	1972	0.035	31-34	0.019	4B②	130	Hyd.		3.5-4.5	700	600
	1973	0.035	31-34	0.019	6B③	130	Hyd.		3.5-4.5	700	600④
	1974	0.035	31-34	0.019	8B⑩	130	Hyd.		3.5-4.5	850⑤	600
	1975	0.060	Elec.	Elec.	10B	130	Hyd.		3.5-4.5	900N	550DR
	1976	0.060	Elec.	Elec.	10B	130	Hyd.		3.5-4.5	900N	550DR
292	1970	0.035	31-34	0.019	TDC①	130	Hyd.		3.5-4.5	750⑥	600⑦
	1971	0.035	31-34	0.019	4B	130	Hyd.		3.5-4.5	550	500
	1972	0.035	31-34	0.019	4B	130	Hyd.		3.5-4.5	700	700
	1973	0.035	31-34	0.019	4B⑧	130	Hyd.		3.5-4.5	700⑨	700⑨
	1974	0.035	31-34	0.019	8B	130	Hyd.		3.5-4.5	700	700
	1975	0.060	Elec.	Elec.	8B	130	Hyd.		3.5-4.5	600	600
	1976	0.060	Elec.	Elec.	8B	130	Hyd.		3.5-4.5	600	600
305C (V6)	1973	0.040	31-34	0.019	7-½B	125	0.012-0.018	3600	5.0-7.0	550	550
	1974	0.035	31-34	0.019	7-½B	125	0.012-0.018	3600	5.0-7.0	600	600
379 (V6)	1973	0.035	31-34	0.019	8B	125	0.012-0.018	4000	5.0-7.0	550	550
	1974	0.035	31-34	0.019	6B	125	0.012-0.018	4000	5.0-7.0	575	575
432 (V6)	1973	0.035	31-34	0.019	8B	125			5.0-7.0	525	525
	1974	0.035	31-34	0.019	6B	125	0.012-0.018	3200	5.0-7.0	525	525
EIGHT CYLINDER											
307	1970	0.035	28-32	0.019	2B⑪	150	Hyd.		5.0-6.5	700	600
	1971 (200hp)	0.035	28-32	0.019	4B⑫	150	Hyd.		5.0-6.5	600	550
	1971 (215hp)	0.035	28-32	0.019	4B	150	Hyd.		5.0-6.5	550	500
	1972	0.035	28-32	0.019	4B⑬	150	Hyd.		5.0-6.5	900⑭	600
	1973	0.035	29-31	0.019	4B⑮	150	Hyd.		5.0-6.5	900⑯	600
350	1970 (215hp)	0.035	28-32	0.019	4B	150	Hyd.		5.0-6.5	500	500
	1970 (250hp)	0.035	28-32	0.019	TDC⑰	150	Hyd.		5.0-6.5	600⑱	500⑲
	1971	0.035	28-32	0.019	4B⑳	150	Hyd.		5.0-6.5	600	550
	1972	0.035	29-31	0.019	4B⑳	150	Hyd.		5.0-6.5	750	600
	1973	0.035	29-31	0.019	㉑	150	Hyd.		5.0-6.5	900㉒	600㉒
	1974	0.035	29-31	0.019	㉓	150	Hyd.		5.0-6.5	900㉔	600㉔
	1975 (2bbl)	0.060	Elec.	Elec.	6B	150	Hyd.		5.0-6.5	——	600
	1975	0.060	Elec.	Elec.	6B㉖	150	Hyd.		5.0-6.5	800㉗	600㉗
	1976	0.060	Elec.	Elec.	6B	150	Hyd.		5.0-6.5	800	600
366	1970	0.035	28-32	0.019	6B	150	Hyd.		5.0-6.5	500	500
	1971	0.035	28-32	0.019	8B	150	Hyd.		5.0-6.5	500	500
	1972	0.035	28-32	0.019	8B	150	Hyd.		5.0-6.5	550	550
	1973	0.035	28-32	0.019	8B	150	Hyd.		5.0-6.5	550㉕	550㉕
	1974	0.035	28-32	0.019	8B	150	Hyd.		5.0-6.5	600	600
	1975 (Fed.)	0.035	28-32	0.019	8B	150	Hyd.		5.0-6.5	700	700
	1975 (w/AT-475)	0.035	28-32	0.019	8B	150	Hyd.	3600	5.0-6.5	700	700
	1975-76 (Calif.)	0.060	Elec.	Elec.	8B	150	Hyd.		5.0-6.5	700	700
400	1975-76 (fed.)	0.060	Elec.	Elec.	4B	150	Hyd.		5.0-6.5	700	700
	1975-76 (Calif.)	0.060	Elec.	Elec.	2B	150	Hyd.		5.0-6.5	700	700
396	1970	0.035	28-32	0.019	4B	150	Hyd.		7.0-8.5	700	600

TUNE-UP SPECIFICATIONS

CU. IN. DISPLACE-MENT (cu. in.)	YEAR	SPARK PLUG GAP (in.)	DISTRIBUTOR POINT DWELL (deg.)	POINT GAP (in.)	IGNITION TIMING (DEGREES)	CRANKCASE COMP. PRESSURE	VALVE CLEARANCE Int. Lot Exh.	GOV. RPM NO LOAD (rpm)	PUMP FUEL PRESS (psi)	IDLE SPEED* (rpm) STD.	AUTO.
402	1971	0.035	28-32	0.019	8B	150	Hyd.		7.0-8.5	600	600
	1972	0.035	28-32	0.019	8B	150	Hyd.		7.0-8.5	750	600
427	1970	0.035	28-32	0.019	6B	150	Hyd.		7.0-8.5	500	500
	1971	0.035	28-32	0.019	8B	150	Hyd.		7.0-8.5	500	500
	1972	0.035	28-32	0.019	8B	150	Hyd.		7.0-8.5	550	550
	1973	0.035	28-32	0.019	8B	150	Hyd.		7.0-8.5	550㉓	550㉓
	1974	0.035	28-32	0.019	8B	150	Hyd.		7.0-8.5	600	600
	1975-76 (Calif.)	0.060	Elec.	Elec.	8B	150	Hyd.		7.0-8.5	700	700
	1975-76 (Fed.)	0.035	28-32	0.019	8B	150	Hyd.		7.0-8.5	700	700
454	1973 (Fed.)	0.035	28-32	0.019	10B	150	Hyd.		7.0-8.5	900④	600④
	1973 (Calif.)	0.035	28-32	0.019	㉘	150	Hyd.		7.0-8.5	900④	600④
	1974	0.035	29-31	0.019	10B㉙	150	Hyd.		7.0-8.5	800④	600④
	1975-76 (Fed.)	0.060	Elec.	Elec.	16B㉙	150	Hyd.		7.0-8.5	——	650④
	1975-76 (Calif.)	0.060	Elec.	Elec.	8B	150	Hyd.		7.0-8.5	600	600

—— Not Applicable
Elec.—Electronic Ignition
Hyd.—Hydraulic valve lifters
N—Neutral
DR—Drive
B—BTDC

①—4B w/automatic transmission
②—TDC on K-20 Suburban California only
③—4B All C-K 20 except Suburban; all C-P 30 series and all G-30 except Sportvan
④—700 rpm All C-K 20 except Suburban; all C-P 30 series and all G-30 except Sportvan
⑤—600 rpm All C-K 20 except Suburban; all C-P 30 series and all G-30 except Sportvan
⑥—600 rpm 20 and 30 series
⑦—550 rpm 20 and 30 series
⑧—8B California
⑨—600 rpm California
⑩—68 All C-K 20 series except Suburban; all C-P 30 series and all G-30 except Sportvan
⑪—8B w/automatic transmission
⑫—8B w/automatic transmission
⑬—8B 10 series w/automatic transmission only
⑭—950 rpm California
⑮—8B All 10 series, C-K 20 Suburban, G-20 & 30 Sportvans w/auto transmission TDC All others
⑯—600 rpm All C-K 20 except Suburban; all C-P 30 series and all G-30 except Sportvan
⑰—4B w/automatic transmission

⑱—700 rpm 20 & 30 series
⑲—600 rpm 20 & 30 series
⑳—8B w/automatic transmission
㉑—C-20 Suburban 2B
All 10 series, K-20 Suburban, G-20, and G-30 Sportvan:
  w/manual transmission 8B
  w/automatic transmission 12B
All others 4B
㉒—All C-K 20 except Suburban; all C-P 30 series and all G-20 & 30 except Sportvan 700 rpm
㉓—Federal except C-K 10 & 20 Suburban and G-20 & 30 Sportvan 8B
Federal C-K 10 & 20 Suburban and G-20 & 30 Sportvan:
  w/automatic transmission 12B
  w/automatic transmission (except Suburban) 8B
  Suburban (w/manual transmission) 6B
California:
  w/automatic transmission 8B
  Suburban (w/manual transmission) 6B
  w/manual transmission 4B
㉔—All C-K 20 except Suburban, all C-P 30 series and all G-20 & 30 except Sportvan 600 rpm
㉕—750 rpm California
㉖—2B California
㉗—700 rpm California
㉘—All 10 series, C-K 20 Suburban, G-20 and G-30 Sportvan 10 B
All C-K 20 except Suburban, all C-P 30 Series and all G-30 except Sportvan:
  w/manual transmission 5B
  w/automatic transmission 8B
㉙—All C-K 20 except Suburban, all C-P 30 series and all G-30 except Sportvan 8B

GENERAL ENGINE SPECIFICATIONS

CU. IN. DISPLACE-MENT (cu. in.)	YEAR	SPARK PLUG GAP (in.)	DISTRIBUTOR POINT DWELL (deg.)	POINT GAP (in.)	IGNITION TIMING (DEGREES)	CRANKCASE COMP. PRESSURE	VALVE CLEARANCE Int. Lot Exh.	GOV. RPM NO LOAD (rpm)	PUMP FUEL PRESS (psi)	IDLE SPEED* (rpm) STD.	AUTO.
				SIX CYLINDER							
250	1970	3.875 x 3.530	1-5-3-6-2-4		155 @ 4200	235 @ 1600	8.5	1V	Hyd.		40-60
	1971	3.875 x 3.53	1-5-3-6-2-4		145 @ 4200	230 @ 1600	8.5	1V	Hyd.		40-60
	1972	3.875 x 3.53	1-5-3-6-2-4		110 @ 3800	185 @ 1600	8.5	1V	Hyd.		40-60
	1973-74	3.875 x 3.53	1-5-3-6-2-4		100 @ 3600	175 @ 2000	8.25	1V	Hyd.		40-60
	1975	3.875 x 3.53	1-5-3-6-2-4		105 @ 3800	185 @ 1200	8.25:1	1V	Hyd.		40-60
	1976 (L.D.)	3.875 x 3.53	1-5-3-6-2-4		105 @ 3800	185 @ 1200	8.25:1	1V	Hyd.		40-60
	1976 (H.D.)	3.875 x 3.53	1-5-3-6-2-4		100 @ 3600	175 @ 1800	8:25:1	1V	Hyd.		40-60
292	1970	3.875 x 4.125	1-5-3-6-2-4		170 @ 4000	275 @ 1600	8.0	1V	Hyd.		40-60
	1971	3.875 x 4.125	1-5-3-6-2-4		165 @ 4000	270 @ 1600	8.0	1V	Hyd.		40-60
	1972	3.875 x 4.125	1-5-3-6-2-4		125 @ 3600	225 @ 2400	8.0	1V	Hyd.		40-60
	1973-74	3.875 x 4.125	1-5-3-6-2-4		120 @ 3600	225 @ 2000	8.0	1V	Hyd.		40-60

Chevrolet Trucks · Vans · Blazer

GENERAL ENGINE SPECIFICATIONS, continued

CU. IN. DISPLACE- MENT	YEAR	BORE AND STROKE	FIRING ORDER	DEVELOPED HORSE POWER @ R.P.M.	DEVELOPED TORQUE @ R.P.M.	COM- PRESSION RATIO	CARBUR- ETOR	VALVE LIFTER TYPE	NORMAL OIL PRESSURE
292	1975	3.87 x 4.12	1-5-3-6-2-4	120 @ 3600	215 @ 2000	8.0:1	1V	Hyd.	40-60
	1976	3.87 x 4.12	1-5-3-6-2-4	120 @ 3600	215 @ 2000	8.0:1	1V	Hyd.	40-60
305C (V6)	1973-74	4.250 x 3.58	1-6-5-4-3-2	148 @ 4000	238 @ 1600	7.5	2V	Mech.	57
379 (V6)	1973-74	3.56 x 3.86	1-6-5-4-3-2	170 @ 3600	280 @ 1600	7.5	2V	Mech.	57
432 (V6)	1973-74	4.875 x 3.86	1-6-5-4-3-2	190 @ 3200	331 @ 1600	7.5	2V	Mech.	60

EIGHT CYLINDER

CU. IN. DISPLACE- MENT	YEAR	BORE AND STROKE	FIRING ORDER	DEVELOPED HORSE POWER @ R.P.M.	DEVELOPED TORQUE @ R.P.M.	COM- PRESSION RATIO	CARBUR- ETOR	VALVE LIFTER TYPE	NORMAL OIL PRESSURE
307	1970	3.875 x 3.25	1-8-4-3-6-5-7-2	200 @ 4600	300 @ 2400	9.0	2V	Hyd.	30-35
	1971	3.875 x 3.25	1-8-4-3-6-5-7-2	200 @ 4600	300 @ 2400	8.5	2V	Hyd.	30
	1971	3.875 x 3.25	1-8-4-3-6-5-7-2	215 @ 4800	305 @ 2800	8.5	2V	Hyd.	30
	1972	3.875 x 3.25	1-8-4-3-6-5-7-2	130 @ 4000	230 @ 2400	8.5	2V	Hyd.	30
	1972	3.875 x 3.25	1-8-4-3-6-5-7-2	135 @ 4000	230 @ 2400	8.5	2V	Hyd.	30
	1973	3.875 x 3.25	1-8-4-3-6-5-7-2	115 @ 3600	205 @ 2000	8.5	2V	Hyd.	30
	1973	3.875 x 3.25	1-8-4-3-6-5-7-2	130 @ 4000	220 @ 2200	8.5	2V	Hyd.	30
350	1970	4.00 x 3.48	1-8-4-3-6-5-7-2	215 @ 4400	320 @ 2400	8.0	2V	Hyd.	30
	1970	4.00 x 3.48	1-8-4-3-6-5-7-2	255 @ 4600	355 @ 3000	9.0	4V	Hyd.	30
	1971	4.00 x 3.48	1-8-4-3-6-5-7-2	215 @ 4000	335 @ 2800	8.0	2V	Hyd.	50-65
	1971	4.00 x 3.48	1-8-4-3-6-5-7-2	245 @ 4800	350 @ 2800	8.5	2V	Hyd.	50-65
	1971	4.00 x 3.48	1-8-4-3-6-5-7-2	250 @ 4600	350 @ 3000	8.5	4V	Hyd.	50-65
	1971	4.00 x 3.48	1-8-4-3-6-5-7-2	255 @ 4600	355 @ 3000	9.0	4V	Hyd.	50-65
	1971	4.00 x 3.48	1-8-4-3-6-5-7-2	270 @ 4800	360 @ 3200	8.5	4V	Hyd.	50-65
	1972	4.00 x 3.48	1-8-4-3-6-5-7-2	155 @ 4000	265 @ 2400	8.0	2V	Hyd.	50-65
	1972	4.00 x 3.48	1-8-4-3-6-5-7-2	165 @ 4000	280 @ 2400	8.5	2V	Hyd.	50-65
	1972	4.00 x 3.48	1-8-4-3-6-5-7-2	175 @ 4000	280 @ 2400	8.5	4V	Hyd.	50-65
	1972	4.00 x 3.48	1-8-4-3-6-5-7-2	175 @ 4000	290 @ 2400	8.5	4V	Hyd.	50-65
	1973	4.00 x 3.48	1-8-4-3-6-5-7-2	145 @ 4000	255 @ 2400	8.5	2V	Hyd.	40
	1973	4.00 x 3.48	1-8-4-3-6-5-7-2	155 @ 4000	255 @ 2400	8.5	4V	Hyd.	40
	1973	4.00 x 3.48	1-8-4-3-6-5-7-2	175 @ 4000	260 @ 2800	8.5	4V	Hyd.	40
	1974	4.00 x 3.48	1-8-4-3-6-5-7-2	145 @ 3600	250 @ 2200	8.5	2V	Hyd.	40
	1974	4.00 x 3.48	1-8-4-3-6-5-7-2	160 @ 3800	255 @ 2400	8.5	4V	Hyd.	40
	1975 (2 bbl)	4.00 x 3.48	1-8-4-3-6-5-7-2	145 @ 3800	250 @ 2200	8.5:1	2V	Hyd.	40-60
	1975 (4 bbl)	4.00 x 3.48	1-8-4-3-6-5-7-2	160 @ 3800	250 @ 2400	8.5:1	4V	Hyd.	40-60
	1976	4.00 x 3.48	1-8-4-3-6-5-7-2	160 @ 4000	265 @ 2400	8.0:1	2V	Hyd.	40-60
366	1970	3.937 x 3.76	1-8-4-3-6-5-7-2	235 @ 4000	345 @ 2600	8.0	4V	Hyd.	50-75
	1971-72	3.937 x 3.76	1-8-4-3-6-5-7-2	200 @ 4000	295 @ 3200	8.0	4V	Hyd.	40-55
	1973-74	3.937 x 3.76	1-8-4-3-6-5-7-2	200 @ 4000	310 @ 2800	8.0	4V	Hyd.	40-55
	1975	3.937 x 3.76	1-8-4-3-6-5-7-2	200 @ 4000	305 @ 2800	8.0:1	4V	Hyd.	40-55
	1976 (sing. exh.)	3.937 x 3.76	1-8-4-3-6-5-7-2	195 @ 4000	290 @ 2800	8.0:1	4V	Hyd.	40-55
	1976 (dual exh.)	3.937 x 3.76	1-8-4-3-6-5-7-2	200 @ 4000	305 @ 2800	8.0:1	4V	Hyd.	40-55
396	1970	4.094 x 3.76	1-8-4-3-6-5-7-2	310 @ 4800	400 @ 3200	9.0	4V	Hyd.	50-75
400	1975	4.125 x 3.75	1-8-4-3-6-5-7-2	175 @ 3600	290 @ 2800	8.5:1	4V	Hyd.	40-60
	1976	4.125 x 3.75	1-8-4-3-6-5-7-2	175 @ 3600	290 @ 2800	8.5:1	4V	Hyd.	40-60
402 240 H.P.	1971	4.126 x 3.76	1-8-4-3-6-5-7-2	240 @ 4400	340 @ 3200	8.5	4V	Hyd.	40
260 H.P.	1971	4.126 x 3.76	1-8-4-3-6-5-7-2	260 @ 4400	345 @ 3200	8.5	4V	Hyd.	40
210 H.P.	1972	4.126 x 3.76	1-8-4-3-6-5-7-2	210 @ 4000	320 @ 2800	8.5	4V	Hyd.	45-55
427	1970	4.250 x 3.76	1-8-4-3-6-5-7-2	260 @ 4000	405 @ 2600	8.0	4V	Hyd.	50-75
	1971-72	4.25 x 3.76	1-8-4-3-6-5-7-2	230 @ 4000	360 @ 2400	8.0	4V	Hyd.	40
	1973-74	4.25 x 3.76	1-8-4-3-6-5-7-2	230 @ 4000	360 @ 2800	8.0	4V	Hyd.	40-55
	1975	4.25 x 3.76	1-8-4-3-6-5-7-2	220 @ 4000	360 @ 2400	8.0:1	4V	Hyd.	40-55
	1976	4.25 x 3.76	1-8-4-3-6-5-7-2	220 @ 4000	360 @ 2400	8.0:1	4V	Hyd.	40-55
454	1971	4.251 x 4.00	1-8-4-3-6-5-7-2	285 @ 4000	390 @ 3200	8.5	4V	Hyd.	40
	1971	4.251 x 4.00	1-8-4-3-6-5-7-2	325 @ 5600	390 @ 3600	9.0	4V	Hyd.	40
	1972	4.251 x 4.00	1-8-4-3-6-5-7-2	270 @ 4000	390 @ 3200	8.5	4V	Hyd.	40
	1973	4.251 x 4.00	1-8-4-3-6-5-7-2	240 @ 4000	355 @ 2800	8.25	4V	Hyd.	40
	1973	4.251 x 4.00	1-8-4-3-6-5-7-2	245 @ 4000	375 @ 2800	8.25	4V	Hyd.	40

GENERAL ENGINE SPECIFICATIONS, continued

CU. IN. DISPLACEMENT	YEAR	BORE AND STROKE	FIRING ORDER	DEVELOPED HORSE POWER @ R.P.M.	DEVELOPED TORQUE @ R.P.M.	COMPRESSION RATIO	CARBURETOR	VALVE LIFTER TYPE	NORMAL OIL PRESSURE
454	1973	4.251 x 4.00	1-8-4-3-6-5-7-2	250 @ 4000	365 @ 2800	8.25	4V	Hyd.	40
	1974	4.251 x 4.00	1-8-4-3-6-5-7-2	230 @ 4000	350 @ 2800	8.25	4V	Hyd.	40
	1974	4.251 x 4.00	1-8-4-3-6-5-7-2	245 @ 4000	365 @ 2800	8.25	4V	Hyd.	40
	1975 (L.D.)	4.251 x 4.00	1-8-4-3-6-5-7-2	215 @ 4000	350 @ 2400	8.15:1	4V	Hyd.	40
	1975 (H.D.)	4.251 x 4.00	1-8-4-3-6-5-7-2	245 @ 4000	355 @ 3000	8.15:1	4V	Hyd.	40
	1976 (L.D.)	4.251 x 4.00	1-8-4-3-6-5-7-2	245 @ 3800	365 @ 2800	8.15:1 ①	4V	Hyd.	40
	1976 (H.D., Fed.)	4.251 x 4.00	1-8-4-3-6-5-7-2	240 @ 3800	370 @ 2800	8.15:1	4V	Hyd.	40
	1976 (H.D., Calif.)	4.251 x 4.00	1-8-4-3-6-5-7-2	250 @ 3800	385 @ 2800	8.15:1	4V	Hyd.	40

Fed.—Federal (all states except California)
Calif.—California only
L.D.—Light duty emissions (under 6,000 lb GVW)
H.D.—Heavy duty emissions (over 6,000 lb GVW)
① 8:25:1 on C-10 w/H.D. chassis and C-10, 20 Suburban

CRANKSHAFT BEARING JOURNAL SPECIFICATIONS

CU. IN. DISPLACEMENT	YEAR	MAIN BEARING JOURNALS				CONNECTING ROD BEARING JOURNALS		
		JOURNAL DIAMETER	OIL CLEARANCE	SHAFT END PLAY	THRUST ON NO.	JOURNAL DIAMETER	OIL CLEARANCE	END PLAY
SIX CYLINDER								
250	1970-72	2.2983-2.2993	.0003-.0029	.002-.006	Rear	1.999-2.000	.0007-.0027	.0009-.0014
	1973-76	2.2983-2.2993	.0003-.0029	.002-006	Rear	1.999-2.000	.0007-.0027	.0006-.0017
292	1970-72	2.2983-2.2993	.0008-.0034	.002-.006	5	2.099-2.100	.0007-.0028	.0009-.0014
	1973-76	2.2983-2.2993	.0008-.0034	.002-.006	5	2.099-2.100	.0007-.0027	.0006-.0017
305C (V6)	1973-74	3.1247-3.1237¹	.0013-.0039	.003-.008	—	2.8112-2.8122	.001-.003	.006-.011
379 (V6)	1973-74	3.1247-3.1237¹	.0023-.0039²	.003-.008	—	2.8112-2.8122	.0015-.0035	.006-.011
432 (V6)	1973-74	3.1247-3.1237¹	.0023-.0039²	.003-.008	—	2.8112-2.8122	.0015-.0035	.006-.011
EIGHT CYLINDER								
307	1970-73	2.4484-2.4493³	⁵	.002-.006	5	2.1990-2.200	.0013-.0035	.008-.014
350	1970	2.4484-2.4493³	⁴	.002-.006	5	2.199-2.200	.0007-.0028	.008-.014
	1971-76	2.4484-2.4493 ③	⑤	.002-.006	5	2.199-2.200	.0013-.0035	.008-.014
366	1970-76	2.7481-2.7490⁶	.0013-.0025⁷	.006-.010	5	2.1985-2.1995	.0014-.0030	.019-.025
396	1970	⁸	⁹	.006-.010	5	2.199-2.200	.0009-.0025	.015-.021
400	1975-76	2.4484-2.4493 ③	⑤	.002-.006	5	2.199-2.200	.0013-.0035	.008-.014
402	1971-72	2.7487-2.7496¹⁰	.0007-.0019¹¹	.002-.006	5	2.1985-2.1995	.0009-.0025	.013-.023
427	1970-75	2.7481-2.7490⁶	.0013-.0025⁷	.006-.010	5	2.199-2.1998	.0014-.0030	.019-.025
454	1971-74	2.7485-2.7494¹²	.0013-.0025¹³	.006-.010	5	2.1985-2.1995	.0009-.0025	.013-.023

1. Rear—3.1229—3.1239 in.
2. No. 4—.0031-.0047 in.
3. Rear—2.4479-2.4488 in.
4. No. 1—.0003-.0015, No. 2, 3, 4—.0006-.0018, No. 5—.0008-.0023
5. No. 1—.0008-.0020; No. 2, 3, 4—.0011-.0023; No. 5—.0017-.0033
6. Rear—2.7473-2.7483 in.
7. Rear—.0029-.0045 in.
8. No. 5 1-2—2.7487-2.7496; No. 5 3-4—2.7481-2.7490 No. 5—2.7478-2.7488
9. No. 1—.0007-.0019; No. 2, 3, 4—.0013-.0025; No. 5—.0024-.0040
10. No. 3-4—2.7841-2.7490; No. 5—2.7473-2.7483
11. No. 2 3-4—.0013-.0025; No. 5—.0019-.0033
12. No. 2 3-4—2.7481-2.7490; No. 5—2.7478-2.7488
13. No. 5—.0024-.0040

VALVE SPECIFICATIONS

CU. DISPLACEMENT	YEAR	LASH (HOT) INCHES INT.	LASH (HOT) INCHES EXH.	ANGLE DEGREE FACE	ANGLE DEGREE SEAT	STEM DIA. INCHES INT.	STEM DIA. INCHES EXH.	STEM CLEARANCE INTAKE	STEM CLEARANCE EXHAUST	CAM LOBE LIFT INCHES	VALVE SPRING LBS @ INCHES OPEN	VALVE SPRING LBS @ INCHES CLOSED	FREE LENGTH INCH
SIX CYLINDER													
250	1970-71	0+1	Turn	45	46	.341	.341	.001-.003	.002-.004	.390	186 @ 1.27	60 @ 1.66	2.08
	1972-75	0+1	Turn	45	46	—	—	.0010-.0027	.0015-.0032	.221	185 @ 1.27	60 @ 1.66	1.90
292	1970-76	0+1	Turn	45	46	—	—	.0010-.0027	.0015-.0032	.2315	185 @ 1.27	60 @ 1.66	1.90

VALVE SPECIFICATIONS

CU. DISPLACE-MENT	YEAR	LASH (HOT) INCHES INT.	EXH.	ANGLE DEGREE FACE	SEAT	STEM DIA. INCHES INT.	EXH.	STEM CLEARANCE INTAKE	EXHAUST	CAM LOBE LIFT INCHES	VALVE SPRING LBS @ INCHES OPEN	CLOSED	FREE LENGTH INCH
305C (V6)	1973-74	.012	.018	—	30	.341	.340	.0015-.003	.002-.0035	.454[2]	203 @ 1.50	80 @ 1.92	2.27
379 (V6)	1973-74	.012	.018	—	30	.373	.438	.0015-.003	.0019-.0036	.454[2]	203 @ 1.50	80 @ 1.92	2.27
432 (V6)	1973-74	.012	.018	—	30	.373	.438	.0015-.003	.0019-.0036	.454[2]	203 @ 1.50	80 @ 1.92	2.27
EIGHT CYLINDER													
307	1970-73	0+1	Turn	45	46	.341	.341	.001-.003	.001-.003	[3]	189 @ 1.20	80 @ 1.61	1.91
350	1970-76	0+1	Turn	45	46	.341	.341	.001-.003	.001-.003	[3]	200 @ 1.25	80 @ 1.70	2.03
366	1970-76	0+1	Turn	45	46	.371	.371	.001-.003	.001-.003	.234	220 @ 1.40	90 @ 1.80	2.05
396	1970	0+1	Turn	45	46	.371	.371	.001-.002	.001-.003	.398	315 @ 1.38	100 @ 1.88	2.09
402	1971-72	0+1	Turn	45	46	—	—	.001-.0027	.0012-.0029	.234	245 @ 1.38	75 @ 1.88	2.06
427	1970-76	0+1	Turn	45	46	.371	.371	.001-.003	.001-.002	[4]	220 @ 1.40	90 @ 1.80	2.05
454	1971-74	0+1	Turn	45	46	—	—	.001-.0027	.001-.0029	.234	290 @ 1.38	80 @ 1.88	2.12

1. .450-Exhaust
2. .464-Exhaust
3. .260-Intake; .273-Exhaust
4. .234-Intake; .253-Exhaust

RING SIDE CLEARANCE (in.)

ENGINE (cu in.)	YEAR	TOP COMPRESSION	BOTTOM COMPRESSION	OIL CONTROL
250	1970-76	.0012-.0027	.0012-.0032	.0000-.0050
292	1970-76	.0020-.0040	.0020-.0040	.0005-.0055
305 (V6)	1973-74	.0030-.0050	①	.0010-.0040
379 (V6)	1973-74	.0030-.0045	②	.0025-.0040
432 (V6)	1973-74	.0030-.0045	②	.0025-.0040
307	1970-73	.0012-.0027	.0012-.0032	.0000-.0050
350	1970-76	.0012-.0032	.0012-.0032	.0000-.0050
366	1970-76	.0018-.0032	.0018-.0032	.0020-.0035
396	1970	.0012-.0032	.0012-.0032	.0012-.0060
400	1975-76	.0012-.0032	.0012-.0032	.0000-.0050
402	1971-72	.0017-.0032	.0017-.0032	.0005-.0065
427	1970	.0018-.0032	.0018-.0032	.0020-.0035
454	1973-76	.0017-.0032	.0017-.0032	.0005-.0065

① —2nd compression—.0030-.0045
   3rd compression—.0025-.0040
② —2nd compression—.0025-.0040
   3rd compression—.0025-.0040

RING GAP SPECIFICATIONS (in.)

ENGINE	YEAR	TOP COMPRESSION	BOTTOM COMPRESSION	OIL CONTROL
250	1970-76	.010-.020	.010-.020	.015-.055
292	1970-76	.010-.020	.010-.020	.015-.055
305 (V6)	1973-74	.017-.027	①	No Gap
379 (V6)	1973-74	.022-.032	②	No Gap
432 (V6)	1973-74	.024-.034	③	No Gap
307	1970-73	.010-.020	.010-.020	.015-.055
350	1970-76	.010-.020	.013-.025	.015-.055
366	1970	.010-.020	.010-.020	.010-.030
	1971-76	.010-.020	.010-.020	.010-.023
396	1970	.010-.020	.010-.020	.010-.030
400	1975-76	.010-.020	.010-.020	.010-.035
402	1971-72	.010-.020	.010-.020	.015-.055
427	1970-76	.010-.020	.010-.020	.010-.023
454	1973-76	.010-.020	.010-.020	.010-.030

① —2nd compression—.015-.025
   3rd compression—.015-.025
② —2nd compression—.022-.032
   3rd compression—.015-.025
③ —2nd compression—.024-.034
   3rd compression—.015-.025

TORQUE SPECIFICATIONS

CU. IN. DISPLACE-MENT	YEAR	CYLINDER HEAD BOLTS FT. LBS.	ROD BEARING BOLTS FT. LBS.	MAIN BEARING BOLTS FT. LBS.	CRANKSHAFT BALANCER BOLT FT. LBS.	FLYWHEEL TO CRANKSHAFT BOLTS FT. LBS.	MANIFOLDS INTAKE FT. LBS.	EXHAUST
SIX CYLINDER								
250	1970-76	95	35-45	65	Pressed on	60	[1]	[1]
292	1970-76	95	40	65	Pressed on	55-65	[1]	[1]
305C (V6)	1973-74	60-65	55-65	170-180[2]	180-200	100-110	30-35	15-20
379 (V6)	1973-74	90-100	55-65	170-180[2]	240-260	100-110	30-35	15-20
432 (V6)	1973-74	90-100	55-65	170-180[2]	240-260	100-110	30-35	15-20
EIGHT CYLINDER								
307	1970-73	65	45	70	Pressed on	60	30	20[3]
350	1970-76	65	45	70	60	60	30	20[3]
366	1970-76	80	55	100[4]	85	60	30	20
396	1970	60-70	45-55	110	85	65	30	20
402	1971-72	80	50	110	85	65	30	20
427	1970-76	80	50	110	85	60	30	20
454	1971-74	80	50	110	85	65	30	20

1 Outer—20 ft. lbs.; others—30 ft. lbs.
2. Rear—90-100 ft lbs.
3. Inside bolts—30 ft lbs.
4. Outer—95 ft. lbs.

FIRING ORDER AND ROTATION

FIRING ORDER 1-5-3-6-2-4

235, 261 engines

FIRING ORDER 1-5-3-6-2-4

250, 292 engines

FIRING ORDER 1-6-5-4-3-2

401, 478 engines

FIRING ORDER 1-8-4-3-6-5-7-2

407, 348 engines

FIRING ORDER 1-8-4-3-6-5-7-2

1970-74—307, 350, 366, 396, 402, 427, 454 engines

FIRING ORDER 1-8-4-3-6-5-7-2

1975-76—305, 350, 366, 400, 454 engines

WHEEL ALIGNMENT SPECIFICATIONS

MODEL	YEAR	CASTER (deg)	CAMBER (deg)	TOE-IN (in.)	KINGPIN INCLINATION (in.)
10-20-30 Series (Light Duty)					
C-10, 20, 30	1970	¼N-¼P	0-½P	⅛-¼	——
	1971	①	①	⅛-¼	——
	1972-76	②	¼P	⅛-¼	——
K-10, 20	1970	3¼P*	1½P*	3/32-3/16	8½
	1971	1½P*	4P*	1/16-5/16	8½
	1972-76	1½P*	4P*	⅛-¼	8½
G-10, 20, 30	1970-71	¼N-¼P	0-½P	⅛-¼	——
	1972	¼N-¼P②	0-½P	⅛-¼	——
	1973-76	②	0-½P	⅛-¼	——
P-10, 20, 30	1970	¼N-¼P	0-½P	⅛-¼	——
	1971	①	①	⅛-¼	——
	1972-76	②	¼P	⅛-¼	——
40 thru 65 Series (Medium Duty)					
C-40, 50, 60	1970	2P-3P	½P-1½P	3/32-3/16	7¼
	1971-72	2P-3P	½P-1½P③	3/32-3/16④	7¼⑤
C-50	1973	2P-3P	½P-1½P	⅛-3/16	7¼
	1974-76	2P-3P	½P-1½P	1/16-⅛	7¼
C-60, 65	1973	2P-3P	½P-1½P	3/32-3/16	7¼
	1974-76	2P-3P	½P-1½P③	1/16-⅛④	7¼⑤
P-40	1970	2P-3P	½P-1½P	3/32-3/16	7¼
P-40, 45	1974-76	2P-3P	½P-1½P	1/16-⅛	7¼
M-50	1970	2P-3P	½P-1½P	3/32-3/16	7¼
M-60	1970	2P-3P	¼P (L.H.) / ¼N (R.H.)	⅛-7/32	5¾ (L.H.) / 6¼ (R.H.)
M-60, 65	1971-73	2P-3P	½P-1½P③	3/32-3/16④	7¼⑤
M-60, 65	1974-76	2P-3P	½P-1½P③	1/16-⅛⑥	7¼⑤
S-50, 60 (exc long w.b.)	1970-72	2P-3P	½P-1½P	3/32-3/16	7¼
S-50 (long w.b.)	1970	1¾P	½P-1½P	3/32-3/16	7¼
S-60	1973	2P-3P	½P-1½P	3/32-3/16	7¼
	1974-76	2P-3P	½P-1½P	1/16-⅛	7¼
T-50, 60	1970	2P-3P	½-1½P⑦	3/32-3/16⑧	7¼⑩
T-50, 60, 65	1971-76	¾P-1¾P	1P-2P⑨	⅛-¼	7⑩

P—Positive
N—Negative
L.H.—Left hand
R.H.—Right hand
*—No provision for adjustment
—— Not Applicable

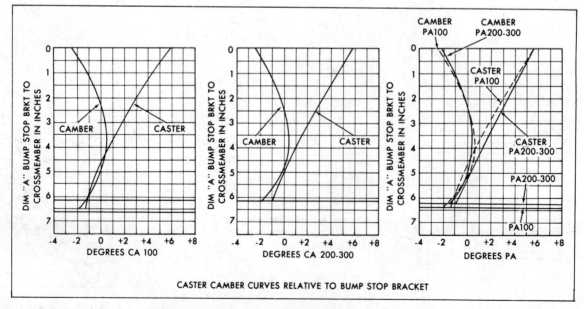

CASTER CAMBER CURVES RELATIVE TO BUMP STOP BRACKET

1971 C-10, 20, 30 and F-10, 20, 30 (©) Chevrolet Div., G.M. Corp.

BUMP STOP BRACKET
LOWER CONTROL ARM

Measure the distance from the bump stop bracket to the frame and consult the appropriate chart. (© Chevrolet Div., G.M. Corp.)

CASTER

Dimension "A" in inches	2½"	2¾"	3"	3¼"	3½"	3¾"	4"	4¼"	4½"	4¾"	5"
1972 C-10	—	—	+2°	+1¾°	+1½°	+1¼°	+1°	+¾°	+½°	+¼°	0°
1972 C-20,30	+2¾°	+2½°	+2°	+1¾°	+1½°	+1¼°	+1°	+¾°	+½°	+¼°	0°
1973-76 C-10	—	—	+2°	+1½°	+1¼°	+1°	+¾°	+½°	+¼°	0°	−½°
1973 C-20, 30	+2°	+1½°	+1¼°	+1°	+¾°	+½°	+¼°	0°	−¼°	−½°	−¾°
1974-76 C-20, 30	+1½°	+1¼°	+1°	+¾°	+½°	+¼°	0°	−¼°	−½°	−¾°	−1°
1972-76 G-10, 20, 30	+2¼°	+2°	+1½°	+1¼°	+1°	+¾°	+½°	+¼°	0°	−¼°	−½°
1972 P-10	—	—	+2°	+1¾°	+1½°	+1¼°	+1°	+¾°	+½°	+¼°	0°
1972 P-20, 30	+2¾°	+2½°	+2°	+1¾°	+1½	+1¼°	+1°	+¾°	+½°	+¼°	0°
1973-76 P-10	—	—	+2°	+1½°	+1¼°	+1°	+¾°	+½°	+¼°	0°	−½°
1973 P-20, 30	+2°	+1½°	+1¼°	+1°	+¾°	+½°	+¼°	0°	−¼°	−½°	−¾°
1974-76 P-20, 30	+1½°	+1¼°	+1°	+¾°	+½°	+¼°	0°	−¼°	−½°	−¾°	−1°

③ C-M 60, 65 w/9000 and 12000 lb axles—¼P (L.H.); ¼N (R.H.)
④ C-M 60, 65 w/9000 and 12000 lb axles—⅛-7/32 in.
⑤ C-M 60, 65 (1971-73) w/9000 and 12000 lb axle—5¾° (L.H.); 6¼° (R.H.)
⑥ C-M 65 (1974-76 w/9000 and 12000 lb axle—⅛-¼in.
⑦ T-50, 60 w/9000 and 11000 lb axles—¼P (L.H.); ¼N (R.H.)

⑧ T-50, 60 w/9000 and 11000 lb axles—⅛-7/32 in.
⑨ T-50, 60, 65 w/9000 and 12000 lb axles—¼N-¾P (L.H.); ¾N-¼P (R.H.)
⑩ T-50, 60 w/9000 and 11000 lb axles and T-50, 60, 65 w/9000 and 12000 lb axles—5¾° (L.H.); 6¼° (R.H.)

TRUCK MODELS AND ENGINE APPLICATION

Identification Plate: The vehicle identification plate containing the VIN is located on the left door pillar of all conventional models. On 1970 Forward Control models, it is located on the steering column; on all later Forward Control models, on the dash and toe panel. On cowl models, the plate is attached to the engine side of the cowl.

Engines (cu in.)	Year	Models Available	Engine Make
250	1970-71	C-10, 20, 30, 40 / K-10, 20 / P-10, 20, 30, 40 / G-10, 20, 30 / S-40	Own
250	1972	C-10, 20, 30, 40 / K-10, 20 / P-10, 20, 30 / G-10, 20, 30	Own
250	1973-74	C-10, 20, 30, 50 / K-10, 20 / P-10, 20, 30 / G-10, 20, 30	Own
250	1975-76	C-10, K-10, G-10	Own
292	1970-71	C-10, 20, 30, 40, ③ / 50 / K-10, 20③ / P-20, 30, 40① / S-40, 50 / T-50	Own
292	1972	C-10, 20, 30, 40, ③ / 50 / K-10, 20③ / P-20, 30 / S-50	Own
292	1973	C-20, 30, 50, 60 / S-60	Own
292	1974	C-20, 30, 50, 60 / K-20 / P-20, 30, 40 / S-60	Own

Engines (cu in.)	Year	Models Available	Engine Make
292	1975-76	C-20, 30, 50, 60 / K-20 / P-10, 20, 30 / G-20, 30 / S-60	Own
305 (V6)	1973	C-60, S-60, T-60	Own
	1974	S-60, T-60	
379 (V6)	1973-74	C-60, 65 / S-60 / T-60, 65	Own
432 (V6)	1973	C-65, T-65	Own
	1974	C-65, M-65, T-65	
307	1970-73	C-10, 20, 30 / K-10, 20 / P-20, 30 / G-10	Own
350	1970-72	C-10, 20, 30, 40, 50 / K-10, 20 / P-20, 30 / G-10, 20, 30 / M-50, S-50,T-50 ②	Own
	1973-74	C-10, 20, 30, 50, 60 / K-10, 20 / P-20, 30 / G-10, 20, 30 / S-60, T-60	Own

Engines (cu in.)	Year	Models Available	Engine Make
350	1975-76	C-10, 20, 30, 50, 60 / K-10, 20 / P-20, 30 / G-20, 30 / S-60, T-60	Own
366	1970	C-50, 60 / M-50, 60, T-60 / S-50, T-50	Own
	1971-72	C-50, 60 / M-60, S-50 / T-50, 60	Own
	1973-76	C-60, 65 / S-60 / T-60, 65 / M-65	Own
396	1970	C-10, 20, 30 ③	Own
400	1975-76	K-10, 20 / G-20, 30	Own
402	1971-72	C-10, 20, 30 ③	Own
427	1970	C-60, M-60	Own
	1971-72	C-60, M-60, T-60	Own
	1973-74	C-65, M-65, T-65	Own
	1975-76	C-65, M-65, T-65	Own
454	1973-76	C-10, 20,30 ③ / P-30	Own

①—P-40 1970 only
②—M-50 1970 only
③—Except Blazer

Six cylinder distributor—typical
(© Chevrolet Div., G.M. Corp.)

Distributor

Detailed information on direction of distributor rotation, cylinder numbering, firing order, point gap, cam dwell, spark plugs, spark advance, and idle speed will be found in the Specifications tables.

Engine diagnosis is found in the General Repair Section.

H.E.I. System—1975-76

Most 1975-76 light duty Chevrolet truck engines use a High Energy Ignition system. Two types are used. V8 distributors combine all ignition components in one unit. The coil is in the distributor cap and connects directly to the rotor. The 6 cylinder distributor has an externally mounted coil. Both units operate in basically the same manner, except that the module and pick-up coil replace the conventional breaker points. The module automatically controls the dwell, stretching it with increased engine speed. The system also features a longer spark duration due to the greater amount of energy stored in the primary coil.

The centrifugal and vacuum advance mechanisms are basically the same type of unit as on a conventional ignition distributor.

The electronic module is serviced by complete replacement.

WARNING: Do not remove the spark plug wires with the engine running. Severe shock could result.

Distributor Removal and Installation

Inline Engines

1. Remove distributor cap, primary wire and vacuum line.
2. Scribe a mark on the distributor body, locating the position of the rotor. Scribe another mark on the distributor body and engine block, showing the position of the body in the block.
3. Remove the distributor hold-down screw and lift the distributor up and out of the engine.

NOTE: As the distributor is removed from engine, the rotor will turn counterclockwise slightly. When reinstalling be sure to allow for this.

4. If the crankshaft was rotated, turn the engine until the piston of No. 1 cylinder is at the top of its compression stroke.
5. Position the distributor in the block so that the vacuum control unit is in its normal postion.
6. Position the rotor to point toward the front of the engine (with distributor held out of the block, but in installed position). Turn rotor counterclockwise about one-eighth turn and push

distributor down to engage camshaft drive. It may be necessary to move the rotor one way or the other to mesh the drive and driven gears properly.

7. While holding the distributor down in place, kick the starter a few times to make sure the oil pump shaft is engaged. Install hold-down clamp and bolt and snug up the bolt.
8. Once again, rotate the crankshaft until No. 1 cylinder is on the compression stroke and the harmonic balancer mark is on 0°.
9. Turn distributor body slightly until points open. Tighten distributor clamp bolt.
10. Place distributor cap in position and see that the rotor lines up with the terminal for the No. 1 spark plug.
11. Install cap, distributor primary wire, and double check plug wires in the cap towers.
12. Start engine and set timing according to the Tune-up chart.
13. Reconnect vacuum hose to vacuum control assembly.

CAUTION: When using an auxiliary starter switch for bumping the engine into position for timing or compression test, the primary distributor lead must be disconnected from the negative post of the ignition coil and the ignition switch must be on. Failure to do this may cause damage to the grounding circuit in the ignition switch. This will also prevent the sudden starting of engine and possible serious injury.

V8 Engines

The distributor is located between the two banks of cylinders at the rear of the block.

The drive gear is attached to the distributor shaft. If it becomes necessary to remove the distributor, carefully mark the position of the rotor so that, if the engine is not turned after the distributor is taken out, the rotor can be returned to the position from which it was removed without difficulty.

1. To remove the distributor, take off the carburetor air cleaner, disconnect the coil primary wire and the vacuum line, remove the distributor cap, take out the single hold-down bolt located under the distributor body. With a pencil, mark the position of the body relative to the block, and then work the distributor up out of the block.

NOTE: If necessary, remove secondary leads from cap after first marking cap tower for No. 1 lead.

2. Remove No. 1 spark plug and, with finger on plug hole, crank the engine until compression is felt in No. 1 cylinder. Continue cranking until pointer lines up with the timing mark on the crankshaft pulley.
3. Position distributor in opening of the block in normal installed attitude; have rotor pointing to front of engine.
4. Turn the rotor counterclockwise about one-eighth of a turn (from straight front toward the left cylinder bank). Push the distributor down to engage the camshaft and while holding, turn the engine with the starter so that distributor shaft engages the oil pump shaft.

V8 distributor—typical (© Chevrolet Div., G.M. Corp.)

5. Return engine to compression stroke of No. 1 piston with timing mark on pulley aligned with the pointer. Adjust the distributor so that the points are opening. Install the cap being sure the rotor points to the contact for No. 1 spark plug. Connect the timing light and check that spark occurs as timing mark and pointer are aligned.

CAUTION: On the V8, the distributor body is involved in the engine lubricating system. The lubricating circuit can be interrupted to the right bank valve train by misalignment of the distributor body. This can cause serious trouble and may be hard to diagnose. See Firing Order and Timing illustrations.

Contact Point Replacement (w/o H.E.I.)

Inline Engines

1. Release distributor cap hold-down screws, remove cap.
2. Remove rotor.
3. Pull primary and condenser lead wires from contact point quick disconnect terminal.
4. Remove condenser hold-down screw and replace condenser.
5. Remove contact set attaching screw, lift contact point set from breaker plate.
6. Clean breaker plate of oil and dirt.
7. Place new contact point assembly in position on breaker plate, install attaching screw.

CAUTION: Carefully wipe protective film from point set prior to installation.

NOTE: Pilot on contact set must engage matching hole in breaker plate.

8. Connect primary and condenser lead wires to quick disconnect terminal on contact point set.
9. Check and adjust points for proper alignment and breaker arm spring tension. Use an aligning tool to bend *stationary contact support* if points need alignment.
10. Set point gap.
11. Reinstall rotor and distributor cap.
12. Start engine and check dwell.

WINDOW
"HEX" TYPE WRENCH

ADJUSTING SCREW

Thru cap point adjustment
(© CHEVROLET Div., G.M. Corp.)

ADJUST DWELL ANGLE SETTING OR POINT OPENING

Adjusting contact points
(© CHEVROLET Div., G.M. Corp.)

PRIMARY LEAD

Distributor head arrangements
(© Chevrolet Div., G.M. Corp.)

V8 Engines

1. The contact point set is replaced as one complete assembly and only dwell angle requires adjustment after replacement. Breaker lever spring tension and point alignment are factory set.
2. Remove the distributor cap by placing a screw driver in the slot head of the latch, press down and turn ¼ turn in either direction. Remove two attaching screws, which hold rotor to weight base, and remove rotor.
3. (On '73-'74 models, remove the two screws which hold R.F.I. shield in place, and remove shield.) Remove the two attaching screws which hold the base of the contact set assembly in place.
4. Remove the primary and condenser leads from their nylon insulated connection in contact set.
5. Reverse Steps 2, 3 and 4 to install new contact set.

CAUTION: Improper installation of the primary and condenser leads will cause lead interference between the cap, weight base and breaker advance plate.

6. Start engine and check the dwell.

With the engine running at idle and operating temperatures normalized, the dwell is adjusted by raising the window provided in the cap and inserting a "Hex" type wrench into the adjusting screw head.

Turn the adjusting screw until the specified dwell angle is obtained.

Dwell Angle—H.E.I. System (1975-76)

The dwell angle is fixed and is not adjustable. No attempt should be made to adjust the unit.

Timing Light Connections— H.E.I. System

Timing light connections should be made in parallel using an adapter at the distributor No. 1 terminal.

Tachometer Connections— H.E.I. System

There is a "tach" terminal on the distributor cap. Connect the tachometer to this terminal and ground. Follow the tachometer manufacturer's instructions.

CAUTION: Grounding the tach terminal could damage the H.E.I. ignition module.

Ignition Timing

On conventional ignition engines, remove the spark plug wire from No. 1 plug and attach a timing light between the wire and the plug. On 1975-76 H.E.I. systems, connect the timing light in parallel at the No. 1 tower on the distributor cap. Disconnect the distributor spark advance hose and plug the vacuum opening. Start the engine and run it at idle speed. Aim the timing light at the degree scale just over the harmonic balancer. The markings on the scale are in 2° increments with the greatest number of markings on the *before* side of the 0. Adjust the timing by loosening the securing clamp and rotating the distributor until the desired ignition advance is achieved, then tighten the clamp. To advance the timing, rotate the distributor opposite to the normal direction of rotor rotation. Retard the timing by rotating the distributor in the normal direction of rotor rotation.

NOTE: On 1971-74 250 engines, if engine miss or rough idle occurs, connect the dwell meter and accelerate the engine to 1700 rpm. If the dwell reading varies more than 3°, check the distributor for worn distributor shaft, worn bushings or a loose distributor breaker plate.

AC Generator (Delcotron)

Alternator

Delcotron, the alternator by Delco-Remy is used on Chevrolet trucks. These units are furnished in two types with companion voltage regulators, which will be a two-unit external regulator or transistorized internal regulator.

Repair and test details on the alternator and its regulators are covered in the General Repair Section.

Alternator Removal and Installation

1. Disconnect the battery ground strap at battery to prevent damaging diodes or wiring harness (also prevents accidentally reversing polarity).
2. Disconnect wiring leads at Delcotron.
3. Remove the alternator brace bolt, (if power steering equipped, loosen pump brace and mount nuts) then detach drive belt(s).
4. Support the generator and remove alternator mount bolt (6.2" Delcotron uses 2 mounting bolts) or bolts and remove from vehicle.
5. Reverse the removal procedure to install, then adjust drive belt(s).
6. If no belt tension tool is available, force alternator away from the engine until fan belt has 5/16 in. deflection when forced downward from normal position with light pressure applied between the alternator and the fan.

CAUTION: Since the Delcotron and regulator are designed for use on a single polarity system, the following precautions must be observed:

1. The polarity of the battery, generator, and regulator must be matched and considered before making any electrical connections in the system.
2. When connecting a booster battery, be sure to connect the negative battery terminals with one another, and the positive battery terminals with one another.
3. When connecting a charger to the battery, connect the charger positive lead to the battery positive terminal. Connect the charger negative lead to the battery negative terminal.
4. Never operate the Delcotron on uncontrolled open circuit. Be sure that all connections in the circuit are clean and tight.
5. Do not short across or ground any of the terminals on the Delcotron regulator.
6. Do not attempt to polarize the Delcotron.
7. Do not use test lamps of more than 12 volts for checking diode continuity.
8. Avoid long soldering times when replacing diodes or transistors. Prolonged heat is damaging to these units.
9. Disconnect the battery ground terminal when servicing any AC system. This will prevent the

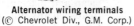

Alternator wiring terminals
(© Chevrolet Div., G.M. Corp.)

Cross section of alternator
(© Chevrolet Div., G.M. Corp.)

possibility of accidentally reversing polarity.

External Voltage Regulator

Removal and Installation

1. Disconnect the ground cable from the battery.
2. Disconnect the wiring harness from the regulator.
3. Remove the mounting screws and remove the regulator.
4. Make sure that the regulator base gasket is in place before installation.
5. Clean the attaching area for proper grounding.
6. Install the regulator. Do not overtighten the mounting screws, as this will cancel the cushioning effect of the rubber grommets.

Voltage Adjustment

10-30 Series (1970-72)

1. Insert a $\frac{1}{4}$ ohm-25 watt fixed resistor into the charging circuit at the horn relay junction block, between both leads and the terminal.
2. Install a voltmeter as shown in the figure.
3. Warm the engine by running it for several minutes at 1,500 rpm or more.
4. Cycle the voltage regulator by disconnecting and reconnecting the regulator connector.
5. Read the voltage on the voltmeter. If it is between 13.5 and 15.2, the regulator does not need adjustment or replacement. If the voltage is not within these limits, leave the engine running at 1,500 rpm.
6. Disconnect the four-terminal connector and remove the regu-

lator cover (except on transistorized regulators). Reconnect the four-terminal connector and adjust the voltage to between 14.2 and 14.6 volts by turning the adjusting screw while observing the voltmeter.
7. Disconnect the terminal, install the cover, and then reconnect the terminal.
8. Continue running the engine at 1,500 rpm to re-establish the regulator internal temperature.
9. Cycle the regulator by disconnecting/reconnecting the regulator connector. Check the voltage. If the voltage is between 13.5 and 15.2, the regulator is good.

CAUTION: Always disconnect the regulator before removing or installing the cover in order to prevent damage by short-circuiting.

Starter

Starter Motor Removal and Installation

The following procedure is a general guide for all vehicles and will vary slightly depending on the truck series and model. (On Forward Control Vans, vehicle must be raised and supported.)

1. Disconnect battery ground cable at the battery.
2. Disconnect engine wiring harness and battery leads at solenoid terminals.
3. Remove starter mounting bolts and retaining nuts and disengage starter assembly from the flywheel housing. Light duty gasoline powered engines use

Overrunning clutch type sta ter (© Chevrolet Div., G.M. Corp.)

1	Bail wire	11	Lock ring
2	Reservoir cover	12	Housing
3	Seal	13	Seal
4	Body	14	Check valve
5	Valve seat	15	Return spring
6	Valve assembly	16	Retainer
7	Spring	17	Primary cup
8	Primary cup	18	Piston
9	Piston	19	Piston seal
10	Secondary cup	20	Snap ring

Single & clutch assist type cylinders (© Chevrolet Div., G.M. Corp.)

conventional nose housing or pad mounting. Intermediate and heavy duty use conventional flange. On these, scribe mark on flange and flywheel housing as nose housing can be mounted in several positions.

4. Position starter motor assembly to the flywheel housing and install the mounting bolts and retaining nuts. Torque the mounting bolts 25 - 35 ft. lbs.
5. Connect all wiring leads at the solenoid terminals.
6. Connect the battery ground cable and check operation of the unit.

Brakes

Reference

Specific information will be found in General Brake Section on adjustments, bleeding, master cylinder and wheel cylinder overhaul procedures and trouble shooting.

Refer to Power Brake Section for details concerning power brakes.

Master Cylinders

Standard

A twin master cylinder, one side for brakes and the other for clutch operations, was used on some light duty trucks. Starting in 1964 a conventional single piston cylinder is used. A dual master cylinder is introduced in 1967 on small trucks. This one designed to be used with separate hydraulic systems for front and rear brakes. This new type cylinder has two separate reservoirs and outlets in a single casting. The front reservoir and outlet is for the front wheel brakes.

Twin (Brake & Clutch) Type

Master Cylinder Removal

1. Disconnect clutch and brake pedal return springs.
2. Detach push rod boots from cylinders.
3. Remove clutch and brake hydraulic lines.
4. Remove three bolts holding cylinder to dash and slide cylinder off push rod.

NOTE: Wipe hydraulic fittings

clean and place dry cloth under lines to absorb any fluid spillage. Cover fittings and lines to prevent any foreign matter from entering system.

Installation

1. Place new gaskets and push rod boots over cylinder tubes.
2. Hold cylinder next to dash and insert push rods, making sure they are centered.
3. Bolt assembly loosely to dash. This freedom of assembly will allow hydraulic lines to be started in cylinder without stripping fittings.
4. Tighten assembly and hydraulic lines securely.
5. Replace pedal return springs.
6. Fill reservoir and bleed both clutch and brake cylinders.
7. Check pedal free play and operation.

Standard Conventional Single

Master Cylinder Removal

1. Clean area at fitting and place dry cloth under line to absorb leakage.
2. Disconnect hydraulic line at cylinder and cover ends with clean

1	Cover
2	Diaphragm
3	Rear piston assembly
4	Snap ring
5	Secondary cups
6	Front piston
7	Cup protector
8	Primary cup
9	Cup retainer
10	Front piston return spring
11	Piston top screw
12	"O" ring
13	Tube seat inserts
14	Check valves
15	Check valve springs

Dual type master cylinder   (© Chevrolet Div., G.M. Corp.)

L-6   V-8

Starter motor & solenoid connections
(© Chevrolet Div., G.M. Corp.)

cloth to prevent any foreign matter from entering system.
3. Disconnect push rod from pedal.
4. Remove the two nuts and washers holding cylinder to firewall. Remove Cylinder.

Installation

1. Position cylinder at dash, align push rod through boot and secure loosely. This freedom of assembly will allow hydraulic line and push rod to be installed with minimum of effort.
2. Tighten nuts and line. Check free play.
3. Fill cylinder and bleed. Bleeding can be accomplished by slowly pressing down on brake pedal and at same time tightening the hydraulic line fitting. Any air still trapped in line at fitting can be expelled by pressing hard on brake pedal to a point of just below free play. By having a slight pressure on pedal, the piston is held forward enough to clear ports in reservoir and check valve is held off its seat, so air can be released.
4. Final check of fluid and brake operation.

Standard Dual

Master Cylinder Removal

1. Clean area at fittings and place dry cloth under lines to absorb leakage.
2. Disconnect both lines at cylinder and cover to prevent foreign matter from entering system.
3. Disconnect any stop light or brake warning light wires.
4. Unbolt cylinder and remove, allowing push rod to fall loose.

Installation

1. Install new boot on push rod.
2. Position cylinder making certain push rod and boot are in proper position and fasten loosely to firewall. This freedom of assembly will allow both hydraulic lines to be started easily.
3. Tighten mounting nuts and lines. Check free play.
4. Connect any stop light or brake warning light wires.
5. Fill reservoir and bleed. Test brakes before moving truck.
   NOTE: Front reservoir and outlet is connected to front wheel brakes.

Wheel Cylinders

Four types of cylinders are used, identified by type of brake system used.
Duo servo—One double-end cylinder mounted at toe ends of shoes.
Twinplex—Two double-end cylinders mounted between shoes at toe and heel.

Wagner F (FA)—Two single end cylinders (single piston, single direction) mounted so as to be an anchor for one and powering other.
Wagner FR3 (FR3A)—Two double-end cylinders mounted between shoes.

Wheel Cylinder Removal

1. Jack up axle and support. Remove wheel and drum.
   NOTE: To remove drum it may be necessary to back off brake adjustment, also if rear drum, release hand brake cable if so equipped.
   CAUTION: Starting in 1964 to gain access to adjusting starwheel, a knockout lanced area is located in web of drum. After knocking out metal be sure to clean all metal particles from brake compartment. A new cover plug must be installed.

2. Release shoe return springs and spread shoes to clear wheel cylinder links. Make sure any lubricant or brake fluid does not get on facings by covering same.
3. At front—Disconnect metal line from flexible hose and remove hose if accessible or remove hose later after cylinder is removed. At rear—Disconnect metal line from cylinder.
4. Remove shield over cylinder and connecting line between cylinders, if so equipped.
5. Remove cap screws and washers holding cylinder to backing plate. Remove cylinder being careful of any fluid spillage.

Installation

1. Clean mounting surface and reverse above procedures.

TYPE "F"

1 Boot
2 Brake shoe guide
3 Piston
4 Piston cup
5 Cup filler
6 Piston spring
7 Cylinder
8 Brake shoe anchor slot
9 Push rod

TYPE "FR-3"
Duo servo and Twin Plex cylinders
(© Chevrolet Div., G.M. Corp.)

DUO-SERVO

TWINPLEX
Wheel cylinder used with "F", "FA", "FR3" & "FR3A" brakes
(© Chevrolet Div., G.M. Corp.)

1 Push rod
2 Boot
3 Piston
4 Piston cup
5 Spring
6 Housing

Piston type hydro vac unit
(© Chevrolet Div., G.M. Corp.)

Moraine unit (© Chevrolet Div., G.M. Corp.)

2. Bleed and readjust brakes. Check pedal before moving vehicle.

NOTE: *Twinplex*—Upper and lower cylinders are not interchangeable due to position of connector tube openings. Upper cylinder has threaded bleeder valve opening drilled at outer edge of bore.

Wagner F & FA—Two wheel cylinders (upper and lower) are identical, however cylinders on right and left brakes have opposite castings.

Wagner FR3 & FR3A—Upper and lower cylinders on both right and left brakes are interchangeable.

Power Brakes (Power Hydraulic)

Reference

Specific information will be found in Power Brake Section on adjustments, bleeding, overhaul and trouble shooting.

General Description

Various vacuum-hydraulic or air-hydraulic brake systems are used, although sizes and shapes differ the basic function is the same.

Hydrovac (Early-piston Type)

When driver presses the brake pedal, brake fluid is compressed in master cylinder and acts to open a valve which allows a power source (air or vacuum) to exert a greater pressure in a second cylinder.

In event of loss of power (reservoir tank empty), the foundation brakes will stop the vehicle but with greater driver pedal effort.

Master-Vac Moraine

Starting in 1963 the master-vac is used. It is a single unit, containing both hydraulic and vacuum systems, using manifold vacuum and atmospheric pressure. It is usually mounted on engine side of firewall. This is also true of the moraine.

Hy-Power Multi-Vac

Bigger and more powerful units such as these are frame mounted. Some are single diaphragm and others double diaphragm.

In the event of vacuum power failure, brake application may still be made. However, it will be necessary to pump the brake pedal rapidly in order to move sufficient fluid from the master cylinder to the wheel brake system for the emergency stop. The amount of pumping required will depend upon the brake shoe clearances. If brakes are kept well adjusted, less pumping will be required in the event of power failure.

Master-Vac

The Master-Vac, a self contained hydraulic and vacuum unit is used on light duty trucks, also the new hydrovac, starting in 1966, replaces the multi-vac. This hydrovac is of the diaphragm type. The multi-vac unit was designed for use with the low input-high output system, while the newer hydrovac is used in equal displacement system. In equal displacement hydraulic system the fluid displaced by the master cylinder is equal to the fluid displaced by the power cylinder. Vacuum powered cylinders on 40-50-60 series, with hydraulic brakes, are either single or tandem diaphragms. The tandem diaphragm unit is used with single master cylinder. Single diaphragm units, two used, are on dual cylinder units. One for each system.

Air-Pak

Air-pak is a self contained hydraulic-air pressure power unit for use on trucks with an air compressor, reservoir, regulator and check valve. It consists of three elements.

1. An air cylinder, consisting of a cylinder, a piston and a push rod that connects power piston to hydraulic piston.
2. A hydraulic cylinder, consists of a hydraulic piston with built in check valve, a residual check valve and a compensating check valve.
3. An air pressure control valve, which controls the power output of the air pressure cylinder in

Bendix master vac unit
(© Chevrolet Div., G.M. Corp.)

Hy-Power vacuum booster unit
(© Chevrolet Div., G.M. Corp.)

relation to the hydraulic pressure in the master cylinder.

The operation of the air-pak is similar to the multi-pak unit. The difference between units is that the air-pak is designed to operate in equal displacement hydraulic systems. The multi-pak is made to work in the low-input, high-output systems. In the equal displacement system, the fluid output of the master cylinder is equal to the fluid output of the power cylinder.

NOTE: The correct master cylinder MUST be used with the proper power unit. Air-pak and multi-pak units are NOT interchangeable.

Power Brakes (Power-Vacuum)

Unit Removal

NOTE: Wipe hydraulic fittings clean, place dry cloth under lines to absorb any fluid leakage, cover lines to keep system clean.
1. Disconnect push rod clevis at pedal, if clearance hole in dash is not large enough, remove clevis. (mark position)
2. Remove vacuum hose from unit. (check valve)
3. Disconnect hydraulic lines.
4. Remove any stop light wires.
5. Remove 4 nuts and washers holding unit to firewall, remove unit (and bracket)

Unit Installation

1. Mount unit in place and install loosely (freedom of assembly will allow easy starting of fittings), secure push rod to pedal and check free-play.
2. Tighten mounting nuts and hydraulic lines.
3. Install vacuum line.
4. Connect any stop light wire.
5. Bleed brakes, (bench-bleed unit before installing, units with 2 bleeder valves. Bleed valve nearest to shell first).

CAUTION: Pressure bleeding must be done with engine off (no vacuum). In manual bleeding, use engine (start engine, allow vacuum to build up).

6. Check brakes and stoplight before moving vehicle.
7. Units requiring lubrication, remove 1/8 inch pipe plug in front end of shell (engine off). Fill with vacuum cylinder oil until oil runs out filler hole.

Power Brakes (Hydro-Boost)

Reference

Specific information will be found in the Power Brake portion of the General Repair Section on adjustments, overhauling and troubleshooting.

Description

The Hydro-boost system was designed to eliminate the need for the remote frame mounted boosters. It utilizes power steering fluid in place of engine vacuum to provide a power assist that operates a dual master cylinder brake system. A spring accumulator is used in conjunction with the hydraulic brake booster. The accumulator is a sealed hydraulic cylinder with a port at each end. On 1974 models the accumulator and booster are mounted separately. In 1975 all "C" model vehicles equipped with the hydro-boost incorporate an accumulator which is integral with the booster.

CAUTION: The accumulator contains a spring compressed under high pressure. Any attempt to disassemble or cut could cause personal injury.

Hydraulic Brake Booster Motor Home Chassis

Removal & Installation

1. Make sure all pressure is discharged from the accumulator by depressing and releasing the brake pedal several times.
2. Raise the vehicle on a hoist.
3. Clean all the dirt from the booster at the hydraulic line connections and master cylinder.
4. Remove the nuts and lockwashers that secure the master cylinder to the booster and support bracket. Support the master cylinder leaving the hydraulic lines attached to the master cylinder.
5. Disconnect and plug the hydraulic lines from the booster ports.
6. Remove the cotter pin, nut, bolt and washers that secure the operating lever to the vertical brake rod.
7. Remove the six nuts, lockwashers and bolts that secure the booster linkage bracket to the front and rear support brackets, then slide the booster off the rear support studs and remove the booster from the vehicle.
8. Remove the cotter pin, nut, washer and bolt that secures

Dual vacuum rooster unit
(© Chevrolet Div., G.M. Corp.)

Hydro-Boost—1974 (© Chevrolet Div., G.M. Corp.)

Hydro-Boost—1975 Cabs, Suburban (© Chevrolet Div., G.M. Corp.)

Booster Installation—Motor Home Chassis (© Chevrolet Div., G.M. Corp.)

the operating lever to the pedal rod.

9. Remove the brake pedal rod lever nut and bolt and then remove the lever, sleeve and bushings.

10. To install reverse the removal procedures. Bleed the booster-power steering hydraulic system and check the brake pedal and stoplamp switch adjustment.

Conventional Cab & Suburban

Removal & Installation

1. Make sure all pressure is discharged from the accumulator by depressing and releasing the brake pedal several times.

2. Remove the nuts and lockwashers that secure the master cylinder to the booster and support bracket. Support the master cylinder leaving the hydraulic lines

attached to the master cylinder.

3. Remove the booster pedal push rod cotter pin, and washer and disconnect the push rod from the brake pedal.

4. Remove the booster support bracket.

5. Remove the booster bracket to dash panel or support bracket nuts and remove the booster assembly.

6. To install reverse the removal procedure. Bleed the booster-power steering hydraulic system and check brake pedal and stoplamp switch adjustment.

Forward Control Chassis— (Vans)

Removal & Installation

1. Make sure all pressure is discharged from the accumulator by depressing and releasing the brake pedal several times.

2. Clean all the dirt from the booster at the hydraulic line connections and master cylinder.

3. Remove the nuts and lockwashers that secure the master cylinder to the booster and the support bracket. Support the master cylinder leaving the hydraulic lines attached to the master cylinder.

4. Remove the booster pedal push rod cotter pin and washer and disconnect the push rod from the booster bracket pivot lever.

5. Remove the booster supper braces.

6. Remove the booster bracket nuts and remove the booster.

7. To install reverse the removal procedure. Bleed the booster-power steering hydraulic system and check the brake pedal and stop lamp switch adjustment.

Booster Installation—Cab & Suburban
(© Chevrolet Div., G.M. Corp.)

Booster Installation—Vans
(© Chevrolet Div., G.M. Corp.)

Bleeding Hydro-Boost System

1. Fill the power steering pump to the proper level.
2. Start the engine for approximately two seconds. Check the fluid and add if necessary.
3. Repeat step 2 until the fluid level remains constant.
4. Raise the front end of the vehicle so that the tires are clear of the ground.
5. Start the engine and run approximately 1500 rpm. Depress and release the brake pedal several times then turn the steering wheel right and left, lightly contacting the wheel stops.
6. Turn off the engine and check the fluid level in the reservoir and add fluid if necessary.
7. Lower the vehicle, start the engine and run at approximately 1500 rpm. Depress and release the brake pedal several times and turn the steering wheel to full right and left.
8. Turn the engine off and check the fluid level in the reservoir. Add fluid if necessary.

NOTE: If the fluid is extremely foamy, or there is an erratic pedal feel allow vehicle to stand a few moments with the engine off and repeat the above procedure.

Brake Pedal Adjustment
Motor Home Chassis

1. With brake pedal pull back spring installed, brake pedal hard into bumper, brake master cylinder assembly and brake pedal rod lever at full return, install the preassembled brake pedal rod assembly (rod end at boot) and adjust to 31.75".
2. Turn the brake pedal rod end and adjust the free pedal travel to .06" to .36".
3. Fasten the boot to the floor pan assembly and compress the boot to 2.54" installed height.

Forward Control Chassis— (Vans)

1. Adjust the pedal rod to 9.90" and install in the vehicle.
NOTE: The brake pedal push rod is not adjustable on cab and Suburban models.

Booster Installation—Forward Control chassis exc. Light duty Vans (© Chevrolet Div., G.M. Corp.)

Stop Lamp Switch Adjustment
All Models

1. Release the brake pedal to its normal position.
2. Loosen the switch locknut and rotate the switch in its bracket. Electrical contact should be made when pedal travel is 3/8"-5/8".

Air Brakes
Reference

Specific information will be found in Power Brake Section on adjustments, overhauling and troubleshooting.

Brake pedal adjustment—forward control chassis (© Chevrolet Div., G.M. Corp.)

Brake pedal adjustment—Vans
(© Chevrolet Div., G.M. Corp.)

Brake pedal and stop lamp adjustments—Motor Home Chassis (© Chevrolet Div., G.M. Corp.)

General Description

Full air brakes completely replace ALL hydraulic parts with more durable components, capable of producing and using greater braking energy.

Brakes are applied by pushing on the pedal, which controls the application valve. Varying amounts of pressurized air will fill the brake chambers depending on brake pedal travel. Cam type shoe actuators (wedge type on stopmaster) are connected to push rods attached to diaphragms in the brake chamber. When air pressure is passed to brake chambers, the diaphragm then converts air pressure energy to mechanical force, the pressured diaphragms move the cam type actuators (wedge type on stopmaster) spreading the brake shoes and thereby applying brakes.

When the brake pedal (application valve) is released, a rapid discharge of air pressure from brake chambers is necessary to speed brake shoe release. A front and rear quick release valve aids in this function.

Many safety devices are used. A low air pressure warning buzzer sounds when pressure falls below a safe level. An air pressure gauge on dash shows the air pressure in system. Normal air pressure, for brake application, is at least 70 lbs. "Wet"

Safety valve
(© Chevrolet Div., G.M. Corp.)

and "dry" reserve tanks (also called primary and secondary) serve to remove moisture from air and also to provide a reserve of braking power. Drain cocks in tanks are provided to drain condensation. A pressure relief valve on the "wet" tank will release pressures over 150 lbs. A check valve located ahead of "wet" tank will retain air pressure in event of compressor failure or leaks.

Components

Compressor

Belt driven on gas engines and usually gear driven on diesel.

The air compressor serves only to supply and maintain sufficient pressure for brakes and air operated accessories. When pressure in system reaches top of normal range, an unloading valve opens and nullifies compressor action.

The average compressor is a single stage reciprocating piston type, usually one cylinder. Larger units are

Air-Pak unit (© Chevrolet Div., G.M. Corp.)

Governor assembly (© Chevrolet Div., G.M. Corp.)

FULL-AIR BRAKE SYSTEM
Full air brake system (© Chevrolet Div., G.M. Corp.)

Relay valve components (© Chevrolet Div., G.M. Corp.)

two cylinders. Compressors are lubricated by the engine system.

NOTE: Water cooled compressors, in event of freezing weather, must be drained as well as engine block.

Governor

Controls load and unload mechanism to automatically maintain maximum and minimum air pressures in reservoirs. Pressure ranges or settings are adjustable. The governor, by regulating the load and unloading mechanism, establishes an intermittent compressor pumping cycle.

Brake Control (Application) Valve (Foot Operated)

Provides quick and sensitive control of air pressure (FORCE) from reservoir to brake chambers. The amount of force applied to brakes is proportional to the amount of pedal depression.

Reservoir(s)

"Wet and Dry" tanks serve to remove moisture and provide a sufficient reserve of air under pressure for several brake applications

1 Valve body	4 Valve disc
2 Washer	5 Screw cap
3 Valve seat	6 Valve spring

Air tank check valve
(© Chevrolet Div., G.M. Corp.)

(safety factor). Drain cocks are provided to drain condensed moisture. A dash mounted gauge will show amount of reservoir pressure.

Safety Valve

Usually mounted on reservoir, allows air to escape when air pressure exceeds a predetermined setting (adjustable).

Check Valve

Between "Wet" tank and compressor to retain air pressure in the event of compression (compressor or lines) failure.

Low Pressure Signal

A safety device (buzzer) sounds when air pressure is absent or low.

Air Guage

Located on instrument panel, shows air pressure in system, works in conjunction with low pressure switch to warn of low pressure.

Pressure Protection Valve

Mounted in the delivery port of application valve. Its function is to close all air lines to auxiliary systems in event of loss of air pressure.

Relay Valve

A relay station to speed the application and release of brakes because of long air lines and volume of air necessary. A relay valve is usually at rear wheels. It is connected to application valve and meters air directly to rear brake chambers from an auxiliary reservoir.

Quick Release Valve

When brake pedal is released, a rapid discharge of air is necessary to speed the return of brake shoes. Two valves are used, one with front brake

Pressure protection valve
(© Chevrolet Div., G.M. Corp.)

Air brake chamber (© Chevrolet Div., G.M. Corp.)

chambers and one with rear chambers.

Moisture Ejector Valve

Mounted on bracket on cab step support close to wet air tank. Valve operates when brakes are applied and released to evacuate moisture from system.

Brake Chambers

Converts energy of compressed air into mechanical force required for brake application.

Cam Type

Air, admitted by control valve, enters brake chamber and pressurizes diaphragm with attached push rod. Push rod rotates lever arm of slack adjuster exerting a turning force on camshaft with an "S" design on end. This "S" cam operates between rollers on free ends of brake shoes and serves to expand shoes. Adjustment is manual at slack adjusters.

Wedge Type

Features two brake chambers per wheel. Wedge type actuators, operating between roller assemblies, force *each* shoe evenly against drum. Stopmaster brakes have automatic adjusters and do not need slack adjusters. *Fail-Safe* and *Super Fail-Safe* can be operated by either air or spring pressure, with additional features such as spring applied parking brake and is a safety factor in event of air brake failure.

NOTE: These units have a manual release bolt, in center of chamber cap, to permit safe handling for service. See note and caution under R&R.

Slack Adjusters

Used with cam type brakes to provide convenient means of adjustment for brake lining wear. With brakes APPLIED the angle formed by slack adjuster lever and brake chamber push rod should be approximately 90 degrees, and all adjusters to be about the same angle. Excessive travel of push rod shortens the life of chamber diaphragms and also results in slow braking response. Some slack adjusters have a locking sleeve, which engages head of worm shaft adjusting bolt, that must be pushed in to clear bolt head in order to make brake adjustments. Re-engage sleeve when finished.

Compressor (Belt Driven)

Compressor Removal

1. Block or hold vehicle by means other than air brakes.
2. Drain air from system, usually at reservoirs.
3. If water cooled, drain cooling system.
4. Disconnect ALL lines. (air, water and oil).
5. Loosen belt adjusting stud and remove drive belt.
6. Remove mounting bolts, remove compressor.

Compressor Installation

1. Run engine briefly to clear and check oil supply lines. Clean oil return lines and passages. Check coolant supply and lines (if used).
2. Clean mounting surface and replace gasket, be sure oil holes in gasket are aligned.
3. Install compressor with mounting cap screws loose, compressor will be movable to allow fittings on lines to be started.
4. Make sure air cleaner is cleaned and properly installed.
5. Align compressor, check drive belt.

6. Tighten mounting bolts and adjust belt tension.
7. Tighten all lines, fill cooling system if drained.
8. Run engine and check compressor for noises, leaks and output. Soapy water will help pin-point any air leaks. Check build-up time and governor.

Compressor (Gear Driven)

Compressor Removal

1. Block or hold vehicle by means other than air brakes.
2. Drain air from system.
3. Drain engine block.
4. Disconnect ALL lines (air, water, oil).
5. Remove four nuts and washers from mounting studs, pull compressor back off studs and remove.

Compressor Installation

1. Run engine briefly to clear and check oil supply lines. Check oil return lines and passages. Check coolant supply and lines. Inspect drive gears and coupling.
2. Make sure mating surfaces of compressor and housing are clean. Place new gasket on studs.
3. Install drive coupling on hub and position compressor on mounting studs. Guide compressor into mesh with driven disc, making sure coupling teeth engage disc. Install nuts and washers and torque to 65 foot pounds.
4. Connect water, air and oil lines securely, fill cooling system.
5. Run engine and check compressor for noise, leaks and output. Check build-up time and governor action.

Governor

Governor Removal

1. Block or hold vehicle by means other than air brakes.
2. Drain air system.
3. Remove dirt and grease from air line fittings, disconnect air lines.
4. Remove mounting bolts, remove governor.

Governor Installation

1. Make sure both air lines, to governor, are clean and open.
2. Place governor in position with exhaust port towards ground, tighten bolts finger-tight allowing unit to move. Start fittings.
3. After fittings are started, tighten governor mounting bolts then securely tighten fittings.
4. Test governor and check for leaks.

PUSH LOCK SLEEVE IN TO DISENGAGE HEAD OF WORM SHAFT TO MAKE ADJUSTMENT

LOCK SLEEVE MUST COME OUT AND ENGAGE HEAD OF WORM SHAFT TO LOCK ADJUSTMENT

Lever

Dowel

Spring

Lock Sleeve

Worm

Worm Shaft

Gear

Cover Plate

Slack adjusters (Ⓒ Chevrolet Div., G.M. Corp.)

Brake Control (Application) Valve

Control Valve Removal

1. Block or hold vehicle by means other than air brakes.
2. Exhaust air system.
3. Remove all lines and wires.
4. Remove pedal clevis pin and pedal.
5. Remove mounting bolts, remove valve.

Control Valve Installation

1. Mount valve in position, fasten loosely.
2. Start all fittings, connect stop lite wires. NOTE. Keep any sealant compound off first two threads of fittings.
3. Tighten mounting bolts, then securely tighten all lines.
4. Replace pedal.
5. Run engine and charge air system.
6. Check all fittings with pedal depressed with soapy water solution.
7. Check (and adjust) pedal free play.
8. Check valve action.

Reservoirs

Reservoir Removal

1. Block or hold vehicle by means other than air brakes.
2. Exhaust air system, open drain cocks.
3. Disconnect all air lines, remove drain cock and valves.
4. Remove mounting bracket bolts and nuts, remove tank.
   CAUTION: Where inside of reservoir is sludged and steam is used to clean, do not plug up reservoir or use excessive steam pressure.
   NOTE—In cold weather, more attention should be given to draining of moisture.

Reservoir Installation

1. Install reservoir in place loosely.
2. Start all fittings, valves and drain cock.
3. Tighten all mounting bolts and nuts to make sure reservoir does not vibrate in service. (Vibration causes premature line failures).
4. Securely tighten all lines, drain cock and valves.
5. Run engine, charge air system.
6. Check for leaks.

Valves, Signals and Gauges

Removal

1. Block or hold vehicle by means other than air brakes.

2. Exhaust air system, make certain ignition is off.
3. Clean work area, remove any wires, air lines and brackets. Remove unit.

Installation

1. Position replacement unit in system, making certain of any markings showing air flow direction, and secure.
2. Connect any wires and air lines.
3. Run engine and charge air system.
4. Test for leaks and operation of unit.

Brake Chamber

Cam type (uses slack adjusters one per wheel.)

Chamber Removal

1. Disconnect air hose from chamber.
2. Remove clevis pin from yoke.
3. Remove nuts and washers from mounting studs.
4. Remove chamber.

Chamber Installation

1. Place chamber on mounting bracket and secure with stud nuts and lock washers.
2. Connect air hose.
3. Install slack adjuster yoke clevis pin, after adjusting for minimum travel. (Angle made by push rod and slack adjuster lever should *not* be less than 90°, brakes applied). Lock yoke with locking nut. Push rod travel should be as short as possible without brakes dragging.
4. Check for leaks, and possible brake shoe adjustment.

Wedge Type (two per wheel) see note and caution below

Chamber Removal

1. Block or hold vehicle by means other than air brakes.
2. Disconnect air hose from chamber.
3. Remove lock washer tangs from notches in spanner nut and spider housing.
4. Loosen spanner nut and unscrew air chamber from housing.

Chamber Installation

1. Screw air chamber in spider housing until it "bottoms", then back off (no more than one turn) until chamber air port aligns with air hose. The plastic guide will assure proper position of wedge. Lock brake chamber in position with spanner nut and lock washer.
2. Start engine, charge air system, check for leaks. Pump brake pedal to allow automatic adjusters to adjust brakes.

NOTE: When brakes are equipped with "fail-safe" brake chambers, cage power spring before starting any disassembly or removal of wheels or drums to avoid possible injury. When a vehicle is disabled, due to low or lost air pressure, cage power spring before attempting to move the vehicle. Cage the power spring by rotating the release bolt approximately 18 to 21 turns clockwise. Caging and uncaging can be made easier by applying air pressure, 65 lbs needed (if possible). This takes spring load off release bolt.

CAUTION: Before removing or caging brake chamber, block wheels since parking brake will not be applied.

1	Brake band
2	Cams
3	Links
4	Clevis pins
5	Cam shoe
6	Lock nut
7	Adjusting nut
8	Locating bolt
9	Tension spring
10	Washer
11	Adjusting nut
12	Lock nut
13	Lock washer
14	Brake lining
15	Release spring
16	Brake drum
17	Adjusting bolt
18	Anchor bar
19	Anchor screw
20	Lock wire

Contracting bank (external) parking brake
(© Chevrolet Div., G.M. Corp.)

Slack Adjusters

Adjuster Removal

1. Remove clevis pin at lever.
2. Remove lock ring and washer on splined camshaft (some front slack adjusters are held on by a retaining screw).
3. Slide adjuster off splined shaft.

Adjuster Installation

1. Make sure spacer washers are in place (if used).
2. Slide slack adjuster on splined camshaft, lock in place with snap ring and washer. If held on by retaining screw, allow .010″ end play. Stake edge of screw to lock.
3. Connect yoke clevis pin. Angle made by push rod and slack adjuster lever should NOT be less than 90° brakes applied. Push rod travel should be as short as possible without brakes dragging.
4. Lubricate adjuster.

Parking Brakes

NOTE: Except in case of an emergency, set parking brake only after vehicle is brought to a complete stop. Parking brakes are not designed to take the place of service brakes.

Propeller Shaft—Band type.

This type, using external band and drum mounted on rear of transmission, provides a hand controlled brake independent of service brakes. Band, with lining, is centered on transmission bracket (anchor) and both sides are arranged to contract equally. Brake is actuated by lever and rod, or cable, to a cam and "J" bolt.

Adjustment

1. Block wheels and release hand brake.
2. Remove locking wire from anchor bolt (19) and adjust to obtain .010″ clearance between lining and drum—rewire anchor.
3. Loosen lock nut (6) on locating bolt and tighten adjusting nut (7) until there is a clearance of .020″ between lining and drum. Measure clearance about 3 inches from end of lining. Tighten lock nut.
4. Loosen lock nut (12) on adjusting "J" bolt (17) and tighten adjusting nut (11) to obtain a clearance of .020″ approximately 3 inches from end of lining. Tighten lock nut.
5. Check hand brake operation by applying lever. If more than ½ the number of notches on sector are needed to lock the propeller shaft, make final adjustment on lever rod, at clevis end. Remove blocks.

Propeller Shaft—Shoe Type

Hand brake drum is mounted on rear of transmission with internal and external shoes (duo-grip) or with two internal expanding shoes. Shoes are forced against drum by lever and cam actuated by cable. Propeller shaft brakes lock the driveline for parking.

Adjustment—Duo-Grip

1. Block wheels and release hand brake.
2. Loosen lock nut (12) and tighten adjusting bolt (13) to obtain .010″ clearance between outer shoe lining and drum at this point. Hold bolt and lock nut securely.
3. Loosen lock nut (6) and tighten adjusting nut (11) to obtain .010″ between inner shoe lining and drum, at center of shoe. Hold nut (11) and tighten nut (6).

NOTE: Some vehicles, such as tilt cab, use a compound hand brake lever with flexible cable that features a cable adjustment. This allows the operator to adjust the "over-center" position of lever required to lock parking brake.

Adjustment—Two Shoe Internal Expanding

1. Block wheels and release hand brake, it may be necessary to remove clevis pin to assure full release of shoes.
2. Align slot in drum with star wheel adjuster. Knock out lanced area in drum, if necessary to gain access to star wheel. Be sure to remove all metal from brake compartment.

1 Brake cable
2 Adjustable clevis
3 Connecting lever
4 Return spring
5 Link
6 Lock nut
7 Operating lever
8 Inner shoe
9 Outer shoe
10 Brake drum
11 Adjusting nut
12 Lock nut
13 Adjusting bolt
14 return spring
15 Adjuster bracket

Two shoe (Duo Grip) parking brake
(© Chevrolet Div., G.M. Corp.)

1 Return springs
2 Anchor pin link
3 Camshaft
4 Control lever
5 Link
6 Relay lever
7 Brake shoe
8 Plate bolt
9 Adjusting screw spring
10 Adjusting screw
11 Support plate

Internal expanding type brake—installed
(© Chevrolet Div., G.M. Corp.)

3. Engage star wheel with brake spoon and rotate star wheel to obtain a .010″ clearance between lining and drum. Moving handle end of spoon down expands shoes. Check with .010″ feeler gauge rotating drum. Shoes can be expanded so as to lock drum then backed off 5 notches similar to a wheel adjustment. Check drum, jack up one rear wheel, for free rotation.

4. Replace clevis, install drum hole cover, remove jack and blocks.

Rear Wheel—Cable Type

Hand lever or foot pedal operated, cable actuated, rear wheel service brakes are used for parking brakes.

Adjustment

1. Block front wheels and apply hand brake two notches from released position.
2. Jack up both rear wheels.
3. All cables and linkage connected, pull back spring in place, loosen cable adjusting lock nut and tighten adjusting nut until a slight drag is felt when rotating rear wheels. Tighten lock nut.
4. Fully release parking brake and check both rear wheels. No drag should be present.
5. Remove jack and blocks.

NOTE: Adjustment of cable should only be made when service brakes are in full adjustment. Cables should be lubricated when rear drums are off.

Rear Wheel—Air Brake

NOTE: For stopmaster fail-safe and super fail-safe information see brake chamber section. (automatic adjusters)

Anchorlok

Anchorlok chamber is mounted "piggy back" on service chamber. It contains a diaphragm under air pressure (60 pounds or more) to contain a powerful spring in compression in normal opration. When air pressure drops below 60 pounds, the coiled spring starts to move out. If air pressure continues to drop, the spring

1	Brake Support Bracket
2	Parallel Adjusting Screws
3	Front Lever Arm Pin
4	Pin Retaining Screw
5	Brake Cable Clevis
6	Brake Lever
7	Brake Shoe Pin Retainer
8	Brake Shoe Pin
9	Front Brake Shoe
10	Rear Brake Shoe
11	Front Lever Arm
12	Brake Disc
13	Tension Spring
14	Spring
15	Rear Lever Arm
16	Adjusting Nut
17	Tie Rod

Tru-stop type parking brake (© Chevrolet Div., G.M. Corp.)

will keep expanding to apply brakes until at approximately 30 pounds the spring will have applied the brakes sufficiently to bring the vehicle to a safe, even stop.

To permit moving vehicle, when air pressure is not available to compress spring, a caging tool consisting

Spring compressor assembly
(© Chevrolet Div., G.M. Corp.)

of a stud and nut will be found stored on service chamber housing. Remove rubber plug in center of anchorlok and insert stud ¼ turn. Turning nut on stud will cage spring.

CAUTION: Cage spring before removing or servicing anchorlok.

TRU-STOP (Disc Type)

This type brake is used only on models equipped with an auxilliary transmission. It uses a ventilated brake disc which is mounted between the propeller shaft flange and the auxiliary transmission shaft companion flange. The brake shoes are mounted in the opposed positions with the brake disc between. When the brake is applied the shoes are forced against the disc.

Adustment

1. Disconnect the brake cable or rod clevis from the brake lever.
2. Tighten the adjusting nut until the spring exerts enough pressure to bring the lever against the front lever arm.
3. Insert a 1/32″ shim between the rear shoe lining and brake disc.
4. Tighten the adjusting nut until the front shoe lining is firmly

Internal expanding type adjustment
(© Chevrolet Div., G.M. Corp.)

"Anchor Lock" brake chamber—installed
(© Chevrolet Div., G.M. Corp.)

against the disc yet still allowing removal of the shim.

5. Make sure that the tensions spring is in place. Make sure that both linings are parallel with the disc by adjusting the parallel adjusting screws. This provides 1/64" clearance between the front and rear shoelinings and brake disc at all points.

6. Check to see that brake lever in the cab is in the full released position. Adjust the clevis on the brake cable as necessary to permit installation of the clevis pin through the clevis and brake lever without changing position of the lever. Install the clevis pin and cotter pin.

7. Make sure the lock nuts on the brake cable and adjusting screws are firmly tightened.

Fuel System

Reference

This section contains brief information on removal, installation and minor external adjustments. For more detailed information and major service operations see carburetor general section.

Data on capacity of the gas tank will be found in the Capacities table. Data on correct engine idle speed and fuel pump pressure will be found in the Tune-up Specifications table. Both can be found at the start of this section.

Carburetors

Various carburetors are designed to meet requirements of engine, transmission and vehicle; therefore carburetors may look alike but are not always interchangeable. All carburetors have conventional float, idle, low speed, power or high speed and accelerating circuits with either manual or automatic chokes.

NOTE: Some symptoms indicate carburetor trouble but in reality are ignition. Before any extensive repairs on carburetor, check first—heat riser, intake manifold and ignition.

Carburetor Removal

1. Remove air cleaner.
2. Disconnect fuel, vacuum, spark control and governor lines.
3. Disconnect choke and hand throttle controls.
4. Disconnect throttle and automatic transmission linkage at carburetor. Remove pull back spring.
5. Remove mounting nuts and washers.
6. Lift carburetor off manifold and drain. Discard gasket.

Mechanical fuel pump
Single
Combination
(© Chevrolet Div., G.M. Corp.)

Carburetor Installation

1. Clean carburetor mounting surface.
2. Install new gasket on manifold. Be sure vacuum port and gasket slots are aligned.
3. Place carburetor on manifold, reconnect finger-tight all lines before (evenly) tightening carburetor mounting nuts.
4. Tighten all lines.
5. Reconnect choke and hand throttle controls, replace throttle and automatic transmission linkage, reconnect all vacuum and electrical lines. Connect pull back spring. Check choke and throttle operation.
6. Install air cleaner, check element.
7. Start engine and warm to operating temperature. During warm-up time, torque intake manifold.
8. Adjust idle mixture and idle speed screws, be sure choke is fully open.

CAUTION: Do not force idle mixture screw against seat, this will damage needle. On transmission controlled spark engines (TCS), fast idle adjustment must be set with electrical leads disconnected at solenoid and transmission in neutral.

NOTE: If possible (safely), fill carburetor bowl before installing, will save time and battery drain as well as reducing possible backfiring. Dirt is greatest troublemaker for carburetors, check all filters. Use starter briefly to clear fuel lines (before reconnecting) of any metal flakes that are always present when fuel lines (metal) are disturbed.

NOTE: For Idle Speed and Mixture adjustments (see Tune-Up de-

cal) *in the engine compartment. For all other adjustments refer to the appropriate carburetor in the General Repair Section.*

Fuel Pumps

Description

Two types of pumps are used, mechanical and electric. Mechanical pump is diaphragm type, consisting of a single fuel chamber or a combination fuel and vacuum chambers. In-line engines the pump is actuated by an eccentric lobe on camshaft, V6 eccentric is attached to front of camshaft, V8 engines use a push rod between eccentric lobe on camshaft and pump rocker arm. The single pump is non-serviceable while the combination pump is rebuildable. Electrical pumps are used with step fuel tanks or as stand-by emergency units.

Fuel Pump Removal

(Diaphragm Type)

1. Disconnect fuel lines at pump, also vacuum lines on combination unit. Be ready to cap gas feed line should it be necessary (trucks without shut-off valve).
2. Remove two cap screws and washers holding pump to block. Remove pump and mounting gasket. Be careful of push rod on V8's.

Fuel Pump Installation

(Diaphragm Type)

1. Crank engine to position camshaft lobe on lowest point.
2. Check feed line for restrictions.
3. On V8s—place heavy grease on one end of push rod and slide into position.
4. Hold fuel pump, with new gasket, in position and start two cap screws finger tight. CAUTION: Be sure rocker arm contacts eccentric in correct position.
5. Start fuel line fittings, using flexibility of pump to insure against crossing threads, also start vacuum lines if dual pump.
6. Tighten mounting bolts and lines. Start engine and check for leaks. (open shut-off valve if closed)

Electric fuel pump
(© Chevrolet Div., G.M. Corp.)

Spinner type governor installation (© Chevrolet Div., G.M. Corp.)

Fuel pump installation
(© Chevrolet Div., G.M. Corp.)

Diagrammatic view of governor
(© Chevrolet Div., G.M. Corp.)

CAUTION: When engine is cranked at starter with jumper cable, remove distributor lead from negative post on coil and ignition switch must be on. Failure to do this can result in damage to the ground circuit of ignition switch.

Fuel Pump Removal

(Electric)

1. Disconnect battery ground cable.
2. Disconnect wiring harness from pump connector.
3. Remove fuel line from pump.
4. Remove bolts and washers holding pump to tank, rotate pump 90 degrees counterclockwise and remove from tank.

Fuel Pump Installation

(Electric)

1. Carefully position pump into tank opening. Reconnect fuel outlet line to fitting.
2. Install attaching bolts and torque to 4-6 ft.-lbs.
3. Reconnect pump wiring harness and battery ground cable.
4. Check operation of pumps by using pump selector switch.

Fuel Tank

Description

Various types and designs of gas tanks are used due to complexity of engine body and chassis combinations. On ½ ton and ¾ ton the tank is located in rear behind drive axle.

Larger vehicles use frame mounted tanks on right side, frame side rail. Cab models, except tilt cab, tank is behind seat in cab. Increased fuel capacity is available by using optional tanks. Tanks may be cylindrical, step, saddle or round. All tanks are equipped with a vented filler neck cap. A large fine-mesh, self cleaning screen is used on bottom of fuel pickup pipe.

Following procedure is intended only as a guide. It will vary according to truck model and tank type.

Fuel Tank Removal and Installation

1. On trucks with dual tanks check shut-off valve position.
2. Be sure ignition switch is off or battery ground is disconnected.
3. Remove seat back rest if cab mounted.
4. Drain tank. If tank does not have a drain plug, disconnect gas line and use opening to drain tank. If not accessible, siphon fuel. Do not siphon by mouth, use equipment for that purpose or make a siphon hose as shown below and use air pressure if available.
5. Remove filler neck, cap and vent hose.
6. Disconnect tank gage wire and any ground lead.
7. Remove tank support straps or mounting bolts. Remove tank.
8. Clean all lines, check filters. (Blow clean only after disconnecting other end of line).

9. To install, reverse removal procedures.

CAUTION: Do not use drop cord in area. A bulb breakage could have disastrous effects. Use only safety cans for fuel storage. Do not overtighten lines, as this could distort or twist and lead to leaks.

Governors

Velocity Type

Governor is mounted between carburetor and intake manifold and automatically governs the maximum speed of engine which in turn limits maximum speed of vehicle.

Operation

Governor is operated by vacuum intake manifold opposing a calibrated (adjusting) spring, which in turn is connected to a throttle shaft and valve. Velocity of gas mixture from carburetor tends to close valve but this action is opposed by governor spring tension. The calibration of velocity versus spring tension is very sensitive.

Adjustment

Adjustment of spring pull is accomplished by number of spring coils operating (active). Turn adjusting cap counter-clockwise for higher speeds. If too sensitive use special hollow wrench to turn adjusting screw nut. Caps are usually wire locked and sealed.

Vacuum Spinner Type

Governor consists of two components connected by tubing. One is in distributor housing and other on carburetor throttle body. This type permits full horsepower usage without excessive engine speeds. An overspeed warning device is usually incorporated in system. A system of calibration of vacuum versus spring tension.

Operation

To limit engine speed while permitting greater throttle openings when additional power is required.

Vacuum is applied to diaphragm in carburetor chamber on throttle housing by internal passages. This vacuum is controlled by distributor air valve thru inter-connecting tube. Distributor centrifugal air valve, by spring pressure, remains open until desired governor speed is reached. Then adjustable centrifugal weight will close air valve in opposition to spring, thereby allowing vacuum to be applied to diaphragm which in turn acts to close throttle valve in opposition to carburetor governor tension.

Increased engine load results in lower distributor speed which allows air valve to open, permitting vacuum to drop, which will in turn allow governor spring to open throttle wider, increasing engine power to meet load increase.

Adjustment

Since governor speed is a function of both distributor and carburetor the best method of setting speed is to adjust spinner on vehicle. The spinner mechanism can be adjusted by holding slotted end of ballast weight with screw driver and turning adjusting nut on other end.

Increase speed by turning nut clockwise, decrease — counter-clockwise.

NOTE: Efficiency of governor depends on keeping all passageways clean and tight, also distributor air filter clean.

Cooling System

Reference

Detailed information on cooling system capacity can be found in the Capacities table.

Type—Description

All models have pressurized cooling system, thermostatically controlled bypass, sealed by radiator cap. System is designed to operate with coolant's boiling point raised which increases efficiency of radiator. Pressure cap contains both pressure and vacuum relief valves, spring loaded. Pressure valve allows excess pressure out overflow and vacuum

valve relieves when system cools off. Thermostat is pellet or poppet construction designed to open and close at predetermined temperatures, and incorporates a by-pass. Two types of cores are used, down-flow and cross-flow, according to vehicle needs and design.

NOTE: Due to various body and chassis designs the following procedures are typical.

Radiator Removal

1. Drain radiator. NOTE: When draining, use short piece of ⅜ hose over draincock to save coolant or anti-freeze.
2. Remove radiator, heater, radiator filler and overflow hoses, also oil cooler lines (and plug).
3. Disconnect battery ground cable at battery. Remove wiring from front-end sheet metal, remove hood on cab-over-engines.
4. Remove grille, lower panel, baffle plates and air duct hoses on step-vans.
5. Remove heater from firewall and raise out of way, remove inspection plate on firewall above engine box on step-vans.
6. Remove shroud, if so equipped, or hang over fan blades for additional clearance.
7. Remove finger guard and surge tank, if so equipped.
8. Loosen fan belt and remove fan blades if necessary.
9. Remove radiator (support) bolts and any braces.
   NOTE: On larger vehicles attach hoist to support assembly before removing bolts as support assembly of core, grille, shroud, surge tank and air cleaner ducts will be removed as a unit.
10. Conventional vehicles—Lift up core to remove, on step-vans and forward control units it may be necessary to raise vehicle and remove from below.

Radiator Installation

Install in reverse order of removal —fill system and check for leaks, adjust fan belt if necessary.

Tests

Test radiator by warming engine to operating temperature, then turning off and feeling core. Radiator should be hot at top and warm at bottom, an even temperature drop from top to bottom. A cool spot indicates stoppage. All radiator fins should be straight and free of bugs and any dirt that might restrict air flow.

CAUTION: Radiator coolant level should be checked when engine is cool otherwise, unless precautions are taken, serious personal injury may result. The radiator cap removal, when system is at operating temperature, will cause the pressure in system to drop to atmospheric pressure.

Since operating temperatures are as high as 247°F., steam pockets will form in system and blow coolant out of radiator. It is important that coolant level be maintained either 1″ below filler neck or at level indicated on radiator.

CAUTION: Do not pour cold water in radiator while engine is hot. Wait until boiling ceases, start engine and while engine is idling then add water slowly.

Water Pump

Types—Description

Pump is belt driven, centrifugal vane impeller type. Bearings are permanently lubricated and sealed against water and dirt. Pump requires no care other than keeping air vent, on top of housing, and drain hole in bottom, open.

Water Pump Removal

1. Drain system.
2. Remove lower radiator and heater hoses.
3. Loosen alternator and remove fan belt (and idler belt if so equipped).
4. Remove fan blade bolts, remove blades and pulley. CAUTION— Thermostatic fans are to be kept in "on the car" position to avoid loss of silicone fluid.
5. Remove pump attaching bolts (or nuts) and pull pump cautiously out of block recess, avoid any contact that might damage impeller.

Water Pump Installation

1. Clean gasket surface on block and install new pump-to-block gasket, sealed on both sides.
2. Guide pump into position and secure evenly.
3. Connect all hoses, use a good sealer.
4. Replace fan blades and pulley.
5. Install fan belt and adjust.
6. Fill cooling system and check for leaks, check heater operation.

Water pump—typical inline engines
(© Chevrolet Div., G.M. Corp.)

Water pump—typical V8 engines
(© Chevrolet Div., G.M. Corp.)

Engine cradle under engine
(© Chevrolet Div., G.M. Corp.)

NOTE: A 5/16 x 1″ sae cap screw (with head removed) will make a guide stud to help align fan blades, pulley and hub.

Tests

Water pump operation may be checked by accelerating engine while squeezing top hose. A pressure surge should be felt. *Under safe conditions* this will also be apparent in top tank of radiator. Do not confuse surge in top tank with gas bubbles due to cylinder head (gasket) leakage.

NOTE: Consult index for procedures on GMC V6 engines.

Engine

Reference

In the specifications tables of this section are listed most of the service references needed by the mechanic.

Where different sized engines are used, identification can be made by refering to Serial Number Location and Engine Identification, near the beginning of this section.

Exhaust Emission Control

Beginning 1966, the California inspired Air Injection System (K-19) is used on all General Motors built trucks (with a few design exceptions) for delivery into that state. This Emission Control System, in some cases, involves removal and installation procedures more complicated than standard R&R procedures. This situation is especially true in the area of Manifolds, Cylinder Heads, or Engine R&R.

Beginning 1968

In compliance with anti-pollution laws involving all of the continental United States, the General Motors Corporation has adopted a special system of terminal exhaust treatment. This plan supersedes (in most cases) the method used to conform to 1966-67 California laws. The new system replaces (except with stick shift and special purpose engine applications) the use of the A.I.R. method previously used.

The new concept, Combustion Control System (C.C.S.) utilizes engine modification, with emphasis on carburetor and distributor changes. Any of the methods of terminal exhaust treatment requires close and frequent attention to tune-up factors of engine maintenance.

Since 1968, all manufacturers post idle speeds, and other pertinent data relative to the specific engine application, in a conspicuous place in the engine compartment.

Evaporative Emission System

This system was designed to reduce fuel vapor emissions that are normally vented into the atmosphere from the gas tank and the carburetor fuel bowl, through the use of a carbon canister and liquid-vapor separator.

Transmission Controled Spark System

This system controls emissions by eliminating the vacuum advance in the low gears. The control is accomplished by the use of a solenoid vacuum switch which regulates the vacuum to the distributor. This system also incorporates a thermal override switch which provides full vacuum in all gears when engine is cold.

Exploded view—V8 engine typical (© Chevrolet Div., G.M. Corp.)

Chevrolet Trucks · Vans · Blazer

Exhaust Gas Recirculation System

This system helps reduce nitrogen oxides emitted by the engine exhaust. This is accomplished by releasing small amounts of exhaust gas into the cylinders by means of the E.G.R. valve. This lowers the peak combustion temperatures, reducing the amounts of oxides produced.

Air Injection Reactor

The A.I.R. system injects compressed air into the exhaust system, close enough to the exhaust valves to continue the burning of the normally unburned segment of the exhaust gases. To do this it employs an air injection pump and a system of hoses, valves, tubes, etc., necessary to carry the compressed air from the pump to the exhaust manifolds. Carburetors and distributors for A.I.R. engines have specific modifications to adapt them to the air injection system; these components should not be interchanged with those intended for use on engines that do not have the system.

A diverter valve is used to prevent backfiring. The valve senses sudden increases in manifold vacuum and ceases the injection of air during fuel-rich periods. During coasting, this valve diverts the entire air flow through the muffler and during high engines speeds, expels it through a relief valve. Check valves in the system prevent exhaust gases from entering the pump.

Early Fuel Evaporation System

1975 models are equipped with this system to reduce engine warm-up time, improve driveability, and reduce emissions. On start-up, a vacuum motor acts to close a heat valve in the exhaust manifold which causes exhaust gases to enter the intake manifold heat riser passages. Incoming fuel mixture is then heated and more complete fuel evaporation is provided during warm-up.

Catalytic Converters

The converters are used to oxidize hydrocarbons (HC) and carbon monoxide (CO). They are necessary because of even stricter emission standards for the 1975 models.

The catalysts are made of noble metals (platinum and palladium) which are bonded to either a monolithic (one-piece) element or to individual pellets. The catalyst causes the HC and CO to break down without taking part in the reaction; hence, a catalyst life of 50,000 miles is expected.

Some engines equipped with the converters require an air injection pump to supply air for the reaction; others will not.

For more detailed information refer to the General Section.
NOTE: Engine details for V6 see GMC

Engine Removal

Conventional Cab, Pickups, Panel and 4 Wheel Drive

1. Disconnect and remove battery.
2. Drain cooling system.
3. Drain engine oil.
4. Remove air cleaner and ducts.
5. Remove hood and radiator (also shroud if equipped) on larger models (1½ ton and up) it will be necessary to remove front end sheet metal. NOTE: Scribe alignment marks on hood hinges.
6. Disconnect wires at:
Starter solenoid.
Delcotron.
Temperature switch.
Oil Pressure switch.
Transmission controlled spark solenoid.
Coil.
Neutral safety switch.
7. Disconnect:
Accelerator linkage.
Choke cable at carburetor (if so equipped).
Fuel line to fuel pump. (capline).
Heater hoses.
Transmission dipstick and tube, plug hole (if so equipped).
Oil pressure line to gauge. (if so equipped).
Oil fill tube (and dipstick).
Vacuum or air lines.
Parking brake cable (if used).
Power steering lines (if so equipped).
Engine ground straps.
Exhaust pipe (support if necessary).
8. Loosen fan belt, remove fan blades and pulley.
9. Remove clutch cross-shaft or disconnect clutch slave cylinder (if so equipped).
10. Remove road draft tube (if so equipped).
11. Remove rocker arm cover (s) and attach engine lifting tool. Take engine weight off mounting bolts.
12. Remove propeller shaft and plug end of transmission housing on light trucks. On 1½ ton and up, support transmission and disconnect from engine.
13. On light duty trucks, disconnect speedometer cable at transmission, shift linkage and any clutch linkage as required.
14. Disconnect transmission cooler lines (if so equipped).
15. On light trucks equipped with automatic or 4 speed transmission, remove rear engine mount bolts and rear crossmember.
16. Remove front engine mount

bolts. CAUTION: Make final check that all necessary disconnects have been made.
17. On light trucks, raise engine and transmission and pull forward until removed. Larger trucks remove rear mounting bolts, raise engine and pull forward until disconnected from transmission continue to raise engine until removed from vehicle. Be careful not to damage clutch disc.

Engine Installation

Install in reverse order of removal, fill cooling system and crankcase (check transmission). Start engine and check for leaks and operation. Adjust carburetor and road test.

Engine Removal

Van (Panel and Sport)

Because of its location, the engine is removed from below and both engine and transmission removed as a unit.
1. Disconnect battery ground cable.
2. Drain cooling system.
3. Remove engine cover.
4. Disconnect:
Air cleaner, extensions and heat tubes.
Accelerator linkage.
Choke cable at carburetor (if used).
Transmission controlled spark solenoid (if used)
Primary wire at coil.
Oil fill tube (and dipstick).
Starter solenoid.
Temperature sender at unit.
Delcotron.
Oil pressure line or sender switch.
Transmission dipstick and tube, plug hole (if so equipped).
Evaporative Control System lines at air cleaner and carburetor.
5. Remove upper radiator hose and heater hoses.
6. Loosen fan belt, remove blades, pulley and shroud (if used).
7. Remove distributor cap and spark plug wiring harness. NOTE: Disconnect any wiring harness retaining clips.
8. Raise vehicle on hosit, drain crankcase and disconnect:
Engine splash shields (if used).
Engine ground straps.
Lower radiator hose.
Neutral safety switch, at transmission (if equipped).
Fuel line to fuel pump. (capline).
Transmission controlled spark switch, at transmission (if used).
Transmission cooler lines (if used).
Speedometer cable at transmission (and plug).

30

Power steering hoses (if equipped).
Parking brake cable (if used).
Steering idler and pitman arms.
Positive battery cable at starter.

9. Disconnect exhaust pipe, support if necessary or block out of way.

10. Remove propeller shaft at transmission and plug extension housing to prevent oil leakage.

11. On manual transmissions, disconnect shift levers and clutch linkage; on automatics, shift linkage.

12. Place jack, with engine cradle attached, under engine and take weight off mounting bolts. CAUTION: Place cradle under engine as far as possible, (to the fifth oil pan cap screw from flywheel at least) and secure with chain over flywheel housing.

13. Remove engine front mounting bolts (and brackets for additional room).

14. Remove bolts at rear mount to crossmember.

15. Remove transmission support crossmember bolts and remove crossmember. CAUTION: Make final check that all necessary disconnects have been made.

16. Lower engine and transmission assembly slowly, pulling to rear to clear front crossmember, and move unit out from under vehicle.

NOTE: On 1974 models, Chevy-Van and Sportvan, provisions have been made so that the grille, filler panels and tie bars can be removed easier than on previous models. This allows removal of the engine from the front of the vehicle instead of from underneath, which makes engine R & R quicker and easier.

Engine Installation

Van (Panel and Sport)

Install in reverse order of removal, fill cooling system and crankcase (check transmission). Start engine and check for leaks and operation. Adjust carburetor and road test.

Engine Removal

Step Vans

1. Disconnect battery and remove.
2. Drain cooling system, drain engine oil.
3. Remove engine box, drivers seat, floor panels at stepwells, floor panel around steering column and pedals, and inspection plate on firewall above engine box.
4. Remove air cleaner (and any ducts).
5. Remove radiator and shroud.
6. Loosen fan belt and remove fan blades.
7. Remove engine splash pans (if used).

8. Disconnect neutral safety wire at converter (if used).
9. Remove upper and lower radiator hoses.
10. Disconnect wires at:
Starter solenoid.
Delcotron.
Transmission controlled spark solenoid (if used).
Temperature switch.
Oil pressure switch.
Coil.
11. Disconnect:
Accelerator Linkage.
Choke cable at carburetor (if so equipped).
Fuel line to pump.
Heater hoses.
Oil pressure gauge line (if so equipped).
Parking brake cable (if used).
Vacuum or airlines.
Power steering lines (if so equipped).
Engine ground straps.
Exhaust pipe (support if necessary).
12. Remove clutch cross-shaft or disconnect clutch slave cylinder (if so equipped).
13. Remove oil fill tube and dipstick also transmission dipstick and tube, plug holes (if used).
14. Remove rocker arm cover (s) and attach engine lift tool.
15. Push arm of engine lift crane in right side door opening. Attach to lifting device or sling and take engine weight off mounts. CAUTION: Make final check that all necessary disconnects have been made.
16. Support transmission and remove shift controls (cover opening), speedometer cable (plug hole), transmission spark

control switch wire and oil cooler lines (if used).
17. Remove propeller shaft at transmission. Plug extension housing to prevent leakage.
18. Remove 2 top transmission to clutch housing cap screws and insert 2 guide pins. NOTE: Take 2 bolts, the same diameter and threads as just removed, but at least 4″ long and cut heads of bolts off. Using a hack saw, slot ends just cut for screwdriver and use for guides.
19. Remove 2 lower transmission to clutch housing cap screws and slide transmission back until clear of clutch disc. When transmission is free from engine, lower and remove from under vehicle.
20. Remove engine mounting bolts, front and rear.
21. Raise engine slightly and push forward to clear crossmember, then lift up and remove engine through door opening.

Engine Installation

Step Vans

A careful check of clutch components should be made. Install in reverse order of removal, fill cooling system and crankcase (check transmission). Start engine and check for leaks and operation. Adjust carburetor and road test.

Engine Removal

Tilt Cab

1. Tilt cab to expose engine area and secure.
2. Block wheels and exhaust air (if so equipped).

(25-30 FT. LBS.)
(15-20 FT. LBS.)   (15-20 FT. LBS.)

Manifold torque (typical)
(© Chevrolet Div., G.M. Corp.)

FRONT   FRONT

"SMALL V8"   "MARK IV V8"

Intake manifold bolt torque sequence (© Chevrolet Div., G.M. Corp.)

3. Disconnect battery ground cable.
4. Drain cooling system.
5. Drain crankcase.
6. Remove air cleaner and any ducts.
7. Remove radiator and heater hoses.
8. Remove radiator support and shroud assembly.
9. Disconnect hoses and remove surge tank.
10. Disconnect choke cable at carburetor.
11. Disconnect hand throttle at carburetor.
12. Disconnect shift linkage at control island.
13. Remove control island bolts and swing island out of way.
14. Remove both right and left island supports.
15. Disconnect cab safety lock and remote cab support.
16. Disconnect emergency brake cable.
17. Remove any engine splash shields.
18. Disconnect wires at:
Starter solenoid.
Delcotron.
Temperature sender.
Oil pressure sender.
Coil.
Governor speed warning.
Transmission controlled spark solenoid at carburetor.
19. Remove:
Accelerator linkage.
Fuel line to pump.
Lines or wires to dash guages.
Vacuum or air lines at engine.
Power steering lines at pump (if equipped).
Engine ground straps.
Exhaust pipe or crossover pipe (support if necessary).
20. Remove fan blades, pulley and support bracket assembly.
21. Remove clutch cross-shaft or disconnect clutch slave cylinder.
22. Remove rocker arm covers and install lift tool or sling.
23. Hoist engine and take engine weight off motor mounts.
NOTE: According to work to be performed select either of the following.

Removal of Engine and Transmission as a Unit

24. Disconnect speedometer (and plug).
25. Disconnect shift linkage at transmission (cover opening).
26. Disconnect any clutch linkage not yet removed.
27. Disconnect and drop propeller shaft at transmission, also any power take-off or auxiliary transmission couplings (cover or plug all openings).
28. Disconnect oil cooler lines or transmission spark control switch (if so equipped).

29. On Roadrangers remove air lines and parking brake drum (if used).
30. Remove all engine mounting bolts and raise slightly to support transmission weight. CAUTION: Make final check that all necessary disconnects have been made.
31. Remove any transmission to support bolts.
32. Raise engine and transmission assembly out of chassis as a unit.

Removal of Engine Only

24. Support transmission, remove flywheel under-pan, and disconnect from engine. NOTE: If possible, install transmission guide pins in top (transmission to clutch housing) holes to allow engine to slide forward to clear clutch disc splines. This will prevent bending clutch hub.
25. Remove all engine mounting bolts. CAUTION: Make final check that all necessary disconnects have been made.
26. Raise slightly and pull forward until clear of transmission.
27. Continue to raise engine until high enough to clear chassis.

Engine Installation

Tilt Cab

Install in reverse order of removal, fill cooling system and crankcase (check transmission). Start engine and check for leaks and operation. Make any minor adjustments and road test.

Engine Manifolds

Reference

Due to various body and chassis designs, it will be necessary to expose engine areas such as raising tilt cabs, hoods and removing engine boxes on vans.
NOTE: The use of a good chemical solvent on exhaust manifold bolts and nuts will facilitate the operation.
CAUTION: Pay particular attention to heat risers, their failure increases warm-up time and failure to open can cause lean mixtures at higher speeds.

In-line Engines (Combination Manifold)

Removal

1. Remove air cleaner (and any ducts).
2. Disconnect throttle controls, rods, linkage and return spring.
3. Disconnect fuel and vacuum lines at carburetor, also choke cable or control (if used).
4. Disconnect crankcase ventilation valve, vacuum brake or trans-

mission spark control hoses (if used).
5. Remove carburetor.
6. Remove oil filter support bracket and swing filter to one side (if so equipped).
7. Disconnect exhaust pipe at flange and support if necessary (discard gasket or packing).
8. Remove manifold attaching bolts and clamps, remove manifold assembly (be careful of locating rings). Discard gaskets.

Installation

Reverse removal procedures after cleaning all gasket surfaces, checking for cracks, check heat riser and alignment. Lay straight edge on manifold to head surface to check. If intake and exhaust are not in line, loosen center bolts where they are joined and do not tighten until assembly is bolted to head, then retighten). Install finger-tight, check that pilot or locating rings and gaskets are in place, then torque to specifications in proper sequence. Torque on end bolts is 15 to 20 ft. lbs., all others are 20-30 ft. lbs.
Warm engine, adjust idle and check for leaks.

V Engines—Intake Manifold

Removal

1. Drain radiator, remove top hose at thermostat housing also any bypass or heater hoses.
2. Remove battery ground cable.
3. Remove carburetor air cleaner and any ducts.
4. Remove oil fill tube and cap.
5. Disconnect gas line, all vacuum hoses, throttle linkage and return spring, choke cable and crankcase ventilation valve.
6. Disconnect wires to temperature sender, coil and transmission spark controlled solenoid (if so equipped).
7. Remove carburetor.
8. Remove distributor cap and mark position of rotor. Remove distributor.
9. Exhaust air and remove air compressor, disconnect oil drain line at manifold (if so equipped and interferes).
10. Remove manifold attaching bolts, remove manifold.
NOTE: If manifold is not to be replaced, some components can be left on such as carburetor, oil fill tube, thermostat housing and temperature sender.

Installation

Clean gasket and seal surfaces on manifold, block and heads. Install new gaskets and seals, coated with a good sealer particularly at water passages. Position manifold, use guide pins to prevent gaskets moving, and check mating angle at heads. (Angle could be incorrect due to excessive cylinder head resurfacing)

Install bolts finger tight, then torque to specifications in proper sequence. Reverse the removal procedures fill radiator, warm engine, adjust timing and carburetor idle if necessary and check for leaks.

V Engines—Exhaust Manifold

Removal

1. Use a good liquid penetrant freely on attaching bolts and nuts.
2. Remove the carburetor heater if so equipped.
3. Remove exhaust pipe (support if necessary).
4. Open french locks and remove manifold attaching bolts. NOTE: A 9 16″, thin wall, 6 point socket sharpened at leading edges, placed over head of bolt then tapped with hammer will speed the opening of french locks.
5. Remove Delcotron (on left side), remove manifold.
NOTE: On 366 and 427 engs. spark plugs must also be removed before removing manifold.

Installation

Clean mating surfaces, install new gaskets where used, check heat riser and check for cracks. Reverse removal procedures. Start engine and check for leaks.

Cylinder Head

Reference

Due to many types of vehicles it will be necessary to remove various access covers to expose engine area.

In-line Engines

Removal

1. Drain cooling system and remove battery ground strap at head.
2. Remove air cleaner and any ducts.
3. Remove choke cable, accelerator rod and return spring, fuel and vacuum lines at carburetor.
4. Remove manifold to head bolts and clamps, pull manifold and carburetor assembly clear of head and support.
5. Remove fuel and vacuum lines from retaining clip at thermostat housing.
6. Disconnect temperature sender wire, remove wiring harness from rocker cover clip. Remove coil wires and coil.
7. Remove top radiator hose, at thermostat housing.
8. Remove spark plug wires and distributor cap.

9. Remove rocker arm cover. CAUTION: Never pry rocker arm cover loose—bump cover rearward in a gasket shearing manner.
10. Engines with rocker arm shafts, back off adjusting nuts, rotate rocker arm to clear push rod and remove push rods. Engines using

V8—366, 396 & 427 engines

V8—283, 307, 327 & 350 engines

V6—401 & 478 engines

6—235 & 261 engines

6—194, 230, 250 & 292 engines

4—153 engine

V-8 400, 454 engines
(© Chevrolet Div., G.M. Corp.)

pedestal rocker arms, remove rocker arm ball nuts, arms and push rods.
11. Remove push rod cover.
12. Remove cylinder head bolts, cylinder head and discard gasket.

NOTE: Place rocker arm mechanism and cylinder head bolts in a rack so they can be re-installed in same locations. (mated)

Check cylinder head for warpage with a straight edge. Inspect for cracks and burnt valves.

Installation

Reverse removal procedures and adjust valves after cleaning gasket surfaces. Engines using a steel (shim) gasket, coat both sides with a good sealer, bead side up. Do not reuse gaskets. Cylinder head bolt threads in block and threads on bolts must be clean. Coat threads on bolts with sealer before installing. Tighten each cylinder head bolt a little at a time, in correct sequence, until specified torque is reached. Engines using composition (steel asbestos) gaskets must have heads retorqued after warm-up. (retightening heads effects valve lash) Refer to specifications at beginning of this section for nut tightening sequence.

V Engines

Removal

1. Remove intake manifold (with carburetor) and exhaust manifold—see manifolds R & R.
NOTE: If only one head is to be removed, remove inlet manifold bolts on that side only and leave inlet manifold assembly in place.
2. Loosen belt and remove power steering pump (if so equipped).
3. Remove rocker arm covers.

CAUTION: Never pry rocker arm cover loose—bump cover rearward in a gasket shearing manner.

SPARK PLUG COOLING HOLES
CYLINDER HEAD GASKET WITH BEAD SIDE UP

Cylinder block spark plug cooling holes
(© Chevrolet Div., G.M. Corp.)

4. Loosen rocker arm adjusting nut, turn rocker arm to clear push rods and remove push rods. Exhaust push rods are longer than intake push rods in some engines so to be sure—place in sequence so that they can be installed in same location (mated).

5. Remove cylinder head bolts, cylinder head and discard gasket.

6. Check cylinder head for warpage with a straight edge. Inspect for cracks and burnt valves.

Installation

Reverse removal procedures and adjust valves, after cleaning gasket surfaces. If heads are to be resurfaced check alignment at intake manifold. Cylinder head bolt threads in block and threads on bolts must be clean, coat threads with sealer. Tighten each cylinder head bolt a little at a time, in correct sequence, until specified torque is reached. Engines using steel (shim) gasket, coat both sides with a good sealer, bead side up. Engines using composition (steel asbestos) gaskets must be retorqued after warm-up (retightening heads effects valve lash).

Refer to specifications at beginning of this section for nut tightening sequence.

3. Back off rocker arm adjusting nut until rocker arm starts to clatter, then turn nut down slowly until clatter stops. This is zero lash position.

4. Turn adjusting nut down ¼ turn and pause 10 seconds until engine runs smoothly. Repeat operation 3 more times until 1 full turn down from zero lash position is reached. NOTE: This 1 turn pre-load adjustment must be done slowly and in stages to allow hydraulic lifter to adjust itself to prevent possibility of internal interference or bent push rods.

5. Repeat for each valve, the use of a vacuum gauge is recommended.

6. Install new rocker cover gaskets and torque rocker covers. Reset engine idle.

Engine Not Running

1. Remove rocker cover (s) (bump off—do not pry off).

2. Tighten cylinder head bolts (and rocker arm supports if used).

3. Disconnect primary wire at negative terminal of coil.

4. Mark distributor housing with chalk at each spark plug tower (double mark no. 1 cylinder).

5. Remove distributor cap and

crank engine until rotor points to No. 1 chalk mark. (No. 1 cylinder is approximately at TDC and both valves can be adjusted). Valve adjustment is made by backing off rocker arm nut until push rod can be rotated and then slowly tightened until push rod does not turn. This is zero lash position. Turn adjusting nut down 1 full turn to complete adjustment.

6. Adjust the remaining valves, one cylinder at a time (following firing order) in same manner.

7. Install distributor cap.

8. Install new rocker cover gasket (s) and torque rocker cover (s).

Noisy Lifters

Locate a noisy lifter by using a mechanic's stethoscope or hose, can also be detected by placing finger on valve spring retainer (a distinct shock will be felt each time valve returns to seat). Forcing push rod down will cause lifter check valve to unload and remain open. A noisy or defective push rod is usually indicated by a free-spinning push rod.

Rocker Arms

Rocker arms are trough shaped, pressed steel levers that transfer lifter motion to valves. Rocker arms are

Valve adjustment (© Chevrolet Div., G.M. Corp.)

LIFTER "A"   LIFTER "B"

Valve System

Adjustments—Hydraulic lifters
Engine Running

1. Run engine to normalize (stabilize oil temperature), remove rocker cover (s) bump off—do not pry off). Leave old gasket on head to aid against oil overflow or use oil deflector clips.

2. Reduce engine idle as low as possible, tighten cylinder head bolts (and rocker supports if used). Check camshaft lobe lift.

1 Lifter body
2 Push rod seat
3 Metering valve (Lifter A) inertia valve (Lifter B)
4 Check ball
5 Check ball retainer
6 Push rod seat retainer
7 Plunger
8 Check ball spring
9 Plunger spring

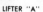

Hydraulic valve lifters (© Chevrolet Div., G.M. Corp.)

© Chevrolet Div. G.M. Corp.

Nut
Rocker Arm Ball
Rocker Arm
Ball Stud
Cap Shield — Valve Spring Cap
Valve Push Rod
Valve Spring
Intake Valve   Exhaust Valve

V8 engine—valve system
(© Chevrolet Div., G.M. Corp.)

Engine (Cu. In.)	Camshaft Part No. & Valve Lift	Gears Properly Indexed	One Tooth Adv.	One Tooth Ret.
250	3864896-.388	.014" ± .004"	.0351"	.0055"
292	384800-.405	.016" ±.004"	.0379"	.0068"

supported on individual pedestals and have an oval hole in center to fit over stud and pivot on ball seats. Oil is fed to rocker arms by means of hollow push rods. Whenever arms or ball seats are being installed, coat all bearing surfaces with engine oil.

Rocker arm studs are pressed in cylinder head and are available in oversize for replacement.

CAUTION: Do not try to press oversize stud in head without reaming stud hole first.

Pressed in studs can be replaced by a stud threaded on both ends. Head is to be threaded in stud hole to accept threaded stud.

Checking Engine Valve Timing 6 cyl. (In Line Engine)

1. Remove the valve rocker arm cover and the push rod front cover.
2. Loosen the nut and the no. 2 intake valve rocker arm, swing the rocker arm away from the push rod and remove the push rod and valve lifter.
3. Temporarily install a flat face mechanical lifter in place of the hydraulic lifter.
4. Turn the crankshaft until the no. 2 exhaust valve opens and the notch on the pulley dampner is aligned with the "O" mark on the timing pointer.
5. Position a deal indicator to measure lifter movement and set the indicator at zero. Turn the crankshaft to 360 degrees and read the indicator. On engines that are correctly timed the indicator will read as follows:
   250 engines .... 0.014"
   292 engines .... 0.016"

If the reading is not as above, reset the indcator at zero and turn the crankshaft 360 degrees, then read the indicator again. If the read is now correct, the engine is timed properly. The following chart shows indicator

readings result from improperly indexed gears.

6. If after checking an out-of-time condition exist, remove the engine front cover and check for proper indexing of time marks on gears.

V-6—Engine

1. Remove the left-hand rocker cover.
2. Facing the front of the engine turn the engine clockwise to the top dead center No. 1 mark at the crankshaft pulley on the compression stroke. Both the intake and the exhaust valve on the No. 1 cylinder will then be closed.
3. On all V-6 engines adjust the clearance to exactly 0.099 inches at the No. 1 exhaust valve (front valve).
4. Turn the engine clockwise until the No. 1 exhaust valve opens and begins to close, then with fingers, try turning the push rod of the No. 1 exhaust valve as the engine is cranked slowly. When the push rod rotates with finger pressure, the 5-degree (before top dead center mark) on the pulley should be at the pointer. This will be about one revolution from the starting point. If the pushrod can be rotated at any point between the 10-degree mark and the top dead center No. 1 mark, the valve timing is correct. After making the timing check be sure to adjust the exhaust valve clearance to 0.018".

NOTE: If the timing chain has been installed improperly, there will be a 15 degrees out-of-time condition for each mismatched tooth on the sprocket.

V-8 Engine

1. Remove the rocker arm covers.
2. Turn the crankshaft so that the timing mark is at the "O" mark on the pointer and the No. 1 cylinder is ready to fire.
3. Move the crankshaft, and the exhaust valve in the No. 6 cylinder will just close and the intake valve will just begin to open.
4. If the exhaust valve or the intake valve is open when the pointer is at the "O" timing mark the camshaft is out of time
5. When the No. 6 cylinder is ready to fire and the pointer is at the "O" timing mark the No. 1 cylinder exhaust valve will have just closed and the intake valve will begin to open.

Timing Gears and Chain

Crankshaft Pulley or Damper Removal

1. Drain radiator; remove hoses.
2. Remove radiator—See Radiator R & R

NOTE: On V-8 engines if additional operations such as camshaft removal are not being performed, radiator removal will not be necessary.

3. Loosen fan belt and remove any accessory drive.
4. Use puller to remove pulley or damper.

NOTE: On some early models, pulley is bolted to Hub. Remove pulley first then, using pulley holes, remove hub. More recent models have the

LOCKS
CAP
SEAL
SHIELD
SPRING
*DAMPER

NOT USED ON 194,230 & 250 CU. IN. L6

Valve spring installation
(inline & small V8 engines)
(© Chevrolet Div., G.M. Corp.)

LOCKS
CAP
SEAL
DAMPER
SPRING
*ROTATOR

Exhaust valve spring installation
(Mark IV V8 truck, 366 and 427 engines)
(© Chevrolet Div., G.M. Corp.)

hub bonded to inertia weight. Care must be exercised when using a puller.

Installation

1. Clean area, inspect oil seal in cover. (Now would be good time to install new seal even if just for preventative maintenance).
2. Coat timing case cover oil seal with light oil, inspect hub for seal (grooved) wear.
3. Position damper (or hub) on crankshaft, aligning keyway, and tap lightly into position.
4. Pull damper (or hub) into position with damper retaining bolt and washer. (Make sure damper retaining bolt has good thread engagement before applying force). Torque to specifications.
5. Reverse balance of removal steps.

Timing Cover Oil Seal Replacement

With Cover On (To Remove Cover Means Removing Oil Pan)

1. Remove torsional damper—see damper R & R.
2. Pry old seal out, be careful not to mar crankshaft or bend cover.
3. Install new seal (lip of seal toward block), tap lightly into position. Coat seal with oil.
4. Reverse removal procedures.

Timing Gear Replacement

In-Line Engines

NOTE: When necessary to install a new camshaft gear the camshaft should be removed. However gear can be removed from camshaft without removing camshaft from engine. Cam gear can be split and hub section pulled off but extreme care must be taken not to allow any impact, either removing or installing gear, on the shaft. Camshaft must be totally blocked so as not to allow any movement to disturb oil sealing welsh plug at camshaft rear bearing.

Removal (Pulling Camshaft)

1. Drain and remove radiator.
2. Remove front end sheet metal or grille.
3. Remove damper or pulley.
4. Remove oil pan (See Oil Pan R & R).
5. Remove timing case cover (2 bolts inside oil pan at front main bearing cap).
6. Remove rocker arm cover(s) and remove lifters.
7. Remove fuel pump and distributor (mark position of rotor).
8. Align timing gear marks (check rotor mark) then remove 2 thrust plate screws by reaching through 2 holes in camgear.
9. Remove camshaft and rear assembly by pulling and turning shaft carefully so lobes will not mar bearings and will clear lifters.
10. Use press to remove cam gear using caution not to damage thrust plate by woodruff key.
11. Clean all gasket surfaces and inspect.
12. Check camshaft alignment and lobes for wear. Check camshaft

TIMING MARKS

Timing mark alignment inline engines

bearings in block, check crank gear and oil spray nozzle.

Installation

1. Support camshaft at back end of front bearing in a press, place thrust plate over end of shaft, install woodruff key in key way, align camgear with key and press gear on shaft until clearance at thrust plate (and front end of front bearing) is .001-.003".
2. Install camshaft and gear assembly in block, turning shaft carefully so lobes clear lifters and bearings, until it almost bottoms. NOTE: Coat lobes and bearing surfaces with engine oil.
3. Turn camshaft and mesh timing marks, tighten thrust plate.
4. Check cam gear for runout (should not exceed .005").
5. Check backlash at gears. (.004-.006").
6. Reverse remaining removal procedures.
7. Fill radiator, and oil and start engine. Adjust valves, check timing and inspect for leaks.

Timing Chain
V Engines

Removal

1. Drain and remove radiator.
2. Remove torsional damper.
3. Remove oil pan (see oil pan R & R).
4. Remove water pump or pulley if necessary.
5. Remove timing case cover.
6. Align timing marks.
7. Remove (3) camshaft sprocket bolts.
8. Remove sprocket and chain. NOTE: sprocket is a light press fit on-camshaft, especially at dowel pin. If sprocket is tight, tap lightly with plastic hammer on lower edge of sprocket.
9. Clean all gasket and seal areas and inspect.
10. Check teeth on both sprockets for wear.

Installing oil seal (cover installed)
(© Chevrolet Div., G.M. Corp.)

Removing torsional damper
(© Chevrolet Div., G.M. Corp.)

Valve timing—V8 engines

Correct relation of piston & rod
153, 194, 230 & 250 engines

PISTON PIN CLAMP BOLT
TOWARD CAMSHAFT SIDE
OF ENGINE

Correct relation of piston & rod
235 & 261 engines

Timing mark alignment 366 & 427 engines

Correct relation of piston and rod 366, 400,
427, 454 engines
(© Chevrolet Div., G.M. Corp.)

Timing mark alignment V6 401 & 478 engines

Correct relation of piston & rod
6—292 engine

Correct relation of piston to rod
293, 307 & 350 engines

Installation

1. Suspend chain on camshaft sprocket with timing mark in approximate position.
2. Place chain over crankshaft sprocket and position camshaft sprocket on dowel. Recheck timing marks.
3. Draw camshaft sprocket in place using the three mounting bolts. Torque to specifications. CAUTION: do not drive sprocket on camshaft as welsh plug at rear of camshaft can be dislodged.
4. Lubricate chain with engine oil, make sure oil slinger is in place.
5. Reverse removal procedures.
6. Fill radiator, add engine oil and start engine. Check for leaks.

Check for Worn Chain

1. Check fan belt tension, adjust if too loose.

Pistons and Connecting Rods

Pistons

Pistons are of various designs, flat, cup, hump and dome. Heads are usually notched to indicate front or pistons are marked on pin boss.

Connecting Rods

Rod forging and cap have mating numbers and must be on same side when installed or cap is on "backwards." Rod number on in-line engines go to camshaft side. Numbers on "V" engines go to outside of block. The oil spurt (cylinder wall oiling) hole goes toward camshaft. On inline engines the spurt hole and number are both on camshaft side. On "V" engines the spurt hole is in center, toward camshaft, and numbers to outside.

2. Remove distributor cap, loosen spark plugs.
3. Move fan blades until rotor moves. Mark distributor housing and balancer at pointer.
4. Move fan in opposite direction until rotor moves, remark both units.
5. Marks in excess of 4° apart, 2 graduations (usually) on balancer, indicate excess wear.

Piston and Rod Removal

1. Drain cooling system and remove cylinder head(s). See cylinder head removal.
2. Drain crankcase oil and remove oil pan. See Oil Pan Removal.
3. Remove any ridge and/or deposits from upper end of cylinder bores with a ridge reamer. NOTE: Move piston to bottom of its travel and place a cloth on top of piston to collect cuttings. After ridge and/or deposits are removed turn crankshaft until piston is at top of its stroke and carefully remove cloth with its cuttings.
4. Check connecting rods and pistons for cylinder number identification and if necessary, mark them.
5. Remove conecting rod nuts and caps. Push rods away from crankshaft and install caps and

RIGHT BANK
2-4-6-8

LEFT BANK
1-3-5-7

Correct relation of piston & rod
348 & 409 engines

Install piston & rod assemblies
(© Chevrolet Div., G.M. Corp.)

NOTCH TO FRONT OF ENGINE

OIL SPURT HOLE

RIGHT BANK
2-4-6-8

LEFT BANK
1-3-5-7

Correct relation of piston & rod
327 engine

nuts loosely to their respective rods.

6. Push piston and rod assemblies away from crankshaft and out of cylinders. See Engine Rebuilding—General Section.

Piston and Rod Installation

1. Lightly coat pistons, rings and cylinder walls with light engine oil, making sure everything is clean and free of dirt and foreign material.
2. With bearing caps removed, and ring compressor tool installed, install each piston in its respective bore.
3. Install bearing caps and check bearing clearance. See Engine Rebuilding—General Section.
4. Install oil pan gaskets, seals and oil pan. See Oil Pan Installation.
5. Install cylinder head gasket(s) and head(s). See Cylinder Head Installation.
6. Refill crankcase and cooling system and check for leaks.

Piston Rings

Piston rings are available in standard size as well as .020″, .030″, and .040″ oversizes.

Piston Ring Removal

1. With pistons removed from cylinders, remove piston rings by expanding them and sliding them off piston.
2. Clean piston ring grooves by removing all particles of carbon. Check for burrs or nicks that might cause rings to hang up.

Piston Ring Installation

See Engine Rebuilding—General Section.

Main and Rod Bearings

Main bearings and connecting rod bearings are replaceable inserts, precision fit and held in place by locking tangs. Excessive bearing clearances reduce oil pressure. Never replace the lower half of any bearing without replacing the upper half. Do not file any bearing cap. Make sure, on main bearings, the upper half oil hole is aligned. Be certain oil passages in the crankshaft are open. Mark rod caps and upper forgings, also main caps

and block, in numerical order to aid in reassembly. Rod bearings are available in standard size as well as .001″, .002″, .010″ and .020″ undersizes. Main bearings are furnished in standard size and .001″, .002″, .009″, .010″, .020″ and .030″ undersizes.

Rod Bearing Replacement

1. Drain crankcase oil and remove oil pan. See Oil Pan Removal.
2. Remove connecting rod bearing cap.
3. Wipe bearing shell and crankpin clean of oil.
4. Inspect bearings for evidence of wear or damage. (Bearings showing the above should not be installed).
5. Measure crankpin for out-of-round or taper with a micrometer. If within specifications measure bearing clearance with plastigage or its equivalent. See Engine Rebuilding—General Section.
6. Install bearing in connecting rod and cap.
7. Coat bearing surface with oil, install rod cap and torque nuts to specifications.
8. Rotate crankshaft after bearing adjustment to be sure bearings are not too tight. Check side clearance.
9. Install oil pan gaskets, seals and oil pan. See Oil Pan Installation.

230 CU. INCH   250 CU. INCH

INSERT PISTONS WITH NOTCHES
TOWARD FRONT OF ENGINES

FRONT OF ENGINE

Pistons installed (inline engines)
(© Chevrolet Div., G.M. Corp.)

V-8

CONNECTING ROD BEARING TANG SLOTS INSTALLED OPPOSITE CAMSHAFT

SLOT

SLOT

Connecting rods installed V8 engines

Measuring connecting rod side clearance V8 engines
(© Chevrolet Div., G.M. Corp.)

Rear main bearing removal (upper half)
(© Chevrolet Div., G.M. Corp.)

Main Bearing Replacement

NOTE: Main bearings may be replaced with or without removing crankshaft.

(Engine in Vehicle)

1. Drain crankcase oil and remove oil pan. See Oil Pan Removal.
2. Remove oil pump.
3. Loosen or remove spark plugs for easier crankshaft rotation.
4. Starting with rear main bearing, remove bearing cap and wipe oil from journal and cap.
5. Inspect bearings for evidence of wear or damage.
6. Measure bearing clearance with plastigage or its equivalent. The crankshaft should be supported at damper and flywheel to remove clearance from upper bearing. Total clearance can then be measured between lower bearing and journal. See Engine Rebuilding—General Section.
7. Remove bearing shell from cap.
8. On in-line engine crankshaft, rear main bearing has no oil hole. Replace rear main bearing upper half as follows:
   a. Use a small drift punch and hammer to start upper bearing half rotating out of block.
   b. Use a pair of pliers (with taped jaws) to hold bearing

thrust surface to oil slinger and rotate crankshaft to remove bearing.
   c. Oil new selected size upper bearing and insert plate (unnotched) and between crankshaft and indented or notched side of block.
   d. Use pliers as in removing to rotate bearing into place. The last ¼ movement may be done by holding just the slinger with pliers or tap in place with a drift punch.
9. All other crankshaft journals (in-line and "V" models) have oil holes. Replace main bearing upper half as follows:
   a. Install a main bearing remov-

ing and installing tool in oil hole in crankshaft journal. NOTE: If such a tool is not available, a cotter pin (with head flattened) may be used.
   b. Rotate crankshaft clockwise as viewed from front of engine. This will roll upper bearing out of block.
   c. Oil new selected size upper bearing and insert plain (unnotched) end between crankshaft and indented or notched side of block. Rotate bearing into place and remove tool from oil hole in crankshaft journal.
10. Oil new lower bearing and install in bearing cap.
11. Install main bearing cap accord-

UPPER

LOWER

Rear main oil seal 6 cyl. engines
(© Chevrolet Div., G.M. Corp.)

Wire attached on oil seal
(© Chevrolet Div., G.M. Corp.)

WICK SEAL

Rear main oil seal installation
(© Chevrolet Div., G.M. Corp.)

ing to markings. Torque bearing cap bolts to specifications.

12. Install oil pump and oil pan. Refill crankcase. Install and tighten spark plugs.

Rear Main Bearing Oil Seal Replacement (Engine in Vehicle)

1. Raise vehicle and drain oil.
2. Remove oil pan and oil pump. See oil pan and oil pump removal.
3. Remove rear main cap and discard seal.
4. Loosen all mains (except no. 1) and block crankshaft down for maximum clearance at rear main.
5. Use wooden dowel, so as not to mar journal, tap lightly until seal can be gripped and removed. Rotating shaft may help.
6. Wick type seal: Use "Chinese Finger" type of tool, or insert a piece of soft wire through seal approximately ¼ from end, then wrap end with wire. Insert wire through seal opening in crankcase and around crankshaft. Start upper half of seal in place, lubricated with light sealer. Pull seal into place (rotating shaft may help) until centered. Cut each end of seal so that ¼″ protrudes. Install new lower half of oil seal in cap and roll or pack into position. Cut ends flush with cap parting face. Replace cap. Molded type seal: Insert new upper half, lubricated with light sealer, into channel and apply firm pressure with hammer handle until seal is centered. (Lip of seal facing toward front of engine.) Install lower half of oil seal in cap (lip toward front), lubricate lip with oil and install cap.
7. Torque all mains, check for drag.

Rear main oil seal removal
(© Chevrolet Div., G.M. Corp.)

Removing lower half—rear oil seal
(© Chevrolet Div., G.M. Corp.)

8. Replace oil pump, oil pan and add oil.
9. Start engine and check for leaks.

Engine Lubrication
Oil Pan Removal and Installation
1970 and Up—Vans

1. Support on stands.
2. Disconnect battery ground cable, loosen fan belt and remove radiator shroud top belt.
3. Remove radiator fan and pulley.
4. Raise vehicle, clean road dirt from oil pan.
5. Drain oil, replace drain plug gasket.

6. Remove engine splash shields if equipped.
7. Remove starter, leave electrical connections intact, swing out of way.
8. Automatic transmisson models —remove oil cooler lines and converter pan.
9. Remove front motor mount bolts.
10. Remove accessory drive pulley (if used).
11. Engines with radiator shroud— drain radiator, remove lower radiator hose, remove lower shroud bolts and lower shroud out of way.
11. Using a jack, raise and support front of engine.
12. Remove crossmember to frame bolts, remove crossmember.
13. Remove oil pan bolts, remove oil pan. CAUTION: If any prolonged operations are planned (with pan off), it would be safer to re-install crossmember and lower engine on mounts.
14. Reverse removal steps to install after cleaning gasket and seal surfaces.
15. Lower vehicle, fill crankcase and radiator, start engine and check for leaks. NOTE: Use gasket sealer as a retainer to hold side gaskets in place on block. Bolts in front cover should be installed last. They are installed at an angle and holes line up after rest of pan bolts are tightened.

1970 and Up (Except Vans)

1. Raise front of vehicle and support on stands.

Engine lubrication 283, 327 & 350 engines (© Chevrolet Div., G.M. Corp.)

Engine lubrication 6 cyl.
235 & 261 engines
(© Chevrolet Div., G.M. Corp.)

OIL PRESSURE SENDING UNIT

DISTRIBUTOR SHAFT OILING

TIMING GEAR OIL NOZZLE

FULL FLOW OIL FILTER

SPLASH OILING

FILTER BY-PASS SYSTEM

Engine lubrication 4 cyl. 153 engine 6 cyl. 194, 230, 250 & 292 engines
(© Chevrolet Div., G.M. Corp.)

2. Remove road dirt from pan and drain plug.
3. Drain oil, replace drain plug gasket.
4. Remove converter pan on automatic transmission.
5. Remove battery ground cable, remove starter (leave electrical connections intact and swing aside).
6. V8—Remove dipstick and tube, remove exhaust crossover pipe.
7. C10-30—Remove front motor mount bolts, using a block of wood under oil pan, raise engine with a jack high enough to insert blocks at motor mounts.
8. Remove oil pan and discard gaskets and seals.
9. Reverse removal steps to install after cleaning all gasket and seal surfaces.
10. Lower vehicle, fill crankcase to level, start engine and check for leaks.
NOTE: Use gasket sealer as a retainer to hold side gaskets in place on block.

Oil Filters

Oil filters are related to oil change periods, which in turn are related to quality of oil used, type of service and operating conditions. Severe conditions such as frequent and prolonged idle periods may warrant more changes. Heavy sludge in pan or filter indicates oil change intervals should be shortened. Filter replacements should be made at time of oil change. It is recommended that filter be replaced with initial oil change and every second oil change thereafter.

Filters on in-line engines are located at right front of engine, "V" engines at left rear.

Replacement—Element Type

1. Remove drain plug (some models) in shell and drain, replace drain plug (if used).
2. Remove center stud, withdraw shell and empty (if no drain plug).
3. Lift out element and clean inside of shell thoroughly.
4. Clean base and replace shell gasket, check bypass valve.
5. Install new element (with element gasket) in shell.

6. Install shell on base, drain plug away from engine, and tighten retaining bolt to engine and check for leaks, check oil level.

Replacement-Disposable (Spin-on) type

1. Turn filter from mounting base and discard.
2. Clean base and inspect gasket area.
3. Apply oil film to gasket and turn filter on stud until gasket seats then tighten ½ turn more.
4. Run engine, check for leaks, check oil level.
NOTE: On some vans the right hand engine splash shield will have to be removed.

Oil Pump

The pumps used are distributor driven gear type. Oil pump consists of two spur gears and a relief valve in a two piece housing. On in-line engines, pump is mounted on cylinder block while on "V" engines pump is mounted on rear main cap inside oil pan. Pump gears and body are not serviced separately, replace pump as a unit. A baffle, incorporated on the pickup screen, eliminates oil pressure loss due to surging.

Removal and Installation

1. Remove oil pan—see oil pan removal.
2. In-line engines—Remove oil suction pipe at housing. CAUTION: Do not disturb screen on pick up pipe.
3. Remove two flange mounting bolts, remove pump.
4. Reverse removal steps to install, using new pan gasket, watch slot alignment with distributor tang.

1 Shaft extension
2 Shaft coupling
3 Pump body
4 Drive gear and shaft
5 Idler gear
6 Pickup screen and pipe
7 pump cover
8 Pressure regulator valve
9 Pressure regulator spring
10 Washer
11 Retaining pin
12 Screws

Oil pump V8 engines
(© Chevrolet Div., G.M. Corp.)

THROW-AWAY TYPE   REPLACEABLE ELEMENT TYPE

Engine oil filters (© Chevrolet Div., G.M. Corp.)

NOTE: Pump should slide easily into place, if not remove and relocate slot.

5. Refill with oil, start engine and check for leaks.

Front Suspension

References

General instructions covering the front suspension and how to repair and adjust it, together with information on installation of front wheel bearings and grease seals, are given in the General Repair Section.

Definitions on the points of steering geometry are covered in the General Repair Section. This article also covers troubleshooting front end geometry and irregular tire wear.

Figures covering the caster, camber, toe-in, kingpin inclination, and turning radius can be found in the Wheel Alignment table of this section.

Types

1963 and Up

Two different types of front end suspension are used, independent coil spring and I-beam with leaf spring. Four wheel drive series uses a driving axle with tapered leaf springs.

Coil Spring Type

This suspension consists of upper and lower control arms, pivoting on steel threaded bushings on upper and lower control arm inner shafts which are attached to the crossmember. Control arms are connected to the steering knuckle by ball joints. A coil spring is seated between the upper and lower control arms, thus the lower control arm is the load carrying member.

I Beam Type

Front axle is the conventional reverse Elliott type with king pins that use full floating bushings up to approximately 7,000 lb. Front leaf spring is semi-elliptical, steel bushed at front eye, shackled at rear and seated on top of axle.

Spring Replacement
Coil Spring
1963 and Up

1. Raise vehicle and place (high) stands under frame allowing control arm to hang free.

2. Disconnect shock absorber (and stabilizer if used) at lower end.
3. Using a floor jack, under center of lower control arm inner shaft, raise and remove tension from shaft. CAUTION: Install a safety chain through spring.
4. Remove both clamps or "U" bolts securing inner shaft to crossmember.
5. Release jack very cautiously, slowly lowering arm with spring until spring is free. Remove safety chain, remove spring.
6. Inspect front end especially at ball joints and both upper and lower control arm inner shaft bushings.
7. Reverse removal steps to install, use a long tapered drift to align holes of inner control arm shaft and crossmember while slowly jacking arm into place.

Leaf Spring
1970 and Up

1. Wire brush all road dirt from threaded areas on U bolts, shock absorbers and stabilizer links, apply a good penetrant on threads.
2. Disconnect shock and stabilizer link at lower bracket.
3. Loosen both spring U bolts.
4. Using jack under I-beam, raise front of vehicle and support at frame side rail with stand. Finish removing U bolts and rebound bumper. Lower jack until spring clears I-beam or tire rests on ground. Remove any caster wedges (shims) and set aside for installation. NOTE: Thick end of shim goes to rear of vehicle for increased caster.
5. Remove front spring eye bolt.
6. Remove rear shackle (and hanger cam if equipped).
7. Remove spring, inspect hangers and spring seat (center bolt index).
8. Reverse removal procedures to install after placing spring on axle with center bolt head indexed in seat and caster shims in place. Torque all nuts and lubricate.

CROSS DRILLED MAIN BEARING JOURNALS WITH HIGH PERFORMANCE ENGINE ONLY.

CRANKCASE AND CRANKSHAFT OILING   VALVE MECHANISM OILING

Engine lubrication 348, 366, 396, 409 & 424 engines (© Chevrolet Div., G.M. Corp.)

Ball Joint Replacement
Coil Spring Suspension
Upper

1. Place jack under lower control arm, at coil spring, and raise vehicle until tire clears floor.
2. Remove tire, wheel and drum assembly.
3. Remove upper ball stud nut and break the stud taper from the steering knuckle by rapping sides of knuckle flats at stud. Separate stud from knuckle.
4. Remove rivets and bolt in new ball joint. Rivets can be chiseled off, ground off or drilled out. CAUTION: Use special hardened bolts only when installing joint (furnished with joint).
5. Reverse remaining removal steps to complete installation.

Coil Spring Suspension
Lower

1. Jack vehicle at lower control arm spring seat and remove tire, wheel and drum assembly.
2. Remove coil spring, see coil spring R&R.
3. Remove ball stud nut at knuckle, use stud jack or rap stud loose from knuckle.
4. Remove lower control arm assembly.
5. Press out ball joint. Press new ball joint into arm. Make sure ball joint assembly is fully seated and square with arm. Check inner shaft bushings.
6. Reverse remaining removal steps to complete installation.

Front Drive Axle
Description

The front axle is a hypoid gear axle unit equipped with steering knuckles.

Coil spring type suspension (© Chevrolet Div., G.M. Corp.)

Axle assembly number and production date are stamped on left tube of assembly.

Conventional truck service brakes are provided on all 4-wheel drive units.

Transfer Case

The transfer case, also known as a drop gear box, is the unit which transmits power from the transmission to the rear and/or front axles and power take-off. Engagement of front wheel drive, power take-off or speed range is accomplished through control levers in the cab. The case is mounted to an adapter at the rear of the transmission.

Model number, ratio and production date are stamped on a plate located on top of the transfer case.

For service on transfer case refer to General Repair Section.

Front Drive Axle

Front Axle Assembly
Removal and Installation

1. Disassemble propeller shaft from front axle differential.
2. Raise front of vehicle until weight is removed from front

Torsion bar suspension 10-40 series (© Chevrolet Div., G.M. Corp.)

Torsion bar suspension 50-80 series (© Chevrolet Div., G.M. Corp.)

Torsion bar anchor bolt
(© Chevrolet Div., G.M. Corp.)

springs. Support truck with stands on frame just behind front springs.
3. Disconnect connecting rod from steering arm.
4. Disconnect brake hoses from frame fittings.
5. Disconnect shock absorbers from axle brackets.
6. Dismount "U" bolts from axle to separate axle from truck springs.
7. Raise truck enough to clear axle and roll axle out from underneath.

8. To install axle, reverse removal procedures.

Front Axle Shaft Assembly Removal and Installation

1. Support vehicle with front wheel free.
2. Place drain pan under wheel and hub grease cap.
3. Remove snap ring from axle shaft.
4. Remove drive flange as follows:
a. On K10 and K14 models, pull splined drive flange from shaft

and hub and remove spacer from hub.
b. On K20 and K25 models remove stud nuts and washers, remove drive flange and gasket.
5. Remove bearing lock nut and lock ring and remove adjusting nut.
6. Remove wheel, hub and drum as an assembly.
7. Remove bolts and lockwashers holding brake flange plate and spindle to steering knuckle.

I beam type suspension P-20—P-20 series
(© Chevrolet Div., G.M. Corp.)

I beam type suspension 40, 50 and 60 series
(© Chevrolet Div., G.M. Corp.)

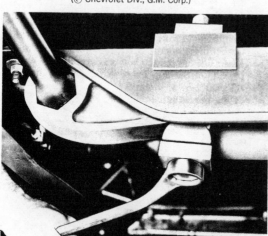

Unloading torsion bar (© Chevrolet Div., G.M. Corp.)

Installing torsion bar lock pin 50-80 series
(© Chevrolet Div., G.M. Corp.)

8. Remove flange plate from steering knuckle and support the plate so brake hose will not be damaged.
9. Slide spindle from shaft.
10. Remove axle shaft and joint assembly.
11. To install, reverse removal procedures. Adjust bearings by tightening nut snug while rotating drum. Loosen nut $\frac{1}{8}$ turn and assemble lock-washer by loosening nut to nearest hole, then assemble outer nut. Tighten nut to 40 ft. lbs. minimum.

Kingpin Trunnion

Adjustment

Front axle trunnion adjustment is generally necessary only when there is excessive play in steering, irregular wear on tires or persistent loosening of the tie rod.

1. Raise front end of vehicle, then place jack stands just inside of front springs.
2. Disconnect connecting rod and tie rod to allow independent movement of each steering knuckle.
3. Remove all cap screws which attach knuckle seal retainers, then move seals and retainers free of the knuckle.
4. At top of knuckle, apply torque wrench to one of the steering arms attaching stud nuts, then check torque necessary to turn the steering knuckle.
   Starting torque should be:
   5 to 10 in. lbs.—Axle 44-5F
   15 to 35 lbs.—Axle 44-5HDF
   NOTE: Knuckle should turn smoothly through turning arc but have no vertical end play.
   IMPORTANT: Temperature will affect turning torque considerably.

Ball Joint Adjustment

Adjustment of the ball joint is necessary only when there is excessive

AXIAL MOVEMENT

Ball joint check—unloaded
(© Chevrolet Div., G.M. Corp.)

TIRE SIDEWALL MOVEMENT

Ball joint check—unloaded
(© Chevrolet Div., G.M. Corp.)

play in the steering, persistent loosening of the tie rod, or wear on the tires.

1. Raise vehicle on hoist and place jack stands just inside of front springs.
2. Disconnect tie rod and connecting rod to allow each steering knuckle to move independently.
3. Apply torque wrench, at top of knuckle, to one of the steering arms attaching and stud nuts and check torque necesstry to turn knuckle.

Maximum torque is:
15 ft.-lbs.   Axle 44-5B
20 ft.-lbs.   Axle 44- B
NOTE: Knuckle should turn smoothly through turning arc and have no vertical end play.
IMPORTANT: Temperature will affect turning torque considerably so allowances should be made.

4. If torque is too low perform the following procedures:
   a. Remove upper ball stud cotter pin and lock nut.
   b. Torque stud adjusting sleeve to 50 ft.-lbs.
   c. Install lock nut and new cotter pin.
   d. Recheck torque necessary to turn steering knuckle. If torque is still too low retorque sleeve to 60-ft.-lbs. and recheck.

NOTE: If torque specifications for turning of knuckle can not be reached, replace required parts.

Steering Knuckle

Removal

1. Remove axle shaft and joint assembly.
2. Disconnect steering connecting rod from steering arm.
3. Disconnect the tie rod from steering knuckle.
4. Remove the seal retainers (2 pieces) from knuckle.
5. Remove the felt seal, rubber seal and the seal ring from knuckle and let them hang on axle housing.
6. Remove upper and lower bearing retainers and shims from knuckle.
7. Remove knuckle from housing and remove bearing cones from axle housing.

NOTE: On K20 HD models the upper kingpin bearing consists of a cup and bushing assembly. The kingpin and bushing are slotted to receive a

FOUR WHEEL DRIVE

Four wheel drive components (© Chevrolet Div., G.M. Corp.)

ENGAGED   DISENGAGED

PUT IN   2 WH. DRIVE   BE FORE   UNLOCK

Locking front hub key positions
(© Chevrolet Div., G.M. Corp.)

1 Lock ring
2 "O" ring seal
3 Hub assembly
4 Wheel hub housing
5 Extension housing
6 Gaskets
7 Bolts (6)
8 Lock washer (6)

MODEL-K10

MODEL-K20

Locking front hub installation
(© Chevrolet Div., G.M. Corp.)

key which acts to connect the two components so that they will pivot together. Removal procedure for this installation is as listed above.

Free Wheeling Hub

Reference

Free-wheeling hubs are available for the front wheels of four wheel drive vehicles. The purpose of these hubs is to reduce friction and wear by disengaging the front axle shafts, differential and drive line from the front wheels when the vehicle is operated under conditions where front wheel drive is not needed.

The engagement and disengagement of free-wheeling hubs is a manual operation which must be performed at each front wheel. The transfer case control lever must be in 2-wheel drive position when locking or unlocking hubs. Both hubs must be in the fully locked or fully unlocked position. They must not be in the free-wheeling position when low all wheel drive is used as the additional torque output in this position can subject the rear axle to severe strain and rear axle failure may result.

Removal

K20 Series

1. Turn hub key to set hub to "*free*" or "*disengage*" position.
2. Remove outer clutch ring, cap and cam assemblies as follows: Remove internal snap ring from hub and pull assembly out of hub.
   a. Remove bolts retaining hub cap assembly to wheel hub, pull assembly and extension housing away from hub and remove gasket.
3. Remove snap ring from end of axle shaft.

4. Pull bushing and inner clutch ring assembly shaft.

Installation

1. Place bushing and inner clutch ring over axle spline with clutch teeth outward. Slide on until bushing bottoms in wheel hub and install snap ring in axle shaft.
2. Install outer clutch ring, cap and cam assembly as follows:
   a. On K20 and K25 models, place gasket on hub, align mounting holes in clutch ring and cap with holes in hub and install bolts and lockwashers.
3. Turn knob to check for proper locking.

Removal

K10 Series 1970 and Up

1. Turn actuator lever to set hub to "lock" position and raise vehicle.
2. Remove retaining plate bolts and remove retaining plate actuating knob and "O" ring.
3. Remove internal snap ring, outer clutch retaining ring and actuating cam body.
4. Remove axle shaft snap ring.
5. Remove axle shaft sleeve and clutch ring assmbly and inner clutch ring and bushing assembly.
6. Remove pressure spring and spring retainer plate.

MODEL-K10

MODEL-K20

1 Key knob
2 Retainer cap
3 Key knob seal
4 Key knob retainer pin
5 Cap aligning pin
6 Spring
7 Outer clutch gear assembly
8 Axle shaft lock ring
9 Collar (bushing) internal clutch gear
10 Internal clutch gear
11 Wheel hub housing
12 Extension housing gaskets
13 Extension housing
14 Snap ring

Hub assembly (© Chevrolet Div., G.M. Corp.)

Installation

1. Lubricate all parts. Install spring retainer plate (flange side facing bearing) over spindle nuts and seat retainer against bearing outer cup.
2. Install pressure spring into position. Large O.D. seats against spring retaining plate. NOTE: When spring is seated, spring extends past the spindle nuts by approximately 7/8".
3. Place inner clutch ring and bushing assembly into axle shaft sleeve and clutch ring assembly and install as an assembly into the axle shaft. Press in on assembly and install axle shaft snap ring. NOTE: Install 7/16x20 bolt in axle shaft end and pull outward on axle shaft to aid in installing snap rings.
4. Install activating cam body (cams facing outward), outer clutch retaining ring and internal snap ring.
5. Install "O" ring on retaining plate and install activating knob and retaining plate. NOTE: Install activating knob with knob in "lock" position, grooves in knob must fit into activator cam body.
6. Install cover bolts and seals.
7. Turn knob to *"free"* position to check for proper operation.
8. Lower vehicle.

Steering Gear

Manual Steering Gear

Instructions covering the overhaul of the steering gear will be found in the General Repair Section.

Power Steering Gears

Troubleshooting and repair instructions covering power steering gears are given in the General Repair Section.

Type

Steering Gear is recirculating ball device with several types of linkage used, on power steering units the power assist is supplied by an engine driven, valve type pump. An oil cooler is used on large trucks.

Steering Gear Replacement

Except Van and Forward Control

1. Set wheels in straight ahead position. Mark alignment of upper and lower steering shafts. Loosen champ bolt at coupling (coupling is splined), or separate at joint. On some models to remove coupling, either lower steering gear or raise mast jacket assembly.
2. Mark pitman arm and sector shaft, for reassembly, and using puller remove pitman arm, or remove drag link from pitman arm if sufficient room between drag link stud and frame rail. If clamp type pitman arm is used, spread just enough to remove.
3. Remove power steering hoses from gear assembly, cap lines and plug openings (if equipped). from vehicle.
4. Remove gear housing to frame rail bolts (watch shims), remove from vehicle.
5. Reverse removal steps to install. NOTE: Do not hammer pitman arm on sector shaft, use nut to pull into position. On power steering vehicles, raise front when bleeding.

Steering Gear Replacement

1970 and Up—Van and Forward Control

1. Disconnect battery ground cable.
2. Set wheels in straight ahead position.
3. Disconnect steering shaft flange bolts at flexible coupling.
4. Mark position of pitman arm on shaft. Remove pitman shaft nut and remove arm using a puller. NOTE: If clamp type pitman arm is used, spread arm, using a wedge, just enough to remove pitman from shaft.
5. Remove steering gear frame mounting bolts and remove steering gear assembly.
6. Reverse removal steps to install. NOTE: Do not hammer pitman arm onto sector shaft, use nut to pull into position.

Adjustments (on Vehicle)

Manual Steering

1. Check tire pressure and inspect steering linkage.
2. Check gear housing for lubricant, tighten cover side plate.
3. Check steering gear housing to frame rail bolts.
4. Set wheels in straight ahead position.
5. Disconnect drag link from pitman arm, remove pitman arm on Vans.
6. Loosen sector (cross) shaft lock nut and back off lash adjuster 1/4 turn. This lessens steering worm bearing load by reducing tooth mesh contact.
7. Check load on steering gear by measuring pull on steering wheel with scale. Pull is measured at rim of wheel with scale tangent to rim of wheel (1/2 to 3 lb. pull according to size of truck).
8. If pull is not within limits, adjust worm bearings. Loosen worm bearing lock nut and turn adjusting nut in until there is no perceptible end play. Tighten lock nut. Using an inch-pound torque wrench and socket on steering wheel nut (remove horn wire and button), measure torque (3 inch pounds to 14 inch pounds according to size of truck). A rough feeling when

Manual steering gear (© Chevrolet Div., G.M. Corp.)

Ball stud removal (typical)
(© Chevrolet Div., G.M. Corp.)

K-10-20 steering linkage
(© Chevrolet Div., G.M. Corp.)

rotating steering wheel indicates defective worm bearings. Some early heavy duty steering gears use shims under steering gear housing top cover, and also use a back-up adjuster. Removal of shims decreases worm bearing end play. Back-up adjuster setting is made last. After adjusting worm bearings and lash, then tighten back-up adjuster until adjuster bottoms against ball nut return guide clamp, then back-off adjuster ⅛ to ¼ turn and secure with lock nut.

9. After proper adjustment of worm bearings is obtained, center steering wheel by turning wheel gently from one stop to the other, counting the number of turns. Turn wheel back exactly half way to center position (high point). Mark steering wheel rim at top or bottom center with tape. Turn lash (slotted) adjuster clockwise to take out all lash in gear teeth and tighten lock nut. Check steering free play. NOTE: If maximum adjustment is exceeded, turn lash adjuster screw back (counter-clockwise) and then come in (clockwise) slowly on adjustment. CAUTION: Do not bounce steering wheel hard

20-40-50-60 ser. steering linkage (typical)
(© Chevrolet Div., G.M. Corp.)

against stops with drag link removed, worm ball guide damage can result.

10. Connect drag link or replace pitman arm, road test and check steering.

Adjustments (on Vehicle)
Power Steering

Power steering gear is adjusted in the same manner as manual steering gear, however starting in 1967, sector lash adjustment is the only power steering gear adjustment that can be made on the vehicle. In order to make this adjustment, it is necessary to check the combined valve drag and worm bearing preload.

1. Check power steering fluid level, check belt tension and hose for leaks or kinks.

2. Remove drag link from pitman arm.

3. Disconnect horn wire, remove horn button assembly.

4. Center steering wheel—turn through its full travel then locate wheel at center of its travel.

5. Loosen sector lash adjusting screw locknut and back off (slotted) adjusting screw to the limit of its travel.

6. Check combined valve drag and worm bearing preload with inch-pound torque wrench and socket on steering shaft nut, by rotating wheel approximately 20° in each direction. Note highest reading.

7. Tighten sector lash adjusting screw until torque at steering wheel meets specifications (4 to 18 inch pounds according to truck size). Secure lock nut.

NOTE: If maximum adjustment is exceeded, turn lash adjuster screw back (counter-clockwise) and then come in (clockwise) slowly on adjustment. CAUTION: Do not bounce steering wheel hard against stops with drag link removed, worm ball guide damage can result. When bleeding hydraulic system, raise front of vehicle.

(© Chevrolet Div., G.M. Corp.)
Chevy Van steering gear mounting

CA-10
PA-10

C-10-20-30 steering linkage
(© Chevrolet Div., G.M. Corp.)

Side mounted power steering cylinder
(© Chevrolet Div., G.M. Corp.)

C-10-20-30 series control valve and power cyl. installed
(© Chevrolet Div., G.M. Corp.)

8. Replace drag link, horn button assembly and connect horn wire.
9. Road test and check steering.

Idler Arm

Removal

1. Jack up front of vehicle and support or raise on hoist.
2. Remove cotter pin and castellated nut from ball stud at relay rod. Remove ball stud from relay rod by using a tapered driver or tapping on relay rod boss. Support relay rod so impact will center on ball stud.
3. Remove idler arm to frame bolts, remove idler arm.

Installation

1. Position idler arm on frame and install mounting bolts. (special plain washers under bolt heads). Torque nuts.
2. Make sure threads on ball stud and in ball stud nut are good—ball stud may turn in sket if threads are damaged. Check ball and seal.
3. Install idler arm ball stud in relay rod (seal in place) and install castellated nut and cotter pin. Torque nut to specifications.
4. Lower vehicle or remove from hoist.

Clutch

Description—Types

Clutches used on inline engines are single (driven) disc with either of two types of pressure (drive) plates, diaphragm or coil spring. "V" engines use a single disc with coil spring pressure plate. Heavy duty clutches use two discs. The two plate clutch consists of three basic assemblies, the cover with rear pressure plate assembly, front pressure plate and two discs. The front pressure plate, lo-

(© Chevrolet Div., G.M. Corp.)

40-50-60 series power steering gear and central valve (typical)

cated between the two driven discs, has two friction surfaces and is coupled to rear pressure plate through steel drive straps bolted at each of its four driving bosses. Diaphragm spring covers operate with light pedal pressure while coil spring levers combine operating ease and high torque capacity. The operating controls are either mechanical or hydraulic. Discs have torsion spring centers.

Adjustments

Free Pedal Travel

This adjustment is for the amount of pedal travel (measured at pedal) before clutch release bearing contacts the levers, or fingers of a coil spring cover or the diaphragm spring of a

Pedal height adjustment (conventional pedal)
(© Chevrolet Div., G.M. Corp.)

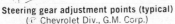

Steering gear adjustment points (typical)
(© Chevrolet Div., G.M. Corp.)

Adjusting sector shaft preload
(© Chevrolet Div., G.M. Corp.)

Adjusting clutch push rod (eccentric method)
(© Chevrolet Div., G.M. Corp.)

CROSS SHAFT LEVER

HOLD THIS DIRECTION

PUSH ROD

SWIVEL

HOLD THIS DIRECTION

¼" APPROX.

Free travel adjustment
(© Chevrolet Div., G.M. Corp.)

Move Release Lever or Fork Until Resistance Is Felt

Wedge

Adjusting Nut

Lock Nut

Push Rod

Force Push Rod To Bottom In Slave Cylinder

Hold Wedge Against Lever Or Fork

Free Travel

Clutch slave cylinder adjustment
(© Chevrolet Div., G.M. Corp.)

Three Bolts
¼"-20 x 2¼" (12" Clutch)
⅜"-16 x 2¼" (14" Clutch)

Lipe clutch hold-down bolts installed (typical)
(© Chevrolet Div., G.M. Corp.)

CLEARANCE 3/16"

ADJUSTING NUT

RETURN SPRING

Adjusting slave cylinder push rod
(© Chevrolet Div., G.M. Corp.)

diaphragm clutch cover. This is called free-play. With normal clutch wear the amount of free-play is reduced and in time this will cause the release bearing to be in constant contact with the cover. This in turn will cause clutch disc slippage resulting in premature failure of disc and release bearing. It is necessary to maintain sufficient free pedal travel for clutch efficiency and long life.

Mechanical Linkage

1. Check linkage for excessive wear (will create false free play).
2. Disconnect fork arm return spring.
3. Back off locknut "A" at least ½" from swivel.
4. Hold fork push rod against fork to keep release bearing touching fingers (or diaphragm). Push rod will slide through swivel at cross shaft.
5. Adjust nut "B" to obtain approximately 3 16" to ¼" clearance between nut "B" and swivel.
6. Release push rod, connect pull back spring at fork and tighten nut "A" to lock swivel against nut "B".
7. Check free play at pedal for ¾" to 1" clearance.

Hydraulic Controls

1. Check master cylinder, cylinder must be filled and no air in system.
2. 1963 and Up—Loosen lock nut on slave cylinder push rod and turn adjusting nut at fork arm to obtain ¼" free pedal travel, tighten lock nut (3/16" at fork arm).
NOTE: This should insure master cylinder piston moving sufficiently to uncover port in master cylinder reservoir.

Total Pedal Travel

Mechanical Linkage

1. Check linkage for excessive wear.
2. Loosen lock nut on adjustable pedal stop. (conventional pedal

—on pedal support bracket under dash).
3. Turn adjustment bolt until clutch pedal is equal in height to brake pedal.
4. Tighten lock nut.
5. Pedal Free Travel must be made after this adjustment.
NOTE: Inverted pedal—additional pedal travel will be gained by cutting rubber bumper stop. Since shorten-

ing the bumper increases free play, the lash must be reduced to gain the additional pedal travel. Insufficient clutch release leads to low and reverse gear clash.

Hydraulic Controls

1. Locate clutch pedal bumper so clutch pedal, in fully released position, is even with brake pedal (if equipped with adjustable stop). Check reservoir.
2. Disconnect clutch fork return spring.
3. Bottom slave cylinder push rod and piston by pushing rod to the front of cylinder as far as it will go.
4. Move clutch fork arm until release bearing contacts pressure plate levers (or diaphragm spring).
5. Adjust clearance between slave cylinder push rod fulcrum (wedge) by adjusting nut behind it to 3/16" clearance between wedge and nut (hold wedge against fork arm).
6. Check pedal free play.
NOTE: Clearance can be checked with shank of 3/16 drill.

Cover Assemblies

While no wear adjustment is needed (except Spicer), original settings at time of manufacture must be retained for good clutch operation. If a diaphragm clutch cover fails to release properly, after first checking pedal travel and pedal lash and linkage for looseness, replace diaphragm retracting springs. This can be done in the vehicle. If trouble still persists the diaphragm is probably overstressed.

With coil spring covers, the finger or lever adjusting screw nut is locked (staked) at time of manufacture and should not be disturbed unless rebuilding. Some Spicer heavy duty covers are internally adjusted for wear. These are covered in the general section.

Clutch Replacement

1. Remove transmission (see transmission R & R).

Use of wood blocks between release levers and cover (© Chevrolet Div., G.M. Corp.)

Mechanical linkage (inverted pedal) (© Chevrolet Div., G.M. Corp.)

Use of blocks between release bearing and spring plate hub (© Chevrolet Div., G.M. Corp.)

2. Block clutch fingers down on coil spring covers for additional clearance. On heavy duty clutches use blocks between release bearing and spring plate hub. On Lipe-Rollaway use bolts and washer in three holes provided

3. Disconnect pedal linkage and fork arm pull back springs.

4. Disconnect slave cylinder from fork arm (if equipped).

5. Remove release bearing from fork arm or disconnect grease hose and remove bearing assembly from yoke.

6. Remove fork arm from ball stud or remove yoke and shaft.

7. Fork arm ball stud can be removed if necessary.

8. Punch mark cover and flywheel for alignment if cover assembly is to be re-used.

9. Loosen cover bolts a turn or two at a time to prevent cover distortion. Support cover and disc with pilot tool (or sling) to

prevent damage to clutch when last cover bolt is removed. A good practice on heavy units is to remove one cover bolt and install a support stud. Rotate flywheel and locate stud at top, loosen all other bolts evenly until pressure is released from disc(s). Disc(s) can be removed and marked for positions. Remove remaining cover bolts and slide cover assembly off stud. Stud will also aid in installation.

10. Clean flywheel and pressure plates, check for scores and heat cracks. Excessive bluing indicates abnormally high operating temperatures. Torque flywheel bolts.

11. Check pilot bearing or bushing (lubricate sparingly), check splines on clutch shaft, check release bearing (do not wash bearing).

12. Reverse removal steps to install. Use pilot tool or dummy shaft to align disc(s). Be certain of disc's position in relation to flywheel. Tighten cover bolts evenly. Do not try to pull clutch into place with impact wrench. This procedure can crack or break pilot shoulders on bolts. Lubricate with a light coat of grease, fork arm ball seat and inside of release bearing. Make sure spring retainer (if used) for release fork ball stud is in correct position. Install retainer with high side up, away from bottom of ball socket and with open end of retainer horizontal. After clutch and transmission are installed and clutch pedal free travel adjusted, check disc(s) for release. This can be done by putting transmission in gear and pulling down slowly on clutch pedal while applying torque to transmission propeller shaft flange. If release can be felt, then complete installation.

101 Diaphragm spring type clutch parts (typical) (© Chevrolet Div., G.M. Corp.)

Coil spring clutch parts (typical) (© Chevrolet Div., G.M. Corp.)

Transfer Case

Removal

1. Raise and support vehicle on hoist. Drain transfer case.
2. Disconnect speedometer cable, back-up lamp and TCS switch.
3. Remove skid plate and crossmember supports as necessary.
4. Disconnect rear prop shaft from transfer case and tie up away from work area.
5. Disconnect front prop shaft from transfer case and tie up shaft away from work area.
6. Disconnect shift lever rod from shift rail link. On full time 4 wheel drive models, disconnect shift levers at transfer case.
7. Remove transfer case to frame mounting bracket bolts.
8. Support transfer case and remove bolts attaching transfer case to transmission adapter.
9. Move transfer case to rear until input shaft clears adapter and lower assembly from vehicle.

Installation

1. Support transfer case in suitable stand and position case to transmission adapter. Install bolts attaching case to adapter and torque to 45 ft. lbs.
2. Remove stand as required and install bolts attaching transfer case to frame rail. Bend lock tabs after assembly.
3. Install connecting rod to shift rail link or connect shift levers to transfer case, as applicable.
4. Connect front prop shaft to transfer case front output shaft.
5. Connect rear prop shaft to transfer case rear output shaft.
6. Install crossmember support and skid plate, If removed.
7. Connect speedometer cable, back-up lamp and TCS switch.
8. Fill transfer case to proper level with lubricant.

9. Lower and remove vehicle from hoist.

CAUTION: Check and tighten all bolts to specified torques.

NOTE: Before connecting prop shafts to companion flanges be sure locknuts are torqued to specifications.

For overhaul—see General Section

Standard Transmission

Transmission refill capacities are in the Capacities table of this section.

Troubleshooting and repair of manual transmissions are covered in the General Repair Section.

Types

The transmission is used to provide suitable gear ratios between engine and rear wheels for all driving conditions. Various types and designs of transmissions are used due to complexity of engines, chassis and body types. Transmission characteristics range from a standard three speed Helical gear, fully synchronized unit to an air controlled combination of a five speed front section and a two speed rear auxiliary, with a range of ten forward speeds. Operations other than those included in this section may be necessary if the vehicle has special equipment.

CAUTION: An important and often overlooked aspect of diagnosis is finding out specifically what the customer is complaining of. For this purpose a short ride with the customer will prove beneficial. It may be found that the condition that the customer wants corrected is standard and should not be altered.

Shift Linkage and Adjustments

3 Speed Column Shift

1. Raise vehicle and support on stands.

2. Disconnect control rods at transmission levers.
3. Place transmission shift levers in neutral (neutral detents in cover must be fully engaged).
4. Place gearshift lever in neutral, on early models remove housing cover at base of mast jacket and make sure shifter gates and inner levers are aligned. If alignment is off, loosen first and reverse control rod swivel clamp at housing outer lever and adjust swivel until shifter gates are aligned.
5. Adjust swivels on control rods until swivels (or rods) enter transmission shift lever holes. Make sure levers remain in neutral position. Lock control rods.
6. Lower vehicle and move gearshift lever through all gear positions to check (keep clutch pedal depressed to aid shifting).

4 Speed Column Shift

1. Place gearshift lever in neutral. Raise vehicle on hoist.
2. Disconnect first and second shift rod from cross shaft lever. Disconnect third and fourth shift rod from transmission lever. Disconnect reverse cable from reverse lever by removing "C" clip. Manually shift all transmission controls into neutral, including reverse lever.
3. Remove engine splash shield. Install a fabricated pin (see illustration for details) through upper control shaft bracket into cutouts in shift levers and into hole provided at base of control shaft as shown.
4. Adjust swivel on end of first and second rod to freely enter cross shaft lever hole. Reconnect rod to lever.
5. Adjust swivel on end of third and fourth rod to freely enter transmission lever. Reconnect rod to lever.

OUTER LEVERS
INNER LEVERS
SHIFTER GATES
LOWER CONTROL SHAFT
CONTROL SHAFT LEVER
CONTROL SHAFT SPRING
GEARSHIFT LEVER
UPPER CONTROL SHAFT
1ST AND REVERSE CONTROL ROD
AXIAL PIVOT
ROTARY SWIVEL
2ND AND 3RD CONTROL ROD
2ND AND 3RD SHIFTER LEVER
1ST AND REVERSE SHIFTER LEVER

Steering column gearshift—3 speed early
(© CHEVROLET Div., G.M. Corp.)

GEARSHIFT CONTROL LEVER
FIRST AND REVERSE TUBE LEVER
SECOND AND THIRD TUBE LEVER
RELAY LEVER
SECOND AND THIRD CONTROL ROD
SECOND AND THIRD SHIFTER LEVER
FIRST AND REVERSE SHIFTER LEVER
FIRST AND REVERSE CONTROL ROD

Steering column gearshift—3 speed late
(© CHEVROLET Div., G.M. Corp.)

Chevrolet Trucks · Vans · Blazer

Steering column gearshift—4 speed (© Chevrolet Div., G.M. Corp.)

6. Adjust swivel on end of reverse cable to freely enter reverse lever hole. If more adjustment is needed at swivel, adjust cable assembly by using cable to bracket attaching nuts. Install washer and "C" clip. Tighten swivel lock nut.
7. Remove fabricated pin, replace splash shield, lower vehicle and move gearshift lever through all gear positions to check. Depressing clutch pedal will aid in shifting.

Van Column Shift

1. Raise vehicle and support on stands.
2. Remove control rods at transmission levers.
3. Move both transmission levers until transmission is in neutral. Neutral detents must be fully engaged.
4. Move gearshift lever into neutral position, align shifter relay levers on mast jacket, install pin in holes of levers to hold levers in alignment and in neutral position.
5. Adjust swivel on end of low and reverse control rod until swivel enters transmission lever freely, lock with retaining ring, tighten swivel locknut.
6. Similarly, install second and third control rod, be sure levers remain in neutral.
7. Lower vehicle and move gearshift lever through all gear positions to check. Keep clutch pedal depressed to aid in shifting.

Floor Shift (and Related Controls)

Removal of gearshift lever, remote control and control island and any linkage adjustments are carried in transmission removal and installation section.

Transmission Removal

3 Speed Except Van and Blazer with 4 Wheel Drive

1. Raise vehicle and support on jack stands.
2. Drain transmission.

Replacing transmission gearshift lever—floor shift (© Chevrolet Div., G.M. Corp.)

3. Disconnect speedometer cable, TCS switch and back-up lamp wire at transmission.
4. Disconnect shift control levers from transmission.
5. Disconnect parking brake lever and controls (if used).
6. Remove drive shaft after marking position of shaft to flange.
7. Position jack under transmission to support weight of transmission.
8. Remove crossmember. Visually inspect to see if other equipment, brackets or lines, must be removed to permit removal of transmission. NOTE: Mark position of crossmember when removing to prevent incorrect installation.
9. Remove flywheel housing underpan.
10. Remove the top two transmission to housing bolts and insert two guide pins. NOTE: The use of guide pins will not only support the transmission but will prevent damage to the clutch disc. Guide pins can be made by taking two bolts, the same as those just removed only longer, and cutting off the heads. (Slot for screwdriver)
11. Remove two remaining bolts and slide transmission straight back from engine. Use care to keep the transmission drive gear straight in line with clutch disc hub. NOTE: Be sure to support release bearing when removing transmission to avoid having bearing fall into flywheel housing.
12. When transmission is free from engine, move from under vehicle.

Transmission Installation

3 Speed Except Van and Blazer with 4 Wheel Drive

1. Place transmission on guide pins, slide forward starting main drive gear into clutch disc's splines. NOTE: Place transmission in gear and rotate transmission flange or output yoke to aid entry of main drive gear into disc's splines. Make sure clutch release bearing is in position.
2. Install two lower transmission mounting bolts, and flywheel lower pan (if equipped).
3. Remove guide pins and install upper mounting bolts.
4. Install propeller shaft, watch align marks.

Column shift linkage—vans (© Chevrolet Div., G.M. Corp.)

"APRON" TYPE
FLYWHEEL HOUSING
ENGINE

"SAE #2" TYPE
FLYWHEEL HOUSING
ENGINE

TRANSMISSION

PAN

TRANSMISSION

CLUTCH HOUSING

"APRON" TYPE

"SAE #2" TYPE

Flywheel housing identification
(© Chevrolet Div., G.M. Corp.)

J-8109

J-8109
MODIFIED

Replacing transfer case gearshift lever
(© Chevrolet Div., G.M. Corp.)

5. Connect parking brake, back-up lamp and T.S.C. switch (if used).
6. Connect shift levers, see section on adjustment if needed.
7. Connect speedometer cable, refill transmission.
8. Lower vehicle and road test.

Transmission Removal

Vans

1. Place heavy cardboard between radiator core and fan blades as a precautionary measure.
2. Raise and support vehicle on stands or hoist, drain transmission.
3. Disconnect speedometer cable at transmission.
4. Disconnect parking brake, back-up lamp and T.S.C. switch (if used).
5. Disconnect propeller shaft and power take off (if equipped).
6. 3 Speed (Column Shift)
   a. Remove shift controls from transmission.
   4 Speed (Floor Shift)
   a. Remove floor mat.
   b. Remove floor pan.
   c. Place transmission in neutral and remove gearshift lever by sliding open side of tool over lever, engage lugs of tool in the open slot of retainer, press down on tool and turn to left to disengage the lugs on retainer. Cover transmission opening. Be careful of pivot pin.
   d. Remove reverse lever cable and bracket at transmission.
   4 Speed (Column Shift)
   a. Remove shift controls from levers.
   b. Remove reverse lever cable and bracket at transmission.
7. Remove clutch shaft frame bolts and accelerator linkage at manifold bellcrank.
8. Place jack under bell housing and raise enough to relieve weight at transmission rear support.
9. Remove transmission rear support crossmember or on early models, remove support bolt and

lower engine carefully to allow transmission rear mount to clear support bracket.
10. Position jack under transmission and adjust to carry weight of transmission (if 4 speed).
11. Remove 2 top transmission to bell housing bolts and install 2 guide pins to prevent damaging clutch disc.
12. Remove two lower transmission mounting bolts.
13. Visually inspect to determine if other equipment or lines need to be removed.
14. Slide transmission back on guide pins, four speed units aided by jack (support release bearing), until transmission clears engine. Remove transmission from under vehicle.
CAUTION: If other work is to be performed support engine more securely after transmission is removed.

Transmission Installation

Vans

1. Clean bell housing and transmission mating surfaces, lightly lubricate main drive gear bearing retainer and clutch pilot bushing or bearing. Make sure release bearing is in position.
2. Move transmission into position on guide pins, shift transmission into any gear.
3. Slide transmission forward rotating transmission flange or yoke to aid entry of main drive gear into clutch disc splines.
4. Install two lower transmission mounting bolts. Remove guide pins and install two upper mounting bolts. Remove transmission jack.
5. Carefully raise engine and transmission to normal position and install transmission rear mounting bolt or crossmember. Remove jack from under bell housing. Remove cardboard from radiator.
6. Connect speedometer cable, parking brake, back-up light and T.S.C. switch (if equipped).

7. Connect propeller shaft and power take off (if equipped).
8. Connect clutch shaft and accelerator linkage.
9. Reinstall shift controls on transmission or gearshift lever on four speed. Install reverse cable and bracket. See section on shift linkage adjustment if needed.
10. Replace floor mat and floor pans on four speed units.
11. Refill transmission, lower vehicle and road test.

Transmission Removal and Installation

4 Wheel Drive (Including Blazer)

1. Floor shift models.
   a. Remove shift lever boots and retainers on both transfer case and transmission.
   b. Remove floor mat or carpet, seat and accelerator pedal.
   c. Center console models: remove center outlet from heater distributor duct and remove console.
   d. Remove transmission floor cover, shift transfer case lever into neutral and rotate floor cover approximately 90° while lifting to clear transfer case lever.
   e. Slide open side of tool over transmission gearshift lever, engage lugs of tool in open slot of retainer, press down and turn counter-clockwise to remove lever. Do same for transfer case lever. Be careful of any pivot pins. Cover transmission openings.
2. Raise vehicle and support on stands or hoist vehicle.
3. Drain transmission and transfer case.
4. Disconnect back-up light and T.S.C. switches (if equipped).
5. Disconnect parking brake.
6. Disconnect speedometer cable (at transfer case on some models).
7. Disconnect front and rear auxiliary drive shafts at transfer case and tie up out of work area.

Gearshift lever and housing
(© Chevrolet Div., G.M. Corp.)

GEARSHIFT LEVER

KNOB

NUT

SEAL

PIVOT PIN

HOUSING

GASKET

WASHER

SPRING

8. 1961-66—Disconnect propeller shaft joint "U" bolts and remove propeller shaft. Disconnect auxiliary shift rod.
1967 and Up—Remove bolts attaching transfer case to adapter (remove side access cover to reach two bolts).

9. Support rear of engine with jack.

10. Support transfer case on cradle or dolly. Remove two transmission adapter mounting bolts.

11. Remove transfer case mounting bolts, remove transfer case (all except Blazer).

12. Column Shift Models:
a. Disconnect shift control rods from levers at transmission.
b. On 4 speed, remove reverse cable and bracket at transmission.

13. Remove two upper transmission mounting bolts and install two guide pins (longer bolts with heads cut off and slotted). Use of guide pins will prevent damage to clutch disc.

14. Remove flywheel under pan and remove two lower transmission mounting bolts.

15. On V-8 engines, remove exhaust crossover pipe.

16. On Blazer, remove transmission frame crossmember bolts. Remove crossmember (rotating to clear frame rails).

17. Visually inspect to determine if other equipment or lines need to be removed.

18. Slide transmission and adapter (transmission with transfer case on Blazer) back on guide pins, aided by transmission dolly, until main drive gear clears clutch (watch clutch release bearing), remove from under vehicle.

19. Lubricate pilot bushing or bearing, make sure clutch release bearing is in position, use guide pins to align transmission and rotate main drive gear to enter clutch disc splines without forcing. Reverse removal procedures to install.

4 and 5 Speed Heavy Duty Transmissions

The procedures required to remove and install the transmissions covered in this section are dependent upon types of cabs, engines and chassis used, also what equipment is available in repair shop. Other operations may be necessary if vehicle has special equipment, therefore, procedures contained herein will serve only as a guide. It is important to note that vehicles covered in this section will have either an "apron" or "S.A.E. 2" type of flywheel housing. The apron type is identified by sheet metal pan, also note it is a one piece housing. The "S.A.E. 2" type completely surrounds the flywheel. A

Removing gearshift lever
(© Chevrolet Div., G.M. Corp.)

Gearshift lever installation
(© Chevrolet Div., G.M. Corp.)

CONTROL LEVER

CAP

CUP

LOCKING PIN HOLE

SPRING

SEAL

SLOTTED PIN

CONTROL LEVER HOUSING

SNAP RING

TRANSMISSION COVER

separate clutch housing is used in addition to the flywheel housing. Transmission replacement procedures are different for each type of flywheel housing used.

Transmission Removal

1. Drain transmission.

2. On transmission equipped with remote controls.
a. Disconnect control rods from shift levers at transmission.

3. On transmissions with a conventional floor gearshift lever.
a. Remove steering jacket grommet from floor and slide grommet up mast jacket out of way (if used).
b. Remove floor mat and accelerator pedal.
c. Disconnect and remove parking brake lever.

Reverse idler gear and adjustment
(© Chevrolet Div., G.M. Corp.)

1 Gearshift lever
2 Island panel
3 Selector finger
4 Clevis
5 Lock nuts
6 Clevis
7 Shift finger
8 Selector and shift rods
9 Selector and shift levers

NOTE: SEE TEXT
90°

Tilt cab transmission control linkage (© Chevrolet Div., G.M. Corp.)

d. Remove transmission floor pan (s), place gearshift lever in neutral.

e. Remove gearshift lever (and control tower on some models). NOTE: On models with New Process Transmissions remove lever by sliding open side of tool over lever. Engage lugs of tool in open slot of retainer, press down on tool and turn to left to disengage lugs on retainer. Lift lever out of cover, be careful of pivot pin. Cover opening in transmision.

On Spicer models, press down on shift lever cup and drive locking pin out of lever. Lift off cup, spring, cap and seal. Remove snap ring from groove on lever housing and tap out slotted pin. Lift lever out of housing and cover opening.

On Clark models remove shift lever housing cover to transmission bolts. Lift lever and control tower from transmission. Cover transmission opening.

On Air Control Shift models, bleed air tanks, remove range shift lines at air valve on transmission. Remove gearshift lever and control tower assembly from transmission. Cover transmission opening and tape or plug air valves.

4. Disconnect and drop propeller shaft at transmission.
5. If unit is equipped with power take-off, disconnect drive shaft and controls.
6. Remove reverse shift control cable and bracket on 4 speed units.
7. Disconnect any clutch control linkage on transmission.
8. Disconnect speedometer cable at transmission.
9. Remove engine ground strap, back up lamp switch and "T.S.C." switch (if used).
10. Place transmission jack into position and adjust to carry weight of transmission. Use locking chain to secure transmission to jack. NOTE: On vehicles which have rear engine mountings attached to the clutch housing (except "apron" type flywheel housing models), position a jack under flywheel housing and adjust to carry the weight of the engine. Remove rear engine mounts.
11. Remove bolts attaching transmission to rear crossmember support brackets (if used).
12. Remove clutch housing-to-flywheel housing bolts. (except on "apron" type flywheel housing models) NOTE: On models with "apron" type flywheel housing, remove flywheel housing under pan (also access panel on Spicer) and transmission to flywheel housing bolts. The use of guidepins in two top holes of "apron" type flywheel housing or in two top side holes on "S.A.E." type will maintain alignment during both removal and installation of transmission.
13. Visually inspect to determine if other equipment or lines must be removed.
14. Move transmission straight back, using guide pins to keep transmission main drive gear in alignment with clutch disc, until free from engine. Be sure to support clutch release bearing during removal of transmission. Lower transmission and move from under the vehicle.

Transmission Installation

1. Clean transmission mating surfaces and apply a light film of grease to main drive gear bearing retainer and clutch pivot bearing.
2. Place transmission on jack and move into position.
3. On "apron" type, place clutch release bearing and support assembly inside flywheel housing. Be sure clutch fork engages bearing. On "S.A.E. 2" type, make sure clutch release bearing is in position.
4. Using guide pins to align transmission main drive gear with clutch disc, move transmission forward rotating main drive gear so gear can enter clutch disc splines without forcing.
5. Reverse removal procedures to install.
NOTE: On transmissions having remote controls make the following control island shift mechanism adjustments if necessary.
1. Place transmission selector and shift levers in neutral.
2. Adjust selector and shift rods to provide 90° angle at the lower end of the gearshift lever to the control island panel. Adjustment is made by rotating the adjustable clevis at either the control island or transmission end of the selector and shift rods. Tighten lock nuts.
3. Check adjustments by moving gearshift lever through shift pattern.
NOTE: On 4 speed transmissions with reverse idler eccentric. To adjust the position of the reverse idler gear, the transmission must be fully assembled except for power take-off cover. Then proceed as follows:
1. Loosen the eccentric nut and rotate the eccentric, using a screwdriver in the slot with end of electric, until slot with dot on end is to the rear. This places the reverse idler in its extreme rear position and will provide for maximum engagement when the transmission is shifted into reverse.
2. Shift transmission into second. Check for interference between reverse idler and first and reverse gear. If interference exists, rotate eccentric in a counter-clockwise direction to obtain approximately 1/32" clearance This clearance can be checked through the power take-off opening.
4. Shift transmission into reverse and check clearance between reverse idler gear and transmission case. If necessary, rotate the eccentric an additional amount, in counter-clockwise direction, to obtain running clearance at this point.
5. Tighten eccentric nut and lock.
6. Install power take-off cover and new gasket.

Auxiliary Transmissions
Description

The spicer auxiliary transmission is supported at the front by a support bracket attached to the frame side rails and at the rear by a support beam attached to frame brackets. The gears are shifted by a lever in the cab, which is interconnected to the auxiliary transmission with control rods. The hand brake and speedometer drive gear are located at the rear of the transmission.

Removal

1. Drain the lubricant.
2. Disconnect and support the propeller shafts from the input and output ends of the transmission.
3. Disconnect the shift control rods from the front of the transmission.
4. Disconnect the speedometer cable from the adapter at the rear of the transmission.
5. Disconnect the parking brake linkage if applicable.
6. Remove all connections to the auxiliary transmission power take-off.
7. Place a suitable dolly or jack under the transmission and adjust its position so it can safely carry the weight.
8. Disconnect the front and rear mountings and lower the transmission away from the chassis.

Installation

1. Make sure the tapered surface of the front mount face the front of the vehicle as shown in the illustration.
2. Move the transmission into position under the vehicle and adjust the front and rear height. (See alignment Data Chart)
3. Torque the attaching parts to the proper specifications (See "AUXILIARY TRANSMISSION MOUNTING" — Illustration).

TRUCK MODELS	ENGINE	MAIN TRANSMISSION	AUXILIARY TRANSMISSION	FRONT MOUNTING	DIMENSION "A" INCHES	REAR MOUNTING	DIMENSION "A" INCHES
ME65	366	NP542	SP6041	View A	1-1/8	View B	2-7/16
ME65	366	CL285V	SP6041	View A	1-1/8	View B	2-7/16
ME65	427	CL325V	SP7041	View B	2-11/16	View B	2-11/16
ME65	427	SP5652B	SP7041	View B	2-11/16	View B	2-11/16

Alignment data chart (© Chevrolet Div., G.M. Corp.)

VIEW A   NOTE: See Chart for Dimension "A"   VIEW B
Auxiliary transmission mounting (© Chevrolet Div., G.M. Corp.)

Front mount installed
(© Chevrolet Div., G.M. Corp.)

Overdrive electrical circuit
(© Chevrolet Div., G.M. Corp.)

4. Reconnect the propeller shafts to the input and output ends of the transmission.

NOTE: It is important that all angels of the driveline be checked with a bevel protractor. Also the auxiliary transmission must be the same as the engine and main transmission. Adjustments may be made by raising or lowering the front or rear of the auxiliary transmission or by adding plates, washers spacers etc. (See Drive shaft alignment in U-joints-Drive Line Section.)

5. Connect the power take-off if applicable.
6. Connect the parking brake linkage.
7. Connect the speedometer cable to the adapter at the rear of the transmission.
8. Connect the shift control rods and adjust if necessary.
9. Refill the transmission with the recommended lubricant.

Linkage Adjustments

1. Disconnect the control rods from the shift control tower under the cab.
2. Place the auxiliary transmission gearshift lever and shift rods in the "Neutral" position.
3. Adjust the length of each control rod by rotating its adjustable clevis to provide a free clevis pin fit.
4. Reconnect the control rods to the control tower and shift the transmission through its entire shift pattern.
5. Replace any worn or damaged cotter pins, tighten the locknuts firmly and lubricate the control linkage.

Overdrive

Reference

The overdrive unit is essentially a two-speed planetary transmission attached to the rear of a conventional three speed transmission. In overdrive, engine speed is approximately thirty per cent slower at a given road speed since the drive train includes planetary gears which provide a lower overall gear ratio than that obtained in high gear with the conventional transmission.

The electrical equipment which controls the automatic action of the mechanical portion of the overdrive unit consists of a solenoid, a governor switch, a relay and a kickdown switch. The circuit including this equipment makes it possible to operate in overdrive above a pre-set cut-in speed, or in conventional drive at any speed.

Repairs to the overdrive housing, output shaft, ring gear assembly, clutch cam, roller retainer, pinion cage, sun gear, shift rail, sun gear control plate, output shaft bearing, oil seal, speedometer drive gear, solenoid pawl and interlock plunger may be performed underneath the vehicle, by removing the overdrive housing without disturbing the transmission.

If the transmission mainshaft overdrive adaptor or transmission rear bearing which is retained in the adaptor require replacement the entire transmission and overdrive assembly should be removed.

For overhaul—see General Section.

Governor Switch

To remove governor switch disconnect wires at switch and screw governor out of housing.

Solenoid

Remove solenoid by taking out the two mounting bolts and lockwashers. Turn solenoid 1/4 turn and pull solenoid plunger out of adapter.

Automatic Transmission

Reference

See specific chapter in general section for overhaul procedures for each make.

Types

Transmissions basically used are Powerglide, Powermatic (Allison) and Turbo Hydra-matic 350 and 400.

Powerglide

Available for light trucks consisting of a 3 element torque converter (a welded unit), and a two speed planetary transmission automatically shifted by a hydraulic control system, in a one piece aluminum case with a single shift occurring between Low and Drive. A forced downshift provides a passing gear by returning transmission to Low range. When gearshift lever is placed in Drive position, the transmission automatically shifts to Low range for initial vehicle movement. As the vehicle gains speed, depending on load and throttle position, an automatic shift is made to high gear.

Powermatic (Allison)

Powermatic or Allison automatic transmissions are designed for medium and heavy duty trucks. It is a torque converter type, using planetary gearing for full power shifting, with 6 speeds forward and one reverse and with automatic lock-up for direct drive from engine to the range gearing. An outstanding feature is the integral hydraulic retarder for controlling truck speed downhill. It is also equipped with two power take-off mounting openings, one on each side of housing.

NOTE: Do not apply hydraulic retarder while checking oil level, it will aerate the oil making an accurate oil level check impossible.

CAUTION: Do not tow or push Powermatic. Disconnect drive line or pull axles.

Turbo Hydra-matic 350

A fully automatic 3 speed transmission in a two piece aluminum casting, consisting primarily of a torque converter and a compound planetary gear set. Four

Turbo Hydra Matic 400 transmission ser. no. is located on plate on right side of transmission
(© Chevrolet Div., G.M. Corp.)

Power Matic (Allison) transmission number and production date on tag left side of case
(© Chevrolet Div., G.M. Corp.)

Power Glide and Turbo Hydramatic 350 identification number located on right rear vertical surface of oil pan
(© Chevrolet Div., G.M. Corp.)

multiple disc clutches, two roller clutches and one band provide the friction elements. The compound planetary gear set produces three forward speeds and one reverse. The cable operated detent system is designed to ensure positive part throttle or full throttle downshifting, depending on throttle position.

NOTE: Do not overfill, with oil level at the full mark on the dipstick it is just slightly below the planetary gear unit. If additional oil is added, bringing oil level above the full mark, the planetary unit will run in oil, foaming and aerating the oil. Aerated oil, carried through various oil pressure passages and converter, may cause malfunction of transmission resulting in cavitation noises in converter, bands and clutches. Overheating will also occur.

Turbo Hydra-matic 400/475

A fully automatic three speed transmission consisting primarily of

a three element torque converter and a compound planetary gear set. Three multiple disc clutches, one sprag unit, one roller clutch and two bands provide the friction elements. The three element torque converter consists of a pump (driving member), a turbine (driven member) and a stator mounted on a one-way (clockwise) roller clutch.

The detent solenoid is activated by an electric switch on the carburetor. When the throttle is fully opened, the switch on the carburetor is closed, activating the detent solenoid, causing transmission to downshift for passing speeds.

NOTE: Park position is not provided for 30 series.

CAUTION: Do not overfill, this transmission is very sensitive to oil level. If fluid is too low, especially when cold, complete loss of drive may result.

Powerglide Transmission

Shift Linkage and Adjustments

Manual linkage adjustment and neutral safety switch are important from a safety stand point. The neutral safety switch should be adjusted so that the engine will start in Park and Neutral positions only. With selector lever in Park position, the parking pawl should freely engage and prevent the vehicle from moving. The pointer on the indicator quadrant should line up with the range indicators in all ranges.

Shift Linkage and Adjustments

Powerglide 1970 & Up

Check for adjustment. With engine off, lift gearshift lever towards steering wheel, allow gearshift lever to be positioned in Drive (D) by the transmission detent. DO NOT use the indicator pointer to position the gearshift lever. Pointer is adjusted (or set) after linkage adjustment is made. Gearshift lever now won't engage reverse range unless lifted. A properly adjusted linkage will prevent the gearshift lever from moving beyond the Neutral detent and drive detent unless lever is raised to pass over mechanical stop in steering column.

Linkage Adjustment

1. Place the gearshift lever in Drive (D) position, as determined by detent.
2. Loosen adjustment swivel at mast jacket lever and rotate transmission lever so that it contacts the Drive stop in the steering column.
3. Tighten the swivel and recheck the adjustment.

Power glide shift linkage adjustment
(© Chevrolet Div., G.M. Corp.)

Adjusting low band
(© Chevrolet Div., G.M. Corp.)

Powerglide shift linkage
(© Chevrolet Div., G.M. Corp.)

4. Readjust indicator pointer, if necessary, to agree with transmission detent positions.
5. Readjust neutral safety switch, if necessary.

Low Band Adjustment

Adjustments should be made at periodical intervals or sooner if necessary, determined by operating performances.

1. Raise vehicle and support on stands.
2. Place gearshift lever in Neutral.
3. Remove protective cap from adjustment screw on transmission. NOTE: On some models it may be necessary to remove rear mounting bolts from crossmember and move transmission slightly to passenger side for additional clearance.
4. Loosen adjusting screw locknut ¼ turn and hold in this position during adjusting procedure.
5. Using an inch-pound torque wrench, adjust band to 70 inch pounds and back off four complete turns for a band which has been in service for 6000 miles or more, or three full turns for one with less than 6000 miles.
6. Tighten adjusting screw locknut to specified torque.

CAUTION: The back-off amount is not an approximate figure, it must be exact.

Throttle valve linkage adjustment
(using special tool)
(© Chevrolet Div., G.M. Corp.)

Throttle valve linkage adjustment
(using special tool)
(© Chevrolet Div., G.M. Corp.)

Throttle Linkage Adjustments

NOTE: Powerglide throttle linkage adjustments are made when carburetor throttle valve(s) is in closed position (hot idle) and transmission throttle lever is back against its internal stop. If shift occurs too early, shorten rod a turn or two and road test. If shift occurs too late, lengthen rod.

Powerglide 1970 and Up (6 Cylinder)

1. Remove air cleaner and disconnect carburetor return spring.
2. Rotate lever (A) to the wide open throttle position and T.V. lever through detent. (Depress accelerator fully).

3. Hold slot on rod (B) against pin on lever (A) as shown in circle Y—adjust swivel on rod so that it freely enters hole on lever (C).
4. Hold rod (B) perpendicular to pin on lever (A) and then tighten swivel nut. Rod must be 1/64"-1/16" off lever stop with transmission lever against internal stop. Connect carburetor return spring.
5. Check for throttle linkage freedom and proper operation.

Powerglide 1970 and Up (V8 Models)

1. Remove air cleaner.
2. Disconnect accelerator linkage at carburetor.

Throttle valve linkage adjustment—V8 engines
(© Chevrolet Div., G.M. Corp.)

Powerglide throttle valve linkage adjustment
—6 cyl.
(© Chevrolet Div., G.M. Corp.)

3. Disconnect accelerator return and throttle valve rod return springs.
4. With right hand, pull T.V. upper rod (F) forward until transmission lever (C) is through detent. With left hand, rotate carburetor lever (A) to wide open throttle position. Carburetor must reach wide open throttle position at the same time pin or ball stud on lever (A) contacts end of slot in upper T.V. rod (F)—see circle Z.
5. Adjust swivel on upper end of T.V. rod (F) to obtain setting described in step 4 (approximately 1/32″).
6. Connect and adjust accelerator linkage. Connect carburetor return springs.
7. Check for throttle linkage freedom and proper operation.

Powerglide Transmission Removal

1. Raise vehicle on hoist or support on stands.
2. Drain transmission oil if equipped with drain plug (or remove oil pan to drain, then replace pan using several bolts). Oil can be drained after transmission removal, if desired.
3. On models with long oil fill pipe, remove dipstick and pipe.
4. Disconnect oil cooler lines (if equipped), vacuum modulator hose and speedometer cable at transmission. Support lines out of work area.
5. Disconnect ground cable, T.S.C. switch, neutral switch and back-up lamp switch (if used).
6. Remove shift and throttle valve controls from transmission.
7. Disconnect propeller shaft from rear of transmission.
8. Position transmission jack and secure transmission to jack with safety chain.
9. Raise jack slightly to relieve engine rear mount on transmission extension and remove transmission support crossmember (Vans—remove thru-bolt). NOTE: Use care to remove any shims (if used) at crossmember. It is vital that exactly the same number be reinstalled.
10. Remove flywheel cover or converter under pan, scribe flywheel-converter marks for reassembly, remove flywheel to converter attaching bolts.
11. Support engine at oil pan rail with a jack to support engine weight when transmission is removed.
12. Vans—Remove linkage cross shaft frame bolts and accelerator linkage at bellcrank before lowering engine. Lower engine to

C10-20 WITH L-6 ENGINE

Throttle valve linkage adjustments L-6 engines
(© Chevrolet Div., G.M. Corp.)

P-10 MODELS

Throttle valve linkage adjustments—P-10 models
(© Chevrolet Div., G.M. Corp.)

P-20 MODELS

Throttle valve linkage adjustments—P20 models
(© Chevrolet Div., G.M. Corp.)

C10-20 WITH V-8 ENGINE

Throttle valve linkage adjustments V8 engines
(© Chevrolet Div., G.M. Corp.)

allow rear mount housing to clear support bracket.
13. Lower rear of transmission slightly so that the upper transmission to engine bolts can be reached using a universal socket and a long extension. Remove upper bolts. CAUTION: On V8 engines do not lower too far because of distributor—firewall interference.
14. Remove remaining transmission mounting bolts.
15. Remove transmission by moving

V-8 ENGINE   **L-6 ENGINE**

Powerglide throttle valve linkage adjustment
(© Chevrolet Div., G.M. Corp.)

it slightly to the rear and downward, remove from under vehicle.
NOTE: Watch converter when moving transmission back. If it does not move with transmission pry it free of flywheel before proceeding.
CAUTION: Keep front of transmission up to prevent the converter from falling out. Install a converter hold tool or improvise.
For Overhaul Procedures—See General Repair Section

Installation

1. Reverse removal procedures. NOTE: If reusing converter align scribed marks, if not through flywheel cover opening align as closely as possible the white stripe painted on engine side of flywheel outer rim (heavy side) with the blue stripe painted on end of converter (light side) to maintain balance.
2. Refill transmission and check for proper operation and leaks.

Turbo-Hydramatic

Shift Linkage

Check for adjustment with engine off, lift gearshift lever towards steering wheel, allow gearshift lever to be positioned in Drive (D) by the transmission detent. DO NOT use the indicator pointer to position the gearshift lever. Pointer is adjusted (or set) after linkage adjustment is made. Release gearshift lever. Lever must drop back into position, with no restriction, and be inhibited from engaging low range (unless lifted). Lift gearshift lever towards steering wheel and allow the lever to be positioned in Neutral (N) by the transmission detent. Release gearshift lever. The lever should now be inhibited from engaging reverse range (unless lifted). A properly adjusted linkage will prevent the gearshift lever from moving beyond both the Neutral detent and the Drive detent unless lever is lifted to pass over the mechanical stop in steering column.

Linkage Adjustment

1970-76 Cabs, Suburbans, 4-wheel drive
1974-76 Forward Control exc. Vans

1. Place gearshift lever in Drive (D), as determined by transmission detent. Obtain Drive position by rotating transmission lever (A) counterclockwise to low detent, then clockwise two detent positions to Drive.
2. Loosen adjustment swivel at mast jacket lever (B) and rotate transmission lever (A) so that it contacts the Drive stop in the steering column.
3. Tighten swivel and recheck adjustment.
4. Readjust indicator pointer, if necessary, to agree with transmission detent positions.
5. Readjust Neutral safety switch if necessary (C).

Linkage Adjustment

1970-73—Forward Control
1970-74—Vans

1. Set transmission lever (E) in Drive position. Obtain Drive position by rotating transmission lever (E) counter-clockwise to Low detent, then clockwise two detent positions to Drive.
2. Attach control rod (D) to lever (E) and shaft assembly (B) with retainers.
3. Assemble ring, washers, grommet, swivel, retainer and nut loosely on shaft (B).
4. Insert control rod (C) in swivel and retainer, attach opposite end to tube and lever assembly.
5. Set tube lever assembly in Drive position and tighten nut (F).

NOTE: When above procedure is adhered to, the following conditions must be met by manual operation of the gearshift lever. From Reverse to Drive position travel, the transmission detent feel must be noted and related to indicated position on dial. When in Drive and Reverse position, pull lever toward steering wheel and

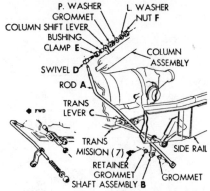

Turbo Hydra Matic Control Rod Linkage—1975-76 Vans (© Chevrolet Div., G.M. Corp.)

then release. It must drop back into position with no restriction.

Linkage Adjustments

1975-76—Vans

1. The shift tube and lever assembly must be free in the mast jacket.
2. Set transmission lever (C) in "neutral" position by one of the following optional methods.
NOTE: Obtain "neutral" position by moving transmission lever (C) counter-clockwise to "LI" detent, then clockwise three detent positions to "neutral" or obtain "neutral" position by moving transmission lever (C) clockwise to the "park" detent then counter-clockwise two detents to "neutral".
3. Set the column shift lever in "neutral" position. This is obtained by rotating shift lever until it locks into mechanical stop in the column assembly.
NOTE: Do not use indicator pointer as a reference to position the shift lever.
4. Attach rod (A) to shaft assembly (B) as shown.
5. Slide swivel (D) and clamp (E) onto rod (A) align the column shift lever and loosely attach as shown.
6. Hold column lever against "neutral" stop "park" position side.
7. Tighten nut (F) to 18 foot pounds.

8. Readjust indicator needle if necessary to agree with the transmission detent positions.
9. Readjust neutral start switch if necessary to provide the correct relationship to the transmission detent positions.

CAUTION: Any inaccuracies in the above adjustments may result in premature failure of the transmission due to operation without controls in full detent position. Such operation results in reduced oil pressure and partial engagement of clutches.

Detent Switch

Turbo Hydra-matic 350

A hydraulic system, pressurized by a gear pump, provides the working pressure required to operate the friction elements and automatic controls. The vacuum modulator is of the aneriod type and is used to automatically sense any change in torque input to the transmission. It transmits this signal to the pressure regulator, to the intermediate clutch accumulator valve and to the shift valves so that all torque and shift speed requirements of the transmission are met and smooth shifts are obtained at all throttle openings. A cable operated detent system controls downshifting for passing speeds.

Adjustment

1. Remove air cleaner.
2. Loosen detent cable screw.
3. With choke off and accelerator linkage properly adjusted, position carburetor lever in wide open throttle position.
4. Pull detent cable rearward until wide open throttle stop in

Detent cable adjustment
(© Chevrolet Div., G.M. Corp.)

Linkage adjustment (typical)
(© Chevrolet Div., G.M. Corp.)

Linkage adjustment (tilt cab)
(© Chevrolet Div., G.M. Corp.)

Turbo Hydra Matic Control Rod Linkage—1970-76 cabs, Suburbans, 4 wheel drive—1974-76 Forward Control exc. Vans (© Chevrolet Div., G.M. Corp.)

Vacuum modulator assembly (© Chevrolet Div., G.M. Corp.)

transmission is felt. NOTE: Cable must be pulled through detent position to reach wide open throttle stop in transmission.

5. Tighten detent cable screw and check linkage for proper operation.

Turbo Hydra-matic 400/475

A hydraulic system pressurized by a gear pump provides the working pressure required to operate the friction elements and automatic controls. A vacuum modulator is used to automatically sense any change in torque input to the transmission. The vacuum modulator transmits this signal to the pressure regulator for line pressure control, to the 1-2 accumulator valve, and to the shift valves so that all torque requirements of this transmission are met and smooth shifts are obtained at all throttle openings. A detent solenoid, activated by an electrical switch on carburetor, controls downshift for passing speeds.

Neutral Safety Switch Adjustment

Mast Jacket Mounted

1. Place gearshift lever in Neutral (N).
2. Loosen retainer screws holding switch, install 3/32" drill (or pin) through hole in lower switch arm and bracket. Adjust position of switch until engine turns over (with ignition switch in start).

Transmission Mounted

1. Place gearshift lever in Neutral (N), loosen transmission lever extension bolt.
2. Pin switch lever in Neutral position with 3/32" drill or pin.
3. Install rod into switch lever, adjust swivel on rod to allow free entry of rod into lever.

Turbo Hydra Matic Control Rod Linkage—1970-73 Forward Control—1974 Vans (© Chevrolet Div., G.M. Corp.)

4. Secure rod with retainer, tighten transmission lever extension bolt.
5. Check adjustment by testing for cranking in both Neutral and Park.

Transmission Removal

Turbo Hydra-matic 350 (Except 4 Wheel Drive)

1. With vehicle on hoist drain oil by removing oil pan or drain plug (if so equipped). NOTE: Oil can be drained after transmission is removed if so desired.
2. Remove the vacuum modulator line and speedometer cable from the transmission and secure out of way.
3. Remove detent cable and manual control lever from the transmission.
4. Disconnect the drive shaft and remove.
5. Place suitable jack or other support under transmission and secure transmission to it.
6. At transmission extension disconnect rear engine mount and then remove support crossmember.
7. Remove converter underpan. Place marks on the flywheel and converter to insure proper in-

stallation and then remove the flywheel-to-converter bolts.

8. Support engine at oil pan rail with jack capable of supporting the weight of the engine when transmission is removed.
9. Lower rear of the transmission slightly so that upper, housing-to-engine, transmission bolts can be reached with a long extension and universal socket. Remove upper bolts. NOTE: Have an assistant watch upper engine parts to make sure everything clears when rear of transmission is being lowered.
10. Remove remaining transmission-to-housing bolts.
11. Remove transmission by moving it slightly to the rear and downward. Remove from under vehicle.

CAUTION: Watch converter when removing transmission to be sure that it moves with transmission. If it does not move, pry it free from flywheel before proceeding any further.

NOTE: On those vehicles so equipped, disconnection of the catalytic converter may be necessary to provide adequate clearance for transmission removal.

NOTE: Keep transmission front upward when removing transmission to prevent converter from falling out. Install converter holding tool after removal from engine.

For overhaul procedures—see General Repair Section.

Transmission Installation

Turbo Hydra-matic 350 (Except 4 Wheel Drive)

1. Mount transmission on transmission lifting equipment installed on jack or other lifting device.
2. Remove converter holding tool. CAUTION: Do not permit converter to move forward after removal of holding tool.

396 V8

Adjust kickdown switch (A) so that actuating lever (B) rests against threaded barrel of switch when carb lever is in wide open throttle position.

CARB LEVER — ACTUATING LEVER (B)

VIEW A — SWITCH (A)

Detent switch adjustment (396 engine)
(© Chevrolet Div., G.M. Corp.)

6 CYLINDER ENGINE

WITH ACCELERATOR CONTROLS PROPERLY ADJUSTED, ROTATE LEVER TO OBTAIN WIDE OPEN THROTTLE. FULLY DEPRESS PLUNGER AND POSITION SWITCH TO OBTAIN DIM. A SHOWN IN TABLE BETWEEN PLUNGER AND LEVER. TIGHTEN SWITCH ATTACHING SCREWS.

LEVER

	DIM. A
ALL EXCEPT 327 - 350	.05
327 - 350	.20

SWITCH   PLUNGER   A

307 V-8 ENGINE

327 350 V8 ENGINE

Detent switch adjustment (© Chevrolet Div., G.M. Corp.)

3. Raise transmission into place at rear of engine and install transmission case to engine upper mounting bolts, then install remainder of the mounting bolts.
4. Remove support from beneath engine, then raise rear of transmission to final position.
5. If scribed during removal, align scribe marks on flywheel and converter cover. Install converter to flywheel attaching nuts and bolts.
6. Install converter underpan.
7. Reinstall transmission support crossmember to transmission and frame.
8. Remove transmission lift equipment.
9. Connect propeller shaft to transmission.
10. Connect manual control lever rod and detent cable to transmission.
11. Connect vacuum modulator line, and speedometer drive cable to transmission.
12. Lower vehicle.
13. Refill transmission.
14. Check transmission for proper operation and for leakage. Check and, if necessary, adjust linkage.
15. Remove vehicle from hoist.

Transmission Removal
Turbo Hydra-matic 350 (4 Wheel Drive)

1. With vehicle on hoist drain oil by removing oil pan or drain plug (if so equipped). NOTE: Oil can be drained after transmission removal if so desired.
2. Remove shift lever and rod from transfer case.
3. Remove speedometer cable and vacuum modulator line from transmission and secure out of way.
4. Disconnect detent cable and manual control lever rod from transmission.
5. Remove front and rear drive shafts from transfer case.
6. Place jack or other support under transfer case and remove transmission - to - adapter case bolts.

7. Place jack or other support under transmission and secure transmission to it.
8. Remove transfer case-to-frame bracket bolts and remove transfer case.
9. On V8 engines remove exhaust crossover pipe.
10. Disconnect and remove rear transmission crossmember.
11. Remove converter underpan. Place marks on the flywheel and converter to insure proper installation and then remove the flywheel-to-converter bolts.
12. Support engine at oil pan rail with jack capable of supporting engine weight when transmission is removed.
13. Lower rear of transmission slightly so that upper housing-to-engine transmission bolts can be removed with a long extension and universal socket. Remove upper bolts. NOTE: Have an assistant watch upper engine parts to make sure everything clears when transmission is lowered.
14. Remove the remaining transmission-to-housing bolts.
15. Remove the transmission by moving it slightly to the rear and downward. Remove from under vehicle.
CAUTION: Watch converter when removing transmission to make sure converter moves with transmission. If it does not, pry it loose from flywheel before proceeding any further.
NOTE: Keep transmission front upwards when removing from engine to prevent converter holding tool

after removal from engine. See General Repair Section for overhaul procedures.

Transmission Installation
Turbo Hydra-matic 350 (4 Wheel Drive)

1. Mount transmission on transmission lifting equipment installed on jack or other lifting device.
2. Remove converter holding tool. CAUTION: Do not permit converter to move forward after removal of holding tool.
3. Raise transmission into place at rear of engine and install transmission case to engine upper mounting bolts, then install remainder of the mounting bolts.
4. Remove support from beneath engine, then raise rear of transmission to final position.
5. If scribed during removal, align scribe marks on flywheel and converter cover. Install converter to flywheel attaching bolts.
6. Install flywheel cover.
7. Place transfer case and adapter assembly at rear of transmission on suitable lift equipment and install transfer case to frame bracket attaching bolts.
8. Reinstall transmission to transfer case adapter attaching bolts and remove lift equipment.
10. Connect front and rear axle propeller shafts to transfer case.
11. Install exhaust system cross pipe.

12. Connect manual control lever rod and detent cable to transmission.
13. Connect vacuum modulator line and speedometer drive cable to transmission.
14. Assemble rod on transfer case shift lever before installing rod to transfer case shift linkage.
15. Lower vehicle.
16. Refill transmission.
17. Check transmission for proper operation and for leakage. Check, and if necessary, adjust linkage.
18. Remove from hoist.

Removal and Installation

Turbo Hydra-matic 400/475

Before raising the truck, disconnect the battery and release the parking brake.
1. Raise truck on hoist.
2. Remove propeller shaft.
3. Disconnect speedometer cable, electrical lead to case connector, vacuum line at modulator, and oil cooler pipes.
4. Disconnect shift control linkage.
5. Support transmission with transmission jack.
6. Disconnect rear mount from frame crossmember.
7. Remove two bolts at each end of frame crossmember and remove crossmember.
8. Remove converter under pan.
9. Remove converter to flywheel bolts.
10. Loosen exhaust pipe to manifold bolts approximately ¼ inch, and lower transmission until jack is barely supporting it.
11. Remove transmission to engine mounting bolts and remove oil filler tube at transmission.
12. Raise transmission to its normal position, support engine with jack and slide transmission rearward from engine and lower it away from vehicle.

CAUTION: Use converter holding tool when lowering transmission or

DIM. "A"

AT 475	1/2-INCH
AT 540	3/8-INCH
MT 640-650	1/4-INCH

Trunion adjustment—Allison Trans.
(© Chevrolet Div., G.M. Corp.)

64

Trunion and Cable Core Assembly—Allison Trans. (© Chevrolet Div., G.M. Corp.)

keep rear of transmission lower than front so as not to lose converter.

The installation of the transmission is the reverse of the removal with the following additional steps.

Before installing the flex plate to converter bolts, make certain that the weld nuts on the converter are flush with the flex plate and the converter rotates freely by hand in this position. Then, hand start all three bolts and tighten finger tight before torquing to specification. This will insure proper converter alignment.

NOTE: After installation of transmission check linkage for proper adjustment and check for leaks.

Shift Linkage Adjustment Allison—(AT475, AT540, MT640, MT650) Transmissions

With engine off and vehicle wheels blocked, shift the selector lever through each drive range "R," "N," "D," "3," "2," "1" (AT 540 and MT 640), "R," "N," "D," "L2," "L1," (AT 475), "R," "N," "2-5," "2-4," "2," "1" (MT 650) while feeling for full engagement in the transmission. The transmission shift control linkage should fully engage all transmission detent positions in the transmission just before the range selector lever hits the stops incorporated in the range selector cover. Note the position of the selector lever after each shift. The transmission detent "R" (Reverse) should not engage until the selector lever is completely out of

the neutral notch. If the selector lever is not properly located or operating, adjust the linkage.

Gas and Diesel Engines

1. Disconnect clevis from transmission shift lever by removing cotter pin and clevis pin.
2. Disconnect control cable from anchor point at bracket on transmission and remove cable retainer clips from underside of cab.
3. Remove four cross recess screws retaining range selector cover to tower or bracket, depending on truck model. Lift range selector assembly out to inspect cable attachment at range selector lever and hanger.
4. Check cable at trunnion for dimension "A" as shown. This dimension is necessary to allow for proper cable length at clevis. If adjustment is necessary, remove cable from range selector lever and hanger assembly as follows:
   a. Remove ½-inch locknut from trunnion.
   b. Disconnect cable from anchor point on hanger by removing two locknuts and U-bolt.
   NOTE: Locknuts can be removed and reinstalled up to six times before their replacement becomes necessary.
   c. Mark location of trunnion. Remove trunnion with attached cable core from lever.
   CAUTION: The trunnion has been placed in the proper hole at the factory. Any change in the location could cause vehicle operation to be dangerous.
5. With control cable removed, loosen jam nut at trunnion.
   NOTE: Do not use pliers on cable core when loosening jam nut or when adjusting trunnion. Cable core finish may be damaged resulting in cable core seal damage.
6. Turn trunnion clockwise, or counterclockwise to attain dimension "A". Tighten jam nut against trunnion.
7. Install trunnion in its original hole and tighten locknut securely.
8. Anchor cable to hanger with U-bolt, washers and locknuts. Tighten locknuts 3-5 foot-pounds torque.
9. Install shift control cover in tower or bracket depending on truck model. Install four cross recess screws. Tighten screws 3-5 foot-pounds torque. Install cable clips to underside of cab.
10. Anchor cable to bracket at transmission. Tighten two cross recess screws securely.
11. Locate transmission shift lever in "R" (Reverse) position.
    NOTE: "R" position if full counterclockwise (except on AT 475 "full clockwise") movement of lever.

12. Locate range selector lever against stop in "R" (Reverse) position.

13. Loosen jam nut at clevis. Turn clevis clockwise or counterclockwise on threaded cable core until holes in clevis align with hole in shift lever. Install clevis pin, note that pin should enter freely, if it does not, adjust clevis slightly by ½ turn in each direction until pin does enter freely.

14. Turn clevis one full turn clockwise to allow for cable backlash.

15. Connect clevis to shift lever with clevis pin and a new cotter pin, but do not spread cotter pin at this time.

16. Move the range selector lever through all drive ranges. The transmission detents should fully engage just before the range selector lever hits the stops incorporated in the shift control cover.

Throttle Valve Linkage Adjustment Diesel Engines

1. Apply parking brake and block vehicle's driving wheels.

2. Disconnect upper TV cable end from accelerator cross shaft.

3. Push upper cable end toward transmission modulator until seated against the stop.

4. Assemble slotted clevis end to cable with locknut.

5. With accelerator linkage in "IDLE" position, upper end of the slotted clevis must be against the clevis pin on the cross shaft lever.

6. Shorten cable at slotted clevis by turning clevis three complete turns clockwise to locate lower end of the cable in actuator ⅛-inch from idle stop.

7. Tighten locknut securely.

8. Assemble slotted clevis to cross shaft lever with clevis pin and a new cotter pin.

9. Attach TV return spring to bracket.

Neutral Safety and Backup Lamp Switch Check and Adjustment
Allison—(AT475) Transmission —1970-74

NOTE: "Shift Linkage Adjustment" should be performed as described previously, prior to adjustment of the neutral safety switch.

1. Block driving wheels, apply parking brake, and perform the following to prevent the vehicle from accidentally starting.

NOTE: Pull the secondary wire out of socket in distributor cap and ground the wire to prevent possible damage to coil.

2. Position the selector lever (B) in "N" (Neutral). Turn ignition switch to "START" position. Engine should turn over but not

Clevis adjustment—Allison Trans.
(© Chevrolet Div., G.M. Corp.)

start. Turn ignition switch to "OFF."

3. Position selector lever in "R" (Reverse). Turn ignition switch to "START" position. Engine should not turn over or start.

4. Move selector lever to "D" (Drive) position. Turn ignition switch to "START" position. Again the engine should not turn over or start. Turn ignition switch to "OFF."

Throttle Valve Linkage (Diesel Engine)—Allison Trans. (© Chevrolet Div., G.M. Corp.)

5. If the conditions in Steps 2 through 4 are not met, the neutral safety and back-up lamp switch (F) must be adjusted as follows:

6. Disconnect and remove swivel (I) from transmission shift lever (H). Position transmission selector lever (B) in "N" (Neutral).

7. Locate the switch lever (F) of the neutral safety and back-up lamp switch in neutral position. Neutral position of the switch lever is achieved by inserting a 3/32-inch diameter pin at location (E) through switch lever and into switch bracket.

8. Position swivel (I) on rod (J) to provide free-entry of swivel into shift lever (H). Secure swivel with two retainers.

9. Repeat Steps 2 through 4. If switch does not operate properly it must be replaced and adjustment procedure repeated.

Allison—(AT475) Transmission —1975-76

NOTE: "Shift Linkage Adjust-

ment" should be performed prior to adjustment of neutral safety switch.

1. Block driving wheels, apply parking brake, and perform the following to prevent vehicle from accidentally starting:
   Pull the secondary wire out of the socket in the distributor cap and ground the wire to prevent possible damage to the coil.

2. Position the range selector lever to "N" (neutral). Turn ignition switch to "Start" position. Engine should crank, but not start. Turn ignition to "Off."

3. Position range selector lever in "R" (reverse). Turn ignition switch to "Start" position. Engine should not crank or start. Turn ignition switch to "Off."

4. Move range selector lever to "D" (drive) position. Turn ignition switch to "Start" position. Again the engine should not crank or start. Turn ignition switch to "Off."

5. If the conditions in Steps 2 through 4 are not met, the neutral safety and back-up lamp switch must be adjusted as follows:
   a. Place range selector lever in "N" (neutral) position.
   b. Loosen two screws attaching switch assembly to transmission mounting bracket. Check to see that actuating rod is secure.
   c. Locate switch in neutral position with a 3/32-inch diameter pin in hole H through switch lever G and bracket.
   d. Tighten switch to bracket screws to 15-20 in.-lbs. torque.
   e. Repeat Steps 2 through 4 to check switch operation. Readjust switch if necessary or replace if found defective.

Neutral Safety and Backup Lamp Switch Adjustment
Allison—(AT540) Transmission Tilt & Schoolbus Models

NOTE: "Shift Linkage Adjustment" should be performed as described previously, prior to adjustment of the neutral safety and back-up lamp switch.

1. Block driving wheels, apply parking brake, and perform the following to prevent the vehicle from accidentally starting.

NOTE: Pull the secondary wire out of center socket in the distributor cap and ground wire to prevent possible damage to coil.

2. Move selector lever (B) to "N" (Neutral) position. Then, loosen jam nuts and adjust length of push rod to dimension shown.

3. With switch push rod properly adjusted, tighten jam nuts securely.

Shift Linkage—AT-475 Trans.
(© Chevrolet Div., G.M. Corp.)

Neutral safety and back-up lamp switch 1975-76-AT-475 Trans. (© Chevrolet Div., G.M. Corp.)

Downshift Switch—AT-475 Trans.
(© Chevrolet Div., G.M. Corp.)

Shift Linkage—AT-540 Trans.
(© Chevrolet Div., G.M. Corp.)

4. Check each range position of shift linkage to make sure the starter does not operate with the selector lever in any position other than "N." Have assistant check for proper operation of back-up lights with selector lever in "R." If necessary readjust switch.

5. Reconnect secondary wire to distributor cap.

NOTE: The neutral safety and back-up lamp switches are non-adjustable on the Allison-MT-640, MT-650 trans. and all diesel engines with automatic transmissions.

Downshift Switch Adjustment Allison—(AT475) Transmission

The downshift switch mounted at the carburetor is activated by the carburetor throttle lever. When the throttle lever reaches wide open position it results in a forced downshift to the transmission unless vehicle is in "L1."

1. Move carburetor throttle lever to wide open position.
2. Loosen two adjusting screws (at slotted holes) on switch bracket.
3. Position switch and bracket assembly so that clearance between throttle lever and switch plunger (fully depressed) is .05-inch.
4. Tighten the two adjusting screws to 20-30 inch-pounds torque.
5. Road test and check for proper operation.

Allison—(AT475) Transmission Removal

NOTE: It may be necessary to remove the air tanks, fuel tanks, special equipment, etc., on some vehicles to provide clearance before the transmission is removed.

1. Block vehicle so that it cannot move. Disconnect ground strap from battery negative post. Remove the spark plugs so the engine can be turned over manually.
2. Remove the level gauge (dipstick). Drain transmission by disconnecting oil filler tube at right side of transmission. Remove bracket holding oil filler tube to transmission and remove filler tube from vehicle. Replace dipstick in tube and cover the oil pan opening to prevent entry of foreign material.
3. Disconnect oil cooler lines from fittings on right side of transmission case. Plug line ends and case openings with lint-free material.
4. Disconnect the shift cable from shift lever at left side of transmission.

5. Disconnect vacuum modulator line from modulator. Disconnect wiring to neutral safety and back-up lamp switch.
6. Disconnect the speedometer shaft fitting from adapter at rear of transmission.
7. Disconnect the propeller shaft from transmission.
8. Disconnect the mechanical parking brake linkage at the right side of transmission (if used).
9. Remove the sheet metal under pan from beneath the converter housing. As the flex-plate is rotated, remove the six bolts retaining flex-plate assembly to converter.
10. Support the transmission with 500-pound (minimum rating) transmission floor jack. The jack must be positioned so transmission oil pan will not support the weight of transmission. Fasten a safety chain over top of transmission and to both sides of jack.
11. Place a support under rear of engine and remove transmission

Engine rear mounting—AT-475 (© Chevrolet Div., G.M. Corp.)

extension-to-engine rear support bolts. Then remove engine rear support from frame of vehicle.

12. Remove the transmission case-to-flywheel housing bolts and washers.

13. Carefully inspect transmission and surrounding area to be sure no lines, hoses, or wires will interfere with transmission removal.

IMPORTANT: When removing transmission, keep rear of case lower than the front so as not to lose the converter. Install converter holding tool (J-5384) when transmission is removed from the vehicle.

14. Move transmission assembly from the engine, lower the assembly carefully and move it out from the vehicle.

Installation

1. Raise vehicle sufficiently to allow installation of transmission. With transmission assembly mounted on transmission jack move transmission into position aligning converter with flex-plate. Check for and clean away any foreign material in flywheel pilot hole and flywheel flex-plate assembly and front face of transmission case. Rotate flywheel ring gear, as necessary, so that the six bolt holes in flex-plate are aligned with bolt holes in converter. Carefully move transmission assembly toward engine so flex-plate-to-converter bolts can be loosely installed and so that pilot on transmission converter enters pilot hole in center of flywheel flex-plate assembly.

2. Install bolts and washers that attach transmission case to flywheel housing. Tighten bolts to 25-30 foot-pounds torque.

3. Tighten the six flex-plate-to-converter bolts.
   In-Line and
   V8 Engines .... 25-30 Ft. Lbs.
   V6 Engines .... 20-25 Ft.-Lbs.

4. Install engine rear support.

NOTE: An arrow is stamped in the center of the engine rear support. This arrow should face the front of vehicle when equipped with 292, 350, or 379 engines. The arrow should face the rear of vehicle when equipped with 366 engine.

5. Carefully lower engine and transmission assembly onto engine rear support. Tighten engine rear support-to-transmission bolts to torques specified. Bend lock tabs down over heads of bolts (where used). Remove lifting equipment from beneath vehicle.

6. Install the sheet metal underpan beneath the converter housing.

7. Remove plugs from oil cooler lines and transmission case fittings. Be sure fittings are clean

Flex plate installed (inline and V-8 engines)—AT-475   (© Chevrolet Div., G.M. Corp.)

Flex plate installed (V-6 engine)—AT-475
(© Chevrolet Div., G.M. Corp.)

and lint-free, then connect oil cooler lines to transmission.

8. Install oil cooler tube and bracket on right side of transmission. Install oil level gauge (dipstick).

9. Connect the speedometer shaft fitting to adapter at rear of transmission.

10. Connect propeller shaft to transmission.

11. Connect parking brake linkage (if used) at side of transmission.

12. Connect the manual selector cable to shift lever at left side of transmission.

13. Connect the vacuum modulator line to modulator. Connect wiring to neutral safety and back-up lamp switch.

NOTE: Make sure the ignition switch is in the off position before proceeding to the next step.

14. Install spark plugs and connect battery ground strap, previously disconnected.

15. Connect any other lines, hoses, or wires which were disconnected to aid in transmission removal.

16. Adjust the shift linkage. (see "Shift Linkage Adjustment")

17. Refill the transmission with the proper lubricant.

Allison—(AT540) Transmission Removal

NOTE: It may be necessary to remove the air tanks, fuel tanks, special equipment, etc., on some vehicles to provide clearance before the transmission is removed.

1. Block vehicle so that it cannot move. Disconnect ground strap from battery negative (−) post. Remove the spark plugs so the engine can be turned over manually.

2. Remove the oil level gauge (dipstick). Drain transmission by disconnecting oil filler tube at right side of transmission oil pan. Remove bracket holding oil filler tube to transmission and remove filler tube from vehicle. Replace dipstick in tube and cover the oil pan opening to prevent entry of foreign material.

3. Disconnect oil cooler lines from fittings on right side of transmission case. Plug line ends and case openings with lint-free material.

4. Disconnect the range selector cable from shift lever at left-side of transmission.

5. Disconnect vacuum modulator line from modulator. Also, on conventional cab models, disconnect wiring from neutral safety and back-up lamp switches.

6. Disconnect the speedometer shaft fitting from adapter at rear of transmission.

7. Disconnect the propeller shaft from transmission.

8. Disconnect the mechanical parking brake linkage at the right side of the transmission (if used).

9. Through the opening in the flywheel housing, use a pry-bar, as necessary to manually turn the flywheel. As the flywheel is rotated, remove the six bolts retaining flywheel flex plate assembly to converter cover.

10. Support the transmission with a 500-pound (minimum) transmission floor jack. The jack must be positioned so transmission oil pan will not support the weight of transmission. Fasten a safety chain over top of transmission and to both sides of jack.

11. Place a support under rear of engine and remove transmission case-to-crossmember support bolts. Raise the engine to remove weight from the engine rear mounts.

12. Remove the transmission case-to-flywheel housing bolts and washers.

13. Carefully inspect transmission and surrounding area to be sure no lines, hoses, or wires will interfere with transmission removal.

NOTE: When removing transmission, keep rear of transmission lower than the front so as not to lose converter.

14. Move transmission assembly from the engine, lower the assembly carefully and move it out from the vehicle.

Installation

1. Raise vehicle sufficiently to allow installation of transmission. With transmission assembly mounted on transmission jack move transmission into position aligning converter with flywheel. Check for and clean away any foreign material in flywheel pilot hole, flywheel flex-plate assembly, and front face of transmission case. Rotate flywheel as necessary so that the six bolt holes in flex-plate are aligned with bolt holes in converter cover. Carefully move transmission assembly toward engine so flex-plate-to-converter cover bolts can be loosely installed and so that pilot on transmission converter enters pilot hole in center of flywheel.
2. Install bolts and washers that attach transmission case to flywheel housing. Tighten bolts to 25-30 foot-pounds torque.
3. Tighten the six flex-plate-to-converter cover bolts to 35-40 foot-pounds torque.
4. Carefully lower engine and transmission assembly onto engine rear mounts. Tighten engine rear mounting bolts to 60-70 foot-pounds torque. Then bend lock tabs down over head of each bolt. Remove lifting equipment from beneath vehicle.
5. Remove plugs from oil cooler lines and transmission case fit-

Flex plate installation (V-8 engine)—AT-540
(© Chevrolet Div., G.M. Corp.)

tings. Be sure fittings are clean and lint-free, then connect oil cooler lines to transmission.
6. Install oil filler tube and bracket on right side of transmission. Install oil level gauge (dipstick).
7. Connect the speedometer shaft fitting to adapter at rear of transmission.
8. Connect propeller shaft to transmission.
9. Connect parking brake linkage (if used) at side of transmission.
10. Connect the range selector cable to shift lever at left side of transmission.
11. Connect the vacuum modulator line to modulator. Also, on conventional cab models, connect wiring to neutral safety and back-up lamp switches.

NOTE: Make sure the ignition switch is in the off position before proceeding to the next step.

12. Install spark plugs and connect battery ground strap, previously disconnected.
13. Connect any other lines, hoses, or wires which were disconnected to aid in transmission removal.
14. Adjust the shift linkage. (see "Shift Linkage Adjustment")
15. Refill the transmission with the proper lubricant.

Allison—(MT640, MT650) Transmission Removal

NOTE: It may be necessary to remove the air tanks, fuel tanks, special equipment, etc., on some vehicles to provide clearance before the transmission is removed.

1. Block vehicle so that it cannot move. Disconnect ground strap from battery negative (—) post. Remove the spark plugs so the engine can be turned over manually.
2. Remove the oil level gauge (dipstick). Drain transmission by disconnecting oil filler tube at right side of transmission oil pan. Remove bracket holding oil filler tube to transmission and remove filler tube from vehicle. Replace dipstick in tube and cov-

er the oil pan opening to prevent entry of foreign materials.
3. Disconnect oil cooler lines from fittings on right side of transmission case. Plug line ends and case openings with lint-free material.
4. Disconnect shift cable from shift lever at left side of transmission.
5. Disconnect vacuum modulator line from modulator. Also, disconnect wiring from back-up lamp switch (right side of transmission) and neutral safety switch (left side of transmission).
6. Disconnect the speedometer shaft fitting from adapter at rear of transmission.
7. Disconnect the propeller shaft from transmission.
8. Disconnect the mechanical parking brake linkage at the right side of the transmission (if used).
9. Through access opening in the flywheel housing, use a pry bar, as necessary to manually turn the flywheel. As the flywheel is rotated, remove the six nuts retaining flex-plate assembly to converter cover.
10. Support the transmission with a 750-pound (minimum rating) transmission floor jack. The jack must be positioned so transmission oil pan will not support the weight of transmission. Fasten a safety chain over top of transmission and to both sides of jack.
11. Place a support under rear of engine and remove transmission case-to-crossmember support bolts. Raise the engine to remove weight from the engine rear mounts.
12. Remove the transmission case-to-flywheel housing bolts and washers.
13. Carefully inspect transmission and surrounding area to be sure no lines, hoses, or wires will interfere with transmission removal.

Flex plate installation (V-6 engine)—AT-540
(© Chevrolet Div., G.M. Corp.)

Flex plate installation—MT-640, MT-650
(© Chevrolet Div., G.M. Corp.)

NOTE: When removing transmission keep rear of transmission lower than the front so as not to lose converter.

14. Move transmission assembly from the engine, lower the assembly carefully and move it out from the vehicle.

Installation

1. Raise vehicle sufficiently to allow installation of transmission. With transmission assembly mounted on transmission jack move transmission into position aligning converter with flywheel. Check for and clean away any foreign material in flywheel pilot hole, flex-plate assembly, and front face of transmission case. Rotate flywheel as necessary so that the six studs in converter cover are aligned with holes in flex plate. Carefully move transmission assembly toward engine so flex-plate-to-converter cover nuts can be loosely installed and so that pilot on transmission converter enters pilot hole in center of flywheel.

2. Install bolts and washers that attach transmission case-to-flywheel housing. Tighten bolts to 12-16 foot-pounds torque.

3. Tighten the six flex-plate-to-converter cover nuts to 34-40 foot-pounds torque.

4. Carefully lower engine and transmission assembly onto engine rear mounts. Tighten engine rear mounting nuts to 190-210 foot-pounds torque. Remove lifting equipment from beneath vehicle.

5. Remove plugs from oil cooler lines and transmission case fittings. Be sure fittings are clean and lint-free, then connect oil cooler lines-to-transmission.

6. Install oil filler tube and bracket on right side of transmission. Install oil level gauge (dipstick).

7. Connect the speedometer shaft fitting to adapter at rear of transmission.

8. Connect propeller shaft to transmission.

9. Connect parking brake linkage (if used) at side of transmission.

10. Connect shift cable to shift lever at left side of transmission.

11. Connect the vacuum modulator line to modulator. Also, connect wiring to neutral safety switch (left side of transmission) and back-up lamp switch (right side of transmission).

NOTE: Make sure the ignition switch is in the off position before proceeding to the next step.

12. Install spark plugs and connect battery ground strap, previously disconnected.

13. Connect any other lines, hoses, or wires which were disconnected to aid in transmission removal.

14. Adjust the shift linkage. (see "Shift Linkage Adjustment")

15. Refill the transmission with the proper lubricant.

U Joints, Drive Lines

Description

Tubular type propeller shafts and needle bearing type universal joints are used on all model trucks. An internally splined sleeve which compensates for variation in distance between rear axle and transmission is located at the forward end of single or rear propeller shafts.

The number of propeller shafts used is dependent upon the wheel base of the vehicle. On vehicles which use two or more propeller shafts, each shaft (except the rear) is supported near its splined end in a rubber cushioned ball bearing which is mounted in a bracket attached to a frame cross member. The ball bearing is a permanently sealed and lubricated type.

An extended-life universal joint, which does not require periodic inspection and lubrication, has been incorporated in several applications on the 10 and 20 series vehicles.

This extended-life universal joint is identified by the absence of the lubrication fitting, which is present on all trunnions not equipped with the extended-life feature.

A lubrication fitting is also provided on each sliding sleeve to lubricate the splines. A plug is staked into the yoke end of sleeve to retain lubricant and a small hole is drilled in the end of this plug to relieve trapped air. The opposite end of the sleeve is sealed by means of a cork packing in a retainer which screws on the end of the sleeve.

Shaft Removal

Single or Rear

Remove rear trunnion "U" clamps, lower the rear of propeller shaft and pull back to disengage the sleeve at front of shaft. Remove shaft from under vehicle.

Front

Remove four front flange nuts at transmission and, if equipped with intermediate propeller shaft, remove the rear trunnion "U" clamps. Remove nuts and lock washers attaching bearing support to frame crossmember and pull shaft assembly from vehicle.

1 Front propeller shaft and bearing suuport assy.	6 Guard	16 Cork packing
2 Front intermediate propeller shaft and bearing support assy.	7 "U" clamp	17 Trunnion
	8 Rear propeller shaft	18 Seal ring
	9 Lock ring	19 Flange and deflector assy.
3 Rear intermediate shaft and bearing support assy.	10 Bearing assembly	20 Brakcet
	11 Lubrication fitting	21 Cushion
4 Rear propeller shaft and sleeve assy.	12 Plug	22 Slinger
	13 Sleeve	23 Grease retainer
	14 Retainer	24 Inner deflector
5 Frame crossmember	15 Washer	25 Dust shield

Propeller shafts, universal joints and bearing supports (© Chevrolet Div., G.M. Corp.)

Intermediate or Rear Intermediate Shaft

Remove the front trunnion "U" clamps and the bearing support mounting bolt nuts and lock washers. Lower the front of the shaft and pull forward to disengage splines at rear of shaft. Remove shaft and bearing support assembly from under vehicle.

Front Intermediate Shaft

Remove the front and rear trunnion "U" clamps and the bearing support mounting bolt nuts and lock washers. Lower shaft and bearing support assembly from vehicle.

Inspection

Wash ends of propeller shaft in cleaning solvent, inspect for damage and excessive wear on splines, trunnions and bearings. Examine sleeve seal, washer and retainer for damage or deterioration.

CAUTION: When trunnion bearing "U" clamps are removed to remove the propeller shaft, tape the bearings to keep them clean and from becoming damaged. Propeller shaft guards may be removed, if necessary, by removing nut at each end of the guard.

Shaft Installation

Propeller shafts may be installed by reversing the procedure used in removal when the following notes are observed.

NOTE 1: Before installing a rear propeller shaft and sleeve assembly, slide seal retainer, steel washer and cork seal on spline of mating shaft. Assemble these parts to sleeve by turning retainer onto sleeve after rear propeller shaft is installed.

NOTE 2: Over torquing "U" clamp nuts will result in bearing cap distortion which will reduce roller bearing life.

NOTE 3: To prevent excessive driveline vibration on some models, the rear propeller shaft must be installed so that centerline of sleeve yoke is positioned from vertical to 7 splines clockwise from vertical. The centerline of either yoke at the transmission end is perpendicular to the ground.

Driving out U-joint bearing cups (snap ring type) (© Chevrolet Div., G.M. Corp.)

Removing U-joint bearing cups (snap ring type) (© Chevrolet Div., G.M. Corp.)

NOTE 4: The propeller shaft to pinion flange fastener is an important attaching part in that it could affect the performance of vital components and systems, and/or could result in major repair expense. It must be replaced with one of the same part number or with an equivalent part if replacement becomes necessary. Do not use a replacement part of lesser quality or substitute design. Torque values must be used as specified during reassembly to assure proper retention of this part.

Universal Joint R&R (Snap Ring Type)

Disassembly

1. Remove trunnion bearings from propeller shaft yoke as follows:
   a. Remove lock rings from yoke and lubrication fitting from trunnion.
   b. Support yoke in a bench vise.
   c. Using soft drift and hammer, drive on one trunnion bearing to drive opposite bearing from yoke.
   NOTE: The bearing cap cannot be driven completely out.
   d. Grasp cap in vise and work out.
   e. Support other side of yoke and drive other bearing cap from yoke and remove as in step d.
   f. Remove trunnion from propeller shaft yoke.
2. If equipped with sliding sleeve, remove trunnion bearings from sleeve yoke in the same manner as above. Remove seal retainer from end of sleeve and pull seal and washer from retainer.

Assembly

1. Assemble trunnion bearings to propeller shaft as follows:
   a. On extended life universal joints when performing service operations that require disassembly of the universal joint, repack bearings with grease as outlined in NOTE below and replace trunnion assembly dust seals.
   b. On all other universal joints lubricate trunnion bearing rollers and install new seal rings.
   c. Insert trunnion in propeller

shaft yoke and press bearings into yoke and over trunnion hubs far enough to install lock rings.
   d. Hold trunnion in one hand and tap propeller shaft yoke lightly to seat bearings against lock rings.
2. On rear propeller shafts, install sleeve yoke over trunnion hubs and install bearings in the same manner as above.

NOTE: In addition to packing the bearings, make sure the lubricant reservoir at the end of each trunnion is completely filled with lubricant. In filling these reservoirs, pack lubricant into the hole so as to fill from the bottom. This will prevent air pockets and ensure an adequate supply of lubricant.

To replace trunnion dust seal, remove the old dust seal and place new seal on trunnion—cavity of seal toward end of trunnion—Press seal onto trunnion exercising caution during installation to prevent seal distortion and to assure proper seating of seal on trunnion.

(Plastic Retaining Ring Type)

Disassembly

1. Support the drive shaft in a horizontal position in line with the base plate of a press. Place the universal joint so that the lower

Using spacer to remove bearing cup (plastic retaining ring type) (© Chevrolet Div., G.M. Corp)

Pressing out bearing cup (plastic retaining ring type) (© Chevrolet Div., G. M. Corp)

Aligning universal joints (© Chevrolet Div., G.M. Corp.)

Install plastic snap rings
(© Chevrolet Div., G.M. Corp.)

ear of the shaft yoke is supported on a 1⅛″ socket. Place the cross press, J-9522-3 or equivalent, on the open horizontal bearing cups, and press the lower bearing cup out of the yoke ear as shown in the illustration. This will shear the plastic retaining the lower bearing cup.

2. If the bearing cup is not completely removed, lift the cross and insert Spacer J-9522-5 or equivalent, between the seal and bearing cup being removed, as shown in figure 2.

   Complete the removal of the bearing cup, by pressing it out of the yoke.

3. Rotate the drive shaft, shear the opposite plastic retainer, and press the opposite bearing cup out of the yoke as before, using Spacer J-9522.

4. Disengage the cross from the yoke and remove.

NOTE: Production universal joints cannot be reassembled. There are no bearing retainer grooves in production bearing cups. Discard all universal joint parts removed.

5. Remove the remains of the sheared plastic bearing retainer from the ears of the yoke. This will aid in reassembly of the service joint bearing cups. It usually is easier to remove plastic if a small pin or punch is first driven through the injection holes..

6. If the front universal joint is being serviced, remove the pair of bearing cups from the slip yoke in the same manner.

Reassembly

1. A universal joint service kit is used when reassembling this joint. This kit includes one pregreased cross assembly, four service bearing cup assemblies with seals, needle rollers, washers, grease and four bearing retainers.

2. Make sure that the seals are in place on the service bearing cups to hold the needle rollers in place for handling.

Installing trunion into yoke (plastic retaining ring type) (© Chevrolet Div., G.M. Corp.)

STRIKE TUBE YOKE EAR IN THIS AREA

Seating plastic snap rings
(© Chevrolet Div., G.M. Corp.)

3. Remove all of the remains of the sheared plastic bearing retainers from the grooves in the yokes. The sheared plastic may prevent the bearing cups from being pressed into place, and this prevents the bearing retainers from being properly sealed.

4. Install one bearing cup part way into one side of the yoke, and turn this yoke ear to the bottom.

5. Insert cross into yoke so that the trunnion seats freely into bearing cup as shown in illustration.

6. Install opposite bearing cup part way. Make sure that both trunnions are started straight and true into both bearing cups.

7. Press against opposite bearing cups, working the cross all of

the time to check for free movement of the trunnions in the bearings. If there isn't, stop pressing and recheck needle rollers to determine if one or more of them has been tipped under the end of the trunnion.

8. As soon as one bearing retainer groove clears the inside of the yoke, stop pressing and snap the bearing retainer into place as shown in the illustration.

9. Continue to press until the opposite bearing retainer can be snapped into place. If difficulty is encountered, strike the yoke firmly with a hammer to aid in seating bearing retainers. This springs the yoke ears slightly.

10. Assemble the other half of the universal joint in the same manner.

11. Check the freedom of rotation of both sets of trunnions of the cross. If too tight, again rap the yoke ears as described above. This will loosen the bearings and help seat the bearing retainers.

Constant Velocity Joint

Disassembly

1. Remove front propeller shaft from vehicle.

2. Remove rear trunnion snap rings from center yoke. Remove grease fitting.

3. Place propeller shaft in vise and drive one rear trunnion bearing cap from center yoke until it protrudes approximately ⅜″. NOTE: Keep rear portion of propeller shaft up to avoid interference of rear yoke half with center yoke.

4. Once the bearing cap protrudes ⅜″, release vise. Grasp protruding portion of cap in vise and drive on center yoke until cap is removed. Remove cap seal by prying off with a thin screwdriver.

5. Repeat steps 3 and 4 for remaining bearing caps.

6. Once the center yoke caps have been removed remove rear yoke half bearing caps. Remove rear trunnion.

7. Gently pull rear yoke half from propeller shaft. Remove all loose needle bearings. Remove spring seal.

8. Remove front trunnion from center and front yoke in same manner as described in Steps 2, 3 & 4.

NOTE: Before front trunnion can be removed all four (4) bearing caps must be removed.

Assembly

1. Clean and inspect all needle bearings, caps, seals, fittings, trunnions and yokes. Assemble all needle bearings in caps (27 per cap) ; assemble needle bearings in front yoke (28 total). Retain bearings with a heavy grease. Assemble seals to bearing caps.

2. Place front trunnion in drive shaft. Place center yoke on front trunnion. Install one bearing cap and seal assembly in front yoke. Drive in to a depth that the snap ring can be installed. Install snap ring. Install remaining cap and seal in front yoke. Install snap ring.

3. Install front trunnion bearing caps in center yoke in same manner.

4. With front trunnion completely installed, install seal on propeller shaft (large face first). Gently slip rear yoke half on propeller shaft using care not to upset rollers. Insert rear trunnion in center yoke. Install rear yoke half bearing caps on rear trunnion. Install one rear trunnion bearing cap in center yoke and press into yoke until snap ring can be installed. Install remaining cap and snap ring.

5. Before assembly is reinstalled in vehicle, grease universal at all three (3) fittings (2 conventional type and one, in rear yoke half), that requires a needle nose grease gun adapter.

Bearing Support

Removal

1. Remove dust shield, or, if equipped with flange, remove cotter pin and nut and pull flange and deflector assembly from shaft.

2. Pull support bracket from rubber cushion and pull cushion from bearing.

3. Pull bearing assembly from shaft. Remove grease retainers and slingers (if used) from bearing.

4. Remove inner deflector from shaft if replacement is necessary.

NOTE: The ball bearing is a permanently sealed and lubricated type.

72

Installation

1. Install inner deflector on propeller shaft, if removed, and prick punch deflector at two opposite points to make sure it is tight on shaft.

2. Pack retainers with grease. Insert a slinger (if used) inside one retainer and press this retainer over bearing outer race.

3. Start bearing and slinger assembly straight on shaft journal. Support propeller shaft and, using suitable length of pipe over splined end of shaft, press bearing and inner slinger against shoulder on shaft.

4. Install second slinger on shaft and press second retainer over bearing outer race.

5. Install dust shield over shaft, small diameter first and press into position against outer slinger or, if equipped with flange, install flange and deflector assembly as follows :

   a. Install deflector on flange, if removed, and prick punch at two opposite points to make sure it is tight on flange.

   b. Align centerline of flange yoke with centerline of propeller shaft yoke and start flange straight on splines of shaft with end of flange against slinger.

   c. Install retaining nut and tighten to 160-180 ft. lbs. torque. Install cotter pin.

6. Force rubber cushion onto bearing and coat outside diameter of cushion with brake fluid.

7. Force bracket onto cushion.

Drive Shaft Alignment

Correct drive line angles are necessary to prevent excessive torsional vibrations, especially tandem rear axle models. On some vehicles adjustable auxiliary transmission mountings are provided for adjusting the angle of the various drive line components. On vehicles not having adjustable auxiliary transmission mountings and adjustable torque rods at rear axles, proper adjustment of the angle of the drive line components must be accomplished by the use of spacers or shims at the frame crossmember or hangers. All angles must be checked with a maximum

Checking pinion angles
(© Chevrolet Div., G.M. Corp.)

amount of exactness. The use of a bubble level is not sufficient, a bevel protractor must be used. The vehicle should be checked on a reasonably flat surface.

Clean machined surface at rear of (main) tranmission to check engine (and transmission) angle. This is the key angle and auxiliary transmission (if equipped) and rear axle pinion must be set to this angle. Make sure all drive line components from (main) transmission to rear axle are properly centered. Clean dirt and paint off machined surface of propeller shaft yoke, make sure surface is free of nicks or burrs. Set bevel protractor to zero, place protractor on yoke surface at right angle to propeller shaft and rotate shaft until bubble is centered in glass. Reposition protractor on yoke, in-line with propeller shaft, and note shaft angle.

Shaft angle must be held within a maximum of 1° less than engine. Check rear axles on machined surfaces on differential carrier housing, at right angle to pinion shaft. Make sure protractor is held straight up to get correct angle. On rear axles that do not have a machined surface it will be necessary to remove propeller shaft. Rotate the pinion yoke into a vertical position, clean the four machined ends of yoke of dirt, paint, nicks and burrs. Place the protractor across ends of yoke, on either side, and in as close as possible to a vertical position. Rear axle angle should be same as engine.

Rear Axle

Chevrolet Semi Floating Single Speed

Description

Two types of rear axles are used. The removable carrier type thru 1962 with Hotchkiss drive and the Salisbury type from 1963 with an integral carrier.

The following applies to both rear axles except where noted.

The drive pinion is mounted on two preloaded taper roller bearings. The ring gear is bolted to the differential case which is mounted on preloaded taper roller bearings. There are two side gears and two differential pinion gears.

Axle Shaft Removal

1. Remove the brake drum.

2. Drain lubricant from the differential and remove the housing cover.

3. Remove the differential pinion shaft lock screw, pinion shaft and axle shaft spacer.

4. Push the axle shaft in and

remove the "C" washer from the inner end of the axle shaft.

5. Remove the axle shaft from the housing.

Installation

NOTE: If a new axle shaft is to be installed.

1. Position the axle shaft gasket to the axle shaft flange.
2. Apply heavy shellac or paint to both sides of the gasket and axle shaft oil deflector.
3. Install the axle shaft oil deflector over the gasket aligning the oil pocket with the notch in the flange.
4. Insert six special axle shaft bolts and force the heads down to the deflector.
5. Peen the end of the shoulder on the bolts into the countersink around the bolt holes in the flange.
6. Slide the axle shaft into place. CAUTION: Exercise care that the splines on the end of the shaft do not cut the axle shaft oil seal and that they engage with the splines of the differential side gears.
7. Install the "C" washer on the inner end of the shaft.
8. Pry the shafts apart so that the "C" washers are seated in the counterbore in the differential side gears and install the pinion gears.
9. Select the proper axle shaft spacer to give free fit to .014" maximum clearance between the end of the axle shaft and the spacer.
10. Install the spacer and pinion shaft, locking in place with the special screw.
11. Install the axle housing cover and gasket and refill the differential.
12. Install the drum and wheel.
13. Road test for leaks and noise.

Axle Shaft Removal (Spline Drive Type)

Procedure for removal of axle shafts is same with assembly removed or installed in the vehicle.

1. Remove cap screws and hub cap from hub.
2. Install slide hammer adapter into tapped hole in axle flange.
3. Install slide hammer into adapter and remove axle shaft.

Installation

1. Dip small end of splined shaft in axle lubricant, and insert shaft into hub.
2. Turn shaft as necessary to index shaft splines with differential side gear splines. As shaft is pushed inward, rotate hub to align axle shaft flange splines to hub. Push shaft into place.

Bearing and oil seal removal
(© Chevrolet Div., G.M. Corp.)

Measuring pinion bearing preload
(© Chevrolet Div., G.M. Corp.)

3. Install new gasket on hub cap and install hub cap to hub with cap screws. Torque cap screws 15 to 20 foot-pounds.

Axle Shaft Bearing or Oil Seal Removal

1. Remove the wheel, drum and axle shaft (see axle shaft removal).
2. Using a slide hammer, remove the bearing, bearing retainer and oil seal.
3. Inspect the bore and dress out the old stake points.

Installation

1. Using the proper driver, place the oil seal, bearing and inside bearing retainer on the driver in that order.
2. Place a light coat of sealer on the outside of the seal to insure proper sealing of the seal in the housing bore.
3. Start the bearing into the axle housing and tap the tool with a hammer to seat the parts.
4. Remove the driver and stake the oil seal in place with a punch.
5. Assemble the axle shafts (see Axle Shaft Installation).

Pinion Flange, Oil Deflector and/or Oil Seal Replacement

1. Raise the vehicle and support the frame on stand jacks, allow the axle to drop for clearance and expand the brake shoes on one wheel to lock the wheel.
2. Check the free wheel for freedom of rotation.

3. Separate the rear universal, tape the trunnion bearings to the joint and lower the rear of the propeller shaft.
4. Using a one inch torque wrench, and proper socket on the pinion flange nut, rotate the pinion through several complete revolutions and record the torque required to keep the pinion turning. If the old flange is to be installed, mark the pinion and flange for reassembly in the same relative position.
5. Hold the pinion flange, remove the pinion flange nut and special washer. Discard the nut and use a new one upon reassembly.
6. Remove the pinion flange. Pry the old oil seal out of the case.
7. Inspect the pinion flange for smooth oil seal surface or worn drive splines. Replace if necessary.
8. Install a new flange oil deflector if the deflector is damaged.
9. Soak the new seal in light engine oil before installation. Wipe the outside of the seal and coat the outside with sealer.
10. Install the new seal using the proper driver.
11. Install the pinion flange, aligning the marks on the pinion and flange if the old flange is being used. If the flange does not go on the shaft easily, pull the flange on the shaft using a special tool. Remove the special tool and install the special washer and new nut.
12. Tighten the nut to remove end play and continue alternately tightening and checking preload with an inch pound torque wrench until it is the same as recorded in step 4.
13. Readjust the brake on the locked wheel.
14. Connect the propeller shaft, lower the vehicle and road test for leaks and noise.

Removable Carrier Differential Removal

1. Remove the wheel, drum and axle shafts (see Axle Shaft Removal).
2. Reinstall the axle shaft spacer, pinion shaft and lock screw to retain assembly for removal from the vehicle.
3. Separate the rear universal, tape the trunnion bearings to the joint and lower the rear of the propeller shaft.
4. Remove the nuts which attach the differential carrier to the axle housing, separate the carrier from the housing and remove the carrier from the vehicle.

For overhaul—see general section.

Installation

1. Clean the axle housing and differential gasket surfaces and install a new gasket.
2. Position the differential carrier to the axle housing, install the nuts and tighten securely.
3. Connect the rear universal joint.
4. Assemble the axle shafts (see Axle Shaft Installation).

Salisbury Differential Removal

1. Remove the wheel, drum and axle shafts (see Axle Shaft Removal).
2. Roll out the differential pinion and thrust washers, then remove the side gears and thrust washers. Mark the pinions and side gears so that they can be reassembled in the original position.
3. Mark one bearing cap and housing for reassembly in the same position. Remove the bearing cap bolts and bearing caps, tap the surface of the bearing caps to loosen. CAUTION: Do not pry the caps off as this may damage the machined face of the caps.
4. Using a pry bar, pry the differential case out of the carrier. NOTE: Exercise caution in prying on the case and gasket sealing surface. If the bearings are preloaded, the case will suddenly fall free when it is pried past a certain point. Make sure the case is properly supported to prevent damage.
5. Place the left and right bearing cups, caps and shims so that they may be reinstalled in the original positions.

Salisbury Drive Pinion Removal

1. Remove the differential as previously outlined.
2. Remove the propeller shaft.
3. Remove the pinion flange nut and washer. Discard the nut and use a new one upon reassembly.
4. Remove the pinion flange. Pry the oil seal out of the bore.
5. Remove the drive pinion by tapping on the front end with a soft faced hammer.
6. Remove the pinion front bearing from the carrier bore. Discard the pinion bearing spacer and use a new one upon reassembly.
7. Clean all gears and bearings and inspect all bearing cups, races and rollers for scoring, chipping or excessive wear. Inspect pinion splines and flange splines. Inspect the ring gear and pinion teeth.

Salisbury Pinion and/or Bearing Replacement

1. If necessary to replace the pinion bearings, tap the old cups out of the carrier using a brass drift.
2. Position the new cup in the carrier, thick edge of the cup toward the shoulder of the carrier. Using a cup installer, tap the cup into the carrier until it is fully seated against the shoulder.
3. Press the rear bearing cone and roller assembly from the pinion and note the shim between the bearing cone and pinion head.
4. When the ring gear and pinion or the pinion rear bearing assembly are replaced, the correct shim thickness must be determined by using special gauges or the trial and error method according to tooth pattern.
5. Position the shim selected on the pinion shaft against the pinion head.
6. Press the new cone and roller assembly on the pinion.

Salisbury Drive Pinion Installation

1. Position the drive pinion and rear bearing cone and roller assembly in the carrier, install a new pinion bearing spacer on the pinion shaft and install the pinion front bearing cone and roller assembly.
2. Soak the new seal in light engine oil before installation. Wipe the outside of the seal and coat the outside with sealer.
3. Install the new seal using the proper driver.
4. Install the pinion flange. If the flange does not go on the shaft easily, pull the flange on the shaft using a special tool. Remove the special tool and pack the cavity between the end of the pinion splines and pinion flange with a non-hardening sealer.
5. Install the pinion flange washer and new nut. Tighten the nut to remove end play and continue alternately tightening and checking preload with an inch pound torque wrench until torque required to rotate the pinion is 20-25 in. lbs. for new bearings and seal, or 5-10 in. lbs. when used parts are installed.

Salisbury Differential Bearing Replacement

1. Using a bearing puller, remove the bearings from the case.
2. Place the new bearing on the hub of the case, thick side of inner race toward case. Using a bearing driver, drive the bearing into place.
3. Before installing the bearing on the opposite hub, support the case on an adapter. This allows the case to rest on the adapter instead of the bearing cage which has already been installed. Install the remaining bearing.

Salisbury Ring Gear Replacement

1. Remove the ring gear bolts and lock washers and, using a soft faced hammer, tap the ring gear off the case.
2. Install five guide pins, made from $3/8''$—$24x1\frac{1}{2}''$ long cap screws with the heads cut off and ends slotted, to the ring gear.
3. Position the ring gear on the case. Install every other ring gear bolt and lock washer, then draw them up evenly and snugly so that the gear face is flush with the case.
4. Remove the guide pins and install the remaining bolts, torque all bolts to 50 ft. lbs.

Salisbury Differential Bearing Preload

1. Place the differential case and bearing assembly in the carrier. If the same bearings and case are used, select new right and left adjusting shims each 0.002'' thicker than the original shim. If new bearings and/or case are being installed, loosely install the left bearing cap and select the preload shim as follows:
   a. Select two shims of known thickness and position them between the right bearing cup and the cup seat in the carrier. (select shims with a total thickness that will permit a feeler gauge of at least .010'' to be inserted between the shim and cup seat in the carrier) Make sure the left bearing cup and case are against the left cup seat. Using a feeler gauge, determine the distance between the shim and cup seat.
   b. Add .010'' to the total of both shims and feeler gauge thickness used in step a, then select two shims of equal thickness which in total are equal to the value obtained in step a plus the additional .010''.

NOTE: Use only one shim at each side.

2. Remove the left bearing cap and position the shim between the bearing cup and cup seat. Wedge the right shim between the bearing cup and cup seat (position the shim so that the chamfered side is outward or next to the cup seat). Tap the shim into position, using a soft faced hammer, while rotating the differential case.
3. Install the bearing caps and torque them alternately to 50-60 ft. lbs.

Installing bearing cap
(© Chevrolet Div., G.M. Corp.)

Salisbury Ring Gear and Pinion Adjustment

1. Mount a dial indicator on the carrier and check the backlash between the ring gear and pinion. The backlash should be within .003"-.010" with .005"-.008" preferred. Check gear lash at four equally spaced positions around the gear. Variations in reading should not exceed .001".
2. If gear lash is not within limits, correct by decreasing shim thickness on one side and increasing thickness of the other shim the same amount. Total shim thickness must be maintained at all times to maintain proper preload. After adjustments have been made, assemble the axle shafts (see Axle Shaft Installation).

Chevrolet Full Floating

Description
Single Speed

The rear axle is a full floating type with hypoid ring gear and pinion. The full floating construction enables removal of the axle shafts without removing the truck load or jacking up the rear axle. The drive pinion is straddle mounted being supported at the rear end on a roller bearing and at the front end on a double row bearing.

The ring gear is bolted to the differential case and some models are provided with a ring gear thrust pad to prevent distortion when starting under heavy loads.

Some models have a two pinion differential while others have a four pinion differential.

Description
Two-Speed

The Chevrolet two-speed axle is available in the 15,000 and 17,000 lb. capacity. In low gear, torque is transmitted to the differential case through the planetary pinions. The straddle mounted drive pinion and the ring gears operate to produce the high range reduction, the planet and sun gears being locked to revolve with the ring gear.

Differential case removal
(© Chevrolet Div., G.M. Corp.)

J 22888

Differential bearing removal
(© Chevrolet Div., G.M. Corp.)

PINION SHIM IDENTIFICATION

Thickness	Identification Notches
.021	None
.024	1
.027	2
.030	3
.033	4

Measuring pinion shim requirement
(© Chevrolet Div., G.M. Corp.)

Early models have a two way vacuum system for axle shifts. Later models use an electric shift system.

Maintenance and adjustments for the two speed axle are performed the same as those outlined for the Chevrolet single-speed axles.

Axle Shaft Removal

5200 and 7200 lb. Axles

1. Remove the bolts and lockwashers that attach the axle shaft flange to the wheel hub.
2. Install two ½" - 13 bolts in the threaded holes provided in the axle shaft flange. By turning

J-0358-1   J-7028

Pinion cone & roller assembly removal
(© Chevrolet Div., G.M. Corp.)

these bolts alternately the axle shaft may be started and then removed from the housing.

Installation

1. Clean both the axle flange and the wheel hub.
2. Place a new gasket over the axle shaft and position the axle shaft in the housing so that the shaft splines enter the differential side gear.
3. Install the bolts and torque to 85-95 ft. lbs.

Axle Shaft Removal

11,000-13,500 and 1500 lb. Axles

1. Remove the hub cap and install a slide hammer and adapter in the tapped hole on the shaft flange
2. Remove the axle shaft.

Installation

1. Clean the old gasket from the hub and hub cap. Clean the axle shaft flange and mating surfaces in the wheel hub.
2. Install the axle shaft so that the shaft splines index into the hub splines.
3. Tap the shaft into position. Install a new hub cap gasket, position the hub cap to the hub and install the attaching bolts. Torque the bolts to 11-18 ft. lbs.

Axle Shaft Removal

17,000 lb. Axle

1. Remove the axle shaft flange-to—hub nuts.
2. Strike the flange with a lead hammer to loosen the flange and dowels.
3. Remove the tapered dowels from the studs and pull the axle shaft from the housing.

Installation

1. Clean the old gasket from the wheel hub and axle shaft flange and install a new gasket over the hub studs.
2. Install the axle shaft so that the splines are aligned with the differential side gear and the flange holes index over the hub studs.

Chevrolet Trucks · Vans · Blazer

3. Install the tapered dowel over each hub stud. Install and tighten the stud nuts to 80-100 ft. lbs

Axle Shaft Removal
(Spline Drive Type)

Procedure for removal of axle shafts is same with assembly removed or installed in the vehicle.
1. Remove cap screws and hub cap from hub.
2. Install slide hammer adapter into tapped hole in axle flange.
3. Install slide hammer into adapter and remove axle shaft.

Installation

1. Dip small end of splined shaft in axle lubricant, and insert shaft into hub.
2. Turn shaft as necessary to index shaft splines with differential side gear splines. As shaft is pushed inward, rotate hub to align axle shaft flange splines to hub. Push shaft into place.
3. Install new gasket on hub cap and install hub cap to hub with cap screws. Torque cap screws 15 to 20 foot-pounds.

Bearing and Bearing Cup
Replacement

Replace the inner cup (all axles) and outer bearing cup for 17,000 lb. axle as follows:
1. Place an appropriate press-out tool behind the bearing cup, index the tool in provided notches, and press out the cup.
NOTE: The hub outer bearing (all axles except 17,000 lb. axle) cannot be replaced with the inner bearings in position; therefore, replace the outer bearings (if required) before proceeding.
2. Position the cup in the hub, with the thick edge of the cup toward the shoulder of the hub. Using an applicable cup installer, press the cup into the hub until it seats on the hub shoulder.
Replace the outer bearing assembly (all axles except 17,000 lb.) as follows:
NOTE: The inner bearing assembly must be removed before attempting to replace the outer bearing.

Removing hub inner bearing cup
(© Chevrolet Div., G.M. Corp.)

1. Using a punch, tap the bearing outer race away from the bearing retaining ring. Then remove the retaining ring from the hub.
2. On 5,200 and 7,200 lb. axles, remove the outer bearing by using a brass drift. On 11,000, 13,500 and 15,000 lb. axles, remove the bearings by driving on the axle spacer, using the splined flange cut from an old axle.
3. On 11,000, 13,500 and 15,000 lb. axles place the axle shaft spacer in the hub first. Place the inner race and roller assembly in the hub, larger O.D. towards the outer end of the hub. Position the bearing cup in the hub, then end of the cup toward the outer end of the hub. Press the cup into the hub, install the retainer ring, then press the cup into positive contact with the retainer ring.
NOTE: The bearing cup to retainer ring seating is essential to assure accurate wheel bearing adjustment.

Wheel Hub Oil Seal
Replacement

Pry out the old seal from the hub bore. Pack the cavity between the new seal lips with wheel bearing grease. Position the seal in the hub bore and press the seal into the bore until it is properly seated.
With the exception of the 15,000 lb. axle with 15x4 inch brakes, the seal should be installed flush with the end of the hub. On the 15,000 lb. axle with 15x4 inch brakes the seal should

be installed so that it makes contact with the bearing race.

Bearing Adjustment

Before checking the bearing adjustment, make sure the brakes are fully released and do not drag. Check bearing play by grasping the tire at the top and pulling back and forth, or by using a pry bar under the tire. If the bearings are properly adjusted, movement of the brake drum in relation to the brake flange plate will be barely noticeable and the wheel will turn freely. If movement is excessive, adjust the bearings as follows:
1. Remove the axle shaft and raise the vehicle until the wheel is free to rotate. (See Axle Shaft Removal)
2. Disengage the nut lock from the lock nut and remove them from the axle housing tube.
3. Using an appropriate tool, tighten the adjusting nut to specifications, at the same time rotating the hub.
5,200 and 7,200 lb. axles—55 ft. lbs.
11,000 and 13,500 lb. axles—90 ft. lbs.
15,000 lb. axle
4 inch brakes—90 ft. lbs.
5 inch brakes—50 ft. lbs.
17,000 lb. axle—65 ft. lbs.
Then back the nut off 1/8 to 1/4 turn to align the nearest slot with the short tang on the nut lock.
3. Install the nut lock.
4. Install the lock nut and tighten to specifications.
5,200 and 7,200 lb. axles—175 ft. lbs.
11,000 and 15,000 lb. axles with 15x4 inch brake—250 ft. lbs.
13,500 lb. axle—135 ft. lbs.
15,000 lb. axle with 15x5 inch brake—135 ft. lbs.
17,000 lb. axle—135 ft. lbs.
5. Bend the tang of the nut lock over the flat or slot of the lock nut.
Final bearing check should show 0.001" to 0.007" end play.
6. Lower the vehicle and install the axle shaft. (See Axle Shaft Installation)

Removing bearing adjusting nut (typical)
(© Chevrolet Div., G.M. Corp.)

Checking ring gear backlash
(© Chevrolet Div., G.M. Corp.)

Measuring differential shim requirement
(© Chevrolet Div., G.M. Corp.)

Drive Pinion Oil Seal Replacement

1. Disconnect the propeller shaft and remove the pinion flange and deflector.
2. Remove the bolts retaining the oil seal retainer to the carrier, and withdraw the retainer from the pinion.
3. Pry the old seal from the bore.
4. Clean all foreign matter from the retainer.
5. Pack the cavity of the new seal with a high melting point bearing lubricant, position the seal on an installer.
6. Press the seal into the retainer until it bottoms against the shoulder.
7. Position the seal retainer over the pinion. Install and tighten the retaining bolts.
8. Reinstall the pinion flange and propeller shaft.

Differential Carrier Removal

1. Drain the lubricant from the differential.
2. Remove the axle shafts. (See Axle Shaft Removal)
3. Disconnect the rear universal joint and swing the propeller shaft to one side.
4. On two speed axles, remove the electric or vacuum lines.
5. Remove the bolts and lock washers which retain the carrier assembly to the axle housing. Support the differential housing with a floor jack and roll it from under the truck.

For overhaul—see General Section.

Installation

1. Clean the axle housing and differential housing gasket surfaces and place a new gasket over the axle housing.
2. Assembly the carrier to the axle housing, install the lockwashers and bolts and tighten securely.
3. Assemble the rear universal joint.
4. On two speed axles, connect the electric or vacuum lines.
5. Install the axle shafts. (See Axle Shaft Installation)
6. Fill with lubricant and road test for proper operation.

Removing bearing rotation ring 5200 and 7200 lb. axle (© Chevrolet Div., G.M. Corp.)

Removing axle shaft—11,000, 13,500 and 15,000 lb. axle (© Chevrolet Div., G.M. Corp.)

Installing differential shim (© Chevrolet Div., G.M. Corp.)

Eaton Full Floating

Description
Single Speed

This axle is equipped with a straddle mounted drive pinion. Pinion bearings are of the opposed tapered roller bearing type.

A straight roller type pilot bearing is pressed onto the inner end of the drive pinion and seats in the bore of the differential case.

The differential carrier assembly may be removed, while the axle is still installed in the truck, after the axle shafts have been removed.

The differential is a conventional four pinion type. On early models the ring gear is riveted to the differential case. On later models the ring gear is bolted to the differential case.

Some models have a thrust pad mounted on the end of an adjusting screw which is threaded into an opening in the differential carrier. This thrust pad limits the deflection of the drive gear under severe loads.

Axle shaft, oil seal, wheel bearings, pinion seal and differential removal and installtion are performed the same as those outlined for Chevrolet axles. Refer to Rear Axle (Chevrolet).

For overhaul—see General Section.

Description
Two Speed

The differential and planetary assembly is installed in a two-piece support case. The ring gear is installed between the thalves of the support case and retained in place by the same bolts which fasten the support case halves together.

The planetary assembly is composed of a high speed clutch plate, and four planetary pinions.

An electric power shifting arrangement is used to assist in making ratio changes. For schematic of Electric Shift see Chevrolet Two Speed Axle.

Axle shaft, oil seal, wheel bearings, pinion seal and differential removal and installation are performed the same as those outlined for Chevrolet Axles. Refer to Rear Axle (Chevrolet).

For overhaul—see General Section.

Rear Suspension

Coil Spring Type

Control Arm Removal

1. Remove the load from the spring by jacking at the frame.
2. Disconnect the parking brake cable from the control arm.
3. Remove the spring clamp bolt from the underside of the control arm.
4. Remove the "U" bolt nuts and separate the shock absorber bracket from the control arm. Separate the control arm from the "U" bolts and lower the rear of the arm.
5. Remove the pivot bolt and remove the arm from the vehicle.

Installation

1. Position the bushed end of control arm and insert the pivot bolt. Place the nut on the bolt finger tight.
2. Position the clamp inside the spring, raise the control arm, then pass the bolt, with the flat washer installed, up through the control arm and clamp. Install the lock washer and nut. Torque from 40 to 50 ft. lbs.
3. Place the arm adjacent to the axle. Pass the "U" bolt over the axle and through the holes in the arm.
4. Place the shock absorber bracket on the "U" bolt, install the nuts and torque from 200 to 225 ft. lbs.

Tightening wheel hub bearing nut (© Chevrolet Div., G.M. Corp.)

5. Lower the vehicle to put full weight of the unloaded vehicle on the front and rear suspension, torque the control arm pivot bolt from 125 to 165 ft. lbs.

Coil Spring Removal

1. Raise the vehicle and adjust the axle to frame height so that the spring is not under tension.
2. Remove the shock absorber bolt from the mounting bracket at the control arm.
3. Remove the upper and lower clamps from the spring.
4. Lower the control arm sufficiently to permit removal of the spring.

Installation

1. Place the spring lower clamp inside the spring. Position the clamp so that the end of the spring coil is within the notch. Locate the spring and clamp over the bolt hole in the control arm.
2. Pass the clamp bolt and washer up through the hole in the control arm and loosely install the nut.
3. Position the upper clamp inside the spring and install the bolt and washer. Torque to 45-55 ft. lbs.
4. Connect the shock absorber. Torque the nut to 110-150 ft. lbs.
5. Torque the spring lower clamp bolt to 40-50 ft. lbs.
6. Lower the vehicle.

Leaf Spring Type

Spring Removal

(Light Duty Trucks with Spring Hanger and Shackle Pin Lubricating Fittings)

1. Jack the vehicle at the frame to relieve tension on the spring.
2. Remove the lubrication fitting from the spring eye and rear shackle pin.
3. Remove the lock bolts and nuts or pins from the shackle pin and spring eye pin.
4. Using appropriate tools, remove the spring eye pin and shackle pin.
5. Remove the "U" bolt nuts, withdraw the "U" bolts and remove the spring from the vehicle.

Installation

1. Position the spring assembly on the axle housing. Install the spacer assembly between the axle housing and spring, if so equipped, then install the "U" bolts.
2. Install the "U" bolt retaining nuts, torque the nuts alternately and evenly to properly seat the spring.

3. Jack as required to align the spring eyes; install the spring eye and shackle pins, lock bolts and nuts or lock pins and lubricating fittings. Lubricate the spring bushings and lower the vehicle.

Spring Removal

(Light Duty Trucks with Rubber Spring Hanger and Shackle Bushings)

1. Jack the vehicle at the frame to relieve tension on the spring.
2. Remove the "U" bolt retaining nuts and withdraw the "U" bolts.
3. Loosen the shackle bolts and remove the lower bolt.
4. Remove the nut and bolt securing the spring to the front hanger.
5. Remove the spring from the vehicle.

Installation

1. Position the spring assembly, and spacers if so equipped, on the axle housing. NOTE: On springs with metal encased pressed in type bushings, the shackle assembly must be attached to the rear spring eye before installing the shackle to the rear hanger.
2. Position the "U" bolts and loosely install the "U" bolt retaining nuts.
3. Jack as required to align the spring eyes with the front hanger and rear shackle, install the eye bolts.
4. Lower the vehicle.
5. Tighten the "U" bolt retaining nuts alternately and evenly to properly seat the spring, and tighten the front hanger and rear shackle bolts.

Spring Removal

(Medium Duty Trucks)

1. Raise vehicle frame to take weight off the spring. Make sure vehicle is supported safely.
2. Remove rear wheels to provide access to spring assembly.

3. Safely support axle on floor jack.
4. Install a C-clamp on radius leaf, to relieve load on radius leaf eye bolt on 45 Series vehicles.
5. On 45 Series at the front and rear hanger, remove rebound pin retainer bolt, then remove retainer. Install suitable puller into tapped hole at end of rebound pin, then remove pin.
6. Remove spring U-bolt nuts, shock absorber bracket (when used) U-bolt anchor plate and U-bolts and U-bolt spacer, then lower axle slightly.
7. Remove spring eye on radius bolt nut and washer, then remove spring eye bolt from spring eye or radius leaf.

NOTE: When tapered shim is used, the position of shim thin and thick edge should be noted so that shim can be installed properly at assembly.

Installation

1. Set spring assembly and tapered shim or spacer (if used) at axle pad.

NOTE: Tapered shim must be installed on axle in same position that was noted at removal.

2. Install U-bolt spacer over center bolt.
3. Seat U-bolts in spacer grooves, then secure spring to axle by installing anchor plates, shock absorber bracket (when used) and nuts on U-bolts.
4. Lower frame until ends of spring enter the hanger and touch the cam surface of hanger. Compress radius leaf with C-clamp until radius leaf eye and hanger holes are aligned and torque to specifications.
5. Remove C-clamp from radius leaf.
6. Install rebound pin at front and rear hangers. Install rebound pin retainer and secure with retainer bolt.
7. Install wheels.
8. Remove blocking and lower frame to place weight on springs. Check U-bolt nuts for proper torque.

TORQUE SPECIFICATIONS

PART	FT. LBS. TORQUE
Spring U-Bolt Nuts (All "C/S" Series)	190-210
(All "T" Series)	190-210
Shock Absorber Nuts (when used) Upper Nut	85-90
Lower Nut	25-30
Rear Spring Radius Leaf Bolt Nut	175-225
(All T Series)	290-320
(All "C/S" Series with ⅝" x 18 Bolt)	60-80
(All "C/S" Series with 1" x 14 Bolt)	150-200
Rebound Pin Retainer Bolt (All Except "T" Series)	10-14
("T" Series)	
60	5-10
65	20-25
Rear Axle Bumper Bolt Nuts (All Except "T" Series)	6-8
("T" Series)	10-12

Index

TUNE-UP SPECIFICATIONS

CU. IN. DISPLACE-MENT	YEAR	SPARK PLUG GAP	DISTRIBUTOR		IGNITION TIMING DEG. BTC (± 2°)	CRANKING COMP. PRESS.	VALVE CLEARANCE		GOV. RPM NO LOAD	FUEL PUMP PRESS	IDLE SPEED	
			POINT DWELL	POINT GAP			INTAKE	EXHAUST			STD.	AUTO.
SIX CYLINDER												
198	1970-71	.035	40-45	.020	TDC	130	.012H	.024H	3500	3½-5	550	650N
225	1970-71	.035	42-47	.020	TDC	125	.012H	.024H	3500	3½-5	650	650N
225	1972	.035	41-46	.020	TDC	100	.012H	.024H	3500	3½-5	750	750N
225 Lt.Duty	1973	.035	Electronic		TDC	100	.012H	.024H	3600	3½-5	700 (800)	700N (800)
225 Heavy Duty	1973	.035	Electronic		TDC (2½A)	100	.012H	.024H	3600	3½-5	700 (800)	700N (800)
225 Lt. Duty	1974	.035	Electronic		TDC	100	.012H	.024H	3600	3½-5	800	750N
225 Heavy Duty	1974	.035	Electronic		2½A	100	.012H	.024H	3600	3½-5	800	750N
225 Lt. Duty	1975	.035①	Electronic		TDC	100	.012H	.024H	3600	3½-5	800	750N
225 Heavy Duty	1975	.035①	Electronic		TDC	100	.012H	.024H	3600	3½-5	700	700N
225	1976	.035①	Electronic		③	100	.012H	.024H	3600	3½-5	③	③
EIGHT CYLINDER												
318 S. Tr.	1970-71	.035	28-32	.017	5B	140	—	—	3900	5-7	500	—
318 A. Tr.	1970-71	.035	28-32	.017	10B	140	—	—	3900	5-7	—	500N
318 w/exh. em.	1970-71	.035	28-32	.017	5A	140	—	—	3800	5-7	650	600N
318-1	1970-71	.035	28-32	.017	5B	140	—	—	3800	5-7	500	500N
318-3	1970-71	.035	28-32	.017	12½B	110	—	—	3800	5-7	500	500N
318	1972	.035	32	.016	TDC	110	—	—	3800	5-7	750	700N
318-1 Lt. Duty	1973	.035	Electronic		2½B②	100	—	—	3900	5-7	750	700(750)N
318-1 Heavy Duty	1973	.035	Electronic		5B (TDC)	100	—	—	3900	5-7	750	700(750)N
318-3 Heavy Duty	1973	.035	Electronic		2½B	100	—	—	3700	5-7	700	700N
318-1 Lt. Duty	1974	.035	Electronic		TDC	100	—	—	3900	5-7	700	700N
318-1 Heavy Duty	1974	.035	Electronic		2½A	100	—	—	3700	5-7	750	750N
318-3 Heavy Duty	1974	.035	Electronic		TDC	100	—	—	3900	5-7	700	700N
318-1 Lt. Duty	1975	.035	Electronic		2B (TDC)	100	—	—	3900	5-7	750	750N
318-1 Heavy Duty	1975	.035	Electronic		2A (TDC)	100	—	—	3800	5-7	750 (700)	750N (700)
318-3 Heavy Duty	1975	.035	Electronic		TDC (2B)	100	—	—	3800	5-7	700	700N
318	1976	.035	Electronic		③	100	—	—	3800	5-7	③	③
318-3	1976	.035	Electronic		③	100	—	—	3800	5-7	③	③
360	1970-72	.035	32	.016	TDC (2½B)	110	—	—	3900	5-7	750	700N
360 Lt. Duty	1973	.035	Electronic		TDC	100	—	—	3900	5-7	750	700N(750)N
360 Heavy Duty	1973	.035	Electronic		TDC	100	—	—	3900	5-7	750	700N(750)N
360 Lt. Duty	1974	.035	Electronic		2½B	100	—	—	3900	5-7	750	750N
360 Heavy Duty	1974	.035	Electronic		TDC	100	—	—	3900	5-7	750	750N
360 Lt. Duty	1975	.035	Electronic		TDC (4B)	100	—	—	3800	5-7	750 (700)	750N (700)
360 Heavy Duty	1975	.035	Electronic		TDC	100	—	—	3800	5-7	750 (700)	750N (700)
360	1976	.035	Electronic		③	100	—	—	3800	5-7	③	③
360-3	1976	.035	Electronic		③	100	—	—	3800	5-7	③	③
361-3, 4	1970-72	.035	28-32	.016	5B	120	—	—	3600	3½-5	500	—
361-3, 4	1973	.035	Electronic		5B	100	—	—	3600	3½-5	600 (700)	700N
361-3, 4	1974-75	.035	Electronic		2½B	100	—	—	3600	6-7½	700	700N
361-3	1976	.035	Electronic		③	100	—	—	3600	6-7½	③	③
383 Std.	1970-71	.035	28-33	.017	TDC	140	—	—	—	3½-5	650	—
383 Auto.	1970-71	.035	28-33	.017	7½B	140	—	—	—	3½-5	—	600N
400	1971-72	.035	32	.016	7½B	—	—	—	—	—	700	700N
400 Lt. Duty	1973	.035	Electronic		10B	100	—	—	—	3½-5	700	700N
400 Heavy Duty	1973	.035	Electronic		2½B	100	—	—	—	3½-5	700	700N
400 Lt. Duty	1974	.035	Electronic		7½B	100	—	—	—	5-7	750	750N
400 Heavy Duty	1974	.035	Electronic		2½B	100	—	—	—	5-7	750	750N
400	1976	.035	Electronic		③	100	—	—	—	5-7	③	③
413	1970-71	.035	27-32	.017	5B	130	—	—	3600	3½-5	500	500N

TUNE-UP SPECIFICATIONS

CU. IN. DISPLACE-MENT	YEAR	SPARK PLUG GAP	DISTRIBUTOR POINT DWELL	DISTRIBUTOR POINT GAP	IGNITION TIMING DEG. BTC (± 2°)	CRANKING COMP. PRESS.	VALVE CLEARANCE INTAKE	VALVE CLEARANCE EXHAUST	GOV. RPM NO LOAD	FUEL PUMP PRESS	IDLE SPEED STD.	IDLE SPEED AUTO.
EIGHT CYLINDER												
413-1, 3	1972	.035	28-32	.015	5B	100	—	—	3600	3½-5	600 (700)	600N (700)N
413-2	1972	.035	28½-32½	.018	5B	100	—	—	3600	3½-5	600 (700)	600N (700)
413-1	1973	.035	Electronic		5B	100	—	—	3600	3½-5	600 (700)	600N (700)N
413-2	1973	.035	Electronic		5B (2½B)	100	—	—	3600	3½-5	600 (700)	500N (700)N
413-3	1973	.035	Electronic		5B	100	—	—	3600	3½-5	600 (700)	600N (700)N
413-2	1974	.035	Electronic		2½B	100	—	—	3600	6-7½	700	700N
413-3 Heavy Duty	1975	.035	Electronic		5B	100	—	—	3600	6-7½	700	700N
413-3 Bus	1975	.035	Electronic		TDC	100	—	—	3600	6-7½	700	700N
413-3	1976	.035	Electronic		③	100	—	—	3600	5-7	③	③
440 Lt. Duty	1974	.035	Electronic		10B (5B)	100	—	—	—	5-7	700	700N
440 Heavy Duty	1974	.035	Electronic		7½B	100	—	—	—	5-7	700	700N
440	1975	.035	Electronic		8B	100	—	—	3800	5-7	700	700N
440	1976	.035	Electronic		③	100	—	—	—	5-7	③	③
440-3	1976	.035	Electronic		③	100	—	—	3800	5-7	③	③
478	1970-73	.035	28-32	.016	10B	140	—	—	3400	4-4¾	500	500N
549	1970-72	.035	28-32	.016	7B	140	—	—	3200	4-4¾	500	500N

① Uses taper seat plug without tube or gasket, torque to 10 ft. lbs.
② TDC with automatic.
③ See underhood specifications sticker.
Lt. Duty—Under 6,000 lbs. GVW.
Heavy Duty—Over 6,000 lbs. GVW.
Figures in parentheses are for California only.

Note: The underhood specifications sticker often reflects tune up specifications changes made in production. Sticker figures must be used if they disagree with those in this Chart.

FIRING ORDER AND ROTATION

Slant six   FIRING ORDER 1-5-3-6-2-4

360 and smaller V8   FIRING ORDER 1-8-4-3-6-5-7-2

361 and larger V8   FIRING ORDER 1-8-4-3-6-5-7-2

GENERAL ENGINE SPECIFICATIONS

CU. IN. DISPLACE-MENT	YEAR	BORE & STROKE	FIRING ORDER	ESTIMATED H.P. @ RPM	ESTIMATED TORQUE @ RPM	COMPRESSION RATIO	CARBU-RETOR	VALVE LIFTER TYPE	NORMAL OIL PRESSURE
SIX CYLINDER									
198	1970-71	3.406 x 3.64	1-5-3-6-2-4	130 @ 4000	182 @ 1600	8.4	1V	Mech.	50
225	1970-71	3.40 x 4.125	1-5-3-6-2-4	140 @ 3900	215 @ 1600	8.4	1V	Mech.	50
225	1972-74	3.40 x 4.125	1-5-3-6-2-4	100 @ 3900	180 @ 1600	8.4	1V	Mech.	55
225	1975-76	3.40 x 4.125	1-5-3-6-2-4	90 @ 3600	170 @ 1600	8.4	1V	Mech.	55

GENERAL ENGINE SPECIFICATIONS

CU. IN. DISPLACEMENT	YEAR	BORE & STROKE	FIRING ORDER	ESTIMATED H.P. @ RPM	ESTIMATED TORQUE @ RPM	COMPRESSION RATIO	CARBURETOR	VALVE LIFTER TYPE	NORMAL OIL PRESSURE
EIGHT CYLINDER									
318-3	1970-71	3.91 x 3.312	1-8-4-3-6-5-7-2	202 @ 3900	288 @ 2400	7.5	2V	Hyd.	70
318	1970-71	3.91 x 3.312	1-8-4-3-6-5-7-2	210 @ 2800	318 @ 2800	8.5	2V	Hyd.	60
318-2	1970-71	3.91 x 3.312	1-8-4-3-6-5-7-2	212 @ 4000	322 @ 2800	8.0	2V	Hyd.	70
318	1972-74	3.91 x 3.312	1-8-4-3-6-5-7-2	150 @ 3600	260 @ 2000	7.8/8.6	2V	Hyd.	30-80
318	1975	3.91 x 3.312	1-8-4-3-6-5-7-2	150 @ 4000	255 @ 1600	7.8/8.6	2V	Hyd.	30-80
318	1976	3.91 x 3.312	1-8-4-3-6-5-7-2	150 @ 4000	255 @ 1600	8.4	2V	Hyd.	30-80
318-3	1976	3.91 x 3.312	1-8-4-3-6-5-7-2	150 @ 4000	255 @ 1600	7.8	2V	Hyd.	30-80
360	1970-75	4.00 x 3.58	1-8-4-3-6-5-7-2	170 @ 4000	285 @ 2400	8.4	2V	Hyd.	30-80
360	1976	4.00 x 3.58	1-8-4-3-6-5-7-2	170 @ 4000	285 @ 2400	8.7	2V	Hyd.	30-80
360-3	1976	4.00 x 3.58	1-8-4-3-6-5-7-2	170 @ 4000	285 @ 2400	7.9	2V	Hyd.	30-80
361-2	1970-75	4.125 x 3.375	1-8-4-3-6-4-7-2	186 @ 4000	300 @ 2400	7.5	2V	Hyd.	70
361-3	1970-76	4.125 x 3.375	1-8-4-3-6-5-7-2	194 @ 3600	310 @ 2400	7.5	2V	Hyd.	70
361-4	1970-75	4.125 x 3.375	1-8-4-3-6-5-7-2	204 @ 3600	335 @ 2400	7.5	2V	Hyd.	70
361	1972-75	4.125 x 3.375	1-8-4-3-6-5-7-2	155 @ 3600	295 @ 2000	7.5	2V	Hyd.	70
383	1970-71	4.25 x 3.38	1-8-4-3-6-5-7-2	258 @ 4400	375 @ 2800	9.2	2V	Hyd.	45-65
400	1971-74	4.34 x 3.38	1-8-4-3-6-5-7-2	180 @ 3600	315 @ 2400	8.2	2V, 4V	Hyd.	30-80
400	1976	4.34 x 3.38	1-8-4-3-6-5-7-2	180 @ 3600	315 @ 2400	8.2	2V	Hyd.	30-80
413-2	1970-71	4.188 x 3.75	1-8-4-3-6-5-7-2	220 @ 3600	386 @ 2200	7.5	2V	Hyd.	70
413-3	1970-71	4.188 x 3.75	1-8-4-3-6-5-7-2	283 @ 3600	407 @ 2000	7.5	4V	Hyd.	70
413	1972-76	4.188 x 3.75	1-8-4-3-6-5-7-2	180 @ 3200	334 @ 2000	7.5	2V	Hyd.	70
440	1973-76	4.32 x 3.75	1-8-4-3-6-5-7-2	235 @ 4000	340 @ 2400	8.2	4V	Hyd.	30-80
440-3	1976	4.32 x 3.75	1-8-4-3-6-5-7-2	235 @ 4000	340 @ 2400	7.5	4V	Hyd.	30-80
478	1970-73	4.50 x 3.75	1-8-7-3-6-5-4-2	206 @ 3400	403 @ 1800	8.2	2V	Hyd.	50-70
549	1970-72	4.50 x 4.312	1-8-7-3-6-5-4-2	230 @ 2300	505 @ 2000	7.6	4V	Hyd.	50-70

CRANKSHAFT BEARING JOURNAL SPECIFICATIONS

CU. IN. DISPLACEMENT	YEAR	MAIN BEARING JOURNALS		SHAFT END PLAY	THRUST ON NO.	CONNECTING ROD BEARING JOURNALS		END PLAY
		JOURNAL DIAMETER	OIL CLEARANCE			JOURNAL DIAMETER	OIL CLEARANCE	
SIX CYLINDER								
198	1970-71	2.7495-2.7505	.0005-.0015	.004-.008	3	2.1865-2.1875	.0005-.0015	.006-.012
225	1970-76	2.7495-2.7505	.0005-.0015	.002-.007	3	2.1865-2.1875	.0005-.0015	.006-.012
EIGHT CYLINDER								
318	1970-76	2.4995-2.5005	.0005-.0015	.002-.007	3	2.124-2.125	.0005-.0015	.006-0.14
360	1970-76	2.8095-2.8105	.0005-.0015	.002-.007	3	2.124-2.125	.0005-.0015	.006-0.14
361	1970-76	2.6245-2.6255	.0015-.0025	.002-.007	3	2.374-2.375	.001-.002	.009-.017
383	1970-71	2.6245-2.6255	.0005-.0015	.002-.007	3	2.374-2.375	.0005-.0015	.009-0.17
400	1971-76	2.6245-2.6255	.0005-.0020	.002-.007	3	2.374-2.375	.0005-.0025	.009-0.17
413	1970-76	2.7495 2.7505	.002-.0022	.002-.007	3	2.374-2.375	.0005-.0015	.009-0.17
440	1973-76	2.7495-2.7505	.002-.0022	.002-.007	3	2.374-2.375	.0005-.0015	.009-0.17
478	1970-73	3.123-3.124	.0014-.0044	.004-.009	3	2.623-2.624	.0017-.0042	.010-.018
549	1970-72	3.123-3.124	.0014-.0044	.004-.009	3	2.623-2.624	.0017-.0042	.010-.018

VALVE SPECIFICATIONS

CU. IN. DISPLACEMENT	YEAR	LASH (HOT) INCHES		ANGLE DEGREE		STEM DIA. INCHES		STEM CLEARANCE		VALVE LIFT INCHES	VALVE SPRING LBS. @ INCHES		FREE LENGTH INCHES
		INT.	EXH.	FACE	SEAT	INT.	EXH.	INTAKE	EXHAUST		OPEN	CLOSED	
SIX CYLINDER													
198	1970-71	.012	.024	①	45	.372	.371	.001-.003	.002-.004	.395	144 @ 1⁵⁄₁₆	53 @ 1¹¹⁄₁₆	1.92
225	1970-72	.012	.024	①	45	.372	.371	.001-.003	.002-.004	③	144 @ 1⁵⁄₁₆	53 @ 1¹¹⁄₁₆	1.92
225	1973-74	.012	.024	①	45	.372	.371	.001-.003	.002-.004	⑰	144 @ 1⁵⁄₁₆	53 @ 1¹¹⁄₁₆	1.92
225	1975-76	.012	.024	①	45	.372	.371	.001-.003	.002-.004	⑱	144 @ 1⁵⁄₁₆	53 @ 1¹¹⁄₁₆	1.92

VALVE SPECIFICATIONS

CU. IN. DISPLACE-MENT	YEAR	LASH (HOT) INCHES		ANGLE DEGREE		STEM DIA. INCHES		STEM CLEARANCE		VALVE LIFT INCHES	VALVE SPRING LBS. @ INCHES		FREE LENGTH INCHES
		INT.	EXH.	FACE	SEAT	INT.	EXH.	INTAKE	EXHAUST		OPEN	CLOSED	
EIGHT CYLINDER													
318-1	1970-72	no adj.	no adj.	①	45	.372	.371	.001-.003	.002-.004	[21]	177 @ 1 5/16	83 @ 1 11/16	2.00
318-3	1970-72	no adj.	no adj.	45	45	.372	.371	.001-.003	.002-.004	[21]	177 @ 1 5/16	83 @ 1 11/16 [20]	2.00 [22]
318-1	1973-74	no adj.	no adj.	①	45	.372	.371	.001-.003	.002-.004	[21]	177 @ 1 5/16	83 @ 1 11/16	2.00
318-3	1973-74	no adj.	no adj.	45	45	.372	.371	.001-.003	.002-.004	[21]	177 @ 1 5/16 [23]	83 @ 1 11/16 [20]	2.00 [25]
318-1	1975-76	no adj.	no adj.	45	45	.372	.371	.001-.003	.002-.004	[21]	185 @ 1 1/4 [26]	93 @ 1 21/32	2.00
318-3	1975-76	no adj.	no adj.	45	45	.372	.371	.001-.003	.002-.004	[21]	177 @ 1 5/16	83 @ 1 11/16	2.00
360	1970-72	no adj.	no adj.	①	45	.373	.372	.001-.003	.002-.004	[14]	177 @ 1 5/16	83 @ 1 11/16	2.00 [25]
360	1973-76	no adj.	no adj.	①	45	.372	.371	.001-.003	.002-.004	[27]	177 @ 1 5/16	83 @ 1 11/16	2.00
361	1970-72	no adj.	no adj.	45	45	.372	.433	.001-.003	.003-.005	.360	⑤	⑥	2.31 [12]
361	1973-76	no adj.	no adj.	45	45	.372	.433	.001-.003	.003-.005	.360	180 @ 1 15/32 [28]	80 @ 1 55/64 [29]	2.31 [12]
383	1970-71	no adj.	no adj.	45	45	.372	.371	.001-.003	.002-.004	⑦	200 @ 1 7/16	125 @ 1 55/64	2.63
400	1970-76	no adj.	no adj.	45	45	.372	.372	.002-.003	.002-.003	.430	200 @ 1 7/16	125 @ 1 55/64	2.63
413	1970-72	no adj.	no adj.	45	45	.372	.433	.001-.003	.003-.005	.360	⑤	⑥	2.31 [12]
413	1973-76	no adj.	no adj.	45	45	.372	.433	.001-.003	.003-.005	.360	180 @ 1 15/32 [28]	80 @ 1 55/64 [29]	2.31 [12]
440	1973-74	no adj.	no adj.	45	45	.372	.372	.002-.003	.002-.003	.464	105 @ 1 55/64	105 @ 1 55/64 [31]	2.23
440	1975-76	no adj.	no adj.	45	45	.372	.372	.002-.003	.002-.003	.425 ⓒ	200 @ 1 7/16 [32]	125 @ 1 7/8 [32]	2.63
478	1970-73	0 + 1 turn		15 ⑧	14 ⑨	.434	.434	.0015-.004	.0025-.005	—	83 @ 1 17/32	⑩	2.28 [13]
549	1970-72	0 + turn		15 ⑧	14 ⑨	.434	.434	.0015-.004	.0025-.004	—	83 @ 1 17/32	⑩	2.28 [13]

① Intake 45, Exhaust 43
② Intake 2.00, Exhaust 43
③ Intake .397, Exhaust .392
④ Intake, Exhaust 185 @ 1 5/32
⑤ Intake 180 @ 1 15/32, Exhaust Outer 115 @ 1 8/8, Inner 49 @ 1 11/64
⑥ Intake 80 @ 1 55/64, Exhaust Outer 57 @ 1 47/64, Inner 27 @ 1 17/32
⑦ Intake .425, Exhaust .435
⑧ Intake, Exhaust 45
⑨ Intake, Exhaust 44
⑩ Inner, Outer 116.5
⑪ Intake, Exhaust 1.890
⑫ Intake, Exhaust (Outer) 2.125, (Inner) 1.875
⑬ Inner, Outer 2.562
⑭ Intake .410, Exhaust .412
⑮ At hot end
⑯ Intake .434, Exhaust .430
⑰ Intake .406, Exhaust .414
⑱ Intake .394, Exhaust .390
⑲ Exhaust 47
⑳ Exhaust 85 @ 1 35/64
[21] Intake, .372 Exhaust .400
[22] Intake, Exhaust 1.88
[23] 185 @ 1 5/64
[24] Exhaust 85 @ 1 31/64
[25] Intake, Exhaust 1.81
[26] Exhaust 192 @ 1 9/32
[27] Intake, .410, Exhaust .400
[28] Intake, Exhaust 175 @ 1 21/64
[29] Intake, Exhaust 85 @ 1 3/4
[30] Intake, Exhaust 2.13
[31] Intake, Exhaust 246 @ 1 23/64
[32] Intake, Exhaust 208 @ 1 5/16
[33] Intake, Exhaust 123 @ 1 3/4

TORQUE SPECIFICATIONS

CU. IN. DISPLACE-MENT	YEAR	CYLINDER HEAD BOLTS (FT. LBS.)	ROD BEARING BOLTS (FT. LBS.)	MAIN BEARING BOLTS (FT. LBS.)	CRANKSHAFT BALANCER BOLT (FT. LBS.)	FLYWHEEL TO CRANKSHAFT BOLTS (FT. LBS.)	MANIFOLD	
							INTAKE (FT. LBS.)	EXHAUST
SIX CYLINDER								
198	1970-71	65	45	85	Press	55	10	10
225	1970-76	65 ①	45	85	Press	55	10	10
EIGHT CYLINDER								
318	1970-72	85	45	85	135	60	30	25
318	1973-76	95	45	85	100	55	35	20
360	1970-76	95	45	85	100	55	35	20
361	1970-76	70	45	85	135	55	35	30
383	1970-71	70	45	85	135	60	50	30
400	1971-76	70	45	85	135	55	40	30
413	1970-76	70	45	85	135	55	45	30
440	1973-76	70	45	85	135	55	45	30
478	1970-73	90-100	60-70	100-110	—	90-100	—	30
549	1970-72	90-100	60-70	100-110	—	90-100	—	30

① 70 starting 1975

WHEEL ALIGNMENT SPECIFICATIONS

YEAR	MODEL	CASTER (Deg.)*	CAMBER (Deg.)	TOE-IN (in.)	KING PIN INCLINATION (Deg.)
1970-71	D100	1½ to 2½	1½	0-⅛	4
1972-76	D100	0 to +½	0 to +½	¹⁄₁₆-⅛	—
1970-76	AW, PW, W100	3	1½	0-⅛	7½
1970-76	B, PB, CB, MB100, 200, 300	½ ⑤	+¼	¹⁄₁₆-⅛	—
1970-71	D200	1½	2	0-⅛	4
1970-71	D200 crew cab	1½	1½	0-⅛	7
1972-76	D200	0 to +½	0 to +½	¹⁄₁₆-⅛	—
1970-72	P200	1½	1½	0-⅛	4
1970-76	W200⑥	3	1½	0-⅛	7½
1970-71	D300	1½	2	0-⅛	7
1973-76	D300	0 to +½	0 to +½	¹⁄₁₆-⅛	—
1970-73	W300	1½	3½	0-⅛	8
1974-76	W300⑥	3	½	0-⅛	8½
1970-72	M375	1½ to 2½	2	0-⅛	7
1970-71	D400, P400	1½ to 2½	2	0-⅛	7
1972-73	P400	1 man/4 power	2	0-⅛	7
1970-76	D500, S500②	½ to 2	2	0-⅛	7
1970-71	S500	0 to +½	1	0-⅛	5½
1970-71	W500	2½	¾	0-⅛	8
1970-72	C600②	½ to 2	2	0-⅛	7
1970-72	C600③	½ to 1	2	0-⅛	7
1970-76	D600②	½ to 2	2	0-⅛	5½
1970-76	S600	0 to +1	1	0-⅛	5½
1972-76	W600	2½	¾	0-⅛	8
1970-72	C700	1④	1	0-⅛	5½
1970-76	D700②	½ to 2	2	0-⅛	7
1970-76	D700③	0 to +1	1	0-⅛	5½
1975-76	S700	0 to +1	1	0-⅛	5½
1970-76	800 All	0-1④	1	0-⅛	5½
1970-76	850 All	1③	1	0-⅛	5½
1970-76	900 All	0 to +1④	1	0-⅛	5½
1970-76	1000 All	0 to +1④	1	0-⅛	5½

* No load
① Not used
② 5000 lb. axle
③ 7000 lb. axle
④ With power steering 4-5 degrees
⑤ 2¼ with power steering
⑥ Use W300 figures for W200 with Spicer 60 or 70F front axle

Truck Model and Engine Application

GASOLINE ENGINES

ENGINE	YEARS AVAILABLE	ENGINE MAKE
6-198	1970-71	Own
6-225	1970-76	Own
V8-318	1970-76	Own
V8-360	1970-76	Own
V8-361	1970-76	Own
V8-383	1970-71	Own
V8-400	1971-76	Own
V8-413	1970-76	Own
V8-440	1973-76	Own
V8-478	1970-73	IH
V8-549	1970-72	IH

DIESEL ENGINES

ENGINE	ENGINE MAKE
6-71N	Detroit
8V-71N	Detroit
8V-71NE	Detroit
NH230	Cummins
NHC250	Cummins
NTC280	Cummins
NTC335	Cummins
V8-210	Cummins
V903	Cummins

NOTE: *Ramcharger and Trailduster service procedures are the same as those for conventional trucks, except where specific and separate procedures are given.*

Distributor

Distributor Removal

1. Disconnect primary lead wire at coil. On electronic ignition, disconnect the distributor lead wire at the connector.
2. Disconnect vacuum hose at distributor.
3. On the Holley distributor, disconnect tachometer drive and governor inlet and outlet lines.
4. Unfasten distributor cap retaining clips and remove distributor cap.
5. Scribe a line on the distributor housing and engine block to indicate positioning of the rotor and housing.

6. Remove distributor hold-down clamp or arm screw.
7. Carefully lift out distributor assembly.

NOTE: *Do not disturb engine position.*

Installation

1. Clean top of cylinder block to insure a good seal between distributor base and block.
2. If the crankshaft has not been rotated, insert distributor into block with the rotor and body aligned to the previously scribed marks. Make sure O-ring seal is in groove of shank. NOTE: *Distributors on 6 cylinder engines have the drive gear mounted on the bottom of the distributor shaft and a slight rotation will occur when installing. Allow for this rotation when aligning rotor with scribed line on housing.*
3. If engine has been cranked while distributor was removed, it will be necessary to correctly time the distributor with the camshaft. This is done by rotating the crankshaft until No. 1 piston is at top dead center of compression stroke. With rotor in No. 1 cylinder firing position with respect to the distributor cap, insert distributor into engine.
4. Connect primary lead or electronic ignition lead wire.
5. Install distributor cap and check that all high tension leads are securely in position.

V8 electronic ignition distributor (© Chrysler Corp.)

Holley governor distributor—361 and 413 engines (© Chrysler Corp.)

6. On the Holley distributor, connect governor lines and tachometer drive cable.
7. Set ignition timing.
8. Tighten distributor arm or clamp screw.
9. Connect vacuum advance line.

Breaker Points and Condenser Replacement, Dwell Angle Adjustment

1. Pull back the spring clips and lift off the distributor cap. Pull off the rotor. You might have to unclip or detach some or all of the plug wires to remove the cap.
2. Clean the cap inside and out with a clean rag. Check for cracks and carbon paths. A carbon path shows up as a dark line, usually from one of the cap sockets or inside terminals to a ground. Check the condition of the button inside the center of the cap and the inside terminals. Replace the cap if necessary.
3. Clean off the metal outer tip of the rotor if it is burned or corroded. Don't file it. Replace the rotor if necessary or if one came in the tune-up kit.
4. The factory says that the points don't need to be replaced unless their surfaces are oily, dark, or pitted. However, it is best to replace them while the distributor is open.
5. Loosen the terminal screw nut and remove the primary and condenser lead wires. Remove the stationary contact lockscrew and remove the point set. Be very careful not to drop any of these screws inside the distributor. If the hold-down screw is lost, it must be replaced with one that is no longer than the original to avoid interference with the distributor advance mechanism workings. Remove the point set, even if it is to be reused.
6. If the points are to be reused, clean them with a few strokes of a fine file. This is done with the points removed to prevent tiny metal filings getting into the distributor.
7. Remove the condenser, retaining screw and the condenser.
8. Rub a matchhead size dab of high melting point grease on the cam lobes, or better yet, on the rubbing block on the points.
9. Install the new condenser.
10. Replace the point set and leave the screw slightly loose. Replace the two wire terminals, making sure that the wires don't interfere with anything.
11. Check that the contacts meet squarely. If they don't, bend the tab supporting the fixed contact.
12. Turn the engine until a high

point on the cam which opens the points contacts the rubbing block on the point arm.
13. There is a screwdriver slot near the contacts. Insert a screwdriver and lever the points open or closed until they appear to be at about the gap specified in the "Tune-Up Specifications" chart.
14. Insert the correct size feeler gauge and adjust the gap until you can push the gauge in and out between the contacts with a slight drag, but without disturbing the point arm. Check by trying the gauges 0.001-0.002 larger and smaller than the setting size. The larger one should disturb the point arm, while the smaller one should not drag at all. Tighten the point set holddown screw. Recheck the gap, as it often changes when the screw is tightened.

NOTE: This adjustment isn't critical if you intend to use a dwell meter later on.

15. After all the point adjustments are complete, pull a white business card through (between) the contacts to remove any traces of oil from the feeler gauge. Oil will cause rapid contact burning.
16. Put one drop of SAE 10 oil on the felt wick in the top of the distributor shaft. Push the rotor firmly into place. It will only go on one way. If the rotor is not installed properly, it will probably break when the starter is operated.
17. Replace the distributor cap.
18. Check the dwell. Dwell can be checked with the engine running or cranking. Decrease dwell by increasing the point gap; increase dwell by decreasing the gap. Dwell angle is simply the number of degrees of distributor shaft rotation during which the points stay closed. Theoretically, if the point gap is correct, the dwell should also be correct or nearly so. Adjustment with a dwell meter produces more exact, consistent results than a feeler gauge since it is a dynamic adjustment. If dwell varies more than 2 degrees from idle speed to 1,500 engine rpm, the distributor is worn.
19. To adjust dwell, trial and error point adjustments are required. On a Holley governor distributor, dwell can be adjusted externally with a 1/8 in. Allen wrench.
20. If the engine won't start, check:
   a. That all the spark plug wires are in place;
   b. That the rotor has been installed;
   c. That the two wires inside the distributor are connected;

Typical distributor—6 cyl. engines
(© Chrysler Corp.)

   d. That the points open and close when the engine turns. This should produce a reading on a dwell meter;
   e. That the gap is correct and the hold-down screw is tight.
21. After the first 200 miles or so on a new set of points, the point gap often closes up due to initial rubbing block wear. For best performance, recheck the dwell (or gap) at this time. Some mechanics get around this problem by adding about .003 in. to the initial gap setting.
22. Since changing the gap and dwell affects the ignition point setting, the timing should be checked and adjusted as necessary after each point replacement or adjustment.

Electronic Ignition System Distributor

No internal distributor maintenance is required with this system; it does not use contact points or a condenser. You can get a dwell meter reading of sorts; but you can't adjust it. This system is easily identified by a double wire lead from the distributor and a control unit in the engine compartment. It is on all engines beginning 1973; there is also an electronic Holley governor distributor.

Electronic Ignition Distributor Air Gap Adjustment

This adjustment is not required at regular intervals. It is not a normal tune-up service.

1. Release the spring clips and remove the distributor cap. Pull off the rotor.
2. Align one reluctor tooth with the pick-up coil tooth by turning the engine. The reluctor is the six or eight-toothed ring around the distributor shaft.
3. Insert an 0.008 in. *nonmagnetic* (brass) feeler gauge between the reluctor tooth and the pick-up coil tooth.
4. Loosen the hold-down screw and adjust the gap using the screwdriver slot in the mounting plate. Contact should be made between the reluctor tooth, the feeler gauge, and the pick-up coil tooth.
5. Tighten the hold-down screw.
6. Remove the feeler gauge. No force should be required.
7. Check the gap with a 0.010 in. *nonmagnetic* feeler gauge. It should not fit; don't force it into the gap.
8. Turn the distributor shaft and apply vacuum to the vacuum advance unit. If it is adjusted properly and nothing is bent, the pick-up coil tooth will not hit the reluctor teeth.

Ignition Timing Marks

On all engines the timing plate is located on the timing case (front) cover and the timing mark is on the crankshaft pulley damper. On all models the ignition is timed to the No. 1 cylinder spark plug. Always remove and plug the vacuum advance line when setting ignition timing.

Holley Governor Distributor

Dwell setting may be adjusted externally with the use of a 1/8" Allen wrench. See Specifications for correct dwell angle. Disconnect and plug the vacuum advance line and connect dwell meter. Insert wrench while engine is running and turn adjusting screw until correct dwell angle reading is obtained.

Alternator

For voltage regulator circuit tests and for alternator off-the-vehicle service, see The Electrical Section.

Removal

1. Disconnect battery ground cable at the negative terminal.
2. Disconnect alternator output "BAT" and field "FLD" leads and disconnect ground wire.
3. Remove mounting bolts and remove alternator.

Installation

1. Install alternator and adjust drive belt.
2. Connect output "BAT" and field "FLD" leads and connect ground wire.
3. Connect battery ground cable.
4. Start engine, and observe alternator operation.
5. Test current output and adjust regulator voltage setting, if necessary. See Electrical Section.
NOTE: Late models use a nonadjustable sealed electronic regulator.

Adjustable Voltage Regulator

Removal and Installation

1. Disconnect the battery ground cable at battery negative terminal.
2. Disconnect the field lead from alternator and ignition lead from regulator terminals.
3. Remove three regulator assembly mounting screws and remove regulator.
4. Installation is the reverse of the above procedure.

Adjustment

1. Turn the adjustment screw in the cover to get the correct voltage. This is 13.5-14.5 Volts, measured at 70°F. There is a stop in the regulator cover to limit the voltage adjustment.
2. If Step 1 didn't produce the cor-

Exploded view of alternator (© Chrysler Corp.)

LOWER CONTACT ARM
ARMATURE-SPRING
FUSIBLE WIRE
SOLDERING POINT
ARMATURE
VOLTAGE COIL
GASKET
UPPER CONTACT ARM
STATIONARY
CONTACT ARM
LIMITED ADJUSTMENT
ARM
ADJUSTING SCREW
LOCK NUT
VOLTAGE COIL
SOLDER POINTS
FUSIBLE WIRE
SOLDERING POINTS

Voltage regulator (cover removed) (© Chrysler Corp.)

rect voltage, remove the cover and check the upper contact gap. It should be .010-.018 in. Adjust by bending the upper contact bracket. Make sure the contacts are in alignment.

3. If voltage still can't be adjusted correctly, adjust the air gap by bending the fixed contact bracket above the winding. If the voltage difference is more than .7 Volt, bend the bracket down. If it is less than .2 Volt, bend the bracket up.

4. When replacing the cover, make sure that the rubber grommet is centered over the adjusting screw.

5. Replace the regulator if voltage cannot be brought within specifications.

Electronic Voltage Regulator

Removal and Installation

1. Release the spring clips and pull off the regulator wiring plug.
2. Unbolt and remove the regulator.
3. Installation is the reverse of removal. Be sure that the spring clips engage the wiring plug.

Regulator Fusible Wire Replacement

Excessive current loads through the two fusible wires in the adjustable regulator will cause them to melt and break the circuit. Remove what is left of the old wire and solder new fusible wire to terminals, using only resin core solder. See the Electrical Section for service and testing of alternator systems.

Starter

For starter motor overhaul procedures see the Electrical Section.

Starter Removal and Installation

1. Disconnect the battery ground cable.

2. Remove the cable at the starter.
3. If the solenoid is mounted on the starter, disconnect the wires at the solenoid terminals. On Diesel engine starters, record the wiring harness color coding at the solenoid to insure proper installation.

4. Remove the starter to flywheel housing mounting bolts. Remove automatic transmission oil cooler tube bracket off the stud if necessary. Remove the starter and removable seal if so equipped.

5. Before installing the starter, make sure the starter and flywheel housing mounting surfaces are free of dirt and oil. These surfaces must be clean.

6. Install the starter to flywheel housing removable seal if so equipped.

7. Position the starter to the flywheel housing and, if necessary, install the automatic transmission oil cooler bracket. Install mounting bolts. Tighten securely.

NOTE: When tightening the mounting bolt and nut on the starter

SLEEVE
VAPOR BARRIER
.010-.045 END PLAY
POLE SHOE (4)
SOLENOID
ARMATURE
MOVABLE CORE
FORK
RETAINER
THRUST
WASHERS
STEEL WASHER
FIBER WASHER
SNAP RING
RING
OVERRUNNING
CLUTCH
FIBER WASHER
(AS REQUIRED)
FRICTION WASHER

Starter motor (reduction gear type) (© Chrysler Corp.)

SOLENOID
SPRING
CORE ASSEMBLY
BOOT
FORK
FORK PIN
PINION
HOUSING
RETAINER
THRUST
WASHER
RING
CLUTCH
ASSEMBLY
SEAL
RETAINER
FRAME AND
FIELD ASSEMBLY
BRUSH
HOLDER
END HEAD
ASSEMBLY
THRUST
WASHER
SCREW
GROMMET

Starter motor (direct drive type) (© Chrysler Corp.)

hold the starter away from the engine for correct alignment.

8. If the solenoid is mounted on the starter, connect the wires to the solenoid terminals.
9. Connect the cable to the starter terminal.
10. Connect the battery ground cable and test operation of the starter for proper engine cranking.

Brakes

For master and slave cylinder overhaul procedures and brake shoe replacement and service procedures, see Brake Section of the General Repair Section.

Master Cylinder Removal and Installation

Firewall Mounted

1. From within the cab, disconnect push rod from brake pedal.
2. Disconnect hydraulic line from master cylinder.
3. Remove four nuts and washers from master cylinder mounting studs and remove master cylinder assembly.
4. Installation is the reverse of the above procedure.
5. Bleed hydraulic system.

Tandem Type Dual Cylinder

The tandem master cylinder is of the compensating type with reservoirs cast integrally on the dash mounted type and with removable reservoirs on the booster mounted type. Both consist of a front and rear piston (in tandem) with two outlets, each containing a residual pressure valve and spring.

The dual hydraulic brake system is basically a safety system in which

the front brakes are actuated by one master cylinder and the rear brakes by the other. A hydraulic safety switch closes a warning light circuit whenever unequal pressure exists between the two systems whenever a pressure failure occurs in either.

The procedure for removing and installing dual master cylinders is the same as that for single master cylinders as described above.

Booster Mounted Type Removal

1. Disconnect both hydraulic lines at master cylinder outlets.
2. Remove capscrew holding lower support strap to cylinder.
3. Remove master cylinder to booster mounting nuts and lift cylinder from vehicle.

Installation

1. Position seal ring in groove on master cylinder body mounting flange, then install unit on power booster. Tighten mounting nuts to 18-20 ft. lbs. torque.
2. Install capscrew holding lower support strap to cylinder.
3. Connect and tighten both hydraulic brake lines at cylinder outlet.
4. Bleed entire brake system.

Frame Mounted Type Removal and Installation

1. Remove bolts and screws that attach the airscoop to the frame.
2. Slide scoop out (toward front) from under vehicle.
3. Disconnect brake tube at rear of master cylinder.
4. Disconnect stop light switch wires.
5. Remove bolts and nuts that attach master cylinder to frame bracket.
6. Slide unit toward rear to clear push rod and remove from under vehicle.

7. Installation is the reverse of the above procedure.

Vans and Wagons Removal

1. Disconnect the front and rear tubes from the master cylinder.
2. Install plugs in the reservoir outlets.
3. Remove mounting nuts.
4. Disconnect the brake pedal push rod from pedal.
5. Slide the master cylinder straight out.

Installation

1. Put the cylinder in position, aligning the push rod with the cowl panel opening or power brake cylinder piston.
2. Slide the cylinder on over the mounting studs. Install the attaching nuts, tightening to 200 inch-pounds.
3. Connect and tighten brake tubes.
4. Bleed brake system.

Bleeding Hydraulic Brakes

Bleed brakes in the conventional manner. Be sure to fill fluid reservoir and to check frequently during bleeding. Start with right rear wheel.

Dual Master Cylinder Bleeding

Before installing master cylinder on vehicle or before bleeding the wheel cylinders, the dual master cylinder must be bled first. If master cylinder is to be bled on the vehicle, disconnect hydraulic lines first.

1. Clamp master cylinder in vise and attach bleeding tubes from the tube seats into the reservoirs.
2. Fill both reservoirs with fluid.
3. Depress push rod slowly several times, letting it return under the pressure of the springs, until all air bubbles are expelled.
4. Remove bleeding tubes from cylinder and install cover and gasket.

Typical tandem master cylinder (© Chrysler Corp.)

INSERT
SPRING
OUTLET TO RIGHT FRONT BRAKE TUBE
FROM MASTER CYLINDER PORT STAMPED "F"
SWITCH BODY
OUTLET TO LEFT FRONT BRAKE TUBE
PISTON SEAL "O" RING
SWITCH SEAL "O" RING
SWITCH ASSEMBLY
PISTON ASSEMBLY
FROM MASTER CYLINDER PORT STAMPED "R"
OUTLET TO REAR BRAKE TUBE
PLUG

AIR BUBBLES
BLEEDING TUBES

Bleeding dual master cylinder (© Chrysler Corp.)

Dual brake system safety switch (© Chrysler Corp.)

Double diaphragm power brake unit (© Chrysler Corp.)

5. Install cover retaining clamp and clamp screw.
6. Install cylinder on vehicle.
7. Bleed hydraulic system.

Power Brakes

Vacuum-Hydraulic Booster
Removal

1. Depress brake pedal several times to remove all vacuum from the system.
2. Disconnect all lines, hoses and wires from the unit.
3. Remove the brake booster mounting brackets, then remove booster.

For overhaul procedures see Brake Section in General Repair Section.

Installation

1. Position the assembly on the mounting brackets, and install the attaching bolts.
2. Connect all lines, hoses and wires to the unit. NOTE: On Tandem Booster units, remove the lubricating plugs from the end and center the plates. Add vacuum cylinder oil to the level of the filler holes, then install the lubricating plugs.
3. Bleed the hydraulic system.

Bleeding Vacuum-Hydraulic Booster Systems

1. Eliminate vacuum in the booster by depressing the brake pedal several times while the engine is not running.
2. On trucks not equipped with reservoir tanks, disconnect the manifold tube at the booster side of the manifold check valve (engine not running).
3. Alternately loosen the brake tube at each unit until all air is expelled. Booster slave cylinder is bled first.

CAUTION: Where air pressure brake bleeding equipment is used to bleed brakes, do not use more than 25-30 psi.

NOTE: A piston stop is provided in the slave cylinder to eliminate the possibility of damaging the return spring while bleeding the system. This damage occurs only when bleeding the brakes with a vacuum present in the booster system.

Parking Brake

External Contracting Driveshaft Type

Removal

1. Disconnect the brake cable.
2. Remove adjusting bolt nut.
3. Remove guide bolt adjusting lock nuts.
4. Remove anchor adjusting screw.
5. Pull band assembly away from transmission and off propeller shaft.

Typical external contracting type parking brake
(© Chrysler Corp.)

2 Parking brake adjusting bolt
3 Parking brake rod yoke nut
4 Parking brake band guide bolt nuts
5 Parking brake adjusting bolt nut

Installation

1. Position brake band and lining assembly over propeller shaft and on brake drum.
2. Install brake band anchor adjusting screw and adjusting guide bolt nut and lock nuts.
3. Connect brake cable.

Internal Expanding Driveshaft Type (Early)

NOTE: This procedure is for the early type brake which has an internal adjuster similar to the type used on wheel brakes. There is an adjusting screw cover plate on the bottom of the backing plate.

Removal

1. Disconnect propeller shaft at transmission.
2. Remove companion flange nut, lockwasher and flatwasher.
3. Install a puller tool on companion flange and remove flange and brake drum while using a holding tool to prevent rotation.
4. Disengage ball end of cable from operating lever.
5. Separate shoes at bottom, allowing brake shoe adjusting nut screws, and sleeve to drop out and release shoes.
6. Pry brake shoe return spring up and over to the right and brake shoe in.
7. Then, work spring out of assembly.
8. Pry out brake shoe retaining washer and remove outer guide.
9. Slide each shoe out from under guide spring (as shoes are removed, the operating lever strut will drop out of place).
10. Separate the operating lever from the right hand brake shoe

by removing nut, lockwasher and bolt.

Installation

1. Assemble operating lever to right hand brake shoe.
2. Slide the right and left parking brake shoes under guide.
3. Spread shoes and insert operating lever.
4. Work return spring under guide spring and upward to engage retaining pin on left hand shoe.
5. Force the other end of return spring upward and over retaining pin on right hand shoe.
6. Install adjusting nut, screw and sleeve.
7. Place outer anchor guide over anchor and secure shoes with retaining washer.
8. Turn shoe adjusting nut until shoes are in a released position and install brake drum.
9. Adjust brake shoe and control cable.

CAUTION: If parking brake is adjusted incorrectly, the automatic shifting of the Load-Flite Transmission will be affected.

Internal Expanding Driveshaft Type (Late)

NOTE: This procedure is for the late type brake that has an external linkage clevis adjustment.

Removal

1. Disconnect the adjuster clevis at the operating lever.
2. Remove the universal joint trunnion bolts and support the driveshaft.
3. Remove the mainshaft locknut and washer. Remove the yoke and drum.

Tandem power brake unit (© Chrysler Corp.)

Typical internal expanding type parking brake (© Chrysler Corp.)

10—ANCHOR SHOE GUIDE
12—OPERATING LEVER STRUT
9—ANCHOR SHOE GUIDE
8—SHOE AND FACING
31—SHOE RETURN SPRING
4—DRUM
30—NUT
29—LOCKWASHER
11—RETAINER WASHER
33—CABLE CLAMP BOLT
13—ANCHOR PIN
35—BALL END
15—CABLE ADJUSTING NUT
14—CABLE ASSY.
16—TRANSMISSION EXTENSION
17—DOWEL PIN
7—SHOE ADJUSTING SLEEVE
6—SHOE ADJUSTING NUT
5—SHOE ADJUSTING SCREW
28—SHOE AND FACING
27—OPERATING LEVER
19—NUT
20—LOCKWASHER
22—SCREW
21—EXTENSION OIL SEAL
23—LOCKWASHER
32—TRANSMISSION MAIN SHAFT
24—ADJUSTING SCREW COVER PLATE
25—SHOE GUIDE SPRING
18—SUPPORT
26—OPERATING LEVER BOLT

4. Unbolt the drum from the yoke.
5. Unbolt the brake assembly from the transmission mounting flange. Separate the shoe assembly from the actuating cam and lever.

Installation

1. Place the brake assembly, with the cam lugs between the ends of the shoes, on the mounting flange.
2. Align the brake on the flange, install the mounting bolts and lockwashers, torquing to 75 ft. lbs.
3. Bolt the drum to the yoke, torquing to 75 ft. lbs.
4. Install the drum to the mainshaft. Torque the nut to 120 ft. lbs.
5. You can check drum runout with a dial indicator. If it exceeds .015 in., loosen the drum to yoke bolts ¼ turn and tap the high side with a soft hammer. Tighten the bolts and recheck the runout. If runout persists, but doesn't exceed .018 in., make 6-8 moderate brake applications from 20 mph and recheck runout. If runout still exceeds .015 in., a new drum is required.

Air Spring Type
Reference

The air spring type parking brake is air actuated and is operated in conjunction with the rear wheel service brake air chamber. The spring is held in the retracted (or off) position by air pressure from a protected third air reservoir. As the air pressure is released from the cylinder housing, the spring is released thereby actuating the service brake push rod and applying the brakes.

Air Spring Type—Removal

1. Back off slack adjuster adjusting screw.
2. Disconnect brake chamber push rod by removing clevis pin.
3. Disconnect air lines.
4. Remove nuts and washers from mounting bolts, remove brake chamber and spring brake assembly.
5. To install reverse the above procedure, and adjust brakes.

Quick Release Valve—Removal

1. Relieve air pressure. Disconnect air line.
2. Remove four capscrews and remove cap.
3. Remove remaining two capscrews holding release valve to body.
4. Remove boot from small end of body, clean all parts with solvent and blow dry with compressed air. All "O" rings and rubber parts must be replaced.
5. To install, reverse the above procedure. Tighten all six capscrews to 15 ft. lb. Connect air line pressurize system and check for leaks.

Fail-Safe

This unit is mounted "Piggy Back" on the air chamber non-pressure housing of the stopmaster brake. The power spring is held in a compressed position as long as the air pressure is 65 PSI or more. Anytime the air pressure drops below 65 PSI the power spring pushes the piston against the diaphragm plate, forcing the wedge head between the rollers, which spreads the plungers apart and applies the brake.

Fail-Safe—Removal

1. Cage power spring. Relieve air pressure and remove air lines from unit.
2. Mark non-pressure housing, pressure housing and cap with punch or chisel to aid in alignment at reassembly. Loosen or remove clamp ring and remove unit from non-pressure housing.

Installation

1. Align cap and housing with marks made during removal.
2. Position unit on non-pressure housing and install clamp ring and bolt.
3. Connect air lines and apply air pressure. Uncage power spring and check operation of system.

Shortstop Spring Brake

This spring type parking brake assembly is used in conjunction with the wedge type air brakes.

Removal

1. Bleed air from system. Disconnect air lines (mark lines for proper assembly).
2. Remove breather cap. Using a 9/16" deep socket, unscrew release bolt completely.
3. Mark clamp ring, spring brake housing and service brake housing to aid in proper alignment at assembly. Remove bolt from clamp ring. Spring brake is now free for further work.

Installation

1. Align service brake housing, spring brake housing and clamp ring. Install and tighten clamp bolt.
2. Connect and tighten air lines using marks made during removal.
3. Charge system with air, screw release bolt down.
4. Check for air leaks, clean and replace breather cap.

Rear Wheel Cable Type

In this system, the rear wheel brakes also act as parking brakes. They are operated mechanically by a lever and strut connected to a steel cable. This cable is connected to the rear wheel brake cables via an equalizer.

Rear Cable Removal

1. Raise the vehicle, release the brakes, and remove the rear wheels.
2. Remove the brake drum from the rear axle.

1 Yoke
2 Jam nut
3 Non press housing
4 Spring
5 Diaphragm
6 Clamp band
7 Push rod

8 Lockwasher
9 Nut
10 Cotter pin
11 Clevis pin
12 Nut
13 Washer
14 Carriage bolt

15 O-ring
16 O-ring
17 O-ring
18 Snap ring
19 Nut
20 Nut
21 Pin

22 Cover plate-sub
   assembly
23 Spring
24 Retaining ring
25 Spring
26 Cylinder
27 Snap ring

28 Boot
29 Washer
30 Spring
31 Ball
32 O-ring
33 Tooth washer
34 Piston
35 Release bolt
36 Screw
37 O-ring
38 Diaphragm
39 Screw
40 O-ring
41 Cap
42 Screw
43 Body
44 O-ring
45 O-ring
46 Plunger
47 Piston shaft
48 Pipe Plug
49 Screw
50 Bushing
51 Cap
52 O-ring
53 Ring
54 Piston nut
55 Retaining ring
56 Screw
57 Lock washer

Spring type parking brake (© Chrysler Corp.)

3. Remove the brake shoe return spring and brake shoe retaining springs.
4. Remove the brake shoe strut and spring from the support plate.
5. Disconnect the cable from the operating arm.
6. Compress the retainers on the end of the cable housing and remove the cables from the support plate.
7. Remove the retaining bolt and nut from the cable bracket. Remove the clips at the frame bracket.
8. Disconnect the cable from the equalizer bar, and remove the assembly.

Installation

1. Lubricate the cable with short fiber grease at the point of contact.
2. Insert the cable and housing into the frame bracket and install the retaining clips.
3. Engage the end with the equalizer bar.
4. Insert the rear end of the cable and housing into the brake support plate. Make sure the housing retainers lock firmly in place.
5. Insert the end of the cable into the brake shoe operating lever and install the brake shoes.
6. Install the retaining springs, re-

turn springs, brake drum, and wheel.
7. Connect the brake cable bracket.
8. Adjust the brakes and cable.

Parking Brake Adjustment

Internal Expanding Driveshaft Type (Early)

Disconnect front end of propeller shaft to permit turning brake drum by hand.

1. Remove adjusting screw cover plate, loosen brake cable clamping bolt and back off the cable adjusting nut.
2. Turn adjusting nut to decrease shoe-to-drum clearances, until a slight drag is felt on drum.

Fail safe unit (© Chrysler Corp.)

3. Back off adjusting nut at least one full notch, using spanner wrench. *CAUTION:* Make sure the two raised shoulders on adjusting nut are seated in the grooves on the adjusting sleeve.
4. The cable length adjusting nut should be positioned against cable housing so there is at least .005 inch but no more than .010 inch clearance, between the operating lever and brake shoe cable. To lock adjustment, tighten cable housing clamp securely.
5. Tighten cable adjusting nut against the housing.
6. Check parking brake lever for travel.
7. Install adjusting screw cover plate and connect propeller shaft.
8. With rear wheels off the floor, start engine, apply brakes a few times, check for binding and proper adjustment.

Internal Expanding Driveshaft Type (Late)

1. Release the brake handle.
2. Adjustment is made by removing the pin and adjusting the length of the clevis. The brake should be free of drag when rotated. Shoe to drum clearance should be .020 in. on the 10 in. brake used on D800 and S600 models.

External Contracting Driveshaft Type

1. Remove the lockwire from the anchor adjusting screw on the left side.
2. Using a feeler gauge between drum and lining tighten or loosen adjusting screw to give .015 to .020 inch clearance. Install lock wire. *CAUTION:* The lockwire which retains anchor screw must not be drawn up tight. It will cause uneven wear and poor brake application.
3. Adjust the small diameter guide bolt on the right side to adjust the clearance of the lower part of the band.
4. Adjust the large adjusting bolt (the one with the springs) on the right side to adjust the clearance of the upper part of the band. Adjust until the drum is free with the brake released.
5. Adjust the cable as necessary.

Rear Wheel Cable Type

1. Inspect all components and correct any deficiencies such as rust, kinks, or bent parts.
2. Raise the vehicle on a lift and release the brake.
3. Loosen the adjustment until both cables have slack.
4. Tighten the cable adjuster until a slight drag is felt while rotating the wheel. Loosen the adjuster until there is no drag, then

back off two turns.
5. Apply the brake several times, then recheck the adjustment.

Fuel System

Fuel Tank

Removal—Conventional, 1970-71

1. Disconnect battery.
2. Drain fuel tank.
3. Disconnect fuel tank gauge unit wire.
4. Disconnect fuel line.
5. Remove support strap nuts and studs, remove tank.
6. Remove gauge unit.

Installation

1. Install gauge unit.
2. Position tank, install support straps and studs and nuts.
3. Connect fuel line.
4. Connect gauge wire.
5. Connect battery.

Removal—Vans and Wagons

1. Disconnect the battery ground cable.
2. Remove the fuel tank filler cap to relieve pressure.
3. Raise the vehicle on a lift. Pump all fuel from the tank into an approved holding tank.
4. Disconnect the fuel line and wire lead to the gauge unit. Remove the ground strap.
5. Remove the vent hose shield and the hose clamps from the hoses running to the vapor vent tube.
6. Remove the filler tube hose clamps and disconnect the hose from the tank.
7. Place a transmission jack under the center of the tank and apply sufficient pressure to support the tank.
8. Disconnect the two J-bolts and remove the retaining straps at the rear of the tank. Lower the tank from the vehicle. Feed the two vent tube hoses and filler tube vent hose through the grommets in the frame as the tank is being lowered. Remove the tank gauge unit with a spanner wrench.

Installation

1. Inspect the rubber seal for cracks and deterioration, and replace it if necessary. Inspect the fuel filter, and if it is clogged or damaged, replace it.
2. Insert a new gasket in the recess of the fuel gauge opening and slide the gauge into the tank. Align the positioning tangs on the gauge with those on the tank. Install the lock ring, and tighten securely with a spanner wrench. Install a new tank insulator if it

was damaged during removal of the tank.
3. Position the tank on a transmission jack and hoist it into place, feeding the vent hoses through the grommets on the way up.
4. Connect the J-bolts and retaining straps, and tighten to 40 inch-lbs. Remove the jack.
5. Connect the filler tube and all vent hoses. Install new clamps and tighten securely.
6. Connect the fuel supply line, ground strap, and gauge unit wire lead.
7. Refill the tank and inspect it for leaks. Connect the battery ground cable.

Removal—Conventional, 1972 and later

1. Disconnect the battery ground cable. Remove the fuel tank filler cap.
2. Pump all fuel out of the tank and the auxiliary tank (if so equipped) into a safe holding tank.
3. Remove all seat mounting nuts from under the cab, and remove the seat from the cab.
4. Disconnect the gauge wire, vent lines, and fuel line and remove the grommet from the outer end of the filler tube. If the vehicle is equipped with an auxiliary fuel tank (through 1973), disconnect the two large hose clamps on the lower filler tube inside the cab and slide the hose down far enough to allow the top filler tube to be removed with the tank. Disconnect the auxiliary fuel tank vent hose from the filler tube.
5. Remove the screw from the filler tube mounting bracket located on the face of the cab pillar.
6. Loosen the four nuts from the mounting studs along the top of the tank and remove two bolts from the bottom of the tank.
7. Tip the bottom of the tank forward and remove the tank from the vehicle, working through the passenger side door opening.
8. Remove the tank gauge unit with a special spanner wrench. Slide the gauge unit assembly from the tank and discard the gasket.

Installation

1. Insert a new gasket and the gauge assembly into the fuel gauge opening recess. Align the gauge positioning tangs with the tangs in the tank. Install the lock ring and secure it.
2. Put the tank into position in the cab and tighten the bolts and nuts securely.
3. Connect the gauge wire, vent tubes, and fuel line. If there is an auxiliary fuel tank, connect

VIEW A

VIEW B

VIEW C

VIEW D

GROMMET VENT HOSE CAP

GROMMET

FRONT

FRONT

FRONT

FRONT

INSULATOR

SILENCER

REINFORCEMENT

Conventional truck in-cab fuel tank, 1972 and later (© Chrysler Corp.)

the lower hoses and tighten the hose clamps.

4. Install the filler tube grommet over the end tube and install the retaining screw into the filler tube mounting bracket.

5. Mount the seat in the vehicle and securely install the nuts on the seat mounting studs under the vehicle.

6. Refill the fuel tank, and inspect for leaks. If no leaks are present, install the battery and ground cable and gauge wire.

Removal—Conventional Chassis Mounted, 1972 and later

1. Disconnect the battery ground. Remove the fuel tank filler cap.

2. Pump all fuel from the tank into an approved holding tank.

3. Put the vehicle on a lift and disconnect the vent hoses and filler hose. Remove the vent hoses from the hose routing bracket.

4. Remove the nut from the outboard end of the center retaining strap, pull off the end of the strap, and allow it to hang free.

5. Place a transmission jack under the tank and apply sufficient pressure to support it.

6. Remove the two remaining outboard retaining strap nuts and lower the tank slightly to permit disconnecting the gauge wire and fuel line. Remove these, and then lower the tank further and remove it from the vehicle.

Installation

1. Place the tank on top of the transmission jack and raise it high enough to connect the fuel line and gauge wire.

2. Connect the fuel line and gauge wire. Raise the tank into position and connect the two retaining straps.

3. Remove the jack and connect the center strap. Tighten all three straps firmly, but cautiously, to

avoid overstraining straps.

4. Route the vent hoses through the hose holding bracket and connect them to the adapters at the back of the cab.

5. Connect the filler hose to the adaptor at the back of the cab.

6. Refill the tank and inspect for leaks, verifying safety before reconnecting battery ground.

Removal—Ramcharger and Trailduster

1. If there is a tank skid plate, remove it.

2. Disconnect the battery ground cable.

3. Remove the tank filler cap.

4. Pump or siphon the contents of the tank into a safe container.
CAUTION: Siphoning should not be started by mouth. Only fuel-safe pumps should be used.

5. Raise the vehicle on a hoist and disconnect the fuel line and tank sending unit wire. Remove the ground strap or wire.

6. Remove the hose clamps from the vent dome hose.

7. Remove the filler tube hose clamps. Detach the hoses from the tank.

8. Support the tank with a padded transmission jack.

9. Disconnect the two J-bolts and remove the straps at the rear of the tank.

10. Remove the tank gauge sending unit.

Installation

1. Use a new tank gauge sending unit gasket. Check the filter on the end of the fuel suction tube.

2. Use a new or undamaged tank to frame insulator. Raise the tank into positon.

3. Connect the J-bolts and retaining straps. Tighten the bolts until about .97 in. of threads protrude.

4. Connect the filler tube and all hoses. Tighten the clamps.

5. Connect the fuel line, ground strap or wire, and tank sending unit wire. Make sure that all fuel line heat shields are in place.

6. Reconnect the battery ground cable and replace the skid plate.

Carburetor

For idle speeds see the Specifications at the beginning of this section.

Removal and Installation

The following is a general removal procedure for all carburetors.

1. Disconnect the battery ground cable.

2. Remove the air cleaner.

3. Remove the fuel tank pressure-vacuum filler cap. The tank could be under a small amount of pressure.

4. Disconnect and plug the fuel lines. Use two wrenches to avoid twisting the fuel line. A container is also useful to catch any fuel which spills from the lines.

5. Disconnect the throttle and choke linkage.

6. Disconnect any vacuum lines.

7. Remove the mounting bolts.

8. Carefully remove the carburetor from the engine and carry it in a level position to a clean work place.

9. Installation is the reverse of removal. Adjust the curb idle speed.

Idle Speed and Mixture Adjustment

NOTE: Adjust with the air cleaner installed.

1. Run the engine at fast idle to stabilize engine temperature.

2. Make sure that the choke plate is fully released.

3. Attach a tachometer to the engine. With electronic ignition, connect the meter to the negative primary coil terminal and to a ground.

NOTE: Not all tachometers or dwell/tachometers will work with electronic ignition; some may be damaged. Check the manufacturer's instructions carefully.

4. Connect an exhaust analyzer to the engine and insert the probe as far into the tailpipe as possible. On vehicles with dual exhaust, insert the probe into the left tailpipe as this is the side without the heat riser valve.

5. Check ignition timing and adjust it as required.

6. If the truck has air conditioning, turn the air conditioner off. On six-cylinder engines, turn the headlights on high beam.

7. Place the manual transmission in neutral; put the automatic in Park. Make sure the hot idle compensator valve (if any) on

Electric assist choke system (© Chrysler Corp.)

the carburetor is fully seated in the closed position.

8. Turn the engine idle speed adjustment screw in or out to adjust idle speed to specification. If the carburetor has an electric solenoid, turn the solenoid adjusting screw in or out to obtain the specified rpm. Then, adjust the curb idle speed screw until it just touches the stop on the carburetor body. Now, back the curb idle speed adjusting screw out one full turn.

9. Turn each idle mixture adjustment screw 1/16 turn richer (counterclockwise). Wait 30 seconds and observe the reading on the exhaust gas analyzer. Continue this procedure until the meter indicates a definite increase in the richness of the mixture.

NOTE: This step is very important. A carburetor that is set too lean will cause the exhaust gas analyzer to give a false reading indicating a rich mixture. Because of this, the carburetor must first be known to have a rich mixture to verify the reading on the exhaust gas analyzer.

10. After verifying the reading obtained on the meter, adjust the mixture screws to get an air/fuel ratio of 14.2:1. Turn the mixture screws clockwise (leaner) to raise the meter reading or counterclockwise (richer) to lower the meter reading.

NOTE: On 1975 and later models, adjust to get the air/fuel ratio and percentage of CO indicated on the engine compartment sticker.

Idle Speed Solenoid Adjustment

This solenoid is energized whenever the ignition circuit is on. Its function is to allow the throttle plates to close farther when the ignition is switched off, thereby preventing running on.

1. Bring the engine to operating temperature and attach a tachometer.
2. With the engine running, adjust the solenod screw to the proper rpm.
3. Adjust the slow curb idle screw until the screw end just contacts the stop on the carburetor body. Back the screw off one full turn.
4. Test the above procedure by disconnecting the solenoid wire at the connector. Be sure not to let the lead short to the engine. The solenoid should de-energize and idle speed should drop down below normal. Now reconnect the wire. After you reconnect the solenoid, move the throttle linkage by hand since the solenoid isn't strong enough to move it.

Well Type Automatic Choke

This choke requires no servicing as the unit is set when manufactured. Move the choke rod up and down to check for free movement in the pivot. If the unit binds, a new choke unit must be installed. *NOTE: Do not attempt to repair or change the setting. When installing the well type choke unit, be certain that the coil housing does not contact the sides of the well in the exhaust manifold.*

Electric Assist Choke System— 1973 and later

Choke Control Switch Test

1. Remove both electrical connectors from the control switch.
2. Connect a test lamp between the "load" (small) terminal and ground.
3. Operate the engine until it reaches normal operating temperature. Apply 12 volts to the "bat" terminal of the control switch. The test light should

light for a period of from a few seconds to five minutes.

4. If the light does not operate for a few seconds, or remains lit for more than five minutes, replace the control switch.

Choke Heating Element Test—

1. Disconnect the electric heating element wire at the control switch.
2. Connect an ohmmeter lead to the crimped junction of the element wire at the choke end, avoiding connection with the heater casing. Ground the other lead of the ohmmeter.
3. Resistance of twelve ohms is acceptable. Replace the unit if resistance is outside this range.
4. Make sure choke linkage moves freely when hot and when cold.

Governors

Sandwich Velocity Type Governor

Speed Adjustment

1. See Specifications at the beginning of this section for engine no load governed rpm.
2. Remove seal.
3. Turn speed screw adjusting cap, one-half turn at a time, counterclockwise to increase speed and clockwise to decrease speed. Each 1/2 turn equals approximately 150 rpm. More than two complete counterclockwise turns from factory setting is not recommended.

Surge Adjustment

1. Remove adjusting screw cap assembly and locate special hollow wrench in calibrating nut.
2. Locate hex wrench through hollow wrench into adjusting screw.
3. Block throttle linkage to produce surge at governed speed.
4. Turn calibrating nut clockwise 1/4 turn at a time while holding adjusting screw with hex wrench until surge is minimized.
5. Reinstall adjusting screw cap assembly and reset governor speed if necessary.

Slow Action Adjustment

If governor does not cut in quickly at maximum speed or does not open promptly at governed speed when load is applied, governor is said to be slow acting. This is corrected by the same procedure as that described for surge adjustments above, except that the calibrating nut is turned counterclockwise.

Holley Governors

Adjustment

1. Connect tachometer to engine. run it up to governed speed.

Vans · Ramcharger · Trailduster

2. After the engine has warmed up, run it up to governed speed.
3. Stop the engine for adjustment.
4. Remove the cover band from the distributor body. Turn the engine until the governor counterweight adjusting screw is accessible.
5. Remove the plug from the counterweight with a ⅛ in. Allen wrench.
6. Insert a slotted adjusting tool into the counterweight hole and engage the adjusting tangs. Turn clockwise to decrease speed and counterclockwise to increase. ¼ turn changes governed speed about 100 rpm.
7. Remove the adjusting tool and replace the plug and cover band before starting the engine.

Sandwich velocity type governor
(© Chrysler Corp.)

1 Non-cheating stabilizer piston
2 Throttle valve
3 Passage to transfer valve chamber
4 Carburetor vacuum connection (not used)
5 Ignition distributor vacuum connection (not used)
6 Vacuum transfer valve plunger
7 Vacuum passage
8 Vacuum by-pass passage
9 Cam and valve shaft assembly
10 Control spring and ribbon assembly
11 Calibrating nut
12 Adjusting screw
13 Adjusting screw cap assembly

Sandwich governor surge adjustment
(© Chrysler Corp.)

Holley governor distributor adjustment—361 and 413 engines (© Chrysler Corp.)

Pierce Governor

Removal
1. Remove distributor.
2. Disconnect oil line, linkage to carburetor and tachometer cable.
3. Remove hold-down bolt at lower end of support housing that also holds down distributor.
4. Remove ignition distributor adapter and governor from engine as an assembly.

Installation
1. With distributor intermediate drive shaft in proper mesh with camshaft gear, install adapter on engine and install hold-down bolt.
2. Install ignition distributor.
3. Connect oil line and tachometer cable.
4. Adjust linkage to proper length and connect to governor.
5. Connect governor adjusting spring.
6. Start and run engine to operating temperature.
7. Adjust tension on governor adjusting spring to control engine speed to specification.

Pierce governor assembly (© Chrysler Corp.)

Fuel Pump

Removal and Installation
1. Disconnect the fuel lines from the inlet and output sides of the fuel pump.
2. Plug these lines to prevent gasoline from leaking out.
3. Unbolt the retaining bolts from the fuel pump and remove the fuel pump from the engine and pushrod (if equipped).
4. Remove the old gasket from the engine and/or fuel pump.
5. Clean all mounting surfaces.

318 and 360 engine fuel pump details
(© Chrysler Corp.)

Slant six fuel pump (© Chrysler Corp.)

6. Using a new gasket, install the fuel pump. Installation is the reverse of removal.

Cooling System

Radiator Removal

Conventional Trucks
1. Drain cooling system.
2. On vehicles with automatic transmission, disconnect oil cooler lines at radiator bottom tank.
3. Remove upper and lower radiator hoses.
4. On vehicles with a two piece shroud remove the lower half of the shroud.
5. On vehicles with a one piece fan shroud, separate shroud from radiator and position rearward on engine for maximum clearance.
6. Remove radiator attaching screws. You may have to remove the air conditioning condenser bolts.
7. Remove radiator from engine compartment. Care should be taken not to damage cooling fins or water tubes during removal.

Installation
1. Slide radiator down into position behind radiator support and install attaching screws.
2. Install fan shroud (if so equipped) connect hoses, and connect transmission oil cooler lines, if so equipped.
3. Fill cooling system as required. Open the system draincock while filling, on the 361/413 engines. After warm-up, with the heater on, re-check coolant level.
4. On vehicles with automatic transmission, measure transmission level after warm-up and add fluid as required.

Vans and Wagons
1. Drain the cooling system through the radiator drain cock and disconnect the battery ground.
2. Detach the upper radiator hose and remove the fan shroud mounting nuts to permit positioning the shroud rearward on the engine.
3. Remove the top radiator mounting screws. Remove the top con-

denser attaching screws on air conditioned vehicles.
4. Raise the vehicle and remove the transmission cooler lines and lower radiator hose. Cap the transmission coolant lines.
5. Holding the radiator in place, remove the lower mounting screws. Then lower the radiator, being careful to avoid damage to it.

Installation
1. Raise the raiator into the yoke carefully to avoid damage, and install the lower attaching screws. Connect the lower hose and transmission cooler lines.
2. Lower the vehicle. Install the upper attaching screws and the condenser mounting screws.
3. Put the fan shroud in position and install the mounting nuts.
4. Install the upper hose and attach the battery ground. Fill the system with coolant to 1¼" below the filler neck.
5. Operate the engine, with the heater on, until operating temperature is reached. Check for leaks and ensure that transmission and coolant fluid levels are correct.

Heater Core Removal and Installation

Conventional Trucks without Air Conditioning through 1971
1. Drain the coolant.
2. Mark and disconnect the coolant hoses from the heater.
3. Disconnect the motor wiring and heater control cables.
4. Remove the three heater mounting bolts or nuts from inside the engine compartment.
5. Lower the heater unit to the floor and remove the defroster hoses and intake duct.
6. Disassemble the heater unit to remove the core.
7. On installation, position the heater unit and install the defroster hoses and intake duct.
8. Install the mounting nuts or bolts.
9. Connect the wiring and control cables. Connect the coolant hoses.
10. Refill the cooling system and let the engine warm up with the heater on. Check the coolant level.

Conventional Trucks with Factory Air Conditioning through 1971
The air conditioning system must be discharged to remove the heater core. Do not attempt this if you are not familiar with air conditioning service.
1. Disconnect the battery ground cable, drain the coolant, remove the air cleaner, disconnect the

coolant hoses and plug the outlets to prevent spillage.

2. Detach the refrigerant lines from the evaporator core tubes. Cap all openings.

3. Disconnect the two vacuum hoses from the water valve and the one from the intake manifold. Push the hoses and the grommet through the firewall.

4. Remove the three mounting nuts from the studs.

5. Remove the glove box and disconnect the actuator vacuum hose cluster from the back of the control switch. Remove both cables from the bellcrank on top of the housing. Disconnect the wiring at the blower motor resistor block and evaporator temperature control switch.

6. Remove the ashtray and disconnect the left spot cooler and defroster ducts. Disconnect the left side support bracket.

7. Remove the three retaining screws from the face of the housing. Remove the appearance shield. Collapse the distribution duct toward the back of the instrument panel to allow the housing to be rolled out.

8. Remove the support bracket bolts at the back of the blower motor housing. Remove the air intake grille in front of the windshield for access to the nuts.

9. Remove both wiper arms.

10. Pull the heater/air conditioner unit to the rear of the cab until the studs are clear, then move it to the right and tilt down.

11. Disassemble the unit to remove the heater or evaporator core.

12. On installation, position the unit, being careful that no hoses or wires are caught behind it. Install the stud nuts, center the studs in their holes, and tighten the nuts. Install the rear support bracket bolts.

13. Install the left and right support bracket.

14. Connect the vacuum hose cluster to the control switch. Connect the control cables to the bellcrank. Connect all electrical and vacuum connectors.

15. Install the left spot cooler, defroster, and distribution ducts.

16. Install the ashtray.

17. Connect the refrigerant lines, using new O-rings lubricated with refrigerant oil. Connect the heater hoses.

18. Replace the glove box.

19. Fill the cooling system, replace the air cleaner, and install the battery cable. Let the engine warm up with the heater on and check the coolant. Charge the air conditioner.

1972 and later Conventional Trucks without Air Conditioning

1. Disconnect the battery ground cable.

2. Drain the radiator.

3. Disconnect the heater hose from the heater.

4. Disconnect the wiring from the resistor.

5. Remove the defroster ducts.

6. Disconnect the ground wire and the cooling tube from the engine side of the blower motor.

7. Remove the bracket from the righthand side of the instrument panel and pull the panel toward the rear of the truck.

8. Remove the seven retaining nuts from the engine side of the firewall. Remove one nut from inside the truck at the right-hand kick panel.

9. Roll the heater out from its mounting.

10. Separate the front and rear housings. Two of the retaining screws are located inside the unit at the right-hand end.

11. Remove the screws at each end of the core, holding the core to the housing. Remove the screws from the front side of the housing, between the inlet and outlet tubes.

12. Installation is the reverse of removal.

1972 and Later Conventional Trucks with Factory Air Conditioning

1. Disconnect the battery ground cable.

2. Drain the coolant and disconnect the heater hoses at the firewall.

3. Remove the glove box and ashtray.

4. Remove the right and left ducts.

5. Remove the four screws and the distribution duct. Remove the two screws and the center air outlet and duct.

6. Disconnect the wiring harness from the resistor. Detach the vacuum lines from the housing.

7. Remove the 22 screws from the housing. Remove the two plugs in order to remove the two inside screws. Hold the defroster door to the heat position and separate the housing.

8. Remove the screw between the heater core tubes from the engine compartment firewall and the two screws from each end of the core. Slide the core out.

9. On installation, position the core and install the retaining screws.

10. Assemble the housing, holding the defroster door to the heat position and making sure that the shaft lines up in the hole.

11. Install the vacuum lines, wiring, ducts, glovebox, and ashtray.

12. Connect the heater hoses and the

battery cable. Fill the cooling system.

13. Let the engine warm up with the heater on, then check the coolant level.

Vans and Wagons without Air Conditioning

1. Disconnect the battery ground cable.

2. Drain the radiator.

3. Cover the alternator with a waterproof cover.

4. Disconnect the blower motor resistor and ground wires from the heater.

5. Disconnect and plug the heater core hoses.

6. Disconnect the control cables.

7. Remove the retaining screws from the water valve. Do not disconnect the hoses from the water valve; place the water valve with hoses attached to one side.

8. Remove the blower motor cooler tube.

9. Remove the nuts holding the housing to the mounting studs and tip the complete unit out through the hood opening.
   To remove the heater core:

10. Remove the 3 retaining nuts and lift the blower with wheel out of the housing.

11. Remove the 4 cover retaining nuts and lift the cover off the housing.

12. Remove the 4 core retaining screws and lift the core out of the housing.

13. Installation is the reverse of removal. Fill the cooling system.

14. Let the engine warm up with the heater on, then check the coolant level.

Vans and Wagons with Factory Air Conditioning

The air conditioning system must be discharged to remove the heater core. Do not attempt if you are not familiar with air conditioning servce.

1. Disconnect the battery ground cable and drain the coolant.

2. Remove the grille, condenser, and radiator.

3. Place a waterproof cover over the alternator.

4. Disconnect the heater hoses at the water valve and remove the valve and bracket. Disconnect and cap the refrigerant lines.

5. Remove the glovebox, spot cooler bezel, and appearance shield.

6. Working through the glovebox opening, remove the evaporator housing to firewall screws and nuts.

7. Remove the wiper motor. Detach all evaporator housing vacuum and electrical connections. Detach the blower motor cooling hose and the drain hoses.

8. Remove the two 2¼ in. bolts from the crossbar and the four screws from the sealplate on the front of the housing. Separate the evaporator and blower motor housings, remove the evaporator housing.

9. Remove the receiver drier and cap all the openings. Carefully pry the heater core out, leaving the air seal at the front intact.

10. On installation, connect the hoses to the core. Position the evaporator housing on top of the blower housing. Install the mounting screws and nuts.

11. Position the crossbar under the lip on the blower housing opening and install the two 2¼ in. bolts. Install the four seal plate screws at the front of the housing.

12. Replace the wiper motor and connect the vacuum and electrical lines. Connect the blower motor cooler hose and the drain hoses.

13. Connect the heater hoses to the water valve.

14. Install the receiver drier and connect the refrigerant lines.

15. Install the radiator, condenser, and grille.

16. Replace the glovebox, spot cooler bezel, and appearance shield.

17. Install the battery ground cable and fill the cooling system. Let the engine warm up with the heater on, then check the coolant. Charge the air conditioner.

Water Pump

Only the 361/413 water pump is rebuildable.

Removal—All Engines

1. Drain cooling system and remove the fan belt and fan shroud. Remove the radiator on 1974 and later V8s.

2. Unscrew fan blade bolts and remove fan blade, spacers and bolts as an assembly. *CAUTION: Silicone drive fans must be kept in their normal attitude. If the shaft points down, silicone fluid will contaminate the fan drive bearing.*

3. Position the six-cylinder lower clamp in the center of the by-pass hose. Disconnect or remove heater and radiator hoses.

4. Remove water pump retaining bolts and remove water pump assembly.

Installation

1. Install a new by-pass hose if necessary, with clamps positioned in the center of the hose.

2. Use a new gasket and install water pump. Install and tighten pump retaining bolts to 30 foot pounds. Position by-pass hose

The 361/413 engines use a rebuildable water pump (© Chrysler Corp.)

EIGHT CYLINDER   SIX CYLINDER
Thermostats (© Chrysler Corp.)

clamps. Install the heater and radiator hoses.

3. Install fan blade, spacer and bolt assembly. Start all bolts, then tighten to 15-18 foot pounds.

4. Install fan belt and adjust belt tension. Fill cooling system.

Thermostat Removal

1. Drain cooling system down to thermostat level or below.

2. Remove upper radiator hose from thermostat housing.

3. Remove thermostat housing bolts and remove thermostat and housing.

4. Installation is the reverse of the above procedure. Use a new gasket.

Engine

Emission Controls

Two basic approaches to emission control have been used on Dodge engines. The first is engine design modifications, which apply to some extent to all engines. The second is a group of specific emission control systems, the application of which varies with model and power train. Those models rated under 6000 lbs GVW are subject to stricter light-duty emission regulations, and therefore use more of these systems.

The design modifications and emission control systems are listed here; tests and adjustments for the systems will be found in the General Repair Section on Emission Controls.

Engine Design Modifications

Intake Manifold

The intake manifolds were modified to provide more rapid vaporization of fuel during warm-up. Thin fins were added to the manifold "hot spot" area below the carburetor to aid in the transfer of heat from exhaust gases in the crossover passage. By the addition of this heat, fuel vaporizes faster allowing the use of leaner mixtures, thus lowering the output of CO (carbon monoxide).

Combustion Chamber Design

Combustion chamber designs were modified to reduce emissions, permit more complete combustion, and allow a substantial reduction in HC (hydrocarbon).

Lower Compression Ratios

Compression ratios on most engines were reduced to allow the use of 91 octane gasoline. This also resulted in a reduction of HC and CO output.

Camshaft

A modified camshaft was installed to use greater valve overlap which lowers the peak combustion temperatures to reduce the emission of NO_x (nitrous oxide).

Electronic Ignition System

The electronic ignition provides for better and more precise spark, thereby reducing emissions.

Carburetion

Modified carburetors are used giving improved fuel distribution,

DISTRIBUTOR
• Electronic Ignition
• Reduced Tolerances
• Permanently Lubricated

CARBURETOR
• Improved Distribution
• Leaner Mixture
• Faster Acting Choke, Electric Assist
• External Idle Mixture Limiter
• Solenoid Throttle Stop
• Gasoline Vapor Control
• Idle Enrichment
• Throttle Positioner (Catalyst Protection)

INTAKE MANIFOLD
• Improved Hot Spot

ORIFICE SPARK ADVANCE
CONTROL VALVE (OSAC)

COOLANT CONTROL
IDLE ENRICHMENT VALVE

CHARCOAL CANISTER

VAPOR VENT TUBE
TO FUEL TANK

OXIDATION
CATALYTIC CONVERTER

CCEGR
TEMPERATURE
VALVE

CLOSED CRANKCASE VENTILATION

INCREASED
CAM OVERLAP

HEATED INTAKE AIR

EXHAUST GAS RECIRCULATION
• EGR Control Valve
• EGR Vacuum Amplifier
• EGR Time Delay

MODIFIED COMBUSTION CHAMBER
AND REDUCED COMPRESSION RATIO

Light Duty (under 6,000 lbs. GVW) emission controls (© Chrysler Corp.)

leaner mixtures, and gasoline vapor control, further reducing emissions.

Emission Control Systems

Electric Assist Choke System

All engines are equipped with an electric assist choke to shorten the period of choke operation when control temperatures are above 60° F. This device consists of a heating element docated in the choke well and a control unit adjacent to the choke well. Heat applied to the thermostatic choke coil by the heating element causes the choke to open in a shorter time than previously.
NOTE: The heating element should not be exposed to or immersed in any fluid for any purpose. This especially applies to cleaning agents. A short in the wiring to the heater will result in a short circuit in the ignition.

Heated Air Intake System

The carburetor air preheater is a device which is part of the air cleaner and which keeps the air entering the carburetor at about 100° F when underhood temperatures are less than 100° F. By using this device, the carburetor can be calibrated much leaner to improve engine warm-up characteristics.

The heated air intake system is basically a two circuit airflow system. When underhood temperatures are less than 100° F, the air will flow into the stove, through a flexible connector, into the adaptor on the bottom of the snorkel, and then into the carburetor. When the underhood tem-

perature is above 100° F, the airflow will be through the snorkel.

Modulation of the induction air is performed through intake manifold vacuum, a temperature sensor, and a vacuum diaphragm which operates the heat control door in the snorkel.

Orifice Spark Advance Control (OSAC)

The OSAC system is used to control NO_x. The system controls the amount of vacuum supplied to the vacuum advance mechanism of the distributor.

Exhaust Gas Recirculation (EGR)

EGR is used in conjunction with the vacuum spark advance control to limit peak flame temperatures and thus retard the formation of NO_x. Two alternate systems are used.

Ported Vacuum Control System

This system uses a slot type port in the carburetor throttle body which is exposed to an increasing percentage of manifold vacuum by the opening movement of the throttle plate. The throttle bore port is directly connected to the EGR valve through an external nipple. The flow rate of exhaust gases is determined by manifold vacuum, throttle position, and exhaust gas backpressure. Wide open throttle recycling of exhaust gases is prevented by calibrating the valve opening point above manifold vacuum available at wide open throttle, since port vacuum cannot exceed manifold vacuum.

Venturi Vacuum Control System

This system uses a vacuum tap at the throat of the carburetor venturi to provide a control signal. Because the signal is so low however, a vacuum amplifier is used to increase the strength of the signal. The amplifier uses stored manifold vacuum to provide the source for amplification. Elimination of EGR at wide open throttle is accomplished by a "dump" diaphragm which compares venturi and manifold vacuum to determine when wide open throttle is achieved. At wide open throttle, the internal reservoir is "dumped", limiting the output of the EGR valve to manifold vacuum. As with the ported vacuum control system, the valve opening point is set above the manifold vacuum available at wide open throttle, permitting the valve to be closed at wide open throttle.

Coolant Control Exhaust Gas Recirculation Valve

Trucks with EGR are equipped with a CCEGR valve located in the top of the radiator tank. When coolant in the top radiator tank reaches 65° F, the valve opens to apply vacuum to the EGR valve to recirculate exhaust gases.

EGR Delay System

Some trucks are equipped with an EGR delay system, which is an electrical timer on the dash to control an engine mounted solenoid. The timer prevents exhaust gas recirculation for about 35 seconds after the ignition is turned on.

Air Injection System

This system adds a controlled amount of air through special passages in the cylinder head, to exhaust gases in the exhaust ports, causing oxidation of the gases and thereby reducing carbon monoxide and hydrocarbon emissions to the required levels.

The air injection system consists of a belt-driven air pump, rubber hose, a check valve to protect the hoses and pump from hot gases, injection tubes, and a combination diverter/pressure relief valve assembly.

Evaporative Control System

The function of the evaporative control system is to prevent the emission of raw gasoline vapors from the fuel tank and carburetor into the atmosphere. When fuel evaporates in the tank or float bowl, the vapors pass through lines and into the charcoal canister where they are temporarily stored until they can be drawn into the intake manifold and burned. A vacuum port located in the base of the carburetor governs vapor flow from the canister to the engine.

Closed Crankcase Ventilation System

The closed PCV system operates as follows:

In place of a vented oil filler cap, an air intake line is installed between the carburetor air filter and a crankcase opening in the valve cover.

A sealed oil filler cap and dipstick are used.

A separate PCV air filter is used when the intake air hose is connected to the "dirty" side of the carburetor air cleaner. The filter is located where the intake air line connects to the valve cover.

Under normal engine operation, air enters through the intake line from the air filter. Under heavy acceleration, any excess vapors back up through the air intake line and are forced to mix with incoming air into the carburetor and are burned in the combustion chamber. Back-up fumes cannot escape into the atmosphere, creating a closed system.

The PCV valve is used to control the rate at which crankcase vapors are returned to the intake manifold. The action of the valve plunger is controlled by intake manifold vacuum and the spring. During deceleration and idle, when manifold vacuum is high, it overcomes the tension of the valve spring and the plunger bottoms in the manifold end of the valve housing. Because of the valve construction, it reduces, but does not stop, the passage of vapors to the intake manifold. When the engine is lightly accelerated or operated at constant speed, spring tension matches intake manifold vacuum pull and the plunger takes a mid-position in the valve body, allowing more vapors to flow into the manifold.

Catalytic Converter

Most 1975 and later models less than 6,000 lbs GVW, are equipped with catalytic converters. These devices are used to oxidize excess carbon monoxide (CO) and hydrocarbons (HC) in the exhaust system before they can escape out the tailpipe and into the atmosphere. The converter is installed in front of the mufflers, underneath the truck, and protected by a heat shield.

The expected catalyst life is 50,000 miles, provided that the engine is kept in tune and unleaded fuel is used.

To keep the catalyst from being overheated by an overly rich mixture during deceleration, a catalyst protection system (CPS) is sometimes used. The system consists of a throttle positioner solenoid (not to be confused with the idle stop solenoid), a control box, and an engine rpm sensor.

Any time that the engine speed is more than 2,000 rpm, the solenoid is energized and keeps the throttle butterfly from fully closing, thus preventing the deceleration mixture from becoming too rich.

Engine Removal

Vans and Wagons

NOTE: Engine removal is a complicated operation. A floor jack is a necessity and you will probably have to fabricate several stands and attaching apparatus. On vehicles equipped with air conditioning, before removing the engine, have an air conditioning expert evacuate the system.

1. Disconnect the battery and drain the coolant from the radiator and engine block. Drain the engine oil. On V8s, remove the oil filter.
2. Remove the engine cover, air cleaner, and starter.
3. Remove the front bumper, grille, and support brace. Disconnect both radiator hoses and remove the radiator and support brace as a unit.
4. Remove the power steering and air pumps with the hoses attached and lay them aside.
5. Disconnect the throttle linkage, heater and vacuum hoses and all electrical connections to the ignition, alternator, and all other electrical connections.
6. Remove the alternator, fan, pulley, and drive belts.
7. Remove the heater blower motor.
8. Remove and plug the inlet line to the fuel pump.
9. Remove the oil dipstick tube. On V8s, remove the intake manifold and left exhaust manifold. If equipped with air conditioning, remove the right side valve cover.
10. To provide clearance for engine removal, the oil pan and transmission must be removed.
11. Raise the engine slightly in preparation for transmission removal. Support it with an engine lifting fixture. This tool can be fabricated from galvanized pipe fittings obtained locally. Use only galvanized parts with an inside diameter of 1½ in. or larger. Be sure they are firmly threaded together to assure maximum strength.
12. Raise the vehicle and support it on jackstands. Remove the starter and distributor.
13. Remove the driveshaft and engine rear support. Remove the rear support by removing the rear mount through-bolt and the U-shaped bracket from the crossmember. Remove the insulator from the bottom face of the transmission housing.
14. If equipped with an automatic transmission, remove the transmission intact with the filler tube and the torque converter separated from the drive plate.
15. Raise the rear of the engine approximately 2 in. and remove the clutch or drive plate and the flywheel.
15a. On V8s, position the cut-out in the crankshaft flange at 3 o'clock. Remove the oil pan screws and lower the oil pan far enough to reach inside and turn the oil pump pick-up tube slightly to the right to clear the pan. Remove the oil pan.
16. Lower the vehicle.
17. Using a boom hoist attached to the engine with the shortest hook-up possible, take up all tension and support the engine. The boom hoist is the ideal tool to use. If one is not available, it may be possible to support the engine on a stationary hoist and roll the vehicle out from under the engine.
18. Remove the engine front mounts and insulators.
19. Carefully remove the engine from the vehicle.
20. Installation is the reverse of removal. Check all fluid levels and perform all tune-up adjustments if the engine was rebuilt.

NOTE: If the engine was rebuilt or new camshaft or lifters installed, add 1 quart of MoPar Engine oil Supplement to aid break-in. This should be left in the engine for at least 500 miles.

Conventional Trucks

1. Drain the coolant.
2. Remove the battery.
3. Mark the outline of the hinges on the hood and remove it.
4. Discharge the air conditioning system safely. If you are not sure of the procedure, do not do it yourself. Disconnect and cap the compressor lines.
5. Disconnect the wiring at the alternator, coil, temperature and oil pressure sending units, starter relay, and engine ground strap.
6. Remove the air cleaner and

Rear engine mount—vans and wagons
(© Chrysler Corp.)

TIGHTENING
TORQUE
30 FT. LBS.
50 FT. LBS.

FRONT

Rear engine mount—100-300 series

TIGHTENING TORQUE	
1	50 FT.LBS.

carburetor. Install an engine lifting fixture.

7. Remove the distributor cap, rotor, and spark plug wires.
8. Disconnect and cap the fuel line.
9. Remove the fan and radiator.
10. Detach the exhaust pipe, driveshaft, linkage, and oil cooler lines.
11. Support the rear of the engine and remove the engine rear crossmember and transmission. On the 361 and 413 engines, remove the transmission only.
12. Unbolt the engine mounts and lift the engine out. On D500 and larger models, the grille and support assembly should be removed first.

Ramcharger and Trailduster, W100, 200, 300

1. Drain the coolant from the radiator and cylinder block.
2. Disconnect the battery ground cable. Remove the V8 battery.
3. Scribe the outline of the hood hinges and remove the hood.
4. If equipped with air conditioning, remove the compressor with lines attached and lay it aside. *CAUTION: Do not disconnect any refrigerant lines. Bodily injury could result.*
5. Disconnect the electrical connections at the alternator, ignition coil, temperature and oil pressure sending units, starter-to-solenoid, and engine/body ground.
6. Remove the air cleaner and carburetor. Install an engine lifting fixture.
7. Remove the distributor cap and rotor.
8. Disconnect and plug the fuel pump line.
9. Disconnect the radiator and heater hoses. Disconnect and plug the oil cooler lines.
10. Remove the fan, spacer, fluid drive, and radiator. Do not store the fan drive unit with the shaft pointing downward. Fluid will leak out.
11. Raise the truck and support the rear of the engine.
12. Disconnect the exhaust pipes at the manifolds.

RIGHT SIDE
(D1-2-3 FRAME SHOWN)

LEFT SIDE
(W1-2-3 FRAME SHOWN)
USE WITH 360 ENGINE

TIGHTENING TORQUE	
1	55 FT.LBS.
2	75 FT.LBS.

V8 engine mounts—100-300 series, conventional trucks (© Chrysler Corp.)

LEFT SIDE

TIGHTENING TORQUE	
1	50 FT.LBS.
2	75 FT.LBS.

RIGHT SIDE

Six cylinder, except 4WD, engine mounts— -100-300 series, conventional trucks

13. Remove the V8 starter.
14. Remove the automatic transmission dust cover and attach a C-clamp to the front bottom of the torque converter housing to prevent it from failing out. Remove the drive plate bolts from the torque converter. On manual transmission models, remove the rear crossmember, transmission, transfer case and adapter. You can leave the transfer case in place on six-cylinder models.
15. Support the transmission and remove the transmission attaching bolts.
16. Lower the truck and attach a hoist to the engine.

17. Remove the front motor mount bolt stud nuts and washers.
18. Carefully remove the engine.
19. Installation is the reverse of removal. Fill the engine with coolant and fresh oil. Adjust the transmission linkage, carburetor, and ignition timing.

Manifolds

Removal and Installation
6 Cylinder Combination Manifold

1. Remove air cleaner.
2. Disconnect vacuum control tube at carburetor.
3. Disconnect fuel line at carburetor.
4. Disconnect crankcase ventilation tube at carburetor.
5. Disconnect automatic choke rod at carburetor and remove choke from intake manifold.
6. Disconnect throttle linkage at carburetor.
7. Remove carburetor from intake manifold.
8. Disconnect exhaust pipe at exhaust manifold flange.
9. Remove nuts and washers securing manifold assembly to cylinder head.
10. Remove manifold from cylinder head.
11. Remove three screws securing intake manifold to exhaust manifold.
12. Separate intake and exhaust manifolds and discard gasket.
13. Clean all gasket surfaces on manifolds in solvent and blow dry with compressed air.
14. Clean manifold gasket surfaces on cylinder head, wash with solvent and blow dry with compressed air.
15. Check mating surfaces of manifolds for parallelism with straightedge. Surfaces should be flat within .008″.
16. Inspect manifolds for cracks or distortion.
17. Check operation of manifold heat control valve. If necessary to free up operation, apply a manifold heat control valve solvent.
18. To install, first install a new gasket between the two manifolds.
19. Install three long screws securing the two manifolds. *Do not tighten screws at this time.*
20. Position manifold assembly on cylinder head, using a new gasket.
21. Install triangular washers and nuts on upper studs and on the four lower studs opposite numbers 2 and 5 cylinders. The eight triangular washers should be positioned squarely on the machined surfaces of both intake and exhaust manifold retaining pads.

Slant six manifold heat control valve (© Chrysler Corp.)

Manifold heat control valve 383 engine
(© Chrysler Corp.)

These washers must be installed with *cup side* against manifold. Install nuts and washers only when engine is cold.

22. Install steel conical washers with cup (concave) side to manifold, one on center upper stud and two on center lower studs. Install the brass washers at each end, with the flat side to the manifold. Install nuts with flat side away from washers. Snug up the nuts.

23. Tighten the inboard intake to exhaust manifold screw to 200 in. lbs. Tighten the outboard screws to 240 in. lbs. Tighten the manifold to head screws and nuts to 120 in. lbs.

24. Attach exhaust pipe to manifold flange, using a new gasket and tighten bolt nuts to 35 ft. lbs.

25. Install carburetor and connect automatic choke rod and throttle linkage. Assemble crankcase ventilation hose, vacuum control tube and fuel line to carburetor. Install carburetor air cleaner, and connect closed breather cap hose to air cleaner inlet tube, if used.

V8 Intake Manifold

1. Drain cooling system and disconnect battery.
2. Remove alternator, carburetor air cleaner, and fuel line.
3. Disconnect accelerator linkage.
4. Remove vacuum control between carburetor and distributor.

5. Remove distributor cap and wires.
6. Disconnect coil wires, temperature sending unit wire, heater hoses and bypass hose.
7. Remove intake manifold, ignition coil and carburetor as an assembly.
8. Installation is the reverse of the above procedure. Tighten the intake manifold to head bolts in the sequence illustrated, from center alternating out. Tighten manifold mounting bolts to torque listed in Specifications, tightening in 15 ft. lb. increments.

V8 Exhaust Manifold Removal

1. Disconnect the exhaust manifold at the flange where it mates to the exhaust pipe.
2. If the vehicle is equipped with air injection and/or a carburetor-heated air stove, remove them.
3. Remove the exhaust manifold by removing the securing bolts and washers. To reach these bolts, it may be necessary to jack the engine slightly off its front mounts. When the exhaust manifold is removed, sometimes the securing studs will screw out with the nuts. If this occurs, the studs must be replaced with the aid of sealing compound on the

coarse thread ends. If this is not done, water leaks may develop at the studs. To install the exhaust manifold, reverse the removal procedure. On the center branch of the 318 and 360 manifold, no conical washers are used.

Manifold Heat Control Valve

Inspect operation of manifold heat control valve by racing engine momentarily to wide open throttle. The counterweight should respond by moving about $\frac{1}{2}''$. If it does not move it may be frozen with deposits or the thermostatic spring may be weak or broken. Use a manifold heat control valve solvent to loosen valve shaft at bushings. *CAUTION:* Be sure that manifold is *cool* when applying solvent and let it soak for a few minutes before attempting to free the valve.

Cylinder Head

Cylinder Head Removal and Installation

6 Cyl. OHV

1. Drain cooling system.
2. Remove air cleaner and fuel line.
3. Remove vacuum line at carburetor and distributor.
4. Disconnect accelerator linkage.
5. Disconnect spark plug wires by pulling boot straight out in line with plugs.

Intake and exhaust manifold installation,
slant six (© Chrysler Corp.)

V8 Intake manifold bolt tightening sequence (© Chrysler Corp.)

Installing 318 and 360 exhaust manifold (© Chrysler Corp.)

Slant six cylinder head bolt tightening sequence

6. Disconnect heater hose and by-pass hose clamp.
7. Disconnect temperature sending wire.
8. Disconnect exhaust pipe at exhaust manifold flange. Disconnect diverter valve vacuum line on engines with air pump.
9. Remove intake and exhaust manifolds.
10. Remove closed vent system (PCV) and rocker cover.
11. Remove rocker shaft assembly.
12. Remove pushrods in sequence and mark them in such a way that they may be put back into their original positions.
13. Remove head bolts.
14. Remove spark plugs and tubes (through 1974).
15. To install, clean all gasket surfaces of cylinder block and cylinder head and install spark plugs.
16. Check all surfaces with a straightedge if there is any reason to suspect leakage.
17. Install gasket, using sealer, and cylinder head.
18. Install cylinder head attaching bolts. Tighten all bolts in the sequence illustrated to 50 ft. lbs. torque, then repeat tightening sequence torquing to 65 ft. lbs.
19. Install rocker arms and shaft assembly with the flat (through 1973) or the oil hole on the end of the shaft on top and to the front. The special bolt goes to the rear. Install rocker shaft retainers between rocker arms so they seat on rocker shaft and not on extended bushing of rocker arm. Be sure to install long retainer in center position only. Tighten bolts to 25 ft. lbs. Tighten the special bolt to 200 in. lbs.
20. Loosen the 3 bolts holding intake manifold to exhaust manifold. This is necessary for proper alignment. Install the manifolds as detailed under manifold removal and installation.
21. Install the manifolds as detailed under manifold removal and installation.
22. Connect heater hose and by-pass hose clamp.

Slant six rocker shaft, 1974 and later models don't have the flat shown (© Chrysler Corp.)

23. Connect heat indicator sending unit wire, the accelerator linkage and spark plug wires.
24. Install the vacuum control tube from carburetor to distributor. Install the air tube assembly with a new gasket to the head, tightening it to 100 inch-pounds. Install the diverter valve vacuum line.
25. Connect exhaust pipe to exhaust manifold flange.
26. Install fuel line and carburetor air cleaner.
27. Fill cooling system, start and warm up engine, and adjust valve tappet clearance.
28. Install valve cover using new gasket, tightening retaining nuts to 3-4 ft. lbs.
29. Install crankcase ventilation system.

V8 Engines

1. Drain cooling system and disconnect battery. On vehicles with 361 or 413 cu. in. engines, remove battery.
2. Remove alternator, air cleaner and fuel line.
3. Disconnect accelerator linkage.
4. Remove vacuum control hose between carburetor and distributor.
5. Remove cooling and heater hoses from head and, if so equipped, remove air compressor.
6. Remove distributor cap and high tension leads as an assembly.
7. Remove heat indicator sending unit wire.
8. Remove crankcase ventilation

Cylinder head bolt tightening sequence, 360 and smaller V8

Cylinder head bolt tightening sequence, 361 and larger V8

system and valve covers.
9. Remove spark plugs and, on 361, 413 cu. in. engines, remove distributor and governor.
10. Remove intake manifold, carburetor and, if attached to manifold, ignition coil as an assembly.
11. Remove tappet chamber cover.
12. On 361, 413 cu. in. engines, remove the bolts that secure water pump housing to each cylinder head.
13. Remove exhaust manifolds. On the 361, 413 cu. in. engines, tag the center bolts for reinstallation in same hole.
14. Remove rocker arms and shaft assemblies.
15. Remove pushrods and *identify to insure installation in original location.*
16. Remove cylinder head bolts and cylinder heads.
17. Before installing cylinder heads, clean all gasket surfaces of block and heads.
18. Inspect all surfaces with a straightedge if there is any indication of leakage.
19. Coat new head gaskets with sealant and install on block.
20. Install cylinder head and head bolts. Tighten bolts in the sequence illustrated, first to 50 ft. lbs. torque, then in sequence again to the specified torque (see Specifications at the beginning of this section). *CAUTION:* Do not retighten cylinder head bolts after engine has been operated if embossed steel head gaskets are used.
21. Inspect pushrods for wear or bending and install in original positions. Use an aligning rod.
22. Install rocker shaft assembly. making sure long stamped steel retainers are in the No. 2 and No. 4 positions. Tighten rocker shaft mounting bolts to 25 ft. lbs. (17 ft. lbs on 318 and 360 cu. in. engine) torque. On the 318 and 360 cu. in. engines, make sure the "NOTCH" end of the rocker assemblies are pointing toward the centerline of the engine and toward the front on

the left bank and toward the rear on the right bank.

23. Install tappet chamber cover. On the 361, 413 cu. in. engines, make sure the 1/8" gasket bleed hole at the crossover is on the right side of the engine. Tighten bolts to 7-8 ft. lbs. torque.

24. Install exhaust manifolds. Use new gaskets. On the 361, 413 cu. in. engines, be sure center bolt is inserted in its original position. Tighten bolts to the specified torque.

25. Set correct gap on spark plugs (see Tune-Up Specifications at the beginning of this section) and install, tightening to 30 ft. lbs. torque.

26. Install intake manifold and carburetor assembly, tightening bolts from center outward, first to 25 ft. lbs. torque, then again to correct torque (see Torque Specifications at the beginning of this section). On the 318 and 360 cu. in. engine, coat the gaskets with sealant and install with bead down.

27. If they were removed, install distributor and governor.

28. Install distributor cap and high tension leads.

29. Connect vacuum control hose between distributor and carburetor, throttle linkage, heat indicator sending unit wire, heater and coolant hoses, fuel line and, if so equipped, manual choke cable.

30. On the 361, 413 cu. in. engines, install bolts which secure water pump housing to each cylinder head.

31. Install rocker cover, using new gasket. Tighten bolts to 3-4 ft. lbs. torque.

32. Install crankcase ventilation system and air cleaner.

33. Install alternator and drive belts. Install air compressor if so equipped.

34. Fill cooling system and install or connect battery.

Valve System

For complete instructions for servicing valves and valve train see the Engine Overhaul Section of the General Repair Section.

For valve angles, stem dimensions, clearances and spring tensions see Valve Specifications at the beginning of this section.

Valve Lash

This adjustment is required only on the six-cylinder engine. It should be done at every tune-up. It should also be done whenever there is excessive noise from the valve mechanism.

No valve lash adjustment is necessary or possible on any other Chry-

Typical hydraulic tappet (© Chrysler Corp.)

sler-built engine. Hydraulic valve lifters automatically maintain zero clearance. After engine reassembly these lifters adjust themselves as soon as engine oil pressure builds up.

NOTE: Do not set the valve lash closer than specified in an attempt to quiet the valve mechanism. This will result in burned valves.

The manufacturer recommends that the valves be adjusted with the engine running, but the following procedure can also be used.

1. The engine must be at normal operating temperature. Mark the crankshaft pulley into three equal 120° segments, starting at the TDC mark.

2. Remove the valve (rocker) cover and the distributor cap.

3. Set the engine at TDC on the No. 1 cylinder by aligning the mark on the crankshaft pulley with the 0° mark on the timing cover pointer. The distributor rotor should point at the position of the No. 1 spark plug wire in the distributor cap. Both rocker arms on the No. 1 cylinder should be free to move slightly. If all this isn't the case, you have No. 6 cylinder at TDC and will have to turn the engine 360° in the normal direction of rotation.

4. The cylinders are numbered from front to rear. The intake and exhaust valves are in the following sequence, starting at

the front: E-I, E-I, E-I, I-E, I-E, I-E. Intake and exhaust valves have different settings.

5. The lash is measured between the rocker arm and the end of the valve.

6. To check the lash, insert the correct size feeler gauge between the rocker arm and the valve. Press down lightly on the other end of the rocker arm. If the gauge cannot be inserted, loosen the self-locking adjustment nut on top of the rocker arm. Tighten the nut until the gauge can just be inserted and withdrawn without buckling.

7. After both valves for the No. 1 cylinder are adjusted, turn the engine so that the pulley turns 120° in the normal direction of rotation (clockwise). The distributor rotor will turn 60°, since it turns at half engine speed.

8. Check that the rocker arms are free and adjust the valves for the next cylinder in the firing order, 5. The firing order is 1-5-3-6-2-4.

9. Turn the engine 120° to adjust each of the remaining cylinders in the firing order. When you are done the engine will have made two complete revolutions (720°) and the rotor one complete revolution (360°).

10. Replace the rocker cover with a new gasket. Replace the distributor cap. Start the engine and check for leaks.

Installing push rods (© Chrysler Corp.)

Rocker Shaft Removal and Installation

Six-Cylinder

1. Remove the closed ventilation system.
2. Remove the evaporative control system (if so equipped).
3. Remove the valve cover with its gasket.
4. Take out the rocker arm and shaft assembly securing bolts and remove the rocker arm and shaft.
5. Reverse the above for installation. The flat (through 1973) or the oil hole on the end of the shaft must be on the top and point toward the front of the engine to provide proper lubrication to the rocker arms. The special bolt goes to the rear. Torque the rocker arm bolts to 25 ft. lbs. and adjust the valves.

V8

The stamped steel rocker arms are arranged on one rocker arm shaft per cylinder head. To remove the rocker arms and shaft:

1. Disconnect the spark plug wires.
2. Disconnect the closed ventilation and evaporative control system (if so equipped).
3. Remove the valve covers with their gaskets.
4. Remove the rocker shaft bolts and retainers, and lift off the rocker arm assembly.
5. Reverse the above procedure to install. The notch on the end of both rocker shafts on the 318 and 360 should point to the engine centerline and toward the front of the engine on the left cylinder head, or toward the rear on the right cylinder head. On the 361, 383, 400, 413, and 440, the rocker arm lubrication holes must point down and toward the valves.

Torque the rocker shaft bolts to 17 ft. lbs. on the 318 and 316, and 25 ft. lbs. on the others.

Valve Stem Oil Seal Replacement

If valve stem oil seals are found to be the cause of excessive oil consumption, they may be replaced without removing the cylinder heads.

1. Remove the air cleaner.
2. Remove the rocker arm covers and spark plugs.
3. Detach the coil wire from the distributor.
4. Turn the engine so that No. 1 cylinder is at Top Dead Center on the compression stroke. Both valves for No. 1 cylinder should be fully closed and the crankshaft damper timing mark at TDC. The distributor rotor will point at the No. 1 spark plug wire location in the cap.
5. Remove the rocker shaft and install a dummy shaft.
6. Apply 90-100 psi air pressure to No. 1 cylinder, using a spark plug hole air hose adaptor.
7. Use a valve spring compressor to compress each No. 1 cylinder valve spring and remove the retainer locks and the spring. Remove the old seals.
8. Install a cup shield on the exhaust valve stem. Position it down against the valve guide.
9. Push the intake valve stem seal firmly and squarely over the valve guide. Do not force the seal against the top of the guide.
10. When installing the valve spring retainer lock, compress the spring only enough to install the lock.
11. Repeat the operation on each successive cylinder in the firing order, making sure that the crankshaft is exactly on TDC for each cylinder. Firing order is

1-5-3-6-2-4 for sixes, and 1-8-4-3-6-5-7-2 for V8s. See the Firing Order and Distributor Rotation illustrations in the Specifications Section of this Chapter for cylinder numbering.

12. Replace the rocker arms, covers, spark plugs, and coil wire.

Timing Cover and Chain

NOTE: On models through 1974 it is normal to find particles of rubber collected between the seal retainer and the crankshaft oil slinger after the seal has been in service. Check the slack in the chain after installation.

Removal and Installation

Six-Cylinder

1. Drain the cooling system and disconnect the battery.
2. Remove the radiator and fan.
3. With a puller, remove the vibration damper.
4. Loosen the oil pan bolts to allow clearance, and remove the timing case cover and gasket.
5. Slide the crankshaft oil slinger off the front of the crankshaft.
6. Remove the camshaft sprocket bolt.
7. Remove the timing chain with the camshaft sprocket.
8. On installation: Turn the crankshaft to line up the timing mark on the crankshaft sprocket with the centerline of the camshaft (without the chain).
9. Install the camshaft sprocket and chain. Align the timing marks.
10. Torque the camshaft sprocket bolt to 35 ft. lbs.
11. Replace the oil slinger.
12. Reinstall the timing case cover with a new gasket and torque the bolts to 17 ft. lbs. Retighten the engine oil pan to 17 ft. lbs.
13. Press the vibration damper back on.
14. Replace the radiator and hoses.
15. Refill the cooling system.

V8

1. Disconnect the battery and drain

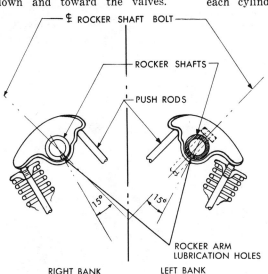

RIGHT BANK   LEFT BANK

‡ ROCKER SHAFT BOLT

ROCKER SHAFTS

PUSH RODS

ROCKER ARM LUBRICATION HOLES

15° 15°

On 361 and larger V8s, the rocker arm lubrication holes should be aligned as shown (© Chrysler Corp.)

Inspection of oil seal for proper seating
(© Chrysler Corp.)

107

the cooling system. Remove the radiator.

2. Remove the vibration damper pulley. Unbolt and remove the vibration damper with a puller. On 318 and 360 engines, remove the fuel lines and fuel pump, then loosen the oil pan bolts and remove the front bolt on each side. On 361 and 413 engines, you will have to remove the front engine mount to get out the two front pan bolts.

3. Remove the timing gear cover and the crankshaft oil slinger.

4. On 318 and 360 engines, remove the camshaft sprocket lockbolt, securing cup washer, and fuel pump eccentric. Remove the timing chain with both sprockets. On 383, 361, 400, 413, and 440 engines, remove the camshaft sprocket lockbolt and remove the timing chain with the camshaft and crankshaft sprockets.

5. To begin the installation procedure, place the camshaft and crankshaft sprockets on a flat surface with the timing indicators on an imaginary centerline through both sprocket bores. Place the timing chain around both sprockets. Be sure that the timing marks are in alignment.

CAUTION: When installing the timing chain, have an assistant support the camshaft with a screwdriver to prevent it from contacting the plug in the rear of the engine block. Remove the distributor and the oil pump/distributor drive gear. Position the screwdriver against the rear side of the cam gear and be careful not to damage the cam lobes.

6. Turn the crankshaft and camshaft to align them with the keyway location in the crankshaft sprocket and the keyway or dowel hole in the camshaft sprocket.

7. Lift the sprockets and timing chain while keeping the sprockets tight against the chain in the correct position. Slide both sprockets evenly onto their respective shafts.

8. Use a straightedge to measure the alignment of the sprocket timing marks. They must be perfectly aligned.

9. On 318 and 360 engines, install the fuel pump eccentric, cup washer, and camshaft sprocket lockbolt and torque to 35 ft. lbs. If camshaft end play exceeds 0.010 in., install a new thrust plate. It should be 0.002-0.006 in. with the new plate.

On 383, 361, 400, 413, and 440 V8s, install the washer and camshaft sprocket lockbolt(s) and then torque the lockbolt to 35-40 ft. lbs. Check to make sure that the rear face of

Alignment of timing gear marks—V8

Alignment of timing gear marks—6 cylinder

the camshaft sprocket is flush with the camshaft end.

Checking Timing Chain Slack

1. Position a scale next to the timing chain to detect any movement in the chain.

2. Place a torque wrench and socket on the camshaft sprocket attaching bolt. Apply either 30 ft. lbs. (if the cylinder heads are installed on the engine) or 15 ft. lbs. (cylinder heads removed) of force to the bolt and rotate the bolt in the direction of crankshaft rotation in order to remove all slack from the chain.

3. While applying torque to the camshaft sprocket bolt, the crankshaft should not be allowed to rotate. It may be necessary to block the crankshaft to prevent rotation.

4. Position the scale over the edge of a timing chain link and apply an equal amount of torque in the opposite direction. If the movement of the chain exceeds 3/16 in. for models through 1972 and all 361 and 413 engines, or 1/8 in. for 1973 and later models, replace the chain.

Timing Gear Cover Seal Replacement

NOTE: A seal remover and installer tool is required to prevent seal damage.

1. Using a seal puller, separate the seal from the retainer.

2. Pull the seal from the case.

3. To install the seal place it face down in the case with the seal lips downward.

4. Seat the seal tightly against the cover face. There should be a maximum clearance of .0014 in. between the seal and the cover. Be careful not to over-compress the seal.

Camshaft Removal and Installation

Six-Cylinder

1. Remove the cylinder head, timing gear cover, camshaft sprocket, and timing chain.

2. Remove the valve tappets, keeping them in order to ensure installation in their original locations.

3. Remove the crankshaft sprocket.

4. Remove the distributor and oil pump.

5. Remove the fuel pump.

6. Install a long bolt into the front of the camshaft to facilitate its removal.

7. Remove the camshaft, being careful not to damage the cam bearings with the cam lobes.

8. Lubricate the camshaft lobes and bearing journals. It is recommended that 1 pt. of Chrysler Crankcase Conditioner be added to the initial crankcase oil fill.

The V8 camshaft should be held forward while installing the chain and sprockets

Measuring timing chain stretch
(© Chrysler Corp.)

9. Install the camshaft in the engine block. From this point, reverse the removal procedure.

V8

1. Remove the cylinder heads. Remove the timing gear cover, the camshaft and crankshaft sprocket, and the timing chain.
2. Remove the valve tappets, keeping them in order to ensure installation in their original location.
3. Remove the distributor and lift out the oil pump and distributor driveshaft.
4. Remove the camshaft thrust plate (on 318 and 360).
5. Install a long bolt into the front of the camshaft and remove the camshaft, being careful not to damage the cam bearings with the cam lobes.
6. Lubricate the camshaft lobes and bearing journals. It is recommended that 1 pt. of Chrysler Crankcase Conditioner be added to the initial crankcase oil fill. Insert the camshaft into the engine block within 2 in. of its final position in the block.
7. Have an assistant support the camshaft with a screwdriver to prevent the camshaft from contacting the plug in the rear of the engine block. Remove the distributor and the oil pump/distributor drive gear. Position the screwdriver against the rear side of the cam gear and be careful not to damage the cam lobes.
8. Replace the camshaft thrust plate. If camshaft end play exceeds 0.010 in., install a new thrust plate. It should be 0.002-0.006 in. with the new plate.
9. Install the oil pump and distributor driveshaft. Install the distributor.
10. Inspect the crown of all the tappet faces with a straightedge. Replace any tappets which have dished or worn surfaces. Install the tappets.
11. Install the timing gear, gear cover, and the cylinder heads.

Measuring camshaft end play
(© Chrysler Corp.)

Camshaft OHV 6 cyl. engines (© Chrysler Corp.)

Pistons and Connecting Rods

The notch on the top of each piston must face the front of the engine.

To position the connecting rod correctly, the oil squirt hole should point to the right-side on all six-cylinder engines. On all V8 engines, the larger chamfer of the lower connecting rod bore must face to the rear on the right bank and to the front on the left bank.

Relation of piston to rod V8 engines
(© Chrysler Corp.)

Relation of piston to rod OHV 6 engines
(© Chrysler Corp.)

Bearings

Detailed procedures for fitting main and rod bearings can be found in the Engine Rebuilding Section.

6 Cylinder Engine

The maximum allowable bearing clearance is .001″. No. 1, No. 2 and No. 4 lower inserts are interchangeable. No. 2 and No. 4 upper inserts are interchangeable. No. 1 upper insert has a chamfer on the tab side for timing chain oiling and is identified by the red mark on the edge of the insert. No. 3 upper and lower inserts are flanged. Bearing caps are not interchangeable and are numbered for correct installation. Maximum end play is .0085″. Replace No. 3 (thrust) bearing if end play exceeds that amount.

V8 Engine

A Maltese Cross stamped on the engine (except on the 318 and 360) numbering pad indicates that the engine is equipped with a crankshaft which has one or more connecting rods and/or main bearing journal finished .001″ undersize. The position of the undersize journal(s) is stamped on a machine surface of the No. 3 counterweight. The letter "R" or "M" signifies whether the undersize journal is a rod or main, and the number following the letter indicates which one it is. A Maltese Cross with an "X" indicates that all those journals are .010″ undersize. On the 318 and 360 engines, .001 in. undersize journals are indicated by marks on the No. 8 crankshaft counterweight. If the "R" or "M" is followed by "X", all those journals are .010 in. undersize.

Upper and lower bearing inserts are not interchangeable on any of the V8 engines due to oil hole and V-groove in the uppers. On the 318 and 360 cu. in. engine lower bearing halves No. 1, No. 2 and No. 4 are interchangeable; No. 1, No. 2 and No. 4 upper bearing halves are interchangeable. No. 3 bearing is the thrust bearing and No. 5 is the wider rear main bearing. On 361, 383, 400, 413, and 440 cu. in. engines the No. 1, No. 2, No. 4 and No. 5 lower bearing halves are interchangeable; No. 2, No. 4 and No. 5 upper bearing halves are interchangeable. No. 1 upper insert has a chamfer on the tab side for timing chain oiling and is identified by the red marking on the edge. No. 3 bearing is a thrust bearing and should be replaced if end play exceeds .007″.

Remove main bearing caps one at a time and check clearance. Check number of cap for proper location.

On the 361, 383, 400, 413, and 440 cu. in. engines, the rear main bearing lower seal is held in place by a

Ring Gap (in.)

Year	Engine No. Cyl- Displacement	Top Compression	Bottom Compression	Oil Control
1970-71	6-198	.010-.020	.010-.020	.015-.055
1970-71	6-225	.010-.020	.010-.020	.015-.025
1972-75	6-225	.010-.020	.010-.020	.015-.055
1970-75	8-318	.010-.020	.010-.020	.015-.055
1970-75	8-360	.010-.020	.010-.020	.015-.055
1970-75	8-361	.013-.025	.013-.025	.013-.025
1970-71	8-383	.013-.052	.013-.052	.015-.062
1971-74	8-400	.013-.052	.013-.052	.015-.062
1970-75	8-413	.013-.025	.013-.025	.013-.025
1973-74	8-440	.013-.052	.013-.052	.015-.062
1975	8-440	.013-.023	.013-.023	.015-.055

Ring Side Clearance (in.)

Year	Engine No. Cyl- Displacement	Top Compression	Bottom Compression	Oil Control
1970-71	6-198	.0015-.0040	.0015-.0040	.0002-.0050
1970-75	6-225	.0015-.0030	.0015-.0030	.0010-.0030
1970-71	8-318	.0015-.0030	.0015-.0030	.0010-.0050
1973-74	8-318	.0015-.0030	.0015-.0030	.0002-.0050
1975	8-318	.0015-.0030	.0015-.0030	.0002-.0050
1970-74	8-360	.0015-.0030	.0015-.0030	.0002-.0050
1975	8-360	.0015-.0030	.0015-.0030	.0005-.0050
1970-75	8-361	.0025-.0040	.0025-.0040	.0010-.0030
1970-71	8-383	.0015-.0030	.0015-.0030	.0002-.0050
1971-74	8-400	.0015-.0030	.0015-.0030	.0002-.0050
1970-74	8-413	.0025-.0040	.0025-.0040	.0010-.0030
1975	8-413	.0010-.0025	.0010-.0025	.0010-.0030
1973-74	8-440	.0015-.0040	.0015-.0040	.0000-.0050
1975	8-440	.0015-.0030	.0015-.0030	.0010-.0030

Location of undersize markings on counter weight; 318 and 360 engines are marked on the No. 8 counterweight (© Chrysler Corp.)

Engine Lubrication

Oil Pan Removal and Installation

Conventional Trucks
1. Remove the dipstick.
2. Raise the vehicle safely and drain the oil. On I-beam axle models, let the axle hang down on the springs.
3. Remove the optional frame reinforcement.
4. Remove the left bellhousing brace.
5. Unbolt the pan and lower it.
6. On installation, make sure that the six cylinder oil pickup screen contacts the bottom of the pan and that it is 1⅛ in. from the inside edge of the block.
7. Install the pan with new gaskets and seals.

Six Cylinder Vans and Wagons
1. Disconnect the battery and remove the dipstick.
2. Remove the engine cover and remove the starter and air cleaner.
3. Raise the van on a hoist and drain the crankcase oil.
4. Install an engine support as described under "Engine Removal."
5. Disconnect and tie out of the way: driveshaft, transmission linkage, and exhaust pipe at the manifold.
6. Remove the clutch torque shaft (if equipped) and the oil cooler lines (if equipped).
7. Disconnect the speedometer cable and electrical connections to the transmission.
8. Remove the support bracket, inspection plate, and drive plate-to-converter attaching screws if equipped.
9. Remove the bolts which attach the transmission to the clutch housing. Carefully work the transmission and converter rearward off the engine dowels and disengage the converter hub from the end of the crankshaft if so equipped. Support the transmission.

seal retainer. On the 318 and 360 cu. in. engine, the rear main bearing lower seal is held in place by the rear main bearing cap. Note that the oil pump is mounted on this cap and that there is a hollow dowel which must be in place when the cap is installed.

Engine numbering pad shows markings indicating undersize crankshaft journals, except on the 318 and 360 (© Chrysler Corp.)

Slant six oil pump pickup screen on conventional trucks must be positioned 1⅛ in. from the inside edge of the block (© Chrysler Corp.)

CAP SEAL—LONG CAP SEAL—SHORT DOWEL

OIL SEAL LOWER

BEARING SHELL

OIL DRAIN HOLE

Rear main bearing cap (© Chrysler Corp.)

RIGHT REAR CYLINDER HEAD SCREW

VALVE ROCKER SHAFT

FILTER BY-PASS VALVE

FILTER ELEMENT

LOW PRESSURE CAVITY

FILTER INLET PRESSURE

FILTER OUTLET PASSAGE

HIGH PRESSURE CAVITY

PRESSURE RELIEF VALVE

DRILLED PASSAGES IN NO. 4 CAMSHAFT JOURNAL

LONGITUDINAL OIL GALLERY

ALL MAIN BEARINGS ARE LUBRICATED AS SHOWN. CONNECTING ROD CRANKPIN END BEARINGS ARE LUBRICATED BY HOLES DRILLED IN THE CRANKSHAFT BETWEEN THE MAIN AND PIN-JOURNALS

PUMP AND FILTER SIDE VIEW

STRAINER

Slant six engine oiling system (© Chrysler Corp.)

10. Support the right rear corner of the engine with a transmission jack and remove the engine attaching fixture.
11. Remove the oil pan attaching bolts. Positioning the crankshaft so that the counterweights will clear the pan, rotate the pan to the steering gear side and remove it. You may have to turn the pump pickup tube for clearance.
12. Installation is the reverse of removal. Make sure that the pickup screen contacts the bottom of the pan. Fill the engine with oil and check for leaks.

1970-71 V8 Vans and Wagons

1. Drain the cooling system and disconnect the battery.
2. Remove the engine cover.
3. Disconnect the radiator hoses.
4. Disconnect the exhaust pipes. Remove the left exhaust manifold, oil dipstick, and tube.
5. Raise the vehicle and support it. Drain the engine oil.
6. Remove the clutch dust pan, inspection plate, and engine-to-torque converter left housing strut.
7. Remove the starter and clutch torque shaft or shifter torque shaft.
8. Disconnect and cap the inlet line to the fuel pump.
9. Remove the front engine mount insulator top nut and insulator.
10. Loosen the transmission mount

through-bolt and jack up and support the engine.
11. Remove the oil pan attaching screws and position the crankshaft so that the pan will clear the counterweights. Remove the pan.
12. Installation is the reverse of removal. Check all fluid levels and be sure that there are no leaks.

1972 and later V8 Vans and Wagons

1. Disconnect the battery ground cable. Remove the dipstick and tube, engine cover, and air cleaner.

2. Disconnect the throttle linkage at the rear of the engine and the clutch or automatic transmission linkage.
3. Raise the engine slightly and support it with the device described under "Engine Removal".
4. Raise the vehicle and drain the oil. Remove the starter.
5. Remove the driveshaft and engine rear support.
6. Remove the transmission from the van. Remove the automatic transmission with the filler tube installed and the torque converter separated from the drive plate.

NOTCH IN CRANKSHAFT FLANGE AT 3 O'CLOCK

TUBE AND STRAINER TURNED TO THIS POSITION FOR OIL PAN REMOVAL/INSTALLATION

NORMAL POSITION OF OIL PICK-UP TUBE AND STRAINER

Crankshaft and oil pickup tube positioned for oil pan removal or installation— six-cylinder van (© Chrysler Corp.)

7. Remove the clutch assembly and flywheel (or driveplate) from the crankshaft.
8. Raise the engine about 2 in.
9. Rotate the crankshaft so that the counterweights will clear the oil pan. Maximum clearance is with the notch in the crankshaft flange at the 3 o'clock position. Remove the oil pan. It will be necessary to reach inside the oil pan and turn the oil pick-up tube and strainer slightly to the right to clear the pan.
10. Installation is the reverse of removal. Be sure to check all fluid levels and be sure that there are no leaks.

Two-wheel Drive Ramcharger and Trail Duster

1. Disconnect the battery cable and remove the dipstick.
2. Raise and support the truck.
3. Drain the oil.
4. Remove the torque converter or clutch housing brace.
5. If necessary, remove the exhaust pipe.
6. Remove the oil pan bolts and remove the pan.
7. Installation is the reverse of removal.

Four-Wheel Drive Ramcharger and Trailduster, W100, 200, 300

1. Raise vehicle on a hoist.
2. Remove the two front engine mounting bolts.
3. Remove the left-side support, connecting the converter housing and cylinder block.
4. Raise the engine approximately 2 in.
5. Drain oil.
6. Remove the oil pan bolts, lower pan down and to the rear. (Do not turn oil pickup out of position)

Oil Pump Removal and Installation

Slant Six Engines

The rotor type oil pump is externally mounted on the rear right-hand (camshaft) side of the engine and is gear driven (helical) from the camshaft. The oil filter screws into the pump body.
1. Remove oil pan and oil pick up tube and screen.
2. Remove oil pump mounting bolts and remove pump and filter assembly from engine.
3. Disassemble oil pump (drive gear must be pressed off) and inspect the following clearances: maximum cover wear is .0015"; outer rotor to body maximum clearance is .014"; maximum clearance between rotors is .010". Inspect the pressure relief valve for scoring and free operation. Relief valve spring should have a free length of 2-9/32 to 2-19/64 in. through 1971 and 2¼ in. beginning 1972.
4. Install new oil seal rings between cover and body, tightening cover attaching bolts to 95 in. lbs.
5. Install oil pump to engine block using a new gasket and tightening mounting bolts to 200 in. lbs.

318, 360 Cu. In. V8 Engine

The rotor type oil pump is gear (helical) driven from the camshaft and is mounted on the rear main bearing cap.
1. Drain engine oil and remove oil pan.
2. Remove oil pump mounting bolts and remove pump from rear main bearing cap.
3. The pressure relief valve cap is pressed in and is destroyed when removed. Remove cotter pin first, then drill cap and use a self-tapping sheet metal screw to get a grip on the cap. Free length of spring is 2 1/32—2 3/64 in.
4. When assembling pump, use a new oil seal ring between cover and body. Prime pump before installing onto rear main bearing cap. The distributor drive gear slot should align with the front left intake manifold bolt with No. 1 cylinder on TDC. Tighten mounting bolts to 35 ft. lbs. tor-

Measuring oil pump cover wear (© Chrysler Corp

Measuring clearance between rotors (© Chrysler Corp.)

que. Use new gaskets when installing oil pan.

361, 383, 400, 413, 440 Cu. In. V8 Engines

The rotor type oil pump is externally mounted and gear driven from the camshaft. The oil filter screws into the pump body.
1. Drain engine oil.
2. Remove oil pump and filter assembly.
3. Disassemble and inspect pump components for wear. If 0.0015" feeler gauge can be inserted between cover and straight edge, replace cover. Install outer rotor in pump body and holding against one side of body measure clearance between rotor and body. If clearance is greater than 0.014", replace oil pump body. Install inner rotor into pump body and place straight edge across pump body between bolt holes. If feeler gauge greater than 0.004" can be inserted be-

Slant six oil pump (© Chrysler Corp.)

318 and 360 V8 oil pump (© Chrysler Corp.)

318 and 360 V8 engine oiling system (© Chrysler Corp.)

tween rotors and body, replace oil pump body. Measure clearance between tips of inner and outer rotor where they are opposed. If clearance exceeds 0.010″, replace inner and outer rotors. Use new oil seal rings between filter base and body. Tighten bolts to 10 ft. lbs. Use a new "O" ring seal on pilot of oil pump before attaching pump to engine block.

4. Install oil pump on engine using new gasket and tightening bolts to 30 ft. lbs. The distributor drive gear slot should parallel the crankshaft with no. 1 cylinder on TDC.
5. Install oil pan and fill crankcase with oil.

Measuring outer rotor clearance (© Chrysler Corp.)

Measuring clearance over rotors (© Chrysler Corp.)

Measuring inner rotor clearance (© Chrysler Corp.)

Front Suspension

I-Beam Axle

I-Beam Axle King Pin and Bushing Removal and Installation

1. Block brake pedal to prevent its being depressed and forcing out brake wheel cylinder cups and fluid necessitating bleeding of brakes.
2. Remove brake support attaching bolts or screws.
3. Lift complete brake shoe and support assembly from steering knuckle (brake hose attached) and wire to frame (don't let it dangle by hose). Check hose for deterioration. Replace hose if necessary and bleed brakes if hose is replaced.
4. Remove steering knuckle arm from steering knuckle.
5. Remove pivot pin locking screw or pin. Some models have two locking screws.
6. Remove upper pivot pin oil seal plug (steel disc) and drive pivot pin down forcing the lower seal plug (steel disc) from assembly.
7. Remove pivot thrust bearing.

D200 I-beam front axle (© Chrysler Corp.)

8. The steering knuckle (spindle) bushings should be pressed out.

9. The bushings should be pressed in, then reamed to fit the new king pin. Make sure that grease holes in bushings line up with the grease fitting hole. Pack bushing grooves with grease.

10. Install king pin.

11. Expansion plugs at top and bottom should be staked in four places.

12. Reverse Steps 1 through 5 to complete assembly.

Front Leaf Spring Removal and Installation

This procedure applies to all models with front leaf springs.

1. Raise truck until weight is removed from springs.

REFER TO WHEEL BEARING ADJUSTMENT PROCEDURES IN THIS GROUP

MAXIMUM TORQUE TO ROTATE KNUCKLE AROUND KING PIN WITH TIE ROD AND DRAG LINK DISCONNECTED AND WHEEL EQUIPMENT INSTALLED 125 IN-LBS (WHEEL RAISED OFF FLOOR)

① 105 ±25 FT LBS

② 125 ±25 FT LBS

③ 85 ±20 FT LBS   ⑦ 30 ±5 FT LBS

④ 60 ±20 FT LBS   ⑧ 55 ±15 FT LBS   ⑪ 24 ±5 FT LBS

⑤ 150 ±30 FT LBS   ⑨ 100 ±20 FT LBS   ⑫ 75 ±20 FT LBS

⑥ 65 ±15 FT LBS   ⑩ 35 ±10 FT LBS   ⑬ 150 ±30 IN-LBS

I-beam front end torques for D100,200 (© Chrysler Corp.)

King pin bushing installation—D100,200
(© Chrysler Corp.)

2. Install stands under side frame members as a safety precaution.
3. Disconnect the sway bar at the spring plate. Remove nuts, lockwashers and U-bolts securing spring to axle.
4. Remove spring shackle bolts, shackles and spring front eye bolt.
5. Remove spring.
6. To install, line up spring fixed eye with bolt hole in bracket and install spring bolt and nut.
7. Install shackle bolts, shackles and nuts. Tighten shackle bolt nuts and fixed eye bolt until slack is taken up.
8. Position spring on axle so spring center bolt enters locating hole in axle pad.
9. Install U-bolts, new lockwashers and nuts, tightening securely.
10. Remove stands from under frame, lower truck so weight is resting on wheels. Tighten

U-bolt nuts, spring eye bolt nuts and shackle bolt nuts.
11. Lubricate spring bolts and shackle bolts with chassis lubricant if equipped with pressure fittings. *Do not lubricate rubber bushings.*

Front Drive Axle

Front Drive Axle Assembly Removal

1. Raise front end of vehicle until wheels clear ground and block up frame at rear of front springs.
2. Disconnect front driveshaft at drive pinion yoke.
3. Disconnect steering linkage at drag link.
4. Disconnect front shock absorbers and brake line at frame. Disconnect the sway bar link assembly from the spring clip plate.
5. Remove nuts from the spring hold down bolts and remove axle assembly from under vehicle.
6. To install, place axle assembly under vehicle and line up spring center bolts with locating hole in axle housing pad.
7. Install spring clips or spring U-bolts, new lock washer and nuts.
8. Connect shock absorbers.
9. Connect brake line at frame.
10. Connect steering linkage to drag link.
11. Connect driveshaft to drive pinion yoke.
12. Lubricate all necessary points on the axle.
13. Lower vehicle and check toe-in and caster.

Front Drive Axle Shaft Removal and Installation
Enclosed U-Joint, Pivot Pin Type

1. After removing wheel assembly and locking hubs, remove grease cap from drive flange.
2. Remove drive flange bolts and snap ring. Then, using a suitable puller, remove drive flange.
3. Remove locknut, lockwasher and adjusting nut.
4. Remove wheel hub and brake drum assembly, being careful not to damage oil seal.
5. Remove brake assembly and wire to frame, leaving hydraulic line connected.
6. Tap end of spindle with a soft hammer and remove spindle.
7. Inspect spindle and bushing for wear. Bushing is pressed on and requires no reaming for proper fit.
8. Remove axle shaft assembly. Inspect universal joint. Disassemble and replace any worn components.
9. Install axle assembly, being careful not to damage inner oil seal.
10. Lubricate flanged bushing and install spindle and brake support assembly.
11. Remove, clean, inspect and repack inner and outer wheel bearings.
12. Install inner wheel bearing, position hub, drum and wheel assembly on spindle, then install outer bearing, washer and adjusting nut.
13. Adjust bearing by tightening adjusting nut to 50 ft. lbs. torque, then back off ¼ to ⅓ turn. Tighten locknut and bend tab of lock-washer.

70F axle & steering knuckle (W-300) (© Chrysler Corp.)

14. Install drive flange, retaining nuts, snap ring and grease cup.

Exposed U-Joint, Ball Joint Type

This procedure is for disc-braked vehicles, but may be adapted to those with drum brakes.

1. Remove the locking hubs. Remove the cotter key and loosen the axle shaft nut.
2. Block the brake pedal up. Remove the wheel.
3. Remove and hang the caliper out of the way. Remove the inner pad.
4. Working through the hole in the disc hub, remove the socket head capscrews.
5. Remove the axle shaft nut and use a hub puller to remove the disc and hub.
6. Remove the O-ring from the steering knuckle. Remove the disc brake adapter from the knuckle. Punch out the inner oil seal from the rear of the knuckle.
7. Slide the axle shaft from the housing.
8. On replacement, first slide the shaft into place, then drive a new seal into the steering knuckle.
9. Install the disc brake adapter and torque the mounting bolts to 85 ft. lbs.
10. Install a new O-ring on the steering knuckle.
11. Slide the disc and hub, retainer and bearing assembly over the shaft and start it into the housing. Install the axle shaft nut.
12. Install the capscrews holding the retainer to the steering knuckle flange. Tighten them to 30 ft. lbs. in a criss-cross pattern.
13. Torque the axle shaft nut to 100 ft. lbs. and tighten further until the cotter key can be installed.
14. Locate the inner pad on the adapter with the shoe flanges in the adapter ways. Slide the caliper into position, being careful not to pull the dust boot from its grooves.
15. Install the anti-rattle springs, making sure that the inner one is on top of the retainer spring plate. Tighten the retaining clips to 200 in. lbs.

Axle housing (W-500) (© Chrysler Corp.)

1 Drum	17 Spring seat	31 Outer cup and cone
2 Backing plate	18 Housing tube	32 Hub and drum stud
3 Backing plate lockwasher	19 Cardon joint axle shaft	33 Outer hub and drum stud nut
4 Backing plate nut	20 Cardon joint needle bearing cap	
5 Brake cylinder	21 Bearing cap retaining ring	34 Wheel bearing jam nut
6 Sterring arm capscrew		35 Jam nut retainer
7 Steering arm capscrew	22 Cardon joint cross	
8 Trunnion pin bushing	23 Needle bearing retainer	36 Wheel bearing adjusting nut
9 Trunnion pin bushing retainer	24 Needle bearing cap	37 Outer cardon joint axle shaft
	25 Lower steering knuckle plate	
10 Steering knuckle boot	26 Steering knuckle spindle	38 Axle shaft retaining ring
11 Oil seal assembly		39 Hub cap
12 Sterring knuckle socket	27 Oil slinger	40 Hub cap capscrew
13 Sterring ball	28 Anchor pin	
14 Steering arm	29 Inner cup and cone	41 Hub cap lockwasher
15 Sterring arm nut	30 Hub and drum inner stud nut	42 Drive flange
16 Steering arm cotter		43 Hub

16. Install the wheel and lower the vehicle.

Front Drive Axle Steering Knuckle Service

Enclosed U-Joint, Pivot Pin Type

1. Remove, wheel, hub, brake drum assembly, brake support assembly, spindle and axle shaft.
2. Disconnect tie rod ends from steering knuckles and drag link from steering knuckle arm.
3. Remove steering knuckle felt and oil seal retainers.
4. Remove lower bearing cap and shims.
5. Remove upper bearing cap or knuckle arm and shims.
6. Remove knuckle housing, felt and oil seal.
7. Remove upper and lower bearing cones, then clean and inspect bearings.
8. Check bearing cups for wear and remove with drift if required.
9. To assemble, place felt and oil seal over end of axle housing.
10. Install steering knuckle arm or upper bearing cap and shim pack and tighten retaining bolts or nuts. If a new shim pack is used, use *only* one which is .060″ thick.
11. Lubricate and install cone (press in) on upper bearing pivot, making sure serration or key and slot are properly located, if so equipped.

Typical brake hub and drum assembly (© Chrysler Corp.)

Steering knuckle flange oil seal (© Chrysler Corp.)

Disconnecting steering linkage joints
(© Chrysler Corp.)

12. Seat bearing cups in yokes of axle housing. Slide knuckle assembly over yoke and enter bronze cone in its cup.

13. Lubricate and insert lower bearing cone, tilting knuckle to provide access. Install lower bearing cap and shim pack. If a new pack is required, use *only* .025" thick pack for 44-3F axle or .055" thick pack for 44-3HF or 70F axle.

14. Using a torque wrench on a top outer knuckle bearing cap retaining bolt or nut, measure bearing preload as knuckle is turning. It must read 5-15 ft. lbs. for 44-3F axle and 15-35 ft. lbs. for the 44-3HDF or 70-F axles. Remove or add shims to adjust preload.

15. Attach oiled felt and oil seal to knuckle housing with retainers and screws.

16. Install axle shaft, spindle and brake support assembly, tightening spindle to steering knuckle flange bolts.

17. Install hub, brake drum and wheel assembly.

18. Fill steering knuckle housing with SAE 140 oil to level of filler plug opening.

19. Check and adjust toe-in and turning radius.

Exposed U-Joint, Ball Joint Type

The ball joints should be replaced if there is any looseness or end-play. The steering knuckle and ball joint must be removed to remove the ball joint.

1. Remove the wheel cover or locking hub.
2. Remove the cotter pin and the outer axle shaft nut.
3. Block the brake pedal in the up position. Raise and support the vehicle with jackstands. Remove the wheel and tire.
4. Remove the caliper retainer and the anti-rattle spring.
5. Remove the caliper from the disc. Hang the caliper aside. Do not allow the caliper to hang by the brake line. Remove the inboard shoe.

6. Using the hole in the flange, remove the six capscrews from the retainer plate.
7. Remove the outer axle shaft nut.
8. Install a puller on the wheel lugs and install the wheel lug nuts.
9. Remove the rotor, hub, and the retainer and bearing.
10. Remove and discard the O-ring from the steering knuckle.
11. Remove the capscrews from the brake splash shield and remove the splash shield. Remove the brake disc adaptor from the steering knuckle.
12. Disconnect the tie-rod from the steering knuckle. On the left side, disconnect the drag link from the steering knuckle arm.
13. Using a punch and hammer, remove the inner oil seal from the rear of the steering knuckle.
14. Carefully, slide the outer and inner axle shaft complete with U-joint from the axle housing.
15. On the left-side, remove the steering knuckle arm by tapping it to loosen the tapered dowels.
16. Remove the cotter pin from the upper ball joint nut. Remove the upper and lower ball joint nuts and discard the lower nut.
17. Separate the steering knuckle from the axle housing yoke with a brass drift and hammer. Remove and discard the sleeve from the upper ball joint yoke on the axle housing.
18. Position the steering knuckle upside down in a vise with soft jaws and remove the snap-ring from the lower ball joint.
19. Press the lower and upper ball joints from the steering knuckle individually.

To install the ball joints and steering knuckle:

20. Position the steering knuckle right side up in a vise with soft jaws. Press the lower ball joint into position and install the snapring.
21. Press the upper ball joint into position. Install new boots on both ball joints.

Steering knuckle (W-100 & W-200) (© Chrysler Corp.)

Caster angle can be adjusted by placing wedges between the spring and axle on both driving and I-beam front axles

22. Screw a new sleeve into the upper ball joint yoke on the axle housing, leaving about two threads showing at the top.
23. Install the steering knuckle on the axle housing yoke and install a new lower ball joint nut, tightening it to 80 ft. lbs.
24. Tighten the sleeve in the upper ball joint yoke to 40 ft. lbs. Install the upper ball joint nut and tighten it to 100 ft. lbs. Align the cotter key hole in the stud with the slot in the castellated nut and install the cotter pin. If the slot and the hole do not align, tighten the nut until they do align. Do not loosen the nut to align the holes.
25. On the left-side, position the steering knuckle arm over the studs on the steering knuckle. Install the tapered dowels and nuts. Tighten the nuts to 90 ft. lbs. Install the drag link on the steering arm. Install the nut and tighten it to 60 ft. lbs. Install the cotter pin.
26. Install the tie-rod end on the steering knuckle. Tighten the nut to 45 ft. lbs. and install the cotter pin.
27. Install the axle shaft. Install the brake splash shield and tighten the screws to 13 ft. lbs. Install the brake disc adaptor and tighten the bolts to 85 ft. lbs.
28. Install a new O-ring in the steering knuckle.
29. Clean any rust from the axle shaft splines.
30. Carefully, slide the hub, rotor and retainer, and bearing onto the axle shaft and start it into the housing. Install the axle shaft nut.
31. Align the retainer with the steering knuckle flange. Install the retainer screws and tighten them in a criss-cross pattern to 30 ft. lbs.
32. Tighten the axle shaft nut to 100 ft. lbs. Tighten the nut until the next slot in the nut aligns with the hole in the axle shaft. Install the cotter pin.

Dana locking hub (© Chrysler Corp.)

Warn locking hub (© Chrysler Corp.)

33. Install the inboard brake shoe on the adaptor with the shoe flanges in the adaptor ways. Install the caliper in the adaptor and over the disc. Align the caliper on the machined ways of the adaptor. Be careful not to pull the dust boot from its grooves as the piston and boot slide over the inboard shoe.

34. Install the anti-rattle springs springs and retaining clips. Torque to 16-17 ft. lbs. The inboard shoe anti-rattle spring must always be installed on top of the retainer spring plate.

35. Install the wheel, tire, and locking hub and lower the truck. Lubricate all fittings.

Warn Front Locking Hubs

Removal

1. Raise wheel until it clears floor.
2. Straighten lock tabs and remove 6 hub mounting bolts.
3. Tap hub gently with mallet to remove.

Installation

1. Position hub assembly over end of axle.
2. Replace 6 hub mounting bolts and tighten to 30 to 35 foot-pounds. Bend lock washer tabs to anchor bolts.
3. Lower vehicle.

Disassembly

1. Remove hub assembly from vehicle.
2. Separate clutch assembly from body assembly.
3. Remove snap-ring from rear of body assembly using snap-ring pliers. Slip axle shaft hub out of body from the front.
4. Remove Allen screw from inner side of clutch.
5. Remove bronze dial assembly from front of clutch housing assembly.
6. Remove clutch assembly from rear of housing complete with 12 roller pins.
7. Wash all parts for burrs, chips, wear, flat spots or cracks. Replace necessary parts.

Assembly

1. Coat moving parts with waterproof grease.
2. Slide axle shaft hub into body from front. Replace snap-ring.
3. Replace bronze dial assembly and inner clutch. Tighten Allen screw. Stake edge of screw with center punch to prevent loosening.
4. With dial in FREE position rotate outer clutch body into inner assembly until it bottoms in housing, back it up to nearest hole, then insert roller pins.
5. Position hub and clutch assembly

together with new gasket in between.

6. Install complete assembly on vehicle with new gasket. Follow installation procedure.

Dana Front Locking Hubs

Removal and Disassembly

1. Place hub in lock position. Remove Allen head mounting bolts and washers.
2. Carefully remove retainer, O-ring seal and knob. Separate knob from retainer.
3. Remove large internal snap-ring. Slide retainer ring and cam from hub.
4. While pressing against sleeve and ring assembly, remove axle shaft snap-ring. Relieve pressure and remove sleeve and ring, ring and bushing, spring and plate.
5. Wash all parts in a suitable solvent, inspect all parts for wear, nicks and burrs. Replace all parts which appear questionable.

Assembly and Installation

1. Slide plate and spring (large coils first) into wheel hub housing.
2. Assemble ring and bushing, sleeve and bushing. Slide complete assembly into housing.
3. Compress spring and install axle shaft snap-ring.
4. Position cam and retainer in housing and install large internal snap-ring.
5. Place small O-ring seal on knob, lubricate with waterproof grease and install in retainer at lock position.
6. Place large O-ring seal on retainer. Align retainer and retainer ring and install washers and Allen head mounting screws.
7. Check operation.

Independent Front Suspension

These procedures apply to all vans,

wagons, and conventional trucks with independent front suspension.

Coil Spring Removal and Installation

1. Raise the vehicle and support it with jackstands under the front ends of the longitudinal rails.
2. Remove the wheel.
3. Remove the shock absorber and upper shock absorber bushing bushing and sleeve.
4. If equipped, remove the sway bar.
5. Remove the strut.
6. Install a spring compressor and tighten finger-tight.
7. Remove the cotter pins and ball joint nuts.
8. Install a ball joint breaker tool and turn the threaded portion of the tool to lock it against the lower stud.
9. Spread the tool to place the lower stud under pressure, then strike the steering knuckle sharply with a hammer to free the stud. Do not attempt to force the stud out of the steering knuckle with the tool.
10. Remove the tool. Slowly release the spring compressor until all tension is relieved from the spring.
11. Remove the spring compressor and spring.
12. Installation is the reverse of removal. Compress the spring until the ball joint can be properly positioned in the steering knuckle.

Shock Absorber Removal and Installation

1. Raise and support the vehicle with jackstands positioned at the extreme front ends of the longitudinal rails.
2. Remove the wheel.
3. Remove the upper nut and retainer.
4. Remove the two lower mounting bolts.
5. Remove the shock absorber.

Independent front suspension alignment points (© Chrysler Corp.)

STRAIGHT PART
OF CONTROL ARM
MUST BE FORWARD

FRONT

1 Nut
2 Retainer
3 Bushing
4 Bolt
5 Nut
6 Coil Spring
7 Shock Absorber
8 Washer
9 Bushing Assembly
10 Capscrew
11 Lower Control Arm

1 Nut
2 Lockwasher
3 Cam
4 Bushing Assembly
5 Ball Joint
6 Lock Nut
7 Upper Control Arm
8 Upper Ball Joint
9 Bumper Assembly
10 Sleeve
11 Cam and Bolt Assembly

FRONT

Lower control arm details (© Chrysler Corp.)

Upper control arm details (© Chrysler Corp.)

6. Installation is the reverse of removal.

Upper Control Arm Removal and Installation

NOTE: Any time the control arm is removed, it is necessary to align the front end.

1. Raise and support the vehicle with jackstands under the longitudinal rails.
2. Remove the wheel.
3. Remove the shock absorber and shock absorber upper bushing and sleeve.
4. Install a spring compressor and tighten it finger-tight.
5. Remove the cotter pins and ball joint nuts.
6. Install a ball joint breaker and turn the threaded portion of the tool, locking it securely against the upper stud. Spread the tool enough to place the upper ball joint under pressure and strike the steering knuckle sharply to loosen the stud. Do not attempt to remove the stud from the steering knuckle with the tool.
7. Remove the tool.
8. Remove the eccentric pivot bolts, after making their relative positions in the control arm.
9. Remove the upper control arm.
10. Installation is the reverse of removal. Tighten the ball joint nuts to 135 ft. lbs. Tighten the eccentric pivot bolts to 70 ft. lbs.
11. Adjust the caster and camber.

Lower Control Arm Removal and Installation

1. Follow the procedure outlined under "Coil Spring Removal and Installation."
2. Remove the mounting bolt from the crossmember.
3. Remove the lower control arm from the vehicle.
4. Installation is the reverse of removal. After the vehicle has been lowered to the ground, tighten the mounting bolt to 210 ft. lbs.

Lower Ball Joint Removal and Installation

1. Remove the lower control arm.
2. Remove the ball joint seal.
3. Using an arbor press and a sleeve, press the ball joint from the control arm.
4. Installation is the reverse of removal. Be sure that the ball joint is fully seated. Install a new ball joint seal.
5. Install the lower control arm. Be sure to install the ball joint cotter pins.

Upper Ball Joint Removal and Installation

1. Install a jack under the outer end of the lower control arm and raise the van.
2. Remove the wheel.
3. Remove the ball joint nuts. Using a ball joint breaker, loosen the upper ball joint.
4. Unscrew the ball joint from the control arm.
5. Screw a new ball joint into the control arm and tighten it as far as possible by hand. Tighten the ball joint to 125 ft. lbs.
6. Install the new ball joint seal, using a 2 in. socket. Be sure that the seal is seated on the ball joint housing.
7. Insert the ball joint into the steering knuckle and install the ball joint nuts. Tighten the nuts to 135 ft. lbs. and install the cotter pins.
8. Install the wheel and lower the truck to the ground.

Steering Gear

Before making any adjustments, inspect steering linkage for lash and wheel bearing adjustment. Ross and Saginaw steering gears, except the model 24J Ross, may be adjusted for cross shaft lash and worm bearing preload without removing the gear from the vehicle. On the 24J, worm bearing preload adjustment must be done with the unit removed.

Worm Bearing Preload Adjustment
All Except Ross Model 24J

1. On Ross gears, remove the horn button and spring.
2. Remove the steering arm from the steering gear cross (sector) shaft. Mark relation of steering arm to shaft before removing.
3. On long worm shaft type gears, check steering column for alignment.
4. Loosen cross (sector) shaft adjusting screw and back out adjusting screw about two turns.
5. Turn steering wheel two complete turns from the straight-ahead position. CAUTION: Do not turn steering wheel hard against the stops as this may damage gear.
6. Using a torque wrench on the steering wheel nut, rotate steering wheel through "lash" area toward straight-ahead position. Torque required to keep wheel moving indicates worm bearing preload.
7. If preload is not within limits, remove or add shims beneath the lower worm bearing cover on Ross gears. Cover retaining bolts are tightened to 20 ft. lbs. torque. Preload on the Saginaw gear is made by turning the large adjuster. Adjuster locknut is tightened to 85 ft. lbs. torque.
8. Recheck preload, adjusting again if necessary.

Cross or Sector Gear Mesh Adjustment

This adjustment is made only after

Model (35J) Ross steering gear (© Chrysler Corp.)

worm bearing preload is adjusted. Steering arm is still removed from cross (sector) shaft.

1. Center steering wheel (worm-shaft) by counting turns from full right to full left and counting back exactly half way.
2. Loosen locknut on cross (sector) shaft adjusting screw and turn adjusting screw in until all lash is gone.
3. Check torque required to move steering wheel (torque wrench on steering wheel nut) through high-spot (center) position.
4. Readjust if necessary and re-tighten locknut.
5. Reinstall steering arm on cross (sector) shaft and tighten clamp bolt to 85 ft. lbs. torque.

Worm Bearing Preload Adjustment Ross Model 24J

This gear must be removed to adjust the worm bearing preload. Torque required to keep the worm shaft moving through "lash" (center position) should be 5-10 in. lbs. Adjustment is made by removing or adding shims between the worm shaft cover plate and the gear body. Tighten cover bolts to 18-20 ft. lbs. torque. Perform cross shaft adjustment after worm gear preload is adjusted.

Steering Gear	Worm Bearing Preload (in. lbs)	Cross or Sector Gear Mesh (in. lbs)
Ross (Gemmer) 24J	5-10	7-11 over worm preload
Ross (Gemmer) Y4D-335, 35J, 376	7-14	20-27 total
Ross (Gemmer) 6D-400	7-14	25-32 total
Saginaw 525	4-6	14 total
Saginaw 553	13-18	25-29 total
All Vans and Wagons, Saginaw	1½-4½	8¼-11¼ total

NOTE: D100,200,300 and W100, 200 use the Ross 24J (early) and Saginaw 525 (1972 and later). W300 uses Ross 35J or 376.

Manual Steering Gear Removal and Installation

Ross Models With Long Shaft

1. Disconnect battery negative cable at battery, horn wire at connector and any gear shift linkage or directional signal controls that are attached to steering column jacket.
2. Remove horn button by pressing down on ornament while turning to release spring.
3. Remove steering wheel and column clamp to instrument panel.
4. Disconnect drag link from steering arm. *Mark relation of arm to cross shaft before removal.*
5. Using a puller, remove steering arm from cross shaft.
6. If so equipped, remove transmission shift linkage.
7. Remove gear housing mounting bolts and lower jacket mounting bolts and remove gear and tube assembly from vehicle.
8. To install, insert gear and tube assembly from below frame.
9. Install mounting bolts.
10. Install clamp bolts and secure tube to instrument panel.
11. Tighten gear housing to frame bolts.
12. Loosen instrument panel to tube clamp bolts. Column tube will not change position if steering gear is in alignment. If column tube shifted position when clamp was loosened, relocate column tube bracket before tightening clamp.
13. Install spring, retainer, steering wheel, horn button spring, re-

tainer and wheel nut, tightening nut to 24 ft. lbs. torque.

14. If so equipped, attach directional signal switch.
15. Install spring, contact plate, horn wire spring and horn button.
16. Connect and adjust shift linkage (see "Manual Transmissions") if so equipped.
17. Install steering arm and drag link, tighten steering arm nut to 85 ft. lbs. torque.

Ross Models With Short Shaft

1. Remove bolt from column coupling clamp at upper end of steering worm shaft. Disconnect turn signal and horn wire connectors and move column upward to clear worm shaft splines.
2. *Mark relation of arm to gear shaft before removal.* Remove steering arm nut and washer from gear shaft and remove steering arm with a puller.
3. Remove steering gear housing mounting bolts. On 6D-400 models, remove two bolts at trunnion cap.
4. Remove steering gear from vehicle.
5. To install, center gear and install in frame, aligning housing with frame. Tighten 7/16" and ½" mounting bolts to 70 ft. lbs. torque and 9/16" bolts to 100 ft. lbs. torque.
6. Install universal joint clamp to worm shaft and tighten to 30 ft. lbs. torque. On pot type joint, center the steering column shaft in the joint to insure adequate travel.
7. Set front wheels straight ahead.
8. Install steering arm (use marks made during removal to position

Model (24J) Ross steering gear (© Chrysler Corp.)

Model 553 Saginaw steering gear (© Chrysler Corp.)

arm in original location). Tighten bolt clamp to 170 ft. lbs. and cross shaft nut to 250 ft. lbs.

Saginaw Models

1. Unbolt the coupling clamp at the bottom of the column.
2. Remove the steering gear arm nut.
3. Use a puller to remove the steering gear arm.
4. Unbolt the steering gear from the frame and remove it. You may have to remove the grille for access on some larger models, with the Saginaw 553 steering box.
5. Align the gear in the straight-ahead position.
6. Bolt the steering gear to the frame.
7. Make sure the front wheels are straight ahead and install the steering arm but not the nut.
8. If both wheels and steering gear are in the straight-ahead position, install the steering arm nut.
9. Install the coupling clamp.

NOTE: On models with the Saginaw 553 steering box, you will have to slide the column up to install the coupling.

Vans and Wagons

1. Remove the drag link from the steering arm.
2. Raise the hood and disconnect the battery. Disconnect the wires from the windshield washer motor and lift the reservoir up and out of the way.
3. Remove the steering column.
4. Remove the retaining bolts and the retaining nut which hold the gear onto the frame.
5. Remove the two bolts from the bottom of the splash shield going in under the left wheel house. Force the bottom of the shield out about ½ inch.
6. Lift the gear up off the mounting stud and out through the hood opening.
7. To replace the gear, position it to the frame in reverse of the above step, and install the mounting

bolts, nut, and lockwasher. Tighten the bolts and nut to 100 ft-lbs.

8. Center the worm shaft and steering wheel.
9. Install the drag link to the steering arm.
10. Install the two splash shield bolts.
11. Install and adjust the steering column.
12. Connect the windshield washer motor wiring and battery. Mount the washer reservoir in its retaining bracket.

Power Steering

The linkage assist type power steering consists of a power cylinder attached to the front axle and tie rod, a control valve installed on the drag link between the steering knuckle arm and the steering arm and a belt-driven hydraulic pump mounted on the engine. Integral Power steering was introduced on light trucks in 1972.

Model (Y4D-335) Ross steering gear (© Chrysler Corp.)

Early model .94 power steering pump, later models have a pear shaped fluid reservoir (© Chrysler Corp.)

Slipper type power steering pump (© Chrysler Corp.)

Power Steering Pump Pressure Test

Model .94, 1.14

This vane type pump is used on D and W 100 through 300 series trucks. The 1.14 pump used on D500 and larger trucks is similar. The number .94 or 1.14 indicates the fluid displacement per revolution.

1. Fill fluid reservoir and check drive belt tension.
2. Disconnect the high pressure hydraulic line going to the control valve at the control valve and install a pressure gauge and valve, connecting the gauge end to the pump and the valve end to the control valve.
3. After warming up the fluid to 150-170° (let engine run and turn steering back and forth), note pressure reading while turning steering wheel to extreme in either direction as engine idles at 600-800 rpm. Maximum pressure should be at least 900 psi.
4. If maximum pressure is below 900 psi, momentarily close valve and note maximum pressure reading. If pressure was less than 900 psi, the pump is faulty. If pressure was at least 1000 psi, then either the control valve, power cylinder, or integral steering gear is faulty.
5. When removing test gauge and valve, be sure to reinstall high pressure line in its original position to avoid interference with engine or sheet metal.
6. For power steering pump overhaul procedures, see "Power Steering" in the General Repair Section.

Model 1.2

This slipper type pump is used on 1972 and later D500 and larger trucks.

The pressure test procedure is the same as that described for the model .94 above. In this test, however, the engine idles at 500 rpm. It is possible with this pump that the pressure relief valve may be faulty if the test indicated that the pump was faulty. Before removing pump and overhauling pump, retest with a new pressure relief valve.

Pump Removal and Installation

See "Power Steering" in General Repair Section for power steering pump overhaul procedures.

1. Loosen pump lower mounting and locking bolts and remove the belt.
2. Place a container under pump and disconnect both pump hoses.
3. Remove mounting and locking bolts and remove pump and brackets.
4. To install, position pump on engine and install retaining and locking bolts.
5. Install drive belt and adjust. Tighten pump brackets to 30 ft. lbs. torque.
6. Connect pressure and return hoses, routing them in the same position they were in before removal.
7. Fill pump reservoir.
8. Start engine and turn steering wheel all the way left and right to bleed the system. Stop engine and recheck fluid level, refilling if necessary.

Linkage Assist Type

Control Valve Removal and Installation

See "Power Steering" in the General Repair Section for control valve overhaul and service procedures.

1. Disconnect pressure and return hoses at valve assembly.
2. Cap hoses and connections at valve assembly. Fasten hoses so that ends are above fluid level in reservoir and tag them for reinstallation identification.
3. Disconnect ball ends at steering arm and steering knuckle arm and remove control valve and drag link assembly.
4. To install, connect control valve sliding sleeve end at steering arm and install nut and cotter pin.
5. Connect drag link end to steering knuckle arm and install nut and cotter pin.
6. Connect pressure and return hydraulic lines at valve assembly, tightening securely.
7. Refill pump reservoir.
8. Bleed system by turning steering wheel back and forth several times while the engine is idling.
9. Recheck fluid level and refill if necessary.

Power Cylinder Removal and Installation

1. Disconnect hydraulic lines at power cylinder and cap ends and connections at cylinder.
2. Remove cotter pin and nut at ball studs (and tie rod clamp U-bolts on lightweight trucks). Remove cylinder.
3. To install, insert ball stud into place on axle bracket and install nut and cotter pin, tighten nut securely.
4. Rotate steering wheel to extreme right turn position.
5. Install tie rod clamp loosely (on medium weight trucks loosen tie rod clamp and install ball stud and nut).
6. Position cylinder piston rod in fully retracted position and tighten U-bolt clamps on tie rod. On medium weight trucks the ball stud will have to be connected to tie rod clamp bracket before tightening clamp bolts.

Labels on image 1: OVAL SHAPED FILLER TUBE, KEY

Labels on image 2: RESERVOIR, SPRINGS(8), ROTOR, RELIEF VALVE, INLET, METERING INSERT, CAM—INSERT, SLIPPERS (4), FLOW CONTROL VALVE, OIL SEAL, SNAP RING, FLOW CONTROL PLUG

Clamp should be mounted on tie rod at a 20° angle to the vertical. Nuts on U-bolts are torqued to 40 ft. lbs.

7. Connect hydraulic lines to power cylinder in their original positions.
8. Bleed system by turning the steering wheel back and forth several times with the engine idling.

Integral Type

Removal and Installation

Conventional Trucks

1. Center the steering gear.
2. Pull off the steering arm.
3. Disconnect the pressure and return hoses.
4. Disconnect the steering shaft coupling.
5. Unbolt the gear from the frame and remove it.
6. Install the mounting bolts finger tight on installation.
7. Connect the coupling. Align the gear to the frame to prevent binding; tighten the bolts.
8. Connect the pressure and return hoses.
9. Center the steering gear, make sure the wheels are straight ahead, replace the steering arm and nut.
10. Idle the engine and turn the steering wheel gently from stop

to stop to bleed the system of air.

Vans and Wagons

1. Disconnect the battery and remove the windshield washer reservoir.
2. Remove the steering column.
3. Remove the optional steering arm shield.
4. Use a puller to remove the drag link from the steering arm.
5. Detach the hoses and raise their ends to prevent spillage.
6. Remove the two gear to frame bolts and the nut from the stud.
7. Remove the two bolts from the bottom of the splash shield (left side) and pull it out to lift the gear off the stud.
8. Turn the steering arm and lift the steering gear out through the hood opening.
9. On installation, move the parking brake cable away from the mounting stud. Position the gear. Install the mounting bolts and nut.
10. Install the drag link to the steering arm.
11. Replace the splash shield bolts.
12. Connect the hoses and check the reservoir fluid level.
13. Replace the steering column.
14. Replace the windshield washer reservoir and connect the battery.
15. Idle the engine and turn the

steering wheel gently from stop to stop to bleed the system of air.

Adjustment

The power steering gear used in conventional trucks should not be adjusted while in the chassis or filled with hydraulic fluid. The unit in vans and wagons may be adjusted in the vehicle.

Sector Adjustment, Vans and Wagons

1. Disconnect the center link from the steering gear arm.
2. Start the engine and allow to run at normal idle speed.
3. Rotate the steering wheel from lock to lock. Carefully count the number of turns required, then rotate the wheel back, exactly to the midpoint of its travel.
4. Loosen the adjusting screw until backlash in the steering gear arm becomes apparent.

NOTE: Backlash is felt by holding the end of the steering gear arm lightly between your thumb and forefinger.

5. Tighten the adjusting screw just enough so that the backlash disappears. Continue to tighten the screw for another 3/8 to 1/2 turn from this point. Tighten the locknut to 28 ft. lbs.
6. Attach the center link to the steering gear arm.

Power cylinder adjustment (© Chrysler Corp.)

Clutch

Clutch slave cylinder (© Chrysler Corp.)

Mechanical Clutch Linkage Adjustment

The only adjustment required is pedal free-play. Adjust the clutch actuating fork rod by turning the self-locking adjusting nut to provide 1/8 in. (3/32 in. on vans and wagons) free movement at the end of the fork. This will provide the recommended 1 1/2 in. (1 in. on Vans, Wagons, Ramcharger, and Trailduster) free-play at the pedal.

Hydraulic Clutch Adjustment, Medium Duty (D400 up) Models through 1971

1. Inside the cab, adjust clutch pedal free play to 3/16 in. by turning adjusting nut to allow .010″ free play between push rod and master cylinder piston.
2. At the slave cylinder, adjust clutch linkage free play at clutch fork pivot pin to 3/16″. Total pedal free play should then be approximately 1-1/2″. This figure should be used as a check and not for setting free play.
3. Inside the cab, check clutch pedal reserve. This is that portion of pedal travel remaining after free play and complete clutch disengagement. There should be a minimum of 1″ pedal reserve. If there is insufficient pedal reserve, bleed the hydraulic system as described below. Extremely low reserve indicates excessive wear in either of the cylinders.
4. Check for binding, incorrect parts or improperly installed parts and make corrections, repeating Steps 1 through 3 if necessary.
5. Over center spring tension (pedal return) is increased by backing off end nut on rod at top of clutch pedal.

Bleeding Hydraulic Clutch System

1. Clean away dirt from around master cylinder reservoir filler cap, remove cap and fill reservoir. Make sure to check reservoir frequently during bleeding process and fill when necessary.
2. Clean bleeder valve on slave cylinder and attach bleeder hose to valve.
3. Place other end of hose in jar half full of brake fluid.
4. Bleed intermittently as clutch pedal is being depressed by opening and closing bleeder valve. Continue bleeding until no air bubbles come from bleeder hose.

Clutch Master Cylinder Removal and Installation

1. Remove pedal return spring.
2. Disconnect push rod end at clutch pedal and hydraulic fluid line at master cylinder.
3. Unbolt master cylinder from firewall.
4. Installation is the reverse of the above procedure. Adjust master cylinder push rod to .010″ free play. Bleed hydraulic system.

Clutch Slave Cylinder Removal and Installation

Slave cylinder is located on the right side of the clutch housing. Disconnect hydraulic line, then remove cylinder mounting bolts. After installation, be sure to bleed hydraulic system and adjust as described above.

Clutch Removal

Conventional Trucks through 1971

1. Support engine on a suitable jack.
2. Remove insulator to crossmember bolts.
3. Remove crossmember to frame bracket mounting bolts.
4. Remove crossmember.
5. Remove transmission. Remove transfer case.
6. Remove clutch housing pan if so equipped.
7. Remove clutch fork, clutch bearing and sleeve assembly if not removed with transmission.
8. Mark clutch cover and flywheel, with a prick punch, to assure correct reassembly.
9. Remove clutch cover retaining bolts, loosening them evenly so clutch cover will not be distorted.

Clutch master cylinder (© Chrysler Corp.)

Hydraulic clutch adjustments (© Chrysler Corp.)

Dodge and Plymouth Trucks •

D and W 100, 200 clutch linkage (© Chrysler Corp.)

10. Pull pressure plate assembly clear of flywheel and, while supporting pressure plate, slide clutch disc from between flywheel and pressure plate.

Vans and Wagons, 1972 and Later Conventional Trucks

Follow Steps 5 through 10 of the preceding procedure.

Clutch Installation

All Models

1. Thoroughly clean all working surfaces of flywheel and pressure plate.
2. Grease radius at back of bushing.
3. Rotate clutch cover and pressure plate assembly for maximum clearance between flywheel and frame crossmember if crossmember was not removed during clutch removal.
4. Tilt top edge of clutch cover and pressure plate assembly back and move it up into the clutch housing. Support clutch cover and pressure plate assembly and slide clutch disc into position.
5. Position clutch disc and plate against flywheel and insert spare transmission main drive gear shaft or clutch installing tool through clutch disc hub and into main drive pilot bearing.
6. Rotate clutch cover until the prick punch marks on cover and flywheel line up.
7. Bolt cover loosely to flywheel. Tighten cover bolts a few turns at a time, in progression, until tight. Then tighten bolts to 20 ft. lbs. torque.
8. Install transmission.
9. On models through 1971, install frame crossmembers and insulator, tighten all bolts.

Manual Transmission

For Manual Transmission overhaul procedures see "Manual Transmission" in the General Service Section.

The transmission model can be identified by a number stamped on a pad on the right side of the case, or a tag under the power take-off cover plate bolts or attached to the left side of the case at the top near the case cover. The three-speed, non-synchronized low gear transmission used only with six-cylinder engines is the A-250 top-cover unit; this is similar in appearance to the A-745 which may found in some 1970-71 models. The fully-synchronized three-speed transmissions are the A-230 side-cover and the A-390 top-cover. The A-390, introduced in 1975, is very similar in design to the Ford 3.03 unit, and is produced by Tremec in Mexico. The wide-ratio (6.68 low gear) four-speed is the New Process 435, while the close ratio (4.56 low) is the New Process 435D with unsynchronized low gear, and 445D with synchronized low gear. Five-speed units are the New Process 540 and 542.

3-Speed Transmission Removal and Installation

Conventional Trucks, Vans and Wagons

1. Drain lubricant.
2. Disconnect driveshaft. On the sliding spline type, disconnect driveshaft at the rear universal joint, then carefully pull the shaft yoke out of the transmission extension housing. Do not nick or scratch splines.
3. Disconnect gearshift control rods and speedometer cable.
4. Remove backup light switch if so equipped.
5. Support engine.
6. Remove crossmember and rubber insulator on models through 1971, and 1975 and later models with A-390 transmission. On all other models, unbolt the insulator or mount from the crossmember. Support the transmission with a jack.
7. Remove transmission to clutch housing bolts.
8. Slide transmission rearward until pinion shaft clears clutch completely, then lower transmission from vehicle.
9. Installation is the reverse order of the above procedure. Before inserting transmission drive shaft into clutch, make sure clutch housing bore, disc and face are aligned. Tighten clutch housing to transmission bolts to 50 ft. lbs. torque.
10. Fill with lubricant.
11. Adjust shift linkage.
12. Road test.

4-Speed Transmission Removal and Installation

Conventional Trucks, Vans and Wagons

1. Shift transmission into any gear.
2. Disconnect universal joint and loosen yoke retaining nut.
3. Disconnect parking brake (if so equipped) and speedometer cables at transmission.
4. Remove lever retainer by pressing down, rotating retainer counter-clockwise slightly, then releasing.

Three-speed manual transmission identification number location, A-390 shown
(© Chrysler Corp.)

5. Remove lever and its springs and washers.
6. Support the rear of the engine and remove the crossmember. Remove transmission to clutch bell housing retaining bolts and pull transmission rearward until drive pinion clears clutch, then remove transmission.
7. To install, place ½ teaspoon of short fibre grease in pinion shaft pilot bushing, taking care not to get any grease on flywheel face.
8. Align clutch disc and backing plate with a spare drive pinion shaft or clutch aligning tool, then carefully install transmission.
9. Install transmission to bell housing bolts, tightening to 50 ft. lbs. torque. Replace the crossmember.
10. Install gear shift lever, shift into any gear and tighten yoke nut to 95-105 ft. lbs. torque.
11. Install universal joint, speedometer cable and brake cable.
12. Adjust clutch as described in "Clutch" above.
13. Install transmission drain plug and fill transmission with lubricant.
14. Road test.

Ramcharger and Trailduster, W100, 200, 300, 3 and 4-Speed Transmission Removal and Installation

1. Raise and support the truck.
2. Remove the skid plate, if any.
3. Disconnect the speedometer cable.

Holding three-speed column shift linkage in neutral position (© Chrysler Corp.)

4. Disconnect the front and rear driveshafts. Suspend each shaft from a convenient place; do not allow them to hang free.
5. Disconnect the shift rods at the transfer case. On 4-speed transmissions, remove the shift lever retainer by pressing down and turning it counterclockwise. Remove the shift lever springs and washers.
6. Remove the rear driveshaft. Matchmark the driveshaft and rear U-joints before removing the driveshaft.
7. Support the transfer case.
8. Remove the extension-to-transfer case mounting bolts.
9. Move the transfer case rearward to disengage the front input shaft spline.
10. Lower and remove the transfer case.

11. Disconnect the back-up light switch.
12. Support the engine.
13. Support the transmission.
14. Remove the transmission crossmember.
15. Remove the transmission-to-clutch housing bolts.
16. Slide the transmission rearward until the mainshaft clears the clutch disc.
17. Lower and remove the transmission.
18. Installation is the reverse of removal. The transmission pilot bushing in the end of the crankshaft requires high-temperature grease. Multipurpose grease should be used. Do not lubricate the end of the mainshaft, clutch splines, or clutch release levers. Adjust the gearshift linkage on 3-speed transmissions.

5-Speed Transmission Removal and Installation

1. Drain lubricant.
2. Remove gearshift lever, floor mat and floor cover over transmission.
3. Disconnect parking brake cable, speedometer cable and driveshaft.
4. Loosen flange nut and drop center bearing if so equipped.
5. Position a transmission jack under transmission and remove clutch housing to transmission bolts.
6. Slide transmission rearward until pinion shaft clears clutch (about 6"), then lower jack slightly. Move transmission to the left just enough for the main drive pinion to clear clutch housing, then lower transmission.

A-250 transmission linkage with clutch interlock—van with six-cylinder (© Chrysler Corp.)

Gearshift lever adjustment (© Chrysler Corp.)

7. Installation is the reverse order of the above procedure. Align clutch backing plate and disc with a spare drive pinion shaft or clutch aligning tool before inserting transmission drive pinion and be sure splines on shaft align with clutch hub splines before inserting. Tighten bell housing to transmission bolts to 100 ft. lbs. torque and driveshaft flange nut to 125 ft. lbs. torque.
8. Fill with lubricant and adjust clutch.
9. Road test.

Column Shift Linkage Adjustment

Conventional Trucks

1. Remove both shift rod swivels from transmission shift levers. Make sure transmission shift levers are in neutral (middle detent) position.
2. Move shift lever to line up locating slots in bottom of steering column shift housing and bearing housing. Install suitable tool in slot, if any.
3. Place screwdriver or suitable tool between crossover blade and second-third lever at steering column so that both lever pins are engaged by cross-over blade.
4. Set first-reverse lever on transmission to reverse position (rotate clockwise).
5. Adjust first-reverse rod swivel by loosening clamp bolt and sliding swivel along rod so it will enter first-reverse lever at transmission. Install washers and clip. Tighten swivel bolt.
6. Remove gearshift housing locating tool and shift column lever into neutral position.
7. Adjust second-third rod swivel by loosening clamp bolt and sliding swivel along rod so it will enter second-third lever at transmission. Install washers and clip. Tighten swivel bolt.
8. Remove tool from crossover blade at steering column, and shift through all gears to check adjustment and cross-over smoothness.

Vans and Wagons

1. Adjust the length of the 2-3 shift rod so the position of the shift lever on the steering column will be correct.
2. Assemble the 1st-reverse and 2-3 shift rods, and place each in its normal position, secured with a clip. Loosen both swivel clamp bolts.
3. Move the 2-3 shift lever into 3rd position (this means moving the forward lever forward). Move the steering column lever until it is about five degrees above the horizontal. Tighten the shift rod swivel clamp bolt.
4. Shift the transmission to neutral. Place a screwdriver between the crossover blade and the 2-3 lever at the steering column so that both lever pins are engaged by the cross over blade.
5. Set the 1st-reverse lever in neutral. Tighten the swivel clamp bolt.
6. Remove the tool from the cross over blade, and check all shifts for smoothness.

Clutch Interlock Adjustment

A-250 3-Speed

This adjustment is required only on the A-250 3-speed transmission. This is a top cover unit used only as base equipment on light duty six cylinder models. It has synchromesh only on second and third gears.
1. Disconnect the clutch rod swivel from the interlock pawl. Adjust the clutch pedal free play.
2. Shift the transmission to neutral. Loosen swivel clamp bolt and slide the swivel onto the rod until the pawl is positioned fully within the slot in the first-reverse lever. Install the washers and clip.

New Process T-233 and T-201 transfer case linkage adjustment, measurement A should be ¼ in. (© Chrysler Corp.)

3. Hold the interlock pawl forward and tighten the swivel clamp bolt. The clutch pedal must be in fully returned position during the adjustment. *NOTE:* Do not pull the clutch rod rearward to engage the swivel in the pawl.

4. Shift the transmission into first and reverse and release the clutch pedal while in either gear to check for normal clutch action. Then, shift halfway between neutral and either gear and release clutch. The interlock should hold it to within one or two inches of the floor.

Transfer Case

See General Section for overhaul procedures.

Transfer Case Removal and Installation

W100, 200, 300 through 1974

This is the new process 205 two-speed transfer case.

1. Drain lubricant.
2. Disconnect speedometer cable.
3. Disconnect input and output shafts, securing driveshafts to frame.
4. Remove shift rod from shift rail link.
5. Using a suitable jack, support transfer case while removing frame crossmember.
6. Remove mounting bolts and lower transfer case from truck.
7. Installation is the reverse of the above procedure. Tighten mounting bolts to 35 ft. lbs. and driveshaft yoke bolts to 300-400 ft. lbs. torque.

Ramcharger and Trailduster, 1975 and Later W100, 200, 300

This is the New Process 203 two-speed, full-time four-wheel drive transfer case. It incorporates a differential unit which allows the front and rear axles to remain in continuous drive in normal HI and LO positions. Both driveshafts transmit power simultaneously at the same rpm in Hi-Loc and Lo-Loc positions with the differential locked. The two-speed feature gives direct drive in High range and 2.01:1 reduction in Low range.

1. Raise and support the truck.
2. Remove the skid plate, if any.
3. Drain the transfer case by removing the bottom bolt from the front output rear cover.
4. Disconnect the speedometer cable.
5. Disconnect the front and rear output shafts. Suspend these from a convenient location; do not allow them to hang free.
6. Disconnect the shift rods at the transfer case.

New Process 203 full-time four-wheel drive shifter positioned for adjustment, note that the shift levers on the transfer case are in the neutral and unlocked positions (© Chrysler Corp.)

7. Support the transfer case.
8. Remove the adaptor-to-transfer case mounting bolts and move the transfer case rearward to disengage the front input splines.
9. Lower and remove the transfer case.
10. Installation is the reverse of removal. Adjust the linkage.

W500, 600

This is the new process T-223 two speed, two lever, transfer case. On Canadian models through 1973, it is the new process T-201.

1. Drain lubricant.
2. Disconnect speedometer and parking brake cables.
3. Disconnect input and output shafts. *Do not allow shafts to hang.*
4. Remove clevis pins, disconnecting de-clutch and shift control rods from transfer case rails. Secure rods out of the way.
5. Using a jack, support transfer case while removing support bracket bolts.
6. Carefully lower transfer case from truck.
7. To install, raise transfer case with a jack and align threaded mounting bolt holes in transfer case with holes in support brackets. Install bolts and tighten securely.
8. Connect speedometer cable and parking brake cable, adjusting parking brake as described in "Parking Brake" above.
9. Install and adjust transfer case shift and de-clutch rods.
10. Connect driveshafts.

Transfer Case Linkage Adjustment

W500, 600

1. Make sure that the front axle drive is engaged (the de-clutch rail on the case must be fully in). Make sure that the transfer case is in low range (the shift rail on the case must be fully out).
2. Disconnect the de-clutch and shift rods at the case by removing the clevis pins.
3. Adjust the de-clutch rod length so that the lever clears the rear end of the cab floor slot by ½ in. Replace the clevis pin.
4. Adjust the shift rod length until the distance between the lever contact surfaces is ¼ in. Replace the clevis pin.

Ramcharger and Trailduster, 1975 and Later W100, 200, 300

1. Loosen the lockscrews in both swivel rod clamps at the shifter assembly. The rods must be free to slide in the swivels.
2. Place the selector lever in the cab in neutral and insert a 11/64 in. diameter rod through the alignment holes in the shifter housing.
3. Place the range shift lever (outboard lever) on the transfer case in the neutral position.
4. Place the lockout shift lever on the transfer case (the inboard lever) in the unlocked position.
5. Retighten the rod swivel screws.
6. Remove the alignment rod from the shifter housing.

W100, 200, 300 through 1974

There is no external linkage adjustment necessary or possible on this unit.

Automatic Transmission

For complete overhaul procedures see "Automatic Transmission" section of the General Repair Section.

The three-speed automatic is the Loadflite A-727, a heavy-duty version of the Torqueflite transmission used in passenger cars. There are three different cases used: one for six-cylinder engines, one for V8s through 360 cu in., and another for larger V8s. There are also short and long extension housings, depending on the application.

The four-speed automatic introduced in 1974 medium duty models is the New Process A-345. It is based on the Loadflite A-727, with the extension housing replaced by a compounder housing and a different lower valve body.

NOTE: Internal components vary with model and drive train. Use the part number stamped on the left side of the fluid pan flange for positive identification.

Transmission Removal and Installation

1. Remove the transmission and converter as an assembly; otherwise the converter drive plate, pump bushing, and oil seal will be damaged. The drive plate will not support a load. Therefore, none of the weight of transmission should be allowed to rest on the plate during removal. Remove the transfer case, as necessary.
2. Attach a remote control starter switch to the starter solenoid so the engine can be rotated from under the vehicle.
3. Disconnect high tension cable from the ignition coil.
4. Remove cover plate from in front of converter assembly to provide access to the converter drain plug and mounting bolts.
5. Rotate engine to bring drain plug to "6 o'clock" position. Drain the converter and transmission.
6. Mark converter and drive plate to aid in reassembly.
7. Rotate the engine with the remote control switch to locate two converter to drive plate bolts at "5 and 7 o'clock" positions. Remove the two bolts, rotate engine again and remove the other two bolts. CAUTION: Do not rotate converter on drive plate by prying with a screwdriver or similar tool as drive plate might become distorted. Also the starter should never be engaged if drive plate is not attached to converter with at least one bolt or if transmission case to engine block bolts have been loosened.
8. Disconnect battery ground cable. Remove engine to transmission struts, if necessary. You may have to drop the exhaust system on some models.
9. Remove the starter.
10. Remove wire from the neutral starting switch.
11. Remove gearshift cable or rod from the transmission and the lever.
12. Disconnect the throttle rod from left side of transmission.
13. Disconnect the oil cooler lines at transmission and remove the oil filler tube. Disconnect the speedometer cable.
14. Disconnect the driveshaft.
15. Install engine support fixture to hold up the rear of the engine.
16. Raise transmission slightly with jack to relieve load and remove support bracket or crossmember. Remove all bell housing bolts and carefully work transmission and converter rearward off engine dowels and disengage converter hub from end of crankshaft. CAUTION: Attach a small "C" clamp to edge of bell

housing to hold converter in place during transmission removal; otherwise the front pump bushing might be damaged.

Installation

1. Install transmission and converter as an assembly. The drive plate will not support a load. Do not allow weight of transmission to rest on the plate during installation.
2. Rotate pump rotors until the rotor lugs are vertical.
3. Carefully slide converter assembly over input shaft and reaction shaft. Make sure converter impeller shaft slots are also vertical and fully engage front pump inner rotor lugs.
4. Use a "C" clamp on edge of converter housing to hold converter in place during transmission installation.
5. Converter drive plate should be free of distortion and drive plate to crankshaft bolts tightened to 55 ft. lbs. torque. Grease converter hub hole in crankshaft with wheel bearing grease.
6. Using a jack, position transmission and converter assembly in alignment with engine.
7. Rotate converter so mark on converter (made during removal) will align with mark on drive plate. The offset holes in plate are located next to the 1/8" hole in inner circle of the plate. A stamped "V" mark identifies the offset hole in converter front cover. Carefully work transmission assembly forward over engine block dowels with converter hub entering the crankshaft opening.
8. Install converter housing to en-

Aligning pump rotors (© Chrysler Corp.)

TOOL

ALIGNMENT HOLES VERTICAL

Converter & drive plate markings (© Chrysler Corp.)

DRAIN PLUG

1/8 INCH HOLE

"V" MARK

gine bolts and tighten to 28 ft. lbs.

9. Install the two lower drive plate to converter bolts and tighten to 270 in. lbs. torque.
10. Install engine to transmission struts, if required. Install starting motor and connect battery ground cable.
11. Rotate engine and install two remaining drive plate to converter bolts.
12. Install crossmember and tighten attaching bolts to 90 ft. lbs. torque. Lower transmission so that extension housing is aligned and rests on the rear mount. Install bolts and tighten to 40 ft. lbs. torque.
13. Remove transmission jack and engine support fixture, then install tie-bars under the transmission.
14. Replace the driveshaft.
15. Connect oil cooler lines, install oil filler tube and connect the speedometer cable.
16. Connect gearshift cable or rod and torqueshaft assembly to the transmission case and to the lever.
17. Connect throttle rod to the lever at left side of transmission bell housing.
18. Connect wire to back-up and neutral starting switch.
19. Install cover plate in front of the converter assembly.
20. Refill transmission with fluid.
21. Adjust throttle and shift linkage.

Loadflite Kickdown Throttle Linkage Adjustment

Conventional Trucks Through 1971

1. Warm up engine until choke and fast idle cam are released.
2. On all except 318 cu. in. V8 engines, remove clip, spring, flat washer and transmission throttle rod from the carburetor pin. Holding transmission throttle lever forward against its stop, adjust rod end so rear of slot contacts carburetor pin. Reinstall washer, spring and clip.
3. On 318 cu. in. engine, remove cotter pin, washer and transmission throttle rod from carburetor pin. Unhook spring from adjustable rod end. Hold transmission throttle lever forward against its stop and adjust rod end so front of slot contacts carburetor pin. Replace spring, washer and cotter pin.
4. Road test vehicle. If transmission does not kickdown, adjust transmission throttle rod one more turn to move the lever at the transmission farther back.

1972 and Later Conventional Trucks, Six-Cylinder

1. Block the choke valve fully open and release the fast idle cam.
2. Hold the transmission lever forward firmly against its stop while adjusting the linkage. If there is a solenoid idle stop, the plunger must be fully extended.
3. Loosen the slotted link lock bolt and pull forward on the slotted adjuster link until it contacts the carburetor lever pin and all slack is removed.
4. Tighten the lock bolt.
5. Check the adjustment by moving the slotted adjuster link all the way back and releasing it slowly. It should return to the full forward position.

1972 and Later Conventional Trucks, V8

1. Set the idle speed to specifications.
2. Disconnect the choke at the carburetor or block the choke open in the wide open position.
3. Open the throttle slightly to release the fast idle cam and return the carburetor to curb idle.
4. It is important that the transmission lever remain firmly against the stop during the next two steps. Have an assistant hold the transmission throttle lever forward against the stop while the adjustment is made. On engines with solenoid idle stops, the solenoid plunger must be fully extended.
5. With a 3/16 in. diameter rod placed in the holes in the upper bellcrank and lever, adjust the length of the intermediate transmission rod by means of the threaded adjustment at the up-

per end. The ball socket must align with the ball end with a slight downward pressure on the rod.

6. Assemble the ball socket to the ball end and remove the 3/16 in. rod from the upper bellcrank and lever.
7. Disconnect the return spring, clip, and washer and adjust the length of the carburetor rod by pushing rearward on the rod with a slight effort (to remove all backlash) and turning the threaded adjustment. The rear end of the slot should contact the carburetor lever pin with no backlash without exerting any forward force on the pin when the slotted adjuster link is in its normal operating position.
8. Assemble the slotted adjustment to the carburetor lever pin and install the washer and retainer clip. Install the transmission linkage return spring.
9. Check the freedom of operation by moving the slotted link at the carburetor to the full rearward position and allow it to return slowly. Be sure that it returns to the full rearward position.
10. Connect the choke rod or unblock the choke plate.

Vans and Wagons

1. Warm the engine to operating temperature.
2. Block the choke plate fully open.
3. Remove the throttle return spring from the carburetor.
4. Remove the clip, washer and slotted throttle rod from the carburetor pin.
5. Rotate the threaded end of the rod so that the rear edge of the slot in the rod contacts the car-

Loadflite transmission kickdown throttle linkage—conventional truck 318 V8 through 1971 (© Chrysler Corp.)

Dodge and Plymouth Trucks ·

Loadflite transmission kickdown throttle linkage—1972 and later V8 conventional truck (© Chrysler Corp.)

1 Adjuster
2 Ball socket
3 Accelerator pivot
4 Clamp bolt
5 Ferrule
6 Upper bellcrank
7 Pivot pin
8 Choke
9 3/16 in. adjusting rod
10 Intermediate transmission rod
11 Transmission throttle lever
12 Carburetor rod
13 Transmission linkage return spring
14 Throttle base
15 Retaining pin

buretor pin when the transmission throttle lever is held forward against its stop.
6. Install the washer and clip to retain the throttle rod to the carburetor.
7. Install the throttle rod return spring.
8. Check the transmission linkage for freedom of operation and unblock the choke plate.

New Process A-345 Kickdown Throttle Linkage Adjustment

1. Block the choke valve fully open and release the fast idle cam.
2. Hold the transmission lever forward against its stop while adjusting the linkage.
3. Remove the spring from the stabilizer and retainer (not the throttle return spring) and loosen the bolt attaching the upper end of the slotted rod to the retainer.
4. Push gently backward on the rod to remove all slack.
5. Tighten the bolt at the retainer and replace the spring.
6. Check that the linkage works freely.

Shift Linkage Adjustment
Loadflite
1. Place the gearshift lever in the Park position.
2. Move the shift control lever on the transmission all the way to the rear (in the Park detent).
3. Set the adjustable rod to the proper length and install it with no load in either direction. Tighten the swivel bolt.

4. The shift linkage must be free of binding and be positive in all positions. Make sure that the engine can start only when the gearshift lever is in the Park or Neutral position. Be sure that the gearshift lever will not jump into an unwanted gear.

New Process A-345
1. Detach the clevis from the transmission lever by removing the pin.
2. Place the shift lever in Neutral.
3. Place the transmission lever in Neutral, the second detent from the rear.
4. Adjust and install the clevis.
5. Make sure that the engine can only be started in Neutral.

Band Adjustments

Kickdown Band
The kickdown band adjusting screw is located on the left-hand side of the transmission case near the throttle lever shaft.
1. Loosen the locknut and back it off about five turns. Be sure that the adjusting screw is free in the case.
2. Torque the adjusting screw to 72 in. lbs.
3. Back off the adjusting screw 2 turns. On 1973 and later six-cylinder engines, and 1974 and later conventional truck V8s back off 2½ turns. On 1974 and later 440 V8, V8 van and wagon, and A-345 four-speed back off 2 turns. Then, keep the screw from turning and torque the locknut to 35 ft. lbs. (29 ft. lbs. through 1972).

Low and Reverse Band
The pan must be removed from the transmission to gain access to the low and reverse band adjusting screw.
1. Remove the skidplate, if any. Drain the transmission and remove the pan.

Loadflite transmission kickdown throttle linkage—V8 van (© Chrysler Corp.)

132

Load flite external controls (© Chrysler Corp.)

A-345 4-speed automatic transmission shift linkage (© Chrysler Corp.)

Loadflite and A-345 low-reverse band adjustment (© Chrysler Corp.)

2. Loosen the band adjusting screw locknut and back it off about five turns. Be sure that the adjusting screw turns freely in the lever.
3. Torque the adjusting screw to 72 in. lbs.
4. Back off the adjusting screw 2 turns. Keep the screw from turning and torque the locknut to 30 ft. lbs.
5. Using a new gasket, install the pan and torque the pan bolts to 150 in. lbs. Refill the transmission.

Neutral Safety/Backup Light Switch Replacement

The neutral safety switch is mounted in the transmission case. When the gearshift lever is placed in either the Park or Neutral position, a cam, which is attached to the transmission throttle lever inside the transmission, contacts the neutral safety switch and provides a ground to complete the starter solenoid circuit.

The back-up light switch is incorporated into the neutral safety switch. The center terminal is for the neutral safety switch and the two outer terminals are for the back-up lamps.

There is .no adjustment for the switch. If a malfunction occurs, first check to make sure that the transmission gearshift linkage is properly adjusted. If the malfunction continues, the switch must be removed and replaced.

To remove the switch, disconnect the electrical leads and unscrew the switch. Use a drain pan to catch the transmission fluid. Using a new seal, install the new switch and torque it to 24 ft. lbs. Refill the transmission.

Pan Removal and Installation, Filter Change

1. Drive the truck until it is thoroughly warmed up.
2. Remove the skidplate, if any. Unbolt the pan. It holds six or more quarts, so be ready with a large container.

NOTE: If the fluid removed smells burnt, serious transmission troubles, probably due to overheating should be suspected.

3. Remove the access plate in front of the torque converter. With the aid of a socket wrench on the vibration damper bolt or the starter, rotate the engine clockwise to bring the converter drain to the bottom. Position the container under the converter, remove the drain plug, and allow the fluid to drain. Drain the compounder housing on the A-345.

Replace the converter drain plug and torque it to 110 in. lbs. for a 7/16 in. head plug and 90 in. lbs. for a 5/16 in. plug. Install the access plate.

4. Unscrew and discard the filter.
5. Install a new filter. The proper torque is 35 in. lbs.
6. Clean out the pan, being extremely careful not to leave any lint from rags inside.
7. Replace the pan with a new gasket. Tighten the bolts to 150 in. lbs. in a crisscross pattern.
8. Pour six quarts (eight on the A-345) of DEXRON® automatic transmission fluid through the dipstick tube.
9. Start the engine in Neutral and let it idle for two minutes or more.
10. Hold your foot on the Brake and shift through D,2,1, and R and back to N.
11. Add enough fluid to bring the level to the ADD ONE PINT mark.
12. Operate the truck until the transmission is thoroughly warmed up, then check the level. It should be between FULL and ADD ONE PINT. Add fluid as necessary.

NOTE: The manufacturer recommends MOPAR automatic transmission sealer be added to reduce fluid leakage resulting from hardening or shrinking of the seals in high-mileage vehicles.

Drive Shaft, U Joints

Driveshaft Removal and Installation

Single Section Type

This driveshaft has a universal joint at either end and no external supports.

1. Raise and support the truck with the rear higher.
2. Matchmark the shaft and pinion flange to assure proper balance at installation.
3. Remove both rear U-joint roller and bushing clamps from the rear axle pinion flange. Do not disturb the retaining strap which holds the bushing assemblies on the U-joint cross.

Typical Loadflite transmission shift linkage (© Chrysler Corp.)

Single section driveshaft (© Chrysler Corp.)

NOTE: Do not allow the driveshaft to hang during removal. Suspend it from the frame with a piece of wire. Before removing the driveshaft, raise the rear end of the truck to prevent loss of transmission fluid.

4. Slide the driveshaft, with the front sliding yoke, off the transmission output shaft.

5. Installation is the reverse of removal. Align the matchmarks made during removal.

Two-Section Type

This driveshaft has a universal joint at either end, with a third universal joint and a support bearing at the center.

1. Matchmark the shaft and the rear axle pinion hub yoke. Matchmark the center bearing spline and slip yoke.

NOTE: Do not allow the driveshaft to hang down during removal. Suspend it from the frame. Raise the rear of the truck to prevent loss of transmission fluid.

2. Remove both rear U-joint roller and bushing assembly clamps from the rear axle pinion yoke. Do not disturb the retaining strap used to hold the bushing assemblies on the U-joint cross.

3. Slide the rear half of the shaft off the front shaft splines at the center bearing. Remove the rear half.

4. At the transmission end of the front half, remove the bushing retaining bolts and clamps, after matchmarking. If there is a driveshaft brake, there will be flange nuts.

5. Unbolt the center bearing mounting nuts and bolts and remove the front half of the shaft.

6. On installation, align the matchmarks at the transmission and start all the bolts and nuts at the front U-joint and the center support bearing.

7. Tighten 1/4 in. clamp bolts to 170 in. lbs, and 5/16 in. bolts to 300 in. lbs. Tighten driveshaft brake flange nuts to 35 ft. lbs. Leave the center bearing bolts just snug.

8. Align the rear shaft matchmarks and slide the yoke onto the front shaft splines.

9. Align the rear U-joint matchmarks and install the bushing clamps and bolts. Tighten the bolts to the torque given in Step 7. Grease the joints and splines.

10. Jack up the rear wheels and let the engine drive the shaft. The center support bearing will align itself.

11. Tighten the center bearing bolts to 50 ft. lbs.

Four-Wheel Drive Front Driveshaft

This applies to Ramcharger and Trailduster, W100, 200, and 300.

1. Remove the four flange retaining bolts and lockwashers from the constant velocity U-joint at the transfer case. Mark the parts to reinstall them in the same position. To prevent the constant velocity joint from turning while removing the nuts, use a press bar.

2. Remove the nuts and lockwashers from the U-bolts at the differential flange and remove the U-bolts.

3. Support the driveshaft and separate the U-joint at the front the driveshaft joint backward to clear the flange. The driveshaft should never be allowed to hang by either universal joint.

4. Remove the driveshaft.

5. Installation is the reverse of removal.

Universal Joint Replacement

Lock Ring Type

Remove lockring bushing retainers, then drive bushing out by tapping on yoke next to bushing opening. Pull out bearings then work cross up and out of yoke. To install, first position washer retainers (use new seals) on cross, then position cross in driveshaft yoke with grease fitting approximately parallel to other fittings on shaft. Grease rollers and tap bearings into place. Install lock rings. Lubricate slip joint.

Snap-ring Type

1. Hammer the bushings (roller cups) slightly inward to relieve pressure on the snap-rings. Remove the snap-rings.

2. Place the yoke in a vise with a socket bigger than the bushing on one side and one smaller than the bushing on the other side.

3. Apply pressure, forcing one bushing out into the larger socket.

4. Reverse the vise and socket arrangement to remove the other bushing and the cross.

Two-section driveshaft (© Chrysler Corp.)

Lock ring type universal joint (© Chrysler Corp.)

Strap clamp type universal joint (© Chrysler Corp.)

Constant velocity joint bearing cup removal sequence (© Chrysler Corp.)

5. On installation, press the new bushings in just far enough to install the snap-rings.

Strap Clamp Type (Rear Axle Yoke)

Unbolt strap bolts and remove straps, bushings, seals and washer retainers. Install new components as required. When assembling, grease bearings. Install with grease fitting parallel to other fittings in drive train. Tighten strap bolts to 20 ft. lbs. torque.

Constant Velocity U-Joint

This is the double universal joint used in the front driveshaft on four-wheel drive models. These are disassembled in the same way as the snap-ring type U-Joint. Original equipment U-joints are held together by plastic retainers which shear when pressed out. The bearing cups in the center part of the joint should be pressed out before those in the yoke. Original equipment constant velocity joints cannot be reassembled. Replacement part kits have bearing cups with grooves for retaining rings.

Slip Joints

When reassembling slip joints make sure that arrows stamped on each side are matched. This will assure proper universal joint alignment.

Rear Axle

Numerous rear axles are used on Dodge and Plymouth trucks. Those used through the 300 series can be identified by the chart.

Maker	Ring Gear Size (in.)	Identification
Chrysler	8³⁄₈	10 bolt cover, front filler plug
Chrysler	8³⁄₄	Welded cover, front filler plug
Chrysler	9¹⁄₄	12 bolt cover, filler plug in cover
Spicer 60, 60HD	9³⁄₄	10 bolt cover, filler plug in cover
Spicer 70	10¹⁄₂	10 bolt cover, filler plug in cover

The gear ratio is usually identified by a metal tag under one of the cover or housing bolts. The tag gives either the gear ratio or the number of teeth on the ring and pinion gears. Larger axles (up to 15,000 lb. capacity) are the Chrysler RA115 12½ in. axle, the F140D 12½ in. Rockwell, the F147 13¼ in. Rockwell, and the Eaton 13802 and 15201 two-speed units.

Axle Assembly Removal and Installation

1. Raise vehicle and support at front of rear springs.
2. Block brake pedal in the up position.
3. Remove rear wheels.
4. Disconnect hydraulic brake hose at "T" fitting or at each wheel.
5. Disconnect parking brake cable.
   NOTE: To insure proper drive line balance when reassembling, make scribe marks on the drive-

shaft universal joint and differential pinion flange before removal.
6. Disconnect driveshaft at rear universal joint bearing clamps and secure with wire to prevent damage to front universal joint.
7. Disconnect shock absorbers and remove rear spring nuts and U-bolts.
8. Remove assembly from vehicle.
9. To install, position rear axle assembly spring pads over the spring center bolts.
10. Install U-bolts and tighten nuts securely.
11. Connect shock absorbers.
12. Connect parking brake cable.
13. Connect hydraulic brake lines. Install brake drums and adjust. Bleed hydraulic brake system.
14. Connect driveshaft universal joint in its original position, matching scribe marks made during removal. Tighten universal joint clamp bolts.

Differential Service

For service and overhaul procedures on differentials see "Drive Axles" in the General Repair Section.

Axle Shaft Removal and Installation

8³⁄₈ and 9¹⁄₄ in. Axles

NOTE: There is no provision for axle shaft end-play adjustment on this axle.

1. Raise the vehicle and remove the rear wheels.
2. Clean all dirt from the housing cover and remove the housing cover to drain the lubricant.
3. Remove the brake drum.
4. Rotate the differential case until the differential pinion shaft lockscrew can be removed. Remove the lockscrew and pinion shaft.
5. Push the axle shafts toward the center of the vehicle and remove the C-locks from the grooves on the axle shafts.
6. Pull the axle shafts from the

8⅜ in. rear axle, 9¼ in. is similar (© Chrysler Corp.)

housing, being careful not to damage the bearing which remains in the housing.

7. Inspect the axle shaft bearings and replace any doubtful parts. Whenever the axle shaft is replaced, the bearings should also be replaced.

8. Remove the axle shaft seal from the bore in the housing, using the button end of the axle shaft.

9. Remove the axle shaft bearing from the housing. Do not reuse the bearing or the seal.

10. Check the bearing shoulder in the axle housing for imperfections. These should be corrected with a fine file.

11. Clean the axle shaft bearing cavity.

12. Install the axle shaft bearing in the cavity. Be sure that the bearing is not cocked and that it is seated firmly against the shoulder.

13. Install the axle shaft bearing seal. It should be seated beyond the end of the flange face.

14. Insert the axle shaft, making sure that the splines do not damage the seal. Be sure that the splines are properly engaged with the differential side gear splines.

15. Install the C-locks in the grooves on the axle shafts. Pull the shafts outward so that the C-

locks seat in the counterbore of the differential side gears.

16. Install the differential pinion shaft through the case and pinions. Install the lockscrew and secure it in position.

17. Clean the housing and gasket surfaces. Install the cover and a new gasket.

NOTE: Replacement gaskets may not be available for differential covers. In this case, the use of a gel type nonsticking sealant is recommended.

Be sure that the rear axle ratio identification tag is replaced under one of the cover bolts. Refill the axle with the specified lubricant to ½ in. below the filler plug hole. Do not overfill.

18. Install the brake drum and wheel.

19. Lower the vehicle to the ground and test the operation of the brakes.

8¾ in. Axle

NOTE: Whenever this axle assembly is serviced, both the brake support plate gaskets and the inner axle shaft oil seal must be renewed.

1. Raise the rear of the vehicle and remove the rear wheels.

2. Detach the clips which secure the brake drum to the axle shaft studs and remove the brake drum.

3. Through the access hole in the axle shaft flange, remove the axle shaft retaining nuts. The right-side axle shaft has a threaded adjuster in the retainer plate and a lock under one of its studs which should be removed at this time.

4. Remove the parking brake strut.

5. Attach a puller to the axle shaft flange and remove the axle shaft.

6. Remove the brake assembly from the axle housing.

7. Remove the axle shaft oil seal from the axle housing.

CAUTION: It is advisable to position some sort of a protective sleeve over the axle shaft seal surface next to the bearing collar to protect the seal surface. Never use a torch or other heat source as an aid in removing any axle shaft components; this will result in serious damage to the axle assembly.

8. Wipe the axle housing seal bore clean. Install a new axle shaft oil seal.

NOTE: All 8¾ in. rear axle shaft bearings are packed with a special lubricant at the factory. If the roller bearing must be repacked, the factory lubricant must be washed out. The service lubricant is not compatible with the factory lubricant.

9. Place the axle shaft housing retaining collar in a vise. With a chisel, cut deeply into the retaining collar at 90° intervals. Remove the bearing with a puller.

10. Remove the bearing roller retainer flange by cutting off the lower edge with a chisel.

11. Grind or file a section off the flange of the inner bearing cone and remove the bearing rollers.

12. Pull the bearing roller retainer down as much as possible and cut it off with side cutters.

13. Remove the roller bearing cup with its protective sleeves.

14. To prevent damage to the seal journal when the bearing cone is removed, protect the journal with a single wrap of 0.002 in. thick shim stock held in place by a rubber band.

15. Using a puller, remove the bearing cone. Remove the seal in the bearing retainer plate and replace it.

16. To assemble the axle, first install the retainer plate and seal assembly on the axle shaft.

17. Grease the wheel bearings and install them.

18. Install a new axle shaft bearing cup, cone, and collar on the shaft. Check the axle shaft seal journal for imperfections and if necessary, polish with No. 600 crocus cloth.

19. Thoroughly clean the axle housing flange face and brake sup-

Grind the flange off the inner cone to remove the 8¾ in. axle bearing rollers (© Chrysler Corp.)

port. Install a new rubber/asbestos gasket onto the axle housing studs. Next, install the brake support plate assembly on the left side of the axle housing.

20. Lightly grease the outside edge of the bearing cup. Install the bearing cup in the bearing bore.

21. Replace the foam gasket on the studs of the left-side axle housing and very carefully slide the axle shaft assembly through the oil seal and engage the splines of the differential side gear.

22. Using a non-metallic hammer, lightly tap the end of the axle shaft to position the axle housing. Install the retainer plate over the axle housing studs and, starting with the bottom securing nut, torque the nuts to 30-35 ft. lbs.

23. Repeat steps 19-22 for the right-side axle housing.

24. At the right side of the axle housing, back off the threaded adjuster until the inner face of the adjuster is flush with the inner face of the retainer plate. Very carefully slide the axle shaft assembly through the oil seal and engage the splines of the differential side gear. Then repeat step four of the installation procedure.

25. Mount a dial indicator on the left brake support. Turn the adjuster clockwise until both wheel bearings are seated and there is zero end-play in the axle shafts. Back off the adjuster about four notches to establish proper end-play (0.008-0.018 for the 8¾ in. axle, and 0.008-0.012 for the 9¾ in. axle).

26. Lightly tap the end of the left axle shaft with a non-metallic hammer. This will seat the right wheel bearing cup against the adjuster. Turn the axle shaft several times so that a true end-play reading is obtained.

27. Remove one retainer plate nut and install the adjuster lock. If the lock tab does not mate with the notch in the adjuster, turn the adjuster slightly until it does.

Refit the nut and torque it to 30-35 ft. lbs.

28. Recheck the axle shaft end-play. If it is not within specifications, repeat the adjustment. When the adjustment is complete, remove the dial indicator.

29. Install the parking brake strut. Replace the brake drum and retaining clips.

30. Install the rear wheels and lower the vehicle.

RA115, Spicer 60 and 70, F147, F140D, Eaton 2-Speed Axles

1. Remove axle shaft flange nuts and washers.
2. Rap axle shafts sharply in center of flange with hammer to free dowels.
3. Remove tapered dowels and axle shafts.
4. Clean gasket contact area with suitable solvent and install a new flange gasket.
5. Install axle shaft into axle housing.
6. On axles having an outer wheel bearing seal, install new gaskets on each side of seal mounting flange.

7. Install tapered dowels, lock washers and nuts. Torque the nuts to 30-35 ft. lbs. on the RA115, 40-70 ft. lbs. on Spicer axles with 7/16 in. thread size, and 65-105 on Spicer with ½ in.

Rear Suspension

Rear Spring Removal and Installation
Conventional Trucks, 100-300

1. Raise rear of truck until weight is removed from springs, wheels just touching the floor.

NOTE: Truck must be lifted by jack or hoist under frame side rail at crossmember behind the axle being careful not to bend flange of side rail.

2. Place stands under side frame members as a safety precaution.
3. Remove nuts, lockwashers and U-bolts securing spring to axle.
4. Remove spring shackle bolts, shackle and spring front bolt, then remove spring.
5. To install, position spring on axle so spring center bolt enters locating hole in axle housing pad.
6. Line up spring front eye with bolt hole in bracket and install spring bolt and nut.
7. Install the rear shackle, bolts and nuts. Tighten shackle bolt nut until slack is taken up.
8. On headless type spring bolts install the bolts with lock bolt groove lined up with lock bolt hole in bracket. Install lock bolt and tighten lock bolt nut. Install lubrication fittings.
9. Install U-bolts, new lockwashers and nuts, tightening until nuts

Spicer (Dana) 60,60HD rear axle (© Chrysler Corp.)

Spicer (Dana) 70 rear axle (© Chrysler Corp.)

push lockwashers against axle. Align auxiliary spring parallel with main spring.

10. Remove stands from under vehicle, lower truck so weight is resting on wheels. Tighten U-bolt nuts, spring eye nuts and shackle bolt nuts.

11. Lubricate spring bolts and shackle bolts with chassis lubricant when equipped with lubrication fittings.

Vans and Wagons

1. Raise the vehicle until springs are accessible. Place jackstands under the bumper brackets.

2. Remove U-bolt nuts, U-bolts, and plate.

3. Remove the front pivot bolt nut. Remove the bolt.

4. Remove the rear shackle bolt nuts. Remove the shackle plate.

5. Remove the outer shackle and bolt assembly from the hanger. Remove the spring. On vehicles equipped with one piece shackles, remove the nut, remove the shackle to spring bolt, and remove the spring.

6. To install, position the spring and shackle assembly in the rear hanger.

7. Install the shackle plates and nuts, tightening the nuts to 40 ft-lbs. On vehicles with the one piece shackle, first position the spring to the shackle, and then install the bolt and nut.

8. Position the spring in the front pivot hanger and install the bolt and nut.

9. Position the spring properly on the axle and install the U-bolt plate.

10. Install the U-bolts and nuts.

Make sure the shackled end of the spring is above the shackle bracket pivot.

11. Lower the vehicle to the floor, and tighten all nuts.

Medium Duty Models, 400-800

1. Raise truck frame until weight is off rear springs with wheels still touching the ground.

2. Remove nuts from spring clips and remove spring clip plate. Remove spring clips.

3. If truck is so equipped, remove the auxiliary spring and spacer.

4. Install a "C" clamp on radius leaf to relieve load on spring eye bolt. Remove front eye bolt retaining nut.

5. Remove spring eye bolt and slowly release tension on radius leaf.

6. Remove rebound pin retaining lock from front bracket. Remove spring rebound pin. Repeat for rear rebound pin.

7. Remove rear spring.

8. If necessary, replace radius leaf eye rubber bushing.

9. To install, position spring in front bracket and install rebound pin. Install retaining lock.

10. Position spring in rear bracket, and install rebound pin. Install retaining lock.

11. Align spring eye and install spring eye bolt and nut. It may be necessary to draw the radius leaf eye into position with a "C" clamp.

12. Install auxiliary spring assembly if so equipped.

13. Install spring U-bolt plate and U-bolt seat. Install spring clips and nuts and washers, tightening nuts until they are snug.

14. Lower truck to the floor and tighten spring U-bolts.

Rear suspension, D100, 200 shown (© Chrysler Corp.)

Rear suspension, W200, W300, and D300 shown (© Chrysler Corp.)

Index

TUNE-UP SPECIFICATIONS

CU. IN. DISPLACE- MENT		YEAR	SPARK PLUG GAP	DISTRIBUTOR POINT DWELL	POINT GAP	IGNITION TIMING DEGREES	CRANKING COMP. PRESSURE	VALVE CLEARANCE INLET	EXHAUST	GOV. R.P.M. NO LOAD	FUEL PUMP PRESS.	IDLE SPEED STD.	AUTO.
				SIX CYLINDER									
170	Std. Tr.	1965-67	.035	37-42	.025	4[1]	175	.018H	.018H	—	4-6	585	—
		1970-72	.034	35-40	.027	6	175	.018H	.018H	—	4-6	525	—
200		1973-75	.034	37	.027	6B	175	Zero		—	4-6	500	650
240		1970	.034	35-40	.027	6	175	Zero		4000	4-6	[1]	[1]
		1971-72	.034	33-38[10]	.027[11]	6B	175	Zero		4000	4-6	500	500
		1973	.034	33-39	.027	[9]	[9]	Zero		4000	4-6	[9]	[9]
		1974	[9]	[9]	[9]	[9]	[9]	[9]		[9]	[9]	[9]	[9]
		1971-72	.034	33-38	.027[11]	6B	175	Zero		—	4-6	775	500[15]
		1973	.034	33-39	.027	[9]	[9]	Zero		—	4-6	[9]	[9]
		1974-76	[9]	[9]	[9]	[9]	[9]	Zero		—	4-6	[9]	[9]
				EIGHT CYLINDER									
300		1970	.034	35-40[12]	.027[13]						4-6	[14]	[14]
302		1970	.030	24-29	.021	6[9]	150	Zero		—	5	800[9]	600[9]
		1971-72	.034	24-29	.017[16]	6B	150	Zero		—	5	500	500
		1973	.034	24-30	.017	[9]	150	Zero		—	5	[9]	[9]
		1974-76	[9]	[9]	[9]	[9]	150	Zero		—	5	[9]	[9]
330		1970-73	.030	24-30[4]	.017[5]	[9]	140	Zero		3900	4½-6½	[9]	[9]
		1974-76	[9]	[9]	[9]	[9]	140	Zero		3900	4½-6½	[9]	[9]
360		1970	.036	24-29	.021	6B	140	Zero		—	4½-6½	500[9]	500[9]
		1971-72	.034	24-29[17]	.021[18]	6B	140	Zero		—	4½-6½	650	550
		1973	.034	24-30	.017	[9]	140	Zero		—	4½-6½	[9]	[9]
		1974-76	[9]	[9]	[9]	[9]	140	Zero		—	4½-6½	[9]	[9]
361		1970-73	.030	26-31[4]	.017[5]	6[9]	140	Zero		3800	4½-6½	550[9]	500[9]
		1974-76	[9]	[9]	[9]	[9]	140	Zero		3800	4½-6½	[9]	[9]
390		1970	.032	24-29	.021	6B	140	Zero		—	4½-6½	500[9]	500[9]
		1971-72	.034	24-39[17]	.021	6	140	Zero		—	4½-6½	650	550
		1973	.034	24-30	.017	[9]	140	Zero		—	4½-6½	[9]	[9]
		1974-76	[9]	[9]	[9]	[9]	140	Zero		—	4½-6½	[9]	[9]
391		1970-73	.030	26-31[4]	.017[5]	6[9]	140	Zero		3800	4½-6½	550[9]	500[9]
		1974-76	[9]	[9]	[9]	[9]	140	Zero		3800	4½-6½	[9]	[9]
401		1970-76	.030	26-31[4]	.017[5]	8[9]	150	.020	.020	3600	8	525[9]	500D[9]
460		1973-76	[9]	[9]	[9]	[9]	140	Zero		—	4½-6½	[9]	[9]
477		1970-76	.030	26-31[4]	.017[5]	8[9]	150	.020	.020	3400	8	525[9]	500D[9]
534		1970-76	.030	22-24	.020	8[9]	150	.020	.020	3200	8	550[9]	500[9]

1—F-250, Auto. 550, Man—600
  F-100 Man. 500, Auto—500
  Econoline—775
  Bronco—775 (Man.) 675 (Auto.)
2—With Exhaust Emission TDC.
3—With Exhaust Emission 6B.
4—Transistor Ignition 22-24.
5—Transistor Ignition .020.
6—Heavy Duty—1969-70.
7—Auto. Trans.
8—Electric.
9—Set to specifications shown on engine decal.

10—F-250 and 1972 Models—34-40.
11—1971 F-250—.025.
12—F-250—37-42.
13—F-250—.025.
14—F-100 Man—775, Auto—550.
  F-250—600.
  F-250 (4WD)—550.
15—Over 6000 GVW California—550.
16—.021 w/Dual Diaphragm Distributor.
17—26-31 on F-250 and 1972 Models.
18—.017 on F-250 and 1972 Models.

GENERAL ENGINE SPECIFICATIONS

CU. IN. DISPLACE- MENT	YEAR	BORE AND STROKE	FIRING ORDER	DEVELOPED HORSE POWER @ R.P.M.	DEVELOPED TORQUE @ R.P.M.	COM- PRESSION RATIO	CARBU- RETOR	VALVE LIFTER TYPE	NORMAL OIL PRESSURE
				SIX CYLINDER					
170	1970-71	3.500x2.94	153624	100 @ 4000	156 @ 2200	8.7	1V	Mech.	35-55
	1972	3.500x2.94	153624	97 @ 4400	137 @ 2600	8.3	1V	Mech.	35-60
200	1973-75	3.683 x 3.26	153624	84 @ 3600	151 @ 1800	8.3	2V	Hyd.	35-55
240	1970-71	4.000x3.18	153624	150 @ 4000	234 @ 2200	9.2-1	1V	Hyd.	35-60
	1972	4.00x3.18	153624	121 @ 4000	186 @ 2400	8.5	1V	Hyd.	.35-60
	1973-74	4.00x3.18	153624	119 @ 3800	190 @ 2200	8.5	1V	Hyd.	40-60

GENERAL ENGINE SPECIFICATIONS

CU. IN. DISPLACE-MENT	YEAR	BORE AND STROKE	FIRING ORDER	DEVELOPED HORSE POWER @ R.P.M.	DEVELOPED TORQUE @ R.P.M.	COM-PRESSION RATIO	CARBU-RETOR	VALVE LIFTER TYPE	NORMAL OIL PRESSURE
			SIX CYLINDER						
300	1970-71	4.000x3.98	153624	165 @ 3600	284 @ 2000	8.8-1	1V	Hyd.	35-60
	1972	4.000x3.98	153624	132 @ 3600	240 @ 2000	8.4	1V	Hyd.	35-60
	1972	4.000x3.98	153624	165 @ 3600	294 @ 2000	7.9	1V	Hyd.	35-60
	1973	4.000x3.98	153624	128 @ 3600	234 @ 1600	7.9	1V	Hyd.	40-60
	1973	4.000x3.98	153624	132 @ 3600	241 @ 1800	7.9	1V	Hyd.	40-60
	1973-74	4.000 x 3.98	153624	N.A.	N.A.	N.A.	1V	Hyd.	40-60
			EIGHT CYLINDER						
302	1970-71	4.00x3.00	15426378	205 @ 4600	300 @ 2600	8.6-1	2V	Hyd.	35-60
	1972	4.00x3.00	15426378	159 @ 4000	250 @ 2400	8.2	2V	Hyd.	35-60
	1973	4.00x3.00	15426378	157 @ 4000	249 @ 2600	8.2	2V	Hyd.	40-60
	1974-76	4.00 x 3.00	15426378	N.A.	N.A.	N.A.	2V	Hyd.	40-60
330	1970-72	3.875x3.50	15426378	190 @ 4000	306 @ 2000	7.4-1	2V	Hyd.	45-70
	1973	3.875x3.50	15426378	154 @ 3600	276 @ 2000	7.4	2V	Hyd.	35-60
	1973	3.875x3.50	15426378	155 @ 3600	262 @ 2600	7.4	2V	Hyd.	35-60
	1974-76	3.815 x 3.50	15426378	N.A.	N.A.	N.A.	2V	Hyd.	35-60
351	1976	4.00 x 3.50	13726548	N.A.	N.A.	N.A.	2V	Hyd.	35-60
360	1970-71	4.05x3.50	15426378	215 @ 4400	327 @ 2600	8.4-1	2V	Hyd.	35-60
	1972	4.05x3.50	15426378	196 @ 4600	291 @ 2000	8.0	2V	Hyd.	35-60
	1973	4.05x3.50	15426378	189 @ 4600	287 @ 2400	8.0	2V	Hyd.	35-60
	1974-76	4.05 x 3.50	15426378	N.A.	N.A.	N.A.	2V	Hyd.	35-60
361	1970-71	4.05 x 3.50	15426378	210 @ 4000	345 @ 2000	7.4-1	2V	Hyd.	45-70
	1972	4.05x3.50	15426378	210 @ 4000	345 @ 2000	7.2	2V	Hyd.	35-60
	1973	4.05x3.50	15426378	169 @ 3600	290 @ 2400	7.2	2V	Hyd.	35-75
	1974-76	4.05 x 3.50	15426378	N.A.	N.A.	N.A.	2V	Hyd.	35-75
390	1970-71	4.050x3.78	15426378	255 @ 4400	376 @ 2600	8.6-1	2V	Hyd.	35-60
	1972	4.05x3.78	15426378	201 @ 4400	316 @ 2600	8.2	2V	Hyd.	35-60
	1973	4.05x3.78	15426378	195 @ 4400	319 @ 2400	8.2	2V	Hyd.	35-75
	1974-76	4.05 x 3.78	15426378	N.A.	N.A.	N.A.	2V	Hyd.	35-75
391	1970-72	4.050x3.79	15426378	235 @ 4000	372 @ 2000	7.2	4V	Hyd.	35-60
	1973	4.05x3.79	15426378	192 @ 3600	333 @ 2400	7.2	4V	Hyd.	35-75
	1974-76	4.05 x 3.79	15426378	N.A.	N.A.	N.A.	4V	Hyd.	35-75
401	1970-72	4.1250x3.75	15486372	226 @ 3600	343 @ 2300	7.5-1	4V	Mech.	35-65
	1973	4.125x3.75	15486372	185 @ 3400	293 @ 3000	7.3	4V	Mech.	35-60
	1974-76	4.125 x 3.75	15486372	N.A.	N.A.	N.A.	4V	Mech.	35-60
460	1973-76	4.36 x 3.85	15426378	N.A.	N.A.	N.A.	4V	Hyd.	35-65
477	1970-71	4.5000x3.75	15486372	231 @ 3400	412 @ 1600	7.5-1	2V	Mech.	35-65
	1972-73	4.500x3.75	15486372	209 @ 3200	353 @ 2800	7.20	4V	Mech.	35-60
	1974-76	4.50 x 3.75	15486372	N.A.	N.A.	N.A.	4V	Mech.	35-60
534	1970-72	4.5000x4.20	15486372	266 @ 3200	481 @ 1700	7.5-1	4V	Mech.	35-65
	1973-76	4.500x4.20	15486372	222 @ 3000	400 @ 1800	7.3	4V	Mech.	35-65

CRANKSHAFT BEARING JOURNAL SPECIFICATIONS

CU. IN. DISPLACE-MENT	YEAR	MAIN BEARING JOURNALS				CONNECTING ROD BEARING JOURNALS		
		JOURNAL DIAMETER	OIL CLEARANCE	SHAFT END PLAY	THRUST ON NO.	JOURNAL DIAMETER	OIL CLEARANCE	END PLAY
			SIX CYLINDER					
170	1970-72	2.2482-2.2490	.0007-.0026	.004-.008	3	2.1232-2.1240	.0006-.0026	.0035-.0105
200	1973	2.2482-2.2490	.0005-.0026	.004-.008	5	2.1232-2.1240	.0002-.0024	.0035-.0105
240	1965-74	2.3982-2.3990	.0005-.0022	.004-.008	5	2.1228-2.1236	.0008-.0024	.006-.013
300	1970-76	2.3982-2.3990	.0009-.0028	.004-.008	5	2.1228-2.1236	.0009-.0027	.006-.013
			EIGHT CYLINDER					
302	1970-76	2.2482-2.2490	.0005-.0015	.004-.008	3	2.1228-2.1236	.0010-.0015	.010-.020
330 MD.	1970-76	2.7484-2.7492	.0011-.0031	.004-.008	3	2.4380-2.4388	.0006-.0023	.010-.020
HD.	1970-76	2.7479-2.7487		.004-.010	3	2.4377-2.4385	.0009-.0027	.010-.020

CRANKSHAFT BEARING JOURNAL SPECIFICATIONS

CU. IN. DISPLACE-MENT	YEAR	MAIN BEARING JOURNALS				CONNECTING ROD BEARING JOURNALS		
		JOURNAL DIAMETER	OIL CLEARANCE	SHAFT END PLAY	THRUST ON NO.	JOURNAL DIAMETER	OIL CLEARANCE	END PLAY
EIGHT CYLINDER								
351	1976	2.9994-3.002	3	.004-.008	3	2.3103-2.311	.0008-.0026	.010-.020
360	1970-76	2.7484-2.7492	.0005-.0024	.004-.010	3	2.4380-2.4388	.0008-.0026	.010-.020
361	1970-76	2.7479-2.7487	1	.004-.010	3	2.4377-2.4385	.0010-.0029	.010-.020
390	1970-76	2.7484-2.7492	.0005-.0024	.004-.010	3	2.4380-2.4385	.0008-.0026	.010-.020
391	1970-76	2.7479-2.7487	.0012-.0033	.004-.008	3	2.4377-2.4385	.0012-.0033	.006-.016
401	1970-76	3.1246-3.1254	.0018-.0025	.004-.008	3	2.7092-2.7100	.0017-.0036	.006-.014
460	1973-76	2.9994-3.002	.0008-.0026 4	.004-.008	3	2.4992-2.500	.008-.0015	.010-.020
477	1970-76	3.1246-3.1254	.0018-.0039	.004-.008	3	2.7092-2.7100	.0017-.0036	.006-.014
534	1970-76	3.1246-3.1254	.0018-.0039	.004-.008	3	2.7092-2.7100	.0017-.0036	.006-.014

MD—Medium Duty.
HD—Heavy Duty.

1—No. 1, 3 .0012-.0036, No. 2, 4, 5 .0010-.0033.
2—No. 1. .0007-.0031, others .0005-.0028.

3—N. 1—.0005-.0015; All others .0008-.0015.
4—No. 1 only—All others, .0008-.0015.

FIRING ORDER AND ROTATION

Six—144, 170 & 200 engines

Six—240 & 300 engines

V8—all

VALVE SPECIFICATIONS

CU. IN. DISPLACE-MENT	YEAR	LASH (HOT) INCHES INT.	EXH.	ANGLE DEGREE FACE	SEAT	STEM DIA. INCHES INT.	EXH.	STEM CLEARANCE INCHES INTAKE	EXHAUST	VALVE LIFT INCHES	VALVE SPRING LBS. @ INCHES OPEN	CLOSED	LENGTH INCH FREE
SIX CYLINDER													
170	1970-72	.018	.018	44	45	.3104	.3102	.0008-.0025	.0010-.0027	.2405[4]	117 @ 1.222	52 @ 1.585	2.00
200	1973-75	Zero	Zero	45	44	.3103	.3101	.0008-.0025	.0010-.0027	—	150 @ 1.20	—	—
240	1970-76	Zero	Zero	44	45	.3420	.3420	.0010-.0027	.0010-.0027	.2330[5]	197 @ 1.300	80 @ 1.70	1.99
300	1970-76	Zero	Zero	44	45	.3420	.3420	.0010-.0027	.0010-.0027	.2490	192 @ 1.180	80 @ 1.58	1.87
MD.	1970-71	Zero	Zero	44	45	.3420	.3420	.0010-.0024	.0028-.0042	.2490	1	2	3
EIGHT CYLINDER													
302	1970-76	Zero	Zero	44	45	.3420	.3420	.0010-.0027	.0010-.0027	.244[7]	180 @ 1.230	75 @ 1.66	1.97
MD.	1970-76	Zero	Zero	44	45	.3715	.3705	.0010-.0024	.0028-.0042	.2446[8]	189 @ 1.420	99 @ 1.82	2.26
HD.	1970-76	Zero	Zero	44	45	.3715	.4343	.0010-.0024	.0020-.0037	.2446[8]	185 @ 1.240	80 @ 1.67	2.00
351	1975-76	Zero	Zero	44	45	.3420	.3415	.0010-.0027	.0010-.0027	.370[11]	200 @ 1.34	75 @ 1.79	2.06[12]
360	1970-76	Zero	Zero	44	45	.3715	.3715	.0010-.0024	.0020-.0034	.238[9]	220 @ 1.380	90 @ 1.82	2.12
361	1970-72	Zero	Zero	44	45	.3715	.4343	.0010-.0024	.0020-.0037	.2448	185 @ 1.240	80 @ 1.67	2.00
	1973-76	Zero	Zero	44	45	.3715	.4343	.0010-.0024	.0020-.0037	.244[10]	185 @ 1.240	80 @ 1.67	2.00
390	1970-76	Zero	Zero	44	45	.3715	.3715	.0010-.0024	.0020-.0034	.248	220 @ 1.380	90 @ 1.82	2.12
391	1970-76	Zero	Zero	44	45	.3715	.4343	.0010-.0024	.0020-.0037	.2448[10]	185 @ 1.240	80 @ 1.67	2.00
401	1970-76	.020	.020	44	45	.4354	.4340	.0010-.0026	.0024-.0040	.278	185 @ 1.280	77 @ 1.70	2.07
460	1973-76	Zero	Zero	44	45	.3420	.3420	.0010-.0027	.0010-.0027	.253[13]	252 @ 1.33	80 @ 1.81	2 03
477	1970-76	.020	.020	44	45	.4354	.4340	.0010-.0026	.0024-.0040	.278	185 @ 1.280	77 @ 1.70	2.07
534	1970-76	.020	.020	44	45	.4354	.4340	.0010-.0026	.0024-.0040	.278	185 @ 1.280	77 @ 1.70	2.07

HD—Heavy Duty.
MD—Medium Duty.
1—Intake 197 @ 1.30, Exhaust 192 @ 1.18.
2—Intake 80 @ 1.70, Exhaust 81 @ 1.58.
3—Intake 1.99, Exhaust 1.87.
4—Exhaust .2395.

5—Exhaust .2490.
6—Exhaust .237.
7—Exhaust .265.
8—Exhaust .2329—Lat Model engines: Intake .2303. Exhaust .2375.

9—Late Model engines: Intake .247. Exhaust .249.
10—Exhaust .233.
11—Intake; Exhaust—.382.
12—Intake; Exhaust—.212.
13—Intake; Exhaust—.278.

RING SIDE CLEARANCE SPECIFICATIONS

ENGINE (CU IN.)	YEAR	TOP COMPRESSION (IN.)	BOTTOM COMPRESSION (IN.)	OIL CONTROL (IN.)
170-6	1970-72	.002-.004	.002-.004	Snug
200-6	1973-75	.0019-.0036	.0025-.0045	Snug
240-6	1970-74	.0019-.0036	.0025-.0045	Snug
300-6	1970-76	.0019-.0036	.0025-.0045	Snug
302-V8	1970-76	.002-.004	.002-.004	Snug
351-V8	1976	.002-.004	.002-.004	Snug
330-V8	1970-76	.0024-.0046	.003-.005	Snug①
360-V8	1970-76	.002-.004	.002-.004	Snug
361-V8	1970-72	.0029-.0046	.0029-.0046	.0036-.0039
361-V8	1973-76	.002-.005	.002-.005	.003-.0046
390-V8	1970-76	.002-.004	.002-.004	Snug
391-V8②	1970-72	.0029-.0046	.0029-.0046	.0036-.0039
391-V8②	1973-76	.003-.005	.003-.005	.003-.0046
401-V8 477-V8 534-V8	1970	.0029-.0046	.0025-.0045	.0014-.0031
401-V8 477-V8 534-V8	1971-72	.0029-.0046	.0025-.0045②	.0014-.0045
401-V8 477-V8 534-V8	1973-76	.0029-.0046	.0029-.0046	.0014-.0031
460-V8	1976	.002-.004	.002-.004	Snug

① 330 Heavy Duty—.0036-.0039
② Intermediate compression same as others

RING GAP SPECIFICATIONS

ENGINE (CU IN.)	YEAR	TOP COMPRESSION (IN.)	BOTTOM COMPRESSION (IN.)	OIL CONTROL (IN.)
170-6	1970-72	.010-.020	.010-.020	.015-.055
200-6	1973-75	.010-.020	.010-.020	.015-.055
240-6	1970-74	.010-.020	.010-.020	.015-.055
300-6	1970-76	.010-.020	.010-.020	.015-.055
302-V8	1970-76	.010-.020	.010-.020	.015-.055
351-V8	1976	.010-.020	.010-.020	.015-.055
330-V8①	1970-76	.010-.015	.010-.015	.015-.055
360-V8①	1970-76	.015-.023	.010-.015	.015-.055
361-V8	1970-72	.015-.023	.010-.020	.015-.030
361-V8	1973-76	.015-.023	.010-.020	.015-.025
390-V8①	1970-76	.015-.023	.010-.020	.015-.055
391-V8	1970-72	.015-.023	.010-.020	.015-.030
391-V8	1973-76	.015-.023	.010-.020	.015-.025
401-V8 477-V8 534-V8	1970-72	.018-.039	.015-.036②	.013-.039
401-V8 477-V8 534-V8	1973	.018-.028	.018-.028②	.013-.028
401V8 477-V8 534-V8	1974-76	.018-.028	.015-.025②	.013-.028
460	1975-76	.010-.020	.010-.020	.015-.055

① If equipped with intermediate ring, gap is .015-.023 in.
② Intermediate ring same as bottom compression.

TORQUE SPECIFICATIONS

CU. IN. DISPLACEMENT	YEAR	CYLINDER HEAD BOLTS (FT. LBS.)	ROD BEARING BOLTS (FT. LBS.)	MAIN BEARING BOLTS (FT. LBS.)	CRANKSHAFT BALANCER BOLT (FT. LBS.)	FLYWHEEL TO CRANKSHAFT BOLTS (FT. LBS.)	MANIFOLD INTAKE (FT. LBS.)	EXHAUST
SIX CYLINDER								
170	1970	70-75	19-24	60-70	85-100	75-85	—	13-18
200	1973-75	70-75	19-24	60-70	85-100	75-85	—	13-18
240	1970-76	70-75	40-45	60-70	130-150	75-85	23-28	23-28
300	1970-76	70-75	40-45	60-70	130-145	75-85	20-25	20-25
EIGHT CYLINDER								
302	1970-76	65-75	19-24	60-70	70-90	75-85	20-22	15-20
330 MD.	1970-76	80-90	40-45	95-105	70-90	75-85	32-35	23-28¹
HD.	1970-76	80-90	40-45	95-105	150-175	75-85	32-35	23-28¹
351	1975-76	65-70	19-24	60-70	70-90	75-85	23-25	18-24
360	1970-76	80-90	40-45	95-105	70-90²	75-85	32-35	12-18
361	1970-76	80-90	40-45	95-105	150-175	75-85	32-35	18-24
390	1970-76		40-45	95-105	70-90²	75-85	32-35	12-18
391	1970-76	80-90	40-45	95-105	150-175	75-85	32-35	18-24
401	1970-76	170-180	60-65	130-150	130-175	100-110	23-28	23-28
460	1973-76	130-140	40-45	95-105	70-90	75-85	25-30	28-33
477	1970-76	170-180	60-65	130-150	130-175	100-110	23-28	23-28
534	1970-76	170-180	60-65	150-165	130-145	100-110	23-28	23-28

MD—Medium Duty.
HD—Heavy Duty.

1—1970, 18-24.
2—1975-76—130-150.

WHEEL ALIGNMENT SPECIFICATIONS — EXCEPT BRONCO

YEAR	MODEL	CASTER (deg)			CAMBER (deg)			TOE-IN (in.)
		MAXIMUM	MINIMUM	OPTIMUM	MAXIMUM	MINIMUM	OPTIMUM	
1970	Econoline	5½P	½P	—	3½P	½P	—	⅛
	F-100, 150 (2WD)	5½P	½P	—	2½P	½N	—	³⁄₃₂
	F-350 (2WD)	5½P	½P	—	3P	0	—	³⁄₃₂
	F-100 (4WD) Bronco	4¼P	2¾P	3½P	2P	1P	1½P	⅛
	F-250 (4WD)	4½P	3½P	4P	1P	2P	1½P	⅛
	P-350 P-3500	5¼P	3¾P	4½P	⅞P	⅜P	⅝P	⅛
	P-400, 500 P-4000, 5000	4¼P	2¾P	3½P	1P	0	½P	⅛
1971	E-100, 200	5½P	½P	—	3½P	½P	—	⅛
	E-300	7½P	2½P	—	3½P	½P	—	⅛
	F-100, 250	5½P	½P	—	2½P	½N	—	³⁄₃₂
	F-350	5½P	½P	—	3P	0	—	³⁄₃₂
	F-100 (4WD) Bronco	3¼P	1¾P	2½P	2P	1P	½P	⅛
	F-250 (4WD)	4½P	3½P	4P	2P	1P	1½P	⅛
	P-350 P-3500	5¼P	3¾P	4½P	⅞P	⅜P	⅝P	⅛
	P-400, 500 P-4000, 5000	4¼P	2¾P	3½P	1P	0	½P	⅛
1972	E-100, 200	8½P	3½P	—	3½P	½P	—	⅛
	E-300	7½P	2½P	—	3½P	½P	—	⅛
	F-100, 250	8½P	3½P	—	2½P	½N	—	³⁄₃₂
	F-350	8½P	3½P	—	3P	0	—	³⁄₃₂
	F-100 (4WD) Bronco	4¼P	2¾P	3½P	2P	1P	1½P	⅛
	F-250 (4WD)	4½P	3½P	2½P	2P	1P	1½P	⅛
	P-350 P-3500	5¼P	3¾P	4½P	⅞P	⅜P	⅝P	⅛
	P-400, 500 P-4000, 5000	4¼P	2¾P	3½P	1P	0	½P	⅛
1973	E-100, 200	8½P	3½P	—	3½P	½P	—	⅛
	E-300	7½P	3½P	—	3½P	½P	—	⅛
	F-150, 250, 350	8½P	3½P	—	3½P	½P	—	⅛
	F-100 (4WD) Bronco	4¼P	2¾P	3½P	2P	1P	½P	⁵⁄₃₂
	F-250 (4WD)	4½P	3½P	2½P	2P	1P	½P	⁵⁄₃₂
	P-350 P-3500	5¼P	3¾P	4½P	⅞P	⅜P	⅝P	⅛
	P-400, 4000 P-500, 5000	4¼P	2¾P	3½P	1P	0	½P	⅛
1974-76	E-100, 150, 200, 250	8½P	2½P	—	3½P	½P	—	⅛
	E-300, 350	7½P	2½P	—	3½P	½P	—	⅛
	F-150, 250	8½P	½P	—	2½P	½N	—	⅛
	F-350	8½P	½P	—	3P	0	—	⅛
	F-100 (4WD) F-150 (4WD) Bronco	4¼P	2¾P	3½P	2P	1P	1½P	⁵⁄₃₂
	F-250 (4WD)	4½P	3½P	4P	2P	1P	1½P	⁵⁄₃₂
	P-350 P-3500	5¼P	3¾P	4½P	⅞P	⅜P	⅜P	⅛
	P-400, 500 P-4000, 5000	4¼P	2¾P	3½P	1P	0	½P	⅛

Note: Maximum variation between wheels—½°
P—Positive
N—Negative

TOE-IN SPECIFICATIONS
— MEDIUM AND HEAVY DUTY TRUCKS

VEHICLE	AXLE CAPACITY (lbs)	YEAR	TOE-IN (in.)① Minimum	Maximum
All Exc. w-wt good w/Center Point	5000, 5500, 6000, 7000, 12000 Center-Point	1970-76	3/16	5/16
All Exc. L-Series conventional or Steer-Ease	9000, 12000 Conventional, 12000 Steer-Ease, 15000, 16000, 18000, 20000	1970-76	5/16	7/16
W-WT 9000 w/Center-Point	1200 Center-Point②	1971-76	3/16	11/16
F-600 (4WD)	7500	1971-76	1/16	3/16
L-Series w/12000 Conv. or 12000 Steer-Ease	12000 Conventional 12000 Steer-Ease	1973-76	3/16	5/16

① Vehicle Unladen
② No part of the tie-rod clamp can be in the area between 10 o'clock and 2 o'clock.

BRONCO

YEAR	MODEL	CASTER (Deg.)	CAMBER (Deg.)	TOE-IN (In.)	KING PIN INCLINATION (Deg.)
1970		3½ ¹	1½ ¹	⅛	8½
1971		2½	1½	⅛	8½
1972		3½	1½	⅛	8½
1973-76		3½	1½	5/32	8½

1—The Caster and Camber angles are designed into the front axle and can not be adjusted.

TRUCK MODEL AND ENGINE APPLICATION

IDENTIFICATION PLATE: On light and medium cowl and windshield vehicles, the rating plate is attached to the right side of the cowl top panel or the upper cowl panel under the hood. The rating plate is on the right side of the radiator support on Parcel Delivery trucks, and on the inside of the glove compartment door on Broncos. On all other models, the plate is attached to the rear face of the left front door.

ENGINE PLATE: An identification tag is attached to the engine, giving the cubic inch displacement, building date and year.

GASOLINE ENGINES

CUBIC INCH DISPLACEMENT	YEAR	ENGINE MAKE
6-170	1970-72	Own
6-200	1973-75	Own
6-240	1970-74	Own
6-300	1970-76	Own
V-8-302	1970-74	Own
V8-330	1970-76	Own
V8-351	1975-76	Own
V8-360	1970-76	Own
V8-361	1970-76	Own
V8-390	1970-76	Own
V8-391	1970-76	Own
V8-401	1970-76	Own
V8-460	1975-76	Own
V8-477	1970-76	Own
V8-534	1970-76	Own

CAMBER SPECIFICATIONS
— MEDIUM AND HEAVY DUTY TRUCKS

VEHICLE	AXLE CAPACITY (lbs)	YEAR	CAMBER (deg)① Minimum	Maximum
All	5000, 5500, 6000, 7000	1970-76	¼P	1P
All Except L-LT-LTS-LN-LNT 800-9000	9000, 12000 Conventional	1970-76	D(L), ½N(R)	¾P(L), ¼P(R)
	12000 Center-Point	1970-76	⅛P(L), ⅜N(R)	⅞P(L), ⅜(PR)
	15000	1970-76	¼P	1P
L-LT-LTS-LN-LNT 800-9000	9000, 12000 Conventional, 12000 Steer-Ease, 16000, 18000, 20000	1970-76	¼P	1P
F-600 (4WD)	7500	1971-76	½P	1½P

① Vehicle Empty
P—Positive
N—Negative
L—Left
R—Right

CASTER SPECIFICATIONS
— MEDIUM AND HEAVY DUTY TRUCKS

VEHICLE	AXLE CAPACITY (lbs)		YEAR	CASTER (deg) ①	
				Minimum	Maximum
F-B 700, 750	All	Manual	1970	3P	4P
		Power		6P	7P
F-B 700, 750	All		1971-76	3P	4P
L-N 500	All	Manual	1970	4P	5P
		Power		7P	8P
L-N 500, 750	All		1971-76	4P	5P
C-CT Series	6000, 7000, 9000, 12000 Conventional, 15000		1970-76	2½P	3½P
	12000 Center-Point		1970-76	0	1P
L-LT-LN-LNT 800-900, 9000	6000, 7000		1970-76	3¼P	4¼P
	9000,		1970, 1973-76	3½P	4½P
	12000 Conventional, 12000 Steer-Ease, 16000, 18000, 20000		1970	3P	4P
	9000, 12000 Conventional		1971-72	3½P	4½P
	12000 Steer-Ease		1972	3¼P	4¼P
	16000, 18000, 20000		1972-76	3P	4P
	12000 Conventional 12000 Steer-Ease		1973-76	1¹⁵⁄₁₆P	3¹⁄₁₆P
W-WT 9000	12000 Conventional 15000 Conventional		1970-73 1970-76	3P	4P
	12000 Center-Point		1970-73	0	1P
	12000 Conventional		1974-76	2½P	3½P
F-600 (4WD)	7500		1971-76	2½P	3½P

① Vehicle unladen
P—Positive
N—Negative

Note: Caster Specifications are for a level frame front to rear. If the frame is lower at the rear, subtract the frame angle from the angle on the checking equipment. If the frame is lower at the front, add the frame angle to the angle on the checking equipment.

Loadomatic distributor spark advance mechanism
(© Ford Motor Co.)

on the body and engine block, indicating the position of the body in the block. These marks will insure that the distributor will be correctly timed when it is reinstalled.

5. Remove hold down bolt and clamp or retaining bolt and lockwasher and lift the distributor out of the block. NOTE: Do not rotate the crankshaft while the distributor is removed, or it will be necessary to time the engine.

6. To install, position the distributor in the block with the rotor aligned to the mark previously scribed on the distributor and the marks on the distributor and block aligned.

7. If the crankshaft has been rotated while the distributor was removed, the distributor must be timed with respect to the crankshaft. Rotate engine until No. 1 piston is at top dead center of compression stroke. Position the distributor in the block with the rotor in No. 1 firing position. Rotate the distributor until points are just about to open. NOTE: Make sure the oil pump intermediate shaft properly en-

Distributor

General Information

1970-76 6-cylinder engines are equipped with Autolite dual advance distributors. All V8 engines have Autolite dual advance distributors. 1970-76 model Autolite distributors may have the dual diaphragm vacuum advance mechanism, depending on which exhaust emission control system is utilized. See "Exhaust Emission Controls" in this section or "Exhaust Emission Controls" in the General Repair Section for detailed information on emission control systems. Rotation is clockwise on 6-cylinder engines and counterclockwise on V8 engines.

Distributor Removal

1. On a conventional ignition system, disconnect the primary wire at the coil. On a transistor ignition system, disconnect the primary wire from the quick disconnect.

2. Disconnect the vacuum line(s) at the distributor.

3. Remove the distributor cap.

4. Scribe a mark on the distributor body, indicating the position of the rotor. Scribe another mark

Autolite dual diaphragm distributor—6 cyl. (© Ford Motor Co.)

Autolite dual advance distributor w/single diaphragm (© Ford Motor Co.)

3. Connect a timing strobe light to the No. 1 spark plug lead and install a tachometer.
4. Start engine and set idle speed.
5. Loosen hold down clamp bolt or retainer bolt and rotate distributor housing until timing is correctly set.
6. Check the operation of the centrifugal advance by accelerating the engine to 2000 rpm. If the timing does not advance 9-14 degrees, the mechanical advance mechanism is faulty and must be removed for service.
7. Unplug vacuum line(s) and connect to distributor diaphragm. Momentarily accelerate engine to 2000 rpm and note timing advance. If it is not considerably more than the mechanical advance alone, the disphragm must be replaced.
8. Remove timing light and tachometer. Reset idle to correct speed.

Breaker Point Replacement

1. Remove the distributor cap and rotor.
2. Disconnect the primary and condenser wires from breaker point assembly.
3. Remove the breaker point assembly and condenser retainer screws and lift the breaker point assembly and condenser out of the vehicle.
4. To install, place breaker point assembly and condenser in position and install retaining screws. Be sure to place the ground wire under the breaker point assembly screw farthest from the

gages (Autolite dual advance) the distributor shaft. It may be necessary to crank the engine with the starter, after the distributor gear is engaged, in order to engage the oil pump intermediate shaft.
8. Install retaining clamp and bolt or retaining bolt and lockwasher, but do not tighten.
9. Connect primary wire and install distributor cap.
10. Check and reset ignition timing as described below.
11. Tighten hold down clamp bolt or retaining bolt.
12. Connect vacuum hose(s).

Setting Ignition Timing

Before checking and adjusting the ignition timing, inspect the breaker points for alignment and adjust if necessary. Rotate the distributor until breaker rubbing block rests on the peak of a cam lobe and check the breaker point gap, adjusting if necessary. See Specifications at the beginning of this section for correct gap setting.
1. Clean and mark timing marks. All timing marks are on the crankshaft belt drive pulley, except on the 240 cu. in. engine in Econoline models and 240 and 300 cu. in. engines in P series models, where the marks are on the flywheel or flexplate (automatic transmission).
2. Disconnect vacuum line(s) and plug the disconnected line(s).

Transistor ignition system (© Ford Motor Co.)

breaker point contacts on V8 engine distributor or under the condenser retaining screw on 6-cylinder engine distributor.

5. Align and adjust the breaker points.
6. Connect primary and condenser wires to the breaker point assembly.
7. Install rotor and distributor cap.
8. Set ignition timing to specifications.

Transistor Ignition System

The tachometer block is used to connect a tachometer or other test equipment into the circuit.

CAUTION: Do not connect test equipment into the circuit in any other manner, or reading will be inaccurate and damage may occur to the resistor, or change its operating characteristics.

Connect the tachometer red lead to the tachometer block small terminal and black lead to the large terminal when making tests.

Ignition timing and breaker point gap are set in the conventional manner as described above.

Breakerless Distributor (Solid State)

In 1975 all engines are equipped with the breakerless type electronic ignition system. The conventional contact breaker points and condenser in the distributor are replaced by a permanent magnet low-voltage generator. The generator consists of an armature with four or six gear-like teeth mounted on the top of the distributor shaft, and a permanent magnet inside a small coil. The coil is riveted in place to provide a preset air gap with the armature. The distributor base, cap, rotor and vacuum and centrifugal spark advance are about the same as the conventional system.

The distributor is wired to a solid state module in the engine compartment. Inside the module is an electronic circuit board which consists of inner connecting resistors, capacitors, transistors and diodes. The module senses a signal from the magnetic generator to perform the switching function of conventional points and it senses and controls dwell.

Unless a malfunction occurs, or the distributor is moved or replaced, the initial ignition timing remains constant. Because the low voltage coil in the distributor is riveted in position, the air gap adjustment with the rear tooth armature is not possible.

Module Test

If the electronic module is suspected of being defective, proceed as follows:

1. Without removing the existing module from the vehicle, unplug the connectors from the electronic module. Connect a known good module. The substitute module does not have to be fastened to the vehicle to operate properly.
2. Attempt to start the engine. If the engine starts and accelerates properly, proceed to step three. If the engine will still not start, the fault is in the wiring or other vehicle systems. Inspect and repair as necessary.
3. Reconnect the original module. Again attempt to start and run the engine. If the engine once again will not start, remove the original module and replace with a new one. If, however, the engine will now start and run on the original module, the module is not defective.
4. With the engine operating, check all connections in the primary wiring of the ignition system for such faults as poor wire crimp to terminal or improper engagement. The faulty connection will be observed when the engine misfires or stops. Correct as necessary.

Tachometer-to-Coil Connection—Electronic Ignition

The new solid state ignition coil connector allows a tachometer test lead with an alligator-type clip to be connected to the DEC (Distributor Electronic Control) terminal without removing the connector.

When engine rpm must be checked, install the tachometer alligator clip into the "TACH TEST" cavity as shown. If the coil connector must be removed, grasp the wires and pull horizontally until it disconnects from the terminals.

COIL CONNECTOR

TO "DEC" TERMINAL (DISTRIBUTOR ELECTRONIC CONTROL)

TO "BAT" TERMINAL

TACH TEST

MUELLER 60 SERIES ALLIGATOR CLIP

TACHOMETER TEST LEAD

Tachometer to coil connection— electronic ignition (© Ford Motor Co.)

Alternator

The alternator charging system is a negative (—) ground system consisting of an alternator, regulator, charge indicator, storage battery and associated wiring. The belt-driven alternator produces power in the form of alternating current which is rectified to direct current by six diodes (eight diodes in 61 ampere alternators) for use in charging the battery and supplying the electrical system.

The alternator is self current limiting and there is therefore no current limiting relay in the regulator. For alternator and regulator electrical testing procedures see the Electrical Diagnosis Section in the General Repair Section.

Alternator Removal and Installation

1. Disconnect battery ground cable.
2. Loosen the alternator mounting bolts and remove the adjustment arm to alternator attaching bolt.
3. Remove the electrical connectors from the alternator. The stator and field connectors are of the push-on type and should be pulled straight off to prevent damage to the terminal studs.
4. Disengage the alternator belt.
5. Remove the alternator mounting bolt and alternator.
6. To install, first install the wiring harness, then position the alternator on engine, installing spacer (if used) and mounting bolt. Tighten bolt only finger tight.
7. Install the adjustment arm to alternator attaching bolt.
8. Adjust belt tension as described below.
9. Tighten adjusting arm bolts and mounting bolt to 22-32 ft. lbs. torque.

Alternator Belt Adjustment

1. Loosen the alternator mounting bolt to a snug position and loosen the adjusting arm bolt.
2. *Apply pressure on the alternator front housing only* and tighten the adjusting arm to alternator bolt.
3. Check for correct tension. Belt tension is correctly adjusted when belt can be deflected by hand 1/2-3/4". Readjust if necessary.
4. Tighten all mounting bolts to 22-32 ft. lbs. torque.

Regulator Adjustments

Motorcraft

The Motorcraft electro-mechanical regulator used in 1968-76 models is not adjustable and must be replaced if charging system tests indicate that it is defective.

Transistorized Regulator

Starting in 1966, some models were equipped with transistorized alternator regulators. In transistorized regulator circuits the electro-mechanical field relay is used. The field relay is mounted separately from the voltage regulator. The field relay is not adjustable and must be replaced if testing indicates that it is faulty. The transistorized voltage re-

65 amp. Leece Neville alternator (© Ford Motor Co.)

Transistorized regulator (© Ford Motor Co.)

Field relay transistor ignition
(© Ford Motor Co.)

gulator voltage limiter 40 ohm variable resistor may be adjusted as described below.

1. Remove regulator mounting screws and regulator.
2. Remove bottom cover from regulator.
3. With regulator at normal operating temperature, use a fiber rod as a screwdriver to turn 40-ohm adjustable resistor.
4. Install bottom cover and mount regulator.

Regulator Removal and Installation

1. Remove battery ground cable.
2. Remove the regulator mounting screws.
3. Disconnect the regulator from the wiring harness.
4. To install, connect wiring harness.
5. Mount the regulator to the regulator mounting plate. The radio supression condenser (electro-mechanical regulator) mounts under one of the mounting screws. The ground lead mounts under the other mounting screw.
6. Connect battery ground cable and test the charging system for proper voltage regulation. See Electrical Diagnosis Section in the General Repair Section for testing procedures.

Fuse Link

The fuse link is a short thin length of insulated wire integral with the engine compartment wiring harness. If there is a heavy reverse current flow (such as caused by an improperly connected booster battery or when a short occurs in the wiring harness), the fuse link burns out and thus protects the alternator from damage. Production fuse links are black and replacement are green or black. All have the words FUSE LINK printed on the insulation. Burn-out of a fuse link may be evidenced by disfigured or bubbled insulation or by bare wire ends protruding from the insulation.

To test continuity of the fuse link (Bronco and F-Series LD) check that the battery is OK, then check with a voltmeter for voltage at the BAT terminal of the alternator. No voltage indicates that the fuse link is probably burned out. On P-Series trucks, disconnect the battery ground cable and, using an ohmmeter or a self-powered test light, check for continuity between points A and B (see illustration). A good fuse link will light the test bulb or show zero resistance on the ohmmeter. If fuse link is burned out, replace as described below.

Fuse Link Replacement

1. If the 5/16″ eyelet terminal is not required, cut it off as close to the terminal as possible.
2. Disconnect battery ground cable.
3. Disconnect the fuse link terminal at the starter relay (alternator on P-Series).
4. Remove the complete fuse link at the splice, when applicable, remove the old terminal from the battery stud of the starter relay.
5. Cut out original splice(s), then splice and solder the new fuse link with the existing wires from the original splice(s). See illustration. Wrap splice completely with tape. If there were two wires connected to the fuse link eyelet, cut link from eyelet and position the second wire with the eyelet back on the starter relay terminal.
6. Install all other wires removed during service.
7. Connect battery ground cable.

Fusible link installation (© Ford Motor Co.)

Starter

Reference

For complete overhaul procedures of starter motor and drive mechanisms, see "Starters" in the General Repair Section.

Autolite & Motorcraft Starter Removal and Installation

This starter utilizes a solenoid integral positive-engagement drive. All starters are mounted on the engine block and flywheel housing.

1. Disconnect starter cable at the starter terminal.
2. Remove the starter mounting bolts.
3. Remove the starter assembly.
4. To install, insert the starter into the pilot hole in the flywheel housing, making sure that the starter housing pilot completely enters the pilot hole all the way around, and that the starter housing face is square and tight to the engine rear cover plate. Install mounting bolts.
5. Snug all bolts, torquing them to 23–28 ft. lbs.
6. Connect starter cable.

Delco Remy Starter Removal and Installation

1. Open battery box and disconnect the battery cables.
2. Remove one bolt and lockwasher securing the battery cable retainer to the right rear cylinder head cover.
3. Remove the starter upper mounting bolt.
4. Remove the clamps securing the resonator inlet pipes to the exhaust manifolds, and position the inlet pipes out of the way.
5. Remove the starter shield retaining bolts.
6. Disconnect starter and solenoid wires. Tag the wires to insure proper reinstallation.
7. Remove the two remaining starter mounting bolts and lockwashers.
8. Remove starter.
9. To install, position the starter on engine and install three mounting bolts and lockwashers. Tighten to 23–28 ft. lbs. torque.
10. Connect solenoid wire to starter terminal.
11. Install starter shield on engine block with two retaining bolts.
12. Connect the remaining starter wires to the terminals.
13. Connect the resonator inlet pipes to the exhaust manifolds, and secure with clamps.
14. Connect the battery cables and close battery box.
15. Check operation of starter.

Prestolite Starter Removal and Installation

1. Disconnect the starter cable at the starter terminals.
2. Remove the heat shield from the manifold.
3. Remove the starter mounting bolts.
4. Tilt the starter slightly so the starter drive clears the flywheel housing and remove the starter.
5. Installation is the reverse of removal. On trucks with automatic transmission the dipstick tube bracket is mounted under the starter mounting bolt.

Brakes

Hydraulic

Starting in 1968, front disc brakes became a standard production option on F-250 and F-350 models and standard equipment on F-250 models with the 390 cu. in. engine.

A dual master cylinder hydraulic system is standard equipment.

Vacuum assist is optional equipment on most models.

For complete hydraulic master and slave cylinder overhaul procedures see the General Repair Section. For brake shoe removal procedure also see General Repair Section.

Brake Pedal Adjustment

1970-72

If the pedal free travel in a standard hydraulic brake system or frame mounted hydraulic booster system is not within 3/16–3/8", the pedal should be adjusted as follows:
1. Push the brake pedal down by

Autolite starter—disassembled (© Ford Motor Co.)

BENDIX

GPD

Typical dual master cylinder (© Ford Motor Co.)

hand pressure, and check the free travel.

2. Loosen locknut on eccentric bolt, and rotate the eccentric bolt until proper free travel is obtained. On P-series trucks rotate the hex head of the push rod to obtain correct free travel.

3. Hold the bolt securely and torque locknut to 30–35 ft. lbs.

4. Recheck brake pedal free travel.

Bleeding Conventional Hydraulic Brake System

1. Fill master cylinder reservoir with fluid. Check level of fluid frequently during bleeding procedure.

2. If hydraulic system is equipped

with a vacuum booster, bleed the booster before bleeding the rest of the system.

3. If vehicle is equipped with dual slave cylinders, bleed the upper one first. If there are two bleeder screws, bleed the one nearest the power chamber first.

4. Bleed the wheel cylinder with the longest hydraulic line first.

5. Attach bleeder tube to bleeder screw and place other end of tube in a container partially filled with fluid.

6. Loosen bleeder screw, then slowly depress the brake pedal by hand, allowing it to return slowly to the fully-released position. Repeat until all bubbles

cease to flow fom bleeder tube.

7. Close bleeder screw and remove tube.

8. Repeat this procedure at each wheel until system is completely free of air bubbles.

Bleeding Dual Hydraulic Brake Systems

The primary and secondary hydraulic brake system are individual systems and are bled separately. Bleed the longest line first on the individual system being serviced. Be sure to keep reservoir filled during bleeding operation

After bleeding it is necessary to centralize the pressure differential valve. On 1970-71 500-950 series

Brake differential valve—100-400 series (© Ford Motor Co.)

Brake differential valve—500-900 series w/split hydraulic brakes (© Ford Motor Co.)

trucks, remove the brake warning light switch from the pressure differential valve to prevent damage to the switch assembly.

1. Bleed master cylinder at the outlet port side of the system being serviced. If there are no bleed screws, loosen the hydraulic line nut. Do not use the secondary piston stop screw located on the bottom of the master cylinder—the stop screw or piston could easily be damaged.
2. Operate pedal slowly until fluid is free of air bubbles, then tighten bleed screw.
3. Follow Steps 1 through 8 of Conventional Bleeding procedure above.
4. Centralize the pressure differential valve. Turn the ignition switch to ACC or ON position. Loosen the pressure differential valve inlet tube nut on the system opposite the system which was bled last. This will result in unequal pressure in the other direction and allow the valve to center. Slowly depress brake pedal until light goes out. Tighten inlet tube nut. On 1970-71 500-900 series trucks, disconnect wires from warning light switch on the differential valve, remove switch. Springs inside valve will center valve. Replace switch and wire.
5. Check fluid level in reservoir and fill to within ¼" of top.

Master Cylinder Removal and Installation

On models equipped with power boosters, depress brake pedal while engine is not running to expel vacuum or air from booster system.

1. If stoplight switch is mounted on the master cylinder, disconnect wires.
2. On dash-mounted master cylinders, disconnect the dust boot from the rear of the master cylinder at the dash panel. If the boot is connected to the master cylinder only, leave it in place.
3. Disconnect the hydraulic line(s) from the master cylinder and pump the brake pedal all the way several times to evacuate all fluid from the master cylinder into a suitable container.
4. Disconnect the pushrod from the brake pedal. On dash-mounted master cylinders the pushrod is connected to the brake pedal lever with a bolt, and there may be a stoplight switch mounted by that bolt. Remove the bolt and stoplight switch. If the master cylinder is under the floorboard, remove clevis pin from pushrod yoke. Mark or tag bushings and spacers for correct position.
5. On trucks equipped with conventional brakes, remove the master cylinder mounting bolts and master cylinder. If the truck is equipped with a dash-mounted booster, remove the retaining nuts and washers and pull master cylinder off mounting studs.
6. To install, position master cylin-

Brake cylinder installation—C series
(© Ford Motor Co.)

der so that mounting bolts or retainer nuts may be installed. Tighten mounting bolts or nuts securely.
7. Connect hydraulic lines(s) loosely to master cylinder fitting(s).
8. If rubber dust boot attaches to both cylinder and dash, make sure it is properly installed at this time.
9. Connect pushrod to brake pedal lever. If there is a bushing in the hole at the end of the pushrod, lubricate bushing. Install stoplight switch at this time if it was removed when disconnecting pushrod from brake pedal lever. Make sure all bushings and spacers are properly installed.
10. Connect stoplight switch wires.
11. Bleed hydraulic system as described above. Bleed master cylinder first.

Power Disc Brake

Floating Caliper

This type power disc brake became available as an option on F-250 and F-350 models in 1968. The brake system consists of a dual master cylinder coupled to a dash-mounted vacuum booster. Both primary and secondary hydraulic lines run to a differential valve and warning light switch unit. A metering valve is located in the front brake line between the pressure differential valve and the disc brake calipers. The double piston housing is mounted on the anchor plate on two mounting pins which travel in bushings in the anchor plate. The anchor plate is bolted directly to the spindle.

The disc brake shoe requires no adjustment as the unit is designed so that it is inherently self-adjusting.

152

Exploded view of floating caliper assembly (© Ford Motor Co.)

Exploded view of sliding caliper assembly (© Ford Motor Co.)

Sliding Caliper

This type of disc brake assembly is used on light duty trucks only. The system uses a sliding caliper with a single piston. The caliper support and the steering arm are cast as a single piece and help to form the spindle assembly. The caliper assembly is cast as a single piece and is machined to slide on the support.

A proportioning valve is located on the frame and helps to keep the pressure equal between the front and rear brake assemblies.

No adjustments are required on the brakes other than setting the brake pedal several times, after the system has been worked on, to set the brake shoes against the rotor. After this is done no other adjustments are necessary. The hydraulic line pressure will maintain the proper clearance between the shoes and the rotor.

Refer to the General Repair Section

for repair procedures on this type of brake assembly.

Bleeding Disc Brake Hydraulic System

The hydraulic system may be bled in the conventional manner, with the following additional steps.

1. First bleed master cylinder, then rear brake cylinders (longest line first).
2. On front disc brakes, the bleeder button on the metering valve must be depressed to allow the brake fluid to reach the caliper assemblies. When the bleeding operation is complete, fill the reservoir to within ¼" of top.
3. Centralize the pressure differential valve as described above in "Bleeding Dual Hydraulic Brake Systems".

Differential Valve Removal and Installation

1. Raise the vehicle on a hoist.
2. Disconnect the brake warning light from the pressure differential valve assembly switch. CAUTION: To prevent damage to the brake warning switch wire connector, expand the plastic lugs to allow removal of the shell-wire connector from the switch body.

Brake metering valve (© Ford Motor Co.)

Floating caliper disc brake (© Ford Motor Co.)

Disc brake system (© Ford Motor Co.)

3. Disconnect the brake hydraulic lines from the differential valve assembly.
4. Remove the screw retaining the pressure differential valve assembly to the frame side rail and remove the valve assembly.
5. Differential valve and switch are separate units and are serviced separately. Remove warning light switch from valve to replace either unit.
6. To install, mount the pressure differential valve assembly on the frame side rail and tighten the attaching bolt.
7. Connect the brake hydraulic lines to the differential valve and tighten the tube nuts securely.
8. Connect the shell-wire connector to the brake warning light switch. Make sure plastic lugs on the connector hold the connector securely to the switch.
9. Bleed the brakes and centralize the pressure differential valve as described above.

Power Boosters

Reference

For power booster overhaul procedures see the General Repair Section.

Bendix Dash-Mounted Vacuum Booster

Push Rod Adjustment

To assure correct operation of the vacuum booster, proper clearance between the booster pushrod and the master cylinder pushrod must be maintained. Too long a booster pushrod can cause brake drag. Too short a pushrod can cause excessive pedal travel and an annoying clunk in the booster area.

1. Fabricate a gauge of the dimensions illustrated.
2. Unbolt nuts and remove master cylinder from mounting studs.
3. Measure booster pushrod length with gauge.
4. If adjustment is necessary, turn adjusting screw until it just touches the inner edge of the gauge.
5. Reinstall master cylinder.

Bendix Booster Removal and Installation

1. Remove retaining nuts and master cylinder from booster.
2. Loosen hose clamp and remove manifold vacuum hose from booster.
3. From inside the cab, remove the attaching bolt, nut and plastic

Bendix booster push rod adjustments (© Ford Motor Co.)

bushings and disconnect the booster pushrod from the brake pedal.
4. Remove nuts that retain the booster mounting bracket to the dash panel.
5. Remove the booster assembly from engine compartment.
6. To install, mount the booster and bracket assembly to the engine side of the dash panel by sliding the bracket mounting bolts and valve operating rod in through the holes in the dash panel.
7. From inside the cab, install the booster mounting bracket to dash panel retaining nuts.
8. Position the master cylinder to the booster assembly and install the retaining nuts.
9. Connect the manifold vacuum hose to the booster and secure with clamp.
10. From inside the cab connect the booster valve operating rod to the brake pedal with the attaching bolt, nut and plastic bushings.
11. Start engine and check operation of the brake system.

Midland-Ross Dash-Mounted Vacuum Booster

Pushrod Adjustment

Checking the adjustment of the pushrod length on the dash-mounted Midland-Ross vacuum brake booster is the same as that described for the Bendix above, with the exception of the gauge dimensions.

Midland-Ross Booster Removal and Installation

Removal and installation proce-

Midland Ross dash mounted vacuum booster (© Ford Motor Co.)

External band type parking brake
(© Ford Motor Co.)

Midland Ross booster push rod adjustments
(© Ford Motor Co.)

dure for the Midland-Ross booster is the same as that described for the Bendix booster above.

Parking Brakes

Adjustment

Orscheln Lever

The Orscheln parking brake is the over center locking type. It is adjusted (in the fully released position) by turning the lever knob. When properly adjusted, it pulls over center with a distinct click. No other adjustment is normally required.

Cable Actuated Rear Wheel Type

Adjust service brakes before attempting to adjust the parking brake cables. Place parking brake lever in fully released position, then check for slack in the parking brake two rear cables. Cables are properly adjusted when the rear brake shoes are fully applied when parking brake is applied, and the brake shoes fully release when the parking brake lever is released.

To tighten cables, loosen locknut and tighten adjusting nut on equali-

zer. Tighten locknut when proper adjustment is obtained.

External Band Type

1. On cable controlled parking brakes, move the parking brake lever to the fully released position. On a vehicle with a rod type linkage, set the lever at the first notch.
2. Check the position of the cam to make sure that the flat portion is resting on the brake band bracket. If the cam is not flat with the bracket, remove the clevis pin from the upper part of the cam and adjust the clevis rod to allow the flat portion of the cam to rest on the brake band bracket. Install the clevis pin and cotter pin.
3. Remove the lock wire from the anchor adjusting screw, and turn the adjusting screw clockwise until a clearance of 0.100″ is obtained between the brake lining and the brake drum at the anchor bracket. Install the lock

wire in the anchor adjusting screw.
4. Adjust the clearance on the upper and lower halves of the band in a similar manner. See illustration for location of adjusting screws. Adjust for a 0.010″ clearance between band and drum.

Internal Shoe Type 9″ Drum

1. Release parking brake lever.
2. Remove cotter pin from the parking brake linkage adjusting clevis pin and remove the clevis pin.
3. Lengthen or shorten adjusting link by turning the clevis. There should be a 0.010″ clearance between the drum and the band all the way around when the clevis pin is installed.
4. Install a new cotter pin in the clevis pin and check brake operation.

12″ Drum

There is no internal adjustment on this brake. Adjust the linkage as follows:

Internal shoe type parking brake (© Ford Motor Co.)

1. Remove clevis pin, loosen the nuts on the adjusting rod and turn clevis until a ¼"—⅜" free play is obtained at the brake lever with pin installed.
2. Tighten locknuts on adjusting rod and reinstall clevis pin.

Parking Brake Drum and Shoe R & R

Transmission Mounted External Band

1. Put the transmission in low gear and disconnect the driveshaft flange from the transmission.
2. Apply the parking brake and remove the nut attaching the transmission output shaft flange. Release the parking brake.
3. Disconnect the adjusting rod from the cam by removing the cotter and clevis pins.
4. Remove the cotter and clevis pins and remove the cam link from the cam.
5. Remove the lockwire and anchor adjusting screw.
6. Remove the brake band adjusting nuts and bolts.
7. Lift the brake band and lining from the drum.
8. The lining should be replaced if the lining is less than 1/32 in. off the top of the rivet.
9. Installation is the reverse of removal. Adjust the parking brake.

Fuel System

On models 1968 and later, all carburetors on Ford trucks are equipped with fuel mixture adjusting limiters. The external type plastic idle limiter cap is installed on the head of the idle fuel mixture adjusting screw(s). The cap limits the maximum idle fuel richness and helps prevent unauthorized persons from making overly rich idle adjustments.

On the Autolite 2-barrel, the limiter stops must be installed under the power valve cover in order that the limiters have positive stops.

If all other engine systems are operating within specifications, a satisfactory idle should be obtainable within the range of idle adjusting limiters. Carburetors on models 1967 and earlier are, of course, adjusted in the conventional manner.

Carburetor specifications may be found in the General Repair Section.

The following idle speed and idle fuel mixture adjustment procedures should be followed in the sequence given. If a satisfactory idle condition cannot be obtained, proceed with the checks and adjustments described in "Additional Idle Speed and Mixture Procedures".

Idle fuel mixture limiter—Holley 4 BBL (© Ford Motor Co.)

Idle Fuel Settings—Engine Off

1. Set idle mixture screw(s) and limiter cap(s) to full counterclockwise position.
2. Back off idle speed adjusting screw until throttle plate(s) seat in throttle bore(s).
3. Be sure dashpot or solenoid (if so equipped) plunger is not interfering with the throttle lever. It may be necessary to loosen the dashpot to allow the throttle plate to seat in the throttle bore.
4. Turn the idle speed adjusting screw inward until it just makes contact with stop on throttle shaft and lever assembly, then turn screw inward 1½ turns to establish a preliminary idle speed adjustment.

IDLE ADJUSTING LIMITERS

LIMITER STOPS

Idle adjusting limiters & stops—Autolite (© Ford Motor Co.)

Idle Fuel Settings—Engine Running

1. Set parking brake, start engine and position idle screw on the intermediate step of the fast idle cam to obtain an engine speed of 1500 rpm. Let the engine run for at least 20 minutes so that engine and underhood temperatures are stabilized.
2. Check ignition timing and advance as described above in this section. These settings must be accurate.

3. On manual transmission model, idle setting is made with transmission in *neutral*. On automatic transmission models, set selector lever in DRIVE position and parking brake on, except as noted when using an exhaust gas analyzer.
4. Be sure choke plate is in full open position.
5. On carburetors equipped with a hot idle compensator or where the idle compensator is in the crankcase ventilation hose, be sure the compensator is seated to allow for proper idle adjustment.
6. Turn headlights on so that alternator is under load.
7. Turn air conditioner OFF for final idle speed adjustment.
8. Adjust curb idle rpm to specifications (see Specifications at the beginning of this section or in the Carburetor section of the General Repair Section). Use a tachometer and leave the air cleaner on. On Carter model YF IV with solenoid throttle modulator, turn solenoid plunger screw to obtain correct curb idle. Disconnect solenoid lead wire at bullet connector near the loom (*not* at solenoid), then adjust the throttle stop screw for 500 rpm. Reconnect solenoid lead wire and open throttle by hand: the throttle plunger should follow the throttle lever and remain in the fully extended position as long as the ignition is on and the solenoid energized. If it is impossible to adjust idle speed with the air cleaner on, remove it to adjust, then reinstall it and check speed, repeating the process until correct idle speed is obtained.

9. Turn idle mixture adjusting screw(s) inward to obtain the smoothest possible idle within range of limiter(s). On 2- and 4-barrel carburetors, turn idle mixture limiters and equal amount. Check for smoothness only with the air cleaner installed.

Additional Idle Speed and Mixture Procedures

If a satisfactory idle is not obtained with the above normal procedures, make the following checks, making corrections if necessary:

1. Vacuum leaks, ignition wiring continuity, spark plugs, breaker point dwell angle, breaker point gap and initial ignition timing.
2. If a satisfactory idle condition is still not obtained with the checks and corrections of Step 1 above, check: fuel level, crankcase ventilation system, valve clearance and engine compression.
3. If the above procedures fail to produce a satisfactory idle condition, it may be due to a lean idle mixture. Check air-fuel mixture with an exhaust analyzer and adjust as described below.

Use of Exhaust Gas Analyzer

1. Connect analyzer in accordance with manufacturer's instructions. All exhaust gas analyzers must be checked for calibration.
2. Observe reading with *air cleaner installed*. Refer to specifications below for correct air-fuel ratio.
3. Turn idle mixture adjusting screw(s) to obtain specified air-fuel ratio. On 2- and 4-barrel carburetors, turn the idle limiters equal amounts. Be sure to check idle speed frequently, correcting if necessary. Allow at least 10 seconds after each mixture adjustment for the analyzer to properly respond and stabilize.
4. If the air-fuel ratio is not to specifications, as shown by analyzer reading, it may be corrected by altering the controlled limits of the idle mixture system. See following paragraph for limiter cap replacement procedure.

Replacing Idle Limiter Caps

1. Cut plastic cap with a knife or side-cutter pliers, then carefully pry limiter apart. On some carburetors it may be necessary to remove the carburetor to remove the limiters. On Holley 4-barrel carburetors, pry limiters out of metering block with a screwdriver.
2. After limiters are removed, set the carburetor to the correct fuel-ratio, using exhaust gas analyzer.
3. When air-fuel ratio is within specified value, install limiter caps. Install cap so that it is the maximum counterclockwise position with the tab of the limiter against the stop on the carburetor. Be careful not to turn the screw, installing cap with a straight, forward push.
4. Recheck air-fuel ratio with the analizer.

Carburetor

Removal and Installation

1. Remove the air cleaner.
2. Remove the throttle cable or rod from the throttle lever. Disconnect the distributor vacuum line, EGR vacuum line, if so equipped, the inline fuel filter and the choke heat tube at the carburetor.
3. Disconnect the choke clean air tube from the air horn. Disconnect the choke actuating cable, if so equipped.
4. Remove the carburetor retaining nuts then remove the carburetor. Remove the carburetor mounting gasket, spacer (if so equipped), and the lower gasket from the intake manifold.
5. Before installing the carburetor, lean the gasket mounting surfaces of the spacer and carburetor. Place the spacer between two new gaskets and position the spacer and gaskets on the intake manifold. Position the carburetor on the spacer and gasket and secure it with the retaining nuts. To prevent leakage, distortion or damage to the carburetor body flange, snug the nuts, then alternately tighten each nut in a criss-cross pattern.
6. Connect the inline fuel filter, throttle cable, choke heat tube, distributor vacuum line, EGR vacuum line, and choke cable.
7. Connect the choke clean air line to the air horn.
8. Adjust the engine idle speed, the idle fuel mixture and anti-stall dashpot (if so equipped). Install the air cleaner.

Idle Speed Adjustment

1. Start the engine and run it until it reaches operating temperature.
2. If it hasn't already been done, check and adjust the ignition timing. After you have set the timing, turn off the engine.
3. Attach a tachometer to the engine.
4. Turn the headlights on to high beam.
5. On trucks with manual transmissions, engage the parking brake and place the transmission in Neutral; vehicles equipped with automatic transmission, engage the parking brake, and place the gear selector in Drive. Block the wheels.
6. Make sure that the choke plate is in the fully open position.
7. Adjust the engine curb idle rpm to the proper specifications. The tachometer reading must be taken with the carburetor air cleaner in place. If it is impossible to make the adjustment with the air cleaner in position, remove it and make the adjustment. Then replace the air cleaner and check the tachometer for the proper rpm reading.

On carburetors equipped with a solenoid throttle positioner, loosen the jam nut on the solenoid at the bracket and rotate the solenoid in or out to obtain the specified curb idle rpm. Disconnect the solenoid lead wire at the connector, set the automatic transmission in Neutral, then adjust the carburetor throttle stop screw to obtain 500 rpm. Connect the solenoid lead wire and open the throttle slightly by hand. The solenoid plunger will follow the throttle lever and remain in the fully extended position as long as the ignition is on and the solenoid energized.

Fuel Pump

All engines except the 401, 477 and 534 cu. in. are equipped with mechanical fuel pumps which are driven by an eccentric on the camshaft. On 6-cylinder engines it is located on the lower, left center of the block. On V-8 engines mechanical pumps are mounted on the left side of the cylinder front cover. Some fuel pumps have an integral filter. Other models have an in-line filter assembly. Filters are replaced (see owner's manual for specified replacement interval) by unscrewing the filter housing and replacing the old filter.

Testing Mechanical Fuel Pump

Install a new filter element before making the following tests. Tests are made with the fuel pump installed on the engine, with the engine warmed up to normal operating temperature, and with the engine idling at proper idle speed.

1. Remove air cleaner assembly and disconnect fuel inlet line at the carburetor. *Avoid fuel spillage due to risk of fire.*
2. Connect pressure gauge and fitting, flexible hose and restrictor clamp as illustrated.
3. Operate engine at idle speed. Momentarily open restrictor clamp to bleed system of air.

Testing mechanical fuel pump (© Ford Motor Co.)

Typical Carter fuel pump
(© Ford Motor Co.)

4. Close restrictor and note reading after pressure has stabilized. See Tune-Up Specifications at the beginning of this section for correct fuel pump pressure. If pressure is below specified value, fuel pump must be replaced or rebuilt.
5. If fuel pump is producing correct pressure, leave engine idling and proceed with volume test.
6. Open restrictor clamp and note time required to expell one pint into the container. It should take no more than 30 seconds.
7. If it takes more than 30 seconds, check for restriction in the fuel line from the tank by connecting pump to an external fuel source. If the volume test still takes more than 30 seconds per pint, then the fuel pump must be replaced.

Testing Electric Fuel Pump

1. Remove air filter and disconnect the fuel inlet line at the carburetor.

Testing electrical fuel pump (© Ford Motor Co.)

2. Using ¼″ pipe fittings (smaller diameter will restrict the flow), connect the pressure gauge, gate valve and flexible hose as illustrated. Use a suitable container to collect expelled fuel.
3. Operate fuel pump with primer switch. *Be sure the battery is fully charged.* Adjust gate valve for a reading of 2 psi, then note time required to expell 1 quart of fuel.
4. If the time required to expell one quart exceeds that specified in the table below, repeat the same test at the outlet at the tank to establish whether or not there is restriction in the fuel line.

Engine	Time (Sec.)
401	36
477	33
534	30

5. If the fuel pump does not fill the quart container fast enough, the pump must be replaced as a unit.
6. Remove test equipment, connect fuel line and install air cleaner.

Mechanical Fuel Pump

Removal and Installation

1. Disconnect inlet and outlet lines from pump.
2. Remove pump mounting bolts and remove pump and gasket. Discard gasket.
3. To install, clean away all gasket material from mounting pad and pump flange. Apply sealant to new gasket and threads of bolts.
4. Position pump and gasket on the mounting pad, being sure the rocker arm is riding on the cam eccentric. Turn engine over until eccentric is on low side of stroke.
5. Install mounting bolts and tighten securely.
6. Connect fuel lines.
7. Operate engine and check for leaks.

Electric Fuel Pump

Removal and Installation

1. Disconnect the battery.
2. Disconnect the fuel outlet line at the pump cover.
3. Remove wire harness housing cover from the fuel pump cover and disconnect the wires.
4. Remove fuel pump cover and reach down into the tank and disconnect the toggle clamp which secures the pump in the retaining bracket and remove the fuel pump.
5. Disconnect the fuel outlet tube and the wire assembly at the cover and at the pump.
6. To install, remove the old gasket

Electric fuel pump installation
(© Ford Motor Co.)

FUEL OUTLET   WIRE HARNESS   FUEL PUMP
LINE   HOUSING COVER   COVER

Electric fuel pump wiring
(© Ford Motor Co.)

from the cover and install a new gasket.
7. Connect the fuel outlet tube and the wire assembly to the pump cover and to the pump.
8. Install fuel pump in the bracket in the tank and fasten the toggle clamp.
9. Position the pump cover assembly on the tank and install the attaching bolts and wire clamps.
10. Connect the fuel line to the fitting on the cover.
11. Position the wiring harness in its housing on the cover and install the wire harness housing cover.
12. Connect the battery and operate the pump and truck engine to check for leaks.

Fuel Tank

Removal and Installation

Bronco

The following procedure can be used to remove either the main or auxiliary fuel tanks.
1. Insert a siphon through the filler neck and drain the fuel into a suitable container.
2. Raise the rear of the vehicle. If you are removing the auxiliary tank, raise the left side of the vehicle.
3. To avoid any chance of sparking at or near the tank(s), disconnect the ground cable from the vehicle battery. Disconnect the fuel gauge sending unit wire at the fuel tank.
4. Loosen the clamp on the fuel filler pipe hose at the filler pipe and disconnect the hose from the pipe.

5. Loosen the hose clamps, slide the clamps forward and disconnect the fuel line at the fuel gauge sending unit.
6. If the fuel gauge sending unit is to be removed, turn the unit retaining ring, and gasket, and remove the unit from the tank.
7. Remove the strap attaching nut at each tank mounting strap, swing the strap down, and lower the tank enough to gain access to the tank vent hose.
8. Disconnect the fuel tank vent hose at the top of the tank. Disconnect the fuel tank-to-separator tank lines at the fuel tank.
9. Lower the fuel tank and remove it from under the vehicle.
To install the fuel tank:
10. Position the forward edge of the tank to the frame crossmember, and connect the vent hose to the top of the tank. Connect the fuel tank-to-separator tank lines at the fuel tank.
11. Position the tank and mounting straps, and install the attaching nuts and flat washers.
12. If the fuel gauge sending unit was removed, make sure that all of the old gasket material has been removed from the unit mounting surface on the fuel tank. Using a new gasket, position the fuel gauge sending unit to the fuel tank and secure it with the retaining ring.
13. Connect the fuel line at the fuel gauge sending unit and tighten the hose clamps securely. Install the drain plug. if so equipped.
14. Connect the fuel gauge sending unit wire to the sending unit.
15. Connect the filler pipe-to-tank hose at the filler pipe and install the hose clamp.
16. Connect the vehicle battery ground cable.
17. Fill the tank and check all connections for leaks.
18. Lower the vehicle.

Econoline

1. Raise the rear of the vehicle.
2. To avoid electrical sparking at the tank, disconnect the ground cable on the vehicle battery. Then disconnect the fuel gauge sending unit wire at the fuel tank.
3. Remove the fuel tank drain plug and drain the fuel into a suitable container.
4. Loosen the hose clamps, slide the clamps forward and disconnect the fuel line at the fuel gauge sending unit. Disconnect the fuel tank vapor lines, if so equipped, by removing the clamps at the emission control valve.
5. If the fuel gauge sending unit is to be removed, turn the unit retaining ring counterclockwise

and remove the sending unit, retaining ring, and gasket.
6. Loosen the clamp on the fuel filler pipe hose at the tank, and disconnect the hose at the tank.
7. Remove the strap retaining nut at each tank mounting strap, swing the strap down, and lower the tank enough to gain access to the tank vent hose.
8. Disconnect the fuel tank vent hose at the top of the tank.
9. Lower the tank and remove it from under the vehicle.
10. Install the fuel tank in the reverse order of removal, using a new sealing gasket at the sending unit if it was removed from the tank.

F-100, 150, 250, 350 In-Cab Fuel Tank

1. Siphon the fuel from the tank into a suitable container through the filler neck.
2. Move the seat to the full forward position and tilt the seat forward.
3. Disconnect the fuel gauge sending unit wire and fuel line from the tank. Disconnect the vapor vent chamber and vapor lines of the fuel evaporative emission control system.
4. Loosen the filler neck hose clamp at the tank end of the hose, and pull the filler neck away from the tank.
5. Remove the fuel tank retaining nuts and bolts and lift the tank out of the cab. If the tank is being replaced, remove the fuel gauge sending unit and install it in the new tank.
6. Install the fuel tank in the reverse order of removal.

In-Frame Fuel Tank

1. Drain the fuel from the tank into a suitable container by either removing the drain plug, if so equipped, or siphoning through the filler cap opening.
2. Disconnect the fuel gauge sending unit wire and fuel outlet line.
3. Disconnect the air relief tube from the filler neck and fuel tank.
4. Loosen the filler neck hose clamp at the fuel tank and pull the filler neck away from the tank.
5. Remove the retaining strap mounting nuts and bolts and lower the tank to the floor.
6. If a new tank is being installed, change over the fuel gauge sending unit to the new tank.
7. Install the fuel tank in the reverse order of removal.

Behind-the-Axle Fuel Tank

1. Raise the rear of the truck.
2. Disconnect the negative battery cable.

3. Disconnect the fuel gauge sending unit wire at the fuel tank.
4. Remove the fuel drain plug or siphon the fuel from the tank into a suitable container.
5. Loosen the fuel line hose clamps, slide the clamps forward and disconnect the fuel line at the fuel gauge sending unit.
6. If the sending unit is to be removed, turn the unit retaining ring counterclockwise and remove the sending unit, retaining ring and gasket. Discard the gasket.
7. Loosen the clamps on the fuel filler pipe and vent hose as necessary and disconnect the filler pipe hose and vent hose from the tank.
8. If the tank is the metal type, support the tank and remove the bolts attaching the tank supports to the frame. Carefully lower the tank and disconnect the vent tube from the vapor emission control valve in the top of the tank. Finish removing the filler pipe and filler pipe vent hose if not possible previously. Remove the tank from under the vehicle.
9. If the tank is the plastic type, support the tank and remove the bolts attaching the combination skid plate and tank support to the frame. Carefully lower the tank and disconnect the vent tube from the vapor emission control valve in the top of the tank. Finish removing the filler pipe and filler pipe vent hose if it was not possible previously. Remove the skid plate and tank from under the vehicle. Remove the skid plate from the tank.
10. Install the tank in the reverse order of removal.

Governors

There are three types of governors used on Ford truck engines. The velocity governor (used on 240, 300, 360, 390 cu. in. engines) is a single unit mounted between the carburetor and the intake manifold. There is not provision for repair of this governor and it must be replaced as a unit when damaged. Some velocity governors are equipped with a coolant passage so that they are also used as a heated carburetor spacer. The velocity governor on the MD 330 V-8 engine may be adjusted for specific altitude.

Vacuum governors consist of a centrifugal valve on the distributor and a throttle actuating mechanism on the carburetor. At governing speed venturi and manifold vacuum, controlled by the controlling unit on the distributor, operates a vacuum diaphragm to close the throttle plates.

Vacuum governor system (© Ford Motor Co.)

Mechanical governors are gear-driven off the camshaft. When governing speed is reached, the centrifugal force of the flyweights pivoted on the governor shaft overcomes the spring retention and close the throttle plates through linkage to the throttle shaft.

Adjusting Velocity Governors

1. Connect a tachometer to the engine, warm up the engine then read engine rpm at wide-open throttle. If governed speed is not within the range stamped on the governor plate, adjustment is required.

2. Remove the governor seal.
3. To increase rpm, turn the cap counterclockwise; to decrease the rpm turn it clockwise.
4. If the truck is to be operated at a consistent altitude, cut the seal wire and remove the adjusting cap. *Do not rotate the cap during removal.* Use a mirror and light to observe the position of the slots in the adjusting bushing. *Do not disturb the center post or adjusting bushing*—if the tool does not engage the slots easily, remove the tool and realign it. For an increase in the average altitude of operation ro-

Coolant heated velocity governor (© Ford Motor Co.)

tate the inserted tool the amount specified in the table below in the counterclockwise direction.

Aver. Operating Altitude—Feet	Amount of Tool Rotation
2000	1/3 turn (120°)
3000	1/2 turn (180°)
4000	2/3 turn (240°)
5000	5/6 turn (300°)
6000	1 turn (360°)

60° or 1/6 turn rotation is equivalent to one flat of the tool hex head.

5. Remove tool and install cap, but *do not turn the adjusting cap.*
6. Install a tachometer and check and adjust the no-load setting. It should be 3900 for no-load at altitude and 3600 for load at altitude. Load and no-load speed should be slightly above these speeds if the governor is being adjusted above anticipated operating altitude and slightly below if it is being adjusted below anticipated operating altitude.
7. If load rpm is below 3600 rpm at operating altitude, repeat Step 4 turning the tool counterclockwise. If load governed speed is above 3600 rpm, repeat Step 4 turning the tool clockwise.
8. Seal adjusting cap to the governor body using service governor seal wire.
9. If the engine is to be operated at varying altitudes, adjust the governor for 3800 rpm no-load for sea-level. Using the adjusting cap only, adjust the no-load speed for 4100 rpm at the anticipated altitude by turning the adjustment cap ¼-turn (clockwise) for each 1000′ difference between the adjusting and anticipated altitudes. If the maximum operating altitude of the truck is lower than the altitude at which the adjustment is being made, adjust the no-load speed to 4100 rpm with the adjusting cap.

Adjusting Vacuum Governor

1. Warm up the engine until normal operating temperature is reached, then connect a tachometer.
2. Momentarily operate engine at wide-open throttle (governed speed) and note rpm reading.

Altitude compensation adjustment
(© Ford Motor Co.)

3. If governed speed is not at the correct value (see Tune-Up Specifications at the beginning of this section), turn off the ignition switch and remove adjusting hole cover from the controlling unit (distributor).
4. Crank engine by hand until adjusting nut is aligned with access hole.
5. Turn adjusting nut clockwise to increase speed and counterclockwise to decrease speed. One full turn equals about 150 rpm.
6. Repeat above procedure until proper governed speed is obtained.
7. Install adjusting access hole cover and tighten securely.
8. Install new locking wire and lead seal.

Adjusting Mechanical Governor

1. Disconnect the throttle control rod at the carburetor.
2. Loosen the top nut on the primary spring adjusting eye bolt.
3. Tighten the bottom nut finger tight, then turn it in two additional turns to pre-load the spring. Tighten the top nut.
4. Move the throttle to the wide-open position and connect the governor throttle control rod to the carburetor control arm.
5. Adjust the governor throttle control rod so that the governor throttle control auxiliary lever is full forward, then back off (shorten) the rod one full turn.

(TO CARBURETOR)

Mechanical governor (© Ford Motor Co.)

6. Check the throttle linkage to be sure that the throttle is wide-open when pedal is depressed to the floor. Be sure the rod or cable is attached to the proper hole in the throttle lever.
7. Check operation of choke plate for proper adjustment. On C-AND W-Series trucks the choke plate does not completely close when the dash knob is fully out.
8. To adjust speed, operate the engine (parking brake on) until normal operating temperature is reached. With throttle wide-open, adjust main spring (higher tension increases rpm and lower tension decreases rpm). Sensitivity of the governor can be sharpened by installing the governor spring in the hole closest to the lower arm pivot. Adjust governed speed after changing spring position.

Cooling System

Radiator Removal and Installation

To remove radiator, drain coolant and disconnect all hoses at the radiator. Fiberglass shrouds are retained to the radiator support with bolts having flat washers between the bolt head and the fiberglass and should always be assembled in this manner. Remove shrouding. On trucks equipped with a fan shroud, remove the fan, spacer, water pump pulley and drive belt.

When replacing radiator with a new one, remove the drain cock from the old one and install it in the new radiator using a sealing compound. If necessary, transfer hose fittings also.

On engines equipped with coolant recovery systems, fill the radiator through the filler cap opening of the radiator upper tank, completely full. The cap may be removed by turning to the stop and, forcing down on the cap, force the cap past the *stop* tangs on the the filler neck. Engine should be running at idle speed to circulate coolant and eliminate any trapped air in the system. Install the radiator cap. Fill coolant reservoir with one quart of coolant and operate vehicle until normal operating temperature is reached. Check coolant reservoir to see if coolant level is noted at the "Engine Hot" level. Add coolant if necessary.

Always check for leaks in the engine and, if so equipped, transmission cooling lines.

On P-Series trucks the hood, grill and headlights must be removed in order to replace radiator. On C-Series trucks remove the tachometer cable clamp from the radiator and disconnect the accelerator linkage to remove radiator.

On E-Series with 240-6, remove the right hood lock bracket and bolts from grill.

On F-Series with fan shroud, loosen the generator or a Hernator adjusting arm bolts and loosen the fan belt. Remove the fan, spacer, water pump pulley and fan belt.

Water Pump Removal and Installation

6-Cylinder Engines

1. Drain cooling system.
2. Disconnect radiator lower hose and heater hose at the water pump.
3. Remove fan belt, fan and water pump pulley.
4. On trucks equipped with air compressors, remove the air compressor belt.
5. Remove water pump retaining bolts, then remove pump and gasket.
6. To install, clean gasket surfaces of pump body and engine block.
7. If a new water pump is being installed, remove the fittings from the old pump and install them on the new pump.
8. Coat new gasket with water-resistant sealer on both sides and install gasket and pump on engine. Tighten mounting bolts securely.
9. Install water pump pulley, fan and fan belt, adjusting fan belt tension.
10. If so equipped, install air compressor belt.
11. Connect radiator and heater hoses.
12. Fill cooling system and operate engine to bleed air. Check for leaks and recheck coolant level.

V-8 Engines

Removal and installation of water pumps on V-8 engines are essentially the same as described for 6-cylinder engines. On V-8 equipped Econolines, the radiator must be removed in order to replace the water pump. On late model F-100 and Bronco vehicles, there may be a radiator shroud which must be unbolted and hung on the fan to permit access to the lower radiator hose. Remove lower radiator hose, then shroud.

Engine

Description

All Ford truck engines are of the conventional overhead valve design, either of six-cylinder in-line or V-8 configuration.

The 240 cu. in. and 300 cu. in.

6-cylinder engines (1970-76) are the large block units found in most medium and some heavy duty trucks. The 300 HD Six has a lower compression ratio to meet the higher torque requirements of heavier vehicles. These are the most common Ford power units.

The 330 cu. in. engine became the most popular V-8 option in medium and heavy duty trucks. The difference between the medium and heavy duty models is that the HD has a longer crankshaft in front.

The 302 cu. in. was the Econoline V-8 for both Econoline and Bronco models. The 351W was added in 1975 and the 460 was added in 1973.

The large block Super Duty 401, 477 and 534 cu. in. V-8 engines are used mainly in heavy trucks and will not be considered here.

Reference

Tune-up and general specifications for Ford truck engines may be found at the beginning of this section.

Crankcase Emission Controls

The crankcase emission control equipment consists of a positive crankcase ventilation (PCV) valve, a closed or open oil filler cap and the hoses that connect this equipment.

When the engine is running, a small portion of the gases which are formed in the combustion chamber leak by the piston rings and enter the crankcase. Since these gases are under pressure they tend to escape from the crankcase and enter into the atmosphere. If these gases were allowed to remain in the crankcase for

any length of time, they would contaminate the engine oil and cause sludge to build up. If the gases are allowed to escape into the atmosphere, they would pollute the air, as they contain unburned hydrocarbons. The crankcase emission control equipment recycles these gases back into the engine combustion chamber, where they are burned.

The most critical component of the system is the PCV valve. This vacuum-controlled valve regulates the amount of gases which are recycled into the combustion chamber. At low engine speeds the valve is partially closed, limiting the flow of gases into the intake manifold. As engine speed increases, the valve opens to admit greater quantities of the gases through connecting hoses to an air manifold and through air nozzles in the exhaust ports adjacent to each exhaust valve. The air, with its normal oxygen content, reacts with the hot but incompletely burned exhaust gases and permits further combustion in the exhaust port or manifold.

Another emission control system common to all of the engines since 1974 is the Exhaust Gas Recirculation (EGR) system. This system is designed to reduce the amount of nitrous oxides (NO_x) emitted into the atmosphere by re-introducing small amounts of exhaust gas into the combustion cycle. The amount of recycled exhaust gas depends chiefly on engine vacuum and temperature.

New for 1975 models is the catalytic converter. The converter is a muffler-type device installed in the vehicle's exhaust system and contains a chemical catalyst. When exhaust gases pass over and through the catalyst, it heats up to such great temper-

Closed crankcase ventilation system (© Ford Motor Co.)

atures that further chemical reaction occurs and the NO_x is broken down into harmless elements.

The above paragraphs are just a brief summary of the main exhaust emission control systems. Individual components of the various systems, their functions, construction, and repair are discussed further in the general repair section.

The above explanation and the troubleshooting procedure which follows applies to all of the engines installed in Ford trucks, since all are equipped with PCV systems.

Evaporative Emission Controls

Beginning 1970, F-100 pick-ups produced for sale in California were equipped with evaporative emission controls on the fuel system. For 1971, the system was modified somewhat and used on all F-100 pick-ups as standard equipment.

After 1974, F-250 pick-ups sold in California were equipped with the evaporative emissions system.

Exhaust Emission Controls

There are many devices used on the engines installed in Ford pick-ups to control emission of exhaust gases into the atmosphere.

All of the engines use the air injection reactor system, the Ford terminology for which is the "Thermactor" exhaust emission control system. This system is used on all engines, from 1970 to the present.

Air Pump

The air injection pump is a posi-

Thermactor system—installation (© Ford Motor Co.)

tive-displacement vane type which is permanently lubricated and requires little periodic maintenance. The only serviceable parts on the air pump are the exhaust tube and relief valve. The relief valve decreases the airflow when the pump pressure reaches a preset level. This occurs at high engine rpm. The relief valve also serves to prevent damage to the pump and to limit maximum exhaust manifold temperatures.

Air Delivery Manifold

The air delivery manifold distributes the air from the pump to each of the air delivery tubes in a uniform manner. This applies only to the 6 cylinder engines, as the air delivery manifold is integral with the cylinder head on the V8 engines.

Air By-Pass Valve

The air by-pass valve prevents engine backfire by briefly interrupting the air being injected into the exhaust manifold during periods of de-

celeration or rapid throttle closure. The valve opens when a sudden increase in manifold vacuum overcomes the diaphragm spring tension. With the valve in the open position, the airflow is vented to the atmosphere. In addition to preventing backfiring in the exhaust manifold as previously mentioned, the valve also prevents possible damage to the engine by not allowing the overly rich fuel mixture from being burned in the exhaust manifold. A rich mixture in the exhaust manifold is the result of deceleration or rapid throttle closure and to promote its further combustion by injecting air would cause backfiring.

Carburetor

The carburetors used on engines equipped with emission controls have specific flow characteristics that differ from the carburetors used on vehicles not equipped with emission control devices. All carburetors have limiter caps installed on the idle fuel mixture adjustment screws. These limiter caps prevent an overly rich mixture adjustment from being made. The correct adjustment can usually be reached within the range of the limiter caps. These carburetors are identified by number. The same

Thermactor exhaust emission control system (© Ford Motor Co.)

type carburetor should be used when replacement is necessary.

Thermostatically Controlled Air Cleaner System (TAC)

This system consists of a heat shroud which is integral with the right-side exhaust manifold, a hot air hose and a special air cleaner assembly equipped with a thermal sensor and vacuum motor and air valve assembly.

The purpose of TAC is to get hot air into the carburetor as soon as possible because the engine will emit less pollutants on a lean mixture.

Dual Diaphragm Distributor

The dual diaphragm distributor has two diaphragms which operate independently. The outer (primary) diaphragm makes use of carburetor vacuum to advance the ignition timing. The inner (secondary) diaphragm uses intake manifold vacuum to provide additional retardation of ignition timing during closed-throttle deceleration and idle, resulting in the reduction of hydrocarbon emissions.

Ported Vacuum Switch Valve (PVS)

The PVS valve is a temperature sensing valve usually found on the distributor vacuum advance line, and is installed in the coolant outlet elbow. During prolonged periods of idle, or any other situation which causes engine operating temperatures to be higher than normal, the valve, which under normal conditions simply connects the vacuum advance diaphragm to its vacuum source within the carburetor, closes the normal source vacuum port and engages an alternate source vacuum port. This alternate source is from the intake manifold which, under idle conditions, maintains a high vacuum. This increase in vacuum supply to the distributor diaphragm advances the timing, increasing the idle speed. The increase in idle speed causes a directly proportional increase in the operation of the cooling system. When the engine has cooled sufficiently, the vacuum supply is returned to its normal source, the carburetor.

These switches are used in several places in the emission systems. They can have anywhere from two to four ports and can be used to turn vacuum on and off, or to switch between two vacuum sources for a third delivery point.

Deceleration Valve

Some engines were equipped with a distributor vacuum advance control valve (deceleration valve) which is used with dual diaphragm distributors to further aid in controlling ignition timing. The deceleration valve is in

Ignition vacuum system with Imco emission (© Ford Motor Co.)

the vacuum line which runs from the outer (advance) diaphragm to the carburetor, the normal vacuum supply for the distributor. During deceleration, the intake manifold vacuum rises causing the deceleration valve to close off the carburetor vacuum source and connect the intake manifold vacuum source to the distributor advance diaphragm. The increase in vacuum provides maximum ignition timing advance, thus providing more complete fuel combustion and decreasing exhaust system backfire.

Exhaust Gas Recirculation System (EGR)

In this system, a vacuum-operated

Distributor modulator schematic (© Ford Motor Co.)

EGR flow valve is attached to the carburetor spacer (except on the 302 V8). A passage in the carburetor spacer mates with a hole in the mounting face of the EGR valve or the intake manifold. The EGR valve on the 302 V8 is located on the rear of the intake manifold. On all engines except the 302 V8, the system allows exhaust gases to flow from the exhaust crossover, through the control valve and through the spacer into the intake manifold below the carburetor. For those engines where exhaust gases cannot be picked up from the exhaust crossover (6 cylinder) as described above, the gases are picked up from the choke stove located on the exhaust manifold or directly from the exhaust manifold. The exhaust gases are routed to the carburetor spacer through steel tubing.

The vacuum signal which operates the EGR valve originates at the EGR vacuum port in the carburetor. This signal is controlled by at least one, and sometimes, two series of valves.

A water temperature sensing valve (the EGR PVS) which is closed until the water temperature reaches either 60° F or 125° F, depending on application, is always used.

Another system working in conjunction with the EGR system is the EGR/CSC system. This system regulates both the distributor spark advance and operation of the EGR valve according to the temperature of the engine coolant. The system consists of: a 95° EGR valve, a spark delay valve, and a vacuum check valve.

When the engine coolant is below 82° F, the EGR PVS valve admits carburetor EGR port vacuum directly to the distributor advance diaphragm through a one-way check valve. At the same time, the EGR PVS valve shuts off carburetor EGR vacuum to the EGR valve and transmission diaphragm.

When the engine coolant temperature is above 95° F, the EGR PVS valve is actuated and directs carburetor EGR vacuum to the EGR valve and transmission instead of the distributor.

The spark delay valve (SDV) delays carburetor spark advance vacuum to the distributor advance diaphragm by restricting the vacuum through the SDV valve for a predetermined time. During normal acceleration, little or no vacuum is admitted to the distributor advance diaphragm until acceleration is completed, because of the time delay of the SDV valve, and the re-routing of the EGR port vacuum, if the engine coolant temperature is 95° F or higher. The check valve blocks vacuum from the SDV valve to the EGR PVS valve so that carburetor spark vacuum will not be dissipated when

the EGR PVS valve is actuated above 95° F. increases and the increase in coolant circulation and fan speed cools the engine.

Cold Temperature Activated Vacuum System

The cold temperature activated vacuum (CTAV) system was used beginning in 1974 on 460 V8 engines in F-100 trucks built for sale in California.

The CTAV system more accurately marches spark advance to the engine requirements under cold ambient temperature conditions. The system can select from two vacuum sources for spark advance depending on the ambient temperature: below 45° F—carburetor spark port vacuum, above 65° F—EGR vacuum. In between these two temperature ranges the system will select either source of vacuum, depending on the cycle it is in.

The CTAV system consists of an ambient temperature switch, a three-way vacuum switch, inline vacuum bleed, and a latching relay.

The vacuum from both the spark port of the carburetor and the EGR port is supplied to the three-way solenoid valve. The ambient temperature switch provides the signal that determines which of the sources will be selected. The latching relay provides for only one cycle each time the ignition switch is turned on.

Vacuum and Spring Controlled Heat Control Valve

The heat control valve, commonly known as the heat riser, is mounted between the exhaust pipe and the exhaust manifold. The purpose of the device is to provide a quick warm-up of the carburetor and the rest of the induction system.

Fuel will condense on the cold surfaces of the induction system, which causes air/fuel ratios to fluctuate. These variations can cause uneven acceleration and increased emissions. The exhaust control valve, which is thermostatically-controlled, is closed when the engine is cold and routes hot exhaust gases through a passage under the carburetor and over to the opposite exhaust manifold which has no heat control valve and thus no restriction to block the flow of exhaust gases. This quickly warms the air/fuel mixture delivery passages and provides improved mixture control and driveability. As the engine warms up, the valve opens and reduces the flow of exhaust gases through the warm-up passage.

The valve is either operated by a bi-metal temperature sensitive spring or vacuum motor operated by intake manifold vacuum routed through a PVS switch.

Electrically-Assisted Choke

Some pick-ups use an electrically heated choke thermostatic spring housing as an aid to fast choke release and better emission characteristics during engine warm-up. The heater operates from a lead off the alternator only when the engine is actually running.

The heater element only operates when ambient temperatures are above 60° F (when long periods of choke operation are not necessary for engine driveability). When temperatures are blow 60° F, the choke thermostatic spring is heated in the normal manner: via a tube running from an exhaust manifold heat stove.

Engine Removal and Installation

Bronco 6-Cylinder

1. Drain cooling system and remove air cleaner.
2. Disconnect battery ground cable from the battery.
3. Disconnect upper and lower hoses at the engine, remove the four radiator mounting bolts, then remove radiator.
4. Disconnect the heater hose at the water pump and at the rear of the carburetor spacer.
5. Disconnect battery ground cable and alternator ground wire from the cylinder block.
6. Remove fan belt and alternator.
7. Disconnect the starter cable at starter, then remove the starter.
8. Remove U-clamp holding exhaust head pipe to the block, remove manifold stud retaining nuts, and remove pipe from the exhaust manifold.
9. Disconnect wiring at the coil and oil and temperature sending units.
10. Disconnect throttle and choke cables from the carburetor.
11. Remove windshield wiper vacuum hose from fuel pump.
12. Remove the crimped clamp, then the flex line from fuel pump.
13. Remove the retaining screws from the equalizer shaft bracket at the block and clutch housing, and remove the bracket.
14. Remove nut and washer from each of the engine mounts.
15. Loosen clutch housing to block bolts just enough so that they may be hand removed later.
16. Remove clutch housing cover retaining bolts.
17. Lower vehicle to the floor.
18. Position a jack under the transmission, and remove the clutch housing to block bolts.
19. Carefully remove engine.
20. To install, lower engine assembly carefully aligning the transmission shaft with the clutch disc splines.

21. Remove hoisting equipment and transmission jack.
22. Raise vehicle on a hoist.
23. Install lower clutch housing to block bolts securely.
24. Install clutch housing cover to clutch housing retaining bolts.
25. Install engine mount washers and retaining nuts, tightening securely.
26. Lubricate the clutch equalizer shaft and bracket and position the bracket and install the retaining bolts.
27. Lower vehicle.
28. Connect flex line (use a new clamp) and vacuum line to fuel pump.
29. Connect and adjust choke and throttle cables.
30. Connect the wiring at the coil and at the oil and temperature sending units.
31. If they were removed, install the water pump pulley, spacer and fan.
32. Place a new gasket on the exhaust inlet pipe, connect the pipe to the exhaust manifold, install the reaining nuts and tighten securely.
33. Install the U-bolt clamp to retain the inlet pipe to the bolck.
34. Install the starter and starter cable.
35. Install alternator and belt. Adjust belt.
36. Connect battery and alternator ground cables to block.
37. Connect heater hose at the rear of carburetor spacer and at the water pump.
38. Install radiator and, using a water-resistant sealer, connect upper and lower hoses to engine.
39. Connect battery ground cable and install air cleaner.
40. Fill cooling system and bleed all air.
41. Fill crankcase with lubricant.
42. Operate engine and check for fuel, lubricant and coolant leaks.

F-100 and Bronco V-8

Removal and installation procedure for the V-8 engine is the same as that for the 170 cu. in. 6-cylinder described above except for the following.
1. Transmission shift rod must be disconnected and retracting spring removed.
2. A left and a right lifting bracket are used, the left bracket on the front of the left cylinder head and the right bracket on the rear of the right cylinder head. A sling is then attached to each bracket to lift out the engine.
3. When lowering the engine into the vehicle, make sure exhaust manifolds are properly aligned with the muffler inlet pipes and the dowels in the block are through the rear cover plate and engage the holes in the flywheel housing. If the engine hangs up after the transmission splined shaft enters the clutch disc, turn the crankshaft slowly (transmission in gear) until the shaft splines mesh with the clutch disc splines.

240, 300 Cu. In. 6-Cylinder Econoline (to 1972), P-350, 500, F-100-600, C, B, LN-500, 600

The engine and transmission are disattached in the following engine removal procedure.
1. Drain cooling system and crankcase.
2. Remove hood or tilt the cab.
3. Remove air cleaner (1973-76). On C-series, remove the oil filler tube.
4. Disconnect the battery positive cable.
5. Disconnect the heater hose from the water pump and coolant outlet housing.
6. Disconnect flexible fuel line from the fuel pump.
7. Remove the radiator following procedure described above.
8. Remove the cooling fan, water pump pulley and fan drive belt.
9. Disconnect the accelerator cable and the choke cable at the carburetor. Remove the cable retracting spring.
10. On a vehicle with power brakes, disconnect the vacuum line at the intake manifold.
11. On a vehicle with automatic transmission, disconnect the transmission kickdown rod at the bellcrank assembly.
12. Disconnect exhaust manifold from the muffler inlet pipe.
13. Disconnect the body ground strap and the battery ground cable at the engine.
14. Disconnect the engine wiring harness at the ignition coil, water temperature and oil pressure sending units.
15. Remove alternator mounting bolts and position the alternator out of the way, leaving wires attached.
16. On a vehicle with power steering, remove the power steering pump from the mounting brackets and position it right side up and to one side, leaving the line attached.
17. If equipped with an air compressor, bleed the air system and disconnect the two air lines at the compressor.
18. Raise vehicle and remove starter and, if so equipped, remove the automatic transmission fluid filler tube.

19. Remove engine rear plate upper right bolt.
20. On a vehicle with manual transmission, remove all the flywheel housing lower attaching bolts. Disconnect the clutch retracting spring.
21. On vehicles with an automatic transmission, remove the converter housing access cover assembly. Remove the flywheel to converter nut and secure the converter assembly in the housing. Remove the transmission oil cooler lines from the retaining clip at the engine. Remove the converter housing to engine lower attaching bolts.
22. On F-100, 250, remove the insulator to intermediate support bracket nut from each engine front support. On other vehicles, remove the engine from support insulator bolt.
23. Lower the vehicle and position a transmission jack under the transmission. Remove the remaining flywheel or converter housing to engine bolts.
24. Attach engine lifting hook and raise the engine slightly and carefully pull it from the transmission. Lift engine out of the chassis.
25. To install, place a new gasket on the muffler inlet pipe.
26. Lower engine carefully into chassis. Make sure the studs on the exhaust manifold are aligned with the holes in the muffler inlet pipe and the dowels in the block engage the holes in the flywheel or converter housing.
27. On a vehicle with an automatic transmission, start the converter pilot into the crankshaft. Remove the retainer securing the converter in the housing.
28. On a vehicle with standard transmission, start the transmission input shaft into the clutch disc. It may be necessary to adjust the position of the transmission with relation to the engine if the transmission input shaft will not enter the clutch disc. If the engine hangs up after the shaft enters, turn the crankshaft slowly (with transmission in gear) until the shaft splines mesh with the clutch disc splines.
29. Install the converter or flywheel housing upper attaching bolts. Remove the transmission jack.
30. Lower the engine until it rests on the engine support(s) and remove the lifting hook.
31. On the F-100, 250, install engine left and right support insulator to intermediate support bracket retaining nuts, tightening securely. Install the front engine

mount bolt and nut on other vehicles.

32. Install the transmission oil cooler lines bracket, if so equipped.
33. Install remaining converter or flywheel housing attaching bolts.
34. Connect clutch return spring.
35. Install starter and connect cable.
36. If so equipped, install transmission fluid filler tube bracket.
37. On a vehicle with automatic transmission, install transmission oil cooler lines in the bracket at the engine block.
38. Install exhaust pipe to exhaust manifold, tightening bolts securely.
39. Connect engine ground strap and battery ground cable.
40. On a vehicle with automatic transmission, connect the kickdown rod to the bellcrank assembly on the intake manifold.
41. Connect the accelerator linkage to the carburetor and install the retrackting spring. Connect the choke cable to the carburetor and hand throttle if so equipped.
42. On a vehicle with power brakes, connect the brake vacuum line to the intake manifold.
43. On a C-series vehicle, install the oil filler tube.
44. Connect coil primary wire, oil pressure and water temperature sending units, flexible fuel line, heater hoses and battery positive cable.
45. Install alternator on mounting bracket. On a vehicle with power steering, install the power steering pump on the mounting brackets.
46. Install water pump pulley, spacer, cooling fan and drive belt, tightening bolts securely.
47. Install radiator.
48. Connect air compressor lines.
49. If so equipped, connect oil cooler lines.
50. Install and adjust hood.
51. Fill and bleed cooling system, checking for leaks.
52. Adjust the carburetor idle speed and mixture.
53. Adjust clutch pedal free travel or automatic transmission control linkage and check transmission fluid level.
54. Install air cleaner.

240, 300 Cu. In. Six, 1973-74
Econoline

1. Disconnect the battery and drain the cooling system. Remove the engine cover and the right hand seat. Remove the grille and bumper.
2. Remove the hood lock support bracket, right and left headlight doors, and grille.
3. Disconnect all hoses and lines to the radiator, and remove the battery deflector. Remove the radiator.
4. Disconnect
   A. The heater hoses, at the engine.
   B. Temperature, oil, and ignition wires.
   C. Starter solenoid, neutral safety switch, and back-up light wiring.
5. Remove the engine oil dipstick and oil filler tube. Remove hoses connecting the rocker cover and air filter. Remove the air cleaner and brackets.
6. Disconnect the choke and accelerator cables at the carburetor. Disconnect the auxiliary heater hose at the front heater. Disconnect the hoses at the right front of the engine, and position them out of the way.
7. Disconnect the fuel pump discharge line at the pump. Disconnect the alternator, and remove it from the brackets.
8. Disconnect the ground wires at the block, and the muffler inlet pipe at the manifold. Disconnect the modulator line at the intake manifold.
9. Put the vehicle on a hoist. Drain the crankcase and remove the oil filter.
10. Disconnect the starter wiring, and remove the starter.
11. Position an engine support bar to the chassis and engine, and adjust it.
12. On manual transmission vehicles:
    A. Disconnect the driveshaft, and remove it. Install a plug in the transmission extension housing.
    B. Disconnect the speedometer cable and housing, and secure the assembly out of the way.
    C. Remove the nut and bolt holding the rear support to the crossmember. Raise the transmission, remove the mounting bolts, and remove the crossmember.
    D. Remove the clutch equalizer arm bolts from the engine. Disconnect the retracting spring, and move the assembly away.
    E. Remove the bolts connecting transmission and clutch, and remove the transmission.
13. On automatic transmission vehicles:
    A. Remove the bolts connecting the adapter plate and inspection cover to the torque converter.
    B. Unbolt and remove the transmission dipstick tube. Drain the transmission.
    C. Remove the nuts attaching the converter to the flex plate. Disconnect the oil cooler and modulator lines at the transmission.
    D. Disconnect the driveshaft at the companion flange.
    E. Disconnect the speedometer cable and housing from the transmission. Disconnect the shift rod at the lever on the transmission. Jack the transmission up slightly.
    F. Remove the nuts and bolts attaching the rear engine mount bracket to the crossmember. Remove the side support bolts, and remove the crossmember.
    G. Secure the transmission to the jack with a safety chain, remove the remaining bolts attaching the transmission to the cylinder block, and remove the transmission from the vehicle.
14. Remove the nuts which attach the engine front support insulator, remove the bellcrank bolt from the block, and position it out of the way.
15. Lower the vehicle, and remove the fan spacer, and water pump pulley. Lift the engine from the vehicle with a lifting hook. Remove the clutch housing on vehicles with manual transmission.
16. Install the clutch housing on manual transmission vehicles. Hoist the engine into the vehicle, and allow it to rest on the front supports and support tool.
17. Raise the vehicle on a hoist.
18. On manual transmission equipped
    A. Raise the transmission and position it behind the clutch housing. Install the mounting bolts.
    B. Raise the transmission slightly further, position the crossmember to the chassis and rear support, and install the attaching bolts. Torque crossmember to body bolts to 20-30 ft-lbs.
    C. Remove the jack and engine support tool. Connect the shift linkage and the speedometer cable housing.
    D. Install and connect the drive shaft.
19. Install the engine front support insulator bolts, and torque to 45-55 ft-lbs.
20. Install the transmission bellcrank.
21. On automatic transmission equipped vehicles:
    A. Position the transmission against the block and install the mounting bolts. Torque to 23-33 ft-lbs.
    B. Position the crossmember to the rear mount bracket and frame side members. Install the attaching nuts and bolts,

and torque to 20-30 ft-lbs.

C. Remove the transmission safety chain, and remove the jack. Remove the engine support bar.

D. Install the converter to the flex plate. Connect the vacuum and oil cooler lines to the transmission.

E. Install the dipstick and tube into the transmission oil pan. Install the tube and vacuum line bracket attaching bolt to the block.

F. Connect the driveshaft to the transmission companion flange. Connect the speedometer cable and housing to the transmission. Connect the shift rods to the transmission levers.

G. Install the adapter plate and inspection cover.

22. Install the starter. Connect the muffler inlet pipe at the manifold.

23. Install the clutch equalizer arm bracket (on manual transmission models). Install the attaching bolts, and connect the retractor spring.

24. Lower the vehicle to the floor, install the remaining automatic transmission mounting bolts.

25. Install the starter ground wire and remaining starter attaching bolt. Connect the starter cable at the starter.

26. Install the water pump pulley, spacer, and fan assembly.

27. Install the alternator onto its mounting brackets, and install and tension the V-belt.

28. Connect the alternator wiring, and back-up light and neutral safety switch leads.

29. Connect the alternator and battery ground wires to the block.

30. Connect the transmission modulator line to the manifold.

31. Connect the fuel line from the tank to the fuel pump.

32. Connect the choke and accelerator cables to the carburetor. Install the dipstick tube, and bolt it to the cylinder head.

33. Connect remaining neutral safety switch and back-up light wires. Position the wiring harness, and connect the coil, oil, and temperature leads.

34. Connect the auxiliary heater hoses. Connect the oil filler tube to the rocker arm cover and install the retaining clamp. Install the filler tube bracket to the dash panel.

35. Install the radiator and battery deflector. Connect the radiator hoses and oil cooler lines.

36. Install the grille, head light and hood lock bracket.

37. Fill the crankcase and cooling system. Fill the automatic transmission.

38. Connect the positive battery cable, and operate the engine to check for leaks. Adjust idle speed and mixture, and automatic transmission linkage.

39. Install the air cleaner and brackets, engine front cover, and right front seat, grille and bumper.

302 and 351 Cu. In. V-8 Econoline

In this procedure the engine is removed without the transmission attached.

1. Remove engine cover.
2. Remove right front seat.
3. Drain cooling system.
4. Remove air cleaner and intake duct assembly (later models), including crankcase ventilation hose.
5. Disconnect battery and alternator ground cables at block.
6. Remove oil filler tube at dash panel and disconnect at the rocker arm cover.
7. Disconnect radiator upper and lower hoses at the radiator and automatic transmission cooler lines (if so equipped).
8. Remove radiator.
9. Disconnect heater hoses at the engine.
10. Remove fan, spacer, pulley and drive belt.
11. Disconnect accelerator linkage at accelerator shaft assembly on the left cylinder head.
12. Disconnect automatic transmission kickdown rod at the carburetor and vacuum line at the intake manifold, if so equipped.
13. Disconnect wiring harness from left rocker arm cover.
14. Remove upper nut attaching right exhaust manifolds to exhaust pipe.
15. Raise vehicle on hoist.
16. Drain crankcase and remove filter.
17. Disconnect fuel pump inlet line at the pump.
18. Disconnect oil dipstick tube bracket from exhaust manifold and oil pan.
19. On vehicles with standard transmission, remove bolts attaching the equalizer arm bracket to cylinder block and clutch housing (this includes clutch linkage disconnection and retracting spring).
20. Disconnect starter cable at starter and remove starter.
21. On a vehicle with standard transmission, disconnect driveshaft at the rear axle and remove driveshaft. Install plug in transmission end.
22. On a vehicle with automatic transmission, disconnect driveshaft at companion flange.
23. Disconnect speedometer cable

and transmission linkage at transmission.

24. Position a transmission jack under transmission. Raise transmission and remove bolts attaching crossmember to chassis. Lower transmission slightly and remove bolt which attaches rear engine support to frame crossmember. Remove crossmember.

25. On a vehicle with standard transmission, remove bolts attaching transmission to clutch housing. Remove transmission.

26. On a vehicle with automatic transmission, remove the lower front cover from converter housing. Remove transmission dipstick tube and drain transmission. Install plastic bag in transmission oil pan. Remove nuts attaching transmission converter to flywheel. Disconnect oil cooler lines and vacuum lines at transmission. Remove remaining bolts fastening transmission to engine. Remove transmission.

27. Position engine support bar (tool T65E-6000-J) to engine and chassis, or improvise a suitable support.

28. Disconnect exhaust pipes at exhaust manifold.

29. Remove front engine mount attaching nuts and washers.

30. Remove bellcrank bolt from side of engine block and position bellcrank aside.

31. Lower vehicle.

32. Remove bolts which fasten alternator and adjusting arm to the block and water pump. Set alternator aside.

33. Remove carburetor air horn stud. Disconnect fuel line at fuel pump.

34. Install engine lifting apparatus and remove engine through side door.

35. On vehicle with standard transmission, remove bolts which fasten adapter plate to clutch housing. Remove clutch housing from block.

36. To install, connect fuel line to fuel pump.

37. On models with manual transmission, position clutch housing to block and install mounting bolts. Install adapter plate to clutch housing.

38. Position alternator and adjusting arm to cylinder block and water pump. Install and tighten attaching bolts.

39. Lift engine and position to chassis and supporting tool.

40. Raise vehicle on hoist.

41. Install front engine support retaining nuts and washers, tightening securely.

42. On vehicle with automatic transmission, position bellcrank as-

sembly to engine block and install attaching bolt, tightening securely. Position transmission to engine and install attaching bolts, tightening securely.

43. On vehicle with standard transmission, position transmission to clutch housing and install attaching bolt, tightening securely.
44. Remove engine support bar.
45. Position rear engine support crossmember to chassis and install retaining bolts. Position transmission with rear engine support attached to crossmember. Install bolt and nut. Tighten all bolts and nuts securely.
46. On vehicle with automatic transmission, install and tighten converter-to-flywheel attaching nuts. Connect oil cooler and vacuum lines at transmission. Install transmission dipstick tube in pan. Install dipstick tube and vacuum line retaining bracket bolt to engine block.
47. Connect transmission shift linkages and speedometer cable.
48. On vehicle with automatic transmission, connect driveshaft to transmission companion flange.
49. On vehicle with standard transmission, remove plug from transmission and install driveshaft yoke into transmission. Connect rear end of driveshaft at rear axle.
50. Install starter and connect cable to starter.
51. Install the exhaust pipe to exhaust manifold, installing all bolts except upper nut on right exhaust manifold.
52. On a standard transmission, install the bolts connecting equalizer arm bracket to block and clutch housing (including clutch linkage connection and retracting spring).
53. Install oil filter, then oil dipstick tube bracket to oil pan and exhaust manifold.
54. Connect fuel line at fuel pump.
55. Lower the vehicle.
56. Install upper nut attaching right exhaust manifold to exhaust pipe.
57. Connect engine wire harness at left rocker arm cover.
58. Connect battery and alternator ground cables at block.
59. If applicable, connect automatic transmission vacuum line at intake manifold and transmission kickdown rod at carburetor.
60. Connect accelerator linkage at accelerator shaft assembly on left cylinder head.
61. Install drive belt, pulley, spacer and fan.
62. Connect heater hoses at engine, then install radiator and connect hoses.
63. Install oil filler tube by connect-

ing to left rocker arm cover and dash panel.
64. Install air cleaner and intake duct assembly, including the crankcase ventilation hose.
65. Fill and bleed cooling system.
66. Fill crankcase and automatic transmission (if so equipped).
67. Install right front seat and engine cover.
68. Operate engine at fast idle and check for leaks.

302 and 351 Cu. In. V-8's F-100 to F-350

1. Drain the cooling system and crankcase. Remove the hood.
2. Disconnect the battery and alternator cables from the cylinder block.
3. Remove the air cleaner and intake duct assembly, plus the crankcase ventilation hose.
4. Disconnect the upper and lower radiator hoses, and, if so equipped the automatic transmission oil cooler lines.
5. Remove the fan shroud and lay it over the fan. Remove the radiator and fan, shroud, fan, spacer, pulley, and belt.
6. Disconnect the alternator leads and the alternator adjusting bolts. Allow the alternator to swing down out of the way.
7. Disconnect the oil pressure sending unit lead from the sending unit.
8. Disconnect the fuel tank-to-pump fuel line at the fuel pump and plug the line.
9. Disconnect the accelerator linkage at the carburetor. Disconnect the automatic transmission kick-down rod and remove the return spring, if so equipped.
10. Disconnect the heater hoses from the water pump and intake manifold. Disconnect the temperature sending unit wire from the sending unit.
11. Remove the upper bellhousing-to-engine attaching bolts.
12. Disconnect the primary wire from the coil. Remove the wiring harness from the left rocker arm cover and position the wires out of the way. Disconnect the ground strap from the cylinder block.
13. Raise the front of the truck and disconnect the starter cable from the starter. Remove the starter.
14. Disconnect the exhaust pipe from the exhaust manifolds.
15. Disconnect the engine mounts from the brackets on the frame.
16. On trucks with automatic transmissions, remove the converter inspection plate and remove the torque converter-to-flywheel attaching bolts.
17. Remove the remaining bellhousing-to-engine attaching bolts.

18. Lower the vehicle and support the transmission with a jack.
19. Install the engine lifting device.
20. Raise the engine slightly and carefully pull it out from the transmission. Lift the engine out of the engine compartment.
21. Install the engine in the reverse order of removal. Make sure that the dowels in the engine block engage the holes in the bellhousing through the rear cover plate. If the engine hangs up after the transmission input shaft enters the clutch disc (manual transmission only), turn the crankshaft with the transmission in gear until the input shaft splines mesh with the clutch disc splines. Tighten the exhaust pipe-to-exhaust manifold nuts to 25-35 ft lbs., and all others as follows:
$\frac{1}{4}$" 20—6-9 ft lbs
$\frac{5}{16}$" 18—12-18 ft lbs
$\frac{3}{8}$" 16—22-32 ft lbs
$\frac{7}{16}$" 14—45-57 ft lbs
$\frac{1}{2}$" 13—55-88 ft lbs
$\frac{9}{16}$" 10—85-120 ft lbs

460 V-8

1. Remove the hood.
2. Drain the cooling system, the radiator, and the cylinder block.
3. Disconnect the negative battery cable and remove the air cleaner assembly.
4. Disconnect the upper and lower radiator hoses and the transmission oil cooler lines from the radiator.
5. Remove the fan shroud from the radiator and remove the fan from the water pump. Remove the fan and shroud from the engine compartment.
6. Remove the upper support and remove the radiator.
7. If the truck is equipped with air conditioning, remove the compressor from the engine and position it out of the way. If the compressor must be removed completely, loosen the air conditioning service valves (disconnect) carefully to discharge the air conditioning system. Remove the compressor.
8. Remove the power steering pump from the engine, if so equipped, and position it to one side. Do not disconnect the fluid lines.
9. Disconnect the fuel pump inlet line from the pump and plug the line.
10. Remove the alternator drive belts and disconnect the alternator from the engine, positioning it aside.
11. Disconnect the ground cable from the right front corner of the engine.
12. Disconnect the heater hoses.
13. Remove the transmission fluid

14. Disconnect all vacuum lines at the rear of the intake manifold.

15. Disconnect the speed control cable at the carburetor, if so equipped. Disconnect the accelerator rod and the transmission kick-down rod and secure them out of the way.

16. Disconnect the engine wiring harness at the connector on the fire wall.

17. Raise the vehicle and disconnect the exhaust pipes at the exhaust manifolds.

18. Disconnect the starter cable and remove the starter. Bring the starter forward and rotate the solenoid outward to remove the assembly.

19. Remove the access cover from the converter housing and remove the fly-wheel-to-converter attaching nuts. Remove the lower converter housing-to-engine attaching bolts.

20. Remove the engine mount through bolts attaching the rubber insulators to the frame brackets.

21. Lower the vehicle and place a jack under the transmission to support it.

22. Remove the converter housing-to-engine block attaching bolts (left-side).

23. Disconnect the coil wire and remove the coil and bracket assembly from the intake manifold.

24. Attach the engine lifting device and carefully lift the engine from the engine compartment.

25. Install the engine in the reverse order of removal.

Tighten the alternator pivot bolt to 45-57 ft lbs and all the rest of the nuts and bolts as is outlined in Step 21 of the preceding "302 and 351 V8, etc. Removal and Installation" procedure.

330, 360, 361, 390, 391 Cu. In. V-8—All Models

1. On B, F and FT series trucks, remove engine hood assembly from vehicle; on C and CT vehicles, release cab lock and tilt the cab forward. On N and NT series vehicles, position a suitable support in front of the truck to accept the hood and fender assembly when it is fully forward, then raise the hood and fender assembly.

2. Disconnect the ground cable from the battery. On N and NT series trucks, disconnect and remove the battery.

3. Drain cooling system and crankcase.

4. On N and NT series trucks, disconnect the check cable assemblies and let the hood swing forward out of the way, resting on the support. Remove radiator to cowl support rod, disconnect water hoses and unbolt and remove radiator.
On C and CT series trucks, remove the heater hoses from the radiator, transmission oil cooler lines (automatic transmission), disconnect upper and lower radiator hoses, disconnect and remove vent line between radiator and supply tank and hose between water outlet housing and supply tank, remove fan (leaving it lay in the shroud), then remove the radiator, shroud and fan as an assembly. Remove radiator supply tank from cab rear support.
On B, F and FT series trucks, disconnect the upper and lower hoses from the engine and water pump, remove the fan, disconnect the transmission oil cooler hoses (if applicable), then unbolt and remove radiator.

5. On a vehicle with power steering, disconnect the power steering pressure line from the pump reservoir and return line from the pump housing. Drain oil, then loosen and remove the power steering drive belt.

6. On N and NT series trucks, remove fan.

7. On N, NT, C and CT series truck, disconnect heater hoses at engine.

8. Remove air cleaner and, if applicable, vent hose from carburetor.

9. Disconnect choke and throttle cables and accelerator linkage.

10. Disconnect tachometer cable (and bracket, if so attached) and position out of the way.

11. Remove ignition coil.

12. On a vehicle with an air compressor, relieve pressure from the system and disconnect main line from the compressor and treadle valve. Remove drive belt if it is still in place.

13. Disconnect fuel line (from tank) at the fuel pump and cap line.

14. Disconnect wires from the alternator and remove wiring harness from engine (or disconnect from junction block).

15. Disconnect cable from starter and remove starter. Remove flywheel lower housing attaching bolts first on L and LT truck. Disconnect engine-to-body ground strap.

16. Unbolt exhaust pipes from right and left exhaust manifolds.

17. Disconnect vacuum lines from intake manifold.

18. Remove clutch return spring and hydraulic clutch slave cylinder

attaching bolts on C and CT trucks.

19. Remove driveshaft center bearing retainer (except on C and CT series) and position a jack under transmission.

20. Remove flywheel housing cover.

21. On B, F and FT series trucks, remove lower clutch housing attaching bolts. Secure lifting apparatus. Remove front engine mount nuts. Remove remaining clutch housing bolts. Raise engine high enough to remove the bolts that attach the engine front mount bracket to the upper insulator. Carefully lift engine away from the transmission and chassis. On C and CT vehicles, remove flywheel housing to engine attaching bolts. Remove nuts and bolts from front engine mount and upper insulator. Attach lifting apparatus and remove engine from chassis. On N and NT trucks, remove flywheel upper housing to engine attaching bolts. Remove the bolt(s) attaching the front engine mounting plate to the front engine mount. Attach lifting apparatus. Raise engine sufficiently to remove the front support bracket-to-upper insulator bolt and nuts. Remove engine.

22. To install, carefully lower engine into chassis, aligning clutch disc splines with transmission shaft and aligning front engine mount bracket with upper insulator.

23. Install flywheel housing to engine attaching bolts, tightening securely.

24. Install flywheel housing cover.

25. Lower engine and remove jack from under transmission, being careful to keep front engine mounting aligned.

26. Install and tighten front engine mount bolts and nuts. On N and NT trucks, install front engine mount to mounting plate.

27. Remove lifting apparatus.

28. Install driveshaft center bearing support to frame crossmember.

29. On vehicle with power steering, install power steering unit if it was removed.

30. Install starter motor and starter cable, attaching engine-to-frame ground cable if applicable.

31. Install left and right exhaust pipes to exhaust manifolds, using new gaskets.

32. Connect alternator wires and engine wiring harness wires. Secure engine wiring harness to bracket on engine.

33. On C and CT trucks, install hydraulic clutch slave cylinder to the flywheel housing and attach the clutch return spring.

34. Secure coil and bracket to cylin-

der head and connect all leads.
35. Connect vacuum line(s) to intake manifold.
36. Connect fuel line to fuel pump.
37. On C and CT trucks install radiator supply tank to cab rear support.
38. Connect accelerator linkage, choke and throttle cables and tachometer cable. Adjust linkage and cables if necessary.
39. Connect heater hoses.
40. On vehicles equipped with air system, install and connect all components.
41. Connect engine-to-body ground strap.
42. On N and NT series trucks, install fan. On B, F, FT, C and CT trucks, place fan in radiator, shroud, then install radiator, shroud and fan (loose) in vehicle. Secure all attaching bolts, insulators and radiator supports. Make sure belts are ready to be installed. Install fan and belts.
43. Connect radiator upper and lower hoses. On C and CT series trucks, connect hoses to radiator supply tank.
44. On vehicle with automatic transmission, connect transmission oil cooler lines to radiator lower tank.
45. On vehicle with power steering, install and tighten the drive belt and connect power steering pressure line to the pump reservoir and return line to the pump housing.
46. On C and CT series trucks, attach the heater hoses, throttle cable, choke cable and tachometer cable to the radiator.
47. Install air cleaner.
48. Install (if removed) and connect battery cables.
49. Fill crankcase and cooling system.
50. On B, F and FT series trucks, install the hood.
51. On N and NT series trucks, raise hood and connect check cables.
52. Adjust clutch as required.
53. Operate engine and check for lubricant and coolant leaks.

Manifolds

Exhaust Manifold Removal and Installation

170, 200 Cu. In. 6-Cylinder
1. Remove air cleaner and, if so equipped (later models), hot air duct.
2. Disconnect exhaust pipe from manifold.
3. Remove retaining bolts and manifold.
4. To install, clean mating surfaces of head and manifold and scrape

gasket material from manifold exhaust pipe flange and pipe.
5. Apply graphite grease to the mating surface of the exhaust manifold.
6. Install manifold, retaining bolts and tab washers, tightening bolts from the center out to 13-18 ft. lbs. Bend tabs to lock bolts.
7. Install exhaust pipe on manifold, using new gasket.
8. Install air cleaner and hot air duct.
9. Start engine and check for exhaust leaks.

302 and 351 Cu. In. V-8
1. Remove air cleaner, intake duct and crankcase ventilation hose as an assembly.
2. Remove air cleaner inlet duct attaching bolts (Bronco and F-100) and oil dipstick tube bracket on right exhaust manifold.
3. Disconnect exhaust pipes from manifolds.
4. Remove bolts, washers and manifolds.
5. To install, clean mating surfaces of cylinder head and manifolds. Clean out exhaust pipe flange of manifolds and exhaust pipe.
6. Apply graphite grease to mating surfaces of manifolds.
7. Install manifolds, tab washers, and bolts, tightening from the center out to 12-16 ft. lbs. torque. Bend tabs to lock bolts.
8. Install exhaust pipe to flange on manifold, using a new gasket.
9. Install air cleaner inlet duct (Bronco and F-100) and oil dipstick tube bracket on the right exhaust manifold.
10. Install air cleaner and intake duct, including crankcase ventilation hose.

330, 360, 361, 390, 391 and 460 Cu. In. V-8—All Models
1. Remove air cleaner and disconnect exhaust pipes from manifolds.
2. Disconnect the power steering pump bracket from the cylinder block and move it out of the way. Position the pump so that the oil will not drain out.
3. Remove dipstick and tube assembly.
4. Remove attaching bolts, washers of cylinder head, manifold, manifold pipe flange and exhaust pipe.
5. To install, clean mating surfaces.
6. Apply graphite grease to mating surface of manifold, then install manifold, tab washers and bolts. Tighten bolts from the center out to specifications. Bend tabs to lock bolts.
7. Install dipstick and tube assembly.
8. Install power steering pump bracket and adjust belt tension.
9. Connect exhaust pipes to manifolds, using new gaskets.
10. Install air cleaner.

Intake Manifold Removal and Installation

302 and 351 Cu. In. V-8
1. Drain cooling system.
2. Remove air cleaner and intake duct assembly, including crankcase ventilation hose.
3. Disconnect accelerator rod, choke cable and automatic transmission kickdown rod (if applicable) at the carburetor. Remove the accelerator retracting spring, where so equipped.
4. Disconnect high tension lead and wires from the coil.
5. Remove spark plug wire from plugs and harness brackets, then remove distributor cap and spark plug wire assembly.
6. Disconnect fuel inlet line at carburetor.
7. Disconnect distributor vacuum hoses and remove distributor.
8. Remove heater hose, radiator hose and water temperature sending unit wire from manifold.
9. Remove water pump bypass hose from coolant outlet housing.
10. Disconnect crankcase ventilation hose from valve rocker cover.
11. Remove intake manifold and carburetor as an assembly, prying manifold from cylinder head if necessary. Throw away gaskets and bolt sealing washers.
12. When disassembling, identify all vacuum hoses before disconnecting them. Remove coolant outlet housing and gasket. Remove ignition coil and engine identification tag, temperature sending unit, carburetor, spacer, gasket, vacuum fitting, accelerator retracting spring bracket and choke cable bracket.
13. To install, first assemble manifold/carburetor unit by installing all components removed in Step 12 above, making sure vacuum lines are positioned correctly.
14. Clean all mating surfaces, using a suitable solvent to remove all oil. Apply block surfaces with adhesive sealer.
15. Position new gaskets and front and rear seals, using a nonhardening sealer at four gasket-seal junctions. Interlock gaskets with seal tabs and be sure all holes are aligned.
16. Carefully position manifold,

Intake manifold—302 and 351 V-8 (© Ford Motor Co.)

Intake manifold torque sequence––302 V-8 (© Ford Motor Co.)

Intake manifold torque sequence—351 V-8 (© Ford Motor Co.)

making sure that gaskets and seals do not shift. Install bolts and new bolt seal washers, tightening in the sequence illustrated. *Retighten after engine has been operated until warmed up.* Torque bolts to 23-25 ft. lbs.

17. Install water bypass hose to coolant outlet housing, radiator upper hose and heater hose.
18. Install distributor as described in "Distributor Removal and Installation" above. Install distributor cap and spark plug wires, positioning wires in harness brackets on valve rocker covers.
19. Connect crankcase ventilation hose, high tension lead and coil wires, accelerator rod and retracting spring, choke cable and automatic transmission kickdown rod (if applicable).
20. Fill and bleed cooling system.
21. Adjust ignition timing.
22. Connect vacuum hoses at distributor.
23. Operate engine until warmed up, checking for leaks.
24. Retorque manifold bolts.
25. Adjust transmission throttle linkage, if so equipped.
26. Install air cleaner and intake

duct assembly including closed crankcase ventilation hose.

330, 360, 361, 390 and 391 Cu. In. V-8—All Models

1. Drain cooling system.
2. Remove air cleaner and crankcase vent hose(s).
3. Disconnect accelerator linkage at the carburetor.
4. If so equipped, remove the accelerator cross shaft bracket from the intake manifold.
5. Disconnect fuel line and distributor vacuum line at the carburetor.
6. Disconnect all leads at the coil and oil pressure and water temperature sending units.
7. Remove wiring harness from the retaining clips on the left valve rocker cover.
8. Disconnect spark plug wires, remove wires from harness brackets, remove distributor cap and spark plug wire assembly.
9. Disconnect and remove distributor vacuum line.
10. Remove distributor.
11. Disconnect radiator upper hose(s) at the water outlet housing, heater hoses and, on C ser-

ies vehicle, the coolant supply tank hose at the water outlet housing.

12. Disconnect water pump bypass hose(s) at the water pump.
13. Remove valve rocker covers and crankcase ventilation hoses.
14. Remove valve rocker shaft assembly as described below in the section, "Rocker Arm Shaft Assembly Removal and Installation."
15. Remove and identify pushrods so that they can be put back in their original positions.
16. Remove manifold attaching bolts.
17. Install eyebolts (5/16-18 thread) in the left front and right rear rocker arm cover screw holes and attach lifting sling.
18. Carefully lift out intake manifold, then remove seals and gaskets.
19. Remove water pump bypass hoses(s), water outlet housing, carburetor, gaskets spacer and water temperature sending unit.
20. Before installing, assemble components removed in Step 19. Use a new gasket and sealing compound when installing water outlet (thermostat) housing. Use electrical-conductive sealer when installing water temperature sending unit.
21. Thoroughly clean all manifold, cylinder head and block mating surfaces (use solvent to remove all traces of oil). Coat block seal surfaces with quick-setting seal adhesive and coat mating surfaces of cylinder heads and block with non-hardening Oil-resistant sealer. Position new seals on

Typical V-8 intake manifold except 302, 351 and 460 V-8 (© Ford Motor Co.)

Intake manifold torque sequence—460 V-8 (© Ford Motor Co.)

block and cylinder heads, *making sure they are properly aligned.* Position manifold gasket slots over the end tabs on the seals and coat these junctions with non-hardening sealer.

22. Install eyebolts in intake manifold and attach lifting sling, then carefully lower manifold onto engine. Position manifold by inserting distributor and check that seals and gaskets are still properly aligned and that all holes line up.

23. Install manifold attaching bolts, coating under side of bolt heads with non-hardening sealer. Tighten bolts to 32-35 ft. lbs. torque in the sequence illustrated. Retorque bolts after engine has been run and warmed up. Remove distributor, lifting sling and eyebolts.

24. Connect water pump bypass hose (s) to water pump, radiator upper hose, heater hoses, water temperature sending unit and, on C series trucks, coolant supply tank hose.

25. Apply lubriplate to both ends of pushrods and install them in their original positions. Install valve rocker shaft as described in "Rocker Arm Shaft Assembly Removal and Installation" below.

26. Install the distributor as described in "Distributor Removal and Installation" above.

27. Install rocker covers, using new gasket and sealer, tightening to 10-12 ft. lbs., waiting two minutes then torquing again.

28. Connect crankcase ventilation hoses.

29. Install carburetor fuel inlet line, spark plug wires, wiring harness, distributor vacuum line and distributor cap.

30. Connect oil pressure sending unit wire and coil wire and lead.

31. Install accelerator cross shaft bracket (if applicable) and accelerator rod.

32. Fill and bleed cooling system.

33. Install air cleaner and vent hose.

34. Start engine, then check ignition timing idle speed and idle fuel mixture, then let engine warm up.

35. Retorque intake manifold bolts to specifications.

Intake manifold torque sequence—V-8 except 302, 351 and 460 (© Ford Motor Co.)

460 V-8

1. Drain the cooling system and remove the air cleaner assembly.

2. Disconnect the upper radiator hose at the engine.

3. Disconnect the heater hoses at the intake manifold and the water pump. Position them out of the way. Loosen the water pump by-pass hose clamp at the intake manifold.

4. Disconnect the PCV valve and hose at the right valve cover. Disconnect all of the vacuum lines at the rear of the intake manifold and tag them for proper reinstallation.

5. Disconnect the wires at the spark plugs, and remove the wires from the brackets on the valve covers. Disconnect the high-tension wire from the coil and remove the distributor cap and wires as an assembly.

6. Disconnect all of the distributor vacuum lines at the carburetor and vacuum control valve and tag them for proper installation. Remove the distributor and vacuum lines as an assembly.

7. Disconnect the accelerator linkage at the carburetor. Remove the speed control linkage bracket, if so equipped, from the manifold and carburetor.

8. Remove the bolts holding the accelerator linkage bellcrank and position the linkage and return springs out of the way.

9. Disconnect the fuel line at the carburetor.

10. Disconnect the wiring harness at the coil battery terminal, engine temperature sending unit, oil pressure sending unit, and other connections as necessary. Disconnect the wiring harness from the clips at the left valve cover and position the harness out of the way.

11. Remove the coil and bracket assembly.

12. Remove the intake manifold attaching bolts and lift the manifold and carburetor from the engine as an assembly. It may be necessary to pry the manifold away from the cylinder heads. Do not damage the gasket sealing surfaces.

13. Install the intake manifold in the reverse order of removal. Clean all gasket material from the mating surfaces of the manifold and cylinder heads and block. Glue the intake manifold end seals in place before installing the manifold. Use sealer at each end of the intake manifold-to-cylinder head gaskets for the full width of the gasket. When the manifold is placed on top of the engine run your fingers around the end

seal areas to make sure that the end seals have not shifted. If they have, remove the manifold and reposition the seals. Tighten the intake manifold bolts in two stages in the proper sequence; first to 15 ft lbs, and then to 25-30 ft lbs. After the engine has been started and has reached normal operating temperature, retorque the intake manifold bolts.

Valve Rocker Arm Shaft Assembly Removal and Installation

330, 360, 361, 390, and 391 Cu. In. Engine

1. Remove air cleaner, disconnect spark plug leads and remove leads from bracket on the valve rocker cover.
2. Remove crankcase ventilation hose from rocker cover, then remove rocker cover. On left rocker cover the wiring harness must be removed.
3. On right side, start at No. 4 cylinder (rearmost) and loosen the support bolts in sequence, two turns at a time. Remove the shaft assembly and baffle plate after all the bolts have been loosened. The same procedure is followed on the left bank, except that the bolt-loosening sequence starts with the No. 5 cylinder (foremost). CAUTION: The above bolt-loosening procedure must be followed to avoid damage to the rocker arm shaft.
4. To install, apply Lubriplate to the pad end of the rocker arms, to the tip of the valve stems and to both ends of the pushrods.
5. Rotate engine to 45 degrees *past* No. 1 cylinder TDC.
6. With the pushrods in place, position rocker arm shaft assembly and baffle plate on the cylinder head such that *oil holes are on the bottom and identification notch is down and toward the front on the right bank and toward the rear on the left bank.* Tighten support bolts finger tight.

Valve rocker arm shaft assembly V8—typical (© Ford Motor Co.)

Manifold tightening sequence—240 & 300 engines (© Ford Motor Co.)

7. On the right bank, start at No. 4 cylinder and tighten the support bolts two turns at a time in sequence (4-3-2-1) until the supports are fully in contact with the cylinder head. Then tighten the support bolts to 40-45 ft. lbs. torque. The same procedure is followed on the left valve rocker arm shaft support bolts, starting with the No. 5 cylinder. This procedure allows time for the hydraulic lifter leakdown and thus prevents damage to pushrods, valves and rocker arms.
8. Check valve clearances and adjust if necessary.
9. Install rocker cover, using new gaskets and sealer.
10. Tighten cover retaining bolts to 10-12 ft. lbs, wait two minutes, then tighten to the same torque again.
11. Install crankcase ventilation regulator valve and hose(s), connect spark plug wires and crankcase vent hose, and install air cleaner.

Intake/Exhaust Manifold Removal and Installation

240 and 300 Cu. In. 6-Cylinder

1. Remove air cleaner and hot air ducts.
2. Disconnect choke cable and accelerator rod or cable at the carburetor. Remove accelerator retracting spring.
3. On LN series vehicles, disconnect the battery and remove the alternator.

4. On vehicle with an automatic transmission, remove the kickdown rod retracting spring and remove the accelerator rod bellcrank assembly.
5. On C series vehicle, remove the engine oil dipstick and tube.
6. Disconnect fuel inlet line and distributor vacuum line from the carburetor, exhaust pipe from the manifold and, if so equipped, power brake vacuum line.
7. Remove manifold attaching bolts and lift manifolds from engine.
8. To separate manifolds, remove the nuts joining the intake and exhaust manifolds. Discard all gaskets.
9. If the exhaust control valve requires replacement, see "Exhaust Control Valve Removal and Installation" below.
10. To install, clean the mating surfaces of cylinder head and manifolds.
11. If a new manifold is to be used, remove the tube fittings on the old manifold and install them on the new one.
12. Before joining exhaust and intake manifolds, coat the mating surfaces lightly with graphite grease. Use a new gasket and tighten the nuts finger tight.
13. Coat the mating surfaces with graphite grease and install the manifold assembly on the cylinder head. Use a new intake manifold gasket. Tighten the bolts and nuts to 23-28 ft. lbs. torque in the sequence illustrated.
14. Tighten the intake to exhaust

Rocker arm shaft identification notch (© Ford Motor Co.)

manifold stud nuts to 28-33 ft. lbs. torque.

15. Connect exhaust pipe to manifold, tightening nuts to 25-30 ft. lbs. torque.
16. Connect crankcase vent hose to intake manifold inlet tube, fuel inlet line and distributor vacuum line to carburetor, accelerator rod or cable and choke cable to carburetor. Install the accelerator retracting spring.
17. On LN series trucks, install the alternator and belts and connect the battery.
18. On C series trucks, install the dipstick and tube.
19. On a vehicle with an automatic transmission, install the bell-crank assembly and kickdown rod retracting spring. Adjust the transmission control linkage.
20. Install the air cleaner and hot air duct.
21. Adjust idle speed and idle fuel mixture.

Exhaust Control Valve Removal and Installation

240 and 300 Cu. In. 6-Cylinder

1. Separate intake and exhaust manifolds.
2. Remove valve tension spring, thermostatic spring and stop pin.

Cylinder head torque sequence—170, 200 cu in. 6-cylinder (© Ford Motor Co.)

3. The valve shaft must be cut with a torch on each side of the valve plate. Remove valve plate and expansion plug.
4. Remove bushings and install new ones. There are two sizes of replacement bushings (OD) so make sure the right ones are used. Ream the ID of bushings to 0.51-0.253″. The shorter bushing (front) is installed 0.010-0.015″ below inside surface of the manifold and the longer bushing (rear) protrudes into the manifold cavity 0.020″ (note that beveled end points inward).
5. Slide new shaft into the bushings, flat washer and valve plate. Note that the flat washer is between the valve plate and the long (rearward) bushing. Install a new stop pin spring on the stop pin.
6. Rotate the counterweight and shaft assembly clockwise until the counterweight contacts the stop pin spring, then place a

0.030″ feeler gauge between the counterweight and the manifold to maintain the specified clearance. Hold the valve plate at a 84 degree angle to the top surface of the manifold as illustrated and tack-weld the plate to the shaft, *using stainless steel welding rod.*
7. Check for free movement of the valve and install expansion plug in the bushing bore.
8. Install the thermostatic spring, positioned so that it will be necessary to wind the spring ½ turn clockwise to hook it over the stop pin.
9. Install a new valve tension spring on the exhaust control valve shaft and the stop pin.

Cylinder Head

Cylinder Head Removal and Installation

170, 200 Cu. In. 6-Cylinder

1. Drain cooling system, remove the air cleaner and oil filler tube, and disconnect the battery cable at cylinder head.
2. Disconnect exhaust pipe from manifold.
3. Disconnect accelerator rod retracting spring, choke control cable and accelerator rod at the carburetor, transmission kickdown rod (automatic transmission), accelerator linkage at bellcrank, fuel inlet line at fuel filter hose, distributor vacuum line at the carburetor and other vacuum lines as necessary for accessibility (identify them for proper reinstallation).
4. Remove upper radiator hose at the coolant outlet housing.
5. Disconnect the distributor vacuum line at the distributor and carburetor fuel inlet line at the fuel pump.
6. Disconnect spark plug wires at the plugs and temperature sending unit wire at the unit.
7. Remove PCV valve and hose from valve rocker cover and disconnect the other end of the hose from the intake manifold.
8. Remove the valve rocker arm cover, then remove the rocker arm shaft support bolts by loosening them two turns at a time in sequence.
9. Lift off rocker arm shaft.
10. Remove cylinder head bolts and cylinder head. *Do not pry.*
11. Before installing, clean gasket surfaces of cylinder head and engine block, install guide studs at each end of block, apply cylinder head gasket sealer evenly to both sides of the head gasket,

Exhaust control valve assy.—240 & 300 engines (© Ford Motor Co.)

Exhaust valve plate position & counterweight clearance (© Ford Motor Co.)

and run the gasket down the guide studs into position on the engine block.

12. Put a new gasket on the flange of the exhaust pipe, then carefully lower the head down the guide studs onto the block, guiding the exhaust manifold studs into the exhaust pipe.

13. Coat the threads of the cylinder head right side end bolts (Nos. 12 and 13 in the illustration) and install them finger tight to hold the head and gasket in position. Install the rest of the head bolts finger tight, then tighten in steps to 55 ft. lbs., 65 ft. lbs. and 70-75 ft. lbs., following the sequence illustrated for each step.

14. Apply Lubriplate to both ends of their original locations.

15. Apply Lubriplate to the rocker arm follower pads and to the valve stem tips, then position rocker arm shaft assembly on the head.

16. Install the rocker arm shaft support bolts and tighten them in sequence two turns at a time until they are torqued to 30-35 ft. lbs.

17. Check and adjust the preliminary (cold) lash as described in "Valve Clearance Adjustment" below.

18. Install lockwashers and nuts to exhaust manifold to exhaust pipe studs and tighten to 25-35 ft. lbs. torque.

19. Connect radiator upper hose at the coolant outlet housing.

20. Install vacuum lines(s) and fuel line.

21. Connect accelerator linkage at the bellcrank assembly, transmission kickdown rod, accelerator rod retracing spring, battery cable at the cylinder head, choke control cable and accelerator rod at carburetor, temperature sending unit wire and spark plug leads. Adjust choke cable.

22. Temporarily install rocker cover and PC valve, then operate engine until it is warmed up. Adjust final (hot) valve lash as de-

scribed in "Valve Clearance Adjustment" below.

23. Clean rocker cover and head gasket surfaces and install cover using a new seal coated on both sides with oil-resistant sealer. Tighten cover retaining bolts to 3-5 ft. lbs. torque, wait two minutes, then retorque to the same value.

24. Connect one end of the crankcase vent hose to the carburetor spacer and the valve end to the rocker cover.

25. Install oil filler tube and air cleaner.

26. Start engine and check for coolant and oil leaks.

240 and 300 Cu. In. 6-Cylinder

1. Drain cooling system and remove air cleaner and crankcase ventilation valve.

2. Disconnect the following: the vent hose at the intake manifold inlet tube, carburetor fuel inlet line, distributor vacuum line, choke cable, accelerator cable and heater hose at the coolant outlet elbow. Remove accelerator cable retracting spring.

3. On a vehicle with automatic transmission, disconnect the kickdown rod at the carburetor.

4. Disconnect upper radiator hose and exhaust pipe.

5. Remove the coil and the valve rocker cover and disconnect spark plug wires.

6. Loosen the rocker arm stud nuts so that the rocker arms can be twisted aside, then remove the pushrods, identifying each so that it may be installed in its original position.

7. Remove head bolts and install eyebolts for lifting (see illustration). Attach lifting apparatus and lift off cylinder head and manifold assembly. *Do not pry between head and block.*

8. Before installing, clean mating surfaces of block, cylinder head and exhaust pipe.

9. Position new gasket over the dowel pins on the cylinder block,

Cylinder head bolt tightening sequence— 6 cyl.—240 & 300 engines (© Ford Motor Co.)

then carefully lower head into place on the block. Remove lifting apparatus.

10. Oil the threads and install head bolts. Tighten the bolts in three steps, following the sequence illustrated in each step: first to 50-55 ft. lbs., then to 60-65 ft. lbs, and finally to 70-75 ft. lbs.

11. Connect exhaust pipe to manifold flange, using a new gasket and tighten the nuts to 25-30 ft. lbs.

12. Apply Lubriplate to both ends of the pushrods and install them in their original positions.

13. Apply Lubriplate to both the rocker arm fulcrum seat and the fulcrum seat socket of each rocker arm and install the rocker arms, tightening the stud nuts just enough to hold the pushrods. Adjust the valve lash as described in "Valve Clearance Adjustment" below.

14. Install the rocker cover, using oil-resistant sealer and a new gasket. Tighten the retaining bolts to 4-7 ft. lbs.

15. Connect the spark plug wires to the plugs, crankcase vent hose to the intake manifold, PCV valve in the valve rocker cover, fuel inlet line, distributor vacuum hose, accelerator cable and choke cable. Install accelerator cable retracting spring.

16. On a vehicle with automatic transmission, connect the kickdown rod to the carburetor.

17. Connect radiator upper hose to the coolant outlet housing and the heater hose to the coolant outlet housing, leaving the clamp loose.

18. Fill the cooling system and bleed. Then tighten the heater hose clamp.

Rocker arm shaft assembly—6 cyl.—typical (© Ford Motor Co.)

19. Operate the engine until it is warmed up, checking for leaks.
20. Adjust engine idle speed and idle fuel mixture.

Cylinder head bolt tightening sequence— all V8 engines

Cylinder Head Removal and Installation
302 and 351 Cu. In. V-8

1. Remove the intake manifold and carburetor as an assembly as described in "Intake Manifold Removal and Installation" above.
2. Remove rocker arm cover.
3. To remove right cylinder head, loosen alternator adjusting arm bolt and remove the alternator mounting bracket bolt and spacer. Swing alternator down out of the way. On Bronco and Econoline trucks, remove the coil and air cleaner inlet duct from the right head. To remove left cylinder head, remove accelerator shaft fastening bolts at the front of the head.
4. Disconnect exhaust pipe from the manifold.
5. Loosen rocker arm stud nuts and twist rocker arms so that the pushrods may be removed. Identify the pushrods when removing so that they may be reinstalled in their original locations.
6. Remove exhaust valve stem caps, on 302 engines.
7. Install cylinder head holding fixtures, remove head bolts and lift off head.
8. To install, clean all gasket surfaces of block, head and rocker cover. Position new head gasket over the dowels onto the block (do *not* use sealer on this composition gasket). Install head and remove holding fixture.
9. Install head bolts and tighten in three steps: first to 50 ft. lbs, then to 60 ft. lbs, and finally to 65-72 ft. lbs. Tighten in the sequence illustrated for each step.
10. Clean pushrods, blowing out oil passage, and check them for straightness. Lubricate pushrod ends, valve stem tips and rocker arm cups, fulcrum sets and followers. Install pushrods in their original positions, install exhaust stem caps and install rocker arms. Adjust the valve clearance as described in "Valve Clearance Adjustment" below.
11. Connect the exhaust pipe to the manifold, using new gasket and tightening nuts to 25-35 ft. lbs. torque.

12. On right cylinder head, position the alternator and install the attaching bolt and spacer, ignition coil (Bronco and Econoline) and air cleaner inlet duct. Adjust drive belt tension. On left cylinder head, install accelerator shaft assembly.
13. Install rocker cover using new gasket and tightening cover bolts to 3-5 ft. lbs.
14. Install intake manifold and carburetor assembly as described in "Intake Manifold Removal and Installation" above.

330, 360, 361, 390 and 391 Cu. In. V-8

Removal and installation of cylinder heads on the larger V-8's is essentially the same procedure as that described above for the 302 and 351 cu. in. engines. The intake manifold and carburetor assembly and rocker arm shaft assembly are removed first (see "Intake Manifold Removal and Installation" above). When installing new head gasket, note the word "front" on the gasket and install accordingly. The head bolts are tightened in three steps, first to 70 ft. lbs., then to 80 ft. lbs., and finally to 85-90 ft. lbs. Tighten in the sequence illustrated for each step.

460 V-8s

1. Remove the intake manifold and carburetor as an assembly.
2. Disconnect the exhaust pipe from the exhaust manifold.
3. Loosen the air conditioning compressor drive belt, if so equipped.
4. Loosen the alternator attaching bolts and remove the bolt attaching the alternator bracket to the right cylinder head.
5. Disconnect the air conditioning compressor from the engine and move it aside, out of the way. Do not discharge the air conditioning system, if possible.
6. Remove the bolts securing the power steering reservoir bracket to the left cylinder head. Position the reservoir and bracket out of the way.
7. Remove the valve rocker arm covers. Remove the rocker arm bolts, rocker arms, oil deflectors, fulcrums and pushrods in sequence so that they can be reinstalled in their original positions.
8. Remove the cylinder head bolts and lift the head and exhaust manifold off the engine. If necessary, pry at the forward corners of the cylinder head against the casting bosses provided on the cylinder block. Do not damage the gasket mating surfaces of the cylinder head and block by prying against them.
9. Remove all gasket material from the cylinder head and block.

Clean all gasket material from the mating surfaces of the intake manifold. If the exhaust manifold was removed, clean the mating surfaces of the cylinder head exhaust port areas and install the exhaust manifold.

10. Position the two long cylinder head bolts in the two rear lower bolt holes of the left cylinder head. Place a long cylinder head bolt in the rear lower bolt hole of the right cylinder head. Use rubber bands to keep the bolts in position until the cylinder heads are installed on the cylinder block.
11. Position new cylinder head gaskets on the cylinder block dowels. Do not apply sealer to the gaskets, heads, or block.
12. Place the cylinder heads on the block, guiding the exhaust pipe connections. Install the remaining cylinder head bolts. The longer bolts go in the lower row of holes.
13. Tighten all the cylinder head attaching bolts in the proper sequence in three stages: 75 ft lbs, 105 ft lbs, and finally, to 135 ft lbs. When this procedure is used, it is not necessary to retorque the heads after extended use.
16. Connect the exhaust pipes to the exhaust manifolds.
17. Install the intake manifold and carburetor assembly. Tighten the intake manifold attaching bolts in the proper sequence to 25-30 ft lbs.
18. Install the air conditioning compressor to the engine.
19. Install the power steering reservoir to the engine.
20. Apply oil-resistant sealer to one side of the new valve cover gaskets and lay the cemented side in place in the valve covers. Install the covers.
21. Install the alternator to the right cylinder head and adjust the alternator drive belt tension.
22. Adjust the air conditioning compressor drive belt tension.
23. Fill the radiator with coolant.
24. Start the engine and check for leaks.

Reference

For cylinder head overhaul procedures see General Repair Section.

Valve Train

Valve Clearance (Lash) Adjustment

All engines used in full-size Ford products are equipped with hydraulic valve lifters except the 401, 477, 534 cu. in. versions. Valve systems with hydraulic valve lifters operate with zero clearance in the valve train, and because of this the rocker arms are non-adjustable. The only means by which valve system clearances can be altered is by installing .060 in. over- or undersize pushrods; but, because of the hydraulic lifter's natural ability to compensate for slack in the valve train, all components of the valve system should be checked for wear if there is excessive play in the system.

STEP 1—SET NO. 1 PISTON ON T.D.C. AT END OF COMPRESSION STROKE ADJUST NO. 1 INTAKE AND EXHAUST

STEP 4— ADJUST NO. 6 INTAKE AND EXHAUST

STEP 2— ADJUST NO. 5 INTAKE AND EXHAUST

STEP 3— ADJUST NO. 3 INTAKE AND EXHAUST

STEP 5— ADJUST NO. 2 INTAKE AND EXHAUST

STEP 6— ADJUST NO. 4 INTAKE AND EXHAUST

6-cylinder preliminary valve adjustment
(© Ford Motor Co.)

Preliminary Valve Adjustment

6-Cylinder

1. Crank the engine until the TDC mark on the crankshaft damper is aligned with timing pointer on the cylinder front cover.
2. Scribe a mark on the damper at this point.
3. Scribe two more marks on the damper, each equally spaced from the first mark (see illustration).
4. With the engine on TDC of the compression stroke (mark A aligned with the pointer), back off the rocker arm adjusting nut until there is end-play in the pushrod. Tighten the adjusting nut until all clearance is removed, then tighten the adjusting nut one additional turn. To determine when all clearance is removed from the rocker arm, turn the pushrod with the fingers. When the pushrod can no longer be turned, all clearance has been removed.
5. Repeat this procedure for each valve, turning the crankshaft 1/3 turn to the next mark each time and following the engine firing order of 1-5-3-6-2-4.

All V-8

NOTE: The early 302 V8 engine has rocker arm mounting studs which do not incorporate a positive stop shoulder on the mounting stud. These engines were originally equipped with this kind of stud. However, due to production differences, it is possible some early 302 engines may be encountered that are equipped with pos-

itive stop rocker arm mounting studs. Before adjusting the valves, verify that the rocker arm mounting studs do not incorporate a positive stop shoulder. On studs without a positive stop, the shank portion of the stud that is exposed just above the cylinder head is the same diameter as the threaded portion, at the top of the stud, to which the rocker arm retaining nut attaches. If the shank portion of the stud is of greater diameter than the threaded portion, this identifies it as a positive stop rocker arm stud and the adjustment specifications for the 351 engine with adjusting nuts should be used. Only the 302 and 351W engines require a preliminary valve adjustment. All other V8s use either a bolt and fulcrum (460) or rocker shafts (330, 360, 361, 390, 391).

ROCKER ARM STUD NUT

FULCRUM SEAT

ROCKER ARM

Stud/nut type rocker arm (© Ford Motor Co.)

302 and 351W
With Rocker Arm Adjusting Nuts

1. Crank the engine until #1 cylinder is at TDC of the compression stroke and the timing pointer is aligned with the mark on the crankshaft damper.
2. Scribe a mark on the damper at this point.
3. Scribe three more marks on the damper, dividing the damper into quarters.
4. With the first mark aligned with the timing pointer, adjust the valves on #1 cylinder by backing off the adjusting nut until the pushrod has free play in it. Then, tighten the nut until there is no free play in the rocker arm. This can be determined by turning the pushrod while tightening the nut; when the pushrod can no longer be turned, all clearance has been removed. After the clearance has been removed, tighten the nut an additional 3/4 of a turn. (302 V8 w/o positive stop rocker arm studs).
5. Rocker arm adjusting nut tightening specifications are: 302 (with positive stop rocker arm studs and 351W—tighten the nut until it contacts the rocker shoulder, then torque it to 18-20 ft lbs.
6. Repeat this procedure for each

valve, turning the crankshaft 1/4 turn to the next mark each time and following the engine firing order.

330, 360, 361, 390, 391

These engines do not require a preliminary valve adjustment. In the event of cylinder head removal or some operation requiring that the valve train be disturbed, torque the rocker arm shaft supports to 40-45 ft lbs.

460

These engines use a bolt and fulcrum rocker arm and require no preliminary valve adjustment. In the event that the valve train is disturbed, install the fulcrum, oil deflector, and tighten the bolt to 18-25 ft lbs.

FULCRUM BOLT

OIL DEFLECTOR

FULCRUM SEAT

ROCKER ARM

Bolt and fulcrum rocker arm (© Ford Motor Co.)

Valve Overhaul

See the General Repair Section for complete valve overhaul procedures. All valves are removed by compressing the spring with a valve spring

LOCKS

POSITIVE ROTATING SPRING RETAINER

FREE TURNING SPRING RETAINER

VALVE SPRINGS

EXHAUST VALVE OIL SEAL

INTAKE VALVE OIL SEAL

EXHAUST VALVE

INTAKE VALVE

Typical valve layout
(© Ford Motor Co.)

compressing tool, then removing the keepers from the end of the valve stem. Most models utilized an O-ring or cup type oil seal as illustrated. Valve spring, stem and seal specifications may be found in the Valve Specifications Table at the beginning of this section.

Valve rocker arm shaft assembly removal and installation procedures may be found immediately following "Intake Manifold Removal and Installation" above (330, 360, 361, 390 and 391 cu. in. V-8) and under "Cylinder Head Removal and Installation" (170 and 200 cu. in. 6-cylinder).

Timing Gears and Chain

Timing (Front) Cover and Seal Removal and Installation

170 and 200 Cu. In. 6-Cylinder

1. Drain cooling system, disconnect the radiator upper hose at the coolant outlet elbow and remove the two radiator upper attaching bolts.
2. Raise vehicle and drain crankcase.
3. Remove splash shield (if applicable) and radiator as described above.
4. Remove drive belts, fan, pulley and crankshaft damper (use a suitable puller).
5. Remove front cover attaching bolts. Before removing the cover, cut the oil pan gasket. Remove cover.
6. Check timing chain deflection and camshaft endplay as described below. Endplay should be within 0.001-0.007" and chain deflection should not exceed 0.500".
7. Rotate crankshaft until sprocket timing marks are aligned, then remove camshaft sprocket attaching bolt and washer. Slide off sprockets and chain.
8. Drive out the old seal with a pin punch and clean out seal recess.

Timing mark alignment—170, 200 cu in. 6-cylinder (© Ford Motor Co.)

9. Coat new seal with grease and install using a suitable installing tool.
10. Clean and oil chain and sprockets, then install as an assembly with timing marks aligned as illustrated. Install camshaft sprocket retaining bolt and washer, tightening to 34-45 ft lbs.
11. Cut and install a piece of new gasket to go between front cover and oil pan, using sealer on all surfaces.
12. Install front cover and new seal, coating all surfaces with sealer. It may be necessary to force the cover downward to compress the new piece of oil pan gasket. Coat threads of cover attaching screws with oil-resistance sealer and install them finger-tight. While holding the front cover in alignment (using an aligning tool if available), tighten oil pan to cover attaching to 7-9 ft. lbs. Tighten the rest of the mounting bolts to the same torque.
13. Apply Lubriplate to the hub of the crankshaft and install damper, tightening attaching bolt to 85-100 ft. lbs.
14. Install fan, pulley, drive belt (adjust), radiator, radiator lower hose and splash shield.
15. Lower the vehicle and connect upper hose.
16. Fill and bleed cooling system.
17. Fill crankcase.
18. Operate engine and check for leaks.

240 and 300 Cu. In. 6-Cylinder

Drain cooling system and crankcase then remove in order: radiator (see "Radiator Removal and Installation" above), alternator adjusting arm bolt, drive belt (swing alternator out of the way), fan, pulley, air compressor and/or steering pump belt, damper cam screw, washer, damper, oil level dipstick, oil pan (see "Oil Pan Removal and Installation" above) and oil pump screen and inlet tube assembly.

Remove front cover retaining bolts and front cover. Discard old seal and gasket and clean out seal recess in cover. New seal is pressed in from the inside of cover.

Check camshaft endplay (0.003-0.007"), gear backlash (0.002-0.004") and timing gear runout (0.006" for camshaft gear and 0.003" and 0.006" for the 240 and 300 crankshaft gears respectively). Replace worn parts.

Before pulling gears, rotate crankshaft until timing marks are aligned. Metal camshaft gear (300 HD) and crankshaft gear may be removed with a puller. *Do not rotate crankshaft while gears are removed.* Fiber camshaft gear (240 and 300 LD) may only be separated from the cam-

Timing mark alignment—6 cyl.— 240 & 300 engines

Tool—T64T-6306-A
Tool—T65L-6306-A

Installing camshaft gear (© Ford Motor Co.)

shaft after the camshaft has been removed. See "Camshaft Removal and Installation" below. Fiber gear is removed with an arbor press. Camshaft, spacer and thrust plate are installed before the gear (metal or fiber) is installed with special tools as illustrated. Be sure to install key in slot and to align timing marks before installing gear. Install thrust plate bolts, tightening to 19-20 ft. lbs.

When installing front cover, use a new gasket and be sure to align the cover before tightening cover retaining bolts to 15 ft. lbs. Lubricate the rubbing surface of the oil seal and damper, then install key and damper. Install oil pan using new gaskets and sealer. Install in reverse order all the other components which were removed. Fill cooling system and crankcase.

Timing Cover and Seal Removal and Installation
302 and 351 Cu. In. V-8

Drain cooling system and crankcase. Remove the following: alternator pivot and adjusting arm bolts, fan shroud, fan, spacer, pulley, drive belts, crankshaft pulley and damper (use a puller), fuel pump (disconnect fuel and vacuum lines), dipstick and dipstick tube. Disconnect the radiator lower hose and heater hose at the water pump. On Econoline models, remove the air cleaner and intake duct assembly, including the crankcase ventilation hose. Then remove the radiator.

In addition to the four front cover to block attaching bolts, the four front oil pan bolts must be removed to get the front cover off. Cut the oil pan gasket flush with the block with a thin-bladed knife before removing front cover. Check the deflection of the timing chain. If the chain deflection exceeds 0.500", the chain must be replaced. To remove chain and sprocket, first rotate crankshaft until the timing marks are aligned, then remove camshaft sprocket bolt, washers, crankshaft oil slinger and fuel pump eccentric. Slide off sprockets and chain as an assembly.

Always install a new front seal when the front cover is removed. Drive out old seal with a pin punch. Coat new seal with grease, then drive in seal until it is fully seated. Check spring position.

Install timing chain and sprockets as an assembly, making sure timing marks are aligned. Install fuel pump eccentric, washers and camshaft sprocket bolt, tightening 40-45 ft. lbs. Install oil slinger on crankshaft. Lubricate chain and sprockets with heavy engine oil.

Using a new front cover gasket and a piece of oil pan gasket cut to size, install front cover, tightening bolts finger tight. Use oil-resistant sealer on gaskets and bolt threads. It may be necessary to force the cover downward to compress the section of oil pan gasket. Align the front cover with respect to the crankshaft (it is best to use an aligning tool). Tighten front cover and front oil pan bolts to 12-15 ft. lbs, oil pan bolts first.

Apply Lubriplate to oil seal to damper rubbing surface, then install key, damper, washer and retaining bolt, tightening bolt to 100-130 ft. lbs.

Install in reverse order all the rest of the components previously removed. Fill and bleed cooling system. Fill crankcase. Operate engine and check for leaks.

330, 360, 361, 390 and 391 Cu. In. V-8

Drain the cooling system and crankcase. Disconnect battery ground cable and distributor vacuum line. Remove the following in the order given: air cleaner, radiator (see "Radiator Removal and Installation"), water pump bypass hose, fan, fan drive belt, power steering pump, air compressor, alternator, water pump, crankshaft damper retaining bolt, damper, fuel pump (leave flex line attached) and crankshaft sleeve (use puller).

Remove all front cover attaching bolts (to oil pan and block). Before removing cover, cut the oil pan gasket flush with the block. Remove front cover, alternator support bracket and adjusting arm bracket, engine front mount bracket and oil slinger. Check timing chain deflection (0.500" for 360 and 390, 0.680" for 330, 361, 391) and camshaft endplay (0.001-0.007"). Rotate crankshaft until timing marks are aligned. Remove camshaft sprocket bolt and fuel pump eccentric, then slide off sprockets and chain as an assembly.

Replace front oil seal by driving out old one with a pin punch, cleaning seal recess, then driving greased new seal into cover (it is best to use a seal installing tool). Make sure the spring is properly seated in seal.

Install camshaft spacer, then timing chain and sprockets as an assembly, making sure slotted spacer is aligned with dowel and timing marks are aligned. Install fuel pump eccentric and sprocket bolt on camshaft, tightening bolt to 34-45 ft. lbs. Check endplay if new camshaft thrust plate was installed. Install oil slinger on crankshaft.

Cut a piece of gasket material to replace the section of oil pan gasket and install front cover, cover gasket and oil pan gasket, using oil-resistant sealer on all surfaces. Align cover (use an aligning tool), position front engine mount bracket and install attaching bolts, tightening 3/8-16 bolts

Crankshaft Sleeve

Tool—T56P-6362-A

Removing crankshaft sleeve— 330 engine
(© Ford Motor Co.)

to 23-28 ft. lbs. or 5/16-18 bolts to 12-15 ft. lbs.

Lubricate the rubbing surface with grease and insert the crankshaft sleeve. Use a new sleeve if the old one is nicked or worn, for seal is easily damaged. Install key, damper and retaining bolt, tightening to 75-85 ft. lbs. torque. Install in reverse order all components which were removed. Fill crankcase. Fill and bleed cooling system. Operate engine and check for leaks.

Checking Timing Chain Deflection

To measure timing chain deflection, rotate crankshaft clockwise to take up slack on the left side of chain. Choose a reference point and measure distance from this point and the chain. Rotate crankshaft in the opposite direction to take up slack on the right side of the chain. Force the left (slack) side of the chain out and measure the distance to the reference point chosen earlier. The difference between the two measurements is the deflection.

Timing chain should be replaced if deflection measurement exceeds specified limit.

Timing mark alignment—302, 351, 401, 477 and 534 V-8 (© Ford Motor Co.)

TIMING MARKS

Timing mark alignment—330, 360, 361, 390, 391 and 460 V-8 (© Ford Motor Co.)

REFERENCE POINT   RIGHT SIDE OF CHAIN

TAKE UP SLACK ON LEFT SIDE, ESTABLISH REFERENCE POINT. MEASURE DISTANCE A. TAKE UP SLACK ON RIGHT SIDE. FORCE LEFT SIDE OUT. MEASURE DISTANCE B. DEFLECTION IS A MINUS B.

Checking timing chain deflection
(© Ford Motor Co.)

Camshaft Endplay Measurement

The fiber camshaft gears used on some engines is easily damaged if pried upon while the valve train load is on the camshaft. Loosen rocker arm nuts or rocker arm shaft support bolts before checking camshaft endplay.

Push camshaft toward rear of engine, install and zero a dial indicator, then pry between camshaft gear and block to pull the camshaft forward. If endplay is excessive, check for correct installation of spacer. If spacer is installed correctly, then replace thrust plate.

1. PUSH CAM TO REAR OF ENGINE
2. SET *Dial* ON ZERO
3. PULL CAM FORWARD AND RELEASE

Measuring camshaft end play
(© Ford Motor Co.)

Measuring Timing Gear Backlash

Use a dial indicator installed on block to measure timing gear backlash. Hold gear firmly against the block while making measurement. If excessive backlash exists, replace both gears.

Checking timing gear backlash
(© Ford Motor Co.)

460 V-8

1. Drain the cooling system and crankcase.
2. Remove the radiator shroud and fan.
3. Disconnect the upper and lower radiator hoses, and the automatic transmission oil cooler lines from the radiator.
4. Remove the radiator upper support and remove the radiator.
5. Loosen the alternator attaching bolts and air conditioning compressor idler pulley and remove the drive belts with the water pump pulley. Remove the bolts attaching the compressor support to the water pump and remove the bracket (support), if so equipped.
6. Remove the crankshaft pulley

from the vibration damper. Remove the bolt and washer attaching the crankshaft damper and remove the damper with a puller. Remove the woodruff key from the crankshaft.

7. Loosen the by-pass hose at the water pump, and disconnect the heater return tube at the water pump.
8. Disconnect and plug the fuel inlet and outlet lines at the fuel pump, and remove the fuel pump.
9. Remove the bolts attaching the front cover to the cylinder block. Cut the oil pan seal flush with the cylinder block face with a thin knife blade prior to separating the cover from the cylinder block. Remove the cover and water pump as an assembly. Discard the front cover gasket and oil pan seal.
10. Transfer the water pump if a new cover is going to be installed. Clean all of the gasket sealing surfaces on both the front cover and the cylinder block.
11. Coat the gasket surface of the oil pan with sealer. Cut and position the required sections of a new seal on the oil pan. Apply sealer to the corners.
12. Coat the gasket surfaces of the cylinder block and cover with sealer and position the new gasket on the block.
13. Position the front cover on the cylinder block. Use care not to damage the seal and gasket or mislocate them.
14. Coat the front cover attaching screws with sealer and install them.

NOTE: it may be necessary to force the front cover downward to compress the oil pan seal in order to install the front cover attaching bolts. Use a screwdriver or drift to engage the cover screw holes through the cover and pry downward.

15. Assemble and install the remaining components in the reverse order of removal. Tighten the front cover bolts to 15-20 ft lbs, the water pump attaching screws to 12-15 ft lbs, the crankshaft damper to 70-90 ft lbs, the crankshaft pulley to 35-50 ft lbs, fuel pump to 19-27 ft lbs, the oil pan bolts to 9-11 ft lbs for the

5/16″ screws and to 7-9 ft lbs for the ¼″ screws, and the alternator pivot bolt to 45-57 ft lbs.

Camshaft

Camshaft Removal and Installation

170 and 200 Cu. In. 6-Cylinder

1. Remove in order front cover, timing chain, cylinder head, distributor and fuel pump. Detailed removal and installation procedures for these components may be found in this section under each component heading.
2. Remove tappets with a magnet.
3. Remove dipstick, headlights, parking lights and the grill and hoodlock assembly.
4. Remove camshaft thrust plate and carefully slide camshaft from block.
5. Blow out rocker arm oil supply passages in the block with compressed air. Oil camshaft journals and apply Lubriplate to lobes. If a new camshaft is being used, transfer the spacer and dowel from old camshaft. Carefully slide camshaft into place.
6. Install thrust plate, tightening bolts to 12-15 ft. lbs.
7. Install timing sprockets, chain and all related front cover components as described in front cover removal and installation procedures above. Be sure to install a new front cover oil seal.
8. Install in reverse order all components removed, following instructions for each component group described topically in this section.
9. Start engine, adjust ignition timing, set idle speed and check for leaks.

240 and 300 Cu. In. 6-Cylinder

1. Remove the front cover following procedure described in "Front Cover Removal and Installation" above.
2. Remove air cleaner and crankcase vent tube at the rocker cover.
3. Disconnect accelerator cable, choke cable and hand throttle cable (if so equipped). Remove accelerator cable retracting spring.

BEARINGS
THRUST PLATE
WASHER
SPACER
CAMSHAFT REAR BEARING BORE PLUG
CAMSHAFT
TIMING CHAIN AND CAMSHAFT SPROCKET

Camshaft—170 and 200 cu in. 6-cylinder (© Ford Motor Co.)

4. If applicable, remove air compressor and power steering belts.
5. Disconnect oil filler hose from rocker cover.
6. Remove distributor cap and wiring as an assembly, then disconnect vacuum line and primary wire and remove distributor.
7. Remove fuel pump.
8. Remove valve rocker cover, loosen rocker arm stud nuts and move rocker arms to one side. Remove pushrods, identifying each so that they may be installed in their original locations.
9. Remove pushrod cover and valve lifters, identifying the position of each.
10. Turn crankshaft to align timing marks, remove camshaft thrust plate bolts and carefully pull camshaft and gear from block. Metal camshaft gear (300 HD) is bolted onto camshaft and gear (240 and 300 LD) is pressed on and must be removed with an arbor press.

Removing fibre camshaft gear
(© Ford Motor Co.)

11. To install camshaft, oil journals and apply Lubriplate to lobes, then carefully install camshaft, spacer, thrustplate and gear as an assembly, making sure timing marks are aligned, then tightening thrustplate bolts to 19-20 ft. lbs. Do not rotate crankshaft until distributor is installed.
12. Install front cover, referring to "Front Cover Removal and Installation" for correct procedure.
13. Install valve lifters, then the pushrods in their original locations. Apply heavy engine oil to the lifters and Lubriplate to the pushrods.
14. Install in order the following components, referring to appropriate sections by topic for detailed instructions if necessary and using new gaskets with sealer: pushrod cover, valve rocker cover (adjust valve lash first), distributor (rotor in No. 1. cylinder firing position), fuel pump, distributor cap and wiring assembly, crankcase ventilation valve (in rocker cover), oil

Camshaft—6 cyl.—240 & 300 engines (© Ford Motor Co.)

filler hose, accelerator cable and retracting spring, choke cable, hand throttle cable, water pump pulley, fan, belt, air compressor and power steering belts, radiator, hood latch, grill and air cleaner.
15. Fill crankcase.
16. Fill and bleed cooling system, checking for leaks.
17. Set the ignition timing, then connect distributor vacuum line.
18. Adjust carburetor idle speed and idle fuel mixture.

240 and 300 CID

1. Drain the cooling system and crankcase. Remove the air cleaner. Remove the crankcase ventilator valve from the rocker cover.
2. Disconnect the accelerator cable at the carburetor, and remove the retracting spring. Disconnect the choke and hand throttle cables.
3. Remove the radiator. Disconnect the oil filler hose. Remove the dipstick and tube on C series.
4. Remove the power steering and air compressor belts. Loosen the adjusting bolt, and remove the alternator drive belt. Remove the water pump pulley.
5. Remove the plug wires and distributor cap as an assembly.
6. Disconnect fuel outlet lines at the pump, and remove the pump.
7. Disconnect the distributor vacuum line and the primary wiring, and remove the distributor.
8. Remove the rocker cover. Loosen the stud nuts, and remove the rocker assembly. Remove pushrods and put down in order of removal.

9. Remove the pushrod cover, and remove the lifters with a special tool, and put them down in order of removal.

V-8 Engines

1. Remove the intake manifold and valley pan, if so equipped.
2. Remove the rocker covers, and either remove the rocker arm shafts or loosen the rockers on their pivots and remove the pushrods. The pushrods must be reinstalled in their original positions.
3. Remove the valve lifters in sequence with a magnet. They must be replaced in their original positions.
4. Remove the timing gear cover and timing chain and sprockets.
5. In addition to the radiator and air conditioning condenser, if so equipped, it may be necessary to remove the front grille assembly and the hood lock assembly to gain the necessary clearance to slide the camshaft out the front of the engine.
6. Remove the camshaft thrust plate attaching screws and carefully slide the camshaft out of its bearing bores. Use extra caution not to scratch the bearing journals with the camshaft lobes.
7. Install the camshaft in the reverse order of removal. Coat the camshaft with engine oil liberally before installing it. Slide the camshaft into the engine very carefully so as not to scratch the bearing bores with the camshaft lobes. Install the camshaft thrust plate and tighten the attaching

Typical camshaft—V8 engines (© Ford Motor Co.)

screws to 9-12 ft lbs. Measure the camshaft end-play. If the end-play is more than 0.009 in., replace the thrust plate. Assemble the remaining components in the reverse order of removal.

Camshaft thrustplate & spacer—330 engine
(© Ford Motor Co.)

Camshaft Bearings and Valve Lifters

Reference

For detailed procedures for camshaft bearing replacement and hydraulic lifter service see the General Repair Section.

Pistons and Connecting Rods

Reference

Instructions for fitting of rings and rod bearings, ridge reaming and cylinder honing may be found in the General Repair Section.

Piston and Rod Removal and Installation

All Models

1. Drain cooling system and crankcase.
2. Remove the cylinder head.
3. Remove oil pan, oil pump pick-up tube and screen assembly and oil pump.
4. Turning crankshaft so that piston is at the bottom of its stroke, then ridge ream the top of the cylinder. *Never cut into the ring travel area in excess of 1/32″ when removing ridges.*
5. Mark each rod bearing cap before removal so that it can be installed in its original location, then remove cap. Caps and rods are numbered on some models.
6. Push connecting rod and piston assembly out the top of the cylinder.
7. Make sure piston is assembled in correct relation to the connecting rod, that is, that the notch on the top of the piston and the oil hole in the rod are positioned as illustrated. Align ring gaps as illustrated and oil the piston rings, pistons and cylinder walls.

Piston ring gap spacing
(© Ford Motor Co.)

Piston-to-rod relationship—302 and 351 V-8
(© Ford Motor Co.)

Piston-to-rod relationship—170 and 200 cu in. 6-cylinder (© Ford Motor Co.)

8. Install a ring compressor and push the piston and rod assembly into the cylinder (if reinstalling an old piston, make sure it is in the same cylinder). On all but the 330, 360, 361, 390 and 391 cu. in. V-8 engines the piston is installed with the notch on the crown toward the front of the engine. On the 330, 360, 361, 390 and 391 cu. in. engines the notch faces in (toward "V").
9. Fit rod bearings, apply oil to journals and bearings, then install bearings and cap, tightening cap bolts to specified torque (see Specifications at the beginning of this section).
10. Check rod bearing side clearance.
11. Thoroughly clean oil pump assembly, then prime it by filling and rotating shaft until pump is full. Install pump assembly.

Correct relation of piston to rod— 6 cyl.—240 & 300 engines

Correct relation of piston to rod— V8—330 engines

Piston and rod relationship—460 V-8
(© Ford Motor Co.)

12. Install oil pan, cylinder head and intake manifold (V-8 engines).
13. Fill and bleed cooling system.
14. Fill crankcase.
15. Set ignition timing and operate engine to check for leaks.
16. Make final (hot) valve lash adjustment.

Main Bearings

Main Bearing Removal and Installation

All main bearings may be replaced with the engine in the vehicle with the exception of the 240 and 300 cu. in. rear main bearing. See the General Repair Section for main bearing fitting procedure.

Remove oil pan and oil pump assembly (see Engine Lubrication System below). Replace one bearing at a time. Remove cap and insert special Ford tool #6331 (-E) or similar bearing removing tool into the crankshaft journal oil hole. Slowly rotate crankshaft in its running direction to force upper bearing insert out of its seat. Fit new bearings (0.001″ and 0.002″ undersize available) for specified main bearing clearance, then oil journal and bearings and install cap, tightening cap bolts to specified torque (see Specifications).

To seat thrust bearing (No. 3 on 144, 170, 200 Six and V-8's; No. 5 on 240, 300 Six), fit bearing inserts, then install bearings and cap, tightening cap bolts finger-tight. While prying crankshaft forward and bearing cap rearward (see illustration), tighten the cap bolts to specified torque.

If the rear main bearing is replaced, install a new rear oil seal as described below.

Rear Oil Seal Removal and Installation

170, 200, Cu. In. Six and 302, 330, 351, 360, 361, 390, 391 and 460 V-8

On all models, remove the oil pan as described below. In some cases it may be necessary to remove the oil pump pick-up and screen or the whole pump assembly.

Use only the split-lip type crankshaft rear oil seal as a replacement.

1. Loosen all main bearing caps, lowering the crankshaft slightly, but not more than 1/32″.
2. Remove the rear main bearing cap.
3. Remove the seal halves from cap and block. Use a seal removing tool on the block half or install a small metal screw in one end so that the seal may be pulled out. *CAUTION:* Do not damage or scratch the crankshaft seal surfaces.
4. If so equipped (not used on split-lip type), remove the oil seal retaining pin from the bearing cap.
5. Thoroughly clean seal grooves in block and cap with brush and solvent.
6. Dip seal halves in engine oil.
7. Carefully install upper half of seal with the lip facing toward the *front* of the engine until ⅜″ is left protruding below parting surface. Be careful not to scrape seal.
8. Tighten all but the rear main bearing caps to specified torque.

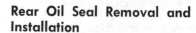

Crankshaft rear oil seal installation (© Ford Motor Co.)

9. Install lower seal half in the rear main bearing cap with the lip facing toward the *front* of the engine. Apply a light coat of oil-resistant sealer to the rear of the top mating surface of the cap. Do not apply sealer to the area forward of the side seal groove.
10. Install rear main bearing cap and tighten bolts to specified torque.
11. Install side seals on the 330, 360, 361, 390 and 391 cu. in. V-8. Dip side seals in oil (do not use sealer as these seals expand when in contact with oil and sealer would retard or stop the

Tool—T65L-6701-A

Installing crankshaft rear oil seal
(© Ford Motor Co.)

expansion). Install seals in grooves, lightly tapping them if necessary. Do not cut off projecting ends. After allowing sufficient time for the seals to expand, squirt oil over the seal end and blow compressed air against the seals from inside the block to check for leakage.
12. Install oil pump and oil pan.
13. Fill crankcase and operate engine to check for leaks.

Rear Oil Seal Removal and Installation

240 and 300 Cu. In. 6-Cylinder

1. Remove the starter.
2. Remove the transmission (see Transmission Removal and Installation). On standard transmission, remove pressure plate and cover assembly and the clutch disc.
3. Remove flywheel and engine rear cover plate.
4. Punch two holes with an awl on each side of the crankshaft just above the bearing cap to cylinder block splint line.
5. Install two sheet metal screws, then pry on both at once to

PRY CRANKSHAFT FORWARD

PRY CAP BACKWARD

TIGHTEN CAP

Aligning thrust bearing (© Ford Motor Co.)

Ford Trucks • Vans • Bronco

remove seal. Be careful not to damage or scratch oil seal surface. Clean out seal recess in cap and block.
6. Lightly oil crankshaft and seal, then install seal with tool as illustrated. Carefully drive the seal straight in.
7. Install engine rear cover plate and flywheel. Coat the flywheel attaching bolt threads with oil-resistant sealer and torque to 75-85 ft. lbs.
8. On standard transmission, install the clutch disc and pressure plate assembly (see Clutch Removal and Installation).
9. Install transmission.

Engine Lubrication System

All models are equipped with rotor type oil pumps, helical gear-driven from the camshaft. The oil flow is from the pan, through the pump, to the oil filter, then crankshaft and bearings and rockers.

Oil Pan Removal and Installation

170 and 200 Cu. In. 6-Cylinder
On some earlier models there is no frame crossmember under the oil pan. Therefore, some of the steps of the following procedure will not be applicable in certain cases.
1. Drain crankcase and cooling system and remove dipstick.
2. Remove fan and water pump pulley.
3. Disconnect the radiator upper and lower hoses, flex fuel line at the fuel pump and starter cable at the starter.
4. Remove the starter.
5. Remove nuts from both front engine support insulators and raise the front of the engine with a transmission jack and wood block. Remove crossmember from beneath the pan and install blocks between front support insulators and side rails. Lower and remove jack.
6. Remove the oil pan attaching bolts and pan.
7. Clean all gasket surfaces and remove seals from their grooves in the front cover and rear main bearing cap.
8. Position oil pan gasket, then pan front seal on front cover, making sure that the tabs on the seal are over the oil pan gasket. Position oil pan rear seal on the rear main bearing cap, making sure the tabs on the seal are over the oil pan gasket.
9. Install oil pan, tightening bolts to 7-9 ft. lbs.

10. Raise the engine with a transmission jack and remove the blocks. Install crossmember and lower the engine. Install washers and nuts on the insulator studs and tighten to 30-40 ft. lbs.
11. Install starter and connect starter cable.
12. Connect radiator hoses and fuel pump flex line.
13. Install water pump pulley, fan and drive belt. Adjust belt.
14. Install dipstick.
15. Fill and bleed cooling system.
16. Fill crankcase.
17. Operate the engine and check for leaks.

240 and 300 Cu. In. 6-Cylinder
1. Drain the crankcase.
2. On the F-100-250, also drain the cooling system.
3. Remove radiator from F-100-250 vehicles.
4. Raise vehicle on a hoist. On F-100-250 trucks disconnect and remove the starter.
5. On F-100-250, remove engine front support insulator to support bracket nuts and washers. Use a transmission jack to raise the front of the engine, then install blocks (1″ thick) between the front support insulators and support brackets. Lower engine onto blocks and remove jack.
6. Remove the attaching bolts and oil pan. It may be necessary to remove the oil pump inlet tube and screen assembly in order to free the pan.
7. Remove the rear main bearing cap and front cover seals. Clean out the seal grooves and all gasket surfaces.
8. Apply oil-resistant sealer in the spaces between the rear main bearing cap and the block as illustrated. Install new rear cap seal, then apply a bead of sealer to the tapered ends of the seal.
9. Install new oil pan side gaskets with sealer and position the front cover seal.
10. Clean oil pump pick-up assembly and place it in the pan.
11. Position pan under the engine and install pick-up assembly.
12. Install pan and attaching bolts, tightening to 10-12 ft. lbs.

Installing oil pan seal—240 & 300 engines
(© Ford Motor Co.)

13. Raise engine enough with a jack and remove wood blocks. Lower engine and install washers and nuts on the support insulator studs, tightening to 40-60 ft. lbs. on LD trucks and 110-150 ft. lbs. on MD and HD trucks.
14. Install starter and starter cable on F-100-250 trucks.
15. Lower vehicle and install radiator if it was removed.
16. Fill crankcase and cooling system and start engine to check for leaks.

All V-8 Engines
1. Remove the oil dipstick.
2. Remove the bolts attaching the fan shroud and position it over the fan.
3. Remove the engine support insulators-to-chassis bracket attaching nuts and washers.
4. If the vehicle is equipped with an

Oil pan gasket and seals—typical V-8
(© Ford Motor Co.)

automatic transmission, disconnect the oil cooler line at the left-side of the radiator.
5. Raise the engine with a jack placed under the crankshaft damper and a block of wood to act as a cushion. Place wood blocks under the engine supports.
6. Drain the crankcase. Remove the oil filter on the 460 V8.
7. Remove the oil pan attaching screws and lower the oil pan onto the crossmember. Remove the two bolts attaching the oil pump pick-up tube to the oil pump. Lower the pick-up tube and screen into the oil pan, then remove the pan.

NOTE: It may be necessary to turn the crankshaft to provide clearance between the crankshaft counterweights and the oil pan.

8. Clean the oil pan and remove all gasket material from the mating surfaces. Repair and straighten any damage due to overtightening the retaining bolts.
9. Place the new oil pan gasket and end seals on the cylinder block. Use sealer to hold them in place.
10. Position the oil pick-up tube and screen to the oil pump, and install the lower attaching bolt and gasket loosely.
11. Place the oil pan on the crossmember. Install the upper pick-up tube bolt.
12. Position the oil pan to the engine and install the attaching screws. Tighten them to 7-9 ft lbs for the 1/4″ screws, and 9-11 ft lbs for the 5/16″ screws.
13. Raise the engine and remove the wooden blocks. Lower the engine and install insulator-to-chassis bracket nuts and washers.
14. Connect the transmission oil cooler lines to the radiator, if so equipped. Install the fan shroud.
15. Fill the crankcase with oil, install the dipstick, and operate the engine until it reaches normal operating temperature and check for leaks.

Oil Pump Removal and Installation

To remove oil pump, remove oil pan as described above. Remove oil pump attaching bolts, then pull pump shaft from engine.

Thoroughly clean all parts in solvent and dry with compressed air. Check the inside of the pump housing for obvious wear or scoring. Check mating surfaces of pump cover and rotors, replacing the cover if it is scored or grooved.

Measure outer race to housing clearance and clearance (rotor endplay) between a straightedge and the rotor. The outer race, shaft and rotor are replaceable only as an assembly. Measure the driveshaft to housing clearance by comparing shaft OD to housing bearing ID.

Checking outer race to housing clearance
(© Ford Motor Co.)

Typical oil pump assembly
(© Ford Motor Co.)

Inspect relief valve spring for collapsed or worn condition. Check the spring tension. Replace the spring if weak or worn.

Check relief valve piston and bore for scores and free operation.

Front Axle, Suspension

Solid I-Beam

Description

Spindles, held in place by bolts, are mounted at each end of the axle. Steel-backed bronze or delrin bushings provide bearing surfaces for the spindle bolt.

Thrust bearings at the lower ends of the axle help support the load. Semi-elliptic, leaf-type springs are mounted parallel to the frame side rails by U-bolt and shackle assemblies.

Front Spring R & R

Econoline

1. Raise the front end of the truck and support the chassis with floor stands. Support the axle with a jack or hoist.
2. Remove front splash shield.
3. Disconnect lower end of shock absorber.
4. Remove the two U bolts and the U-bolt (spring clip) plate.
5. Lower the spring, then remove rear shackle nuts and outside plate.
6. Remove rear shackle assembly and rubber bushings from bracket and spring.
7. Remove nut and bolt attaching front of spring to shackle bracket. Remove spring.

Installation is a reversal of the removal procedure, in addition to noting the following:

1. Install new rubber bushings in the rear shackle bracket and rear spring eye.

2. Do not tighten attaching bolts and nuts until after connecting shock absorber.

Front Spring R & R

F-100, F-250, P Series

1. Raise truck until weight is off front springs, but with wheels still touching ground.
2. Remove spring clips (U-bolts) and spring clip plate.
3. Remove attaching nut, then drive out spring to frame bracket bolt with a brass drift.
4. Remove attaching nut, then drive out lower shackle bolt.
5. Remove lubrication fittings (if so equipped). Remove the spring.

Installation is a reversal of the removal procedure, in addition to noting the following:

1. Replace bushings in spring and shackle bracket.
2. Install caster wedge (if so equipped) pointing in same direction as before removal.
3. Position bolt through bracket and spring eye with head toward inside. NOTE: Install bolt with head toward outside on P Series trucks.
4. Install attaching nuts and bolts, but do not fully tighten until truck has been lowered to floor.

Front Spring R & R

F-350

1. Raise truck until weight is off front springs, but with wheels still touching ground.
2. Disconnect lower end of shock absorber.
3. Remove spring clips (U-bolts) and plate.
4. Remove attaching nut, then drive out rear bracket bolt with a brass drift.
5. Support spring; then, remove cotter pin, rebound pin and rubber bushing from front bracket.
6. Remove spring, noting position of caster wedge (if so equipped).

Installation is a reversal of the removal procedure, in addition to noting the following:

1. Install caster wedge (if so equipped) pointing in same direction as before removal.
2. Install attaching nuts and bolts, but do not fully tighten until truck has been lowered to floor.

Front Spring R & R

N-500, N-600
Early Model F-500 Thru 750

NOTE: On F Series trucks, the locking bracket is at the rear end of the spring and the supporting bracket at the front. On N Series trucks, the bracket positions are reversed.

1. Raise truck until weight is off spring.

2. Remove attaching locking bolt and nut, then drive shackle pin out of locking bracket.
3. Remove shackle pin lubrication fitting.
4. Support spring, then remove supporting bracket cotter pin, rebound pin and rubber bushing.
5. Remove attaching nuts and spring clips (U-bolts), then remove spring and caster wedge (if so equipped).

Installation is a reversal of the removal procedure, in addition to noting the following:

1. Install shackle pin with lubricator opening facing outward.
2. Install caster wedge (if so equipped) pointing in same direction as before removal.
3. Fully tighten attaching nuts and bolts only after truck has been lowered to ground.

Front Spring R & R

Late Model F-B-500 Thru 750

1. Raise truck until weight is off front springs, but with wheels still touching ground.
2. Support front axle.
3. Remove attaching nuts and U-bolts.
4. Remove rear hanger cotter pin, nut, washers and bolt.
5. Remove securing cotter pin, then remove spring front hanger pin.
6. Remove spring.

Installation is a reversal of the removal procedure, in addition to noting the following:

1. Make certain that front U-bolt enters shock absorber lower bracket.
2. Raise or lower axle to align spring eye with bolt hole in rear hanger. Install bolt and one washer on each side of bracket; then, with the weight of the truck on the springs, tighten rear hanger bolt nut and install cotter pin.
NOTE: Do not back-off nut to align castellation with cotter pin hole. If necessary, tighten nut.

Front Spring R & R

L-LT-LN-LNT-800-900, 8000-9000, C-CT And W Series

1. Raise truck until weight is off front springs, but with wheels still touching ground.
2. Remove attaching nuts, then drive out front and rear mounting studs.
3. Remove attaching nuts, spring clips, plate, shock absorber lower mounting bracket and spring. Note position of caster wedge and spacer (if so equipped).
4. Installation procedure is given in Steps 5 through 11.

Front spring installation—F-B 500-750 (© Ford Motor Co.)

5. Position spring on seat and align front eye with bracket.
6. Remove lubrication fitting from front stud, then drive stud (lubricator opening facing outward) through bracket and front eye. Install nut and tighten snugly; then, back off 1/3 turn. Install cotter pin at inner end of stud and lubrication fitting at outer end.
7. Align rear spring eye with shackle bars.
8. Repeat Step 6 at the rear mounting stud and bracket.
9. Install caster wedge (if so equipped) pointing in same direction as before removal.
10. Install shock absorber lower bracket. Secure with lockwasher and nut.
11. Lower the truck, then fully tighten all attaching nuts and bolts. Lubricate stud fittings.

Spindle R & R

Econoline

1. Raise truck and support frame with floor stands. Do not use a bumper jack.
2. Remove front wheel hub and drum assembly.

3. Remove attaching bolts and brake backing (carrier) plate. Secure plate to frame with wire.
4. Remove spindle arm attaching nut, then drive arm off spindle with a soft-faced hammer. NOTE: If removing left spindle, disconnect steering drag link.
5. Drive out spindle bolt locking pin.
6. Remove threaded caps from top and bottom of spindle.
7. Drive bolt out of spindle and axle, then remove spindle and bearing.

Installation is a reversal of the removal procedure, in addition to noting the following:

1. Make certain that notch in spindle bolt is correctly aligned with locking pin hole in axle.
2. Lubricate spindle fittings. Adjust brakes and front wheel bearings.
3. After lowering truck, adjust toe-in and tighten spindle connecting rod clamps.

Spindle R & R

P Series, Early Model C, F, N Series

1. Raise truck until wheels clear floor. Place a support under axle.

2. Remove wheel, drum, bearing and hub assembly. NOTE: It may be necessary to back-off brakes adjustment in order to remove drum.
3. Remove brake backing (carrier) plate, then remove spindle arm bolt and nut. Tie plate and arm to frame with wire.
4. Remove attaching nut, lockwasher and spindle bolt locking pin.
5. Remove top spindle bolt seal, then drive bolt out from top of axle. Remove the spindle from the axle.

Installation is a reversal of the removal procedure, in addition to noting the following:
1. Coat all spindle parts with oil.
2. Pack bearing with chassis lubricant.
3. Install bearing with open end of seal facing downward.
4. Install a new top spindle bolt seal.
5. Make certain that notch in spindle bolt is aligned with locking pin hole in axle.
6. Install new bottom spindle bolt seal (except F-350).
7. After lowering truck, check and adjust toe-in.

Spindle R&R

Late Model C, F, N Series (5000, 5500, 6000, 7000 Lb. Axles)

1. Raise truck and support front axle.
2. Remove wheel, hub, drum bearing.
3. Remove brake backing plate. Tie plate to frame with wire.
4. Disconnect spindle arm. NOTE: F-250 and F-350 models with BX or disc brakes have an integral spindle arm.
5. Remove top spindle bolt seal.
6. Remove attaching nut, then drive out spindle bolt locking pin.
7. Using a suitable drift, drive out spindle bolt from top of axle.
8. Remove spindle assembly.

Installation is a reversal of the removal procedure, in addition to noting the following:
1. Install thrust bearing with seal (retainer) lip downward.
2. Late model trucks, excluding F Series, are equipped with shims between top of axle and spindle. A clearance of .003-010" between axle and spindle must be maintained on all models.
3. Excluding F Series, install spindle bolt with letter "T" upward.
4. Install new top and bottom spindle bolt seals.
5. On 5000 and 5500 lb. axles, excluding F Series, make certain that hardened flat washers, of

Spindle installation—P-Series
(© Ford Motor Co.)

Spindle installation—5000-5500 lb. axles
(© Ford Motor Co.)

Spindle installation—6000-7000 lb. axles
(© Ford Motor Co.)

the same type removed, are placed between backing plate and attaching bolt heads.
6. On 6000 lb. and larger axles, install spindle arm before backing plate.
7. Lubricate spindle bushings.
8. Adjust front wheel bearings and toe-in.

Spindle Bushing Replacement

1. Remove bronze bushings by driving them out with a drift slightly smaller than spindle bore. If a drift is not available, carefully drive a small center punch between the bushing and the spindle bore. Collapse the bushing, then remove.

2. Remove Delrin bushings, using a small center punch as described in Step 1.
3. Thoroughly clean spindle bores and make certain that lubrication holes are not obstructed in any way.
4. Place new bushing in spindle bore with lubricating holes properly aligned. Position open end of bushing oil groove toward axle.
5. Drive bronze bushing into spindle bore, using a drift as a pilot.
6. It is not necessary to drive Delrin bushings into spindle bores.
7. Install remaining bushing(s) in the same manner.
8. Ream bronze bushings .001 to .003" larger than spindle bolt diameter.
9. DO NOT ream Delrin bushings.
10. After reaming bronze bushings, clean out spindle bore to remove metal shavings.

Reaming bronze bushing
(© Ford Motor Co.)

Removing bronze bushing
(© Ford Motor Co.)

Installing bronze bushing
(© Ford Motor Co.)

11. Apply a light coat of oil to all bushings before spindle assembly and installation.

Twin I-Beam

Description

One end of each axle is attached to a spindle and radius arm; the other end is attached to a frame pivot bracket on the opposite side of the truck. Each spindle is held in place by a bolt, which pivots in steel-backed bronze bushings. A thrust bearing, between the spindle and the lower end of the axle, helps support the load. An arm is bolted to the spindle for attachment to the steering linkage.

NOTE: F-100 and F-250 models with standard brakes utilize Delrin spindle bolt bushings.

NOTE: F-250, F-350 and E-300 models with BX or disc brakes are equipped with an integral arm and spindle.

Front Coil Spring R & R

Econoline (1970-75)

1. Remove floor mat retainer from lower end of door opening.
2. Fold mat to one side, then remove attaching screws and shock absorber cover plate.
3. Remove spring upper retainer attaching screws, insulator and clamp.
4. Support frame side rails with a jack stand.
5. Position a floor jack under axle, then remove lower retainer attaching bolt, retainer and spring support.
6. Slowly lower axle to release tension, then remove spring.
7. Installation procedure is given in steps 8-14.
8. Position spring on axle with pigtails toward rear end of truck.
9. Position spring lower support and retainer. Install attaching bolt loosely.
10. Place upper insulator on spring.
11. Raise jack to apply light spring pressure.
12. Install upper retainer and clamp. NOTE: Make certain that all upper retainer parts are correctly seated.
13. Remove jack stand.
14. Install shock absorber cover plate and floor mat retainer.

Econoline (1976)

1. Raise and support the front of the van. Support the front axle.
2. Disconnect the shock absorber from the lower bracket.
3. Remove the 2 upper spring attaching bolts from the upper spring seat. Remove the retainer.
4. Remove the nut from the lower

Twin I-beam front axle (© Ford Motor Co.)

spring retainer and remove the retainer.
5. Install a spring compressor.
6. Lower the axle carefully, and remove the spring.
7. Installation is the reverse of removal.

Front Spring R & R

F-100, 150, 250, 350

1. Raise front end of truck and support frame with floor stands.
2. Position a jack under axle.
3. Disconnect shock absorber from lower bracket.
4. Remove attaching bolt, nut and rebound bracket.
5. On pre-1966 F-100 and F-250, lower axle and remove spring.
6. On 1966-71 F-100 and F-250, perform the following:
   a. Remove attaching bolts and retainer.
   b. Remove attaching nut and lower spring retainer.
   c. Lower axle and remove spring.
7. On F-350, perform the following:
   a. Remove bolts attaching upper spring clip to seat. Remove clip.
   b. Remove attaching nut and lower spring retainer.
   c. Lower axle and remove spring.
Installation is a reversal of the removal procedure.

Radius Arm R & R

All Models

1. Raise front end of truck and support frame with floor stands.
2. Position a jack under axle or appropriate wheel.
3. Remove coil spring.
4. Disconnect steering rod from spindle arm.

5. Remove coil spring lower seat and shim.
6. Remove radius arm front attaching bolt and nut.
7. Remove cotter pin, nut and washer from radius arm rear attachment.
8. Remove bushing (insulator) from rear end of arm.
9. Remove radius arm.
10. Remove inner bushing (insulator).
Installation is reversal of the removal procedure.

Refer to Wheel Alignment Specifications for toe-in, caster, camber and kingpin (spindle bolt) inclination values.

Front Drive Axle

Description

Bronco

The Dana Model 441F drive axle is used on Bronco trucks. The axle has an open yoke welded to the outer ends of the axle housing. Cardan-type universal joints transmit power to the front driving wheels.

NOTE: Early Bronco models used the Dana Model 30F, utilizing kingpins rather than ball joints, as on the Model 441F. This is the only significant difference between the two models.

F-100

The Dana Model 44-7F drive axle is used on F-100 four wheel drive trucks. The axle has an open spindle assembly, utilizing Cardan-type universal joints to transmit power to the front drive wheels.

NOTE: Early model F-100 trucks were equipped with a Spicer 2559 drive axle. Follow repair procedures given for F-250.

F-250

Dana Models 44-6BF and 44-7BF-HD are used on early F-250 four wheel drive trucks. The axle has a spherical,

STEERING KNUCKLE

Removing axle shaft (© Ford Motor Co.)

Knuckle removal (© Ford Motor Co.)

closed spindle and enclosed universal joint.

NOTE: Some early model F-250 trucks were equipped with a Spicer 2559 or optional Spicer 2558. Follow repair procedures given for F-250 with Dana drive axle.

Late model trucks use the Dana model 44-6CF or model 44-6CF-HD. These axles are identical to the other 44 series except for a few minor differences.

F-600

The Rockwell-Standard Single-Reduction Final Drive Axle was made available on 1971-74 F-600 trucks. The axle has a heavy duty spiral bevel or hypoid pinion and gear. The differential and gear assembly is carried in tapered roller bearings.

Refer to the General Repair Section for complete overhaul procedures on the front wheel drive axles.

With the exception of specialized components required for front drive application, the Dana and Rockwell-Standard models are identical to their rear axle counterparts (i.e. Dana 44-7F—Dana Model 44, Rockwell - Standard Single - Reduction— same, etc.). Spicer and Dana front drive axles are identical. The Dana Model 44IF, used on Bronco models, is similar to the other Dana axles except in size.

Axle Shaft and Steering Knuckle R & R

Bronco, F-100 and F-150

1. Raise vehicle on a hoist.
2. Remove front hub grease cap. Remove driving hub retaining snap-ring, then slide splined

driving hub from between axle shaft and wheel hub.
3. Remove driving hub spring. NOTE: If equipped with free-wheeling hubs, see hub removal.
4. Remove lock nut, washer, and wheel bearing adjusting nut from spindle. Remove wheel, hub and drum as an assembly. The wheel outer bearing will be forced off the spindle at the same time. Remove wheel inner bearing cone.
5. Remove capscrews that attach brake backing plate and spindle to steering knuckle. Remove brake backing plate and secure it to one side. Carefully remove the spindle.
6. Pull shaft assembly from axle housing, working universal joint through bore in steering knuckle.
7. To remove steering knuckle (housing), disconnect the steering connecting rod end from the steering knuckle and remove the bearing caps. Remove the steering knuckle.
8. Remove the three retaining nuts and remove the steering arm. Remove the cotter key from the upper ball socket.
9. Remove the nut from the upper ball socket. Remove the nut from the lower ball socket. NOTE: Discard the nut from the bottom socket.
10. Remove the knuckle from the yoke. If the top socket remains in the yoke it can be dislodged with a rawhide hammer.
11. Remove the bottom socket, the adjusting sleeve and the top socket from the knuckle. On F-100, F-150 remove the snap-ring before removing the socket.
12. Installation is given in steps 13 thru 30.
13. Place knuckle in vise and assemble bottom socket. Place new socket into knuckle making sure it is not cocked; place the driver over the socket; place forcing screw into driver as shown. Apply torque to screw and force socket into knuckle.

14. Make sure socket shoulder is seated against knuckle. Use a .0015″ feeler gauge between socket and knuckle. Feeler gauge is not to enter at minimum area of contact.
15. Assemble top socket into knuckle. Assemble holding plate onto backing plate screw. Tighten nuts snug. Place new socket into knuckle. Be sure socket is straight and not in a cocked position. Place driver over socket.
16. Make sure socket shoulder is seated against knuckle. Use a .0015″ feeler gauge between socket and knuckle. Feeler gauge is not to enter at minimum area of contact.
17. Assemble new adjusting sleeve into top of yoke. Leave approximately two threads exposed. This will protect the threads in the yoke.
18. Assemble knuckle with sockets to yoke. Assemble new nut to bottom socket. Tighten nut finger loose. This will serve as a holding device.
19. Place spanner wrench and step plate over adjusting sleeve. Position puller, and turn forcing screw. This will pull the knuckle assembly into the yoke. With torque still applied, tighten the bottom nut on the socket. Torque nut to 70-90 ft. lbs. NOTE: If the bottom stud should turn with the nut, add more torque to the puller forcing screw.
20. Torque adjusting sleeve to 50 ft. lbs. Remove spanner wrench.
21. Assemble top socket nut. Torque to 100 ft. lbs. Line up cotter key hole of stud with the castellation or slot of the nut. Tighten nut when it is being lined up with the hole of the stud. Do not loosen nut. Assemble cotter key.
22. Assemble steering arm, three stud adapters, and three nuts. Torque nuts to 80-100 ft. lbs.
23. Assemble the tie rod to the knuckle arm. Torque the nut to

Top socket assembly
(© Ford Motor Co.)

Inch-Pound
Torque Wrench

Checking steering knuckle bearing preload
(© Ford Motor Co.)

STEERING KNUCKLE

Removing axle shaft—F-100 (© Ford Motor Co.)

specifications and install the cotter key.

24. Assemble the protective inner slinger on to the axle shaft. The outer wheel bearing spindle nut will serve as a guide to assemble the slinger. Place the nut in a vise and the slinger on the end of the shaft. Tap on the shaft with a rawhide hammer until the slinger is seated.

25. Assemble the protective outer slinger on to the shaft. One of the wheel spindles will serve as a guide. Place the spindle in a vise. Do not clamp on the bearing diameters. Place the slinger on the shaft. Tap on the end of the shaft with a rawhide hammer until the slinger is seated. NOTE: Take care not to damage the seal diameter of the slinger.

26. Assemble the axle shaft joint assembly into the housing.

27. Place the spindle in a vise and install the needle roller bearings, using driver and rawhide hammer.

28. Assemble the grease seal into the spindle, flush with the spindle face.

29. After assembly of the needle bearing and oil seal, pack wheel bearing grease around the needle bearing and lip of the seal.

30. Assemble the axle shaft joint assembly, bronze spacer and spindle to the knuckle.

NOTE: The chamfer of the spacer should be inboard against the shaft.

F-250 (1970-75)

1. Raise the vehicle and support it with jackstands placed under the frame side rails.
2. Remove the front wheel free-running hub. Remove the hub and brake drum.
3. Place a drain pan under the steering knuckle assembly.
4. Remove the capscrews which hold the brake backing plate and spindle to the steering knuckle. Remove the backing plate and spindle. Support the brake backing plate with a piece of wire so that the tension is removed from the brake fluid hose.
5. Slide the axle shaft out through the opening in the steering knuckle.
6. Disconnect the steering drag link from the steering knuckle.
7. Disconnect the spindle tie-rod at both ends.
8. Remove the unitized seal from the steering arm of the steering knuckle, if so equipped.
9. Remove the upper and lower kingpin bearing caps and shims. Keep the shims in the same order side-to-side in which they are removed for proper installation.
10. Remove the steering knuckle from the axle housing and remove the bearings.
11. If the bearing cups (races) are to be removed from the housing, tap them out with a hammer and drift.
12. Place a new steering knuckle seal over the axle housing tube,

if the seal is being replaced. The seal is attached to the rear of the steering knuckle with the split facing up to prevent leakage. Do not attach the seal until the steering knuckle turning torque is checked.

13. Install and assemble the steering knuckle and axle shaft in the reverse order of removal. Install the shims under the kingpin bearing caps in the same order in which they were removed and tighten the cap attaching bolts to 30-40 ft lbs on the Dana Model 44-6CF and 80-90 ft lbs on the Dana Model 44-6CF-HD.

14. Place a torque wrench on the inside/forward bearing cap retaining bolt and check the torque required to turn the steering knuckle. The torque required should be 5-10 ft lbs on the 44-6CF and 10-15 ft lbs on the 44-6CF-HD. Adjust the number and thickness of the shims under the bearing cap to obtain the correct turning breakaway torque.

NOTE: Check the steering turning torque with the seal not yet attached to the back of the knuckle, the axle shaft removed, and the steering linkage unattached.

F-250 (1976)

1. Raise and support the front of the truck.
2. Remove the wheel.
3. Remove the caliper from the rotor and suspend it from the frame.
4. Remove the dust cap, cotter pin, nut, washer and outer bearing and remove the rotor from the spindle.

5. Remove the inner bearing cone and seal.

6. Remove the axle shaft, working the U-joint through the bore of the steering knuckle. Be careful not to damage the seal.

7. At this point, the axle shaft, U-joints, spindle bore seals and bearings can be replaced without further disassembly.

8. Disconnect the steering connecting rod end from the steering knuckle.

9. Remove the cotter key from the upper ball socket. Loosen the nuts from the upper and lower ball sockets and discard the nuts.

10. Remove the knuckle from the yoke. If the top socket sticks in the yoke, it can be removed with a plastic mallet.

11. Remove and discard the bottom socket.

12. Remove and discard the adjusting sleeve.

13. Remove the top socket from the knuckle.

14. Place a new knuckle in a vise and install a new bottom socket. The socket shoulder should be seated against the knuckle so that a .0015 in. feeler blade cannot be inserted between the socket and the knuckle.

15. Install the top socket as in Step 14.

16. Install a new adjusting sleeve, leaving about 2 threads exposed.

17. Assemble the knuckle to the yoke and tighten the nut finger-tight.

18. Pull the knuckle assembly into the yoke and tighten the bottom nut on the socket to 70-90 ft lbs.

19. Tighten the adjusting sleeve to 40 ft lbs.

20. Assemble the top socket nut. Tighten it to 100 ft lbs and align the keyway with the castellations on the nut. Tighten the nut to align the holes. Install a new cotter pin.

21. Test the steering knuckle turning effort with a spring scale hooked at the tie rod hole. If it is more than 26 lbs, the ball joints should be replaced.

22. Connect the steering rod to the steering knuckle and tighten the nut.

23. Further installation is the reverse of removal. Adjust the wheel bearings.

Front Drive Axle R & R

Bronco

1. Raise the vehicle on a hoist or jack and install safety stands under the radius arm brackets.

2. Follow the procedure given in Axle Shaft and Steering Knuckle Removal and remove the front wheels, tires, brake drums or brake calipers, brake backing plates, spindles and axle shaft.

3. Remove the hydraulic brake line brackets from each end of the axle without breaking the hydraulic connection. Disengage the hydraulic lines from the axle clips. Tie the lines to the frame to keep them out of the working area.

4. Disconnect the steering tie rod at the knuckle connecting rod ends and tie it out of the working area. Disconnect the axle stablizer bar.

5. Disconnect the front drive shaft at the pinion companion flange and universal joint. Secure the drive shaft out of the working area.

6. Lower the vehicle onto the safety stands and place a jack under the axle to support it while disconnecting it from the radius arms.

7. Each radius arm and cap is numbered from 1 through 100 for proper assembly, since they are manufactured as matched pairs. Remove the bolts attaching the radius arms to the radius arm caps. Remove the rubber insulators and roll the axle form under the vehicle.

8. Installation is given in steps 9 thru 15.

9. Position the front drive axle under the vehicle, using a floor jack, and install the radius arms, insulators and caps to the axle. The numbers enscribed on cap and arm should be matched. Torque the attaching bolts to specifications, tightening them diagonally in pairs.

10. Raise the vehicle to working height and install the drive shaft to the pinion companion flange at the universal joint. Torque the universal joint U-bolt nuts to specifications.

11. Connect the axle stabilizer bar. Connect the steering tie rod to the steering knuckle by the steering connecting rod ends. Torque the attaching nuts to specifications, then install cotter pins.

12. Follow the procedure detailed in Axle Shaft and Steering Knuckle Installation and install the axle shafts, spindles and brake backing plates.

13. Position the hydraulic brake lines and brackets, then install the retaining clips.

14. Install the front brake drums, wheels and tires. Adjust the front wheel bearings. Install the dust cap or locking hub cap and the wheel cover on each front wheel.

15. Lower the truck and fill the axle housing with the specified lubricant.

F-100 and F-150

1. Raise the vehicle on a hoist or jack and install safety stands under the radius arm brackets.

2. Follow the procedure detailed in Axle Shaft and Steering Knuckle Removal and remove the front wheels, tires, brake drums, brake carrier plates, spindles and axle shafts.

3. Remove the hydraulic brake line brackets from each end of the axle without breaking the hydraulic connection. Disengage the hydraulic lines from the axle clips. Tie the lines to the frame.

4. Disconnect the steering tie rod at the spindle connecting rod ends. Disconnect the axle stabilizer bar.

5. Disconnect the front drive shaft at the pinion companion flange and universal joint. Secure the drive shaft out of the working area.

6. Lower the vehicle onto the safety stands and place a jack under the axle to support it while disconnecting it from the radius arms.

7. Each radius arm and cap is marked, since they are manufactured as matched pairs (parts are numbered 1 through 100). Remove the bolts attaching the radius to the radius arm caps. Remove the rubber insulators and roll the axle from under the truck.

8. Installation is given in steps 9 thru 15.

9. Position the front drive axle under the vehicle, using a floor jack, and install the radius arms, insulators and caps to the axle. Numbers on radius arm and cap should be matched. Torque the attaching bolts to specifications, tightening them diagonally in pairs.

10. Raise the vehicle to working height and install the drive shaft to the pinion companion flange at the universal joint. Torque the universal joint U-bolt nuts to specifications.

11. Connect the axle stablizer bar. Connect the steering tie rod to the spindle arms by means of the steering connecting rod ends. Torque the attaching nuts to specifications, then install the cotter pins.

12. Follow the procedure detailed in Axle Shaft and Spindle Arm Installation and install the axle shafts, spindles and brake backing plates.

13. Position the hydraulic brake lines and brackets, then install the retaining clips.

14. Install the front brake drums, wheels and tires. Adjust the front wheel bearings. Install the dust cap or locking hub cap and the wheel cover on each front wheel. NOTE: If a dust cap is used, install it with a coat of non-hardening sealer on the sealing surface.

15. Lower the truck and fill the axle housing with the specified lubricant.

Front Drive Axle R & R
F-250

1. Raise the vehicle on a hoist so that no weight is supported by the front axle.
2. Remove the hubs, rotors, brake carrier plates, axle shafts and steering knuckle as given in Axle Shaft and Steering Arm.
3. Disconnect both front axle shock absorbers at their lower ends.
4. Disconnect the front axle drive shaft at the pinion flange.
5. Support the front axle on a transmission jack, then remove the spring clip (U-bolt) nuts and the spring seats.
6. Lower the axle assembly and roll it from under the truck.
7. Installation is given in steps 8 thru 11.
8. Position axle under truck and raise it so that the spring clips and spring seats can be installed.
9. Connect the front axle shock absorbers.
10. Connect the front axle drive shaft.
11. Complete the assembly as given in Axle Shaft and Steering Knuckle Installation.

Steering Knuckle R & R
F-600

1. Raise the vehicle and support with safety stands.
2. Remove the plug from the bottom of the axle housing and drain the lubricant.
3. Disconnect the driveshaft at the pinion shaft.
4. Remove one front wheel from the brake drum and hub assembly.
5. Remove the outer hub cap retaining screws and cap.
6. Remove the retaining lock ring.
7. Remove the retaining screws and the splined drive plate.
8. Bend the tab of the lockwasher from the locknut, then remove the locknut.
9. Remove lockwasher and discard. Remove the adjusting nut.
10. Remove the drum and hub assembly from the spindle.
11. Remove the brake backing plate retaining screws and carefully lift out the backing plate and wire it out of the way.

Front drive axle—F-100 and F-150 (© Ford Motor Co.)

Axle shaft removal—F-600 (© Ford Motor Co.)

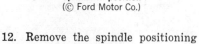

Spindle in position
(© Ford Motor Co.)

Removing king pin bearing cup
(© Ford Motor Co.)

**Removing or installing steering knuckle—
F-250**
(© Ford Motor Co.)

12. Remove the spindle positioning screw and spindle.
13. Remove the axle shaft from the housing.
14. Repeat steps 4 thru 13 to remove the opposite axle shaft.
15. Remove the carrier to housing stud nuts and washers. Loosen two top nuts and leave on studs to prevent carrier from falling.
16. Break carrier loose from axle housing with rawhide mallet. NOTE: A roller jack should be positioned and fastened to the carrier at this point.
17. Remove the top nuts and washers, then work the carrier free. A small pinch bar may be used to straighten the carrier in the housing bore. However, the end must be rounded to prevent identing the carrier flange. A roller jack may be used to facilitate removal of the carrier.
18. Installation is given in steps 21 thru 39.
19. Remove all traces of old gasket material from the carrier and housing surfaces, then position a new gasket over the housing mounting studs.
20. Using a roller jack, ease the carrier into position in the housing bore.
21. Position two washers and run two nuts part way on to the studs to hold the carrier; then align it properly with the housing.
22. Install the housing stud nuts and torque them to specifications.
23. Install one axle shaft in the housing.
24. Install the spindle and secure it with the positioning screw.
25. Position the brake backing plate, install the retaining screws and torque to specifications.
26. Carefully position the drum, and hub assembly on the axle spindle, and tighten the adjusting nut.
27. Adjust wheel bearing. Position a new lockwasher against the ad-

justing nut and apply a film of oil to the outer face of the lockwasher.
28. Run the lock nut against the lockwasher, then torque it to specifications.
29. Bend one tab of the lockwasher over the adjusting nut.
30. Bend other tab of the lockwasher (in the opposite direction) over the lock nut.
31. Apply Silastic Sealer to the front and rear mounting faces of the splined drive plate. Position the drive plate and install the plate retaining screws, then torque to specifications.
32. Install the retaining lock ring.
33. Position the outer hub cap and install the retaining screws, then torque to specifications.
34. Install the front wheel.
35. Connect the drive shaft at the pinion shaft.
36. Repeat steps 23 through 34 for the other axle shaft assembly.
37. Make sure that the housing drain plug has been installed.
38. Fill the axle housing with the correct grade and quantity of lubricant.
39. Lower the vehicle.

Wheel Bearing Adjustment
F-100, F-150, F-250, F-350, Econoline P-350-500 (1970-76)
1. Remove the hub cap and hub grease cap.
2. Clean the end of the spindle and remove the cotter pin and nut-lock.
3. While rotating the wheel, torque the adjusting nut to 17-25 ft lbs. (40-55 ft lbs.—P-350-500), to seat the bearings.
4. Install the nut-lock so that the cotter pin hole in the spindle is aligned with the hole in the nut-lock.
5. Back the adjusting nut off, 2 slots and install the cotter pin. Be sure that the wheel rotates freely with no noticeable endplay.

6. Install the grease cap and hub cap.

4-Wheel Drive (1970-76)

NOTE: On 1971 Bronco and F-100 models, the hub spacer has been replaced with a pressure spring.

1. Raise the vehicle and support with safety stands.
2. Back off the brake adjusting screw, if necessary. Remove the wheel cover.
3. Remove the front hub grease cap. Remove the driving hub retaining snap-ring and slide the splined driving hub from between the axle shaft and the wheel hub. Remove the driving hub spacer. NOTE: If equipped with free-wheeling hubs, see Free-Wheeling Hub Removal.
4. Remove lock nut and lock ring from the spindle.
5. Tighten the bearing adjusting nut to 50 ft. lbs., while rotating the wheel back and forth to seat the bearings.
6. Continue rotating the wheel and then, loosen and re-torque the adjusting nut to 30-40 ft. lbs.
7. Back the adjusting nut off approximately ¼ turn (90 degrees). Assemble the lock ring by turning the nut to the nearest notch where the dowel pin will enter.
8. Install the outer lock nut and torque to 50 ft. lbs. (80-100 ft. lbs—1973-76). Final endplay of the wheel on the spindle should be 0.001 to 0.010.
9. Install the driving hub, spacer, snap-ring and hub grease cap. Apply a thin coat of non-hardening sealer to the seating edge of the grease cap before installation. NOTE: If equipped with free-wheeling hubs, installation refer to Free-Wheeling Hub.
10. Adjust the brake.
11. Remove safety stands and lower the vehicle.

Wheel Bearing Adjustment

F-600

1. Remove the outer hub cap retaining screws, then remove the cap.
2. Remove the retaining lock ring.
3. Remove the retaining screws and the splined drive plate.
4. Bend the tab of the lockwasher away from the locknut, then remove the locknut.
5. Remove the lockwasher and discard.
6. While rotating the wheel back and forth to correctly seat the bearings, torque the adjusting nut to 50 ft. lbs.
7. Back-off the adjusting nut from 1/4 to 1/3 turn.
8. Position a new lockwasher against the adjusting nut and apply a film of oil to the outer face of the lockwasher.
9. Run the lock nut up against the lockwasher, then torque it to 100-150 ft. lbs.
10. Bend one tab of the lockwasher over the adjusting nut.
11. Bend other tap (in the opposite direction) over the lock nut. NOTE: Use a blunt tool when bending the tabs.
12. Apply Silastic Sealer to the front and rear mounting faces of the spined drive plate.
13. Position the drive plate, install the retaining screws and torque to specifications.
14. Install the retaining lock ring.
15. Position the outer hub cap and install the retaining screws. Torque to specifications.

Free-Wheeling Lock-out Hubs

Description

Free-Wheeling lock-out hubs are available on Bronco, F-100 and F-250 front wheel drive models. An internal design hub is used on Bronco and F-100 trucks; an external type on F-250 trucks.

Free Wheeling Hub R&R

Bronco, F-100, F-150, F-250 (Except H.D.)

1. Remove the three screws (six screws on Bronco) attaching the lock-out actuating knob and retaining plate assembly to the wheel hub. Remove the actuating knob and retaining plate assembly and large O-ring.
2. Remove the large internal snap-ring, the outer clutch retaining ring and the actuating cam body.
3. While pressing inward against the axle shaft sleeve and ring assembly, remove the snap-ring

that secures the axle sleeve and ring assembly to the axle shaft.
4. Remove the axle shaft sleeve and ring assembly and the inner clutch and bushing assembly.
5. Remove the pressure spring (or spacer) and spring retainer plate.
6. Installation is given in steps 7 thru 13.
7. Insert the spring retainer plate into the wheel hub with the flange side facing inward. Be sure spring retainer plate bottoms against the outer wheel hub bearing cap.
8. Position the pressure spring (or spacer), with the large end seating against the spring retainer plate, inside the wheel hub.
9. Assemble the inner clutch ring and bushing assembly to the axle shaft sleeve and ring assembly, sliding both assemblies as a unit on to the axle shaft splines. Using a new axle shaft snap-ring, lock the axle shaft sleeve and ring assembly to the shaft.
10. Place the actuating cam body in position against the axle shaft sleeve and ring assembly, inside the wheel hub.
11. Install the outer clutch retaining ring and the internal snap-ring

into position in the wheel hub. Make certain the snap-ring is well seated in the groove on the inside diameter of the hub.
12. Coat the large O-ring seal with O-ring lubricant. Install the large O-ring seal onto the actuating knob and retaining plate and place the knob and retaining plate assembly into position in the wheel hub.
13. Install the three (six on Bronco) knob and retaining plate assembly attaching screws and copper washers. Tighten screws securely.

F-250 Heavy-Duty

1. Remove the free-running hub screws and washers.
2. Loosen the gear hub housing and slide it away from the hub and drum assembly.
3. Remove and discard the inner metal gasket, remove the gear hub housing, and remove and discard the outer gasket. Wipe the exposed parts clean with a clean rag.
4. Remove the snap-ring while holding pressure on the clutch gear.
5. The actuator knob should be in the lock position while perform-

External lock-out hub—disassembled (© Ford Motor Co.)

Internal lock-out hub—disassembled (© Ford Motor Co.)

ing this operation. Ease the clutch gear and pressure spring out of the assembly.

6. Turn the actuator knob to the free position. Drive the cam lock pin out of the assembly with a drift.
7. Remove the actuating cam from the knob.
8. Remove the knob retainer snap-ring and remove the knob from the knob retainer.
9. Using a capscrew, pull out slightly on the axle shaft and remove the snap-ring which retains the bushing and inner clutch gear assembly.
10. Remove the inner clutch gear and the bushing behind it. Replace these two components as a set if excessive wear or damage is evident.
11. Inspect the splines of the axle shaft for nicks or burrs. Clean the threaded holes in the wheel hub.
12. Apply Moly XL Hi-Speed grease to the back face and thrust face of the bushing and the splines of the inner clutch gear.
13. Assemble the inner clutch gear into the bushing.
14. Install the bushing and inner clutch gear onto the axle shaft mating the splines of the axle and the gear.
15. Install a new snap-ring to retain the bushing and gear. It may be necessary to pull out the axle with a capscrew to gain clearance for the snap-ring to be installed. Make sure that the snap-ring is fully seated.
16. Apply a small amount of O-ring lubricant on the actuator knob and assemble the O-ring to the actuator knob.
17. Install the actuating knob into the knob retainer with the arrow pointing to the free position.
18. Install the knob retainer snap-ring.
19. Install the actuating cam onto the knob, aligning the ears of the cam with the slots of the retainer. Position the parts on a small block of wood.
20. Assemble the cam lock pin through the groove of the cam and the holes in the actuating knob. Be sure that the ends of the pin are flush with the outside diameter of the cam.
21. Turn the actuator knob to the lock position and apply a small amount of Moly XL Hi-Speed grease to both grooves of the cam.
22. Install the pressure spring and outer clutch gear. Compress the pressure spring by forcing the clutch gear down, then install the snap-ring. Be sure that the snap-ring is fully seated in the groove.

GEAR ATTACHING BOLTS
STEERING GEAR
PITMAN ARM
FLEX COUPLING

Steering gear installation—Econoline (© Ford Motor Co.)

23. Turn the actuator knob to the free position. Assemble the six dished washers to the six retaining screws.
24. Install two screws with washers into the knob retainer to properly align the parts. Apply a small amount of Moly XL Hi-Speed grease to the outer spline and teeth of the outer clutch gear. Remove any excess lubricant from the gasket surface of the retainer.
25. Install a new outer retainer gasket. Assemble the gear hub housing by aligning the splines of the housing with those on the outer clutch gear. Then install a new inner metal gasket on the hub housing.
26. Position the free-running hub assembly to the axle and tighten the two installed retaining screws. Turn the actuator knob to the lock position.
27. Install the remaining four retainer screws with washers and tighten all screws in sequence to 30-36 ft lbs.
NOTE: The hubs may be hard to engage and disengage at first, but should loosen up after some use. Make sure that both the hubs are either engaged or disengaged before driving the truck.

Reference
Front wheel and steering alignment procedures may be found in the General Repair Section.

Steering Gear

Manual Steering Gear
Steering Gear R&R
Econoline
1. Raise the vehicle on a hoist.

2. Remove the flex coupling lower attaching bolt.
3. Disconnect the pitman arm from the drag link.
4. Remove the three attaching bolts and remove the gear.
5. Remove the pitman arm attaching nut and remove the pitman arm.
6. To install, center the input shaft (approximately three turns from either stop).
7. Install pitman arm pointing downward, tightening attaching nut securely.
8. Fill the steering gear to the proper level with lubricant.
9. Position the steering gear in the truck, aligning the input shaft splines to engage the flexible coupling. Install and tighten the three steering gear mounting bolts.
10. Connect drag link to pitman arm. Install attaching bolt and tighten securely. Install cotter pin.
11. Install flexible coupling attaching bolt and tighten securely.
12. Lower vehicle.

F-100, 150, 250, 350 (4x2)
1. Remove flex joint attaching bolt and remove the brake line bracket.
2. Raise the front of the vehicle.
3. Disconnect the pitman arm from the sector shaft.
4. Remove the steering gear attaching bolts and the gear.
5. Before installing gear, align the wheels and the sector shaft to the straight-forward position.
6. Install steering gear, tightening attaching bolts securely.
7. Install the brake line bracket to the gear cover studs.
8. Connect the pitman arm to the sector shaft.

9. Install and tighten flex coupling bolt.
10. Remove the steering gear filler plug and housing lower cover bolt. Turn the steering wheel to the left to move the ball nut away from the filler hole. Fill the steering gear with lubricant (until lubricant comes out of the housing cover lower bolt hole). Install filler plug and cover bolt.

Bronco and F-100, 150, 250 (4x4)

1. Raise the vehicle on a hoist.
2. Remove the pitman arm.
3. Remove the three gear to frame attaching bolts, then lower the vehicle.
4. Remove the flex coupling clamp bolt at the steering gear input shaft and loosen the other clamp bolt (steering column). Remove the coupling from the steering gear input shaft. Discard clamp, bolt and nut.
5. Remove the steering gear from the vehicle.
6. When installing, first mount the steering gear to the frame, but do not tighten attaching bolts.
7. Install steering shaft flex coupling to the gear input shaft using a new clamp and bolt. Tighten bolt securely.
8. Install the flex coupling to the steering column shaft with a new clamp and bolt. Tighten bolt securely.
9. Raise the vehicle and tighten the steering gear attaching bolts securely.
10. Install the pitman arm on the

steering gear sector shaft, tightening attaching nut securely.
11. Lower the vehicle and fill the steering gear with lubricant.

Steering gear installation—4 wheel drive (© Ford Motor Co.)

Steering linkage—F100 & 4x4 Bronco (© Ford Motor Co.)

Steering Gear R & R

P, F, B, and C-Series Trucks

On P-Series trucks the steering wheel must be removed first. Raise the vehicle and remove the sector shaft arm and the gear attaching bolts, then disconnect the horn wire, loosen the steering column lower clamp and remove the steering gear. Install in reverse order of removal, leaving all bolts loose. Tighten bolts in this order: upper steering bolts (leave 1/16" clearance between top of tube and steering wheel hub), lower steering column clamp bolts, steering gear attaching bolts.

On F and B-Series trucks the steering gear is removed after first loosening and removing steering column lower clamp and the pitman arm. Install in this order: steering gear in frame (bolts loose), steering column lower clamp, tighten steering gear attaching bolts, install pitman arm.

On C-Series trucks remove the horn wire brush from the steering column just below instrument panel bracket, disconnect universal joint from steering gear, turn the wheels to the right, remove the pitman arm from the steering gear, then remove

CONCENTRIC BRACKET

LOWER BEARING RETAINER

FLEXIBLE COUPLING

STEERING COLUMN LOWER CLAMP

STEERING GEAR

GEAR ATTACHING BOLTS

PITMAN ARM

Steering gear installation—
F100, 250 & 350, 4x2
(© Ford Motor Co.)

the steering gear. Install in reverse order of removal, tightening bolts as you go.

Worm Bearing Preload Adjustment

F-100, 150, 250, 350 (4x2)

Always check and adjust worm and roller mesh after check checking and adjusting worm bearing preload (see below for worm and roller mesh adjustment).

1. Remove the pitman arm from sector shaft and the horn button and spring from the steering wheel. Disconnect the horn wire at the relay.
2. Turn steering wheel to end of travel.
3. Use a torque wrench on the steering wheel nut and measure the lowest torque required to move the wheel at a constant speed. This torque is the worm bearing preload.
4. If the preload is not 4-5″ lbs. (manual) or 3-4″ lbs. (power assist), adjust the preload as follows: loosen the steering shaft bearing adjuster locknut and turn adjuster to set the preload.
5. Tighten bearing adjuster locknut, install the pitman arm and horn components.

F-100 (4x4)

Follow Steps 1 through 3 of the procedure for F-100, 250, 350 (4x2) above. If adjustment is necessary, remove or add shims between the worm shaft bearing retainer cover and the steering gear housing. If erratic readings are experienced, disconnect the steering shaft joint at the steering gear and check torque

required to rotate the steering shaft. If that torque is measurable, add it to the preload specification.

Bronco

Remove the gear from the vehicle, loosen locknut and back off the mesh and roller adjusting nut. Check the torque required to rotate the input shaft 1½ turns either side of center. If bearing preload is not 5-10″ lbs., add or remove shims between the worm shaft bearing retainer cover and the steering gear housing until proper preload is obtained.

F and C-Series

Remove the steering gear and use a 12-point socket and torque wrench on the lower steering serrated shaft to measure preload at a constant speed rotation. If bearing preload is not within 9-11″ lbs. (C-series) or 5-9″ lbs. (F-series), add or remove gasket shims between the worm shaft bearing retainer and the gear housing. Adjust the worm and roller mesh preload. Install steering gear in vehicle.

Worm and Roller Mesh Adjustment

Always check and adjust worm bearing preload before making the mesh adjustment (see above).

1. Remove the steering gear from the vehicle.
2. Measure the torque required to move the gear through middle (straight-ahead) position with a torque wrench on the input shaft. The highest reading is used. If it is not 24-29″ lbs. (C-series), 14-22″ lbs. (F-500-750) or 12-21″ in. lbs. (F-100 4x4 and Bronco), loosen locknut and turn adjusting screw until correct mesh load is obtained. Tighten locknut.
3. Recheck mesh load, install steering gear in vehicle and fill gear with lubricant.

Steering Worm and Sector Adjustment

Econoline (1970-74)

1. Remove the steering gear from the vehicle.
2. Loosen locknut on the sector shaft adjusting screw and turn adjusting screw out (counterclockwise) approximately three turns.
3. Using a torque wrench on the input shaft, rotate shaft about 1½ turns either side of center. If the preload is not 4-5″ lbs. (manual) or 3-4″ lbs. (power assist), loosen input shaft bearing adjuster locknut and tighten or loosen bearing adjuster to obtain the correct bearing preload.

Tighten locknut and recheck preload.
4. Center the input shaft (turn against stops gently as it is easy to damage the ball return guides).
5. Turn sector shaft adjusting screw clockwise until an over-center meshload of 9-10″ lbs. (manual) or 8-9″ lbs. (power assist) is obtained (measured at input shaft). Tighten the locknut.
6. Check the total gear lash by holding the sector shaft solid in the center position and pulling with the torque wrench 15 in. lbs. in each direction. If the travel of the wrench exceeds 1¼″, then the whole gear must be replaced.
7. Recheck total over-center preload, then install steering gear in vehicle.

Econoline (1975-76)

1. Remove the steering gear.
2. Tighten the worm bearing adjuster plug until all end-play is removed. Loosen it ¼ turn.
3. Using a socket on an in. lb torque wrench, turn the worm shaft full right and back ½ turn.
4. Tighten the adjuster plug until 5-8 in. lbs is reached. Tighten the locknut to 85 ft. lbs.
5. Turn the worm shaft from stop to stop, counting the number of turns. Turn the shaft back exactly half the number of turns to the center position.
6. Turn the sector shaft adjuster screw clockwise to remove all lash between the ball nut and sector teeth. Tighten the locknut.
7. Using a socket and in. lb torque wrench, note the highest reading required to rotate the gear through the center position, which should be 16 in. lbs.
8. If necessary, adjust the sector shaft adjuster screw to obtain the proper torque and recheck it.

Power Steering Gear

Reference

For power steering gear overhaul procedures, see the General Repair Section.

Ford Integral Power Steering Gear

F-100, 250, 350 (4x2)

This torsion-bar type power assist unit consists of a worm and one-piece rack piston, a hydraulic valve, valve actuator, input shaft and torsion bar assembly. The double acting power cylinder is integral with the housing. The hydraulic pump is belt driven with integral reservoir.

Over Center Preload

1. Disconnect pitman arm from the sector shaft.
2. Disconnect the fluid return line at the reservoir and cap the reservoir return line.
3. Place the end of the return line in a clean container and cycle the steering wheel in both directions to discharge the fluid from the gear.
4. Turn the steering wheel to 45-degrees from the left stop and measure the torque (at the steering wheel nut) required to turn $\frac{1}{8}$-turn from there.
5. Determine the torque required to turn the steering gear through center position. Loosen adjusting screw locknut and turn adjusting screw to obtain a torque reading 11-12 in. lbs. greater than the torque 45-degrees from the stop.
6. Hold adjusting screw while tightening locknut.
7. Install the pitman arm and steering wheel hub cover.
8. Connect the fluid return line and fill reservoir with fluid.

Steering Gear Removal and Installation

1. Disconnect pressure and return lines from the steering gear, *being sure to tag them for identification*. Plug lines and ports.
2. Remove brake lines attached to bracket on the steering gear.
3. Remove the two bolts that secure the flex coupling to the steering gear and to the column steering shaft assembly.
4. Raise the vehicle.
5. Remove the pitman arm from the sector shaft, using a puller if necessary.
6. If vehicle has a standard transmission, remove the clutch release lever retracting spring.
7. Remove the steering gear attaching bolts and steering gear, working the steering gear free of the flex coupling.
8. To install, slide the flex coupling into place on the bottom of the steering shaft.
9. Set the steering wheel so that the spokes are horizontal and center the steering gear input shaft.
10. Slide the steering gear input shaft into the flex coupling. Install the three steering gear attaching bolts and tighten them securely.
11. With wheels in the straight ahead position, install the pitman arm on the sector shaft.
12. Install the flex coupling and tighten the bolts securely.
13. Connect fluid pressure and return lines to steering gear. Rein-

stall brake lines on bracket on steering gear.
14. Remove the coil wire, fill the power steering pump reservoir and, while engaging the starter, cycle the steering wheel to distribute the fluid. Add fluid if reservoir is not full.
15. Connect the coil wire, start the engine and check for leaks while cycling the steering wheel.

Integral Power Steering Gear (Saginaw)

Removal and Installation

Bronco

1. Disconnect the pressure and return lines and plug the lines and ports.
2. Raise the truck and disconnect the Pitman arm.
3. Remove the Pitman arm.
4. Unbolt the gear from the frame rails and lower the truck.
5. Remove the pinch-bolt from the flange and insulator.
6. Unbolt the horn and hold it outward.
7. Remove the attaching bolts and remove the gear from the truck, with the shaft and joint assemblies as a unit.
8. Remove the pinch-bolt from the shaft and joint.
9. Remove the shaft and joint from the gear.
10. Installation is the reverse of removal.

Econoline

1. Disconnect the pressure and return lines and plug the ports.
2. Raise the van and remove the drag link from the Pitman arm.

3. Unbolt the flex coupling from the steering shaft.
4. Support the gear and remove the attaching bolts.
5. Remove the pinch bolt from the flex coupling and remove the coupling from the gear.
6. Remove the Pitman arm from the sector shaft.
7. Installation is the reverse of removal.

Mesh Load Adjustment

1. On Econolines, remove the drag link from the Pitman arm and remove the horn pad. On Broncos, disconnect the Pitman arm from the sector shaft and remove the horn pad.
2. Disconnect the fluid return line and cap the reservoir return line. Put the end of the return line in a clean container and cycle the wheel several times to discharge fluid from the gear.
3. Using an in. lb torque wrench on the steering wheel nut, check the torque required to rotate the wheel through a 180° arc on each side of center. The new gear over center torque should be 4-8 in. lbs greater than the end readings but the total should not exceed 18 in. lbs. Used gears should be 4-5 in. lbs greater than the end reading, but should not exceed 14 in. lbs.
4. To adjust, make sure the Pitman shaft over center adjusting screw is backed all the way out. Turn it in $\frac{1}{2}$ turn.
5. Rotate the shaft from one stop to the other. Count the number of turns and locate the center position. Check the combined preload

Ford integral power steering gear (© Ford Motor Co.)

Ross model HF-64 integral steering gear (© Ford Motor Co.)

on the ball and thrust bearing by rotating the shaft through the center of travel. Note the highest reading.

6. Tighten the adjusting screw until the torque wrench reads 3-6 in. lbs, higher than the reading in Step 5. The total should not exceed 14 in. lbs.

7. Hold the adjusting screw and tighten the locknut to 35 ft lbs.

Ross HF-54 and HF-64 Integral Power Steering Gears
F, B, L-500 through 9000 Series

Reference

Complete power steering gear overhaul procedures may be found in the General Repair Section.

Unloader Valve Adjustment

This adjustment is made for *right turn only* on the HF-54 gear and for *both turns* on the HF-64 gear.

Before making this adjustment, establish the straight-forward center of the steering system by driving the truck forward with hands off the wheel until the steering finds its own center. Stop the truck and mark the steering column to steering wheel with chalk or masking tape.

1. With wheels straight ahead engine warm and idling, turn the steering wheel 1¾ turns to the right (HF-54), 1½ turns (2 port HF-64) or 1¼ turns (4 port HF-64). Hold this position.

2. Loosen locknut and turn the unloader valve pressure adjusting screw until an audible hiss is heard. Tighten locknut.

3. While vehicle is moving, let the steering wheel center (straight-forward), then stop the truck

and turn the wheel the prescribed number of turns (Step 2 above) and listen for audible hiss. Repeat Step 2 if necessary. NOTE: The pitman arm on the HF-64 must not contact the stop cast on the gear housing prior to contacting the unloader valve. The distance between the pitman arm and the stop should be 1/16" to ⅛" when the hiss is heard.

4. To adjust the unloader valve for left turn (HF-64 ONLY), repeat Steps 1 through 3 above turning the steering wheel to the left.

Sector Shaft Adjustment

1. Disconnect the drag link from the pitman arm and center the steering wheel. Check for lash between the sector shaft and the rack piston by moving the pitman arm. If there is noticeable lash, remove the gear from the vehicle.

2. Loosen the sector shaft adjustment screw locknut on the side cover.

3. Rotate the input shaft through its full travel at least five times, then adjust the sector shaft adjusting screw for a 15-20 in. lb. (20-25 in. lbs. 1974-76) torque as shaft is rotated 90 degrees each side of center.

4. Back off adjusting screw one turn and note torque required to move the input shaft 90 degrees each side of center. Move the adjusting screw in to provide for an increase of 2-4 in. lbs. at a point within 45 degrees each side of center after locknut is first tightened snugly. Torque locknut to 20-25 ft. lbs.

5. Input torque of assembled gear (no fluid) should not exceed 15 in. lbs. over the full travel of output shaft.

6. Install steering gear in the vehicle.

7. Connect the drag link to the pitman arm.

8. Connect the pump lines and fill the system with fluid.

Steering Gear R & R

1. Position a drain pan under the steering gear and disconnect the pressure line from the gear, the return line from the gear and the turning hoses if so equipped. Mark all lines for identification.

Ross model HF-54 integral steering gear (© Ford Motor Co.)

2. Remove the pitman arm from the sector shaft.
3. Disconnect the universal joint from the input shaft of the gear, sliding it up and off the shaft.
4. Remove the steering gear attaching bolts and remove the gear.

On Ford B-6000-7000 and F-880 with manual transmission: The front engine mount must be loosened. Remove the exhaust pipes shields and loosen the exhaust pipes. Remove the clutch spring bracket, from under the left side pipe. Unbolt the transmission mount and jack the transmission. Remove the mounting pads. Unbolt the clutch bracket from the steering gear. Unbolt the gear from the frame. Remove the floor board covering the gearshift and brake levers. Move the engine and transmission to the right and remove the gear.

5. To install, first position gear in vehicle and install and tighten attaching bolts.
6. Connect universal joint to the steering gear input shaft.
7. Install pitman arm on the sector shaft.
8. Connect all hydraulic lines in their original locations.
9. Fill power steering hydraulic system, start engine and check for leaks.

Clutch

Mechanical Clutch Linkage Adjustment

The clutch pedal free travel is the distance between the clutch pedal in the fully released position and the pedal position at which the clutch release fingers contact the clutch release bearing (this can be felt).

The clutch pedal total travel is the distance between the floor pan and the top of the pedal when the clutch is in the fully released position.

Only the clutch pedal free travel is adjusted. If the pedal free travel is not within 11/16″ to 1 1/8″, adjust clutch release rod until correct free travel is obtained.

1970-76 Econoline

First the clutch pedal total travel is adjusted. It should be between 7 1/2″ and 7 3/4″. Adjustment is made by loosening the locknut on the pedal stop eccentric bolt and turning the eccentric bolt until correct total travel is obtained. Tighten locknut.

Check the clutch pedal free travel. It should be 1 1/8″ to 1 3/8″. Adjustment is made at the clutch release rod turnbuckle.

Bronco

If the clutch pedal total travel is

CLUTCH RELEASE ROD AND LEVER

Clutch adjustment—Econoline
(© Ford Motor Co.)

not within 6-43/64″ and 6-11/16″ (1970) or 6-11/16″ and 15/16″ (1971), or 6 3/4″ to 7″, move the clutch pedal bumper and bracket up or down to obtain required free travel.

Check and adjust pedal free travel. For 1970-71 Bronco's it is 1-7/32″ to 1-27/64″ and the 1972-76 is 3/4″ to 1 1/2″. Adjustment is made at the clutch release rod turnbuckle.

F- and N-Series

Total pedal travel is adjusted at the pedal bumper stop. Pedal free travel is made at the clutch release rod.

F-Series

1. Measure the clutch pedal free-play by depressing the pedal slowly until the free-play between the release bearing assembly and the pressure plate is removed. Note this measurement. The difference between this measurement and when the pedal is not depressed is the free-play measurement.
2. If the free-play measurement is less than 3/4″, the clutch linkage must be adjusted.
3. Loosen the two jam nuts on the release rod under the truck and back off both nuts several turns.
4. Loosen or tighten the first jam nut (nearest the release lever) against the bullet (rod extension) until a free-play measurement of 3/4-1 1/2″ is obtained. A free-play measurement closer to 1 1/2″ is more desirable.
5. When the correct free-play measurement is obtained, hold the first jam nut in position and securely tighten the other nut against the first.
6. Recheck the free-play adjustment.

NOTE: Total pedal travel is fixed and is not adjustable.

Hydraulic Actuated Clutch Adjustment

Before adjusting hydraulic clutch, check the level of fluid in the master cylinder reservoir, filling to within 1/2″ of the top if necessary. Bleed the hydraulic system as described below.

Bleeding Hydraulic Clutch

1. Attach a funnel to the bleeder screw of the slave cylinder by means of a transparent bleeder hose. The funnel must be higher than the master cylinder.
2. Pour fluid into the funnel as the system is filling, *being careful not to pour bubbles in the fluid.* Bleeder screw must be open.
3. Close the bleeder screw when master cylinder reservoir is full.
4. Check the slave cylinder pushrod total travel which should be 1 1/8″.
5. The clutch master cylinder relief port must be open in order to bleed the system. Clutch master cylinder pushrod lash of 1/4″ is required on the P-500 and 5000 series vehicles to permit the conventional type master cylinder piston to return to the piston stop ring and open the relief port. The clutch master cylinder cannot be adjusted on the P-350, 400, 3500 and 4000 series vehicles. In the case of tilt-cab (C-series) master cylinder, the O-ring seal on the end of the pushrod must not seat against the piston. Uncovering of the piston port is accomplished by adjustment of the pushrod to a piston lash of 1/4″. Forcing the clutch pedal to compress the pedal bumper more than normal by jamming a screwdriver between the pedal pad and the floor insures a complete uncovering of the relief port.

Hydraulic Clutch Adjustment

There are two adjustments for obtaining clutch pedal free travel. The initial pedal free travel should be 1/4″ for all models. On F, N, NT, and T Series vehicles the pedal height is first adjusted to 8-1/16″ to 8-3/16″ at the pedal stop. Turn eccentric bolt on pedal to obtain an initial pedal free travel of 3/16″ to 3/8″. Remove retracting spring, push slave cylinder pushrod as far forward as possible and release lever back until it contacts the release fingers. Adjust the nut on the pushrod for a clearance of 1/4″ between pushrod adjusting nut and release lever. A total pedal travel of at least 2″ should result.

On P and C Series trucks, the initial pedal free travel is that distance of pedal travel before the master cylinder pushrod contacts the piston. On C Series vehicles this adjustment is made with the eccentric bolt and on P Series it is made by rotating the master cylinder pushrod. Obtain an initial pedal free travel of ¼". With the retracting spring removed, the slave cylinder pushrod held completely forward and the release lever held in contact with the release fingers, turn adjusting nut on the slave cylinder pushrod to obtain a final pedal free travel of approximately 2".

Spicer clutch adjustment
(© Ford Motor Co.)

Internal clutch adjustment
(© Ford Motor Co.)

Internal Clutch Adjustment

1. Remove inspection cover from the bottom of the clutch housing.
2. Disconnect the retracting spring and hold the release lever against the throwout bearing. Measure the distance between the throwout bearing and the clutch spring hub (synchromatic transmission) or clutch brake (non-synchromatic transmission). On vehicles with the 14" single plate clutch, this distance should be 11/32" to 13/32". On all Spicer clutches, also adjust the adjusting ring to obtain a ⅛" clearance between release yoke fingers and the throwout bearing.

3. If adjustment is necessary, rotate the clutch assembly to get at the adjusting lockring and bolt. Remove the bolt and lockring.
4. With clutch pedal held or blocked in the released position, rotate the adjusting ring (use a pry bar) clockwise to move the throwout bearing toward the flywheel or counterclockwise to move the throwout bearing away from the flywheel. Rotating the adjusting ring one lug position moves the throwout bearing about 1/32".
5. Let clutch pedal return to engage the clutch, then recheck clearance.
6. Install lock and bolt.
7. Adjust clutch linkage.
8. Connect the retracting spring and replace the clutch housing cover.

Clutch Removal and Installation

9.37", 10", 11", 11.5", 12" and 13" Single Disc

1. Disconnect the release lever retracting spring and pushrod at the lever.
2. If so equipped, remove the slave cylinder attaching bolts.
3. Remove the transmission.
4. If there is no dust cover on the flywheel housing remove the starter. Remove the release lever and bearing.
5. Mark the pressure plate and cover, remove the dust cover, release lever and bearing.
   If the flywheel housing has a dust cover assembly and the flywheel so that they may be assembled in the same relative position.
6. Loosen the pressure plate attaching bolts evenly until the springs are loose then remove the bolts, pressure plate assembly and clutch disc. Do not remove the pilot bushing unless it is to be replaced.
7. To install, position the disc on the flywheel and install a pilot tool or spare transmission spline shaft.
8. Install the pressure plate assembly over the aligning tool and align the marks made during removal. Install the retaining bolts, tightening securely.
9. Remove pilot tool and apply a light coat of lithium-base grease to the hub splines of the clutch disc.
10. Apply lithium-base grease to the sides of the driving lugs.
11. Position throwout bearing and bearing hub on the release lever and install release lever on the trunnion in the flywheel housing.
12. Apply a light film of lithium-base grease to the release lever

Pressure plate lubrication point
(© Ford Motor Co.)

fingers and to the lever trunnion or fulcrum. Fill the angular groove of the release bearing hub with grease.
13. If removed, install the flywheel housing, tightening bolts securely.
14. Install the starter motor if it was removed.
15. Apply a light film of lithium-base grease to the transmission front bearing retainer and install the transmission assembly on the clutch housing, tightening attaching bolts securely.
16. Install the slave cylinder, if applicable.
17. Adjust the clutch linkage and install the clutch housing dust cover.

Clutch Removal and Installation

14" Single Plate Clutch

1. Disconnect the clutch pedal assist spring, removing the left-hand exhaust pipe from the manifold if necessary.
2. Disconnect the release lever retracting spring and remove the slave cylinder attaching bolts, if applicable.
3. Remove the transmission.
4. Insert two ¾" wood blocks between the throwout bearing housing and the rear surface of the pressure plate assembly.
5. Remove the clutch to flywheel bolts and remove the flywheel ring and pressure plate assembly. Remove the clutch disc.
6. To install, position the clutch disc and pressure plate assembly on the flywheel and start the bolts. NOTE: the long hub of the clutch disc faces the rear.
7. Insert a spare transmission splined shaft or a disc aligning tool through the disc and into the pilot bushing. Tighten pressure plate bolts evenly and securely.

8. Remove the wood blocks and aligning tool or shaft.
9. Install the transmission.
10. Install the clutch slave cylinder.
11. Connect the release lever retracting spring and exhaust pipe.
12. Connect the clutch pedal assist spring.
13. Check internal clutch adjustment, linkage adjustment and correct if necessary.

Manual Transmission

Reference

For complete manual transmission overhaul procedures see the General Repair Section.

Transmission R & R

Bronco

1. Shift the transfer case into Neutral.
2. Remove the bolts attaching the fan shroud to the radiator support, if so equipped.
3. Raise the vehicle on a hoist.
4. Support the transfer case shield with a jack and remove the bolts that attach the shield to the frame side rails. Remove the shield.
5. Drain the transmission and transfer case lubricant. To drain the transmission lubricant, remove the lower extension housing-to-transmission bolt.
6. Disconnect the front and rear driveshafts at the transfer case.
7. Disconnect the speedometer cable at the transfer case.
8. Disconnect the T.R.S. switch, if so equipped.
9. Disconnect the shift rods from the transmission shift levers. Place the First-Reverse gear shift lever into the First gear position and insert the fabricated tool. The tool consists of a length of rod. the same diameter as the holes in the shift levers, which is bent in such a way to fit in the holes in the two shift levers and hold them in the position stated above. More important, this tool will prevent the input shaft roller bearings from dropping into the transmission and output shaft. THIS TOOL IS A MUST.
10. Support the engine with a jack.
11. Remove the two cotter pins, bolts, washers, plate and insulators that secure the crossmember to the transfer case adapter.
12. Remove the crossmember-to-frame side support attaching bolts.
13. Position a transmission jack under the transfer case and remove the upper insulators from the crossmember. Remove the crossmember.
14. Roll back the boot enclosing the transfer case shift linkage. Remove the threaded cap holding the shift lever assembly to the shift bracket. Remove the shift lever assembly.
15. Remove the two lower bolts attaching the transmission to the flywheel housing.
16. Reposition the transmission jack under the transmission and secure it with a chain.
17. Remove the two upper bolts securing the transmission to the flywheel housing. Move the transmission and transfer case rearward and downward out of the vehicle.
18. Move the assembly to a bench and remove the transfer case-to-transmission attaching bolts.
19. Slide the transmission assembly off the transfer case.

To install the transmission:
20. Position the transfer case to the transmission. Apply an oil-resistant sealer to the bolt threads and install the attaching bolts. Tighten to 42-50 ft lbs.
21. Position the transmission and transfer case on a transmission jack and secure them with a chain.
22. Raise the transmission and transfer case assembly into position and install the transmission case to the flywheel housing.
23. Install the two upper and two lower transmission attaching bolts and torque them to 37-42 ft lbs.
24. Position the transfer case shift lever and install the threaded cap to the shift bracket. Reposition the rubber boot.
25. Raise the transmission and transfer case high enough to provide clearance for installing the crossmember. Position the upper insulators to the crossmember and install the crossmember-to-frame side support attaching bolts.
26. Align the bolt holes in the transfer case adapter with those in the crossmember, then lower the transmission and remove the jack.
27. Install the crossmember-to-transfer case adapter bolts, nuts, insulators, plates and washers. Tighten the nuts and secure them with cotter pins.
28. Remove the engine jack.
29. Remove the fabricated tool and connect each shift rod to its respective lever on the transmission. Adjust the linkage.
30. Connect the speedometer cable.
31. Connect the T.R.S. switch. if so equipped.
32. Install the front and rear driveshaftshafts to the transfer case.
33. Fill the transmission and transfer case to the bottom of the filler hole with the recommended lubricant.
34. Position the transfer case shield to the frame side rails and install the attaching bolts.
35. Lower the vehicle.
36. Install the fan shroud, if so equipped.
37. Check the operation of the transfer case and the transmission shift linkage.

Econoline

1. Raise the vehicle on a hoist and drain the lubricant from the transmission by removing the drain plug if the vehicle is so equipped. For models without drain plugs, remove the lower extension housing-to-transmission bolt.
2. Disconnect the drive shaft from the flange at the transmission. Secure the front end of the drive shaft out of the way with lock wire.
3. Disconnect the speedometer cable from the extension housing and disconnect the gear shift rods from the transmission shift levers. Remove the wire to the TCS switch if so equipped.
4. Position a transmission jack under the transmission. Secure the transmission to the jack.
5. Raise the transmission slightly and remove the four bolts retaining the transmission support crossmember to the frame side rails. Remove the bolt retaining the transmission extension housing to the crossmember.
6. Remove the four transmission-to-flywheel housing bolts.
7. Position engine support bar (Tool T65E-6000-J) to the frame.
8. Lower the transmission.
9. To install, make certain that the machined surfaces of the transmission case and the flywheel housing are free of dirt, paint and burrs.
10. Install a guide pin in each lower mounting bolt hole.
11. Start the input shaft through the release bearing. Align the splines on the input shaft with the splines in the clutch disc. Move the transmission forward on the guide pins until the input shaft pilot enters the bearing or bushing in the crankshaft. If the transmission front bearing retainer binds up on the clutch release bearing hub, work the release bearing lever until the hub slides onto the transmission front bearing retainer. Install the two transmission-to-flywheel housing upper mounting bolts and lock washers. Remove the two guide pins and install the

lower mounting bolts and lock washers.

12. Raise the jack slightly and remove the engine support bar.
13. Position the support crossmember on the frame side rails and install the retaining bolts. Install the extension housing-to-crossmember retaining bolt.
14. Connect the gear shift rods and the speedometer cable.
15. Install the drive shaft and torque the attaching bolts to specification.
16. Fill the transmission to the bottom of the filler hole with the recommended lubricant.
17. Adjust the clutch pedal free travel and shift linkage as required.

F-100-250

1. Raise the vehicle and position safety stands.
2. Drain the transmission lubricant by removing the drain plug if the vehicle is so equipped. For models without drain plugs, remove the lower extension housing-to-transmission bolt.
3. Position a transmission jack under the transmission.
4. Disconnect the gear shift linkage at the transmission.
5. If the vehicle has a four-wheel drive, remove the transfer case shift lever bracket from the transmission.
6. Disconnect the speedometer cable.
7. Disconnect the drive shaft from the transmission.
8. Remove the transmission-to-clutch housing attaching bolts.
9. Move transmission to the rear until the input shaft clears the clutch housing and lower the transmission. *Do not depress the clutch pedal while the transmission is removed...*
10. Before installing the transmission, apply a light film of lubricant to the clutch disc splines, release bearing inner hub surfaces, release lever fulcrum and fork and the transmission front bearing retainer. Exercise care to avoid contaminating the clutch disc with excessive grease.
11. Place the transmission on a transmission jack. Raise the transmission until the input shaft splines are in line with the clutch disc splines. The clutch release bearing and hub must be properly positioned in the release lever fork.
12. Install a guide stud in each lower clutch housing-to-transmission case mounting bolt and align the splines on the input shaft with the splines on the clutch disc.
13. Slide the transmission forward

on the guide studs until it contacts the clutch housing.

14. Install the two transmission to flywheel housing upper mounting bolts and nuts. Remove the two guide studs and install the lower mounting bolts.
15. Connect the speedometer cable and the driven gear.
16. Install the drive shaft.
17. Connect each shift rod to its respective lever on the transmission.
18. If the vehicle is equipped with four-wheel drive, install the four-wheel drive shaft bracket.
19. Fill the transmission to the proper level with an approved lubricant.
20. Adjust the clutch pedal free travel and shift linkage as required.

Warner T-89F, T-87G

Removal and Installation

1. Raise and support the truck.
2. Drain the lubricant.
3. Support the transmission with a jack.
4. Disconnect the gearshift linkage at the transmission.
5. If the vehicle is a 4WD, remove the transfer case shift lever bracket from the transmission.
6. Disconnect the brake cable clevis at the cam and remove the cable clamp.
7. Disconnect the speedometer cable.
8. Remove the driveshaft and wire it aside.
9. Remove the transmission attaching bolts and remove the transmission.
10. Installation is the reverse of removal.

Warner T85N 3-Speed With Overdrive

Transmission R & R

F-100

The overdrive unit cannot be removed from the vehicle as a separate assembly. Drain both the transmission and the overdrive unit, and then remove the transmission and overdrive as a unit.

To remove the overdrive transmission, follow the same procedure as that for the standard three-speed transmission plus the following:

1. Disconnect the solenoid and governor wires at the connectors near the solenoid.
2. Remove the overdrive wiring harness from its clip on the transmission.
3. Disconnect the overdrive control cable.

To install the overdrive transmis-

sion, follow the same procedure as that for the standard transmission, plus the following:

1. Connect the overdrive control cable so that there is 1/4" clearance between the handle shank and dash bracket when the lever at the overdrive housing is against its rear stop.
2. Connect the solenoid and governor wires, and replace the overdrive wiring harness in its clip.
3. Fill only the transmission with lubricant.

Warner T-18, T-19 4-Speed

Transmission R & R

1. Disconnect the back-up light switch located at the rear of the gearshift housing cover.
2. Remove the rubber boot, floor mat, and the body floor pan cover, and remove the transmission shift lever. Remove the weather pad and pad retainer.
3. Raise the truck and position safety stands. Position a transmission jack under the transmission, and disconnect the speedometer cable.
4. If the truck is equipped with band-type parking brake, disconnect the brake cable clevis at the cam. Remove the brake cable conduit clamp.
5. Remove the front U-joint flange attaching bolts. Remove the bolts that attach the coupling shaft center support to the crossmember and wire the coupling shaft and drive shaft to one side. On F-100-350 Series trucks, remove the transmission rear support.
6. Remove the transmission attaching bolts.
7. Move the transmission to the rear until the input shaft clears the clutch housing, and lower the transmission.

Before installing the transmission, apply a light film of lubricant to the clutch disc splines, release bearing inner hub surfaces, release lever fulcrum and fork, and the transmission front bearing retainer. Care must be exercised to avoid excessive grease from contaminating the clutch disc.

8. Place the transmission on a transmission jack, and raise the transmission until the input shaft splines are aligned with the clutch disc splines. The clutch release bearing and hub must be properly positioned in the release lever fork.
9. Install guide studs in the clutch housing and slide the transmission forward on the guide studs until it is in position on the clutch housing. Install the attaching bolts and nuts. Remove

Ford Trucks · Vans · Bronco

Model T87G Three-Speed Heavy-Duty Transmission

Warner T19 Four-Speed Transmission

Warner T18 Four-Speed Transmission

the guide studs and install the two lower attaching bolts.

5. Connect the speedometer cable and driven gear and parking brake clevis. Install the brake cable conduit clamp, and shift linkage.

6. Install the bolts attaching the coupling shaft center support to the crossmember.

7. Install the bolts attaching the front U-joint flange to the transmission output shaft flange. On F-100-350 Series trucks, install the transmission rear support.

8. Connect the back-up light switch.

9. Install the shift lever and lubricate the spherical ball seat with lubricant.

10. Install the weather pad and pad retainer. Install the floor pan cover, floor mat and boot.

New Process 435 4-Speed

Transmission R & R

1. On F-, LN- or B-Series truck, remove the rubber boot and floor mat.

2. On a F-, LN- or B-Series truck, remove the floor pan transmission cover plate. Remove the weather pad and pad retainer. It may be necessary first to remove the seat assembly.

3. Disconnect the back-up light switch located in the rear of the gearshift housing cover.

4. Raise the truck and position safety stands. Position a transmission jack under the transmission, and disconnect the speedometer cable.

5. Disconnect the parking brake lever from its linkage, and remove the gearshift housing. On a C-Series truck, disconnect parking brake cable and bracket at the transmission.

6. Disconnect the drive shaft. Remove the bolts that attach the coupling shaft center support to the cross-member and wire the coupling shaft and drive shaft to one side. In F-100-350 Series Trucks, remove the transmission rear support.

7. Remove the two transmission upper mounting nuts at the clutch housing.

8. Remove the transmission attaching bolts at the clutch housing, and remove the transmission.

9. Before installing the transmission, apply a light film of lubricant to the clutch disc splines, release bearing inner hub surfaces, release lever fulcrum and fork, and the transmission front bearing retainer. Care must be exercised to avoid excessive

grease from contaminating the clutch disc.

10. Place the transmission on a transmission jack, and raise the transmission until the input shaft splines are aligned with the clutch disc splines. The clutch release bearing and hub must be properly positioned in the release lever fork.

11. Install guide studs in the clutch housing and slide the transmission forward on the guide studs until it is in position on the clutch housing. Install the attaching bolts and nuts. Remove the guide studs and install the two lower attaching bolts.

12. Install the bolts attaching the coupling shaft center support to the crossmember.

13. Connect the drive shaft and the speedometer cable. On F-100-350 Series trucks, install the transmission rear support.

14. Connect the parking brake to the transmission.

15. Connect the back-up light switch.

16. On an F-, LN- or B-Series truck, install the weather pad, the pad retainer and the transmission cover plate. Install the seat assembly if it was removed.

17. On an F-, LN- or B-Series truck, install the weather pad, the pad retainer, the floor mat and rubber boot.

Gearshift Linkage Adjustment

Ford 3.03 3-Speed & T-85N 3-Speed E and F-100, 150, 250 & Bronco

1. Place the shifter in the Neutral position and insert a gauge pin (3/16″ diameter) through the steering column shift levers and the locating hole in the spacer.

2. If the shift rods at the transmission are equipped with threaded sleeves, adjust the sleeves so that they enter the shift levers on the transmission easily with the shift levers in the Neutral position. Now lengthen the rods seven turns of the sleeves and insert them into the shift levers.

3. If the shift rods, are slotted, loosen the attaching nut, make sure that the transmission shift levers are in the Neutral position, then retighten the attaching nuts.

4. Remove the gauge pin and check the operation of the shift linkage.

Warner T85N 3-Speed With Overdrive

1. Check the operation of the gear shift linkage for smooth operation.

2. To adjust the gear shift linkage, move the selector lever to the neutral position.

3. If the selector lever position must be changed, disconnect the adjustable rods at the transmission, and install the gauge pin.

4. Loosen the lock nuts and adjust the swivels on the rods so that ends enter the levers freely, but do not put them in. Now adjust the swivels 7 turns to lengthen the rods by that amount. Connect the rods and lock the lock nuts.

5. Move the selector lever through all shift positions as a final check for smooth operation.

6. Adjust the position of the steering column tube if there is interference.

Gearshift linkage adjustment—Bronco
(© Ford Motor Co.)

Gearshift linkage adjustment—Econoline
(© Ford Motor Co.)

Overdrive Control Cable Adjustment

1. Loosen the overdrive cable lock nut at the overdrive control lever.

2. Position the overdrive cable until there is 1/4″ clearance between the cable control handle and bezel.

3. Move the overdrive control lever to the rear against the stop. When moving the lever, be careful not to move the cable out of position.

4. Tighten the control cable lock nut on the overdrive.

Ford Trucks · Vans · Bronco

Overdrive Kickdown Switch Adjustment

1. With the accelerator shaft held in the full throttle position, slide the switch up or down on the elongated slots until the accelerator shaft is just touching the switch plunger. If at the closest position the plunger is still not touching the shaft, an adjustment not exceeding 4 turns counterclockwise may be made at the switch plunger.
2. The accelerator shaft can now be returned to the normal position and an additional adjustment of 5 turns counterclockwise performed at the switch plunger.

Transfer Case

Reference

For transfer case overhaul procedures see the General Repair Section.

Transfer Case R & R

Bronco (Dana 20)

1. Shift the transfer case into neutral and remove the fan shroud. Raise vehicle, support transfer case shield, then remove shield.
2. Drain the transmission and transfer case lubricant then disconnect driveshafts from transfer case.
3. Disconnect speedometer cable and shift rods.
4. A tool must be placed in the transmission shift levers to keep the input shaft roller bearings from falling out.
5. Remove the frame crossmember from side frame and transfer case, first raising transmission and removing adapter insulators.
6. Disconnect the shift rod from the transfer case shift lever bracket.
7. Remove the shift lever bracket to transfer case adapter bolt and let the assembly hang.
8. Position a transmission jack under the transfer case, remove the transfer case to transmission attaching bolts, then pull the transfer case back until it clears the transmission output shaft.
9. To install, place the transfer case in position and install the attaching bolts, tightening securely.
10. Install the shift lever to transfer case adapter. Connect the shift rod to the shift lever bracket.
11. Raise the transmission and transfer case high enough to provide clearance for installing the crossmember. Position the upper insulators on the crossmember, install the crossmember, then lower the transmission

and install the bolts, tightening securely.
12. Remove fabricated tool from shift levers and install the shift rods.
13. Connect the speedometer cable.
14. Install the forward and rear driveshafts.
15. Fill the transmission and transfer case with lubricant.
16. Install transfer case shield.

F-100, 150 (4x4) (Dana 21)

1. Raise the vehicle on a hoist and disconnect the front and rear driveshafts.
2. Disconnect the shift rod from transfer case shift lever.
3. Remove transmission extension housing to transfer case attaching bolts and remove the transfer case.
4. To install, position transfer case and new gasket to extension housing and install attaching bolts.
5. Connect shift rod to shift lever.
6. Connect the front and rear driveshafts.
7. Lower vehicle and check for proper operation.

F-250 (4x4) (Dana 24)

1. Raise the vehicle on a hoist and drain transfer case lubricant.
2. Disconnect front and rear driveshafts, speedometer cable and shift rods.
3. Position a transmission jack under the transfer case and remove mounting bolts. Remove transfer case.
4. To install, raise transfer case on the jack and install nuts on mounting studs.
5. Connect shift rod, speedometer cable and driveshafts.
6. Fill transfer case to filler plug with lubricant.

Transfer Case R & R

F-100 and F-250 (New Process 205)

1. Drain the Transfer case and remove the rear drive shaft.
2. On F-250 models remove the front drive shaft from the transfer case. On F-100 models remove the front drive shaft and remove the transmission adapter to transfer case bolts.
3. Disconnect the shift rod and speedometer cable. Disconnect the reaction bar.
4. Support the transfer case with a jack and remove the transfer case mounting bolts.
5. Remove the transfer case from the vehicle.
6. To install reverse the removal procedures.

Transfer Case R & R

F-600 (4x4) (Rockwell 223-C9)

1. Drain transfer case and disconnect speedometer cable.
2. Disconnect front and rear driveshafts and secure with wire or rope *so that they do not hang.*
3. Disconnect parking brake at the bellcrank and secure rod out of the way.
4. Disconnect de-clutch and shift rods.
5. Support the transfer case with a transmission jack and remove the support bracket bolts. Remove transfer case.
6. Install with the use of a transmission jack. Install and tighten mounting bolts.
7. Connect and adjust parking brake rod at the bellcrank.
8. Connect de-clutch and shift rods.
9. Connect front and rear driveshafts.
10. Connect speedometer.
11. Fill transfer case with lubricant.

New Process Model 203

1. Drain the transfer case by removing the power take-off lower bolts and the front output rear cover lower bolts.
2. Disconnect the front axle driveshaft from the flange at the transfer case.
3. Disconnect the shift rods from the transfer case.
4. Disconnect the speedometer cable and lockout light switch wire from the transfer case rear output shaft housing.
5. On F-250 pick-ups, disconnect the front input and output shafts from the transfer case flanges. On F-100 trucks, remove the transfer case-to-transmission adapter attaching bolts. Disconnect the rear axle driveshaft at the transfer case flange.
6. Position a transmission jack under the transfer case and secure it with a chain.
7. Remove the transfer case mounting bolts and remove the unit from the vehicle. On F-250 models, remove the stabilizer bar-to-transfer case attaching bolt before lowering the case.
8. Install the transfer case in the reverse order of removal.

Transfer Case Shift Linkage Adjustment

New Process Model 205—F-250

Manual Transmission

Adjust the length of the shift rod between the transfer case and the shift lever with the lever in 4WD-Low so that the distance between the rear face of the transmission and the shift lever-to-rod clevis pin is 3.94 to 3.82".

208

TO
FRONT

20-25 FT-LB.

REAR DRIVE SHAFT
INSTALLATION

TO
FRONT

20-25 FT-LB

FRONT DRIVE SHAFT
INSTALLATION

CAP
7220

SEAT
7A138

SPRING
7227

TRUNNION
7B125

LEVER
7202

GASKET
7085-AA

BRACKET
7A147

GASKET
7207

20-30 FT.LB

35-45
FT-LB

21-30 FT-LB

40-50 FT-LB

AUTOMATIC TRANSMISSION

SPACER
6A027

INSULATOR
6A061

LOCKWASHER

40-60 FT-LB

PLATE
6070

INSULATOR
6A061

45-55
FT-LB

REAR ENGINE SUPPORT

LEVER
7220

HOSE CLAMP
97330-S35

BOOT
7C455

MAIN VIEW

GASKET
7085-A

MANUAL TRANSMISSION

Transfer Case Installation

Automatic Transmission

Adjust the length of the shift rod between the transfer case and the shift lever with the lever in 4WD-Low so that the distance between the upper surface of the automatic transmission extension housing and the upper horizontal edge of the shift lever is 0.640 to 0.600".

New Process 203 Full-Time 4WD F-100, F-150

1. Place the shift lever in the Low position.
2. Remove the adjusting stud nuts from the shift rods under the truck.
3. Disconnect the front driveshaft at the transfer case.
4. Remove the transfer case shifter.
5. Unsnap the top snap of the splash boot, peel the boot back and install a new adjustment pin in the rear of the shifter bracket. The pin is 1.5" long, ¼" in diameter and must be of breakable material. The pin cannot be reached once the shifter is installed.
6. Reinstall the shifter. tightening the rear bolt to 12-17 ft lbs and the front bolt to 70-90 ft lbs.
7. Move the lower lever on the transfer case completely forward and the upper lever completely rearward.
8. Install new adjusting stud nuts and tighten them to 20-25 ft lbs.
9. Connect the front driveshaft.

F-250

1. Move the transfer case shifter to the low position.
2. Loosen the adjusting stud nuts.
3. Unsnap the top splash boot snap and peel the boot back. Install a new adjustment pin in the rear of the shifter bracket. The pin is the same size as previously mentioned for the F-100. If the pin is made of steel, it must be removed after tightening the adjusting studs.
4. Move the lower lever on the transfer case completely forward and the upper lever completely rearward.
5. Install new adjusting nuts and tighten them to 15-20 ft lbs.

Automatic Transmission

Reference

For complete automatic transmission overhaul procedures see the General Repair Section.

Shift Linkage Adjustment

F-100, 250, 350 (1970-71)

1. Remove and discard shift rod

trunnion retainer clip and grommet.
2. Install a new grommet and position selector lever against stop in D position.
3. Shift lever on transmission in D position (third from rear).
4. Adjust shift rod length until trunnion fits easily into the column shift lever, then lengthen rod seven additional turns.
5. Install trunnion in column shift lever and secure with new retainer clip.
6. Tighten trunnion locknut.
7. Check operation of selector lever in all positions.

P-350, 400, 500

1. Disconnect shift rod from column shift lever.
2. Position selector lever against the stop in N position.

Manual linkage adjustment P-350-400-500 (© Ford Motor Co.)

3. Shift lever on transmission to N position (fourth from the rear).
4. Rotate trunnion until it is easily inserted in column lever, then turn trunnion two full turns to lengthen rod.
5. Connect trunnion to column lever.
6. Check operation in all shift positions, adjusting trunnion one turn at a time if necessary. Relocate quadrant to selector indicator if necessary.

Econoline (1970-71)

1. Position selector lever in drive position.
2. Loosen the locknut on the shift rod at the transmission and disconnect the manual shift rod.
3. Place transmission lever in drive position.
4. Adjust trunnion so that it fits into the lower column lever, then rotate the trunnion four additional turns to lengthen rod.
5. Connect trunnion and tighten the locknut.

Manual linkage adjustment F-100-250-350 (© Ford Motor Co.)

6. Check operation of linkage in all positions, adjusting the rod length one turn at a time if necessary.

7. Adjust selector indicator to quadrant if necessary.

1972

1. With the engine stopped, place the transmission selector lever in the D position against the D stop.
2. Shift the manual lever at the transmission into the D position, second detent position from the rear.
3. With the transmission manual lever in the D position, connect the trunnion to the manual lever.
4. Turn the nuts on each side of the trunnion against the face of the trunnion finger-tight.
5. While holding the upper nut stationary tighten the lower nut to 12-18 ft lbs.

1973-76

1. With the engine stopped, place the transmission selector lever at the steering column in the D position against the D stop.
2. Loosen the shift rod adjusting nut at the transmission lever.
3. Shift the manual lever at the transmission to the D position, two detents from the rear. On an F-100 with 4WD, move the bell-crank lever.
4. With the selector lever and transmission manual lever in the D position, tighten the adjusting nut to 12-18 ft lbs. Do not allow the rod or shift lever to move while tightening the nut.
5. Check the operation of the shift linkage.

C-4 Automatic Transmission
Intermediate Band Adjustment

1. Clean adjusting screw, apply penetrating lubricant and remove and discard locknut.
2. Install a new locknut (loosely) and torque adjusting screw to 10 ft. lbs., then *back off 1 3/4 turns.*
3. Hold adjusting screw and tighten locknut.

Low-Reverse Band Adjustment

The adjusting procedure is exactly the same as that described for the intermediate band above except the *adjusting screw is backed off 3 full turns.*

C-6 Automatic Transmission

Intermediate Band Adjustment

F-100, 150, 250, 350

The adjusting procedure is exactly the same as that described for the C4 intermediate band adjustment above except that the adjusting screw is *backed off 1 1/2 turns.*

Adjusting intermediate band
(© Ford Motor Co.)

Adjusting low-reverse band
(© Ford Motor Co.)

C6 intermediate band adjustment
(© Ford Motor Co.)

MX-HD Automatic Transmission

P-350, 400, 500 and F-350
Front Band Adjustment

1. Disconnect filler tube and drain fluid.
2. Remove and clean transmission pan and screen. Discard pan gasket.
3. Loosen locknut and adjusting screw, then insert a 1/4" spacer between the servo piston stem and the adjusting screw.
4. Tighten adjusting screw to 10 in. lbs., then remove spacer and *tighten adjusting screw an additional 3/4 turn.*
5. Hold adjusting screw and tighten locknut.
6. Install screen and pan using a new gasket.
7. Install the filler tube and fill transmission with fluid.

FMX front band adjustment (© Ford Motor Co.)

FMX rear band adjustment (© Ford Motor Co.)

Rear Band Adjustment

1. Clean adjusting screw threads and apply oil.
2. Loosen locknut and tighten adjusting screw to 10 ft. lbs., then *back off adjusting screw 1 1/2 turns.*
3. Hold adjusting screw and tighten locknut.

FMX Automatic Transmission

Front Band Adjustment

1. Remove the transmission oil pan.
2. Loosen the front servo adjusting screw locknut.
3. Pull back on the actuating rod, and insert a 1/4" spacer between the adjusting screw and the servo piston stem.
4. Tighten the adjusting screw to 10" lbs.
5. Remove the spacer and tighten the adjusting screw an additional 3/4 turn.
6. Hold the adjusting screw stationary and tighten the locknut. Tighten the locknut to 20-25 ft lbs.
7. Install the oil pan and a new gasket in the reverse order of removal.

Rear Band Adjustment

1. Remove all dirt away from the adjusting screw threads then oil the threads.
2. Loosen the rear band adjusting screw locknut.

SPECIFICATIONS

APPROXIMATE REFILL CAPACITIES — C4 TRANSMISSION

Trans. Model	U.S. Measure	Imp. Measure
F-100-250 and Econoline	10 1/4	8 1/4
Bronco	11	9 1/4

CHECKS AND ADJUSTMENTS — C4 TRANSMISSION

Operation	Specification
Transmission End Play	0.008-0.042 inch (Selective Thrust Washers Available
Turbine and Stator End Play	New or Rebuilt 0.023 Max. Used 0.040 Max.
Intermediate Band Adjustment	Remove and discard lock nut. Adjust screw to 10 ft-lbs torque, then back off 1-3/4 turns. Install new lock nut and torque to specification.
Low Reverse Band Adjustment	Remove and discard lock nut. Adjust screw to 10 ft-lbs torque, then back off 3 turns, Install new lock nut and torque to specification.
Forward High Clutch Pressure Plate to Snap Ring Clearance	0.025-0.050
Reverse High Clutch Pressure Plate to Snap Ring Clearance	0.050-0.071
Selective Snap Ring Thickness	0.050-0.054, 0.064-0.068, 0.078-0.082, 0.092-0.096

TORQUE LIMITS — C4 TRANSMISSION

Item	Ft-Lb	Item	Ft-Lb	Item	In-Lb
Converter to Flywheel	23-28	Pressure Gauge Tap	9-15	Lower to Upper Valve Body	40-55
Converter Hsg. to Trans. Case	28-40	Band adj. Screw Locknut to Case	35-45	Reinforcement Plate to Body	40-55
Front Pump to Trans. Case	28-40	Yoke to Output Shaft	60-120	Screen and Lower to Upper Valve Body	40-55
Overrunning Clutch Race to Case	13-20	Reverse Servo Piston to Rod	12-20	Neutral Switch to Case (Econoline)	55-75
Oil Pan to Case	12-16	Converter Drain Plug	20-30	Neutral Switch to Column	20
Rear Servo Cover to Case	12-20	Manual Valve Inner Lever to Shaft	30-40	Separator Plate to Lower Valve Body	40-55
Stator Support to Pump	12-20	Downshift Lever to Shaft	12-16	Control Assy. to Case	80-120
Converter Cover to Converter Hsg.	12-16	Filler Tube to Engine	20-25	Gov. Body to Collector Body	80-120
Intermediate Servo Cover to Case	16-22	Filler Tube to Pan	32-42	Cooler Line Fittings	80-120
Diaphragm Assy. to Case	15-23	Transmission to Engine	40-50	Detent Spring to Lower Valve Body	80-120
Extension Assy. to Trans. Case	28-40	Distributor Sleeve to Case	12-20	Upper Valve Body to Lower Valve Body	80-120
Engine to Transmission	23-33	T.R.S. Switch to Case	4-8	Oil Tube Connector	80-120
		Transfer Case to Transmission	21-30	End Plates to Body	20-35

CHECKS AND ADJUSTMENTS

C6 TRANSMISSION

Operation	Specification
Transmission End Play	0.008 – 0.044 inch (Selective Thrust Washers Available)
Turbine and Stator End Play	New or Rebuilt 0.021 Max. Used 0.030 Max. ①
Intermediate Band Adjustment	Remove and discard lock nut. Adjust screw to 10 ft-lbs torque, then back off 1-1/2 turns, install new lock nut and tighten lock nut to specification.
Forward Clutch Pressure Plate-to-Snap Ring Clearance	0.031 – 0.044
Selective Snap Ring Thicknesses	0.056 – 0.060 0.065 – 0.069 0.074 – 0.078 0.083 – 0.087 0.092 – 0.096
Reverse-High Clutch Pressure Plate-to-Snap Ring Clearance	0.022 – 0.036
Selective Snap Ring Thickness	0.056 – 0.060 0.065 – 0.069 0.074 – 0.078 0.083 – 0.087 0.092 – 0.096

① To check end play, exert force on checking tool to compress turbine to cover thrust washer wear plate. Set indicator at zero.

APPROXIMATE REFILL CAPACITIES

C6 TRANSMISSION

Trans. Model	U.S. Measure	Imp. Measure
All	12-1/2 qts.	10 qts.

APPROXIMATE REFILL CAPACITIES

FMX TRANSMISSION

Transmission Model	U.S. Measure	Imperial Measure
All	11 qts.	9-1/4 qts.

CHECKS AND ADJUSTMENTS

FMX TRANSMISSION

Operation	Specifications
Transmission End Play Check	0.010-0.029 plus end play between output shaft ball bearing and retainer. Not to exceed a total of 0.044 inch (Selective Thrust Washers Available)
Turbine and Stator End Play Check	New or rebuilt 0.023 maximum. Used 0.040 maximum.
Front Band Adjustment (Use 1/4 inch spacer between adjustment screw and servo piston stem)	Adjust screw to 10 in-lbs torque. Remove spacer, then tighten screw an additional 3/4 turn. Hold screw and tighten lock nut.
Rear Band Adjustment	Adjust screw to 10 ft-lbs torque, and back off 1-1/2 turns. Hold screw and tighten lock nut.
Primary Sun Gear Shaft Ring End Gap Check	0.002-0.009

GENERAL SPECIFICATIONS
AT-540 TRANSMISSION

Dry Weight	275 Lbs.
Lubricant Capacity	15 Quarts (Dry)
Maximum Oil Temperature:	
Sump	250°F Max.
To Cooler-Converter Out	300°F Max.
Power Take-Off Mounting	SAE Regular Duty – 6-Bolt
Power Take-Off Drive Gear	55 Teeth, 6/8 Pitch
Speedometer Drive Gear	5 Teeth, 29 Normal Pitch

MAIN PRESSURE CHECKS
AT-540 TRANSMISSION

Forward and Neutral	150 psi
Reverse	250 psi

3. Tighten the adjusting screw to 10 ft lbs.
4. Back off the adjusting screw *exactly 1 1/2 turns.*
5. Hold the adjusting screw stationary and tighten the adjusting screw locknut to 35-40 ft lbs.
6. Reinstall the oil pan and a new gasket.

C4 Automatic Transmission R & R

F-100, 150, 250

1. Raise the vehicle and disconnect the transmission fluid filler tube from the pan. Drain the transmission fluid.
2. At the front lower edge of the converter housing, remove the cover attaching bolts and remove the dust cover. Remove the splash shield at the control levers.
3. Remove the drive shaft or coupling shaft. Remove the converter drain plug. Allow the converter to drain and install the drain plug.
4. Disconnect the oil cooler lines from the transmission.
5. Disconnect the manual and downshift linkage rods from the transmission control levers. Be sure to use tool T67P-7341-A when removing the manual rod from the transmission lever.
6. Remove the speedometer gear from the extension housing.
7. Remove the four converter to flywheel attaching nuts. Disconnect the starter cable. Remove the three starter to converter housing attaching bolts. Remove the starter.
8. Disconnect the vacuum line from the diaphragm unit and the vacuum line retaining clip.
9. Position the transmission jack to support the transmission. Install the safety chain to hold the transmission on the jack.
10. Remove the two engine rear support crossmember-to-frame attaching bolts.
11. Remove the two engine rear support-to-extension housing attaching bolts.
12. Raise the transmission and remove the rear support. Remove the six converter housing-to-engine attaching bolts.
13. Move the transmission away from the engine. Lower the transmission and remove it from under the vehicle.
14. To install secure the transmission in a transmission jack. Align the transmission with the engine and move it into place. Install the converter housing-to-engine attaching bolts. Make sure that the converter studs are entered in the flywheel.

15. Install the rear support. Install the rear support-to-extension housing attaching bolts.
16. Position the starter into the converter housing and install the three attaching bolts. Install the starter cable.
17. Remove the transmission jack. Install the four converter to flywheel attaching nuts.
18. Connect the transmission filler tube to the transmission pan. Connect the oil cooler lines to the transmission.
19. Install the speedometer driven gear in the extension housing.
20. Connect the transmission linkage rods to the transmission control levers. Be sure to use tool T67P-7341-A to install a new grommet into the manual lever, and to install the manual linkage rod into the ground.
21. Install the drive shaft or coupling shaft.
22. Install the vacuum line in the retaining clip. Connect the vacuum line to the diaphragm unit.
23. At the front lower area of the converter housing, install the lower cover and the control lever dust shield. Install the attaching bolts.
24. Secure the fluid filler tube to the pan.
25. Lower the vehicle.
26. Fill the transmission to the proper level.
27. Raise the vehicle and check for transmission fluid leakage. Lower the vehicle and adjust the throttle and manual linkage.

Econoline

1. Working from inside the vehicle, remove the engine compartment cover.
2. Disconnect the neutral start switch wires at the plug connector.
3. If the vehicle is equipped with a V8 engine, remove the flex hose from the air cleaner heat tube.
4. Remove the upper converter housing-to-engine attaching bolts (three bolts on 6-cylinder engines; four bolts on 8-cylinder engines).
5. On V8 engines, remove the upper muffler inlet pipe-to-exhaust manifold flange nut (right side of engine).
6. Raise the vehicle on a hoist.
7. On V8 engines, remove the three remaining muffler inlet pipe-to-exhaust manifold flange nuts and allow the exhaust pipe to hang.
8. Disconnect the transmission filler tube at the pan and drain the transmission fluid.
9. At the front lower edge of the converter housing, remove the dust cover attaching bolts and remove the cover.

10. Remove the converter-to-flywheel attaching nuts. As the flywheel is being rotated, remove the converter drain plug and drain the fluid from the converter.
11. Disconnect the drive shaft from the transmission companion flange and position it out of the way.
12. Remove the bolt retaining the fluid filler tube to the engine and remove the tube.
13. Disconnect the starter cable at the starter. Remove the starter-to-converter housing attaching bolts and remove the starter.
14. Position the engine support bar (Tool T65E-6000-J) to the side rail and engine oil pan flanges.
15. Disconnect the cooler lines from the transmission. Disconnect the vacuum line from the vacuum diaphragm unit.
16. Remove the speedometer driven gear from the extension housing.
17. Disconnect the manual and downshift linkage rods from the transmission control levers.
18. Install the converter drain plug. If the converter is not going to be cleaned, torque the drain plug to specification.
19. Position a transmission jack to support the transmission. Install the safety chain to hold the transmission on the jack.
20. Remove the bolt and nut securing the rear mount to the crossmember. Remove the four bolts retaining the crossmember to the side rails. Then, with the transmission jack, raise the transmission and remove the crossmember.
21. Remove the remaining converter housing-to-engine attaching bolts. Lower the transmission and remove it from under the vehicle.
22. Position the transmission on the jack and secure the transmission and converter to the jack with the safety chain.
23. Raise the transmission and guide the transmission and converter into position. The converter-to-flywheel retaining studs must line up with the holes in the flywheel. The converter hub must enter the end of the crankshaft.
24. Install the converter engine attaching bolts. Install the converter-to-flywheel attaching nuts.
25. Install the crossmember. Install the rear mount-to-crossmember attaching bolt and nut.
26. Remove the safety chain and remove the jack from under the vehicle. Remove the engine support bar.
27. Connect the cooler lines to the transmission. Connect the vac-

uum line to the vacuum diaphragm unit.

28. Install the speedometer driven gear into the extension housing.
29. Connect the transmission linkage rods to the transmission control levers.
30. Connect the transmission filler tube to the transmission pan. Secure the tube to the engine with the attaching bolt.
31. Install the converter dust cover.
32. Position the starter into the converter housing and install the attaching bolts. Install the starter cable.
33. Install the drive shaft.
34. If equipped with a V8 engine, install the muffler inlet pipe on the exhaust manifolds and install and torque the three retaining nuts.
35. Lower the vehicle.
36. On V8 engines, install and torque the upper muffler inlet pipe-to-exhaust manifold flange nut.
37. Install the upper converter housing-to-engine attaching bolts.
38. On V8 engines, install the flex hose to the air cleaner heat tube.
39. Connect the neutral start switch wires at the plug connector.
40. Fill the transmission to the proper level with the specified fluid.
41. Raise the vehicle and check for transmission fluid leakage. Lower the vehicle and adjust the throttle and manual linkage.
42. Install the engine compartment cover.

C-6 Automatic Transmission R & R

1. Drive the vehicle on a hoist, but do not raise at this time.
2. Remove the two upper converter housing-to-engine bolts.
3. Remove the bolt securing the fluid filler tube to the engine cylinder head.
4. Raise the vehicle and drain the fluid from the transmission and converter.
5. Disconnect the coupling shaft or driveshaft from the transmission companion flange and position it out of the way.
6. Disconnect the speedometer cable from the bearing retainer.
7. Disconnect the throttle and manual linkage rods from the levers at the transmission.
8. Disconnect the oil cooler lines from the transmission.
9. Remove the vacuum hose from the vacuum unit. Remove the vacuum line retaining clip.
10. Disconnect the cable from the terminal on the starter motor. Remove the three attaching bolts and remove the starter motor.
11. Remove the four flywheel attaching nuts. Place a wrench on

the crankshaft pulley attaching bolt to turn the converter to gain access to the nuts.
12. Remove the two engine rear support crossmember-to-frame attaching bolts.
13. Remove the two engine rear support-to-extension housing attaching bolts.
14. Remove the eight bolts securing the No. 2 crossmember to the frame side rails.
15. Raise the transmission with a transmission jack and remove both crossmembers.
16. Secure the transmission to the jack with the safety chain.
17. Remove the remaining converter housing-to-engine attaching bolts.
18. Move the transmission away from the engine. Lower the transmission and remove it from under the vehicle.
19. Install the converter on the stator support.
20. Secure the transmission to the jack with the safety chain.
21. Rotate the flywheel to place the two converter mounting stud holes in a vertical position.
22. Rotate the converter so that studs and drain plug are in alignment with those in the flywheel.
23. Move the transmission toward the cylinder block until they are in contact. Install attaching bolts.
24. Remove the transmission jack safety chain from around the transmission.
25. Position the No. 2 crossmember to the frame side rails. Install the attaching bolts.
26. Position the engine rear support crossmember to the frame side rails. Install the rear support to extension housing mounting bolts.
27. Lower the transmission and remove the jack.
28. Secure the engine rear support crossmember to the frame side rails with the attaching bolts.
29. Connect the vacuum line to the vacuum diaphragm making sure that the metal tube is secured in the retaining clip.
30. Connect the oil cooler lines to the transmission.
31. Connect the throttle and manual linkage rods to their respective levers on the transmission.
32. Connect the speedometer cable to the bearing retainer.
33. Secure the starter motor in place with the attaching bolts. Connect the cable to the terminal on the starter.
34. Install a new O-ring on the lower end of the transmission filler tube and insert the tube in the case.

35. Secure the converter-to-flywheel attaching nuts. Use a wrench on the crankshaft pulley attaching nut to rotate the flywheel. Do not use a wrench on the converter attaching nuts to rotate it.
36. Install the converter housing dust shield and secure it with the attaching bolts.
37. Connect the coupling shaft drive shaft.
38. Adjust the shift linkage.
39. Lower the vehicle. Then install the two upper converter housing-to-engine bolts.
40. Position the transmission fluid filler tube to the cylinder head and secure with the attaching bolt.
41. Fill the transmission to the correct level with the specified lubricant. Start the engine and shift the transmission thru all ranges, then re-check the fluid level.

MX-HD and FMX Automatic Transmission R & R

1. Drive the vehicle onto a hoist, but do not raise it at this time.
2. After removing the converter access hole covers, remove the two upper bolts and lockwashers which attach the converter housing to the engine.
3. Raise the vehicle, and remove the cover from the lower front side of the converter housing.
4. Remove the converter drain plug. Drain the converter and reinstall the plug. If desired, the converter may be drained after the unit has been removed from the vehicle.
5. Disconnect the fluid filler tube from the transmission pan.
6. When the fluid has stopped draining from the transmission, remove the flywheel to converter bolts. Wedge the converter to hold it in place when the transmission is removed.
7. Disconnect the starter cable from the starter, and disconnect the transmission to body ground cable from the transmission. Remove the starter.
8. On a transmission that has an oil cooler in the radiator, disconnect the fluid lines. On models equipped with a sidemounted cooler, disconnect the radiator-to-cooler coolant lines at the cooler. Plug the lines to prevent coolant loss from the radiator.
9. Disconnect the manual and throttle linkages from the transmission.
10. Remove the vacuum hose from the vacuum unit. Remove the vacuum line retaining clip.
11. Disconnect the speedometer cable from the extension hous-

ing, and remove the drive shaft and/or coupling shaft.

12. Remove both engine rear support bolts.

13. With the transmission jack, raise the engine and transmission high enough to remove the engine rear supports.

14. Lower the engine against a floor stand or engine support bar so that the converter housing is clear of the cross member when all weight is off the transmission jack.

15. Remove the remaining converter housing to engine attaching bolts.

16. Remove the flywheel to converter attaching bolts. Then move the assembly toward the rear and lower it, leaving the flywheel attached to the crankshaft. If additional clearance is needed, tilt the rear of the assembly upright slightly and to the rear (enough to allow removal of the six flywheel to crankshaft bolts). Move the assembly to the rear, and remove it.

17. If the converter has been removed from its housing, position the converter in the housing, and install a wedge to prevent the converter from slipping out of the housing.

18. Rotate the converter until the studs are in the vertical position. Position the flywheel on the crankshaft flange and install the six attaching bolts.

19. Raise the transmission and converter with the jack to align it with the engine. Remove the wedge from the converter housing. Carefully move the transmission toward the engine and at the same time engage the converter studs with the holes in the flywheel.

20. Install the converter engine lower bolts.

21. Raise the engine and transmission with the transmission jack, and remove the engine support stand or support bar.

22. Place the engine rear supports in position on the cross member.

23. Lower the engine and transmission against the supports, and at the same time install the support bolts.

24. Rotate the flywheel, and tighten the attaching bolts.

25. Install the four converter-to-flywheel attaching nuts. Install the converter drain plug and the access plate.

26. Connect the oil cooler inlet and outlet lines to the transmission or side-mounted cooler.

27. Install the vacuum line and retaining clip. Install the vacuum hose on the vacuum unit.

28. Coat the universal joint knuckle with transmission fluid, and install the drive shaft and/or coupling shaft.

29. Connect the speedometer cable to the transmission.

30. Connect the manual linkage rod to the transmission manual lever.

31. Connect the throttle linkage to the transmission throttle lever.

32. Install the linkage splash shield.

33. Install the starter motor. Connect the transmission to frame ground cable to the transmission.

34. Connect the fluid filler tube to the pan.

35. Lower the hoist. Then install the upper two converter housing-to-engine bolts.

36. Install the access hole covers, and position the floor mat.

37. Fill the transmission with fluid.

38. Check the transmission, converter assembly, and oil cooler lines for fluid leaks. Then adjust the transmission control linkage.

Hydraulic control system—typical (© Ford Motor Co.)

Drive Shaft, U Joints

Driveshaft R & R

Except Bronco

1. Disconnect the driveshaft from the rear axle flange.

2. On a 117″ wheelbase vehicle, disconnect the driveshaft rear flange from the flange on the rear axle.

3. If vehicle has a coupling shaft, slide the driveshaft off the coupling splines.

4. Working from the center support nearest to the rear of the vehicle, remove the two attaching bolts and support the bearing.

5. On a vehicle with more than one coupling shaft, disconnect the rear shaft from the front one.

6. Remove the remaining center support attaching bolts and support the bearing.

7. Remove the transmission coupling shaft flange attaching nuts and remove the shaft and center bearing(s) as an assembly.

8. Thoroughly clean all driveshaft components before installing.

9. To install, connect the front flange or joint to the transmission flange.

10. Secure the center bearing to the frame bracket, tightening the bracket attaching bolts securely.

11. If vehicle has more than one coupling shaft, connect the rear shaft to the forward one, then

FLYWHEEL   DRAIN PLUG HOLE

Converter drain plug location
(© Ford Motor Co.)

Coupling shaft and center support bearing (© Ford Motor Co.)

install the remaining center support.

12. Connect the rear universal to the rear axle flange, tightening nuts or bolts securely.

13. Be sure all driveshaft and coupling shaft yokes are in phase.

Driveshaft R & R

Bronco

1. Disconnect the double cardan joint from the transfer case flange and at the rear axle. Remove axle.

2. Remove the front axle by disconnecting the double cardan joint from the flange at the transfer case and the universal joint flange at the front axle. Remove the driveshaft.

3. Install axles connecting the universal joint ends before the cardan ends.

U-Joints

E-100, 150, 250, F-100, 150, 250, 350, P-350-500, Bronco

Disassembly and Assembly

1. Mark the position of the spiders, the center yoke, and the centering socket as related to the stud yoke which is welded to the front of the driveshaft tube. The spiders must be assembled with the

bosses in their original positions to provide proper clearance.

2. Remove the snap-rings that secure the bearings in the front of the center yoke.

3. Position the driveshaft in a vise so that the bearing caps that are pressed into the center yoke can be pressed or driven out with a drift and hammer. Do this for all of the spiders.

4. Clean all the serviceable parts in cleaning solvent. If you are using a repair kit, install all of the parts supplied with the kit.

NOTE: If the driveshaft is damaged in any way, replace the complete driveshaft to insure a balanced assembly.

5. Assemble the U-joints in the reverse order of disassembly.

Rear Axles, Suspension

Reference

See the Unit Repair Section for overhaul procedures for rear axles.

Integral Carrier Axle R & R

1. Loosen the wheel stud nuts and the axle shaft retaining bolts.

2. Disconnect the rear shock absorbers from the spring seat

caps. Then raise the rear end of the vehicle frame until the weight is off the rear springs. Place safety stands under the frame in this position.

3. Disconnect the flexible hydraulic line at the frame and disconnect the axle vent hose at the axle connection.

4. Disconnect the parking brake cable (if so equipped) at the equalizer, and remove the cables from the cable support brackets.

5. Disconnect the drive shaft from the rear U-joint flange.

6. Remove the nuts from the spring clips (U-bolts), and remove the spring seat caps.

7. Roll the axle from under the vehicle, and drain the lubricant. Remove the wheels. Mount the axle in a work stand.

8. Replace the hub inner grease seal. Install the axle shafts through the housing ends so that they will spline to the differential side gears. Install the shaft retaining bolts and lock washers.

9. After installing rear wheels, roll the axle assembly under the vehicle.

10. Install the spring clips (U-bolts) and spring seat caps. Torque the nuts to 165-185 ft-lbs.

11. Connect the rear shock absorbers.

12. Lower the vehicle to the floor. Connect the drive shaft to the rear universal joint flange.

13. Connect and adjust the parking brake cables (if so equipped).

14. Connect the hydraulic brake hose and bleed the brakes. Also connect the axle vent hose to the axle fitting.

15. Fill the axle with the proper grade and amount of lubricant.

Ford Removable Carrier Axle

Carrier Assembly R & R

1. Raise the vehicle on a hoist and remove the two rear wheel and tire assemblies.

2. Remove the two brake drums (3 Tinnerman nuts at each drum) from the axle shaft flange studs. If difficulty is experienced in removing the drums, back off the brake shoes.

Drive shaft components—115″ wheelbase (© Ford Motor Co.)

Drive shaft components—132″ wheelbase (© Ford Motor Co.)

Ford integral carrier differential (© Ford Motor Co.)

7. Position the differential carrier on the studs in the axle housing using a new gasket between carrier and housing. Install the carrier-to-housing attaching nuts.

8. Remove the oil seal replacer tool from the transmission extension housing. Position the drive shaft so that the front U-joint slip yoke splines to the transmission output shaft.

9. Connect the drive shaft to the axle U-joint flange, aligning the scribe marks made on the drive shaft end yoke and the axle U-joint flange during the removal procedure. Install the U-bolts and nuts and torque to specifications.

10. Wipe a small amount of an oil-resistant sealer on the outer edge of each seal before it is installed. Do not put any of the sealer on the sealing lip. Install the oil seals in the ends of the rear axle housing with tool shown in illustration.

3. Working through the hole provided in each axle shaft flange, remove the nuts that secure the rear wheel bearing retainer plate. Pull each axle shaft assembly out of the axle housing using axle shaft remover, Tool 4235-C. Care must be exercised to prevent damage to oil seal, if so equipped. Any roughing or cutting of the seal element during removal or installation can result in early seal failure. Install a nut on one of the brake carrier plate attaching bolts to hold the plate to the axle housing after the shaft has been removed. Whenever a rear axle shaft is replaced, the wheel bearing oil seals must be replaced. Remove the seals with tool 1175-AB.

4. Make scribe marks on the drive shaft end yoke and the axle U-joint flange to insure proper position at assembly. Disconnect the drive shaft at the rear axle U-joint, remove the drive shaft from the transmission extension housing. Install oil seal replacer tool T57P-7657-A in the housing to prevent transmission leakage.

5. Place a drain pan under the carrier and housing, remove the carrier attaching nuts, and drain the axle. Remove the carrier assembly from the axle housing.

6. Synthetic wheel bearing seals must not be cleaned, soaked or washed in cleaning solvent. Clean the axle housing and shafts using kerosene and swabs. To avoid contamination of the grease in the sealed ball bearings, do not allow any quantity of solvent directly on the wheel bearings. Clean the mating surfaces of the axle housing and carrier.

Ford banjo type differential—exploded view (© Ford Motor Co.)

Ford banjo (removable carrier) type differential (© Ford Motor Co.)

LOCK NUT · FLANGE · SPACER · O-RING · REAR BEARING · PILOT BEARING RETAINER

SEAL · FRONT BEARING · FRONT BEARING CUP · RETAINER · SHIM · CUP · CONE AND ROLLER · PINION · PILOT BEARING

Pinion and bearing retainer components (© Ford Motor Co.)

11. Install the two axle shaft assemblies in the axle housing. Care must be exercised to prevent damage to the oil seals. The shorter shaft goes into the left side of the housing. When installing an axle shaft, place a new gasket between the housing flange and the brake backing plate, and carefully slide the axle shaft into the housing so that the rough forging of the shaft will not damage the oil seal. Start the axle splines into the differential side gear, and push the shaft in until the bearing bottoms in the housing.

12. Install the bearing retainer plates on the attaching bolts on the axle housing flanges. Install and tighten the nuts on the bolts.

13. Install the two rear brake drums and the drum attaching nuts.

14. Install the rear wheel and tire assemblies.

15. If the rear brake shoes were backed off, adjust the brakes.

16. Fill the rear axle with lubricant.

Axle Housing R & R

1. Remove the carrier assembly from the axle housing as outlined in the foregoing procedure.

2. Position safety stands under the rear frame members, and support the axle housing with either a floor jack or hoist.

3. Disengage the brake line from the clips that retain the line to the axle housing.

4. Disconnect the vent tube from the rear axle housing.

5. Remove the brake backing plate assemblies from the axle housing, and support them with wire. Do not disconnect the brake line.

6. Disconnect each rear shock absorber from the mounting bracket stud on the axle housing.

7. Lower the rear axle slightly to reduce some of the spring tension. At each rear spring, remove the spring clip (U-bolt) nuts, spring clips, and spring seat caps.

8. Remove the rear axle housing from under the vehicle. If the axle housing is new, install a new vent. The hose attaching portion must face toward the front of the vehicle.

9. Install new rear wheel bearing oil seals in the ends of the rear axle housing. If leather-type wheel bearing service seals are to be installed, soak the new rear wheel bearing oil seals in SAE 10 oil for ½ hour before installation.

10. Position the rear axle housing under the rear springs. Install the spring clips (U-bolts), spring seat caps, and nuts. *Torque the spring clip nuts evenly.*

11. If a new axle housing is being installed, remove the bolts that attach the carrier plate and bearing retainer from the old housing flanges. Position the bolts in the new housing flanges to hold the brake backing plates in position. Install the backing plates with new gaskets between the housing flange and the brake backing plate.

12. Connect the vent tube to the axle housing.

13. Position the brake line to the axle housing, and secure with the retaining clips.

14. Raise the rear axle housing and springs enough to allow connecting the rear shock absorbers to the mounting bracket studs on the axle housing.

15. Install the carrier assembly and the two axle shaft assemblies in the axle housing as outlined in this section.

Axle Shaft

Removal and Installation

Ford Removable Carrier Type

1. Raise and support the vehicle and remove the wheel/tire assembly from the brake drum.

2. Remove the nuts which secure the brake drum to the axle flange, then remove the drum from the flange.

3. Working through the hole provided in each axle shaft flange, remove the nuts which secure the wheel bearing retainer plate.

4. Using an axle puller, pull the axle shaft assembly out of the axle housing. ·

NOTE: The brake backing plate must not be dislodged. Install one nut

to hold the plate in place after the axle shaft is removed.

To replace the axle shaft:

5. Remove the one nut which holds the brake backing plate and carefully slide the axle shaft into the housing, so that the rough forgings on the shaft will not damage the oil seal.

6. Start the axle splines into the side gear and push the shaft in until the bearing bottoms in the housing.

7. Install the bearing retainer plate and the nuts which secure it.

8. Install the brake drum and the drum attaching nuts.

9. Install the wheel/tire assembly and lower the vehicle.

Dana Integral Carrier Type

1. Remove the lockbolts and lockwashers which hold the axle flange to the hub and drum assembly.

NOTE: It is not necessary to raise the vehicle to remove the axle shafts.

2. Carefully slide the axle shaft out of the axle housing.

3. Clean the mating surfaces of the axle flange and the hub and drum assembly.

4. Position a new gasket on the axle flange and carefully slide the axle shaft into the axle housing. When the splined end of the axle shaft reaches the side gear, gently rotate the shaft until it is inserted into the side gear.

5. Position the gasket between the axle flange and the hub and drum and install the lockbolts and lockwashers.

Rear Spring

Rear Spring R & R

F-100, 150, 200

1. Raise the vehicle frame until the weight is off the rear spring, with the wheels touching the floor.

2. Remove the nuts from the spring clips (U-Bolts) and drive the clips out of the spring seat cap. If so equipped, remove the auxiliary spring and spacer.

3. Remove the spring to bracket nut and bolt at the front of the spring.

Rear spring F-100-250 (© Ford Motor Co.)

12. Lower the vehicle to the floor, tighten the spring bolt nuts and spring clip nuts (U-bolts), tighten the front spring bolt and nut, the rear shackle bolt and nut and the compensating shackle bolt and nut.

E-100, 150, 200

1. Raise the rear end of the vehicle and support the chassis with safety stands. Support the rear axle with a floor jack or hoist.
2. Disconnect the lower end of the shock absorber from the bracket on the axle housing.
3. Remove the two U-bolts and plate.
4. Lower the axle and remove the upper and lower rear shackle bolts.
5. Pull the rear shackle assembly and rubber bushings from the bracket and spring.
6. Remove the nut and mounting bolt that secures the front end of the spring. Remove the spring assembly from the front shackle bracket.
7. Install new rubber bushings in the rear shackle bracket and in the rear eye of the replacement spring.
8. Position the spring assembly and connect the front eye of the spring to the front shackle bracket by installing the front mounting bolt and nut. Do not tighten the nut.
9. Mount the rear end of the spring by inserting the upper bolt of the rear shackle assembly through the eye of the spring and lower bolt through the rear spring hanger.

4. Remove shackle lower nut and bolt at the rear of the spring, and remove the spring and shackle assembly from the rear bracket. Remove the spring and compensating shackle from the rear bracket.
5. Remove the shackle from the spring. If the bushing in the spring or the bushing in the shackle are worn or damaged, remove them.
6. If required, install new bushings in the spring and the shackle.
7. Position the spring in the shackle, and install the upper

shackle to spring bolt and nut with the bolt head facing outboard.
8. Position the front end of the spring in the bracket and install the bolt and nut.
9. Position the shackle in the rear bracket and install the bolt and nut.
10. Position the spring on top of the axle with the spring tie bolt centered in the hole provided in the seat. If so equipped, install the auxiliary spring and spacer.
11. Install the spring clips, spring seat cap, and nuts.

Rear spring E-100—E-200 (© Ford Motor Co.)

219

10. Position the spring center bolt to the pilot hole in the axle and install the plate. Install the U-bolts through the plate. Do not tighten the attaching nuts at this time.
11. Raise the axle with a floor jack or hoist until the vehicle is free of the stands and connect the lower end of the shock absorber to the bracket on the axle housing.
12. Tighten the spring front mounting bolt and nut, the rear shackle nuts and the U-bolt nuts.
13. Remove the safety stands and lower the vehicle.

E-250, 300, 350

1. Raise the rear end of the vehicle and support the chassis with safety stands. Support the rear axle with a floor jack or hoist.
2. Disconnect the lower end of the shock absorber from the bracket on the axle housing.
3. Remove the two spring clips (U-bolts) and the spring clip cap.
4. Lower the axle and remove the spring front bolt from the hanger.
5. Remove the two attaching bolts from the rear of the spring. Remove the spring and the shackle.
6. Assemble the upper end of the shackle to the spring with the attaching bolt.
7. Connect the front of the spring to the front bracket with the attaching bolt.
8. Assemble the spring and shackle to the rear bracket with the attaching bolt.
9. Place the spring clip plate over the head of the center bolt.
10. Raise the axle with a jack and guiding it so that the center bolt enters the pilot hole in the pad on the axle housing.
11. Install the spring clips, cap and attaching nuts. Tighten the nuts snugly.
12. Connect the lower end of the shock absorber to the lower bracket.
13. Tighten the spring front mounting bolt and nut, the rear shackle nuts and spring clip nuts.
14. Remove the safety stands and lower the vehicle.

F-100, 150, F-250 4-Wheel Drive and P-Series

1. Raise the vehicle frame until the weight is off the rear springs with the wheels still touching the floor.
2. Remove the nuts from the spring clips (U-bolts) and drive the clips out of the spring seat

Rear spring F-350 (© Ford Motor Co.)

cap and remove the spring clip plate. If the truck is so equipped, remove the auxiliary spring and spacer.
3. Remove the shackle pin locking bolts from each end of the spring (bolt and nut on F-250 4 x 4 front eye).
4. Working from the inner side of the frame, insert a drift in the hole provided in the frame for removing the shackle pin. Drive the shackle pin out of each spring bracket (bolt on F-250 4 x 4 front eye).
5. Remove the spring and shackle from the vehicle. On F-100-250 4 x 4 models, remove the spring to axle spacer.
6. Drive out the remaining shackle pin from the rear spring eye and remove the shackle from the spring.
7. Position the shackle to the rear spring eye.
8. Install the shackle pin through the shackle and spring eye with the lubricator fitting on the shackle pin facing outward.
9. Line up the shackle pin lock bolt groove with the lock bolt hole in the shackle. Install the lock bolt, lock washer, and nut.
10. Position the spring on the axle, making sure that the spring tie bolt is in the hole provided in the axle spring seat or spacer. On F-100-250 4 x 4 models, first install the spacer between the spring seat and the spring, making sure the spacer dowel is positioned in the pilot hole of the axle spring seat.

11. Install a shackle pin through the shackle and rear bracket, with the lubricating fitting on the shackle pin facing outward. Line up the pin groove with the lock bolt hole in the bracket, and install the lock bolt, lock washer, and nut as before.
12. Repeat this operation to install a shackle pin at the front bracket and spring eye (bolt on F-250 4 x 4).
13. If so equipped, install the auxiliary spring and spacer. Place the spring clip plate on top of the spring at the tie bolt, and put the spring clips over the spring assembly and axle.
14. Position the spring seat cap, and install the nuts on the spring clips.
15. Lower the vehicle to the floor and tighten the spring clip nuts. Lubricate the fittings on the shackle pins.

Bronco

1. Raise the vehicle by the axles and install safety stands under the frame.
2. Disconnect the shock absorber from the axle.
3. Remove the U-bolt attaching nuts and remove the 2 U-bolts and the spring clip plate.
4. Lower the axle to relieve spring tension and remove the nut from the spring front attaching bolt.
5. Remove the spring front attaching bolt from the spring and hanger with a drift.

Rear Spring Installation

Rear Suspension—Bronco

6. Remove the nut from the shackle to hanger attaching bolt and drive the bolt from the shackle and hanger with a drift and remove the spring from the vehicle.

7. Remove the nut from the spring rear attaching bolt. Drive the bolt out of the spring and shackle with a drift.

8. Position the shackle (closed section facing toward front of vehicle) to the spring rear eye and install the bolt and nut.

9. Position the spring front eye and bushing to the spring front hanger, and install the attaching bolt and nut.

10. Position the spring rear eye and bushing to the shackle, and install the attaching bolt and nut.

11. Raise the axle to the spring and install the U-boats (when an axle cap is not used, the U-bolt shank should contact the leaf edges) and spring clip plate. Align the spring leaves.

12. Tighten the U-bolt nuts and the spring front and rear attaching bolt nuts. The U-bolts should contact the spring assembly edges or axle seat.

13. Connect the shock absorber to the axle and tighten the nut.

14. Remove the safety stands and lower the vehicle.

F-350

1. Raise the vehicle frame until the weight is off the rear springs with the wheels still touching the floor.

2. Remove the nuts from the spring U-bolts.

3. Drive the U-bolts out of the shock absorber lower bracket and the spring cap and remove the U-bolts.

4. Remove the spacer from the top of the spring.

5. If equipped with auxiliary springs, remove the auxiliary spring and spacer.

6. Remove the shackle to bracket bolt and nut from the rear of the spring.

7. Remove the spring to hanger bolt and nut from the front of the spring and remove the spring.

8. Remove the shackle to spring bolt and nut and remove the shackle from the spring.

9. Position the shackle to the spring and install the attaching bolt and nut. The bolt must be installed so the nut is away from the frame.

10. Position the spring to the spring front hanger and install the attaching bolt and nut.

11. Position the shackle to the bracket and install the attaching bolt and nut.

12. Align the spring toe bolt with the pilot hole in the axle spring seat and, if so equipped, install the auxiliary spring and spacer.

13. Position the spacer on top of the spring and install the U-bolts over the spacer, spring and axle.

14. Position the spring cap and shock lower bracket to the axle and U-bolts. Install the U-bolt attaching nuts.

15. Lower the vehicle and tighten the front spring bracket bolt and nut and the rear shackle bolts and nuts.

C-Series

1. Raise the vehicle frame until the weight is off the rear springs with the wheels still touching the floor.

2. Remove the nuts from the spring clips (U-bolts) and drive the clips out of the spring seat cap. If so equipped, remove the auxiliary spring and spacer.

3. Remove the shackle pin locking bolts from each spring bracket.

4. A hole is provided in the frame opposite each spring bracket for removing the shackle pin. Insert a drift from the inside of the frame through these holes and drive the shackle pin out of each bracket.

Rear spring C-series (© Ford Motor Co.)

5. Remove the spring and shackle assembly from the truck. Separate the spring from the shackle by removing the locking bolt and driving out the shackle lower pin from the shackle and spring eye.
6. Remove the lubricating fittings from the shackle pins.
7. Align the upper bore of the shackle with the holes in the rear bracket. Drive the shackle upper pin through the shackle and bracket with the pin lubricator hole facing outward.
8. Line up the shackle pin groove with the locking bolt hole in the bracket and install the locking bolt, washer and nut.
9. Install the spring seat and the wedge (if so equipped) between the axle and the spring. Position the spring on the axle, being

sure that the spring tie bolt is in the hole provided in the axle or spring seats. If so equipped, install the auxiliary spring and spacer.
10. Drive the shackle lower pin through the shackle and spring rear eye. Install the locking bolt, washer and nut as before. Repeat the operation to install the shackle pin through the spring front bracket and eye.
11. Place the spring clip plate on top of the spring at the tie bolt, and put the spring clips over the

spring assembly and the axle.
12. Install the spring seat cap on the spring clips and install the spring clip nuts on the clips.
13. Lower the vehicle to the floor and tighten the spring clip nuts.

L-LN-B-W Series

1. Lift the vehicle until the weight is off of the rear spring but the wheels still touch the ground.
2. Remove the nuts from the U-bolts and drive the bolts out of the spring seat caps.
3. Remove the auxiliary spring and spacer.
4. Support the spring and remove the front shackle pins. The lower pin is held in place by a lock bolt and the upper is held by a cotter pin.
5. Remove the cotter pin in the rear shackle pin and remove the pin. Remove the spring from the vehicle.
6. To install place the spring in the rear shackle bracket and install the shackle pin and cotter pin.
7. With a jack or C-clamp press the front eye of the spring up into the bracket until the eye is lined up with the hole in the bracket. Install the shackle pins in the spring and secure them in place with the lock bolt or the cotter pin.
8. Install the spring seat and the wedge (if so equipped) between the axle and spring and install the U-bolts over the axle and install the nuts on the bolts after installing the spring seat cap.
9. Lower the vehicle and tighten the nuts on the U-bolts securely.

**REAR SUSPENSION TORQUE LIMITS –
500—9000 SERIES**

Dia. Inches	Torque Limit
1/4	85–115 (In-Lb)
5/16	12–17 (Ft-Lb)
3/8	31–42 (Ft-Lb)
7/16	50–70 (Ft-Lb)
1/2	75–105 (Ft-Lb)
9/16	110–150 (Ft-Lb)
5/8	150–205 (Ft-Lb)
3/4	220–300 (Ft-Lb)
7/8	360–480 (Ft-Lb)
1.0	540–730 (Ft-Lb)

Torque limits are determined by these bolt and nut diameters

**REAR SUSPENSION TORQUE LIMITS –
F-SERIES, ECONOLINE, BRONCO, P-SERIES**

Description	Model	Ft-Lb
Rear Shock Upper Mounting	F-100-250, F-100 (4x4), P-350-3500-400	15-25
	P-500	100-120
	F-250 (4x4), F-350, E-Series, Bronco	40-60
Rear Shock Lower Mounting	All F-Series, E-300, Bronco	40-60
	All P-Series	35-45
	E-100-200	45-60
Rear Spring to Axle U-Joint	F-100-250, F-100 (4x4), E-100-200	(1/2-13 Nut) 45-70 (9/16-12 Nut) 85-115
	P-350-3500-400, F-250 (4x4), F-350	150-190
	P-500	220-260
	E-300	150-200
	Bronco	45-60
Rear Spring to Front Hanger	All except P-Series	(9/16-12 Nut) 75-105 (5/8-11 Nut) 150-190
Rear Spring to Rear Hanger	F-100-350, Bronco	75-105
	F-200-250 (4x4)	150-190
	Econoline	55-90
Rear Axle Bumper to Frame	All except P-350-3500	20-30
	P-350-3500	12-17
Rear Shackle, Front Hanger Bracket, Rear Hanger Bracket Locking Pins	P-Series	15-25

Index

TUNE-UP SPECIFICATIONS

CU. IN. DISPLACEMENT (cu. in.)	YEAR	SPARK PLUG GAP (in.)	DISTRIBUTOR POINT DWELL (deg.)	POINT GAP (in.)	IGNITION TIMING (DEGREES)	CRANKCASE COMP. PRESSURE	VALVE CLEARANCE Int. Lot Exh.	GOV. RPM NO LOAD (rpm)	PUMP FUEL PRESS (psi)	IDLE SPEED* (rpm) STD.	AUTO.
SIX CYLINDER											
250	1970	0.035	31-34	0.019	TDC①	130	Hyd.		3.5-4.5	750⑥	600⑦
	1971	0.035	31-34	0.019	4B	130	Hyd.		3.5-4.5	550	500
	1972	0.035	31-34	0.019	4B②	130	Hyd.		3.5-4.5	700	600
	1973	0.035	31-34	0.019	6B③	130	Hyd.		3.5-4.5	700	600④
	1974	0.035	31-34	0.019	8B⑩	130	Hyd.		3.5-4.5	850⑤	600
	1975	0.060	Elec.	Elec.	10B	130	Hyd.		3.5-4.5	900N	550DR
	1976	0.060	Elec.	Elec.	10B	130	Hyd.		3.5-4.5	900N	550DR
292	1970	0.035	31-34	0.019	TDC①	130	Hyd.		3.5-4.5	750⑥	600⑦
	1971	0.035	31-34	0.019	4B	130	Hyd.		3.5-4.5	550	500
	1972	0.035	31-34	0.019	4B	130	Hyd.		3.5-4.5	700	700
	1973	0.035	31-34	0.019	4B⑧	130	Hyd.		3.5-4.5	700⑨	700⑨
	1974	0.035	31-34	0.019	8B	130	Hyd.		3.5-4.5	700	700
	1975	0.060	Elec.	Elec.	8B	130	Hyd.		3.5-4.5	600	600
	1976	0.060	Elec.	Elec.	8B	130	Hyd.		3.5-4.5	600	600
305C (V6)	1973	0.040	31-34	0.019	7-½B	125	0.012-0.018	3600	5.0-7.0	550	550
	1974	0.035	31-34	0.019	7-½B	125	0.012-0.018	3600	5.0-7.0	600	600
379 (V6)	1973	0.035	31-34	0.019	8B	125	0.012-0.018	4000	5.0-7.0	550	550
	1974	0.035	31-34	0.019	6B	125	0.012-0.018	4000	5.0-7.0	575	575
432 (V6)	1973	0.035	31-34	0.019	8B	125			5.0-7.0	525	525
	1974	0.035	31-34	0.019	6B	125	0.012-0.018	3200	5.0-7.0	525	525
EIGHT CYLINDER											
307	1970	0.035	28-32	0.019	2B⑪	150	Hyd.		5.0-6.5	700	600
	1971 (200hp)	0.035	28-32	0.019	4B⑫	150	Hyd.		5.0-6.5	600	550
	1971 (215hp)	0.035	28-32	0.019	4B	150	Hyd.		5.0-6.5	550	500
	1972	0.035	28-32	0.019	4B⑬	150	Hyd.		5.0-6.5	900⑭	600
	1973	0.035	29-31	0.019	4B⑮	150	Hyd.		5.0-6.5	900⑯	600
350	1970 (215hp)	0.035	28-32	0.019	4B	150	Hyd.		5.0-6.5	500	500
	1970 (250hp)	0.035	28-32	0.019	TDC⑰	150	Hyd.		5.0-6.5	600⑱	500⑲
	1971	0.035	28-32	0.019	4B⑳	150	Hyd.		5.0-6.5	600	550
	1972	0.035	29-31	0.019	4B⑳	150	Hyd.		5.0-6.5	750	600
	1973	0.035	29-31	0.019	㉑	150	Hyd.		5.0-6.5	900㉒	600㉒
	1974	0.035	29-31	0.019	㉓	150	Hyd.		5.0-6.5	900㉔	600㉔
	1975 (2bbl)	0.060	Elec.	Elec.	6B	150	Hyd.		5.0-6.5	——	600
	1975	0.060	Elec.	Elec.	6B㉖	150	Hyd.		5.0-6.5	800㉗	600㉗
	1976	0.060	Elec.	Elec.	6B	150	Hyd.		5.0-6.5	800	600
366	1970	0.035	28-32	0.019	6B	150	Hyd.		5.0-6.5	500	500
	1971	0.035	28-32	0.019	8B	150	Hyd.		5.0-6.5	500	500
	1972	0.035	28-32	0.019	8B	150	Hyd.		5.0-6.5	550	550
	1973	0.035	28-32	0.019	8B	150	Hyd.		5.0-6.5	550㉕	550㉕
	1974	0.035	28-32	0.019	8B	150	Hyd.		5.0-6.5	600	600
	1975 (Fed.)	0.035	28-32	0.019	8B	150	Hyd.		5.0-6.5	700	700
	1975 (w/AT-475)	0.035	28-32	0.019	8B	150	Hyd.	3600	5.0-6.5	700	700
	1975-76 (Calif.)	0.060	Elec.	Elec.	8B	150	Hyd.		5.0-6.5	700	700
400	1975-76 (fed.)	0.060	Elec.	Elec.	4B	150	Hyd.		5.0-6.5	700	700
	1975-76 (Calif.)	0.060	Elec.	Elec.	2B	150	Hyd.		5.0-6.5	700	700
396	1970	0.035	28-32	0.019	4B	150	Hyd.		7.0-8.5	700	600
402	1971	0.035	28-32	0.019	8B	150	Hyd.		7.0-8.5	600	600

TUNE-UP SPECIFICATIONS

CU. IN. DISPLACE-MENT (cu. in.)	YEAR	SPARK PLUG GAP (in.)	DISTRIBUTOR POINT DWELL (deg.)	POINT GAP (in.)	IGNITION TIMING (DEGREES)	CRANKCASE COMP. PRESSURE	VALVE CLEARANCE Int. Lot Exh.	GOV. RPM NO LOAD (rpm)	PUMP FUEL PRESS (psi)	IDLE SPEED* (rpm) STD.	AUTO.
	1972	0.035	28-32	0.019	8B	150	Hyd.		7.0-8.5	750	600
427	1970	0.035	28-32	0.019	6B	150	Hyd.		7.0-8.5	500	500
	1971	0.035	28-32	0.019	8B	150	Hyd.		7.0-8.5	500	500
	1972	0.035	28-32	0.019	8B	150	Hyd.		7.0-8.5	550	550
	1973	0.035	28-32	0.019	8B	150	Hyd.		7.0-8.5	550㉓	550㉓
	1974	0.035	28-32	0.019	8B	150	Hyd.		7.0-8.5	600	600
	1975-76 (Calif.)	0.060	Elec.	Elec.	8B	150	Hyd.		7.0-8.5	700	700
	1975-76 (Fed.)	0.035	28-32	0.019	8B	150	Hyd.		7.0-8.5	700	700
454	1973 (Fed.)	0.035	28-32	0.019	10B	150	Hyd.		7.0-8.5	900④	600④
	1973 (Calif.)	0.035	28-32	0.019	㉘	150	Hyd.		7.0-8.5	900④	600④
	1974	0.035	29-31	0.019	10B㉙	150	Hyd.		7.0-8.5	800④	600④
	1975-76 (Fed.)	0.060	Elec.	Elec.	16B㉙	150	Hyd.		7.0-8.5	—	650④
	1975-76 (Calif.)	0.060	Elec.	Elec.	8B	150	Hyd.		7.0-8.5	600	600

—— Not Applicable
Elec.—Electronic Ignition
Hyd.—Hydraulic valve lifters
N—Neutral
DR—Drive
B—BTDC

① —4B w/ automatic transmission
② —TDC on K-20 Suburban California only
③ —4B All C-K 20 except Suburban; all C-P 30 series and all G-30 except Sportvan
④ —700 rpm All C-K 20 except Suburban; all C-P 30 series and all G-30 except Sportvan
⑤ —600 rpm All C-K 20 except Suburban; all C-P 30 series and all G-30 except Sportvan
⑥ —600 rpm 20 and 30 series
⑦ —550 rpm 20 and 30 series
⑧ —8B California
⑨ —600 rpm California
⑩ —68 All C-K 20 series except Suburban; all C-P 30 series and all G-30 except Sportvan
⑪ —8B w/ automatic transmission
⑫ —8B w/ automatic transmission
⑬ —8B 10 series w/ automatic transmission only
⑭ —950 rpm California
⑮ —8B All 10 series, C-K 20 Suburban, G-20 & 30 Sportvans w/ auto transmission TDC All others
⑯ —600 rpm All C-K 20 except Suburban; all C-P 30 series and all G-30 except Sportvan
⑰ —4B w/ automatic transmission

⑱ —700 rpm 20 & 30 series
⑲ —600 rpm 20 & 30 series
⑳ —8B w/ automatic transmission
㉑ —C-20 Suburban 2B
All 10 series, K-20 Suburban, G-20, and G-30 Sportvan:
   w/ manual transmission 8B
   w/ automatic transmission 12B
All others 4B
㉒ —All C-K 20 except Suburban; all C-P 30 series and all G-20 & 30 except Sportvan 700 rpm
㉓ —Federal except C-K 10 & 20 Suburban and G-20 & 30 Sportvan 8B
Federal C-K 10 & 20 Suburban and G-20 & 30 Sportvan:
   w/ automatic transmission 12B
   w/ automatic transmission (except Suburban) 8B
   Suburban (w/ manual transmission) 6B
California:
   w/ automatic transmission 8B
   Suburban (w/ manual transmission) 6B
   w/ manual transmission 4B
㉔ —All C-K 20 except Suburban, all C-P 30 series and all G-20 & 30 except Sportvan 600 rpm
㉕ —750 rpm California
㉖ —2B California
㉗ —700 rpm California
㉘ —All 10 series, C-K 20 Suburban, G-20 and G-30 Sportvan 10 B
All C-K 20 except Suburban, all C-P 30 Series and all G-30 except Sportvan:
   w/ manual transmission 5B
   w/ automatic transmission 8B
㉙ —All C-K 20 except Suburban, all C-P 30 series and all G-30 except Sportvan 8B

GENERAL ENGINE SPECIFICATIONS

CU. IN. DISPLACE-MENT	YEAR	BORE AND STROKE	FIRING ORDER	DEVELOPED HORSEPOWER @ R.P.M.	DEVELOPED TORQUE @ R.P.M.	COM-PRESSION RATIO	CARBU-RETOR	VALVE LIFTER TYPE	NORMAL OIL PRESSURE
SIX CYLINDER									
250	1970	3⅞ x 3¹⁷⁄₃₂	153624	150 @ 4200	235 @ 1600	8.5-1	1V	Hyd.	40-60
	1971	3⅞ x 3¹⁷⁄₃₂	153624	145 @ 4200	230 @ 1600	8.5-1	1V	Hyd.	40-60
	1972	3⅞ x 3¹⁷⁄₃₂	153624	110 @ 3800	185 @ 1600	8.5-1	1V	Hyd.	40-60
	1973-74	3⅞ x 3¹⁷⁄₃₂	153624	100 @ 3600	175 @ 2000	8.25-1	1V	Hyd.	40-60
	1975-76	3⅞ x 3¹⁷⁄₃₂	153624	105 @ 3800	185 @ 1200	8.25-1	1V	Hyd.	40-60
292	1970	3⅞ x 4⅛	153624	170 @ 4000	275 @ 1600	8.0-1	1V	Hyd.	40-60
	1971	3⅞ x 4⅛	153624	165 @ 4000	270 @ 1600	8.0-1	1V	Hyd.	40-60
	1972	3⅞ x 4⅛	153624	125 @ 3600	225 @ 2400	8.0-1	1V	Hyd.	40-60
	1973-74	3⅞ x 4⅛	153624	120 @ 3600	215 @ 2000	8.0-1	1V	Hyd.	40-60
	1975-76	3⅞ x 4⅛	153624	120 @ 3600	215 @ 2000	8.0-1	1V	Hyd.	40-60
		3⅞ x 4⅛	153624	130 @ 3600	225 @ 2000	8.0-1	1V	Hyd.	40-60

GENERAL ENGINE SPECIFICATIONS

CU. IN. DISPLACE-MENT	YEAR	BORE AND STROKE	FIR'NG ORDER	DEVELOPED HORSEPOWER @ R.P.M.	DEVELOPED TORQUE @ R.P.M.	COM-PRESSION RATIO	CARBU-RETOR	VALVE LIFTER TYPE	NORMAL OIL PRESSURE
V-6 ENGINES									
305	1970	4¼ x 3.58	165432	170 @ 4000	277 @ 1600	7.75-1	2V	Mech.	60
	1971	4¼ x 3.58	165432	165 @ 4000	270 @ 1600	7.75-1	2V	Mech.	60
	1972	4¼ x 3.58	165432	125 @ 3600	225 @ 1600	7.75-1	2V	Mech.	60
	1973-74	4¼ x 3.58	165432	120 @ 3600	220 @ 1600	7.75-1	2V	Mech.	60
351	1970	4⁹⁄₁₆ x 3.58	165432	195 @ 3600	314 @ 1600	7.5-1	2V	Mech.	60
401	1970	4⅞ x 3.58	165432	237 @ 4000	372 @ 1600	7.5-1	2V	Mech.	60
	1971	4⅞ x 3.58	165432	230 @ 4000	365 @ 1600	7.5-1	2V	Mech.	60
	1972	4⅞ x 3.58	165432	175 @ 3600	298 @ 1600	7.5-1	2V	Mech.	60
432	1973-74	4⅞ x 3⁵⁵⁄₆₄	165432	190 @ 3200	331 @ 1600	7.5-1	2V	Mech.	60
478	1970	5⅛ x 3.86	165432	254 @ 3700	442 @ 1400	7.5-1	2V	Mech.	60
	1971	5⅛ x 3.86	165432	250 @ 3700	435 @ 1400	7.5-1	2V	Mech.	60
	1972	5⅛ x 3.86	165432	192 @ 3200	371 @ 1400	7.5-1	2V	Mech.	60
EIGHT CYLINDER									
305	1976	3.736 x 3.48	18436572	140 @ 3800	245 @ 2000	8.5-1	2V	Hyd.	40-60
307	1970	3⅞ x 3.25	18436572	200 @ 4600	300 @ 2400	9.0-1	2V	Hyd.	30
	1971	3⅞ x 3.25	18436572	200 @ 4600	300 @ 2400	8.5-1	2V	Mech.	60
	1972	3⅞ x 3.25	18436572	130 @ 4000	230 @ 2400	8.5-1	2V	Hyd.	30
	1973	3⅞ x 3.25	18436572	115 @ 3600	205 @ 2000	8.5-1	2V	Hyd.	30
350	1970	4.0 x 3.48	18436572	215 @ 4000	335 @ 2800	8.0-1	2V	Hyd.	30
	1970	4.0 x 3.48	18436572	255 @ 4600	355 @ 3000	9.0-1	4V	Hyd.	30
	1971	4.0 x 3.48	18436572	250 @ 4600	350 @ 3000	8.5-1	2V	Hyd.	30
	1972	4.0 x 3.48	18436572	165 @ 4000	280 @ 2400	8.5-1	2V	Hyd.	30
	1973	4.0 x 3.48	18436572	145 @ 4000	255 @ 2400	8.5-1	2V	Hyd.	30
	1974	4.0 x 3.48	18436572	145 @ 4000	250 @ 2400	8.5-1	2V	Hyd.	30
	1975	4.00 x 3.48	18436572	145 @ 3500	250 @ 2200	8.5-1	2V	Hyd	40
		4.00 x 3.48	18436572	160 @ 4000	265 @ 2400	8.5-1	2V	Hyd.	30
		4.00 x 3.48	18436572	155 @ 3800	250 @ 2800	8.5-1	4V	Hyd.	40
		4.00 x 3.48	18436572	160 @ 3800	250 @ 2400	8.5-1	4V	Hyd.	40
	1976	4.00 x 3.48	18436572	145 @ 3800	250 @ 2200	8.5-1	2V	Hyd.	40
		4.00 x 3.48	18436572	165 @ 3800	260 @ 2400	8.5-1	4V	Hyd.	40
		4.00 x 3.48	18436572	185 @ 4000	275 @ 2400	8.5-1	4V	Hyd.	40
		4.00 x 3.48	18436572	210 @ 5200	255 @ 3600	9.0-1	4V	Hyd.	40
366	1970	3¹⁵⁄₁₆ x 3.76	18436572	235 @ 4000	345 @ 2600	8.0-1	4V	Hyd.	50-75
	1971	3¹⁵⁄₁₆ x 3.76	18436572	230 @ 4000	340 @ 2400	8.0-1	4V	Hyd.	50-75
	1972	3¹⁵⁄₁₆ x 3.76	18436572	211 @ 4000	312 @ 2800	8.0-1	4V	Hyd.	40-55
	1973	3¹⁵⁄₁₆ x 3.76	18436572	200 @ 4000	310 @ 2800	8.0-1	4V	Hyd.	40-55
	1974	3¹⁵⁄₁₆ x 3.76	18436572	200 @ 4000	310 @ 2800	8.0-1	4V	Hyd.	40-55
	1975	3¹⁵⁄₁₆ x 3.76	18446572	200 @ 4000	305 @ 2800	8.0-1	4V	Hyd.	40-55
	1976	3¹⁵⁄₁₆ x 3.76	18436572	—	—	8.0-1	4V	Hyd.	40-55
396	1970	4³⁄₃₂ x 3.76	18436572	310 @ 4800	400 @ 3200	9.0-1	4V	Hyd.	50-75
400	1974	4.125 x 3.75	18436572	150 @ 3200	295 @ 2000	8.5-1	2V	Hyd.	40
		4.125 x 3.75	18436572	180 @ 3800	290 @ 2400	8.5-1	4V	Hyd.	40
	1975-76	4.125 x 3.75	18436572	175 @ 3600	305 @ 2000	8.5-1	4V	Hyd.	40
402	1971	4³⁄₃₂ x 3.76	18436572	300 @ 4600	400 @ 3200	8.5-1	4V	Hyd.	50-75
	1972	4³⁄₃₂ x 3.76	18436572	210 @ 4000	320 @ 2800	8.5-1	4V	Hyd.	50-75
427	1970	4.25 x 3.76	18436572	260 @ 4000	405 @ 2600	8.0-1	4V	Hyd.	50-75
	1971	4·25 x 3.76	18436572	260 @ 4000	405 @ 2600	8.0-1	4V	Hyd.	45-55
	1972	4.25 x 3.76	18436572	230 @ 4000	360 @ 2400	8.0-1	4V	Hyd.	45-55
	1973	4.25 x 3.76	18436572	230 @ 4000	360 @ 2800	8.0-1	4V	Hyd.	45-55
	1974	4.25 x 3.76	18436572	230 @ 2800	360 @ 2800	8.0-1	4V	Hyd.	40-55
	1975	4.25 x 3.76	18436572	220 @ 4000	360 @ 2400	8.0-1	4V	Hyd.	40-55
	1976	4.25 x 3.76	18436572	—	—	8.0-1	4V	Hyd.	40-55
454	1972	4.25 x 4.00	18436572	270 @ 4000	390 @ 3200	8.25-1	4V	Hyd.	40
	1973	4.25 x 4.00	18436572	240 @ 4000	355 @ 2800	8.25-1	4V	Hyd.	40
	1974	4.25 x 4.00	18436572	230 @ 4000	350 @ 2800	8.25-1	4V	Hyd.	40
	1975	4.25 x 4.00	18436572	245 @ 4000	350 @ 2400	8.25-1	4V	Hyd.	40

GENERAL ENGINE SPECIFICATIONS

CU. IN. DISPLACE-MENT	YEAR	BORE AND STROKE	FIR'NG ORDER	DEVELOPED HORSEPOWER @ R.P.M.	DEVELOPED TORQUE @ R.P.M.	COM-PRESSION RATIO	CARBU-RETOR	VALVE LIFTER TYPE	NORMAL OIL PRESSURE
		4.25 x 4.00	18436572	245 @ 4000	355 @ 3000	8.25-1	4V	Hyd.	40
		4.25 x 4.00	18436572	245 @ 4000	375 @ 2800	8.25-1	4V	Hyd.	40
637	1970-71	5⅛ x 3.86	18436572	275 @ 2400	600 @ 1600	8.0-1	2V	Mech.	60
	1972	5⅛ x 3.86	18436572	219 @ 2800	478 @ 1600	8.0-1	2V	Mech.	60

CRANKSHAFT BEARING JOURNAL SPECIFICATIONS

CU. IN. DISPLACE-MENT	YEAR	MAIN BEARING JOURNALS				CONNECTING ROD BEARING JOURNALS		
		JOURNAL DIAMETER	OIL CLEARANCE	SHAFT END PLAY	THRUST ON NO.	JOURNAL DIAMETER	OIL CLEARANCE	END PLAY
SIX CYLINDER								
230	1970	2.2983-2.2993	.0003-.0019[1]	.002-.006	Rear	1.999-2.000	.0007-.0028	.0085-.0135
250	1970-74	2.2983-2.2993	.0003-.0029	.002-.006	Rear	1.999-2.000	.0007-.0027	.0085-.0135[10]
250	1975	2.2983-2.2993	.0003-.0029	.002-.006	Rear	1.999-1.2000	.0007-.0027	.0007-.0016
292	1970	2.2983-2.2993	.0008-.0024	.002-.006	Rear	2.099-2.100	.0007-.0028	.0085-.0135
	1971-72	2.2983-2.2993	.0008-.0034	.002-.006	5	2.099-2.100	.0007-.0027	.0009-.0014
	1973-75	2.2983-2.2993	.0008-.0034	.002-.006	5	2.099-2.100	.0007-.0027	.0006-.0017
V-6 ENGINES								
305	1970-74	3.1237-3.1247[2]	.0013-.0039	.003-.008	3	2.8112-2.8122	.0013-.0039	.006-.011
351	1970	3.1237-3.1247[2]	.0013-.0039	.003-.008	3	2.8112-2.8122	.0013-.0039	.006-.011
401	1970-72	3.1237-3.1247[2]	.0013-.0039	.003-.008	3	2.8112-2.8122	.0013-.0039	.006-.011
478	1970-72	3.1237-3.1247[2]	.0013-.0039	.003-.008	3	2.8112-2.8122	.0013-.0039	.006-.011
EIGHT CYLINDER								
305	1976	[17]	[18]	.002-.006	5	1.8682-1.8692	.0013-.0035	.008-.0014
307	1970	2.4484-2.4493[3]	.0008-.0024[4]	.003-.011	5	2.099-2.100	.0007-.0028	.009-.013
	1971-73	2.4684-2.4693[11]	.0011-.0023[12]	.002-.006	5	2.199-2.200	.0013-.0035	.008-.014
327	1970	2.4484-2.4493[3]	.0008-.0024[4]	.003-.011	5	2.099-2.100	.0007-.0028	.009-.013
350	1970	2.4484-2.4493[3]	[5]	.002-.006	5	2.099-2.100	.0007-.0028	.008-.014
	1971-74	2.4484-2.4493[11]	.0011-.0023[12]	.002-.006	5	2.199-2.200	.0013-.0035	.008-.014
350	1975	[19]	[20]	.002-.006	5	2.199-2.200	.0013-.0035	.008-.0014
350	1976	[17]	[21]	.002-.006	5	2.099-2.100	.0013-.0035	.008-.0014
366	1970-76	2.7481-2.7490[6]	.0013-.0025[7]	.006-.010	5	2.1988-2.1998	.0007-.0030	.019-.025
396	1970	2.7481-2.7490[6]	.0013-.0025[7]	.006-.010	5	2.1988-2.1998	.0007-.0028	.019-.025
400	1975-76	[22]	[20]	[23]	5	2.099-2.100	.0013-.0035	.008-.0014
402	1971-72	2.7487-2.7496[13]	.0013-.0025[14]	.006-.010	5	2.1985-2.1995	.0009-.0025	.013-.023
427	1970-76	2.7481-2.7490[8]	.0013-.0025[9]	.006-.010	5	2.1988-2.1998	.0007-.0028	.019-.025
454	1972	2.7481-2.7490[15]	.0013-.0025[16]	.006-.010	5	2.199-2.200	.0009-.0025	.015-.021
	1973-76	2.7481-2.7490[15]	.0013-.0025[16]	.006-.010	5	2.1985-2.1995	.0009-.0025	.013-.023
637	1970	3.1237-3.1247	.0013-.0039	.003-.008	4	2.8112-2.8122	.0010-.0031	.006-.011

1—Rear .0008-.0024.
2—Rear No. 4—3.1229-3.1239.
3—Rear 2.4478-2.4488.
4—Rear .0010-.0026.
5—No. 1—.003-.0015,
   No. 2, 3, 4—.0006-.0018,
   No. 5—.0008-.0023.
6—Rear 2.7478-2.7488.
7—Rear .0015-.0031.
8—Rear 2.7473-2.7483.
9—1969 Rear .0015-.0031,
   1970—.0029-.0045.
10—1971-72 .0009-.0014,
   1973-74 .0006-.0017.
11—No. 5—2.4479-2.4488.

12—No. 1—.0008-.0020,
   No. 5—.0017-.0033.
13—Applies to No.'s 1-2. For No.'s 3-4,
   figures are 2.7481-2.7490. For No.
   5, figures are 2.7473-2.7483.
14—Applies to No.'s 2-3-4. For No. 1, figures
   are .0007-.0019. For No. 5, figures are
   .0019-.0033.
15—Applies to No.'s 2-3-4. For No. 1 figures
   are 2.7485-2.7494. For No. 5, figures
   are 2.7478-2.7488.
16—For No. 5, figures are .0024-.0040.
17—#1—2.4484-2.4493
   #2, 3, 4—2.4479-2.4490
   #5—2.4479-2.4488

18—Auto.—#1, .0019-.0031
   #2, 3, 4—.0013-.0025
   #5—.0023-.0033
   Man.—#1, 2, 3, 4—.0013-.0025
   #5—.0023-.0033
19—#1, 2, 3, 4—2.4484-2.4493
   #5—2.4479-2.4488
20—#1—.0008-.0020
   #2, 3, 4—.0011-.0023
   #5—.0017-.0033
21—#1, 2, 3, 4—.0013-.0025
   #5—.0023-.0035
22—#1, 2, 3, 4—2.6484-2.6493
   #5—2.6479-2.6488
23—2 bbl.—.002-.006
   4 bbl.—.006-.0010

VALVE SPECIFICATIONS

CU. IN. DISPLACEMENT	YEAR	LASH (HOT) INCHES INT.	EXH.	ANGLE DEGREES FACE	SEAT	STEM DIA. INCHES INT.	EXH.	STEM CLEARANCE INTAKE	EXHAUST	VALVE LIFT INCHES	VALVE SPRING LBS. @ INCHES OPEN	CLOSED	FREE LENGTH INCH
						SIX CYLINDER							
230	1970	0 + 1 Turn		45	46	.341	.341	.001-.003	.002-.004	.335	171 @ 1.33	82 @ 1.66	2.03
250	1970	0 + 1 Turn		45	46	.341	.341	.001-.003	.002-.004	.390	186 @ 1.27	60 @ 1.66	2.08
	1971-72	0 + 1 Turn		45	46	.341	.341	.0010-.0027	.0015-.0032	.390	186 @ 1.27	59 @ 1.66	1.90
	1973	0 + 1 Turn		45	46	.341	.341	.0010-.0027	.0010-.0027	.390	186 @ 1.27	59 @ 1.66	1.90
	1974-75	0 + 1 Turn		45	46	.341	.341	.0010-.0027	.0015-.0032	.390	186 @ 1.27	59 @ 1.66	1.90
250	1976	0 + ¾ Turn		45	46	—	—	.0010-.0027	.0015-.0032	—	175 @ 1.26	82 @ 1.06	2.08
292	1970	0 + 1 Turn		1	46	.341	.341	.001-.003	.001-.003	.400	179 @ 1.30	89 @ 1.69	1.90
	1971-72	0 + 1 Turn		45	46	.341	.341	.0010-.0027	.0015-.0032	.400	179 @ 1.30	89 @ 1.69	
	1973	0 + 1 Turn		45	46	.341	.341	.0010-.0027	.0010-.0027	.400	179 @ 1.30	89 @ 1.69	
	1974-75	0 + 1 Turn		45	46	.341	.341	.0010-.0027	.0015-.0032	.400	179 @ 1.30	89 @ 1.69	
						V-6 ENGINES							
305	1970-74	.012H	.018H	7	7	.341	.340	.001-.003	.002-.004	—	204 @ 1.50	—	—
351	1970	.012H	.018H	7	7	—	—	.001-.003	.002-.004	—	204 @ 1.50	—	—
401	1970-72	.012H	.018H	2	3	.373	.434	.001-.003	.002-.004	.442	204 @ 1.49	80 @ 1.92	2.27
478	1970-72	.012H	.018H	2	3	.373	.434	.001-.003	.002-.004	.442	204 @ 1.49	80 @ 1.92	2.27
						EIGHT CYLINDER							
305	1976	0 + ¾ Turn		45	46	—	—	.0010-.0027	.0010-.0027	—	200 @ 1.25	80 @ 1.70	2.03
283	1970	0 + 1 Turn		45	46	.341	.341	.001-.003	.001-.003	4	200 @ 1.25	80 @ 1.70	2.03
	1971	0 + 1 Turn		45	46	.341	.341	.0010-.0027	.0010-.0027	4	200 @ 1.25	80 @ 1.70	
	1972	0 + 1 Turn		45	46	.341	.341	.0010-.0027	.0012-.0029	4	200 @ 1.25	80 @ 1.70	
	1973	0 + 1 Turn		45	46	.341	.341	.0010-.0027	.0010-.0027	4	200 @ 1.20	80 @ 1.61	
350	1970	0 + 1 Turn		1	46	.341	.341	.001-.003	.001-.003	4	174 @ 1.26	92 @ 1.66	2.08
	1971	0 + 1 Turn		45	46	.341	.341	.0010-.0027	.0010-.0027	4	200 @ 1.20	80 @ 1.61	
	1972	.024H	.030H	45	46	.341	.341	.0010-.0027	.0012-.0029	4	200 @ 1.25	80 @ 1.70	
	1973	0 + 1 Turn		45	46	.341	.341	.0010-.0027	.0010-.0027	4	200 @ 1.25	80 @ 1.70	
	1974	0 + 1 Turn		45	46	.341	.341	.0010-.0027	.0010-.0027	4	200 @ 1.20 8	80 @ 1.61 8	
350	1975	0 + ¾ Turn 14		45	46	—	—	.0010-.0027	.0010-.0027 15	—	12	12	13
366	1970-76	0 + 1 Turn		1	46	.371	.371	.001-.003	.001-.003	.400	220 @ 1.40	90 @ 1.80	2.05
400	1975	0 + 1 Turn		45	46	—	—	.0010-.0027	.0012-.0027	—	200 @ 1.25	80 @ 1.70	2.03
	1976	0 + ¾ Turn		45	46	—	—	.0010-.0027	.0010-.0027	—	200 @ 1.25	80 @ 1.70	2.03
402	1971	0 + 1 Turn		45	46	.372	.372	.0010-.0027	.0012-.0029	9	240 @ 1.38 10	75 @ 1.88 11	
	1972	0 + 1 Turn		45	46	.372	.372	.0010-.0027	.0012-.0027	9	215 @ 1.48 10	90 @ 1.80	2.05
427	1970-73	0 + 1 Turn		5	46	.371	.371	.001-.003	.001-.003	6	220 @ 1.40	90 @ 1.88	
454	1975	0 + 1 Turn		45	46	—	—	.0010-.0027	.0012-.0029	—	305 @ 3.05	80 @ 1.88	2.12
637	1970	.010H	.018H	45	45	.373	.434	.001-.003	.002-.004	—	154 @ 1.60	—	—

1—Intake 45, Exhaust 46.
2—Inlet 29, Exhaust 44.
3—Inlet 30, Exhaust 44.
4—Intake 390, Exhaust 410.
5—1969 Intake 45, Exhaust 46.
  1970 Intake and Exhaust 46.
6—Intake .398, Exhaust .430.
7—Inlet 30, Exhaust 45.

8—Use 1973 figures for 160 hp engines.
9—Intake .398, Exhaust .430
10—Inner spring 90 @ 1.28
11—Inner spring 30 @ 1.78
12—Exhaust—Closed-80 @ 161, Open-189 @ 120
  Intake—Closed-80 @ 170, Open-200 @ 125
  1975 Sprint—Closed-80 @ 170, Open-200 @ 125

13—Exhaust—1.91
  Intake—2.03
  Sprint-In & Exh—2.03
14—1975-Sprint-0 + 1 turn
15—1975 Sprint—.0012-.0029

TORQUE SPECIFICATIONS

CU. IN. DISPLACEMENT	YEAR	CYLINDER HEAD BOLTS FT. LBS.	ROD BEARING BOLTS FT. LBS.	MAIN BEARING BOLT FT. LBS.	CRANKSHAFT DAMPER BALANCER BOLT FT. LBS.	FLYWHEEL TO CRANKSHAFT BOLTS FT. LBS.	MANIFOLD INTAKE FT. LBS.	EXHAUST
				SIX CYLINDER				
230	1970	90-95	35-45	60-70	Pressed on	55-65	1	1
250	1970-75	90-95 4	35-45	60-70	Pressed on	55-65	1	1
292	1970	90-95	30-35	60-70	Pressed on	55-65	1	1
	1971-75	90-95	40	60-70	Pressed on	55-65	1	1

TORQUE SPECIFICATIONS

CU. IN. DISPLACE-MENT	YEAR	CYLINDER HEAD BOLTS FT. LBS.	ROD BEARING BOLTS FT. LBS.	MAIN BEARING BOLT FT. LBS.	CRANKSHAFT DAMPER BALANCER BOLT FT. LBS.	FLYWHEEL TO CRANKSHAFT BOLTS FT. LBS.	MANIFOLD	
							INTAKE FT. LBS.	EXHAUST
V-6 ENGINES								
305	1970-74	65-72	50-55	130-140[3]	200-210	100-105	20-25	15-20
351	1970	65-72	50-55	130-140[3]	200-210	100-105	20-25	15-20
401	1970-72	65-72	50-55	130-140[3]	200-210	100-105	20-25	15-20
478	1970-72	65-72	50-55	130-140[3]	200-210	100-105	20-25	15-20
EIGHT CYLINDER								
305	1976	65	45	70[5]	Pressed on	60	30	20
307	1970	65	35	70	Pressed on	60	30	20
	1971-73	90-95	40	60-70	Pressed on	55-65	30	[1]
350	1970	65	35	80	Pressed on	60	30	20
	1971-75	65	45	70	Pressed on	60	30	20[6]
366	1970-76	60-70	45-55	90-100	85	65	—	—
396	1970	60-70	45-55	90-100	85	65	30	20
400	1975-76	65	45	70[5]	Pressed on	60	30	20
402	1971	80	50	110	Pressed on	65	30	20
	1972	80	50	105	Pressed on	65	30	20
427	1970-73	60-70	45-55	90-100	85	100-105	30	20
454	1972-73	80	50	105	Pressed on	65	30	20
	1974-75	80	50	110	Pressed on	65	30	20
637	1970	130-135	55-65	170-180[2]	200-210	100-105	25	20

1—Outer 20, others 30. Exhaust to intake, 25.
2—Rear and side ½", 90-100.
3—Rear 55-65.
4—1976 Sprint-L.F.-80-90
5—Outer bolts on engine with four bolt caps-65
6—Inside bolts-30

FIRING ORDER AND ROTATION

1970-74—307, 350, 366, 396, 402, 427, 454 engines

6 Cyl- 250 & 292 engines

V6-engines

V8-637 engines

1975-76—305, 350, 366, 400, 454 engines

WHEEL ALIGNMENT SPECIFICATIONS

YEAR	MODEL	CASTER (Deg.)	CAMBER (Deg.)	TOE-IN (In.)	KING PIN (Deg.)
1500 thru 3500 Series					
1970-72	K1500	+4	+1-3	1/8	—
	CP1500, C1550	+1/4-1/4	0+1/2	1/8-1/4	—
	G1500-2500	+3¼	+¼-1¾	3/32-3/16	7¼
	K1500-2500	+3¼	+½-1½	3/32-3/16	—
	P2500-3500	−¼+¼	0+½	1/8-1/4	—
	Sprint	±½	±½	±1/16	—
1973	GA10-30	±1	+¼	±1/16	—
	CA, PA10	±1	+¼	±1/16	—
	CA, PA20-30	±1	+¼	±1/16	—
	K10-20	±1	+1½	±1/16	—
	GE, GS1500, 2500, 3500	±½	±½	±1/16	—
1973-74	Sprint⑤	−½-1½	⑦	0-1/8	—
	Sprint⑥	−½±½	⑦	0-1/8	—
1975-76	Sprint⑤	+½-1½	⑦	0-1/8	—
	Sprint⑥	+1½-2½	⑦	0-1/8	—

Note: For 1974-76 Alignment Specifications for series 150 thru 3500 see the chart & illustration following these tables.

YEAR	MODEL	CASTER (Deg.)	CAMBER (Deg.)	TOE-IN (In.)	KING PIN (Deg.)
4000 thru 6500 Series					
1970-72	CP4500	+2-3	+½-1½	1/8-3/16	7¼
	CS5500	+2-3	+½-1½	3/32-3/16	7¼
	CM6500①	+2-3	+½-1½	3/32-3/16	7¼
	M6500	+2-3	0±¼	1/8-7/32	6
	CM6500③	+2-3	0±¼	1/8-7/32	6
	T5500, T6500①	+¾-1¾	+1-2	1/8-1/4	7
	T5500, T6500③	+¾-1¾	0±¼	1/8-1/4	6
1973	C4500	2½±½	1±½	1/8-3/16	7¼
	S/C5500	2½±½	1±½	3/32-3/16	7¼
	C/M6500①	2½±½	1±½	3/32-3/16	7¼
	C/M6500③	2½±½	+¼	1/8-7/32	5¾
	T5500①	1¼±½	1½±½	1/8-1/4	7
	T5500③	1¼±½	¼±½	1/8-1/4	5¾
	T6500①	1¼±½	1½±½	1/8-1/4	7
	T6500③	1¼±½	¼±½	1/8-1/4	5¾
	T6500②	1¼±½	¼±½	1/8-1/4	5¾
1974	P40-45	2½±½	1±½	1/16-1/8	7¼
	C-50	2½±½	1±½	1/16-1/8	7¼
	S/C-60	2½±½	1±½	1/16-1/8	7¼
	C/M-65①	2½±½	1±½	1/16-1/8	7¼
	C/M-65②③	2½±½	−0¼	1/8-1/4	L-5¾, R-6¼
	T-60①	1¼±½	1½±½	1/16-1/8	7
	T-60④	1¼±½	−¼±½	1/8-1/4	L-5¾, R-6¼
	T-65①	1¼±½	1½±½	1/16-1/8	7
	T-65④	1¼±½	−¼±½	1/8-1/4	L-5¾, R-6¼
	T-65②	1¼±½	−¼	1/8-1/4	L-5¾, R-6¼
1975-76	CE/CS-50, 60	+1½-2½	+1±2	1/16-1/8	7
	SE-60	+1½-2½	+1±2	1/16-1/8	7
	CE/ME-65①	+1½-2½	+1±2	1/16-1/8	7
	CE/ME-65④	+1½-2½	−¼±¾	1/16-1/8	L-5¾, R-6¼
	CE/ME-65②	+1½-2½	−¼±¾	1/16-1/8	5¾
	TE-60, 65①	+3½-4½	+1±2	1/16-1/8	7
	TE-60, 65④	+3½-4½	−¼±¾	1/16-1/8	L-5¾, R-6¼
	TE-60, 65②	+3½-4½	−¼±¾	1/16-1/8	5¾

①—W/F070 Axle
②—W/F120 Axle
③—W/F160 Axle
④—W/F090 Axle

⑤—Manual Steering
⑥—Power Steering
⑦—Left +½° to +1½°
   right 0° to +1°

Caster—1974-76-1500-thru 3500 Series

All caster specifications are given assuming a frame angle of zero. Therefore, it will be necessary to know the angle of the frame (whether "up" in rear or "down" in rear) before a corrected caster reading can be determined. Camber and toe can be read "as is" from the alignment equipment.

How to Determine Caster

1. With the vehicle on a level surface, determine the frame angle "B" in the illustration, using a bubble protractor or clinometer.
2. Draw yourself a graphic as shown in the illustration that is representative of the frame angle (either "up" in rear or "down" in rear).
3. Determine the caster angle from the alignment equipment and draw a line that is representative of the caster reading.
4. To determine an "actual (corrected) caster reading" with various frame angles and caster readings one of the following rules applies:
   a. A "down" in rear" frame angle must be subtracted from a positive caster reading.
   b. An "up in rear" frame angle must be added to a positive caster reading.
   c. A "down in rear" frame angle must be added to a negative caster reading.
   d. An "up in rear" frame angle must be subtracted from a negative caster reading
5. Add or subtract as necessary to arrive at the corrected caster angle.
6. Measure dimension "A" (bump stop bracket to frame) and check the specifications for that dimension.
7. Correct the actual caster angle, as arrived at in Step 4, as necessary to keep within the specifications by adding or subtracting shims from the front or rear bolt on the upper control arm shaft.

A

HORIZONTAL

FRAME ANGLE = 1¼° DOWN

90°

← CASTER ANGLE READING = +(2¼°)

ACTUAL (CORRECTED) CASTER ANGLE = +(1°)

C

HORIZONTAL

FRAME ANGLE = ½° DOWN

90°

← CASTER ANGLE READING = −(1¼°)

ACTUAL (CORRECTED) CASTER ANGLE = −(1¾°)

B

HORIZONTAL

FRAME ANGLE = 1° UP

90°

← CASTER ANGLE READING = +(2°)

ACTUAL (CORRECTED) CASTER ANGLE = +(3°)

D

HORIZONTAL

FRAME ANGLE = 1¼° UP

90°

← CASTER ANGLE READING = −(¼°)

ACTUAL (CORRECTED) CASTER ANGLE = +(1°)

ANGLE (B)

POSITIVE CASTER

CROSSMEMBER

◀ FWD

JOUNCE BUMPER BRACKET

DIMENSION (A)

Determining Caster—Typical—1974-76—Series 1500 thru 3500

WHEEL ALIGNMENT SPECIFICATIONS
1974-76—1500 thru 3500 Series
CASTER

Dimension "A" in inches	2½"	2¾"	3"	3¼"	3½"	3¾"	4"	4¼"	4½"	4¾"	5"
GA10-30 PA 30	+2¼°	+2°	+1½°	+1¼°	+1°	+¾°	+½°	+¼°	0°	−¼°	−½°
CA PA 10			+2°	+1½°	+1¼°	+1°	+¾°	+½°	+¼°	0°	−½°
CA PA 20-30	+1½	+1¼°	+1°	+¾°	+½°	+¼°	0°	−¼°	−½°	−¾°	−1°
K10-20					+4° —no provision for resetting						
PA 10-20	—	—	—	+1½°	+1¼°	+1°	+¾°	+½°	+¼°	0°	−¼°

CAMBER	
CA GA PA 10-20-30	+¼°
KA 10-20 .... No provision for resetting	+1½°
TOE-IN (TOTAL)	
CA GA PA 10-20-30 K 10-20	3/16"†
K 10-20	0°

* See Column 1, 2 or 3 under Vehicle Alignment Tolerances for applicable tolerances.
† K-10 with full time four wheel drive toe-in = 0".

VEHICLE ALIGNMENT TOLERANCES

	FIELD USAGE	
	Column 1 *Service Checking	Column 3 @ Service Reset
Camber	±¾°	±½°
Caster	±1°	±½°
①Toe-in	±⅛″	±¹/₁₆″
Camber (Side to Side)	1°	½°
Caster (Side to Side)	1°	½°

* Caster and Camber must not vary more than 1° from side to side.
@ Caster and Camber must not vary more than ½° from side to side.
① Toe setting must always be made after caster and camber.

VEHICLE INSPECTION TOLERANCES

	Column 2
Caster	± 2°
Camber	± 1½°
Toe	± ⅜″

TRUCK MODELS AND ENGINE APPLICATION

ENGINE IDENTIFICATION—The identification plate is located inside the cab or on the firewall. The plate shows the model of engine, transmission, auxiliary transmission, brakes, front and rear axles. All identifications are for equipment on the vehicle when it was shipped from the factory.

Series	Engines— HP-Rating
SPRINT	G 100-230
JIMMY	
C1550 Jimmy	G 100-160
K1550 Jimmy	G 100-180
VANDURA SERIES①	
G1500	G 100-160
G2500	G 120-180
G3500	G 120-180
P SERIES②	
P1500	G 120
P2500	G 120-160
P3500	G 120-245
PICKUP MODELS③	
C1500 Wide-side, Fender-side	G 100-230
C2500 Wide-side④, Fender-side	G 120-230
C3500 Wide-side,④ Fender-side	G 120-230
K1500 Wide-side, Fender-side	G 100-180
K2500 Wide-side, Fender-side	G 120-180
SUBURBAN MODELS	
C1500	G 100-230
C2500	G 160-230
K1500	G 160-180
K2500	G 160-180

Series	Engines— HP-Rating
C & M SERIES (97½-in. BBC)	
C5000	G 130-160
C6000	G 130-200
C6500	G 200-220
M6500	G 200-220
H & J SERIES	
H7500	G 220
H7500	D 190*
H9500	D 201-319*
J7500	G 220
J7500	D 190*
J9500	D 201-319*
M SERIES (114-in. BBC)	
M9500	D 242-289*
T SERIES	
T6000	G 160-200
T6500	G 200-220
F & D SERIES (Astro)	
F9502	D 201-319*
D9502	D 201-390*

① Vandura Series also available with windows as Rally, Magnavan and Rally Camper Special Series.
② P2500 and P3500 available as van or stripped chassis.
③ C2500, 3500 and K2500 available as cab-chassis.
④ Also available with crew cab.
* Net hp.
** Sleeper cabs offered in 74 and 86-in. BBC.
G Gasoline Engines
D Diesel Engines

Distributor

(w/o H.E.I)

Distributor used on in-line engines is driven from the engine camshaft by spiral cut gears and is located on the right side of the engine. A gasket is used between the distributor flange and cylinder block. The distributor is held in place by a hold-down clamp and cap screw. The lower end of the distributor shaft is tongued and fits a slot in the upper end of the oil pump shaft to drive the oil pump.

Distributor used on V6 and V8 engines is mounted on top center of cylinder block at the rear end, and is driven from the camshaft by spiral cut gears. A gasket is used between distributor flange and engine block. The distributor is held in place by a hold-down clamp and cap screw. The lower end of the distributor shaft has a hexagonal opening that fits the end of the oil pump shaft to drive the oil pump. Model number is stamped on distributor housing.

Distributor Removal (w/o H.E.I)

In Line, V6 Engines

1. Locate and mark the No. 1 cylinder spark plug wire position on distributor cap and on adjacent distributor housing.
2. Release distributor cap hold-down screws, remove and place cap clear of work area.
3. Disconnect distributor primary wire from coil terminal.
4. Disconnect vacuum line from

Distributor with cover removed—inline engine (typical)
(© G.M.C.)

Distributor and coil—V6 engine (typical)
(© G.M.C.)

distributor, noting vacuum advance mechanism position relative to engine. Mark rotor position on distributor body.

5. Remove distributor.
6. Set distributor in upright position to prevent oil on distributor shaft from contacting breaker plate and points.

(V8 Engines) Models 1000-5000

1. Locate and mark the No. 1 cylinder spark plug wire position on distributor housing.
2. Disconnect distributor primary wire from coil terminal.
3. Disconnect vacuum line and remove distributor cap.
4. Remove single hold-down bolt located under the distributor body.
5. Mark position of distributor body relative to block, then remove distributor.
6. Set distributor in upright position to prevent oil on distributor shaft from contacting breaker plate and points.

(Inline, V6, V8 Engines) Models 5500-7500

1. Locate and mark the No. 1 cylinder spark plug wire position on distributor cap and on adjacent distributor housing.
2. Release distributor cap hold-down screws, remove and place cap clear of work area.
3. Disconnect distributor primary wire from coil terminal.
4. Operate starter intermittently until crankshaft pulley timing mark aligns with pointer or timing tab. With pointer and timing mark properly aligned, rotor should point towards mark made in Step (1). If rotor points 180° from mark, rotate engine one complete revolution and re-align timing mark with tab.
5. Disconnect vacuum line, drive cable, etc. Remove cap screw and mounting clamp. Lift distributor

straight up until spiral gear disengages from camshaft gear. Rotor will move clockwise as the gears disengage. Mark this position on distributor housing. Also note position of vacuum advance mechanism relative to engine. To complete removal, lift distributor straight up and remove cylinder block to distributor flange gasket.

6. Set distributor in upright position to prevent oil on distributor shaft from contacting breaker plate and points.

Distributor Installation (w/o H.E.I)

(Inline Engines) Engine Has Not Been Cranked

1. Turn rotor in clockwise direction 1/8 turn past previously marked rotor position on distributor housing.
2. Lubricate distributor drive gear with engine oil and place new distributor flange to cylinder gasket on block.
3. Push distributor down into engine block to the "normal" position. It may be necessary to move rotor a few degrees to mesh with camshaft gear; however, rotor will align with mark on distributor housing when properly in place.
4. Install cap screw and hold-down clamp, tightening clamp bolt firmly. Connect vacuum line and primary wire to coil terminal. Install No. 1 spark plug wire in socket adjacent to No. 1 firing position mark on distributor housing. Continue installing spark plug wires clockwise around cap in correct firing sequence.

(V8, V8 Engines) Engine Has Not Been Cranked

1. From old distributor, locate No.

1 firing position and mark made on housing after gears were disengaged.
2. Lubricate distributor drive gear with engine oil and place new distributor flange to cylinder gasket on block.
3. Turn rotor to point toward mark made after gears were disengaged. As distributor is inserted into place, spiral gear will cause rotor to turn counter-clockwise. It may be necessary to insert the assembly several times in order to find the correct position to bring rotor to No. 1 firing position.
4. Install cap screw and hold-down clamp, tightening clamp bolt firmly. Install No. 1 spark plug wire in socket adjacent to No. 1 firing position mark on distributor housing. Continue installing spark plug wires clockwise around cap in correct firing sequence.
5. Connect vacuum line and primary wire to coil terminal.

(Inline Engines) Engine Has Been Cranked

1. Locate No. 1 cylinder firing posi-

Distributor and coil—V8 engine (typical)
(© G.M.C.)

305, 351, 401, AND
478 ENGINES

Distributor assembly—inline, V6 engines (typical)
(© G.M.C.)

1 Distributor cap
2 Rotor
3 Contact point attaching screw
4 Contact point assy.
5 Weight cover attaching screws
6 Weight cover
7 Weight springs
8 Advance weights
9 Wick (felt)
10 Cam assy.
11 Main shaft assy.
12 Roll pin
13 Drive gear
14 Pin
15 Washer
16 Cushion assy.

17 Drive gear
18 Housing
19 Oil seal—292, 351, and 401 engines
20 Flat washer—292 eng.
21 Vacuum control attaching screws
22 Vacuum control assy.
23 Oil wick
24 Breaker plate assy.
25 Condenser
26 Condenser attaching screw
27 Breaker plate attaching screws
28 Tension spring

intake valve begins to close. Continue cranking very slowly until timing mark on crankshaft pulley aligns with timing tab.

2. Place new distributor flange gasket on cylinder block and position distributor at the opening. Note position of vacuum advance mechanism.

3. Turn rotor to point toward front of engine (distributor held in "installed" attitude), then turn rotor ⅛ turn counter-clockwise and push distributor down. It may be necessary to move rotor slightly until gears engage.

4. Press down on distributor and engage starter several times to make certain oil pump shaft is engaged. Install hold-down clamp and bolt.

5. Rotate distributor body slightly until points just begin to open, then tighten clamp boot.

6. Install distributor cap, aligning rotor with terminal for No. 1 spark plug wire.

7. Install No. 1 spark plug wire in socket adjacent to No. 1 firing position mark on distributor housing. Proceed installing spark plug wires clockwise around cap in correct firing sequence.

8. Connect vacuum line and then primary wire to negative (-) terminal on ignition coil.

("P/PB" Models)

Use same procedure as for other inline models except time to No. 2 cylinder, piston, spark plug, and intake valve instead of No. 1.

Distributor Installation (w/o H.E.I)

(V6, V8 Engines) Engine Has Been Cranked

1. Remove left side rocker arm cover. Intermittently operate starter and observe No. 1 intake valve as it begins to close. Continue cranking until timing mark on crankshaft pulley or damper aligns with timing tab.

2. Install distributor as previously described. It may be necessary to rotate oil pump drive shaft to engage distributor drive gear.

3. Install distributor hold-down clamp, cap screw and cap.

4. Install No. 1 spark plug wire in socket adjacent to No. 1 firing position mark on distributor housing. Continue installing spark wires clockwise around cap in correct firing order.

5. Connect vacuum line and then primary wire to negative (-) terminal on ignition coil.

tion by one of two methods below:

a. Remove No. 1 spark plug, put finger over hole trnd crank engine until compression is

felt. Continue cranking until timing mark on crankshaft pulley aligns with timing tab.

b. Remove rocker arm cover and crank engine until No. 1

Distributor view—V8 engine (typical)
(© G.M.C.)

Contact Point Replacement (w/o H.E.I)

Cleaning

Dirty breaker points should be cleaned with a few strokes of a fine-cut contact file. File should be kept free of grease, dirt and should not be used on other metals. Never use emery cloth to clean breaker points. Do not attempt to file point surface smooth, just remove scale or dirt.

NOTE: Highly pitted or burnt points are often caused by improper condenser capacity.

Removal—Inline, V6 Engines

1. Remove distributor cap and place it away from work area.
2. Lift off rotor.
3. Pull primary and condenser lead wires from quick-disconnect terminal.
4. Remove attaching screws and lift breaker point set from plate.

Distributor point set replacement
(© G.M.C.)

5. Remove oil, dirt and smudge from breaker plate.

Removal V8 Engines

1. Remove distributor cap and place it away from work area.
2. Remove two screws attaching rotor to weight assembly, then pull primary and condenser lead wires from quick-disconnect terminal.
3. Remove two screws holding point set to distributor housing, and lift out set. Clean housing.
4. Remove cam lubricating wick, if so equipped, with long nose pliers. Clean old lubricant from cam surface.

Installation—Inline, V6 Engines

1. Carefully remove protective covering from points and place set on breaker plate. Install attaching screw.
2. Connect primary and condenser leads to terminals. Assemble clips "back to back". Do not push on spring.
3. Apply slight amount of petroleum jelly to breaker cam and a few drops of S.A.E. #20 oil to top of shaft.
4. Check points for alignment and breaker arm spring for proper tension.
5. Set point gap to specifications.
6. Install rotor and distributor cap.

Installation V8 Engines

NOTE: Breaker point set is replaced as a complete assembly; point alignment and spring tension are pre-adjusted.

1. If equipped with cam lubricator, adjust wick to touch cam lobe only.
2. Install new contact set assembly on housing and attach with two screws.
3. Connect primary and condenser leads to terminals. Assemble clips "back to back".
4. Install rotor on weight assembly with two screws and washers.
5. Install distributor cap and lock into position with screw latches.

Ignition Timing (w/o H.E.I)

NOTE: To use a timing light, disconnect vacuum advance line to carburetor and tape open end. Carburetor trouble can affect ignition timing adjustments. Without a power timing unit, an accurate method of setting timing with engine stopped is by using a jumper light.

1. Remove distributor cap and rotor, set breaker gap to specifications.
2. Rotate engine until No. 1 cylinder is at firing position (timing mark on crankshaft pulley aligned with timing tab).
3. Connect jumper light between

Checking breaker arm spring tension
(© G.M.C.)

Breaker plate parts
(© G.M.C.)

distributor ignition terminal and ground.
4. Turn on ignition.
5. Loosen distributor and move in normal rotation until light goes out (points closed), then slowly turn distributor back until light just comes on. Tighten distributor.

Refer to Troubleshooting section for ignition problem analysis.

High Energy Ignition

Most 1975-76 GMC truck engines use a High Energy Ignition system. Two types are used. V8 distributors combine all ignition components in one unit. The coil is in the distributor cap and connects directly to the rotor. The 6 cylinder distributor has an externally mounted coil. Both units operate in basically the same manner, except that the module and pick-up coil replace the conventional breaker points. The module automatically controls the dwell, stretching it with increased engine speed. The system also features a longer spark duration due to the greater amount of energy stored in the primary coil.

The centrifugal and vacuum advance mechanisms are basically the same type of unit as on a conventional ignition distributor.

The electronic module is serviced by complete replacement.

WARNING: *Do not remove the spark plug wires with the engine running. Severe shock could result.*

Distributor Removal

Removal

1. Disconnect wiring harness connectors at side of distributor cap.
2. Remove distributor cap and position out of way.
3. Disconnect vacuum advance hose from vacuum advance mechanism.
4. Scribe a mark on the engine in line with rotor. Note approximate position of distributor housing in relation to engine.
5. Remove distributor hold-down nut and clamp.
6. Lift distributor from engine.

Installation

1. Install distributor using same procedure as for standard distributor.
2. Install distributor hold-down clamp and snugly install nut.
3. Move distributor housing to approximate position relative to engine noted during removal.
4. Position distributor cap to housing with tab in base of cap aligned with notch in housing and secure with four latches.
5. Connect wiring harness connector to terminals on side of distributor cap. Connector will fit only one way.
6. Adjust ignition timing.

Dwell Angle—H.E.I System (1975-76)·

The dwell angle is fixed and is not adjustable. No attempt should be made to adjust the unit.

Timing Light Connections— H.E.I System

Timing light connections should be made in parallel using an adapter at the distributor No. 1 terminal.

Tachometer Connections— H.E.I System

There is a "tach" terminal on the distributor cap. Connect the tachometer to this terminal and ground. Follow the tachometer manufacturer's instructions.

CAUTION: Grounding the tach terminal could damage the H.E.I. ignition module.

Ignition Timing — H.E.I.

On 1975 H.E.I. systems, connect the timing light in parallel at the No. 1 tower on the distributor cap. Disconnect the distributor spark advance hose and plug the vacuum opening.

Start the engine and run it at idle speed. Aim the timing light at the degree scale just over the harmonic balancer. The markings on the scale are in 2° increments with the greatest number of markings on the *before* side of the 0. Adjust the timing by loosening the securing clamp and rotating the distributor until the desired ignition advance is achieved, then tighten the clamp. To advance the timing, rotate the distributor opposite to the normal direction of rotor rotation. Retard the timing by rotating the distributor in the normal direction of rotor rotation.

Alternator

Alternating Current Generator

(Integral and non-integral)

All generators used are the self-rectifying, alternating current type with a direct current output. The generator consists of a stator and a rotor. The rotor revolves within the stator (a large number of windings within a laminated core) and is carried in bearings at either end of the generator frame. Two brushes carry current through slip rings to the field coils which are wound concentric with the rotor shaft.

Due to design and equipment variations, the removal and installation procedures will vary accordingly. Additional operations may be required to permit access to generator, belts and mounting bolts. The following procedures are intended as a guide.

A.C. Alternator Removal

1. Disconnect negative (-) cable from battery.

CAUTION: Alternator will be damaged if terminals or wiring is accidentally shorted or grounded with negative (-) cable connected to battery.

2. Depress lock and pull connector out of socket on generator. Remove rubber boot from "BAT" terminal and remove terminal nut. Disconnect wire from "GRD" terminal and remove clip.

NOTE: On 130 amp alternator, remove nuts and washers from harness leads at alternator terminals. Remove harness clip from alternator, then pull leads from terminals.

3. Loosen alternator mounting bolts and adjusting arm pivot bolt, then remove drive belt(s).
4. Remove alternator mounting bolts and adjusting arm pivot bolt. Lift alternator assembly from engine.

A.C. Generator Installation

CAUTION: Make certain negative (-) cable is disconnected from battery.

1. Attach alternator to mounting bracket and install adjusting arm. Tighten lock nuts.
2. Install drive belt(s) and adjust to specifications. Torque lock

Delcotron installation
(© G.M.C.)

AC generator installed (typical)
(© G.M.C.)

NO. 1 TERMINAL

NO. 2 TERMINAL

"BAT" TERMINAL

Integral AC generator (typical)
(© G.M.C.)

nuts and mounting bolts to specifications.

3. Push connector into socket, making certain that it locks; place clip on "GRD" terminal and connect ground wire. NOTE: On 130 amp alternator, connect leads to respective terminals, install attaching nuts and washers.
4. Install harness clip.
5. Attach red wire to "BAT" terminal on generator and fit rubber boot.

Voltage Regulator

Removal-Non-Integral

1. Disconnect negative (-) cable from battery.
2. Carefully remove wiring harness connector from regulator.
3. Remove regulator mounting screws; lift off regulator assembly.

Installation-Non-Integral

CAUTION: Make certain negative (-) cable is disconnected from battery.

1. Place regulator ground wire on mount and install attaching screws.

THIN BLADE SCREWDRIVER

TO LOWER SETTING   TO RAISE SETTING

Adjusting voltage setting (typical)
(© G.M.C.)

2. Lift regulator terminal latch and insert wiring harness connector. Make certain connector is locked.
3. Connect negative (-) cable to battery.

Adjustment-Non-Integral

1. Connect (POS) voltmeter lead to battery (POS) terminal on regulator and (NEG) voltmeter lead to ground on regulator.
2. Adjust engine speed to approximately 1500 rpm, turn heater to medium speed and turn all other electrical load "OFF." Disconnect negative cable from battery.
3. Place a thermometer approximately 1/4" from regulator cover and operate engine 15 minutes.
4. Compare voltmeter reading with those given in specifications.
5. If voltmeter is not within limits listed in specifications, remove plug from regulator cover and insert thin-bladed screwdriver into adjustment screw. NOTE: After two notches in either direction there is a positive stop. CAUTION: Forcing screw beyond normal stop will destroy regulator.
6. For an undercharged battery, turn adjusting screw one notch clockwise.
7. For an overcharged battery, turn adjusting screw one notch counterclockwise.
8. Check battery condition after a service period of reasonable length.
9. If regulator cannot be adjusted to within limits listed in specifications, repair or replace the regulator.

Refer to General Section for alternator/voltage regulator overhaul.

Starter

Starter Motor used on all models is the over-running clutch type, having an enclosed shift lever. Entire shift lever mechanism and solenoid plunger are enclosed in the extended drive end housing. A compression type lever return spring is used to operate the over-running clutch. Oil saturated wicks lubricate armature shaft through bronze bushings in the drive end, commutator end and nose housing.

Starter Motor Removal

1. Remove ground strap from negative (-) post on battery.
2. Disconnect wires from terminals on starter solenoid. Reinstall nuts as each wire is disconnected.
3. Loosen front bracket mounts where applicable. Remove bolts, nuts and washers attaching starter to flywheel housing.
4. Remove starter and spacer (when used).

Starter Motor Installation

1. Install spacer (when used) and position starter against flywheel housing.
2. Install bolts, nuts and washers and torque to specifications.
3. Connect wires to proper terminals on starter solenoid and tighten attaching nuts.
4. Connect ground strap to negative (-) post on battery.

Refer to General Section for starter motor overhaul.

Brakes

Master Cylinder

Three different types of master cylinders are used on GMC trucks covered by this manual: double-barrel dash mounted type, single-barrel dash mounted type and single-barrel frame mounted type.

Removal-Standard Models

1. Hold container under master cylinder to catch fluid when hydraulic lines are disconnected. *Do not re-use this fluid.*
2. Disconnect hydraulic lines from outlets of brake and clutch cylinders. Disconnect compensating line (when used) from master cylinder reservoir.
3. Pull pushrod boots off master cylinder tubes. Boots will remain

1/4"

Correct Fluid Level (© G.M.C.)

on pushrods when master cylinder is removed.
4. Remove three bolts and lock washers attaching master cylinder to dash.
5. Remove master cylinder assembly.

Installation-Standard Models

1. Place gasket over each cylinder tube. Position assembly at dash while assistant inside cab guides pushrods into pistons. Attach cylinder to dash with three bolts and lock washers.
2. Connect hydraulic lines to brake and clutch cylinder outlets. Connect compensating line (when used) to reservoir.
3. Place pushrod boots over ends of cylinder tubes.
4. Adjust pushrods.
5. Fill reservoir and bleed brake system.

Removal-Tilt Cab Models

1. Hold container under master cylinder to catch fluid when hydraulic lines are disconnected. *Do not re-use this fluid.*
2. Disconnect hydraulic lines from brake and clutch cylinders. Disconnect compensating line (when used) from master cylinder reservoir.
3. Pull pushrod boots off master cylinder. Boots will remain on pushrods when master cylinder is removed.
4. Remove three bolts attaching master cylinder to support bracket.
5. Remove master cylinder assembly.

Installation-Tilt Cab Models

1. Position master cylinder assembly at support bracket and guide pushrods into pistons. Attach cylinder with three bolts and tighten.
2. Connect hydraulic lines to brake and clutch cylinder outlets. Connect compensating line (when used) to reservoir.
3. Place pushrod boots over ends of master cylinder brackets.
4. Adjust pushrods.
5. Fill reservoir and bleed brake system.

Master Cylinder Removal

P/PB1000, P3500-7500 Models

The master cylinder on the P/PB1000 and P3500-7500 is a double barrel cylinder and is mounted on the dash panel in front of the clutch and brake pedal assemblies. Since it is not readily accessible from outside the vehicle, it should be removed

through access door above instrument panel.
1. Hold container beneath cylinder to catch fluid. *Do not re-use this fluid.*
2. Disconnect hydraulic lines from brake and clutch cylinders.
3. Pull pushrod boots off master cylinder. Boots will remain on pushrods when master cylinder is removed.
4. Remove three bolts which fasten master cylinder to dash panel. Remove master cylinder through access door.

Installation

P/PB1000, P3500-7500 Models

1. Insert master cylinder through access door.
2. Install three bolts which fasten cylinder to dash panel. Make certain pushrods are in proper location.
3. Install pushrod boots on master cylinder.
4. Connect hydraulic lines to brake and clutch cylinder outlets.

Master Cylinder Removal

P/PB1500-P/P2500 Models

1. Disconnect brake pedal return spring.
2. Disconnect hydraulic line from master cylinder head nut.
3. Remove pin connecting pushrod clevis to pedal lever.
4. Remove bolts and lock washers attaching master cylinder to mounting bracket. Remove master cylinder assembly.
5. Remove adjustable clevis and lock nut from piston pushrod.

Installation

P/PB1500-P/P2500 Models

1. Install lock nut and clevis on master cylinder pushrod.
2. Position master cylinder at mounting bracket and attach with bolts and lock washers. Tighten bolts.
3. Connect hydraulic line to head nut.
4. Connect pushrod clevis to pedal lever with clevis and cotter pins.
5. Connect brake pedal return spring.
6. Adjust pushrod.
7. Fill master cylinder and bleed brake system.

Master Cylinder Removal

SPV/DSPV5000 Models

1. Disconnect hydraulic lines from master cylinder head nut and from reservoir port at inner side of mounting bracket.
2. Disconnect brake pedal return spring.
3. Remove eccentric bolt attaching

piston pushrod to pedal lower half.
4. Remove nuts, lock washers, and flat washers from master cylinder mounting bolts.
5. Remove shaft from pedal and supports, then drop pedal down.
6. Remove mounting bolts and master cylinder assembly.

Installation

SPV/DSPV5000 Models

1. Position master cylinder assembly at mounting bracket and insert bolts from inner side of bracket through master cylinder housing.
2. Position pedal lower half between supports and install shaft. NOTE: Shaft must be installed with milled notch at outer side of bracket, facing rearward.
3. Install retaining bracket on mounting bolts, with forward end of bracket engaging notch in pedal shaft. Install flat washer, lock washer, and nut on each mounting bolt and tighten.
4. Connect hydraulic lines to master cylinder head nut and reservoir port.
5. Install bolt connecting piston pushrod to pedal lower half. Adjust pedal to toeboard clearance.
6. Fill master cylinder and bleed brake system.

Master Cylinder Removal

1972-74 Series 1500-3500

1. Wipe the cylinder assembly and lines, and place dry cloths below the unit.
2. Disconnect the hydraulic lines at the master cylinder. Cover the ends of the lines with a clean, lint-free material.
3. Disconnect the push rod from the brake pedal on manually actuated brake systems.
4. Remove the mounting bolts or nuts and remove the master cylinder.

Installation

1. If necessary, install the push rod into the retainer.
2. Push the retainer over the end of the master cylinder. Install a new rubber boot over the push rod and press it down over the retainer.
3. Install a new gasket and mount the cylinder assembly to the dash panel with mounting bolts or stud nuts. *Do not substitute any replacement part of lesser quality during reassembly.*
4. On vehicles with manual brakes, connect the push rod clevis to the brake pedal with a pin and retainer.
5. Connect the master cylinder

brake lines. Fill the reservoirs to the level shown in the illustration.

6. Bleed the system. Check pedal and stoplamp switch adjustment as necessary.

Master Cylinder Removal

1972-74 Series 5000-6500 Tilt Cabs

1. Tilt the cab forward. Place a container suitable for collection of waste fluid under the master cylinder.
2. Disconnect the hydraulic lines at the cylinder assembly. Remove the support bracket bolts and pull the cylinder away, leaving rubber boots on the push rods. Discard lost fluid.

Installation

1. Position the cylinder support assembly onto the support bracket and guide the push rods into the pistons. Firmly install the mounting bolts.
2. Connect the hydraulic lines to the brake and clutch cylinder outlets.
3. Adjust the push rod so there is 1/8″ free play of the brake pedal before the end of the pushrod contacts the piston. Fill the reservoir and bleed the brakes.

Master Cylinder Removal

Conventional Models

1. Place a container suitable for collection of waste fluid under the master cylinder.
2. Disconnect the hydraulic lines leading to the cylinder and cover the open ends wtih a clean, lint free material. Discard the lost fluid.
3. Remove the master cylinder mounting nuts, bolts, and washers. Pull the cylinder straight off the push rod.

Installation

1. Position the master cylinder assembly on the dash, and have someone else guide the push rod into the piston from inside. Attach the cylinder to the dash with the bolts and washers.
2. Adjust the push rod so there is 1/8″ free play of the brake pedal before the end of the push rod contacts the end of the piston. Fill the master cylinder and bleed the system.

Master Cylinder Removal

S Models and Conventional Vehicles with Tandem Cylinder

1. Wipe the master cylinder and lines with a clean cloth. Place rags below the cylinder to collect spillage.

2. Disconnect all hydraulic lines at the cylinder and cover the ends with a clean, lint free material.
3. Remove all mounting bolts, nuts, and lockwashers, pull the cylinder straight off the push rod, and remove it.
4. Remove the cover, pour out the fluid, and then pump the remaining fluid out of the cylinder by depressing the piston.

Installation

1. Place the cylinder in position in the engine compartment. Check the position of the push rod and boot to ensure proper installtion.
2. Install mounting bolts, nuts, and washers.
3. Connect the brake lines.
4. Fill the cylinder with fluid and bleed the system. Adjust the brake pedal free play for 1/8″ pedal travel at the push rod.

Air Brakes

Application Valve Removal

1. Relieve air pressure from system.
2. Disconnect all air lines from valve. On "L" models, disconnect hose from exhaust tube.
3. Remove valve as follows:

All Except SPA5000

Remove three attaching bolts and valve assembly.

SPA5000

Remove bolts attaching valve and treadle mounting plate to toeboard and then remove the complete assembly from the truck. Remove three bolts attaching valve to mounting plate and remove valve.

Installation

Except SPA5000 Models

Position valve assembly on mounting bracket with pushrod inserted into piston cup. On dash mounted units, the exhaust opening (with filter screen) must be down; on "L" models, exhaust tube must be toward right side of cab. Attach valve to mounting bracket with three bolts. Check pushrod or stop screw adjustment and correct if necessary.

Installation

SPA5000 Models

Connect valve assembly to mounting plate, with pushrod inserted into plate. Attach with three bolts and lock washers. Check for free travel between end of pushrod and piston cup. If necessary, remove treadle pin, then remove treadle stop bumper and add shims under bumper as necessary to remove clearance. Install treadle pin and secure with cotter pin. Install the complete assembly on toeboard and attach with three bolts, lock washers, and nuts.

All Models

Connect air lines to valve. When installing connector fittings in valve,

Brake treadle installation (SPA5000)
(© G.M.C.)

1 Shims	6 Treadle
2 Treadle stop bumper	7 Push rod
3 Mounting plate to application valve bolt	8 Push rod boot
	9 Mountain plate
4 Treadle pin	10 Application valve piston cup
5 Push rod pin	11 Application vlave

Power cylinder (conventional)
(© G.M.C.)

Power cylinder (tilt cab)
(© G.M.C.)

Application valve—models 1000-4500 (typical)
(© G.M.C.)

Application valve—model 6500 (typical)
(© G.M.C.)

check for leaks, and test brakes for proper operation.

Compressor (Belt Driven)

Compressor Removal

1. Block or hold vehicle by means other than air brakes.
2. Drain air from system, usually at reservoirs.
3. If water cooled, drain cooling system.
4. Disconnect ALL lines (air, water and oil).
5. Loosen belt adjusting stud and remove drive belt.
6. Remove mounting bolts, remove compressor.

Compressor Installation

1. Run engine briefly to clear and check oil supply lines. Clean oil return lines and passages. Check coolant supply and lines (if used).

use sealing compound on threads. *Keep sealing compound off first two threads of fittings.* Sealing compound inside the valve could foul valve seats and block compensating port. On "L" models, connect hose to exhaust tube. Build up air pressure in system and test application valve operation.

Application Valve Removal

Tilt Cab 5000-6500 Models, 1971-74

1. Block the vehicle wheels, drain air pressure from the brake system, and disconnect the air lines from the application valve.

2. Disconnect the exhaust hose from the exhaust port of the valve.
3. Remove the bolts which attach the valve to the support bracket, and remove the valve.

Installation

1. Position the valve on the support bracket and install the attaching bolts.
2. Connect the exhaust hose to the exhaust port of the valve.
3. Connect the air lines to the valve.
4. Operate the engine until operating air pressure is built up,

2. Clean mounting surface and re-place gasket, be sure oil holes in gasket are aligned.

3. Install compressor with mounting cap screws loose, compressor will be movable to allow fittings on lines to be started.

4. Make sure air cleaner is cleaned and properly installed.

5. Align compressor, check drive belt.

6. Tighten mounting bolts and adjust.

Compressor (Gear Driven)

Compressor Removal

1. Block or hold vehicle by means other than air brakes.
2. Drain air from system.
3. Drain engine block.
4. Disconnect ALL lines (air, water, oil).
5. Remove four nuts and washers from mounting studs, pull compressor back off studs and remove.

Compressor Installation

1. Run engine briefly to clear and check oil supply lines. Check oil return lines and passages. Check coolant supply and lines. Inspect drive gears and coupling.
2. Make sure mating surfaces of compressor and housing are clean. Place new gasket on studs.
3. Install drive coupling on hub and position compressor on mounting studs. Guide compressor into mesh with driven disc, making sure coupling teeth engage disc. Install nuts and washers and torque to 65 ft lbs.
4. Connect water, air and oil lines securely, fill cooling system.
5. Run engine and check compressor for noise, leaks and output. Check build-up time and governor action.

Brake Chamber

Cam type (uses slack adjusters one per wheel.)

Chamber Removal

1. Disconnect air hose from chamber.
2. Remove clevis pin from yoke.
3. Remove nuts and washers from mounting studs.
4. Remove chamber.

Chamber Installation

1. Place chamber on mounting bracket and secure with stud nuts and lock washers.
2. Connect air hose.
3. Install slack adjuster yoke clevis pin, after adjusting for mini-

mum travel. (Angle made by push rod and slack adjuster lever should not be less than 90°, brakes applied). Lock yoke with locking nut. Push rod travel should be as short as possible without brakes dragging.

4. Check for leaks, and possible brake shoe adjustment.

Wedge Type (two per wheel) see note and caution below

Chamber Removal

1. Block or hold vehicle by means other than air brakes.
2. Disconnect air hose from chamber.
3. Remove lock washer tangs from notches in spanner nut and spider housing.
4. Loosen spanner nut and unscrew air chamber from housing.

Chamber Installation

1. Screw air chamber in spider housing until it "bottoms," then back off (no more than one turn) until chamber air port aligns with air hose. The plastic guide will assure proper position of wedge. Lock brake chamber in position with spanner nut and lock washer.
2. Start engine, charge air system, check for leaks. Pump brake pedal to allow automatic adjusters to adjust brakes.

NOTE: When brakes are equipped with "fail-safe" brake chambers, cage power spring before starting any disassembly or removal of wheels or drums to avoid possible injury. When a vehicle is disabled, due to low or lost air pressure, cage power spring before attempting to move the vehicle. Cage the power spring by rotating the release bolt approximately 18 to 21 turns clockwise. Caging and un-caging can be made easier by applying air pressure, 65 lbs needed (if possible). This takes spring load off release bolt.

CAUTION: Before removing or caging brake chamber, block wheels since parking brake will not be applied.

Slack Adjusters

Adjuster Removal

1. Remove clevis pin at lever.
2. Remove lock ring and washer on splined camshaft (some front slack adjusters are held on by a retaining screw).
3. Slide adjuster off splined shaft.

Adjuster Installation

1. Make sure spacer washers are in place (if used).
2. Slide slack adjuster on splined camshaft, lock in place with snap

ring and washer. If held on by retaining screw, allow .010 in. end play. Stake edge of screw to lock.

3. Connect yoke clevis pin. Angle made by push rod and slack adjuster lever should NOT be less than 90° brakes applied. Push rod travel should be as short as possible without brakes dragging.

4. Lubricate adjuster.

NOTE: See "Air Brake" section of the General Repair section.

Bleeding Brakes

Pressure Bleeding

CAUTION: Stop engine and relieve vacuum or exhaust pressure from system before following procedures.

1. Make certain lever in pressure tank is up to petcock above outlet and that tank is charged with 40 to 50 psi.
2. Clean dirt from around master cylinder filler cap. Connect pressure tank hose to filler cap or cover opening. Bleed air from hose before tightening connection. Open valves at both ends.
3. Bleed slave cylinder and control valve first. (when used). Slip end of bleeder hose over bleeder valve No. 1 and place other end in glass jar containing enough hydraulic fluid to cover end of hose. Open bleeder valve with wrench and observe flow of fluid. On Models 4000 and 5000, start engine and make at least two power brake applications with bleeder valve open to force air out of slave cylinder. Close bleeder valve as soon as bubbles stop and fluid flows in solid stream. Stop engine and relieve vacuum from system.
4. Bleed valve No. 2 (on power cylinder control valve), then bleed wheel cylinders in sequence. Repeat bleeding operations at power cylinder. On Models 4000 and 5000, repeat power brake applications with engine running as in Step (3).
5. If, after bleeding, the pedal "feel" is not satisfactory, inspect residual check valve in the master cylinder and the check valve in the power cylinder piston. Improper operation of either or both of these valves will result in same pedal "feel" as air in the system, since malfunction permits recirculation of fluid through compensating line and back to master cylinder reservoir. Refer to applicable procedures for repair.

DUO-SERVO   DUO-SERVO

1000; 1500; 2500

DUO-SERVO   TWIN-ACTION

3500 (POWER OPT.)—ALL 4000 (EXCEPT "L" AND "H")

TYPE "F"   TWIN-ACTION

L4000

TYPE "F"   TYPE "FR-3"

H 4000—ALL 5000 (EXCEPT "W")

TYPE "F"   W5000   TYPE "FR-3"

Brake bleeding sequence (© G.M.C.)

Manual Bleeding

Manual bleeding follows the same procedures as pressure bleeding, except that brake fluid is forced through lines by pumping the brake pedal instead of by air pressure. Fluid in master cylinder must be replenished after bleeding at each valve. Brake pedal should be pumped up and down slowly, and should be on downstroke as valve is closed.

Split System ("S" Models)

The system consists of a dash mounted master cylinder and two power cylinders mounted on the frame. The main system consists of the front wheel brakes and one cylinder on each rear wheel brake. The secondary system consists of one cylinder on each secondary wheel brake. Each system must be bled separately using a tool like that shown in the illustration.

Power Brakes

(Power Vacuum)

Power Cylinder Removal

Exc. 1975-76 Sprint

1. For easier accessibility, it is recommended that cab step be removed on conventional models and that cab be tilted forward on tilt cab models.

Hydro-boost—1974.

Hydro-Boost—1975—Cabs, Suburban.

2. Clean away road dirt and grease to prevent contamination of vacuum or hydraulic systems.
3. Have a container available to catch hydraulic brake fluid which will flow from system. *Do not re-use this fluid.*
4. Disconnect all hydraulic, vacuum and atmospheric lines and hoses from power cylinder. Plug vacuum line.
5. On light duty models, disconnect the push rod from the brake pedal. Remove bolts and nuts fastening cylinder to frame and support brackets.
6. Remove power cylinder.

Installation

1. Place power cylinder in position and fasten with nuts and bolts to frame and support brackets. Connect the push rod to the brake pedal.
2. Connect all hydraulic, vacuum, and atmospheric lines and hoses to power cylinder.
3. Bleed master cylinder and vacuum power cylinder as directed under "Bleeding Brakes." If ONLY the power cylinder has been removed, it should not be necessary to bleed the wheel cylinders IF the master cylinder and power cylinders are bled first AND lines to wheel cylinder have not been disturbed.

Power Cylinder Removal

1975-76 Sprint

1. Remove vacuum hose from check valve.
2. Remove master cylinder to power cylinder nuts.
3. Pull forward on the master cylinder until the cylinder clears the power cylinder mounting studs. Carefully move the master cylinder aside (brake lines attached). Support the cylinder to avoid stress on the brake lines.

NOTE: Move the master cylinder

only enough to allow room for removal of the power cylinder.

4. Remove nuts securing power unit to dash.
5. Remove the brake line clip from the power booster. Install the clip on reassembly of the booster to the vehicle.
6. Remove push rod to pedal retainer and slip push rod off pin. Remove power cylinder assembly.
7. Push brake pedal to floor. This action will push the power unit away from the dash and provide adequate clearance for removing the push rod pin.
8. If an overhaul is necessary, refer to the applicable General Repair Section.

Installation

1. To install reverse the removal procedure.

Hydro-Boost Reference

Specific information will be found in the Power Brake portion of the General Repair Section on adjustments, overhauling and troubleshooting.

Description

The Hydro-boost system was designed to eliminate the need for the remote frame mounted boosters. It utilizes power steering fluid in place of engine vacuum to provide a power assist that operates a dual master cylinder brake system. A spring accumulator is used in conjunction with the hydraulic brake booster. The accumulator is a sealed hydraulic cylinder with a port at each end. On 1974 models the accumulator and booster are mounted separately. In 1975 all "C" model vehicles equipped with the hydro-boost incorporate an accumulator which is integral with the booster.

CAUTION: The accumulator contains a spring compressed under high pressure. Any attempt to disassemble or cut could cause personal injury.

Hydraulic Brake Booster Motor Home Chassis

Removal & Installation

1. Make sure all pressure is discharged from the accumulator by depressing and releasing the brake pedal several times.
2. Raise the vehicle on a hoist.
3. Clean all the dirt from the booster at the hydraulic line connections and master cylinder.
4. Remove the nuts and lockwashers that secure the master cylinder to the booster and support bracket. Support the master cylinder leaving the hydraulic lines attached to the master cylinder.
5. Disconnect and plug the hydraulic lines from the booster ports.
6. Remove the cotter pin, nut, bolt and washers that secure the operating lever to the vertical brake rod.
7. Remove the six nuts, lockwashers and bolts that secure the booster linkage bracket to the front and rear support brackets, then slide the booster off the rear support studs and remove the booster from the vehicle.
8. Remove the cotter pin, nut, washer and bolt that secures the operating lever to the pedal rod.
9. Remove the brake pedal rod lever nut and bolt and then remove the lever, sleeve and bushings.
10. To install reverse the removal procedures. Bleed the booster-power steering hydraulic system and check the brake pedal and stoplamp switch adjustment.

Conventional Cab & Suburban

Removal & Installation

1. Make sure all pressure is discharged from the accumulator by depressing and releasing the brake pedal several times.
2. Remove the nuts and lockwashers that secure the master cylin-

Booster Installation—Motor home chassis.

der to the booster and support bracket. Support the master cylinder leaving the hydraulic lines attached to the master cylinder.
3. Remove the booster pedal push rod cotter pin and washer, and disconnect the push rod from the brake pedal.
4. Remove the booster support bracket.
5. Remove the booster bracket to dash panel or support bracket nuts and remove the booster assembly.
6. To install reverse the removal procedure. Bleed the booster-power steering hydraulic system and check brake pedal and stop-lamp switch adjustment.

Forward Control Chassis (Vans)

Removal & Installation
1. Make sure all pressure is discharged from the accumulator by depressing and releasing the brake pedal several times.
2. Clean all the dirt from the booster at the hydraulic line

connections and master cylinder.
3. Remove the nuts and lockwashers that secure the master cylinder to the booster and the support bracket. Support the master cylinder leaving the hydraulic lines attached to the master cylinder.
4. Remove the booster pedal push rod cotter pin and washer and disconnect the push rod from the booster bracket pivot lever.
5. Remove the booster upper braces.
6. Remove the booster bracket nuts and remove the booster.
7. To install reverse the removal procedure. Bleed the booster-power steering hydraulic system and check the brake pedal and stop lamp switch adjustment.

Bleeding Hydro-Boost System
1. Fill the power steering pump to the proper level.
2. Start the engine for approximately two seconds. Check the fluid and add if necessary.

3. Repeat step 2 until the fluid level remains constant.
4. Raise the front end of the vehicle so that the tires are clear of the ground.
5. Start the engine and run approximately 1500 rpm. Depress and release the brake pedal several times then turn the steering wheel right and left, lightly contacting the wheel stops.
6. Turn off the engine and check the fluid level in the reservoir and add fluid if necessary.
7. Lower the vehicle, start the engine and run at approximately 1500 rpm. Depress and release the brake pedal several times and turn the steering wheel to full right and left.
8. Turn the engine off and check the fluid level in the reservoir. Add fluid if necessary.

NOTE: If the fluid is extremely foamy, or there is an erratic pedal feel allow vehicle to stand a few moments with the engine off and repeat the above procedure.

Booster Installation—Cab and Suburban.

Booster Installation—Vans

Brake pedal adjustment—Forward Control Chassis.

Booster Installation—forward control chassis exc. Light Duty Vans.

Brake pedal and stop lamp adjustments—Motor Home Chassis.

Brake Pedal Adjustment Motor Home Chassis

1. With brake pedal pull back spring installed, brake pedal hard into bumper, brake master cylinder assembly and brake pedal rod lever at full return, install the preassembled brake pedal rod assembly (rod end at boot) and adjust to 31.75 in.
2. Turn the brake pedal rod end and adjust the free pedal travel to .06 in. to .36 in.
3. Fasten the boot to the floor pan assembly and compress the boot to 2.54 in. installed height.

Forward Control Chassis— (Vans)

1. Adjust the pedal rod to 9.90 in. and install in the vehicle.

Brake pedal adjustment—Vans

NOTE: *The brake pedal push rod is not adjustable on cab and Suburban models.*

Stoplamp Switch Adjustment

All Models

1. Release the brake pedal to its normal position.
2. Loosen the switch locknut and rotate the switch in its bracket. Electrical contact should be made when pedal travel is 3/8 in.-5/8 in.

(Electro-Hydraulic)

General Description

The booster unit is hydraulically operated with an electrical pump attached as a back-up unit in the event of primary pump failure. The booster system features a dual braking system, increased pressure output, excellent pedal feel, separate hydraulic pump, and an electrical powered back-up system.

The hydraulic booster is powered by a standard power steering vane type pump.

Electro-Hydraulic Pump Removal

NOTE: *The pump may be removed from the booster assembly while in the vehicle.*

1. Block vehicle wheels.
2. Disconnect battery ground.
3. Disconnect E.H. pump lead.
4. Position a container to catch fluid and remove bracket-to-booster 9/16 in. hex-head bolt.
5. Remove two 9/16 in. hex-head mounting bolts. Remove pump and two O-rings.

Installation

1. To install reverse the removal procedure. Use new O-rings and torque the two 3/8-16 x 1 1/8 in mounting bolts to 16-30 ft. lbs.

Booster Assembly Removal Conventional Cab

1. Block vehicle wheels.
2. Disconnect battery ground cable.
3. Disconnect electrical leads to E.H. pump and flow switch.

NOTE: *Booster head may be re-*

Booster assembly mounting—Conv. cab.

Booster assembly mounting—Tilt cab.

moved from vehicle without removing master cylinder and disconnecting brake lines. Remove two nuts retaining brake line clips to line support. Remove bolt and clips in booster head. Remove four 9/16 in. hex head master cylinder to booster head mounting bolts and move master cylinder forward from booster. Secure in an upright position. Complete booster assembly removal procedure following:

4. Disconnect hydraulic lines from booster. Use a suitable container to catch fluid. DO NOT reuse fluid.
5. Remove cotter key from push rod pin. Remove nut and bolt from pedal push rod eye. Thread push rod and nut from booster push rod.
6. Remove line and hose supports from booster head.

NOTE: Use care when proceeding to next two steps. This is a heavy unit, approximately 50 pounds including master cylinder, and should be handled as such. After removing from vehicle, use care in handling so that flow switch or E.H. pump is not damaged and bail or cover on master cylinder is not damaged.

7. Remove two 3/8-24 thread hex-head nuts and washers from inside cab at dash panel.

8. Remove upper two mounting bolts and washers from booster head at dash. Remove booster assembly.
9. Remove four 9/16 in. hex-head bolts which attach brake master cylinder to booster head (Fig. 8). Remove master cylinder, gasket, and brake line support.

Installation

1. To install reverse the removal procedure. Torque the four 3/8-16 x 1 3/8 in. hex-head bolts attaching the master cylinder to the booster head to 16-30 ft lbs. The two hex-nuts on the 3/8-24 in. studs are torqued to 25-30 ft lbs. The two mounting bolts are torqued to 25-30 ft lbs.

Tilt Cab

1. Block vehicle wheels.
2. Disconnect battery ground cable.
3. Disconnect electrical lead to E.H. pump.
4. Disconnect hydraulic lines from booster and master cylinder. Use a suitable container to catch fluid. Do not reuse fluid.
5. Loosen nuts on each end of push rod extension. Turn extension until free of booster push rod. Bellcrank ball joint may have to be removed to facilitate turning extension.

6. Remove two 9/16 in. hex-head bolts and nuts retaining support to cab sill.
7. Remove two 9/16 in. hex-head bolts and nuts retaining bracket to sill.
8. Remove booster assembly. Move push rod end forward and down while revolving unit to clear E.H. pump, support, and bracket.
9. Remove four 9/16 in. hex-head bolts which attach brake master cylinder to booster head and remove master cylinder and gasket.

Flow Switch Removal

1. Position container to catch fluid from disconnected hose at flow switch.
2. Loosen outer hose clamp at switch and remove hydraulic line from hose. Drain fluid into previously placed container. DO NOT reuse fluid.
3. Loosen inner hose clamp at switch and remove hose.
4. Disconnect electrical lead to switch.
5. Remove switch using a one-inch thin blade wrench.

Installation

1. Use a new O-ring seal and torque to 20-30 ft lbs.

Brake Hydraulic pump installation—(V-8)

Brake Hydraulic pump installation—(L-6)

Brake Hydraulic Pump
Removal

V-8 Engines

1. Disconnect E.H. pump electrical lead.
2. Disconnect hydraulic lines at pump. Cap or otherwise restrict flow of fluid from lines.
3. Remove hose to reservoir (if used).
4. Remove pulley.
5. Remove adjusting nut and washers at rear of pump at bracket slot.
6. Remove adjusting bolt and washers from front of pump at bracket slot.
7. Remove front mounting bolt and washers and remove pump.

Installation

1. To install reverse the removal procedure. Use a belt tension gauge and adjust the belt to 90-100 lbs (new belt).

L-6 Engines

1. Disconnect E.H. pump electrical lead.
2. Disconnect hydraulic lines at pump. Cap or otherwise restrict flow of fluid from lines.
3. Remove pulley.
4. Remove adjusting bolt and washer from slot at front bracket.
5. Remove nut and washer from support at rear of pump.
6. Remove mounting bolt at front bracket and remove pump.

Installation

1. To install reverse the removal procedure. Use a belt tension gauge and adjust the belt to 90-100 lbs (new belt).
   NOTE: See the "Power Brake" section of the General Repair section.

Parking Brakes

Adjustments

NOTE: Parking brake adjustments can be accomplished only when service brakes are in adjustment.

Foot Pedal Type

1. Jack up rear wheels.
2. Apply parking brake 1 notch from fully released position.
3. Loosen equalizer check nut and tighten the adjusting nut until moderate drag is felt when rear wheels are rotated.
4. Tighten check nut securely.
5. Fully release parking brake and rotate rear wheels. No drag should be present.

Orscheln Lever Type

1. Turn adjusting knob on parking

---

1 Brake support bracket
2 Parallel adjusting screws
3 Front lever arm pin
4 Pin retaining screw
5 Brake cable clevis
6 Brake lever
7 Brake shoe pin retainer
8 Brake shoe pin
9 Front brake shoe
10 Rear brake shoe
11 Front lever arm
12 Brake disc
13 Tension spring
14 Spring
15 Rear lever arm
16 Adjusting nut
17 Tie Rod

Tru-stop (disc) parking brake
(© G.M.C.)

---

brake lever counter-clockwise to stop.
2. Apply parking brake.
3. Jack up rear wheels.
4. Loosen lock nut at intermediate cable equalizer and adjust front nut to give light drag at rear wheels.
5. Re-adjust parking brake lever knob to give definite snap-over-center feel.
6. Fully release parking brake and rotate rear wheels. No drag should be present.

Driveshaft Type (Drum On)

1. Jack up at least one rear wheel. Block wheels and release hand brake.
2. Remove cotter pin and clevis pin connecting pull rod to relay lever. NOTE: It may be necessary to knock out lanced area in brake drum with punch and hammer to gain entry to adjusting screw through brake drum.
3. Rotate brake drum to bring an access hole into line with adjusting screw at bottom of shoes.
4. Expand shoes by rotating adjusting screw with screw driver.

Move outer end of screw driver away from drive shaft. Continue adjustment until shoes are tight against drum and drum cannot be rotated by hand. Back off adjustment ten notches and check drum for free rotation.
5. Place parking brake lever in fully released position. Take up slack in brake linkage by pulling back on cable just enough to overcome spring tension. Adjust clevis of pull rod or front cable to line up with hole in relay levers.
6. Insert clevis pin and cotter pin, tighten clevis locknut.
7. Install new hole cover in drum to prevent dirt contamination.
8. Lower rear wheels. Remove jack and wheel blocks.

Driveshaft Type (Drum Off)

1. With parking brake drum off, check diameter of drum clearance surface.
2. Turn tool to the opposite side and fit over brake shoes by turning star wheel until gauge just slides over linings.
3. Rotate gauge around brake shoe

Parking brake system ("C"-"K" models)
(© G.M.C.)

Parking brake system (P2500-3500 models)
(© G.M.C.)

Parking brake system (P1500 models)
(© G.M.C.)

lining surface to insure proper clearance.

4. Install driveshift flange at mainshaft.
5. Lower rear wheels. Remove jack and wheel blocks.

Stopmaster "Fail-Safe" Type

Stopmaster "Fail-Safe" parking brakes are used as standard equipment on some models and as optional equipment on others. When Stopmaster service brakes with "Fail-Safe" feature are used, no other parking brake system is required.

Anchorlok Type

The "Anchorlok" brake chamber is used as optional equipment on some models. This chamber incorporates a spring applied, air pressure released parking/emergency brake.

Tru-Stop (Disc) Type

This type brake is used only on "W" models when equipped with 3-speed or 4-speed auxiliary transmission. The ventilated brake disc is mounted between propeller shaft flange and auxiliary transmission shaft companion flange. Brake shoes are mounted in opposed positions with brake disc between, as shown in illustration. When brake is applied, the shoes are forced against disc. Brake should be adjusted before a full application requires parking brake lever to be pulled to travel limit.

1. Disconnect brake cable clevis (5) from brake lever (6).
2. Tighten adjusting nut (16) until spring (14) exerts enough pressure to bring lever (6) against front lever arm (11).
3. Insert a 1/32" shim between rear shoe lining and brake disc.
4. Tighten adjusting nut (16) until front shoe lining is firmly against disc, yet allowing removal of shim.
5. Make certain tension spring (13) is in place. Turn adjusting screws (2) so that both linings are parallel with disc. This provides 16¼" clearance between front and rear shoe linings and brake disc at all points.

6. Make certain parking brake lever is in fully released position. Adjust clevis (5) on brake cable to permit installation of clevis pin through clevis and brake lever (6) without changing position of lever. Install clevis pin and cotter pin.
7. Make certain lock nuts on brake cable and adjusting screws are firmly tightened.

Fuel System

The following procedures are for gasoline engines only. Refer to General Repair Section for diesel engine service.

Carburetors

Bendix-Stromberg Carburetor —1970-74

Removal
1. Remove air cleaner and gasket.
2. Disconnect fuel and vacuum lines from the carburetor.
3. Disconnect choke cable or rod.
4. Disconnect accelerator linkage.
5. Remove carburetor attaching nuts or bolts and remove carburetor.

Installation
1. Be certain throttle body and intake manifold sealing surfaces are clean.
2. Install new gasket between carburetor and manifold flange.
3. Install the carburetor over the manifold studs.
4. Start vacuum and fuel lines at carburetor.
5. Install attaching nuts or bolts and tighten to 20-25 foot-pounds torque.
6. Tighten fuel and vacuum lines.
7. Connect and adjust accelerator linkage.

8. Connect choke cable or choke rod.
9. Adjust idle speed and mixture.

Idle Speed and Mixture Adjustment

All V6 Engines—1970-71

1. Dwell reading on all V6 engines should be 31 to 34 degrees.
2. Disconnect and plug distributor vacuum lines.
3. Set ignition timing to:
   305C Engine ...... 7½° BTDC
   351C Engine .... 5° BTDC
4. Connect distributor vacuum lines except to vacuum idle stop.
5. With engine running, vacuum idle stop disconnected, check reduced engine rpm. The engine speed should be 400 rpm. If necessary, readjust.
6. Connect vacuum line from carburetor to vacuum idle stop. With engine running, vacuum idle stop connected, idle speed should be 550 rpm. If necessary to readjust, perform the following:
   a. Place a ¼" open end wrench on diaphragm extension of vacuum idle stop to prevent its rotation while adjusting plunger.
   b. Adjust the plunger with a ⅜" open end wrench until the face of the plunger hex contacting the carburetor throttle lever results in an idle speed of 550 rpm.
7. Adjust the idle mixture screws. With engine running and idling speed set, turn each mixture screw "in" until engine begins to slow down or run unevenly, then back out screws until engine runs smoothly with highest vacuum gauge reading.
8. Reset the engine idle speed to 575 rpm, by adjusting plunger

Adjusting Vacuum Idle Stop (© G.M.C.)

ACCELERATOR
PUMP PISTON
ROD

CHOKE-TO-THROTTLE
ADVANCE LEVER

IDLE SPEED
SCREW

THROTTLE LEVER

ACCELERATOR
PUMP LEVER

ACCELERATOR
PUMP LINK

Bendix-Stromberg carburetor
(© G.M.C.)

on vacuum idle stop as previously described.

9. Turn "in" idle mixture screws equally to reduce idle speed to 550 rpm.

Idle Speed and Mixture Adjustment

401, 478, 637 — 1972

1. Idle the engine until the choke is wide open and it is hot. Adjust the ignition timing and dwell. Dwell is 31-34 on V6 engines, and 28-32 on V8 engines. Timing is 7½° BTDC on V6 engines, 5° BTDC on V8 engines.

2. Place a ¼ in. open end wrench on the diaphragm extension of the vacuum idle stop as shown in the illustration. This will prevent its rotation while the plunger is adjusted.

3. Adjust the plunger (with a ⅜ in. wrench) for the idle speeds as follows:

   401M,   478M   575
   478SN,   637   525

4. Adjust the engine idle mixture screws for a too-lean condition, and then screw them out just until highest idle speed and vacuum reading are obtained.

5. Drive the idle mixture screw caps on in the rich position as shown. Make sure both cap tangs contact the main body of the carburetor, and that the idle mixture screws will not be bent.

6. Set the idle speed back to specifications. Then, turn screws inward until the following idle speeds are produced:

   401M,   478M   525
   478SN   500
   637   475

305C, 379, 432 — 1973

1. Idle adjustments should be performed with the engine at operating temperature, air cleaner installed, parking brake applied, driving wheels blocked, air conditioning (if used) should be turned "OFF," transmission in "N" (Neutral), and on the California vehicles equipped with a carbon canister, disconnect fuel tank hose from canister.

2. Check and adjust distributor dwell reading to 33 degrees.

3. Adjust ignition timing with vacuum advance port at carburetor plugged.
   305C Engine ......7½° BTDC
   379, 432 Engines .....8° BTDC

4. Using a ⅜ in. open-end wrench, adjust plunger on idle stop solenoid until engine idle speed is 575 RPM.

5. With engine running at idle speed, adjust plastic limiter caps to obtain highest steady idle speed.
   NOTE: If plastic limiter caps have been removed due to carburetor repairs, simply rotate idle mixture screws until highest steady idle speed is attained.

6. Readjust plunger of idle stop solenoid until engine idle speed is 575 RPM.

7. Turn plastic limiter caps (idle mixture screws) IN, equally, by rotating clockwise to LEAN mixture until the engine idle speed is 525 RPM.

8. Disconnect electrical connector from idle stop solenoid with engine idling. Adjust idle speed screw until engine speed is 400 RPM (reduced idle speed).

9. Reconnect electrical connector to solenoid and check for proper idle speed of 525 RPM.

10. Connect fuel tank vapor hose at carbon canister (when used).

350C, 379, 432 — 1974

1. Idle adjustments should be performed with the engine at operating temperature, air cleaner installed, parking brake applied, driving wheels blocked, air conditioning (if used) should be turned "OFF," transmission in "N" (Neutral), and on the California vehicles equipped with a carbon canister, disconnect fuel tank hose from canister.

2. Check and adjust distributor dwell reading to 33 degrees.

3. Adjust ignition timing as follows:
   305C Engine ......7½° BTDC
   379, 432 Engines ....6° BTDC

4. With engine running at idle speed, adjust plastic limiter caps to obtain highest steady idle speed.
   NOTE: If plastic limiter caps have been removed due to carburetor repairs, simply rotate idle mixture screws until highest steady idle speed is attained.

5. Readjust plunger of idle stop so-

IDLE STOP
SOLENOID

PLUNGER

3/8" WRENCH

Adjusting idle stop solenoid—Bendix Stromberg Carb.

lenoid with ⅜ in. open-end wrench until engine idle speed is as follows:

305C engine ....675 RPM
379 engine ....650 RPM
432 engine ....575 RPM

6. Turn IN each mixture screw, one at a time, until a slight drop in rpm is noted.
7. Then turn IN each mixture screw an equal amount, one at a time, until the speed is as follows:

305C engine ....600 RPM
379 engine ....575 RPM
432 engine ....525 RPM

If idle is not steady, repeat the above procedure or have tachometer checked for accuracy and then repeat above procedure.

8. Reconnect tank hose to canister (if used).

Holley Carburetor—1970-76

Removal

1. Remove air cleaner and gasket.
2. Disconnect fuel and vacuum lines from carburetor.
3. Disconnect choke cable or rod.
4. Disconnect accelerator linkage.
5. If equipped with automatic transmission, disconnect TV linkage. Remove vacuum hoses and carburetor solenoid connectors.
6. Remove carburetor attaching nuts.
7. Remove carburetor.

Installation

1. Be certain throttle body and intake manifold sealing surfaces are clean.
2. Install new carburetor to manifold flange gasket or insulator as required.
3. Install carburetor over manifold studs.
4. Start vacuum and fuel lines at carburetor.
5. Install attaching nuts and tighten to specified torque.
6. Tighten fuel and vacuum lines.
7. Connect and adjust accelerator and TV linkage (when used).
8. Connect choke cable or rod.

Idle Speed and Mixture Adjustment — 1970-72

1. Check dwell reading.
NOTE: The dwell reading should be 28 to 32 degrees. Readjust if necessary.
2. Set ignition timing as follows:
Manual Transmission 8° BTDC
Automatic Trans. ....8° BTDC
3. Set the engine idle speed to 500 rpm.
4. Adjust mixture screws for maximum steady idle speed.
5. Adjust each carburetor mixture

CARBURETOR PART NO.
FUEL TRANSFER TUBE
PLASTIC LIMITER CAP (IDLE MIXTURE SCREW)
FUEL INLET
ACCELERATOR PUMP
IDLE SPEED SCREW
THROTTLE LEVER
IDLE STOP SOLENOID (CALIFORNIA ONLY)

Holley 4150G Carb. assy.

screw to obtain a 20 rpm drop (lean roll).
6. Adjust each mixture screw out ¼ turn.
7. Check idle speed and re-adjust to 500 rpm.

Idle Speed Adjustment — 1973

1. Idle adjustments should be performed with the engine at operating temperature, air cleaner installed, parking brake applied, driving wheels blocked, air conditioning (if used) should be turned "OFF," transmission in "N" (Neutral), and on California vehicles equipped with a carbon canister, disconnect fuel tank hose from canister.
2. Check and adjust distributor dwell reading to 30 degrees.
3. Adjust ignition timing to 8° BTDC.
4. On all vehicles (except those sold in the State of California) adjust idle speed screw until speed reaches 550 RPM.
5. Vehicles sold in the State of California are equipped with an idle stop solenoid. Adjust idle speed as follows:
   a. Using a ⅜ in. open-end wrench, adjust plunger on solenoid until an idle speed of 750 RPM is attained.
   b. Disconnect electrical connector from solenoid with engine idling.
   c. Adjust idle speed screw until engine speed is 450 RPM (reduced idle speed).
   d. Reconnect electrical connector to solenoid and check for proper idle speed (refer to Step a.).

Idle Mixture Adjustment — 1973

1. Turn mixture screws IN until they lightly contact seat, then back mixture screws out four full turns.

2. Perform "Idle Speed Adjustment" as described earlier in this section.
3. With engine running at idle speed, adjust idle mixture screws to give highest steady idle speed.
4. Readjust engine idle speed by adjusting idle speed screw (except California) to 600 RPM. On vehicles sold in the State of California adjust the plunger of the idle stop solenoid until speed reaches 800 RPM.
5. Turn idle mixture screws IN equally, by rotating clockwise to LEAN mixture until the engine idle speed is as follows:
California engines only ....750 RPM
All Other Engines ...550 RPM
6. Connect fuel tank vapor hose at carbon canister (when used).

Idle Speed Adjustment — 1974-76

1. Idle adjustments should be performed with the engine at operating temperature, air cleaner installed, parking brake applied, driving wheels blocked, air conditioning (if used) should be turned "OFF," transmission in "N" (Neutral), and on California vehicles equipped with a carbon canister, disconnect fuel tank hose from canister.
2. Check and adjust distributor dwell reading to 30 degrees.
3. Adjust ignition timing to 8° BTDC.
4. On all vehicles adjust curb idle stop solenoid plunger hex (½ in.) screw until speed reaches 700 rpm.
5. Disconnect electrical connector from solenoid with engine idling.
6. Adjust low idle speed screw until engine speed is 400 rpm (reduced idle speed).
7. Reconnect electrical connector to solenoid, open throttle release

and check for proper curb idle speed (700 rpm).

Idle Mixture Adjustment — 1974-76

1. Turn mixture screws IN until they lightly contact seat, then back mixture screws out four full turns.
2. Perform "Idle Speed Adjustment" as described earlier in this section.
3. With engine running at idle speed, adjust idle mixture screws equally to give highest steady idle speed.
4. Readjust engine curb idle speed by adjusting the plunger of the idle stop solenoid as follows:
   366 engine .... 825 RPM
   427 engine .... 800 RPM
5. Turn idle mixture screws IN equally, to obtain 700 rpm.
6. Connect fuel tank vapor hose at carbon canister (when used).

Rochester Carburetor—1970-76

Removal

1. Remove air cleaner and gasket.
2. Disconnect fuel and vacuum lines from carburetor.
3. Disconnect choke cable or rod.
4. Disconnect accelerator linkage.
5. If equipped with Automatic transmission (MT Models), disconnect TV linkage. Remove vacuum hoses and carburetor solenoid connectors.
6. Remove carburetor attaching nuts and remove carburetor.
NOTE: *Fill the carburetor bowl before installing the carburetor. This reduces the strain on the starter motor and battery and reduces the possibility of backfiring while attempting to start the engine.*

Installation

1. Be certain throttle body and intake manifold sealing surfaces are clean.
2. Install new carburetor to manifold flange gasket or insulator as required.
3. Install carburetor over manifold studs.
4. Start vacuum and fuel lines at carburetor.
5. Install attaching nuts and tighten to specified torque.
6. Tighten fuel and vacuum lines.
7. Connect and adjust accelerator and TV linkage (when used).
8. Connect choke cable or coil rod.

Idle and Mixture Adjustment — 1970-71

1. Have engine at operating temperature choke open, and air cleaner installed.

2. Air conditioning (when used) must be turned ON. Hot idle compensator must be held closed.
3. When equipped with automatic transmission, apply parking brake and block driving wheels.
4. Check the distributor dwell reading.
5. Adjust idle speed and mixture as follows:
NOTE: *When setting ignition timing, the term BTDC means BEFORE TOP DEAD CENTER.*

Inline Engines

1. Turn mixture screw IN until it lightly contacts seat, then back screw OUT 4 full turns.
2. Disconnect and plug distributor vacuum line. Set ignition timing:
   Manual Transmission 4° BTDC
   Automatic Trans. ....4° BTDC
3. Connect distributor vacuum line.
4. Adjust idle speed screw to 600 rpm (manual transmission in neutral) or 530 rpm (automatic transmission in drive).
5. Adjust mixture screw IN to obtain 550 rpm (manual transmission in neutral), or 500 rpm (automatic transmission in drive).

350 V8 Engine

1. Adjust the mixture screws for maximum steady idle speed.
2. Disconnect and plug distributor vacuum advance line. Set ignition timing as follows:
   Manual Transmission 4° BTDC
   Automatic Trans. ....4° BTDC
3. Connect distributor vacuum line.
4. Adjust idle speed screw to 500 rpm.
5. Adjust mixture screws IN for a 20 rpm drop.
6. Adjust each mixture screw out ¼ turn.
7. Check idle speed and re-adjust screw to 500 rpm.

Idle Speed Adjustments — 1972

One Barrel Carburetor

Preliminary Checks (All Engines)
NOTE: *Idle settings must follow the procedure on decal located under hood.*
1. Engine idle speed adjustments should be performed with the engine at operating temperature, air cleaner installed, parking brake applied, driving wheels blocked and thermostatic air cleaner valve must be in full open position.
2. Air conditioning (when used) must be turned "OFF."
3. Disconnect fuel tank vapor hose at canister distributor vacuum advance hose at the distributor and plug hose lead to carburetor.

(Disconnecting hoses is necessary to obtain proper adjustments.)
4. Check the distributor dwell reading. (Inline engines 33°, and V8 engines 30°.)
5. Adjust ignition timing to "Specifications."

One Barrel Carburetor

1. Use a 9/16 in. open-end wrench on hexagonal portion of solenoid, rotate solenoid until engine speed reaches 700 rpm with manual transmission and 600 rpm with automatic transmission (clockwise to increase rpm and counterclockwise to decrease rpm).
IMPORTANT: DO NOT turn in too far or damage to idle stop solenoid will result.
NOTE: *If necessary to rotate solenoid more than one full revolution (360°), disconnect electrical connector, straighten wiring and reconnect to solenoid.*
2. Disconnect electrical connector from solenoid with engine idling. Adjust ⅛ Allen-head screw on end of solenoid to achieve 450 rpm (reduced idle speed).
3. Reconnect electrical connector and check for proper idle speed (Step 1 previously).
NOTE: *The idle stop solenoid should be checked to assure that it permits the throttle plate to close further when the ignition switch is turned "OFF." An inoperative solenoid should be replaced.*
4. Reconnect vacuum advance hose to distributor (after unplugging) and fuel tank vapor hose to canister.

Two and Four Barrel Carb.

1. Disconnect electrical connection at end of idle stop solenoid.
2. Adjust carburetor low idle (adjustment screw on low step of cam) until engine speed is 450 rpm.
3. Reconnect electrical connector to the solenoid. Open the throttle momentarily and adjust the solenoid plunger screw to curb idle speed (rpm).
900 rpm on 307 and 350 engines, 750 rpm on 402 and 454 engines with mechanical transmissions and 600 rpm on all engines with automatic transmissions in "DRIVE" range.
NOTE: *The idle stop solenoid should be checked to assure that it permits the throttle plate to close further when the ignition switch is turned "OFF." An inoperative solenoid should be replaced.*
4. Reconnect vacuum advance hose and fuel tank vapor hose to canister.

CEC SOLENOID

IDLE SPEED (SOLENOID) SCREW   IDLE SPEED (SOLENOID) SCREW   IDLE SPEED (SOLENOID) SCREW

Idle solenoid screw—Rochester—One, tow, four barrel carb.

Idle Speed Adjustments — 1973

Preliminary Checks (All Engines)

NOTE: Idle settings must follow the procedure on decal located under hood.

1. Engine idle speed adjustments should be performed with the engine at operating temperature, air cleaner installed, parking brake applied, driving wheels blocked and thermostatic air cleaner valve must be in full open position.
2. Air conditioning (when used) must be turned "OFF."
3. Disconnect fuel tank vapor hose at canister, distributor vacuum advance hose at the distributor and plug hose lead to carburetor. (Disconnecting hoses is necessary to obtain proper adjustments.)
4. Check the distributor dwell reading. (Inline engines 33°, and V8 engines 30°.) 5. Adjust ignition timing to "Specifications."

Series 10-30

Emission system requirements necessitate the division of the Series 10-30 trucks into two groups as follows:
1. Light Duty Emission Vehicles—Includes all 10 Series; C-K20 Suburban Models; All G20 Series and G30 Passenger Models.
2. Heavy Duty Emission Vehicles—Includes all C-K-P20 Series (Except C-K20 Suburban Models); all C-P30 Series and all G30 Series (Except Sportvan Models).

250-Engine-One Barrel Carb.

Adjust Idle Stop Solenoid (turn solenoid body, using hex nut) to obtain:

700 rpm on all Heavy-Duty Vehicles and all Light-Duty vehicles equipped with manual transmission (in neutral).

600 rpm on Light-Duty vehicles equipped with automatic transmissions (in "Park").

NOTE: On Light-Duty vehicles do not adjust the CEC solenoid screw or

a decrease in engine breaking may result.

292 Engine-One Barrel Carb.

Adjust Idle Stop Solenoid (turn solenoid body, using hex nut) to obtain:

600 rpm on vehicles equipped with Air Injection Reactor System (State of California Vehicles).

700 rpm on vehicles not equipped with Air Injection Reactor System.

307 Engine-Two Barrel Carb.

On Light-Duty Vehicles—C-G-K10 and C20 Suburban—adjust Idle Stop Solenoid (turn solenoid body, using hex nut) to obtain 600 rpm with automatic transmission in Drive—900 rpm with manual transmission in neutral.

On Light-Duty vehicles, disconnect the Idle Stop Solenoid electrical lead. Adjust low idle screw (located inside the solenoid hex nut) with screw on low step of cam, to obtain 450 rpm—automatic transmission in Drive and manual transmission in neutral—reconnect Idle Stop Solenoid electrical lead.

350 Engine-Four Barrel

On Heavy-Duty vehicles, adjust carburetor Idle Speed Screw to obtain 600 rpm with automatic transmission in "Park" and manual transmission in neutral.

On Light-Duty vehicles, adjust Idle Stop Solenoid (turn solenoid body, using hex nut) to obtain 600 rpm with automatic transmission in Drive; 900 rpm with manual transmission in neutral.

On Light-Duty vehicles with automatic transmission, reconnect distributor spark advance hose. Adjust fast idle screw to obtain 1600 rpm with screw on top step of fast idle cam.

On Light-Duty vehicles with manual transmission, adjust fast idle screw to obtain 1300 rpm with screw on top step of fast idle cam and distributor spark advance hose disconnected.

454 Engine-Four Barrel

Adjust Idle Stop Solenoid (turn solenoid body, using hex nut) to obtain:

700 rpm on all Heavy Duty vehicles —automatic transmission in "Park"; manual transmission in neutral.

600 rpm on Light-Duty vehicles with automatic transmission (in Drive).

900 rpm on Light-Duty vehicles with manual transmission (in neutral).

On Light-Duty vehicles with automatic transmission, reconnect distributor spark advance hose. Adjust fast idle screw to obtain 1600 rpm with screw on top step of fast idle cam.

On Light-Duty vehicles with manual transmission, adjust fast idle screw to obtain 1600 rpm with screw on top step of fast idle cam and distributor spark advance hose disconnected.

Reconnect "Fuel Tank" line to vapor canister and reconnect distributor spark advance hose.

Series 40-65

250, 292 Engine-One Barrel Carb.

1. Use a 9/16-in. open-end wrench on hexagonal portion of solenoid, rotate solenoid until engine speed reaches proper idle:
250 & 292 Engines ...600 RPM

NOTE: If necessary to rotate solenoid more than one full revolution (360°), disconnect electrical connector, straighten wiring and reconnect to solenoid.

2. Disconnect electrical connector from solenoid with engine idling. Adjust 1/8 in. Allen-head screw on end of solenoid to achieve 450 rpm (reduced idle speed).
3. Reconnect electrical connector to solenoid and check for proper idle speed (given in Step 1).
4. Connect fuel tank vapor hose to carbon canister (when used).

350 Engine-Two Barrel Carb.

1. Adjust idle speed screw to 600 rpm.
2. Reconnect the fuel tank vapor to the canister.

Sprint

250 Engine-One Barrel Carb.

Adjust Idle Stop Solenoid screw to

obtain 700 rpm with manual transmission in neutral; 600 rpm with automatic transmission in drive.

NOTE: Do not adjust the CEC solenoid screw or engine braking may result.

307, 350, 400 Engine- Two Barrel Carb.

With air conditioning off, adjust Idle Stop Solenoid screw to obtain 900 rpm with manual transmission in neutral; 600 rpm with automatic transmission in drive.

With automatic transmission in drive or manual transmission in neutral, and idle stop solenoid de-energized; adjust carburetor idle cam screw (with screw on low step of cam) to obtain 450 rpm on 307 cu. in. engines; 400 rpm on 350 and 400 cu. in. engines with automatic transmission; and 500 rpm on 350 cu. in. engine with manual transmission.

Reconnect "Fuel Tank" line to vapor canister and reconnect distributor spark advance hose.

350, 454 Engine- Four Barrel Carb.

With air conditioning off, adjust Idle Stop Solenoid screw to obtain 900 rpm with manual transmission in neutral; 600 rpm with automatic transmission in drive.

Idle Speed Adjustments — 1974-76

Preliminary Checks (All Engines)

NOTE: Idle settings must follow the procedure on decal located under hood.

1. Engine idle speed adjustments should be performed with the engine at operating temperature, air cleaner installed, parking brake applied, driving wheels blocked and thermostatic air cleaner valve must be in full open position.
2. Air conditioning (when used) must be turned "OFF."
3. Disconnect fuel tank vapor hose at canister, distributor vacuum advance hose at the distributor and plug hose lead to carburetor. (Disconnecting hoses is necessary to obtain proper adjustments.)
4. Check the distributor dwell reading. (Inline engines 33°, and V8 engines 30°.)
5. Adjust ignition timing to "Specifications."

Series 10-30

Emission system requirements necessitate the division of the Series 10-30 trucks into two groups as follows:
1. Light-Duty Emission Vehicles—Includes all 10 Series; C-K20

Suburban Models; All G20 Series and G30 Sportvan Models.
2. Heavy-Duty Emission Vehicles—Includes all C-K-P20 Series (Except C-K20 Suburban Models; All C-P30 Series and all G30 Series (Except Sportvan Models).

250 Engine-One Barrel Carb.

Adjust Idle Stop Solenoid (turn solenoid body, using hex nut) to obtain:

600 rpm on all Heavy-Duty Vehicles and 850 rpm on all Light-Duty vehicles equipped with manual transmission (in neutral).

600 rpm on Light-Duty vehicles equipped with automatic transmissions (in "Park").

292 Engine-One Barrel Carb.

Place transmission in neutral and adjust Idle Stop Solenoid (turn solenoid body, using hex nut) to obtain 600 rpm on all vehicles with automatic transmission in "Park" and manual transmission in neutral.

350 Engine-Four Barrel Carb.

On Heavy-Duty vehicles, adjust carburetor Idle Stop Solenoid Screw to obtain 600 rpm with automatic transmission in "Park" and manual transmission in neutral.

On Light-Duty vehicles, adjust Idle Stop Solenoid Screw to obtain 600 rpm with automatic transmission in Drive; 900 rpm with manual transmission in neutral.

454 Engine-Four Barrel

Adjust Idle Stop Solenoid Screw to obtain:

700 rpm on all Heavy-Duty vehicles—automatic transmission in "Park"; manual transmission in neutral.

600 rpm on Light-Duty vehicles with automatic transmission (in Drive).

800 rpm on Light-Duty vehicles with manual transmission (in neutral).

Series 40-60

250-292 Engine- One Barrel Carb.

1. Use a 9/16-in. open-end wrench on hexagonal portion of solenoid, rotate solenoid until engine speed reaches proper idle speed: 250 & 292 Engines ...600 RPM
NOTE: If necessary to rotate solenoid more than one full revolution (360°), disconnect electrical connector, straighten wiring and reconnect to solenoid.
2. Disconnect electrical connector from solenoid with engine idling. Adjust 1/8 in. Allen-head screw on end of solenoid to achieve 450 rpm (reduced idle speed).
3. Reconnect electrical connector to

solenoid and check for proper idle speed (given in Step 1).
4. Connect fuel tank vapor hose to carbon canister (when used).

350 Engine-Two Barrel Carb.

1. Adjust idle speed screw to 600 rpm.
2. Reconnect the fuel tank vapor to the canister.

Sprint

250 Engine-One Barrel Carb.

Adjust Idle Stop Solenoid screw to obtain 700 rpm with manual transmission in neutral; 600 rpm with automatic transmission in drive.
NOTE: Do not adjust the CEC solenoid screw or engine braking may result.

307, 350, 400 Engine- Two Barrel Carb.

With air conditioning off, adjust Idle Stop Solenoid screw to obtain 900 rpm with manual transmission in neutral; 600 rpm with automatic transmission in drive.

With automatic transmission in drive or manual transmission in neutral, and idle stop solenoid de-energized; adjust carburetor idle cam screw (with screw on low step of cam) to obtain 450 rpm on 307 cu. in. engines; 400 rpm on 350 and 400 cu. in. engines with automatic transmission; and 500 rpm on 350 cu. in. engine with manual transmission.

Reconnect "Fuel Tank" line to vapor canister and reconnect distributor spark advance hose.

350, 454 Engine- Four Barrel Carb.

With air conditioning off, adjust Idle Stop Solenoid crew to obtain 900 rpm with manual transmission in neutral; 600 rpm with automatic transmission in drive.
NOTE: See the "Carburetor" section in the General Repair Section.

Fuel Pump

All models covered by this manual utilize single—diaphragm, dual—diaphragm or electric fuel pumps.

Mechanical Fuel Pump

Removal

1. Disconnect all inlet and outlet pipes from fuel pump.
2. Remove fuel pump mounting bolts.
3. Remove fuel pump and gasket. NOTE: On V8 engines, remove fuel pump adapter and gasket if pushrod is to be removed.
4. Transfer fittings if new pump is to be installed.

Installing electric fuel pump
(© G.M.C.)

Installing V8 engine fuel pump
(© G.M.C.)

Installing V6 engine fuel pump
(© G.M.C.)

Fuel pump—inline engine (typical)
(© G.M.C.)

Fuel pump—V6 engine (typical)
(© G.M.C.)

Installation

1. On V8 engines, install fuel pump pushrod and adapter.
2. Install fuel pump, using new gasket and sealer on mounting bolt threads.
3. Connect fuel lines to pump.
4. Start engine and check for leaks.
   NOTE: On V8 engines use mechanical fingers or heavy grease to hold push rod up while installing pump.

Electric Fuel Pump

Removal

1. Disconnect battery ground cable.
2. Disconnect pump wiring harness from connector.
3. Disconnect fuel outlet fitting from hose.
4. Remove cap screws and washers.
5. Rotate pump 90° counterclockwise and lift out.

Installation

1. Insert pump outlet line into tank and connect to fitting.
2. Carefully install fuel pump and cap screws with washers. Tighten to specifications.
3. Connect pump harness to connector.
4. Connect battery ground cable.

Governor

All models covered by this manual utilize single-throat, dual-throat or hydraulic governors. Governors are adjusted for correct maximum speed and sealed at the factory.

Adjustments

Governor adjustments are pre-set at the factory. However, minor adjustments to satisfy local conditions may be accomplished by turning adjusting cap counterclockwise for higher speed and clockwise for lower speed. One turn on the adjusting cap will vary speed 300-400 rpm or 4-5 mph.

VELOCITY TYPE GOVERNOR

King-Seeley Model (Stamped)	GMC No. (Stamped)	Engine Model	Max. Governed Speed (rpm) *(No Load)	Spark Advance
651-640B	2456730	230	2400-2600	YES
601-641	2456731	230	3700-3900	YES
901-623	2440843	305E	3600-3800	YES
		305C	3600-3800	YES
900-639	2442733	351	3600-3800	NO
901-685	2472969	351	3600-3800	YES

*With engine broken-in. Full Load RPM is approximately 300 RPM less than No Load RPM and will vary from engine to engine.

HYDRAULIC TYPE GOVERNOR

SPINNER VALVE*
   Location .... At Engine Oil Pump
   Type .... Centrifugal, Pre-Set
SLAVE UNIT*
   Location .... Carburetor Throttle Body
ENGINE GOVERNED SPEED (FULL LOAD)
   401 Engine .... 3400 rpm
   351 Engine (option) .... 3400 rpm

SINGLE THROAT TYPE

WITH DISTRIBUTOR VACUUM ADVANCE

DUAL THROAT TYPE

1 Governor body
2 Valve shaft
3 Throttle valve
4 Throttle valve arm
5 Stabilizer piston rod
6 Stabilizer piston
7 Stabilizer piston plug
8 Adjusting screw cap
9 Adjusting screw
10 Adjusting screw bushing
11 Governor cover
12 Operating spring
13 Cam ribbon
14 Cam ribbon clip
15 Roller bearing
16 Vacuum by-pass passage
17 Roller bearing
18 Shaft plug
19 Transfer valve spring
20 Transfer valve

Velocity type governor (© G.M.C.)

Fuel Tank

Description

Various types and designs of gas tanks are used due to complexity of engine body and chassis combinations. On ½ ton and ¾ ton the tank is located in rear behind drive axle. Larger vehicles use frame mounted tanks on right side, frame side rail. Cab models, except tilt cab, tank is behind seat in cab. Increased fuel capacity is available by using optional tanks. Tanks may be cylindrical, step, saddle or round. All tanks are equipped with a vented filler neck cap. A large fine-mesh, self cleaning

Governor mounting (© G.M.C.)

screen is used on bottom of fuel pickup pipe.

Following procedure is intended only as a guide. It will vary according to truck model and tank type.

Fuel Tank Removal and Installation

1. On trucks with dual tanks check shut-off valve position.
2. Be sure ignition switch is off or battery ground is disconnected.
3. Remove seat back rest if cab mounted.
4. Drain tank. If tank does not have a drain plug, disconnect gas line and use opening to drain tank. If not accessible, siphon fuel. Do not siphon by mouth, use equipment for that purpose or make a siphon hose as shown below and use air pressure if available.
5. Remove filler neck, cap and vent hose.
6. Disconnect tank gage wire and any ground lead.
7. Remove tank support straps or mounting bolts. Remove tank.
8. Clean all lines, check filters. (Blow clean only after disconnecting other end of line).
9. To install, reverse removal procedures.

CAUTION: Do not use drop cord in area. A bulb breakage could have disastrous effects. Use only safety cans for fuel storage. Do not overtighten lines, as this could distort or twist and lead to leaks.

Cooling System

Reference

Detailed information on cooling system capacity can be found in the Capacities table.

Radiator

Due to various types of radiator mountings, the following general information applies to all models.

The radiator assembly may include a fan shroud and an oil cooler at the base of radiator core. If equipped with a fan shroud, remove attaching bolts and then lay shroud back over fan blade. When oil lines are removed, make provisions for catching oil drainage from cooler tank and lines. Do not re-use this oil. Replenish transmission to recommended level with fresh fluid after installing radiator.

Some models may be equipped with a separate power steering oil cooler which is attached in front of radiator core by means of cooler support

V6 engine water pump
(© G.M.C.)

braces. It may be necessary to remove power steering oil cooler in order to replace the radiator core.

Water Pump

Removal

1. Drain cooling system.
2. Remove fan spacers (when used) and pulley(s) from water pump drive hub.
3. Remove all hoses connected to water pump.
4. Remove mounting bolts and washers.
5. Remove pump and gasket.

Installation

Reverse removal procedure, installing new water pump gasket.

Overhaul

Due to various models, overhaul procedures vary considerably. The following basic guide may be used.

1. Support fan hub in an arbor press and press shaft out of hub.
2. Drive seal out of pump body.
3. Clean and inspect water pump components. Check all surfaces for wear and bearings for excessive play. NOTE: Do not clean bearing and shaft assembly in solvent as it will dissolve lubricant.
4. Replace water pump seal and necessary parts.
5. Reassemble and install water pump.

Engine

Exhaust Emission Control Systems

For service and adjustment procedures on various types used, refer to General Repair Section.

Engine Assembly

Three types of gasoline engines are used by models covered in this man-

V8 engine water pump
(© G.M.C.)

Inline engine water pump
(© G.M.C.)

ual: Inline, V6 and V8. Removal and installation procedures will vary according to engine used and model of truck. Basic guides for various engine and truck models are provided below.

Engine Removal

Inline Engines In Conventional Models

1. Drain radiator.
2. Disconnect battery.
3. Remove hood and attaching parts.
4. Remove grille and radiator support braces.
5. Remove radiator and heater hoses.
6. Remove radiator and grille assembly.
7. Disconnect fuel line at fuel pump.
8. Remove air cleaner and cover carburetor to protect it from dirt.
9. Disconnect choke control and accelerator linkage.
10. Disconnect exhaust pipe from manifold.
11. Disconnect wiring harness and battery cable.
12. Remove hand brake lever and gearshift lever from transmission.
13. Disconnect driveshaft from transmission flange.
14. Attach lifting equipment, remove mounting bolts and rear crossmember.
15. Lift out engine and transmission assembly.

Engine Installation

Inline Engines In Conventional Models

1. Attach lifting equipment and

GMC Trucks · Vans · Jimmy

lower assembly into chassis. Install support crossmember and engine mountings.
2. Connect driveshaft.
3. Install handbrake and gearshift levers.
4. Connect exhaust pipe to manifold.
5. Connect wiring harness and carburetor control linkage.
6. Install hood and attaching parts.
7. Install air cleaner, connect fuel line.
8. Fill cooling system.
9. Fill crankcase with oil to the proper level.
10. Install battery.
11. Start engine and check for leaks.

Engine Removal

Inline Engines in Tilt Cab Models
1. Drain cooling system.
2. Disconnect battery cables.
3. Tilt cab forward; remove radiator and shroud.
4. Disconnect shift linkage at control island.
5. Disconnect throttle and choke controls at carburetor.
6. Disconnect parking brake cable and housing.
7. Remove control island mounting bolts; swing control island forward.
8. Disconnect hoses and remove surge tank.
9. Remove right and left island supports.
10. Disconnect cab safety lock, remove cab rear support.
11. Disconnect electrical wiring from engine units.
12. Disconnect all fuel, heater, oil lines from engine.
13. Disconnect exhaust pipe from manifold.
14. Remove engine fan and pulley.
15. Remove rocker arm cover and attach lifting brackets at cylinder head bolts.
16. Attach hoist and take up slack.
17. Remove engine mounting bolts and bolts attaching transmission to engine. Support transmission.
18. Move engine forward until it is disengaged from transmission.
19. Lift engine from the chassis.

Installation

Inline Engines in Tilt Cab Models
Install engine by reversing the removal procedure. Be certain to maintain cleanliness and to avoid damaging the engine parts. After engine is installed, check operation of all control linkages, fill cooling system and check for leaks. Fill crankcase with oil to the proper level.

Engine Removal

V6 Engines in Conventional Models
1. Drain radiator.

2. Disconnect battery.
3. Remove hood and attaching parts.
4. Remove grille and radiator braces.
5. Remove radiator and heater hoses.
6. Disconnect oil cooler lines (when used).
7. Remove grille, radiator, and front bumper.
8. Disconnect fuel line.
9. Disconnect air lines (when used).
10. Disconnect engine ground strap.
11. Disconnect exhaust pipes from manifolds.
12. Disconnect accelerator and choke controls from the carburetor.
13. Disconnect tachometer drive and oil gauge pressure line (when used).
14. Attach lifting equipment and take up slack.
15. Remove clutch housing to flywheel housing bolts.
16. Move engine forward to disengage transmission.
17. Lift engine from the chassis.

Engine Installation

V6 Engines in Conventional Models
Install engine by reversing the removal procedure. Be certain to maintain cleanliness and to avoid damaging the engine parts. After engine is installed, check operation of all control linkages, fill cooling system and check for leaks. Fill crankcase with oil to the proper level.

Engine Removal

V6 Engines in Tilt Cab Models
1. Drain radiator.
2. Disconnect battery.
3. Disconnect oil cooler lines (when used).
4. Disconnect electrical wiring and cables from the engine units.
5. Disconnect engine ground strap.
6. Disconnect accelerator and choke controls at the carburetor.
7. Disconnect transmission control rods, surge tank hoses, air cleaners and hoses.
8. Remove control island and rear cab support.
9. Disconnect exhaust pipes from manifolds.
10. Disconnect clutch control cylinder, parking brake control and speedometer drive from the rear of the transmission.
11. Disconnect cooling system and heater hoses.
12. Disconnect air lines from compressor (when used).
13. Disconnect driveshaft from transmission.
14. Attach lifting equipment and take up slack.

15. Remove bolts from front and rear mountings.
16. Lift assembly from the chassis.

Engine Installation

V6 Engines in Tilt Cab Models
Install engine by reversing the removal procedure. Be certain to maintain cleanliness and to avoid damaging the engine parts. After engine is installed, check operation of all control linkages, fill cooling system and check for leaks. Fill crankcase with oil to the proper lever.

Engine Removal

V8 Engines in Conventional Models
1. Disconnect battery cables and remove battery.
2. Drain cooling system.
3. Disconnect air intake hose (when used).
4. Disconnect all wiring to engine units and as necessary to remove front end sheet metal.
5. Disconnect radiator and heater hoses.
6. Disconnect fuel line.
7. Remove front end sheet metal, including hood.
8. Remove engine fan and drive belts.
9. Remove power steering pump.
10. Remove air compressor and disconnect air lines (when used).
11. Remove air cleaner and disconnect accelerator and choke cables at the carburetor.
12. Disconnect exhaust pipes from manifolds.
13. Disconnect clutch and transmission controls as necessary.
14. Remove valve covers and attach lifting brackets at cylinder head bolts.
15. Attach lifting equipment and take up slack.
16. Remove bolts from front and rear mountings.
17. Remove bolts attaching transmission to engine.
18. Move engine forward to disengage transmission.
19. Lift engine from the chassis.
NOTE: Engines coupled to an automatic transmission must be removed as a unit. Disconnect all transmission controls accordingly. Transmission may be removed from engine assembly after power plant removal.

Engine Installation

V8 Engines in Conventional Models
Install the engine by reversing the removal procedure. Be certain to maintain cleanliness and to avoid damaging the engine parts. After engine is installed, check operation of all control linkages, fill cooling system and check for leaks. Fill crankcase with oil to the proper level.

NOTE: Engines coupled to an automatic transmission must be installed as a unit.

1. Remove radiator, support and shroud.
2. Disconnect shift linkage at control island, accelerator and choke cables at carburetor.
3. Disconnect parking brake control.
4. Disconnect surge tank hoses.
5. Remove surge tank and control island rear support.
6. Remove cab safety lock control and cab rear support.
7. Disconnect all wiring to engine units.
8. Disconnect fuel line.
9. Disconnect heater hoses and vacuum/air lines (when used).
10. Disconnect engine ground straps.
11. Disconnect exhaust pipes from manifolds.
12. Disconnect clutch control.
13. Remove engine fan and pulley.
14. Remove valve covers and install lifting brackets at cylinder bolts.
15. Attach lifting equipment and take up slack.
16. Remove bolts attaching transmission to engine.
17. Remove bolts from front and rear mountings.
18. Move engine forward to disengage transmission.
19. Lift engine from the chassis.

Engine Installation

V8 Engines in Tilt Cab Models

Install the engine by reversing the removal procedure. Be certain to maintain cleanliness and to avoid damaging engine parts. After engine is installed, check operation of all control linkages, fill cooling system and check for leaks. Fill crankcase with oil to the proper level.

Manifolds

Removal

Inline Engine

1. Remove air cleaner.
2. Disconnect both throttle rods at bellcrank, remove throttle return spring.
3. Disconnect fuel and vacuum lines, choke cable at carburetor.
4. Disconnect crankcase ventilation hose.
5. Disconnect exhaust pipe at manifold flange. Discard packing.
6. Remove heat stove (when used).
7. Remove attaching bolts and clamps and manifold.

Installation

Inline Engine

1. Clean all surfaces.
2. Place new gasket over manifold end studs on head.
3. Position manifold and install bolts and clamps while holding manifold in place.
4. Torque bolts to specifications.
5. Connect exhaust pipe to manifold using new packing.
6. Connect crankcase ventilation hose.
7. Connect fuel and vacuum lines.
8. Connect choke cable, throttle rods, and install throttle return spring.
9. Install air cleaner.

Intake Manifold Removal

V8 Engines

1. Drain radiator and remove air cleaner.
2. Disconnect battery cables, radiator and heater hoses, water pump by-pass, accelerator linkage, choke control, and fuel line at carburetor. If necessary, remove crankcase ventilation lines and spark advance connections.
3. Where necessary, remove the distributor cap, mark the rotor position with chalk, and remove the distributor.
4. Remove, as necessary, the oil filler bracket, air cleaner bracket, air compressor and bracket, coil, accelerator return spring and bracket, and accelerator bellcrank.
5. Remove the attaching bolts, and remove the manifold.

Intake Manifold Installation

V8 Engines

1. Clean all surfaces.
2. Install manifold seals on block and gaskets on cylinder heads.
3. Install manifold and torque bolts to specifications.
4. To finish installation, reverse removal procedure. Fill cooling system and check for leaks.

Exhaust Manifold Removal

V8 Engines

1. Remove carburetor bracket as required. Remove generator and bracket from manifold, as required. NOTE: On large V8 engines, remove spark plugs.

Exhaust manifold installed (V8 engine) (© G.M.C.)

1 Engine lifting bracket
2 Spark plug wires
3 Plug wire supports
4 Intake manifold gasket
5 Crankcase ventilation valves
6 Intake manifold
7 Water outlet hose
8 Exhaust manifold bolt locks
9 Exhaust manifold
10 Dip stick tube clip
11 Exhaust manifold gasket
12 Rocker arms, shaft, and brackets

Intake manifold bolt tightening sequence
(350 V8 engine)
(© G.M.C.)

← FRONT —

Intake manifold bolt tightening sequence
(366, 427 V8 engines)
(© G.M.C.)

Intake manifold gaskets and seals (V8 engine)
(© G.M.C.)

Manifold heat stove (inline engine)
(© G.M.C.)

2. Disconnect exhaust pipe from manifold.
3. On 1975-76 models remove the carburetor heat choke tube assembly.
4. Bend back bolt lock tabs and remove manifold bolts.
5. Remove exhaust manifolds.

Exhaust Manifold Installation

V8 Engines

1. Clean all surfaces.
2. Install bolts with locks and torque in proper sequence to specifications.
3. Connect exhaust pipe to manifold with new packing.
4. On 1975-76 models install the carburetor heat choke tube with a new gasket.
5. Install generator and bracket and carburetor bracket as re-
NOTE: Install spark plugs on large engines.

Cylinder Head

Cylinder Head Removal

Inline Engines

1. Remove manifold assembly.
2. Remove valve mechanism.
3. Drain cooling system (block).
4. Remove fuel and vacuum lines from retaining clip and disconnect wires at temperature sending units.

5. Disconnect radiator hose at water outlet and ground strap at cylinder head.
6. Remove coil.
7. Remove cylinder head bolts, cylinder head and gasket.

Installation

Inline Engines

1. Clean all surfaces and make certain there are no nicks or deep scratches. Cylinder head bolt threads must also be cleaned.
2. Place gasket over dowel pins with the bead up.
3. Place cylinder head over dowel pins carefully.
4. Apply sealer to head bolts and tighten down finger tight.
5. Tighten cylinder head bolts a little at a time in proper sequence and to torque specifications.
6. Install valve mechanism.
7. Connect wires to temperature sending units, connect fuel vacuum lines to retaining clip. NOTE: Make certain to follow proper cylinder head tightening sequence.

Cylinder Head Removal

V6 Engines

1. Drain cooling system.
2. Remove exhaust manifold.
3. Remove valve covers and valve mechanism.

4. Disconnect spark plug wires from plugs.
5. Remove water outlet and intake manifolds.
6. Remove cylinder head bolts, cylinder head and gasket. NOTE: If lifters are removed, always install them in the same bores they were removed from.

Installation

V6 Engines

1. Clean all surfaces and make certain there are no nicks or deep scratches. Cylinder head bolt threads must also be cleaned.
2. Place gasket over dowel pins, the word "top" facing up.
3. Place cylinder head over dowel pins carefully.
4. Apply sealer to head bolts and tighten down finger tight.
5. Tighten cylinder head bolts a little at a time in proper sequence and to torque specifications.
6. Install exhaust manifolds, using new gaskets.
7. Install intake manifold and water outlet manifold, using new gaskets.
8. Lubricate and install valve mechanism. Install valve cover with new valve cover gasket.

Cylinder Head Removal

V8 Engines

1. Drain cooling system (block).

259

Cylinder Head bolt tightening sequence—
inline engines
(© G.M.C.)

Cylinder head bolt tightening sequence
V8 engines
(© G.M.C.)

Cylinder head gasket installed (inline engine)
(© G.M.C.)

Cylinder head bolt tightening sequence
V6 engines
(© G.M.C.)

2. Remove intake manifold.
3. Remove exhaust manifolds.
4. Remove valve mechansim.
5. Remove cylinder head bolts, cylinder head and gasket.

Installation

V8 Engines

1. Clean all surfaces and make certain there are no nicks or deep scratches. Cylinder head bolt threads must also be cleaned.
2. Coat both sides of gasket with a thin coat of sealer. NOTE: Use no sealer on a composition steel-asbestos gasket.
3. Place gasket over dowel pins with bead facing up.
4. Place cylinder head over dowel pins carefully.
5. Apply sealer to head bolts and tighten down finger tight.
6. Tighten cylinder head bolts a little at a time in proper sequence and to torque specifications.
7. Install exhaust manifolds.
8. Install intake manifold.
9. Install valve mechanism and adjust.

Refer to the specifications area for proper head bolt tightening sequences and torques for all Inline, V6 and V8 engines.

Valve Train

Adjustments

Inline and V8 Engines

1. Remove rocker arm cover.
2. With engine running at idle speed, install oil deflector clips to prevent oil splatter.
3. Back off rocker arm stud nut at one rocker arm until it begins to clatter, then tighten it slowly until the clatter just stops. This is zero lash position.
4. Turn nut down ¼ turn and pause

for 10 seconds. Repeat this procedure until nut has been turned down for one complete revolution. This allows the hydraulic lifter to adjust itself while the valve completely closes each time.
5. Repeat the above procedure on all rocker arm assemblies.
6. Remove the oil deflector clips and install rocker arm cover using new gasket.

Adjustments

V6 Engines

1. Run engine until it reaches normal operating temperature.
2. Remove rocker arm covers.
3. Using a feeler gauge and a box end wrench, adjust exhaust and intake valve clearance to specifications.

Timing gear marks and thrust plate screws (inline engine)
(© G.M.C.)

Measuring camshaft thrust plate clearance (inline engine)
(© G.M.C.)

Crankshaft gear removal (inline engine)
(© G.M.C.)

4. Repeat the above procedure for all rocker arms, and check to make certain that all valve rocker arms are receiving sufficient lubrication.

Valve Rocker Arm Removal

Inline and V8 Engines

1. Remove rocker arm cover.
2. Remove rocker arm nuts, rocker arm balls, rocker arms and push rods. NOTE: Place assemblies in a specific order so that they may be installed in their previous positions.

Installation

Inline and V8 Engines

1. Install push rods, making certain they seat in the lifter socket.
2. Install rocker arms, rocker arm balls and rocker arm nuts. Tighten all rocker arm nuts until all lash is eliminated.
3. Adjust valves.

Refer to Engine Rebuilding Section for more details.

Refer to valve specifications for valve spring, stem and seat angle specifications.

NOTE: Whenever installing new rocker arms or rocker arm balls, coat bearing surfaces with Molykote or its equivalent.

Valve Rocker Arm and Shaft Removal

V6 Engines

1. Remove rocker arm covers.
2. Loosen rocker arm shaft bracket bolts until spring pressure is fully relieved from rocker arms.
3. Lift off rocker arm shaft and brackets as an assembly.
4. Remove push rods and place them in a specific order so that they may be installed in their original positions.

Installation

V6 Engines

1. Install push rods in their proper positions.
2. Install rocker arm shaft and bracket assembly.
3. Set clearance between rocker arm shaft end brackets and adjacent rocker arms to specifications. Set initial valve clearance to 0.014″-intake, 0.022″-exhaust.
4. Lubricate rocker arms with engine oil, temporarily install rocker arm covers.
5. Run engine until operating temperature is reached, then stop engine.
6. Adjust valves.

Checking Engine Valve Timing

6 cyl. Inline Engine

1. Remove the valve rocker arm cover and the push rod front cover.
2. Loosen the nut and the No. 2 intake valve rocker arm, swing the rocker arm away from the push rod and remove the push rod and valve lifter.
3. Temporarily install a flat face mechanical lifter in place of the hydraulic lifter.
4. Turn the crankshaft until the no. 2 exhaust valve opens and the notch on the pulley dampener is aligned with the "0" mark on the timing pointer.
5. Position a deal indicator to measure lifter movement and set the indicator at zero. Turn the crankshaft to 360 degrees and read the indicator. On engines that are correctly timed the indicator will read as follows:

250 engines .... 0.014 in.
292 engines .... 0.016 in.

If the reading is not as above, reset the indicator at zero and turn the crankshaft 360 degrees, then read the indicator again. If the reading is now correct, the engine is timed properly. The following chart shows indicator readings with gears properly indexed for each engine and indicator readings resulting from improperly indexed gears.

6. If after checking an out-of-time condition exists, remove the engine front cover and check for proper indexing of timing marks on gears.

V-6—Engine

1. Remove the left-hand rocker cover.
2. Facing the front of the engine turn the engine clockwise to the top dead center No. 1 mark at the crankshaft pulley on the compression stroke. Both the intake and the exhaust valve on the No. 1 cylinder will then be closed.
3. On all V6 engines adjust the clearance to exactly 0.099 in. at the No. 1 exhaust valve (front valve).
4. Turn the engine clockwise until the No. 1 exhaust valve opens and begins to close. then with fingers, try turning the push rod of the No. 1 exhaust valve as the engine is cranked slowly. When the push rod rotates with finger pressure, the 5-degree (before top dead center mark) on the pulley should be at the pointer. This will be about one revolution from the starting point. If the push rod can be rotated at any point between the 10-degree mark and the top dead center No. 1 mark, the valve timing is correct. After making the timing check be sure to adjust the exhaust valve clearance to 0.018 in.

NOTE: If the timing chain has been installed improperly, there will be a 15 degree out-of-time condition for each mismatched tooth on the sprocket.

V-8 Engine

1. Remove the rocker arm covers.
2. Turn the crankshaft so that the timing mark is at the "0" mark on the pointer and the No. 1 cylinder is ready to fire.
3. Move the crankshaft, and the exhaust valve in the No. 6 cylinder will just close and the intake valve will just begin to open.
4. If the exhaust valve or the intake valve is open when the pointer is at the "0" timing mark the camshaft is out of time.
5. When the No. 6 cylinder is ready to fire and the pointer is at the "0" timing mark the No. 1 cylinder exhaust valve will have just closed and the intake valve will begin to open.

Engine (Cu. In.)	Camshaft Part No. & Valve Lift	Gears Properly Indexed	One Tooth Adv.	One Tooth Ret.
250	3864896-.388	.014″±.004″	.0351″	.0055″
292	3848000-.405	.016″±.004″	.0379″	.0068″

Timing gears and fuel pump eccentric installed
(401M and 478M engines
(© G.M.C.)

Timing chain and alignment marks (V8 engine)
(© G.M.C.)

Timing Gears

Crankshaft Gear Removal

Inline Engines

1. Attach gear puller to crankshaft gear (puller screw holes are provided on gear).
2. Turn puller screw and remove gear.
3. Check condition of timing gear key; replace if necessary.

Installation

Inline Engines

1. Install key in crankshaft and coat gear seat with oil.
2. Align key way in gear to key on crankshaft with timing mark toward front of crankshaft.
3. Drive gear into place.

Camshaft Gear Removal

Inline Engines

1. Gear is press fit on camshaft. Place in arbor press and apply pressure to front end of camshaft.
2. Press camshaft out of gear and remove key and spacer.

Installation

Inline Engines

1. Install spacer and key, apply transmission oil on gear seat.
2. Support camshaft at journal, then position gear with timing mark forward and keyway aligned with key in camshaft.
3. Press gear on to camshaft until gear hub stops at spacer.
4. Measure clearance at thrust plate with a feeler gauge. A clearance of 0.001-0.005" is necessary for proper lubrication.

Idler Gearshaft Removal

V6 and V8 Engines

1. Bend back lock and remove idler gear plate bolts, lock, and plate.
2. Remove idler gear assembly from idler gear shaft.
3. Remove bolts holding idler gear shaft to cylinder block and remove shaft.

Idler Gearshaft Installation

V6 and V8 Engines

Due to different configurations of engines, the following procedures are a basic guide. Although the configurations vary, installation steps are similar.

1. Turn crankshaft and camshaft so that the timing marks on gears are towards the idler gearshaft.
2. Install idler gearshaft, mating marks with those corresponding on other gears in train.
3. Install retainer plates and secure with bolts and lock plates.

Removal (Pulling Camshaft)

1. Drain and remove radiator.
2. Remove front end sheet metal or grille.
3. Remove damper or pulley.
4. Remove oil pan (See Oil Pan R & R).
5. Remove timing case cover (2 bolts inside oil pan at front main bearing cap).
6. Remove rocker arm cover(s).

7. Loosen adjusters to relieve lifters.
7. Remove fuel pump and distributor (mark position of rotor).
8. Align timing gear marks (check rotor mark) then remove 2 thrust plate screws by reaching through 2 holes in camgear.
9. Remove camshaft and rear assembly by pulling and turning shaft carefully so lobes will not mar bearings and will clear lifters.
10. Use press to remove cam gear using caution not to damage thrust plate by woodruff key.
11. Clean all gasket surfaces and inspect.
12. Check camshaft alignment and lobes for wear. Check camshaft bearings in block, check crank gear and oil spray nozzle.

Crankshaft Pulley or Damper

Removal

1. Drain radiator; remove hoses.
2. Remove radiator—See Radiator R & R.
3. Loosen fan belt and remove any accessory drive.
4. Use puller to remove pulley or damper.

NOTE: On some early models, pulley is bolted to hub. Remove pulley first then, using pulley holes, remove hub. More recent models have the hub bonded to inertia weight. Care must be exercised when using a puller.

Timing Cover Oil Seal Replacement

1. Remove torsional damper—See Damper R & R.
2. Pry old seal out, be careful not to mar crankshaft or bend cover.
3. Install new seal (lip of seal toward block), tap lightly into position. Coat seal with oil.
4. Reverse removal procedures.

Timing Case Cover Removal

1. Remove bolts, washers and cylinder block cap (V6, V8 engines).
2. Carefully remove front cover; discard gasket and oil seal.

Installation

1. Clean all surfaces and glue new gasket to cylinder block.
2. Press new oil seal squarely into bore with seal lip on inner side of cover.
3. Install attaching bolts, washers and cylinder block cap (V6, V8 engines). Torque to specifications.

Piston and Connecting Rod

Removal

1. Ream out top of bore if a piston ring travel ridge is present.
2. Position crankshaft so that a pair of connecting rods can be moved without interference.
3. Remove nuts from connecting rod cap bolts, remove rod cap and lower bearing half.
4. Mark all parts for reassembly.

Installation

1. Clean and coat piston pin, rings, and cylinder bore with engine oil.
2. Stagger piston ring gaps.
3. Place connecting rod bearing halves in rod and cap.
4. Use a ring compressor to install piston and connecting rod assembly in cylinder bore.

Ring-Groove Clearance	
Top Ring 230 & 250 Eng.	0.0012"-0.0027"
Top Ring 292 Eng.	0.0020"-0.0040"
2nd Ring 230 & 250 Eng.	0.0012"-0.0032"
2nd Ring 292	0.0020"-0.0040"
Oil Ring 230 & 250 Eng.	0.0000"-0.0050"
Oil 292	0.0005"-0.0055"
Ring Gap	
Compression Rings (All Eng.)	0.0100"-0.0200"
Oil Rings (All Eng.)	0.0150"-0.0550"
Piston Ring Groove Width	
Compression Ring Grooves	
Top Groove	0.0965"-0.0975"
2nd Compression Ring Groove	
All Except 637 Engines	0.0960"-0.0970"
637 Engines	0.0955"-0.0965"
3rd Compression Ring Groove	
305E & 637 Engines	None
Other Engines	0.0955"-0.0965"
Oil (Bottom) Ring Groove	
All Engines	0.1885"-0.1895"
Piston Ring Clearance in Groove	
Top Groove	
305 Series Engines	0.0030"-0.0045"
Other Engines	0.0030"-0.0055"
2nd Compression Ring	
305C, 351C, 351M Engines	0.0030"-0.0055"
401M Engines	0.0030"-0.0045"
478M and 637 Engines	0.0025"-0.0040"
3rd Compression Ring	
305E & 637 Engines	None
Other Engines	0.0025"-0.0040"
Oil (Bottom) Ring	
305C, 351C, 351M & 401M Engines	0.0010"-0.0030"
478M & 637 Engines	0.0020"-0.0035"
478M & 637 Engines	0.0020"-0.0035"
Piston Ring Gap	
Top Ring	
305C & 305E	0.017"-0.027"
351C, 351E & 351M	0.022"-0.032"
401M	0.024"-0.034"
478M & 637	0.026"-0.036"
2nd Ring	
All Except 478 & 637	0.015"-0.025"
478 & 637	0.017"-0.027"
3rd Ring	
All Except 305E, 478M & 637	0.015"-0.025"
478M	0.017"-0.027"
305E & 637	(No. #3 Compression Ring Used)
Oil Control Ring	
Rails on 305E Only	0.015"-0.055"
No Gap on Oil Ring on 305C, 351C, 351M, or 401M, 478M & 637	0.017"-0.032"
	(© G.M.C.)

Sleeve type piston ring compressor
(© G.M.C.)

APPLY SEALANT TO SHADED AREAS ONLY

Applying sealer to rear bearing cap area
(© G.M.C.)

Cylinder numbering and size selection (V6 engine)
(© G.M.C.)

ENGINE FRONT

NOTCH ON PISTON MUST FACE
FRONT OF ENGINE

230 CU. IN   250 CU. IN. & 292 CU. IN.

Piston installation (inline engines)
(© G.M.C.)

ENGINE FRONT

NOTCH IN PISTON

"A" OIL RING SPACER GAP
(Tang in Hole or Slot within Arc)

"B" OIL RING RAIL GAPS

"C" 2ND COMPRESSION RING GAP

"D" TOP COMPRESSION RING GAP

IN LINE-ALL CYL.

Piston ring gap locations (inline engine)
(© G.M.C.)

COMPRESSION RING

OIL RING

PISTON

PISTON RING SPREADER

Installing piston rings with spreader tool
(© G.M.C.)

5. Install cap and lower bearing half. Lubricate nut threads and torque to specifications.
6. Check bearing clearances.

Refer to General Engine Rebuilding Section for further details on piston and connecting rod assembly and disassembly.

Piston Rings

Piston rings are removed and installed with the use of a spreader tool. Use care not to break the rings.

Crankshaft Bearings

Remove crankshaft bearings very carefully; place in a specific order with corresponding bearing caps and bolts.

Installation

Inline Engines

1. Match service main bearings with crankshaft to be installed, i.e., standard size with new

1 Side seal
2 Crankshaft oil seal
3 Rear bearing cap
4 Bearing cap rear bolts
5 Bolt hole plugs
6 Cylinder block

CUT OFF ENDS OF PACKING CLEANLY AND FLUSH WITH SURFACE

POINT "A"

POINT "A"

DIP SIDE SEALS (1) IN DIESEL OIL AND INSERT INTO GROOVE IN CAP (3) AFTER CAP IS INSTALLED. CHAMFER ON END OF SEALS MUST BE LOCATED AT POINTS "A"

INSERT PLUGS (5) WITH CAVITY TOWARD BOLTS

Cross section of rear seals
(© G.M.C.)

BEARING CAPS

SIDE BOLTS

CYLINDER BLOCK

12-POINT SOCKET

Installing bearing cap side bolts (V8 engine)
(© G.M.C.)

crankshaft and undersize with reconditioned crankshaft.
2. Install bearing upper halves in cylinder block and rear oil seal upper half, seal lip pointing forward.
3. Lubricate inserts and oil seal lip with S.A.E. #10W oil. NOTE: Do not lubricate oil seal ends.
4. Install crankshaft.
5. Install all except rear bearing caps and tighten to specifications.
6. Check for any binding bearings, then apply sealer to illustrated area.
7. Initially install rear main bearing cap, then move crankshaft fore and aft to seat the inserts. Tighten to specifications.
8. Check bearing clearances and crankshaft end play.

Installation

V6 Engines

1. Install bearing upper halves in #10W oil and apply sealer to crankshaft rear bearing cap where it joins the crankcase.
2. Lubricate bearings with S.A.E. cylinder oil.
3. Install crankshaft.
4. Install all bearing caps and tighten to specifications.

5. Check for any binding bearings.
6. Install rear bearing bolt caps.

Installation

V8 Engines

1. Main bearing installation on V8 engines follows the same procedure as those outlined for V6 engines, with one exception; thread side bolts into bearing cap before tightening cap to cylinder bolts.

Engine Lubrication

Oil Pan Removal
Series 10-30

6 cyl.-1970-72

1. Disconnect battery ground cable then remove starter.
2. On CS 15, 25, 35 (1970-71) and CS 10, 20, 30 (1972):
   a. Remove engine front mount bolts (frame bracket-to-mount).
   b. Using a suitable jack with a flat piece of wood (to prevent damaging oil pan), raise engine enough to insert 2 in. x 4 in. wood blocks between the engine mounts and frame brackets.

OIL PRESSURE
SENDING UNIT

DISTRIBUTOR SHAFT
OILING

TIMING GEAR
OIL NOZZLE

SPLASH
OILING

FULL FLOW OIL FILTER

FILTER BY-PASS
SYSTEM

Engine lubrication system (inline engine) (© G.M.C.)

3. Remove bolts securing engine mounts to crossmember brackets —then, using a suitable jack with a flat piece of wood to protect oil pan, raise engine sufficiently to insert 2 in. x 4 in. wood block between engine mounts and cross-member brackets.
4. Drain engine oil and remove flywheel (converter) cover.
5. Remove engine mount spacer on C Series vehicles.
6. Remove oil pan bolts and withdraw oil pan from engine.

Installation

1. Discard old gaskets and seals, thoroughly clean all gasket sealing surfaces.
2. Install new rear seal in rear main bearing cap.
3. Install new front seal on crankcase front cover.
4. Install new side gaskets on cylinder block.
   NOTE: DO NOT USE SEALER.
5. Position oil pan to block, making sure that seals and gaskets remain in place, install and torque pan screws to specifications.
6. Raise engine as outlined above and remove blocks used to support engine.
7. Lower engine, install and torque mount-to-crossmember bracket bolts.
8. Install starter and flywheel (converter) cover.
9. Install engine mount spacer on C Series vehicles.
10. Fill engine with specified quantity of oil, then start engine and check for leaks.

Series 10-30

V-8-1970-72

Removal

1. Drain engine oil.
2. Remove oil dip stick and tube.
3. On vehicles equipped with automatic transmission remove converter housing under pan.
5. Remove starter brace and inboard bolt, swing starter aside.
6. On CE 15, 25, 35 (1970-71) and CE 10, 20, 30 (1972):
   a. Remove engine front mount bolts (frame bracket-to-mount).
   b. Using a suitable jack with a flat piece of wood (to prevent damaging oil pan), raise engine enough to insert 2 in. x 4 in. wood blocks between the engine mounts and frame brackets.
7. Remove oil pan and discard gaskets and seals.

Installation

1. Thoroughly clean all gasket and seal surfaces on oil pan, cylinder

---

3. Drain engine oil.
4. Remove oil pan and discard gaskets and seals.

Installation

1. Thoroughly clean all gasket sealing surfaces.
2. Install new rear seal in rear main bearing cap.
3. Install new front seal on crankcase front cover pressing tips into holes provided in cover.
4. Install new side gaskets on cylinder block.
   NOTE: DO NOT USE SEALER.
5. Install oil pan and torque bolts to specifications.
6. Complete installation as follows on CS 15, 25, 35 and CS 10, 20, 30:
   a. Using a suitable jack with a flat piece of wood (to prevent damaging oil pan), raise en-

gine enough to remove 2 in. x 4 in. wood blocks from between the engine mounts and frame brackets.
   b. Lower engine, install front mount bolts and torque to specifications.
   c. Install starter and connect battery cable.
7. Fill with engine oil then start engine and check for leaks.

Series 10-30

6 cyl.-1973-76

Removal

1. Disconnect battery ground cable.
2. Raise vehicle on a hoist and disconnect starter at engine block— leave electrical connections intact and position starter out of way.

BALANCE SHAFT BEARING AND IDLER SHAFT GEAR LUBRICATION (637, V-8 ENGINE)

FROM PASSAGE "A"
FROM PASSAGE "B"
FROM PASSAGE "C"

1 To timing gears	7 Oil from camshaft rear bearing	14 Timing idler gear shaft
2 Cylinder heads	8 Rocker arms	15 Cylinder block
3 Oil from camshaft front bearing	9 Oil drain back holes	16 Balance shaft idler gear shaft
4 Rocker arm shaft front bracket	10 Oil filter	17 Balance shaft idler gear
5 Rocker arm shafts	11 Oil pump inlet screen	18 Balance shaft gear
6 Rocker arm shaft rear bracket	12 Oil pump	19 Balance shaft
	13 Piston pin splash lubricated	

Engine lubrication system (V6, V8 engines with gear driven cam) (© G.M.C.)

Series 10-30

V-8-1973-76

Removal

1. Drain engine oil.
2. Remove oil dip stick and tube.
3. On vehicles so equipped remove exhaust crossover pipe.
4. On vehicles equipped with automatic transmission remove converter housing under pan.
5. Remove starter brace and inboard bolt, swing starter aside.
6. Remove oil pan and discard gaskets and seals.

Installation

1. Thoroughly clean all gasket and seal surfaces on oil pan, cylinder block, crankcase front cover and rear main bearing cap.
2. Install new oil pan side gaskets on cylinder block using gasket sealer as a retainer. Install new oil pan rear seal in rear main bearing cap groove, with ends butting side gaskets. Install new oil pan front seal in groove in crankcase front cover with ends butting side gaskets.
3. Install oil pan and torque bolts to specifications.
4. Install starter brace and attaching bolts. Torque bolts to specifications.
5. Install converter housing under pan (if removed).
6. Install exhaust crossover pipe (if removed).
7. Install oil dip stick tube and dip stick.
8. Fill with oil, start engine and check for leaks.

Oil Pan Removal Sprint

6-cyl.-1971-76

1. Disconnect battery positive cable.
2. Remove radiator upper mounting panel or side mount bolts.
3. Place a piece of heavy cardboard between fan and radiator.
4. Disconnect fuel suction line at the fuel pump.
5. Raise vehicle on hoist and drain engine oil.
6. Disconnect and remove starter.
7. Remove either flywheel underpan or converter housing underpan and splash shield.
8. Rotate crankshaft until timing mark on torsional damper is at 6:00 o'clock position.
9. Remove bolts attaching brake line to front crossmember and move brake line away from crossmember.
10. Remove "through" bolts from engine front mounts.
11. Remove oil pan bolts.

block, crankcase front cover and rear bearing cap.

2. Install new oil pan side gaskets on cylinder block using gasket sealer as a retainer. Install new oil pan rear seal in rear main bearing cap groove, with ends butting side gaskets. Install new oil pan front seal in groove in crankcase front cover with ends butting side gaskets.
3. Install oil pan and torque bolts to specifications.
4. Install starter brace and attach-

ing bolts. Torque bolts to specifications.
5. On CE 15, 25, 35 and CE 10, 20, 30:
   a. Lower engine and install front mount through bolts.
   b. Torque bolts to specifications.
6. Install converter housing under pan (if removed).
7. Install exhaust crossover pipe (if removed).
8. Install oil dip stick tube and dip stick.
9. Fill with oil, start engine and check for leaks.

1 Suction tube and screen assy.
2 Bracket bolt (20-25 ft.-lbs.)
3 Flange bolts and lock washers
4 Gaskets
5 Cylinder block
6 Pump drive shaft
7 Pump to block bolts (30-35 ft.-lbs.)
8 Oil Pump
9 Bracket
10 Oil pan

Engine oil pump installation
(© G.M.C.)

12. Raise engine slowly until motor mount through bolts can be removed—remove bolt—continue to raise engine until it is raised approximately three inches.
13. Lower oil pan and remove.

Installation

1. Thoroughly clean all gasket sealing surfaces.
2. Using a new gasket set, install rear seal in rear main bearing cap.
3. Install front seal on crankcase front cover, pressing tips into holes provided in cover.
4. Install side gaskets to engine block, using a gasket sealer with sufficient body to act as a retainer.
5. Install oil pan, torquing the retaining bolts to specifications. Roll pan under engine and then upward and install pan bolts. Torque pan bolts to specifications. Install left engine mount and bracket.
6. Raise engine sufficiently to allow removal of wood blocks—install engine mounts, lower engine and install mount "through" bolts. Torque bolts to specifications.
7. Reinstall and secure brake line to front crossmember.
8. Connect and secure steering rod at idler lever.
9. Install flywheel underpan or converter housing underpan and splash shield as applicable.
10. Install and connect starter.
11. Install radiator upper mounting panel or side mount bolts as applicable.
12. Remove cardboard previously placed between fan and radiator.
13. Connect fuel suction line at fuel pump and connect battery positive cable.

Sprint

V-8-1971-76

Removal

1. Disconnect battery negative cable.
2. Remove distributor cap from distributor (to prevent breaking cap when engine is raised).
3. Remove fan shroud retaining bolts on all models.
4. On 454 cu. in. engine models, place a piece of heavy cardboard between the radiator and fan to avoid damage from contact when engine is raised.
5. Raise vehicle on hoist and drain engine oil.
6. Disconnect exhaust pipes or crossover pipe.
7. On vehicles equipped with automatic transmission, remove converter housing under pan and splash shield.
8. Rotate crankshaft until timing mark on torsional damper is at 6:00 o'clock position.
9. For all engines except 350 cu. in. and 454 cu. in. with automatic transmissions, disconnect starter brace at starter. Remove inboard starter bolt and loosen outboard starter bolt. Starter can now be swung outboard to gain adequate clearance to remove oil pan.
10. Remove both "through" bolts from the engine front mounts.
11. For all engines, use a suitable

jack and a block of wood (to avoid pan damage) and raise the engine.
12. Engine should be raised until wood blocks of 3 in. can be inserted under engine mounts. Lower engine until supported by blocks.
13. Remove oil pan bolts and remove oil pan. Discard used gaskets and seals.

Installation

1. Thoroughly clean all gasket sealing surfaces.
2. If crankshaft was rotated while oil pan was off, place timing mark at 6:00 o'clock position.
3. Using new gaskets, install side gasket on pan rails using gasket sealer as a retainer.
4. Install front and rear pan seals, making sure their ends butt with side gaskets.
5. Install oil pan and torque retaining bolts to specifications.
6. Raise engine, remove wood blocks and lower engine onto front mounts.
7. Complete installation as follows:
   a. Install engine front mount "through" bolts and torque to specifications.
   b. Install inboard starter bolt and connect starter brace, torque bolt to specifications.
   c. On vehicles equipped with automatic transmissions install converter under pan and splash shield.
   d. Connect exhaust pipes or crossover pipe.
   e. Lower vehicle and fill engine with oil.
   f. Install fan shroud retaining bolts on all models.
   g. Install distributor cap on distributor and connect battery positive cable.

Oil Pan Removal
Series 40-60

1. Clean all dirt and accumulated material from oil pan attaching bolts and drain plug.
2. Drain oil out of crankcase.
3. Remove oil pan bolts, then remove oil pan. Scrape off any portions of gaskets which adhere to oil pan flange or bolting flange on engine block and front cover. Gasket at front cover is neoprene type. Remove seal at crankshaft rear bearing cap.

Installation

1. Install seal at rear bearing cap.
2. Install front seal on timing gear cover, pressing tips into holes in cover.
3. Use grease or cement to hold side gaskets in place on cylinder block. Side gasket tabs must

index with front seal on timing gear cover.

4. Install oil pan.

Oil Cooler Service

Should foreign matter be suspected of contaminating oil system, back flush oil cooler and lines, using cleaning solvent and compressed air. Do not exceed 100 psi.

Oil Pump Removal

Inline Engines

1. Remove oil pan.
2. Remove oil suction pipe bolt and two bolts attaching the pump flange to engine.
3. Remove oil pump and screen.

Installation

Inline Engines

1. Install oil pump, aligning drive shaft with distributor tang. Install suction pipe support bolt.
2. Install oil pan.

Oil Pump Removal

V6 Engines

1. Remove oil pan.
2. Remove two mounting bolts and oil pump.

Installation

V6 Engines

1. Place new gasket on pump flange and install pump, turning shaft as necessary to engage gears.
2. Install mounting bolts and torque to specifications.
3. Install oil pan.

Oil Pump Removal

V8 Engines

1. Remove oil pan.
2. Remove pump to rear main bearing cap bolt.
3. Remove pump and extension shaft.

Installation

V8 Engines

1. Install pump and extension shaft, aligning slot with tang on lower end of distributor drive shaft.
2. Install attaching bolt and torque to specifications.
3. Install oil pan.

Front Axle, Suspension

Solid Axle

Front Spring Removal

1. Raise truck frame and support front axle with a floor jack.

2. Remove spring shackle U-bolts and lower the axle.
3. Remove all attaching retainer pins, bolts and nuts from rear hanger.
4. Remove U-bolts, spacers, tow eyes and dowel pins as necessary, then remove spring.

Installation

1. Install rear end of spring with all attaching parts.
2. Raise front end of spring and install attaching parts.
3. Raise front axle to spring and install attaching U-bolts, nuts and washers.
4. Torque all bolts and nuts to specifications.
5. Lower vehicle.

King Pins and Bushings
Removal

1. Jack up axle and remove hubs and bearings.
2. Remove steering arm from knuckle.
3. Remove king pin draw key by using a brass drift and hammer.
4. Remove king pin cap screws, caps and gaskets.
5. Drive out king pin using a brass drift and hammer.
6. Remove bearings, shims and O-ring.

Installation

1. Clean all parts and coat king pin with S.A.E. #10W oil.
2. Install thrust bearing and knuckle, then raise to take up all clearance.
3. Check thrust bearing minimum clearance with specifications and correct with shims, if necessary.
4. Align king pin holes and partially install king pin.
5. Drive king pin into place, aligning milled slot with draw key (when used).
6. Install required king pin bushings and nuts and torque to spec-

ifications. Install dust caps and gaskets.

7. Install remaining parts, lubricate according to specifications, then install bearings and hubs.

Coil Spring Suspension

Coil Spring Removal

1. Raise vehicle and place jack stands under frame, allowing control arms to hang free.
2. Disconnect lower end of shock absorber.
3. Install chain through spring and lower control arm as a safety precaution.
4. Raise cross-shaft to relieve load; remove U-bolts securing shaft to crossmember.
5. Slowly lower control arm until the coil spring can be removed.
6. Remove coil spring.

Installation

1. Install spring and then lift control arm. Position cross-shaft with crossmember and install attaching U-bolts.
2. Connect lower end of shock absorber.
3. Torque all nuts to specifications.
4. Lower vehicle.

Lower Control Arm Removal

1. Remove coil spring.
2. Remove cotter pin from lower ball stud and loosen stud nut.
3. Loosen lower ball stud in steering knuckle, then remove nut.
4. Remove control arm.

Installation

1. Install lower ball stud through steering knuckle and tighten nut.
2. Install spring and control arm.
3. Torque stud to specifications and install cotter pin.

**REAR HANGER
CE, ME4500-6500 SERIES**

PIN RETAINER — RETAINER BOLT
REBOUND PIN

"T" MODELS ONLY

**FRONT MOUNTING
ALL MODELS**

Front spring mounting (typical)
(© G.M.C.)

Front spring center mounting (tilt cab models)
(© G.M.C.)

Upper Control Arm Removal

1. Raise vehicle and support lower control arm.
2. Remove wheel assembly.
3. Remove cotter pin from upper ball stud and loosen stud nut.
4. Loosen upper ball stud in steering knuckle, then remove nut.
5. Remove nuts attaching control arm to crossmember bracket. Remove control arm.

Installation

1. Install control arm in position on bracket. Make certain camber and caster shims are in proper order.
2. Install ball joint stud, nut and cotter pin.
3. Remove lower control arm support and lower vehicle.

Adjustments

Refer to wheel alignment specifications area for necessary information.

Ball Joint Inspection

Lower Ball Joint

1. Support the control arms at the wheel hub and at the drum.
2. Measure the distance between the tip of the ball stud and the tip of the grease fitting below the ball joint.
3. Remove the support under the control arm, and measure the distance between the tip of the ball stud and the tip of the grease fitting, as in 2.
4. Subtract the smaller measurement from the larger. If the difference exceeds .094″ (or 3/32″), the ball joint must be replaced.

Upper Ball Joint

1. Check the stud for perceptible lateral shake.
2. Attempt to twist the stud in its socket with the fingers. If either test produces positive results, replace the ball joint.

Upper Ball Joint Removal

1. Put the vehicle on a hoist. Support the lower control arm, using a floor jack, if necessary.

2. Remove the cotter pin from the upper ball stud. Loosen the stud nut just two turns.
3. Remove the brake caliper assembly and wire it to the frame for clearance.
4. Install a special tool between the ball studs, as shown.
5. Extend the bolt from the special tool to loosen the ball stud in the steering knuckle. When the stud is loose, remove the tool and stud nut.
6. Center punch the rivet heads. Drill out the rivets.
7. Remove the assembly.

Installation

1. Install a new service ball joint with fasteners supplied, torquing nuts to 45 ft lbs.
2. Install the ball stud in the steering knuckle, and install the stud nut, torquing the nuts, as specified below:
   10 Series—40-60 ft lbs
   20, 30 Series—80-100 ft lbs, plus additional torque required to cotter pin—not to exceed 130 ft lbs
3. Install a new cotter pin.
4. Install the lube fitting, and lubricate the joint.
5. Install the brake caliper assembly and tire and wheel.

Lower Ball Joint Removal

1. Put the vehicle on a hoist. Support the lower control arm using a floor stand, if necessary.
2. Remove the tire and wheel.
3. Remove the lower stud cotter pin and loosen the stud nut just two turns.
4. Remove the brake caliper assembly and wire it to the frame for clearance.
5. Install a special tool between the ball studs, as shown.
6. Extend the bolt from the special tool to loosen the ball stud in the steering knuckle. When the stud is loosened, remove the tool and ball stud nut.
7. Pull the brake disc and knuckle assembly off the ball stud and support the upper arm with a block of wood.

8. If working on a 20 or 30 Series vehicle, cut a piece of 3″ water pipe to a length of 2⅝″. Install the special tools and, on 20 and 30 Series vehicles the pipe, as shown in the illustration.
9. Press the ball joint out of the control arm with the hex head screw. Remove the ball joint.

Installation

1. Start the new joint into the control. Then, install the special installation tools shown. Make sure bleed vent in rubber boot is inward.
2. Turn the hex head screw just far enough to seat the new joint in the control arm.
3. Lower the upper arm and start the lower ball stud into the steering knuckle.
4. Install the brake caliper assembly.
5. Install the ball stud nut and torque to 80-100 ft lbs. Then continue to torque the nut until the cotter pin hole is in alignment. The maximum torque must not exceed 130 ft lbs.
6. Install a lube fitting and lubricate the new joint. Install the tire and wheel.

Wheel Bearing Adjustment Check
1500-3500 Series

1. Raise the vehicle and support it at the front lower control arm.
2. Grip the tire at the top and bottom and move the wheel assembly in and out on the spindle. Measure the movement of the hub assembly, if movement is less than .001 in. or greater than .005 in. adjust the bearings.
3. If bearings are noisy, tight, or excessively loose, they should be cleaned, inspected and lubricated prior to adjustment.

Adjustment
1500-3500 Series

1. Remove the hub cap or wheel disc from the wheel.
2. Remove the dust cap from the hub.
3. Remove the cotter pin from the spindle and spindle nut.
4. Tighten the spindle nut to 12 ft lbs. while turning the wheel assembly forward by hand to fully seat the bearings.
5. Back off the nut to the "just loose" position.
6. Hand tighten the spindle nut then loosen the spindle nut until either hole in the spindle lines up with a slot in the nut and install a new cotter pin.
7. Measure the looseness in the hub assembly. If properly adjusted

the end play will be from .001-
.005 in.

8. Install the dust cap, hub cap and
lower the vehicle.

Wheel Bearing Adjustment Check
4500-6500 Series

1. Make sure the brakes are fully
released and jack up the front
axle until the wheels clear the
floor.
2. Check the bearing play, by
grasping the tire at the top and
pulling back and forth, or by
using a pry bar under the tire. If
the bearings are properly adjusted, movement of the brake
drum in relation to the backing
plate will be barely noticeable
and the wheel will turn freely.

Wheel Bearing Adjustment
4500-6500 Series

1. Raise the vehicle and safely
support the axle.
2. Remove the hub cap and gasket.
3. Remove the cotter pin from the
adjusting nut.
4. Tighten the adjusting nut to 50
ft. lbs. while rotating the wheel
in both directions.
5. Back off the nut 1/3 turn and install a new cotter pin. This adjustment should result in bearing end play of .001-.007 in.
6. Install the dust cap and wheel
and lower the vehicle.

Four Wheel Drive Axle

*For service on transfer case, see
general repair section.*

Description

GMC uses two different types of
front driving axles. The type used
on K1000, K1500 series is a hypoid,
single reduction type, consisting of a
housing, differential and carrier assembly, axle shaft and universal joint
assemblies, steering tie rod assembly
and steering knuckle support at outer
ends of housing.

The second type KV400 is a single
speed spiral bevel type consisting of
a housing with removable stub ends
that are piloted and bolted to the
flange ends of the housing. The outer
ends of the hollow stubs are designed
to accept upper and lower pivot bearings, which allow the front wheels to
steer as well as help drive the vehicle
when all wheel drive is necessary.

Removal

1. Disconnect driveshaft from
front differential.
2. Raise front end and support
with jack stands behind the
front springs.
3. Disconnect rod from steering
arm.

Removing snap-ring at axle shaft
(© G.M.C.)

4. Disconnect brake hoses from
frame fittings.
5. Disconnect shock absorbers
from axle brackets.
6. Remove attaching U-bolts and
remove front axle assembly.

Installation

1. Place axle in position under
truck.
2. Install attaching U-bolts.
3. Connect shock absorbers to axle
brackets.
4. Connect brake hoses to frame fittings.
5. Connect rod to steering arm.
6. Remove jack stands and connect
driveshaft.
7. Lower truck.

K1000, K1500
Series Axle

Reference

For overhaul procedures refer to
Spicer, Single, Reduction Rear Axles
in General Repair Section.

Hub Removal

1. Remove hub cap, using block of
hard wood and hammer on
K1000; on K1500 use pry bar.
NOTE: Some vehicles are
equipped with free-wheeling unit
as front hub which must first be
removed.
2. On 1500 series vehicles, remove
six nuts and lock washers attaching drive flange to hub.
3. Using snap-ring pliers, remove
snap-ring attaching drive flange
(K1500) or drive gear (K1000)
to axle shaft, then remove flange
or gear.
4. Using spanner wrench, remove
outer lock nut, then remove retainer plate and bearing adjusting nut.
5. Remove hub and brake drum assembly with bearings and oil
seal. Use caution that outer bearing cone is not damaged, due to
being dropped.

Removing axle shaft and universal joint
(© G.M.C.)

Hub Installation

1. If bearing cups have been removed, install new cups, being
sure they are seated solidly
against shoulders in hub.
2. Lubricate hub and bearing cones,
then install inner bearing cone
in hub.
3. Coat oil seal bore in hub with a
thin layer of sealing compound,
then press seal in until against
shoulder in hub. Lip of seal must
be toward inside of hub. Coat lip
of seal with wheel bearing
grease.
4. Install hub assembly over spindle, then install outer bearing
cone and adjusting nut.
5. Using spanner wrench, tighten
adjusting nut. During tightening, rotate hub to prevent bearing damage.
6. Loosen adjusting nut and again
tighten until snug. Loosen nut
1/8 turn and install locking
washer, being sure that pin in
adjusting nut is in one of the
holes in washer.
7. Again using spanner wrench,
install and tighten outer locking
nut. Tighten nut to 40 foot-
pounds torque minimum.
8. On Series 1000 vehicles, install
spacer in hub, then install drive
gear into end of hub and one
end of axle shaft. During installation, rotate gear as necessary
to mate hub and shaft splines.
9. On Series 1500 vehicles, install
drive flange and gasket at end of
hub, with drive shaft and flange
mating flange over hub studs.
Install and tighten stud nuts and
lock washers.
10. Install bolt in threaded end of
drive shaft, then pull drive shaft
outward to facilitate installation
of snap-ring.
11. Install snap-ring at end of drive
shaft, using pliers. Remove bolt
from threaded end of drive shaft,
then install hub cap at end of
hub.
12. Apply recommended lubricant

MODEL K1000

H.D. K1500 (OPT.)

Sectional view of front axle at steering knuckle and wheel hub (© G.M.C.)

1 Drive flange—K-1500	12 Knuckle bearing—upper	23 Hub oil seal
2 Hub cap—K-1000	13 Axle shaft U-joint	24 Hub bearing—inner
3 Snap ring	14 Axle shaft—inner	25 Hub spindle
4 Wheel hub—K-1000	15 Axle housing	26 Hub bearing—outer
5 Drive gear—K-1000	16 Knuckle bearing—lower	27 Adjusting nut
6 Axle shaft—outer	17 Seal ring	28 Lock washer
7 Wheel hub—K-1500	18 Rubber seal	29 Lock nut
8 Brake drum	19 Felt seal	30 Hub cap—K-1500
9 Brake backing plate	20 Seal retainer	31 Bushing woodruff key
10 Adjusting shims	21 Bearing retainer	32 Knuckle bushing
11 Steering arm	22 Steering knuckle	33 Bearing retaining snap ring

in steering knuckle through pipe plug provided for this purpose.

Axle Shaft and Joint

Removal

1. Remove six cap screws and lock washers attaching brake backing plate and spindle to steering knuckle.
2. Remove backing plate from steering knuckle spindle.
3. Grasp outer shaft and pull shaft and universal joint assembly straight out of housing.
4. Remove snap-ring retainer bearing in yoke. NOTE: Snap-rings retaining bearings in yoke are installed in yoke at outer end of bearing on heavy duty K1500, and are installed in bearing cage at inner end of yoke on K1000 and standard K1500.
5. Strike end of journal sharply, using a rawhide mallet or soft hammer. This will force bearing

out of yoke far enough to permit removal of trunnion.

Installation

1. Lubricate bearings with high melting point grease, working grease into space around rollers.
2. On K1000 and standard K1500, position trunnion in yoke, then press bearings into yoke over trunnion far enough to install lock rings. Hold journal and lightly tap yoke to seat bearings out against snap-rings. On heavy duty K1500, press bearings into yoke far enough to clear snapring grooves, then install snaprings.
3. Slide axle shaft and universal joint assembly into housing, engaging splines with differential side gear.
4. Install spindle and bushing assembly over axle shaft and against steering knuckle. Install brake backing plate over spindle.

Align holes in backing plate and spindle with steering knuckle then install six cap screws and lock washers. Tighten bolts to torque given in "Specifications."

Steering Knuckle

Removal

1. Remove cotter pin and nut attaching tie rod end to steering knuckle.
2. Remove cap screws attaching oil seal retainers, seal felt, and rubber seal and ring assembly to steering knuckle.
3. Using spring scale at steering knuckle arm check pound pull required to rotate steering knuckle. Record this information for reference at time of reassembly.
4. At bottom of steering knuckle, remove four cap screws and lock washers attaching steering knuckle bearing cap to knuckle.

Removing steering knuckle bearing cap
(© G.M.C.)

Remove bearing cap from knuckle.

5. At top of steering knuckle remove cap screws and lock washers or stud nuts. At left side remove tapered dowels from four studs by striking arm sharply with hammer to loosen dowels.

6. Remove bearing cap at right or steering arm at left. Remove and tag shims for reassembly reference.

7. Remove steering knuckle, also upper and lower bearing cones on K1000 and standard K1500. On heavy duty K1500, remove Woodruff key, then remove bushing from upper steering knuckle.

Installation

1. In the order named, install new felt seal and rubber seal and ring assembly, also metal seal ring over end of axle housing.

2. Install steering knuckle bearing cones (or bushing on heavy duty K1500—make sure that Woodruff key is installed properly when installing bushing) in cups at end of axle housing, while steering knuckle is being placed in position.

3. Install lower bearing cap, and secure with cap screws and lock washers tightened to recommended torque.

4. Install upper bearing cap at right side or steering arm at left side, using same shims removed and tagged at time of disassembly. Tighten cap screws or stud nuts to recommended torque. Observe that clearance exists between nut and arm. If no clearance exists, this indicates excessive wear at studs, dowels, or arm holes. Replace worn parts.

5. Check bearing preload, using spring scale in manner illustrated. Add shims to decrease preload or remove shims to increase preload, whenever scale reading is not within limits given in "Specifications."

6. Position rubber seal and ring assembly around housing bell and inside opening in steering knuckle, followed by felt seal. Two retainer plates with cap screws and lock washers are used to hole seals in their proper location. NOTE: A film of grease can be used to hole seals in place during installation, which also provides initial lubrication.

7. Install tie rod end to steering knuckle arm. Tighten nut securely and install cotter pin.

Axle Shaft Guide and Oil Seal

Axle shaft guides and oil seals, are located at inner ends of axle housing tube, just outside of the differential bearings. Purpose of guides is to permit installation of axle shaft without damaging oil seal. Seals effectively prevent differential lubricant losses along axle shaft.

Replacement

1. Remove axle shaft and universal joint assembly as instructed in this section.

2. Remove differential assembly as instructed in respective rear axle section.

3. Drive guide and oil seal inward and out of housing.

4. Install new guides in housing tube.

5. Apply axle lubricant to lip of oil seal, then install seal in housing tube with lip of seal inward or toward differential.

K10, K20 Series Axles—1972-74

Free Wheeling Hub Removal, K10 Series

1. Turn the actuator lever to the "Lock" position. Raise the vehicle on a hoist.

Axle Vent Hose Routing—Typical (© G.M.C.)

Removing Pitman Arm—Typical (© G.M.C.)

2. Remove the six retaining plate bolts. Remove the retaining plate actuating knob and O-ring.
3. Remove the internal snap ring, outer clutch retaining ring, and actuating cam body.
4. Relieve the pressure on the axle shaft snap ring and remove it.
5. Remove the axle shaft sleeve and clutch ring assembly and the inner clutch ring and bushing assembly.
6. Remove the pressure spring and its retainer plate.

Installation

1. Lubricate all parts with a high speed grease.
2. Install the spring retainer plate with the flange side facing the bearing. The retainer plate goes over the spindle nuts and seats against the outer bearing cup.
3. Install the pressure spring, large o.d. against spring retainer plate. When the spring is properly seated, it extends beyond the spindle nuts approx. 7/8".
4. Place the inner clutch ring and bushing into the axle shaft sleeve and clutch ring. Install the entire assembly onto the axle shaft, press in on it, and install the axle shaft snap ring. Note: Installing a 7/16 x 20 bolt in the axle shaft end and pulling it outward during installation may be of help.
5. Install the actuating cam body with the cams facing outward, the outer clutch retaining ring, and internal snap ring.
6. Install the O-ring on the retaining plate. Install the actuating knob and retaining plate with the knob in "Lock" position. The grooves in the knob must fit into the actuator cam body.
7. Install the cover bolts and seals. Turn the knob to the "Free" position and check for proper operation.

Free Wheeling Hub Removal, K20 Series

1. Raise the vehicle on a hoist.

Straddle Type Torque Rod (© G.M.C.)

Turn the hub key knob to "Free" position.
2. Remove the allen head bolts, and remove the hub cap assembly and gasket from the wheel hub. Remove the exterior sleeve extension housing and gasket.
3. Turn the hub key knob to the locked position. Drive out the key knob retainer roll pin.
4. Remove the outer clutch gear assembly.
5. Remove the lock ring. Remove the slotted adjustment sleeve.
6. Remove the spring, and then remove the lock ring securing the plastic key knob to the hub retainer cap.
7. Remove the O-ring from the plastic hub key knob.
8. Remove the snap ring from the end of the axle shaft. Pull the internal clutch gear and its collar.

Installation

1. Apply a high speed grease to both faces of the bushing, the splines, the teeth of the inner and outer clutch gears, and to the actuating cam.
2. Install the internal clutch collar and gear. Install the lock ring at the end of the axle shaft.
3. Lubricate the O-ring and install it in the groove of the plastic hub key knob. Insert the knob into the retainer cap.
4. Install the lock ring into the hub retainer cap. Push outward on the plastic knob to ensure that the lock ring is fully engaged, and correct its position as necessary.
5. Install the slotted adjustment sleeve with the two tabs outward.
6. Install the key knob retaining

Removing Pitman Arm—Typical (© G.M.C.)

Torque Rod Installation (© G.M.C.)

BEARING ADJUSTING WEDGE
WEDGE ADJUSTING SCREW
SCREW LOCKNUT
BRAKE DRUM
TIE ROD ARM
ADJUSTING CLAMP RING
HUB
WHEEL BEARING CUP
WHEEL BEARING CONE
BEARING ADJUSTING PLATE SEAL
ADJUSTING PLATE
HUB COVER
INSPECTION COVER
UPPER PIVOT BEARING CONE AND CUP
AXLE SHAFT
POWER YOKE
AXLE SHAFT DOWEL
LOWER PIVOT BEARING CONE AND CUP
LOCK PIN
COMPENSATING RING
RING BUSHING
COMPENSATING RING PIN
AXLE HOUSING STUB
STEERING ARM
BOOT
SPINDLE
PIPE PLUG

Sectional view of axle outer end (© G.M.C.)

roll pin with the knob in the locked position. Install the spring.

7. Place the outer clutch gear assembly on top of the spring, compress the spring, and install the lock ring at the sleeve end. Turn the key knob to the "Free" position.

8. Install a ⅜" bolt 5 inches long into one of the hub housing bolt holes.

9. Install the new exterior sleeve extension housing gasket and the housing and retainer cap assembly and gasket. Install the allen head bolts, and tighten securely.

10. Turn the hub key knob to the locked position and check for proper engagement. Install the wheel and tire.

Axle Assembly Removal

1. Disconnect the drive shaft from the front axle. Raise the vehicle far enough to take the weight off the front springs and place jack stands under the truck.

2. Disconnect the connecting rod at the steering arms.

3. Disconnect the brake hoses at the frame fittings, and cover all open ends.

4. Disconnect the shock absorbers at the axle brackets.

5. Disconnect the axle vent tube clip at the differential housing.

6. Unfasten the U-bolts, raise the

truck further, as necessary, and roll the axle out from underneath.

Installation

1. With truck on axle stands, roll the axle under the truck. Lower the truck until axle and truck are in proper relative positions. Again support the vehicle with axle stands.

2. Attach the shock absorbers to the axle brackets. Connect the brake hoses to the frame fittings and fill and bleed the brake system.

3. Attach the steering connecting rod at the steering arms.

4. Connect the drive axle to the front differential.

Model KV4000 Axle

Reference

For overhaul procedures refer to Rockwell Single Reduction Rear Axle in General Repair section.

Hub and Drum

Removal

1. Bend tangs on lock plate, then remove lock plate bolts, bearing adjusting plate and adjusting shims from spindle. NOTE: Wire adjusting shims together

so that same number of shims will be installed that were removed.

2. Remove seal from bearing adjusting plate.

3. Using suitable hoist or chainfall, pull hub and brake drum assembly from spindle. CAUTION: As hub and drum are removed from spindle, outside wheel bearing cone will be removed. Use care not to drop or damage bearing cone.

4. Remove cap screws attaching hub and brake drum together. Using a soft drift, remove bearing cups from hub, being careful not to drop or damage cups.

Installation

1. Press bearing cups into hub.

2. Install brake drum on hub and attach with new cap screws. Tighten cap screws to torque listed in "Specifications" at end of this section.

3. Using suitable hoist or chainfall, place hub and drum over spindle, rotating back and forth to ease hub and drum over the spindle seal. Place outer bearing cone on end of spindle and press into place.

4. Install seal in groove in bearing adjusting plate. Install wheel bearing shims, adjusting plate, lock plates and lock plate bolts.

NOTE: Refer to "Radial (Wheel)

Hub key positions (typical)
(© G.M.C.)

Installing rear bearing cone
(© G.M.C.)

Bearing Adjustment" for number of shims to use. After proper alignment, secure lock bolts by bending.

Axle Shaft Removal

1. Remove demountable rim or disc wheel cover by removing nuts and washers (when used) from studs and lifting off cover. The wheel cover for demountable rim (spoke type wheels) comes off when the rim is removed. Remove inspection cover from the disc wheel cover.
2. Remove lock wire from bolts, then remove bolts and dowels, withdraw axle shafts from housing, using care not to dam-age oil seal in housing.

Installation

1. Install axle shafts into housing, using care not to damage oil seals in housing.
2. Install dowels and bolts attaching axle shaft to power yoke. Tighten bolts firmly, then secure bolts with lock wire.
3. On disc wheel type, install hub cover, then install inspection cover on studs.
4. Hub cover for demountable rim type is installed when the rim is installed.
5. Adjust pivot bearings and check wheel bearing adjustment as directed below.

Spindle Removal

1. At inner side of spindle, loosen lock nut and remove wedge adjusting screw and washer.
2. Using a long thin punch, tap adjusting wedge. This operation will relieve pressure on pivot bearing cones and pivot bearing adjusting wedge clamp ring.
3. Using suitable puller, remove wedge clamp from spindle.
4. Remove 12 screws and lock washers attaching spindle boot and retainers to spindle. Loosen clamp and attaching other end of boot to axle housing stub.

Typical method of installing upper and lower bearing cone, cup and cap
(© G.M.C.)

Driving wedge outward on spindle
(© G.M.C.)

Pivot bearing adjustment
(© G.M.C.)

Spanner Wrench

Adjusting wheel bearing
(© G.M.C.)

5. Using a long thin punch through knock-out holes in rear of spindle, tap inner wheel bearing cone ½ inch away from spindle flange. Then, using suitable puller, remove bearing cone from spindle. CAUTION: Remove bearing cone evenly or bearing cone may bind and score spindle. Do not drop or damage bearing cone.

6. Spindle and brake backing plate assembly will now drop and rest on stub.

7. Remove pivot bearing cups by driving thin punch through upper and lower knockout holes on inside end of axle housing stub. Lift out top pivot bearing cap, bearing adjusting wedge, and top pivot bearing cone. CAUTION: Do not attempt to remove spindle from housing stub until pivot bearing cups have been driven from housing stub. Also, use extreme caution not to drive punch after cup is loose or punch may slip past cups and damage bearing cage.

8. Tilt back of spindle upward and lift from housing stub. If spindle does not come off readily, DO NOT FORCE, since bearing cup probably is not completely free of housing stub. In this case, repeat preceding step 7.

9. Place spindle on bench and, using a thin punch, drive out lower pivot bearing cone through knock-out holes in bottom of spindle.

10. Remove seal from spindle.

11. Remove cap screws and lock washers attaching tie rod arm, and steering arm (left wheel only) to back of brake backing plate. NOTE: At right wheel, a blank plate is installed in place of steering arm. Separate spindle and brake backing plate by removing bolts and lock washers.

Installation

1. Position brake backing plate assembly on spindle and attach with bolts and lock washers.

2. Position tie rod arm and steering arm (11) (left wheel) or blank plate (right wheel) to brake backing plate; attach with cap screws and lock washers.

3. Lubricate lower pivot bearing cone with clean chassis grease, then press cone into spindle. CAUTION: Make sure that spindle is held firmly during this operation.

4. Place lower pivot bearing cup over lower pivot bearing cone.

5. Position brake backing plate assembly and spindle over end of stub, tilting back upward slightly as the lower pivot cup and cone approach the end of stub.

6. Lubricate upper pivot bearing cup with clean chassis grease, then press cup into spindle.

7. Lubricate and press upper pivot bearing cone into pivot bearing cap. Insert this assembly into pivot bearing hole in top of spindle.

8. Install pivot bearing adjusting wedge into slot on top of pivot bearing cap with rounded surfaced of wedge upward.

9. Using an improvised tool similar to the one illustrated, tighten nuts alternately and evenly until pivot bearing cap is even with surface of spindle. CAUTION: Make sure that hardwood blocks are used between tool and spindle as shown, otherwise damage will occur to spindle and cap.

10. With tool holding pivot bearing cap down, install pivot bearing clamp ring until it is centered over pivot bearing.

11. Using a thin punch through wedge adjusting screw hole in back of spindle, drive pivot bearing adjusting wedge outward in slot until it feels solid. Measure distance from end of wedge to end of spindle as shown. If distance is less than 1⅜ inches, add approximately 0.012 inch shim stock under lower pivot bearing cone for each ⅛ inch it

is less than the foregoing distance. Release pressure on pivot bearing clamp ring by driving pivot bearing wedge back with punch, then remove clamp ring.

12. Reinstall clamp or through-bolts and bars as shown, then install inner (wheel) bearing cone over spindle. Lubricate wheel bearing cone. Press inner (wheel) bearing cone onto spindle over pivot bearing cap.

13. Remove clamp or through-bolts and bars, then continue pressing bearing cone until it is against flange on spindle.

14. Press pivot bearing clamp ring over spindle. The clamp ring should be pressed as far as it will go but must not contact the cage of the inner bearing cone.

15. Using wedge adjusting screw in inner side of spindle, move pivot bearing wedge outward in pivot bearing cap slot until it feels solid.

16. Install seal in groove in spindle flange. Pack additional bearing grease around bearing clamp ring and inner bearing cone to fill the space between the hub and the spindle when the hub is installed.

17. Position spindle boot to spindle and attach with two retainers and twelve retainer screws and lock washers. Tighten boot clamp at opposite end of housing stub.

Power Yoke and Compensating Ring

Removal and Disassembly

1. Remove pipe plugs from hub, then remove pins holding power yoke and compensating ring to hub. NOTE: Pins have a ⅜ inch tapped hole to assist in removal of pins.

2. Remove power yoke and compensating ring as an assembly from hub.

3. Remove roll pin, then push out compensating ring to power yoke pin. Power yoke and compensating ring are now separated.

Assembly

1. Position power yoke and compensating ring together, install power yoke pins, and roll pin.

2. Position power yoke and compensating ring assembly (if removed) to hub, then install compensating ring pins and lock pins in hub and compensating ring. Lock pins in hub by installing pipe plugs in hub.

Radial (Wheel) Bearing Adjustment

Radial (wheel) bearing adjustment must be maintained at all times. Adjustment is made each time the bearings are repacked (10,000 miles). However, bearings should be checked for looseness each time the pivot bearings are lubricated and an adjustment made if required. Radial (wheel) bearings are adjusted by means of shims between the bearing adjusting plate spindle end. These shims are in 0.002″, 0.010″, and 0.050″ thicknesses. Sufficient shims should be used to cause only a slight drag when rotating the wheel. Remove tire and rim, disc or case wheel cover, axle shaft, adjusting plate bolts and lock plates, and adjusting plate. Then remove enough shims until a slight drag can be felt when the adjusting plate is attached in place. Bearing adjustment is correct when no play can be felt. After correct adjustment is obtained, secure adjusting plate bolts with lock plates, install axle shaft, wheel cover, and tire and rim.

Free Wheeling Hubs

Free wheeling hubs are available for front wheels on four wheel drive trucks. By disengaging the hubs when four wheel drive is not needed, wear on the front wheel drive train is reduced. The engagement and disengagement of the hubs is a manual operation which must be performed on each front wheel. The hubs must be either fully locked or unlocked and the transfer case control lever must be in two wheel drive position when adjustments are made.

Steering Gear

Standard Steering Gear

Medium and Heavy Trucks

Removal

1. Disconnect steering linkage from pitman arm.
2. Scribe alignment marks on worm shaft and clamp yoke for reassembly.
3. Remove bolts attaching clamp yoke or coupling to steering gear worm shaft.
4. Remove pitman arm nut and washer, then use a puller to remove arm.
5. Remove attaching bolts, nuts and washers, then remove steering gear.

Installation

1. Turn steering wheel to straight-ahead position and center steering gear.
2. Position the steering gear, matching the alignment marks.

3. Install attaching bolts, washers and nuts.
4. Connect clamp yoke or coupling to steering gear worm shaft with attaching parts and torque to specifications.
5. Align pitman arm and shaft; press arm onto shaft and torque to specifications.

Adjustments

Before proceeding to adjust steering gear, check lubricant, front end alignment, tire pressures, shock absorbers, king pins, pitman arm and all mounting bolts for looseness, wear or incorrect adjustment. These are common causes for steering wheel shimmy, clunking or chucking movements.

Adjustment—Worm Bearing

1. Loosen adjuster lock nut and turn screw clockwise until there is no perceptible play.
2. Tighten adjuster lock nut.

Adjustment—Pitman Shaft Lash

1. Center steering wheel and mark its position.

2. Loosen adjuster nut and turn screw clockwise to remove all backlash between gear teeth.
3. Check steering rim pull.

Light Duty Trucks

Removal

1. Drive the vehicle a short distance and move the wheels to the straight ahead position.
2. On P models, remove the lower universal joint pinch bolt. On C and K models, remove the bolts from the flexible coupling to steering shaft flange. Mark the relationship between the universal yoke and the wormshaft.
3. Mark the relationship between the pitman arm and the pitman shaft, and remove the pitman shaft nut or pitman arm pinch bolt.
4. Remove the pitman arm from the shaft with a special puller.
5. Remove the bolts between steering gear and frame. Remove the steering gear.
6. On C and K models, remove the flexible coupling pinch bolt and

Steering gear and shaft (with flexible coupling)
(© G.M.C.)

Steering gear and linkage—"T" models (typical)
(© G.M.C.)

1 Worm shaft adjuster lock nut	6 Pitman shaft nut
2 Spacer washer	7 Drag link
3 Pitman shaft	8 Steering arm
4 Frame	9 Lubrication fitting
5 Pitman arm	10 Drag link stud nut
	11 Steering gear

Pitman arm installed (typical)
(© G.M.C.)

Steering gear and linkage—convential models (typical)
(© G.M.C.)

Steering gear adjustment points (typical)
(© G.M.C.)

Power steering gear—models 1500-3500 (typical)
(© G.M.C.)

remove the coupling from the wormshaft.

Installation

1. On C and K models:
   a. Install the flexible coupling onto the steering gear wormshaft. The flats in the coupling and on the shaft must line up. Then, push the coupling onto the shaft until the wormshaft bottoms on the coupling reinforcement. Install the pinch bolt. *Note that the coupling bolt must pass through the shaft undercut.*
   b. Position the steering gear, guiding the coupling bolt into the steering shaft flange.
   c. Install the steering gear to frame bolts. Torque to 65 ft-lbs.

   d. In cases where plastic spacers are used on the flexible coupling alignment pins, make sure they are bottomed on the pins, torque the flange bolt nuts, and then remove the spacers.
   e. If plastic spacers are not used, center the pins in the steering shaft flange slots, and install and torque the flange bolt nuts.
2. On P models:
   a. Position the steering gear, guiding wormshaft into the U-joint assembly. Line up the marks made at removal. In cases where a new steering gear is being installed, line up the mark on the wormshaft with the slit in the yoke of the U-joint.

   b. Install the steering gear to frame bolts, and torque to 65 ft-lbs.
   c. Install and torque the universal joint pinch bolt. Make sure the bolt passes through the shaft undercut.
3. Install the pitman arm onto the shaft, lining up marks made at removal. Install the shaft nut or pinch bolt and torque to 140 ft-lbs.

Power Steering Gear

Medium and Heavy Trucks
Integral (Type 553-DU)

Removal
1. Mark steering gear worm shaft

Pitman arm removal—Dial indicator and wedge shaped tool installed.

and clamp yoke or coupling for reassembly.

2. Remove connecting rod from pitman arm.
3. Remove attaching pinch bolt, nuts and washers from pitman arm; press pitman arm from shaft.
4. Drain as much fluid as possible from steering gear.
5. Disconnect all tubes from the control valve ports. Plug all tubes and cover all ports to prevent any dirt from entering the system.
6. Remove attaching bolts, nuts and washers from the steering gear and control valve assembly. Remove steering gear.

Installation

1. Center steering wheel and steering gear.
2. Install steering gear by reversing the removal procedure. Make certain to match all alignment marks and to torque all nuts to specifications.
3. Bleed the system and fill reservoir to the proper level.

Integral (Type 710-D)

Removal

1. Center steering gear by position-

ing tires straight ahead and remove Pitman arm clamp bolt.
2. Install Pitman arm puller and remove Pitman arm.

NOTE: It may be necessary to spread the Pitman arm clamp bosses slightly to remove arm. Install a dial indicator as shown. Insert a wedge shaped tool and spread clamp bosses .004 in.

3. Remove pot joint to stub shaft clamp bolt (conventional cab) or carden joint to stub shaft clamp bolt (school bus model). Remove steering column plastic cap and metal cover at dash. Remove column clamp cap screws. Pull steering shaft up until shaft coupling clears stub shaft.
4. Remove steering gear mounting bolts. It will be necessary to use two technicians to remove ear bolt as shown.
5. Disconnect lines from steering gear and plug lines. Turn gear in a vertical position (stub shaft up) and work gear down between frame and inner fender panel and remove gear.
6. Remove adapter to gear bolts.

Installation

1. Install adapter to gear with washers under bolt heads and torque bolts to specifications.

NOTE: One adapter plate to frame bolt and washer (lower forward bolt as shown) must be installed before adapter is bolted to the gear.

2. Holding gear in the vertical position (stub shaft up) push gear up between inner fender panel and frame and position ear on adapter plate over frame and push the bolt previously installed into frame and install washer and nut only finger tight. With gear loose, reach between gear and frame and remove line plugs and install line fittings to gear.
3. Install steering gear to frame mounting bolts with washers and torque to specifications.
4. With one technician inside cab centering steering wheel and one at steering gear with steering gear centered, install pot joint or carden joint over stub shaft. Push steering shaft down until coupling lines up with the cross groove in stub shaft. Install clamp bolt and adjust pot joint to 3.08 in. Tighten steering column clamp cap screws, replace metal cover panel and column plastic cap.
5. Install Pitman arm to Pitman shaft, install clamp bolt and torque to specifications.
6. Bleed the system and fill reservoir to the proper level.

Adjustments
(Type-553-DU)

The only adjustment that can be made on the vehicle is the over-center adjustment.

1. Disconnect pitman arm from shaft, marking the alignment positions.
2. Loosen pitman shaft adjusting screw nut and turn screw out to its limit of travel.
3. Disconnect battery ground cable.
4. Remove horn button.

Steering gear installation.

Over center adjustment
(© G.M.C.)

5. Center steering wheel.
6. Check combined ball and thrust bearing preload by using an in. lbs. torque wrench. Note the highest reading.
7. Tighten pitman shaft adjusting screw and torque steering shaft nut to specifications.
8. Install horn button and connect battery ground cable.
9. Connect pitman arm to shaft, making certain to match alignment marks.
   NOTE: There are no on-vehicle adjustments of the type 710-D steering gears.
   Refer to the General Repair Section for overhaul procedures.

Light Duty Trucks

Removal
1. Disconnect the hoses at the gear and secure the open ends in a raised position.
2. Cap the open ends of the hoses and plug the openings of the steering unit.
3. Remove the flexible coupling to flange bolts on G, C, and K models, or the U-joint pinch bolt on P models. Mark the relationship filler tube from vehicle. Replace dipstick in tube and cover the oil pan opening to prevent entry of foreign material.
3. Disconnect oil cooler lines from fittings on right side of transmission case. Plug line ends and case openings with lint-free material.
4. Disconnect the shift cable from shift lever at left side of transmission.
5. Disconnect vacuum modulator line from modulator. Disconnect wiring to neutral safety and back-up lamp switch.
6. Disconnect the speedometer

shaft fitting from adapter at rear of transmission.
7. Disconnect the propeller shaft from transmission.
8. Disconnect the mechanical parking brake linkage at the right side of transmission (if used).
9. Remove the sheet metal under pan from beneath the converter housing. As the flex-plate is rotated, remove the six bolts retaining flex-plate assembly to converter.
10. Support the transmission with 500-pound (minimum rating) transmission floor jack. The jack must be positioned so transmission oil pan will not support the weight of transmission. Fasten a safety chain over top of transmission and to both sides of jack.
11. Place a support under rear of engine and remove transmission extension-to-engine rear support bolts. Then remove engine rear support from frame of vehicle.
12. Remove the transmission case-to-flywheel housing bolts and washers.
13. Carefully inspect transmission and surrounding area to be sure no lines, hoses, or wires will interfere with transmission removal.
    IMPORTANT: When removing transmission, keep rear of case lower than the front so as not to lose the converter. Install converter holding tool (J-5384) when transmission is removed from the vehicle.
14. Move transmission assembly from the engine, lower the assembly carefully and move it out from the vehicle.
    between the universal yoke and stub shaft.
4. Mark the relationship between the pitman arm and shaft. Remove the shaft nut or pinch bolt from the pitman arm.
5. Remove the arm from the shaft with a special puller.
6. Remove the steering gear mounting bolts, and remove the gear. On G, C, and K models, also remove the pinch bolt from the flexible coupling, and remove the coupling.

Installation
1. Where applicable, install the flexible coupling, aligning the flats in coupling and on shaft. Make sure the stub shaft bottoms on the coupling reinforcement. Install the pinch bolt and torque to 18 in lbs. Make sure the bolt passes through the shaft undercut.
2. Position the steering gear, guiding the coupling bolt into the shaft flange.
3. Install the mounting bolts and torque to 65 ft-lbs. (110 ft-lbs on G series).

4. If plastic spacers are used in the are bottomed on the pins, tighten flexible coupling, make sure they the flange bolt nuts to 18 in-lbs (20 ft-lbs on P series), and then remove the spacers. Where plastic spacers are not used, center the pins in the steering shaft flange slots and install the bolt nuts and torque as above.
5. On P Models:
   a. Position the steering gear. guiding the stub shaft into the U-joint assembly and lining up marks made at removal or, with a new unit, lining up the mark on the stub shaft with the mark on the universal yoke.
   b. Install the gear to frame bolts and torque to 65 ft-lbs.
   c. Install the U-joint pinch bolt and torque to 20 ft-lbs. Make sure the bolt passes through the shaft undercut.
6. Install the pitman arm, lining up the marks made at removal. Install the shaft nut or pinch bolt and torque to 180 ft-lbs on C series, 90 ft-lbs on K series, and 180 ft-lbs on G and P series.
7. Remove the plugs and caps from the fluid fittings and reinstall both hoses.

Standard Transmission

The following procedures for removing and installing the transmission are intended as a guide only. Procedures will vary according to optional equipment and individual truck requirements.

Transmission Removal

Except "K" Models
1. Remove floor mat and transmission floor pan cover, then place transmission in neutral and remove gearshift lever and control tower. NOTE: On trucks equipped with SM465 or New Process transmission, remove gearshift only.
2. Place a clean cloth over the transmission opening to prevent the entrance of dirt.
3. Disconnect back-up light switch at transmission and, where applicable, TCS connection.
4. Drain transmission lubricant.
5. Disconnect speedometer cable at transmission and remove parking brake controls.
6. Disconnect driveshaft from transmission.
7. Remove power take-off unit (when used) and cover opening.
8. Position a jack or dolly under the

transmission and make certain that all attaching lines and brackets are disconnected.

9. Support rear of engine when mounts are located on the clutch housing.

10. Remove transmission to flywheel housing bolts.

11. Move transmission straight back from the engine, keeping mainshaft in alignment. CAUTION: Do not let the weight of the transmission hang on the clutch disc hub.

12. When transmission is free of the engine, lower jack or dolly and remove transmission.

Installation

Except "K" Models

1. Apply a light coating of high temperature grease to main drive gear bearing retainer and splined portion of driveshaft. CAUTION: Do not apply an excessive amount of grease as it will be thrown onto the clutch facings.

2. To complete transmission installation, place transmission in fourth gear, reverse the removal procedures and torque mounting bolts to specifications. Fill transmission with lubricant to the proper level.

Transmission Removal

"K" Models (3 Speed)

1. Drain transfer case and transmission.

2. Disconnect speedometer cable and TCS connections at transmission.

3. Disconnect driveshaft at U-joint.

4. Remove attaching shift assembly bolt, then push assembly to one side.

SECOND AND THIRD SHIFTER LEVER

RELAY LEVER

SECOND AND THIRD TUBE LEVER

FIRST AND REVERSE TUBE LEVER

SECOND AND THIRD CONTROL ROD

SECOND AND THIRD SHIFTER LEVER

FIRST AND REVERSE SHIFTER LEVER

GEARSHIFT CONTROL LEVER

3-speed column shift controls
(© G.M.C.)

5. Supporting transfer case in cradle, remove attaching bolts and case.

6. Disconnect shift control rods from transmission.

7. Support engine rear and remove adapter mount bolts.

8. Remove top 2 transmission to flywheel housing mount bolts and install guide pins.

9. Remove remaining mount bolts and slide transmission straight back on guide pins until it is disengaged from engine.

10. Remove transmission and adapter as an assembly.

Installation

"K" Models (3 Speed)

To install transmission, reverse the removal procedures and fill with lubricant to the proper level.

Transmission Removal

"K" Models (4 Speed)

1. Remove transfer case shift lever retainer.

2. Remove floor mat, shift lever, console and heater duct (when used).

3. Remove transmission floor cover and disconnect shift lever link assembly.

4. Remove all attaching wiring and clamps.

5. Support engine. Drain transmission and transfer case.

6. Disconnect front and rear driveshafts at transfer case.

7. Remove transmission and transfer case to frame bolts and place jack or dolly under transmission assembly.

8. Remove frame crossmember.

9. Remove flywheel housing cover

1 Gearshift lever	6 Clevis
2 Island panel	7 Shift finger
3 Selector finger	8 Selector and shift rods
4 Clevis	9 Selector and shift levers
5 Lock nuts	

Manual transmission control linkage—tilt cab models (typical) (© G.M.C.)

and exhaust crossover pipe (when used).

10. Remove transmission to flywheel housing bolts. Using guide pins, slide assembly back until it disengages the engine.
11. Remove transmission assembly.

Installation

"K" Models (4 Speed)

To install the transmission, reverse the removal procedure and torque mounting bolts to specifications. Fill transmission with lubricant to the proper level.

Shift Linkage Adjustment

Column Shift

1. Disconnect central rods and align both second/third and first/reverse shifter tube levers in neutral position.
2. Install gauge in holes provided to maintain alignment.
3. Position relay levers so that gearshift is in neutral position.
4. Connect control rods to tube levers and then remove gauge.
5. Move gearshift through pattern to check adjustment.

Tilt Cab Models

Shift Linkage Adjustment

1. Place transmission selector and shift levers in "neutral" position.
2. Adjust selector and shift rods to provide 90° angularity at the lower end of the gearshift lever to the control island panel by rotating adjustable clevis on each rod to the desired position and then connecting rods and tightening lock nuts.
3. Check adjustment by moving the gearshift through the pattern.
4. Install new cotter pins and lubricate linkage.

Refer to the General Repair Section for complete overhaul procedures, illustrations and out of truck adjustments.

Clutch

Pedal Free Play Adjustment

1. Disconnect return spring and loosen nuts.
2. Apply approximately 5 lbs. force to pushrod in direction of letter "G" in the illustration.
3. Move lever until pedal makes contact with stop.
4. Turn nut as necessary to obtain a clearance of 3/16-1/4" between nut and swivel.
5. Tighten lock nut and connect return spring.
6. Check pedal free play. The

HOLD-DOWN BOLTS ¼"-20 x 2¼"

Use of hold-down bolts (Lipe-Rollway)
(© G.M.C.)

Clutch linkage (CE, CS4500; CS, SS5500)
(© G.M.C.)

Clutch linkage (CE, ME6500—427 V8 engine)
(© G.M.C.)

clutch pedal free play should be ¾"-1" on all models.

Clutch Removal

1. Remove transmission assembly from truck.
2. Remove clutch release fork from ball stud.
3. Install aligning tool or old transmission main drive gear into the clutch hub to support the clutch components during removal. NOTE: To facilitate the remov-

Linkage adjustment
(all models, except V6, 427 engines)
(© G.M.C.)

366 ENGINE ONLY

Clutch linkage (CE, SE5500; CE, ME6500)
(© G.M.C.)

al of Long or Borg and Beck clutch cover assemblies, install hardwood wedges between release levers and cover.
4. On Lipe- Rollway clutches, install three flat washers and hold down bolts.
5. Make alignment marks on the clutch cover and engine flywheel for reassembly.
6. Loosen the cover bolts one turn at a time and then remove the clutch assembly.

Installation

1. Install clutch assembly.
2. Install clutch cover assembly using the alignment tool or old transmission main drive gear. Make certain alignment marks match.
3. Install cover to flywheel bolts and torque slowly one turn at a time to specifications.
4. Remove aligning tool and wood wedges or hold-down bolts.
5. Connect clutch release mechanism. Lubricate clutch release bearing sparingly and apply a small amount of high temperature grease to recess in release

fork. Tighten ball stud to specifications.
6. Install transmission assembly.
Refer to General Repair Section for clutch overhaul procedures.

Automatic Transmission

The automatic transmissions covered in this section are Allison and Turbo-Hydramatic. Removal and installation procedures are covered separately for each. It may be necessary to remove air tanks, fuel tanks, and optional equipment in order to gain access to the transmission.

Transmission Removal

Turbo Hydra-Matic 350, 400 (Except "K" Models)

1. Raise truck and drain oil. Disconnect TCS wire where necessary.
2. Disconnect vacuum modulator line, speedometer drive cable, manual control lever rod and detent cable from transmission.
3. Disconnect driveshaft.
4. Support transmission with jack or dolly.
5. Disconnect engine rear mount on transmission and remove support crossmember.
6. Remove converter underpan, scribe flywheel—converter alignment marks. then remove attaching bolts.
7. Support engine at oil pan rail.
8. Lower rear end of transmission slightly and remove upper transmission to engine mounting bolts.
9. Remove remaining mounting bolts.
10. Remove transmission, making

certain to keep front end up so that converter does not fall out.
NOTE: On those models so equipped, disconnection of the catalytic converter may be necessary to provide adequate clearance for transmission removal.

Installation

NOTE: Do not permit converter to move forward after removing holding tool or strap.

To install transmission, reverse the removal procedures and torque mounting bolts to specifications. Fill transmission with oil to the proper level.

Transmission Removal

Turbo Hydra-Matic 350, 400 ("K" Models)

1. Raise truck and drain oil.
2. Remove transfer case shift lever and rod. Disconnect TCS wire where necessary.
3. Disconnect vacuum modulator line, speedometer drive cable, manual control lever rod and detent cable from transmission.
4. Disconnect front and rear axle driveshafts at transfer case.
5. Remove attaching transmission to adapter case bolts and support transfer case.
6. Support transmission with jack or dolly.
7. Remove attaching bolts and transfer case.
8. Remove exhaust crossover pipe (when used).
9. Remove support rear crossmember.
10. Remove converter underpan, scribe flywheel—converter alignment marks, then remove flywheel to converter bolts.
11. Support engine at oil pan rail.
12. Lower rear end of transmission slightly and remove upper trans-

mission to engine mounting bolts.
13. Remove remaining mounting bolts.
14. Remove transmission, making certain to keep front end up so that converter does not fall out.
NOTE: On those models so equipped, disconnection of the catalytic converter may be necessary to provide adequate clearance for transmission removal.

Installation

To install transmission, reverse the removal procedures and torque mounting bolts to specifications. Fill transmission with oil to the proper level.

Allison (AT 475) Transmission

Removal

NOTE: It may be necessary to remove the air tanks, fuel tanks, special equipment, etc., on some vehicles to provide clearance before the transmission is removed.

1. Block vehicle so that it cannot move. Disconnect ground strap from battery negative post. Remove the spark plugs so the engine can be turned over manually.
2. Remove the oil level gauge (dipstick). Drain transmission by disconnecting oil filler tube at right side of transmission. Remove bracket holding oil filler tube to transmission and remove

Installation

1. Raise vehicle sufficiently to allow installation of transmission. With transmission assembly mounted on transmission jack move transmission into position aligning converter with flex plate. Check for and clean away any foreign material in flywheel

Engine rear mounting—AT-475

55-70 FT. LBS. (292 & 350 ENGINES)
60-70 FT.LBS. (366 ENGINE)

FLEX PLATE

25-30 FT.LBS.

CONVERTER

REAR FACE OF ENGINE BLOCK

Flex plate installed (in line and V-8 engines) AT-475

CONVERTER

20-25 FT.-LBS.

WASHER

FLEX PLATE

CRANKSHAFT

100-110 FT.-LBS.

FLYWHEEL

Flex plate installation (V-6 engine)—AT-475

pilot hole and flywheel flex-plate assembly and front face of transmission case. Rotate flywheel ring gear, as necessary, so that the six bolt holes in flex plate are aligned with bolt holes in converter. Carefully move transmission assembly toward engine so flex-plate-to-converter bolts can be loosely installed and so that pilot on transmission converter enters pilot hole in center of flywheel flex-plate assembly.

2. Install bolts and washers that attach transmission case to flywheel housing. Tighten bolts to 23-30 ft lbs torque.
3. Tighten the six flex plate-to-converter bolts.

In-Line and V8 Engines . 25-30 ft lbs
V6 Engines . . . . 20-25 ft lbs

4. Install engine rear support.

NOTE: An arrow is stamped in the center of the engine rear support.

This arrow should face the front of vehicle when equipped with 292, 350, or 379 engines. The arrow should face the rear of vehicle when equipped with 366 engine.

5. Carefully lower engine and transmission assembly onto engine rear support. Tighten engine rear support-to-transmission bolts to torques specified. Bend lock tabs down over heads of bolts (where used). Remove lifting equipment from beneath vehicle.
6. Install the sheet metal underpan beneath the converter housing.
7. Remove plugs from oil cooler lines and transmission case fittings. Be sure fittings are clean and lint-free, then connect oil cooler lines to transmission.
8. Install oil cooler tube and bracket on right side of transmission. Install oil level gauge (dipstick).
9. Connect the speedometer shaft fitting to adapter at rear of transmission.
10. Connect propeller shaft to transmission.
11. Connect parking brake linkage (if used) at side of transmission.
12. Connect the manual selector cable to shift lever at left side of transmission.
13. Connect the vacuum modulator line to modulator. Connect wiring to neutral safety and back-up lamp switch.

NOTE: Make sure the ignition switch is in the off position before proceeding to the next step.

14. Install spark plugs and connect battery ground strap, previously disconnected.
15. Connect any other lines, hoses, or wires which were disconnected to aid in transmission removal.
16. Adjust the shift linkage. (See "Shift Linkage Adjustment.")
17. Refill the transmission with the proper lubricant.

Allison (M-40, AT-41, AT 540) Transmission

Removal

NOTE: It may be necessary to remove the air tanks, fuel tanks, special equipment, etc., on some vehicles to provide clearance before the transmission is removed.

1. Block vehicle so that it cannot move. Disconnect ground strap from battery negative (-) post. Remove the spark plugs so the engine can be turned over manually.
2. Remove the oil level gauge (dipstick). Drain transmission by disconnecting oil filler tube at right side of transmission oil pan. Remove bracket holding oil

filler tube to transmission and remove filler tube from vehicle. Replace dipstick in tube and cover the oil pan opening to prevent entry of foreign material.

3. Disconnect oil cooler lines from fittings on right side of transmission case. Plug line ends and case openings with lint-free material.
4. Disconnect the range selector cable from shift lever at left side of transmission.
5. Disconnect vacuum modulator line from modulator. Also, on conventional cab models, disconnect wiring from neutral safety and back-up lamp switches.
6. Disconnect the speedometer shaft fitting from adapter at rear of transmission.
7. Disconnect the propeller shaft from transmission.

55-70 FT.-LBS. (350 ENGINE)
60-70 FT.-LBS. (366 ENGINE)

FLEX PLATE

35-40 FT.-LBS.

CONVERTER

REAR FACE OF ENGINE BLOCK

Flex plate installation (V-8 engine)—AT-540.

20-25 FT.-LBS.

CONVERTER

WASHER

FLEX PLATE

CRANKSHAFT

100-110 FT.-LBS.

FLYWHEEL

Flex plate installation (V-6 engine)—AT-540.

Converter holding strap
(© G.M.C.)

8. Disconnect the mechanical parking brake linkage at the right side of the transmission (if used).
9. Through the opening in the flywheel housing, use a pry-bar, as necessary to manually turn the flywheel. As the flywheel is rotated, remove the six bolts retaining flywheel flex plate assembly to converter cover.
10. Support the transmission with a 500-pound (minimum) transmission floor jack. The jack must be positioned so transmission oil pan will not support the weight of transmission. Fasten a safety chain over top of transmission and to both sides of jack.
11. Place a support under rear of engine and remove transmission case-to-crossmember support bolts. Raise the engine to remove weight from the engine rear mounts.
12. Remove the transmission case-to-flywheel housing bolts and washers.
13. Carefully inspect transmission and surrounding area to be sure no lines, hoses, or wires will interfere with transmission removal.
NOTE: When removing transmission, keep rear of transmission lower than the front so as not to lose converter.
14. Move transmission assembly from the engine, lower the assembly carefully and move it out from the vehicle.

Installation

1. Raise vehicle sufficiently to allow installation of transmission. With transmission assembly mounted on transmission jack move transmission into position aligning converter with flywheel. Check for and clean away any foreign material in flywheel pilot hole, flywheel flex plate assembly, and front face of transmission case. Rotate flywheel as necessary so that the six bolt holes in flex plate are aligned with bolt holes in converter cover. Carefully move transmission assembly toward engine so flex plate-to-converter cover bolts can be loosely installed and so that pilot on transmission converter enters pilot hole in center of flywheel.
2. Install bolts and washers that attach transmission case to flywheel housing. Tighten bolts to 25-30 ft lbs torque.
3. Tighten the six flex plate-to-converter cover bolts to 35-40 ft lbs torque.
4. Carefully lower engine and transmission assembly onto engine rear mounts. Tighten engine rear mounting bolts to 60-70 ft lbs torque. Then bend lock tabs down over head of each bolt. Remove lifting equipment from beneath vehicle.
5. Remove plugs from oil cooler lines and transmission case fittings. Be sure fittings are clean and lint-free, then connect oil cooler lines to transmission.
6. Install oil filler tube and bracket on right side of transmission. Install oil level gauge (dipstick).
7. Connect the speedometer shaft fitting to adapter at rear of transmission.
8. Connect propeller shaft to transmission.
9. Connect parking brake linkage (if used) at side of transmission.
10. Connect the range selector cable to shift lever at left side of transmission.

11. Connect the vacuum modulator line to modulator. Also, on conventional cab models, connect wiring to neutral safety and back-up lamp switches.
NOTE: Make sure the ignition switch is in the off position before proceeding to the next step.
12. Install spark plugs and connect battery ground strap, previously disconnected.
13. Connect any other lines, hoses, or wires which were disconnected to aid in transmission removal.
14. Adjust the shift linkage. (See "Shift Linkage Adjustment.")
15. Refill the transmission with the proper lubricant.

Allison (MT 640, MT 650) Transmission

Removal

NOTE: It may be necessary to remove the air tanks, fuel tanks, special equipment, etc., on some vehicles to provide clearance before the transmission is removed.

1. Block vehicle so that it cannot move. Disconnect ground strap from battery negative (-) post. Remove the spark plugs so the engine can be turned over manually.
2. Remove the oil level gauge (dipstick). Drain transmission by disconnecting oil filler tube at right side of transmission oil pan. Remove bracket holding oil filler tube to transmission and remove filler tube from vehicle. Replace dipstick in tube and cover the oil pan opening to prevent entry of foreign material.
3. Disconnect oil cooler lines from fittings on right side of transmission case. Plug line ends and case openings with lint free material.
4. Disconnect shift cable from shift lever at left side of transmission.
5. Disconnect vacuum modulator line from modulator. Also, disconnect wiring from back-up lamp switch (right side of transmission) and neutral safety switch (left side of transmission).
6. Disconnect the speedometer shaft fitting from adapter at rear of transmission.
7. Disconnect the propeller shaft from transmission.
8. Disconnect the mechanical parking brake linkage at the right side of the transmission (if used).
9. Through access opening in the flywheel housing, use a pry bar, as necessary to manually turn the flywheel. As the flywheel is rotated, remove the six nuts re-

taining flex plate assembly to converter cover.

10. Support the transmission with a 750-pound (minimum rating) transmission floor jack. The jack must be positioned so transmission oil pan will not support the weight of transmission. Fasten a safety chain over top of transmission and to both sides of jack.

11. Place a support under rear of engine and remove transmission case-to-crossmember support bolts. Raise the engine to remove weight from the engine rear mounts.

12. Remove the transmission case-to-flywheel housing bolts and washers.

13. Carefully inspect transmission and surrounding area to be sure no lines, hoses, or wires will interfere with transmission removal.

NOTE: When removing transmission keep rear of transmission lower than the front so as not to lose converter.

14. Move transmission assembly from the engine, lower the assembly carefully and move it out from the vehicle.

Installation

1. Raise vehicle sufficiently to allow installation of transmission. With transmission assembly mounted on transmission jack move transmission into position aligning converter with flywheel. Check for and clean away any foreign material in flywheel pilot hole, flex plate assembly, and front face of transmission case. Rotate flywheel as necessary so that the six studs in converter cover are aligned with holes in flex plate. Carefully move transmission assembly toward engine so flex plate-to-converter cover nuts can be loosely installed and so that pilot on transmission converter enters pilot hole in center of flywheel.

2. Install bolts and washers that attach transmission case-to-flywheel housing. Tighten bolts to 12-16 ft lbs torque.

3. Tighten the six flex plate-to-converter cover nuts to 34-40 ft lbs torque.

4. Carefully lower engine and transmission assembly onto engine rear mounts. Tighten engine rear mounting nuts to 190-210 ft lbs torque. Remove lifting equipment from beneath vehicle.

5. Remove plugs from oil cooler lines and transmission case fittings. Be sure fittings are clean and lint-free, then connect oil cooler lines-to-transmission.

6. Install oil filler tube and bracket on right side of transmission. In-

stall oil level gauge (dipstick).

7. Connect the speedometer shaft fitting to adapter at rear of transmission.

8. Connect propeller shaft to transmission.

9. Connect parking brake linkage (if used) at side of transmission.

10. Connect shift cable to shift lever at left side of transmission.

11. Connect the vacuum modulator line to modulator. Also, connect wiring to neutral safety switch (left side of transmission) and back-up lamp switch (right side of transmission).

NOTE: Make sure the ignition switch is in the off position before proceeding to the next step.

12. Install spark plugs and connect battery ground strap, previously disconnected.

13. Connect any other lines, hoses, or wires which were disconnected to aid in transmission removal.

14. Adjust the shift linkage. (See "Shift Linkage Adjustment.")

15. Refill the transmission with the proper lubricant.

Refer to the General Repair Section for overhaul procedures.

Adjustments

Before making any checks or adjustments on automatic transmission linkage, test the engine performance. It is important that performance meets specifications. Many times the cause for poor shifting can be traced to the engine, and unnecessary linkage adjustments need not be made.

The following procedures are intended as a guide only. Different models utilize various linkage arrangements, and the adjustment steps followed will vary accordingly.

Flex plate installation—MT—640, MT-650.

Allison

TV Linkage Adjustment

Type (MT-40, AT-41)

1. Start engine and adjust idle speed. Stop engine. NOTE: Letters A through K refer to illustrations.

2. Disconnect clevis (G) from TV lever (F) and position lever (A) 0.060″ from stop (B).

3. Set throttle lever (C) at idle and adjust swivels on rod (I) for free entry into levers (A, B).

4. Shorten clevis (G) 2 full turns. Install clevis pin, tighten nut and secure (G) to (F) with cotter pin.

5. With accelerator pedal (D) just touching detent button (E), the throttle lever should be in full open position. Shorten or lengthen rods to achieve correct relationship.

6. Road test truck. Upshift should occur at 50 rpm below top governed engine speed. To raise the shift point, shorten rod (H); to lower shift point, lengthen rod (H).

Manual Linkage Adjustment

Type (MT-40, AT-41)

1. Locate selector lever in the illustrated position.

2. Adjust cable as shown in illustration.

3. Disconnect clevis from manual shift lever.

4. Adjust clevis for free entry of pin, then lengthen clevis by 1½ turns, install pin, tighten lock nut, and secure with cotter pin.

Turbo-Hydra-Matic

Shift Linkage

Check for adjustment with engine off, lift gearshift lever towards steering wheel, allow gearshift lever to be positioned in Drive (D) by the transmission detent. DO NOT use the indicator pointer to position the gearshift lever. Pointer is adjusted (or set) after linkage adjustment is made. Release gearshift lever. Lever must drop back into position, with no restriction, and be inhibited from engaging low range (unless lifted). Lift gearshift lever towards steering wheel and allow the lever to be positioned in Neutral (N) by the transmission detent. Release gearshift lever. The lever should now be inhibited from engaging reverse range (unless lifted). A properly adjusted linkage will prevent the gearshift lever from moving beyond both the Neutral detent and the Drive detent unless lever is lifted to pass over the mechanical stop in steering column.

TILT CAB MODELS

TV linkage adjustment—Allison—MT-40, AT-41.

Manual linkage adjustment—Allison—MT-40, AT-41

Manual selector linkage—"P" models (Turbo Hydra-Matic)
(© G.M.C.)

Detent cable adjustment (Turbo Hydra-Matic 350)
(© G.M.C.)

Linkage Adjustment

1970-1976 Cabs, Suburbans, 4-Wheel Drive
1974-76—Forward Control Exc. Vans

1. Place gearshift lever in Drive (D), as determined by transmission detent. Obtain Drive position by rotating transmission lever (A) counterclockwise to low detent, then clockwise two detent positions to Drive.
2. Loosen adjustment swivel at mast jacket lever (B) and rotate transmission lever (A) so that it contacts the Drive stop in the steering column.
3. Tighten swivel and recheck adjustment.

4. Readjust indicator pointer, if necessary, to agree with transmission detent positions.
5. Readjust Neutral safety switch if necessary (C).

Linkage Adjustment

1970-73—Forward Control
1970-74—Vans

1. Set transmission lever (E) in Drive position. Obtain Drive position by rotating transmission lever (E) counter-clockwise to Low detent, then clockwise two detent positions to Drive.

2. Attach control rod (D) to lever (E) and shaft assembly (B) with retainers.
3. Assemble ring, washers, grommet, swivel, retainer and nut loosely on shaft (B).
4. Insert control rod (C) in swivel and retainer, attach opposite end to tube and lever assembly.
5. Set tube lever assembly in Drive position and tighten nut (F).

NOTE: When above procedure is adhered to, the following conditions must be met by manual operation of the gearshift lever. From Reverse to Drive position travel, the transmis-

GMC Trucks • Vans • Jimmy

Linkage adjustment—Turbo Hydra-matic—1970-76 Cabs. 1974-76 Forward control exc. Vans

Linkage adjustment—Turbo Hydra-Matic 1975-76 Vans.

sion detent feel must be noted and related to indicated position on dial. When in Drive and Reverse position, pull lever toward steering wheel and then release. It must drop back into position with no restriction.

Linkage Adjustment

1975-76—Vans

1. The shift tube and lever assembly must be free in the mast jacket.
2. Set transmission lever (C) in "neutral" position by one of the following optional methods.

NOTE: Obtain "neutral" position by moving transmission lever (C) counter-clockwise to "L1," detent, then clockwise three detent positions to "neutral" or obtain "neutral" position by moving transmission lever (C) clockwise to the "park" detent then counter-clockwise two detents to "neutral."

4. Set the column shift lever in "neutral" position. This is obtained by rotating shift lever until it locks into mechanical stop in the column assembly.

NOTE: Do not use indicator pointer as a reference to position the shift lever.

4. Attach rod (A) to shaft assembly (B) as shown.

Linkage adjustment—Turbo-Hydra-Matic 1970-73 Forward control, 1970-74 Vans.

5. Slide swivel (D) and clamp (E) onto rod (A). Align the column shift lever and loosely attach as shown.
6. Hold column lever against "neutral" stop "park" position side.
7. Tighten nut (F) to 18 ft lbs.
8. Readjust indicator needle if necessary to agree with the transmission detent positions.
9. Readjust neutral start switch if necessary to provide the correct relationship to the transmission detent positions.

CAUTION: Any inaccuracies in the above adjustments may result in premature failure of the transmission due to operation without controls in full detent position. Such operation results in reduced oil pressure and partial engagement of clutches.

Detent Switch

Turbo Hydra-matic 350

A hydraulic system, pressurized by a gear pump, provides the working pressure required to operate the friction elements and automatic controls. The vacuum modulator is of the aneroid type and is used to automatically sense any change in torque input to the transmission. It transmits this signal to the pressure regulator, to the intermediate clutch accumulator valve and to the shift valves so that all torque and shift speed requirements of the transmission are met and smooth shifts are obtained at all throttle openings. A cable operated detent system controls downshifting for passing speeds.

Adjustment

1. Remove air cleaner.
2. Loosen detent cable screw.
3. With choke off and accelerator linkage properly adjusted, position carburetor lever in wide open throttle position.
4. Pull detent cable rearward until wide open throttle stop in transmission is felt.

NOTE: Cable must be pulled through detent position to reach wide open throttle stop in transmission.

5. Tighten detent cable screw and check linkage for proper operation.

Turbo Hydra-matic 400/475

6. A hydraulic system pressurized by a gear pump provides the working pressure required to operate the friction elements and automatic controls. A vacuum modulator is used to automatically sense any change in torque input to the transmission. The vacuum modulator transmits this signal to the pressure regulator for line pressure control, to the 1-2 accumulator valve, and to the shift valves so that all torque requirements of this transmission are met and smooth shifts are obtained at all throttle openings. A detent solenoid, activated by an electrical switch on carburetor, controls downshift for passing speeds.

Neutral Safety Switch Adjustment

1. Place gearshift lever in Neutral (N).
2. Loosen retainer screws holding switch, install 3/32 in. drill (or pin) through hole in lower switch arm and bracket. Adjust

288

6 CYLINDER ENGINE

WITH ACCELERATOR CONTROLS PROPERLY ADJUSTED, ROTATE LEVER TO OBTAIN WIDE OPEN THROTTLE. POSITION SWITCH TO OBTAIN DIM. A SHOWN IN TABLE BETWEEN PLUNGER AND LEVER. TIGHTEN SWITCH ATTACHING SCREWS.

	DIM. A
ALL EXCEPT 350 V8	.05
350 V8	.20

LEVER

SWITCH — PLUNGER — A

307 V-8 ENGINE

350 ENGINE

Detent switch adjustment (Turbo Hydra-Matic 400) (© G.M.C.)

position of switch until engine turns over (with ignition switch in start).

Transmission Mounted

1. Place gearshift lever in Neutral (N), loosen transmission lever extension bolt.
2. Pin switch lever in Neutral position with 3/32 in. drill or pin.
3. Install rod into switch lever, adjust swivel on rod to allow free entry of rod into lever.
4. Secure rod with retainer, tighten transmission lever extension bolt.
5. Check adjustment by testing for cranking in both Neutral and Park.

Shift Linkage Adjustment

Allison (AT 475, AT 450, MT 640, MT 650) Transmissions

With engine off and vehicle wheels blocked, shift the selector lever through each drive range "R," "N," "D," "3," "2," "1" (AT 540 and MT 640), "R," "N," "D," "L2," "L1" (AT 475), "R," "N," "2-5," "2-4," "2," "1" (MT 650) while feeling for full engagement in the transmission. The transmission shift control linkage should fully engage all transmission detent poitions in the transmission just before the range selector lever hits the stops incorporated in the range selector cover. Note the position of the selector lever after each shift. The transmission detent "R"

(Reverse) should not engage until the selector lever is completely out of the neutral notch. Kf the selector lever is not properly located or operating, adjust the linkage.

RANGE SELECTOR LEVER

CABLE CORE
TRUNNION
JAM NUT
"A"
LOCK NUT
CONTROL CABLE ASSEMBLY
SEAL
HANGER
LOCK NUT
U-BOLT

Trunion and cable core assembly—Allison Trans.

Gas and Diesel Engines

1. Disconnect clevis from transmission shift lever by removing cotter pin and clevis pin.
2. Disconnect control cable from anchor point at bracket on transmission and remove cable retainer clips from underside of cab.
3. Remove four cross recess screws retaining range selector cover to tower or bracket, depending on truck model. Lift range selector assembly out to inspect cable attachment at range selector lever and hanger.
4. Check cable at trunnion for dimension "A" as shown. This dimension is necessary to allow for proper cable length at clevis. If adjustment is necessary, remove cable from range selector lever and hanger assembly as follows:
   a. Remove ½-inch locknut from trunnion.
   b. Disconnect cable from anchor point on hanger by removing two locknuts and U-bolt.

NOTE: Locknuts can be removed and reinstalled up to six times before their replacement becomes necessary.

   c. Mark location of trunnion. Remove trunnion with attached cable core from lever.

CAUTION: The trunnion has been placed in the proper hole at the factory. Any change in the location could cause vehicle operation to be dangerous.

DIM. "A"
AT 475   1/2-INCH
AT 540   3/8-INCH
MT 640-650 1/4-INCH

Trunion adjustment—Allison Trans.

Clevis adjustment—Allison Trans.

5. With control cable removed, loosen jam nut at trunnion.

NOTE: Do not use pliers on cable core when loosening jam nut or when adjusting trunnion. Cable core finish may be damaged resulting in cable core seal damage.

6. Turn trunnion clockwise, or counterclockwise to attain dimension "A." Tighten jam nut against trunnion.

7. Install trunnion in its original hole and tighten locknut securely.

8. Anchor cable to hanger with U-bolt, washers and locknuts. Tighten locknuts 3-5 ft lbs torque.

9. Install shift control cover in tower or bracket depending on truck model. Install four cross recess screws. Tighten screws 3-5 ft lbs torque. Install cable clips to underside of cab.

10. Anchor cable to bracket at transmission.

11. Locate transmission shift lever in "R" (Reverse) position.

NOTE: "R" position if full counterclockwise (except on AT 475 "full clockwise") movement of lever.

12. Locate range selector lever against stop in "R" (Reverse) position.

13. Loosen jam nut at clevis. Turn clevis clockwise or counterclockwise on threaded cable core until holes in clevis align with hole in shift lever. Install clevis pin, note that pin should enter freely, if it does not, adjust clevis slightly by ½ turn in each direction until pin does enter freely.

14. Turn clevis one full turn clockwise to allow for cable backlash.

15. Connect clevis to shift lever with clevis pin and a new cotter pin, but do not spread cotter pin at this time.

15. Move the range selector lever through all drive ranges. The transmission detents should fully engage just before the range selector lever hits the stops incorporated in the shift control cover.

Throttle Valve Linkage Adjustment Diesel Engines

1. Apply parking brake and block vehicle's driving wheels.
2. Disconnect upper TV cable end from accelerator cross shaft.

3. Push upper cable end toward transmission modulator until seated against the stop.
4. Assemble slotted clevis end to cable with locknut.
5. With accelerator linkage in "IDLE" position, upper end of the slotted clevis must be against the clevis pin on the cross shaft lever.
6. Shorten cable at slotted clevis by turning clevis three complete turns clockwise to locate lower end of the cable in actuator ⅛-inch from idle stop.
7. Tighten locknut securely.
8. Assemble slotted clevis to cross shaft lever with clevis pin and a new cotter pin.
9. Attach TV return spring to bracket.

Neutral Safety and Back-up Lamp Switch Check and Adjustment

Allison (AT 475) Transmission 1970-74

NOTE: "Shift Linkage Adjustment" should be performed as de-

Throttle valve linkage (diesel engine)—Allison Trans.

Neutral safety and back-up lamp switch—1975-76 AT-475 trans.

Shift linkage—AT-475 trans.

Shift linkage—AT-540 trans.

scribed previously, prior to adjustment of the neutral safety switch.

1. Block driving wheels, apply parking brake, and perform the following to prevent the vehicle from accidentally starting.

NOTE: Pull the secondary wire out of socket in distributor cap and ground wire to prevent possible damage to coil.

2. Position the selector lever (B) in "N" (Neutral). Turn ignition switch to "START" position. Engine should turn over but not start. Turn ignition switch to "OFF."

3. Position selector lever in "R" (Reverse). Turn ignition switch to "START" position. Engine should not turn over or start.

4. Move selector lever to "D" (Drive) position. Turn ignition switch to "START" position. Again the engine should not turn over or start. Turn ignition switch to "OFF."

5. If the conditions in Steps 2 through 4 are not met, the neutral safety and back-up lamp switch (F) must be adjusted as follows:

6. Disconnect and remove swivel (I) from transmission shift lever (H). Position transmission selector lever (B) in "N" (Neutral).

7. Locate the switch lever (F) of the neutral safety and back-up lamp switch in neutral position.

Neutral position of the switch lever is achieved by inserting a 3/32-in. diameter pin at location (E) through switch lever and into switch bracket.

8. Position swivel (I) on rod (J) to provide free-entry of swivel into shift lever (H). Secure swivel with two retainers.

9. Repeat Steps 2 through 4. If switch does not operate properly it must be replaced and adjustment procedure repeated.

Allison (AT 475) Transmission 1975-76

NOTE: "Shift Linkage Adjustment" should be performed prior to adjustment of neutral safety switch.

1. Block driving wheels, apply parking brake, and perform the following to prevent vehicle from accidentally starting:
   Pull the secondary wire out of the socket in the distributor cap and ground the wire to prevent possible damage to the coil.

2. Position the range selector lever to "N" (Neutral). Turn ignition switch to "Start" position. Engine should crank, but not start. Turn ignition to "Off."

3. Position range selector lever in "R" (Reverse). Turn ignition switch to "Start" position. Engine should not crank or start. Turn ignition switch to "Off."

4. Move range selector lever to "D" (Drive) position. Turn ignition

switch to "Start" position. Again the engine should not crank or start. Turn ignition switch to "Off."

5. If the conditions in Steps 2 through 4 are not met, the neutral safety and back-up lamp switch must be adjusted as follows:
   a. Place range selector lever in "N" (Neutral) position.
   b. Loosen two screws attaching switch assembly to transmission mounting bracket. Check to see that actuating rod is secure.
   c. Locate switch in neutral position with a 3/32-in. diameter pin in hole H through switch lever G and bracket.
   d. Tighten switch to bracket screws to 15-20 in lbs torque.
   e. Repeat Steps 2 through 4 to check switch operation. Readjust switch if necessary or replace if found defective.

Neutral Safety and Back-Up Lamp Switch Adjustment

Allison (AT 540) Transmission Tilt & Schoolbus Models

NOTE: "Shift Linkage Adjustment" should be performed as described previously, prior to adjustment of the neutral safety and back-up lamp switch.

1. Block driving wheels, apply

THROTTLE RETURN SPRING

ADJUSTING SCREWS

.05"

THROTTLE LEVER (WIDE OPEN POSITION)

DOWNSHIFT SWITCH (PLUNGER FULLY DEPRESSED)

Downshift linkage—AT-475 trans.

parking brake, and perform the following to prevent the vehicle from accidentally starting.

NOTE: Pull the secondary wire out of center socket in the distributor cap and ground wire to prevent possible damage to coil.

2. Move selector lever (B) to "N" (Neutral) position. Then loosen jam nuts and adjust length of push rod to dimension shown.
3. With switch push rod properly adjusted, tighten jam nuts securely.
4. Check each range position of shift linkage to make sure the starter does not operate with the selector lever in any position other than "N." Have assistant check for proper operation of back-up lights with selector lever in "R". If necessary, readjust switch.
5. Reconnect secondary wire to distributor cap.

NOTE: The neutral safety and back-up lamp switches are non-adjustable on the Allison-MT-640, MT-650 transmission and all diesel engines with automatic transmissions.

Downshift Switch Adjustment

Allison (AT 475) Transmission

The downshift switch mounted at the carburetor is activated by the carburetor throttle lever. When the throttle lever reaches wide open position it results in a forced downshift to the transmission unless vehicle is in "L1."

1. Move carburetor throttle lever to wide open position.
2. Loosen two adjusting screws (at slotted holes) on switch bracket.
3. Position switch and bracket assembly so that clearance between throttle lever and switch plunger (fully depressed) is .05 in.
4. Tighten the two adjusting screws to 20-30 in lbs torque.
5. Road test and check for proper operation.

Drive Axle, Suspension

Driveshaft and Universal Joint

Removal

1. Raise vehicle.
2. Mark shaft and companion flange alignment.
3. Disconnect rear universal joint by removing attaching U-bolt or strap.
4. Remove bearing support bolts as necessary.
5. Slide driveshaft forward to disengage trunnion, then back to disengage transmission.

Installation

1 Piece Driveshaft

1. Slide shaft into transmission and connect rear U-joint.
2. Torque bolts to specifications.

Installation

2 Piece Driveshaft

1. Insert front shaft into transmission and bolt support to crossmember.
2. Install grease cap and gasket on rear splines.
3. Align all U-joint trunnions in the same vertical position, then install rear shaft.
4. Connect rear U-joint to axle.
5. Torque all bolts to specifications and tighten grease cap.

Universal Joint Overhaul

Snap Ring Type

1000-3500 Models

1. Remove bearing lock rings.
2. Support yoke in an arbor press and apply pressure on trunnion until bearing cup is almost out. NOTE: Bearing cup cannot be fully pressed out.

3. Grasp cup with vise and work out of yoke.
4. Repeat procedure on the opposite side.
5. Clean and inspect all parts; replace as necessary. Pack bearings and make certain to fill lubricant reservoirs at end of each trunnion. Place dust seals on trunnions and press into position.
6. Position trunnion into yoke and partially install one bearing cup.
7. Partially install opposite cup and then press them both into place.
8. Install lock rings.

Plastic Retaining Ring Type

Disassembly

1. Support the drive shaft in a horizontal position in line with the base plate of a press. Place the universal joint so that the lower ear of the shaft yoke is supported on a 1⅛ in. socket. Place the cross press, J-9522-3 or equivalent, on the open horizontal bearing cups, and press the lower bearing cup out of the yoke ear as shown in the illustration. This will shear the plastic retaining the lower bearing cup.
2. If the bearing cup is not completely removed, lift the cross and insert Spacer J-9522-5 or equivalent, between the seal and bearing cup being removed, as shown in figure 2.

   Complete the removal of the bearing cup, by pressing it out of the yoke.
3. Rotate the drive shaft, shear the opposite plastic retainer, and press the opposite bearing cup out of the yoke as before, using Spacer J-9522.

Driveshaft U-bolt attachment
(© G.M.C.)

Driveshaft strap attachment
(© G.M.C.)

MULTI-SHAFT TYPE

Transmission

Axle

WITH AUXILIARY TRANSMISSION

Transmission

Axle

SINGLE SHAFT TYPE

Transmission

Axle

1 Universal joint
2 Slip yoke
3 Shaft
4 Center bearing

Transmission

Axle

Transmission

DUAL SHAFT TYPE

Axle

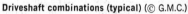

Driveshaft combinations (typical) (© G.M.C.)

1 Trunnion
2 Seal
3 Bearings
4 Cap
5 Snap ring

Universal joint repair kit—(snap ring type)

Bearing cap removal—(Snap ring type)

CENTER YOKE

FRONT YOKE

REAR TRUNNION

REAR YOKE HALF

Driving out bearing caps (Snap ring type)

Installing U-joint trunnion (Snap ring type)

Pressing out bearing cup (Plastic retaining ring type)

Using spacer to remove bearing cup (Plastic retaining ring type)

4. Disengage the cross from the yoke and remove.

NOTE: Production universal joints cannot be reassembled. There are no bearing retainer grooves in production bearing cups. Discard all universal joint parts removed.

5. Remove the remains of the sheared plastic bearing retainer from the ears of the yoke. This will aid in reassembly of the service joint bearing cups. It usually is easier to remove plastic if a small pin or punch is first driven through the injection holes.

6. If the front universal joint is being serviced, remove the pair of bearing cups from the slip yoke in the same manner.

Reassembly

1. A universal joint service kit is used when reassembling this joint. This kit includes one pregreased cross assembly, four service bearing cup assemblies with seals, needle rollers, washers, grease and four bearing retainers.

2. Make sure that the seals are in place on the service bearing cups to hold the needle rollers in place for handling.

3. Remove all of the remains of the sheared plastic bearing retainers from the grooves in the yokes.

Aligning U-joints (© G.M.C.)

The sheared plastic may prevent the bearing cups from being pressed into place, and this prevents the bearing retainers from being properly sealed.

4. Install one bearing cup part way into one side of the yoke, and turn this yoke ear to the bottom.

5. Insert cross into yoke so that the trunnion seats freely into bearing cup as shown in illustration.

6. Install opposite bearing cup part way. Make sure that both trunnions are started straight and true into both bearing cups.

7. Press against opposite bearing cups, working the cross all of the time to check for free movement of the trunnions in the bearings.

Installing trunnion into yoke (Plastic retaining ring type)

Installing plastic snap rings.

If there isn't, stop pressing and recheck needle rollers to determine if one or more of them has been tipped under the end of the trunnion.

8. As soon as one bearing retainer groove clears the inside of the yoke, stop pressing and snap the bearing retainer into place as shown in the illustration.

9. Continue to press until the opposite bearing retainer can be snapped into place. If difficulty is encountered, strike the yoke firmly with a hammer to aid in seating bearing retainers. This springs the yoke ears slightly.

10. Assemble the other half of the universal joint in the same manner.

11. Check the freedom of rotation of both sets of trunnions of the cross. If too tight, again rap the yoke ears as described above. This will loosen the bearings and help seat the bearing retainers.

Seating plastic snap rings.

Universal Joint Overhaul

4500-7500 Models

1. Remove bearing retaining snap rings or U-bolts.

2. Strike one side of yoke with hammer to remove bearing. Repeat on opposite side.

3. Tilt journal and remove yoke.
4. Remove remaining bearings in the same manner as step (2).
5. Clean all parts with cleaning fluid. Make certain lubricating passages in journal cross are clear, and all old lubricant has been removed. Check for wear and any missing bearing rollers. If any excessive wear is noted, discard bearings and journal; replace with new parts. Lubricate as recommended in specifications.
6. Install lubrication fitting in journal.
7. Install journal in yoke, then install bearings using a mallet to tap them in place.
8. Install bearing retaining snap rings or U-bolts and torque nuts (when used) to specifications.

Rear Axle Assembly

Removal

3500 and 5500 Lbs Capacity Axle (Models 1500-3500)

1. Raise truck and support rear axle to relieve load from springs, tie-rod, and shock absorbers.
2. Disconnect tie-rod at axle (when used).
3. Disconnect driveshaft. NOTE: Secure bearing caps to trunnion with tape.
4. Disconnect shock absorbers.
5. Disconnect vent hose.
6. Disconnect brake hose on axle housing. Remove brake drum and disconnect parking brake cable.
7. Make certain coil springs (when used) are compressed, then remove U-bolts, spacers and clamp plates.
8. Withdraw axle assembly.

Installation

3500 and 5500 Lb. Capacity Axle (Models 1500-3500)

To install axle assembly, reverse the removal procedure, bleed brake system, adjust parking brake and torque all bolts to specifications.

Removal

11,000 Lb. Capacity Axle (Models 1500-3500)

1. Raise truck, support frame side rails and remove rear wheels.
2. Disconnect driveshaft. NOTE: Secure bearing caps to trunnion with tape.
3. Disconnect brake hose and shock absorbers.
4. Remove drum and disconnect parking brake.
5. Support axle, remove spring U-bolts and then withdraw assembly.

Installation

11,000 Lb. Capacity Axle (Models 1500-3500)

To install axle assembly, reverse the removal procedure, bleed brake system, adjust parking brake and torque all bolts to specifications.

Removal

11,000 Lb. Capacity Axle (Models 4500-7500)

1. Raise rear of truck and support frame rails.
2. Disconnect brake lines and electrical wiring.
3. Disconnect driveshaft and torque or radius rods (when used).
4. Remove spring U-bolts and withdraw axle assembly.

Installation

11,000 Lb. Capacity Axle (Models 4500-7500)

To install axle assembly, mount wheels and tires, roll axle under truck and reverse the removal procedure. Bleed brake system, fill axle with lubricant to proper level and torque all bolts to specifications. Refer to General Repair Section for complete overhaul procedures and out of truck adjustments.

Locking Differentials

Refer to General Repair Section for complete overhaul procedures.

Leaf Spring Removal

(1500-3500 Models)

1. Raise truck.
2. Loosen, but do not remove, spring to shackle retaining nut.
3. Remove shackle to spring hanger attaching bolt.
4. Remove attaching spring to front hanger bolt.
5. Remove U-bolts and then remove spring.

Installation

(1500-3500 Models)

To install leaf spring assembly, reverse the removal procedure and torque nuts and bolts to specifications. NOTE: Torque nuts and bolts *after* lowering the truck.

Coil Spring Removal

1500-3500 Models

1. Raise truck on hoist and support rear axle.
2. Disconnect shock absorber at control arm bracket.
3. Remove upper and lower spring clamps.
4. Lower control arm enough to remove spring.

Installation

1500-3500 Models

1. Position clamp in spring.
2. Install spring and clamp loosely; torque upper clamp nut to specifications.
3. Connect shock absorber and torque to specifications.
4. Torque lower clamp nut to specifications.
5. Remove axle support and lower truck.

Leaf Spring Removal

4500-7500 Models

1. Remove rebound pin locks or retainers, then remove rebound pins.
2. Install a C-clamp on radius leaf, remove eye bolts or radius lead pin clamp bolts, then remove C-clamp.
3. Remove lubrication fitting and disconnect spring at rear mounting.
4. Remove U-bolts, spacer plate and shock absorber bracket.
5. Remove spring and spacer or shim.

Installation

4500-7500 Models

To install leaf spring, reverse the removal procedure and torque all bolts to specifications. NOTE: Torque U-bolts *after* lowering truck.

Auxiliary Springs

Some models are equipped with auxiliary springs. They are mounted to brackets on the frame and are usually held to the main spring by long U-bolts. The purpose of these springs is to provide additional stability under unusual operating conditions.

NOTE: Coil spring suspension uses an auxiliary spring as shown in illustration.

Shock Absorbers

Shock absorbers used are non-adjustable and non-repairable. Maintenance operations are limited to periodic tightening and replacement of rubber mounting grommets. If a shock absorber is worn, the complete unit must be replaced.

Tie Rod Removal

CP1500-C2500 Models

1. Raise truck.
2. Remove attaching nuts and bolts, then remove rod.

Installation

1. Position rod ends in mounting brackets, insert pivot bolts and install nuts finger tight.
2. Lower truck and torque pivot nuts to specifications.

Rear leaf spring suspension (© G.M.C.)

Installing rebound pin (typical)
(© G.M.C.)

Using C-clamp at radius leaf
(© G.M.C.)

Control Arm Removal
CP1500-C2500 Models

1. Raise truck and relieve load on springs by supporting axle.
2. Place jack under control arm.
3. Remove spring clamp bolt from underside of arm.
4. Remove U-bolt nuts; disconnect shock absorber bracket, and lower end of control arm.
5. Disconnect parking brake lever, then remove pivot bolt and control arm.

Installation

To install control arm, reverse the removal procedure. Torque spring clamp and shock absorber BEFORE lowering truck, torque pivot bolts AFTER.

Stabilizer Shaft

P3500 Model

1. Raise truck and support axle to relieve load on U-bolts.
2. Remove the forward U-bolt re-

taining nuts, and remove shaft anchors.
3. Remove shaft retaining brackets and then remove shaft.

Installation

To install stabilizer shaft, reverse the removal procedure. Alternately torque all nuts and bolts to specifications.

NOTE: Make certain that both ends of shaft protrude equally from the anchors.

Alignment for Phasing—C and G Models Only

Index

TUNE-UP SPECIFICATIONS

CYL x CID	YEAR	SPARK PLUG GAP	DISTRIBUTOR POINT DWELL	POINT GAP	IGNITION TIMING DEGREES	CRANKING COMPRESSION PRESSURE	VALVE CLEARANCE IN	EXH	GOVERNOR NO LOAD RPM	FUEL PRESS.	IDLE SPEED STD	AUTO
4-196	1970-71	.030	68-72	.019⑤	TDC	143	0	0	——	5	475	——
4-196	1972-75	.030	26-32	.017①	TDC	143	0	0	——	5	475	——
6-232	1970-72	.035	32	.016	TDC	130	0	0	——	5	725	550
6-258	1972-74	.035	32	.016	TDC	130	0	0	——	5	675	675
8-304	1970-71	.027	30	.019	TDC	145	0	0	——	5	700	600N
8-304	1972-73	.030	30	.019	TDC	145	0	0	——	5	700	600N
8-304	1974-75	.030	30	.017①⑤	TDC	145	0	0	——	5	700	600N
6-308	1970-74	.030	32	.019	5B	110	.019H	.019H	3200	5	475	
8-345	1970-75	.027	30	.019①⑤	TDC②	143	0	0	3800	5	700	600N
8-392	1970-71	.027	30	.019	TDC	143	0	0	3600	5	700	600D
8-392	1972-75	.030	30	.019①⑤	TDC③	140	0	0	3600	5	700	600D
8-400	1973-74	.035	30	.016	5B	140	0	0	——	5	700	
8-401	1970-74	.027	30	.017	7B	140	0	0	3400	5	700	
8-404(399)	1975	.030	——	①	9B	140	0	0	3600	5	525	575
6-406	1970-74	.030	32	.019	5B	120	.025H	.025H	2450	5	475	——
8-446	1975	.030	——	①	5B	145	0	0	3600	5	525	
6-450	1970-74	.030	32	.019	5B	120	.025H	.025H	2800	5	525	—
8-478	1970-74	.027	32	.017	10B	135	0	0	3400	5	550	550
6-501	1970-74	.030	32	.019	5B	120	.025H	.025H	2800	5	525	
8-549	1970-74	.027	32	.017	7B④	140	0	0	3200	5	475	——
8-605	1975	.030	——	①	7B	N/A	0	0	N/A	5	600	650

① .008 on breakerless ignition
② LPG—10B
　Low compression—5B
③ with thermoquad—5B
④ FTV models—9B
⑤ 1972 -.016 on light duty vehicles

GENERAL ENGINE SPECIFICATIONS

CYL x CID	YEAR	BORE x STROKE	FIRING ORDER	SAE HORSEPOWER @ RPM	SAE TORQUE @ RPM	COMP. RATIO	CARBU- RETOR	VALVE LIFTER	OIL PRESSURE
4-196	1970-71	4.125 x 3.656	1-3-4-2	111 @ 4000	180 @ 2000	8.1	1V	Hyd.	50
4-196	1972-75	4.125 x 3.656	1-3-4-2	103 @ 4000	177 @ 2000	8.1	1V	Hyd.	50
6-232	1970-72	3.75 x 3.50	1-5-3-6-2-4	145 @ 4300	215 @ 1600	8.5	1V	Hyd.	32
6-258	1972	3.75 x 3.895	1-5-3-6-2-4	140 @ 3800	235 @ 1200	8.0	1V	Hyd.	32
6-258	1973-74	3.75 x 3.895	1-5-3-6-2-4	115 @ 3800	199 @ 2000	8.0	1V	Hyd.	32
8-304	1970-72	3.875 x 3.218	1-8-4-3-6-5-7-2	193 @ 4400	273 @ 2800	8.1	2V	Hyd.	45
8-304	1973-75	3.875 x 3.218	1-8-4-3-6-5-7-2	147 @ 3900	240 @ 2400	8.2	2V	Hyd.	45
8-304	1973-74	3.875 x 3.218	1-8-4-3-6-5-7-2	153 @ 3900	246 @ 2400	8.2	4V	Hyd.	45
6-308	1970-74	3.812 x 4.50	1-5-3-6-2-4	136 @ 3200	274 @ 1800	6.5	2V	Mech.	45
8-345	1970-72	3.875 x 3.656	1-8-4-3-6-5-7-2	197 @ 4000	309 @ 2200	8.0	2V	Hyd.	45
8-345	1973-75	3.875 x 3.656	1-8-4-3-6-5-7-2	157 @ 3800	266 @ 2400	8.1	2V	Hyd.	45
8-345	1973-75	3.875 x 3.656	1-8-4-3-6-5-7-2	163 @ 3800	273 @ 2400	8.1	4V	Hyd.	45
8-392	1970-72	4.125 x 3.656	1-8-4-3-6-5-7-2	236 @ 4000	357 @ 2800	8.0	4V	Hyd.	45
8-392	1973-74	4.125 x 3.656	1-8-4-3-6-5-7-2	191 @ 3600	299 @ 2800	8.0	2V	Hyd.	45
8-392	1973-75	4.125 x 3.656	1-8-4-3-6-5-7-2	194 @ 3600	308 @ 2800	8.0	4V	Hyd.	45
8-400	1973-74	4.166 x 3.680	1-8-4-3-6-5-7-2	211 @ 4000	326 @ 2800	8.25	2V	Hyd.	50
8-401	1970-72	4.125 x 3.750	1-8-7-3-6-5-4-2	206 @ 3600	355 @ 1800	7.69	2V	Hyd.	55
8-401	1973-74	4.125 x 3.750	1-8-7-3-6-5-4-2	186 @ 3400	322 @ 2400	7.69	2V	Hyd.	55
8-404 (399)	1975	4.125 x 3.740	1-2-7-3-4-5-6-8	188 @ 3600	311 @ 2300	8.1	2V	Hyd.	55
8-404 (399)	1975	4.125 x 3.740	1-2-7-3-4-5-6-8	210 @ 3600	336 @ 2800	8.1	4V	Hyd.	55
6-406	1970-72	4.375 x 4.50	1-5-3-6-2-4	193 @ 3200	373 @ 1600	7.13	2V	Mech.	50
6-406	1973-74	4.375 x 4.50	1-5-3-6-2-4	160 @ 2750	336 @ 1400	7.13	2V	Mech.	50
8-446	1975	4.125 x 4.180	1-2-7-3-4 5-6-8	235 @ 3600	385 @ 2600	8.1	4V	Hyd.	55
6-450	1970-72	4.375 x 5.0	1-5-3-6-2-4	202 @ 3000	422 @ 1600	7.06	2V	Mech.	50
6-450	1973-74	4.375 x 5.0	1-5-3-6-2-4	168 @ 2600	372 @ 1400	7.1	2V	Mech.	50
8-478	1970-72	4.50 x 3.750	1-8-7-3-6-5-4-2	234 @ 3600	431 @ 1800	7.64	2V	Hyd.	50

GENERAL ENGINE SPECIFICATIONS

CYL x CID	YEAR	BORE x STROKE	FIRING ORDER	SAE HORSEPOWER @ RPM	SAE TORQUE @ RPM	COMP. RATIO	CARBU-RETOR	VALVE LIFTER	OIL PRESSURE
8-478	1973-74	4.50 x 3.750	1-8-7-3-6-5-4-2	209 @ 3400	384 @ 2200	7.6	2V	Hyd.	55
6-501	1970-72	4.50 x 5.250	1-5-3-6-2-4	215 @ 3000	451 @ 1600	6.8	4V	Mech.	40
6-501	1973-74	4.50 x 5.250	1-5-3-6-2-4	181 @ 2600	406 @ 1400	6.8	4V	Mech.	40
8-549	1970-72	4.50 x 4.312	1-8-7-3-6-5-4-2	257 @ 3400	505 @ 2000	7.6	4V	Hyd.	55
8-549	1973-74	4.50 x 4.312	1-8-7-3-6-5-4-2	227 @ 3200	446 @ 2000	7.6	4V	Hyd.	55
8-605	1975	4.625 x 4.50	1-8-7-3-6-5-4-2	N/A	N/A	N/A	4V	Hyd.	55

N/A = Not Available

CRANKSHAFT SPECIFICATIONS

CYL x CID	MAIN BEARING JOURNALS JOURNAL DIAMETER	OIL CLEARANCE	SHAFT END PLAY	THRUST ON NO.	CONNECTING ROD JOURNALS JOURNAL DIAMETER	OIL CLEARANCE	ROD SIDE CLEARANCE
4-196	2.7484-2.7494	.0015-.0035	.003-.008	3	2.373-2.374	.0011-.0036	.008-.014
6-232	2.4981-2.500	.001-.002	.0015-.007	3	2.0934-2.0955	.001-.002	.008
6-258	2.498-2.500	.001-.002	.0015-.007	3	2.0934-2.0955	.001-.002	.008
8-304	2.7484-2.7494	.001-.004	.001-.005	3	2.373-2.374	.0011-.0036	.008-.016
6-308	2.7005-2.7015	.0013-.0043	.006-.014	4	2.122-2.123	.0007-.0032	.006-.012
8-345	2.7484-2.7494	.001-.004	.001-.005	3	2.373-2.374	.0011-.0036	.008-.016
8-392	2.7484-2.7494	.001-.004	.001-.005	3	2.373-2.374	.0011-.0033	.010-.018
8-400	2.7474-2.7489	.001-.002	.003-.008	3	2.2485-.2.2464	.001-.002	.006-.018
8-401	3.123-3.124	.0014-.0044	.006-.011	3	2.623-2.624	.0017-.0042	.010-.018
8-404(399)	3.1228-3.1236	.0010-.0036	.0025-.0085	—	2.4980-2.4990	.0011-.0036	.008-.016
6-406	3.2495-3.2505	.0013-.0043	.006-.015	7	2.751-2.752	.0012-.0037	.007-.013
8-446	3.1228-3.1236	.0010-.0036	.0025-.0085	—	2.4980-2.4990	.0011-.0036	.008-.016
6-450	3.2495-3.2505	.0013-.0043	.006-.015	7	2.751-2.752	.0012-.0037	.007-.013
8-478	3.123-3.124	.0014-.0044	.006-.001	3	2.623-2.624	.0017-.0042	.010-.018
6-501	3.2495-3.2505	.0013-.0043	.006-.015	7	2.751-2.752	.0012-.0037	.007-.013
8-549	3.123-3.124	.0014-.0044	.006-.011	3	2.623-2.624	.0017-.0042	.010-.018
8-605	3.1228-3.1236	.0015-.0035	.006-.011	3	2.623-2.624	.0017-.0042	.010-.018

VALVE SPECIFICATIONS

CYL x CID	ANGLE FACE	SEAT	STEM DIA. IN	EX	STEM-TO-GUIDE CLEARANCE IN	EX	VALVE LIFT IN.	VALVE SPRING LBS @ INCHES	SPRING FREE LENGTH
4-196	45	45	.372	.371	.001-.0035	.0015-.004	①	188 @ 1.428	2.065
6-232	⑥	—	.371	.371	.001-.003	.001-.003	.254	190 @ 1.437	2.265
6-258	⑥	—	.371	.371	.001-.003	.001-.003	.254	190 @ 1.437	2.265
8-304	45	45	.372	.371	.001-.0035	.0015-.004	①	180-195 @ 1.429	2.065
6-308	②	②	.372	.371	.0015-.004	.002-.0045	.407	182-190 @ 1.468	2.187
8-345	45	45	.372	.371	.001-.0035	.0015-.004	①	180-195 @ 1.429	2.065
8-392	⑥	⑥	.372	.414	.001-.0035	.0015-.004	①	180-195 @ 1.429	2.065
8-400	⑥	⑥	.372	.372	.001-.003	.001-.003	.286	210-226 @ 1.365⑧	2.200⑨
8-401	⑤	⑤	.435	.434	.001-.0035	.0015-.004	.426	113-121 @ 1.663⑩	2.562⑦
8-404(399)	45	45	—	—	—	—	—	188 @ 1.429	2.065
6-406	②	②	.435	.434	.0015-.004	.002-.0045	.449	133-141 @ 1.703③	2.562④
8-446	45	45	—	—	—	—	—	188 @ 1.429	2.065
6-450	②	②	.435	.434	.0015-.004	.002-.0045	.449	133-141 @ 1.703③	2.562④
8-478	⑤	⑤	.435	.434	.001-.0035	.0015-.004	.426	113-121 @ 1.663⑩	2.562⑦
6-501	②	②	.435	.434	.0015-.004	.002-.0045	.449	133-141 @ 1.703③	2.562④
8-549	⑤	⑤	.435	.434	.001-.0035	.0015-.004	.426	113-121 @ 1.663⑩	2.562⑦
8-605	②	⑥	—	—	—	—	—	188 @ 1.429	2.5625⑦

① Intake .440; Exh. 395
② Intake 15; Exh. 45
③ Inner 83-88 @ 1.50
④ Inner 2.343
⑤ Intake 15; Exh. 45
⑥ Intake 30; Exh. 45
⑦ Inner 2.281
⑧ Exhaust 210-226 @ 1.183
⑨ Exhaust 2.00
⑩ Inner 79-87 @ 1.538

TORQUE SPECIFICATIONS

CYL x CID	HEAD BOLTS	ROD CAP BOLTS	MAIN CAP BOLTS	CRANKSHAFT BALANCER BOLT	FLYWHEEL BOLTS	MANIFOLDS	
						IN.	EX.
4-196	90-100	40-45	75-80	100-110	45-55	40-45	40-45
6-232,258	80-85	25-30	75-85	Press-Fit	100-110	20-25	20-25
8-304	90-100	45-55	75-85	100-110	45-55	40-55	40-45
6-308	100-110	65-75	100-110	Press-Fit	90-100	25-30	25-30
8-345,392	90-100	45-55	75-85	100-110	45-55	40-55	40-45
8-400	110	35-40	95-105	50-60	100-110	40-45	20-30
8-401	90-100	60-70	100-110	Press-Fit	90-100	25-30	25-30
8-404(399)	100-110	42-46	70-90	80-100	—	—	15-20
6-406	100-110	65-75	100-110	Press-Fit	150-160	25-30	25-30
8-446	100-110	42-46	70-90	80-100	—	—	15-20
6-450	100-110	65-75	100-110	Press-Fit	150-160	25-30	25-30
8-478	90-100	60-70	100-110	Press-Fit	90-100	25-30	25-30
6-501	100-110	65-75	100-110	Press-Fit	150-160	25-30	25-30
8-549	90-100	60-70	100-110	Press-Fit	90-100	25-30	25-30
8-605	90-100	65-70	125-135	Press-Fit	90-100	—	—

FRONT END ALIGNMENT SPECIFICATIONS

AXLE	CODE	CASTER LEVEL FRAME	CAMBER	TOE-IN	KING PIN INCLINATION
FA-1	02001	2° ± 1° (Not Metro) 2° ± ½° (Metro)	1½° ± ½°	1/16 ± 1/16	4°
FA-10	02010	3° ± ½°	1½° ± ½°	1/16 ± 1/16	4°
FA-12	02012	2° ± 1° (Not Motor Home) 4° ± ½° (Motor Home)	½° ± ½°	1/16 ± 1/16	4°
FA-28	02028	1° ± 1° (Not Motor Home or Metro) 4° ± ½° (Motor Home) 3° ± ½° (Metro)	½° ± ½°	1/16 ± 1/16	4°
FA-48	02048	2° ± 1° (Not Motor Home) 4° ± ½° (Motor Home)	½° ± ½°	1/16 ± 1/16	4°
FA-68	02068	2° ± 1°	½° ± ½°	1/16 ± 1/16	4°
FA-69	02069	3° ± ½° (Cargostar Manual Strg.) 4½° ± ½° (Cargostar Power Strg.)	½° ± ½° ½° ± ½°	1/8 ± 1/16 1/8 ± 1/16	4° 4°
FA-71	02071	2° ± ½°	½° ± ½°	1/16 ± 1/16	LT 4¼° RT 4½°
FA-72	02072	2° ± ½°	½° ± ½°	1/16 ± 1/16	4°
FA-73	02073	2° ± ½°	½° ± ½°	1/16 ± 1/16	LT 4¼° RT 4½°
FA-74	02074	3° ± ½° (Manual Strg.) 4½° ± ½° (Power Strg.)	½° ± ½°	1/8 ± 1/16	LT 4¼° RT 4½°
FA-91	02091	2° ± 1° (Not CO-190) 2° ± ½° (CO-190)	½° ± ½°	1/16 ± 1/16	4°
FA-98	02098	2° ± 1° (Not Fleetstar A) 2° ± ½° (Fleetstar A 4x2) 4° ± ½° (Fleetstar A 4x4)	½° ± ½°	1/16 ± 1/16	4°
FA-99	02099	3° ± ½° (Cargostar Manual Strg.) 4½° ± ½° (Cargostar Power Strg.)	½° ± ½°	1/8 ± 1/16	4°
FA-101	02101	2° ± ½° (Not Fleetstar 6x4) 4° ± ½° (Fleetstar 6x4)	½° ± ½° ½° ± ½°	1/16 ± 1/16 1/16 ± 1/16	LT 4¼° RT 4½° LT 4¼° RT 4½°
FA-103	02103	3° ± ½° (Manual Strg.) 4½° ± ½° (Power Strg.)	½° ± ½°	1/8 ± 1/16	LT 4¼° RT 4½°

ENGINE APPLICATIONS

SERIES	AXLES	ENGINES—HP RATING
SCOUT SERIES (with or without top)		
Scout II	4x2	G 86-158
Scout II	4x4	G 86-158
MULTI-STOP SERIES		
MS-1210	4x2	G 158-163
MS-1510	4x2	G 158-163
PICKUP MODELS		
150 Bonus Load, Regular	4x2	G 140-163
200 Bonus Load, Regular	4x2	G 140-163
150 Bonus Load, Regular	4x4	G 140-163
200 Bonus Load, Regular	4x4	G 140-163
TRAVELALL		
150	4x2	G 187-196
200	4x2	G 187-196
150	4x4	G 187-196
200	4x4	G 187-196
LIGHT-DUTY SERIES		
150	4x2	G 140-196
200	4x2	G 140-196
500	4x2	G 140-196
150	4x4	G 140-196
200	4x4	G 140-196
LOADSTAR SERIES		
1600	4x2	G 157
1700	4x2	G 190
1750	4x2	D 150-175
1800	4x2	G 205-235
1850	4x2	D 170-210
1600	4x4	G 147
1700	4x4	G 157
F-1800	6x4	G 205-235
F-1850	6x4	D 170-210

SERIES	AXLES	ENGINES—HP RATING
FLEETSTAR A SERIES		
2010A	4x2	G 209-227
2050A	4x2	D 170-216
2070A	4x2	D 228-290
F-2010A	6x4	G 209-227
F-2050A	6x4	D 170-216
F-2070A	6x4	D 228-290
TRANSTAR SERIES		
4270	4x2	D 260-350
4370	4x2	D 290-350
F-4270	6x4	D 260-430
F-4370	6x4	D 290-450
PAYSTAR SERIES		
5050	4x4	D 190-210
5070	4x4	D 228-304
F-5050	6x4	D 190-210
F-5070	6x4	D 228-400
F-5050	6x6	D 190-210
F-5070	6x6	D 228-400
CARGOSTAR SERIES		
CO-1610B	4x2	G 157
CO-1710B	4x2	G 205
CO-1810B	4x2	G 205-235
CO-1850B	4x2	D 170-190
CO-1910B	4x2	G 209-227
CO-1950B	4x2	D 170-210
COF-1810B	6x4	G 205-235
COF-1910B	6x4	G 209-227
COF-1950B	6x4	D 170-210
CO TRANSTAR II SERIES		
CO-4070B	4x2	D 290-350
COF-4070B	6x4	D 290-450

G = Gasoline
D = Diesel

CYLINDER NUMBERING SEQUENCE

4-CYL. FIRING ORDER:
1 3 4 2

6-CYL. FIRING ORDER:
1 5 3 6 2 4

8-CYL. FIRING ORDER:
1 8 4 3 6 5 7 2

1966-72

1966-67;
1968 wo/Exhaust
Emission Control

1968 w/Exhaust
Emission Control

1969-74

1966
1972-74 ex.
400 eng.

1967-71

1973-74
400 eng.

TIMING MARK

1966-72 4-cyl. eng.;
1966-74 8-cyl. eng.
ex. 400 eng.

1966-68 6-cyl. eng.
wo/Exhaust Emission Control
(Lift cover on flywheel housing)

1967-68 6-cyl. eng.
w/Exhaust Emission Control

1969-74
6-cyl. eng.

1973-74
400 eng.

Distributor

Distributor Removal

1. Remove distributor cap.
2. Mark position of rotor by scribing a mark on the distributor body.
3. Mark position of distributor body on the engine block or mounting bracket.
4. If so equipped, remove vacuum advance line, governor lines, and tachometer cable.
5. Loosen clamp screw or hold-down bolt and remove distributor from engine.
6. To install, reverse the above procedure, making sure to align marks which position rotor and distributor body.
7. If the engine has been disturbed (crankshaft position unknown), rotate engine until engine is in No. 1 firing position (No. 8 on V-304, 345, and 392 engines). Compression stroke may be felt by placing finger tightly over spark plug hole as engine is rotating. Holding distributor shaft so that rotor is in No. 1 (or No. 8 on V-304, 345, 392) firing position, insert distributor, rotating slightly until it drops into keyed position.
8. Adjust ignition timing before tightening clamp screw or hold-down bolt.

Reference

For ignition tune-up settings see tune-up specifications at the beginning of this section.

Breaker Points Replacement

1. Unsnap and remove distributor cap.
2. Remove rotor and dust cover if so equipped.
3. Loosen nut retaining primary and condenser leads and remove leads.
4. Remove breaker assembly mounting screws.
5. Remove breaker assembly, carefully freeing conductor spring. Do not lose eccentric screw which may fall out.
6. To install, follow the above procedure in reverse order,

1 Spring, weight
2 Wick, oil
3 Cam, asm.
4 Cap
5 Rotor
6 Condenser
7 Contact points
8 Plate, breaker
9 Nut
10 Clip
11 Stud, terminal
12 Bushing, outside
13 Bushing, inside
14 Washer
15 Nut
16 Plug, pipe
17 Bushing, shaft
18 Coupling
19 Pin
20 Washer, spacer
21 Washer
22 Housing (body)
23 Support, spring
24 Spring, cap
25 Washer
26 Shaft, asm.
27 Weight
28 Plate, hold down

Typical distributor
(© International Harvester Co.)

Adjusting point gap—slots
(© International Harvester Co.)

Removing primary condenser
(© International Harvester Co.)

being sure to include eccentric screw.
7. Lightly lubricate cam with distributor cam grease.
8. Set breaker gap and ignition timing.

Breaker Point Setting
Internal Adjustment Type

1. Remove distributor cap.
2. Loosen distributor housing clamp screw or hold-down bolt.
3. Rotate distributor until cam positions breaker points at maximum gap.
4. Inspect alignment of breaker points and, if necessary, gently bend the stationary contact support (never bend arm) with needle-nose pliers.
5. Loosen lock screws which mount breaker assembly and adjust gap using a small screwdriver in slots of contact bracket and upper plate. On models without slots and with eccentric adjusting screw instead, rotate adjusting screw until proper gap is obtained.
6. Replace cap and set ignition timing.

External Adjustment Type

1. With engine idling, raise window in distributor cap and insert proper "hex" wrench into adjustment screw.

Ignition timing marks BD232, 308 engines
(© International Harvester Co.)

Ignition timing marks BG engine
(© International Harvester Co.)

MISALIGNMENT   PROPER ALIGNMENT

CORRECT MISALIGNMENT BY BENDING FIXED CONTACT SUPPORT NEVER BEND BREAKER LEVER

Adjusting point gap—eccentric screw
(© International Harvester Co.)

Ignition timing marks—OHV4 and V8 engines
(© International Harvester Co.)

Ignition timing marks RD engine
(© International Harvester Co.)

2. Turn wrench clockwise until engine begins to miss, then back off ½ turn, or until dwell meter reads specified dwell angle. NOTE: To remove distributor cap, press down in slot of latch head with a screwdriver and twist.

Magnetic Pulse Distributor

The Delco-Remy transistor ignition system differs from the conventional breaker point/condenser coil system in that the control of primary coil currents results from magnetic induction. The rotating timer core has vanes which, when lined up with the vanes of the stationary pole piece, establish a magnetic path, whereby inducing a small voltage in a pickup coil. The small current surge is then amplified by a transisterized pulse amplifier which passes a current pulse to the primary windings of the coil.

In the event of engine misfire or surging, other possible sources of misfunction should be checked first, such as carburetion and fuel supply. Then check for breaks in the wiring and for corroded or loose connections.

The timing may be set in the conventional way: rotate the distributor housing while the timing marks are viewed with a timing strobe light.

If the engine will not run at all, remove a lead from one of the spark plugs and hold ½" from the engine block while cranking engine. If there is no spark, check wiring and connections.

Actual repairs to either the dis-

tributor or the amplifier should only be performed by technicians skilled in the handling of electronic equipment.

CAUTION: Never disconnect the high voltage lead between the coil and distributor and never disconnect more than three spark plugs at a time unless the ignition switch is off. To make compression checks, disconnect the harness plug at the amplifier or disconnect the lead at the negative terminal of the coil.

Since the ignition pulse amplifier is completely static and the distributor shaft and bushings have permanent-type lubrication, no periodic maintenance of these components is required.

Ignition Timing

See tune-up specification table at the beginning of this section for timing settings. Timing light is connected to the No. 1 spark plug lead (No. 8 on V-304, 345, 392).

Typical transistor ignition wiring (© International Harvester Co.)

Alternator

Generator Removal

1. Remove leads from generator and tag for identification.
2. Loosen generator mounting bolts and adjusting bracket bolt.
3. Push generator towards engine block to remove fan belt. On some models, a tension idler pulley must be loosened.
4. Remove mounting and adjusting bracket bolts, then remove generator.
5. To install, reverse the above procedure. Be sure to pull generator away from engine block while tightening adjusting bracket bolt so that there will be sufficient tension on the fan belt to avoid slippage. Tighten mounting bolts.

Precautions—Alternators

Rectifiers and regulators in alternator systems are easily damaged by incorrect polarity. Observe the following precautions when wiring and testing circuits:

1. Always be certain of battery polarity.
2. Always connect booster battery negative to negative and positive to positive.
3. Never ground alternator output terminal.
4. When adjusting voltage regulator, be careful not to short adjusting tool.
5. Before making any tests, turn off ignition switch and disconnect battery ground.
6. Never use a fast charge with the battery connected unless charging unit is equipped with a special alternator protector.
7. Never try to polarize the alternator regulator, this will cause severe damage to the regulator and alternator.

Polarizing DC Generator

After service or testing, the generator must be polarized with respect to the battery. Check wiring connec-

Polarizing D.C. generator
(© International Harvester Co.)

tions and start engine. Momentarily short the "GEN" and "BAT" terminals of the voltage regulator with a screwdriver. Generator will be polarized by the surge of current from the battery.

Voltage Regulators—Reference

For adjustment procedures for AC and DC generator regulators see Electrical Diagnosis Section of General Section.

Voltage Regulator Removal
Three Unit Type

1. Disconnect clamp lead at the hot terminal of battery.
2. Disconnect leads from the "GEN", "BAT", and "F" (field) terminals of voltage regulator. Tag leads for identification.
3. Remove mounting screws and regulator unit from vehicle.
4. To install, reverse the above procedure.
5. Field and Armature ("F" and "GEN") wires may be identified by tracing wires to the generator and looking for the "F" and "A" stamped near the terminals.
6. Connect lead to hot terminal of battery.

Two Unit Type
(Used with Alternator)

1. Disconnect clamp lead at the hot

terminal of battery.
2. Lift latch and pull off wiring harness connector at regulator terminals.
3. Remove mounting screws and regulator unit from vehicle.
4. To install, reverse the above procedure.
5. Reconnect cable clamp to battery terminal, checking polarity first.

Starter

Reference

For servicing and overhauling starter motors, see Electrical Diagnosis Section of General Section.

Starter Motor—Removal

1. Disconnect cable clamp from hot terminal of battery.
2. Disconnect cable and wire leads from terminals of solenoid assembly, identifying leads with tags. If the solenoid is not mounted directly on the starter motor, disconnect the cable from the solenoid to the motor at the motor terminal.
3. Remove starter motor mounting bolts or stud nuts.
4. Pull starter assembly forward to clear housing and remove starter.
5. To install, reverse the above procedure, installing new tang lockwashers where removed.

Brakes

Hydraulic Brakes

Late model trucks are equipped with a dual hydraulic brake system in which there are separate hydraulic systems for the front and rear brakes. In this dual system a warning light switch operates a warning light on the dashboard when there is a pressure failure in either the front or rear system. A power system may be employed to reduce the effort applied to the brake pedal. See General Repair Section for hydraulic brake service and overhaul.

Master Cylinder—R & R

1. Disconnect hydraulic lines from master cylinder.
2. Disconnect master cylinder pushrod at brake pedal and remove nuts securing cylinder to dash panel.
3. If master cylinder is mounted on power unit, remove nuts securing master cylinder to power unit and remove cylinder from vehicle.
4. Installation is the reverse of the above procedure.
5. Bleed system.

Typical three unit regulator wiring (© International Harvester Co.)

Warning light switch—circuit closed
(© International Harvester Co.)

Tandem master cylinder disconnect points
(© International Harvester Co.)

Resetting the Warning Light Switch

Once a difference of 85-150 psi pressure between the front and rear systems has activated the warning light switch, it will not go off by itself and must be manually reset.

1. Clean switch and disconnect wire from terminal.
2. Unscrew and completely remove switch from body. This will allow the pistons to center and hold the switch in "off" position.
3. Screw switch back into body and reconnect wire to terminal.
4. NOTE: If fluid is in the switch cavity, press brake pedal to see if piston O-ring seals are leaking. If there is leakage, the O-rings must be replaced.
5. Warning light switch should be checked periodically for proper function and the presence of foreign matter and dirt.

Adjusting Brake Shoes

1. Remove rubber dust cover from access hole.
2. Using an adjusting tool or screwdriver, turn star screw until shoes drag on the drum.

Bleeding brake system
(© International Harvester Co.)

Backing off adjusting screw—self adjusting brakes
(© International Harvester Co.)

Adjusting brakes
(© International Harvester Co.)

3. Rotate star screw back from drag position until drag is completely eliminated.
4. On brakes equipped with automatic adjusters it will be necessary to hold the adjusting lever away from the star wheel with a screwdriver while the adjustment is made.

Bleeding Hydraulic Brakes

1. Before bleeding the brake system, disconnect electrical wire from warning light switch and remove any foreign material or dirt accumulation around warning light switch. Then remove the switch from body. The switch must be removed to prevent shearing of the end of the pin due to unequal pressures created between front and rear systems while bleeding.
2. Fill master cylinder reservoir(s) with clean brake fluid.
3. Attach bleeder hose to bleeder valve on wheel cylinder and place free end of bleeder hose in a jar partially filled with fluid. On some models it may be necessary to take the wheel off to get at the bleeder valve.
4. While the brake pedal is being pressed steadily, open the bleeder valve until the fluid coming from the hose is clean and free of air bubbles, then close bleeder valve and release brake pedal.
5. If the brake pedal goes to the floorboard before the bleeding becomes clean, more fluid will have to be added to the reservoir and the above process repeated.
6. Repeat the above procedure for each wheel cylinder, making sure to check the level of fluid in the reservoir frequently. NOTE: On models equipped with power boosters, the booster must be bled first.

Vacuum Power Brakes

The vacuum power cylinder used with the single and dual hydraulic brake systems assists braking differently than a power booster in that its activation results directly from the foot pedal and not from the master cylinder. There are single and tandem dual types. Both types are mounted on the engine side of the firewall.

Typical standard dual brake system (© International Harvester Co.)

Vacuum Power Brake Cylinder—R & R

1. Disconnect vacuum hose from check valve.
2. Disconnect hydraulic lines from master cylinder.
3. Disconnect pedal link from pedal from inside the cab.
4. Remove bolts which mount the bracket to the firewall.
5. To install reverse the above procedure.
6. Bleed master cylinder output ports while connecting tube nuts which secure lines to ports.
7. Bleed hydraulic brake system.

Vacuum Brake Boosters

Vacuum boosters add pressure to the hydraulic brake system. The activation and amount of pressure is controlled by a hydraulic line from the master cylinder. Disassembly and service procedures for vacuum boosters may be found in the General Repair Section.

Booster—R & R

1. On units lacking integral air filter, remove air inlet hose (from engine air cleaner).
2. Disconnect vacuum inlet tube (coming from engine manifold).
3. Disconnect hydraulic line from master cylinder and hydraulic line going to wheel cylinders.
4. Remove mounting bolts and lift out vacuum unit.
5. To install, reverse the above procedure.
6. Bleed complete hydraulic system, starting with cylinder on vacuum unit as described below.

Bleeding Vacuum Booster Systems

1. The booster must be bled before proceeding to wheel cylinders.
2. All vacuum boosters have a bleed valve on the control valve as indicated in the figures by the number "1". This valve must always be bled first.
3. On boosters having an additional bleeder valve on the hydraulic cylinder indicated by the number "2", bleed this cylinder after control valve.
4. Bleed wheel cylinders as described in preceding section.

Trailer Brake Hand Control— Adjustment

The advance control valve is used in conjunction with the Hydrovac and trailer brake system to vary the initial braking of the trailer.

1. Place advance plate in full released position (rotate counter-clockwise).
2. While coasting on smooth road at 20 mph, apply valve by rotating clockwise until a slight drag is felt from the trailer brakes.

Power cylinder disconnect points
(© International Harvester Co.)

3. Rotate advance plate to where it just touches the valve operating handle. This releases the brakes on the trailer but sets the advance effect.
4. Leaving advance valve controls as set above, gently apply tractor brakes to check the "advance" of the trailer brakes.

Power brake air chamber
(© International Harvester Co.)

Parking Brake Adjustment— Rear Brake Type

1. Loosen locknut on the equalizer rod and turn front nut forward several turns.
2. Turn the locknut (rear) forward just enough to remove any slack but not so much that the brake shoes lift of their anchors.

Typical single cylinder power booster (© International Harvester Co.)

Power cylinder with integral air cleaner (© International Harvester Co.)

Parking brake cable adjustment (© International Harvester Co.)

3. Tighten both nuts against the equalizer.

Drive Shaft Band Type

1. Leaving parking brake lever in the extreme release position, check that the cam lever is resting squarely on upper brake band bracket. This is adjusted by removing the clevis pin and readjusting yoke.
2. Adjust screw nut (1) until a clearance of .020-.030″ is reached.
3. Adjusting nuts (4) on bolt (5), obtain .020-.030″ clearance on lower half of lining and drum.
4. Adjust nuts (2) on bolt (3) for a clearance of .020-.030″ clearance on top half of lining.
5. Lock all adjustment with lock nuts.

NOTE: Hydraulic Switch shown on Hydrovac. Some installations provide for Hydraulic Switch located at Master Cylinder.

Advance control valve assembly
(© International Harvester Co.)

Air Brake System

Air brake systems are composed of a compressor, a reservoir, brake actuating chambers and a network of lines and valves which control operation. The piston-type air compressor is belt driven directly from the engine and is dependent upon the engine for its lubrication. Pressure in

the system is regulated by a governor which starts loading the compressor when the system pressure drops below 95 psi and unloads the compressor when the system pressure reaches 110 psi. See General Section for overhaul of air brake components.

Air Compressor Governor Adjustment

Early Models

1. Check governor filter and supply line for any restriction.
2. Loosen adjusting screw locknut and exhaust valve housing.
3. Remove exhaust valve housing with adjusting screw locknut, and shims as a complete unit.
4. Replace exhaust valve housing, adjusting screw, locknut and

Typical advance trailer brake control valve installation (© International Harvester Co.)

Air compressor governor—early models (© International Harvester Co.)

Air compressor governor—late models (© International Harvester Co.)

three shims into governor body and tighten.

5. Turn adjusting screw until it sticks out ⅜″ from exhaust valve housing.

6. Start truck engine and build up pressure in air brake system until it reaches 115 psi then shut off engine. If governor cuts out before 115 psi then turn adjusting screw out one complete turn and repeat this step.

7. With pressure holding at 115 psi slowly turn adjusting screw out until governor cuts out (dull pop).

8. Start truck engine and slowly bleed pressure until governor cuts in. Cut-in should be between 93-98 psi.

9. If cut-in is below 93 psi, remove

exhaust valve housing unit and add shims (one shim equals 4 psi) to adjust cut-in and install as in step 4.

10. If cut-in is above 98 psi, remove exhaust valve housing unit and remove shims to lower cut-in pressure.

11. Check cut-in and cut-out pressure after each adjustment and repeat appropriate steps if necessary.

12. When adjustments are completed, tighten locknut.

Air Compressor Governor Adjustment

Late Models

1. Check governor filter and supply line for any restriction.

2. Loosen adjusting screw locknut and exhaust valve housing locknut.

3. Unscrew adjusting screw four turns.

4. Screw in exhaust valve housing until it bottoms (do not tighten—seats are easily ruined).

5. Back off exhaust valve housing ¾ turn.

6. While holding exhaust valve housing, turn in adjusting screw three turns after it has made contact with the spring. A slight resistance should be felt when contact is made. If this contact cannot be felt, turn adjusting screw until it sticks out ⅜″ from exhaust valve housing.

7. Start engine and build up air pressure to 115 psi and shut off

Typical air brake system (© International Harvester Co.)

Adjusting brakes
(© International Harvester Co.)

Loosening collect nut—air brake power unit
(© International Harvester Co.)

J H H F C A B
Safety valve
(© International Harvester Co.)

DUST SHIELD
NOT SHOWN

RDA brake with integral plunger housings (© International Harvester Co.)

engine. If governor cuts out before 115 psi, turn adjusting screw out one turn and repeat this step.

8. With pressure holding at 115 psi, turn in adjusting screw until governor cuts out (dull pop).
9. Start truck engine and bleed pressure down until governor cuts in. Cut-in pressure should be 93-98 psi.
10. If cut-in pressure is below 93 psi, hold adjusting screw and turn out exhaust valve housing (1/6 turn equals 5 psi).
11. If cut-in pressure is above 98 psi, hold adjusting screw and turn in exhaust valve housing.
12. Repeat steps until proper cut-in pressure is reached.
13. Check cut-out pressure and adjust if necessary.
14. Tighten adjusting screw locknut and exhaust valve housing locknut.

Air Reservoir Safety Valve Adjustment

1. Connect an accurate air pressure gauge to the emergency line at

the rear of the truck and open emergency line valve. With truck engine running, turn air supply valve to the air supply position to bypass governor. Let pressure rise in reservoir until 150 psi is reached then quickly shut off air supply valve.
2. If the safety valve did not blow off at 150 psi or blew off before that pressure, loosen locknut (A) and turn adjusting screw (B) either in for higher pressure setting or out for lower pressure setting.
3. When adjustment is complete, tighten locknut and reduce pressure in system to normal 100 psi by applying and releasing brakes.

Plunger Actuated Brake—Adjustment

1. Jack or hoist wheels free of ground.
2. Remove dust cover from adjusting slot—two places on each brake.

3. Turn the star wheel until heavy drag on drum is developed.
4. Back off bolt barely past light drag.
5. Replace dust covers in adjusting slots.
6. Repeat for other brakes.
7. If brakes are equipped with automatic adjusters, check drum to lining clearance. If it is more than .060″, adjust brakes manually until they can be serviced. See Unit Repair section for servicing air brakes.

Air Power Unit—Adjustment

1. Determine whether the power unit is the adjustable or bottoming type. Bottoming units have an identification tag fastened to the clamp ring bolt of the air chamber. Adjustable units have no identification markings. Loosen collet nut.
2. Bottoming units automatically provide optimum useful chamber

stroke and need only be screwed in until they bottom.

3. Adjustable units are adjusted manually by screwing the unit in until the wedge is just starting to lift the plungers off the abutment seats at the first movement of the diaphragm.

4. After screwing in air chamber unit to proper depth, tighten collet nut to lock position.

Air Brake Slack Adjusters—Adjustment

Cam actuated air brakes should be adjusted for lining wear every 2000 miles. Adjustment is made by turning a worm screw on a gear which positions stack adjuster angle.

1. With wheel free to rotate, disconnect pushrod from the slack adjuster to determine whether or not it is in fully released position.

2. Reinsert clevis pin through bottomed pushrod and slack adjuster arm, adjusting worm gear if necessary.

3. Holding the locking sleeve in, adjust worm screw until shoes drag against drum, then back off enough to eliminate drag.

4. Angle that slack adjuster makes when brake is fully applied should not "go over" 90° point.

5. If the slack adjuster goes over the 90° point the maximum force will not be exerted and the pushrod must be adjusted as follows:

6. Carefully disconnect slack adjuster from pushrod—it may snap into the air chamber with considerable force.

7. Loosen locknut on pushrod clevis and thread clevis onto pushrod towards air chamber several turns.

8. Connect pushrod and clevis with pin.

9. Check pushrod-to-slack adjuster angle again as the brake is applied to make sure that it is not still going over the 90° point.

10. Readjust if necessary.

11. When adjustment is correct tighten locknut on pushrod clevis and install cotter pin which secures clevis pin.

Fuel System

Carburetor Adjustment

Single-Barrel Holley Model 1904

1. With choke fully off and engine warm, adjust throttle stop screw for 450 rpm (700 rpm for standard transmission and exhaust emission, 600 rpm for automatic transmission and exhaust emission).

Foundation air brake slack adjuster
(© International Harvester Co.)

2. Set idle adjusting screw to give highest steady manifold vacuum or, if no vacuum gauge is available, for the smoothest maximum idle speed.

3. Reset throttle stop screw for rpm as above.

4. For engines with automatic transmissions, set the dashpot adjusting screw for 0.100" clearance. The dashpot diaphragm rod is in fully compressed position while this clearance is set.

Carburetor Removal

Single-Barrel Holley Model 1904

1. Remove air filter, fuel line and vacuum line, if fitted.

2. Remove throttle linkage from throttle lever and unscrew choke cable from choke lever.

3. Remove bolts from mounting studs and lift off carburetor.

4. To install, fit a new carburetor flange gasket on the manifold and mount carburetor without tightening the stud nuts.

5. Install fuel and vacuum lines.

6. Tighten bolts on mounting studs, alternating from one to the other so that a good seal is obtained.

7. Connect throttle and choke linkages, making sure choke plate is fully open and choke knob on dashboard is all the way in.

8. Clean and install air cleaner.

9. Adjust carburetor as described in preceding section.

Carburetor Adjustment

Single-Barrel Holley Model 1920

1. These settings must be made with the engine at normal operating temperature with the air cleaner on, the transmission in neutral, the choke open and the air conditioner on, if so equipped.

2. With the engine off, connect a tachometer to the engine and turn the idle mixture screw out against the tab stop.

3. Start the engine and warm it up

Model 1920 carburetor
(© International Harvester Co)

to normal operating temperature and adjust the idle speed to 720 rpm.

4. Turn the idle mixture screw in to reduce the idle speed to 700 rpm.

NOTE: The removal of the limiter caps may be necessary to obtain the proper rpm setting.

5. If the idle speed of the engine with an automatic transmission in the drive range is not 550 rpm, adjust the idle speed to obtain the required speed.

Carburetor Removal

Single-Barrel Holley Model 1920

1. Remove the air cleaner, fuel lines, vacuum lines and any other hoses and linkage attached to the carburetor.

2. Remove the attaching bolts from the base of the carburetor and remove the carburetor from the manifold. Remove and discard the old gasket under the base of the carburetor.

3. To install reverse the removal procedure making sure to install a new gasket under the carburetor base.

Carburetor Adjustment

Single-Barrel Holley Model 1940

1. When making these adjustments the engine must be at normal operating temperature with the air cleaner in place, the transmission in neutral and the air conditioner off, if so equipped.

2. Connect a tachometer to the engine and with the engine off adjust the idle mixture screw out until it contacts the tab stop.

3. Start the engine and adjust the curb idle to 700 rpm. Adjust the curb idle by the following procedure:

   a. With the engine running make sure the idle stop solenoid is fully extended.

   b. Adjust the curb idle speed by using the screw that contacts the solenoid plunger.

4. Increase the idle speed to 730 rpm by using the low idle speed screw.

5. Adjust the idle mixture until the engine speed drops to 700 rpm. If the correct rpm can not be

obtained, the idle limiter caps will have to be removed to make the proper adjustment.

6. Disconnect the tachometer from the engine and road test the vehicle.

Fast Idle Adjustment (Automatic Choke)

Single-Barrel Holley Model 1940

1. With the engine at normal operating temperature and the engine off, remove the air cleaner and disconnect the vacuum hose from the EGR valve and plug the end, if so equipped.
2. Connect a tachometer to the engine and open the throttle and move the choke plate to the closed position.
3. Holding the plate closed, close the throttle. This will hold the fast idle cam in place.

NOTE: Do not touch the throttle linkage after this step until the adjustments are made. If the linkage is disturbed it will release the fast idle cam.

4. Start the engine and allow the speed to stablize. The speed should be 2000 rpm.

Curb and low speed adjustment screws
(© International Harvester Co)

Idle adjustment
(© International Harvester Co)

5. If the speed is incorrect use the fast idle stop screw to adjust.
6. Reinstall the air cleaner and the hose to the EGR valve.

Carburetor Removal

Single-Barrel Holley Model 1940

1. Remove the air cleaner, fuel lines, vacuum lines and any other lines or linkage attached to the carburetor.
2. Remove the attaching bolts from the base of the carburetor and remove the carburetor from the manifold. Remove and discard the old gasket from under the carburetor.
3. To install reverse the removal procedure making sure to install a new gasket under the carburetor base.

Carburetor Adjustment

Two-Barrel Holley Models 2110 and 852-FFG

1. With the vehicle on the level and engine warm, adjust throttle stop screw for an idle of 350-400 rpm. If carburetion is so far out of adjustment that the engine will not idle, seat idle adjusting needles lightly and back them off one full turn.
2. Adjust each of the idle adjustment screws, first one then the

Model 1904 Holley carburetor
(© International Harvester Co.)

Model 1904 Holley carburetor with dashpot
(© International Harvester Co.)

Model 4150G carburetor with automatic transmission operating cam
(© International Harvester Co.)

Model 2110G Holley 2 BBL carburetor
(© International Harvester Co.)

311

other, for maximum steady manifold vacuum or, if a vacuum gauge is not available, for the smoothest maximum idle speed.

3. If the resulting idle speed exceeds 350-400 rpm, reset throttle stop screw.

4. If equipped with a dashpot (automatic transmission), set the adjusting screw for a clearance of .045-.065" with the dashpot diaphragm fully depressed.

Governor Adjustment

Two-Barrel Holley Models 2110 and 852-FFG

1. Connect tachometer to engine.

2. After engine has warmed up, briefly hold throttle at wide open to determine governor cut-out speed. See specifications table at the beginning of this section for correct governor cut-out speeds.

3. If adjustment is required, stop engine and remove the adjusting hole cover or cover band from the governor valve housing on the distributor.

4. With the ignition off, crank engine until governor valve adjusting screw at the end of the governor valve body appears at the opening.

5. Insert screwdriver and turn the adjusting screw: clockwise to increase cut-out speed and counterclockwise to decrease cut-out speed. One full turn of the adjusting screw equals about 150 rpm.

6. When correct cut-out speed is obtained, replace adjusting hole cover or cover band and tighten securely.

Carburetor Removal

Two-Barrel Holley Models 2100 and 852-FFG

1. Remove air cleaner, throttle linkage and choke cable.

2. Disconnect fuel line and distributor and governor vacuum lines.

3. Remove bolts from mounting studs and lift off carburetor.

4. To install, clean manifold mating surface and install a new flange gasket.

5. Install carburetor but do not tighten down stud nuts.

6. Connect fuel line and vacuum lines.

7. Tighten nuts on mounting studs in an alternating fashion so that flange gasket compresses evenly for a good seal.

8. Connect throttle linkage and choke cable, making sure that choke plates are fully open when the choke knob is pushed in.

9. Check throttle for complete travel.

10. Install air cleaner.

Adjusting spinner governor—distributor
(© International Harvester Co.)

11. Adjust carburetor as described in preceding section.

Carburetor Adjustment

Two-Barrel Carburetor Model 2210-C

1. With the engine warmed to operating temperature and the air cleaner in place, transmission in neutral, and the air conditioner off, connect a tachometer to the engine.

2. With the engine off turn the idle mixture screws out until they contact the tab stops.

3. With the engine running adjust the curb idle to 700 rpm. Do this by the following procedure:
   a. Make sure that the throttle stop solenoid is fully extended.
   b. Loosen the jam nut on the solenoid and turn the solenoid to obtain the correct rpm.

NOTE: Be careful not to twist the wire off the solenoid when making the adjustment. Be sure to tighten the nut after making the adjustment.

4. Using the low idle speed screw, increase the idle speed to 750 rpm.

5. Adjust the idle mixture screws in equally until the engine speed drops to 700 rpm.

NOTE: If the correct RPM can not be obtained the idle limiter caps will have to be removed.

Fast Idle Adjustment (Automatic Choke)

Two-Barrel Carburetor Model 2210-C

1. Run the engine until it reaches normal operating temperature. Shut the engine off and remove the air cleaner. Disconnect the hose to the EGR valve and plug the end, if so equipped.

2. Connect a tachometer to the engine.

3. Holding the choke plate closed open the throttle, then close the throttle still holding the plate in place. This will hold the fast idle cam in place.

4. Without touching the accelerator pedal, start the engine and allow the speed to stablize. The speed should be 2200 rpm. If it is not adjust the fast idle stop screw to obtain the proper rpm.

NOTE: The throttle linkage should not be touched between steps 3 and 5. If the linkage is disturbed it will release the fast idle cam and make it necessary to reset the fast idle cam to make proper adjustment.

Carburetor Removal

Two-Barrel Carburetor Model 2210-C

1. Remove the air cleaner, fuel line, vacuum hoses, throttle linkage, and anything else attached to the carburetor.

2. Remove the attaching bolts from the base of the carburetor and remove the carburetor from the manifold. Remove and discard the old gasket from under the carburetor base.

3. To install reverse the removal procedure making sure to install

LPG carburetion—V401, 461 & 549 engines (© International Harvester Co.)

a new gasket under the carburetor base.

Carburetor Adjustment

Two-Barrel Holley Models 2300 and 2300G

1. First set fast idle by adjusting fast idle stud so as to have .018-.020" clearance between stud and fast idle cam when throttle plates are set for curb idle and choke plate is fully open (2300G). On model without governor (2300), set throttle lever stop screw so that screw just touches fast idle cam at curb idle.
2. With the truck on the level, gently seat idle adjusting screws, then back each off one turn.
3. With warm engine idling, adjust throttle stop screw for an idle of 450-500 rpm.
4. Set one idle adjusting screw to obtain highest steady manifold vacuum reading or, if a vacuum gauge is not available, the smoothest running maximum speed. There should be no more than a ½-turn difference between the two screws at final setting.
5. If the above adjustment has resulted in increased idle speed, reset idle speed as described in Step 3.
6. On vehicles equipped with automatic transmissions, loosen dashpot jam nut and rotate complete dashpot assembly to obtain .095-.105" clearance between dashpot pushrod and throttle lever.

Fuel Level Adjustment

Two-Barrel Holley Models 2300 and 2300G

1. Before changing fuel level, check fuel pump output for proper functioning. See Tune-Up Specifications at the beginning of this section for correct fuel pump output rate.
2. With ignition off and air cleaner removed, drain fuel bowl by loosening bottom left bowl mounting screw.
3. Tighten bowl screw.
4. With engine running, remove the sight plug from the bowl. Fuel level should be on line with the threads at bottom of sight plug hole.
5. To adjust fuel level, loosen and hold locknut with a ½" wrench and turn the adjusting nut with a screwdriver or ⅝" wrench. Turning clockwise lowers fuel level and turning counterclockwise raises fuel level.
6. Tighten locknut.
7. Check fuel level after engine has run enough to stabilize fuel level

and repeat above procedure if necessary.

Pump Discharge Adjustment

Two-Barrel Holley 2300 and 2300G

1. With choke wide open and throttle set for curb idle, lengthen or shorten adjusting bolt (located at override spring on the accelerator pump lever) until bolt touches diaphragm lever and takes up linkage slack.
2. Then lengthen adjusting bolt ½ turn.
3. Tighten nut.

Governor Adjustment

Two-Barrel Holley Model 2300G

Governor adjustment is the same as that described for the Holley model 2110 above. For correct speed setting see table.

Governor Speed RPM

Engine Model	RPM
BD-308	3200
RD-406	2750
RD-450	2600
RD-501	2600
V-345	3800
V-392	3600
V-401	3400
V-478	3400
VS-478	3400
V-549	3200
VS-549	3200

Carburetor Removal

Two-Barrel Holley Models 2300 and 2300G

1. Remove air filter and disconnect fuel line, distributor and governor vacuum lines and throttle and choke linkages.
2. Remove mounting stud nuts and lift off carburetor.
3. Remove flange gasket and discard.
4. To install, clean manifold mating surface and install a new flange gasket.
5. Operate choke and throttle levers to be sure they are functioning properly.
6. Install carburetor and mounting stud nuts, but do not tighten nuts.
7. Connect fuel line, vacuum lines and throttle and choke linkage.
8. Tighten down mounting stud nuts in an alternating criss-cross pattern to make sure that flange gasket is compressed evenly.
9. Check to see that choke plate is fully open and dashboard knob is in when connecting choke.
10. Make all adjustments described in preceding text.
11. Install air cleaner.

Carburetor Removal

Four-Barrel Holley Model 4150

All adjustments and installation procedures are the same for the four-barrel carburetor as for the model 2300 described above except that the four-barrel has two float bowls and the fuel level adjustment is made for each. On trucks equipped with automatic transmissions, make idle adjustments with transmission selector lever in 1-2 drive range while parking brake is on.

Mechanical Spark Advance

Holley Model 2150

On Holley models 4150 and 885 the throttle lever is provided with three (885) or two (4150) pump link hole positions for seasonal requirements. The longer stroke positions are for cold weather conditions and the medium and short stroke positions are for normal and warm weather respectively.

Mechanical Spark Advance Adjustment

Holley Model 2150

1. Place cable wire in hole of pin in the spark advance lever, but do not tighten.
2. Place cable sleeve in clamp, but do not tighten.
3. Holding a .105" feeler gauge between spark advance lever and spark advance lever stop, set a 15-degree reading on the dampener (use timing light) by adjusting the spark advance cable sleeve in relation to the cable clamp.
4. Tighten clamps and check the 15-degree timing advance reading.
5. Remove feeler gauge and recheck timing which should now be 3 degrees advance.

Carburetor Adjustment

Four-Barrel Holley Model 4160C

1. These adjustments must be made with the engine at operating temperature, the air cleaner in place, the transmission in neutral and the air conditioner off if so equipped. If the vehicle is equipped with a fuel vapor canister, remove the vacuum hose from the canister, remove the vacuum hose from the canister and plug the end. After the adjustments are made reconnect the hose.
2. Connect a tachometer to the engine and with the engine off adjust the idle mixture screws in until they rest against the tab stops.
3. With the engine running and at operating temperature, adjust

the curb idle speed to 700 rpm. This is done by the following procedure:

a. Make sure that the idle stop solenoid is extended all the way.

b. Turn the adjusting screw that contacts the soldnoid to obtain the correct curb idle rpm.

4. Increase the idle speed to 730 rpm and turn the idle mixture screws, equally, leaning out the mixture until the rpm drops to 700 rpm.

5. Disconnect the tachometer and reconnect any parts that were removed.

Automatic Choke Fast Idle Adjustment

Four-Barrel Holley Model 4160C

1. Run the engine until it reaches normal operating temperature. Shut the engine off and remove the air cleaner. Disconnect and plug the vacuum from the EGR valve to the carburetor if the vehicle is so equipped. Connect a tachometer to the engine.

2. Open the throttle all the way and move the choke plate to the closed position. Holding the plate in the closed position release the throttle. This will hold the fast idle cam in position.

3. Without touching the accelerator pedal start the engine and check the tachometer. The speed should be 1650 rpm. If the speed is not correct adjust the fast idle lever to obtain the correct rpm.

NOTE: The throttle linkage should not be touched or moved between steps 2 and 3. If this happens the linkage will release the fast idle cam and it will be necessary to reset the fast idle cam for proper adjustment of the fast idle.

Carburetor Removal

Four-Barrel Holley Model 4160C

1. Remove the air cleaner and disconnect the fuel line, vacuum lines, any wires, and choke and throttle linkage.

2. Remove the retaining bolts or nuts and carefully remove the carburetor from the manifold. Remove the old gasket from under the carburetor.

3. To install reverse the removal procedure.

NOTE: Install a new gasket on the intake manifold before installing the carburetor or the carburetor will not be sealed properly.

Carburetor Adjustment

Carter ThermoQuad

1. Run engine at normal operating temperature.

Adjusting carburetor idle speed
(© International Harvester Co)

Checking fast idle adjustment
(© International Harvester Co)

2. With solenoid energized turn the idle adjusting screw to obtain 800 rpm on 345 engines and 700 rpm on 392 engines.

3. Adjust the low curb idle screw until the end of the screw just touches the stop. Back off one full turn. Disconnect solenoid; speed should be 525-575. Reconnect the wire. Shut off engine.

4. Open the throttle slightly and position the fast idle screw on the second step of the cam. Plug the EGR vacuum line. Start engine.

5. Adjust fast idle screw to 1550-1600 rpm.

Carburetor Adjustment

LPG (propane-butane) RD-501, V-304, 345, 401, & 549 Engines

Setting the idle fuel adjustment automatically gives the correct mixture for part and full throttle operation.

CAUTION: Liquefied petroleum gas is extremely flammable. Observe all safety precautions regardless of the nature of work being performed. No work is to be done on fuel tanks except by qualified concerns who normally service such containers.

1. Set throttle for fast idle by turning throttle stop screw in from closed position 3 or 4 turns.

2. Start engine and adjust idle adjusting screw in drag link (either end) until engine runs smoothly. Turning screw in (clockwise) enriches mixture.

3. Adjust throttle stop screw for idle of 600 rpm.

4. Readjust idle adjusting screw in drag link for maximum engine speed. If engine speed starts to go above 900 rpm, set back speed with throttle stop screw to 600 rpm and continue adjusting drag link screw for maximum engine speed.

5. Adjust idle to 400 rpm and replace cotter pin in drag link adjusting screw to lock adjustment.

Carburetor Adjustment

LPG (Propane-Butane) Carburetor Adjustment

All OHV 6 Engines Except PT 6 & RD 501

1. Loosen locknut on starting adjusting screw and turn screw clockwise until it bottoms, then back it out the required number of turns (see table). Tighten locknut.

2. Turn idle adjusting screw on the regulating unit clockwise until it bottoms gently, then back it out the required number of turns (see table).

3. On BD engines, loosen the large lock nut on the economizer unit and turn load adjusting screw clockwise to extreme position, then turn counterclockwise the required number of turns (see table). Tighten locknut. On BD engines (engine not running),

1 Fuelock-strainer, assembly
2 Fuelock, connection to ignition switch
3 Governor, diaphragm housing
4 Governor, spinner box air line
5 Drag, link idle adjusting screw
6 Spacer (insulator)
7 Throttle, control rod
8 Metering, valve lever
9 Throttle, lever

LPG carburetor
(© International Harvester Co.)

LPG Carburetor Adjustment Specifications

Engine	BD-308	RD-406	RD-450
Starting Adjusting Screw (number turns off seat)	2	1	2
Economizer (load adjustment) (number turns off seat)	9-1/2	5 4-11/16	4-3/4 3-3/4

disconnect vacuum line from economizer before setting load adjustment. Then loosen locknut and turn entire economizer assembly clockwise until it bottoms in carburetor, then counterclockwise the specified number of turns (see table). Temporarily plug the vacuum line and start engine. After the engine is warmed up, set hand throttle at about ⅔ governed speed. Screw economizer body in until engine speed starts to drop and then out until the engine speed starts to drop, then set in between the two extremes and tighten locknut. For part throttle adjustment, loosen small locknut on economizer cover and turn economizer adjusting screw clockwise the required number of turns from bottom position (see table) and tighten locknut.

Fuel Pumps

Reference

Fuel pumps are of conventional design and instructions for servicing may be found in the Unit Repair Section.

Fuel Pump Pressure Test

1. Disconnect fuel line at carburetor inlet and attach pressure gauge between the inlet and disconnected line.
2. Start engine and take reading. Consult Tune-up Specifications at the beginning of this section for correct fuel pump pressure.
3. When engine is stopped, the pressure should remain constant or very slowly return to zero.

Fuel Pump Capacity Test

1. Disconnect fuel line from the fuel pump.
2. Connect a piece of hose to the line so that fuel can be directed into a measuring container.
3. Start engine and note time it takes to fill a pint container. Pump should fill one pint within 20-30 seconds.

Fuel Pump Removal

1. Disconnect inlet and outlet fuel lines from pump.
2. Disconnect windshield wiper vacuum hose if so equipped.
3. Remove mounting stud nuts or bolts and remove pump from engine.

4. To install, reverse the above procedure.

Cooling System

Radiator Removal

1. Drain radiator and block.
2. Remove inlet and outlet water hoses.
3. Remove radiator mounting bolts. On some models it may be necessary to remove radiator shell and support rods or, if the radiator assembly is bolted to the fenders, unbolted at those points.
4. Lift radiator straight up and remove.
5. To install, reverse the above procedure, being sure to check for leaks when filling the cooling system.

Water Pump Removal

1. Drain cooling system.
2. If radiator shrouds hinder access they must be removed before proceeding (large V-8's and cab-forward models).
3. Loosen generator pivot bolts and adjusting bolt on bracket to relieve tension on the fan belt and remove belt from water pump pulley. On V(S)-401, 478, 549 engines all accessories are driven by belts from the water pump pulley and are removed by loosening the generator and power steering pump adjusting brackets and pivots. The idler pulley on the belts between the crankshaft and water pump pulleys is then loosened so that these belts may be removed.
4. On V(S)-401, 478, 549 engines the fan blades and pulley are removed.

5. Remove all pipes and hoses connected to the water pump.
6. Remove mounting bolts or stud nuts and water pump. On all models except 4-196 and V-304, 345, 392, only the front half of the pump housing is removed for water pump servicing.
7. Installation is the reverse of the above procedure. Be sure to install new gaskets and, if applicable, new O-rings on pipe end fittings.

Water Pump Service

PT-6 Engines

This water pump is nonadjustable, has a packless seal and must be serviced as a complete unit: in the event of malfunction the whole assembly is replaced.

1. Remove pump as described in the preceding section.
2. Clean impeller cavity before installing new pump.
3. Spin shaft on new pump to be sure it rotates freely.
4. Install as described in preceding section, using a new gasket.

Water Pump Disassembly

All Models Exc. 8-400

1. Drain cooling and remove water pump as described previously.
2. If applicable, remove fan pulley nut and washer.
3. Remove pulley from shaft by pressing or by using a puller.
4. On BD series engines, remove screws and cover plate from impeller end of housing.
5. Remove clip retaining ring from pulley end of shaft.
6. Supporting housing assembly on arbor press, push shaft forward, removing impeller, bearing(s), shaft slinger and seal.
7. If bearing is of smooth type, it cannot be removed from shaft and whole shaft assembly must be replaced if they are damaged. If roller bearings are worn, remove them with a press or puller.
8. On pumps from BD-308 engines, remove snap ring from impeller assembly and take out washer, seal, spring guide, spring and clamp ring.

FEELER GAUGE
SCALE →
IMPELLER
WATER PUMP HOUSING

Checking water pump cover to impeller clearance
(© International Harvester Co.)

Water pump impeller parts BD282 & 308 engines (© International Harvester Co.)

Water pump—V-266, 304, 345 & 392 engines
(© International Harvester Co.)

Water pump cover to impeller clearance
—BG engines
(© International Harvester Co.)

Water pump cross section
—typical BD & BG engines
(© International Harvester Co.)

PCV valve RD engines
(© International Harvester Co.)

9. Clean and examine all parts for damage and wear to determine which need replacement.

Water Pump Assembly

Water pump assembly is the reverse of the above procedure except for the following variations.

Model BD-308: Assemble bearings, slinger and lock rings on shaft end, after filling bearing

PCV system—BD & BG engines
(© International Harvester Co.)

cavity with grease, press shaft assembly into body as a unit. Assemble seal components into impeller and press impeller assembly onto shaft. Press on pulley and install cover with new gasket.

Engine

Positive Crankcase Ventilation Valve

The same PCV valve is used on all engines except the PT-6 and RD series. On V-8 engines it is located in the ventilation line which runs from the intake manifold to the top rear of the crankcase. On RD engines a different PCV valve is mounted on the intake manifold. Another different PCV valve is mounted on the valve cover of the PT-6 engine. These

valves should be replaced every 10,000 miles. The direction of ventilation flow is always towards the manifold or carburetor.

Engine Removal

The following is an outline of general engine removal. Removal procedure will vary from truck to truck due to the variety of body models and accessory equipment. Before lifting out engine be certain that everything has been disconnected. Remove anything that might be in the way of the actual lifting.

1. Drain water from radiator and engine block.
2. Drain crankcase oil.
3. Disconnect battery ground cable and remove cable clamp from hot terminal of battery.
4. Remove all water hoses to radiator and heater.

5. Remove fan blades and fan shroud.
6. Remove any radiator cross-brace rods or brackets.
7. Remove radiator mounting bolts and lift out radiator. WARNING: On vehicles with LPG fuel systems observe all safety precautions. Be sure shop procedures are in compliance with local fire regulations. Close all tank valves and exhaust fuel from lines before working on fuel system.
8. On conventional chassis, remove hood hinge bracket mounting bolts and remove hood assembly. On CO models, tilt cab forward and prop securely. On cab-forward models, remove all front end sheet metal: bumper, fenders, radiator shell and disconnect any wiring that goes to these parts.
9. Disconnect and remove air filter from engine. Remove breather hose from air cleaner, if applicable.
10. Disconnect fuel pump inlet line.
11. Remove vacuum lines from manifold and all other components,

Engine lifting sling—V8 engines
(© International Harvester Co.)

and lines from air compressor, and air pump, if applicable.
12. Disconnect throttle linkage, choke control wire and hand throttle control wire, if applicable. On V-304, 345, 392 engines the carburetor must be removed for the fitting of the lifting fixture.
13. If so equipped, disconnect wire from heater control valve.

14. Disconnect all wiring from engine:
    a. Water temperature gauge sender.
    b. Oil pressure gauge sender.
    c. Generator wires.
    d. Primary ignition wire to resistor.
    e. Starter solenoid wires and battery cable.
15. On V(S)-401, 478, 549 engines, loosen alternator belts and disconnect alternator strap bracket to swing alternator away from thermostat housing. Then remove thermostats and housing.
16. If so equipped, remove tachometer drive at the distributor on the small V-8—or at the rear of the block on the big V-8.
17. Disconnect exhaust pipes at manifolds.
18. If so equipped, remove automatic transmission filler tube, freon compressor lines and disconnect power steering pump line and hose.
19. Install lifting fixtures and suitable sling. On the V(S)-401, 478, 549 engines an eye bolt is installed at rear of intake mani-

Engine removal using lifting sling
(© International Harvester Co.)

Manifold heat control valve—PT-6 engines
(© International Harvester Co.)

Intake manifold removal OHV4 & V8 engines
(© International Harvester Co.)

Exhaust manifold removal OHV4 & V8 engines
(© International Harvester Co.)

fold and a plate where the thermostat was mounted. On V-304, 345, 392 models the lifting fixture is mounted on the intake manifold where the carburetor was removed. On 400 engines, lifting eyes are installed in pre-drilled holes at front right and left rear of intake manifold. On six cylinder engines two brackets are secured by the two extreme head bolts and sling attached as illustrated.

20. Connect hoisting equipment to lifting fixture and hoist enough to support engine.
21. Remove bell housing mounting bolts. On the PT-6 and V-8 engines the flywheel housing front cover is removed before the flywheel housing is removed from crankcase. On the BD-308 engines the transmission is unbolted from the bell housing. On vehicles with RD engines the floor panel is removed to provide access to the bolts securing bell housing.
22. Disconnect clutch linkage.
23. Remove front engine mounting bolts. On some models it is easier to unbolt the mount from the frame crossmember.
24. Remove side engine mount bolts.
25. In hoisting out engine, first pull engine forward to clear clutch assembly from transmission, then tilt front up and carefully out of the chassis. CAUTION: Avoid damaging clutch driven disc.
26. Installation of the engine is in general the reverse of the above described procedure. Be careful when installing that wires are not pinched between engine and frame. Lower the engine until transmission main drive gear spline can be aligned with the clutch driven disc. The weight of the engine must remain supported until the bell housing is secured to flywheel housing. After engine has been secured to chassis, remove hoisting equipment and lifting fixtures.

Manifolds

Intake Manifold Removal & Installation

4 Cylinder and V8 Engines

1. If engine is in vehicle, remove air cleaner and, if applicable, governor vacuum line.
2. Disconnect throttle linkage, choke cable and fuel line.
3. Remove carburetor.
4. On V-304, 345, 392, 400 engines, disconnect hose from thermostat housing and bracket for spark plug wires.

5. On 4 cylinder models, remove coil, coil mounting bracket and ignition resistor from intake manifold.
6. Remove positive crankcase ventilation pipe and vacuum line.
7. Remove mounting bolts, manifold and gasket.
8. Installation is the reverse of the above procedure. Install new gaskets and tighten the mounting bolts from the center out, torquing to 40-45 ft. lbs.

Exhaust Manifold Removal & Installation

4 Cylinder and V8 Engines

1. Disconnect exhaust pipe from manifold.
2. Unbolt exhaust manifold from head.
3. Remove manifold.
4. Installation is the reverse of the above procedure. Install new manifold-to-head gasket and new manifold-to-pipe gasket.
5. Torque manifold-to-head bolts to 25-30 ft.lb.

Manifolds Removal & Installation

6 Cylinder Engines

1. Remove exhaust pipe from manifold.
2. Disconnect PCV line and vacuum lines from intake manifold.
3. Disconnect throttle linkage, fuel line and choke cable from carburetor.
4. Remove air filter and carburetor.
5. Remove exhaust/intake manifold unit and gaskets.
6. Separate intake from exhaust manifold.
7. The PT-6, engines are equipped with a manifold heat control valve in the exhaust manifold. To remove this valve, first note position of counter-weight in relation to valve plate. Remove thermostatic spring from end of shaft. With a hacksaw blade or cutting torch, cut the shaft on both sides of the valve plate and remove plate and shaft pieces, being careful not to ruin bushings. If bushings need replacement, remove and install, spacing them .3175-.3185" on BD engines and .3120-.3130" on PT-6 engines. With valve plate in the "heat on" position, insert shaft, hold counterweight in the correct position and secure plate with screw or tack weld (BD). Install thermostatic spring and hook spring over stop pin. Lubricate with a mixture of penetrating oil and graphite.
8. Intake and exhaust manifolds must be assembled properly to

insure alignment. Position intake manifold to exhaust manifold using new gasket.
9. Install nuts and bolts holding the two manifolds together but do not tighten.
10. Position manifolds to cylinder head with intake manifold pilot rings in place and install mounting bolts, but do not tighten.
11. Tighten nuts and bolts which hold manifolds together, torquing to 25-28 ft. lbs.
12. Tighten manifold mounting bolts, torquing to 25-28 ft. lbs.

Cylinder Head

Cylinder Head Removal & Installation

6 Cylinder Engines

1. If the engine is to remain in the vehicle, first do the following: Drain cooling system, disconnect water hose(s) and disconnect the fuel line from the carburetor. On the PT-6 engine, positive crankcase ventilation and vacuum advance lines must also be removed. In some cases, depending on the model, various accessory or other equipment may have to be removed.
2. Disconnect spark plug wires and, if applicable, remove wires from bracket on cylinder head. Identify cylinder number of each wire with tags or marks.
3. Disconnect ignition coil wires and remove coil from cylinder head.
4. Remove manifolds as described in preceding section.
5. On BD engines, disconnect water by-pass hose at cylinder head and

Rocker arm assembly—PT6 engines
(© International Harvester Co.)

Rocker arm shaft oil feed bolt—RD engines
(© International Harvester Co.)

remove water pump as described in preceding section.

6. Remove rocker arm cover bolts and remove rocker arm cover and gasket. If there are any dowel sleeves in brackets, note their location.

7. Remove push rods and keep them in order so that they may be replaced in the same locations.

8. Remove cylinder head bolts, marking any odd length or oil feed bolts for proper reinstallation.

9. Remove cylinder head and gasket.

10. Installation is the reverse order of the above instructions. Be sure to note the following steps where applicable.

11. Align new head gasket with bolt holes and carefully place cylinder head into position without damaging or shifting gasket.

12. Install all short head bolts and flat washers, but do not tighten.

13. On the PT-6 engine, apply No. 2 Permatex or equivalent sealant to the threads of the long (4¼") bolt at position "11". On this engine, proceed to tighten the head bolts to 80-85 ft. lbs. torque in the sequence illustrated. Tighten in approximately 20 ft. lb. steps until proper torque readings are obtained.

14. Install push rods into original positions.

15. Install rocker arm assembly, installing any dowel sleeves which were removed. On BD engines, rocker arm bolts serve as head bolts and all should be tightened in the sequence illustrated at this point. Tighten to 85-95 ft. lbs. torque, except on BD-308 engines (100-110 ft. lbs.).

16. On RD engines, leave the long oil bolt out and tighten only the short head bolts to 100-110 ft. lbs. torque.

17. On the PT-6 engine, the long rocker arm assembly mounting bolt is placed in the fifth (next to rear) position. Tighten rocker arm assembly mounting bolts to 20-23 ft. lbs. torque, inner first, then outer.

18. On RD engines, insert drilled oil bolt in special oil connector and tighten rocker arm shaft mounting bolts to 25-30 ft. lbs. torque. Be sure to install those bolts with the cover mounting studs in the correct position. Note lock washers which key into end brackets.

19. Adjust rocker to valve clearance. See the following section, "Valve Clearance Adjustment," for correct procedure. The PT-6 engine has hydraulic lifters and cannot be adjusted. See Unit Repair

Cylinder head bolt tightening sequence—PT-6-232 engines

Cylinder head bolt tightening sequence—RD engines

Cylinder head bolt tightening sequence—4-152, 196, V-266, 304, 345 & 392 engines

Cylinder head bolt tightening sequence—BD269, 282 & 308 engines

Cylinder head bolt tightening sequence—401, 561 & 549 engines

Correct pulley location for installing pushrods—OHV-4 & small V8 engines
(© International Harvester Co.)

Cylinder head dowel sleeve location—OHV-4 and V8 engines
(© International Harvester Co.)

Rocker arm shaft dowel sleeve—OHV-4 and V8 engines (© International Harvester Co.)

Section for hydraulic lifter service operations.

20. Reinstall any components which were removed and have not yet been put back. Replace rocker cover gasket if necessary.

Cylinder Head Removal

V-8 and 4 Cylinder Engines

1. Remove intake and exhaust manifolds as described in preceding section. On V-8's, this may entail removal of the air compressor and air compressor mounting bracket.

2. Head removal is facilitated by the use of a lifting sling which is attached with bolts in the intake manifold mounting bolt holes.

3. Remove cylinder head covers and gaskets.

4. Loosen rocker arm shaft bracket bolts and remove the rocker arm assembly. NOTE: Be sure to remove and keep track of the two dowel sleeves on the end brackets of the rocker arm assembly.

5. Remove pushrods, marking them so that they may be installed in their same locations.

6. Remove spark plug wires.

7. Remove cylinder head bolts.

8. When lifting off cylinder, do not lose the two locating dowel sleeves.

Head bolt torque sequence—V8-400

Checking rotating valve cap clearance—
RD, BD & BG engines
(© International Harvester Co.)

Valve rotators RD, BD & BG engines
(© International Harvester Co.)

9. Installation is basically the reverse of the above procedure, with the exception of the following additional steps.

10. Be sure to use a new head gasket and to reinstall dowel sleeves when positioning the head and mounting the rocker assembly. Reinstall pushrods in their original locations.

11. On 4-196 and V-304, 345, 392, turn engine crankshaft until leading edge of balance weight on crankshaft pulley is aligned with the zero degree mark on the timing indicator before installing rocker arm assembly.

12. On 4-196 engines, be sure to install rocker assembly so that the oil feed shaft bracket is third from the rear.

13. On V-304, 345, 392 engines, install rocker arm assembly so that the notches at the end of the shaft are facing upward. Oil feed brackets are third from the rear on the right (even numbers) bank and third from the front on the left (odd numbers) bank.

14. On the V(S)-401, 478, 549 engines, rocker arm assembly mounting bolts serve as head bolts and are tightened in the head bolt torque sequence. Torque head bolts in the sequence pattern illustrated to 80-90 ft. lbs. torque. *CAUTION:* Do not use a power wrench on heads of engines with hydraulic lifters. Torque head bolts slowly so that the leakdown of the lifters may relieve strain from the valve train.

15. On 4-196 and V-304, 345, 392, 400 engines, tighten the head bolts in the sequence illustrated to 110 ft. lb. on 400 engines and 90-100 ft. lb. on all others.

16. Retorque head bolts to the specified torque after 1000 miles of operation.

17. Install rocker covers and any other equipment removed for head work. Replace rocker cover gasket if necessary.

Valves

Valve Rotators

RD Engines

Exhaust valves on RD engines have a special stem and valve cap which permit the valve to rotate for an instant during each cycle. The clearance between the valve cap and the valve stem is critical for service life of the valve. The clearance is measured with a special gauge as illustrated. Grind bottom of valve cap to decrease clearance. To increase clearance, grind top of valve stem. If valve keys are removed they must be reinstalled with the wear on the top side.

Valve Train Service

Reference

The PT-6, 4-196 and V-8 engines utilized hydraulic lifters for which there is no lash adjustment. Excess noise in the valve train of these engines indicates that service is required. Instructions for servicing hydraulic lifters may be found in the General Repair Section.

Valve removal, service, and installation procedures may be found in the Engine Rebuilding Section. See Specifications table at the beginning of this section for valve spring and valve seat angle specifications.

Valve Adjustment

BD and RD Engines

1. Remove valve rocker cover and gasket.

2. Rotate crankshaft until No. 1 cylinder is at top dead center of the compression stroke (both valves closed). Timing marks on the crankshaft pulley of RD and BD-308 engines should be aligned for zero degrees (TDC). On all other 6 cylinder engines the timing marks are located on the flywheel.

3. Clearance is adjusted on both valves. Loosen lock nut.

4. Holding the proper feeler gauge between adjusting screw on the end of the rocker arm and the valve stem, turn adjusting screw until specified clearance is obtained (feeler gauge just held snugly).

5. While holding adjusting screw, tighten lock nut.

6. Recheck clearance.

7. Rotate crankshaft $1/3$ turn so that No. 5 cylinder is at top dead center of compression stroke and repeat Steps 3 to 6.

8. Repeat for each cylinder following the sequence of the firing order.

9. Replace rocker cover, using a new gasket if necessary.

10. Valve clearance should be rechecked with engine at normal running temperature and after 500 miles when new or reground valves have been installed.

Rocker Arm Removal & Installation

1. Remove rocker cover and gasket.

2. Remove rocker arm assembly mounting bolts and flat washers.

3. Remove rocker assembly.

4. If applicable, remove clip-ring and retainer to disassemble

Timing mark alignment for valve adjustment
(© International Harvester Co.)

SNAP RING
ROCKER ARM
FRONT SHAFT
WASHER (KEY)
WASHER
SPRING WASHER
SPRING
BRACKET
CONNECTOR
REAR SHAFT
OIL FEED HOLE BRACKET

Rocker arm assembly—RD engines (© International Harvester Co.)

Exhaust valve rocker arm
Intake valve rocker arm
Spring
Front rocker arm shaft
Shaft bracket
Rocker arm adjusting nuts
Spacers
End bracket
Oil connection bracket

Rocker arm assembly—BD-282 & 308 engines (© International Harvester Co.)

rocker components. Be sure to keep all parts in order so that they may be replaced in their original positions.

5. Clean all parts thoroughly, making sure that oil passages are clear. If necessary to remove plugs from ends of shaft, drill a hole in one plug, knock out the other with a steel rod, then knock out the drilled plug.

6. Inspect shaft for wear and warpage. Replace bent or worn shaft.

7. On engines without hydraulic lifters (all 6 cyclinder except the PT-6), inspect rocker arm adjusting screws for wear at the contact surface and for damaged threads. Replace any that are defective.

8. Inspect rocker arm shaft bushings for wear. On V(S)-401, 478, 549 and early V-304, 345 engines the rocker arm bushings may be pressed out and new bushings pressed in. On all

FRONT OF ENGINE
SPACERS
NOTCH (indicates top of shaft)
SUPPORT WITH OIL FEED HOLE
ROCKER ARMS
SHAFT SUPPORTS

Rocker arm assembly—and V8 engines
(© International Harvester Co.)

other engines the bushing is integral with the rocker arm, and if the bushing is worn, the whole rocker arm must be replaced.

9. Inspect valve stem contact pad surfaces of rocker arm and resurface if wear is excessive. Do not remove more than .010″ of material when resurfacing.

10. If applicable, replace any defective tension springs.

11. Remove and inspect push rods one by one (to insure original position). Roll them on a flat surface to check for straightness. Replace any pushrods that are bent, have loose ends or are worn.

12. Reassemble all rocker arm assembly components in their original order. On RD engines, note that lock washers key into shaft and the end brackets.

13. Install rocker arm assembly, making sure that the oil feed bracket is in the proper position and that dowel sleeves are in place. On 4-196 and V-304, 345, 392 engines turn the crankshaft until leading edge of

balance weight on crankshaft pulley is aligned with the zero degree mark on the timing indicator before installing rocker arm assembly.

14. Tighten mounting bolts.

15. Adjust rocker arm to valve stem clearance as described above.

16. Install rocker cover, replacing gasket if necessary.

Timing Case & Gears

Crankshaft Pulley Removal

Accessibility of the crankcase pulley and front (timing) cover will vary according to the model. On some vehicles the timing case will be accessible only if the engine is completely removed. The following instructions are general and apply to most front cover repairs and service.

1. Drain cooling system.

2. Disconnect radiator hoses and remove radiator. In some cases the radiator shroud and truck hood must be removed.

3. Loosen front engine mounts and jack up engine enough to pro-

CAMSHAFT GEAR
INSTALLER
TIMING MARKS

Installing camshaft gear
(© International Harvester Co.)

Marking exact position of timing indicator—V8 engines
(© International Harvester Co.)

Installing front cover oil seal—BD & BG engines
(© International Harvester Co.)

Timing gear installation—BD282 & 308 engines
(© International Harvester Co.)

Removing camshaft
(© International Harvester Co.)

vide access to the crankshaft pulley with a puller.

4. Loosen and remove fan belts and remove fan blades.

5. Remove crankshaft pulley retaining bolt. On V(S)-401, 478, 549 engines, scribe a line alongside the timing indicator and remove the indicator from front cover. The line is for reassembly purposes. The 400 engine has a pulley which is removed simply by removing 4 capscrews. The vibration damper behind the pulley must be removed with a puller.

6. Using a suitable puller, remove the pulley from the crankshaft. On some models the pulley is in two pieces and the pulley must be unbolted from its hub before the hub is removed with a puller.

Front Oil Seal Removal & Installation

1. Remove crankshaft pulley as described in Steps 1 through 6 above.

2. Remove seal. It is preferable to use an appropriate seal puller. Use a new gasket when installing front cover and be sure to align cover before tightening.

3. Install a new seal using a suitable seal installing tool if possible. Lubricate first and be careful not to damage seal or seating surface of cover.

4. Install crankshaft pulley, fan belt and fan blades.

5. Lower engine and tighten mounting bolts.

6. Install radiator, shroud, hoses and whatever else was removed.

7. Fill cooling system.

Timing Gear Removal

Timing gears can be removed without disassembling the engine. In some cases, however, the engine must be removed.

1. Remove crankcase pulley as described in Steps 1 through 6 above.

2. Remove engine front cover.

3. Rotate engine to align timing marks on crankshaft gear and camshaft gear.

4. To remove either gear, remove bolt and washer. Use a suitable puller. On the PT-6 engine, first remove master link and chain.

5. Use a suitable installing tool to install gears. Lubricate with engine oil and insert key in shaft to align gear. Align timing marks as illustrated. Be careful not to damage threads on shaft. Install and tighten retaining bolt.

6. Rotate engine to check that gears are not binding.

7. Check gear backlash with a dial indicator. It should be within .004-.007″ on OHV6 engines and .0005-.0045″ on OHV4 and V8 engines.

8. Use a new gasket when installing front cover and be sure to align cover before tightening. On some models there is an oil slinger on the crankshaft.

9. Install crankshaft pulley, belt and fan blades. Tighten retaining bolt.

10. Lower engine and tighten engine mounting bolts.

11. Install radiator and hoses.

12. Fill cooling system.

Camshaft Removal & Installation

1. Remove cylinder head as described previously in "Cylinder Head R&R."

Timing gear alignment marks except PT6 engines

TIMING MARKS

Timing gear alignment marks PT6 engines

Step, Arrow, Front and Cam Mark Away from Camshaft Side of Engine

Cast Letters Away from Camshaft Side of Engine

Stamped Numbers Toward Camshaft Side of Engine

Tangs

Piston & rod assembly—RD engines
(© International Harvester Co.)

Bearing Tangs

Right Bank 2,4,6,8

Left Bank 1,3,5,7

Correct assembly of piston & rods— V8 engines
(© International Harvester Co.)

Hammer handle

Ring compressor

Piston

Piston installation
(© International Harvester Co.)

Vertical Slot Toward Camshaft

Tangs

Numbers Toward Camshaft

Piston & rod assembly—BD & BG engines

Notch Toward Front of Engine

Numbers Toward Camshaft

Piston & rod assembly PT-6—232 engines

2. Remove pushrods and tappets. On RD engines the tappets are of the mushroom type and must be removed from the bottom. In order that they be out of the way for removing camshaft, either the engine must be turned upside down or they must be pushed up until the spring loaded retainers snap into a groove in the tappet.
3. Remove crankshaft pulley as described above.
4. Remove distributor and fuel pump.
5. Remove oil pan and oil pump.
6. Remove front (timing) cover.
7. Remove two screws which secure the camshaft thrust flange to the crankcase.
8. Remove camshaft and gear. To prevent nicking and damaging camshaft it is best to use a camshaft removing tool.
9. When installing camshaft and gear coat the bearing surfaces and lobes with lubricant and use an installing tool if possible. Make sure the timing marks are aligned.
10. Working through the two large holes in the gear, insert the two thrust flange screws and tighten them to the specified torque.
11. Check timing gear backlash. If the end play exceeds the limits

listed in Specifications, replace thrust flange.
12. Place oil slinger over end of crankshaft.
13. Install front cover using a new gasket. Be sure to align cover before tightening cover bolts to specified torque.
14. Install crankshaft pulley, tightening pulley retaining bolt to specified torque.
15. Install cylinder head (see "Cylinder Head R&R").
16. Install fan belt, fan blades, fuel pump and distributor.
17. Install oil pump and oil pan.
18. If engine was raised, lower engine and tighten engine mounts to specified torque.

Pistons and Connecting Rods

Reference

For piston and connecting rod overhaul procedures see Engine Rebuilding General Section. Bearings are fitted and their clearances checked in the usual manner.

Piston Removal & Installation

1. Remove oil pan and oil pump. On some models this may re-

quire loosening the engine mounts and jacking up the engine until spacer blocks can be installed. When removing oil pump on big V8's turn crank until counter weight is out of the way.
2. Remove cylinder head. See "Cylinder Head R&R" above.
3. Using a ridge reamer, remove the ridge from the top of the cylinders.
4. Rotate the crankshaft until journal is in lowermost position for removal of connecting rod assemblies. Remove the cap and push the connecting rod and piston up through the cylinder bore. Replace the cap and bearing inserts on the rods so the numbered sides match. The numbers indicate position.
5. To install pistons and connecting rods, rotate crankshaft until No. 1 crankpin is at the bottom of its stroke. Correctly seat rod bearing insert in rod then dip piston assembly in clean oil to lubricate rings. Using a ring compressor, install piston and rod in cylinder. Push piston in, do not strike. On the PT-6 engines, the notch on the top of piston perimeter faces toward the front of the engine (number on connecting rod toward the camshaft).

Proper installation of connecting rods to crankshaft (© International Harvester Co.)

On 4-196 and all V8 engines, except the 400, the piston assembly is installed with the word "UP" toward the top (camshaft) side of the engine block. On the 400, the piston is installed with the notch facing front. On all OVH 6 except the PT-6, install piston assembly with the arrow stamped on piston crown toward camshaft.

6. Place lower half of bearing insert in rod cap and lubricate with oil. Assemble bearing cap to connecting rod with the number side of cap on the same side as the number on the connecting rod. Lubricate threads of bolts with engine oil and install bolts, tightening to the correct torque (see Specifications at the beginning of this section).

7. Rotate crankshaft and repeat installation procedure with the rest of the pistons and connecting rods.

8. Install oil pump and oil pan, using a new pan gasket if necessary.

9. Install cylinder head as described in "Cylinder Head R&R" above.

10. If engine was raised, remove spacers and lower engine. Tighten engine mount bolts.

Piston Rings Replacement

1. Remove pistons as described above.

2. Remove both compression rings and three-piece oil ring.

3. Using rings which correspond to the piston size (standard or oversize), check rings for gap clearance and ring-to-groove side clearance.

4. Install rings on piston with a suitable ring expander tool.

Checking ring groove clearance (© International Harvester Co.)

Checking piston ring gap (© International Harvester Co.)

5. Install piston assembly as described above.

Main Bearing Replacement

On most models it is possible to replace main bearings without removing the engine from the vehicle. However, it is easier to do a better job with the engine removed and, if facilities are available for pulling the engine, this is the preferable method. See "Engine R&R" above. For detailed procedures on main bearing, rod bearing and crankshaft servicing see General Repair Section.

1. Remove crankshaft pulley and front (timing) cover.

2. Remove cylinder head(s) and piston assemblies.

3. If the bell housing and transmission were not removed during engine removal, remove them now.

4. On many engines the clutch plate may be compressed by installing three cap screws ($\frac{3}{8}$"-16x2$\frac{1}{2}$" for RD and V(S)-401, 478, 549 engines or $\frac{3}{8}$"-16x2" for V-304, 345, 392 engines). If the clutch plate cannot be compressed in this way, cut three $\frac{1}{2}$"x1"x3" wood blocks and insert them between the clutch fingers and back plate. Loosen backing plate mounting bolts slightly if it is difficult to insert wood blocks. A third alternative procedure for compressing the clutch plate is to insert three retaining clips as illustrated. The clutch plate is compressed during removal and installation of the clutch to prevent warpage.

5. Remove the backing plate mounting bolts and clutch assembly.

6. Remove flywheel bolts and pull off flywheel.

7. On BD-308 and RD engines remove the upper and lower rear main bearing oil seal retainers.

8. Remove main bearing caps. On OHV4, V-304, 345, 392, engines use a rear main bearing cap puller to remove rear main bearing cap. On RD engines the lower oil seal retainer must be removed before the cap can be unbolted. Note that the caps are numbered and should be reinstalled in their original positions.

9. When installing new main bearings make sure that the oil holes are properly aligned and that bearing tangs are fitted into tang recesses. Thoroughly clean

all surfaces and coat lightly with oil. Be sure to align timing marks when positioning crankshaft. On the PT-6 engine main bearing caps have an arrow which indicates front of engine. On the OHVA and V-304, 345, 392, 400 engines the numbered sides of the main bearing caps face the left side of the engine. On the BD and RD engines the numbered side of the bearing caps face the camshaft side of the engine. On V(S)-401, 478, 549 engines the bearing caps are installed with the numbered side facing to the right side of the engine. When tightening main bearing caps, first tap them lightly into place, then tighten bolts in an alternating manner until the specified torque is reached. See Specifications for correct torque.

10. Install a new rear main bearing oil seal. On OHV4 and V-304, 345, 392, 400 engines the round seal is pressed in after the rear main bearing cap is installed. Rear main bearing cap side oil seals are installed on these engines with an installer tool made from a piece of 1/8" welding rod. Puddle a ball on the end of the rod and file the ball to approximately 5.32" diameter. On BD-308 and RD engines the rear upper seal and retainer are installed before the crankshaft and the lower main bearing lower oil seal is installed after the rear main bearing cap, using new gaskets on each side of the lower seal retainer. On V(S)-401, 478, 549 engines the rear main bearing cap side seals are marked for right and left side. On PT-6, and V(S)-401, 478, 549 engines, the top and bottom rear main bearing oil seals are made of felt material which fits into slots in the block and bearing cap. These must be cut to the correct length while

Installing rear main oil seal
(© International Harvester Co.)

Rear main bearing oil seals—BD-282, 308 & RD engines (© International Harvester Co.)

the seal is being held in place with a seal compressing tool as illustrated.

11. Check main bearing clearance and crankshaft endplay and compare to clearance limits listed in Specifications at the beginning of this section. See Engine Rebuilding General Section for clearance measurement and service procedures.

12. Reassemble engine following Steps 1 through 7 in reverse order. Be sure to align clutch driven disc with transmission shaft or clutch aligning tool before tightening clutch plate mounting bolts.

Rear Main Bearing Seal Replacement

OHV 4 and V-304, 345 & 392, 400 Engines

1. Remove transmission, clutch and flywheel.
2. Using remover tool and protector plate, insert remover between seal retainer and crankshaft flange at long notch of protector plate and pry outward. Repeat prying at various locations around the seal. Use short notch of protector plate to pry seal out of position. If the seal retainer is too tight to fit in removing tool, it will be necessary to use a hammer to pierce the retainer in several places first.

3. Using pilot and installing tool, drive new seal into bore until it is flush with the rear face of the crankcase.
4. Install flywheel, clutch and transmission.

Rear Main Bearing Oil Seal Replacement

PT 6

1. PT-6 Drain crankcase and remove oil pan.
2. Remove rear main bearing cap.
3. Remove oil seal from bearing cap and clean cap thoroughly.
4. Loosen all remaining main bearing cap mounting bolts.
5. Using a brass drift and hammer, tap the upper seal until sufficient seal is protruding on the other side to permit pulling it out with pliers.
6. Wipe crankshaft seal surface clean and coat lightly with oil.
7. Coat crankcase surface of upper seal with soap and the lip of seal with No. 40 engine oil.
8. Install upper seal with lip toward front of engine.
9. Coat mating surfaces of crankcase and cap with No. 2 Permatex or equivalent, back surface of seal with soap and lip of seal with No. 40 engine oil.
10. Seat seal firmly into seal recess of cap and apply No. 2 Permatex or equivalent to both chamfered edges of the rear main bearing cap.
11. Install main bearing halves and cap.
12. Tighten all main bearing cap mounting bolts to specified torque.
13. Install oil pan.

Installation of oil seal in rear main bearing cap
(© International Harvester Co.)

Installing rear main bearing cap side oil seals
(© International Harvester Co.)

Engine Lubrication

Oil Filter Replacement

On all models except the PT-6 and the 400 the oil filter unit is on the left side of the engine block. On these engines it is on the right side and the whole filter is replaced using a strap wrench.

1. Remove drain plug from bottom of filter body, drain oil and replace drain plug.
2. Loosen filter body retaining bolt and remove filter body and element. Check condition of body to base gasket and replace if necessary.
3. Wash filter body with cleaning solvent, being sure to remove all sediment.
4. Install new filter element onto filter base with seal end away from base. Be sure element is fully seated onto base.
5. Install oil filter body and bolt with spring, making sure body

ENGINE LUBRICATION CHART
V-266   V-304   V-345
DIAGRAMATIC-SHOWING CIRCUIT OF OIL IN ENGINE

Engine lubrication system V8—engines (© International Harvester Co.)

Oil filter bypass valve & spring—
PT-6 engines
(© International Harvester Co.)

seats evenly on gasket. Tighten filter body retaining bolt to 30-35 ft. lbs. torque on all engines.
6. Start engine and run for at least 5 minutes until oil is warm and check for leaks.
7. Check crankcase oil level. Lubricant capacity of oil filter is about one quart.

Engine lubrication system PT-6 engines (© International Harvester Co.)

Oil pump installation BD & BG engines
(© International Harvester Co.)

Oil pump shaft sleeve installation—OHV4, V266, 304, 345 & 392 engines
(© International Harvester Co.)

Typical gear type oil pump
(© International Harvester Co.)

Typical front axle mounting
(© International Harvester Co.)

Oil Pump Removal & Installation

1. Drain crankcase and remove oil pan.
2. Remove oil pump mounting bolts and pull straight down on pump to remove.
3. When installing oil pump, guide pump shaft into position and rotate shaft until tang of drive gear is engaged. On PT-6 and V(S)-400, 401, 478, 549 engines install a new oil pump gasket when installing. On BD and RD engines the oil pump shaft drives the distributor shaft and must be installed so that it is correctly timed to the crankshaft. Rotate the crankshaft until No. 1 cylinder is in firing position. On BD-308 engines the slot on the top of the oil pump shaft must be at right angles to the side of the engine (transverse to the vehicle). On RD engines the oil pump is installed so that the slot in the top of the shaft is at a 60-degree angle to the side of the engine.
4. Tighten oil pump mounting bolts to:
   25-30 ft. lb. for all exc. 400.
   400-55 in. lb.
5. Install oil pan and fill crankcase.

Oil Pump Service

1. Thoroughly clean oil pump. Do not disturb or remove pickup tube unless absolutely necessary.

Oil pump installation—RD engines
(© International Harvester Co.)

2. Remove pump cover bolts and pump cover.
3. Check gear to body clearance. If it is not within .0025-.0055" on the OHV6 engines or .0007-.0027" on the OHV4 and V8 engines, obtain new parts.
4. Check gear backlash. If it exceeds .011" on OHV4 and V8 engines or .006" on OHV6 engines, replace gears.
5. Check pump shaft clearance in bore. If it exceeds .004" on OHV6 engines or .003" on V8 and OHV4 engines, replace the whole pump assembly.
6. Remove relief valve and spring. Remove any burrs and clean. Be sure to install with bevelled or pointed end in seat. Check that volve moves freely in bore.
7. Check body and gear clearance. This is the distance between the pump gears and the pump cover, except on the PT-6 where it is the distance the gears protrude beyond the pump body. Adjust-

ment of this clearance is made by the addition or removal of cover gaskets. On V(S)-401, 478, 549 engine oil pumps the clearance must be .0015-.009". On the OHV4 and V-304, 345, 392 engines the clearance is .0015-.006". On all OHV6 except the PT-6 (which is .000-.004" *above* pump body) the clearance is .0025-.0055".

8. When installing drive gears on pump shaft be sure that the correct drive gear to pump body clearance is obtained. On RD engines the clearance is .025-.035" and on BD-308 engines it is .015-.020". On OHV4 and V-304, 345, 392 engines the oil pump shaft sleeve is crimped onto the shaft. On the OHV4 the assembly dimension is .200" and on the V-304, 345, 392 engines the assembly dimension is .375". On V(S)-401, 478, 549 engines the distance "A" is 2⅞" for front-mounted distributors, 1-15/16" for rear-mounted distributors.

Front Suspension

Front I-Beam Suspension

Spring Removal

1. Disconnect shock absorber at lower mount.

2. Raise front of vehicle just enough to take weight off spring.
3. Unbolt U-bolts, tapered caster wedge and U-bolt.
4. Remove lube fittings from spring mountings.
5. Remove spring pins and spring.
6. To install, reverse the above procedure, mounting fixed end of spring first.

King Pin and Bushings Replacement

1. Remove spindle nuts and spindle bearing retaining nuts.
2. Remove wheels, inner bearings and grease retainers from spindles.
3. Remove dirt shields.
4. Remove bolts holding backing plates and place backing plate assemblies over ends of axle I-beam.
5. Remove tapered draw keys holding the knuckle pins.
6. Remove expansion plugs or cap and gasket from the top and bottom of steering knuckles. (Remove expansion plugs by drilling a hole in one of the plugs and driving king pin with a punch to remove the other).
7. Drive out king pin.
8. Remove steering knuckles, thrust bearings and any spacer shims present.
9. Clean all parts thoroughly and inspect for wear and damage.
10. Remove old bushings with an arbor or drift.
11. Install new bushings with an

Typical steering knuckle— expansion type seal plugs
(© International Harvester Co.)

Checking front suspension height
(© International Harvester Co.)

Typical front spring installation (medium duty)
(© International Harvester Co.)

arbor or bushing installing tool, making sure that the grease holes are aligned.
12. Ream or hone bushings to fit king pin with .001-.002″ clearance.
13. Lubricate and install steering knuckle, thrust bearings, spacer shims and king pins.
14. Install draw key (front side of axle) and tighten securely.
15. Insert expansion plugs or cap and gasket seals in the top and bottom of the steering knuckles.
16. Install brake backing plates, tightening bolts securely.
17. Install dirt shields, their retaining screws, cleaned and repacked

SPECIFICATIONS

IH MODEL	FA1 FA10	FA12 FA28 FA48	FA68 FA72	FA91 FA98 FA99	FA69
IH CODE	02001 02010	02012 02028 02048	02068 02072	02091 02098 02099	02069
Knuckle Pin Bushing Diameter (Inch)	.8625 .8615	1.111 1.110	1.236 1.235	1.236 1.235	1.236 1.235
Knuckle Pin Diameter (Inch)	.861 .860	1.110 1.109	1.234 1.233	1.234 1.233	1.234 1.233
Knuckle Pin Length (Inch)	5-7/16	6-1/4	6-3/4	7-21/32	6-3/4
Steering Knuckle Spindle Diameter At Inner Bearing (Inch)	Early Prod. 1.312 1.311 Late Prod. 1.374 1.371	Early Prod. 1.562 1.561 Late Prod. 1.687 1.686	1.749 1.748	2.1248 2.1240	1.874 1.873
At Outer Bearing (Inch)	Early Prod. .812 .811 Late Prod. .843 .842	.937* .936	1.124 1.123	1.312 1.311	1.124 1.123

*FA12 .9998
.9988

SPECIFICATIONS

IH Model	FA-71	FA-73	FA-74	FA-101	FA-103
IH Code	02071	02073	02074	02101	02103
Knuckle Pin Bushing Diameter (inch)	1.360	1.360	1.360	1.360	1.360
Knuckle Pin Diameter (inch)	1.358	1.358	1.358	1.358	1.358
Knuckle Pin Length (inch)	7.97	7.97	7.97	7.97	7.97
Steering Knuckle Spindle Diameter: At Inner Bearing (inch) At Outer Bearing (inch)	1.967 1.374	1.967 1.374	1.967 1.374	2.164 1.374	2.164 1.374

Torsion bar front wheel suspension (© International Harvester Co.)

1 Nut, hex., slotted
2 Washer
3 Seal, oil, front wheel
4 Arm, upper, asm.
5 Cushion, rubber, strut
6 Washer, lower arm strut
7 Washer
8 Bushing, upper control arm, front
9 Spindle, upper control arm
10 Bushing, upper control arm, rear
11 Frame
12 Bar, torsion
13 Seal, torsion bar
14 Nut, adjusting, torsion bar
15 Lever, retainer, torsion bar
16 Washer, adjusting, torsion bar
17 Bolt, hex.-hd.
18 Washer, retaining
19 Cushion, rubber

20 Shock absorber, front
21 Knuckle, steering
22 Bumper, control arm
23 Strut, lower control arm
24 Link, sway bar
25 Retainer, sway bar link cushion
26 Cushion, rubber, sway bar link
27 Arm, steering, left
28 Arm, lower, asm.
29 Link, vertical, left (or tie rod)
30 Arm, pitman
31 Rod, tie, asm.
32 Bar, sway
33 Bolt, hex.-hd.
34 Cam, lower control arm
35 Arm, idler, asm.
36 Link, vertical, right (or tie rod)
37 Arm, steering, right
38 Spacer, lower control arm

wheel bearings and new grease seals.

18. Install wheel and spindle nuts, rotating wheel while tightening nut until slight drag is felt. Back off to the first castellation and install new cotter pin. Install

19. Lubricate and check and align front wheels if necessary.

Torsion Bar Front Suspension

Torsion Bar Removal

Right and left torsion bars are not interchangeable. The bars are marked with an "L" or "R" on one end and the bars should always be installed with the marked end towards the rear of the vehicle. There is an arrow indicating the direction of wind-up on the end of the bar.

1. Jack up the vehicle by the frame crossmember and release the load from the torsion bar by loosening the retainer lever adjusting bolt.

2. Remove retainer lever adjusting bolt and slide retainer lever from end of torsion bar.

3. Remove torsion bar by sliding it rearward. CAUTION: Do not nick or scratch torsion bars—this may create a fracture.

4. To install torsion bar, position torsion bar in upper control arm, observing right and left side and rearward direction as indicated above.

5. Install retainer lever on end of torsion bar and position bar nut in bracket on frame so that torsion bar adjusting bolt may be installed.

6. Insert bolt in bar washer, then through retainer lever and bracket and thread into bar nut.

7. Adjust height by lowering vehicle to ground (check for correct tire pressure), bouncing front end up and down, then turning bolt on torsion bar adjusting lever until correct height is achieved. Measure height between top of lower control arm

and lower edge of rubber bumper frame bracket (vehicle unloaded).

Upper Control Arm Removal

1. Jack up vehicle by front frame crossmember until front wheels are off the ground.

2. Remove wheel and torsion bar (see preceding section).

3. Disconnect top mount of shock absorber.

4. Remove cotter pin, nut and dust seal (cut away seal) from lower ball joint.

5. Drive out lower ball joint stud (do not damage threads) or use special ball stud remover and nut.

6. Remove fender splash panel front shield.

7. Remove nut and washers from front end of upper control arm spindle and carefully drive out spindle with hammer.

8. Remove upper control arm.

9. To install, position upper control

1 Plug, expansion
2 Flange, wheel drive
3 Knuckle, wheel
4 Ball, steering arm
5 Arm, steering
6 Pin, cotter
7 Shaft, axle outer
8 Spider
9 Bearing, trunnion
10 Ring, snap
11 Shaft, axle inner
12 Bushing, knuckle
13 Bearing trunnion
14 Bushing, steering knuckle
15 Pin, king cone
16 Key, woodruff
17 Yoke, trunnion
18 Gasket, yoke mounting
19 Housing, axle
20 Pin
21 Gasket
22 Knuckle, steering
23 Shim
24 Cap, king pin bearing
25 Pin
26 Cone, bearing

Front drive axle (© International Harvester Co.)

arm and install spindle through arm and bracket from rear.

10. Install flat washer, lock washer and nut. Tighten securely.

11. Install fender splash panel front shield.

12. Install new dust seal on ball stud, then line up shock absorber with hole in control arm and position ball stud into steering knuckle. Use jack to raise lower control arm until ball stud is well into steering knuckle.

13. Install nut on ball stud. Tighten securely.

14. Install top mounting of shock absorber, tightening just enough to squash rubber cushion slightly.

15. Install torsion bar on upper control arm as described in preceding section.

16. Mount front wheel.

17. Check alignment (see General Repair Section) of steering.

Lower Control Arm Removal

1. Raise vehicle by jacking frame crossmember. Remove wheel.

2. Disconnect sway bar link from strut and remove two bolts which secure strut to lower control arm.

3. Cut away dust seal from lower ball stud and remove cotter pin and nut from lower ball stud.

4. Either drive out ball stud with a soft hammer while supporting control arm or use special ball stud remover and nut.

5. Disconnect tie rod end from either side of vehicle.

6. Remove nut, lockwasher, cam and bolt from lower control arm and frame bracket.

7. Remove control arm and spacer in bushing.

8. To install, place new dust seal on ball stud and position ball stud into steering knuckle.

9. Tighten nut on ball stud and install cotter pin.

10. Position spacer in bushing and, while holding control arm in position, install bolt from front. Install cam, lockwasher, and nut, tightening to 81-135 ft. lbs. torque.

11. Mount strut to lower control arm tightening bolts securely.

12. Connect tie rod end.

1 Seal axle shaft
2 Bushing, axle shaft
3 Pin, cotter
4 Nut
5 Ball, steering arm
6 Bracket, ball stud
7 End, stub
8 Spindle
9 Screw, adjusting
10 Wedge, adjusting
11 Cap, upper brg.
12 Bearing cone
13 Bearing cup
14 Bearing cup
15 Bearing cone
16 Seal
17 Plate, retaining
18 Seal, wheel
19 Nut, bearing adjusting
20 Plate lock
21 Pin, lock plate
22 Bearing
23 Bearing
24 Ring, clamp
25 Shaft, left axle
26 Bolt, hex-hd.
27 Dowel, shaft flange
28 Yoke, power
29 Pin, ring to yoke
30 Ring, compensating
31 Bushing, ring
32 Bushing, yoke
33 Pin, hub to ring
34 Plug, pipe
35 Hub
36 Drum
37 Washer, lock
38 Bolt, hex-hd.
39 Arm, steering
40 Lubricator
41 Bolt, tie-rod end
42 Bushing, steering
43 Nut, tie-rod end bolt
44 Yoke, tie-rod
45 Rod, tie

Front drive axle (drive gear type) (© International Harvester Co.)

13. Position cushion and retainer on sway bar link and place sway bar link into strut with cushion, retainer and nut. Tighten nut until cushion is slightly squished. Insert cotter pin.
14. Mount front wheel.
15. Check alignment (see General Repair Section) and tighten nut on strut to 120-150 ft. lbs. torque and camber adjusting bolt nut to 81-135 ft. lbs. torque.

Front Drive Axle

For Service on Transfer Case—see General Repair Section.

Description

The front drive axles are units incorporating hypoid gears and spherical steering knuckles. The axle shaft assemblies are full-floating and may be removed without disassembling the steering knuckles.

Two different means of transmitting driving torque from the axle shaft to the wheel are employed. One type uses a drive flange having a splined ID to mate with the axle shaft splines. The second type has a drive gear splined both internally and externally. The internal splines mate with the axle shaft splines and the external splines index with the splines of the inside of the wheel hub.

Front Drive Axle Removal

1. Jack up truck until load is removed from springs and block up frame to safely hold weight.
2. Drain lubricant from main housing and, if applicable, from wheel end housings.

1 Cap, grease
2 Ring, snap
3 Bolt, drive flange
4 Washer
5 Flange, drive
6 Gasket, drive flange
7 Bolt, spindle
8 Washer
9 Spindle, wheel
10 Bushing, wheel spindle
11 Shaft, joint
12 Ring, snap
13 Joint, universal assembly
14 Shaft, axle
15 Bolt, king pin bearing cap
16 Knuckle, steering
17 Washer
18 Cap, king pin bearing
19 Shim
20 Plug, filler
21 Ring, oil seal
22 Seal, oil (rubber)
23 Seal, oil (felt)
24 Plate, knuckle retainer
25 Cone, bronze bearing
26 Cup, bronze bearing
27 Housing, axle w/ball yoke
28 Bolt, metal plate retainer
29 Rod, tie

3. Disconnect brakes.
4. Disconnect drag link from ball stud bracket.
5. Disconnect drive shaft from pinion shaft yoke.
6. Supporting axle with a portable floor jack, remove spring U-bolts.
7. Roll axle assembly out from under truck.
8. To install, reverse the above procedure.

Front Drive Axle Adjustments

FA-57, 59, 140 Models

Preload on the knuckle bearings of these front axles must be maintained at all times. Check for looseness each time knuckle is lubricated.
1. Jack up front end of truck until off-center weight of the wheel is relieved (wheel just barely touching ground).
2. Remove wheel and wheel adapter from hub.
3. Disconnect tie rod and drag link.
4. Remove axle shaft.
5. To remove play (check for play by pushing and pulling on top and bottom of knuckle) and increase preload drag, turn adjusting bolt into back of knuckle. Preload should read (spring scale hooked into end of steering arm) 12 lbs. on FA-57, 59 and 14 lbs. on FA-140.

Front Wheel Bearing Adjustment FA-140

1. Remove wheel and adapter from hub.
2. Remove axle shaft, and adjusting nut lock plate.
3. Tighten nut until just against bearing.
4. Rotate the wheel forward and backward until a slight drag can be felt. Turn nut back to the first lock hole to obtain about a ½ hole relief.
5. Bearing adjustment is correct when no play can be felt when pushing and pull at top and bottom of wheel.

Front Wheel Bearing Adjustment FA-57 & 59

1. Remove wheel cover, axle shaft, adjusting plate bolts and lock plate assembly.
2. Remove or add enough shims until a slight drag can be felt when the adjusting plate is installed.

NOTE: Be certain to add or remove the same number of shims at Top and Bottom.

Models FA 15, 16, 18 and FA 52

Reference for overhaul procedures see International Single Reduction Rear Axle in General Repair Section.

Front drive axle (drive flange type) (© International Harvester Co.)

Axle Shaft and Universal Joint

(Axles having drive flange)
Removal

1. Raise vehicle, support with floor stands and remove wheel from vehicle.
2. Remove grease cap and snap ring from end of axle shaft.
3. Remove drive flange cap screws, lock-washer, flange and gasket. If equipped with locking hubs, bend up locking tab, take out capscrews and remove clutch body. NOTE: Lift off clutch body holding it errect so as not to let drive pins fall out of body. If they do fall out, be certain to install them during reassembly. Remove hub body. Loosen setscrew and unscrew drag shoe from spindle.
4. Remove brake drum countersunk setscrews, where applicable and remove drum.
5. Bend the lip on the wheel bearing lockwasher away from the outer wheel bearing nut and remove the nut and lockwasher. Remove wheel bearing adjusting nut (inner) and bearing lockwasher.
6. Remove the wheel hub with wheel bearing.
7. Remove backing plate and wheel spindle retaining bolts and lockwashers. Support backing plate to prevent damage to brake hose if hose is not disconnected.
8. Remove wheel bearing spindle with bushing. If spindle bushing requires replacing, press out bushing using an adapter of correct size. An alternate method of bushing removal is the use of a cape chisel or punch to collapse the bushing.
9. Pull axle shaft and universal joint assembly out of axle housing.

Installation

1. Insert axle shaft and universal joint assembly into axle housing. Position splined end of axle shaft into differential pinion gear and push into place.
2. If wheel bearing spindle bushing was removed, press new bushing into spindle using an installer tool or adapter of proper size. Lubricate ID of bushing with chassis lube when installed to provide initial lubrication. Bushing should be pressed in until bushing flange is seated against shoulder in spindle. Assemble wheel spindle and backing plate to steering knuckle. Secure with six (6) bolts and lockwashers and tighten to specifications. Connect hydraulic brake fluid line if disconnected.

3. Pack wheel bearings using a pressure lubricator or by carefully working lubricant into bearing cones by hand. Slide lubricated inner wheel bearing on spindle until it stops against spindle shoulder.
4. Apply thin coating of lubricant specified for wheel bearings to seal lip and install seal into wheel hub using an adapter of correct diameter. Lip of seal should extend towards wheel (away from backing plate assembly).
5. Assemble wheel hub on spindle. Install lubricated outer wheel bearing cone on spindle. Push cone on spindle until it rests against bearing cup.
6. Install wheel bearing lockwasher and adjusting (inner) nut. Tighten adjusting nut until there is a slight drag on the bearings when the hub is turned; then back-off approximately one-sixth turn.
7. Install tang-type lockwasher and lock nut (outer). Tighten nut and bend lockwasher tang over lock nut. If axle is equipped with locking hubs, install drag shoe on spindle and tighten setscrews.
8. Align splines of drive flange with those of axle shaft and secure drive flange and new gasket to wheel hub with capscrews and lockwashers. Tighten capscrews securely. If equipped with locking hubs, lightly lubricate hub body and clutch using a light grade chassis lubricant and install new gasket, hub body, snap ring and hub clutch. Be certain that all drive pins are positioned in locking hub clutch when clutch is installed. Secure hub clutch to wheel hub with capscrews and lock. Tighten to specifications and bend tang over head of capscrew.
9. Install snap ring and grease cup if not equipped with locking hubs.
10. Assemble brake drum and wheels to wheel hub. Bleed and adjust brakes. CAUTION: Be certain that master cylinder is full of brake fluid after completing bleeding operation.

Axle Shaft and Universal Joint

(Axles having drive gear)
Removal

1. Raise and support vehicle with floor stands placed under frame rails. Remove wheel from vehicle.
2. Lightly tap alternately around edge of hub cap with hammer and screwdriver or similar tool until hub cap is removed.

3. If axle is equipped with locking hubs, remove the eight (8) socket-head setscrews securing hub clutch assembly to wheel hub assembly. NOTE: Drive pins may fall out of hub clutch when separated from wheel hub assembly. Be certain to replace them during installation.
4. Remove retaining ring from wheel hub if equipped with locking hubs.
5. Remove snap ring from axle shaft.
6. Pull drive gear out of wheel hub. If difficulty is encountered in removing drive gear, obtain a screwdriver or similar tool having the end bent approximately 90° with the handle. Insert end of tool into groove in drive gear and withdraw gear. If necessary, move wheel alternately backward and forward to aid removal of gear.
7. Remove retaining ring and locking hub body, if so equipped.
8. Using Wheel Bearing Adjusting Nut Wrench, remove wheel bearing outer nut and slide lock ring off of axle shaft. Again using wrench, remove wheel bearing inner nut.
9. Pull drive gear spacer out of wheel hub.
10. Remove brake drum from wheel hub and slide wheel hub assembly off of spindle. NOTE: Do not allow tapered roller bearings to drop on floor as bearings may be damaged.
11. Remove screws retaining grease guard to backing plate. Take off grease guard and gasket.
12. Remove the six (6) bolts securing wheel spindle and backing plate to steering knuckle. Pull spindle with bushing off of axle shaft. If spindle bushing requires replacing, press or drive out bushing using an adapter of correct size. An alternate method of bushing removal is the use of a cape chisel or punch to collapse the bushing.
13. Pull axle shaft and universal joint assembly out of axle housing.

Installation

1. Proceed with steps 1 through 5 of *Axle Shaft and Universal Joint Installation* (Axles having drive flange).
2. Insert drive gear spacer over spindle and against outer wheel bearing cup.
3. Position wheel bearing inner adjusting nut Wheel Bearing Adjusting Nut wrench with pin in nut extending toward handle end of wrench. Install nut on spindle and tighten until it is snug against outer wheel bearing; then loosen adjusting nut ¼ turn.

Align tang on adjusting nut lock ring with groove in wheel spindle. Slide ring on spindle and index pin on adjusting nut with hole in lock ring. If pin will not index with hole in lock ring, turn adjusting nut to the left (Loosen) until it will index. NOTE: When attempting to index pin with hole in lock ring, turn nut very slightly since adjusting nut should be locked with first hole in lock ring past ¼ turn loose. Position wheel bearing outer nut in adjusting nut wrench and install on spindle. Tighten nut securely.

4. Align splines on axle shaft and splines in wheel hub with those of drive gear. Insert drive gear on axle shaft. Push gear into hub until it rests against drive gear spacer. NOTE: Groove on side of gear must be toward hub cap.

5. If axle is equipped with locking hubs, lightly lubricate locking hub body using a light grade chassis lubricant. Align splines and insert hub body into wheel hub.

6. Install snap ring on end of axle shaft.

7. Place retaining ring in groove in wheel hub, if equipped with locking hub.

8. If applicable, lightly grease hub clutch assembly using a light grade chassis lubricant. Be sure that all eight (8) drive pins are positioned in the locking hub clutch. Assemble hub clutch to hub body and secure with eight (8) socket head setscrews.

9. Position hub cap on wheel hub and lightly tap alternately around cap until flange is against edge of hub.

10. Assemble brake drum and wheel to wheel hub. Bleed and adjust brakes. CAUTION: Be certain that the master cylinder is full of brake fluid after bleeding operation.

Steering Knuckle

Removal

1. Remove drag link at steering arm and tie-rod at steering knuckle.

2. Remove oil seal retaining bolts from inner flange of steering knuckle and remove oil seals.

3. Remove bolts and lockwashers securing king pin lower bearing cap. Remove bearing cap and shim pack. Retain shim pack for use during reassembly.

4. Remove capscrews or self-locking nuts, which ever is applicable, securing steering arm or upper bearing cap to steering knuckle.

5. Lift steering arm assembly and knuckle until bronze bearing cone will clear ball yoke. Separate steering knuckle from ball yoke. NOTE: Do not allow lower tapered roller bearing cone to drop on floor during removal of steering knuckle.

6. Support steering knuckle and with a long brass drift, drive or press king pin out of bronze bearing cone. NOTE: Be careful not to damage end of king pin during removal of cone.

Installation

1. Assemble steering arm to knuckle using original shim pack. Install self-locking nuts or capscrews and tighten securely.

2. Coat king pin and bronze bearing cone ID and OD with chassis lubricant to prevent galling. Align serrations of new bronze bearing cone with serrations of king pin and press cone on king pin. NOTE: Make sure the cone is pressed all the way on or against the shoulder.

3. With bronze cone and tapered roller bearing pre-lubricated, place tapered roller bearing cone into cup at lower end of ball yoke. While retaining lower bearing cone in position, assemble steering knuckle to ball yoke. Seat bronze cone into cup at upper end of ball yoke.

4. Lubricate lower king pin with chassis lubricant and using original shim pack, install lower bearing cap to knuckle securing with bolts and lockwasher. Tighten bearing cap bolts securely.

5. Assemble opposite knuckle proceeding with instructions similar to those outlined above.

6. Individually check knuckle bearing preload by placing a torque wrench on any one (1) of the steering arm or bearing cap bolts or nuts. Read the starting torque (not rotating torque). Remove or add shims at the lower bearing cap until the specified preload is obtained. Knuckle bearing preload should be checked without ball joint oil seal, drag link or tie-rod installed.

7. Assemble the knuckle oil seals with the split on top. Knuckle retainer plate must be adjacent to ball yoke; followed by rubber seal, felt seal and metal retainer. Install seal retainer bolts and tighten securely.

8. Connect tie-rod to steering knuckle and tighten nut. Connect drag link to steering arm ball. Install cotter keys.

Cleaning, Inspection

All parts of the wheel end assembly should be thoroughly cleaned and dried with compressed air or a lint-free clean cloth.

Inspect all parts for wear, cracks or other damage. Replace all oil seals, felts and gaskets to prevent lubricant leakage.

Front Drive Locking Hubs

Two types of locking hubs are used: manual and Lock-O-Matic. Manual locking hubs are either engaged or disengaged, depending on how they are set. Lock-O-Matic hubs, when in "free" position, automatically engage axle and wheel when forward torque is applied by the axle shaft. Thus, whenever front wheel drive is disengaged at the transmission, the wheels free wheel. "Lock" position is required only when engine braking control on the front wheel is desired.

Front Locking Hubs Removal

1. Bend up tabs on mounting bolt lock washers.

2. Remove six (eight) mounting bolts using a thin-walled socket

GASKET RING   BODY   HUB   RING   RING   DISC   SCREW SEAL   PIN   GASKET   BODY WASHER   BOLT

PIN   PIN   SCREW   CONTROL SEAL

Manual type locking hub (© International Harvester Co.)

or appropriate hex wrench (externally splined type).

3. When clutch body is lifted off, immediately tilt it up so that the drive pins do not fall out.
4. Remove lock ring holding hub body onto axle shaft and pull off hub body.
5. Remove drag shoe (Lock-O-Matic only) from axle spindle by loosening hex-head set screw and unscrew drag shoe.
6. To install, reverse the above procedure.

Steering Linkage

See General Repair Section for steering alignment procedures. See specifications at the beginning of this section for steering alignment specifications.

Tie Rods

Tie rods are of three-piece construction: rod and two end assemblies. The end assemblies are threaded into the end of the tie rod and adjustment is made by turning them either in or out to shorten or lengthen the tie rod. When tightening the clamp it is important to make sure that the end assembly is threaded in far enough so that the clamping action of the clamp is right over the end pieces. Ball studs are integral in the end assemblies.

When disconnecting ball studs, loosen ball stud nut, then strike the nut with one hammer while another larger hammer is backing up the nut.

Steering Gear

Steering Gear Removal

1. Loosen collar clamp at bottom of steering wheel column.
2. Remove nut or loosen clamp bolt which secures steering arm to lever shaft, removing steering arm from lever shaft using a suitable puller if necessary.
3. Remove mounting bolts and steering gear assembly.
4. To install, reverse the above procedure, taking special care not to bind steering column if there is no universal joint.

Steering Gear Adjustment

Twin Stud Levershaft Type

1. Free steering gear of all load by disconnecting drag link from steering arm and loosening bracket clamp on steering gear jacket tube.
2. To adjust end play on cam (ball thrust bearings), loosen lock nut and adjusting screw, then unscrew four upper cover (steering column) bolts.

1 Nut, adjusting lock
2 Cover, housing side
3 Gasket, side cover
4 Ring, snap
5 Washer, thrust
6 Screw, adjusting
7 Levershaft, w/roll-assembly
8 Plug, vent
9 Clamp, w/bolt jacket tube
10 Seal, housing oil, upper
11 Housing, steering gear
12 Bearing, roller (bushing)
13 Seal, levershaft
14 Arm, steering
15 Washer, lock
16 Nut, steering arm
17 Cup, bearing upper (small)
18 Bearing, w/retainer
19 Tube, w/worm
20 Cup, bearing lower (large)
21 Shim housing cover .002", .005", .010"
22 Cover, housing

Cam (worm) and roller type steering gear
(© International Harvester Co.)

Twin stud levershaft steering gear (© International Harvester Co.)

3. Remove (cut) or add shims, replacing and tightening down upper cover to test drag. Drag should be just slight enough so that steering wheel can be moved from lock to lock with one finger.
4. To adjust lever shaft cams for backlash, place steering wheel in middle (straight-forward) position and turn adjusting screw until very slight drag is felt through mid-position range.
5. Tighten lock nut and give final test for drag.
6. Install drag link onto levershaft and tighten clamp on steering gear jacket tube.

Triple Roller Steering Gear

1. To check cam preload, disconnect linkage from steering arm and turn steering wheel through entire range, noting lash area.
2. Check the preload in lash area. It should be 7-13 inch-pounds.
3. If adjustment is necessary, drain lubricant and remove four lower cover bolts.
4. Remove top shim with a knife, being careful not to mutilate remaining shims.
5. Replace lower cover and tighten bolts to 13-22 ft. lbs. torque.
6. Recheck preload and repeat above procedure if necessary.

Power steering gear with toggle type
integral valve
(© International Harvester Co.)

Model S-36 power steering gear
with integral concentric valve
(© International Harvester Co.)

1 Seal, housing upper oil	12 Plug, housing filler
2 Housing	13 Spacer, steering gear mounting
3 Bushing, housing	14 Levershaft
4 Seal, housing side oil	15 Screw, levershaft adjusting
5 Arm, steering	16 Washer, thrust
6 Bearing, upper cup	17 Ring, snap
7 Bearing, cone	18 Gasket, housing side cover
8 Tube, with cam	19 Cover, housing side
9 Bearing, lower cup	20 Nut, hex. jam
10 Shim, housing lower cover	21 Bracket, steering gear mounting
11 Cover, housing lower	

Triple roller steering gear
(© International Harvester Co.)

In-line type power steering booster
(© International Harvester Co.)

7. Refill with SAE multi-purpose type gear lubricant.
8. To adjust levershaft, raise the vehicle and centralize the steering.
9. Rotate the steering 180° through center and check preload:
   S-161: 2-3⅜ lbs.
   S-108, S-165: 1 11/16-3¼ lbs.
   S-109: 2⅝-3⅞ lbs.
10. To adjust:
    a. Loosen lock nut.
    b. Turn slotted adjusting screw clockwise to increase preload; counterclockwise to decrease.
    c. when preload is within specifications, hold adjusting screw and tighten lock nut to 16-20 ft. lb.

Cam (Worm) and Roller Type

1. Disconnect linkage from pitman arm and drain lubricant.
2. Loosen locknut (1) at housing side cover, then turn adjusting screw (6) counterclockwise one turn to assure release of levershaft preload.
3. Turn steering wheel tube to about center of travel and check bearing preload (should register 9/16 to 1⅛ ft. lbs. @ 9" radius).
4. If preload needs adjustment, drain lubricant and remove four housing cover bolts and housing.
5. Remove one shim.
6. Replace housing cover and bolts, torquing bolts to 18-22 ft. lbs.
7. Check preload and repeat the above procedure if necessary.
8. Adjust levershaft preload by turning adjusting screw (6). Correct levershaft preload is ¾ to 1¼ ft. lbs. @ 9" radius (over cam preload).
9. Refill with SAE-90 SP type lubricant.

Recirculating Ball Type

1. Set front wheels in a straight-ahead position. This can be checked by driving the vehicle a short distance on a flat surface to determine steering wheel position when vehicle is following a straight path.
2. Raise vehicle and check number of turns required from center point to extreme right and left. The number of turns should be the same in each direction.
3. If step 2 moves wheels off of straight-ahead, loosen adjusting sleeve clamps on both left and right-hand tie rods, then turn both sleeves an equal number of turns in the same direction to bring gear back on high point.

Power Steering Gear
Reference

For overhaul of power steering systems, see General Section.

In-Line Booster Removal

1. Disconnect and plug hydraulic lines from valve and cylinder unit.

EXTERNAL LEAKAGE

Separate control valve type power steering installation
(© International Harvester Co.)

.030"

NEEDLE BEARING
SINGLE LIP SEAL
DOUBLE LIP SEAL
SEAL RETAINING RING
OUTPUT SHAFT
BACK-UP WASHERS

Correct installation of output shaft seals and bearing
S-281, 282
(© International Harvester Co.)

2. Loosen clamp bolts and disconnect cylinder link from cylinder.
3. Remove nut and lockwasher from piston rod and remove rod from frame bracket.
4. Loosen clamp bolt and unscrew cylinder assembly from pivot on relay.
5. Installation is the reverse of the above procedure. Be sure to center steering wheel and wheels before tightening clamp bolts of cylinder link. Bleed hydraulic system.

Hydraulic Cylinder Removal

1. Disconnect hydraulic lines from cylinder and plug lines.
2. Unbolt piston rod from frame bracket, noting approximate position of clamp.
3. Disconnect cylinder assembly from steering linkage.
4. Installation is the reverse of the above procedure. Approximate original position of clamp on piston rod, center adjusting steering wheel if necessary.

Separate Control Valve Removal

1. Disconnect and plug hydraulic lines from control valve.

Rotary valve power steering gear with horizontal output shaft
(© International Harvester Co.)

2. Loosen clamp bolts at each end of control valve and remove valve.
3. Installation is the reverse of removal. Since the control valve in this type of power steering system serves, in a sense, as a relay arm, it must be adjusted to center the steering wheel for straight-forward running. Tighten clamp bolts after adjustment is made.

Hydraulic Pump Removal

1. Disconnect hydraulic lines at pump. When hoses are disconnected, secure them in a raised position to prevent leakage. Plug fittings of pump.
2. Remove drive pulley attaching nut.
3. Loosen bracket-to-pump mounting bolts, and remove pump belt.
4. Slide pulley from shaft. CAUTION: Do not hammer pulley off shaft as this will damage the pump.
5. Remove bracket-to-pump bolts and take off pump assembly.
6. Installation is the reverse of the above removal procedure. Do not tighten mounting bolts or pulley nut until installation is complete. Move pump until belt is tight, then tighten mounting bolts. Tighten pulley attaching nut last, torquing to 35-45 ft. lbs.

Power Steering Gear Adjustments

S-36 Integral Valve Toggle Type Thrust Bearing Adjustment

1. Free steering gear of load by disconnecting drag link.
2. Turn gear off center to free stud in the cam groove.

OUTPUT SHAFT
WORM SHAFT
HOUSING

PRESSURE PORT — RETURN PORT
CHECK VALVE
NEEDLE BEARING
TORSION BAR
LOCK NUT
STUB SHAFT
DUST SEAL
SEAL
ADJUSTER PLUG
UPPER THRUST BEARING
VALVE BODY
VALVE SPOOL
LOWER THRUST BEARING
RECIRCULATING BALLS
RACK PISTON
HOUSING END PLUG
PISTON END PLUG

Rotary valve type power steering gear (© International Harvester Co.)

3. Remove yoke and joint assembly from stub shaft.
4. Remove key from stub shaft.
5. Remove upper cover.
6. Reassemble actuator housing screws with a ⅜" thick spacer under each head to hold actuator and cam assembly in the gear.
7. Remove the adjusting nut, lock washer, thrust washer and thrust housing.
8. Clean threads on nut and camshaft so that nut can be run freely by hand.
9. Reassemble nut, washers, and bearing.
10. Tighten nut to 10 ft. lb., then back off 10-20°. Bend locknut.
11. Attach cover and other parts.

Stud in Cam Groove

1. Tighten side cover adjusting screw until a very slight drag can be felt when turning through mid-position. If no drag is felt, remove shims until it can be felt. Back off adjusting nut 1/16 turn and lock.
2. If a drag can be felt without removing shims, it will be necessary to add shims, then remove enough shims to reestablish a very slight drag.
3. After adjustment, back off nut 1/16 turn and lock.

S-19 Integral Valve Toggle Type Thrust Bearing Adjustment

1. Disconnect drag link.
2. Remove valve from actuator housing.
3. Pull out actuator lever.
4. Remove actuator housing.
5. Remove adjusting nut, lock washer, thrust washer and bearing.
6. Clean threads in nut and on shaft so that nut can be hand run on shaft.
7. Reassemble bearing, washers and nut.

8. Tighten nut to 10 ft. lb. and back off 10-20°. Lock nut.
9. Reassemble parts. Valve mounting screws should be torqued evenly to 10-15 ft. lb.

Stud in Cam Groove

1. Turn side cover adjusting screw clockwise until a slight drag is felt when turning through midpoint.
2. Lock adjusting nut and turn gear full range to check adjustment.

S-281, 282 Integral Rotary Valve Type

Adjustment

1. Check steering gear blacklash by positioning gear in the straight-ahead position. If steering wheel can be rotated without moving steering arm, lash should be removed by the over-center adjustment.
2. Disconnect steering arm and remove horn ring.
3. Count the number of turns necessary to move wheels from lock to lock and from lock to center.
4. Turn steering wheel one-half turn off of center. Using an inch-pound torque wrench on steering wheel retaining nut, determine the torque necessary to rotate the shaft slowly through a 20° arc.
5. Turn gear back to center. Again rotate wheel with torque wrench. If second torque reading is 4-8 inch lbs. more than the first, no adjustment is necessary.
6. If adjustment is necessary, loosen adjuster screw, locknut and turn screw in until second

reading is 4-8 in. lb. more than the first. Tighten lock nut.

S-276, 299 Integral Type

Adjustment

1. With gear under load, install a suitable pressure gauge in the line between the pump and steering. valve pressure port.
2. Actuate the steering to provide full travel to wheel stops and note pressure.
3. Adjust pressure relief screw clockwise to obtain a minimum of 400 psi below the pressure noted above.

NOTE: Do not hold pressure more than 15 sec. or heat damage will result.

S-261, 277, 301, 302, 320 321, 322, 323, 325 Integral Type

Adjustment

1. Adjust screw in side cover to provide a 15-20 in. lb. torque at the input shaft as the gear is moved 90° either side of center.
3. Move the adjusting screw in to provide a torque vise of 2-4 in lb. at a point within 45° of center after the jam nut is locked at 20-25 ft. lb.
4. Install a pressure guage in line between the pump and steering valve pressure port.
5. Turn the steering lock to lock and note the pressure.
6. Adjust the pressure relief screw clockwise to give a pressure at lead 400 psi below pressure noted above.

NOTE: Do not hold pressure more than 15 seconds or heat damage will result.

Types S-276, 299 Integral power steering gear

Types S-261, 277, 301, 302, 320, 321, 322, 323, 325 Integral power steering gear

Steering Gear Removal

Concentric and Toggle Valve Steering Gear

1. Remove horn button from steering wheel. Unscrew retaining screws and remove base plate assembly. Remove steering wheel nut.
2. Using a suitable puller, remove steering wheel. NOTE: Where the steering column is the jointed type, the steering column and wheel need not be removed. Loosen nut on steering column shaft collar and remove steering column shaft from gear. Retain woodruff key.
3. Using suitable puller, remove pitman arm from levershaft.
4. Identify hydraulic connecting lines by tagging and marking the valve ports to which they are connected. Disconnect hydraulic lines from valve. Plug all openings.
5. Remove mounting flange bolts and remove gear from chassis.
6. To install, mount steering gear in chassis and fasten securely.
7. Place woodruff key in stud end of steering gear and install collar of steering column shaft. Secure with bolt and nut.
8. Center steering gear. Center steering wheel. Set front wheels straight ahead.
9. Connect drag link to ball on steering arm.
10. Install steering arm on levershaft of gear. If arm does not line up with splines of shaft, turn steering wheel to the right or left ¼ turn until it does.

11. Secure arm to levershaft with lockwasher and nut. Tighten nut to 250 ft. lbs.
12. Install hydraulic lines to control valve.
13. Fill steering gear housing with SAE-90 multi-purpose lubricant.
14. Fill hydraulic power system reservoir to indicated level with SAE-10 engine oil.

Output Shaft Preload Adjustment

Rotary Valve Type Gear

1. Position steering in the straight-ahead position. Check for lash by moving steering wheel. If there is steering wheel movement without moving the steering arm, over-center adjustment must be made.
2. Disconnect steering arm and remove horn ring.
3. Position steering wheel at center of travel, then turn ½ turn off center.
4. Using an inch pound torque wrench and socket on the steering wheel retaining nut, determine the torque required to rotate the shaft slowly through a 20-degree arc. Turn gear to center and take a second reading. If second torque reading is 4-8 inch pounds in excess of first reading, no preload adjustment is necessary.
5. If adjustment is required, loosen adjuster screw locknut and turn screw until second reading exceeds first reading by 4-8 inch pounds.

6. Tighten locknut while holding adjusting screw in place to 27-37 ft. lbs. torque.
7. Recheck torque reading after adjustment is made.
8. Install steering arm, tightening nut to 120-125 ft. lbs. torque.
9. Install horn ring.

Steering Gear Removal

Horizontal Output Shaft Type

1. Apply parking brake and raise front of vehicle. Place drip pan under steering gear.
2. Position front wheels straight-ahead and tie steering wheel in centered position.
3. Disconnect and plug hydraulic lines from gear. Tag the lines for identification.
4. Remove nut and lockwasher securing steering arm to output shaft and remove arm from shaft with a suitable puller.
5. Remove lower flexible coupling clamp bolt.
6. Remove steering gear mounting bolts and remove gear from chassis.
7. To install, set gear assembly on center and position gear in chassis.
8. Insert gear stub shaft into lower flexible coupling and install and tighten gear mounting bolts to 55-60 ft. lbs. torque.
9. Install and tighten lower flexible coupling bolt clamp to 30-35 ft. lbs. torque.
10. With steering wheel centered and front wheels straight ahead, place steering arm on output

1 Ring, retaining	7 Ball, recirculating
2 Plug, housing end	8 Guide, ball return
3 Seal, O-ring	9 Clamp, ball return guide
4 Plug, rack piston end	10 Screw, clamp
5 Ring, rack piston	11 Nut, lock output shaft adjuster
6 O-Ring, rack piston backu-up	12 Cover, housing side

13 Seal, O-ring side cover
14 Shaft, output
15 Housing, gear
16 Seat, pressure connector
17 Valve, poppet check
18 Spring, poppet check valve
19 Seat, return connector
20 Shaft, worm
21 Seal, O-ring
22 O-Ring, valve body back-up
23 Valve, control
24 Ring, valve body
25 Nut, lock adjuster plug
26 Ring, retainer
27 Seal, dust
28 Seal, oil
29 Bearing, Needle
30 Plug, adjuster
31 Seal, O-ring
32 Race, thrust bearing, upper
33 Bearing, thrust upper
34 Race, thrust bearing, upper
35 Retainer, thrust bearing
36 Spacer, thrust bearing
37 Race, thrust bearing, lower
38 Bearing, thrust lower
39 Bearing, needle
40 Seal, output shaft
41 Washer, back-up
42 Ring, seal retaining
43 Arm, steering
44 Nut, steering arm retaining
45 Rack piston

Integral rotary valve type power steering gear (© International Harvester Co.)

shaft by matching master serrations of arm with shaft. Secure arm to shaft with lockwasher and nut, tightening nut to 120-125 ft. lbs. torque. Untie steering wheel.

11. Remove plugs and connect hydraulic lines to proper ports, tightening connections to 20-30 ft. lbs. torque.

12. Fill power steering system with fluid and start engine. Bleed system.

13. Check system for operation and leaks.

14. Remove drip pan and lower vehicle.

Steering Gear Removal

Vertical Output Shaft Type

1. Follow Steps 1 through 6 of the horizontal shaft gear removal above, leaving out Step 2 (centering and tying steering wheel). Disconnect battery cables, remove battery and battery box from chassis to permit gear removal.

2. To install, follow Steps 7 through 11 of horizontal output shaft gear installation described above.

3. Install battery box, battery and cables.

4. Follow Steps 12 through 14 of horizontal output shaft installation described above.

Power System Bleeding

Rotary Valve Type Gear

1. Fill pump reservoir to correct level with fluid.

2. Start engine and turn steering wheel through entire travel two or three times. This will permit air to escape and be replaced with fluid.

3. Check fluid level and refill if necessary.

Clutch

Cable Actuated Clutch Adjustment

1. Adjust outer clutch housing lever until pedal free travel is 1.2-1.5".

2. With pedal adjusted and released, adjust bumper until it just contacts upper pedal arm.

Hydraulic Clutch Adjustment

10", 11" and 12" Clutches

1. Check clutch pedal height. If it is not approximately $7\frac{3}{4}$" from the floorboard (measured at right angles from floorboard), loosen two bolts on the clutch

Hydraulic clutch master cylinder—1600 thru 1890 models (© International Harvester Co.)

Clutch and brake master cylinder installation (© International Harvester Co.)

pedal stop bracket and move bracket either way until proper pedal height is achieved. Tighten bracket mounting bolts.

2. Clutch pedal push rod to master cylinder piston clearance is adjusted by loosening the locknut on the pushrod and turning the rod either in or out until 3/16" pedal stroke is obtained before clutch pedal push rod contacts master cylinder. Tighten locknut on pushrod and recheck pedal stroke.

3. Release bearing to clutch lever (finger) clearance is adjusted at the slave cylinder pushrod. Measure stroke of clutch pedal required to produce contact of clutch release bearing to clutch release levers. If it is not $1\frac{7}{8}$" $\pm \frac{1}{8}$", loosen locknut on slave cylinder pushrod and rotate pushrod either in or out until proper pedal travel is obtained. Tighten locknut on pushrod and recheck pedal free travel.

Hydraulic Clutch Adjustment

1600 thru 1890 Models

1. Clutch pedal push rod stroke is adjusted by loosening the locknut on the master cylinder pushrod and turning the pushrod in either direction until a pedal height of $5\frac{5}{8}$" is achieved. Tighten locknut and recheck pedal height.

2. After adjusting pedal height (step 1), clutch release bearing clearance adjustment is made at the slave cylinder pushrod. Loosen locknut on slave cylinder pushrod and remove cotter pin and yoke pin. Holding clutch release lever forward so that release bearing is in contact with the release fingers and holding slave cylinder pushrod in released (bottomed) position, turn yoke until yoke indexes with clutch release lever hole. Install yoke pin. Check that release

Hydraulic clutch control system (© International Harvester Co.)

Clutch compressing cap screws
(© International Harvester Co.)

Using wood blocks to compress clutch fingers
(© International Harvester Co.)

bearing is in contact with fingers while slave cylinder push rod is fully bottomed, then remove yoke pin and shorten linkage by turning yoke four (4) complete turns. Connect yoke and clutch release lever with yoke pin and insert cotter pin. Tighten locknut on push rod assembly.

Hydraulic Clutch Adjustment

GM-80, 1100 Models

1. Clutch pedal pushrod stroke adjustment is made by disconnecting clutch pedal from pushrod (remove yoke pin). Holding master cylinder pushrod out snugly against the stop in the end of the cylinder and making sure that the spring is holding the clutch pedal against its stop, adjust yoke on pushrod until yoke can be connected to pedal. Install yoke pin and cotter pin. Tighten locknut on yoke. A clutch pedal free travel of 5-1/6" should result.
2. Clutch finger to bearing clearance is adjusted at the slave cylinder pushrod. Clutch pedal should travel 1½" before clutch bearing makes contact with release fingers. Loosen locknut on slave cylinder pushrod and turn pushrod to obtain correct pedal travel. Tighten locknut and recheck pedal travel.

Clutch Master Cylinder Removal

1. Remove hydraulic line from master cylinder and remove yoke pins connecting pedal to master cylinder pushrod. On models with dual cylinders (brake-/clutch integral unit), disconnect brake hydraulic line, stoplight switch wire and brake pedal. If the fluid reservoir is separate from the cylinder unit, disconnect reservoir fluid line.
2. Remove cylinder assembly mounting bolts and remove cylinder.

3. To install, first mount the cylinder unit, then connect hydraulic lines.
4. Adjust clutch pedal as described above.
5. Bleed hydraulic clutch system.

Slave Cylinder Removal

1. Disconnect slave cylinder pushrod from clutch release lever.
2. Disconnect hydraulic line.
3. Unbolt and remove slave cylinder unit.
4. To install, reverse Steps 1 through 3.
5. Adjust clutch pedal as described above.
6. Bleed hydraulic clutch system.

Bleeding Hydraulic Clutch System

1. Fill fluid reservoir with hydraulic brake fluid.
2. Remove dust cover from bleeder screw on slave cylinder and open bleeder screw approximately ¾ turn.
3. Attach a short bleeder tube to bleeder screw and place the other end in clear container filled with brake fluid.
4. Pump clutch pedal slowly through full stroke repeatedly until only clear (no air bubbles) fluid flows from bleeder hose.
5. Tighten bleeder screw on down stroke of clutch pedal and remove bleeder tube. Replace rubber bleeder screw dust cover.
6. Refill fluid reservoir if necessary.

Clutch Removal

1. Remove transmission. Extreme care should be taken to support the transmission until it is completely removed so that the main shaft splines will clear the driven member. For transmission removal procedures see "Transmission—R&R" immediately following this section.

2. Remove flywheel housing cover.
3. Disconnect clevis yoke from clutch release lever.
4. Compress clutch assembly. On the 13", 14", 15" and 10" (9 spring) clutches, the pressure plate is drilled and tapped so that three retaining cap screws and flat washers may be installed. Tighten the cap screws until flat washers and cap screw heads are seated on the back plate. On the 11", 12" and 10" (6 spring, open back plate type) clutches, three retaining spacers are used to hold the clutch assembly compressed during removal. Slightly loosen the back plate to flywheel mounting screws to wedge the retaining spacers into place. On the 10" six spring (full back plate type) clutch, three ⅝"x3"x¼" hardwood blocks are used to compress the clutch during removal. Loosen back plate to flywheel retaining screws enough to wedge the blocks between the back plate inner flange and release fingers.
5. Remove back plate to flywheel screws and remove back plate assembly and driven disc.
6. When removing the clutch assembly, observe that the balance mark (spot of white paint) on the back plate flange is located as near as possible to the balance mark ("L") stamped on the flywheel face. These balance marks should be located in the same relative position at clutch installation. If there are no marks, scribe a line to indicate correct position.
7. To install clutch, position the clutch driven member so that the long portion of the hub is toward the rear (all except the 10" 6 spring open back plate type, which may be fitted either

way). Clutch must be compressed for correct installation.

8. Place clutch assembly over the driven member on the flywheel so that the balance mark (spot of white paint) is as near as possible to the flywheel balance mark ("L"). Loosely install two or three back plate to flywheel mounting screws.

9. Using a clutch aligning arbor or transmission main drive gear shaft to hold the driven member in place, complete installation of the remaining back plate to flywheel mounting screws and lockwashers. Tighten capscrews alternately and evenly.

10. Remove retaining capscrews, wood blocks or retaining spacers which were used to hold the clutch compressed.

11. Install transmission as described in "Transmission—R&R".

12. Connect linkage to clutch release lever.

13. Install flywheel housing cover.

14. Bleed hydraulic clutch system.

15. Adjust hydraulic clutch actuating system.

Standard Transmission

Reference

For manual transmission overhaul procedures see the Manual Transmission General Section.

Manual Transmission Removal

Removal and installation of manual transmissions will vary in detail, depending on which vehicle is being serviced. The following general procedure includes the basic steps common to all models.

1. Access to the transmission may be improved by removing cab floor panels.

2. Raise vehicle on a hoist or jack up and support with jack stands.

3. Drain the transmission lubricant.

4. Disconnect drive shaft at the transmission. If the vehicle is equipped with a transfer case which is not mounted directly to the transmission, disconnect the shaft between the transfer case and transmission at the yoke. If the vehicle is equipped with a transfer case which is mounted directly to the transmission, it must be removed with the transmission as a unit and the forward and rear drive shafts must be disconnected. Secure shaft out of the way with wire.

5. Disconnect shift linkage from transmission shift levers. If the

vehicle is equipped with a transfer case which is mounted directly to the transmission, disconnect the shift linkage from the transfer case shift levers.

6. If the vehicle is equipped with a transmission mounted handbrake, disconnect the handbrake cable at the relay lever.

7. Disconnect speedometer cable from the transmission.

8. Remove the clutch slave cylinder from its mount. Do not disconnect the hydraulic line from the slave cylinder. Secure the push rod to the slave cylinder to avoid ejection of the internal components. Keeping the hydraulic system sealed eliminates the necessity of bleeding.

9. On some models it may be necessary to remove the starter motor.

10. Support the rear of engine by means of a hydraulic jack.

11. Remove the transmission mounting bolts and insulators at the engine rear crossmember. If possible, remove the rear engine crossmember. Remove gear shift lever and housing from top of transmission if applicable.

12. Attach suitable hoisting equipment or jack to transmission and raise enough to support the transmission assembly.

13. Remove top transmission to clutch housing bolts and install transmission guide pins.

14. Remove remaining transmission to clutch housing bolts.

15. Carefully pull transmission rearward, keeping it in line until the main drive gear shaft is clear of the clutch. CAUTION: Extreme care must be exercised to insure that the weight of the transmission does not rest on the hub of the clutch driven disc.

16. Depending on vehicle model, either lift the transmission up through the floorboard and out the right door or lower it with a jack.

17. Installation is the reverse of the above procedure.

18. Fill transmission with fluid.

Automatic Transmission

For automatic transmission overhaul procedures see Automatic Transmission General Section, Load Flite Transmission repair procedures.

Dual Range Automatic
Removal

1. Raise the vehicle with a hoist.

2. Disconnect the fluid filler tube at

Pilot studs

Pilot stud location—automatic transmission
(© International Harvester Co.)

the oil pan, and drain the fluid. Loosening the tube clip capscrew at the extension on the starting motor will permit rotating filler tube for transmission removal.

3. Disconnect the vacuum line at vacuum unit located at rear of transmission.

4. Disconnect the speedometer cable at speedometer adapter on transmission.

5. Disconnect the hand brake cable at drive shaft brake if chassis is so equipped.

6. Disconnect the shift linkage at manual shift lever on transmission.

7. Disconnect the two oil cooler lines on right side of transmission if chassis is so equipped.

8. Disconnect the drive shaft at transmission companion flange. NOTE: Wire the end of the drive shaft to the frame to permit transmission removal.

9. Place the hydraulic hoist with a suitable transmission lift cradle in position under the transmission oil pan. Adjust the hoist to align the cradle to the transmission oil pan flange so that the weight of the transmission case is supported by the hoist.

10. Remove the transmission case to converter housing upper capscrews and install two pilot studs into the capscrew holes.

11. Remove the transmission case to converter lower capscrews.

12. With the hydraulic hoist and cradle adjusted so the transmission case is in alignment with the converter housing, pull the transmission rearward with the hydraulic hoist to disengage the transmission from the converter housing and converter assembly. Lower transmission and remove from the vehicle.

13. To install, place two transmission pilot studs in the upper transmission to converter housing mounting screw holes.

14. Mount the transmission on a jack and position it under vehicle.

15. Rotate engine until the front

pump drive lugs on the converter are in a vertical position.

16. Rotate the front pump until the slots in the pump drive gear are in a vertical position.

17. Apply lubricant similar to lubriplate to seal the surface of converter impeller cover hub.

18. Being extremely careful to align the turbine shaft splines with the turbine hub splines and the converter impeller lugs with the slots in the front pump drive gear, raise transmission and move it forward into the converter housing and converter.

19. Install the transmission to converter housing lower mounting screws. Remove two pilot studs and install upper mounting screws. Tighten all mounting screws securely.

20. Install oil cooler lines on the right side of the transmission if so equipped.

21. Connect the shift linkage at the manual shift lever on the transmission.

22. Connect the hand brake cable to the drive shaft brake if so equipped.

23. Connect the speedometer cable to the transmission.

24. Connect the vacuum line to the vacuum unit located at the rear of transmission.

25. Connect the fluid filler tube to the oil pan, tightening securely. Also tighten tube clip capscrews at the extension on the starter motor.

26. Connect the drive shaft to the transmission companion flange. Tighten mounting screws securely and lock with lock plates.

27. Lower vehicle to floor and fill transmission with type "A" automatic transmission fluid.

28. Road test vehicle to check performance and shift points.

Torque Converter Removal

1. Remove transmission as described above.

2. Disconnect and remove starter motor.

3. If vehicle has conventional chassis, remove floormat and transmission floor opening cover.

4. Install a rear engine support or support the rear weight of the engine with a jack.

5. Remove converter housing to crossmember mounting bolts, lower insulators and retainers.

6. Unbolt and remove rear engine crossmember.

7. Remove eight capscrews and lockwashers which attach converter housing to crankcase adapter and remove converter housing. On some models it may be necessary to lower the engine to provide clearance for converter removal.

8. Remove six nuts which attach the converter assembly to the flywheel assembly and remove converter.

9. To install, carefully place converter into position (do not damage bolt mounting threads) and install six nuts which attach converter to converter drive plate, but do not tighten nuts at this time.

10. After thoroughly cleaning crankcase converter housing adapter, install converter housing and engage the dowels being careful not to damage the dowels or the converter housing.

11. Install eight converter housing mounting capscrews and lockwashers.

12. Install rear engine crossmember.

13. Install upper and lower insulators and retainers, the converter to crossmember mounting bolts and lockwashers. Lower converter housing and engine. With insulators and retainers firmly seated, hand tighten bolts, then give bolts one-half additional turn and lock.

14. Remove rear engine support or jack.

15. If vehicle has conventional chassis, install floormat and transmission floor opening cover.

16. Install starter motor and wiring.

17. Install transmission as described above.

18. Rotate engine and converter assembly through two complete revolutions to center converter (to rotate, remove spark plugs and pry on drive plate ring gear).

19. Tighten converter to the converter drive plate attaching nuts.

20. Install converter housing adapter cover.

Transmission Fluid

1. Transmission fluid should be changed and band adjusted every 15,000 miles.

2. Remove converter housing front plate.

3. Remove one of the converter drain plugs, then rotate converter 180 degrees and remove other converter drain plug.

4. Disconnect fluid filler tube at the transmission oil pan.

5. Drain fluid and remove oil pan. Clean oil pan.

6. Connect filler tube to oil pan and tighten securely.

7. Install drain plugs in converter cover and tighten them to 7-10 ft. lbs. torque.

8. Install converter housing front plate.

9. Add five quarts of type "A" automatic transmission fluid through filler tube.

10. Run engine at idle (do not race) for about two minutes, then add five more quarts of fluid. Let engine idle until it reaches normal operating temperature.

11. Move selector lever through all positions, then place it in "P" (park). Check fluid level and add enough fluid to bring level up to the "F" (full) mark on indicator.

Front Band Adjustment

1. Drain fluid from transmission and remove oil pan (disconnect filler tube from oil pan).

2. Loosen front servo adjusting screw locknut two full turns and check the adjusting screw for free rotation.

3. Pull back on the actuating rod and insert gauge block of the

Adjusting rear band
(© International Harvester Co.)

Adjusting front band
(© International Harvester Co.)

front band adjusting tool (SE-1910) between the servo piston stem and adjusting screw. Tighten adjusting screw until adjusting tool handle overruns. Holding adjusting screw stationary, tighten locknut to 20-25 ft. lbs. torque. Remove gauge block.

4. Install fluid screen and pan, using a new gasket. Connect filler tube to pan.
5. Refill transmission as described above, adding new fluid if necessary.

Rear Band Adjustment

1. If vehicle is conventional model, remove floor mat and transmission cover plate from floor board.
2. Clean adjusting screw threads thoroughly and oil threads.
3. Loosen rear band adjusting locknut.
4. Using tool SE-1909, tighten adjusting screw until wrench overruns, at 10 ft. lbs. torque. NOTE: If adjusting screw is tighter than overrun of wrench, loosen screw and retighten.
5. Back off adjusting screw one and one-half turns, then hold adjusting screw stationary and tighten locknut to 25-40 ft. lbs. torque. CAUTION: Severe damage may result if the adjusting screw is not backed off exactly one and one-half turns.
6. Install transmission cover plate and floor mat to floor board.

Manual Linkage Adjustment

1. With engine off, disconnect the manual shift rod from the selector lever on the steering column and the transmission lever on the conventional chassis, or bellcrank on the Metro chassis.
2. Position selector lever in "D" and place transmission manual lever in the "D" detent (second from the top of the transmission).
3. Position the manual shift rod into the ball joint on the steering column. The opposite end of the rod should be installed in the transmission shift lever on the conventional chassis and secured with a washer and cotter pin. On the Metro chassis, the rod yoke should be positioned on the bellcrank and secured with the clevis pin, washer and cotter pin.
4. Tighten ball joint nut at the steering column lever.
5. Move the selector lever through all positions, checking the alignment of the pointer in all positions.

Kickdown Switch Adjustment

1. On the conventional chassis the kickdown switch is located in the toeboard under the throttle pedal. On the Metro chassis it is mounted on a bracket under the toeboard and operated by a pad welded to one of the throttle linkage rods.
2. Loosen two mounting nuts and turn them either direction until a clearance of ¼" is obtained between switch and throttle pedal on the conventional chassis and between switch and throttle linkage pad on the Metro chassis.

Vacuum Control Adjustment

1. Connect a tachometer to the engine.
2. Remove the ⅛ inch pipe plug located on the left front of the transmission case. Install a pressure gauge line connection at this point, then connect a pressure gauge to the line and place gauge in cab.
3. Start engine and move selector lever to "D" (drive) position. Apply hand brake and accelerate engine until 1000 rpm is reached. Pressure reading on gauge should be 82-88 psi.
4. If correct pressure is not obtained, loosen locknut on vacuum control unit (located at rear of transmission) and turn vacuum unit clockwise to increase pressure or counterclockwise to decrease pressure. Adjust for proper pressure, then tighten locknut. CAUTION: Do not operate engine over 10 seconds at any one time while performing the above.

Transmission Model T-407
Aluminum Case LoadFlite

For all repair procedures on this transmission refer to the General Repair Section.

Drive Shaft, U Joints

Drive Shaft Assembly

It is imperative that all components of the drive train be tight to insure balance. Check companion flanges at the axles and transmission,

Silent spin type center driveshaft bearing
(© International Harvester Co.)

center bearing mounts and engine mounts.

When assembling drive train, lubricate slip joint (splined) assemblies and universal joint bearings. Make sure that universal joints are kept on parallel planes by observing the arrows stamped on the shaft end and slip yoke.

Universal Joints

To remove universal joints, bend down tabs on bearing bolt lock plate and remove four bolts at each universal joint. Joint and shaft assembly must be removed as a unit to service "R" type trunnion bearings. Do not disassemble drive shaft from slip yoke unless these parts are to be replaced. On vehicles equipped with "CL" type trunnion bearings, the universal joint may be unbolted from both the drive shaft and the companion flange and the whole shaft assembly does not have to be removed to service one joint.

When replacing trunnion bearings, remove retaining clips then carefully drive out one, then the other, bearing. Use new packing washers (seals) when reassembling.

CL type universal joint
(© International Harvester Co.)

Correct slip joint assembly
(© International Harvester Co.)

"R" TYPE BEARING

DRIVE

"C" TYPE BEARING

CR type universal joint
(© International Harvester Co.)

Rear Axles, Suspension

Reference

For overhaul procedures and out of truck adjustments see Rear Axle General Section.

Rear Axle Assembly Removal

1. Jack and block up truck until load is removed from springs and rear wheels are clear of the ground.
2. Drain differential housing.
3. Disconnect brake lines and parking brake cables (where used).
4. On two speed differentials, disconnect control wires or air hoses from the shift mechanism.
5. Disconnect driveshaft at rear axle companion flange.
6. Support differential on portable floor jack and take off U-bolts at springs.
7. Roll out axle from under truck.
8. Installation is the reverse of the above procedure. Be sure to bleed hydraulic brake systems. Remove axle housing breather valve and clean thoroughly with solvent.

Rear Axle Shaft Removal

Semi-Floating Type

1. Remove wheel and nut from axle shaft end.
2. Remove hub and drum assembly with a suitable puller.
3. Unbolt and remove brake backing plate and bearing retainer.
4. Pull axle shaft and bearing using suitable puller. Bearings are pressed on.
5. When installing axle shaft assembly, use new oil seals and be careful not to damage seals.
6. Lightly tap bearing cap into axle housing.
7. Install shims on end of axle housing flange and insert backing plate bolts to retain shims.
8. Install backing plate, bearing retainer and seal retainer. Tighten nuts to specified torque.
9. Install wheel hub. Grasp wheel hub and pull outward to be sure

that axle shaft is withdrawn as far as possible.
10. Check axle shaft end play as follows: Mount dial indicator on stationary location at right-hand side of axle assembly. Position indicator against end of axle shaft and check shaft end play. If end play is not within .006″, shims must be added or removed between backing plate and axle housing flange.
11. Place key in axle shaft and install hub and drum assembly on shaft, securing with washer and nut. Tighten nut and install cotter pin.

Rear Axle Shaft Removal

Full-Floating Type

1. Axle shaft is removed without taking off wheels. Remove axle shaft nuts from studs in the wheel hub.
2. Install puller screws in the two tapped holes provided in the axle shaft flange.
3. Turn in puller screws until axle shaft is loose, then pull axle.
4. Installation is the reverse of the above procedure. Be sure puller screws are removed.

Rear Axle Shaft Removal

Full-Floating Type With Tapered Dowel Mounting

1. Remove flange nuts from studs of wheel hub.
2. Using a heavy hammer, strike sharply on the center of the flange of the axle shaft. This will unseat and loosen tapered dowels.
3. Remove tapered dowels.
4. Push axle flange back into position against wheel hub and strike again with a hammer to spring axle shaft away from the wheel hub. Do not pry on flange.
5. When installing axle shaft, make sure there is between the axle shaft driving flange and lockwasher. Dowel must not be "sunken in."

Locking Differentials

Reference

For overhaul procedures of differentials with "NoSPIN" and "Powr-Lok" locking units see Rear Axle portion of General Section.

Rear Spring Removal

1. Place floor jack under truck frame and raise truck sufficiently to relieve weight from spring to be removed.
2. Remove shock absorbers where used.
3. Remove U-bolts, spring bumper and retainer or U-bolt seat.

Two speed planetary gear type axle final drive
(© International Harvester Co.)

4. Remove lubricators (not used where springs are equipped with rubber bushings).
5. Remove nuts from spring shackle pins or bracket pins.
6. Slide spring off bracket pin and shackle pin.
7. If spring is rubber bushed, bushing halves may be removed from each side of spring and shackle eye.

Installation

1. Install pivot end of spring first. Align shackle end to other frame bracket. When installing nuts on spring pins which are welded or pressed in, be sure that washer is tightened against shoulder of pin. Spring pins which are driven in must be installed so that slot for lock bolt is aligned. Spring pins which are threaded in must be installed so that the lubrication hole is facing up. Tighten pin into bracket, then back off one-half turn. Install locknut tightly and install cotter pin. Turn pin out to permit installation of cotter pin.
2. Install lubricators.
3. Install U-bolt seat or retainer and U-bolts. Install U-bolt nuts, but do not tighten.
4. Install shock absorber where used.
5. Lower vehicle.
6. Tighten U-bolt nuts securely.

Differential case halves

Straddle mounting for pinion

Single reduction type axle final drive
(© International Harvester Co.)

Index

TUNE-UP SPECIFICATIONS

When analyzing compression test results, look for uniformity among cylinders rather than specific pressures.

Year	ENGINE No. Cyl Displacement (cu. in.)	hp	SPARK PLUGS Type	Gap (in.)	DISTRIBUTOR Point Dwell (deg)	Point Gap (in.)	IGNITION TIMING (deg) ▲	VALVES Intake Opens (deg) ■	Fuel Pump Pressure (psi)	IDLE SPEED (rpm) • Man Trans	Auto Trans
'70-'71	4—134	75	J8	.030	40	.020	5B	9	3	600	N.A.
'70-'71	6—232	140	N-14Y	.035	32	.016	①	12½	5	650⑤	700⑤
'71	6—258	150	N-14Y	.035	32	.016	5B	12½	4-5½	600	700
'70-'71	6—225	160	44S	.035	30	.016	5B	24	5	550	N.A.
'70-'71	8—350	230	H-14Y	.035	30	.016	④	24	5	650⑤	700⑤
'71	8—304	210	N-12Y	.035	30	.016	2½B	18½	4-5½	650	700
'71	8—360	245	N-12Y	.035	30	.016	2½B	18½	4-5½	650	750
'72	6—232	100	N-12Y	.035	32	.016	5B⑥	12½	4-5	700	600
'72	6—258	110	N-12Y	.035	32	.016	3B⑥	12½	4-5	700	600
'72	8—304	150	N-12Y	.035	30	.016	5B⑥	14¾	5-6½	750	650
'72	8-360	175	N-12Y	.035	30	.016	5B⑥	14¾	5-6½	750	650
'73-'74	6—232	100	N-12Y	.035	32	.016	5B⑥	12½	4-5	700⑦	——
'73-'74	6—258	258	N-12Y	.035	32	.016	3B⑥	12½	4-5	700⑦	550
'73-'74	8—304	150	N-12Y	.035	30	.016	5B⑥	14¾	5-6½	750	700
'73-'74	8—360	175	N-12Y	.035	30	.016	5B⑥	14¾	5-6½	750	700
'73-'74	8—360	195	N-12Y	.035	30	.016	5B⑥	14¾	5-6½	750	700
'74-'75	8—401	225	N-12Y	.035	30	.016	5B⑥⑧	25½	5-6½	750⑨	700
'75	6—232	100	N-12Y	.035	Electronic		5B	12	4-5	700(600)	——
	6—258	110	N-12Y	.035	Electronic		3B	12	4-5	700⑩(600)	550
	8—304	150	N-12Y	.035	Electronic		5B	14¾	5-6½	750	—
	8—360	175	N-12Y	.035	Electronic		2-5B	14¾	5-6½	750	700
	8—360	195	N-12Y	.035	Electronic		2-5B	14¾	5-6½	750	700
	8—401	215	N-12Y	.035	Electronic		2-5B	25½	5-6½	750	700
'76-'77	6—232	90	N-12Y	.035	Electronic		8B	12	4-5	600	——
	6—258	95	N-12Y	.035	Electronic		6B⑪	12	4-5	600	550(700)
	8—304	120	N-12Y	.035	Electronic		5B⑫	14¾	5-6½	750	700
	8—360	175	N-12Y	.035	Electronic		5B⑬	14¾	5-6½	750	700
	8—401	215	N-12Y	.035	Electronic		5B⑬	25½	5-6½	750	700

NOTE: Figures in parentheses are for California engines
▲ With vacuum advance disconnected
■ All figures before TDC (BTDC)
• With manual transmission in Neutral and automatic transmission in Drive
B Before top dead center (BTDC)
① W/o emission control, 5B on dist. model 1110340, 0 on dist. model 110444, 0 w/ emission control
② 5B w/o emission control, 0 w/ emission control
③ 650/700 rpm w/o emission control
④ 0 on dist. model 1111330, 1111474, and 1111938, 5B on model 11116964

⑤ 100 rpm less w/o emission control
⑥ At 550 rpm in 1973; 700 rpm in 1974-75
⑦ 700 rpm for CJ, 600 rpm Commando and Wagoneer
⑧ 2.5° B on heavy-duty engine (painted red)
⑨ 650 rpm on heavy-duty engine (painted red)
⑩ 650 rpm w/EGR
⑪ 8B w/Automatic transmission
⑫ 10B w/Automatic transmission; 5B in California
⑬ 8B w/Automatic transmission; 5B in California

GENERAL ENGINE SPECIFICATIONS

Year	Engine Cu In. Displacement	Carburetor Type	Advertised Horsepower @ rpm ■	Advertised Torque @ rpm (ft lbs) ■	Bore and Stroke (in.)	Advertised Compression Ratio	Oil Pressure @ 30 mph (psi)
'70-'71	4-134	1 bbl	75 @ 4000	114 @ 2000	3.125 x 3.375	7.4:1/6.9:1/7.8:1	35
'70-'71	6-232	1 bbl	145 @ 4300	215 @ 1600	3.750 x 3.500	8.5:1	50
'71	6-258	1 bbl	150 @ 3800	240 @ 1800	3.750 x 3.895	8.0:1/7.6:1	37

GENERAL ENGINE SPECIFICATIONS

Year	Engine Cu In. Displacement	Carburetor Type	Advertised Horsepower @ rpm ■	Advertised Torque @ rpm (ft lbs) ■	Bore and Stroke (in.)	Advertised Compression Ratio	Oil Pressure @ 30 mph (psi)
'70-'71	6-225	2 bbl	160 @ 4200	235 @ 2400	3.750 x 3.400	9.0:1	33
'70-'71	8-350	2 bbl	230 @ 4400	350 @ 2400	3.800 x 3.850	9.0:1	37
'71	8-304	2 bbl	210 @ 4400	300 @ 2600	3.750 x 3.440	8.4:1	37
'71	8-360	2 bbl	245 @ 4400	365 @ 2600	4.080 x 3.440	8.5:1	37
'72-'73	6-232	1 bbl	100 @ 3600	185 @ 1800	3.895 x 3.500	8.0:1/7.6:1	37
'72-'73	6-258	1 bbl	110 @ 3500	195 @ 2000	3.750 x 3.500	8.0:1/7.6:1	37
'72-'73	8-304	2 bbl	150 @ 4200	245 @ 2500	3.750 x 3.440	8.4:1	37
'72-'73	8-360	2 bbl	175 @ 4000	285 @ 2400	4.080 x 3.440	8.5:1	37
'72-'73	8-360	4 bbl	195 @ 4400	295 @ 2900	4.080 x 3.440	8.5:1	37
'74-'75	6-232	1 bbl	100 @ 3600①	185 @ 1800②	3.750 x 3.500	8.0:1	37
	6-258	1 bbl	110 @ 3500③	195 @ 2000④	3.750 x 3.900	8.0:1	37
	8-304	2 bbl	150 @ 4200⑤	245 @ 2500⑥	3.750 x 3.440	8.4:1	37
	8-360	2 bbl	175 @ 4000⑦	285 @ 2400⑧	4.080 x 3.440	8.3:1	37
	8-360	4 bbl	195 @ 4400⑨	295 @ 2900⑩	4.080 x 3.440	8.3:1	37
	8-401	4 bbl	215 @ 4200	320 @ 2800	4.165 x 3.680	8.4:1	37

■ Beginning in 1972, horsepower and torque are SAE net figures. They are measured at the rear of the transmission with all accessories installed and operating. Since the figures vary when a given engine is installed in different models, some are representative rather than exact.

① 90 @ 3050 1976-77
② 170 @ 2000 1976-77
③ 95 @ 3050 1976-77
④ 180 @ 2100 1976-77
⑤ 120 @ 3200 1976-77
⑥ 220 @ 2200 1976-77
⑦ 140 @ 3300 1976-77
⑧ 251 @ 1600 1976-77
⑨ 180 @ 3600 1976-77
⑩ 2800 @ 2800 1976-77

VALVE SPECIFICATIONS

Year	Engine No. Cyl. Displacement (cu in.)	Seat Angle (deg) ●	Face Angle (deg) ■	Spring Test Pressure (lbs @ in.)	Spring Installed Height (in.)	Stem to Guide Clearance (in.) Intake	Exhaust	Stem Diameter (in.) Intake	Exhaust
'70-'71	4-134	45①	46②	73 @ 1 27/32	⑥	.0014	.0035	.3730	.3710
	6-232	45③	45③	90 @ 1 13/16	2 13/64⑦	.0020	.0020	.3730	.3730
	6-258	45③	44	195 @ 1 7/16	N.A.	.0020	.0020	.3720	.3720
	6-225	45④	45④	⑤	1 23/32	.0020	.0025	.3407	.3407
'71	8-304	45	44½	195 @ 1 7/16	N.A.	.0020	.0020	.3720	.3720
	8-360	45	44½	195 @ 1 7/16	N.A.	.0020	.0020	.3720	.3720
'72-'77	6-232	44½	44	100 @ 1 13/16⑨	2 15/64⑦⑧	.0010-.0030	.0010-.0030	.3720	.3720
	6-258	44½	44	100 @ 1 13/16⑨	2 15/64⑦⑧	.0010-.0030	.0010-.0030	.3720	.3720
	8-304	44½	44	84 @ 1 13/16⑨	2 7/32⑦⑧	.0010-.0030	.0010-.0030	.3720	.3720
	8-360	44½	44	84 @ 1 13/16⑨	2 7/32⑦⑧	.0010-.0030	.0010-.0030	.3720	.3720
'74-'77	8-401	44½	44	84 @ 1 13/16⑨	2 7/32⑦⑧	.0010-.0030	.0010-.0030	.3720	.3720

● Exhaust valve seat angle given; all intake valve seat angles are 30° unless otherwise noted
■ Exhaust valve face angle given; all intake valve face angles are 29° unless otherwise noted
— Not applicable
N.A. Not available
① Intake valve seat angle 45°

② Intake valve face angle 46°
③ Intake valve angle 30°
④ Intake valve angle 45°
⑤ Intake: 64 @ 1 11/16; exhaust 64 @ 1 5/8
⑥ Free length of intake spring 1 31/32 in.; exhaust 2½ in.
⑦ Free length
⑧ 1974 and later only; other years N.A.
⑨ Without rotators

TORQUE SPECIFICATIONS
All readings in ft lbs

Engine No. Cyl. Displacement (cu in.)	Cylinder Head Bolts	Rod Bearing Bolts	Main Bearing Bolts	Crankshaft Balancer Bolt	Flywheel to Crankshaft Bolts	MANIFOLD	
						Intake	Exhaust
4-134	60-70	35-45	65-75	60-70	35-41	29-35	29-35
6-232, 258	95-115③	26-30	75-85	50-64	95-120④	37-47②	20-30②
6-225	65-80	30-40	95-120	140-160	50-65	25-35	15-20
8-350	①	35	110	140-180	60	50	18
8-304, 360	100-120⑤	26-30⑥	90-105⑦	48-64⑧	95-120④	37-47⑨	20-30⑥
8-401	100-120	35-40⑥	90-105⑦	48-64⑧	95-120④	37-47⑨	20-30⑥

① Metal gasket 75; composition 80
② 20-25 for 1970-72, 18-28 for 1974-'77
③ 80-85 for 1970-72
④ 100-110 for 1970-72
⑤ 105-115 for 1970-72
⑥ 30-35 for 1976-77
⑦ 95-100 for 1970-72
⑧ 50-60 for 1970-72
⑨ 40-45 for 1970-72

CRANKSHAFT AND CONNECTING ROD SPECIFICATIONS
All measurements are given in inches

Engine No. Cyl. Displacement (cu in.)	CRANKSHAFT				CONNECTING ROD		
	Main Brg. Journal Dia	Main Brg. Oil Clearance	Shaft End-Play	Thrust on No.	Journal Diameter	Oil Clearance	Side Clearance
4-134	2.333	.0019	.005	1	1.9375	.0014	.007
6-225	2.4995	.0009	.006	2	2.0000	.0021	.010
6-232	2.4986-2.5001	.001-.003	.0015-.0065	3	2.0934-2.0955	.001-.002	.005-.014①
6-258	2.4986-2.5001	.001-.002	.0015-.0065	3	2.0934-2.0955	.001-.002	.005-.014①
8-350	2.9995	.0010	.006	3	2.0000	.0012	.010
8-304	2.7489-2.7474②	.001-.003	.003-.008	3	2.0934-2.0955	.001-.002	.006-.018
8-360	2.7489-2.7474②	.001-.003	.003-.008	3	2.0934-2.0955	.001-.002	.006-.018
8-401	2.7489-2.7474②	.001-.003	.003-.008	3	2.2464-2.2485	.001-.002	.006-.018

① .008-.010 1973-only
② Rear main, 2.7479-2.7464

WHEEL ALIGNMENT

Model	CASTER Pref. Setting (deg)	CAMBER Pref. Setting (deg)	Toe-In (in.)	King-Pin Inclination (deg)	WHEEL PIVOT RATIO	
					Inner Wheel	Outer Wheel
CJ-5, CJ6, CJ-7, DJ-5, DJ-6, CJ-5A, CJ-6A	3	1°30'	3/64-3/32	7½①	20	20
Jeepster, Commando	3	1°30'	3/64-3/32	7½	N.A.	N.A.
Wagoneer, Cherokee	3②	1°30'	3/64-3/32	7½①	N.A.	N.A.

N.A. Not available
① 8½° in 1974-'75
② 4° in 1974-77

FIRING ORDER

FIRING ORDER 1-3-4-2

4 cylinder F head 134 engines

FIRING ORDER 1-6-5-4-3-2

V6 225 engines

FIRING ORDER 1-8-4-3-6-5-7-2

V8 350 engines

LEFT BANK

7 5 3 1

CLOCKWISE ROTATION
1-8-4-3-6-5-7-2

RIGHT BANK

8 6 4 2

FRONT

V-8 ENGINES

American Motors V8 engines. Circles indicate the position of the distributor cap latches on 1972-74 models; squares indicate the latches on 1975-76 models.

6 5 4 3 2 1

FRONT

SIX-CYLINDER ENGINES
CLOCKWISE ROTATION
1-5-3-6-2-4

232 and 258 Sixes. Circles indicate the position of the distributor cap latches on 1970-74 models; squares indicate the latches on 1975-76 models.

TRUCK MODEL AND ENGINE APPLICATION

(All Jeep engines are gas engines)

| Truck Model | ENGINE | | | |
	Cu. In.	Carb.	H.P.	Torque (ft lbs)
(CJ-5, CJ-6 and CJ-7	134-4 Cyl.	1 bbl	75	114
	225-V6	2 bbl	160	235
	232	1 bbl	100①	185②
	258	1 bbl	110③	195④
	304-V8	2 bbl	150⑤	245⑥
Wagoneer	232⑦	1 bbl	145	215
	232	1 bbl	100①	185②
	258	1 bbl	110③	195④
	304-V8	2 bbl	150⑤	245⑥

TRUCK MODEL AND ENGINE APPLICATION

(All Jeep engines are gas engines)

| Truck Model | ENGINE | | | |
	Cu. In.	Carb.	H.P.	Torque (ft lbs)
Wagoneer	350-V8	2 bbl	230	350
	360-V8	2 bbl	175	285
	360-V8	4 bbl	195	295
	401-V8	4 bbl	215	320
Cherokee	258	1 bbl	110③	195④
	360-V8	2 bbl	175	285
	360-V8	4 bbl	195	295
	401-V8	4 bbl	215	320
Jeepster and Commando	134-4 Cyl.	1 bbl	75	114
	225-V6	2 bbl	160	235
	232	1 bbl	100	185
	258	1 bbl	110	195
	304-V8	2 bbl	150	245
J-100 (Station Wagon 1970), and Truck	232⑦	1 bbl	145	215
	232	1 bbl	100①	185②
	258	1 bbl	110③	195④
	304-V8	2 bbl	150⑤	245⑥
	327-V8	2 bbl	250	340
	350-V8	2 bbl	230	350
	360-V8	2 bbl	175	285
	360-V8	4 bbl	195	295
	401-V8	4 bbl	215	320

① 90 HP in 1976-77
② 170 ft lbs in 1976-77
③ 95 HP in 1976-77
④ 180 ft lbs in 1976-77
⑤ 120 HP in 1976-77
⑥ 220 ft lbs in 1976-77
⑦ 1970 only

Distributor

Refer to the Electrical General Repair section for detail procedures on the different distributors.

Starting in the 1975 model year all engines use the American Motors Breakerless Inductive (BID) Ignition System. This system consists of five major components: an electronic ignition control unit, an ignition coil, a distributor, high tension spark plug wires, and spark plugs. This system uses a conventional coil, spark plug wires, and spark plugs. The main difference in components from a conventional system is the points and condensor are eliminated from the distributor and are replaced by a trigger wheel and an electromagnetic sensor, and an electronic control unit is added.

Distributor R & R

1. Remove the high-tension wires from the distributor cap terminal towers, noting their positions to assure correct reassembly. For diagrams of firing orders and distributor wiring, refer to the front of this section.
2. Remove the primary lead from the terminal post at the side of the distributor.
3. Disconnect the vacuum tube if there is one.
4. Unlatch the two distributor cap retaining hooks and remove the distributor cap.
5. Note the position of the rotor in relation to the base. Scribe a mark on the base of the distributor and on the engine block to facilitate reinstallation. Align the marks with the direction the metal tip of the rotor is pointing.
6. Remove the screw that holds the distributor to the engine.
7. Lift the distributor assembly from the engine.

If the engine has not been disturbed, install the distributor as follows:

1. Insert the distributor shaft and assembly into the engine. Line up the mark on the distributor and the one on the engine with the metal tip of the rotor. Make sure that the vacuum advance diaphragm is pointed in the same direction as it was pointed originally. This will be done automatically if the marks on the

engine and the distributor are lined up with the rotor.

NOTE: On the F4 the distributor shaft fits into a slot in the end of the oil pump shaft.

2. Install the distributor hold-down bolt and clamp. Leave the screw loose enough so that you can move the distributor with heavy hand pressure.

3. Connect the primary wire to the distributor side of the coil. Install the distributor cap on the distributor housing. Secure the distributor cap with the spring clips or the screw type retainers, whichever is used.

4. Install the spark plug wires. Make sure that the wires are pressed all of the way into the top of the distributor cap and firmly onto the spark plugs.

NOTE: Design of the V6 engine requires a special form of distributor cam. The distributor may be serviced in the regular way and should cause no more problems than any other distributor, if the firing pin is thoroughly understood. The distributor cam is not ground to standard six cylinder indexing intervals. This particular form requires that the original pattern of spark plug wiring be used The engine will not run in balance if number one spark plug wire is inserted into number six distributor cap tower, even though each wire in the firing sequence is advanced to the next distributor tower. There is a difference between the firing intervals of each succeeding cylinder through the 720° engine cycle.

5. Adjust the point cam dwell and set the ignition timing.

If the engine has been turned while the distributor has been removed, or if the marks were not drawn, it will be necessary to initially time the engine. Follow the procedure below:

1. It is necessary to place the No. 1 cylinder in the firing position to correctly install the distributor. To locate this position, some engines have marks placed on the flywheel while other engines have marks placed on the timing gear covers and crankshaft pulleys. The flywheel marks may be viewed through a covered opening directly in back of the starting motor by loosening the hole cover and sliding it to one side.

2. Remove the No. 1 cylinder spark plug. Turn the engine until the piston in No. 1 cylinder is moving up on the compression stroke. This can be determined by placing your thumb over the spark plug hole and feeling the air being forced out of the cylinder. Stop turning F-head engines when either the 5° mark on the flywheel is in the middle of the

flywheel inspection opening, or the marks on the crankshaft pulley and the timing gear cover are in alignment.

3. Oil the distributor housing lightly where the distributor bears on the cylinder block.

4. Install the distributor so that the rotor, which is mounted on the shaft, points toward the No. 1 spark plug terminal tower position when the cap is installed. Of course you won't be able to see the direction in which the rotor is pointing if the cap is on the distributor. Lay the cap on the top of the distributor and make a mark on the side of the distributor housing just below the No. 1 spark plug terminal. Make sure that the rotor points toward that mark when you install the distributor.

5. When the distributor shaft has reached the bottom of the hole, move the rotor back and forth slightly until the driving lug on the end of the shaft enters the slot, which is cut in the end of the oil pump gear on the F4, or when the drive gears of the distributor and cam mesh on the other engines, and until the distributor assembly slides down into place.

On models that have a gear on the end of the distributor shaft and a gear on the end of the oil pump drive, these gears have to mesh with the same teeth as originally installed when the distributor is inserted into the engine. Once again, the marks that were placed on the engine and the base of the distributor housing come into play. If the distributor shaft gear and the oil pump drive gear are but one tooth off from what they are supposed to be, the engine will not run correctly.

6. When the distributor is correctly installed, the breaker points should be in such a position that they are just ready to break contact with each other. This is accomplished by rotating the distributor body after it has been installed in the engine. Once again, line up the marks that you made before the distributor was removed from the engine.

7. Install the distributor hold-down screw and the hold-down bracket. Be sure that the models that have vacuum advance units are free to turn in the mounting socket. Note that the vacuum advance control of some distributors is connected directly to the plate on which the points are mounted. When this is the case, the plate must be free to turn rather than the distributor body.

8. Install the spark plug into the No. 1 spark plug hole and con-

tinue from Step 3 of the distributor installation procedure.

Contact Points R & R

F4

1. Pry the distributor cap hold-down clips loose from the cap and remove the cap and rotor.

2. Loosen the nut which holds the condenser lead and spring arm of the points assembly and remove the lead.

3. Remove the condenser and points assembly hold-down screws and remove the assembly and condenser from the distributor.

4. Install the new points assembly and condenser in the reverse order of removal.

5. Turn the engine until the fiber block on the breaker arm is resting on one of the cam lobes at the highest point.

6. Loosen the lock screw and turn the adjusting eccentric until the proper gap is obtained. Tighten the lock screw.

7. Replace the rotor and cap and start the engine to check the ignition timing and point dwell. Make any necessary adjustments to obtain the correct timing and dwell.

225 V6 With Prestolite Distributor

1. Remove the distributor cap from the distributor. Remove the rotor.

2. The condenser and primary leads are retained by breaker point spring tension. Relieve the spring tension to remove the leads.

3. Remove the contact set retaining screw and remove the contact set.

4. Remove the condenser screw and remove the condenser.

5. Install the new parts by reversing the removal procedure. Relieve the spring tension of the breaker point spring to install the primary and condenser leads.

6. Rotate the crankshaft until the distributor cam holds the distributor points to a wide-open position. Check the gap between the points. Then, slightly loosen the contact set mounting screw and adjust the contact point gap to the proper specification. Tighten the mounting screw when the correct gap is obtained. Check the point dwell with a dwell meter and make any necessary readjustments.

225 V6 With Delco Distributor

1. Remove the distributor cap by inserting a screwdriver in the upper slotted end of the cap retainers, press down and turn 90° counterclockwise. Push the distributor cap aside and remove

the rotor. Disconnect the condenser and primary leads from their terminal by loosening the retaining screw. If there is no retaining screw, simply slip the leads out.

2. Loosen the two screws and lock washers which hold the contact point set in place. Remove the point set.

3. Slide the new point set over the boss on the breaker plate and under the two screw heads. Tighten the two screws and lockwashers.

4. Install the condenser and primary leads. The leads must be properly positioned so that they will not come in contact with the bottom of the base or rotor.

5. Install the rotor and distributor cap.

6. If the engine does not readily start, position the contact arm rubbing block on a peak of a cam lobe of the distributor cam, insert a 1/8 in. allen wrench in the adjusting screw and turn the screw in (clockwise) until the contact points just close. Then back the screw out (counterclockwise) 1/2 turn to obtain a point gap of about 0.016 in. for a preliminary setting.

7. Connect a dwell meter and check and adjust the point dwell with the engine running, adjusting the points with the allen wrench inserted through the adjustment window in the side of the distributor cap.

8. Check and adjust the ignition timing.

232 and 258 Sixes

The condenser and primary leads are retained by spring tension. Remove the distributor rotor and cap, release the tension and remove the leads. Loosen contact base screw and remove contact point assembly. Install a new condenser, set approximate point gap of new contact set, lubricate cam lobes or reverse lubricator and install rotor and cap. Check dwell and adjust if necessary.

V8 Engines

Remove the distributor cap, condenser and primary leads which are attached to the nylon terminal. Loosen the two base screws and remove points. When installing points, make sure pilot hole is properly positioned over hole in breaker plate. Install new condenser, then attach primary and condenser leads to nylon terminal. Reverse lubricator and check that terminal leads will not touch rotor. Install rotor, making sure round and square holes are lined up with their respective dowels. Adjust point dwell to specification by turning Allen screw on point set through window in side of cap.

Ignition Timing

All Engines

1. Locate the timing marks on the crankshaft pulley and the front of the timing case cover.

2. Clean off the timing marks, so that you can see them.

3. Use chalk or white paint to color the mark on the scale that will indicate the correct timing, when aligned with the mark on the pulley or the pointer. It is also helpful to mark the notch in the pulley or the tip of the pointer with a small dab of color.

4. Attach a tachometer to the engine.

5. Attach a timing light to the engine.

6. Disconnect the vacuum lines to the distributor at the distributor and plug the vacuum lines. Disconnect the TCS switch if so equipped. Loosen the distributor lock-bolt just enough so that the distributor can be turned with a little resistance.

7. Check to make sure that all of the wires clear the fan and then start the engine.

8. Adjust the idle to the correct specification.

9. With the timing light aimed at the pulley and the marks on the engine, turn the distributor in the direction of rotor rotation to retard the spark, and in the opposite direction of rotor rotation to advance the spark. Align the marks on the pulley and the engine with the flashes of the timing light.

Alternator

Refer to the Electrical General Repair Section for detailed alternator test and overhaul procedures.

CAUTION: Since the AC generator and regulator are designed for use on only one polarity system, the following precautions must be observed:

a. The polarity of the battery, generator and regulator must be matched and considered before making any electrical connections in the system.

b. When connecting a booster battery, be sure to connect the negative battery terminals together and the positive battery terminals together.

c. When connecting a charger to the battery, connect the charger positive lead to the battery positive terminal. Connect the charger negative lead to the battery negative terminal.

d. Never operate the AC generator on open circuit. Be sure that all connections in the circuit are clean and tight.

e. Do not short across or ground any of the terminals on the AC generator.

f. Do not attempt to polarize the AC generator.

g. Do not use test lamps of more than 12 V for checking diode continuity.

h. Avoid long soldering times when replacing diodes or transistors. Prolonged heat is damaging to these units.

i. Disconnect the battery ground terminal when servicing any AC system. This will prevent the possibility of accidentally reversing polarity.

Alternator R & R

Unfasten the bolt holding the tension bar to the alternator. Push the alternator in toward the engine to release the drive belt. Unfasten the mounting bolt to release the alternator from the engine.

When reinstalling, adjust the drive belt to allow 1/2 in. play on the longest run between pulleys.

Starter

Refer to the Electrical General Repair Section for detailed starter test and overhaul procedures.

Starter R & R

232 and 258 Sixes

Remove the oil filler pipe and disconnect the battery and solenoid leads from the starter. From underneath the vehicle, remove the bolts that attach the starter to the bellhousing and lift out the starter.

Install in the reverse of removal.

304 V8, 360 V8, 401 V8

Disconnect the battery lead and solenoid lead from the starter. From underneath the vehicle, remove the attaching bolts and lift out the starter. Install in the reverse of removal.

225 V6

Disconnect the negative battery cable from the battery. Note the locations of the wiring connections and disconnect the electrical leads from the starter. Remove the capscrew which secures the starter motor to the angle bracket on the side of the engine. Remove the two capscrews which secure the drive end of the starter motor to the cylinder block and remove the starter. Install the starter in the reverse order of removal.

Brakes

Refer to the Brakes General Repair Section for detail troubleshooting and brake hydraulic system repair procedures.

Master Cylinder R & R

1. Disconnect and plug the brake lines at the master cylinder.
2. Disconnect the wires from the stoplight switch.
3. Disconnect the master cylinder push rod at the brake pedal on vehicles with manual brakes 1972-76.
4. Remove all attaching bolts and nuts and lift the master cylinder from the vehicle.
5. Install the master cylinder in the reverse order of removal and bleed the hydraulic system.

Power Unit R & R

1. Clean the master cylinder and booster unit.
2. Remove the cotter and clevis pins securing the booster pushrod to the pedal linkage.
3. Disconnect the vacuum hose from the booster check valve.
4. Disconnect the fluid lines from the master cylinder. Plug the ends and catch any escaping fluid. *Do not reuse brake fluid.*
5. Disconnect the stoplight wires from the switch.
6. Remove the attaching nuts, booster unit assembly, and block spacers.
7. Remove the attaching nuts and separate the master cylinder from the booster.

To install the booster unit, reverse the removal procedure and bleed the brakes.

CAUTION: Do not pressure-bleed power-assisted brake systems.

Wheel Cylinder R & R

1. Raise and support the vehicle and remove the brake drums and brake shoes.
2. Disconnect the brake line. Do not bend the line away from the wheel cylinder. When the cylinder is removed from the support plate, the line will separate from the wheel cylinder easily.
3. Remove the wheel cylinder mounting bolts and remove the wheel cylinder from the brake backing plate.
4. Clean the wheel cylinder mounting surface on the brake support plate. Clean the brake line fitting and threads.
5. Start the brake line fitting into the wheel cylinder and attach the wheel cylinder to the support plate and tighten the brake line fitting. Tighten the wheel cylinder mounting bolts to 18 ft lbs.

Parking Brakes

Adjustments

Transmission Brake

Make sure that the brake handle on the instrument panel is fully released. Check the operating linkage and the cable to make sure that they don't bind. If necessary, free the cable and lubricate it. Rotate the brake drum until one pair of the three sets of holes are over the shoe adjusting screw wheels in the brake. Use the edge of the holes in the brake drum as a fulcrum for the brake adjusting

Transmission brake adjustment
(ⓒ Willys Corp.)

1 Ball nut
2 3/32" clearance
  [2,38 mm.]
3 Adjusting screw

tool or a screwdriver. Rotate each notched adjusting screw by moving the handle of the tool away from the center of the drive shaft until the shoes are snug against the drum. Back off seven notches on the adjusting screw wheels to secure the proper running clearance between the shoes and the drum.

Rear Wheel

1. Make sure that the hydraulic brakes are in satisfactory adjustment.
2. Raise the rear wheels off the ground and disengage the parking brake pedal.
3. Loosen the locknut on the brake cable adjusting rod, located directly behind the frame center crossmember.
4. Spin the wheels and tighten the adjustment until the rear wheels drag slightly. Loosen the adjustment until there is no drag and the wheels spin freely.
5. Tighten the locknut to lock the adjusting nut.

Transmission Brake Shoes R & R

The condition of the brake lining on the transmission brake can be visually checked through the adjusting holes in the brake drum.

1. Disconnect the driveshaft from the transmission brake drum and lower it out of the way.
2. Remove the retracting spring clevis pin and spring clip.
3. Remove the hug locknut and the nut and washer from the transfer case output shaft.
4. Use a screw-type puller to remove the driveshaft companion flange and the transmission brake drum.
5. Remove the two brake shoe retracting springs and remove the brake shoes.
6. Turn both adjusting screw wheels away from the center to the fully retracted position.
7. Place a light film of grease on the brake actuating cam and install the brake shoes.
8. Install the black shoe return spring next to the cam and the yellow spring next to the notch adjusting wheel screw.
9. Place the brake drum and driveshaft flange in position and install the transfer case output shaft washer, nut and hug locknut.
10. Adjust the parking brake and connect the driveshaft to the driveshaft flange at the brake drum.

Fuel System

Refer to the Carburetor General Repair Section for exploded views of carburetors and specifications.

Carburetor R & R

To remove the carburetor from any engine, first remove the air cleaner from the top of the carburetor. Remove all lines and hoses, noting their positions to facilitate installation. Remove all throttle and choke linkage at the carburetor. Remove the carburetor attaching nuts which hold it to the intake manifold. Lift the carburetor from the engine along with the carburetor base gasket. Discard the gasket. Install the carburetor in the reverse order of removal, using a new base gasket.

Idle Speed and Mixture Adjustments

1970-71

1. Start the engine and run it until it reaches operating temperature.
2. If it hasn't already been done, check and adjust the ignition timing. After you have set the timing, turn off the engine.
3. Attach a tachometer to the engine.

4. Remove the air cleaner, except on American Motors engines. Leave the air cleaner on these models. Turn on the headlights to high beam.

5. Start the engine and check the idle speed on the tachometer. If the reading on the tachometer is correct, turn off the engine and remove the tachometer. If it is not correct, proceed to the following steps.

6. Turn the idle adjusting screw at the bottom of the carburetor with a screwdriver—clockwise to increase the idle speed and counterclockwise to decrease it.

The idle mixture screw is located at the very bottom of the carburetor.

1. Turn the screw until it is all the way in. Do not force the screw in any further because it is very easy to damage the needle valve and its seat by screwing the adjusting screw in too tightly.

2. Turn the screw out ¾-1¾ turns. This should be the normal adjustment setting. For a richer mixture, turn the screw in. The ideal setting for the mixture adjustment screw results in the maximum engine rpm.

1972

Use the 'lean best idle' procedure to adjust the idle speed and mixture on 1972 Jeep vehicles.

1. Start the engine and allow it to reach normal operating temperature. If the engine is equipped with an air pump, disconnect the bypass valve air inlet hose.

2. Adjust the idle speed to the specified rpm by turning either the idle adjustment screw or the throttle stop solenoid.

NOTE: If the idle adjustment procedure is not completed within 3 minutes, run the engine at 2000 rpm for 1 minute to stabilize the engine temperature.

3. Turn the mixture screw(s) counterclockwise (richer until loss of rpm is noticed, then turn mixture screw(s) clockwise (leaner), past original starting point, counting the number of the screws(s).

4. Continue turning mixture screw(s) clockwise until engine looses rpm due to an overly lean mixture.

5. Return the screw(s) to the midpoint between the two extremes and the highest rpm reading.

6. Turn the mixture adjusting screw(s) clockwise (leaner) to the point where the engine rpm just begin to drop, then counterclockwise the minimum amount to obtain the previously established highest rpm. This is the 'lean best idle'.

NOTE: This procedure should first

be attempted with the limiter caps installed on the mixture adjustment screw(s). If a satisfactory idle cannot be obtained with the caps in place, then carefully remove them by threading a sheet metal screw into the center of the cap and make the adjustment as outlined above. Once the 'lean best idle' has been established, install service limiter caps with the tabs positioned against the full rich stops.

1973-76

The procedure for adjusting the idle speed and mixture on 1973-76 Jeep vehicles is called the lean drop procedure and is made with the engine operating at normal operating temperature and the air cleaner in place as follows:

1. Turn the mixture screws to the full rich position with the tabs on the limiters against the stops. Note the position of screw head slot inside limiter cap slots.

2. Remove idler limiter caps.

3. Remove limiter caps by threading a sheet metal screw in center of cap and turning clockwise. Discard limiter caps.

4. Reset adjustment screws to same position noted before limiter caps were removed.

5. Start engine and allow it to reach normal operating temperature.

6. Adjust idle speed to 30 rpm above the specified rpm in the Tune-Up Specifications.
   a. On 6 cylinder engines with throttle stop solenoid, turn nut on solenoid plunger in or out to obtain specified rpm. This is done with solenoid wire connected.
   b. On V8 engines with throttle stop solenoid, turn hex screw on throttle stop solenoid carriage to obtain specified rpm. This is done with solenoid wire connected.
   c. Tighten solenoid locknut, if so equipped.
   d. Disconnect solenoid wire and adjust curb idle speed screw to obtain idle speed of 500 rpm.
   e. Re-connect solenoid wire.

7. Starting from the full rich position, as was determined before limiter caps were removed, turn mixture adjusting screws clockwise (leaner) until a loss of engine speed is noticed.

8. Turn screws counterclockwise (richer) until the highest rpm reading is obtained at lean best idle setting. The lean best idle setting is on the lean side of the highest rpm setting without changing rpm.

9. If the idle speed changed more than 30 rpm during the mixture

adjustment procedure, reset the idle speed to 30 rpm above the specified rpm with idle speed adjusting screw or the throttle stop solenoid and repeat the mixture adjustment.

10. The final adjustment is to turn the mixture adjusting screws clockwise until engine rpm drop as follows:

1973-74

6 Cylinder Automatic	20 rpm
6 Cylinder Manual	35 rpm
V8 All	40 rpm

1975

6 Cylinder Automatic	25 rpm
6 Cylinder Manual with EGR and Catalytic Converter	35 rpm
6 Cylinder Manual with EGR only	50 rpm
V8 Automatic	20 rpm
V8 Manual	40 rpm

1976-77

6 Cylinder Automatic	25 rpm
6 Cylinder Manual	50 rpm
V8 Automatic	20 rpm
V8 Manual	100 rpm

11. Install new limiter caps over mixture adjusting screws with tabs positioned against full rich stops. Be careful not to disturb idle mixture setting while installing caps.

Fuel Pump R & R

All Engines

1. Disconnect the fuel lines leading to the carburetor and from the fuel tank.

2. Remove the two attaching bolts that hold the fuel pump to the engine and lift the fuel pump off of the engine.

3. Before installing the fuel pump, make sure that all of the mating surfaces are clean.

4. Cement a new gasket to the mating surface of the fuel pump.

5. Position the fuel pump on the cylinder block so that the cam lever of the pump rests on the camshaft.

6. Secure the pump to the engine with the two bolts and lock washers.

7. Connect the fuel lines to the fuel pump.

Fuel Tank R & R

1970-71 CJ-5 and CJ-6

The fuel tank on these models is installed under the driver's seat.

To remove the fuel tank, first make sure that the tank is either completely drained or that the level is at least below any of the vent lines or filler openings so that when these lines are disconnected fuel will not run out.

Remove the driver's seat from the vehicle.

Disconnect all of the ventline hoses, the fuel gauge electrical lead, the fill hose and the fuel outlet line at the tank.

Remove the tank hold down screws from the mounting brackets, or the hold down strap, and lift the tank from the vehicle.

If there is still gas in the tank, be careful not to spill any fuel when lifting it out of the vehicle. Also, empty the tank of all fuel and flush it with water before soldering or welding the tank.

Install the tank in the reverse order of removal.

1972-76 All Models

The fuel tank on 1972-76 models is attached to the frame by brackets and bolts. The brackets are attached to the tank at the seam flange.

Before removing the fuel tank, make sure the level of the fuel inside the tank is at least below any of the various hoses connected. It is best to either drain or siphon the majority of fuel out of the tank to make it easier to handle while removing it.

To remove the tank, loosen all of the clamps retaining hoses to the tank and disconnect the hoses from the tank. It may be necessary to remove the fuel tank-to-mounting bracket screws and lower the tank slightly to gain access to some of the connecting hoses. Disconnect the tank from the mounting brackets, if not already done, and lower the tank from under the vehicle. Be careful not to spill any fuel in the tank while removing it.

Empty the tank of all fuel and flush it with water before soldering or welding the tank.

Install the fuel tank in the reverse order of removal.

Cooling System

See the Capacities Chart in the front of this section for cooling system capacities.

Radiator R & R

1. Drain the radiator by opening the drain cock and removing the radiator pressure cap.
2. Remove the upper and lower hose clamps and hose at the radiator. On vehicles with an automatic transmission, disconnect the oil cooler lines. Plug the lines to prevent dirt from entering the transmission oil.
3. Remove the cap screws, lock washers, and flat washers that hold the radiator to the radiator support.
4. Remove the radiator.
5. Install the radiator in the reverse order of removal.

Water Pump R & R

F4

1. Drain the coolant from the system by opening the petcock.
2. Remove the fan belt, fan, and fan pulley.
3. Remove the bolts which attach the water pump to the block and remove the pump.
4. Install the pump in the reverse order of removal, using a new gasket.

225 V6

1. Drain the cooling system.
2. Remove the fan belt and the fan and pulley from the hub on the water pump.
3. Disconnect the hoses from the water pump.
4. Remove the capscrews which secure the water pump to the engine and remove the pump from the vehicle.
5. Clean all of the mating surfaces, install new gaskets with sealer applied and install the water pump in the reverse order of removal.

232 and 258 Sixes

1. Drain the cooling system at the radiator.
2. Disconnect the radiator and heater hoses from the water pump.
3. Loosen the alternator adjustment strap screw, upper pivot bolt, and remove the drive belt.
4. If the vehicle is equipped with a radiator shroud, separate the shroud from the radiator to facilitate removal and installation of the cooling fan and hub.
5. Remove the cooling fan and hub assembly.
6. Remove air conditioning intermediate idler pulley and mounting bracket, if so equipped.
7. Remove the power steering pump front mounting bracket, if so equipped.
8. Remove the water pump and gasket from the engine.
9. Clean all the old gasket material from the gasket surface of the engine.
10. Install the new water pump and assemble the engine in the reverse order of removal, tightening the water pump retaining bolts to 13 ft lbs.

V8 All

1. Disconnect the negative battery cable.
2. Drain the radiator and disconnect the upper radiator hose at the radiator.
3. Loosen all the drive belts.
4. Remove the fan and hub assembly.
5. Separate the radiator shroud from the radiator, if so equipped.
6. If the vehicle is equipped with a viscous fan, remove the fan assembly and shrould all at the same time. Do not unbolt the fan blades.

NOTE: The studs in the water pump may back out of the water pump while removing the nuts, preventing the fan assembly from clearing the water pump. If this happens, install a double nut on the stud(s) and remove the studs.

7. If the vehicle is equipped with air conditioning, install a double nut on the air conditioning compressor bracket to water pump stud and remove the stud. Removal of this stud eliminates removing the compressor mounting bracket.
8. Remove the alternator and mounting bracket assembly and place it aside. Do not disconnect the alternator wires.
9. Remove the two nuts attaching the power steering pump to the rear half of the pump mounting bracket, if so equipped.
10. Remove the two bolts attaching the front half of the bracket to the rear half.
11. Remove the remaining upper bolt from the inner air pump support brace, loosen the lower bolt and drop the brace away from the power steering front bracket.
12. Remove the front half of the power steering bracket from the water pump mounting stud.
13. Disconnect the heater hose, bypass hose, and lower radiator hose at the water pump.
14. Remove the water pump and gasket from the timing chain cover and clean all old gasket material from the gasket surface of the timing chain cover.
15. Install the new water pump and assemble the remaining components in the reverse order of removal, tightening the water pump-to-engine block screws to 25 ft lbs and the water pump-to-timing case cover screws to 4 ft lbs (48 in. lbs).

Engine

Refer to the Engine General Repair Section for troubleshooting and rebuilding procedures. Also, Emission Control Systems are discussed in the General Repair Section.

Cylinder Head R & R

F4

1. Drain the coolant.
2. Remove the upper radiator hose. Remove the carburetor.
3. On early engines, remove the bypass hose from the front of the cylinder head.
4. Remove the rocker arm cover.
5. Disconnect the oil line.
6. Remove the rocker arm attaching stud nuts and rocker arm shaft assembly.

Cylinder head bolt tightening sequence—four-cylinder F-head engines

7. Remove the cylinder head bolts. One head bolt is located below the carburetor mounting, inside the intake manifold.
8. Lift off the cylinder head.
9. Remove the pushrods and valve lifters.
10. Reverse the procedure for installation. Tighten the cylinder head bolts in the proper sequence to the proper torque.

225 V6

1. Remove the intake manifold.
2. Remove the rocker cover.
3. Remove the exhaust pipes at the flanges.
4. Remove the alternator in order to remove the right head.
5. Remove the dipstick and power steering pump, if so equipped, in order to remove the left head.

Cylinder head bolt tightening sequence—V6-225 engines

6. Remove the valve cover and the rocker assemblies. Mark these parts so that they can be reinstalled in exactly the same positions.
7. Unbolt the head bolts and lift off the cylinder head(s). It is very important that the inside of the engine be protected from dirt. The hydraulic lifters are particularly susceptible to being damaged by dirt.
8. To install, use the reverse procedure. Tighten the cylinder head bolts in the proper sequence to the proper torque.

Cylinder head bolt tightening sequence—232 and 258 Sixes.

232 and 258 Sixes

1. Drain the cooling system and disconnect the hoses at the thermostat housing.
2. Remove the cylinder head cover (valve cover), the gasket, the rocker arm assembly, and the pushrods.

NOTE: The pushrods and rockers must be replaced in their original positions.

3. Remove the intake and exhaust manifold from the cylinder head.
4. Disconnect the spark plug wires and remove the spark plugs to avoid damaging them.
5. Disconnect the temperature sending unit wire, ignition coil and bracket assembly and battery ground cable from the engine.
6. Remove the cylinder head bolts, the cylinder head and gasket from the block.
7. To install, reverse the above procedure. Tighten the cylinder head bolts to the specified torque, in the proper sequence.

All American Motors V8 Engines

1. Drain the cooling system and the cylinder block.
2. When removing the right cylinder head, it may be necessary to remove the heater core housing from the firewall.
3. Remove the valve cover(s) and gasket(s).
4. Remove the rocker arm assemblies and push rods.

NOTE: The valve train components must be replaced in their original positions.

5. Remove the spark plugs to avoid damaging them.
6. Remove the intake manifold with the carburetor still attached.
7. Remove the exhaust pipes at the

flange of the exhaust manifold. When replacing the exhaust pipes, it is advisable to install new gaskets at the flange.

8. Loosen all of the drive belts.
9. Disconnect the battery ground cable and the alternator bracket.
10. Disconnect the air pump and power steering pump brackets from the left cylinder head.
11. Remove the cylinder head bolts and lift the head(s) from the cylinder block.
12. Remove the cylinder head gasket(s) from the head(s) or the block.
13. To install, reverse the above procedure.

NOTE: Apply an even coat of sealing compound to both sides of the new head gasket only. Wire brush the cylinder head bolts, then lightly oil them prior to installation. First, tighten all bolts to 80 ft lbs, then tighten them to the specified torque. Follow the correct tightening sequence.

350 V8

1. Drain the cooling system at the radiator and at the engine block.
2. Disconnect the battery cables from the battery and remove the alternator and alternator bracket assembly from the engine.
3. Remove the air cleaner assembly.
4. Remove the rocker covers and gaskets and remove the rocker assemblies together with the pushrods.

NOTE: The pushrods must be reinstalled in the same positions from which they were removed. Identify each pushrod so that this can be accomplished.

5. Disconnect the exhaust pipes from the exhaust manifolds by removing the nuts from the at-

Cylinder head bolt tightening sequence—V8—304 & 360 engines

350 V8

taching bolts of the clamp. Remove the donut gasket.

6. Remove the distributor.
7. Remove the cap screws, lockwashers, nuts, and flat washers that secure the intake manifold to the cylinder heads.
8. Remove the intake manifold with the carburetor attached from the engine. Remove the gaskets and discard them.
9. Remove the bolts holding the cylinder head to the block. Removing one head bolt on the left bank frees the oil dipstick and tube which may now be lifted off. There is a rubber bushing on the lower end of the tube; take care not to lose the rubber bushing.
10. Lift the heads off the block and remove and discard the cylinder head gaskets. Remove all traces of gasket material from all mating surfaces on both the heads and the intake manifold.
11. Install the cylinder heads and assemble the engine in the reverse order of removal and disassembly. Torque the head bolts and intake manifold bolts in the correct sequence and to the proper specifications.

Engine Mounts R & R

F4

The front of the engine is supported by two rubber insulator mountings attached to the frame side rail brackets. The rear of the engine-transmission assembly is supported by a rubber insulator mounting under the rear of the transmission on the frame center crossmember. This crossmember is bolted to the frame side rails so that it can be dropped when removing the transmission or engine-transmission assembly. The rubber insulators allow free side and vertical oscillation to effectively neutralize engine vibration at the source.

The rubber insulator mountings should be inspected for separation and deterioration by jacking the power plant away from the frame, near the supports. Vibration cannot be effectively absorbed by separated or worn insulators. They should be replaced if faulty.

225 V6

The engine-transmission unit is mounted to the chassis at three points by rubber pads. The two front mounts are bolted to the engine cylinder block and the frame members. These mounts support most of the engine weight, and absorb vibration which would otherwise be caused by changes in engine output torque. The single rear mount is placed between the transmission and the transmission support. It supports part of the engine and transmission weight, and locates the rear of the engine with respect to the centerline of the vehicle.

232 and 258 Sixes and All V8

Resilient rubber mounting cushions support the engine and transmission at three points. A cushion is located at each side on the center line of the engine, with the rear supported by a cushion between the transmission extension housing and the rear engine support crossmember.

Replacement of the cushion may be accomplished by supporting the weight of the engine or transmission at the area of the cushion.

Manifolds R & R

F4

The intake manifold is cast as an integral part of the cylinder head.

The exhaust manifold is removed by removing the five nuts from the manifold studs, removing the two bolts that hold the manifold to the exhaust pipe, and lifting the manifold off of the mounting studs. Remove the center and two end gaskets from the cylinder block. Install in the reverse order of removal, using new gaskets.

NOTE: On engines with the AIR exhaust emission control devices, the rubber hose leading from the air pump to the air injection manifold must be disconnected in order to remove the exhaust manifold.

Intake Manifold

225 V6

1. Disconnect the crankcase vent hose, exhaust manifold line, choke heat tube, distributor vacuum hose, and the fuel line at the carburetor.
2. Disconnect the two distributor leads from the ignition coil.
3. Disconnect the wiring harness from the coolant temperature sending unit.

4. Remove the 10 capbolts which attach the intake manifold to the cylinder heads.
5. Remove the intake manifold and carburetor as an assembly.
6. Clean all the mating surfaces of the intake manifold and cylinder heads, removing all traces of gasket material.
7. Install a new rubber intake manifold seal at the front and rear rails of the cylinder block. Be sure that the pointed ends of the seals fit snugly against the block and cylinder heads.
8. Set the intake manifold in place on the cylinder block between the cylinder heads. Thread two capbolts through the manifold into each cylinder head as guide bolts. Lift the manifold slightly and insert each of the two gaskets into position between the manifold and corresponding cylinder head. Be certain that the gasket is installed with its 3 apertures aligned with the ports of the head and manifold. One gasket should be installed in position on the right-side and the other gasket reversed and installed on the left-side.
9. Install the manifold attaching bolt in the open bolt hole at the right center side of the intake manifold. During manufacture, this open bolt hole is held to close tolerances so that the bolt in this location serves to locate the manifold front and rear.
10. Install the remaining intake manifold attaching bolts. The longer bolts are installed in the two forward holes on either side.
11. Tighten the intake manifold bolts to the proper torque in the proper sequence.
12. Assemble the remaining components to the engine in the reverse order of removal.

232 and 258 Sixes

The intake and exhaust manifold are mounted externally on the left side of the engine and are attached to the cylinder head. They are removed as a unit. On later engines, an exhaust gas recirculation valve is mounted on the side of the intake manifold.

1. Remove the air cleaner and carburetor.
2. Disconnect the accelerator cable from the accelerator bellcrank.
3. Disconnect the PCV vacuum hose from the intake manifold.
4. Disconnect the distributor vacuum hose and electrical wires at the TCS solenoid vacuum valves.
5. Remove the TCS solenoid vacuum valve and bracket from the intake manifold. In some cases it might not be necessary to remove the TCS unit.

Exploded view of the intake and exhaust manifold on 232 and 258 Sixes.

Intake manifold torque sequence for 350 V8.

6. If so equipped, disconnect the EGR valve and back pressure sensor hoses.

7. Remove the power steering mounting bracket and pump and set it aside without disconnecting the hoses.

8. Remove the EGR valve and backpressure sensor, if so equipped.

9. Disconnect the exhaust pipe from the manifold flange.

10. Remove the manifold attaching bolts, nuts and clamps.

11. Separate the intake manifold and exhaust manifold from the engine as an assembly, and discard the gasket.

12. If either manifold is to be replaced, they should be separated at the heat riser area.

13. Clean the mating surface of the manifolds and the cylinder head before replacing the manifolds. Replace them in reverse order of the above procedure with new gasket. Tighten the bolts and

nuts to the specified torque in the proper sequence.

350 V8

1. Drain the cooling system.
2. Remove the carburetor air cleaner. Disconnect all tubes and hoses from the carburetor. Disconnect and remove the ignition coil.
3. Disconnect the temperature indicator wire from the sending unit.
4. Disconnect the accelerator and transmission linkage at the carburetor.
5. Slide the front thermostat bypass hose clamp back on the hose. Disconnect the upper radiator hose at the outlet.
6. Disconnect the heater hose at the temperature control valve inlet. Force the end of the hose down to allow the coolant to drain from the intake manifold.
7. Remove the intake manifold-to-head attaching bolts.
8. Remove the intake manifold and

carburetor as an assembly, by sliding the assembly rearward to disengage the thermostat bypass hose from the water pump. Remove all traces of gasket material from the mating surfaces of the intake manifold and the cylinder heads and block.

9. Install the intake manifold in the reverse order of removal, tightening the attaching bolts in the correct sequence and to the proper torque.

304, 360 and 401 V8s

1. Drain the coolant from the radiator.
2. Remove the air cleaner assembly.
3. Disconnect the spark plug wires. Remove the spark plug wire brackets from the valve covers, and the bypass valve bracket.
4. Disconnect the upper radiator hose and the by-pass hose from the intake manifold. Disconnect the heater hose from the rear of the manifold.
5. Disconnect the ignition coil bracket and lay the coil aside.
6. Disconnect the TCS solenoid vacuum valve from the right side valve cover.
7. Disconnect all lines, hoses, linkages and wires from the carburetor and intake manifold and TCS components as required.
8. Disconnect the air delivery hoses at the air distribution manifolds.
9. Disconnect the air pump diverter valve and lay the valve and the bracket assembly, including the hoses, forward of the engine.
10. Remove the intake manifold after removing the cap bolts that hold it in place. Remove and discard the side gaskets and the end seals.
11. Clean the mating surfaces of the intake manifold and the cylinder head before replacing the intake

232 and 258 Six intake/exhaust manifold torque sequence.

manifold. Use new gaskets and tighten the cap bolts to the correct torque. Install in reverse order of the above procedure.

NOTE: There is no specified tightening sequence for the V8 304, 360 and 401 intake manifold. Begin at the center and work outward.

Exhaust Manifold

225 V6

1. Remove the five attaching screws, one nut, and exhaust manifold(s) from the side of the cylinder head(s).
2. Use a new gasket when replacing the exhaust manifolds. Make sure that the mating surfaces of the manifold and the cylinder head are clean. Tighten the manifold nuts and bolts to the correct torque.

232, 258 Sixes

The intake and exhaust manifolds of the 232 and 258 cu in. Sixes must be removed together. See the procedure for removing and installing the intake manifold.

304, 360 and 400 V8

1. Disconnect the spark plug wires.
2. Disconnect the air delivery hose at the distribution manifold.
3. Remove the air distribution manifold and the injection tubes.
4. Disconnect the exhaust pipe at the manifold.
5. Remove the exhaust manifold attaching bolts and washers along with the spark plug shields.
6. Separate the exhaust manifold from the cylinder head.
7. Install in reverse order of the above procedure. Clean the mating surfaces and tighten the attaching bolts to the correct torque.

350 V8

1. Disconnect the exhaust pipe at the exhaust manifold/exhaust pipe joining flange by removing the retaining nuts.
2. Remove the donut gasket and save it, if it is in good condition. If not, discard and replace it.
3. Remove the bolts attaching the exhaust manifold to the cylinder head, leaving one upper bolt toward the center until last.
4. Remove all traces of gasket material from the exhaust manifold and cylinder head mounting surfaces.

NOTE: The sheet metal heat stove is removed with the left exhaust manifold.

Engine Assembly R & R

F4

1. Drain the cooling system.

2. Disconnect the battery ground cable.
3. Remove the air cleaner and disconnect the breather hose at the oil filter.
4. Disconnect the choke and throttle controls.
5. Disconnect the fuel line and windshield wiper hose at the fuel pump.
6. Remove the radiator stay bar, if so equipped.
7. Remove the radiator and heater hoses.
8. Remove the fan blades, fan hub, radiator, and shroud.
9. Remove the starter motor.
10. Disconnect:
    a. The alternator or generator.
    b. The ignition primary wire at coil.
    c. The oil pressure and temperature sending units.
    d. The exhaust pipe from manifold.
    e. The engine ground strap.
11. Attach a lifting device to the engine. Unbolt and remove the front engine supports.
12. Remove the flywheel housing bolts.
13. Pull the engine forward until the clutch clears the flywheel housing. Lift the engine from the vehicle.
14. Install the engine by reversing the removal procedure.

225 V6

1. Remove the hood if necessary.
2. Disconnect the battery ground cable.
3. Remove the air cleaner.
4. Drain the coolant.
5. Disconnect the radiator hoses.
6. Remove the radiator support bars.
7. On the Universal series, remove the radiator. On the Jeepster series, disconnect the headlamp wiring from the block on the left fender, the horn wiring from the horn, the oil cooler lines if equipped with automatic transmission, and remove the front fenders, radiator, and grille as a unit.
8. Disconnect the engine wiring from the connectors on the firewall.
9. Remove the starter motor.
10. Disconnect the fuel hoses at the right frame rail. Plug the hoses.
11. Disconnect the throttle and choke.
12. Disconnect the exhaust pipes.
13. Place a jack under the transmission and support the weight.
14. Remove the front motor mount bolts.
15. Support the engine with a lifting device.
16. Remove the flywheel housing bolts.

17. Raise the engine slightly and slide the engine forward until the engine is free of the transmission shaft. Remove the engine.
18. Install in reverse order of the above procedure.

350 V8

1. Remove the hood.
2. Remove the air cleaner.
3. Drain the radiator and cylinder block.
4. Disconnect the radiator and heater hoses.
5. If equipped with an automatic transmission, disconnect the oil cooler lines at the radiator. Remove the radiator.
6. Remove the fan, belt, and hub.
7. Drain the engine oil and remove the filter.
8. Disconnect the temperature-sender lead, pressure-sender lead, coil, starter solenoid, and alternator and distributor leads.
9. Disconnect the accelerator cable at the carburetor throttle shaft lever and at the cable support bracket.
10. Disconnect the heater system vacuum valve hose at the intake manifold.
11. Disconnect the flexible fuel line from the frame-to-crankcase at the frame end. Plug the end of the hose.
12. Disconnect the exhaust pipes at both manifolds.
13. Remove the air conditioning compressor (if so equipped). Do not disconnect the hoses.
14. If equipped with a manual transmission, disconnect the linkage at the clutch. Disconnect the clutch cross-shaft support brackets at the flywheel housing and frame.
15. Install a suitable lifting fixture on the engine.
16. Support the transmission on a jack.
17. Remove the nuts from the engine-to-front support brackets.
18. With a manual transmission, remove the cap screws from the transmission-to-clutch housing. With an automatic transmission, remove the cap screws attaching the transmission housing-to-flywheel housing adapter.
19. Pull the engine forward and upward until free from the transmission or clutch.
20. Install by reversing the removal procedure.

232, 258 Sixes

NOTE: This operation requires discharging the air conditioning system. This requires special tools and skills for safety reasons. It should not be attempted by untrained persons.

1. Remove the hood after marking the hinge locations. The hood need not be removed on the CJ series.
2. Remove the air cleaner.
3. Drain the coolant. Disconnect the radiator hoses. Disconnect automatic transmission cooler lines from the radiator. If there is a radiator shroud, remove it, then remove the radiator.
4. Remove the fan.
5. Remove and set aside the power steering pump and belt. Do not disconnect the hydraulic lines.
6. Bleed the compressor refrigerant charge. See the note at the start of this procedure. Remove the condenser and receiver assembly.
7. Disconnect all wires, lines, linkage, and hoses from the engine.
8. Drain the oil and remove the filter.
9. Remove both engine front support cushion-to-frame retaining nuts.
10. Disconnect the exhaust pipe at the support bracket and the manifold.
11. Support the engine with the lifting equipment.
12. Remove the front support cushion and bracket assemblies from the engine.
13. Remove the transfer case lever boot, the floor mat, and the transmission access cover.
14. On automatic transmissions, remove the upper bolts holding the bellhousing to the engine adapter plate. On manual transmissions, remove the upper bolts holding the clutch housing to the engine.
15. Remove the starter.
16. On automatics, remove the two adapter plate inspection covers. Mark the relationship of the converter to the flex plate and remove the converter-to-flex plate bolts. Remove the rest of the bolts holding the bellhousing to the adapter plate. On manual transmissions, remove the clutch housing lower cover and the rest of the bolts holding the clutch housing to the engine.
17. Support the transmission with a floor jack and remove the engine by pulling it forward and upward.

To install the engine:

18. Lower the engine into place and align it with the bellhousing or clutch housing. Make sure the manual transmission clutch shaft aligns with the splines of the clutch driven plate.
19. On automatics, install the bellhousing-to-engine adapter plate bolts. On manuals, install the clutch housing-to-engine bolts. Torque the bolts to 25-28 ft lbs

at the top and 40-45 ft lbs at the bottom.
20. Remove the floor jack.
21. Align the marks made in step 16 and install the converter-to-flex plate bolts, torquing them to 21-23 ft lbs.
22. Install the two engine adapter plate inspection covers or the clutch housing lower cover.
23. Replace the starter.
24. Install the front support cushion and bracket assemblies to the engine, torquing the bolts to 25-30 ft lbs. Lower the engine onto the frame supports. Install the front support cushion retaining nuts, torquing them to 25-30 ft lbs.
25. Connect the exhaust pipe at the support bracket and manifold. A new manifold seal is advisable.
26. Install the oil filter.
27. Replace all the items removed in step seven.
28. Replace the air conditioning condenser and receiver assembly and recharge the system.
29. Replace the power steering pump and belt. Install the fan and tighten the bolts to 15-25 ft lbs.
30. Replace and reconnect the radiator. Replace the oil cooler lines. Fill the cooling system.
31. Fill the crankcase and replace the air cleaner. Install the transmission access cover, floor mat, and transfer case lever boot. Replace the hood.

304, 360 and 401 V8

NOTE: This operation requires discharging the air conditioning system. This requires special tools and skills. For safety reasons, it should not be attempted by untrained persons.

The engine is removed without the transmission and bellhousing.

1. On the Commando, Cherokee, and Wagoneer, the hood must be removed. Mark the hinge locations at the hood panel for alignment during installation. Remove the hood from the hinges.
2. Remove the air cleaner assembly.
3. Drain the cooling system and disconnect the upper and lower radiator hoses. If equipped with automatic transmission, disconnect the cooler lines from the radiator.

NOTE: If the vehicle is equipped with a radiator shroud, it is necessary to separate the shroud from the radiator to facilitate removal and installation of the radiator and engine fan.

4. Remove the radiator.
5. Remove the engine fan.
6. If equipped with power steering, remove the pump from the engine and lay it aside. Do not disconnect the hoses.

7. If equipped with air conditioning, turn both service valves clockwise to the front seated position. Bleed the compressor refrigerant charge by slowly loosening the service valve fittings. Disconnect the condenser and evaporator lines from the compressor. Disconnect the receiver outlet at the disconnect coupling. Remove the condenser and receiver assembly.
8. Remove the battery and tray on CJ models only (1972-75).
9. On Wagoneers and Cherokees, remove the heater core housing and charcoal canister from the firewall.
10. Disconnect all wires, lines linkage, and hoses which are connected to the engine.
11. If equipped with automatic transmission, disconnect the transmission filler tube bracket from the right cylinder head. Do not remove the filler tube from the transmission.
12. Remove both engine front support cushion-to-frame retaining nuts.
13. Support the weight of the engine with a lifting device.
14. On CJ and Commando models, remove the transfer case shift lever boot, floor (if so equipped), and transmission access cover.
15. Remove the upper bolts which secure the transmission bellhousing to the engine adapter plate on vehicles equipped with automatic transmission. If equipped with manual transmission, remove the upper bolts which secure the clutch housing to the engine.
16. Disconnect the exhaust pipes at the exhaust manifolds and support bracket.
17. Remove the starter motor.
18. Support the transmission with a floor jack.
19. If equipped with automatic transmission, remove the two engine adapter plate inspection covers. Mark the assembled position of the converter and flex plate and remove the converter-to-flex plate cap screws. Remove the remaining bolts which secure the transmission bellhousing to the engine adapter plate.
20. If equipped with manual transmission, remove the clutch housing lower cover and the remaining bolts which secure the clutch housing to the engine.
21. Remove the engine by pulling upward and forward.

NOTE: If equipped with power brakes, care must be taken to avoid damaging the power unit while removing the engine.

To install the engine:

22. Lower the engine slowly into the engine compartment and align with the transmission bellhousing (automatic transmission) or clutch housing (manual transmission). On manual transmissions, make certain the clutch shaft is aligned properly with the splines of the clutch driven plate.

23. Install the transmission bellhousing-to-engine adapter plate bolts (automatic transmission) or the clutch housing to engine bolts (manual transmission). Tighten the bolts to the specified torque. Remove the floor jack which was used to support the transmission.

24. If equipped with automatic transmission, align the marks previously made on the converter and flex plate, install the converter-to-flex plate cap screws and tighten to the specified torque.

25. Install the two engine adapter plate inspection covers (automatic transmission) or the clutch housing lower cover (manual transmission).

26. Install the starter motor.

27. Lower the engine onto the frame supports, remove the lifting device and install the front support cushion retaining nuts. Tighten the nuts to the specified torque.

28. Connect the exhaust pipes at the exhaust manifolds and support bracket.

29. If equipped with automatic transmission, connect the transmission filler tube bracket to the right cylinder head.

30. On Wagoneers and Cherokees, install the heater core housing and charcoal canister to the firewall.

31. If removed, install the battery and tray.

32. Connect all wires, lines, linkage and hoses which were previously disconnected from the engine.

33. If removed, install the air conditioning condenser and receiver assembly. Connect the receiver outlet to the disconnect coupling. Connect the condenser and evaporator lines to the compressor. Purge the compressor of air.

NOTE: Both service valves must be open before the air conditioning system is operated.

34. If equipped with power steering, connect the power steering, pump to the engine.

35. Install the engine fan and tighten the retaining bolts to the specified torque.

36. Install the radiator and connect the upper and lower hoses. If equipped with automatic transmission, connect the cooler lines.

37. Fill the cooling system to the specified level.

38. Install the air cleaner assembly.

39. Start the engine. Check all connections for leaks. Stop the engine.

40. If removed, install the transmission access cover, floor mat and transfer case shift lever boot.

41. If removed, install the transmission access cover, floor mat and transfer case shift lever boot.

Valve Adjustment

F4

NOTE: While all valve adjustments must be made as accurately as possible, it is better to have the valve adjustment slightly loose than slightly tight, as a burned valve may result from overly tight adjustments.

The only engine in which the valves can be adjusted is the F-Head 4 cylinder. The V6-225, 232 and 258 sixes, 304, 350, 360 and 401 V8s all have hydraulic lifters and are not adjustable in service.

NOTE: The engine must be cold when the valves are adjusted on the F-Head engine.

1. Start the engine and let it run until it has reached operating temperature. Remove the valve cover and check all the cylinder head bolts to make sure they are tightened to the correct torque specifications.

2. While the engine is cooling, remove the side valve spring cover. Be careful not to burn yourself on the exhaust pipe; it may still be hot.

3. After the engine has cooled to ambient temperature, turn the engine until the lifter for the front intake valve is down as far as it will go. The lifter should be resting on the center of the heel (back) of the cam lobe for that valve. You can observe the position of the lifter by looking through the side valve spring cover opening. Put the correct size feeler gauge between the rocker arm and the valve stem for that particular intake valve. There should be a very slight drag on the feeler gauge when it is pulled through the gap. If there is a slight drag, you can assume that the valves are at the correct setting. If the feeler gauge gannot pass between the rocker arm and the valve stem, the gap between them is too small and must be increased. If the gauge can be passed through the gap without any drag, the gap is too large and must be decreased. Loosen the locknut on the top of the rocker arm (pushrod side) by turning it counterclockwise.

Measuring the clearance between the exhaust valve and tappet adjusting screw on an F4 engine

Turn the adjusting screw clockwise to lessen the gap and counterclockwise to increase the gap. When the gap is correct, turn the locknut clockwise to lock the adjusting screw. Follow this procedure for all of the intake valves, making sure that the lifter is all the way down for each adjustment.

4. Turn the engine so that the first exhaust valve is completely closed and the lifter that operates that particular valve is all the way down and on the heel of the cam lobe that operates it.

5. Insert the correct size feeler gauge between the valve stem of the exhaust valve and the adjusting screw. This is done through the side of the engine in the space that is exposed when the side valve spring cover is removed. If there is a slight drag on the feeler gauge, you can assume that the gap is correct. If there is too much drag or not enough, turn the adjusting screw clockwise to increase the gap and counterclockwise to decrease the gap.

6. When all of the valves have been adjusted to the proper clearance, replace the valve covers. If the gaskets are in good shape then they can be used again. If they are cracked, torn, or squashed out of shape, they must be replaced because they will surely leak.

Timing Gear Cover and Oil Seal R & R

F-Head

1. Remove the drive belts and crankshaft pulley.

2. Remove the attaching bolts, nuts and lock washers that hold the timing gear cover to the engine.

3. Remove the timing gear cover.

4. Remove the timing pointer.

5. Remove the timing gear cover gasket.

6. Remove and discard the crankshaft oil seal from the timing gear cover.

7. Replace in reverse order of the

above procedure. Replace the crankshaft oil seal. Use a new timing gear cover gasket.

225 V6

1. Remove the water pump and crankshaft pulley.
2. Remove the two bolts that attach the oil pan to the timing chain cover.

Timing gear cover and water pump attaching bolt locations on the 225 V6.

3. Remove the five bolts that attach the timing chain cover to the engine block.
4. Remove the cover and gasket.
5. Remove the crankshaft front oil seal.
6. From the rear of the timing chain cover, coil new packing around the crankshaft hole in the cover so that the ends of the packing are at the top. Drive in the new packing with a punch. It will be necessary to ream out the hole to obtain clearance for the crankshaft vibration damper hub.

232, 258 Sixes

1. Remove the drive belts, engine fan and hub assembly, the accessory pulley and vibration damper.
2. Remove the oil pan to timing chain cover screws and the screws that attach the cover to the block.
3. Raise the timing chain cover just high enough to detach the retaining nibs of the oil pan neoprene seal from the bottom side of the cover. This must be done to prevent pulling the seal end tabs away from the tongues of the oil pan gaskets which would cause a leak.
4. Remove the timing chain cover and gasket from the engine.

Trim the timing gear cover-to-oil pan seal as shown on 232 and 258 Sixes.

5. Use a razor blade to cut off the oil pan seal end tabs flush with the front face of the cylinder block and remove the seal. Clean the timing chain cover, oil pan, and cylinder block surfaces.
6. Remove the crankshaft oil seal from the timing chain cover.
7. Install in reverse order of the above procedure. It will be necessary to cut the same amount from the end tabs of a new oil pan seal as was cut from the original seal, before installing the new gasket.

304, 360 and 401 V8

1. Remove the negative battery cable.
2. Drain the cooling system and disconnect the radiator hoses and by-pass hose.
3. Remove all of the drive belts and the fan and spacer assembly.
4. Remove the alternator and the front portion of the alternator bracket as an assembly.
5. Disconnect the heater hose.
6. Remove the power steering pump, and/or the air pump, and the mounting bracket as an assembly. Do not disconnect the power steering hoses.
7. Remove the distributor cap and note the position of the rotor. Remove the distributor. (See the Engine Electrical Section.)
8. Remove the fuel pump.
9. Remove the vibration damper and pulley.
10. Remove the two front oil pan bolts and the bolts which secure the timing chain cover to the engine block.

NOTE: The timing gear cover retaining bolts vary in length and must be installed in the same locations from which they were removed.

11. Remove the cover by pulling forward until it is free of the locating dowel pins.
12. Clean the gasket surface of the cover and the engine block.
13. Pry out the original seal from inside the timing chain cover and clean the seal bore.
14. Drive the new seal into place from the inside with a block of wood until it contacts the outer flange of the cover.
15. Apply a light film of motor oil to the lips of the new seal.
16. Before reinstalling the timing gear cover, remove the lower locating dowel pin from the engine block. The pin is required for correct alignment of the cover and must either be reused or a replacement dowel pin installed after the cover is in position.
17. Cut both sides of the oil pan gasket flush with the engine block with a razor blade.
18. Trim a new gasket to correspond to the amount cut off at the oil pan.
19. Apply seal to both sides of the new gasket and install the gasket on the timing case cover.
20. Install the new front oil pan seal.
21. Align the tongues of the new oil pan gasket pieces with the oil pan seal and cement them into place on the cover.
22. Apply a bead of sealer to the cutoff edges of the original oil pan gaskets.
23. Place the timing case cover into

Installation of the timing gear cover-to-oil pan seal on Americans Motors V8s.

position and install the front oil pan bolts. Tighten the bolts slowly and evenly until the cover aligns with the upper locating dowel.

24. Install the lower dowel through the cover and drive it into the corresponding hole in the engine block.

25. Install the cover retaining bolts in the same locations from which they were removed, tightened to 25 ft lbs.

26. Assemble the remaining components in the reverse order of removal.

350 V8

1. Drain the cooling system and remove the radiator, shroud, fan, pulleys and drive belts.

2. Remove the crankshaft pulley, fuel pump and distributor.

3. Remove the alternator and the power steering pump, if necessary.

4. Loosen and slide rearward the front clamp on the thermostat by-pass hose.

5. Remove the vibration damper.

6. Remove the bolts attaching the timing chain cover to the cylinder block and oil pan. Remove the timing chain cover assembly and gasket.

7. Use a punch to drive the old seal out of the cover. Drive the seal from the front toward the rear of the timing chain cover.

8. Tap the new seal into place from the rear of the timing case cover. If a rope seal is used, position the joint of the two ends at the top, then drive in a new shedder with a suitable punch. Stake the shedder in at least 3 places to secure it in position. Size the packing by rotating a hammer handle or similar smooth tool around the inside of the seal to obtain clearance for the crankshaft hub.

9. If the oil pump has not been removed from the timing chain cover, remove the attaching screws, oil pump cover and gasket from the timing chain cover.

10. Completely pack the space around the oil pump gears with petroleum jelly. There must be no air space left inside the pump. Secure the oil pump cover and a new gasket to the timing chain cover with the 5 slotted attaching screws. Torque the screws alternately and evenly to 8-12 ft lbs.

NOTE: Unless the oil pump gears are packed with petroleum jelly, the pump may not prime itself when the engine is started, thus oil will not be pumped throughout the engine for lubrication.

11. The gasket surfaces of the cylinder block and the timing chain cover must be smooth and clean before positioning the gasket in place on the engine. Use sealer on the engine and timing chain cover mating surfaces.

12. Position the timing chain cover to the engine block. Be sure that the dowel pins on the engine engage the holes in the cover before installing the bolts.

13. Install the attaching bolts and tighten them evenly to 30 ft lbs.

Timing Chain or Gears and Tensioner R & R

F4

1. Remove the timing gear cover.

2. Use a puller to remove both the crankshaft and the camshaft gear from the engine after removing all attaching nuts and bolts.

3. Remove the Woodruff keys.

Installation is as follows:

1. Install the Woodruff key in the longer of the two keyways on the front end of the crankshaft.

2. Install the crankshaft timing gear on the front end of the crankshaft with the timing mark facing away from the cylinder block.

3. Align the keyway in the gear with the Woodruff key and then drive or press the gear onto the crankshaft firmly against the thrust washer.

4. Turn the camshaft or the crankshaft as necessary so that the timing marks on the two gears will be together after the camshaft gear is installed.

5. Install the Woodruff key in the keyway on the front of the camshaft.

TIMING MARKS

Aligning timing marks—4 cylinder
(© Willys Corp.)

6. Start the large timing gear on the camshaft with the timing mark facing out.

NOTE: Do not drive the gear onto the camshaft as the camshaft may drive the plug out of the rear of the engine and cause an oil leak.

7. Install the camshaft retaining screw and torque it to 30-40 ft lbs. This will draw the gear onto the camshaft as the screw is tightened. Standard running tolerance between the timing gears is 0.000 to 0.002 in.

225 V6

1. Remove the timing chain cover.

2. Make sure that the timing marks on the crankshaft and the camshaft sprockets are aligned. This will make installing the parts easier.

NOTE: It is not necessary to remove the timing chain dampers (tensioners) unless they are worn or damaged and require replacement.

3. Remove the front crankshaft oil slinger.

4. Remove the bolt and the special washer that hold the camshaft distributor drive gear and fuel pump eccentric at the forward end of the camshaft. Remove the eccentric and the gear from the camshaft.

5. Alternately pry forward the camshaft sprocket and then the crankshaft sprocket until the camshaft sprocket is pried from the camshaft.

6. Remove the camshaft sprocket, sprocket key, and timing chain from the engine.

7. Pry the crankshaft sprocket from the crankshaft.

Install as follows:

1. If the engine has not been disturbed proceed to step Number 4 for installation procedures.

2. If the engine has not been disturbed turn the crankshaft so that number one piston is at top dead center of the compression stroke.

3. Temporarily install the sprocket key and the camshaft sprocket on the camshaft. Turn the camshaft so that the index mark of the sprocket is downward. Remove the key and sprocket from the camshaft.

4. Assemble the timing chain and sprockets. Install the keys, sprockets, and chain assembly on the camshaft and crankshaft so

Alignment of the timing chain sprockets timing marks on the 225 V6.

that the index marks of both the sprockets are aligned.

NOTE: It will be necessary to hold the spring loaded timing chain damper out of the way while installing the timing chain and sprocket assembly.

5. Install the front oil slinger on the crankshaft with the inside diameter against the sprocket (concave side toward the front of the engine).
6. Install the fuel pump eccentric on the camshaft and the key, with the oil groove of the eccentric forward.
7. Install the distributor drive gear on the camshaft. Secure the gear and eccentric to the camshaft with the retaining washer and bolt.
8. Torque the bolt to 40-55 ft lbs.

232, 258 Sixes

1. Remove the drive belts, engine fan and hub assembly, accessory pulley, vibration damper and timing chain cover.
2. Remove the oil seal from the timing chain cover.
3. Remove the camshaft sprocket retaining bolt and washer.
4. Rotate the crankshaft until the timing mark on the crankshaft sprocket is closest to and in a center line with the timing pointer of the camshaft sprocket.
5. Remove the crankshaft sprocket, camshaft sprocket and timing chain as an assembly. Disassemble the chain and sprockets.

Installation is as follows:
1. Assemble the timing chain, crankshaft sprocket and camshaft sprocket with the timing marks aligned.
2. Install the assembly to the crankshaft and the camshaft.

Alignment of the timing chain sprockets timing marks on 232 and 258 Sixes.

364

3. Install the camshaft sprocket retaining bolt and washer and tighten to 45-55 ft lbs.
4. Install the timing chain cover and in a new oil seal.
5. Install the vibration damper, accessory pulley, engine fan and hub assembly and drive belts. Tighten the belts to the proper tension.

304, 360 and 401 V8s

1. Remove the timing chain cover and gasket.
2. Remove the crankshaft oil slinger.
3. Remove the camshaft sprocket retaining bolt and washer, distributor drive gear and fuel pump eccentric.
4. Rotate the crankshaft until the timing mark on the crankshaft sprocket is adjacent to, and on a center line with, the timing mark on the camshaft sprocket.
5. Remove the crankshaft sprocket, camshaft sprocket and timing chain as an assembly. Disassemble the chain and sprockets.

Alignment of the timing chain sprockets timing marks on the American Motors V8s.

Installation is as follows:
1. Assemble the timing chain, crankshaft sprocket and camshaft sprocket with the timing marks on both sprockets aligned.
2. Install the assembly to the crankshaft and the camshaft.
3. Install the fuel pump eccentric, distributor drive gear, washer and retaining bolt. Tighten the bolt to 25-35 ft lbs.
4. Install the crankshaft oil slinger.
5. Install timing chain cover using a new gasket and oil seal.

350 V8

1. Remove the timing chain cover, and rotate the crankshaft until the timing marks on both the crankshaft and camshaft sprockets are aligned.
2. Remove the crankshaft oil slinger from the crankshaft.

1 Camshaft sprocket 3 Timing chain
2 Crankshaft sprocket 4 Timing marks

Alignment of the timing chain sprockets timing marks on the 350 V8.

3. Remove the fuel pump eccentric from the face of the camshaft sprocket by removing the bolt, lockwasher and flat washer. Remove the distributor drive gear.
4. Pry the camshaft sprocket and the crankshaft sprocket forward a little at a time until the camshaft sprocket is free from the camshaft. Remove the timing chain from both sprockets.
5. Continue prying the crankshaft sprocket forward until it is free of the crankshaft.

To install the timing chain and sprockets:
6. If the engine has been disturbed while the timing chain was removed from the engine or the timing marks on both the sprockets were not aligned prior to being removed, then it is necessary to establish the correct valve timing.
7. Index the "0" marks on the camshaft and crankshaft sprockets on an imaginary line drawn vertically through the centerline of each sprocket. See Step 1.
8. Adjust the positioning of the crankshaft and camshaft so that the sprockets can be installed in the position described in Step 7.
9. Without disturbing the positioning of the indexed sprockets and

chain assembly, lift up the indexed assembly and slide the sprockets onto their shafts. Make sure the longer hubs of both sprockets face the block.

10. To check the assembly, rotate the crankshaft until the timing mark on the camshaft sprocket is on a horizontal line at either the 3 or 9 o'clock position. Count the number of links or pins on the timing chain between the two timing marks. There should be 10 links or 20 pins between the timing marks.

11. On the 350 V8, install the fuel pump eccentric and the distributor drive gear. Install the bolt and washer and torque to 50-55 ft lbs.

12. Install the oil slinger on the crankshaft with the flange facing outward. Install any timing chain cover studs that may have been removed and install the timing chain cover.

Pistons and Connecting Rods R & R

F4

1. Remove the cylinder head and the oil pan.
2. Remove the ridge from the tops of the cylinder bores, using a ridge reamer.
3. Remove the oil pan and, one at a time, remove the connecting rod caps and push the piston assemblies out the top of the block. Number all pistons, connecting rods, and caps on removal.
4. Remove the old rings with a ring expander.
5. Release the piston pin lockscrews and force out the pins.
6. Check the cylinder bores for distortion, taper, and other evidence of excessive wear. Bore and hone as necessary.
7. Assemble the piston to the rod by pushing in and locking the pin.
8. Using a ring expander, install the piston rings. Install the bottom (oil) ring first, center ring second, and top ring last.
9. Coat all the bearing surfaces and rings, and the piston skirt, with engine oil.
10. Turn down the crankpin of the cylinder being worked on.
11. Make sure that the gaps in the rings are not in line.
12. Using a ring compressor, install the piston and rod assembly into the cylinder with the connecting rod identifying number toward the camshaft and oil spray hole away from the camshaft. Carefully tap down until the rod bearing is solidly seated on the crankpin.

1 Oil spray hole
2 Piston skirt T-slot
3 Relative position of the camshaft

Piston and connecting rod assembly for the F4 engine.

13. Install the cap and lower bearing shell. Torque to the specified figure.
14. Install all piston assemblies in the same manner.
15. Install the cylinder head and oil pan.

225 V6

1. Remove the intake manifold, cylinder head(s) and the oil pan.
2. Examine the cylinder bores. If the bores are worn so that a shoulder or ridge exists at the top of the piston ring travel, remove the ridges with a ridge reamer.
3. Mark the cylinder number on all of the pistons, connecting rods and caps. Starting at the front end of the crankcase, the cylinders in the right bank are numbered 2-4-6, and in the left bank are numbered 1-3-5.
4. Remove the cap and lower connecting rod bearing half from the No. 1 connecting rod.
5. Push the piston and the rod assembly up and away from the crankshaft and remove it from the top of the cylinder bore. Install the cap and the lower bearing half on the connecting rod to avoid mixing the parts.
6. Remove each of the connecting rod and piston assemblies as described above.
7. When the piston and connecting rod assembly is properly installed, the oil spurt hole in the connecting rod will face the cam-

shaft. The rib on the edge of the bearing cap will be on the same side as the conical boss on the connecting rod web. These marks on the rib and boss will be toward the other connecting rod on the same crankpin. The notch on the piston will face the front of the engine.

8. Be certain that the cylinder bores, pistons, connecting rod bearings and crankshaft journals are clean. Coat all the bearing surfaces with engine oil.
9. Before installing a piston and connecting rod assembly into its bore, rotate the crankshaft so that the corresponding crankpin is moved downward, away from the cylinder bore.
10. Remove the bearing cap from the connecting rod. With the upper bearing half seated in the connecting rod, install connecting rod guides on the cap bolts. Lengths of rubber hose covering the bolts do a good job.
11. Be sure that the gap in the oil ring faces upward toward the center of the engine. The gaps of the compression rings are not to be aligned with each other or with the oil ring gap.
12. Lubricate the piston and rings with engine oil. Compress the rings around the piston with a suitable ring compressor. Install

Piston and rod assembly for the right bank in the 225 V6

Piston and rod assembly for the left bank in the 225 V6

the piston and connecting rod assembly from the top of the cylinder bore.

13. Install the connecting rod bearing cap with the lower half of the bearing shell in place on the connecting rod. Tighten the nuts to the proper torque.

14. Install the other piston and connecting rod assemblies in the same manner.

15. Check the end clearance between the connecting rods on each crankpin with a feeler gauge.

16. Assemble the oil pan, cylinder head(s) and intake manifold in the reverse order of removal.

232 and 258 Sixes

1. Remove the cylinder head cover and gasket.

2. Remove the rocker arm assemblies. If the engine is equipped with the individual bridged pivot type of rockers, back off each capscrew a turn at a time to prevent breaking the bridge.

3. Remove the push rods.

4. Remove the cylinder head and gasket.

5. Position the pistons one at a time near the bottom of their stroke and use a ridge reamer to remove any ridge from the top end of the cylinder walls.

6. Drain the engine oil.

7. Remove the oil pan and gaskets.

8. Remove the connecting rod bearing caps and inserts and retain them in the same order as removed. The connecting rods and caps are stamped with the number of the cylinder when they are installed.

9. Remove the connecting rod and piston assemblies through the top of the cylinder bores.

NOTE: Be careful the connecting rod bolts do not scratch the connecting rod journals or cylinder walls. Short pieces of rubber hose can be slipped over the rod bolts to prevent damage.

10. After thoroughly cleaning the cylinder bores, apply a light film of clean engine oil to the cylinder bores with a clean cloth.

11. Position the piston rings on the pistons with:
    a. Oil ring spacer gap on centerline of piston skirt.
    b. Oil ring rail gaps 180° apart on center line of piston pin.
    c. Second compression ring gap 180° from top oil rail gap.
    d. First compression ring gap 180° from second compression ring gap with at least 30° between each ring gap.

12. Lubricate the piston and rings with clean engine oil.

13. With the notch in the top of the piston facing forward and the oil squirt hole in the connecting rod

Install the piston and connecting rod assembly on 232 and 258 Sixes and all American Motors V8s. The notch in the top of the pistons must face forward.

facing the camshaft, use a piston ring compressor to install the connecting rod and piston assemblies through the top of the cylinder bores. Make sure you have the little pieces of hose over the connecting rod bolts so as not to scratch the cylinder bores or the crankshaft journals.

14. Install the connecting rod bearing caps and inserts in the same order as removed. Tighten the retaining nuts to 28 ft lbs.

15. Install the oil pan with new gaskets.
    Tighten the drain plug.

16. Install a new gasket and the cylinder head.

17. Install push rods.

18. Install the rocker assemblies.

19. Install the cylinder head cover and gasket.

20. Fill the crankcase with new oil.

V8 All

1. Remove the cylinder head covers.

2. Remove the rocker arms and bridged pivot assemblies, loosening each capscrew one turn at a time to avoid breaking the bridge.

3. Remove the push rods.

4. Remove the intake manifold assembly.

5. Remove the cylinder head and gasket.

6. Position the pistons, one at a time, near the bottom of their stroke and use a ridge reamer to remove any ridge from the top end of the cylinder walls.

7. Drain the engine oil.

8. Remove the oil pan.

9. Remove the connecting rod bearing caps and inserts. Keep these parts in the same order as they are removed. The connecting rods and caps are stamped with the number of the cylinder from which they are removed.

10. Remove the connecting rod and piston assemblies through the

Location of the connecting rod identifying numbers and the oil squirt hole on American Motors V8 engines. The numbers and the squirt hole are on the same side of the connecting rod on the 232 and 258 Sixes. In both cases, the oil squirt hole must face the camshaft when installed in the engine.

top of the cylinder bores. Be careful not to scratch the cylinder bores or the crankshaft connecting rod bearing journals with the connecting rod bolts. Install short pieces of rubber hose over the bolts for protection.

11. After thoroughly cleaning the cylinder bores, apply a light film of clean engine oil to the bores with a clean cloth.

12. Arrange the piston ring gaps around the piston as follows:
    a. Oil spacer gap on centerline of either skirt face.
    b. Oil rail gaps 180° apart and in line with piston pin centerline.
    c. Second compression ring gap 180° from top oil rail gap.
    d. First compression ring gap 180° from second compression ring gap.

13. Lubricate piston and ring surfaces with clean engine oil.

14. With the notch on the top of the pistons facing forward and the oil squirt hole in the connecting rod facing the camshaft, use a ring compressor to install the piston assemblies through the top of the cylinder bores. Place the lengths of rubber hose over the connecting rod bolts so to protect the cylinder bores and crankshaft bearing journals.

15. Install the connecting rod bearing caps and inserts in the same order as removed. Tighten the

1 Oil squirt hole facing camshaft
2 Boss on rod and cap facing forward (rearward on left side assembly)
3 Notch in piston facing forward

Piston and connecting rod assembly for the 350 V8 (right side).

nuts to the proper torque (see Torque Specifications).

16. Install the oil pan with new gaskets and tighten the drain plug.
17. Install the cylinder heads and gaskets.
18. Install the push rods and rocker assemblies.
19. Install the intake manifold assembly.
20. Install the cylinder head covers with new gaskets.
21. Fill the crankshaft with new oil.

Crankshaft Main Bearings

F4

The bearings are positioned and prevented from rotating in their supports in the cylinder block by dowel pins. Dowel pins are used in both the center and the rear bearing caps. No dowel pins are used in the front bearing cap because the bearing has a flange. The front main bearing takes the end thrust of the crankshaft. The main bearings are of premium type which provides long bearing life. They are replaceable and when correctly installed, provide proper clearance without filing, boring, scraping, or shimming. Crankshaft bearings can be removed from this engine only with the engine out of the vehicle. Crankshaft bearings must be replaced as a complete set of three bearings, each bearing consisting of two halves. Main bearings are available in the standard size and the following undersizes:

.001 in., .002 in., .010 in., .012 in., .020 in., .030 in.

The .001 in. and .002 in. undersize main bearings are for use with standard size crankshafts having slightly worn journals. The .010 in., .020 in., and .030 in. undersize bearings are for use with undersize crankshafts in those sizes. The .012 in. undersize bearings are for use with .010 in. undersize crankshafts having slightly worn journals. Bearing sizes are rubber stamped on the reverse side of each bearing half.

225 V6 and 350 V8

The crankshaft bearings consists of two halves which are neither alike nor interchangeable. One half is carried in the corresponding main bearing cap; the other half is located between the crankshaft and cylinder

block. The upper (cylinder block) half of the bearing is grooved to supply oil to the connecting rod bearings, while the lower (bearing cap) half of the bearing is not grooved. The two bearing halves must not be interchanged. All crankshaft bearings except the thrust bearing and the rear main bearing are identical. The thrust bearing (No. 3) (No. 2 on 225 V6) is longer and it is flanged to take crankshaft end thrust, and the rear main upper bearing groove does not extend the full length of the bearing. When the bearing halves are placed in cylinder block and bearing cap, the ends extend slightly beyond the parting surfaces. When cap bolts are tightened, the halves are clamped tightly in place to ensure positive seating and to prevent turning. The ends of bearing halves must never be filed flush with parting surface of crankshaft or bearing cap.

If the thrust bearing shell is disturbed or replaced it is necessary to line up the thrust surfaces of the bearing shell before the cap bolts are tightened. To do this, move the crankshaft fore and aft the limit of its travel several times (the last movement fore) with the bearing cap bolts finger tight.

Crankshaft bearings are the precision type which do not require reaming to size or other fitting. Shims are not provided for adjustment since worn bearings are readily replaced with new bearings of proper size. Bearings for service replacement are furnished in standard size and undersizes. Under no circumstances should crankshaft bearing caps be filed to adjust for wear in the old bearings.

232 and 258 Sixes

The crankshaft main bearings are steel-backed, micro-babbit, precision type. Each bearing is selectively fitted to its respective journal to obtain the desired operating clearance. In production, the select fit is obtained by using various sized color coded vearing inserts. The color code appears on the edge of the insert. Bearing size is not stamped on the inserts used in production.

The main bearing journal size is identified in production by a color coded paint mark on the adjacent cheek toward the rear end of the crankshaft, except for the rear main

journal which is on the crankshaft rear flange.

When required, different sized upper and lower bearing inserts may be used as a pair. A standard size insert is sometimes used in combination with a 0.001 in. undersize insert to reduce clearance by 0.0005 in.

NOTE: Never use bearing inserts in pairs with greater than 0.001 in. difference in size. When replacing inserts, all the odd size inserts must be either on the top (in the block) or the bottom (in the main bearing cap).

Service replacement bearing inserts are available as pairs in the following sizes: standard, 0.001, 0.002, 0.010, and 0.012 in. undersize. The size on these service replacement bearings is stamped on the back of the inserts.

NOTE: The 0.012 in. undersize insert is not used in production.

204, 360, and 401 V8

The main bearing caps are numbered from front to rear 1 through 5, with an arrow indicating forward. The upper inserts are grooved while the lower inserts have a smooth surface on the 304 and 360 V8. The 401 V8 has a groove in both the upper and lower insert.

Each bearing is a select fit to its respective journal to obtain the desired operating clearance. In production the select fit is obtained by using various sized color coded bearing inserts. The bearing code color appears on the edge of the insert. The bearing size is not stamped on production inserts.

The main bearing journal size is identified in production by a color coded paint mark on the adjacent cheek toward the rear end of the crankshaft except for the rear main journal. The paint mark for the rear main journal is on the crankshaft rear flange.

When required, different sized upper and lower bearing inserts may be used as a pair to reduce clearance by 0.0005 in.

NOTE: When using upper and lower inserts of different sizes, install all the same size inserts together either on the top (block) or bottom (bearing cap). Never use bearing inserts with greater than 0.001 in. difference in pairs.

Main Bearing Fitting Chart (232 and 258 Sixes)

Crankshaft Main Bearing Journal Color Code and Diameter in Inches (Journal Size)		Bearing Color Code			
		Upper Insert Size		Lower Insert Size	
Yellow	— 2.5001 to 2.4996 (Standard)	Yellow	— Standard	Yellow	— Standard
Orange	— 2.4996 to 2.4991 (0.0005 Undersize)	Yellow	— Standard	Black	— .001-inch Undersize
Black	— 2.4991 to 2.4986 (0.001 Undersize)	Black	— .001-inch Undersize	Black	— .001-inch Undersize
Green	— 2.4986 to 2.4981 (0.0015 Undersize)	Black	— .001-inch Undersize	Green	— .002-inch Undersize
Red	— 2.4901 to 2.4896 (0.010 Undersize)	Red	— .010-inch Undersize	Red	— .010-inch Undersize

Main Bearing Fitting Chart (304, 360, and 401 V8)

Crankshaft Main Bearing Journal Color Code and Diameter (Journal Size)		Bearing Color Code			
		Upper Insert Size		Lower Insert Size	
Yellow	— 2.7489 to 2.7484 in.	Yellow	— Standard	Yellow	— Standard
Orange	— 2.7484 to 2.7479 in.	Yellow	— Standard	Black	— .001-in. undersize
Black	— 2.7479 to 2.7474 in.	Black	— .001-in. undersize	Black	— .001-in. undersize
Green	— 2.7474 to 2.7469 in.	Black	— .001-in. undersize	Green	— .002-in. undersize
Red	— 2.7389 to 2.7384 in.	Red	— .010-in. undersize	Red	— .010-in. undersize

Service replacement bearings are available as pairs in the following sizes: standard, 0.001, 0.002, 0.010, and 0.012 in. undersize. The size on the service replacement inserts is stamped on the back of the inserts.

NOTE: The 0.012 in. undersize inserts are not used in production.

Connecting Rod Bearings

F4

The connecting rod bearings, like the crankshaft main bearings, are of the replaceable type. When correctly installed, the bearings provide proper clearance without filing, boring, scraping, or shimming.

Main bearings with maximum wearing surfaces are obtained through the use of offset connecting rods. When the rods are installed, the offset is placed away from the nearest main bearing.

The oil spray hole should be on the "follow" side or away from the camshaft, toward the right side of the vehicle. Because of the offset and oil spray hole, No. 1 and 2 or No. 3 and 4 connecting rods cannot be interchanged for if they are reversed, the oil spray hole will be on the wrong side. No. 1 and 3 or No. 2 and 4 can be interchanged.

Connecting rod bearings should be replaced as a complete set. Each bearing consists of two halves. Connecting rod bearing sets are available in standard size and the following undersize:

.001 in., .002 in., .010 in., .012 in., .020 in., .030 in.

The .001 and .002 in. undersize bearings are for use with standard size crankshafts having slightly worn crankpins that do not requre grinding. The .012 in. undersize bearings are for use with slightly worn crankshafts that have been previously ground for .010 in. undersize bearings.

Should it be necessary to replace the bearings due to wear, replacement of piston rings and piston pins is also recommended.

232 and 258 Sixes, 304, 360 and 401 V8

the connecting rod bearings are steel-backed aluminum-alloy, precision type.

Each bearing is selectively fitted to its respective journal to obtain the desired operating clearance. In production, the select fit is obtained by using various sized, color coded bearing inserts. The color code appears on the edge of the insert. Bearing size is not stamped on production inserts.

The rod journal size is identified in production by a color coded paint mark on the adjacent cheek or counterweight toward the rear end of the crankshaft.

When required, different sized upper and lower bearing inserts may be used as a pair, thus reducing clearance by 0.0005 in.

NOTE: Never use a pair of bearing inserts with more than 0.001 in. difference in size.

Service replacement bearing inserts are available as pairs in the following sizes: standard, 0.001, 0.002, 0.010, and 0.012 in. undersize. The bearing size is stamped on the back of the service replacement bearing inserts.

NOTE: The 0.002 and 0.012 in. undersize inserts are not used in production.

Connecting Rod Bearing Fitting Chart (232 and 258 Sixes)
(in.)

Crankshaft Connecting Rod Journal Color and Diameter in Inches (Journal Size)		Bearing Color Code			
		Upper Insert Size		Lower Insert Size	
Yellow	— 2.0955 to 2.0948 (Standard)	Yellow	— Standard	Yellow	— Standard
Orange	— 2.0948 to 2.0941 (0.0007 Undersize)	Yellow	— Standard	Black	— .001 Undersize
Black	— 2.0941 to 2.0934 (0.0014 Undersize)	Black	— .001-Inch Undersize	Black	— .001 Undersize
Red	— 2.0855 to 2.0848 (0.010 Undersize)	Red	— .010-Inch Undersize	Red	— .010 Undersize

Connecting Rod Bearing Fitting Chart (304, 360 and 401 V8)
(in.)

Crankshaft Connecting Rod Journal Color and Diameter in Inches (Journal Size)		Bearing Color Code			
		Upper Insert Size		Lower Insert Size	
		304-360 CID Engines			
Yellow	— 2.0955 to 2.0948 (Standard)	Yellow	— Standard	Yellow	— Standard
Orange	— 2.0948 to 2.0941 (0.0007 Undersize)	Yellow	— Standard	Black	— .001 Undersize
Black	— 2.0941 to 2.0934 (0.0014 Undersize)	Black	— .001-inch Undersize	Black	— .001 Undersize
Red	— 2.0855 to 2.0848 (0.010 Undersize)	Red	— .010-inch Undersize	Red	— .010 Undersize

Connecting Rod Bearing Fitting Chart (304, 360 and 401 V8)
(in.)

Crankshaft Connecting Rod Journal Color and Diameter in Inches (Journal Size)	Bearing Color Code			
	Upper Insert Size		Lower Insert Size	
	401 CID Engine			
Yellow — 2.2485 to 2.2478 (Standard)	Yellow	— Standard	Yellow	— Standard
Orange — 2.2478 to 2.2471 (0.0007 Undersize)	Yellow	— Standard	Black	— .001 Undersize
Black — 2.2471 to 2.2464 (0.0014 Undersize)	Black	— .001-inch Undersize	Black	— .001 Undersize
Red — 2.2385 to 2.2378 (0.010 Undersize)	Red	— .010-inch Undersize	Red	— .010 Undersize

Rear Main Bearing Oil Seal R & R

F4

1. Drain the oil from the engine and remove the oil pan.
2. Remove the screws and lock-washers that attach the rear main bearing cap to the cylinder block.
3. Remove the bearing cap with a lifting bar to pry the cap off of the mounting dowels. Do not apply too much pressure to the cap. Lift the cap off a little at a time from one side to the other until the cap is removed.
4. Remove the two pieces of rear main bearing cap packing out of position between the side of the bearing cap and the cylinder block.
5. Remove the lower half of the oil seal from the bearing cap and install a new half.
   NOTE: Coat the seal with oil to facilitate installation.
6. Remove the upper half of the seal by pushing it out with a suitable tool.
7. Coat the new seal with oil and, using a wire to pull it around the crankshaft, install the new upper half of the seal.
   NOTE: For better sealing, make the joints of the seal off-set from the joints of the rear main bearing cap and the cylinder block.
8. Reinstall the bearing cap, being careful not to bend the dowel pins and making sure that the seal is inserted correctly. Tighten to the correct torque.
9. Apply a small amount of plastic type gasket cement to the rubber packings to be inserted into the holes between the bearing cap and the crankcase. Insert the packings in these holes. Do not trim the packings. They are trimmed to the correct length at the time of manufacture. They will protrude about 1/4 in. from the crankcase. When the oil pan is installed, it will force them tightly into the holes and seal any spaces between the bearing cap and the crankcase.
10. Reinstall the oil pan and fill the crankcase with the correct amount of oil.

225 V6

1. Remove the oil pan and the crankshaft. When the rear main bearing cap is removed, remove the fabric packing type seal from the radius portion of the cap and the neoprene seals from the grooves on the side of the cap.
2. With an ice pick or similar tool pry the upper half of the seal from the block.
3. Place the new seal in the groove in the rear main bearing cap with both ends protruding above the parting surface of the cap. Force the seal into the groove by rubbing down with a hammer handle or similar tool until the seal projects above the groove no more than 1/16 in. Cut the ends off flush with the mating surface of the cap with a razor blade. Lubricate the seal with engine oil just before installing it in the engine.
4. Lubricate all of the main bearings and install the crankshaft. Install all the main bearing caps and tighten them to the correct torque.
5. Dip the neoprene main bearing cap side seals in kerosene (any light oil will do) for 1½ minutes. This will cause the seals to swell; so you will have to work quickly. Install the seals into the bearing cap grooves. The protruding ends of the seals should then be squirted with kerosene (or oil), wiped off, and peened over with a hammer to be sure of a seal at the upper mating surface of the cap and cylinder block.
   NOTE: Do not cut the seals to length before installing them.
6. Attach the connecting rods to the crankshaft and install the oil pan in the reverse order of removal.

232 and 258 Sixes, 304, 350, 360, and 401 V8

1. Remove the engine from the vehicle.
2. Remove the timing chain cover and the crankshaft timing gear.
3. Remove the oil pan, oil float support and the oil float.
4. Slide the crankshaft thrust washer and all of the end-play adjusting shims off the front end of the crankshaft.
5. Move the two pieces of the rear main bearing cap packing away from the side of the bearing cap and the cylinder block.
6. You will now be able to see the marks on the bearing caps and the cylinder block for bearing number and position.
7. Remove the screws and lock-washers that attach the main bearing caps to the cylinder block. Use a lifting bar beneath the ends of each bearing cap. Be careful not to exert too much pressure which could damage the cap or the dowels they fit onto. Lift each cap evenly on both sides until free of the dowels. If there is any reason to believe that any of the dowels have become bent during bearing cap removal, remove them and install new dowels. Remove the connecting rod caps and bearings.
8. Remove the crankshaft.
9. Remove the upper half of the rear main bearing oil seal from the cylinder block and the lower half from the oil seal groove in the rear main bearing cap.
10. Install the main bearing caps and bearings on the cylinder block in their original positions.
11. Reassemble the engine in reverse order of the above procedure.
    NOTE: It is possible to replace the rear main rubber seal without removing the crankshaft. The procedure is as follows:

1. Loosen the crankshaft cap bolts and lower the crankshaft not more than 1/32 in. Remove the rear main bearing cap. Do not turn the crankshaft while it is loosened.
2. Push the seal around the groove until it can be gripped and removed with a pair of pliers.
3. Coat the new seal with clean motor oil and slide it into the groove until 3/8 in. protrudes from the groove. On American Motors engines push the seal

LIP OF SEAL

OUTSIDE OF SEAL

PERMATEX NO. 2 TOP AND BOTTOM BOTH SIDES OF SEAL

PERMATEX NO. 2 ON CHAMFERED EDGES

PERMATEX NO. 2 ON CHAMFERED EDGES

Rear main oil seal on 232 and 258 Sixes and American Motors V8s.

around until its ends are flush with the block.

4. Install the other half of the seal in the bearing cap with ⅜ in. protruding from the opposite side. This is so that the juncture of the two halves of the seal is not at the same point as the juncture of the bearing cap and the cylinder block. On American Motors engines install the seal so that the ends are flush.

5. Install the rear main bearing cap and tighten all the caps to the proper torque. Be sure that the caps have not fallen out of place and that they are tightened in a straight manner.

Oil Pan R & R

Due to the variety of engines used in 1970-71 Jeep vehicles, removal and installation procedures for the oil pan could range from simply removing the attaching screws to removing front end components for access.

On 1972 and later CJ and Commando models equipped with 232 and 258 Sixes, remove the starter, drain the oil pan and disconnect the right engine support cushion bracket from the engine block and raise the engine with a jack placed under the transmission bell housing. The oil pan can then be removed with sufficient clearance.

On all 1972 and later Jeep vehicles equipped with V8 engines, simply drain the oil pan, remove the starter motor, and remove the oil pan.

In all cases, install the oil pan in the reverse order of removal.

Front Axle, Suspension

Refer to the Drive Axles General Repair Section for application, troubleshooting overhaul, and specifications.

370

Front Spring R & R
Prior to 1972

1. Raise the vehicle with a jack under the axle and place a jackstand under the frame side rail. Then lower the axle jack so that the load is relieved from the spring and the wheels rest on the floor.
2. Remove the nuts which secure the spring clip bolts. Remove the spring plate and clip bolts. Free the spring from the axle by raising the axle jack.
3. Remove the pivot bolt nut and drive out the pivot bolt. Disconnect the shackle either by removing the lower nuts and bolts on the rubber-bushed shackles, or by removing the threaded bushings on the U-shackles.
4. To replace, first install the pivot bolt. Then, connect the shackle using the following procedures.
5. On bronze-bushed pivot bolts, install the bolt and nut and tighten the nut. Then back it off two cotter pin slots and install the cotter pin. The nut must be drawn up tightly but must be sufficiently loose to allow the spring to pivot freely. Otherwise the spring might break.
6. On rubber-bushed pivot bolts and locknuts (or lockwasher and nut), only tighten the bolt enough to hold the bushings in position until the vehicle is lowered from the jack.
7. Connect the shackle. On rubber-bushed shackles install the bolts as in Step 6 above. For U-shackles, insert the shackle through the frame bracket and eye of the spring. Holding the U-shackle tightly against the frame, start the upper bushing on the shackle, taking care that when it enters the thread in the frame it does not cross-thread. Screw the bushing on the shackle tightly against the spring eye and thread the bushing in approximately half way. Then, alternately from top bushing to lower bushing, turn them in until the head of the bushing is snug against the frame bracket and the bushing in the spring eye is 1/32 in. away from the spring as measured from the inside of the hexagon head to the spring. Lubricate the bushing and then-try the flex of the shackle, which must be free. If a shackle is tight, rethread the bushings on the shackle.
8. Move the axle into position on the spring by lowering or raising the axle jack. Install the spring clip bolts, spring plate, lockwashers, and nuts. Torque the nuts to

50-55 ft lbs. Avoid over-tightening. Be sure the spring is free to move at both ends.
9. Remove both jacks. On rubber bushed shackles and pivot bolts, allow the weight of the vehicle to seat the bushings in their operating positions. Then torque the nuts to 27-30 ft lbs.

1972 and Later

1. Raise the vehicle with a jack under the axle. Place a jackstand under the frame side rail. Then lower the axle jack so the load is relieved from the spring and the wheels rest slightly on the floor.
2. Disconnect the shock absorber from the spring clip plate.
3. Remove the nuts which secure the spring clips (U-bolts). Remove the spring plate and spring clips. Free the spring from the axle by raising the axle.
4. Remove the pivot bolt nut and drive out the pivot bolt. Disconnect the shackle from the shackle bracket by removing the lock nut, lock nut and bolt or nut, or lockwasher and bolt.
5. With the spring removed, the spring shackle and/or shackle plate may be removed from the spring by removing the lock nut, lock nut and shackle bolt or nut, or lockwasher and shackle bolt.
6. Inspect the bushings in the eye of the main spring leaf and the bushings of the spring shackle for excessive wear. Replace if necessary.
7. The spring can be disassembled, for replacing an individual spring leaf, by removing the clips and the center bolt.
8. To install the spring on the vehicle with the bushings in place and the spring shackle attached to the springs, position the spring in the pivot hanger and install the pivot bolt and lock nut. Only tighten the lock nut enough to hold the bushings in position until the vehicle is lowered from the jack.
9. Position the spring and install the shackle, shackle bolts, shackle plate if applicable, lockwasher, and nuts. Only finger tighten the nuts at this time.
10. Move the axle into position on the spring by lowering the axle jack. Place the spring center bolt in the axle saddle hole. Install the spring clips, spring plate, lockwashers and nuts. Torque the 7 1/6 in. nuts to 36-42 ft lbs and the ½ in. nuts to 45-65 ft lbs.

NOTE: Be sure that the center bolt is properly centered in the axle saddle.

11. Connect the shock absorber.
12. Remove the axle and allow the

weight of the vehicle to seat the bushings in their operating positions. Then torque the 7/16 in. spring pivot bolt nuts and spring shackle nuts to 25-40 ft lbs. Torque the 5/8 in. shackle nuts to 55-75 ft lbs.

Axle Shaft R & R

Without Disc Brakes

1. Remove the wheel.
2. Remove the hub dust cap.
3. Remove the axle shaft drive flange snap ring.
4. Remove the axle shaft driving flange bolts.
5. Apply and hold the foot brakes. Remove the axle shaft flange with a puller.
6. Release the lip on the lockwasher, remove the outer nut, lockwasher, adjusting nut, and bearing lockwasher. Use a special wrench for these nuts.
7. Remove the wheel hub and drum assembly with the bearings.
8. Remove the hydraulic brake tube, backing plate screws, and backing plate.
9. Remove the spindle and spindle bearing.
10. Remove the axle shaft and universal joint assembly.
11. Install in reverse order. Tighten the wheel bearing adjusting nut with the special wrench until there is a slight drag on the bearings, then back off about 1/4-1/6 of a turn.

With Disc Brakes

1. Raise and support the vehicle.
2. Remove the wheel and dust cover.
3. Remove the axle shaft snap ring, drive flange, pressure spring and spring retainer. If the drive flange is stuck to the shaft, use a screwdriver to pry it out.
4. Use the special nut wrench to remove the wheel bearing locknut, lockring, and wheel bearing adjusting nut.
5. Remove the two bolts securing the brake caliper assembly to the disc brake shield and move the caliper assembly aside.
6. Remove the rotor and hub assembly. The spring retainer and outer wheel bearing will slide out as the hub assembly is removed.
7. Remove the nuts and bolts attaching the spindle and disc brake shield.
8. Remove the spindle and disc brake shield. It may be necessary to tap the spindle lightly to free it.
9. Remove the axle shaft.
10. Install the new axle shaft, spindle, and bearing assembly.
11. Install the hub, brake shield, rotor, and the brake caliper as-

sembly.
12. Install the inner wheel bearing adjusting nut. This is the nut with the peg on the side. Tighten the nut to 50 ft lbs with the special wheel bearing nut wrench. Rotate the hub and back off the adjusting nut 1/4 turn maximum.
13. Install the lockwasher with the inner tab lined up with the keyway spindle. Turn the inner adjusting nut until the peg engages the nearest hole in the lockwasher. Install the outer locknut and tighten it to 50 ft lbs. Install the spring retainer, pressure spring and drive flange.
14. Push the drive flange inward to provide clearance and install the axle shaft snap ring.
15. Install the wheel and dust cover and lower the vehicle.

Steering Gear

Manual Steering Gear

Refer to the Manual Steering Gear General Repair Section for troubleshooting and overhaul procedures.

Steering Gear R & R

1. Remove the bolt and nut attaching the coupling to the wormshaft, disconnecting the steering gear from the lower steering shaft.
2. Disconnect the steering arm from the connecting rod using a puller.
3. Remove the upper steering gear-to-frame bracket bolt.
4. Remove the two lower steering gear-to-frame bracket bolts and remove the steering gear.
5. Install in the reverse order.

Power Steering Gear

Refer to the Power Steering Gear General Repair Section for troubleshooting and overhaul procedures. Power steering pump services are also covered in the general repair section.

Steering Gear R & R

1. Disconnect the hoses from the return port and pressure port. Raise the hoses above the level of the pump to prevent any further lose of power steering fluid.
2. On CJ models, disconnect the intermediate shaft coupling at the steering gear stub shaft. On the other models, disconnect the flexible coupling at the intermediate shaft.
3. Remove the pitman arm nut, lockwasher, and remove the pit-

man arm using a puller.
4. Remove the mounting bolts attaching the steering gear assembly to the frame, and remove the steering gear assembly.
5. To install the steering gear, mount the steering gear on the frame and install the attaching bolts, tightening them to 65 ft lbs.
6. Install the pitman arm on the pitman shaft and install the lockwasher and pitman arm nut. Tighten the nut to 190 ft lbs.
7. On CJ models, connect the stub shaft to the intermediate shaft. Tighten the clamp bolt to 40 ft lbs.
8. On the other models, install the flexible coupling on the stub shaft, if it was removed, and tighten the clamp to 30 ft lbs. Connect the intermediate shaft to the flexible coupling and tighten the attaching bolts and nuts to 20 ft lbs.
9. Connect the hoses to the gear and tighten the hose fittings to 30 ft lbs.
10. Check the level of the fluid in the reservoir and add as necessary.

Power Steering Pump R & R

Before working on the power steering pump, clean the exterior of the pump and the reservoir assembly.

NOTE: On all engines except the pre-1972 232 Six, the power steering pump need not be removed to service the pressure relief/flow control valve. The valve is located behind a pressure union on all the other engines, except the pre-1971 232 Six with a Thompson pump. The pressure relief valve in the Thompson unit is removed after the pump has been disassembled.

1. Loosen the drive belt tension adjustment bolt and remove the belt (power steering and air pump, if so equipped).
2. Place a receptacle under the pump/reservoir assembly and disconnect the pressure and return hoses from the pump. Fluid will drain out of the pump and hoses. Lay the ends of the hoses up higher than the steering gear to prevent all of the fluid from draining out. Cover the ends of the hoses to prevent dirt from entering.
3. Remove either the bolts that hold the pump to the mounting bracket or the bolts that hold the bracket and pump to the engine, whichever is easiest. Remove the pump from the engine.
4. Install the pump in the reverse order of removal and install the correct type and amount of fluid.

Clutch

CJ Models Pre-1972

Vehicles with the F-head engine have a 8½ or 9¼ in. clutch plate. The clutch is either a three pressure spring, three fingered Auburn clutch or a six pressure spring, three fingered Rockford clutch.

Jeeps with the V6 engine have a General Motors diaphragm type clutch.

Commando, Wagoneer, and Truck Pre-1972

The clutch installed in pre-1971 Commandos is either a 3-pressure-springed, 3-fingered, 9¼ in. diameter Auburn clutch installed behind the F-Head engine with 1150 lbs of plate pressure or, a diaphragm type, 10.4 in. diameter G.M. clutch installed behind the V6 engine with 1600 lbs of plate pressure.

The clutch installed in the pre-1971 Wagoneers are as follows:

Behind the 232 Six, there is a Borg & Beck, 10½ in. diameter, 9-pressure-springed, 3-fingered clutch with 1350 lbs of plate pressure.

The clutch installed behind the 350 V8 is a G.M. diaphragm type, 11 in. in diameter with 2450-2750 lbs of plate pressure.

All Models 1972 and Later

A single plate, dry disc-type clutch is used with two types of steel covers; a 10½ in. diameter direct spring pressure type and an 11 in. diameter semi-centrifugal type. Both types are similar in function in that they both apply direct spring pressure to the pressure plate. But, the semicentrifugal cover also utilizes six rollers that are forced outward by centrifugal force to apply extra force to the pressure plate and provide extra positive clutch engagement.

Clutch Pedal Free-Play Adjustment

CJ Prior to 1972

When sufficient wear occurs, the pedal clearance must be adjusted to 1-1½ in. The free pedal clearance is adjusted by lengthening or shortening the clutch fork cable. To make this adjustment, loosen the jam nut on the cable clevis and lengthen or shorten the cable to obtain the proper clearance at the pedal pad, then tighten the jam nut.

CJ and Commando—1972 Only

The clutch pedal has an adjustable stop located on the pedal support bracket directly behind the instrument cluster.

1 Throwout bearing
2 Throwout bearing carrier spring
3 Bracket
4 Dust seal
5 Ball stud
6 Pad
7 Retainer
8 Control tube spring
9 Control lever and tube
10 Ball stud and bracket
11 Frame bracket
12 Ball stud nut
13 Yoke locknut
14 Adjusting yoke
15 Bolt
16 Pedal release rod
17 Pedal clamp bolt
18 Control cable
19 Clutch pedal
20 Screw and lockwasher
21 Draft pad
22 Pedal pad and shank
23 Retracting spring
24 Pedal to shaft key
25 Washer
26 Pedal shaft
27 Master cylinder tie bar
28 Control lever
29 Bearing carrier

Clutch linkage on CJ models prior to 1972.

Adjust the stop to provide the specified clearance between the top of the pedal pad and the closest point on the bare floor pan. The distance must be 8 in.

1. Lift up the clutch pedal against the pedal support bracket stop.
2. Unhook the clutch fork return spring.
3. Loosen the ball adjusting nut until some cable slack exists.
4. Adjust the ball adjusting nut until the slack is removed from the cable and the clutch throwout bearing contacts the pressure plate fingers.

Pre-1971 Commando

There are two types of clutch linkage used on pre-1971 Commandos: the cross-shaft tube and lever type and the clutch control cable type. Both use a cable to actuate the release and engagement of the clutch.

To adjust the cross-shaft lever and tube type linkage:

1. With the clutch cross-shaft tube and lever assembly positioned at a 52° angle for the F-Head engine and 58° angle for the V6 engine, adjust the clutch control cable assembly from the clutch pedal to the cross-shaft lever, making sure that the clutch pedal is against the pedal support bracket stop.
2. With the cross-shaft assembly positioned as above, push the clutch housing release lever rearward, until the clutch throwout bearing contacts the clutch pressure plate release levers or diaphragm plate.
3. Adjust the clutch fork cable from the release lever to the clutch cross-shaft lever, until the cable clevis just enters the lever hold.

1 Retainer
2 Cable housing
3 Support bracket
4 Retracting spring
5 Clutch pedal assembly
6 Cross shaft tube
7 Pull-back spring
8 Frame bracket
9 Clutch control cable
10 Cable bracket
11 Clutch fork control lever
12 Clutch fork cable
13 Jam nut

Clutch linkage—Jeepster (© Willys Corp.)

arm of the clutch pedal cross-shaft is at a 30° angle with a 350 V8 and 49° with a 232 Six and 327 V8, in relation to the top of the left frame side rail.

4. To adjust clutch pedal free-play, adjust the cross-shaft-to-throwout lever link, so that the clutch pedal can be depressed 1 in. before the clutch starts to disengage.

NOTE: There is a special tool available for setting the angle of the arm of the clutch pedal cross-shaft as outlined in Step 3 of the above procedure. Tool W-341 is for the vehicle equipped with a 350 V8 and gives the 30° angle and tool W-317 is for the vehicle equipped with a 232 Six and gives the 49° angle.

1972 Wagoneer

1. The clutch pedal has an adjustable stop located on the pedal support bracket, directly behind the instrument cluster. Adjust the stop to provide 8⅜ in. between the top of the pedal pad and the closest point, 90° on the bare floor pan.
2. Lift the clutch pedal up against the pedal support bracket stop.
3. Unhook the clutch fork return spring.
4. Loosen the ball adjusting nut until some cable slack exists.
5. Adjust the ball adjusting nut until the slack is removed from the cable and the clutch throwout bearing contacts the pressure fingers.
6. Back off the ball adjusting nut ¾ of a turn to provide free-play.
7. Tighten the jam nut.
8. Hook the clutch fork return spring.

All Models 1973-76

1. Adjust the bellcrank outer support bracket to provide about ⅛

4. Remove the clevis pin and lengthen the cable 2½ turns of the clevis for the V6 engine and 3 turns for the F-Head engine, to obtain about ¾ in. of freeplay.
5. Release the clutch lever and insert the cable clevis pin and lock the clevis jam nut.

To adjust the clutch control cable type linkage:
1. With the clutch pedal against the pedal support bracket stop, adjust the ball adjusting nut until the slack is removed from the cable and the clutch throwout bearing contacts the clutch pressure plate, release levers or diaphragm plate.
2. Loosen the ball adjusting nut 2½ turns to obtain about ¼ in. of free-play.
3. Lock the hex nut.

Pre-1972 Wagoneer

1. Disconnect the adjustable rod from the clutch pedal.
2. Adjust the clutch pedal stop bolt for a positive overcenter position. This is done by turning the bolt in or out of the crossmember to obtain ¼-½ in. of clutch pedal travel before the overcenter spring assists the pedal to the floorboard. The pedal may be ⅜-⅝ in. higher than the pad on the brake pedal. This is a normal condition.
3. With the clutch pedal resting against the stop bolt, adjust the length of the adjustable rod by turning the ball joint in or out on the rod, so that when the adjustable rod is connected, the

Clutch linkage for 1972 Commandos and CJs (© Jeep Corp)

A Pedal height adjustment point
B Cross shaft arm position adjustment
C Clutch pedal free play adjustment
D Special tool for adjusting angle of clutch pedal cross shaft

Clutch linkage adjustment on Pre-1971 Wagoneers.

Clutch linkage on a 1972 Wagoneer (© Jeep Corp)

in. of bellcrank end play.

2. Lift up the clutch pedal against the pedal stop.

3. On the clutch push rod (pedal-to-bellcrank), adjust the lower ball pivot assembly onto or off the rod, as required, to position the bellcrank inner lever parallel to the front face of the clutch housing (slightly forward from vertical).

NOTE: There is no lower ball pivot assembly on 1976 CJ models, so step 3 does not apply.

4. Adjust the clutch fork release rod (bellcrank-to-release fork) to obtain the maximum specified

clutch pedal free play of ¾ in. on 1973-74 models and 1 in. on 1975-76 models.

Clutch R & R

Pre-1971 CJ and Commando —F4

1. Remove the transmission and transfer case from the vehicle.
2. Remove the flywheel housing.
3. Mark the clutch pressure plate and engine flywheel with a center punch so that the clutch assembly can be reinstalled in the same position after adjustments or replacement are completed.

4. Remove the clutch pressure plate bracket bolts equally, a little at a time, to prevent distortion and to relieve the clutch springs evenly.

5. Remove the pressure plate assembly and clutch disc from the flywheel. Before the clutch is reinstalled, it should be inspected for warpage. If grease or oil is evident on the disc friction facings, the facings should be replaced and the cause of the oil accumulation corrected.

6. Put a small amount of cup grease in the flywheel pilot bushing and install the clutch disc with the short end of the hub toward the flywheel. Next, place the pressure plate assembly in position.

7. With a clutch disc aligning arbor or a spare transmission mainshaft, align the clutch disc splines leaving the arbor in position while tightening the pressure plate screws evenly.

8. Assemble the flywheel housing to the engine and reinstall the transmission and transfer case. Make sure that the clutch release bearing carrier return spring is hooked in place.

9. Assemble the rest of the components in the reverse order of removal. Adjust the clutch control cable so that there is 1 in. of free pedal travel.

Pre-1971 CJ and Commando— 225 V6

1. Remove the transmission.
2. Remove the clutch throwout bearing and pedal return spring from the clutch fork.
3. Remove the flywheel housing from the engine.
4. Disconnect the clutch fork from the ball stud by forcing it toward the center of the vehicle.
5. Mark the clutch cover and flywheel with a center punch so that the cover can later be installed in the same position on the flywheel. This is necessary to maintain engine balance.
6. Loosen the clutch attaching bolts alternately, one turn at a time, to avoid distorting the clutch cover flange, until the diaphragm spring is released.
7. Support the pressure plate and cover assembly while removing the last bolts.
8. Remove the pressure plate and clutch disc from the flywheel.

NOTE: Use extreme care to keep the clutch disc clean.

Before installing the clutch, lubricate the inner surface of the pilot bushing in the crankshaft; the splines of the transmission drive gear shaft, sliding the clutch disc over the shaft and wiping off excess lubricant; the front bearing retainer of the

Clutch linkage for 1973-76 Wagoneers and Cherokees (© Jeep Corp).

b. Tighten the clutch attaching bolts alternately, so that the clutch is drawn into position squarely on the flywheel. Turn each bolt one turn at a time to avoid bending the clutch cover flange. Tighten the attaching bolts to 30-40 ft lbs.

c. Be certain the dowel pins on the flywheel housing are installed in the cylinder block when the housing is installed.

Pre-1971 Wagoneer—350 V8

Remove and install the clutch in the same manner as outlined under "Pre-1971 CJ and Commando—225 V6."

Pre-1971 Wagoneer—232 Six

Remove and install the clutch in the same manner as outlined under "Pre-1971 CJ and Commando—F4."

1971-76 All Models

1. Remove the transmission.
2. Remove the starter, throwout bearing and sleeve assembly and clutch housing.
3. Mark the clutch cover, pressure plate and flywheel with a center punch to insure correct alignment during assembly.
4. Loosen the attaching screws in sequence, one or two turns at a time until the spring tension on the cover is released. This is to prevent the clutch cover from becoming warped, which could result in clutch chatter when reinstalled.
5. Install the clutch in the reverse order of removal, tighten the attaching bolts of the cover in sequence, one or two turns at a time to 40 ft lbs.

NOTE: The clutch pedal is not to be depressed until the transmission has been installed.

Transfer Cases

Refer to the Transfer Case General Repair Section for troubleshooting and overhaul procedures.

Linkage Adjustments

Spicer Model 18 (Pre-1972 CJ Only)

An adjustment nut is provided on the shift rod at the base of the shifter lever. Adjust the length of the link to provide ½ in. clearance between the floor pan and the shift lever bend when the shift lever is moved to the 4WD Low position.

Spicer Model 20

The shifter rails of the transfer case lever assembly connect to the shifter rails of the transfer case either directly or through non-adjust-

Shift linkage adjustment.

able links. The linkage should be lubricated periodically.

Warner Quadra-Trac

Since the Quadra-Trac system is a "full time 4WD" system, and is constantly engaged in 4WD, there is no "shift linkage" as such. There are two features which can be operated manually concerning the transfer case: the "Lock-Out" feature and the engagement of the optional "Low Range Reduction Unit."

Since the "Lock-Out" feature is a vacuum actuated unit, there are no external adjustments that can be made other than making sure that all vacuum lines are in place, connected and not damaged in any way.

The reduction unit is actuated by a shift cable and can be adjusted in the following manner:

1. Loosen the nut which clamps the cable to the shift lever pivot. Be sure that the cable can move freely in the pivot.
2. Move the reduction shift lever to the most rearward detent position (Hi-Range position).
3. Push the Low Range lever inward until it stops. Pull the Low Range lever out slightly, no more than 1/16 in.
4. Tighten the cable clamp nut at the reduction unit shift lever.

NOTE: This procedure only applies to the Quadra-Trac transfer case equipped with a reduction unit.

Manual Transmission

Refer to the Manual Transmission General Repair Section for applica-

tion, troubleshooting and overhaul.

Linkage Adjustments

Jeepster—Console Shift

1. Remove the plug from the hole in the left side of the console. If there is no hole, cut a 1⅛ in. dia. hole or remove the console.
2. Lift the shift tower rubber cover and remove the plug in the shift transmission, sliding the throwout bearing along the retainer several times and removing any excess grease; the groove in the throwout bearing collar; and the ball stud in the flywheel housing together with the seat in the clutch fork.

NOTE: Use wheel bearing grease SPARINGLY to lubricate all of the above. If excessive grease is applied, operating heat will cause it to run out onto the clutch disc, ruining it.

9. Install and reassemble the clutch in the reverse order of removal, taking note of the following:
   a. Be certain that the mark on the clutch cover is aligned with the mark made on the flywheel during clutch removal.
   tower. Move the selector lever to the neutral position.
3. Loosen the adjusting nuts at the transmission.
4. Insert a 3/16 in. dia. rod through the holes in the console and shift tower, and through the aligning holes in the two shift levers. Check to see that the transmission shift levers are in neutral positions.
5. Torque the adjusting nuts to 15-20 ft lbs.
6. Remove the adjusting rod, replace the plugs, and check the shifting action. If the selector lever interferes with the console, relocate the console.

Wagoneer—Column Shift

1. Put the selector lever in Neutral position.
2. Loosen the shift rod adjusting nuts at the transmission. Place the shift levers in Neutral position.
3. Insert a 3/16 in. dia. rod through the remote control shift levers and housing at the bottom of the steering column.
4. Torque the adjusting nuts to 15-20 ft lbs. Remove the adjusting rod.

Transmission R & R

The transmission and transfer case can be removed as a unit. These instructions apply to both three and four-speed transmissions.

Universal (CJ) Series through 1971

1. Drain the transmission and transfer case.

2. Remove the floor pan inspection plate.
3. Remove the shift lever and housing, or disconnect the remote control rods, depending on the model.
4. If the vehicle has a power takeoff, remove the shift lever.
5. Disconnect the front and rear driveshafts from the transfer case. Disconnect the power takeoff driveshaft.
6. Disconnect the speedometer cable.
7. Disconnect the handbrake cable.
8. Disconnect the clutch release cable or rod.
9. Place the jacks under the engine and transmission, protecting the oil pan with a wooden block.
10. Remove the rear crossmember.
11. Unbolt the transmission from the flywheel housing.
12. Force the transmission to the right to disengage the clutch control lever tube ball joint.
13. Lower the jacks. Slide the transmission and transfer case rearward until the clutch shaft clears the flywheel housing.
14. Lower the transmission jack. Remove the assembly from beneath the vehicle.
15. To install, reverse the procedure.

Jeepster through 1971

The procedure for these models is the same as that for the Universal series, with the substitution of the following steps:

2. Remove the right front seat, floor mat, and floorboard center section. Disconnect the back-up switch wires.
10. Remove the rear crossmember. Remove the transmission and transfer case stabilizer brackets.

Wagoneer through 1971

The procedure for these models is the same as that for the Universal series, with the substitution of the following step:

2. Remove the transmission access cover.

All Models—1972 and Later

1. Remove the shift lever knobs, trim rings, and boots.
2. On three-speed floorshift models, remove the floor covering. Remove the floor pan section from above the transmission. Remove the shift control and lever assembly. On four-speed models, remove the shift control housing cap, washer, spring, shift lever, and pin.
3. Remove the transfer case shift lever and bracket.
4. Raise the vehicle on a lift.
5. Disconnect the column shift rods.
6. Remove the front driveshaft and

disconnect the front of the rear driveshaft. Disconnect the vacuum line and electrical lead on a Quadra-Trac unit.
7. Disconnect the clutch cable, if so equipped and remove the cable mounting bracket from the transfer case.
8. Disconnect the speedometer cable, TCS switch, and back-up light switch. Disconnect the parking brake cable if it is connected to the crossmember.
9. On models equipped with V8 engines, disconnect and lower the exhaust pipes from the exhaust manifolds.
10. Support the transmission with a floor jack.
11. Unbolt the crossmember from the frame. Unbolt the transmission from the clutch housing.
12. Lower the transmission slightly and move it to the rear to disengage the clutch shaft. Remove the unit.

To replace the transmission:

13. Place the wave washer and throw-out bearing and sleeve assembly in the fork. Center the bearing over the release levers.
14. Slide the transmission into place, being careful to align the transmission splines with those on the clutch plate. Bolt the transmission to the clutch housing and torque the bolts to 55 ft lbs.
15. Bolt the crossmember to the frame. Torque the bolts to 30-35 ft lbs. Remove the jack.
16. On models equipped with V8 engines, connect the exhaust pipes to the exhaust manifolds.
17. Connect the speedometer cable, back-up light switch, TCS switch, parking brake cable, clutch cable and cable mounting bracket.
18. Install the driveshafts. Flange bolts should be torqued to 25-45 ft lbs.
19. Replace the column shift linkage.
20. Lower the vehicle.
21. Replace the transfer case shift lever and bracket.
22. On four-speeds, install the lever pivot pin, shift lever, spring, washer, and control housing cap. On three-speeds, install the shift control and lever assembly. Set the gears and the cover in the neutral position. Install the cover, placing the shift forks into the sleeves. Torque the cover bolts to 8-15 ft lbs.
23. Replace the floor covering, boots, trim rings, and shift lever knobs.

Automatic Transmission

All Jeep vehicles use the General

Motors Turbo-Hydramatic 400 3-speed automatic transmission. Refer to the Automatic Transmission General Repair Section for troubleshooting and overhaul procedures.

Linkage Adjustment

1. Place the steering column gearshift lever in the Neutral position.
2. Raise the vehicle on a hoist.
3. Loosen the locknut on the gearshift rod trunnion just enough to permit movement of the gearshift rod in the trunnion.
4. Place the outer range selector lever at the transmission, fully into the Neutral detent position and tighten the locknut at the trunnion to 9 ft lbs.
5. Lower the car and operate the steering column gearshift in all ranges. The car should start in Park and Neutral only and the column gearshift lever engage properly in all detent positions.

Neutral Switch Adjustment

1. Apply the parking brake.
2. Check and adjust the manual linkage, if necessary.
3. Remove the Neutral switch from the steering column.
4. Place the selector lever in Park and lock the steering column.
5. Move the switch actuating lever until it is aligned with the letter "P" stamped on the back of the switch.
6. Insert a 3/32 in. drill in the hole located below the letter "N" stamped on the back of the switch.
7. Move the switch actuating lever until it stops against the drill.
8. Position the switch on the steering column, install the attaching screws and remove the drill.
9. Check the operation of the switch. The engine should start in Park and Neutral only. The backup light should glow only in the Reverse position.

U Joints, Drive Lines

The drive of four-wheel drive Universal and Jeepster models from the transfer case to the front and rear axles is through two tubular driveshafts. Each driveshaft has two cross and roller universal joints. Two-wheel drive models drive through a single driveshaft with two universal joints. Each driveshaft has a splined slip joint at one end to allow for variations in length.

Jeepster V6 models have a front driveshaft made up of two shafts with three universal joints and one slip joint. The shorter of the two shafts, directly ahead of the transfer case, has a shaft support bearing.

Wagoneer models use several types and sizes of driveshafts, depending upon various transmission and equipment options. These are divided into two basic types. The first is that with two cross and roller joints and a slip joint. The second has a cross and roller joint at one end, and a ball and trunnion universal joint at the other end. Automatic transmission Wagoneer models have the slip joint end of the front driveshaft at the axle rather than at the transfer case, as on all other models.

Drive Shaft R & R

In order to remove the front and rear driveshafts, unscrew the attaching nuts from the universal joint's U-bolts, remove the U-bolts and slide the shaft forward or backward toward the slip-joint. The shaft can then be removed from the end yokes and removed from under the vehicle. Install the driveshaft in the reverse order.

NOTE: Some driveshafts are marked at the slip-joints with arrows on the spline and sleeve yoke. When installing the driveshaft, align the arrows to have the yokes at the front and rear of the shaft in the same parallel plane.

U-Joint Overhaul
Cross and Roller

Snap-Ring Type Disassembly and Repair

1. Remove the snap-rings.
2. Press on the end of one bearing until the opposite bearing is pushed from the yoke arm.
3. Turn the joint over. Press the first bearing back out of the arm by pressing on the exposed end of the journal shaft. Repeat this operation for the other two bearings, then lift out the journal assembly by sliding it to one side.
4. Wash all parts in solvent and inspect for wear. Replace all worn parts.
5. Install new gaskets on the journal assembly. Make certain that the grease channel in each journal trunnion is open.
6. Pack the bearing cones one-third full of grease and install the rollers.
7. Assemble in the reverse order of disassembly. If the joint binds when assembled, tap the arms lightly to relieve any pressure on the bearings at the end of the journal.

U-Bolt Type Disassembly and Repair

Remove the attaching U-bolts to

Exploded view of the Ball and Trunnion type universal joint.

release one set of bearing races. Slide the driveshaft into the yoke flange to remove the races. The rest of the disassembly and repair procedure is the same as that given above for the snap-ring type of cross and roller joint. The correct U-bolt torque is 15-20 ft lbs.

Ball and Trunnion

Disassembly and Repair

1. Clamp the shaft firmly in a vise.
2. Bend the grease cover lugs away from the universal joint body. Remove the cover and gasket.
3. Remove the two clamps from the dust cover. Push the joint body toward the driveshaft tube. Remove two each; centering buttons, spring washers, ball and roller bearings, and thrust washers, from the trunnion pin.
4. Press the trunnion pin from ballhead.
5. If the ballhead is bent out of alignment or if the trunnion pin bore is worn or damaged, replace the driveshaft.

To reassemble:

6. Secure the larger end of the dust cover to the joint body with the larger of two clamps. Install the smaller clamp. Fit the cover over the ballhead shaft.
7. Push the universal joint cover toward the driveshaft tube. Press the trunnion pin into the centered position. If the trunnion pin is not centered, imbalance will result.
8. Install the thrust washers, ball and roller bearings, spring washer, and centering buttons on the trunnion pin. Compress the centering buttons. Move the joint body to hold the buttons in place.
9. Insert the breather between the dust cover and the ballhead shaft, along the length of the shaft. The breather must extend no more than ½ in. beyond the dust cover. Tighten the clamp screw to secure the cover to the shaft. Cut away any portion of

dust cover protruding under the clamps.
10. Pack the raceways around the ball and roller bearings with about 2 oz of universal joint grease.
11. Position the gasket and grease cover on the body. Bend the lugs of the cover into the notches of the body. Move the body back and forth to distribute grease in the raceways.

Rear Axles, Suspension

Refer to the Drive Axle General Repair Section for application, troubleshooting, and overhaul procedures.

Axle Shaft R & R

Tapered Shaft—CJ Models Prior to 1972

1. Jack up the wheel and remove the hub cap.
2. Remove the axle shaft nut.
3. Use a puller to remove the wheel hub and key.
4. Remove the screws which attach the brake dust shield, grease and bearing retainers, and brake assembly. Remove the shield and retainer.
5. Pull out the axle shaft with a puller, being careful not to lose the adjusting shims. Should the axle shaft be broken, the inner end can usually be drawn out of the housing with a wire loop, after the outer seal is removed. However, if the broken end is less than 8 in. long, it will be necessary to remove the differential.
   If both shafts are to be removed, keep the shims from each shaft separate and replace them on the shaft from which they were removed in order to maintain the correct bearing adjustment.
6. Install in the reverse order of removal. Use a new grease seal when installing the hub assem-

bly. Install the hub assembly. then the key.

Tapered Shaft—Wagoneer, Commando, and Cherokee

1. Jack up the vehicle and remove the hub cap.
2. Remove the wheel.
3. Remove the axle nut dust cap.
4. Remove the axle shaft cotter pin, castle nut and flat washer.
5. Back-off the brake adjustment.
6. Use a puller to remove the wheel hub.
7. Remove the screws attaching the brake dust protector, grease and bearing retainers, brake assembly and shim to the housing.
8. Remove the hydaulic line from the brake assembly.
9. Remove the dust shield and oil seal.
10. Use a puller to remove the axle shaft.
11. Install the axle shaft in the reverse order of removal, using a new grease seal and installing the hub assembly before the woodruff key.

NOTE: Should the axle shaft be broken, the inner end can usually be drawn out of the housing with a wire loop after the outer oil seal is removed. However, if the broken end is less than 8 in. long, it usually is necessary to remove the differential assembly.

Flanged Shaft—Wagoneer, Commando, Cherokee, Truck, and 1972-75 CJ Models

1. Jack up the vehicle and remove the wheels.
2. Remove the brake drum spring lock nuts and remove the drum.
3. Remove the axle shaft flange cup plug by piercing the center with a sharp tool and prying it out.
4. Using the access hole in the axle shaft flange, remove the nuts which attach the backing plate and retainer to the axle tube flange.
5. Remove the axle shaft from the housing with an axle puller.
6. Install in reverse order of removal.

1976—CJ Models Only

1. With the wheel on the ground, remove the axle shaft cotter pin and nut. Loosen the wheel nuts.
2. Raise and support the rear of the car, preferably with jackstands under the axle housing.
3. Remove the wheel.
4. Remove the drum retaining screws, 3 per drum.
5. Remove the drum from the hub. If the brake shoes hold the drum, the brake adjustment will have to be backed off slightly.
6. Attach a puller to the wheel bolts and pull off the hub.

CAUTION: Don't use a knock-out type puller. It could damage the rear wheel bearings or the differential.

7. Disconnect the parking brake cable at the equalizer. The equalizer is where the single cable from the parking brake pedal joins the double cable from the rear wheels.
8. Disconnect the brake tube at the wheel cylinder and remove the brake support plate assembly (backing plate), oil seal, and shims (left-side only).
9. Use a puller to remove the axle shaft and bearing.
10. Remove and discard the axle shaft inner oil seal.
11. The bearing cone is pressed onto the shaft. A hydraulic press must be used to remove it.
12. Before installation, pack the axle shaft bearings with high quality grease. Place a healthy glob of grease in the palm of one hand and force the edge of the bearing into it so that grease fills the bearing. Do this until the whole bearing is packed. Grease packing tools are available which make this task much easier.
13. Press the axle shaft bearings onto the axle shafts with the small diameter of the cone toward the outer end of the shaft.

CAUTION: Always press on the inner bearing race.

14. Coat the inner axle shaft seal with light oil.
15. Coat the outer surface of the metal seal retainer with sealant.
16. Use a seal driver to install the inner oil seal in the axle housing.
17. Install the axle shaft(s), turning them as necessary to fit the splines into the differential.
18. Install the outer bearing cup.
19. Apply sealant to the axle housing flange and brake support plate mounting areas. Install the original shims in their original locations, oil seal assembly, and brake support plate. Tighten the retaining bolts to 35 ft lbs.

NOTE: The oil seal and retainer go on the outside of the brake support plate.

20. Axle shaft end-play can be measured by installing the hub retaining nut on the shaft so it can be pushed and pulled with relative ease. Strike the end of each axle shaft with a lead hammer to seat the bearing cups against the support plate. Mount a dial indicator on the left side support plate with the stylus resting on the end of the axle shaft. Check the end-play while pushing and pulling on the axle shaft. End play should be within 0.004-0.008 in., with 0.006 in. ideal. Add shims to increase end play and subtract whims to decrease end-

play. Remove the hub retaining nut when finished checking end-play.

NOTE: When a new axle shaft is installed. a new hub must also be installed. However, a new hub can be installed on an original axle shaft if the serrations on the shaft are not worn or damaged. The procedures for installing an original hub and a new hub are different.

21. Install an original hub in the following manner:
    a. Align the keyway in the hub with the axle shaft key.
    b. Slide the hub onto the axle shaft as far as possible.
    c. Install the axle shaft nut and washer.
    d. Install the drum, drum retaining screws, and wheel.
    e. Lower the vehicle onto its wheels and tighten the axle shaft nut to 250 ft lbs. If the cotter pin hole is not aligned, tighten the nut to the next castellation and install the pin. Do not loosen the nut to align the cotter pin hole.
22. Install a new hub in the following manner:
    a. Align the keyway in the hub with the axle shaft key.
    b. Slide the hub onto the axle shaft as far as possible.
    c. Install two well-lubricated thrust washers and the axle shaft nut.
    d. Install the brake drum, drum retaining screws, and wheel.
    e. Lower the vehicle onto its wheels.
    f. Tighten the axle shaft nut until the distance from the outer face of the hub to the outer end of the axle shaft is 1-19/64 in. Pressing the hub onto the axle to the specified distance is necessary to form the hub serrations properly.
    g. Remove the axle shaft nut and one thrust washer.
    h. Install the axle shaft nut and tighten it to 250 ft lbs. If the cotter pin hole is not aligned, tighten the nut to the next castellation and install the pin. Do not loosen the nut to install the cotter pin.
23. Connect the brake line to the wheel cylinder and bleed the brake hydraulic system and adjust the brake shoes.

Full-Floating Axle Shaft— Truck Only

It is not necessary to raise the rear wheels in order to remove the rear axle shaft on full-floating rear axles.

1. Remove the axle flange nuts, lock washers, and split washers retaining the axle shaft flange.
2. Remove the axle shaft from the axle housing.

WHEEL HUB PULLER

BEARING PULLER

3. Clean the axle flange mating area on the hub and axle, removing all old gasket material.
4. Install a new flange gasket onto the hub studs.
5. Insert the axle shaft into the housing. It may be necessary to rotate the axle shaft to align the shaft splines with the differential gear splines and the flange attaching holes with the hub studs.
6. Install the split washers, lock-washers, and flange nuts. Tighten the nuts securely.

Pinion Oil Seal R & R

Semi-Floating Axle with Tapered Shaft

1. Raise and support the vehicle and remove the rear wheels and brake drums.
2. Mark the driveshaft and yoke for reassembly and disconnect the driveshaft from the rear yoke.
3. With a socket on the pinion nut and an in. lb torque wrench, rotate the drive pinion several revolutions. Check and record the torque required to turn the drive pinion.
4. Remove the pinion nut. Use a flange holding tool to hold the flange while removing the pinion nut. Discard the pinion nut.
5. Mark the yoke and thee drive pinion shaft for reassembly reference.
6. Remove the rear yoke with a puller.
7. Inspect the seal surface of the yoke and replace it with a new one if the seal surface is pitted, grooved, or otherwise damaged.
8. Remove the pinion oil seal.
9. Before installing the new seal, coat the lip of the seal with rear axle lubricant.
10. Install the seal, driving it into place with the proper driving tool.

11. Install the yoke on the pinion shaft. Align the marks made on the pinion shaft and yoke during disassembly.
12. Install a new pinion nut. Tighten nut until end play is removed from the pinion bearing. Do not overtighten.
13. Check the torque required to turn the drive pinion. The pinion must be turned several revolutions to obtain an accurate reading.
14. Tighten the pinion nut to obtain the torque reading observed during disassembly (step 3) plus 5 in. lbs. Tighten the nut minutely each time, to avoid overtightening. Do not loosen and then retighten the nut.

NOTE: If the desired torque is exceeded a new collapsible pinion spacer sleeve must be installed and the pinion gear preload reset. Refer to the General Repair Section and Overhaul procedures for this operation.

15. Install the driveshaft, aligning the index marks made during disassembly. Install the rear brake drums and wheels.

Semi-Floating and Full-Floating Axles with Flange Shaft

1. Raise and support the vehicle.
2. Mark the driveshaft and yoke for reference during assembly and disconnect the driveshaft at the yoke.
3. Remove the pinion shaft nut and washer.
4. Remove the yoke from the pinion shaft, using a puller.
5. Remove the pinion shaft oil seal.
6. Install the new seal with a suitable driver.
7. Install the pinion shaft washer and nut. Tighten the nut to 210 ft lbs on the semi-floating axles and 260 ft lbs on the full-floating axles.
8. Align the index marks on the driveshaft and yoke and install the driveshaft. Tighten the attaching bolts or nuts to 16 ft lbs.
9. Remove the supports and lower the vehicle.

Rear Suspension

Spring R & R

Mounted Below the Axle

1. Raise the vehicle and support the

PINION AND BEARING REMOVER AND REPLACER

TYPICAL REAR SPRING

1—Cotter Pin	7—Bolt	14—Nut and Lockwasher	20—Cotter Pin
2—Special Washer	8—Rear Spring	15—Bolt	21—Silent Bloc Bushing
3—Bushing	9—Plate and Shaft	16—Axle Bumper	22—Bolt
4—Bracket and Shaft	10—Lockwasher	17—Clip	23—Nut
5—Rear Spring Hanger	11—Nut	18—Rear Shock Absorber	24—Lockwasher
6—Lubrication Fitting	12—Rear Spring Eye Bushing	19—Rear Spring Shackle	25—Spring Shackle Side Plate
	13—Nut		

axle.

2. Disconnect the shock absorber and stabilizer bar, if so equipped.
3. Remove the U-bolts and tie plates.
4. Disconnect the front and rear ends of the spring and remove the spring.
5. The spring can be disassembled by removing the spring rebound clips and the center bolt.
6. Mount the spring in the vehicle, but do not tighten the pivot bolts.
7. Align the spring center bolt and install the tie plate and U-bolts.
8. Connect the shock absorber and stabilizer bar, if so equipped.
9. Remove the axle support and lower the vehicle.
10. Tighten the pivot bolts with the weight of the vehicle on the springs to 45 ft lbs on CJ models and 75 ft lbs on all other models. Tighten 9/16 in. U-bolt nuts to 100 ft lbs, 1/2 in. nuts to 55 ft lbs and 7/16 in. U-bolt nuts to 40 ft lbs.

Mounted Above the Axle

1. Raise the vehicle and support the frame ahead of the axle.
2. Remove the U-bolts.
3. Unclip the axle vent hose from the frame.
4. Disconnect the shock absorber.
5. Remove the spring pivot bolts.
6. Lower the axle enough so the spring can be turned over and remove the spring. The spring can be disassembled by removing

the rebound clips and center bolt.
7. Mount the spring in the vehicle and install the pivot bolts and nuts.
8. Raise the axle, align the spring center bolt, and install the U-bolts.
9. Connect the shock absorber, vent hose, and remove the supports and lower the vehicle.
10. Tighten the spring pivot bolts with the weight of the vehicle on the springs. Tighten the pivot bolts to 75 ft lbs. Tighten 9/16 in. U-bolt nuts to 100 ft lbs, 1/2 in. nuts to 55 ft lbs, and 7/16 in. U-bolt nuts to 40 ft lbs.

Spring Bushing R & R

Small Bushing

1. Install an 8 in. length of threaded rod halfway through the bushing and place a 1 1/8 in. socket with the open end toward the bushing, one 1/2 in. flat

washer, and one 3/8 in. hex nut on one end of the rod.
2. Place a 2 in. section of 1 5/8 in. or 1 3/8 in. ID pipe, one 3/4 in. flat washer, or 1/2 in. flat washer and on 3/8 in. hex nut on the opposite end of the threaded rod.
3. Tighten both of the 3/8 in. nuts finger-tight and align all of the components. Make sure the socket is positioned in the eye of the spring and aligns with the bushing. The pipe section must butt against the spring eye so the bushing can pass through it. The socket will act as a press and will press the bushing out of the spring eye.
4. Tighten the nut at the socket end of the rod until the bushing is pressed out of the spring eye. Remove the tools and the bushing.
5. Install the replacement bushing on the threaded rod and assemble the bushing tools as outlined in steps 1 and 2, and press the bushing into the spring eye. Make sure the bushing is centered in the spring eye.

Set-up for removing small spring eye bushings.

Set-up for removing large spring eye bushings.

Index

Electrical Diagnosis

To satisfy the growing trend toward organized engine diagnosis and tune-up, the following gauge and meter hook-ups, as well as diagnosis procedures are covered. The most sophisticated tune-up and diagnostic facilities are no more than a complex of the basic gauges and meters in common, everyday use. Therefore, to understand gauge and meter hook-ups, their applications and procedures, it is to be equipped with the know-how to perform the most exacting diagnosis.

Testing the Battery

Specific Gravity Test— Hydrometer

Before attempting any electrical checks, it is important to check the condition of the battery.

While not technically exact, a practical measurement of the chemical condition of the battery is indicated by measuring the specific gravity of the acid (electrolyte) contained in each cell. The electrolyte in a fully charged battery is usually between 1.260 and 1.280 times as heavy as pure water at the same temperature (80°F). Variations in the specific gravity readings for a fully charged battery may differ. Therefore, it is most important that all battery cells produce an equal reading.

As a battery discharges, a chemical change takes place within each cell. The sulfate factor of the electrolyte combines chemically with the battery plates, reducing the weight of the electrolyte. A reading of the specific gravity of the acid, or electrolyte, of any partially charged battery, will therefore be less than that taken in a fully charged one.

The hydrometer is the instrument in general use for determining the specific gravity of liquids. The battery hydrometer is readily available from many sources, including local auto replacement parts stores. The following chart gives an indication of specific gravity value, related to battery charge condition. If, after charging, the specific gravity between any two cells varies more than 50 points (.050), the battery is probably bad.

Specific Gravity Reading	Charged Condition
1.260-1.280	Fully charged
1.230-1.250	Three-quarter charged
1.200-1.220	One-half charged
1.170-1.190	One-quarter charged
1.140-1.160	Just about flat
1.110-1.130	All the way down

Testing Battery Polarity

Battery polarity is very important, especially since the introduction of AC generators. Permanent damage to the diodes of alternators (AC generators) will result from reversing polarity.

To determine battery polarity, turn the voltmeter selector to the high reading scale. Connect voltmeter leads to the battery posts. If the gauge needle moves in the correct direction, the positive lead of the meter is on the positive (+) post of the battery. If the gauge needle moves in the wrong direction, polarity is reversed.

Testing the Delco "Sealed Top" Battery

Some GM trucks have a "sealed top" battery which does not require the usual maintenance. Because the battery has a greater amount of electrolyte and a reduced need for water, the top of the battery has no filler caps and is sealed. A small vent is provided at one edge of the battery top.

There are two types of sealed batteries used: one has a charge indicator eye and the other does not. Both types may be tested in the following manner:

1. Check the condition of the battery case. If the case is damaged so that loss of electrolyte is possible, the battery must be replaced.

2. If the battery has a charge indicator eye, check the following:
   a. If the eye is dark, the battery has enough electrolyte. If the eye is light, the electrolyte level is too low and the battery must be replaced.
   b. If a green dot appears in the middle of the eye, the battery is sufficiently charged; go on to Step 4. If there is no green dot visible, charge the battery as in Step 3.

3. Charge the battery if there is no green dot visible in the eye, or if it is the type without an eye, at the following rates:

Amps	Time
75	40 min
50	1 hr
25	2 hr
10	5 hr

   CAUTION: Do not charge the battery for more than 50 ampere-hours. If the green dot appears or electrolyte squirts out of the vent, stop the charge and go on with Step 4.

4. Either disconnect the high-tension coil wire or the engine harness (electronic ignition) and crank the starter motor for 15 seconds, to remove the surface charge.

5. Connect a voltmeter and a 230 amp load across the battery terminals.

6. Take a voltmeter reading after the load has been connected for 15 seconds, then disconnect the load.

7. Consult the chart. If the battery voltage is that specified (or more) for the given ambient temperature, the battery is good. If the voltage falls below that specified, then the battery is bad and must be replaced.

Ambient Temperature (°F)	Minimum Voltage
70 (or above)	9.6
60	9.5
50	9.4
40	9.3
30	9.1
20	8.9
10	8.7
0	8.5

Know Your Instruments

Ohmmeter

An ohmmeter is used to measure electrical resistance in a unit or circuit. The ohmmeter has a self-contained power supply. In use, it is connected across (or in parallel with) the terminals of the unit being tested.

Ammeter

An ammeter is used to measure current (amount of electricity) flowing through a unit, or circuit. Ammeters are always connected in the line (in series) with the unit or circuit being tested.

Voltmeter

A voltmeter is used to measure voltage (electrical pressure) pushing the current through a unit, or circuit. The meter is connected across the terminals of the unit being tested.

The meter reading will be the difference in pressure (voltage drop) between the two sides of the unit.

Boost Charging Rates

12-volt Battery: 1,000 ampere/minutes (50 amps. x 20 min.)
6-volt Battery: 1,800 ampere/minutes (60 amps. x 30 min.)

Testing the Starting Motor

Testing the Starter Circuit

The starter circuit should be divided and tested in four separate phases:

1. Cranking voltage check.
2. Amperage draw.
3. Voltage drop—grounded side.
4. Voltage drop—battery side.

NOTE: The battery must be in good condition for this test to have significance. To accurately check battery condition, use equipment designed to measure its capacity under a load. Instructions accompanying the equipment should be followed.

Cranking Voltage

Turn voltmeter selector to 8-10 volt scale for trucks equipped with 6-volt systems, and to the 16-20 volt scale for trucks equipped with 12-volt systems.

Connect voltmeter leads to prods tapped into the battery posts (observe polarity and reverse meter leads if necessary). Remove the high tension wire from the distributor cap and ground it to prevent starting. With electronic ignition, disconnect the control box harness from the distributor. Now, turn the key. Observe both voltmeter reading and cranking speed. The cranking speed should be even, and at a satisfactory rate of speed, with a voltmeter reading of 4.8 volts or more for 6-volt systems, and at least 9.6 volts for 12-volt systems.

Amperage Draw

The amount of current the starter motor draws is usually (but not always) associated with the mechanical problems involved in cranking the engine. (Mechanical trouble in the engine, frozen or worn starter parts, misaligned starter or starter components, etc.) Because starter motor amperage draw is directly influenced by anything restricting the free turning of the engine, or starter, it is important that the engine and all components be at operating temperatures.

To measure starter current draw, remove the high tension wire from the center of the distributor cap and ground it. With electronic ignition, disconnect the control box harness from the distributor. A very simple and inexpensive starter current indicator is available at auto stores. This indicator is an induction type gauge and shows, without disconnecting any wires, starter current draw.

Place the yoke of the meter directly over the insulated starter supply cable (cable must be straight for a minimum of 2 in.). Close the starter switch for about 20 seconds, watch the meter dial and record the average reading. If the indicator swings in the wrong direction, reverse the position of the meter. On 6-volt systems, normal draw for small to medium size engines is 150 to 225 amperes. Larger and high compression engines may draw as much as 400 amperes. On 12-volt systems, the current draw should be about one-half the amount registered for the 6-volt system.

More accurate but complex equipment is available from many name brand manufacturers. This equipment consists of a combination voltmeter, ammeter, and carbon pile rheostat. When using this equipment, follow the equipment manufacturer's procedures and recommendations.

High amperage and lazy performance would suggest an excessively tight engine, friction in the starter or starter drive, grounded starter field or armature.

Normal amperage and lazy performance suggest high resistance, or possibly poor connections somewhere in the starter circuit.

Low amperage and lazy or no performance suggest battery condition poor, bad cables or connections along the line.

Voltage Drop—Grounded Side

With a voltmeter on the 3-volt scale, without disconnecting any wires, connect negative test lead of the voltmeter to a prod secured in the grounded battery post. The positive test lead is connected to a cleaned, bare metal portion of the starter motor housing. Close the starter switch and note the voltmeter reading. If the reading is the same as battery reading, the ground circuit is open somewhere between the battery and the starter. In many cases the reading will be very small. The reading shown will indicate voltage drop (loss) between battery ground post and starter housing. The drop should not exceed 0.2 volt. If the voltage drop is above the specified amount, the next step is to isolate and correct the cause. It can be a bad cable or connection anywhere in the battery-to-starter ground circuit. A check of this type should progress along the various points of possible trouble, between the battery ground post and the starter motor housing, until the trouble spot has been located.

NOTE: due to the design of the Chrysler reduction gear starter, testing is limited to measuring voltage drop to starter cable connection.

Voltage Drop—Battery Side

Bad starter cranking may result from poor connections or faulty components of the battery or hot phase of the starter motor circuit. To check this phase of the circuit, without disconnecting any wires, connect one lead of a voltmeter to a prod secured in the hot post of the battery and the other voltmeter lead to the field terminal of the starting motor. The meter should be set to the 16-20 volt scale. Before closing the starter switch, the voltmeter reading will be that of the battery. After closing the starter switch, change the selector on the voltmeter to the 3-volt scale. With a jumper wire between the relay battery terminal and the relay starter switch terminal, crank the engine. If the starting motor cranks the engine, the relay (solenoid) is operating.

While the engine is being cranked, watch the voltmeter. It should not register more than 0.5 volt. If more than this, check each part of the circuit for voltage drop to isolate the trouble, (high resistance).

Without disturbing the voltmeter-to-battery hook-up, move the free voltmeter lead to the battery terminal of the relay (solenoid), and crank the engine. The voltmeter should show

Typical Autolite hook-up

Typical Delco-Remy hook-up

no more than 0.1 volt.

If this reading is correct, move the same voltmeter lead to the starting motor terminal of the relay (solenoid). While the engine is being cranked, the voltmeter should show no more than 0.3 volt. If it does, the trouble lies in the relay.

If the reading is correct, the trouble is in the cable or connections between the relay and the starting motor.

Diagnosis

Starter Won't Crank the Engine
1. Dead battery.
2. Open starter circuit, such as:
   a. Broken or loose battery cables.
   b. Inoperative starter motor solenoid.
   c. Broken or loose wire from starter switch to solenoid.

Typical early model Chrysler products hook-up

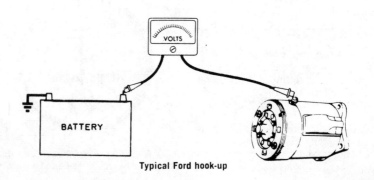

Typical Ford hook-up

d. Poor solenoid or starter ground.
e. Bad starter switch.

3. Defective starter internal circuit, such as:
   a. Dirty or burnt commutator.
   b. Stuck, worn or broken brushes.
   c. Open or shorted armature.
   d. Open or grounded fields.
4. Starter motor mechanical faults, such as:

a. Jammed armature end bearings.
b. Bad bearing, allowing armature to rub fields.
c. Bent shaft.
d. Broken starter housing.
e. Bad starter worm or drive mechanism.
f. Bad starter drive or flywheel driven gear.
5. Engine hard or impossible to crank such as:
   a. Hydrostatic lock, water in

combustion chamber.
b. Crankshaft seizing in bearings.
c. Piston or ring seizing.
d. Bent or broken connecting rod.
e. Seizing of connecting rod bearing.
f. Flywheel jammed or broken.

Starter Spins Free, Won't Engage
1. Sticking or broken drive mechanism.

Switches and Solenoids

Schematic diagram of a magnetic switch with two control terminals

Wiring diagram showing starter solenoid mounted on cranking motor

Pictorial drawing of solenoid with a built-in relay

Pictorial drawing of solenoid with a separate relay

Magnetic Switches

Magnetic switches serve only to make contact for the starter motor. Usually, such switches are located on the inner fender panel, although they are found mounted on the starter in a few cases.

Magnetic Switches with Two Control Terminals

On this type of magnetic switch current is supplied from the ignition switch or transmission neutral button to one of the magnetic switch control terminals. The other control terminal is connected to the transmission neutral safety switch (on the transmission) where it is grounded.

Magnetic Switches with Ignition Resistor By-Pass Terminals

Used with 12-volt systems. All

normally use a magnetic switch with a single control terminal. The second terminal is an ignition resistor by-pass terminal.

Solenoids Without Relays

This type of starter solenoid is always mounted on the starter. Makes electrical contact for the starter and pulls the starter and drive clutch into mesh with the flywheel. The Chrysler reduction gear starter has this solenoid embodied in the starter housing.

There is only one control terminal on the solenoid.

The ignition by-pass terminal is usually marked R or IGN, if it is used.

Solenoids With Separate Relays

The solenoid itself is always mounted on the starter. In addition to making contact for the starter, it also pulls the starter drive clutch gear into mesh with the flywheel. A single control terminal is used on the solenoid itself. The relay is usually found mounted to the inner fender panel or on the firewall.

Solenoids With Built-In Relays

These units are always mounted on the starter and are connected, through linkage, to the starter drive clutch. The relay portion is a square box built into and integral with the front end of the solenoid assembly.

Neutral Safety Switches

The purpose of the neutral safety switch is to prevent the starter from cranking the engine except when the transmission is in neutral or park.

On some trucks the neutral safety switch is located on the transmission. It serves to ground the solenoid or magnetic switch, whichever is used.

On other trucks the neutral safety switch is located either at the bottom of the steering column, where it contacts the shift mechanism, on the steering column, underneath the dash, or on the shift linkage (console).

Reduction gear starting motor (solenoid side)

Reduction gear starting motor (reduction gear side)

Some manual transmission models have a clutch linkage safety switch to prevent starter operation unless the clutch pedal is depressed.

On most trucks the neutral safety switch and the backup light switch are combined into a single switch mechanism.

See the truck sections for specific details.

Troubleshooting Neutral Safety Switches—Quick Test

If the starter fails to function and the neutral safety switch is to be checked, a jumper can be placed across its terminals. If the starter then functions the safety switch is defective.

In the case of neutral safety switches with one wire, this wire must be grounded for testing purposes. If the starter works with the wire grounded, the switch is defective.

Neutral Safety Switch— Back-Up Light Switch

When the neutral safety switch is built in combination with the back-up light switch, the easiest way to tell which terminals are for the back-up lights is to take a jumper and cross every pair of wires. The pair of wires which light the back-up lamps should be ignored when testing the neutral safety switch. Once the back-up light wires have been located, jump the other pair of wires to test the neutral safety switch. If the starter functions only when the jumper is placed across these two wires, the neutral safety

switch is defective or requires adjustment.

Reduction-Gear Starter Motor
(Chrysler Corporation)

The housing is die-cast aluminum. A 3.5 to 1 reduction, combined with the starter to ring gear ratio, results in a total gear reduction of about 45 to 1.

NOTE: the high-pitched sound is caused by the higher starter speed.

The positive shift solenoid is enclosed in the starter housing and is energized through the ignition switch When ignition switch is turned to start, the solenoid plunger engages drive gear through a shifting fork. At the completion of travel, the plunger closes a switch to revolve the starter.

The tension of the spring-type shifting prevents a butt-tooth lock up and motor will not start before total shift.

An overrunning clutch prevents motor damage if key is held on after engine starts.

No lubrication is required due to Oilite bearings.

Disassembly

1. Support assembly in a vise equipped with soft jaws. Do not clamp. Care must be used not to distort or damage the die cast aluminum.
2. Remove the thru-bolts and the end housing.
3. Carefully pull the armature up and out of the gear housing, and the starter frame and field assembly. Remove the steel and fiber thrust washer.

NOTE: on eight cylinder engines the starting motors have the wire of the shunt field coil soldered to the brush terminal. Six cylinder engines have the four coils in series and do not have a wire soldered to the brush terminal. One pair of brushes is connected to this terminal. The other pair of brushes is attached to the series field coils by means of a terminal screw. Carefully pull the frame and field assembly up just enough to expose the terminal screw and the solder connection of the shunt field at the brush terminal. Place two wood blocks between the starter frame and starter gear housing to facilitate removal of the terminal screw and unsoldering of the shunt field wire at the brush terminal.

4. Support the brush terminal with a finger behind terminal and remove screw.
5. On eight cylinder engine starters unsolder the shunt field coil lead from the brush terminal and housing.
6. The brush holder plate with terminal, contact and brushes is serviced as an assembly.
7. Clean all old sealer from around plate and housing.
8. Remove the brush holder attaching screw.
9. On the shunt type, unsolder the solenoid winding from the brush terminal.
10. Remove 11/32 in. nut, washer and insulator from solenoid terminal.
11. Remove brush holder plate with brushes as an assembly.
12. Remove gear housing ground screw.
13. The solenoid assembly can be removed from the well.

Removing terminal screw—reduction gear motor
(© Chrysler Corp)

Removing retainer ring—reduction gear motor
(© Chrysler Corp)

Removing drive gear snap ring—reduction gear motor
(© Chrysler Corp)

Shift fork and clutch arrangement—reduction gear
(© Chrysler Corp)

Removing clutch assembly—reduction gear motor
(© Chrysler Corp)

14. Remove nut, washer and seal from starter battery terminal and remove terminal from plate.
15. Remove solenoid contact and plunger from solenoid and remove the coil sleeve.
16. Remove the solenoid return spring, coil retaining washer, retainer and the dust cover from the gear housing.
17. Release the snap-ring that locates the driven gear on pinion shaft.
18. Release front retaining ring.
19. Push pinion shaft toward the rear and remove snap-ring, thrust washers, clutch and pinion, and two shift fork nylon actuators.
20. Remove driven gear and friction washer.
21. Pull shifting fork forward and remove moving core.
22. Remove fork retainer pin and shifting fork assembly. The gear housing with bushings is serviced as an assembly.

Replacement of Brushes

1. Brushes that are worn more than one-half the length of new brushes, or are oil-soaked, should be replaced.
2. When resoldering the shunt field and solenoid lead, make a strong, low-resistance connection using a high-temperature solder and resin flux. Do not use acid or acid-core solder. Do not break the shunt field wire units when removing and installing the brushes.

Starter Clutch and Pinion Gear Inspection

1. Do not immerse the starter clutch unit in a cleaning solvent. The outside of the clutch and pinion must be cleaned with a cloth so as not to wash the lubricant from the inside of the clutch.
2. Rotate the pinion. The pinion gear should rotate smoothly and in one direction only. If the starter clutch unit does not function properly, or if the pinion is worn, chipped, or burred, replace the starter clutch unit.

Commutator Inspection

1. Inspect the commutator and the surface contacted by the brushes when the starter is assembled, for flat spots, out-of-roundness, or excessive wear.
2. Reface the commutator if necessary, removing only a sufficient amount of metal to provide a smooth, even surface.
3. Using light pressure, clean the grooves of the face of the commutator with a pointed tool. Neither remove any metal or widen the grooves.

Assembly

1. The shifter fork consists of two spring steel plates held together by two rivets. Before assembling the starter, check the plates for side movement. After lubricating between the plates with a small amount of SAE 10 engine oil, they should have about 1/16 in. side movement to insure proper pinion gear engagement.
2. Position the shift fork in the drive housing and install the shifting fork retainer pin. One tip of the pin should be straight and the other bent at a 15 degree angle away from the housing. The fork and retainer pin

should operate freely after bending the tip of the pin.
3. Install the solenoid moving core and engage the shifting fork.
4. Place the pinion shaft into the drive housing and install the friction washer and drive gear.
5. Install the clutch and pinion assembly, thrust washer, and retaining washer.
6. Engage the shifting fork with the clutch actuators.

CAUTION: The friction washer must be positioned on the shoulder of the splines of the pinion shaft before the driven gear is positioned.

7. Install the driven gear snap ring.
8. Install the pinion shaft retaining ring.
9. The starter solenoid return spring can now be inserted in the moveable core.
10. Install the solenoid contact plunger assembly into the solenoid and reform the double wires so they can be curved around the contactor. This will allow the terminal stud to enter the brush holder properly.

CAUTION: The contactor must not touch these double wires after assembly is complete.

11. Assemble the battery terminal stud in the brush holder.
12. Position the seal on the brush holder plate.
13. Run the solenoid lead wire through the hole in the brush holder and attach the solenoid stud, insulating washers, flat washer, and nut.
14. Wrap the solenoid lead wire tightly around the brush terminal post and solder it.
15. Fix the brush holder to the solenoid attaching screws.
16. Gently lower the solenoid coil and brush plate into the gear housing.

Reduction gear starter motor

Chrysler direct drive motor—exploded view (© Chrysler Corp)

Brush lead arrangement—Chrysler direct drive motor
(© Chrysler Corp)

Removing shift fork—direct drive motor
(© Chrysler Corp)

17. Position the brush plate assembly into the starter gear housing, install the nuts, and tighten.
18. Solder the shunt coil lead wire to the starter brush terminal.
19. Install the brush terminal screw.
20. Position the field frame on the gear housing and start the armature into the housing, carefully engaging the splines on the shaft with the reduction gear by rotating the armature.
21. Install the fiber thrush washer and the steel washer on the armature shaft.
22. Replace the starter end housing and starter through bolts; tighten securely.

Direct Drive Starter Motor

(Chrysler Corporation)

This starter was used through 1972. It can be identified by the externally mounted solenoid bolted to the case.

Disassembly

1. Remove through bolts and tap commutator end head from frame.
2. Remove thrust washers from armature shaft.
3. Lift brush holder springs and remove brushes from holders.
4. Remove brush holder plate.
5. Disconnect the field coil wires at the solenoid connector, and remove the solenoid screws.
6. Remove solenoid and boot.
7. Drive out shift fork pivot pin.
8. Remove drive end pinion housing and spacer washer.
9. Remove shift fork from starter drive.
10. Slide overrunning clutch pinion gear toward commutator, drive stop retainer toward clutch pinion gear and remove the now-exposed snap-ring.
11. Remove overrunning clutch drive from armature shaft.
12. If field coils are good, stop disassembly at this point. If field coils must be replaced, remove ground brushes terminal screw and remove brushes, terminal and shunt wire. Remove pole shoe screws, using a ratchet-type impact driver and special wide screwdriver blade, then remove field coils.
13. Replacement of the brushes, inspection of the starter clutch and pinion, and inspection of the commutator procedures are the same as the reduction-gear starter procedures.

Assembly

1. Install field coils into frame, if removed.
2. Lubricate armature shaft and splines with engine oil.
3. Install starter drive, stop retainer, lock ring and spacer washer.
4. Install shift fork, with *narrow* leg of fork toward commutator.
5. Install pinion housing onto armature shaft, indexing shift fork with slot in housing.
6. Install shift fork pivot pin.
7. With clutch drive, shift fork, and pinion housing assembled onto the armature, slide armature into frame until pinion housing indexes with slot.
8. Install solenoid and boot, tightening bolts to 60-70 in. lbs.
9. Conect field coil wires to solenoid connector, making sure they do not touch frame.
10. Install brush holder plate, indexing tang in frame hole.
11. Place brushes in holders, making sure field coil wires do not interfere.
12. Install thrust washers on commutator end of armature shaft to obtain a maximum of 0.010 in. end-play.
13. Install commutator end head and through bolts. Tighten bolts to 40-50 in. lbs.
14. Measure drive gear pinion clearance; it should be $\frac{1}{8}$ in. Adjust by moving solenoid fore and aft as required.

FRONT END PLATE — STARTER FRAME — FIELD COILS — REAR END HOUSING — STARTER DRIVE — BRUSH COVER BAND — ARMATURE — BRUSHES — STARTER DRIVE PLUNGER LEVER — PLUNGER RETURN SPRING — STOP RING — STOP RING RETAINER — COVER

Starter motor

GROUND BRUSH — STARTER DRIVE ACTUATING COIL AND HOLDING COIL — TERMINAL SCREW — FIELD COILS — GROUND BRUSH — FIELD COIL BRUSHES

Field coil assembly

Autolite Positive Engagement Starter Motor

(Ford Motor Co.)

This starting motor is a series-parallel wound, four pole, four brush unit. It is equipped with an over-running clutch drive pinion, which is engaged with the flywheel ring gear by an actuating lever, operated by a movable pole piece. This pole piece is hinged to the starter frame and can drop into position through an opening in the frame.

Three conventional field coils are located at three pole piece positions. The fourth field coil is designed to serve also as an engaging coil and a hold-in coil for the operation of the drive pinion.

When the ignition switch is turned to the start position, the starter relay is energized and current flows from the battery to the starter motor terminal. This prime surge of current first flows through the starter engaging coil, creating a very strong magnetic field. This magnetism draws the movable pole piece down toward the starter frame, which then causes the lever attached to it to move the starter pinion into engagement with the flywheel ring gear.

When the movable pole shoe is fully seated, it opens the field coil, grounding contacts, and the starter is then in normal operation. A holding coil is used to hold the movable pole shoe in the fully seated position during the engine cranking operation.

Trucks, equipped with automatic transmissions have a starter neutral switch circuit control. This is to prevent operation of the starter if the selector lever is not in Neutral or Park.

This type starter is used on both Ford and late-model American Motors products.

Disassembly

1. Remove brush cover band and starter drive gear actuating lever cover. Observe the brush lead locations for reassembly, then remove the brushes from their holders.

   NOTE: factory brush length is $\frac{1}{2}$ in.; wear limit is $\frac{1}{4}$ in.
2. Remove the through bolts, starter drive gear housing and the drive gear actuating lever return spring.
3. Remove the pivot pin retaining the starter gear actuating lever and remove the lever and the armature.
4. Remove the stop ring retainer. Remove and discard the stop ring holding the drive gear to the armature shaft; then remove the drive gear assembly.
5. Remove the brush end plate.
6. Remove the two screws holding the ground brushes to the frame.
7. On the field coil that operates the starter drive gear actuating lever, bend the tab up on the field retainer and remove the field coil retainer.
8. Remove the three coil retaining screws. Unsolder the field coil leads from the terminal screw, then remove the pole shoes and coils from the frame (use a 300 watt iron).
9. Remove the starter terminal nut, washer, insulator and terminal from the starter frame.
10. Check the commutator for runout. If the commutator is rough, has flat spots, or is more than 0.005 in. out of round, reface the commutator. Clean the grooves in the commutator face.
11. Inspect the armature shaft and the two bearings for scoring and excessive wear. Replace if necessary.
12. Inspect the starter drive. If the gear teeth are pitted, broken, or excessively worn, replace the starter drive.

Assembly

1. Install starter terminal, insulator, washers and retaining nut in the frame. (Be sure to position the slot in the screw perpendicular to the frame end surface.)
2. Position coils and pole pieces, with the coil leads in the terminal screw slot, then install the retaining screws. As the pole screws are tightened, strike the frame several sharp hammer blows to align the pole shoes. Tighten, then stake the screws.
3. Install solenoid coil and retainer and bend the tabs to hold the coils to the frame.
4. Solder the field coils and solenoid wire to the starter terminal, using rosin-core solder and a 300 watt iron.
5. Check for continuity and ground connections in the assembled coils.

BATTERY — TO GENERATOR REGULATOR — STARTER RELAY — TO IGNITION COIL — S — I — STARTER — *Red-Blue Stripe* — AUTOMATIC TRANSMISSION ONLY STARTER NEUTRAL SWITCH CLOSED WITH SELECTOR IN N OR P POSITION — *Red-Blue Stripe* — STARTER SWITCH (ON IGNITION SWITCH) — TO BATTERY TERMINAL OF GENERATOR REGULATOR

Starting circuit

Starter Cranks Engine Slowly

CHECK THE BATTERY AND STARTER CABLES FOR GOOD ELECTRICAL CONTACT. LOOK FOR CORRODED OR LOOSE CONNECTIONS. IN PARTICULAR, ASSURE GOOD GROUND CONNECTIONS. CLEAN AND TIGHTEN THE CABLES AS NECESSARY.

CHECK BATTERY SPECIFIC GRAVITY.

| BATTERY SPECIFIC GRAVITY OK | BATTERY SPECIFIC GRAVITY LOW |

* PERFORM BATTERY TESTS. CHARGE OR REPLACE THE BATTERY AS NECESSARY. CHECK THE BATTERY AND STARTER RELAY FOR EXCESSIVE RESISTANCE.

* CHECK THE STARTER CRANKING VOLTAGE AND CURRENT DRAW.

| CURRENT DRAW LOW | CURRENT DRAW NORMAL OR HIGH |

* REMOVE THE STARTER, INSPECT TEST AND REPAIR IT AS NECESSARY.

* REMOVE THE STARTER AND CHECK THE CURRENT DRAW AT NO LOAD.

| CURRENT DRAW ABOVE OR BELOW SPECIFICATIONS | CURRENT DRAW IS NORMAL |

* INSPECT, TEST AND REPAIR THE STARTER AS NECESSARY.

6. Position the solenoid coil ground terminal over the nearest ground screw hole.
7. Position the ground brushes to the starter frame and install retaining screws.
8. Position the brush end plate to the frame, with the end plate boss in the frame slot.
9. Lightly Lubriplate the armature shaft splines and install the starter drive gear assembly in the shaft. Install a new retaining stop ring and stop ring retainer.
10. Position the fiber thrust washer on the commutator end of the armature shaft, then position the armature in the starter frame.
11. Position the starter drive gear actuating lever to the frame and starter drive assembly, and install the pivot pin.
NOTE: fill drive gear housing bore ¼ full of grease.
12. Position the drive actuating lever return spring and the drive gear housing to the frame, then install and tighten the through bolts. Do not pinch brush leads between brush plate and frame. Be sure that the stop ring retainer is properly seated in the drive housing.
13. Install the brushes in the brush holders and center the brush springs on the brushes.
14. Position the drive gear actuating lever cover on the starter and install the brush cover band with a new gasket.
15. Check starter no-load amperage draw.

Autolite Solenoid Actuated Starter Motor

(Ford Motor Co.)

This starter motor, usually used with late-model 460 engines, is a four-brush, four-field, four-pole wound unit. The frame encloses a wound armature, which is supported at the drive end by caged needle bearings and at the commutator end by a sintered copper bushing. The four pole shoes are retained to the frame by one pole screw apiece, and on each pole shoe is wound a ribbon-type field coil connected in series-parallel.

The solenoid is mounted to a flange on the starter drive housing, which encloses the entire shift mechanism and solenoid plunger. The solenoid, following standard industry practice, utilizes two windings—a pull-in winding and a hold-in winding.

Disassembly

1. Disconnect the copper strap from the solenoid starter terminal, remove the remaining screws and remove the solenoid.
2. Loosen the retaining screw and slide the brush cover band back far enough to gain access to the brushes.
3. Remove the brushes from their holders, then remove the through bolts and separate the drive end housing from the frame and brush end plate.
NOTE: factory brush length is ½

Ford solenoid starter motor (© Ford Co)

1 Drive housing
2 Shift lever bolt
3 Shift lever nut and lockwasher
4 Pin
5 Shift lever
6 Solenoid plunger
6A Solenoid return spring

7 Solenoid case
8 Screw and lockwasher
9 Grommet
10 Field frame
11 Through bolts
12 Thrust collar
13 Snap-ring
14 Retainer

15 Overrunning clutch assembly
16 Armature
17 Braking washer
18 Commutator end frame
19 Brush springs
20 Washer
21 Insulated brush holders

22 Grounded brush holder
23 Brushes
24 Screws
25 Field coils
26 Insulators
27 Pole shoes
28 Screws

Typical Delco-Remy starter motor (exploded view) light duty Chevrolet illustrated
(© Chevrolet Div., G.M. Corp)

in., wear limit 1/4 in.

4. Remove the solenoid plunger and shift fork. These two items can be separated from each other by removing the roll pin.
5. Remove the armature and drive assembly from the frame. Remove the drive stop ring and slide the drive off the armature shaft.
6. Remove the drive stop ring retainer from the drive housing.
7. Inspection of the commutator, armature and bearings, and pinion gear procedures is the same as the positive engagement starter procedures.

Assembly

1. Lubricate the armature shaft splines with Lubriplate, then install drive assembly and a new stop ring.
2. Lubricate shift lever pivot pin with Lubriplate, then position solenoid plunger and shift lever assembly in the drive housing.
3. Place a new retainer in the drive housing. Apply a small amount of Lubriplate to the drive end of the armature shaft, then place armature and drive assembly into the drive housing, indexing the shift lever tangs with the drive assembly.
4. Apply a small amount of Lubriplate to the commutator end of the armature shaft, then position the frame and field assembly to the drive housing.
5. Position the brush plate assembly to the frame, making sure it

properly indexes. Install through bolts and tighten to 45-85 in. lbs.
6. Install brushes into their holders and make sure leads are not touching any interior starter components.
7. Place the rubber gasket between the solenoid mount and the frame surface.
8. Place the starter solenoid in position with metal gasket and spring, install heat shield (if so equipped) and install solenoid screws.
9. Connect copper strap and install cover band.

Delco-Remy Starter Motor

(General Motors Corp.)

There are many different versions of the Delco-Remy starter, depending upon application. In general, six-cylinder engines use a unit having four field coils in series between the terminal and armature. Standard V8 engines use, depending on displacement, one of three types: one has two field coils in series with the armature and parallel to each other; another has two field coils in parallel between the field terminal and ground, and another has three field coils in series with the armature and one field connected between the motor terminal and ground. Heavy-duty starter motors, such as used on some of the largest G.M. high-output engines (over 400 cu. in.) have series compound windings.

In spite of these differences, all Delco-Remy starters are disassembled and assembled in essentially the same manner.

Disassembly

1. Disconnect the field coil connectors from the motor solenoid terminal.
NOTE: on models so equipped, remove solenoid mounting screws.
2. Remove the through bolts.
3. Remove commutator end frame, field frame and armature assembly from drive housing.
4. Remove the overruning clutch from the armature shaft as follows:
   a. Slide the two-piece thrust collar off the end of the armature shaft.
   b. Slide a standard 1/2 in. pipe coupling or other spacer onto the shaft so that the end of the coupling butts against the edge of the retainer.
   c. Tap the end of the coupling with a hammer, driving retainer towards armature end of snap-ring.

Delco-Remy starter solenoid
(© Chevrolet Div., G.M. Corp)

Forcing snap ring over armature shaft-Delco-Remy motor

(© Chevrolet Div., G.M. Corp)

Prestolite starter motor—exploded view
(© American Motors Corp)

d. Remove snap-ring from its groove in the shaft using pliers. Slide retainer and clutch from armature shaft.

5. Disassemble brush assembly from field frame by releasing the V-spring and removing the support pin. The brush holders, brushes and springs now can be pulled out as a unit and the leads disconnected.

6. On models so equipped, separate solenoid from lever housing.

Cleaning and Inspection

1. Clean parts with a rag, but do not immerse the parts in a solvent. Immersion in a solvent will dissolve the grease that is packed in the clutch mechanism and damage the armature and field coil insulation.

2. Test overrunning clutch action. The pinion should turn freely in the overrunning direction and must not slip in the cranking direction. Check pinion teeth to see that they have not been chipped, cracked, or excessively worn. Replace the unit if necessary.

3. Inspect the armature commutator. If the commutator is rough or out of round, it should be turned down and undercut.
CAUTION: Undercut the insulation between the commutator bars by 1/32 in.
This undercut must be the full width of the insulation and flat at the bottom; a triangular groove will not be satisfactory. Some starter motor models use a molded armature commutator design and no attempt to undercut the insulation should be made or serious damage may result to the commutator.

Assembly

1. Install brushes into holders. Install solenoid, if so equipped.
2. Assemble insulated and grounded brush holder together using the

V-spring and position the assembled unit on the support pin. Push holders and spring to bottom of support and rotate spring to engage the slot in support. Attach ground wire to grounded brush and field lead wire to insulated brush, then repeat for other brush sets.

3. Assemble overruning clutch to armature shaft as follows:
   a. Lubricate drive end of shaft with silicone lubricant.
   b. Slide clutch assembly onto shaft with pinion outward.
   c. Slide retainer onto shaft with cupped surface facing away from pinion.
   d. Stand armature up on a wood surface, commutator downwards. Position snapring on upper end of shaft and drive it onto shaft with a small block of wood and a hammer. Slide snap-ring into groove.
   e. Install thrust collar onto shaft with shoulder next to snap-ring.
   f. With retainer on one side of snap-ring and thrust collar on the other side, squeeze together with two sets of pliers until ring seats in retainer. On models without thrust collar, use a washer. Remember to remove washer before continuing.

4. Lubricate drive end bushing with silicone lubricant, then slide armature and clutch assembly into place, at the same time engaging shift lever with clutch.

5. Position field frame over armature and apply sealer (silicone) between frame and solenoid case. Position frame against drive housing, making sure brushes are not damaged in the process.

6. Lubricate commutator end bushing with silicone lubricant, place a leather brake washer on the armature shaft and slide commutator end frame onto shaft. Install through bolts and tighten to 65 in. lbs.

7. Reconnect field coil connector's

to the solenoid motor terminal. Install solenoid mounting screws, if so equipped.

8. Check pinion clearance; it should be 0.010-0.140 in. on all models.

Prestolite Starter Motor

Disassembly

1. Disconnect solenoid by removing motor terminal nut and lockwasher and the two retaining bolts.
2. Remove link cover boot and solenoid.
3. Remove starter through bolts, then remove commutator end head and frame.
4. Remove shift lever pin retainer, boot and pivot pin.
5. Remove armature, drive and shift lever from pinion housing.
6. Remove drive assembly as follows:
   a. Slide thrust collar off armature shaft.
   b. Using a standard 1/2 in. pipe connector drive snap-ring retainer off shaft.
   c. Remove snap-ring from groove, then remove drive assembly.
7. See the Delco-Remy starter section for cleaning and inspection procedures.

Assembly

1. Assemble overruning clutch to

Forcing snap ring into retainer—Delco-Remy motor
(© Chevrolet Div., G.M. Corp)

armature shaft as follows:
a. Lubricate drive end and splines with Lubriplate.
b. Install clutch assembly onto shaft.
c. Install snap-ring retainer, cuped surface facing end of shaft.
d. Install snap-ring into groove. Use a new snap-ring if necessary.
e. Install thrust collar onto shaft, shoulder against snap-ring.

f. Force retainer over snap-ring in the same manner as for Delco-Remy starter.
2. Lubricate overrunning clutch shift collar and drive end bushing with engine oil.
3. Hold shift lever in position on collar and assemble armature, drive and shift lever into housing.
4. Install shift lever pivot pin, boot and retainer.
5. Install frame and field coil as-

sembly, making sure brushes are not damaged in the process.
6. Saturate felt washer (commutator head) with engine oil, drain excess and install washer.
7. Install through bolts and tighten to 65 in. lbs.
8. Check armature end-play; it should be 0.005-0.030 in. Adjust, if necessary, by adding or removing thrust washers at commutator end of shaft.
9. Check pinion clearance; it should be 0.010-0.140 in.

Ignition System

The Ignition System is divided into two circuits; a low voltage or primary circuit, and a high voltage or secondary circuit.

The primary circuit carries current, (usually modified for ignition by a resistor, on 12-volt systems) at battery voltage. It includes the battery, ignition-starter switch, starter relay, ignition ballast resistor, primary winding of the coil, condenser, contact points, and ground.

The secondary circuit begins with the ignition coil. Secondary voltage is a product of the coil and emerges from the secondary terminal and flows through a cable to the distributor cap. It is distributed by the rotor, through the distributor cap and cables, to the spark plugs, and to ground.

CAUTION: Secondary circuit pressure could reach as high as 30,000 volts.

Coil Polarity

Coil polarity is predetermined and must match the circuit polarity of the system being tested. It is an established fact that the electron flow through the spark plug is better from the hotter center plug electrode-to-ground than by the opposite route, from ground-to-center electrode. Therefore, negative ground polarity has been established as standard. There is about a 14% difference in required voltage of the two polarity designs at idling speed. This differ-

ential increases with engine speed.

Correct coil polarity can be checked on the truck by connecting a voltmeter negative lead to the ignition coil secondary wire, and the positive voltmeter lead to engine ground. If the voltmeter reading is up-scale, polarity is correct: if voltmeter reading is down-scale, polarity is reversed.

Lately, automotive batteries are designed with the battery posts on the same side of the battery, opposed to the earlier diagonal post design. Therefore, terminal size and cable length will discourage improper battery installation. This results in the battery and distributor terminals of the coil being the most likely points of possible reversal of polarity.

Another tentative, but less precise, method is to hold a regular carbon-cored wooden lead pencil in the gap between a disconnected spark plug wire and ground. It is possible to observe the direction of spark flow, from wire-to-pencil-to-ground when polarity is correct.

CAUTION: Hold the pencil with a heavy glove or you may observe the spark flow along your fingers.

Primary Circuit Test

A quick, tentative check of the 12 volt ignition primary circuit (including ballast resistor) can be made with a simple voltmeter, as follows:
1. With engine at operating temperature, but stopped, and the distributor side of the ignition coil grounded with a jumper wire, hook up a voltmeter between the ignition coil (switch

side) and a good ground.
2. Jiggle the ignition switch (switch on) and watch the meter. An unstable needle will indicate a defective ignition switch.
3. With ignition switch on (engine stopped) the voltmeter should read 5.5 to 7 volts for 12-volt systems.
4. Crank the engine. Voltmeter should read at least 9 volts during cranking period.
5. Now remove the jumper wire from the coil. Start the engine. Voltmeter should read from 9.0 volts to 11.5 volts (depending upon generator output) while running.

COIL

Coil Resistance, with Ohmmeter —Primary Circuit

To check ignition coil resistance, primary side, switch ohmmeter to low scale. Connect the ohmmeter leads across the primary terminals of the coil and read the low ohms scale.

RIGHT **WRONG**

COIL   BATTERY

NOTE: If just one side opens up, the resistance will be doubled.

SHORTED

OPEN

Ballast resistor

Coils requiring ballast resistors should read about 1.0 ohm resistance. 12-volt coils, not requiring external ballast resistors, should read about 4.0 ohms resistance.

Coil Resistance, with Ohmmeter —Secondary Circuit

To check ignition coil resistance, secondary side, switch ohmmeter to high scale. Connect one test lead to the distributor cap end of the coil secondary cable. Connect the other test lead to the distributor terminal of the coil. A coil in satisfactory condition should show between 4 K and 8 K on the scale. Some special coils (Mallory, etc.) may show a resistance as high as 13 K. If the reading is much lower than 4 K, the coil probably has shorted secondary turns. If the reading is extremely high (40 K or more) the secondary winding is either open, there is a bad connection at the coil terminal, or resistance is high in the cable.

If both primary and secondary windings of the coil test good, but the ignition system is still unsatisfactory, check the system further.

Ballast Resistor

Some sort of ballast resistor is used with most trucks equipped with 12-volt ignition systems. This resistance may be built into the ignition coil, or it may be a special wire of specific resistance, comprising the primary ignition circuit.

To provide a greater safety margin of sufficient voltage for high speed operation, a special ignition coil is used with whatever type of ballast

resistance is used. Other reasons for ballast resistance are to limit to a safe maximum the primary current flow through the coil and through the distributor contact points. This helps protect the contact points at slow engine speed when they are closed for a longer period of time. The resistor also protects against excessive build-up of primary current when the ignition switch is on with the engine stopped and ignition points closed.

On some systems, the resistor is removed from the ignition circuit during engine cranking, then with the ignition connected directly to battery voltage. This keeps ignition voltage as high as possible while cranking. The by-pass type system can have the by-pass factor built into the ignition switch, or it may be part of the starter solenoid.

Primary Circuit—Distributor Side

With the voltmeter on the 16-20 volt scale, connect one voltmeter lead to ground. Connect the other voltmeter lead to the distributor side of the coil. Remove the high tension wire from the coil and ground it. Close ignition switch and slowly bump the starter switch to open and close the points. When the distributor contacts make and break during cranking, the voltmeter reading should be from one-third to one-half battery voltage. Normally, with engine stopped and with points open,

the reading will be the same as battery voltage. Furthermore, with the engine stopped and the points closed and in good condition, the reading will be close to zero.

If while cranking, the voltmeter reading remains zero or close to it, the trouble may be one or more of the following:

A. No current at distributor. Disconnect the distributor primary wire from the top of the coil. Now, take a voltmeter reading from the distributor terminal of the coil to make sure that the current is going through the circuit.

B. Points are not opening because of mechanical (points or cam) failure or maladjustment. Dual points in parallel, one set not opening.

C. The movable point, the stud at the primary distributor wire terminal, or the pigtail wire is grounded.

D. The condenser has a dead short. An ohmmeter check of the condenser will show this condition. Connect one test lead of an ohmmeter to the body of the condenser and the other test lead to the pigtail. If the meter shows the slightest reading, the condenser is shorted. With a few exceptions, a visual inspection of the distributor contact points will generally indicate the condition of the condenser. An open, or shorted condenser will not function. A condenser of too great capacity will cause metal to transfer from the movable distributor point to the stationary point. This will cause a pit on the movable point. An under-capacity condenser, causes metal to leave the stationary point and build up on the movable point.

Pitting caused by low capacity

Pitting caused by high capacity

Any excessive resistance in either the primary or secondary circuits will upset the sensitive balance of the ignition system and cause the ignition points to pit.

Ignition Point Dwell

It is very important that point dwell be adjusted to exact specifications before any attempt is made to time the engine.

Point dwell (cam angle) is the degree value for the closed attitude of ignition points for each make-and-break period of a distributor cycle. It is that phase of ignition system functioning during which the coil becomes saturated (builds up to voltage capacity) for its next discharge at the moment of point opening.

Some current production truck engines demand in excess of 23,000 spark plug firings per minute to fire their cylinders. This places a tremendous demand upon the ignition system, particularly the aspect of coil

build up (saturation) and discharge time.

While it is true that ignition points can be adjusted by using a thickness gauge, the results, even when using new points, are sometimes inconclusive. Point gap is incidental to particular distributor cam shape and could be misleading. This is one reason for the use of a dwell meter.

Another point in favor of the dwell meter is its ability to detect high resistance, (oxidized points, poor connections, etc.). The dwell meter, a modified voltmeter, often includes a band on the extreme high end of the scale to indicate excessive point resistance. Follow instrument manufacturer's instructions to get the most out of your particular equipment.

The most informative procedure is to use both methods (dwell meter and point gap) then compare the two. Many times the comparison is surprising, and leads to the location of previously unnoticed distributor troubles.

Using the Dwell Meter

1. With distributor vacuum control line disconnected and plugged, turn the meter selector switch to the eight lobe position (eight cylinder engines) or the six lobe position (six cylinder engines). On four cylinder engines, follow instrument makers' instructions, or select the eight lobe position and double the reading for eight cylinder engines.

2. Connect one tach-dwell meter

lead to the coil terminal of the distributor and the other meter lead to ground.

3. Start the engine and operate it at idle speed. Note reading on dwell meter. On eight cylinder engines, (single contacts) dwell should read 26°-32°. Double contacts should read 26°-32° (each set), or 34°-40° combined. Six cylinder engines should show a dwell of 36°-45° and four cylinder engines, a dwell in the area of 40°. These are tentative figures and cover a wide latitude. It is therefore, urgent that manufacturers' specifications be followed without exception.

An excessive variation in dwell, (over 3°) as engine speed is increased usually indicates a worn distributor shaft, bushing, breaker plate or secondary circuits.

NOTE: on some Auto-Lite or Ford distributors, a pivoted, movable type breaker plate is used. This pivoted plate, operated by the vacuum control unit, carries the contacts and rotates on its own center, independent of the distributor cam center. This design affects a running dwell variation of as much as 12°. To check this type distributor, hook up the distributor vacuum control line. Increase engine rpm and observe dwell changes at various engine rpm and throttle attitudes.

NOTE: experience dictates that all distributor adjustments are best performed with the use of a good off-car distributor tester.

Dwell information at idle speed is given for each engine in the Tune-up Specification Table in the truck Section.

Ignition Timing

Ignition timing is a term applied to the relationship of piston travel and moment of spark in a gas engine.

Due to the many variables involved, such as compression ratio,

CARBON FOULED	OIL FOULED	GAP BRIDGED	OVERHEATING	PRE-IGNITION
IDENTIFIED BY BLACK, DRY FLUFFY CARBON DEPOSITS ON INSULATOR TIPS, EXPOSED SHELL SURFACES AND ELECTRODES. CAUSED BY TOO COLD A PLUG, WEAK IGNITION, DIRTY AIR CLEANER, DEFECTIVE FUEL PUMP, TOO RICH A FUEL MIXTURE, IMPROPERLY OPERATING HEAT RISER OR EXCESSIVE IDLING. CAN BE CLEANED.	IDENTIFIED BY WET, BLACK DEPOSITS ON THE INSULATOR, SHELL BORE AND ELECTRODES. CAUSED BY EXCESSIVE OIL ENTERING COMBUSTION CHAMBER THROUGH WORN RINGS AND PISTONS, EXCESSIVE CLEARANCE BETWEEN VALVE GUIDES AND STEMS, OR WORN OR LOOSE BEARINGS. CAN BE CLEANED.	IDENTIFIED BY DEPOSIT BUILD-UP CLOSING GAP BETWEEN ELECTRODES. CAUSED BY OIL OR CARBON FOULING. IF DEPOSITS ARE NOT EXCESSIVE, THE PLUG CAN BE CLEANED. **Spark Plug Inspection**	IDENTIFIED BY A WHITE OR OR LIGHT GRAY INSULATOR WITH SMALL BLACK OR GRAY BROWN SPOTS AND WITH BLUISH-BURNT APPEARANCE OF ELECTRODES. CAUSED BY ENGINE OVERHEATING, WRONG TYPE OF FUEL, LOOSE SPARK PLUGS, TOO HOT A PLUG, LOW FUEL PUMP PRESSURE OR INCORRECT IGNITION TIMING.	IDENTIFIED BY MELTED ELECTRODES AND POSSIBLY BLISTERED INSULATOR. METALLIC DEPOSITS ON INSULATOR INDICATE ENGINE DAMAGE. CAUSED BY WRONG TYPE OF FUEL, INCORRECT IGNITION TIMING OR ADVANCE, TOO HOT A PLUG, BURNT VALVES OR ENGINE OVERHEATING. REPLACE THE PLUG.

temperature, humidity, elevation, fuel octane value, engine condition, work load, etc. published timing data must be considered approximate; some tolerance permitted.

Ignition timing consists of basic (prime) timing and dynamic (variable) timing.

It is very important that point dwell be correct before setting timing.

Basic Timing

Basic timing can be checked quite accurately by using one of the many timing lights, (strobe-flashers) available. A timing light, when properly connected to No. 1 spark wire, (or the exact opposite cylinder in firing sequence of any multiple cylinder, four stroke cycle automotive engine) will indicate the moment of ignition for that cylinder.

NOTE: Some International Harvester engines are timed on No. 8 cylinder.

Index markings may be on either the rotating member of the crankshaft, (vibration damper or flywheel) with the pointer stationary, or the index may be on an engine stationary member, with the pointer or scribe mark rotating.

NOTE: because ignition timing is directly affected by distributor contact spacing, points should be adjusted to specifications before timing is attempted.

1. Unless otherwise stated by the manufacturer, the distributor control vacuum line should be disconnected, and plugged, to prevent fuel induction disturbance.
2. Hook up the timing light, (power or otherwise) according to the equipment instructions.
3. With engine at operating temperature and adjusted to function smoothly, run engine at low idle. Use a tachometer and be sure the rpm is below the speed of governor advance influence.
4. Shine the timing light on the indexing area (balancer or flywheel) and note the degree value indicated by the pointer.

TIMING LIGHT

TIMING MARKS
CRANKSHAFT PULLEY

5. Rotate the distributor body one way or the other until the pointer appears to correspond with the index value published.

CAUTION: Power timing (on the road adjusting for ping cannot be tolerated, especially on engines equipped with exhaust emission control devices.

Possible Indications and Causes

If The Flash Is Intermittent:
A. The test light is defective.
B. The test light has a bad connection.
C. Distributor points are bad or badly out of adjustment.
D. Distributor grounding is poor.
E. Distributor cap is cracked or tracking.
F. Spark plug gaps too small.
G. Broken or badly worn rotor.

If Pointer Appears To Move On The Index Scale (Unfixed At Constant Engine Speed):
A. Distributor governor weights loose or with broken springs.
B. Distributor shaft or bushing worn.
C. Rotor loose or broken.
D. Distributor base plate loose.
E. Cam lobes worn.

Dynamic Timing

To accurately check and calibrate dynamic timing through all attitudes of engine operation, more sophisticated equipment than the common strobe-light is needed. A distributor tester, an oscillograph, or one of the more complex timing lights equipped with an advance value index is needed.

It is possible, however, to determine to some degree, the action of both governor advance and vacuum control mechanisms with a tachometer and a timing light.

NOTE: before checking dynamic timing with a timing light, extend the index graduations on the timing member involved, by about 30°. This should be done with chalk or white paint, in increments of 5°, on the rotating member, whether that member carries the index or the pointer. Some measurements and extreme care will be necessary in making this extension.

Governor Control

1. Repeat Steps 1 through 4 of basic timing procedures.
2. By watching the timing light flash on the timing index, determine the exact engine rpm that starts the distributor to advance. Compare this with published specifications.
3. It is equally important that distributor advance progresses steadily with engine speed. It is

just as important that a decrease in engine speed will smoothly and gradually return the index pointer to its original position.
4. After checking the indications against specifications, turn the engine off and make corrections, if necessary.

NOTE: dynamic timing cannot be accurately checked using the above method; therefore it is recommended that no attempt be made to modify advance curves (especially on exhaust emission equipped engines) unless the proper distributor test facilities are available.

Vacuum Control

Vacuum control action can be observed and evaluated by using a tachometer and a timing light.

This type of spark control, whether used as the only means of control or used in conjunction with a governor type mechanism, operates through a spring loaded vacuum chamber. This chamber is attached to the side of the distributor, then, through linkage, to the breaker plate (or pick-up assembly of transistorized distributors).

Carefully metered vacuum is piped to one side of the spring loaded diaphragm of the vacuum unit. Vacuum controlled timing is then the result of differential (vacuum-spring) pressures.

In the case of vacuum-only controls, (Ford Loadmatic, etc.) metering is more critical; therefore, a manometer or a very accurately calibrated vacuum gauge is required, in conjunction with the tachometer and timing light.

To Check Vacuum Control:

1. Hook up a tachometer and the timing light in the conventional manner.
2. Connect a good vacuum gauge or a manometer into the vacuum line between the carburetor and distributor.
3. With engine at operating temperature and adjusted to function smoothly, run engine at low idle.
4. Shine timing light on the indexing area and observe the vacuum reading and timing light index relationship.
5. Compare these readings with published vacuum advance data.

Indications and Causes

If timing is not within degree range as specified vacuum reading, a faulty vacuum or mechanical control mechanism, or Loadmatic control mechanism is defective.

If all parts are good, adjustments in control valve can sometimes be

STEP STOP

CALIBRATION WASHERS

DIAPHRAGM

RETURN SPRING

VACUUM FITTING

SPACING WASHER

made by changing the calibration washers between the vacuum chamber spring and the spring retaining nut. Adding washers will decrease the amount of advance. Removing washers will increase the advance. After one vacuum setting has been adjusted, the others should be checked. Do not change original rpm setting when going to a different vacuum setting.

If other settings are not within limits, there is incorrect spring tension, leakage in the vacuum chamber and/or the line, or the wrong stop has been used in the vacuum chamber of the diaphragm housing.

Electronic Ignition Systems

Ford-Autolite Breaker Point System

This transistorized system uses conventional breaker points, but does not use a condenser. The only external components that serve to distinguish this system from a conventional ignition are an external ballast resistor, a tachometer connecting block, a cold-start relay and an amplifier (transistor switching device).

The major hurdle to increasing primary ignition circuit voltage in point-type is that the points burn very easily. This system uses a transistor to by-pass that weakness.

The design of the main transistor in this system allows it to conduct current from the wire running into it

to the wire running out of it—if it is connected to a complete electrical circuit. However, as the current passes through the transistor, it breaks that current down into two paths, one of high voltage and one of low voltage. This transistor is called a PNP transistor because of its three component parts. The top part of the transistor is called a collector (C), the middle part the base (B), and lower part the emitter ·(E). The two currents that form inside the transistor are the high current one, or power current, which runs from E to C and the low current, or the switching current, which runs from B to E.

The power current is connected to the primary side of the ignition coil and the switching current is connected to the ignition points. This allows high current to energize the primary circuit in the coil while permitting a much smaller current to pass through the points.

In order for the transistor to pass current, both the power circuit and the switching circuit must make a complete circuit. This has made adaptation of this transistor system to an

automotive ignition system relatively simple.

When the ignition key is turned on and the breaker points are closed, current passes from the battery, through the ignition switch, to the amplifier which contains the PNP transistor. As the current from the battery passes through the transistor, the two transistor circuits are connected as follows: the power current is connected to the coil, and the switching current is connected to the points. Since the points are closed, both transistor circuits are complete and the primary side of the ignition coil builds up a magnetic field. When the ignition points open, the switching circuit in the transistor (B to E) opens causing the transistor to stop passing current. When the transistor stops passing current, the primary ignition circuit breaks down, and the induction of the magnetic field from the primary circuit in the coil into the secondary circuit in the coil takes place. However, since the initial voltage in the primary circuit in the coil was much higher than in a conventional system, the voltage buildup in

Autolite transistor distributor (© Ford Motor Co.)

Autolite amplifier assembly (© Ford Motor Co.)

Autolite resistor block (© Ford Motor Co.)

the coil will be much quicker and will rise to a higher level than in a conventional ignition system.

The other components of the system, all of which are contained in the amplifier housing with the PNP transistor, are a condenser, a zener diode, a toroid, a base-to-emitter resistor, and a collector resistor.

The base reisstor is similar to the conventional ignition resistor wire and is located between the distributor and the transistor (heat sink). It provides an 8.0 ohm resistance which is necessary for current limitation and it should not be replaced with any other wire, resistance or otherwise. To do so would result in immediate transistor destruction.

The collector and emitter resistors both are located in a ballast resistor block made of white ceramic for electrical and thermal insulation. Both resistors serve the same purpose —limiting system current and control of voltages within their respective circuits. The two resistors are in series in the collector-emitter circuit, together with the ignition coil, toroid and transistor. The emitter resistor also is in series with the base resistor, the toroid, and the transistor, in the base-emitter circuit. The transistor and emitter resistance therefore are common to both circuits. The combined resistances in each circuit permit a base current of approximately 1.0 amp. and a collector current of approximately 12 amps.

A tach block is included in the circuit for attaching tachometer and dwellmeter leads. In the conventional system, these leads are connected to the distributor primary lead and ground, but in the transistorized circuit, the connection of the leads in this manner would jump the contact

gap, contributing to a current buildup in the base circuit and in the collector circuit which would overheat and burn out the transistor. The area surrounding the collector terminal is colored *red* for the meter red lead while the area surrounding the emitter terminal is colored *black* for the meter black lead.

A cold start relay is incorporated into the circuit at the starter relay, interrupting the conventional battery-to-coil lead. The purpose of this is to furnish additional current to the coil primary windings during situations when the starter draw is excessive. The cold start relay contacts normally are closed; only opening during the cranking cycle. However, when the available battery voltage drops below a predetermined value during the cranking cycle, they again close, bypassing the ignition resistor and furnishing full battery current to the system.

The distributor differs from the conventional distributor only in the absence of the condenser and in the highly polished breaker cam. Because one of the big advantages of the transistor ignition is long breaker point life, wear on the rubbing block must be reduced to a minimum. Because the current at the breaker points is so small, the amount of pitting that occurs during normal operation is hardly measurable and point life should be indefinite. The points should be set to .020 in. gap and high-temperature grease used for cam lubrication.

When testing the transistor ignition distributor in a test machine, incorporate a condenser into the primary-to-ground circuit using a jumper wire. This will prevent point pitting or oxidation during testing.

CAUTION: When connecting an in-car tachometer to the Ford System, always shut the tachometer leads that go to the coil IGN terminal and ignition switch with a 10 in. length of Ford ignition resistor wire, part No. COLF-12250-A, to prevent

Autolite tach block (© Ford Motor Co.)

tachometer damage. The higher current draw of the transistor system can ruin a tach is this precaution is not taken.

Troubleshooting

Ignition problems are caused by a failure in the primary or secondary circuit, or incorrect ignition timing. Isolate the trouble as follows:

1. Remove the coil high tension lead from the distributor cap.
2. Disconnect the brown wire from the starter relay "I" terminal and the red and blue wire from the starter relay "S" terminal.
3. Turn the ignition switch on.
4. While holding the high tension lead approximately 1/4 in. from the engine block, crank the engine by using a remote starter switch between the starter relay "S" and battery terminals.

If the spark is good, the trouble lies in the secondary (high voltage) circuit. If there is no spark or a weak spark, the trouble is in the primary (low voltage) circuit.

A breakdown or energy loss in the primary circuit can be caused by:

1. Defective primary wiring.
2. Improperly adjusted, contaminated or defective distributor points.
3. Defective amplifier assembly.

The trouble can be isolated by performing a primary circuit test.

A breakdown or enery loss in the secondary circuit can be caused by:

1. Fouled or improperly adjusted spark plugs.
2. Defective high voltage wiring.
3. High voltage leakage across the

Autolite cold start relay (© Ford Motor Co.)

Primary circuit connected to PNP transistor (© Ford Motor Co.)

Autolite transistor ignition system schematic (© Ford Motor Co.)

coil, distributor cap, or rotor.

To isolate a problem in the secondary circuit, turn the ignition switch off, remove the remote starter switch from the starter relay, install the coil high tension lead in the distributor cap, the red and blue wire to the starter relay (this goes on the "S" terminal) and the brown wire to the starter relay (this goes on the "I" terminal) and perform a secondary circuit test.

Primary Circuit Tests

CAUTION: Do not use any other procedure, conventional short-cut, or connect test equipment in any other manner than described, or extensive damage can be caused to the transistor ignition system.

Connect a dwell meter to the tachometer block. Connect the black lead to the black (large) terminal and the red lead to the red (small) terminal.

With the remote starter switch installed and the ignition switch on, ground the coil high tension wire and crank the engine and observe the dwell reading.

0° Dwell

1. The distributor points are contaminated or are not closing.
2. An open circuit in the distributor lead to the amplifier.

To determine which item listed is causing the trouble, proceed as follows:

Disconnect the distributor lead at the bullet connector and connect a voltmeter red lead to the red (small) tach block terminal and the voltmeter black lead to the distributor lead from the distributor. *Do not connect the voltmeter to the lead from the amplifier.* Crank the engine and note the voltmeter reading.

If a steady indication of voltage is obtained, the trouble is in the distributor lead to the amplifier. Absence of any voltage indication on the voltmeter shows that there is an open circuit between the distributor lead and the breaker point ground.

0-45° Dwell

1. The transistor and the primary circuit are functioning properly.
2. The trouble could be in the secondary circuit.

45° Dwell

1. No power from the ignition switch.
2. The distributor points are closed and not opening.
3. Defective amplifier assembly.

To determine which of the three items listed is causing the trouble, proceed as follows:

Disconnect the distributor lead at the bullet connector, and crank the engine. If the dwellmeter indicates 0° dwell, the distributor points are not opening. If 45° dwell is indicated, the amplifier is malfunctioning

Autolite transistor ignition troubleshooting chart (© Ford Motor Co.)

or there is no power from the ignition switch.

Use a voltmeter or test light to determine if the transistor (amplifier assembly) is at fault. Connect the voltmeter to the red-green lead terminal of the ballast resistor and to ground. Crank the engine.

Absence of any voltage indication on the voltmeter shows there is an open circuit, or no power between the ignition switch and the amplifier. The ballast resistor could be defective. Replace it with a good ballast resistor, and repeat the test.

A steady indication of voltage on the voltmeter indicates either a defective amplifier or the coil to amplifier lead is defective or improperly connected to the ballast resistor. Proceed as follows:

1. Disconnect the amplifier at the quick disconnect.
2. Connect an ohmmeter across the outside terminals of the amplifier side of the quick disconnect.
3. Reverse the ohmmeter leads.

If a very high resistance is obtained one way and a very low or *zero* resistance is obtained the other way, the amplifier is not defective. Check the coil to amplifier wiring for a loose connection or defective wiring.

After a repair has been made, run through the test again to check for any other malfunctions.

Secondary Circuit Tests

Use conventional system test procedures.

Ford-Motorcraft Solid-State Ignition System

The Ford-Motorcraft Solid-State Ignition System is a pulse triggered, breakerless, transistor controlled ignition system. The system utilizes most of the standard ignition components, but substitutes an amplifier module and magnetic pickup assembly for the conventional ignition contact points.

Operation

With the ignition switch "on", the primary circuit is on and the ignition coil is energized. When the armature "spokes" approach the magnetic pickup coil assembly, they induce a voltage which tells the amplifier to turn the coil primary current off. A timing circuit in the amplifier module will turn the current on again after the coil field has collapsed. When the current is "on", it flows from the battery through the ignition switch, the primary windings of the ignition coil, and through the amplifier module circuits to ground. When the current is off, the magnetic field built up in the ignition coil is allowed to collapse, inducing a high voltage into the secondary windings of the coil. High

Ford solid state ignition system
(© Ford Motor Co.)

voltage is produced each time the field is thus built up and collapsed.

The high voltage flows through the coil high tension lead to the distributor cap where the rotor distributes it to one of the spark plug terminals in the distributor cap. This process is repeated for every power stroke of the engine.

Ignition system troubles are caused by a failure in the primary and/or the secondary circuit; incorrect ignition timing; or incorrect distributor advance. Circuit failures may be caused by shorts, corroded or dirty terminals, loose connections, defective wire insulation, cracked distributor cap or rotor, defective pick-up coil assembly or amplifier module, defective distributor points, fouled spark plugs, or by improper dwell angle.

If an engine starting or operating trouble is attributed to the ignition system, start the engine and verify the complaint. On engines that will not start, be sure that there is gasoline in the fuel tank and that fuel is reaching the carburetor. Then locate the ignition system problem by an oscilloscope test or by a spark intensity test.

Primary Circuit Testing

A breakdown or energy loss in the primary circuit can be caused by: defective primary wiring, loose or corroded connections, inoperative or defective magnetic pick-up coil assembly, or defective amplifier module.

A complete test of the primary circuit consists of checking the circuits in the ignition coil, the magnetic pick-up coil assembly and the amplifier module. Wiring harness checks will be included as a part of basic component circuit tests.

Always inspect connectors for dirt, corrosion or poor fit before assuming you have spotted a possible problem.

Troubleshooting

Make sure that the battery is fully charged before beginning tests. Perform a Spark Intensity Test. If no spark is observed, make sure that the high tension coil wire is good. Disconnect the three-way and four-way connectors at the electronic module.

The first trouble isolation test will be conducted on the harness termin-

Electronic module connectors—harness side
(© Ford Motor Co.)

als, with the electronic module disconnected from the circuit. The pin numbers shown in the schematic correspond to those shown in the trouble isolation test table.

Make the following tests using a sensitive volt-ohmmeter. These tests will direct you to the proper follow-up test to determine the actual problem.

If the circuit checks good at all these test points, connect a known good electronic module in place of the vehicle module and again perform the spark intensity test. If the substitution corrects the malfunction again reconnect the vehicle module and perform the spark intensity test. If the malfunction still exists, the problem is in the module and it must be replaced. If the problem is gone, it may be in the wiring connectors.

If the substitute module does not correct the problem, reconnect the original module and make repairs elsewhere in the system.

Module Bias Test

Measure the voltage at Pin 3 to engine ground with the ignition key "on". If the voltage observed is less than battery voltage, repair the voltage feed wiring to the module for running conditions (re-wire).

Battery Source Test

1. Connect the voltmeter leads from the battery terminal at the coil to engine ground, without disconnecting the coil from the circuit.
2. Install a jumper wire from the DEC terminal of the coil to a good engine ground.
3. Turn the lights and all accessories off.
4. Turn the ignition switch "on".
5. If the voltmeter reading is between 4.9 and 7.9 volts, the primary circuit from the battery is satisfactory.
6. If the voltmeter reading is less than 4.9 volts, check the following:
   a. The primary wiring for worn insulation, broken strands, and loose or corroded terminals.
   b. The resistance wiring for defects.
7. If the voltmeter reading is greater than 7.9 volts, the resistance wire should be replaced after verifying a defect.

Solid state distributor exploded view (© Ford Motor Co.)

	TEST VOLTAGE BETWEEN	SHOULD BE	IF NOT, CONDUCT
KEY ON	Pin # 3 and Engine Ground	Battery Voltage	Module Bias Test
	Pin # 5 and Engine Ground	Battery Voltage	Battery Source Test
CRANKING	Pin # 1 and Engine Ground	8 to 12 volts	Cranking Test
	Pin # 5 and Engine Ground	8 to 12 volts	Starting Circuit Test
	Pin # 7 and Pin # 8	½ volt A.C. or D.C. volt wiggle	Distributor Hardware Test

	TEST RESISTANCE BETWEEN	SHOULD BE	IF NOT, CONDUCT
KEY OFF	Pin # 7 and Pin # 8	400 to 800 ohms	Magnetic Pick-up (Stator) Test
	Pin # 6 and Engine Ground	0 ohms	
	Pin # 7 and Engine Ground	more than 70,000 ohms	
	Pin # 8 and Engine Ground	more than 70,000 ohms	
	Pin # 3 and Coil Tower	7000 to 13000 ohms	Coil Test
	Pin # 5 and Pin # 4	1.0 to 2.0 ohms	
	Pin # 5 and Engine Ground	more than 10.0 ohms	Short Test
	Pin # 3 and Pin # 4	1.0 to 2.0 ohms	Resistance Wire

Solid state ignition system diagnosis (© Ford Motor Co.)

Electronic module schematic—solid-state ignition (© Ford Motor Co.)

Cranking Test

Measure the voltage at Pin 1 to engine ground with the engine cranking. If the voltage observed is not 8 to 12 volts, repair the voltage feed to the module for starting conditions (white wire).

Starting Circuit Test

If the reading is not between 8 and 12 volts, the ignition by-pass circuit is open or grounded from either the starter solenoid or the ignition switch to Pin 5. Check the primary connections at the coil.

Distributor Hardware Test

1. Disconnect the three-wire weatherproof connector at the distributor pigtail.
2. Connect a D.C. voltmeter on a 2.5 volt scale to the two parallel blades. With the engine cranking, the meter needle should oscillate.
3. Remove the distributor cap and check for visual damage or misassembly.
   a. Sintered iron armature (6 or 8-toothed wheel) must be tight on the sleeve, and the roll pin aligning the armature must be in position.
   b. Sintered iron stator must not be broken.
   c. Armature must rotate when the engine is cranked.
4. If the hardware is alright, but the meter doesn't oscillate, replace the magnetic pick-up assembly.

Magnetic Pick-up Tests

1. Resistance of pick-up coil measured between two parallel pins in the distributor connector must be 400-800 ohms.
2. Resistance between the third blade (ground) and the distributor bowl must be zero ohms.
3. Resistance between either parallel blade and engine ground must be greater than 70,000 ohms.
4. If any test fails, the distributor stator assembly is defective and must be replaced.
5. If the above readings are not the same as measured in the original test, check for a defective harness. If the readings are the same, proceed.
6. If these tests check alright, the signal generator portion of the distributor is working properly.

Ignition Coil Test

The breakerless ignition coil must be diagnosed separately from the rest of the ignition system.

1. Primary resistance must be 1.0-2.0 ohms, measured from the BAT to the DEC terminals.
2. Secondary resistance must be 7,000-13,000 ohms, measured from the BAT or DEC terminal to the center tower of the coil.
3. If resistance tests are alright, but the coil is still suspected, test the coil on a coil tester by following the test equipment manufacturer's instructions for a standard coil. If the reading differs from the original test, check for a defective harness.

Module Test 1975 and later

1. Unplug the electronic module connector, but don't remove the existing module from the car.
2. Connect a module which is known to be good to the connector. There is no need to attach the module to the car in order to have it work.
3. Start the engine; if it starts and operates correctly go on to the next step. If it won't start and run the trouble is somewhere else. Check and repair the wiring and other systems, as required.
4. If the engine started in step 3, reconnect the original module and try to start the engine again. If the engine won't start, replace the module.
5. If the engine starts in step 4, the original module is not defective. Check all the wiring and connections in the ignition system.

Short Test

If the resistance from Pin 5 to ground is less than 10 ohms, check

Magnetic pulse amplifier schematic
(© Chevrolet Div., G.M. Corp.)

for a short to ground at the DEC terminal of the ignition coil or in the connection wiring to that terminal.

Resistance Wire Test

Replace the resistance wire if it is out of specifications (See "Ignition Resistor Wire").

Adjustments

The air gap between the armature and magnetic pick-up coil in the distributor is not adjustable, nor are there any adjustments for the amplifier module. Inoperative components are simply replaced. Any attempt to connect components outside the vehicle may result in component failure.

Component Replacement

Magnetic Pick-up Assembly Removal and Installation

1. Remove the distributor cap and rotor and disconnect the distributor harness plug.
2. Using a small gear puller or two screwdrivers, lift or pry the armature from the advance plate sleeve. Remove the roll pin.
3. Remove the large wire retaining clip from the base plate annular groove.
4. Remove the snap-ring which secures the vacuum advance link to the pick-up assembly.
5. Remove the magnetic pick-up assembly ground screw and lift the assembly from the distributor.
6. Lift the vacuum advance arm off the post on the pick-up assembly and move it out against the distributor housing.
7. Place the new pick-up assembly in position over the fixed base plate and slide the wiring in position through the slot in the side of the distributor housing.
8. Install the fine wire snap-ring securing the pick-up assembly to the fixed base plate.

9. Position the vacuum advance arm over the post on the pick-up assembly and install the snap-ring.
10. Install the grounding screw through the tab on the wiring harness and into the fixed base plate.
11. Install the armature on the advance plate sleeve making sure that the roll pin is engaged in the matching slots.
12. Install the distributor rotor cap.
13. Connect the distributor wiring plug to the vehicle harness.

Delco-Remy Magnetic Pulse System

Components

The Delco-Remy magnetic pulse, fully transistorized ignition system uses a magnetic pulse distributor having no breaker points. This system switches power electronically rather than with ignition contact points. Instead of the familiar cam and breaker plate assembly, this distributor uses a rotating iron timer core and a magnetic pickup assembly. The magnetic pickup assembly consists of a bearing plate on which are sandwiched a ceramic ring-type permanent magnet, two pole pieces and a pick-up coil. The pole pieces are doughnut shaped steel plates with accurately spaced internal teeth, one tooth for each cylinder of the engine.

A critically important part is the iron timer core. It has a number of equally spaced projections or vanes and is attached to, and rotates with, the distributor shaft.

The transistor control unit, the switchbox of the system, is mounted in an aluminum case and contains three transistors, a zener diode, a condenser and five small resistors. The zener diode is a circuit protection device. Remaining components control and switch ignition-coil current electronically; there are no moving parts in the control unit.

The ignition coil is of standard design except for a special winding. The external primary resistor is a ceramic type, similar to those used on various conventional systems.

Operation

The ignition primary circuit is connected from the battery, through the ignition switch, through the ignition pulse amplifier assembly, through the primary side of the ignition coil, and back to the amplifier housing where it is grounded externally. The secondary circuit is the same as in conventional ignition systems: the secondary side of the coil, the coil wire to the distributor, the

rotor, the spark plug wires and the spark-plugs.

The magnetic pulse distributor is also connected to the ignition pulse amplifier. As the distributor shaft rotates, the distributor rotating pole piece turns inside the stationary pole piece. As the rotating pole piece turns inside the stationary pole piece, the eight teeth on the rotating pole piece align with the eight teeth on the stationary pole piece eight times during each distributor revolution (two crankshaft revolutions since the distributor runs at one-half crankshaft speed). As the rotating pole piece teeth move close to, and align with, the teeth on the stationary pole piece, the magnetic rotating pole piece induces voltage into the magnetic pole piece through the stationary pole piece. This voltage pulse is sent to the ignition pulse amplifier from the magnetic pole piece. When the pulse enters the amplifier, it signals the ignition pulse amplifier to interrupt the ignition primary circuit. This causes the primary circuit to collapse and begins the induction of the magnetic lines of force from the primary side of the coil into the secondary side of the coil. This induction provides the required voltage to fire the spark plugs.

The advantages of this system are that the transistors in the ignition pulse amplifier can make and break the primary ignition circuit much faster than conventional ignition points, and higher primary voltage can be utilized since this system can be made to handle higher voltage without adverse effects, whereas ignition breaker points cannot. The shorter switching time of this system allows longer coil primary circuit saturation time and longer induction time when the primary circuit collapses. This increased time allows the primary circuit to build up more current and the secondary circuit to discharge more current.

Troubleshooting

Cautions

1. Don't use 18 volts or 24 volts for emergency starting.

Magnetic pulse system circuit diagram
(© Chevrolet Div., G.M. Corp.)

2. Never crank engine with coil high-tension lead or more than three spark plug leads disconnected.
3. Don't short circuit between coil positive terminal and ground.
4. On any repair that necessitates replacement of control unit or ignition resistor, perform complete charging system check before releasing the unit. Basic cause of trouble may be high or uncontrolled charging rate.

Engine Surge or Intermittent Miss

Since there are so many possible causes for this problem, all other possible defects must be ruled out before the specialized components of the electronic ignition system are judged defective.

As a general rule, a miss or surge that is caused by an ignition problem will be much more pronounced than a similiar problem that is caused by carburetion. Also, carburetion is usually affected by temperature more than the ignition system is. A carburetor or intake manifold vacuum leak is often compensated for by the choke when the engine is cold. When the engine warms up and the choke is released, the engine surge will show up.

If the ignition system is found to be the source of the problem, first check all connections in the system to make sure that they are *clean and tight*. Check the coil and spark plug high-tension wires with an ohmmeter to be sure they have the correct resistance. Check the inside and outside of the distributor cap and the tower on the ignition coil for cracks which would allow the high voltage intended for the spark plugs to short to ground.

If none of the above checks uncovers a defective component, the distributor pick-up coil leads may be reversed in the connector, or the pickup coil itself may have an intermittent open.

Engine Will Not Start or Is Hard to Start

1. Disconnect a spark plug wire from one spark plug and hold the wire 1/4 in. from a good ground with a pair of insulated pliers.
2. Crank the engine over and observe whether a spark jumps from the plug wire to ground.
3. *If spark occurs*, the problem is not in the ignition system.
4. *If spark does not occur*, reconnect the spark plug wire that was disconnected and connect a tachometer between the positive (+) coil primary terminal and the pink wire in the three-wire connector to the ignition pulse amplifier.
5. Crank the engine over and observe the tachometer.

Connector details for V8 HEI system (© Chevrolet Div., G.M. Corp.)

6. *If the tachometer needle deflects* while cranking the engine, perform "Ignition Distributor Test" to locate the problem.
7. *If the tachometer needle does not deflect* while cranking the engine, perform "Circuit Resistance Test" to pinpoint the problem.

Circuit Resistance Test Ignition Distributor Check

1. Disconnect the distributor leads from the engine wiring harness.
2. Connect the two leads of an ohmmeter to the distributor leads at the connector.
3. Rotate the magnetic pick-up assembly in the distributor through full vacuum advance travel and read the ohmmeter. If the reading is not within a range of 500-700 ohms, replace the magnetic pick-up assembly.
4. If the reading is within the 500-700 ohms range, disconnect one ohmmeter lead from the distributor connector and connect it to a good ground. If the reading is less than infinity (needle moves to end of scale), replace the magnetic pick-up assembly.
5. If the reading is infinite, and there was no spark when the spark plug wire was disconnected from the plug, the amplifier is defective.

Delco-Remy High Energy Ignition (HEI) System

Components

The Delco-Remy High Energy Ig-

Connector details for inline six-cylinder HEI system (© Chevrolet Div., G.M. Corp.)

nition (HEI) System is a breaker-less, pulse triggered, transistor controlled, inductive discharge ignition system.

It is similar in operation to the Magnetic Pulse System. There are only nine external electrical connections; the ignition switch feed wire, and the eight spark plug leads. On V8 engines, the ignition coil is located within the distributor cap, connecting directly to the rotor.

Operation

The magnetic pick-up assembly located inside the distributor contains a permanent magnet, a pole piece with internal teeth, and a pick-up coil. When the teeth of the rotating timer core and pole piece align, an induced voltage in the pick-up coil signals the electronic module to open the coil primary circuit. As the primary current decreases, a high voltage is induced in the secondary windings of the ignition coil, directing a spark through the rotor and high voltage leads to fire the spark plugs. The dwell period is automatically controlled by the electronic module and is increased with increasing engine rpm. The HEI System features a longer spark duration which is instrumental in firing lean and EGR diluted fuel/air mixtures. The condenser (capacitor) located within the HEI distributor is provided for noise (static) suppression purposes only and is not a regularly replaced ignition system component.

Major Repair Operations (distributor in engine)

Ignition Coil Replacement V8 Engines

1. Disconnect the feed and module wire terminal connectors from the distributor cap.
2. Remove the ignition set retainer.
3. Remove the 4 coil cover-to-distributor cap screws and the coil cover.
4. Remove the 4 coil-to-distributor cap screws.
5. Using a blunt drift, press the coil wire spade terminals up out of distributor cap.
6. Lift the coil up out of the distributor cap.
7. Remove and clean the coil spring, rubber seal washer and coil cavity of the distributor cap.
8. Coat the rubber seal with a dielectric lubricant furnished in the replacement ignition coil package.
9. Reverse the above procedures to install.

Six Cylinder Engines

On 6 cylinder engines, a separate ignition coil is used. To remove and install it, proceed as follows:

V8 HEI distributor components (© Chevrolet Div., G.M. Corp.)

1. Remove the ignition switch-to-coil lead from the coil.
2. Unfasten the distributor leads from the coil.
3. Remove the screws which secure the coil to the engine and lift it off.

Installation is the reverse of removal.

Distributor Cap Replacement

1. Remove the feed and module wire terminal connectors from the distributor cap.
2. Remove the retainer and spark plug wires from the cap.
3. Depress and release the 4 distributor cap-to-housing retainers and lift off the cap assembly.
4. Remove the 4 coil cover screws and cover (V8 only).
5. Using a finger or a blunt drift, push the spade terminals up out of the distributor cap (V8 only).
6. Remove all 4 coil screws and lift the coil, coil spring and rubber seal washer out of the cap coil cavity (V8 only).
7. Using a new distributor cap, reverse the above procedures to assemble being sure to clean and lubricate the rubber seal washer with dielectric lubricant.

Rotor Replacement

1. Disconnect the feed and module

wire connectors from the distributor.
2. Depress and release the 4 distributor cap to housing retainers and lift off the cap assembly.
3. Remove the two rotor attaching screws and rotor.
4. Reverse the above procedure to install.

Vacuum Advance Unit Replacement

1. Remove the distributor cap and rotor as previously described.
2. Disconnect the vacuum hose from the vacuum advance unit. Remove the module.
3. Remove the two vacuum advance retaining screws, pull the advance unit outward, rotate and disengage the operating rod from its tang.
4. Reverse the above procedure to install.

Module Replacement

1. Remove the distributor cap and rotor as previously described.
2. Disconnect the harness connector and pick-up coil spade connectors from the module (note their positions).
3. Remove the two screws and module from the distributor housing.
4. Coat the bottom of the new module with dielectric lubricant. Re-

V8 HEI secondary wiring (© Chevrolet Div., G.M. Corp.)

CYL NO. 6
CYL NO. 5
CYL NO. 4
CYL NO. 3
CYL NO. 2
CYL NO. 1
COIL
DISTRIBUTOR
FWD
COIL
VIEW A
VIEW B
DISTRIBUTOR
VIEW C

Inline six-cylinder HEI secondary wiring (© Chevrolet Div., G.M. Corp.)

verse the above procedure to install. Be sure that the leads are installed correctly.

Distributor Removal

1. Disconnect the ground cable from the battery.
2. Disconnect the feed and module terminal connectors from the distributor cap. (Don't use a screwdriver).
3. Disconnect the hose at the vacuum advance.
4. Depress and release the 4 distributor cap-to-housing retainers and lift off the cap assembly.
5. Using crayon or chalk, make locating marks on the rotor and module and on the distributor housing and engine for installation purposes.
6. Loosen and remove the distributor clamp bolt and clamp, and lift distributor out of the engine. Noting the relative position of the rotor and module alignment marks, make a second mark on the rotor to align it with the one mark on the module.

Distributor Installation

1. With a new O-ring on the distributor housing and the second mark on the rotor aligned with the mark on the module, install the distributor, taking care to align the mark on the housing with the one on the engine. It may be necessary to lift the distributor and turn the rotor slightly to align the gears and the oil pump driveshaft.
2. With the respective marks aligned, install the clamp and bolt finger-tight.
3. Install and secure the distributor cap.
4. Connect the feed and module connectors to the distributor cap.
5. Connect a timing light to the engine and plug the vacuum hose.

6. Connect the ground cable to the battery.
7. Start the engine and set the timing.
8. Turn the engine off and tighten the distributor clamp bolt. Disconnect the timing light and unplug and connect the hose to the vacuum advance.

Service Procedures (distributor removed)

Driven Gear Replacement

1. With the distributor removed, use a 1/8 in. pin punch and tap out the driven gear roll pin.
2. Hold the rotor end of shaft and rotate the driven gear to shear any burrs in the roll pin hole.
3. Remove the driven gear from the shaft.
4. Reverse the above procedure to install.

Mainshaft Replacement

1. With the driven gear and rotor removed, gently pull the mainshaft out of the housing.
2. Remove the advance springs, weights and slide the weight base plate off the mainshaft.
3. Reverse the above procedure to install.

HEI system basic wiring schematic (© Chevrolet Div., B.M. Corp.)

Pole Piece, Magnet or Pick-up Coil Replacement

1. With the mainshaft out of its housing, remove the 3 retaining screws, pole piece and magnet and/or pick-up coil.
2. Reverse the removal procedure to install making sure that the pole piece teeth do not contact the timer core teeth by installing and rotating the mainshaft. Loosen the 3 screws and realign the pole piece as necessary.

Chrysler Electronic Ignition

Components

This system consists of a special pulse-sending distributor, an electronic control unit, a two-element ballast resistor, and a special ignition coil.

The distributor does not contain breaker points or a condenser, these parts being replaced by a distributor reluctor and a pick-up unit.

Operation

The ignition primary circuit is connected from the battery, through the ignition switch, through the primary side of the ignition coil, to the control unit where it is grounded. The secondary circuit is the same as in conventional ignition systems: the secondary side of the coil, the coil wire to the distributor, the rotor, the spark plug wires, and the spark plugs.

The magnetic pulse distributor is also connected to the control unit. As the distributor shaft rotates, the distributor reluctor turns past the pick-up unit. As the reluctor turns past the pick-up unit, each of the eight teeth on the reluctor pass near the pick-up unit once during each distributor revolution (two crankshaft revolutions since the distributor runs at one-half crankshaft speed). As the reluctor teeth move close to the pick-up unit, the magnetic rotating reluctor induces voltage into the magnetic pick-up unit. This voltage pulse is sent to the ignition control unit from the magnetic pick-up unit. When the pulse enters the control unit, it signals the control unit to interrupt the ignition primary circuit. This causes the primary circuit to collapse and begins the induction of the magnetic lines of force from the primary side of the coil into the secondary side of the coil. This induction provides the required voltage to fire the spark plugs.

The advantages of this system are that the transistors in the control unit can make and break the primary ignition circuit much faster than conventional ignition points can, and higher primary voltage can be uti-

Chrysler electronic ignition system (© Chrysler Corp.)

lized, since this system can be made to handle higher voltage without adverse effects, whereas ignition breaker points cannot. The quicker switching time of this system allows longer coil primary circuit saturation time and longer induction time when the primary circuit collapses. This increased time allows the primary circuit to build up more current and the secondary circuit to discharge more current.

Pick-up Coil Replacement

1972-74

1. Remove the distributor.
2. Remove the pick-up coil mounting screw.
3. Remove the wires from the retainers on the upper plate and distributor housing.
4. Remove pick-up coil from the upper plate.

Exploded view of V8 electronic ignition distributor (© Chrysler Corp.)

5. Position the pick-up coil on the pivot of the upper plate and install the mounting screw. Do not tighten.
6. Insert the wires into the appropriate retainers in the distributor.
7. Install the distributor.
8. Set the air gap.

1975 and later

1. Remove the distributor from the engine.
2. Using two small pry-bars or screwdrivers (maximum 7/16 in. wide), pry the reluctor off the shaft from the bottom.

   CAUTION: Do not damage the teeth on the reluctor.
3. Unfasten the vacuum advance-to-distributor housing screws. Remove the vacuum unit, after disconnecting the arm from the upper plate.

Chrysler electronic ignition system schematic (© Chrysler Corp.)

TROUBLESHOOTING CHRYSLER ELECTRONIC IGNITION

Condition	Possible Cause	Correction
ENGINE WILL NOT START (Fuel and carburetion known to be OK)	a) Dual Ballast	Check resistance of each section: Compensating resistance: .50-.60 ohms @ 70°-80°F Auxiliary Ballast: 4.75-5.75 ohms Replace if faulty. Check wire positions.
	b) Faulty Ignition Coil	Check for carbonized tower. Check primary and secondary resistances: Primary: 1.41-1.79 ohms @ 70°-80°F Secondary: 9,200-11,700 ohms @ 70°-80°F Check in coil tester.
	c) Faulty Pickup or Improper Pickup Air Gap	Check pickup coil resistance: 400-600 ohms Check pickup gap: .010 in. feeler gauge should not slip between pickup coil core and an aligned reluctor blade. No evidence of pickup core striking reluctor blades should be visible. To reset gap, tighten pickup adjustment screw with a .008 in. feeler gauge held between pickup core and an aligned reluctor blade. After resetting gap, run distributor on test stand and apply vacuum advance, making sure that the pickup core does not strike the reluctor blades.
	d) Faulty Wiring	Visually inspect wiring for brittle insulation. Inspect connectors. Molded connectors should be inspected for rubber inside female terminals.
	e) Faulty Control Unit	Replace if all of the above checks are negative. Whenever the control unit or dual ballast is replaced, make sure the dual ballast wires are correctly inserted in the keyed molded connector.
ENGINE SURGES SEVERELY (Not Lean Carburetor)	a) Wiring	Inspect for loose connection and/or broken conductors in harness.
	b) Faulty Pickup Leads	Disconnect vacuum advance. If surging stops, replace pickup.
	c) Ignition Coil	Check for intermittent primary.
ENGINE MISSES (Carburetion OK)	a) Spark Plugs	Check plugs. Clean and regap if necessary.
	b) Secondary Cable	Check cables with an ohmmeter, or observe secondary circuit performance with an oscilloscope.
	c) Ignition Coil	Check for carbonized tower. Check in coil tester.
	d) Wiring	Check for loose or dirty connections.
	e) Faulty Pickup Lead	Disconnect vacuum advance. If miss stops, replace pickup.
	f) Control Unit	Replace if the above checks are negative.

4. Unfasten the pick-up coil wires from the distributor housing.
5. Unfasten the two screws which secure the lower plate to the distributor housing. Lift out the lower plate together with the upper plate and pick-up coil.
6. Separate the upper and lower plates by depressing the retaining clip on the underside of the plate and slide it away from the stud. The pick-up coil will come off with the upper plate; they cannot be separated; they must be serviced as an assembly.

Installation is the reverse of removal. Place a small amount of distributor grease on the support pins on the lower plate.

Air Gap Adjustment
1. Align one reluctor tooth with the pick-up coil tooth.
2. Loosen the pick-up coil hold-down screw.
3. Insert a 0.008 in. nonmagnetic feeler gauge between the reluctor tooth and the pick-up coil tooth.
4. Adjust the air gap so that contact is made between the reluctor tooth, the feeler gauge, and the pick-up coil tooth.
5. Tighten the hold-down screw.
6. Remove the feeler gauge.
NOTE: No force should be required in removing the feeler gauge.
7. Check the air gap with a 0.010 in. feeler gauge. A 0.010 in. feeler gauge should not fit into the air gap.
CAUTION: A 0.010 in. feeler gauge can be forced into the air gap. DO NOT FORCE THE GAUGE INTO THE AIR GAP.
8. Apply vacuum to the vacuum unit and rotate the governor shaft. The pick-up pole should not hit the reluctor teeth. The gap was not properly adjusted if any hitting occurs. If hitting occurs on only one side of the reluctor, the distributor shaft is probably bent, and the governor and shaft assembly should be replaced.

AMC Breakerless Inductive Discharge (BID) Ignition

Components
The AMC breakerless inductive discharge (BID) ignition system consists of five components:
Control unit
Coil
Breakerless distributor
Ignition cables
Spark plugs

The control unit is a solid-state, epoxy-sealed module with waterproof connectors. The control unit has a built-in current regulator, so no separate ballast resistor or resistance wire is needed in the primary circuit. Battery voltage is supplied to the ignition coil positive (+) terminal when the ignition key is turned to the "ON" or "START" position; low voltage is also supplied by the control unit.

The coil used with the BID system requires no special service. It works just like the coil in a conventional ignition system.

The distributor is conventional, except for the lack of points, condenser and cam. Advance is supplied by both a vacuum unit and a centrifugal advance mechanism. A standard cap, rotor, and dust shield are used.

In place of the points, cam, and condensor, the distributor has a sensor and trigger wheel. The sensor is a small coil which generates an electromagnetic field when excited by the oscillator in the control unit.

Standard spark plugs and ignition cables are used.

Operation
When the ignition switch is turned on, the control unit is activated. The control unit then sends an oscillating signal to the sensor which causes the sensor to generate a magnetic field. When one of the trigger wheel teeth enters this field, the strength of the oscillation in the sensor is reduced. Once the strength drops to a predetermined level, a demodulator circuit operates the control unit's switching transistor. The switching transistor is wired in series with the coil primary circuit; it switches the circuit off when it gets the demodulator signal.

From this point on, the BID ignition system works in the same manner as a conventional ignition system.

Troubleshooting
1. Check all of the BID ignition system electrical connections.
2. Disconnect the coil-to-distributor high tension lead.
3. Hold the end of the lead ½ in. away from a ground. Crank the engine. If there is a spark, the trouble is not in the ignition system.
4. If there was no spark in step 3, connect a test light with a No. 57 bulb between the positive coil terminal (+) and a good ground. Have an assistant turn the ignition switch to "ON" and

BID system schematic (© AMC)

BID distributor components (© AMC)

1	Cap	7	Distributor body
2	Rotor	8	Vacuum unit screw
3	Dust shield	9	Vacuum advance unit
4	Trigger wheel	10	Shim
5	Felt lubricator	11	Drive gear
6	Sensor assembly	12	Pin

"START" (Do not start the engine). The bulb should light in both positions; if it doesn't, the fault lies in the battery-to-coil circuit. Check the ignition switch and related wiring.

5. If the test light lit in step 4, disconnect the coil-to-distributor leads at the connector and connect the test light between the positive (+) and negative (—) coil terminals.

6. Turn the ignition switch on. If the test light doesn't come on, check the control unit's ground lead. If the ground lead is in good condition, replace the control unit.

7. If the bulb lights in step 6, leave the test light in place and short the terminals on the coil-to-distributor connector together with a jumper lead, (connector separated) at the coil side of the connector. If the light stays on, replace the control unit.

8. If the test light goes out, remove it. Check for a spark, as in step 2, each time that the coil-to-distributor connector terminals are shorted together with the jumper lead. If there is a spark, replace the control unit; if there is no spark, replace the coil.

Coil Testing

Test the coil with a conventional coil checker or an ohmmeter. Primary resistance should be 1-2 ohms and secondary resistance should be 8-12 kilohms. The open output circuit should be more than 20 kilovolts. Replace the coil if it doesn't meet specifications.

Sensor Testing

Check the sensor resistance by connecting an ohmmeter to its leads. Resistance should be 1.8 ohms (±10%) at 77° F. Replace the sensor if it doesn't meet these specifications.

Distributor Overhaul

NOTE: If you must remove the sensor from the distributor for any reason, it will be necessary to have the special sensor positioning gauge in order to align it properly during installation.

1. Scribe matchmarks on the distributor housing, rotor, and engine block. Disconnect the leads and vacuum lines from the distributor. Remove the distributor. Unless the cap is to be replaced, leave it connected to the spark plug cables and position it out of the way.

2. Remove the rotor and dust cap.

3. Place a small gear puller over the trigger wheel, so that its jaws grip the inner shoulders of the wheel and not its arms. Place a thick washer between the gear puller and the distributor shaft to act as a spacer; do not press against the smaller inner shaft.

4. Loosen the sensor hold-down screw with a small pair of needle-nosed pliers; it has a tamper-proof head. Pull the sensor lead grommet out of the distributor body and pull out the leads from around the spring pivot pin.

5. Release the sensor securing spring by lifting it. Make sure that it clears the leads. Slide the sensor off the bracket. *Remember, a special gauge is required for sensor installation.*

6. Remove the vacuum advance unit securing screw. Slide the vacuum unit out of the distributor. Remove it only if it is to be replaced.

7. Clean and dry the vacuum unit and sensor brackets. Lubrication of these parts is not necessary.

BID distributor assembly is as follows:

1. Install the vacuum unit, if it was removed.

2. Assemble the sensor, sensor guide, flat washer, and retaining screw. Tighten the screw only far enough to keep the assembly

Using the special gauge to align the BID sensor coil (© AMC)

together; don't allow the screw to project below the bottom of the sensor.

NOTE: Replacement sensors come with a slotted-head screw to aid in assembly. If the original sensor is being used, replace the tamper-proof screw with a conventional one. Use the original washer.

3. Secure the sensor on the vacuum advance unit bracket, making sure that the tip of the sensor is placed in the notch on the summing bar.
4. Position the spring on the sensor and route the leads around the spring pivot pin. Fit the sensor lead grommet into the slot on the distributor body. Be sure that the lead can't get caught in the trigger wheel.
5. Place the special sensor positioning gauge over the distributor shaft, so that the flat on the shaft is against the large notch on the gauge. Move the sensor until the sensor core fits into the small notch on the gauge. Tighten the sensor securing screw with the gauge in place (through the round hole in the gauge).
6. It should be possible to remove and install the gauge without any side movement of the sensor. Check this and remove the gauge.

7. Position the trigger wheel on the shaft. Check to see that the sensor core is centered between the trigger wheel legs and that the legs don't touch the core.
8. Bend a piece of 0.050 in. gauge wire, so that it has a 90° angle and one leg ½ in. long. Use the gauge to measure the clearance between the trigger wheel legs and the sensor boss. Press the trigger wheel on the shaft until it just touches the gauge. Support the shaft during this operation.
9. Place 3 to 5 drops of SAE 20 oil on the felt lubricator wick.
10. Install the dust shield and rotor on the shaft.
11. Install the distributor on the engine using the matchmarks made during removal and adjust the timing. Use a new distributor mounting gasket.

IH Electronic Ignition

There are two versions of the system. The first, with a black control box, was used on 1974 V8 models, while the second, with a gold control box, was introduced in 1975 on four-cylinder and V8 models. The two versions of the system are very similar in appearance; the main external difference is that the gold control box combines all wiring into a single plug.

The system uses a standard ignition coil with no ballast resistor or resistance wire, since the control box regulates the primary, low-voltage, current. The distributor part of the system consists of a metal detecting sensor and a toothed trigger wheel in place of the distributor cam. The only adjustment is for sensor to trigger wheel air gap. The control box components are permanently sealed in a waterproof and vibration resistant compound. Most of these systems use vacuum spark advance in addition to mechanical advance.

Disassembly and overhaul of the distributor is very similar to that for International V8 point-type distributors.

Fabricated BID trigger wheel clearance gauge (© AMC)

Sensor to Trigger Wheel Air Gap Adjustment

1. Align the trigger wheel so that one tooth is aligned with the centerline of the sensor. The tooth should be at right angles to the flat side of the sensor.
2. The gap should be .014 in. for 1974 units and .008 in. for 1975 and later models.
3. A distributor machine or a dwell/tachometer calibrated for electronic ignition systems can be used to measure dwell.

NOTE: Most ordinary dwell/tachometers will give a reading, but this will not be accurate.

On 1974 models, dwell should be 27-30 degrees at curb idle; on a distributor machine the reading will be 22-28 degrees at 2000 distributor rpm with 12-13 volts primary input. On 1975 and later models, dwell should be 26-32 degrees at curb idle and also at 300 distributor rpm with 12-13 volts primary input.

4. Adjust the gap and dwell by moving the sensor. Move the sensor toward the trigger wheel to decrease dwell or away to increase dwell. .001 in. of sensor movement equals about ½ degree of dwell change.

Troubleshooting

1. Make sure that the battery is

IH electronic ignition system schematic (© IH)

Sensor to trigger wheel air gap (© IH)

Voltmeter connected to coil negative terminal (© IH)

Spark gap for testing electronic ignition system (© IH)

fully charged, delivering 12-13 volts. Make sure that all wiring, connections, and mounting bolts are in good condition.

2. Disconnect one spark plug wire and insert an extension of some sort into the boot. Hold the wire with insulated pliers and a heavy glove so that there is a gap of about ¼-½ in. between the extension and a ground. If the spark jumps the gap when the engine is cranked with the starter, the system is in good condition. If not, replace the wire and go on.

3. Detach the coil wire from the center of the distributor cap. Attach one end of a jumper wire to a ground and the other around the coil wire (don't pierce the insulation) ¼-½ in. from the metal tip. If there is a spark when the engine is cranked, the distributor cap, rotor, or spark plug and coil wires may be faulty. If not, keep the jumper in place and go on.

4. Disconnect the primary wiring plug near the distributor and plug a tester switch, part no. SE-2503, into the wiring harness. The switch replaces the distributor sensor in the circuit. Turn the ignition switch on and press the tester switch button. If there is a spark at the jumper, the sensor is defective and must be replaced. If not, go on.

5. Disconnect the primary wiring plug near the control box and install the tester switch. Turn the ignition switch on and press the tester switch button. If there is a spark at the jumper now, the primary wiring harness is defective. If not, go on.

6. Connect a voltmeter between the coil negative terminal and a ground. Voltage should be 12-13 volts. A low reading indicates high resistance between the battery and the coil, probably due to defective wires or ignition switch.

7. Connect the voltmeter between the coil negative terminal and a ground. With the ignition switch on, voltage should be 5-8 volts. A lower or higher reading indicates a bad coil. Press the tester switch button; voltage should go up to 12-13 volts and go back down when the button is released. If the voltage doesn't go up and down, the control box is faulty and must be replaced. If the voltage goes up and down but there is no spark at the jumper, the coil is defective.

8. Reconnect the system and make a final check for spark at the plug wire, as in Step 2.

Alternators and Regulators

Is it the Alternator or the Voltage Regulator?

The first step in diagnosing troubles of the charging system, is to identify the source of failure. Does the fault lie in the alternator or the regulator? The next move depends upon preference or necessity; either repair or replace the offending unit.

It is just as easy to separate an alternator, electrically, from the AC regulator as it is to separate its counterpart, the DC generator from its regulator.

AC generator output is controlled by the amount of current supplied to the field circuit of the system.

Unlike the DC generator, an AC generator is capable of producing substantial current at idle speed. Higher maximum output is also a possibility. This presents a potential danger when testing. As a precaution, a field rheostat should be used in the field circuit when making the following isolation test. The field rheostat permits positive control of the amount of current allowed to pass through the field circuit during the isolation test. Unregulated alternator capacity could ruin the unit.

NOTE: most manufacturers of precision gauges offer special test connectors, in sets, that will adapt to the leads and connections of any AC charging system.

CAUTION: Before attempting the isolation test, disconnect the field wire from the regulator. Failure to take this precaution can cause instant burning and permanent damage to the regulator.

Isolation Test

(By-passing the Regulator)

1. Connect voltmeter leads to two prods driven into the battery posts.

2. Disconnect field wire from the FLD terminal of the voltage regulator.

3. Connect one lead of a field rheostat to the undisturbed IGN terminal of the regulator, and the other field rheostat lead to the wire that was removed from the FLD terminal of the regulator.

4. With field rheostat turned to the low side of the scale, (high resistance) start the engine and adjust throttle to about 2,000 rpm.

5. Slowly move field rheostat control knob to decrease resistance, (allowing more current to flow through the field circuit) until voltmeter reading slightly exceeds manufacturers' specifications.

NOTE: under load conditions, observe the alternator for arcing or any other evidence of malfunction.

6. If alternator performs satisfactorily, repair or replace the regulator. Conversely, if the voltmeter reading is zero, or below specifications, repair or replace the alternator.

Alternator Test Plans

There are certain precautionary measures that apply to alternator tests in general. These items are listed in detail to avoid repetition when testing each make of alternator,

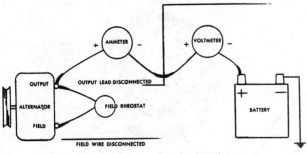

Plan to check charging circuit resistance

Alternator system with ammeter in the circuit

and to encourage a habit of good test procedure.

1. Check alternator drive belt for condition and tension.
2. Disconnect battery cables, check physical, chemical, and electrical condition of battery.
3. Be absolutely sure of polarity before connecting any battery in the circuit. Reversed polarity will ruin the diodes.
4. Never use a battery charger to start the engine.
5. Disconnect both battery cables when making a battery recharge hook-up.
6. Be sure of polarity hook-up when using a booster battery for starting.
7. Never ground the alternator output or battery terminal.
8. Never ground the field circuit between alternator and regulator.
9. Never run any alternator on an open circuit with the field energized.
10. Never try to polarize an alternator.
11. Do not attempt to motor an alternator.
12. The regulator cover must be in place when taking voltage limiter readings.
13. The ignition switch must be in off position when removing or installing the regulator cover.
14. Use insulated tools only to make adjustments to the regulator.
15. When making engine idle speed adjustments, always consider potential load factors that influence engine rpm. To compensate for electrical load, switch on the lights, radio, heater, air conditioner, etc.

Diagnosis

Low or No Charging

1. Blown fuse.
2. Broken or loose fan belt.
3. Voltage regulator not working.
4. Brushes sticking.
5. Slip ring dirty.
6. Open circuit.
7. Bad wiring connections.
8. Bad diode rectifier.
9. High resistance in charging circuit.
10. Voltage regulator needs adjusting.
11. Grounded stator.
12. May be open rectifiers (check all three phases).
13. If rectifiers are found blown or open, check capacitor.

Noisy Unit

1. Damaged rotor bearings.
2. Poor alignment of unit.
3. Broken or loose belt.
4. Open diode rectifiers.

Regulator Points Burnt or Stuck

1. Regulator set too high.
2. Poor ground connections.
3. Shorted generator field.
4. Regulator air gap incorrect.

Chrysler Isolated Field Alternator (Electronic Regulator)

The Chrysler isolated field alternator derives its name from its construction. Both of the brushes are insulated from ground and there is no heat sink connection, thereby isolating the internal field.

Troubleshooting

NOTE: see the "Alternator Test Plans" section before proceeding further. Make sure that the continuous running blower, if equipped, is disconnected. This blower will run with the key turned on even if the blower controls are off unless disconnected.

Fusible Links

Chrysler Corporation trucks have a single fusible link which is connected between the starter relay and the junction block. Failure of this link will cause all electrical systems to stop functioning.

Charging System Operation

NOTE: if the current indicator is to give an accurate reading, the battery cables must be of the same gauge and length as the original equipment.

1. With the engine running and all electrical systems off, place a current indicator over the positive battery cable.
2. If a charge of about 5 amps is recorded, the charging system is working. If a draw of about 5 amps is recorded the system is not working. The needle moves toward the battery when a charge condition is indicated and away from the battery when a draw condition is indicated. If a draw is indicated, proceed to the next testing procedure. If an overcharge of 10-15 amps is indi-

Plan to check current output

Plan to check field current draw

OUTPUT TERMINAL SCREW · HEAT SINK · GROUND BRUSH · POSITIVE (DIODES) RECTIFIERS · NEGATIVE (DIODES) RECTIFIERS · INSULATED BRUSH · FIELD TERMINAL

VOLTS

BATTERY

RHEOSTAT

Disconnect field wire from the "FLD" terminal of the Voltage Regulator.

Typical Chrysler type

cated, check for a faulty regulator.

Ignition Switch-to-Regulator Circuit Check

1. Disconnect the regulator wires at the regulator.
2. Turn the key on but do not start the engine.
3. Using a voltmeter or test light, check for voltage across the I and F terminals. If there is current present, the circuit is good. If there is no current, check for bad connections, a bad ballast resistor, a bad ammeter, broken wires, or bad ground at the alternator or voltage regulator. Also, check for voltage from the I wire to ground; current should be present. Check for voltage from the F terminal to ground; current should not be present.

Isolation Test

This test determines whether the regulator or alternator is bad if everything else in the circuit was OK.

1. Disconnect, at the alternator, the wire that runs between one of the alternator field connections and the voltage regulator.
2. Run a jumper wire from the disconnected alternator terminal to ground.
3. Connect a voltmeter to the battery. The positive voltmeter lead connects to the positive battery terminal, and the negative lead goes to the negative terminal. Record the reading.
4. Make sure that all electrical systems are turned off. Start the engine. Do not race the engine.
5. Gradually raise engine speed to 1500-2000 rpm. There should be an increase of one to two volts on the voltmeter. If this is true, the alternator is good and the voltage regulator should be repaired. If there is no voltage increase, the alternator is faulty.

NOTE: the following tests require the use of a carbon pile and an ammeter.

CARBON PILE · BATTERY · CAR AMMETER · IGNITION SWITCH · BALLAST RESISTOR · BLUE WITH WHITE TRACER · ELECTRONIC VOLTAGE REGULATOR 2875400 · BLUE · GREEN · I F · ISOLATED FIELD ALTERNATOR · BATT FLD · FLD · JUMPER WIRE

Current Output test hook-up—Chrysler isolated field alternator

BATTERY · CAR AMMETER · IGNITION SWITCH · VOLTS · BALLAST RESISTOR · TO IGNITION COIL · BLUE WITH WHITE TRACER · ELECTRONIC VOLTAGE REGULATOR 2875400 · BLUE · GREEN · I F · ISOLATED FIELD ALTERNATOR · BATT FLD · FLD

Voltage regulator test hook-up—Chrysler isolated field alternator

Current Output Test

1. The ammeter and carbon pile hookup should remain the same as for the circuit resistance test.
2. Connect the voltmeter negative lead to the battery negative post.
3. Move the positive voltmeter lead to the alternator "BATT" post.
4. Start the engine and adjust speed to 1250 rpm.
5. Note voltmeter and ammeter readings. Maintain a 15 volt reading by adjusting the carbon pile control.
6. Compare ammeter reading with manufacturer's specifications The reading should be no less than specified, 3 amps.
7. If below specifications, internal trouble is indicated. Remove the alternator for further testing.

Electronic Voltage Regulator Test

1. Make sure battery terminals are clean and battery is charged.
2. Connect the positive lead of a test voltmeter to ignition Terminal No. 1 of the ballast resistor.
3. Connect the negative voltmeter lead to a good *body* ground.
4. Start engine and allow it to idle at 1250 rpm, all lights and accessories turned off. Voltage should be as follows:

Ambient Temp. 1/4 in. from Regulator	Voltage
-20°F.	14.3-15.3
80°F.	13.8-14.4
140°F.	13.3-14.0

5. If the voltage is *below* specifications, check the following:
   a. Voltage regulator ground—check voltage drop between regulator cover and ground.
   b. Harness wiring—disconnect regulator plug (ign. switch off), then turn on ign. switch and check for battery voltage at the terminal having the blue and green leads. *Wiring harness must be disconnected from the regulator when checking individual leads.* If no voltage is present in either lead, the problem is in the truck wiring or alternator field.
6. If Step 5 tests showed no malfunctions, install a new regulator and repeat Step 4.
7. If voltage is *above* specifications (Step 4), or fluctuates, check the following:
   a. Ground between regulator and body, and between body and engine.
   b. Ignition switch circuit between switch and regulator.
8. If voltage is still more than 1/2 volt above specifications, install a new regulator and repeat Step 4.

Insulator brush

Removing the pulley

Pulling bearing from rotor shaft

Removing a rectifier

Chrysler Overhaul and Internal Testing

Alternator disassembly, repair and assembly procedures are basically the same for all Chrysler alternators. Certain variations in design, or in-production modifications, could require slightly different procedures that should be obvious upon inspection of the unit being serviced.

Disassembly

To prevent damage to the brush assemblies they should be removed before proceeding with the disassembly of the alternator. The insulated brush is mounted in a plastic holder that positions the brush vertically against one of the slip rings.

1. Remove the retaining screw, flat washer, nylon washer and field terminal and carefully lift the plastic holder containing the spring and brush assembly from the end housing.
2. The ground brush is positioned horizontally against the remaining slip ring and is retained in the holder that is integral with the end housing. Remove the retaining screw and lift the clip, spring and brush assembly from the end housing.

CAUTION: The stator is laminated, don't burr the stator or end housings.

3. Remove the through bolts and pry between the stator and drive end housing with a thin blade screwdriver. Carefully separate the drive end housing, pulley and rotor assembly from the stator and rectifier housing assembly.
4. The pulley is an interference fit on the rotor shaft. Remove with a puller and special adapters.
5. Remove the three nuts and washers and, while supporting the end frame, tap the rotor shaft with a plastic hammer and separate the rotor and end housing.
6. The drive end ball bearing is an interference fit with the rotor shaft. Remove the bearing with puller and adapters.

NOTE: further dismantling of the rotor is not advisable, as the remainder of the rotor assembly is not serviced separately.

7. Remove the DC output terminal nuts and washers and remove terminal screw and inside capacitor (on units so equipped).
8. Remove the insulator.

NOTE: three positive rectifiers are pressed into the heat sink and three negative rectifiers in the end housing. When removing the rectifiers, it is necessary to support the end housing and/or heat sink to prevent damage to these castings. Another caution is in order relative to the diode rectifiers. Don't subject them to unnecessary jolting. Heavy vibration or shock may ruin them.

   a. Cut rectifier wire at point of crimp.
   b. Support rectifier housing.

INSULATOR

HEAT SINK

Heat sink and insulator

NOTE: the factory tool is cut away and slotted to fit over the wires and around the bosses in the housing. Be sure that the bore of the tool completely surrounds the rectifier, then press the rectifier out of the housing.

NOTE: the roller bearing in the rectifier end frame is a press fit. To protect the end housing it is necessary to support the housing with a tool when pressing out the bearing.

Bench Tests

Testing Silicon Diode Rectifiers With Ohmmeter

Preferred method—rectifiers open in all three phases.

Disassemble the alternator and separate the wires at the Y-connection of the stator.

There are six diode rectifiers mounted in the back of the alternator. Three of them are marked with a plus (+), and three are marked with a minus (−). These marks indicate diode case polarity.

To test, set ohmmeter to its lowest range. If case is marked positive (+), place positive meter probe to case and negative probe to the diode lead. Meter should read between 4 and 10 ohms. Now, reverse leads of ohmmeter, connecting negative meter probe to positive case and positive meter probe to wire of rectifier. Set meter on a high range. Meter needle should move very little, if any (infinite reading). Do this to all three positive diode rectifiers.

The three with minus (−) marks on their cases are checked the same way as above. Only now the negative ohmmeter probe is connected to the case for a reading of 4 to 10 ohms. Reverse leads as above for the other part to test.

If a reading of 4 to 10 ohms is obtained in one direction and no reading (infinity) is read on the ohmmeter in the other direction, diode rectifiers are good. If either infinity or a low resistance is obtained in both directions on a rectifier, it must be replaced.

If meter reads more than 10 ohms when ohmmeter positive probe is connected to positive on diode, and

negative probe to negative, replace diode rectifier.

NOTE: with this test, it is necessary to determine the polarity of the ohmmeter probes. This can be done by connecting the ohmmeter to a DC voltmeter. The voltmeter will read up-scale when the positive probe of the ohmmeter is connected to the positive side of the voltmeter and the negative probe of the ohmmeter is connected to the negative side of the voltmeter.

Alternate method—test light.

Make up a tester as shown in the sketch. Be sure that the lead from the center of the diode rectifiers is disconnected.

To test rectifiers with plus (+) case, touch positive probe of tester to case and minus (−) probe to lead wire of rectifier. Bulb should light if rectifier is good. If bulb does not light, replace rectifier.

Now reverse tester probe connections to rectifier. Bulb should not light. If bulb does light, replace rectifier.

For testing minus (−) marked cases, follow above procedure, except that now bulb should light with negative probe of tester touching rectifier case and positive probe touching lead wire.

Rectifier is good if the bulb lights when tester probes are connected one way, and does not light when tester connections are reversed.

Rectifier must be replaced if the bulb does not light either way. Also, replace rectifier if bulb lights both ways.

NOTE: the usual cause of an open or blown diode or rectifier is a defective capacitor or a battery that has been installed in reverse polarity. If the battery is installed properly and the diodes are open, test the capacitor.

Capacitor capacity:
(int. installed)
..........158 microfarad, min.
(ext. installed) ....5 microfarad

Alternator Bench Tests

Field Coil Draw

1. Connect a jumper between one FLD terminal and the positive terminal of a fully charged 12 volt battery.
2. Connect the positive lead of a test ammeter to the other field (FLD) terminal and the negative test lead to the negative battery terminal.
3. Slowly rotate the rotor by hand and observe the ammeter. The proper field coil draw is 2.3-2.7 amps at 12 volts.

Field Circuit Ground Test

1. Touch one test lead of a 110 volt AC test bulb to one of the alternator brush (field) terminals

and the other test lead to the end shield.
2. If the lamp lights, remove the field brush assemblies and separate the end housing by removing the three thru-bolts.
3. Place one test lead on a slip ring and the other on the end shield.
4. If the lamp lights, the rotor assembly is grounded internally and must be replaced.
5. If the lamp does not light, the cause of the problem was a grounded brush.

Grounded Stator

1. Disconnect the diode rectifiers from the stator leads.
2. Test from stator leads to stator core, using a 110-volt test lamp. Test lamp should not light. If it does, stator is grounded and must be replaced.

Low Output

(About 50% output accompanied with a growl-hum caused by a shorted phase or a shorted rectifier.)

Perform Steps 1, 2 and 3 (rectifier open in all three phases). If the rectifiers are found to be within specifications, replace the stator assembly.

Current Output Too High (No Control) Caused by Open Rectifier or Open Phase

Perform Steps 1, 2 and 3 (rectifier open in all three phases). If the rectifier tests satisfactorily, inspect the stator connections before replacing the stator.

Assembly

1. Support the heat sink or rectifier end housing on circular plate.
2. Check rectifier identification to be sure the correct rectifier is being used. The part numbers are stamped on the case of the rectifier. They are also marked, red for positive and black for negative.
3. Start the new rectifier into the casting and press it in squarely.

CAUTION: Do not start rectifier with a hammer or it will be ruined.

4. Crimp the new rectifier wire to the wires disconnected at removal, or solder (using a heat sink with rosin core solder).
5. Support the end housing on tool so that the notch in the support tool will clear the raised section of the heat sink, then press the bearing into position with tool SP-3381, or equivalent.

NOTE: new bearings are pre-lubricated, additional lubrication is not required.

6. Insert the drive end bearing in the drive end housing and install the bearing plate, washers and nuts to hold the bearing in place.

7. Position the bearing and drive end housing on the rotor shaft and, while supporting the base of the rotor shaft, press the bearing and housing in position on the rotor shaft with an arbor press and arbor tool.

CAUTION: Be careful that there is no cocking of the bearing at installation; or damage will result. Press the bearing on the rotor shaft until the bearing contacts the shoulder on the rotor shaft.

8. Install pulley on rotor shaft. Shaft of rotor must be supported so that all pressing force is on the pulley hub and rotor shaft.

NOTE: Do not exceed 6,800 lbs. pressure. Pulley hub should just contact bearing inner race.

9. Some alternators will be found to have the capacitor mounted internally. Be sure the heat sink insulator is in place.

10. Install the output terminal screw with the capacitor attached through the heat sink and end housing.

11. Install insulating washers, lockwashers and locknuts.

12. Make sure the heat sink and insulator are in place and tighten the locknut.

13. Position the stator on the rectifier end housing. Be sure that all of the rectifier connectors and phase leads are free of interference with the rotor fan blades and that the capacitor (internally mounted) lead has clearance.

14. Position the rotor assembly in the rectifier end housing. Align the through bolt holes in the stator with both end housings.

15. Enter stator shaft in the rectifier end housing bearing, compress stator and both end housings manually and install through bolts, washers and nuts.

16. Install the insulated brush and terminal attaching screw.

17. Install the ground screw and attaching screw.

18. Rotate pulley slowly to be sure the rotor fan blades do not hit the rectifier and stator connectors.

Delcotron 5.5 Series 1D and 6.2 Series 2D (General Motors Corporation)

Description

The Delcotron continuous output AC generator consists of two major parts—the stator and the rotor. The stator is composed of many turns of wire on the inside of a laminated core that is attached to the generator frame. The rotor is mounted on bearings at each end. Two brushes carry

Installing diode rectifier

Installing end frame bearing

Installing drive end frame and bearing on rotor shaft

Installing the pulley

current through slip rings to the field coils, which are wound on the rotor shaft.

The 5.5 Series 1D Delcotron is similar in operation to the 6.2 Series 2D perforated Stator Delcotron. Where differences exist, the two units are mentioned separately.

Six diodes, mounted on internal

Inside capacitor

heat sinks, change the AC current output into DC current. This current is controlled by the regulator. The regulator is a double-contact unit combined with a field relay or a triple-contact unit containing an indicator lamp relay as well as the field relay and voltage relay. Transistor regulators were also used in production intermittently.

On high-output Delcotron units, the regulator incorporates a field discharge diode.

Troubleshooting

NOTE: see the "Preliminary Charging System Inspection" section before proceeding further. Make sure that the continuous running blower, if equipped, is disconnected. This blower will run with the key on and even if the blower control is off, it is not disconnected.

Fusible Links

There are four fusible links on all GM trucks.

1. The 14 gauge wire that runs from the junction block to the positive battery terminal serves as a fusible link.

2. There is a second link in the circuit between the horn relay and the ignition switch.

3. A third link is in the wire running to the No. 3 voltage regulator terminal. Its purpose is to protect the regulator contacts and the alternator field circuit.

4. The fourth link is connected between the main junction block and the horn relay.

These links must be inspected before proceeding with troubleshooting

Charging System Operation

NOTE: if the current indicator is to give an accurate reading, the battery cables must be the same gauge and length as the original equipment.

1. With the engine running and all electrical systems turned off, place a current indicator over the positive battery cable.

2. If a charge of about 5 amps is recorded, the charging system is working. If a draw of about 5 amps is recorded, the system is

Electrical Section

Voltage regulator circuit diagrams (© Chevrolet Div., G.M. Corp)

Mechanical voltage regulator
(© Chevrolet Div., G.M. Corp)

not working. The needle moves toward the battery when a charge condition is indicated, and away from the battery when a draw condition is indicated. If a draw is indicated, proceed with further testing. If an excessive charge (10-15 amps) is indicated, check for an overcharge, caused by a faulty regulator.

Indicator Light Circuit Testing

The indicator lights is important in AC charging systems, for it provides initial field excitation current to the alternator. The light goes out when the field relay closes, which applies battery current to both sides of the bulb. If the light does not go on when key is turned, the bulb could be faulty, there could be an open circuit in the wiring or a positive diode in the alternator could be shorted to ground.

1. Disconnect plug from regulator and connect a test light between terminal No. 4 (in plug) and ground. Turn on ignition switch and observe the light. If light does not go on, check bulb, socket or wiring between switch and regulator plug. If light goes on, check regulator, wiring between regulator F terminal and alternator, or Delcotron itself.
2. Disconnect jumper wire at ground end and reconnect to F terminal in plug. Turn on ignition for a second and note light. If light goes on, problem is in regulator. If light does not go on, problem is in wire between F terminals (regulator and alternator).
3. Disconnect light at plug F terminal and reconnect the free end to F terminal at alternator. Turn on ignition switch for a second and note light. If light goes on, the problem is an open circuit in the wire connecting the regulator and alternator F terminals. If light does not go on, the alternator field windings are defective.

If the indicator light does not extinguish when engine is started,

check for a loose drive belt, faulty field relay, faulty alternator, open parallel resistance wire (usually shows up at idle). If the light stays on with the key turned off, an alternator positive diode is shorted to ground.

Isolation Test

1. Disconnect the wiring harness from the voltage regulator. With a jumper wire connect the F wire to the no. 3 wire in the wire harness plug.
2. Connect a voltmeter across the battery terminals, the positive voltmeter lead to the positive battery terminal, and the negative lead to the negative terminal. Record the reading.
3. Start the engine. Do not race the engine.
4. Gradually raise engine speed to 1500-2000 rpm. The reading on the voltmeter should increase one to two volts over the initial reading. If there is no increase in the reading, repair the alternator. If there is an increase in the voltmeter reading, replace the regulator.

Field Relay Test

1. Connect a voltmeter between the No. 2 terminal and the ground on the regulator.
2. Turn ignition switch on; do not

start the engine. Voltmeter should read battery voltage.
3. If voltmeter reads zero, check circuit connecting regulator terminal No. 2 and Delcotron R terminal.
4. Start engine and run at 1,500-2,000 rpm. If voltage exceeds closing voltage (field relay), and light remains on, field relay is faulty and must be checked.

Field Relay Adjustment

1. Connect a voltmeter between No. 2 regulator terminal and ground.
2. To adjust, connect a 50 ohm rheostat between wiring harness terminal No. 3 and regulator terminal No. 2, after disconnecting the spade lug on the end of the No. 2 regulator terminal wire. Connect a voltmeter between regulator terminal No. 2 and ground, then turn the resistor to "open" position, turn off ignition switch and slowly decrease resistance until relay closes (noting voltage at this point). Voltage can be adjusted by bending heel iron.

Field Circuit Resistance Testing

The resistance wire is an integral part of the ignition wiring harness. The wire cannot be soldered; any connections must be made using crimp-type connectors. Resistance is

Initial field excitation circuit test hook up (© Chevrolet Div., G.M. Corp)

10 ohms, 6¼ watts.

1. Connect a voltmeter between the wiring harness terminal No. 4 and ground.
2. Turn on ignition switch, needle must indicate or resistor is open.

Delcotron Current Output Test

NOTE: disconnect battery ground cable while making test connections, then reconnect cable after completing Step 5. Disconnect battery ground cable again before removing test set-up. This test yields the same information as the isolation test but requires the use of an ammeter and a carbon pile.

1. Disconnect lead from BAT. terminal of Delcotron.
2. Hook an ammeter to the lead just disconnected, and to the BAT. terminal of the Delcotron.
3. Hook up the voltmeter leads to the BAT. terminal and a good ground on the alternator.
4. Disconnect the lead from the FR. terminal of the Delcotron.
5. Hook up a jumper wire between BAT. and F terminals of the Delcotron.
6. With a carbon pile load control hooked up to the battery posts, start the engine and set engine to 1,500 rpm, while adjusting carbon pile to obtain 14 volts. With a 6.2 in. alternator, only 600-800 rpm is required.

CAUTION: Be careful not to exceed the recommended regulator voltage setting. This is controlled by the carbon pile load.

7. Ammeter should read within 10% of rated output, as stamped on frame of each unit.

Alternator Overhaul (5.5 and 6.2 Delcotron)

Disassembly—5.5 Series 1D

1. Remove four bolts.
2. Separate drive end frame and rotor from stator assembly by prying with screwdriver. Note that separation is between stator frame and drive end frame.
3. Place tape over slip ring end

Testing field relay
(© Chevrolet Div., G.M. Corp)

frame bearing to seal dirt.

4. Lightly clamp rotor in vise to remove shaft nut.

CAUTION: Do not distort rotor by overtightening vise.

5. After nut removal, take off washer, pulley, fan and collar.
6. Separate drive end frame from rotor shaft.
7. Remove three stator lead attaching nuts and separate stator from end frame.
8. Remove screws, brushes and holder assembly.
9. Remove BAT., GND., and attaching screw terminals, then remove heat sink.

Disassembly—6.2 Series 2D

1. Clamp drive end mounting flange in a vise, remove the two screws that secure the cover to the brush holder and remove the cover.

Testing field relay closing voltage
(© Chevrolet Div., G.M. Corp)

2. Remove the nut that holds the indicator light wire to the blade connector post; disconnect wire lead from post.
3. Remove the two screws that hold the condenser and brush holder to rear end frame, then remove brush holder. Allow condenser to remain with alternator.
4. Remove three slip ring end frame bolts and tab nuts, then carefully pry end frame and case apart, working evenly around the circumference.
5. Remove the three drive end frame bolts and tab nuts, then remove end frame, rotor and pulley as an assembly.
6. Remove shaft nut, washer, pulley and Woodruff key from rotor shaft, then slide rotor from end frame.
7. Remove drive end frame bearing retainer plate and bearing from end frame.
8. Bearing can be removed, if necessary, at this time. Use puller to prevent damage.

Adjusting field relay closing voltage
(© Chevrolet Div., G.M. Corp)

Delcotron output test hook up
(© Chevrolet Div., G.M. Corp)

Checking rotor for grounds or opens
all Delcotron models
(© Chevrolet Div., G.M. Corp)

Testing diodes (© Chevrolet Div., G.M. Corp)

9. Disconnect the three stator leads by cutting between coils and diodes.

NOTE: diode leads can be cleaned and unsoldered, if proper heat sinks are used to prevent diode damage.

10. Remove heat sink-to-case retaining screws, then remove heat sinks. Insulated heat sink (BATT. terminal) holds positive diode.

Diode Tests

All diodes are marked with either a + or — on the head or are marked with *red* paint for + diodes, *black* paint for — diodes to identify the polarity of the case. On a generator to be used with a negative ground system, the negative case diodes are mounted into the slip ring end frame and the positive case diodes are mounted into the insulated heat sink. Diodes with a negative case have positive polarity leads, whereas positive case diodes have negative polarity leads.

Diodes can be checked for shorts or opens with an ohmmeter.

With the stator leads disconnected, connect one ohmmeter test prod to the diode lead and the other test prod to the heat sink. Reverse the test prods and note the ohmmeter readings. The meter should read high ohms in one direction, low ohms in the other. If both readings are the same, either both high or both low, the diode is faulty and must be replaced. A 1½ volt test light also will indicate a faulty diode. It will light in one direction and not in the other if the diode is good. If it lights in both directions, or in neither direction, the diode is bad.

Diode Replacement

Early Delcotrons had screwed-in diodes, as does the extremely heavy-duty 6.6 Series 4D Delcotron. Models covered here use pressed-in diodes exclusively. If there is any doubt about the year and model of the Delcotron being serviced, not the diode construction—screwed-in diodes have hexagonal heads and the later, pressed-in, units have straight sides with no hex head. Old-style, screwed-in diodes have both right-and left-hand threads. Plus (+) diodes have left-hand and minus (—) have right-hand threads.

5.5 Series 1D

1. Support end frame on a deep socket with a larger inside diameter than the diode outside diameter.
2. Carefully *press* out the diode with a brass drift and an arbor press, or a large bench vise. Be extremely careful so as not to distort the end frame.
3. Select a new diode (red or black), noting that the red (+) diodes go into the heat sink and the black (—) diodes into the end frame.
4. Support end frame on a flat, smooth surface around diode hole and carefully *press* the new diode into position. Diode must be square when starting or both diode and frame will be ruined.

6.2 Series 2D

1. Cut leads connected to diode stem as close as possible to stem, then support end frame as for 5.5 Delcotron and press out diode.
2. Select diode with proper color

marking (same as for 5.5 Delcotron), then press new diode into position.

3. Scrape enough insulation from diode stem and leads to ensure good contact, then install a sleeve over diode and place the T-clip from diode package over diode stem.
4. Place the flexible lead and stator lead (if applicable) into the T-clip, crimp clip and solder with rosin core solder only, using heat sinks (pliers) to avoid destroying diode.
5. Tape the leads together to prevent vibration damage.

Rotor Checks—All Models

The rotor may be checked electrically for grounded, open, or shorted field coils.

To check for grounds, connect a 110-volt test light from either slip ring to the rotor shaft or to the laminations. If the lamp lights, the field windings are grounded.

To check for opens, connect the leads of a 110-volt test light to each slip ring. If the lamp fails to light, the windings are open.

The windings are checked for short-circuits by connecting a battery and ammeter in series with the two slip rings. Note the ammeter reading.

An ammeter reading greater than that specified indicates shorted windings.

Since the field windings are not serviced separately, the rotor assembly must be replaced if the windings are defective.

Stator Checks—All Models

Stator windings may be checked for grounded, open, or shorted windings. If a 110-volt test lamp lights when connected from any stator lead to the stator frame, the windings are grounded. If the lamp fails to light when successively connected between each pair of stator leads, the windings are open.

Brush Assembly—5-5 Delcotron
(© Chevrolet Div., G.M. Corp)

A short circuit in the stator windings is difficult to locate without laboratory equipment, due to the low resistance of the windings. However, if all other electrical checks are normal and the generator fails to supply the rated output, shorted stator windings are indicated.

Slip Ring Servicing and Replacement—All Models

Slip rings which are rough or out of round should be trued in a lathe to .001 in. maximum indicator reading. Remove only enough material to make the rings smooth and round. Finish with 400 grit or finer polishing cloth and blow away all dust.

Slip rings which must be replaced can be removed from the shaft with a gear puller, after the leads have been unsoldered. The new assembly should be pressed on with a sleeve which just fits over the shaft; this will apply all the pressure to the inner slip ring collar and prevent damage to the outer slip ring. Only pure tin solder should be used when reconnecting field leads.

Brush Replacement— All Models

The extent of brush wear can be determined by comparison with a new brush. If brushes are one-half worn, they should be replaced.

1. Remove brush holder assembly from end frame by removing two holder assembly screws.
2. Place springs and brushes in the holder and insert straight wire or pin into holes at bottom of holder to retain brushes.
3. Attach holder assembly onto end frame.

Brush lead arrangement after assembly 6-2 Delcotron
(© Chevrolet Div., G.M. Corp)

Assembly—5.5 Series 1D

1. Install stator assembly into slip ring end frame and locate diode connectors over the relay, diode and stator leads. Tighten terminal nuts.
2. Install rotor into drive end frame.
3. Install fan, spacer, pulley washer and nut.
4. Install Allen wrench (5/16 in.) into end of shaft to hold drive shaft, then tighten pulley nut to 40-50 ft. lbs. using a crowsfoot wrench (15/16 in.) and torque wrench.
5. Assemble slip ring end frame and stator assembly to drive end frame and rotor.
6. Install four through bolts and tighten securely.

Assembly—6.2 Series 2D

1. Install stator assembly into slip ring end frame and locate diode connectors over the relay, diode and stator leads. Tighten terminal nuts.
2. Install the front frame over the rotor.
3. Install the front frame over the key, pulley, washer and nut.
4. Clamp pulley in a padded-jaw vise and tighten shaft nut to 50-60 ft. lbs.
   CAUTION: Do not clamp rotor, or segments will be distorted.
5. Position rotor and drive end frame assembly into slip ring end frame and stator. Install through bolts and tighten securely.
6. Push the brushes into the holder and secure the leads.
7. Attach brush assembly and condenser to the end frame with left-hand hex stud only.
8. Arrange the leads with the right-hand brush lead connected under the right-hand hex stud.
9. Attach terminal cover with two screws, making sure not to pinch the leads.

Delcotron 10-SI Series 100 (General Motors Corp.)

This system is an integrated AC generating system containing a built-in voltage regulator. Removal and replacement is essentially the same as for the standard AC generator.

The regulator is mounted inside the slip ring end frame. All regulator components are enclosed in an epoxy molding, and the regulator cannot be adjusted. Rotor and stator tests are the same as for the 5.5 Delcotron, covered previously.

6-2 Delcotron assembly sequence: 1) drive end frame, 2) rotor 3) stator 4) end frame
(© Chevrolet Div., G.M. Corp)

Troubleshooting

NOTE: see the "Alternator Test Plans" section before proceeding further. Make sure that the continuous running blower, if equipped, is disconnected. This blower will run with the key on even if the blower control is off, unless disconnected.

Charging System Test—Low Charging Rate

1. After battery condition, drive belt tension, and wiring terminals and connections have been checked, charge the battery fully and perform the following test:
2. Connect a test voltmeter between the alternator BAT. terminal and ground, ignition switch on. Connect the voltmeter in turn to alternator terminals No. 1 and No. 2, the other voltmeter lead being grounded as before. A zero reading indicates an open circuit between the battery and each connection at the alternator. If this test discloses no faults in the wiring, proceed to Step 3.
3. Connect the test voltmeter to the alternator BAT. terminal (the other test lead to ground), start the engine and run at 1,500-2,000 rpm with all lights and electrical accessories turned on. If the voltmeter reads 12.8 volts or greater, the alternator is good and no further checks need be made. If the voltmeter reads less than 12.8 volts, ground the field winding by inserting a screwdriver into the test hole in the end frame.

HOOK LEAD OVER STUD   **TEMPORARILY SECURE CLIP WITH NUT**

RUN LEAD BETWEEN TERMINALS

Brush lead arrangement during assembly 6-2 Delcotron (© Chevrolet Div., G.M. Corp)

Electrical Section

10-S1 charging circuit schematic
(© Chevrolet Div., G.M. Corp)

CAUTION: Do not force tab more than ¾ in. into end frame.
   a. If voltage increases to 13 volts or more, the regulator unit is defective.
   b. If voltage does not increase significantly, alternator is defective.

Alternator Output Test

1. Connect a test voltmeter, ammeter and 10 ohm 6 watt resistor into the charging circuit. Do not connect the carbon pile to the battery posts at this time.

**Brush lead clip ground test—
10-S1 Delcotron**
(© Chevrolet Div., G.M. Corp)

420

2. Increase alternator speed and observe voltmeter—if voltage is uncontrolled with speed and increases to 16 volts or more, check for a grounded brush lead clip as covered previously. If brush lead clip is not grounded, the voltage regulator is faulty and must be replaced.
3. Connect the carbon pile load to the battery terminals.
4. Operate the alternator at moderate speed and adjust the carbon pile to obtain maximum alternator output as indicated on the ammeter. If output is within 10% of rated output as stamped on the alternator frame, alternator is O.K. If ouput is not within specifications, ground the alternator field by inserting a screwdriver into the test hole in the end frame. If output now is within 10% of rating, replace the voltage regulator; if still not within specifications, check field winding, diode trio, rectifier bridge and stator, as described later. Disassembly of alternator up to and including Step 6 is necessary.

Disassembly and Assembly

1. Place alternator in a vise, clamped by the mounting flange only.
2. Remove the four through bolts and separate the slip ring end frame and stator assembly from the drive end and rotor assembly, using a screwdriver to pry the two sections apart. Use the slots provided for the purpose.
3. Place a piece of tape over the slip ring end frame bearing to prevent entry of dirt; also tape shaft at slip ring end to prevent scratches.
4. Clean brushes, if they are to be reused, with trichloroethylene or carbon tetrachloride solvent. Use these solvents only in an adequately ventilated area.
5. Remove the stator lead nuts and separate the stator from the end frame.
6. Remove the screw that secures the diode trio and remove diode trio.
NOTE: at this point, test the rotor, rectifier bridge, stator and diode trio if these tests are necessary.
7. Remove the rectifier bridge hold-down screw and the BAT. terminal screw, then disconnect condenser lead. Remove rectifier bridge from end frame.
8. Remove the two securing screws and brush holder and regulator assemblies. Note the insulating sleeves over the screws.
9. Remove the retaining screw and condenser from the end frame.
10. Remove the slip ring end frame

10-S1 basic wiring diagram
(© Chevrolet Div., G.M. Corp)

bearing, if it is to be replaced, using the procedure given later in this section.
11. Remove the pulley nut, washer, pulley, fan and spacer from the rotor shaft, using a 5/16 in. Allen key to hold the shaft while loosening the nut.
12. Remove rotor and spacers from drive end frame assembly.
13. Remove drive end frame bearing retainer plate, screws, plate, bearing, and slinger from end frame, if necessary.
14. To assemble, reverse order of disassembly. Pulley nut must be tightened to 40-50 ft. lbs.

Cleaning and Inspection

1. Clean all metal parts, except stator and rotor assemblies, in solvent.
2. Wipe off bearings and inspect them for pitting or roughness.
3. Inspect rotor slip rings for scoring. They may be cleaned with 400 grit sandpaper (not emery), rotating the rotor to make the rings concentric. Maximum out-of-true is 0.001 in. If slip rings are deeply scored, the en-

10-S1 Delcotron output test hook up
(© Chevrolet Div., G.M. Corp)

Testing diode trio—10-S1 AC Generator

tire rotor must be replaced as a unit.
4. Inspect brushes for wear; minimum length is ¼ in.

Charging System Test—High Charging Rate

1. With the battery fully charged, connect a voltmeter between alternator terminal no. 2 and ground. If the reading is zero, no. 2 circuit from the battery is open.
2. If no. 2 circuit is OK, but an obvious overcharging condition still exists, proceed as follows:
   a. Remove the alternator and separate the end frames.
   b. Connect a low-range ohmmeter between the brush lead clip and the end frame, as illustrated (test no. 1), then reverse the lead connections. If both readings are zero, either the brush lead clip is grounded or the regulator is defective. A grounded brush lead clip can be due to a damaged insulating sleeve or omission of the insulating washer.

Diode Trio Initial Testing

1. Before removing this unit, connect an ohmmeter between the brush lead clip and the end frame. The lowest reading scale should be used for this test.

Brush holder—10-S1 Generator

2. After taking a reading, reverse the lead connections. If the meter reads zero, the brush lead clip is probably grounded, due to omission of the insulating sleeve or insulating washer.

Diode Trio Removal

1. Remove the three nuts which secure the stator.
2. Remove stator.
3. Remove the screw which secures the diode trio lead clip, then remove diode trio.
NOTE: The position of the insulating washer on the screw is critical; make sure it is returned to the same position on reassembly.

Diode Trio Testing

1. Connect an ohmmeter, on lowest range, between the single brush connector and one stator lead connector.
2. Observe the reading, then reverse the meter leads. Repeat this test with each of the other two stator lead connectors. The readings on each of these tests should NOT be identical, there should be one low and one high reading for each test. If this is not the case, replace the diode trio.
CAUTION: Do not use high voltage on the diode trio.

Rectifier Bridge Testing

1. Connect an ohmmeter between the heat sink (ground) and the

Rectifier bridge testing—10-S1 Delcotron
(© Chevrolet Div., G.M. Corp)

base of one of the three terminals. Then, reverse the meter leads and take a reading. If both readings are identical, the bridge is defective and must be replaced.
2. Repeat this test with the remaining two terminals, then between the INSULATED heat sink (as opposed to the GROUNDED heat sink in previous test) and each of the three terminals. As before, if any two readings are identical, on reversing the meter leads, the rectifier bridge must be replaced.

Rectifier Bridge Removal

1. Remove the attaching screw and the BAT. terminal screw.
2. Disconnect the condenser lead.
3. Remove the rectifier bridge.
NOTE: The insulator between the insulated heat sink and the end frame is extremely important to the operation of the unit. It must be replaced

10-S1 Delcotron (© Chevrolet Div., G.M. Corp)

Charging system schematic with transistor regulator and ammeter (© Ford Motor Co)

in exactly the same position on re-assembly.

Brush and/or Voltage Regulator R & R

1. Remove two brush holder screws and stator lead to strap nut and washer, brush holder screws and one of the diode trio lead strap attaching screws.

NOTE: The insulating washers must be replaced in the same position on reassembly.

2. Remove brush holder and brushes. The voltage regulator may also be removed at this time, if desired.

3. Brushes and brush spring must be free of corrosion and must be undamaged and completely free of oil or grease.

4. Insert spring and brushes into holder, noting whether they slide freely without binding. Insert wooden or plastic toothpick into

bottom hole in holder to retain brushes.

NOTE: The brush holder is serviced as a unit; individual parts are not available.

5. Reassemble in reverse order of disassembly.

Slip Ring End Frame Bearing and Seal R & R

1. With stator removed, press out bearing and seal, using a socket or similar tool that fits inside the

Charging system schematic with integral regulator (© Ford Motor Co)

end frame housing. Press from outside to inside, supporting the frame inside with a hollow cylinder (large, deep socket) to allow the seal and bearing to pass.

2. The bearings are sealed for life and permanently lubricated. If a bearing is dry, do not attempt to repack it, as it will throw off the grease and contaminate the inside of the generator.

3. Using a flat plate, press the new bearing from the outside toward the inside. A large vise is a handy press, but care must be exercised so that end frame is not distorted or cracked. Again, use a deep socket to support the inside of the end frame.

4. From inside the end frame, insert seal and press flush with housing.

5. Install stator and reconnect leads.

Ford-Autolite (Ford Motor Co.) with Electro-Mechanical Regulator

The Ford-Autolite charging system is a negative ground system. It includes an alternator, an electro-mechanical regulator, a charge indicator, and a storge battery.

NOTE: Late model Ford systems have replaced the electro-mechanical regulator with either a non-adjustable transistorized regulator or an adjustable transistorized regulator. The adjustable transistorized unit used with high output systems has a single, voltage limit adjusting screw under the cover. Do not use a metal screwdriver for adjustment.

Troubleshooting

NOTE: see the "Alternator Test Plans" section before proceeding further.

Fusible Links

1. Check the fusible link located between the starter relay and the alternator. Replace the link if it is burned or open.

Charging System Operation

NOTE: if the current indicator is to give an accurate reading, the battery cables must be of the same gauge and length as the original equipment.

1. With the engine running, and all electrical systems turned off, place a current indicator over the positive battery cable.

2. If a charge of about 5 amps is recorded, the charging system is working. If a draw of about 5 amps is recorded, the system is not working. The needle moves

CHARGING NO LOAD VOLTAGE
CHARGING VOLTAGE UNDER LOAD
BATTERY NO LOAD VOLTAGE

12 13 14 15

OVERVOLTAGE
OVERCHARGE

VOLTMETER TEST
TYPICAL VOLTAGE BANDS SHOWN

Voltmeter reading isolation test (© Ford Motor Co)

toward the battery when a charge condition is indicated, and away from the battery when a draw condition is indicated. If a draw is indicated, continue to the next testing procedure. If an overcharge of 10-15 amps is indicated, check for a faulty regulator or a bad ground at the regulator or the alternator.

Testing the Ignition Switch to Regulator Circuit

1. Disconnect the regulator wiring harness from the regulator.

2. Turn on the key. Using a test light or voltmeter, check for voltage between the I wire and ground. Check for voltage between the A wire and ground. If voltage is present at this part of the system, the circuit is OK. If there is no voltage at the I wire, check for a burned-out charge indicator bulb, a burned-out resistor, or a break or short in the wiring. If there is no voltage present at the A wire, check for a bad connection at the starter relay or a break or short in the wire.

Isolation Test

This test determines whether the regulator or the alternator is faulty, after the rest of the circuit is found to be in good working order.

1. Disconnect the regulator wiring harness from the regulator.

2. Connect a jumper wire from the A wire to the F wire in the wiring harness plug.

3. Connect a voltmeter to the battery. The positive voltmeter lead goes to the positive terminal and the negative lead to the negative terminal. Record the reading on the voltmeter.

4. Turn off all of the electrical systems and start the engine. Do not race the engine.

5. Gradually increase engine speed to 1500-2000 rpm. The voltmeter reading should increase above the previously recorded battery voltage reading by at least one to two volts. If there is no increase, the alternator is not working correctly. If there is an increase, the voltage regulator needs to be replaced.

Overhaul—Autolite

Disassembly—Except 65 AMP Autolite

1. Mark both end housings with a scribe mark for assembly.

2. Remove the three housing through bolts.

3. Separate the front housing and rotor from the stator and rear housing.

4. Remove the nuts from the rectifier to rear housing mounting studs, and remove the rear housing.

5. Remove the brush holder mounting screws and the holder, brushes, springs, insulator, and terminal.

6. If replacement is necessary, press the bearing from the rear

USE JUMPER WIRE
TO CONNECT "A" AND "F" TERMINALS
AT REGULATOR PLUG

USE OF JUMPER WIRE AT REGULATOR PLUG
TO TEST ALTERNATOR FOR NORMAL OUTPUT AMPS
AND FOR FIELD CIRCUIT WIRING CONTINUITY

Isolation test jumper wire (© Ford Motor Co)

end housing, support housing on inner boss.

7. If rectifiers are to be replaced, carefully unsolder the leads from the terminals.

CAUTION: Use only a 100-watt soldering iron. Leave the soldering iron in contact with the diode terminals only long enough to remove the wires. Use pliers as temporary heat sinks in order to protect the diodes.

8. There are various types of rectifier assembly circuit boards installed in production. One type has the circuit board spaced away from the diode plates and the diodes are exposed. Another type consists of a single circuit board with integral diodes; and still another has integral diodes with an additional booster diode plate containing two diodes. This last type is used only on the eight-diode, 61-amp. 1971-72 Autolite alternator. To disassemble, use the following procedures:

a. Exposed Diodes—remove the screws from the rectifier by rotating bolt heads 1/4 turn clockwise to unlock, then unscrewing.

b. Integral Diodes—press out the stator terminal screw, making sure not to twist it while doing this. Do not remove grounded screw.

c. Booster Diodes—press out the stator terminal screw about 1/4 in., then remove the nut from the end of the screw and lift screw from circuit board, making sure not to twist it as it comes out.

9. Remove the drive pulley and fan. On alternator pulleys with threaded holes in the outer end of the pulley, use a standard puller for removal.

10. Remove the three screws that hold the front bearing retainer, and remove the front housing.

11. If the bearing is to be replaced, press from housing.

Cleaning and Inspection

1. The rotor, stator, diode rectifier assemblies, and bearings are not to be cleaned with solvent. These parts are to be wiped off with a clean cloth. Cleaning solvent may cause damage to the electrical parts or contaminate the bearing internal lubricant. Wash all other parts in solvent and dry them.

2. Rotate the front bearing on the driveshaft. Check for any scraping noise, looseness or roughness that indicates that the bearing is excessively worn. As the bearing is being rotated, look for excessive lubricant leakage. If any of these conditions exist, replace the bearing. Check rear bearing and rotor shaft.

3. Place the rear end housing on the slip ring end of the shaft and rotate the bearing on the shaft. Make a similar check for noise, looseness or roughness. Inspect the rollers and cage for damage. Replace the bearing if these conditions exist, or if the lubricant is missing or contaminated.

4. Check both the front and rear housings for cracks.

5. Check all wire leads on both the stator and rotor assemblies for loose soldered connections, and for burned insulation. Solder all poor connections. Replace parts that show burned insulation.

6. Check the slip rings for damaged insulation and runout. If the slip rings are more than 0.0005 in. out of round, take a light cut (minimum diameter limit 1.22 in.) from the face of the rings to true them. If the slip rings are badly damaged, the entire rotor will have to be replaced, as they are serviced as a complete assembly.

7. Replace any parts that are burned or cracked. Replace brushes that are worn to less than 5/16 in. in length. Replace the brush spring if it had less than 7-12 oz. tension.

Field Current Draw Test

NOTE: alternator must be removed from the truck.

1. Connect a test ammeter between the alternator frame and the positive post of a 12-volt test battery.

2. Connect a jumper wire between

Rectifier assembly (© Ford Motor Co)

Terminal insulators—fiber circuit board (© Ford Motor Co)

Stator Terminal screw removal—61 amp. booster diode model (© Ford Motor Co)

Stator and rectifier assembly—61 amp. booster diode model
(© Ford Motor Co)

Testing diodes—all except 65 amp. autolite
(© Ford Motor Co)

Testing diodes—65 amp. Autolite
(© Ford Motor Co)

the negative test battery post and the alternator field terminal.
3. Observe the ammeter:
   a. Little or no current flow indicates high brush resistance, open field windings, or high winding resistance.
   b. Current in excess of specifications (approximately 2.9 amps. for most models) indicates shorted or grounded field windings, or brush leads touching.

NOTE: sometimes the alternator produces current output at low engine speeds, but ceases to put out at higher speeds. This can be caused by certrifugal force expanding the rotor windings to the point where they short to ground. Place in a test stand and check field current draw while spinning alternator.

Diode Tests

Disassemble the alternator. Disconnect diode assembly from stator and make tests. To test one set of diodes, contact one ohmmeter probe to the diode plate and contact each of the three stator lead terminals with the other probe. Reverse the probes and repeat the test. All six tests (eight for 1971-72 61 amp. Autolite eight-diode models) should show a reading of about 60 ohms in one direction and infinite ohms in the other. If two high readings, or two low readings,

are obtained after reversing probes the diode is faulty and must be replaced.

Stator Tests

Disassemble the stator from the alternator assembly and rectifiers. Connect test ohmmeter probes between each pair of stator leads. If the ohmmeter does not indicate equally between each pair of leads, the stator coil is open and must be replaced.

Connect test ohmmeter probes between one of the stator leads and the stator core. The ohmmeter should not show any reading. If it does show continuity, the stator winding is grounded and must be replaced.

Assembly—Except 65 AMP Autolite

1. Press the front bearing into the front housing boss, putting pressure on outer race only. Install bearing retainer.
2. If the stop ring on the driveshaft was damaged, install a new

stop ring. Push the new ring onto the shaft and into the groove.
3. Position the front bearing spacer on the driveshaft against the stop ring.
4. Place the front housing over the shaft, with the bearing positioned in the front housing cavity.
5. Install fan spacer, fan, pulley, lockwasher and retaining nut and tighten nut to 60-100 ft. lbs. holding the drive shaft with an Allen key.
6. If rear bearing was removed, press a new one into rear housing.
7. Assemble brushes, springs, terminal and insulator in the brush holder, retract the brushes and insert a short length of 1/8 in. rod or stiff wire through the hole in the holder to hold the brushes in the retracted position.
8. Position the brush holder assembly in the rear housing and install mounting screws. Position

Charging system schematic with electro-mechanical regulator and charging light
(© Ford Motor Co)

Brush lead positioning
(© Ford Motor Co)

brush leads to prevent shorting.

9. Wrap the three stator winding leads around the circuit board terminals and solder them using only rosin core solder and a 100-watt iron. Position the stator neutral lead eyelet on the stator terminal screw and install the screw in the rectifier assembly.

10. A. Exposed Diodes—insert the special screws through the wire lug, dished washers and circuit board. Turn 1/4 turn counterclockwise to lock in place.

   B. Integral Diodes—insert the screws straight through the holes.

   NOTE: the dished washers are to be used on the molded circuit boards only. Using these washers on a fiber board will result in a serious short circuit, as only a flat insulating washer between the stator terminal and the board is used on fiber circuit boards.

   C. Booster Diodes—position the stator wire terminal on the stator terminal screw, then position screw on rectifier. Position square insulator over the screw and into the square hole in the rectifier, rotate terminal screw until it locks, then press it in finger-tight. Position the stator wire, then press the terminal screw into the rectifier and insulator with a vise.

11. Place the radio noise suppression condenser on the rectifier terminals. With molded circuit board, install the STA and BAT terminal insulators. With fiber circuit board, place the square stator terminal insulator in the square hole in the rectifier assembly, then position BAT terminal insulator.

   Position the stator and rectifier assembly in the rear housing, making sure that all terminal insulators are seated properly in the recesses. Position STA, BAT and FLD insulators on terminal bolts; install nuts.

12. Clean the rear bearing surface of the rotor shaft with a rag, then position rear housing and stator assembly over rotor. Align matchmarks made during

disassembly and install through bolts. *Remove brush retracting wire and place a dab of silicone sealer over the hole.*

Disassembly—65 AMP Autolite

1. Remove the brush holder and cover assembly from the rear housing.
2. Mark both end housings and the stator.
3. Remove the three housing through bolts.
4. Separate the front housing and rotor from the stator and rear housing.
5. Remove the drive pulley nut, lockwasher, flat washer, pulley, fan, fan spacer and rotor from the front housing.
6. Remove the three screws that hold the front bearing retainer and remove the retainer. If the bearing is damaged or has lost its lubricant, support the housing close to the bearing boss and press out the bearing.
7. Remove all the nut and washer assemblies and insulators from the rear housing and remove the rear housing from the stator and rectifier assembly.
8. If necessary, press the rear bearing from the housing, supporting the housing on the inner boss.
9. Unsolder the three stator leads from the rectifier assembly, and separate the stator from the assembly. Use a 200-watt soldering iron.
10. Perform a diode test and an open and grounded stator coil test.

Cleaning and Inspection

Nicks and scratches may be removed from the rotor slip rings by turning down the slip rings. Do not go beyond the minimum diameter limit of 1.22 in. If the slip rings are badly damaged, the entire rotor must be replaced. The rectifier also is serviced as an assembly. See Lower Ampere Alternator Section for test procedures.

Assembly—65 AMP. Autolite

1. If the front bearing is being replaced, press the new bearing into the bearing boss, putting pressure on the outer race only. Install the bearing retainer and tighten the retainer screws until the tips of the retainer touch the housing.
2. Position the rectifier assembly to the stator, wrap the three stator leads around the diode plate terminals and solder them using a 200-watt soldering iron.
3. If the rear housing bearing was removed, press in a new bearing from the inside of the housing, putting pressure on the outer race only.
4. Install the BAT-GRD insulator, and position the stator and rectifier assembly in the rear housing.
5. Install the STA (purple) and BAT (red) terminal insulators on the terminal bolts and install the nut and washer assemblies. *Make certain that the shoulders on all insulators, both inside and outside of the housing, are seated properly before tightening the nuts.*
6. Position the front housing over the rotor and install the fan spacer, fan, pulley, flat and lockwasher and nut on the rotor shaft.
7. Wipe the rear bearing surface of the rotor shaft with a clean rag.
8. Position the rotor with the front

Disassembled view of 65 amp. autolite alternator (© Ford Motor Co)

GROUND TERMINAL   FIELD TERMINAL

INTEGRAL
REGULATOR

REGULATOR SUPPLY TERMINAL
(TO IGNITION SWITCH)

REGULATOR
BATTERY
TERMINAL

Alternator with integral regulator
(© Ford Motor Co)

housing into the stator and near housing assembly, and align the matchmarks made during disassembly. Seat the machined portion of the stator core into the step in both housings and install the through bolts.

9. If the field brushes have worn to less than $\frac{3}{8}$ in., replace both brushes. Hold the brushes in position by inserting a stiff wire into the brush holder.

10. Position the brush holder assembly into the rear housing and install the three mounting screws. Remove the brush retracting wire and put a dab of silicone cement over the hole.

Brush Replacement—65 AMP Autolite

1. Remove the brush holder and cover assembly from the rear housing.

2. Remove the terminal bolts from the brush holder and cover assembly, then remove the brush assemblies.

3. Position the new brush terminals on the terminal bolts and assemble the terminals, bolts, brush holder washers and nuts. The insulating washer mounts under the FLD terminal nut. The entire brush and cover assembly also is available for service.

4. Depress the brush springs in the brush holder cavities and insert the brushes on top of the springs. Hold the brushes in position by inserting a stiff wire in the brush holder as shown. Position the brush leads as shown.

5. Install the brush holder and cover assembly into the rear housing. Remove the brush retracting wire and put a dab of silicone cement over the hole.

Autolite Alternator with Integral Regulator

Description

Some vehicles are equipped with an Autolite alternator having an integral regulator mounted to the rear end housing. The regulator is a hybrid unit featuring use of solid state integrated circuits. These circuits

may consist of transistors, diodes and resistors. The unusual feature of this type of micro-electronic circuit is that the entire circuit is within a silicone crystal approximately $\frac{1}{8}$ in. square. Because of the small size of the circuit, it is not repairable or adjustable and must be replaced as a unit if found to be defective. It should be noted that the size of the regulator housing is dictated only by the fact that some means of connecting the regulator to the alternator is necessary. Overhaul is the same as for other Autolite alternators.

Troubleshooting

NOTE: see the "Alternator Test Plans" section before proceeding further.

Fusible Links

1. Check the fusible link located between the starter relay and the alternator. Replace the link if it is burned or open.

Output Test

1. Place transmission in Neutral or Park.

2. Remove the positive battery cable and install a battery adapter switch in the line.

3. Attach one lead of a test voltmeter to the negative battery post and the other test lead to the circuit side of the adapter switch.

4. Connect a test ammeter to each side of the adapter switch, so that charging current will go through the ammeter when the switch is opened.

5. Connect a jumper wire between the alternator frame and the integral regulator field terminal (cover plug removed).

6. Close adapter switch, start engine and open adapter switch.

VOLT-AMP-ALTERNATOR TESTER

ALTERNATOR
OUTPUT
TEST

Yellow

ARE 27-38   Green

CONNECT JUMPER WIRE FROM
REGULATOR FIELD TERMINAL
TO GROUND

STARTER
RELAY

BATTERY
ADAPTER
SWITCH

Red

Black

COVER REMOVED

BATTERY

Output test hook-up integral regulator alternator
(© Ford Motor Co)

7. Running engine at 2,000 rpm, observe voltmeter and ammeter. At 15 volts indicated, the ammeter should read 50-57 amps. If so, and there is still a no-charge condition, the regulator is probably faulty and must be replaced. An output 2-8 amps. below 50 amps. usually indicates an open diode rectifier, while an output 10-15 amps. below minimum specifications usually indicates a shorted diode. An alternator with a shorted diode usually will whine at idle speed.

Field Test (Voltmeter)

1. Turn ignition switch to OFF position.

2. Remove wire from regulator supply terminal.

VOLT-AMP-ALTERNATOR TESTER

Yellow   Green

ARE 27-38

STARTER RELAY

WIRE REMOVED FROM
REGULATOR SUPPLY
TERMINAL

TO BATTERY

FIELD
VOLTMETER TEST

COVER REMOVED

Field voltmeter test hook-up—integral regulator alternator
(© Ford Motor Co)

3. Remove cover plug from regulator field terminal and connect one test voltmeter lead to this terminal. A ¼ ohm resistor should be in the circuit.
4. Connect the other test voltmeter lead to a good engine ground.
5. The voltmeter should read 12 volts. If *no* voltage is present, the field circuit is open or grounded.
6. If voltmeter reads more than I volt, but still less than battery voltage, there is probably a partial ground in the alternator field circuit and the circuit should be checked with an ohmmeter.

Field Test (Ohmmeter)

1. Disconnect battery ground cable; remove alternator from truck.
2. Remove the regulator from the alternator (covered later).
3. Make the ohmmeter tests as illustrated. If any of the tests indicates a field circuit problem, disassemble the alternator to further isolate the trouble.
   a. Contact each ohmmeter probe to a slip ring. Resistance should be 4-5 ohms. A higher reading indicates a damaged slip ring soldered connection or a broken wire. A lower reading indicates a shorted wire or slip ring assembly.
   b. Contact one ohmmeter probe to a slip ring and the other probe to the rotor shaft. Any reading other than infinite ohms indicates a short to ground. If neither of these tests (A and B) isolates the trouble, the brushes or brush assembly are the probable cause.

Voltage Limiter Test

1. Check the battery specific gravity. If it is not at least 1.230, charge the battery or install a charged battery for the test.
2. Make sure all lights and accessories are turned off, including such items as dome lights.
3. Make the test connections as illustrated.
4. Place transmission in Neutral or Park, close battery adapter switch and start the engine.
5. Open the battery adapter switch and operate engine at 2,000 rpm for 5 minutes. The voltmeter should read 13.3-15.3 volts.
6. If voltage does not rise above 12 volts, perform a regulator supply voltage test to determine whether or not the regulator is getting voltage from the battery. Before replacing a regulator, check the wiring of the entire

VOLT-AMP-ALTERNATOR TESTER

ARE 27-38

VOLTAGE LIMITER TEST

STARTER RELAY

BATTERY ADAPTER SWITCH

Red

Yellow

Green

BATTERY

Voltage limiter test-hook-up—integral regulator alternator
(© Ford Motor Co)

charging system for shorts, opens, or high resistance connections.

Regulator Supply Voltage Test

The regulator is "turned on" by the application of battery voltage through a 10 ohm resistor wire. If the supply circuit is defective, the regulator will not function and the alternator will not put out current.

1. Connect a 12-volt test light or voltmeter between the regulator supply lead and ground.
2. Turn on the ignition switch. The test light should glow or the voltmeter indicate. If not, the supply circuit should be checked back to the battery, especially the resistance wire.

Overhaul

The overhaul procedures for the alternator are the same as for the Ford Autolite electro-mechanical alternator.

The Motorola System

The Motorola alternator is designed to pass all the DC current through an isolation diode, or diodes, mounted in an external aluminum heat sink.

Due to the nature of the alternator, residual magnetism is at near zero when the unit is at rest. It is, therefore, necessary to provide some small current to excite the field prior to generating current. With Motorola, this priming current is supplied by

CENTER SCALE READINGS INDICATE POTENTIAL LOSS OF CONTROL AT VARIOUS TEMPERATURES OR ENGINE SPEEDS

INFINITE READING INDICATES FIELD CIRCUIT NOT GROUNDED

ZERO READING INDICATES FIELD CIRCUIT SHORTED TO GROUND

OHMMETER ARE 27-42

Red WIRE   Black WIRE

KEEP TERMINAL CENTERED IN HOLE

PULL OUTWARD ON TERMINAL
Red
Black

OHMMETER GROUNDED FIELD CIRCUIT TEST

NORMAL FIELD CIRCUIT IS INDICATED WHEN READING IS 4 TO 10 OHMS. VARIATION IS CAUSED BY BRUSHES SLIDING ON SLIP-RINGS.

INFINITE READING INDICATES AN OPEN FIELD CIRCUIT

ZERO READING INDICATES A SHORTED FIELD CIRCUIT

OHMMETER ARE 27-42

KEEP TERMINAL CENTERED IN HOLE

Black

PULL OUTWARD ON TERMINAL

OHMMETER SHORTED OR OPEN FIELD CIRCUIT TEST

Field circuit test hook-up with ohmmeter—integral regulator alternator (© Ford Motor Co)

Supply voltage test hook-up—integral regulator alternator
(© Ford Motor Co)

Typical Motorola alternator system charging circuit
(© American Motors Corp)

means of a 75 ohm resistance unit between the ignition coil and the alternator (inside the regulator). It is quite important that this resistance unit be checked and found satisfactory before proceeding with subsequent tests.

The charge indicator light on some trucks operates in the same way as this resistor by furnishing the necessary initial field starting current. If this resistor circuit is open (a burned out indicator lamp) on some models, the alternator will not function. On later models, a resistor is placed in parallel with the bulb to provide excitation current if the bulb burns out.

The regulator is a sealed unit and should require no adjustment. It is therefore, recommended that non-functioning regulators be replaced.

Troubleshooting

NOTE: see the "Alternator Test Plans" section before proceeding further.

Fusible Link Test

There are many fuse links in the truck however the fuse link located in the wiring between the battery terminal of the horn relay to the main wire harness is the only one that concerns the charging system. This link protects the entire wiring harness. If it fails, all the electrical systems will fail to function.

Charging System Operation

NOTE: if the current indicator is to give an accurate reading, the battery cables must be of the same gauge and length as the original equipment.

1. With the engine running and all electrical systems off, place a current indicator over the positive battery cable.
2. If a charge of about 5 amps is

recorded, the charging system is working. If a draw of about 5 amps is recorded, the system is not working. The needle moves toward the battery when a charge condition is indicated, and away from the battery when a draw condition is indicated. If a draw is indicated, continue to the next testing procedure. If an overcharge of 10-15 amps is indicated, check for a faulty regulator, or a bad ground at the regulator or the alternator.

Testing the Ignition Switch to Regulator Circuit

1. Disconnect the regulator wires from the regulator.
2. Turn on the key. Using a test light or voltmeter, check for current between the voltage supply wire and ground. This wire is usually orange and has another wire connected to it, usually blue or orange with a tracer.
3. If current is present, this part of the system is OK. If no voltage is present, check for broken or shorted wiring, a bad indicator bulb, a bad fuse in the fuse panel, or a bad connection at the ignition switch or on the battery side of the starter relay.

Isolation Test

This test determines whether the regulator or the alternator is faulty, after the rest of the circuit is found to be in good working order.

1. Disconnect the regulator wiring harness from the regulator.
2. Connect a jumper wire from the voltage supply wire from the battery, orange, to the field wire for the alternator, green.
3. Connect a voltmeter to the battery. The positive voltmeter lead

goes to the positive terminal and the negative lead to the negative terminal. Record the reading on the voltmeter.
4. Turn off all of the electrical systems and start the engine. Do not race the engine.
5. Gradually increase engine speed to 1500-2000 rpm. The voltmeter reading should increase above the previously recorded battery voltage reading by at least one to two volts. If there is no increase, the alternator is not working correctly. If there is an increase, the voltage regulator needs to be replaced.

Field Current Draw Test

1. With battery disconnected, disconnect the wires from the alternator output terminal and the alternator field terminal.

35 amp. alternator—Motorola
(© American Motors Corp)

55 amp. alternator—Motorola
(© American Motors Corp)

Field current test

Brush test points

2. With a field rheostat in the open position, connect its leads to the disconnected alternator output wire and to the positive lead of the test ammeter.
3. Connect the negative ammeter lead to the alternator field terminal.
4. Connect the positive voltmeter lead to the alternator field terminal.
5. Connect the negative voltmeter lead to the alternator ground terminal.
6. Reconnect the battery.
7. Start and run the engine at fast idle.
8. Adjust field rheostat to closed position, then note the voltmeter and ammeter readings.
9. Adjust field rheostat control to the open position.
10. Compare the readings obtained in Step 8 with manufacturers' specifications.
11. If readings are zero, there is an indication of trouble in the field coil, or the connections between field coil and slip ring.
12. If readings are low, there is probable trouble in the slip rings or brushes.

In-circuit diode test points

13. If readings are high, the field coil is probably shorted.
14. If readings are normal, on an alternator which failed to produce its rated output, the probable cause lies in the stator or diodes. Replace the alternator in this case.

Alternator Disassembly

1. Remove the two self-tapping screws and the cover. Pull the brush assembly straight up to clear the locating pins, then lift out the brush assembly.
2. Remove the two locknuts and remove the isolation diode assembly from the rear housing.
3. Scribe a matchmark across the front housing, stator, and rear housing. Remove the four thru-bolts and nuts, then carefully separate the rear housing and stator from the front housing using two screwdrivers in the slots provided.

CAUTION: Do not insert screwdrivers deeper than 1 16 in., to avoid damaging stator winding.

4. Remove the four locknuts and insulating washers that hold the stator and diode assembly, then separate the assembly from the rear housing. Avoid bending the stator wires—do not unsolder the wires without using pliers as a heat sink.
5. There is no reason to remove the rotor from the front housing unless there is a defect in the field coil or front bearing. Front and rear bearings are lubricated for life and sealed and, as a rule, do

not go bad unless the drive belt has been adjusted with too much tension. If the rotor must be removed, use a puller to remove the front drive pulley, then unseat the split-ring washer using long-nose pliers through the front housing to compress the washer while pulling on the rotor. Tap the rotor shaft lightly to remove the rotor and front bearing, then reach in and remove the split-ring washer. Bearings must be removed using a puller and new bearings must be pressed into place.

Bench Tests

Isolation Diode Circuit Test

Excessive leakage through the isolation diode will discharge the battery. The rate of discharge depends upon the degree of leakage. Normal and tolerable leakage is less than .001 amperes.

1. To check isolation diode leakage, connect the regulator to the battery. Do not operate the alternator.
2. Measure the voltage from auxiliary terminal F to ground terminal G. The voltage appearing at the auxiliary terminal should not exceed 0.1 volt. Voltage greater than this indicates leakage through the isolation diode. Check the isolation diode with a commercial diode tester, or with a 12-volt DC test lamp.

Rotor Open Circuit Test

An ohmmeter may be used to check

Motorola alternator—exploded view
(© American Motors)

Alternator and regulator bench test   MODEL A12NX451

Rotor leakage test points

Stator leakage test points

In-circuit stator leakage test points

continuity of the rotor. Connect ohmmeter probes to field terminal and ground terminal (test points B and G). Resistance should be about 6 ohms. If resistance is high, field coil is open.

Isolation Diode Test

If a commercial diode tester is not available, use a 12-volt DC test lamp only, otherwise diodes can be damaged.
1. Connect the test lamp to output terminal and auxiliary terminal. Then reverse the test probes. Test lamp should light in one direction only. If test light lights in both directions, the isolation diode is shorted. If lamp won't light in either direction, the diode is open.

Rotor Leakage Test

This is a check of the field coil for leakage or shorts to rotor poles. An ohmmeter or test lamp (12V or 120V) may be used.
1. Remove the brush assembly to gain access to rotor slip rings.
2. Connect ohmmeter or test lamp probes to one of the slip rings and the ground terminal, points G and P.
Ohmmeter resistance should be infinite or test lamp should not light. If condition is contrary, leakage or a short exists between field coil and rotor.
Repeat test after rotor has been removed from the alternator to pinpoint findings.

Out-of-Circuit Stator Leak Test

Disassemble alternator and remove the rectifier-diode plates and stator as an assembly.
An ohmmeter or 12-volt DC test lamp may be used.
1. Connect ohmmeter or test lamp probes to one of the rectifier diode terminals and to the stator

test points N and Q.
Resistance reading should be infinite (or the test light should not light). If result is contrary, high leakage or a short exists between stator winding and stator. In either case, stator should be replaced.

Stator Coil Leak and Continuity Test

This check is for shorts or leakage between stator coil windings. The 30 and 40 amp. alternators use a Wye-Type winding. 45 ampere models use a Delta type winding.

Wye Type (30 and 40 Amp. Models)

1. Separate winding ends. An ohmmeter or 12-volt DC test lamp may be used.
2. Connect one lead of the ohmmeter or test lamp to point 1. Connect the other test lead to point 2 and then to point 3. Ohmmeter reading should be infinite or the test lamp should not light.
3. Connect test leads to points 2 and 3. Ohmmeter reading should be infinite, or the test lamp should not light.
In test 2 or test 3, if the test results are contrary, excess leakage or a short exists between stator windings; replace the stator.
4. Check continuity by measuring the resistance of each winding in the stator with an ohmmeter, between test points, 1 to 1A, 2 to 2A and 3 to 3A.
Resistance should be very low (about 0.1 ohm).
Never replace stator until all other components have been checked and proven satisfactory.

Delta Type (45 Amp. Models)

1. Separate stator winding ends. An ohmmeter or 12-volt DC test

lamp may be used.
2. Connect one lead of the ohmmeter or test lamp to point 4. Connect the other test lead to point 5 and then to point 6. Ohmmeter reading should be infinite or the test lamp should not light.
3. Connect test leads to test points 5 and 6. Ohmmeter reading should be infinite, or the test lamp should not light.
In test 2 or test 3, if the test results are contrary, excess leakage or a short exists between stator windings; replace the stator.
4. Check continuity by measuring the resistance of each winding in the stator with an ohmmeter placed between test points 4 to 4A, 5 to 5A and 6 to 6A.
Resistance should be very low (about 0.1 ohm).

Electrical Section

Stator coil test points (Delta-type)

Single and two-unit Prestolite circuits

Never replace stator until all other components have been checked and proven satisfactory.

Out-of-Circuit Rectifier Diode Test

If a commercial diode tester is not available, check the diodes with a 12-volt DC test lamp only.

CAUTION: When unsoldering the stator wires from the rectifier diode assembly, provide a heat sink to the diode terminal with a pair of long-nosed pliers.

1. Connect test lamp probes to diode terminal and diode plate stud, then reverse test lamp probes. The test light should light in one direction but not in the other.

   If the test lamp lights in both directions, the diode is shorted. If test lamp does not light in either direction, the diode is open.

   Test the remaining diodes of the assembly in the same manner. Replace entire assembly if one of the diodes is found to be bad.

Alternator Assembly

1. Clean the bearing and the inside of the bearing hub in the front housing, then gently seat the bearing using a socket of appropriate size and a small hammer.
2. Insert the split-ring washer into the hub of the front housing and seat the washer in its groove. Be extremely careful doing this, because the bearing seal is easily damaged.
3. The front bearing now must be seated against the shoulder on the rotor shaft. Install the fan and pulley spacer, then the Woodruff key, fan and pulley. Using a 7/16 in. socket or equivalent tool to fit inside the rear bearing race, apply pressure to drive the bearing against the shoulder of the rotor shaft.
4. Assemble the front and rear housing assemblies by hand, making certain that the rear bearing is properly seated in the rear housing hub and that the diode wires are not touching the rotor at any point.
5. Align the matchmarks made during disassembly, then spin the rotor to make sure sufficient clearance exists between it and the diode wires. Install the through bolts and tighten them evenly, using only a hand wrench. Continue assembly in reverse of disassembly.

The Prestolite System

The Prestolite AC generator regulator with a circuit break (C. B. type) incorporates a polarity sensing feature for the purpose of isolating generator output from battery potential when the system is out of operation. This feature prevents damage to the components of the charging system in the event of battery polarity reversal.

Late model Prestolite alternators incorporate an *isolation diode,* mounted as a component part of the internal positive heat sink assembly. Such alternators are almost identical to late model Motorola units in operation. Test procedures for the Motorola alternator also apply to the diode-equipped Prestolite.

Troubleshooting

NOTE: see the "Alternator Test Plans" section before proceeding further.

Fusible Link Test

See the Motorola system section for the fuse link test.

Charging System Operation

See the Motorola system section for the "Charging System Operation" tests.

Testing the Ignition Switch-to-Regulator Circuit

1. Disconnect the regulator wires from the regulator.
2. Turn on the key. Using a test light or voltmeter, check for current between the I terminal and ground and the L terminal ground. If voltage is present, this part of the system is OK. If no voltage is present, check for broken or shorted wires, a bad indicator bulb, a bad ammeter (if so equipped), or bad connections.

Isolation Test—2 Unit Regulator

This test determines whether the

Typical wiring circuit diagram, Prestolite alternator system

Plan to make charging circuit resistance check

AC Generators and Regulators

Plan to make alternator output test

Plan to make field current draw test

regulator or the alternator is faulty, after the rest of the circuit is found to be in good working order.

1. Disconnect the regulator wiring harness from the regulator.
2. Connect a jumper wire from the A wire to the F wire.
3. Connect a voltmeter to the battery. The positive voltmeter lead goes to the positive terminal and the negative lead to the negative terminal. Record the reading.
4. Turn off all of the electrical system and start the engine. Do not race the engine.
5. Gradually increase engine speed to 1500-2000 rpm. The voltmeter reading should increase by at least one to two volts. If there is no increase, the alternator is not working correctly. If there is an increase, the voltage regulator needs to be replaced.

Isolation Test—Single Unit Regulator

1. Disconnect the field wire from the alternator. Do not allow the wire to touch ground.
2. Connect a jumper wire from the alternator A terminal to the alternator F terminal.
3. Connect a voltmeter to the battery. The positive voltmeter lead goes to the positive terminal and the negative lead goes to the negative terminal. Record the reading on the voltmeter.
4. Turn off all of the electrical systems and start the engine. Do not race the engine.
5. Gradually increase engine speed to 1500-2000 rpm. The voltmeter reading should increase above the previously recorded battery voltage reading by at least one to two volts. If there is no increase, the alternator is not working correctly. If there is an increase, the voltage regulator needs to be replaced.

Field Current Draw Test— C. B. Type

1. Disconnect the generator F ter-

Alternator

	Model No. ALC 5001	Model No. ALD 5001	Model No. ALD 5005
Rotation—Clockwise, Drive End	Yes	Yes	Yes
Voltage	12	12	12
Rated Output (Amps.)	45	40	40
Brushes (No.)	2	2	2
Rotor Field Coil Draw (At 70°F) at 10 Volts	2.34—2.43 Amps.	2.32—2.42 Amps.	2.32—2.42 Amps.
Current Output—4200 rpm (Engine speed 1750 rpm)	42 Amps. 14.2 Volts	38 Amps. 14.2 Volts	38 Amps. 14.2 Volts
Ground Polarity	Negative	Negative	Negative
Control	VR	VR	VR

Voltage Regulator

	Model No. VBS 6201A	Model No. VBT 6201A	Model No. VBS 6201A-1
Volts	12	12	12
Ground Polarity	Negative	Negative	Negative
Point Gap (in.)	.010	.010	.010
Air Gap (in.)	.034-.038	.034-.038	.034-.038
Relay Air Gap (in.)	.015-.020	——	.015-.020
Relay Opening (Amps.)	2.0-2.5	——	2.0-2.5
Relay Closing (Amps.)	1.5 Max.	——	1.5 Max.
Operating Voltage (Upper Contact) 50°F 80°F 110°F 140°F Tolerance 14.3 14.1 13.0 13.7 ±.2		—All Models—	
Voltage Spread (Between upper and lower contact operation)	.1-.3 Volts	.1-.3 Volts	.1-.3 Volts
Capacitor (Color band indicates ground end)	.1 MFD	.1 MFD	.1 MFD
Resistance R^1	10 Ohms.	10 Ohms.	10 Ohms.
R^2	20 Ohms.	20 Ohms.	20 Ohms.
VR Winding	52-58 Ohms.	52-58 Ohms.	52-58 Ohms.
1600-1800 rpm Alternator Speed, 15 minute warm-up, 10 Amp. load		—All Models—	
3400-3600 rpm Alternator Speed, 15 Amp. load Upper contacts—2-7 Amp. Charge rate—lower grounding contacts		—All Models—	
All tests to be made with a fully charged battery		—All Models—	

433

minal and insulate the lead to prevent accidental grounding.

2. Connect an ammeter and a field rheostat in series, between the generator F terminal and the generator A terminal in the following manner:

  A. With a field rheostat set in the open position, connect one of its leads to the generator A terminal and the other lead to the test ammeter.

  B. Connect the other test ammeter lead to the generator F terminal.

3. Hook up a voltmeter by connecting one voltmeter lead to the generator F terminal and the other lead to the generator frame.

4. Reconnect the battery ground cable.

5. Turn ignition switch on.

6. Adjust the field rheostat to obtain recommended voltage.

7. Now, read the ammeter. This represents the rotor field current draw.

8. Adjust field rheostat to open position, and turn ignition switch off.

9. Compare the reading with manufacturers' specifications.

  A. If the reading is too low, it indicates trouble, probably slip rings or brushes.

  B. If the reading is too high, it indicates a short in the field winding.

  C. If the reading is as specified on a generator which did not deliver its rated output, look for trouble in the diodes.

Voltage Regulator Setting— C. B. Type

1. With the battery ground cable disconnected at the battery and the ignition switch in off position, hook up an ammeter to the generator A terminal and to the lead just disconnected from this A terminal.

2. Connect a field rheostat to the generator F terminal and to the lead just disconnected from this F terminal. Adjust rheostat to open position.

3. Connect a voltmeter to the regulator B terminal and a good ground on the frame of the regulator.

4. Connect the battery ground cable.

Plan to make voltage regulator check

5. Hook up a carbon pile (load control turned to the off position) between the battery posts.

6. Start the engine and while operating at 850 rpm, adjust the field rheostat to obtain a 10 amp. charge. Be careful not to exceed factory voltage recommendation. Run engine long enough to develop normal regulator operating temperature.

7. Open, then fully close the field rheostat to cycle the system.

8. Adjust the carbon pile load to obtain a 10 amp. generator output while reading the voltmeter. This reading is on the upper contacts.

9. Turn carbon pile to off position and increase engine rpm to 1750, then read the voltmeter. This voltage should increase and the amperage decrease if the regulator lower point set is working. This is known as spread.

10. If the battery is in fully charged condition, the spread may be checked in the following manner.

  A. Adjust load control to produce 15 amps. of charge, then read the voltmeter. This reading is on the upper set of points.

  B. Adjust load control to off position, wait about one-half minute, then read the voltmeter. This reading is on the lower set of points. The difference between the two readings is spread.

  C. Spread should be 0.2 to 0.5 volts higher when operating on lower grounding contact.

Operation on lower contacts must not exceed 14.7 volts. If necessary, adjust regulator so as not to exceed 14.7 volts.

11. If regulator does not operate within specifications, renew the regulator.

Disassembly—C.B. Type

1. Remove thru bolts and tap ends lightly with plastic hammer to separate ends from rotor.

2. Remove nuts and washers from negative rectifier brackets, and the nuts, washers and insulator bushings from the positive rectifier brackets, and separate the slip ring end head.

3. Remove insulated brush, gripping brass terminal on brush head with pliers and pulling from field terminal insulator.

4. Remove screw that attaches ground brush. Do not lose brush springs.

5. To remove pulley nut, grip pulley with fan belt and vise to hold while breaking nut loose. Then remove pulley with suitable puller.

6. To remove drive end head, remove key, fan and spacer. Then, using suitable puller remove head.

7. Remove retaining plate and press out drive end head bearing.

8. The slip end head bearing can be removed with a puller.

9. The rectifiers can now be pressed out and in. In cutting and crimping leads keep as close to the sleeve as possible.

Alternator Disassembly— Diode Type

1. Remove the two brush mounting screws and cover, then tip the brush assembly away from the alternator and remove.

2. Matchmark the rear housing, stator and drive end housing, then remove the four retaining screws. The stator and rear

Exploded view—Prestolite alternator

Testing diode trio—C.S.I. AC generator

Testing rectifier bridge diodes—C.S.I. AC generator

Grounding tab for voltage regulator test—C.S.I. AC generator

Brush holder—C.S.I. generator

housing are removed as a unit by tapping lightly with a fiber hammer to separate them from the front housing.

3. The rotor should not be removed unless it or the front bearing is defective. To remove the rotor under these conditions, first remove the pulley nut and pulley (using a two-jaw puller), then remove the fan, Woodruff key and spacer. The rotor is removed from the front housing using a three-paw puller.

4. The front bearing is easily removed, after taking out the retaining ring, by pressing it out in a large vise using sockets to support the housing from the rear.

Stator Coil Test—Diode Type

1. Using a No. 57 bulb, connected in series with a 12-volt battery, as a test light, touch one test lead to the connection of the three stator windings and the other test lead to each stator lead that is connected to the diodes. If the bulb does not light, the winding is open.

2. To test for a grounded stator, use a 110-volt test lamp. First disconnect the diodes from the stator leads, then touch one test lead to the stator core and the other test lead to each of the three stator leads. If the test lamp lights, the winding is grounded.

NOTE: if all other components are O.K. and alternator still does not work, it can be assumed that the stator windings are internally shorted. This type of short is impossible to detect by using the previous test. Diode tests are the same as for the Motorola alternator.

Alternator Assembly— Diode Type

1. Press the front bearing into the front housing, making sure the dust seal faces the rotor. Install the bearing retaining snap-ring, then press the shoulder of the shaft against the inner bearing race using a tool that fits over the shaft and against the race.

Install the spacer, Woodruff key, fan and pulley, then install lockwasher and pulley nut.

2. Install the diode heat sink, negative diodes and stator. Solder any stator to diode connections that were unsoldered, using pliers as a heat sink to prevent overheating.

3. Install the rotor and front drive housing to stator and rear housing, aligning matchmarks made during disassembly. Install the four retaining screws, then the brush holder assembly and retaining screws.

4. Make sure the stator leads and brush holder assembly clear the rotor and that the rotor can be spun by hand without binding.

C.S.I. AC Generator

The C.S.I. system is an integrated AC generating system containing a built-in voltage regulator. Removal and replacement is essentially the same as for the standard AC generator. Specialized service procedures are as follows:

Diode Trio Initial Testing

1. Before removing this unit, easily identified in the illustration, connect an ohmmeter between the brush lead clip and the end

frame. The lowest reading scale should be used for this test.

2. After taking a reading, reverse the lead connections. If the meter reads zero, the brush lead clip is probably grounded, due to omission of the insulating sleeve or insulating washer.

Diode Trio Removal

1. Remove the three nuts which secure the stator.
2. Remove stator.
3. Remove the screw which secures the diode trio lead clip, then remove diode trio.

NOTE: The position of the insulating washer on the screw is critical; make sure it is returned to the same position on reassembly.

Diode Trio Testing

1. Connect an ohmmeter, on lowest range, between the single brush connector and one stator lead connector.
2. Observe the reading, then reverse the meter leads. Repeat this test with each of the other two stator lead connectors. The readings on each of these tests should NOT be identical, there should be one low and one high reading for each test. If this is not the case, replace the diode trio.

CAUTION: Do not use high voltage on the diode trio.

Rectifier Bridge Testing

1. Connect an ohmmeter between the heat sink (ground) and the base of one of the three terminals. Then, reverse the meter leads and take a reading. If both readings are identical, the bridge is defective and must be replaced.

2. Repeat this test with the remaining two terminals, then between the INSULATED heat sink (as opposed to the GROUNDED heat sink in previous test) and each of the three terminals. As before, if any two readings are identical, on reversing the meter leads, the rectifier bridge must be replaced.

Rectified Bridge Removal

1. Remove the attaching screw and the BAT. terminal screw.
2. Disconnect the condenser lead.
3. Remove the rectifier bridge.

Brush and/or Voltage Regulator R & R

1. Remove two brush holder screws and lead to strap nut and washer, brush holder screws and one of the diode trio lead strap attaching screws.

NOTE: The insulating washers must be replaced in the same position on reassembly.

2. Remove brush holder and brushes. The voltage regulator may also be removed at this time, if desired.

3. Brushes and brush springs must be free of corrosion and must be undamaged and completely free of oil or grease.

4. Insert spring and brushes into holder, noting whether they slide freely without binding. Insert wooden or plastic toothpick into bottom hole in holder to retain brushes.

NOTE: The brush holder is serviced as a unit; individual parts are not available.

5. Reassemble in reverse order of disassembly.

Voltage Regulator Testing

NOTE: The voltage regulator must be tested with the C.S.I. unit still in place.

1. Disconnect battery ground strap.
2. Connect an ammeter in series with the BAT. terminal of the generator and the lead removed from that terminal.
3. Reconnect battery ground strap, then turn on all accessoris to place a load on the system.
4. Connect a carbon pile across the battery terminals.
5. Ground the field winding by inserting an insulated screwdriver into the test hole in the alternator frame and depressing the tab. Do not push the tab into the generator more than 1 in.
6. Run the engine at moderate rpm, equivalent to 30-40 mph in high gear, and adjust the carbon pile to obtain maximum current output.
7. If the output is within 10% of the rated output of the alternator and the system does not charge properly, the voltage regulator is defective and must be replaced.

Generator—C.S.I.
Amps.—cold rating 55
Output @ rpm .... 30 @ 2000
Output @ rpm .... 55 @ 5000
Field current draw 4.0-4.5
Regulator—C.S.I.
Model 1116368
Normal range ..... 13.5-16.0 volts

Slip Ring End Frame Bearing and Seal R & R

1. With stator removed, press out bearing and seal, using a socket

Wiring plan of Leece-Neville 6000 negative ground system, ammeter equipped

or similar tool that fits inside the end frame housing. Press from outside to inside, supporting the frame inside with a hollow cylinder (large, deep socket) to allow the seal and bearing to pass.

2. The bearings are sealed for life and permanently lubricated. If a bearing is dry, do not attempt to repack it, as it will throw off the grease and contaminate the inside of the generator.

3. Using a flat plate, press the new bearing from the outside toward the inside. A large vise is a handy press, but care must be exercised so that end frame is not distorted or cracked. Again, use a deep socket to support the inside of the end frame.

4. From inside the end frame, insert seal and press flush with housing.

5. Install stator and reconnect leads.

The Leece-Neville System

Field and Lamp Relay Test

1. Disconnect the battery wire from B terminal of the regulator.
2. Disconnect the N wire from the regulator.
3. With the field rheostat in the open position, connect its leads to the disconnected battery wire and the N terminal of the regulator.
4. Hook up a voltmeter to the regulator N terminal and to a good ground.
5. Slowly adjust the field rheostat toward the closed position. The field relay contacts should close somewhere between 1.9 and 2.4 volts.

Load Relay Test

1. Disconnect the battery wire from B terminal of the regulator.
2. With field rheostat in the open position, connect its leads to the disconnected battery wire and the regulator Ign. terminal.
3. Hook up a voltmeter to the regulator Ign. terminal and to a good ground.

4. Slowly adjust field rheostat toward the closed position while watching the voltmeter. The load relay contacts should close somewhere between 5.8 and 6.2 volts.

Rated Output Test

1. With battery disconnected, ignition switch in off position, and the wire disconnected at the alternator B+ terminal, hook an ammeter between the alternator B+ terminal and the wire that was just disconnected from this terminal.
2. Disconnect wire from the alternator F terminal.
3. With the field rheostat adjusted to open position, connect its leads to the alternator F terminal and the alternator B+ terminal.
4. Hook up a voltmeter between the alternator B+ terminal and ground.
5. Reconnect battery cables.
6. Connect a carbon pile load control between the battery posts.
7. With a tachometer connected to the engine, start the engine and set its speed at the recommended rpm.
8. While watching both ammeter and voltmeter, adjust the carbon pile load control to maintain 15 volts. When field rheostat control is fully closed, note voltmeter and ammeter readings.
9. Adjust field rheostat to open position and carbon pile control to off.
10. Compare readings with specifications. Readings should be at least equal to rated output specified by the manufacturer. If output complies with specifications, proceed to the voltage regulator test. If readings are below rated output, it indicates possible internal troubles.

Field Current Draw Test

1. Disconnect battery ground cable.
2. Disconnect carbon pile, voltmeter, ammeter and field rheostat from the previous check.
3. Reconnect the regular circuit wire to the alternator B+ terminal.

TEMPERATURE COMPENSATOR MUST MAKE GOOD MAGNETIC CONTACT WITH YOKE

ARMATURE FLOATING

REGULATOR ARMATURE ADJUSTMENT

CORE GAP INNER CONTACTS CLOSED

HINGE GAP PRE-SET

CONTACT GAP INNER CONTACTS CLOSED

REGULATOR GAP SETTINGS

Adjusting Leece-Neville regulator

CORE GAP CONTACTS CLOSED

HINGE GAP PRE-SET

CONTACT GAP CONTACTS OPEN

RELAY GAP SETTINGS

4. With the field rheostat adjusted to the open position, connect one of its leads to the alternator B+ terminal and the other lead to a test ammeter lead.

5. Connect the remaining ammeter lead to the alternator F terminal.

6. Connect one voltmeter lead to the alternator F terminal and the remaining voltmeter lead to ground.

7. Reconnect battery ground cable, start the engine, and run it at about 1,000 rpm.

8. With field rheostat in closed position, read the ammeter and voltmeter for a very brief period.

9. Compare these readings with specifications.

10. If readings are low, it indicates trouble in slip rings or brushes.

11. If readings are too high, it indicates trouble in the rotor field windings.

12. If readings are as specified on an alternator which did not deliver its rated output, look for trouble in the stator or diodes.

Voltage Regulator Test

NOTE: manufacturers' recommended settings are established with the regulator cover off. Generally, a decrease of 0.2 to 0.3 volt will result when the cover is installed and the regulator brought to normal operating temperature.

1. Disconnect battery, be sure the ignition switch is off, and disconnect the alternator B+ terminal.

2. Hook up an ammeter to the alternator B+ terminal and to the wire just disconnected from this terminal.

3. Disconnect the wire from the alternator F terminal.

4. With the field rheostat turned to the open position, connect one rheostat lead to the alternator F terminal and the other rheostat lead to the wire just disconnected from the F terminal.

5. Connect voltmeter leads to the B terminal of the regulator and to a good ground.

6. Reconnect battery cables.

7. Hook up a carbon pile across the battery posts.

8. Connect a pair of 1,000 ohm +

earphones to the regulator F terminal and the L (gen.) regulator terminal.

9. Start the engine and gradually increase its speed while listening for a vibrating sound in the earphones. This indicates the operation of the regulator top contacts. Note voltmeter reading, compared with manufacturers' specifications.

10. Continue to increase engine rpm until earphones cease to pick up vibration. Voltage should read maximum just before vibrating sound stops. Compare with manufacturers' specifications. The silencing of the vibration indicates transfer of action to the lower contacts.

11. Resume a gradual increase in engine rpm until the vibrating sound starts again. This sound is produced by the lower contacts. Compare voltmeter reading with specifications.

Final Regulator Setting

This is a final setting, to be made at operating temperature through all variations of speed and vibration.

1. Run the engine about 15 minutes, or enough to develop normal operating temperature at the regulator.

2. Set engine speed at 1,750 rpm.

3. Adjust carbon pile load to pro-

duce a 25 amp. charging rate.

4. Open and close the field rheostat four or five times.

5. Turn carbon pile load to full off.

6. With field rheostat fully closed, note the voltmeter reading and compare it with regulator operating specifications.

7. If regulator does not operate within specified limits, replace it.

Disassembly

1. Remove two brush-holder assembly screws and remove holder with brushes.

2. Remove shaft nut, preventing pulley from slipping by gripping a fan belt around pulley and in vise. Remove pulley.

3. Remove four thru-bolts and carefully pry two end housings apart.

4. Place tape over slip ring end housing bearing to keep out dirt.

5. Remove fan, key and spacer and with puller remove drive end housing.

6. Bearings from both housings can be removed after taking off retainer at drive end or tape from slip ring end.

7. To remove individual rectifier, loosen solder around cell while pressing it out. A piece of asbestos or fiber will help concentrate heat.

Exploded view Leece-Neville alternator

1 Rotor shaft nut	14 Slip ring	27 Washer
2 Shaft nut washer	15 Screw terminal	28 Hex nut
3 Woodruff key	16 Bushing insulator	29 Capacitor assembly
4 Fan assembly	17 Terminal screw	30 Washer
5 Fan spacer	18 Rectifier assembly	31 Hex nut
6 Bolt nut	19 Rectifier	32 Roller bearing
7 Drive end frame	20 Rectifier	33 Nut
8 Ball bearing	21 Insulator bushing	34 Lockwasher
9 Ball bearing retainer plate	22 Support-rectifier	35 Guard washer
10 Bearing retainer plate screws	23 Slip ring end housing	36 Insulation washer
11 Spacer	24 Thru bolt	37 Brush and spring assembly
12 Rotor and slip ring assembly	25 Guard washer	38 Brush holder assembly
13 Rotor	26 Washer	39 Screw

40 Brush holder only
41 Guard washer
42 Lockwasher
43 Nut
44 Screw
45 Insulator bushing
46 Terminal screw
47 Terminal screw
48 Rectifier assembly
49 Rectifier
50 Rectifier mount
51 Spacer insulator
52 Eyelet
53 Stator assembly

Disassembled 65-Ampere Leece Neville Alternator

BEND ADJUSTING ARM DOWN TO INCREASE VOLTAGE SETTING. BEND ADJUSTING ARM UP TO DECREASE VOLTAGE SETTING.

Regulator Adjustments

Ambient Air Temperature °F	Voltage Limiter Setting (Volts)
50	14.1–15.1
75	13.9–14.9
100	13.7–14.7
125	13.6–14.6

Voltage Limiter Setting
Versus Ambient Air Temperature

VOLTAGE LIMITER TEST

FIELD RELAY TEST

Alternator Regulator Test

Index

HYDRAULIC BRAKE SYSTEM TROUBLE DIAGNOSIS

Condition	Possible Cause	Correction
Insufficient brakes	1. Improper brake adjustment. 2. Worn lining. 3. Sticking brakes. 4. Brake valve pressure low. 5. Slack adjuster to diaphragm rod not adjusted properly. 6. Master cylinder low on brake fluid.	1. Adjust brakes. 2. Replace brake lining and adjust brakes. 3. Lubricate brake pivots and support platforms. 4. Inspect for leaks and obstructed brake lines. 5. Adjust slack adjuster. 6. Fill master cylinder and inspect for leaks.
Brakes apply slowly	1. Improper brake adjustment or lack of lubrication. 2. Low air pressure. 3. Brake valve delivery pressure low. 4. Excessive leakage with brakes applied. 5. Restriction in brake line or hose.	1. Adjust brakes and lubricate linkage. 2. Check belt tension and compressor for output. Adjust as necessary. 3. Check valve pressure and clean or replace as necessary. 4. Inspect all fittings and lines for leaks and repair as necessary. 5. Clean or replace brake line or hose.
Spongy pedal	1. Air in hydraulic system. 2. Swollen rubber parts due to contaminated brake fluid. 3. Improper brake shoe adjustment. 4. Brake fluid with low boiling point. 5. Brake drums ground excessively.	1. Fill and bleed hydraulic system. 2. Clean hydraulic system and recondition wheel cylinders and master cylinder. 3. Adjust brakes. 4. Flush hydraulic system and refill with proper brake fluid. 5. Replace brake drums.
Erratic brakes	1. Linings soaked with grease or brake fluid. 2. Primary and secondary shoes mounted in wrong position.	1. Correct the leak and replace brake lining. 2. Match the primary and secondary shoes and mount in proper position.
Chattering brakes	1. Improper adjustment of brake shoes. 2. Loose front wheel bearings. 3. Hard spots in brake drum. 4. Out-of-round brake drums. 5. Grease or brake fluid on lining.	1. Adjust brakes. 2. Clean, pack and adjust wheel bearings. 3. Grind or replace brake drums. 4. Grind or replace brake drums. 5. Correct leak and replace brake lining.
Squealing brakes	1. Incorrect lining. 2. Distorted brakedrum. 3. Bent brake support plate. 4. Bent brake shoes. 5. Foreign material embedded in brake lining. 6. Dust or dirt in brake drum. 7. Shoes dragging on support plate. 8. Loose support plate. 9. Loose anchor bolts. 10. Loose lining on brake shoes or improperly ground lining.	1. Install correct lining. 2. Grind or replace brake drum. 3. Replace brake support plate. 4. Replace brake shoes. 5. Replace brake shoes. 6. Use compressed air and blow out drums and support plate and shoes. 7. Sand support plate platforms and lubricate. 8. Tighten support plate attaching nuts. 9. Tighten anchor bolts. 10. Replace brake shoes and cam-grind lining.
Brakes fading	1. Improper brake adjustment. 2. Improper brake lining. 3. Improper type of brake fluid. 4. Brake drums ground excessively.	1. Adjust brakes correctly. 2. Replace brake lining. 3. Drain, flush and refill hydraulic system. 4. Replace brake drums.
Dragging brakes	1. Improper brake adjustment. 2. Distorted cylinder cups. 3. Brake shoe seized on anchor bolt. 4. Broken brake shoe return spring. 5. Loose anchor bolt. 6. Distorted brake shoe. 7. Loose wheel bearings. 8. Obstruction in brake line. 9. Swollen cups in wheel cylinder or master cylinder. 10. Master cylinder linkage improperly adjusted.	1. Correct adjust brakes. 2. Recondition or replace cylinder. 3. Clean and lubricate anchor bolt. 4. Replace brake shoe return spring. 5. Adjust and tighten anchor bolt. 6. Replace defective brake shoes. 7. Lubricate and adjust wheel bearings. 8. Clean or replace brake line. 9. Recondition wheel or master cylinder. 10. Correctly adjust master cylinder linkage.
Hard pedal	1. Incorrect brake lining. 2. Incorrect brake adjustment. 3. Frozen brake pedal linkage. 4. Restricted brake line or hose.	1. Install matched brake lining. 2. Adjust brakes and check fluid. 3. Free up and lubricate brake linkage. 4. Clean out or replace brake line hose.
Wheel locks	1. Loose or torn brake lining. 2. Incorrect wheel bearing adjustment. 3. Wheel cylinder cups sticking. 4. Saturated brake lining.	1. Replace brake lining. 2. Clean, pack and adjust wheel bearings. 3. Recondition or replace the wheel cylinder. 4. Reline front, rear or all four brakes.

Condition	Possible Cause	Correction
Brakes fade (high speed)	1. Improper brake adjustment. 2. Distorted or out of round brake drums. 3. Overheated brake drums. 4. Incorrect brake fluid (low boiling temperature). 5. Saturated brake lining.	1. Adjust brakes and check fluid. 2. Grind or replace the drums. 3. Inspect for dragging brakes. 4. Drain flush and refill and bleed the hydraulic brake system. 5. Reline brakes as necessary.

Hydraulic Brakes

Servicing the hydraulic system is chiefly a matter of adjustments, replacement of worn or damaged parts and correcting the damage caused by grit, dirt or contaminated brake fluid. It is highly important to make sure the brake system is clean and tightly sealed when a brake job is completed and that only approved heavy duty brake fluid is used.

The approved heavy duty type brake fluid retains the correct consistency throughout the widest range of temperature variation, will not affect rubber cups, helps protect the metal parts of the brake system against failure and assures long trouble-free brake operation.

Never use brake fluid from a container that has been used for any other liquid. Mineral oil, alcohol, anti-freeze, or cleaning solvents, even in very small quantities, will contaminate brake fluid. Contaminated brake fluid will cause piston cups and the valve in the master cylinder to swell or deteriorate.

Brake adjustment is required after installation of new or relined brake shoes. Adjustment is also necessary whenever excessive travel of pedal is needed to start braking action.

Low Pedal

Normal brake lining wear reduces pedal reserve. Low pedal reserve may also be caused by the lack of brake fluid in the master cylinder. The wear condition may be compensated for by a minor brake adjustment. Check fluid level in master cylinder and add as required.

Fluid Loss

If the master cylinder requires constant addition of hydraulic fluid, fluid may be leaking past the piston cups in the master cylinder or brake cylinders, the hydraulic lines; hoses or connections may be loose or broken. Loose connections should be tightened, or other necessary repairs or parts replacement made and the hydraulic brake system bled.

Fluid Contamination

To determine if contamination exists in the brake fluid, as indicated by swollen, deteriorated rubber cups, the following tests can be made.

Place a small amount of the drained brake fluid into a small clear glass bottle. Separation of the fluid into distinct layers will indicate mineral oil content. Be safe and discard old brake fluid that has been bled from the system. Fluid drained from the bleeding operation may contain dirt particles or other contamination and should not be reused.

Brake Adjustment

Normally self adjusting brakes will not require manual adjustment but in the event of a brake reline it may be advisable to make the initial adjustment manually to speed up adjusting time.

Automatic Adjuster Check

Place vehicle on a hoist, with a helper in the driver's seat to apply brakes. Remove plug from rear adjustment slot in each brake support plate to observe adjuster star wheel.

Then, to exclude possibility of maximum adjustment; that is, the adjuster refuses to operate because the closest possible adjustment has been reached; the star wheel should be backed off approximately 30 notches. It will be necessary to hold adjuster lever away from star wheel to allow backing off of the adjustment.

Spin the wheel and brake drum in reverse direction and apply brakes vigorously. This will provide the necessary inertia to cause the secondary brake shoe to leave the anchor. The wrap up effect will move the secondary shoe, and cable will pull the adjuster lever up. Upon release of brake pedal, the lever should snap downward, turning star wheel. Thus, a definite rotation of adjuster star wheel can be observed if automatic adjuster is working properly. If by the described procedure one or more automatic adjusters do not function properly, the respective drum must be removed for adjuster servicing.

Hydraulic Line Repair

Steel tubing is used in the hydraulic lines between the master cylinder and the front brake tube connector, and between the rear brake tube connector and the rear brake cylinders. Flexible hoses connect the brake tube to the front brake cylinders and to the rear brake tube connector.

When replacing hydraulic brake tubing, hoses, or connectors, tighten all connections securely. After replacement, bleed the brake system at the wheel cylinders and at the booster, if so equipped.

Differential valve system—with split hydraulic brakes (© Ford Motor Co.)

Brake Tube

If a section of the brake tube becomes damaged, the entire section should be replaced with tubing of the same type, size, shape, and length. *Copper tubing should not be used in the hydraulic system.* When bending brake tubing to fit the frame or rear-axle contours, be careful not to kink or crack the tube.

All brake tubing should be double flared to provide good leak-proof connections. Always clean the inside of a new brake tube with clean isopropyl alcohol.

Brake Hose

A flexible brake hose should be replaced if it shows signs of softening, cracking, or other damage.

When installing a new brake hose, position the hose to avoid contact with other truck parts.

Pressure Differential Switch

The hydraulic system safety switch is used to warn vehicle operator that one of the hydraulic systems has failed. A failure in one part of the brake system does not result in failure of the entire hydraulic brake system.

As an example, failure of rear brake system will leave front brake system still operative.

As pressure falls in one system the other system's normal pressure forces piston to inoperative side contacting switch terminal, causing a red warning light to come on in instrument panel, thus, warning operator of vehicle that one of the systems has failed and should be repaired.

The safety switch body is mounted in a vertical position, with the brake tubes connected to opposite sides.

The component parts of the switch body are not serviced. However, terminal unit can be removed if a malfunction occurs and a new terminal unit installed.

Centralizing the Pressure Differential Valve

1. Turn the ignition switch to the ACC or ON position. Loosen the pressure differential valve inlet tube nut of the system that remained operative, or the side opposite the system that was bled last. Operate the brake pedal carefully and gradually until the pressure differential valve is returned to a centralized position and the brake warning light goes out. Tighten the tube nut.
2. Check the fluid level in the master cylinder reservoirs and fill them to within 1/4" of the top with the specified brake fluid.
3. Turn the ignition switch to the OFF position.

With Split Hydraulic Brakes

The pressure differential valve used with the split hydraulic brake system has a self-centering spring. Use the following procedure to reset the valve:

1. Remove the switch connector wire.
2. Remove the threaded hex-shaped electrical switch body from the center of the valve. This allows the valve centering springs to re-position the valve.
3. Install the electrical switch and connect the wire.
4. Apply the brakes a few times and check the operation of the warning light. The light should go on with the ignition switch in the START position only.

Bleeding Brakes

Manual Bleeding

Conventional, Single-Brake System Hydraulic Master Cylinder

1. Attach a rubber drain tube to the bleeder screw of the brake wheel cylinder. The end of the tube should fit snugly around the bleeder screw.
2. Submerge the free end of the tube in a container partially filled with clean brake fluid. Loosen the bleeder screw.
3. Push the brake pedal down slowly by hand, allowing it to return slowly to the fully-released position. Repeat this operation until air bubbles cease to appear at the submerged end of the tube.
4. When the fluid is completely free of air bubbles, close the bleeder screw and remove the drain tube.
5. Repeat this procedure at each brake cylinder. Refill the master cylinder reservoir after each brake cylinder is bled and when the bleeding operation is completed.

Manual Bleeding

Dual-Brake System Hydraulic Master Cylinder

The primary and secondary hydraulic brake systems are individual systems and are bled separately. Bleed the longest line first on the individual system being serviced. *During the complete bleeding operation, do not allow the reservoir to run dry. Keep the master cylinder reservoirs filled with the specified brake fluid. Never use brake fluid that has been drained from the hydraulic system.*

1. Bleed the master cylinder at the

Split hydraulic brake system—with frame mounted booster (© Ford Motor Co.)

Dual master cylinder—with split hydraulic brakes and frame mounted booster
(© Ford Motor Co.)

Dual master cylinder—with midland ross dash mounted booster (© Ford Motor Co.)

outlet port side of the system being serviced.

NOTE: On a master cylinder without bleed screws, loosen the master cylinder to hydraulic line nut. Operate the brake pedal slowly until the brake fluid at the outlet connection is free of bubbles, then tighten the tube nut to the specified torque. Do not use the secondary piston stop screw located on the bottom of the master cylinder to bleed the brake system. Loosening or removing this screw could result in damage to the secondary piston or stop screw. Operate the brake pedal slowly until the brake fluid at the outlet connection is free of air bubbles, then tighten the bleed screw.

2. Position a suitable ⅜" box wrench on the bleeder fitting on the brake wheel cylinder. Attach a rubber drain tube to the bleeder fitting. The end of the

tube should fit snugly around the bleeder fitting.

3. Submerge the free end of the tube in a container partially filled with clean brake fluid, and loosen the bleeder fitting approximately ¾ turn.

4. Push the brake pedal down slowly thru its full travel. Close the bleeder fitting, then return the pedal to the fully-released position. Repeat this operation until air bubbles cease to appear at the submerged end of the bleeder tube.

5. When the fluid is completely free of air bubbles, close the bleeder fitting and remove the bleeder tube.

6. Repeat this procedure at the brake wheel cylinder on the opposite side. Refill the master cylinder reservoir after each wheel cylinder is bled.

When the bleeding operation is complete, the master cylinder fluid level should be filled to within ¼" from the top of the reservoirs.

7. Centralize the pressure differential valve.

Master Cylinder Service

Bendix Tandem

Disassembly

1. Clean the outside of the master cylinder assembly. Remove the residual pressure valves.

2. Remove the tube seats by installing "easy outs" firmly into the seats. Tap lightly with a hammer to loosen, remove seats.

3. Slide clamp off master cylinder cover and remove the cover and its gasket. Drain the brake fluid from the master cylinder.

COVER

GASKET

CLAMP

MASTER CYLINDER BODY

FRONT PISTON ASSEMBLY

REAR PISTON ASSEMBLY

TUBE SEATS

RESIDUAL PRESSURE
VALVE AND SPRING

FRONT PISTON RETAINING
SET SCREW AND "O" RING

WASHER

SNAP RING

Bendix tandem master cylinder—exploded view (© Chrysler Corp.)

4. Remove the snap ring from the open end of the cylinder with snap ring pliers. Remove the washer from cylinder bore.
5. Remove the front piston retaining screw. Carefully remove the rear piston assembly.
6. Remove the front piston assembly.

Cleaning and Inspection

1. Clean all parts with a suitable solvent and dry with filtered compressed air. Wash cylinder bore with clean brake fluid and check for damage or wear.
2. If cylinder bore is lightly scratched or shows slight corrosion it can be cleaned with crocus cloth. Heavier scratches or corrosion can be removed by honing, providing that diameter of cylinder bore is not increased by more than .002 inch. If master cylinder bore does not clean up at .002 inch when honed, the master cylinder should be replaced.
3. If master cylinder pistons are badly scored or corroded, replace them with new ones. All caps and seals should be replaced when rebuilding a master cylinder.

Assembly

NOTE: Before assembly of master cylinder, dip all parts in clean brake fluid and place on clean paper. Assembling master cylinder dry can damage rubber seals.

1. Coat master cylinder bore with brake fluid and carefully slide the front piston into cylinder body.

2. Slide the rear piston assembly into the cylinder bore. Compress pistons and install the front piston retaining screw.
3. Position washer in cylinder bore and secure with snap ring.
4. Install the residual pressure valve and spring in the outlet port and install tube seats firmly.

Chrysler Tandem

1. Clean the outside of the master cylinder assembly. Remove the master cylinder cover and drain the brake fluid.
2. Remove the front piston retainer screw from inside reservoir and the snap ring from the outer end of cylinder bore. Slide the rear piston assembly out of cylinder bore.
3. Tamp the master cylinder assembly lightly on bench, open end down, to remove the front piston and spring. If the front piston sticks in cylinder bore, use air pressure to force it out.
4. Remove the front piston compression spring from the cylinder bore.
5. Remove the tube seats by installing "easy outs" firmly into the seats. Tap lightly with a hammer to loosen, remove the seats.
6. Take note of the position of cup lips and remove them from pistons. DO NOT remove the center cup of the rear piston. If this cup is damaged or worn, install a new rear piston assembly.

Cleaning and Inspection

1. Clean all parts with a suitable solvent and dry with filtered

compressed air. Wash cylinder bore with clean brake fluid and check for damage or wear.
2. If cylinder bore is slightly scratched or shows slight corrosion it can be cleaned with crocus cloth. Heavier scratches or corrosion can be removed by honing, providing that the diameter of the cylinder bore is not increased by more than .002 inch. If master cylinder bore does not clean up at .002 inch when honed, the master cylinder should be replaced.
3. If master cylinder pistons are badly scored or corroded, replace them with new ones. All caps and seals should be replaced when rebuilding a master cylinder.

Assembly

NOTE: Before assembly of master cylinder, dip all parts in clean brake fluid and place on clean paper. Assembling a master cylinder dry can damage the new seals.

1. Carefully work the primary cup on the end of the front piston with the lip facing away from the piston.
2. Carefully, work the second seal cup over the rear end of the piston and into the second land. Be sure that the lip of the cup is facing the front of piston.
3. Carefully work the rear secondary cup over the piston and into the rear land. The lip must face the rear of the piston.
4. Slide the cup retainer over the stem of the front piston with the beveled side away from the piston cup.

5. Position the small end of the pressure spring into the retainer, then slide the assembly into the master cylinder bore.

CAUTION: Be sure that the cups enter the cylinder bore evenly in order that the sealing quality of the cups is not damaged, keep the seals and cylinder bore well lubricated with brake fluid.

6. Carefully work the secondary cup over the rear end of the rear piston with the lip facing towards the front.

7. Center the spring retainer of the rear piston assembly over the shoulder of the front piston. Push the piston assemblies into the cylinder bore. Carefully work the cup lips into bore, then seat piston assemblies.

8. Holding the pistons in their seated position, install the piston retaining screw and tighten securely.

9. Install new tube seats. (When bench bleeding is performed, the tube seats will be correctly positioned.)

Wagner Single

Disassembly

1. Clean the outside of the master cylinder assembly. Remove the master cylinder cover and drain the fluid.
2. Remove the boot, stop retainer, piston stop and the end plug.
3. Remove the piston, cups, return spring and the valve assembly.

Cleaning and Inspection

1. Clean all parts with a suitable solvent and dry with filtered compressed air. Wash cylinder bore with clean brake fluid and check for damage and wear.
2. If cylinder bore is slightly scratched or shows slight corrosion it can be cleaned with

Wagner single master cylinder—exploded view (© Ford)

crocus cloth. Heavier scratches or corrosion can be removed by honing, providing that the diameter of the cylinder bore is not increased by more than .002 inch. If the master cylinder bore does not clean up at .002 inch when honed, the master cylinder should be replaced.

3. If the master cylinder piston is badly scored or corroded, replace it with a new one. All caps and seals should be replaced when rebuilding a master cylinder.

Assembly

NOTE: Before assembly of master cylinder, dip all parts in clean brake fluid and place on clean paper. Assembling a master cylinder dry can damage the new seals.

1. Install the check valve and spring in the cylinder, with the valve facing toward the outlet of the master cylinder.
2. Install the cylinder cup in the cylinder with the open end of the cup over the closed end of the return spring.

3. Install the secondary cup on the piston and install the piston, piston stop and stop retainer.
4. Install the boot and push rod.

Wagner Tandem

Disassembly

1. Clean the outside of the master cylinder. Remove the cylinder cover screw or spring retaining clip. Lift off the cover and the diaphragm gasket and pour off excess brake fluid. Use the push rod to stroke the cylinder forcing fluid from the cylinder through the outlet ports.
2. Loosen and remove the piston stop screw and gasket from the right hand side of the cylinder.
3. Pull back the push rod boot and remove the snap ring from the groove in the end of the cylinder bore.
4. Remove the push rod and stop plate from the master cylinder.
5. Remove the internal parts from the master cylinder. If the parts will not slide out apply air pressure at the secondary outlet port. If after applying air, parts still do not move easily, check bore carefully for extensive damage which may eliminate possibility of rebuilding master cylinder.

Chrysler tandem master cylinder—exploded view (©Chrysler Corp.)

Inspection and Repair

1. Clean all parts in clean brake fluid. Inspect the parts for chipping, excessive wear or damage. Replace them as required. When using a master cylinder repair kit, install all the parts supplied.
2. Check all recesses, openings and internal passages to be sure they are open and free of foreign matter. Passages may be probed with soft copper wire, 0.020" OD, or smaller.
3. Minor scratches or blemishes in the cylinder bore can be removed with crocus cloth or a clean up hone. Do not oversize the bore more than 0.007".

Assembly

1. Dip all parts except the master cylinder in clean hydraulic brake fluid of the specified type.
2. Install the rear rubber cup on the secondary piston with the cup lip facing the rear. All other cups face the front or closed end of the cylinder.
3. Assemble and install the secondary piston spring, front cup, and the secondary piston.
4. Install the piston stop screw and gasket, making sure the screw enters the cylinder behind the rear of the secondary piston.
5. Assemble and install the primary piston and push rod parts.
6. Locate the stop plate in the seat in the bore and engage the snap ring into the groove at the rear of the cylinder.
7. Install the push rod boot onto the push rod and the groove of the cylinder housing.
8. Bleed the master cylinder.

Bench Bleeding the Master Cylinder

Before the master cylinder is installed on the vehicle, the unit should be bled.

1. Support the master cylinder body in a vise, and fill both fluid reservoirs with the specified brake fluid. CAUTION: Do not tighten the vise too tightly on the master cylinder as this can cause damage to the cylinder which can not be repaired.
2. Loosely intall plugs in the front and rear brake outlet bores. Depress the primary piston several times until air bubbles cease to appear in the brake fluid.
3. Tighten the plugs and attempt to depress the piston. The piston travel should be restricted after all air is expelled.
4. Remove the plugs. Install the cover and diaphragm gasket assembly, and make sure the cover screw is tightened securely.

Midland-Ross Tandem (Removable Reservoir Type)

Disassembly

1. Clean the outside of the cylinder and remove the filler cap and gasket (diaphragm). Pour out any brake fluid that may remain in the reservoir. Stroke the push rod several times to remove fluid from the cylinder bore.
2. Remove the reservoir retainers, washers, and reservoir from the master cylinder body.
3. Remove the two rubber washers from the reservoir and the two O-rings from the reservoir retainers.
4. Remove the snap ring, spring retainer and push rod spring.
5. Unscrew the retainer bushing counterclockwise and remove the push rod, retainer bushing, seal retainer and primary piston from the master cylinder.
6. Remove the primary piston from the push rod and discard it.
7. Remove the seal retainer, and retainer bushing from the push rod. Remove the two lip seals and the two Orings from the retainer bushing.
8. Unscrew the end cap counterclockwise and remove the end cap and secondary piston assembly from the master cylinder.
9. Remove the snap ring from the secondary piston and remove the piston and return spring from the end cap and stop rod assembly.
10. Remove the two lip seals from the piston.
11. Remove the snap ring from the end cap and remove the secondary piston stop rod, relief port seal spring, the two snap rings and the two split washers from the end cap.
12. Remove the relief port seal from the secondary piston stop rod.
13. Remove the O-rings from the end cap.
14. Remove the primary and secondary port caps and discard.
15. Remove the check valves and springs from the ports.
16. Remove the pipe plug from the end of the master cylinder.

Assembly

1. Wash all metal parts in clean brake fluid before assembly. Dip all parts except the master cylinder body in clean hydraulic brake fluid of the specified type. When using a master cylinder repair kit, install all of the parts supplied.
2. Install the pipe plug in the end of the master cylinder.
3. Install a new primary piston into the front end of the master cylinder bore. Push the piston through the bore until it is flush with the retainer bushing recess. Use a non-metallic object which will not scratch the bore.
4. Assemble the O-rings and the two lip seals on the retainer bushing. Be sure the lip seals fit into the undercuts in the center of the bushing with their large diameters toward the piston end.
5. Install the retainer bushing onto the closed end of the push rod and push it onto the push rod approximately half way. Be sure the lip seal at the piston end of the retainer bushing remains in the undercut portion of the retainer bushing.
6. Install the seal retainer onto th closed end of the push rod with the raised lip toward the retainer bushing.
7. Insert the push rod into the master cylinder bore and hook the push rod onto the primary piston.
8. Slide the seal retainer into the recess in the master cylinder bore.
9. Screw the retainer bushing into the master cylinder body and tighten to 15-20 ft-lbs torque.
10. Install the push spring with the large end toward the master cylinder and install the spring retainer and snap ring.
11. Install the O-rings on the end cap.
12. Install the relief port seal on the secondary piston stop rod.
13. Place the port seal spring, split washer (largest of two), and snap ring (largest of two) on the piston stop rod.
14. Slide the assembly into the end cap and engage the snap ring into its groove.
15. Install the lip seals on the secondary piston with the large diameters facing outward.
16. Place the secondary piston return spring on the end cap assembly.
17. Compress the spring and place the remaining snap ring and split washer on the piston stop rod.
18. Slide the piston stop rod into the secondary piston and engage the snap ring in its groove.
19. Slide the end cap and piston assembly into the master cylinder bore and screw the end cap into the master cylinder body. Tighten the cap to 15-20 ft-lbs torque.
20. Install washers on the reservoir retainer and place the retainers in the mounting holes of the reservoir.
21. Place the rubber washers and O-rings on the retainers.
22. Place the reservoir and retainer

Wheel cylinder (typical) (© Chrysler Corp.)

assembly on the master cylinder body and tighten the retainers to 15-20 ft-lbs torque.

23. Replace the springs and check valves in the output ports of the cylinder.

24. Replace the primary and secondary port caps. Tighten to 15-20 ft-lbs torque.

25. Install the mounting seal on the flange of the master cylinder. Install the filler cap and gasket (diaphragm).

Wheel Cylinders

Disassembly

1. In case of a leak, remove brake shoes (replace if soaked with grease or brake fluid), boots, piston wheel cylinder cups and wheel cylinder cup expansion spring. NOTE: A slight amount of fluid on boot may not be a leak, but may be preservative oil used on assembly.

2. Wash wheel cylinder bore with clean brake fluid and inspect for scoring or pitting.

Use extreme care in cleaning the wheel cylinder after reconditioning. Remove all dust or grit by flushing the cylinder with clean brake fluid; wipe dry with a clean lintless cloth and clean a second time with brake fluid. Dry the wheel cylinder with air pressure, then flush with clean brake fluid. (Be sure the bleeder screw port and the bleeder screw are clean and open.)

Wheel cylinder bores or pistons that are badly scored or coroded should be replaced. The old piston cups should be discarded when reconditioning wheel cylinders.

Cylinder walls that have light scratches, or show signs of corrosion, can usually be cleaned with crocus cloth, using a circular motion. However, cylinders that have deep scratches or scoring may be honed, providing the diameter of the cylinder bore is not increased more than .002". *A cylinder that does not clean up at .002" should be discarded and a new cylinder installed. (Black stains on the cylinder walls are caused by the piston cups and will do no harm.)*

Should inspection reveal the necessity of installing a new wheel cylinder proceed as follows:

1. Disconnect brake hose from brake tube at frame bracket (front wheels) or disconnect the brake tube from wheel cylinder (rear wheels).

2. Disconnect brake hose from wheel cylinder (front wheels only) and remove wheel cylinder attaching bolts, then slide wheel cylinder out of backing plate.

Assembly (Front or Rear)

Before assembling pistons and new cups in wheel cylinder, dip them in brake fluid. If boots are deteriorated, cracked or do not fit tightly on brake shoe push rod, as well as wheel cylinder casting, new boots should be installed.

1. Wash wheel cylinder with clean brake fluid and wipe dry.

2. Install expansion spring in cylinder. Install wheel cylinder cups in each end of cylinder with open end of cups facing each other.

3. Install wheel cylinder pistons in each end of cylinder with recessed end of pistons facing open ends of cylinder.

4. Install boots over ends of cylinder. Keep assembly compressed with aid of a brake cylinder clamp until brake shoes are assembled.

Brake Service

Non-Servo Type

This brake is a non-servo, floating shoe type brake. Upper ends of shoes extend through wheel cylinder boots and contact inserts in wheel cylinder pistons. Shoe ends are held firmly against pistons by the brake shoe return spring. Lower ends of shoes are held against a fixed anchor plate by the anchor spring. Hold-down spring at center of each shoe holds shoes in alignment. Lining-to-drum clearance adjustment is made through eccentric cam type adjusting studs.

Brake Shoe Removal

1. Back off brake adjustment, then remove brake drum.

2. Remove brake shoe return spring. Spread upper end of shoes until they are clear of wheel cylinders and hold-down springs, then disengage shoes from anchor plate at bottom. Remove anchor spring from shoes.

3. Do not depress brake pedal while shoes are removed.

Cleaning and Inspection

1. Clean all dirt out of brake drum. Inspect drum for roughness, scoring, or out-of-round. Replace or recondition drum as necessary.

2. Carefully pull lower edge of each wheel cylinder boot away from

cylinder and note whether interior is excessively wet with brake fluid. Excessive fluid indicates leakage past piston cups, requiring overhaul of wheel cylinder. NOTE: A slight amount of fluid is nearly always present and acts as a lubricant for pistons.

3. Check backing plate attaching bolts to make sure they are tight. Clean all rust and dirt from ledges on backing plate where shoe rims make contact using fine emery cloth.
4. Inspect the shoe return and anchor springs and hold-down springs. If broken, cracked, or weakened by rust or corrosion, replace springs.
5. If brake linings are worn to the extent that replacement is necessary, replace linings.

Brake Shoe Installation

1. Inspect brake shoe lining assemblies and make sure there are no nicks or burrs on edges of shoes which contact backing plate.
2. Apply a light film of grease at the following points: where shoe webs contact hold-down springs; where anchor ends of shoe webs contact anchor plate; and at six places where shoe rims contact ledges on backing plate.
3. Install hold-down springs on backing plate. Hook anchor spring into slot at bottom of each shoe. Swing upper ends of shoes apart and position at backing plate, with lower ends of shoe webs engaging anchor plate

and with anchor spring behind extension on anchor plate. NOTE: The shoe with the shorter lining must be to the rear of the vehicle.

4. Swing shoes up into position with center of shoe webs engaging hold-down springs, and with upper ends inserted through wheel cylinder boots.
5. Install brake shoe return spring, being sure short end is hooked into slotted hole in rear shoe and long end in round hole in front shoe.
6. Install brake drum and wheel. Adjust brakes.

Wagner

Twin Action Type

Twin-action brake is a four-anchor type. Brake shoes are self-centering in operation, and both shoes are self-energizing in both forward and reverse.

Two wheel cylinders are mounted on opposite sides of the backing plate. One brake shoe is mounted above wheel cylinders and one below. Sliding pivot type anchor is used at front end of upper shoe and at rear end of lower shoe. Adjustable anchor is used at front end of lower shoe and at rear end of upper shoe. Four shoe return springs hold shoe ends firmly against anchors when brakes are released.

Anchor brackets are steel forgings,

attached to flange on axle housing in conjunction with the backing plate. At adjustable anchor end of each shoe, shoe web bears against flat head of adjusting screw which threads into anchor bracket. The adjusting screw heads are notched and are rotated for brake adjustment through access holes in backing plate. A lock spring which fits over anchor bracket holds adjusting screw in position.

The brake backing plate has six machined bearing surfaces, three for each shoe, against which the inner edge of each shoe bears. Two brake shoe guide bolts are riveted to backing plate and extend through holes in center of brake shoe web. Shoes are retained on guide bolts by flat washers, nuts, and cotter pins.

Wheel cylinder push rods make contact between wheel cylinder pistons and brake shoes.

Inner edge of brake drum has a groove which fits over a flange on the edge of backing plate, forming a seal against the entrance of dirt and mud.

Twin-Action Type Rear Brake

Brake Shoe Removal

1. Remove brake drums. NOTE: If brake drums are worn severely, it may be necessary to retract the adjusting screws.
2. Remove the brake shoe pull back springs. NOTE: Since wheel cyl-

Non servo type brake installed (© G.M.C.)

1 Secondary shoe	5 Shoe return spring
2 Adjusting cam	6 Primary shoe
3 Backing plate	7 Shoe hold-down spring
4 Wheel cylinder	8 Shoe anchor spring

◄ FRONT ►

Twin action self adjusting brakes (© G.M.C.)

1 Hold-down pin spring lock	9 Adjusting lever pivot	17 Adjusting lever pin sleeve
2 Hold-down pin	10 Adjusting lever cam	18 Hold-down spring
3 Adjusting screw	11 Adjusting lever bolt	19 Brake backing plate
4 Adjusting lever	12 Wheel cylinder sheild	20 Hold-down pin retainer
5 Adjusting lever pin spring	13 Wheel cylinder	21 Hold-down pin spring
6 Hold-down spring cup	14 Brake shoe return spring	22 Adjusting lever link
7 Lever override spring	15 Brake shoe anchor	
8 Brake shoe and lining	16 Lever return spring	

inder piston stops are incorporated in the anchor brackets, it is not necessary to install wheel cylinder clamps when the brake shoes are removed.

3. Loosen the adjusting lever cam cap screw, and while holding the star wheel end of the adjusting lever past the star wheel, remove the cap screw and cam.
4. Remove the brake shoe hold down springs and pins by compressing the spring and, at the same time, pushing the pin back through the flange plate toward the tool. Then, keeping the spring compressed, remove the lock ("C"-washer) from the pin with a magnet.
5. Lift off the brake shoe and self-adjuster lever as an assembly.
6. The self-adjuster lever can now be removed from the brake shoe by removing the hold-down spring and pin. Remove lever return spring also. NOTE: The adjusting lever, override spring and pivot are an assembly. It is not recommended that they be disassembled for service purposes unless they are broken. It is much easier to assemble and disassemble the brake leaving them intact.
7. Thread the adjusting screw out of the brake shoe anchor and remove and discard the friction spring.
8. Clean all dirt out of brake drum. Inspect drums for roughness, scoring or out-of-round. Replace or recondition drums as necessary.

9. Carefully pull lower edges of wheel cylinder boots away from cylinders. If brake fluid flows out, overhaul of the wheel cylinders is necessary. NOTE: A slight amount of fluid is nearly always present and acts as a lubricant for the piston.
10. Inspect flange plate for oil leakage past axle shaft oil seals. Install seals if necessary.

Brake Shoe Installation

1. Put a light film of lubricant on shoe bearing surfaces of brake flange plate and on threads of adjusting screw.
2. Thread adjusting screw completely into anchor without friction spring to be sure threads are clean and screw turns easily. Then remove screws, position a new friction spring on screw and reinstall in anchor.
3. Assemble self-adjuster assembly and lever return spring to brake shoe and position adjusting lever link on adjusting lever pivot.
4. Position hold-down pins in flange plate.
5. Install brake shoe and self-adjuster assemblies onto hold down pins. Insert ends of shoes in wheel cylinder push rods and legs of friction springs. NOTE: Make sure the toe of the shoe is against the adjusting screw.
6. Install cup, spring and retainer on end of hold-down pin. With spring compressed, push the hold-down pin back through the flange plate toward the tool and install the lock on the pin.
7. Install brake shoe return springs.
8. Holding the star wheel end of the adjusting lever as far as possible past the star wheel, position the adjusting lever cam into the adjusting lever link and assemble with cap screw.
9. Check the brake shoes for being centered by measuring the distance from the lining surface to the edge of the flange plate. To center the shoes, tap the upper or lower end of the shoes with a plastic mallet until the distances at each end become equal.
10. Locate the adjusting lever .020" to .039" above the outside diameter of the adjusting screw thread by loosening the cap screw and turning the adjusting

Twin action type brake installed (© G.M.C.)

1 Heat shield	6 Brake shoe guide
2 Front wheel cylinder	bolt
3 Dust shield	7 Adjusting screw
4 Brake shoe	8 Hydraulic line
5 Brake shoe return	9 Rear wheel cylinder
spring	10 Brake shoe anchor

Type "F" brake assembly (© G.M.C.)

1 Wheel cylinder	7 Brake shoe guide
2 Brake shoe return	washer
spring	8 Brake shoe guide
3 Backing plate	C-washer
4 Brake shoe	9 Adjusting cam and
5 Brake lining	shoe guide stud
6 Brake shoe adjusting	10 Shoe guide anti-
cam	rattle washer
	11 Adjusting cam spring

cam. NOTE: To determine .020" to .039", turn the adjusting screw 2 full turns out from the fully retracted position. Hold a .060" wire gauge at a 90° angle with the star wheel edge of the adjusting lever. Turn the adjusting cam until the adjusting lever and threaded area on the adjusting screw just touch the wire.

11. Secure the adjusting cam cap screw and retract the adjusting screw.
12. Install brake drums and wheels.
13. Adjust the brakes by making several forward and reverse stops until a satisfactory brake pedal height results.

Wagner

Type "F"

Two identical brake shoes are arranged on backing plate so that their toes are diagonally opposite. Two single-end wheel cylinders are arranged so that each cylinder is mounted between the toe of one shoe and the heel of the other. The two wheel cylinder pistons apply an equal amount of force to the toe of each shoe. Each cylinder casting is shaped to provide an anchor block for the brake shoe heel.

Each shoe is adjusted by means of an eccentric cam which contacts a pin pressed into brake shoe web. Each cam is attached to the backing plate by a cam and shoe guide stud which protrudes through a slot in the shoe web and, in conjunction with flat washers and C-washers, also serves as a shoe hold-down. Two return springs are connected between the shoes, one at each toe and heel.

With vehicle moving forward, both shoes are forward acting (primary shoes), self-energizing in forward direction of drum rotation. With vehicle in reverse, both shoes are reverse acting since neither is self-energized in the reverse direction of drum rotation.

Brake Shoe Removal

1. Remove both brake shoe return springs, using brake spring pliers.
2. Remove C-washer and flat washer from each adjusting cam and hold-down stud. Lift shoes off backing plate.

Cleaning and Inspection

1. Clean all dirt out of brake drum. Inspect drum for roughness, scoring, or out-of-round. Replace or recondition brake drum as necessary.
2. Inspect wheel bearings and oil seals.
3. Check backing plate attaching bolts to make sure they are tight. Clean all dirt off backing plate.

4. Inspect brake shoe return springs. If broken, cracked, or weakened, replace with new springs.
5. Check cam and shoe guide stud and friction spring on backing plate for corrosion or binding. Cam stud should turn easily with a wrench but should not be loose. If frozen, lubricate with kerosene or penetrating oil and work free.
6. Examine brake shoe linings for wear. Lining should be replaced if worn down close to rivet heads.

Brake Shoe Installation

1. Install anti-rattle spring washer on each cam and shoe guide stud, pronged side facing adjusting cam.
2. Place shoe assembly on backing plate with cam and shoe guide stud inserted through hole in shoe web; locate shoe toe in wheel cylinder piston shoe guide and position shoe heel in slot in anchor block.
3. Install flat washer and C-washer on cam and shoe guide stud. Crimp ends of C-washer together.
4. After installing both shoes, install brake shoe return springs. To install each spring, place spring end with short hook in toe of shoe, then using brake spring pliers, stretch spring and secure long hook end in heel of opposite shoe.
5. Install hub and brake drum assembly.
6. Adjust brake.
7. After checking pedal operation, road test vehicle.

Wagner

Type "FA"

Brake Shoe Removal

1. Block brake pedal in up position. Raise vehicle off ground and support.
2. Remove the brake drums. Disconnect the shoe retaining springs and hold down clips and lift off shoes.
3. Unhook the wedge actuating coil spring from the wedge.
4. Unhook the lever actuating spring from the shoe web, work the spring coil off the lever pivot pin and slide the spring "U" hook off the contact plug-lever pin.
5. Pull the adjuster lever from the opposite side of the shoe web, the contact plug through the shoe table and lift off the wedge washer, wedge and the wedge guide.
6. Clean all parts with the excep-

tion of the brake shoe linings in a suitable solvent. Inspect all components for wear or damage. Replace all parts that are in questionable condition.

Brake Shoe Installation

1. Install the automatic adjuster, contact plug flush with the lining surface.
2. Position the wedge guide on the back side of the shoe with serrations facing away from the shoe table.
3. Position the wedge on the shoe with the serrations against matching serrations on the wedge guide with the slot aligned on the lever pivot pin hole.
4. Working from the drum side of the shoe, insert the contact plug, with the guide shank through the hole in the shoe table and over wedge guide and wedge.
5. Insert the adjuster lever pins through the shoe web from the opposite side, guiding actuating (center) pin into the mating hole of the contact plug shank.
6. Install the wedge washer over the shoulder of the pivot pin. Slide the "U" hook of adjuster spring on the pin over the contact plug shank.
7. Attach the end of the wedge actuating spring to the "U" hook of the adjusting spring. Position the coil of the adjuster torsion spring over the pivot pin and pull spring hook over the edge of shoe web.
8. Connect the wedge actuating spring on the raised hook of wedge fork.
9. Fully retract the wedge against the lever pivot pin, pressing upon contact plug to permit this movement. If the plug protrudes more than 0.005 in. above lining, clamp shoe in vise so that jaws press against adjuster lever. With a file, press down on the plug until it is even with the brake lining. Exercise caution when filing so as not to create a flat spot on the brake lining. If the fully extended plug is more than 0.005 below the surface of the lining, replace with a new contact plug.
10. Locate the shoe on hold-downs. Install the retracting springs, long ends of springs are at the ends of shoes.

Initial Adjustment

1. Fully release the manual cams.
2. Center each shoe by sliding up or down on its anchor slot until the leading and trailing edges of the lining are equal distant from the inner curl of the support plate.
3. Install the wheel and drum.

Wagner Type "FA" brake assembly—exploded view (© Chrysler Corp.)

1 Connector tube	8 Brake shoe	16 Adjuster wedge spring
2 Cylinder anchor bolt	9 Brake lining	17 Adjuster torsion spring
3 Anchor bolt washer	10 Rivet	18 Shoe guide washer
4 Screw & lockwasher	11 Automatic adjuster lever	19 Shoe guide wave washer
5 Support plate	12 Adjuster wedge guide	20 Shoe guide 'C' washer
6 Bleeder screw	13 Automatic adjuster wedge	21 Shoe retracting spring
7 Wheel cylinder	14 Drum contact plug	22 Complete shoe assembly
	15 Wedge retainer washer	

4. Rotate the manual adjuster cam in the direction of forward drum rotation, while rotating the drum in the same direction, until the shoe slightly drags on the brake drum. Back off adjuster until drag is just relieved. Use only sufficient adjustment torque to obtain drag that will just allow turning the wheel by hand (approximately 120 to 130 inch pounds) as excessive torque may damage the adjuster mechanism.

5. Adjust other manual adjuster in the same manner, forward to tighten, and reverse to relieve drag.

6. Lower vehicle and road test. Automatic adjusters should operate from this point and additional manual adjustment should not be necessary.

Wagner

Type "FR-3"

Each brake is equipped with two double-end wheel cylinders which apply hydraulic pressure to both the toe and the heel of two identical, self-centering shoes. The shoes anchor at either toe or heel, depending upon the direction of rotation. Each adjusting screw is threaded into or out of its support by means of an adjusting wheel. Adjusting wheels are accessible through adjusting slots in the backing plate.

Brake Shoe Removal

1. Remove hub and brake drum assembly.
2. Install wheel cylinder clamps to hold pistons in cylinders.

3. Remove brake shoe return springs.
4. Remove lock wires, nuts, and washers from brake shoe guide bolts, then remove brake shoe assemblies.
5. Remove screws attaching adjusting wheel lock springs to anchor supports. Thread each adjusting screw from the shoe side of its anchor support by turning adjusting wheels, then lift adjusting wheels out of slots in anchor supports.

Brake Shoe Installation

1. *Install adjusting screws and wheels in anchor supports dry; use no lubricant.* Insert each adjusting wheel in slot in anchor

1 Wheel cylinder heat sheild
2 Upper wheel cylinder
3 Anchor pin
4 Return spring (short)
5 Guide washer
6 Guide bolt
7 Guide bolt nut lock wire
8 Brake shoe and lining assembly
9 Return spring (long)
10 Adjusting wheel lock spring
11 Adjusting wheel
12 Lower wheel cylinder
13 Backing plate

support, insert threaded end of adjusting screw in anchor support, then turn adjusting wheel to thread adjusting screw into anchor support. Insert anchor pins into holes in anchor supports, with slots in pins facing slots in supports.

2. Install brake shoes with cutaway end of shoe web next to adjusting screw and with ends of shoes engaging slots in wheel cylinder push rods and anchor pins. Install flat washer and nut on each brake shoe guide bolt. Tighten nuts finger-tight, then back off nuts only far enough to allow movement of shoes without binding.

3. Install brake shoe return springs, hooking one end of each spring in brake shoe web, then hook other end over anchor pins.

4. Remove wheel cylinder clamps.

5. Install hub and brake drum assembly.

6. Adjust brakes.

7. After checking pedal operation, road test vehicle.

Type "FR-3A" & "FR-5A"

The FR-3A brake system is basically the same as the FR-3 except in that the FR-3A employs a self-adjuster assembly and the FR-3 does not. Each shoe is individually adjusted to compensate for wear by a link-crank system. This serves to maintain a high, firm brake pedal at all times.

Brake Shoe Removal

1. Remove the hub and brake drum assemblies.
2. Remove the two springs for the automatic adjusters.
3. Remove the two long crank links from the adjuster assemblies by turning back the star wheel

Type "FR3" brake assembly (© G.M.C.)

Wagner Type "FR-3A" and "FR-5A" brake assembly (© Chrysler Corp.)

cranks until their slots align with the crank link "U" hooks. Lift out the links and then slide the "S" hooks out of the adjuster cranks.

4. Remove the short crank links by rotating the adjuster cranks until the link "U" hooks clear the eccentrics on the brake shoe webs, then remove the small "U" hooks from the adjuster cranks.

5. Spread the C-washers for the ad-

juster cranks and remove the cranks.

6. Remove the hold down bolt which holds the star wheel crank to the anchor support and remove the crank.

7. Remove the adjuster eccentric screw and eccentric from the brake shoe.

8. Remove the two long and the two short brake shoe return springs.

9. Remove the lock wires, hold-

down nuts and washers from the hold down bolt and remove the brake shoes from the backing plate.

10. Thread each star wheel screw out of the anchor support from the shoe side of the support and lift the star wheels from the support slots.

NOTE: There is a friction ring on each star wheel. DO NOT attempt to remove the friction ring from the star wheel screw. If necessary replace the star wheel and friction as an assembly.

Brake Shoe Installation

1. Install the star wheels into the anchor support slots and thread the star wheel screws in from the shoe side with the friction ring end towards the shoe. NOTE: Do not put any lubricant on the star wheel screws.

2. Position one brake shoe with the "toe" (cut away portion of web) in the adjuster slot and the "heel" in the anchor pin slot of the anchor supports. Install the brake shoe hold down bolt, washer and hold down nut. Tighten the nut finger tight and back off one turn and insert the lock wire in the nut.

3. Install the other brake shoe in the same manner as described in step 2.

Wagner Type "FR-3A" and "FR-5A"—exploded view (© Chrysler Corp.)

1 Connector tube	8 Starwheel adjuster screw	15 Short shoe retracting spring	22 Long starwheel crank link
2 Adjuster slot cover	9 Shoe adjuster starwheel	16 Brake shoe	23 Automatic adjuster anchor crank
3 Screw and lockwasher	10 Shoe hold-down carriage bolt	17 Brake lining	24 Anchor crank 'C' washer
4 Wheel cylinder cover	11 Shoe hold-down washer	18 Rivet	25 Short anchor crank link
5 Wheel cylinders	12 Shoe hold-down castellated nut	19 Automatic adjuster hex eccentric	26 Automatic adjuster spring
6 Bleeder screws	13 Hold-down nut lockwire	20 Eccentric self-tapping screw	27 Support plate
7 Forward-acting anchor pin	14 Long shoe retracting spring	21 Starwheel crank assembly	28 Complete shoe assembly

**Wagner Type "FR-3A" and "FR-5A"—
—alignment marks** (© Chrysler Corp.)

4. Install the long return springs in the shoe and hook them over the anchor pins. Then install the short springs in the same manner.

5. Install the adjuster eccentrics on the brake shoes and fasten them with a self-tapping screw, only make the screw finger tight to allow for final adjustment.

6. Install the adjuster cranks on the anchor pins with the long arm towards the shoe and the bushing towards the backing plate so that they rotate easily while resting against the return springs hooks.

7. Install the C-washer for the ad-

juster crank and crimp in place.

8. On the anchor support place the star wheel and fasten with the crank bolt.

9. On each adjuster crank assembly install the short links small hook into the short arm of the crank from the lower side and hook the other end of the link around the eccentric on the shoe web.

10. Install the long link "S" hook into the long arm of the adjuster crank from the upper side. Then rotate the star wheel crank so the slot lines up with the "U" hook on the long link. Insert the hook and rotate the crank back to its adjusting position.

11. Install the adjuster springs with the short hooks on the star wheel crank fingers and the long hook on the outer groove of the anchor pin on the wheel cylinder side.

12. Adjust the brakes in the following manner:
    a. Center the shoes on the backing plate.
    b. On the shoe web, rotate the eccentrics until the linkage aligns the star wheel crank pawl with the center line of the star wheel screw.
    c. When they are aligned, tighten the self-tapping screw to 19 ft lbs torque.
    d. Install hub and drum assembly and remove the plugs from the slots in the backing plate.
    e. Adjust the brakes in the normal manner to achieve the required amount of drag on each wheel.

13. Road test the vehicle to check for proper braking action.

Bendix
Duo Servo Type

Removing Front Brake Shoes

With the vehicle elevated on a

hoist, jack or suitable stands remove front wheel and drums.

1. Remove brake shoe return springs. (Note how secondary spring overlaps primary spring.)

2. Remove brake shoe retainer, spring and nails.

3. Slide eye of automatic adjuster cable off anchor and unhook from lever. Remove cable, cable guide and anchor plate.

4. Disconnect lever spring from lever and disengage from shoe web. Remove spring and lever.

5. Remove the primary and secondary brake shoe assemblies and adjusting star wheel from support. Install wheel cylinder clamps to hold pistons in cylinders.

Removing Rear Brake Shoes

1. With the vehicle elevated on a hoist, jack or suitable stand, loosen parking brake equalizer nut, remove rear wheel, and drum retaining clips. Remove drum.

2. Remove brake shoe return springs. (Note how secondary spring overlaps primary spring.)

3. Remove brake shoe retainers, springs and nails.

4. Slide eye of automatic adjuster cable off anchor and then unhook from lever. Remove cable, cable guide and anchor plate.

5. Disconnect lever spring from lever and disengage from shoe web. Remove spring and lever.

6. Spread anchor ends of the primary and secondary shoes and remove parking brake strut and spring.

7. Disengage parking brake cable from parking brake lever and remove brake assembly.

8. Remove the primary and second-

Brake assemblies front (© Chrysler Corp.)

453

Removing or installing parking brake strut and spring—rear
(© Chrysler Corp.)

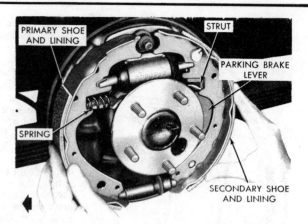

Installing brake shoes (© Chrysler Corp.)

ary brake shoe assemblies and adjusting star wheel from support. Install wheel cylinder to hold pistons in cylinders.

Installing Front Brake Shoes

1. Match a primary with a secondary brake shoe and place them in their relative position on a work bench.
2. Lubricate threads of adjusting screw and install it between the primary and secondary shoes with star wheel next to secondary shoe. The star adjusting wheels are stamped "R" (right side) and "L" (left side), and indicate their location on vehicle.
3. Overlap anchor ends of primary and secondary brake shoes and install adjusting spring lever.
4. Spread anchor ends of brake shoes to maintain adjusting lever and spring in position.
5. Holding brake shoes in their relative position, place brake shoe assembly on support and over the anchor pin.
6. Install nails, cups, springs and retainers.
7. Install anchor pin plate.
8. Install cable guide in the secondary shoe and place the "eye" of adjusting cable over anchor pin.
9. Install return spring in primary shoe. Slide spring over anchor.
10. Install return spring in secondary shoe and slide over anchor. (Be sure the secondary spring overlaps primary).
11. Place adjusting cable cover guide and engage hook of cable into adjusting lever.
12. Install brake drum.
13. Adjust brakes.
14. After checking brake pedal operation, road test vehicle.

Installing Rear Brake Shoes

1. Inspect the platforms of support for nicks or burrs. Apply a thin coat of lubricant to support platforms.
2. Attach parking brake lever to

the back side of the secondary shoe.
3. Place the secondary and primary shoe in their relative position on a work bench.
4. Lubricate threads of adjusting screw and install it between the primary and secondary shoes with star wheel next to secondary shoe. The star adjusting wheels are stamped "R" (right side) and "L" (left side), and indicate their location on vehicle.
5. Overlap anchor ends of the primary and secondary brake shoes and install adjusting spring and lever.
6. Hold the brake shoes in their relative position and engage parking brake cable into parking brake lever.
7. Install parking brake strut and spring between the parking brake lever and primary shoe.
8. Place brake shoes on the support and install retainer nails, springs and retainers.
9. Install anchor pin plate.
10. Install "eye" of adjusting cable over anchor pin and install return spring between primary shoe and anchor pin.
11. Install cable guide in secondary shoe then install secondary return spring. (Be sure secondary spring overlaps primary.)
12. Place adjusting cable in groove of cable guide and engage hook of cable into adjusting lever.
13. Install brake drum and retaining clips.
14. Adjust brakes.

Bendix

Two-Piston Single Cylinder Hydraulically Actuated Type

Description

Both shoes pivot on anchor pins at the bottom of the support plate. The shoes are actuated by one wheel cylinder which is of the double piston

type. Specification for heel and toe clearance of shoes should be strictly followed to obtain efficient brake operation.

Brake Shoe Removal

1. Back off the adjusting cam and remove wheel and drum assembly.
2. Remove brake shoe return spring.
3. Install wheel cylinder brake clamp to prevent pistons from being forced out of cylinder.
4. Remove "C" washer, oil washer and retainer, guide spring retainer and guide spring from anchor bolts to remove brake shoes.

Brake Shoe Installation

1. Install brake shoes, oil washers and retainers on anchor bolts and secure with "C" washers.
2. Install brake return spring.
3. Install wheel and drum assembly.

Adjustments

Since tapered brake lining is thicker at the center than at the ends, the adjustment procedures outlined in the paragraphs that follow must be performed in order to assure maximum braking efficiency.

Minor Adjustment

1. Jack up truck so that one wheel can be rotated freely.
2. Then, while rotating that wheel forward and backward, bring the shoe out to the drum with the adjusting cam until a light drag is obtained.
3. Back off the adjustment until the wheel is free to turn.
4. Repeat this procedure on the other shoe.

Major Adjustment

1. Inspect the fluid level in the master cylinder and add fluid if the level is $\frac{3}{8}$" to $\frac{1}{2}$" from the top of the reservoir or lower.

Uni-servo single anchor brake assembly
(© Ford Motor Co.)

Duo-servo single anchor brake assembly
(© Ford Motor Co.)

2. Loosen lock nuts and turn brake shoe anchor bolts to the fully released position.
3. Adjust the anchor bolt and cam and the minor adjustment cam at the top of the shoe to give equal clearance at the toe and heel. Make sure that sufficient center contact is maintained to produce a slight drag.
4. Lock anchor adjusting nut. After adjusting the clearance on one shoe, repeat the procedure on the other shoe. Then apply the brakes a couple of times to make sure adjustment is up to specifications.

NOTE: Whenever cams are adjusted, check brakes by applying pressure on the brake pedal a couple of times so as to make sure wheel drag has not increased, since the spring loaded cams may cause shoe adjustment to change by shifting position. Wheel should only have a slight drag at room temperature.

Bendix

Single Anchor Brake Shoe Replacement

Brake Shoe Removal

1. Remove the wheel and drum. *Do not push down the brake pedal after the brake drum has been removed.* On a truck equipped with a vacuum or air booster, be sure the engine is stopped and there is no vacuum or air pressure in the system before disconnecting the hydraulic lines.
2. Clamp the brake cylinder boots against the ends of the cylinder, and remove the brake shoe retracting springs from both shoes.
3. Remove the anchor pin plate.
4. Remove the hold-down spring

cups and springs from the shoes, and remove the shoes and the adjusting screw parts from the carrier plate. *Do not let oil or grease touch the brake linings.* If the shoes on a rear brake assembly are being removed, remove the parking brake lever, link, and spring with the shoes. Unhook the parking brake cable from the lever as the shoes are being removed.
5. If the shoes are from a rear brake assembly, remove the parking brake lever from the secondary shoe.

Brake Shoe Installation

1. Coat all points of contact between the brake shoes and the other brake assembly parts with Lubri-plate or a similar lubricant. Lubricate the adjusting screw threads.
2. Place the adjusting screw, socket, and nut on the brake shoes so that the star wheel on the screw is opposite the adjusting hole in the carrier plate. Then install the adjusting screw spring.
3. Position the brake shoes and the adjusting screw parts on the carrier plate, and install the hold-down spring pins, springs, and cups. When assembling a rear brake, connect the parking brake lever to the secondary shoe, and install the link and spring with the shoes. Be sure to hook the parking brake cable to the lever.
4. Install the anchor pin plate on the pin.
5. Install the brake shoe retracting springs on both shoes. *The primary shoe spring must be installed first.*
6. Remove the clamp from the

brake cylinder boots.
7. Install the wheel and drum.
8. Bleed the system and adjust the brakes. Check the brake pedal operation after bleeding the system.

Bendix

Double Anchor Brake Shoe Replacement

1. Remove the wheel and drum. *Do not push down the brake pedal after the brake drum has been removed.* On trucks equipped with vacuum boosters, be sure the engine is stopped and there is no vacuum in the system before disconnecting the hydraulic lines.
2. Clamp the brake cylinder boots against the ends of the cylinder, and remove the brake shoe retracting springs from both shoes.
3. At each shoe, remove the 2 brake shoe retainers and washers from the hold-down pins and remove the spring and pin from the carrier plate. Remove the anchor pin retainers and remove the shoes from the anchor pins. *Do not allow grease or oil to touch the linings.*
4. Clean all brake assembly parts. If the adjusting cams do not operate freely apply a small quantity of lubricating oil to points where the shaft of the cam enters the carrier plate. Wipe dirt and corrosion off the plate.
5. Clean the ledges on the carrier plate with sandpaper. Coat all points of contact between the brake shoes and the other brake assembly parts with high temperature grease.
6. Position the brake shoes on the

Anchor adjustment
(© Ford Motor Co.)

carrier plate with the heel (lower) end of the shoes over the anchor pins and the toe (upper) end of the shoes engaged in the brake cylinder link. Install the hold-down spring pins, spring, washers and retainers.

7. Install the anchor pin retainers and then install the brake shoe return spring.
8. Turn the brake shoe adjusting cams to obtain maximum clearance for brake drum installation.
9. Install the wheel and drum assembly.
10. Bleed the brake system and adjust the brakes.
11. Check brake pedal operation and road test.

Bendix

Two-Cylinder Brake Shoe Replacement

Removal

1. Remove the wheel, and then remove the drum or the hub and drum assembly. *Mark the hub and drum to aid assembly in the same position.* On trucks equipped with vacuum or air boosters, be sure the engine is stopped and there is no vacuum or air pressure in the system before disconnecting the hydraulic lines.
2. Clamp the brake cylinder boots against the ends of the cylinder and remove the four brake shoe retracting springs.
3. Remove the brake shoe guide bolt cotter pin, nut, washer, and bolt from both shoes, and remove the shoes from the carrier plate.
4. Remove the clamp-type adjusting wheel lock from the anchor pin support, and unthread the adjusting screw and wheel assembly from the anchor pin support.

Installation

1. Clean the carrier plate ledges

with sandpaper. Coat all points of contact between the brake shoes and other brake assembly parts with high temperature grease.

2. Thread the adjusting screw and wheel assembly into the anchor pin support and install the clamp-type adjusting wheel lock. Thread the adjusting wheel into the support so that the brake shoe will rest against the adjusting wheel end.
3. Place the brake shoe over the two brake shoe anchor pins, insert the ends in the brake cylinder links, and install the shoe guide bolt, washer, and nut. Finger tighten the nut, then back off one full turn, and install the cotter pin.
4. Install the four retracting springs.
5. Remove the cylinder clamps, install the drum or the hub and drum assembly, then install the wheel assembly. Align the marks on the hub and drum during installation.
6. Bleed and adjust the brakes.
7. Check pedal operation and road test.

Bendix

Brake Shoe Adjustment

The brake drums should be at normal room temperature, when the brake shoes are adjusted. If the shoes are adjusted when the shoes are hot and expanded, the shoes may drag as the drums cool and contract.

A minor brake adjustment reestablishes the brake lining-to-drum clearance and compensates for normal lining wear.

A major brake adjustment includes the adjustment of the brake shoe anchor pins as well as the brake shoes. Adjustment of the anchor pin permits the centering of the brake shoes in the drum.

Adjustment procedures for each type of brake assembly are given under the applicable heading.

Duo-servo brake shoe adjustment
(© Ford Motor Co.)

Minor Adjustment

The brake shoe adjustment procedures for the uniservo single anchor brake assmebly are the same as those for the duo-servo single anchor type.

A major brake adjustment should be performed when dragging brakes are not corrected by a minor adjustment, when brake shoes are relined or replaced, or when brake drums are machined.

Duo-Servo Single Anchor Brake

The duo-servo single-anchor brake is adjusted by turning an adjusting screw located between the lower ends of the shoes.

1. Raise the truck until the wheels clear the floor.
2. Remove the cover from the adjusting hole at the bottom of the brake carrier plate, and turn the adjusting screw inside the hole to expand the brake shoes until they drag against the brake drum.
3. When the shoes are against the drum, back off the adjusting screw 10 or 12 notches so that the drum rotates freely without drag.
4. Install the adjusting hole cover on the brake carrier plate.
5. Check and adjust the other three brake assemblies. When adjust-

Double anchor brake assembly
(© Ford Motor Co.)

LEFT FRONT
Kelsey hayes hydraulic brake assembly
(© Ford Motor Co.)

LEFT REAR
Kelsey hayes rear brake assembly
(© Ford Motor Co.)

ing the rear brake shoes, check the parking brake cables for proper adjustment. Make sure that there is clearance between the ends of the parking brake link and the shoes.

6. Apply the brakes. If the pedal travels more than halfway down between the released position and the floor, too much clearance exists between the brake shoes and the drums. Repeat steps 2 and 3 above. Internal inspection and/or bleeding may be necessary.

7. When all brake shoes have been properly adjusted, road test the truck and check the operation of the brakes. *Perform the road test only when the brakes will apply and the truck can be safely stopped.*

Single Anchor Pin Adjustment

Major Adustment

A major brake adjustment should be made when dragging brakes are not corrected by a minor adjustment, when brake shoes are relined or replaced, or when brake drums are machined.

1. Raise the truck until the wheel clears the floor.

Measuring brake shoes
(© Ford Motor Co.)

2. Rotate the drum until the feeler slot is opposite the lower end of the secondary (rear) brake shoe.

3. Insert a 0.010-inch feeler gauge through the slot in the drum. Move the feeler up along the secondary shoe unit it is wedged between the sedondary shoe and the drum.

4. Turn the adjusting screw (star wheel) to expand the brake shoes until a heavy drag is felt against the drum. Back off the adjusting screw just enough to establish a clearance of 0.010", between the shoe and the drum at a point 1½" from each end of the secondary shoe. This adjustment will provide correct operating clearance for both the primary and secondary shoes. If the 0.010" clearance cannot be obtained at both ends of the secondary shoe, the anchor pin must be adjusted.

5. To adjust the anchor pin setting, loosen the anchor pin nut just enough to permit moving the pin up or down by tapping the nut with a soft hammer. *Do not back the nut off too far or the shoes will move out of position when the nut is tightened.* Tap the anchor pin in a direction that will allow the shoes to center in the drum and provide an operating clearance of 0.010". Torque the anchor pin nut to 80-100 ft-lbs. Recheck the secondary shoe clearance at both the heel and toe ends of the shoe.

6. When all brake shoes and anchor pins have been properly ad-

justed, road test the truck and check the operation of the brakes. *Perform the road test only when the brakes will apply and the truck can be safely stopped.*

Double Anchor Pin Adjustment

Major Adustment

1. Raise the truck until the wheels clear the floor.

2. Rotate the drum until the feeler slot is opposite the lower (heel) end of the secondary (rear) brake shoe.

3. Insert a 0.007" feeler gauge through the slot in the drum. Move the feeler up along the secondary shoe until it is wedged between the shoe and the drum.

4. Loosen the secondary shoe anchor pin nut. Turn the secondary shoe anchor pin until the brake shoe-to-drum clearance at a point 1½" from the heel end of the shoe is 0.007", Remove the feeler gauge.

Measuring brake drum
(© Ford Motor Co.)

Two cylinder brake—equal length springs (© Ford Motor Co.)

Two cylinder brake—unequal length springs
(© Ford Motor Co.)

5. Rotate the drum until the feeler slot is opposite the upper (toe) end of the secondary brake shoe.
6. Insert a 0.010" feeler gauge through the slot in the drum. Move the feeler gauge down along the secondary shoe until it is wedged between the shoe and the drum. Turn the adjusting cam, to expand the brake shoe, until a heavy drag is felt against the drum.
7. Turn the anchor pin until the brake shoe-to-drum clearance at a point 1½" from the toe end of the shoe is 0.010". Remove the feeler gauge.
8. Torque the anchor pin nut to 80-100 ft-lbs. Recheck the heel and toe clearances.
9. Using the preceding secondary brake shoe adjustment procedure as a guide, adjust the primary brake shoe-to-drum clearance.
10. Road test the truck and check the operation of the brakes. *Perform the road test only when the brakes will apply and the truck can be safely stopped.*

Kelsey Hayes

Front Brake Shoes

Removal

1. Raise the vehicle until the wheel clears the floor. Remove the wheel, drum and hub assembly.
2. Clamp the wheel cylinder boots against the ends of the cylinder.
3. Remove the brake shoe retracting springs from both shoes.
4. Remove the adjusting lever link, anchor plate and the adjusting lever spring.
5. Remove the hold down spring cups, springs and the adjusting lever.
6. Remove the brake shoes and adjuster screw assembly from the backing plate.

Installation

1. Clean all brake dust from the brake assembly parts with a *clean dry* rag.
2. Coat all points of contact between the shoes and other brake parts with high temperature grease.
3. Coat the adjuster screw with high temperature grease before assembly. Thread the adjuster screw into the adjuster screw sleeve.
4. Position the brake shoes on the backing plate and install the adjusting lever, hold down pins, springs and cups.
5. Position the adjuster screw assembly on the brake shoes so that the star wheel is opposite the adjusting slot in the backing plate. Install the adjusting lever spring.
6. Install the anchor plate and adjusting lever link.
7. Install the secondary brake shoe retracting spring.
8. Install the primary brake shoe retracting spring.
9. Remove the clamp from the wheel cylinder boots.
10. Install the wheel, drum and hub assembly.
11. Adjust the brakes. Subsequent adjustment will be automatic.

Rear Brake Shoes

Removal

1. Raise the truck until the wheel clears the floor.
2. Remove the wheel, hub and drum assembly.
3. Clamp the brake cylinder boots against the ends of the cylinder with brake piston clamps.
4. Note the two different types of brake shoe retracting springs and remove the springs.
5. Remove the brake shoe hold down post cotter key, nut, and shoe hold down washer.
6. Loosen and remove the eccentric adjuster bolt, lock washer, eccentric and adjusting link.
7. Remove the shoe and lining assembly from the backing plate.
8. Remove the anchor block spring and slide the adjuster assembly from the shoe web.
9. Remove the adjuster star wheel and screw from the adjuster block. Unthread the star wheel from the adjuster screw.

Installation

1. Wipe all brake dust from the brake assembly parts with a *clean dry* rag. Coat all points of contact between brake shoes and other parts with high temperature grease.
2. Coat the adjuster screw and the inside of the adjuster block with high temperature grease.
3. Thread the adjuster screw onto the star wheel and insert the adjuster screw assembly into the adjuster block. Maintain a 2.12-2.18 inch dimension from the end of the adjuster block to the adjuster screw web slot.
4. Install the adjuster assembly onto the shoe web and attach the anchor block spring.
5. Place the brake shoe over the retracting spring toggle pin and insert the ends of the shoe in the wheel cylinder links.
6. Install the shoe hold down washer and nut. Do not install the cotter pin.
7. Install the four brake shoe retracting springs. Make sure the retracting springs are installed.

Typical external band type parking brake
(© Ford Motor Co.)

On 15 x 5" brakes the inner hook ends face the wheel cylinders. On 15 x 4" brakes the inner hook ends face the center of the axle.

8. Install the adjusting link, eccentric, lockwasher and adjuster bolt. Do not tighten.
9. Remove the brake piston clamps.
10. Tighten the shoe hold down nut until there is 0.015-0.025" clearance between the shoe and hold down washer with the shoe held against the backing plate. Install the cotter pin.
11. Center the shoes on the backing plate. Using a ½" wrench, rotate the adjuster eccentric until the adjusting lever is at the index mark. Tighten the eccentric adjuster bolt to specification.
12. Install the wheel, hub and drum assembly.
13. Adjust the brake to obtain a slight drag. Subsequent adjustments will be automatic.

Brake Shoe Adjustment

The brake drums should be at normal room temperature, when the brake shoes are adjusted. If the shoes are adjusted when the shoes are hot and expanded, the shoes may drag as the drums cool and contract.

The brake shoes are automatically adjusted when the vehicle is driven in reverse and the brakes applied. A manual adjustment is required only after the brake shoes have been relined or replaced. *The manual adjustment is performed while the drums are removed, using the tool and the procedure detailed below.*

When adjusting the rear brake shoes, check the parking brake cables for proper adjustment. Make sure that the equalizer operates freely.

To adjust the brake shoes:
1. Use special tool (see illustra-

tion) and adjust to the inside diameter of the drum braking surface.
2. Reverse the tool as shown in illustration and adjust the brake shoes to touch the gauge. The gauge contact points on the shoes must be parallel to the vehicle with the center line through the center of the axle. Hold the automatic adjusting lever out of engagement while rotating the adjusting screw, to prevent burring the screw slots. Make sure the adjusting screw rotates freely.
3. Apply a small quantity of high temperature grease to the points where the shoes contact the carrier plate, being careful not to get the lubricant on the linings.
4. Install the drums. Install the retaining nuts and tighten securely.
5. Install the wheels on the drums and tighten the mounting nuts to specification.
6. Complete the adjustment by applying the brakes several times while backing the vehicle.
7. After the brake shoes have been properly adjusted, check the operation of the brakes by making several stops while operating in a forward direction.

Self Adjusting Brake— Two-Cylinder Front

Two-cylinder front brakes are adjusted by means of exposed, hex-head, self-locking cam adjusters. The brakes are to be manually adjusted initially. Subsequent adjustment is automatic. To adjust this brake:
1. Raise the vehicle and check the front brakes for drag by rotating the wheels.
2. Adjust one shoe by rotating the wheel backward and forward while turning the cam hex-head with a wrench. Bring the shoe out to the drum until a light drag is felt. *Do not apply excessive force on the hex head cam, as automatic adjuster parts can be damaged.* Back off the adjustment until the wheel turns freely. Adjust the other cam on the same wheel in the same manner.
3. Adjust the other front wheel brake using the procedure above.
4. Apply the brakes and recheck the adjustment.

Self Adjusting Brakes—Rear

The brake shoes are automatically adjusted when the vehicle is driven in reverse and the brakes applied. A manual adjustment is required only after the brake shoes have been relined or replaced.

The two-cylinder brake assembly brake shoes are adjusted by turning

Shoe type parking brake
(© Ford Motor Co.)

adjusting wheels reached through slots in the backing plate.

Two types of two-cylinder brake assemblies are used on truck rear wheels. The assemblies differ primarily in the retracting spring hookup, and in the design of the adjusting screws and locks. However, the service procedures are the same for both assemblies.

The brake adjustment is made with the vehicle raised. Check the brake drag by rotating the drum in the direction of forward rotation as the adjustment is made.
1. Remove the adjusting slot covers from the backing plate.
2. Turn the rear (secondary shoe) adjusting screw inside the hole to expand the brake shoe until a slight drag is felt against the brake drum.
3. Repeat the above procedure on the front (primary) brake shoe.
4. Replace the adjusting hole covers.
5. Complete the adjustment by applying the brakes several times while backing the vehicle.
6. After the brake shoes have been properly adjusted, check the operation of the brakes by making several stops while operating in a forward direction.

Parking Brakes

Internal Shoe Type

Adjustment

Nine-Inch Diameter Drum
1. Release the parking brake lever in the cab.
2. From under the truck, remove the cotter pin from the parking brake linkage adjusting clevis pin. Remove the clevis pin.
3. Lengthen the parking brake adjusting link by turning the clevis. Continue to lengthen the adjusting link until the shoes seat against the drum when the clevis pin is installed.
4. Remove the clevis pin and shorten the linkage adjustment until there is 0.010" clearance between the shoes and the drum.

Spring type parking brake (© Chrysler Corp.)

1 Screw	12 Retaining ring	24 Diaphragm
2 Bushing	13 Cylinder housing	25 Clamp band
3 Plunger	14 Protective boot	26 Push rod
4 Cap	15 Seal "O" ring	27 Spring
5 Pin	16 Handle W/O stop	28 Non-pressure housing
6 Cross bar	17 Piston nut	29 Lock washer
7 Nut	18 Piston	30 Nut
8 Piston-cover-spring (sub-assy).	19 Piston shaft	31 Yoke
9 Cover (sub assy.)	20 Rlease bolt	32 Cotterpin
10 Spring	21 Screw	33 Clevis pin
11 Retaining ring (sub assy.)	22 Seal "O" ring	34 Bolt
	23 Seal "O" ring	35 Nut

36 Seal "O" ring
37 Jam nut
38 Washer
39 Snap ring
40 Tooth washer
41 Lock spring
42 Pipe plug
43 Rivet
44 Spring
45 Handle with stop
46 Piston-cover-spring

The measurement should be taken at all points around the drum with the clevis pin installed.

5. Install a new cotter pin in the clevis retaining pin and check the brake operation.

Twelve-Inch Diameter Drum

There is no internal adjustment on this brake. Adjustment is made on the linkage. Remove the clevis pin, loosen the nuts on the adjusting rod, and turn the clevis on the rod until a ¼-⅜" free play is obtained at the brake lever. Tighten the nuts, and connect the clevis to the bellcrank with the clevis pin.

External Band Type

Adjustment

1. On cable-controlled parking brakes, move the parking brake lever to the fully released position. On a vehicle with a rod-type linkage, set the lever at the first notch.

2. Check the position of the cam to make sure the flat portion is resting on the brake band bracket. If the cam is not flat with the bracket, remove the clevis pin from the upper part of the cam, and adjust the clevis

rod to allow the flat portion of the cam to rest on the brake band bracket. Install the clevis pin and cotter pin.

3. Remove the lock wire from the anchor adjusing screw, and turn the adjusting screw clockwise until a clearance of 0.010" is established between the brake lining and the brake drum at the anchor bracket. Install the lock wire in the anchor adjusting screw.

4. Loosen the lock nut on the adjusting screw for the lower half of the brake band, and adjust the screw to establish a 0.010" clearance between the lining and the brake drum at the lower half of the brake band. Tighten the lock nut.

5. Turn the upper band adjusting rod nut until a 0.010 clearance is established between the upper half of the band and the drum.

6. Apply and release brake several times to insure full release.

Disc Type

This type of parking brake is used only on models equipped with auxiliary transmissions. A ventilated disc is mounted between the drive shaft and the auxiliary transmission shaft flange. The brake shoes are mounted

on opposite sides of the disc. The brake is applied through use of me chanical linkage which forces the brake shoes against the disc.

Adjustment

1. Disconnect the brake cable or the rod clevis from the brake lever.

2. Tighten the adjusting nut until the spring pressure pushes the brake lever against the front lever arm.

3. Insert a 1/32" shim between the rear shoe and the disc.

4. Tighten the adjusting screw so that the front shoe is firmly against the disc, yet still allowing removal of the shim.

5. Remove the shim and adjust the parallel adjusting screws so that both linings are parallel to the disc. This should provide 1/64" clearance between the shoes and disc.

6. Making sure the brake lever in the cab is fully released, adjust the clevis on the brake cable as much as necessary to allow installation of clevis pin through the clevis and brake lever without changing position of the lever. Install the pin and cotter pin.

7. Make sure all lock nuts and adjusting screws are tightened securely.

POWER BOOSTER TROUBLE DIAGNOSIS

Condition	Possible Cause	Correction
Vacuum leak (booster in released position)	1. End plate, center plate or control valve body gaskets leak. 2. Distortion of end plate. 3. Misalignment of control valve poppet. 4. Loose vacuum cylinder bolts. 5. Loose control valve body screws. 6. Large control valve poppet spring not centered in spring retainer.	1. Recondition booster unit. 2. Replace end plate. 3. Disassemble, clean and correctly reassemble. 4. Coat vacuum cylinder bolts lightly with a suitable sealing compound and tighten to specified torque. 5. Tighten control valve body screws to specified torque. 6. Disassemble unit and correctly reassemble.
Vacuum leak (booster in applied position)	1. Leak at control valve poppet and seat. 2. Dry or faulty piston leather packing. 3. Faulty control valve diaphragm assembly.	1. Clean and inspect poppet and seat for damage and repair as necessary. 2. Clean and lubricate piston leather or replace. 3. Replace faulty parts.
External hydraulic leaks	1. Gasket ("O" ring) leaking at hydraulic end plate joint. 2. Fluid leaking at copper gasket under hydraulic cylinder end cap.	1. Disassemble clean and replace ("O" ring) gasket and reassemble. 2. Remove end cap and inspect copper gasket and seat install new copper gasket.
Internal hydraulic leak at low pressures	1. Control valve hydraulic piston cup failure. 2. Faulty push rod seal.	1. Recondition control valve unit. 2. Replace push rod seal.
Internal leaks at high pressure	1. Fluid passing copper gasket under hydraulic fitting in control valve. 2. Inspect cups and seals of master cylinder for cuts and scores. 3. Inspect cups of the control valve hydraulic piston.	1. Clean and inspect gasket and fitting, replace if faulty. 2. Hone master cylinder and replace cups and seals. 3. Replace faulty cups.
Hydraulic pressure buildup (without added input)	1. Check hydraulic piston check valve and slot for foreign material under valve.	1. Clean or replace valve and seats as condition indicates.
Failure to release	1. Weak vacuum cylinder piston return spring. 2. Dry vacuum piston leather packing. 3. Swollen rubber cups due to inferior or contaminated brake fluid. 4. Damaged or dented vacuum cylinder shell. 5. Dirty or sticky control valve piston.	1. Replace vacuum cylinder piston return spring. 2. Lubricate vacuum piston leather packing. 3. Flush hydraulic system and recondition or replace all cylinders. 4. Replace vacuum cylinder shell. 5. Recondition control valve assembly.
Failure of booster to operate within specified pressures	1. Rusty, dirty or distorted vacuum cylinder shell. 2. Dry or worn vacuum cylinder leather packing. 3. Swollen rubber cups due to inferior brake fluid. 4. Worn or scored hydraulic cups. 5. Dirt, rust or foreign matter in any component of the system.	1. Clean or replace vacuum cylinder shell. 2. Recondition and lubricate the vacuum booster. 3. Recondition the master cylinder. Replace brake fluid. 4. Recondition the master cylinder. 5. Recondition and lubricate the brake booster assembly.
Loss of fluid	1. Fluid leaking past cup in master cylinder. 2. Brake wheel cylinders leaking. 3. Loose hydraulic hose connectors. 4. Leaking stop light switch.	1. Recondition master cylinder or replace. 2. Recondition or replace wheel cylinders. 3. Inspect and tighten all hydraulic connections. 4. Replace stop light switch.
Presence of brake fluid on hy-power vacuum cylinder	1. Piston cup or push rod seal leaking.	1. Recondition master cylinder.
Pedal kicks back against foot when brakes are applied	1. Vacuum leakage. 2. Dirt under control valve or damaged seat. 3. Weak or broken spring.	1. Inspect and correct vacuum leak. 2. Clean and recondition booster assembly. 3. Replace spring.
Brakes are slow to release Note: First, jack up truck and determine whether or not the wheels are dragging.	1. Incorrect pedal linkage adjustment. 2. Compensating port of master cylinder plugged. 3. Brake shoes sticking. 4. Weak brake shoe return spring. 5. Booster control valve piston sticking. 6. Booster air filter clogged. 7. Control valve diaphragm return spring missing.	1. Adjust and lubricate pedal linkage. 2. Clean master cylinder with compressed air. 3. Free up and lubricate brake shoes. 4. Replace brake shoe return spring. 5. Clean booster control valve piston and lubricate. 6. Clean air filter in mineral spirits. 7. Install new control valve return spring.

Condition	Possible Cause	Correction
	8. Defective check valve in slave cylinder piston.	8. Recondition slave cylinder pistons.
	9. Dirt under atmospheric valve disc.	9. Clean atmospheric valve.
Engine runs unevenly at idle with brakes released	1. Vacuum leakage.	1. Inspect and tighten all vacuum fittings.
	2. Dirt under control valve disc or damaged seat.	2. Clean control valve or replace.
	3. Defective spring.	3. Replace defective spring.
Engine runs evenly and pedal is hard with brakes applied	1. Control valve piston assembly not seating on vacuum disc.	1. Clean or replace control valve piston assembly.
	2. Defective control valve plate and diaphragm.	2. Replace control valve plate and diaphragm.
	3. Defective pressure plate and diaphragm.	3. Replace pressure plate and diaphragm.
Brake pedal is hard at different intervals	1. Defective manifold check valve.	1. Clean or replace manifold check valve.
	2. Slave cylinder piston sticking due to dirt or inferior brake fluid.	2. Clean and recondition slave cylinder.
	3. Brake booster air cleaner clogged.	3. Clean air cleaner in mineral spirits and blow dry with compressed air.

Power Brake Boosters

Brake System Preliminary Checks

Always check the fluid level in the brake master cylinder reservoir (s) before performing the test procedures. If the fluid level is not within 1/4" of the top of the master cylinder reservoirs, add the specified brake fluid.

Push the brake pedal down as far as it will go. If the pedal travels more than halfway between the released position and the floor, adjust the brakes. If the vehicle is equipped with automatic brake adjusters, several sharp brake applications while backing up may be necessary to adjust the brakes.

Road test the vehicle and apply the brakes at a speed of about 20 mph to see if the vehicle stops evenly. If not, the brakes should be adjusted. *Perform the road test only when the brakes will apply and the vehicle can be safely stopped.*

Dual Brake Warning Light System Tests

1. Turn the ignition switch to the ACC or ON position. If the light on the brake warning lamp remains on, the condition may be caused by a shorted or broken switch, grounded switch wires or the differential pressure valve is not centered. Centralize the differential pressure valve. If the warning light remains on, check the switch connector and wire for a grounded condition and repair or replace the wire assembly. If the condition of the wire is good, replace the brake warning lamp switch.
2. Turn the ignition switch to the start position. If the brake warning lamp does not light, check the light and wiring and replace or repair wiring as necessary. When both brake systems are functioning normally, the equal pressure at the pressure differential valve during

brake pedal application keeps the valve centered. The brake warning light will be on only when the ignition key is in the start position.
3. If the brake warning lamp does not light when a pressure differential condition exists in the brake system, the warning lamp may be burned out, the warning lamp switch is inoperative or the switch to lamp wiring has an open circuit. Check the bulb and replace it, if required. Check the switch to lamp wires for an open circuit and repair or replace them, if required. If the warning lamp still does not light, replace the switch.

Power Brake Function Test

With the engine stopped, eliminate all vacuum from the system by pumping the brake pedal several times. Then push the pedal down as far as it will go, and note the effort required to hold it in this position. If the pedal gradually moves downward under this pressure, the hydraulic system is leaking and should be checked by a hydraulic pressure test.

With the brake pedal still pushed down, start the engine. If the vacuum system is operating properly, the pedal will move downward. If the pedal position does not change, the vacuum system is not operating properly and should be checked by a vacuum test.

Vacuum Booster Check Valve Test

Disconnect the line from the bottom of the vacuum check valve, and connect a vacuum gauge to the valve. Start the engine, run it at idle speed, and check the reading on the vacuum gauge.

The gauge should register 17-19" with standard transmission and 14-15" in Drive range if equipped with an automatic transmission. Stop the engine and note the rate of vacuum drop. If the vacuum drops more than one inch in 15 seconds, the check

valve is leaking. If the vacuum reading does not reach 18" or is unsteady, an engine tuneup is needed.

Remove the gauge and reconnect the vacuum line to the check valve.

Vacuum Booster Test—Bendix Piston Type

Disconnect the vacuum line from the booster end plate. Install a tee fitting in the end plate, and connect a vacuum gauge (No. 1) and vacuum line to the fitting. Install a second vacuum gauge (No. 2) in place of the pipe plug in the booster control valve body.

Start the engine, and note the vacuum reading on both gauges. If both gauges do not register manifold vacuum, air is leaking into the vacuum system. If both gauges register manifold vacuum, stop the engine and note the rate of vacuum drop on both gauges. If the drop exceeds one inch in 15 seconds on either gauge, air is leaking into the vacuum system. Tighten all vacuum connections and repeat the test. If leakage still exists, the leak may be localized as follows:

1. Disconnect the vacuum line and gauge No. 1 from the booster.
2. Connect vacuum gauge No. 1 directly to the vacuum line. Start the engine and note the gauge reading. Stop the engine and check the rate of vacuum drop. If gauge No. 1 does not register manifold vacuum, or if the vacuum drop exceeds 1" in 15 seconds, the leak is in the vacuum line or check valve connections.
3. Reconnect vacuum gauge No. 1 and the vacuum line to the tee fitting. Start the engine, and run it at idle speed for one minute. Depress the brake pedal sufficiently to cause vacuum gauge No. 2 to read from zero to 1 inch of vacuum. Gauge No. 1 should register manifold vacuum of 17-19" with standard transmission and 14-16" in Drive range if equipped with an automatic

transmission. If the drop of vacuum on gauge No. 2 is slow, the air cleaner, or air cleaner line, may be plugged. Inspect and if necessary, clean the air cleaner.

4. Release the brake pedal and observe the action of gauge No. 2. Upon releasing the pedal, the vacuum gauge must register increasing vacuum until manifold vacuum is reached. The rate of increase must be smooth, with no lag or slowness in the return to manifold vacuum. If the gauge readings are not as outlined, the booster is not operating. properly and should be removed and overhauled.

Vacuum Booster Test— Diaphragm Type

This procedure can be used to test all diaphragm boosters which are equipped with a pipe thread outlet on the atmosphere portion of the diaphragm chamber.

Remove the pipe plug from the rear half of the booster chamber, and install a vacuum gauge. Start the engine and run it at idle speed. The gauge should register 18-21" of vacuum.

1. With the engine running, depress the brake pedal with enough pressure to show a zero reading on the vacuum gauge.

Hold the pedal in the applied position for one minute. Any downward movement of the pedal during this time indicates a brake fluid leak. Any kickback (upward movement) of the pedal indicates brake fluid is leaking past the hydraulic piston check valve.

2. With the engine running, push down on the brake pedal with sufficient pressure to show a zero reading on the vacuum gauge. Hold the pedal down, and shut the engine off. Maintain pedal position for one minute. A kickback of the pedal indicates a vacuum leak in the vacuum

Tandem power brake unit (© Chrysler Corp.)

1 Tube & bushing	23 Screw & lockwasher	valve
2 Clamp—hose	24 Plug—(3/8")	46 Center plate & seals
3 Hose—vacuum 3/4x2 1/2"	25 Seal—poppet valve	47 Screw & lockwasher fast
4 Tube # fitting—vacuum	26 Valve—poppet	application valve
5 Plug—pipe (1/8")	27 Washer—poppet valve	48 Seat—poppet (fast application
6 Clamp—hose (1")	28 Nut—Hex (#6-32)	valve)
7 Hose—vacuum 1"x3"	29 Spring—poppet valve (small)	49 Gasket—poppet seat
8 Tee—1" hose 3/4" pipe, male	30 Gasket—A. C. tube & cover	50 Spring—return—valve poppet
& female	31 Tube & cover—air inlet	51 Elbow—inverted flared tube
9 Gasket—center plate & end	32 Snap ring—air inlet tube &	52 Plate—diaphragm
plate	cover	53 Gasket—diaphragm plate
10 Plate—cylinder end	33 Nut—piston rod	54 Diaphragm—F. A. valve
11 Valve—bleeder	34 Push rod—piston	55 Gasket—cover (F. A. valve)
12 Cup—hydraulic valve piston	35 Plate—piston (outer)	56 Nut—thin hex. check (1/4"-28)
13 Piston—hydraulic valve	36 Packing—piston	57 Cover—fast application valve
14 Seal—hyd. valve fitting	37 Seal—vacuum piston	58 Pin—retainer (push rod)
15 Fitting—hyd. valve piston	38 Plate—piston (inner)	59 Spring—return (vac. piston)
16 Washer—stop	39 Wick—piston	60 Piston rod & thrust cup
17 Ring—retainer	40 Ring—piston expander	61 Cap—end—hydraulic cylinder
18 Diaphragm & plates—control	41 Plate—retainer (piston felt	66 Gasket—end cap
valve	& exp. ring)	67 Tube—hydraulic cylinder
19 Gasket—poppet (valve body)	42 Shell—vac. cyl.	68 Nut—hyd. cyl. tube
20 Shaft & vac. poppet—control	43 Shaft & seal (fast application	69 Seal—hyd. cyl. tube nut
valve	valve)	70 Seal—hyd. cyl.
21 Spring—poppet valve	44 Seal—center plate piston rod	71 Snap ring—ball retainer
22 Body—control valve	45 Seal—Center plate poppet	72 Retainer—ball

73 Spring—ball return
74 Ball (hyd. piston check valve)
75 Cup—hyd. piston
76 Piston—hydraulic
77 Pin—retainer, hydraulic piston
78 Snap ring
79 Washer—stop
80 Spring—retainer
81 Sleeve—retainer
82 Retainer—seal
83 Hyd. seal
84 Washer—guide
85 End plate & seal
86 Seal—oil (end plate)
87 Tube—vacuum by-pass
88 Screw & lockwasher—clip attached
89 Clip—tube (1/4")
90 Stud—cylinder attaching
91 Lockwasher—cylinder attaching
92 Nut—hex. (1/2"-20) cylinder attaching
93 Tube—hyd. by-pass

Tandem power brake (sectional view) (© Chrysler Corp.)

check valve, in the vacuum line connections, or in the booster.

Hydraulic Tandem Brake Unit

Disassembly

1. Disconnect hydraulic and vacuum by-pass tube from valve body.
2. Remove control valve air inlet fitting from control valve body.
3. Remove control valve body and valve parts from end plate.
4. Make a special tool. NOTE: If this to be a regular service this tool is recommended. For one time or emergency, a vise, "C" clamps, and a guide tube 10" long may be used.
5. Insert tool through end plate opening, and force vacuum cylinder piston forward.
6. Attach flange of tool to end plate with three valve body cover screws.
7. Loosen slave cylinder check nut, and remove slave cylinder.
8. Compress push rod pin retaining spring, remove retainer pin, then remove hydraulic piston from push rod.
9. Hold end cap in a vise, and remove hydraulic cylinder from cap.
10. Loosen vacuum hose clamps, then slide both hoses on the vacuum tube toward center plate.
11. Remove hydraulic by-pass tube from rear end plate, then remove return spring compression tool from end plate.
12. Remove the nuts and studs from power cylinder, then disassemble end plates, cylinder shells and center plate assembly.

Compressor tool for vacuum piston return spring
(© Chrysler Corp.)

13. Force center plate and vacuum piston together, and insert a rod through hole in piston rod to hold piston return spring in the compressed position.
14. Place assembly ring over piston, then remove piston assembly, but keep piston parts assembled in assembly ring. After vacuum tubes and tee fittings have been removed from center plate, position plate on a flat surface.
15. Remove fast application valve cover.
16. To disassemble the diaphragm assembly, hold valve shaft with a screw driver, and remove nut.
17. Lift retainer and diaphragm off valve shaft.
18. Turn center plate upside down, then remove valve seat plate screws and plate, gasket, valve, and spring from center plate.
19. Position front end plate assembly on a flat surface with flat side down.
20. Remove the "O" ring seal, snap ring and retainer washer, push rod seal spring and flange washer, push rod rubber cup seal, and guide washer from end plate.
21. Drive push rod leather seal out of end plate.
22. Position end plate in a holding fixture, then remove hydraulic valve fitting with a 1-7/8" socket wrench.
23. Push hydraulic piston out of valve fitting, and remove gasket from fittings.

Clean all metal parts in a suitable cleaning fluid. After cleaning, wash all the hydraulic system parts in alcohol.

Examine the bore of the cylinder shells for rust and corrosion, and polish with fine steel wool or crocus cloth if necessary.

If the cylinders are badly pitted or scored, install new cylinders.

If felt type wicks are worn, replace them with cotton type wicks.

Use overhaul kit and install ALL parts contained. Do not gamble on ANY old parts that the kit replaces.

Assembly

1. Install nut on piston rod with flat side of nut upward.
2. Position larger diameter piston plate on piston rod with chamfered side of hole at top. Guide rubber seal ring over threads of piston rod.
3. Place assembly ring on a flat surface, then install leather packing, with lip side upward; and smaller diameter piston plate with chamfered side of hole downward in the ring.
4. Cut a new piece of wick to the required length, then place it

against inner face of leather packing lip.

5. Assemble expander ring against wick with gripper points upward, and hook notched end of spring under the clip near opposite end of spring. Position cut of retainer plate over loop of the spring.

6. Hold piston parts in the assembly ring, assemble them on end of piston rod, then install nut on tip of piston assembly. Tighten nut until it is flush with end of rod. Stake nuts securely at two places.

7. Clamp staked nut firmly in a vise, and tighten nut on opposite side of piston plate solidly against piston plate.

8. Press the fast application valve stem and push rod seals into center plate. The application valve seal must be flush with bottom of hole. The push rod seal should rest against the shoulder of center plate. Position center plate. Then place valve spring on top of seal with the small end at top.

9. Install the bullet-nosed tool at threaded end of valve shaft, and insert valve shaft through seal. Position gasket on center plate.

10. Place valve seat plate, with seat side downward, on gasket, and install screws and lockwashers.

11. Turn center plate over. Place lower diaphragm plate on valve shaft with rounded edge at top, then place diaphragm gasket at top of plate. Position diaphragm on top of gasket so screw holes and the bypass hole index with the identical holes in center plate.

12. Install the other diaphragm plate with rounded edge facing diaphragm.

13. Install valve shaft nut on valve shaft. Use a screw driver to prevent shaft from turning, and tighten nut. Stake nut securely at opposite points.

14. Position cover gasket and cover plate, then install screw and lockwashers.

15. Place piston return spring over piston rod with small end of spring at bottom.

16. Carefully guide piston rod through leather seal in center plate, with piston stop flanges of center plate facing upward. Press center plate down against spring, and insert a rod in piston rod. Thread piston rod nut on piston rod, with flat side of nut upward to limit of threads.

17. If forward piston was disassembled to replace leather piston packing, cotton wicking, or other parts, assemble the piston parts in the ring and turn assembly ring over.

18. Remove larger piston plate and "O" ring seal.

19. With assembly ring still in place, guide the remaining piston parts over end of push rod and against piston nut. Carefully install "O" ring seal over threads of piston rod.

20. Place the larger diameter piston plate on piston rod with chamfered side of hole toward "O" ring seal.

21. Assemble large end of push rod in end of piston rod and install retainer pin. Install piston rod nut on end of piston rod with flat side downward. Tighten nut until it is flush with face of piston rod, then stake nut securely at opposite points.

22. Hold piston rod nut in a vise or with a wrench, and tighten inner nut securely against piston. Care must be exercised when tightening inner nut to prevent expander spring retainer plate from shifting.

23. Remove assembly ring, then remove rod holding return spring compressed. Install a new copper gasket in end cap.

24. The hydraulic cylinder must be assembled with milled flats next to end cap. Tighten hydraulic cylinder solidly in end cap, then thread check nut on hydraulic cylinder up to the limit of the threads.

25. Install check nut seal (if used) in groove of cylinder tube. Install bleeder screw in cap.

26. Press push rod leather seal into hydraulic cylinder bore of front end plate from inner side of plate with lip of seal toward outer end of the plate. Install push rod seal parts.

27. The chamfered side of stop washer is down, lip of cup is up, flat side of washer is next to cup, and small end of spring is down. Place washer against spring. Install snap ring in inner groove of end plate.

28. Install stop washer with flat side in control valve hydraulic fitting. Install stop washer retaining ring.

29. Dip hydraulic piston cups in brake fluid, and assemble them on the hydraulic piston with lips of cups positioned away from each other. Insert piston into the fitting with open end of piston toward stop washer.

30. Install a new gasket on the hydraulic fitting (copper gasket on fitting without the groove, and a rubber seal gasket on fitting with the groove). Install the hydraulic fitting in end plate with a 1-7/8" socket wrench. Tighten fitting equipped with a rubber gasket firmly, and fitting

equipped with a copper gasket to 324-330 foot-pounds.

31. Assemble vacuum control parts in control body. Install a new lead washer.

32. Hold slave cylinder end cap in a vise, and thread cylinder into end plate. Install T-fitting and tubes on center plate.

33. Position an end plate gasket on the plate, place cylinder shell on end plate, and coat interior of cylinder with vacuum cylinder oil.

34. Dip cylinder piston on packing in vacuum cylinder oil and allow the excess oil to drain off the wickings.

35. Position a gasket on ledge of center plate, then carefully guide push rod through seal in front end plate. At the same time, align the vacuum tube in end plate with vacuum tube on center plate. Slide hose in place to contact the two vacuum tubes.

36. Position a new gasket at center plate ledge.

37. Coat the interior of cylinder shell with vacuum cylinder oil, then tip cylinder at a 45 degree angle to prevent damage to the piston leather packing.

38. Carefully push the cylinder over piston and onto center plate.

39. Place a new gasket on ledge of end plate, then install end plate on cylinder, aligning end plate vacuum tube and center plate tube. Install cylinder studs and tighten nuts evenly.

40. To assemble the hydraulic piston parts, place large end of spring in retainer cup, then install check ball in piston body behind spring.

41. Dip piston cup in brake fluid, then install it on piston with lip of cup toward check ball.

42. Position the vacuum hoses on tubes, and tighten hose clamps firmly.

43. Connect hydraulic by-pass tube to front and rear end plate.

44. Remove slave cylinder from end plates, then insert and attach return spring compressing tool.

45. Assemble hydraulic piston on push rod.

46. Make certain lock ring is positioned over the retainer pin. Install hydraulic gasket in the plate. Carefully guide the hydraulic cylinder over piston cup, and thread cylinder into end plate.

47. Adjust cylinder 7-3/4", measuring between points shown in illustration.

48. Align bleeder screw in end cap with bleeder screw in control valve.

49. Remove spring compressing tool. After cylinder length adjust-

ment is completed, tighten cylinder check nut solidly.

50. Install guide pins, made from 8-32 x 2½" machine screws with the heads cut off, in end plate.
51. Install diaphragm with diaphragm stem inserted into hydraulic control piston hole. Place diaphragm return spring and control valve body on top of diaphragm.
52. Remove guide pins, one at a time, and replace each guide pin with an attaching screw and a new lock washer. Tighten screws progressively and firmly.
53. Install air inlet fitting in control body, then install retainer.
54. Install vacuum by-pass tube.
55. Inspect assembly to see that all bolts, nuts, screws, washers, and plugs are in place, and that all tubes, clamps, and fittings are firmly tightened.

Installation

1. Position assembly on mounting brackets, and install attaching bolts.
2. Tighten bolts firmly.
3. Connect stop light wires and hydraulic lines to stop light switch.
4. Attach vacuum hose to booster.
5. Connect master cylinder hydraulic line to booster control valve.
6. Connect wheel cylinder hydraulic line to booster end cap.
7. Attach air inlet hose to control valve air inlet fitting, then check and tighten connections.

8. Remove lubricating plugs from end and center plates.
9. Add vacuum cylinder oil to level of filler holes, install plugs, then bleed hydraulic system.

Bendix Hydro-Boost

The Bendix Hydro-Boost uses the hydraulic pressure supplied by the power steering pump to provide a power assist to brake application.

Disassembly

1. Place the booster in a vise with the bracket end up. Using a hammer and chisel, cut the bracket nut that holds the linkage bracket to the booster assembly. The nut should be cut at the open slot in the booster cover threads. Care must be exercised to avoid damage to the threads. Spread the nut and remove the bracket.
2. Remove the pedal boot by pulling it off over the pedal rod eyelet.

3. Position pedal rod removing tool around the pedal rod. The tool should be resting on the booster cover. Insert a punch through the pedal rod from the lower side of the special tool. Push the punch through until it rests on the higher side of the tool. Push up on the punch to shear the pedal rod retainer; remove the pedal rod.
4. Remove the grommet from the groove near the end of the pedal rod and from the groove in the input rod.
5. Disengage the tabs of the spring retainer from the ledge inside the opening near the master cylinder mounting flange of the booster. Remove the retainer and piston return spring from the opening.
6. Pull straight out on the output push rod to remove the push rod and push rod retainer from inside the booster piston.

Bendix Hydro Boost (Typical) (© G.M.C.)

Bendix Hydro-Boost—exploded view (© G.M.C.)

1 Pedal push rod	7 Cover to housing seal	13 Spacer	19 Booster housing	25 Plug 'O' ring
2 Pedal push rod grommet	8 Input rod seals	14 Spacer	20 Tube seat inserts	26 Spool plug
3 Pedal push rod boot	9 Input rod and piston assy.	15 Check valve ball	21 Output push rod	27 Snap ring
4 Bracket nut	10 Spool assembly	16 Accumulator check valve	22 Push rod retainer	28 Piston return spring
5 Linkage bracket	11 Plunger seat	17 'O' ring	23 Spiral snap ring	29 Spring retainer
6 Booster cover	12 'O' ring	18 Piston seal	24 Spool spring	30 Housing to cover bolts

Removing the spool plug from booster-Bendix
Hydro-Boost (© G.M.C.)

Removing the booster pedal rod-Bendix
Hydro-Boost (© G.M.C.)

7. Press in on the spool plug, and insert a small punch into the hole on top of the housing. This unseats one side of the spool plug snap ring from the groove in the bore. Remove the snap ring.
8. Remove the spool plug from the bore with a pair of pliers. Remove the 'O' ring from the plug and discard. Remove the spool spring from the bore.
9. Place the booster cover in a soft-faced vise and remove the cover retaining bolts. Remove the booster assembly from the vise and separate the booster cover from the housing. Remove the large seal ring and discard.
10. Press in on the end of the spool assembly, and use a spiral snap ring removing tool to remove the snap ring from the forward groove in the spool. Discard the snap ring.
11. Remove the input rod and piston assembly, and the spool assembly from the booster housing.
12. Remove the input rod seals from the input rod end, and the piston seal from the piston bore in the housing. Discard the seals.

Staking linkage bracket nut—Bendix
Hydro-Boost (© G.M.C.)

13. Remove the plunger, seat, spacer and ball from the accumulator valve bore in the flange of the booster housing. Remove the 'O' ring from the seat and discard.
14. Thread a screw extractor into the opening in the check valve in the bottom of the accumulator valve bore, and remove the check valve from the bottom of the bore. Discard the check valve and 'O' ring.
NOTE: Using a screw extractor damages the seat in the check valve. A new check valve, 'O' ring and valve must be installed whenever the check valve is removed from the accumulator valve bore.
15. Using a ¼" or a 5/16" spiral flute type screw extractor, remove the tube seats from the booster ports.

Cleaning & Inspection
1. Clean all parts in a suitable solvent.
2. Inspect the valve spool and the valve spool bore for any damage or ware. Discoloration of the spool or bore is normal, particulary in the grooves. If any damage is noted, replace the valve spool and housing.
NOTE: The clearance between the valve spool and the bore is very important. Because of this, the valve spool and housing are to be replaced only as an assembly.
3. Inspect the input rod and piston assembly for any damage or ware. Replace any defective components.
4. Inspect the piston bore in the housing for any damage or ware. If defective, replace the booster housing and spool valve assembly.

Assembly
CAUTION: Parts must be kept VERY clean. If there is any reason to doubt the cleanliness of the components, re-wash before assembly.
Lubricate all seals and metal friction points with power steering fluid

before assembly. Whenever the booster is disassembled, be sure that seals, tube inserts, spiral snap ring, check valve and ball are replaced.
1. Position a tube seat in each booster port and screw a spare tube nut in each port to press the seat down into the port. Do not tighten the tube nuts in the port as this may deface the seats. Remove the spare tube nuts and check for aluminium chips in the ports. Be sure that there is no foreign matter in the ports.

Engage notched end of tool under first coil, then rotate to remove the remaining coils from the snap ring groove.

Removing spiral snap ring—Bendix
Hydro-Boost (© G.M.C.)

2. Coat the piston bore and piston seal with clean power steering fluid. Assemble the seal in the piston bore. The lip of the seal must be towards the rear (away from the master cylinder mounting flange). Be sure that the seal is fully seated in the housing.
3. Lubricate the input rod end, input rod seals and the seal installer tool with clean power steering fluid. Slide the seals on the tool with the lip of the cups towards the open end of the tool. Slide the tool over the input rod end end down to the second groove; then slide the forward seal off the tool and into the groove. Assemble the other seal in the first groove. Be sure that both seals are fully seated.
4. Lubricate the piston and piston installing tool with clean power steering fluid. Insert the large end of the tool into the piston and the tool and piston into the piston bore, through the seal.
5. Position the 'O' ring on the accumulator check valve and coat the assembly with clean power steering fluid. Insert the check valve in the accumulator valve recess in the housing flange. Place the ball and spacer in the same recess.
6. Place the 'O' ring on the changing valve plunger seat and insert the plunger into the seat. Dip the assembly in clean power steering fluid and insert it into the changing valve recess.

Power Brakes

Installing input rod seals—Bendix Hydro-Boost (© G.M.C.)

Installing input rod and piston assembly in booster-Bendix Hydro-Boost (© G.M.C.)

Installing spiral snap ring—Bendix Hydro-Boost (© G.M.C.)

Installing linkage bracket nut (typical)—Bendix Hydro-Boost (© G.M.C.)

7. Coat the spool assembly with clean power steering fluid and insert in the spool bore. Be sure that the pivot pins on the upper end of the input rod lever assembly are engaged in the groove in the sleeve. Remove piston installing tool.

8. Separate the two components of the snap ring installation tool and place the spiral snap ring on the tool. Insert the rounded end of the installer into the spool bore. While pressing on the rear of the spool, slide the snap ring off the tool and into the groove near the forward end of the spool by pressing in on the tool sleeve. Check to be sure that the retaining ring is fully seated.

9. Place the housing seal in the groove in the housing cover. Join the booster housing and cover and secure with five attaching bolts. Tighten the bolts to 18-26 ft. lbs.

CAUTION: It is very important that the same cover attaching bolts are used as they are designed for the booster only. If they are damaged, replace with the same part numbers.

10. Place an 'O' ring on the spool plug. Insert the spool spring and the spool plug in the forward end of the spool bore. Press in on the plug and position the snap ring in its groove in the spool valve bore.

11. Place the linkage bracket on the booster assembly. The tab on the inside of the large hole in the bracket should fit into the slot in

the threaded portion of the booster cover.

12. Install the bracket nut with a staking groove outward on the threaded portion to the booster cover. Use special tool and tighten to 95-120 ft. lbs.

13. Insert a small punch into the staking groove of the nut, at the slot in the booster cover, and with a hammer stake the nut in place. Be sure that the threads on the nut are deformed so the nut will not loosen.

14. Position a new boot and grommet on the pedal rod. Moisten the grommet and insert the grommet end of the pedal rod into the input rod of the booster. When the grommet is fully seated, the pedal rod will rotate freely.

15. Install the boot on the booster cover.

Bendix Master Vac

Removal

1. Disconnect clevis at brake pedal to push rod.
2. Remove vacuum hoses from power cylinder.
3. Disconnect hydraulic line from master cylinder.
4. Remove the four attaching nuts and lock washers that hold the unit to the firewall. Remove the power brake unit.

Disassembly

2. Remove four master cylinder to vacuum cylinder attaching nuts and washers.

2. Separate master cylinder from vacuum cylinder, then remove the rubber seal from the outer groove at end of master cylinder.

3. Remove the push rod from the power section. (Do not disturb adjusting screw.)

4. Remove push rod boot and valve operating rod.

5. Scribe alignment marks across the rear shell and vacuum cylinder. Remove all but two of the end plate attaching screws (opposite each other). Hold down on the rear shell while removing the two remaining screws to prevent the piston return spring from expanding.

6. Scribe a mark across the face of the piston, to index the mark on the rear shell, and remove rear shell with vacuum piston and piston return spring.

7. Remove vacuum hose from vacuum piston and from vacuum tube on inside of rear shell. Separate rear shell from vacuum piston.

8. Remove air cleaner and vacuum tube assembly, and air filter from the rear shell.

9. Spring the felt retaining ring enough to disengage ring from grooves in bosses on rear piston plate.

10. Remove piston felt and expander ring from piston assembly.

11. Remove six piston plate attaching screws and separate front piston plate and piston packing from piston plate.

468

Bendix master vac unit (© Ford Motor Co.)

Adjusting hydraulic cylinder length
(© Chrysler Corp.)

12. Remove valve return spring, floating control valve and diaphragm assembly, valve spring and diaphragm plate. Separate floating control valve spring-retainer and control valve diaphragm from control valve.

13. Remove rubber reaction disc and shim (if present) from front piston plate. NOTE: Do not remove the valve operating rod and valve plunger from the rear piston plate unless it is necessary to replace defective parts. Normally, the next two steps can be omitted.

14. When it is necessary to replace the valve operating rod or valve plunger, remove valve rod seal from groove in piston plate and pull seal over end of rod.

15. Hold piston with valve plunger side down and inject alcohol into valve plunger through opening around valve rod. This will wet the rubber lock in the plunger. Then drive or pry valve plunger

off the valve rod. NOTE: If master cylinder is not to be rebuilt, omit Steps 16-19.

16. Remove snap-ring from groove in base at end of master cylinder.

17. Remove piston assembly, primary cup, retainer spring, and check-valve from master cylinder.

18. Remove filler cap and gasket from master cylinder body.

19. Remove secondary cup from master cylinder piston.

Cleaning Note

After disassembly, cleaning of all metal parts in satisfactory commercial cleaner solvent is recommended. Use only alcohol or Declene on rubber parts or parts containing rubber. After cleaning and drying, metal parts should be rewashed in clean alcohol or Declene before assembly.

Assembly

Steps 1-5 apply to a completely disassembled master cylinder. Otherwise, omit these steps (1-5).

1. Coat bore of master cylinder with brake fluid.
2. Dip secondary cup in brake fluid and install on master cylinder piston.
3. Dip other piston parts in brake fluid and assemble the piston. Install piston.

Bendix Single Diaphragm, Frame-Mounted Booster (© Ford Motor Co)

Power Brakes

4. Install snap-ring into groove of cylinder.
5. Use new gasket and install filler cap.
6. Assemble valve rod seal on rod and insert valve rod through the piston. Dip valve plunger in alcohol and assemble to ball end of valve rod. Be sure ball end of rod is locked in place in plunger.
7. Assemble floating control valve diaphragm over end of floating control valve. Be sure diaphragm is in recess of floating control valve. Press control valve spring retainer over end of control valve and diaphragm.
8. Clamp valve operating rod in a vise with rear piston plate up. Lay leather piston packing on rear piston plate with lip of leather over edge of piston plate.
9. Install floating control valve return spring over end of valve plunger.
10. Assemble diaphragm plate to diaphragm and assemble floating control valve with diaphragm in recess of rear piston plate.
11. Install floating control valve spring over retainer. Align and assemble front piston plate with rear piston plate. Center the floating control valve spring on front piston plate and center valve plunger stem in hole of piston.
12. Holding front and rear piston plates together, loosely install six piston plate cap screws.
13. Install shim and rubber reaction disc in recess at center of front piston plate. NOTE: A piston assembling ring is handy in assembling the piston.

14. Place the assembling tool over piston packing, turn piston assembly upside down and assemble the expander ring against inside lip of leather packing. Saturate felt with Vacuum Cylinder Oil or shock absorber fluid—type A, then assemble in expander ring. Assemble retainer ring over bosses on rear piston plate. Be sure retainer is anchored in grooves of piston plate.
15. Assemble air cleaner filter over vacuum tube of air cleaner and attach air cleaner shell in position with screws.
16. Slide vacuum hose onto vacuum inlet tube of piston and align hose to lay flat against piston.
17. Wipe a coat of vacuum cylinder oil on bore of cylinder. Remove assembling ring from vacuum piston and coat leather piston packing with vacuum cylinder oil.
18. Install rear shell over end of valve operating rod and attach vacuum hose to tube end on each side of end plate.
19. Center small diameter end of piston return spring in vacuum cylinder. Center large diameter of spring on piston. Check alignment mark on piston with marks on vacuum cylinder and rear shell, compress spring and install two attaching screws at opposite sides to hold rear shell and cylinder together. Now, install balance of screws and tighten evenly.
20. Dip small end of pushrod boot in alcohol and assemble guard over end of valve operating rod and over flange of shell.

21. Insert large end of pushrod through hole in end of vacuum cylinder and guide into hole of front piston plate. NOTE: Before going on with assembly, check the distance from the outer end of the pushrod to the master cylinder mounting surface on the vacuum cylinder. This measurement should be 1.195-1.200″.
22. After pushrod adjustment is correct, replace rubber seal in groove on master cylinder body.
23. Assemble master cylinder to the vacuum cylinder at four studs. Replace lock washers and nut and securely tighten.

Bendix Single Diaphragm Type Frame Mounted

Disassembly

1. Remove the booster unit and hydraulic cylinder from frame mounting bracket.
2. Scribe marks across front and rear shells and across flange of hydraulic cylinder. Disconnect the control tube nut from the control valve seat and remove the seal from the tube.
3. Remove the clamp band from the booster unit and disassemble the rear shell. NOTE: The plug in the rear shell should be removed only if it is damaged.
4. Roll the bead of the diaphragm back from the front shell flange and compress the return spring for the diaphragm slightly. Remove the snap ring from groove

Bendix Frame-Mounted, Piston-Type Booster (© Ford Motor Co)

WICKING

EXPANDER RING

PISTON PLATES

NUT

RETAINER PLATE

PISTON PACKING

SEAL RING

Assembly Ring

Bendix Vacuum Piston (© Ford Motor Co)

ring is seated properly before releasing pressure on the spring.

10. Coat both sides of the diaphragm lightly with talcum powder or silicone lubricant. Align scribe marks made on front and rear shells and press the rear shell flange and diaphragm bead into position against the front shell flange.

11. Install the clamp band on the shells and secure with bolt. Install a new seal on the control vacuum tube and assemble the tube and hose onto the rear shell tube and tighten nut.

12. Reinstall on vehicle and check for vacuum leaks and road test to check for proper operation.

NOTE: Be sure to bleed all air from hydraulic cylinder and brake lines before attempting to road test vehicle.

Bendix Piston Type Frame Mounted

Disassembly

1. Remove all vacuum and hydraulic lines to booster and remove unit from vehicle.

2. Scribe marks across end plate and vacuum cylinder, also across the control valve body and flange on the end plate.

3. Clamp the end nut of the hydraulic cylinder in a soft jawed vise and unscrew the lock nut on the control tube and remove the tube and O-ring seal.

4. Remove the four bolts securing the valve body to the end plate and remove the control valve body, valve return spring and diaphragm from the end plate.

5. From the valve body remove the snap ring, tube and cover, gasket, the two poppet return springs and the valve seal. From the valve housing remove the valve poppet seal.

6. Remove the four hook bolts that hold the shell to the end plate and separate the shell from the end plate.

7. Compress the return spring and hold in place with two hook type clamps.

8. Loosen the lock nut on the hydraulic cylinder and separate the cylinder from the end plate. Remove the retaining ring from the hydraulic piston and press out the retaining pin in the piston. Remove the piston from the push rod and remove the piston cup from the piston.

9. Compress the piston return spring and remove the hook clamps. Separate the piston and push rod assembly from the end plate, and remove the return spring from the push rod.

near the end of the hydraulic cylinder. Remove the hydraulic parts, push rod and diaphragm as an assembly.

5. Remove diaphragm return spring from piston end of push rod. Remove bolts securing hydraulic cylinder to front shell and remove the cylinder gasket from the shell. NOTE: The diaphragm assembly should be removed from the push rod only if necessary to remove damaged parts.

6. Remove the retaining ring from groove in hydraulic piston and press the retaining pin from hole in push rod and piston. Remove the cup from the piston and if a new seal is to be installed in end of push rod, remove old push rod seal. NOTE: Be careful to avoid damaging push rod.

Carefully slide the seal retainer, seal, O-ring, guide bearing, retainer washer and snap ring from push rod.

7. Scribe marks across the flanges of valve body and housing and remove the four attaching bolts. Remove the valve body and remove cups from the control valve piston.

Assembly

1. Install check valve, spring, washer and snap ring in hydraulic cylinder end fitting. Next assemble O-ring seal and end fitting on the hydraulic cylinder.

2. Install cups, back to back, on control valve piston. Then assemble piston, diaphragm retainer and valve diaphragm. NOTE: Make sure inner bead of diaphragm is seated in the piston groove.

3. Install the spring retainer, with the flange down, on the spring in

the valve body. Install the piston and diaphragm assembly on the retainer and press the outer bead of the diaphragm into the groove in the valve body.

4. Coat the valve piston with clean brake fluid and assemble the piston in the control valve cylinder bore. Align the scribe marks on the valve cylinder body and housing and attach with bolts. Torque bolts to 40-60 in. lbs.

5. If installing new seal on push rod, place new seal on clean block of wood, with the rubber side down. Place the push rod vertically on the seal stem and strike the threaded end with a soft mallet to seat the seal stem in the push rod. NOTE: Make sure the shoulders of the push rod and seal are in contact.

6. Slide snap ring, retaining washer, guide bearing with O-ring seal in outer groove of guide, seal cup and seal retainer on push rod.

7. Attach the piston to the push rod with retaining ring and pin. Dip the piston cup in clean brake fluid and install on piston.

8. Install new gasket in groove at flange end of hydraulic cylinder and install cylinder on front shell with the hold down bolts.

9. Install the diaphragm return spring, with the large coil first, against the diaphragm plate. Lubricate the cylinder bore with clean brake fluid and carefully insert the piston, cups and seals into cylinder bore. Roll back the edge of the diaphragm and press against the diaphragm to compress the return slightly. When push rod and parts are installed all the way into the cylinder bore, install the retaining snap ring. NOTE: Be sure the snap

Bendix Tandem Diaphragm—Frame-Mounted Booster (© Ford Motor Co)

10. From the end plate remove the seal O-ring, stop washer, snap ring, spring, sleeve, retainer, seal cup, push rod washer and small seal O-ring. On the opposite of the end plate remove the large seal O-ring.

11. From the control valve opening in the end plate, remove the retaining snap ring, piston stop washer and valve fitting. Remove the O-ring seal from the valve fitting.

12. Remove the hydraulic piston from the valve fitting and remove the piston cups from the piston.

13. To prevent damaging the push rod when disassembling the vacuum power piston, clamp the push rod in a soft jawed vise. Next remove the nut, piston felt retainer, packing ring, packing wick, rear plate, packing, front plate and washer from the push rod.

14. To remove the end cap on hydraulic cylinder, loosen the lock nut on the cylinder and remove the cap. Remove the seal O-ring, snap ring, check valve spring and residual pressure check valve from the end cap.

Assembly

1. Assemble the residual pressure check valve, check valve spring, snap ring and seal O-ring in the end cap. Screw the end cap on the cylinder tube until the tube bottoms in the cap and lock in place with the lock nut.

2. Make a vacuum piston assembly ring by cutting a one inch wide section from an old cylinder shell of the proper size. Install the flat washer over the threaded end of the push rod, then install the front piston plate on the rod with the chamfered side of the hole away from the washer. Guide the O-ring seal over the threads of the push rod.

3. Place the assembly ring over the piston plate and install the leather packing with the lip of the packing up. Install the rear piston plate keeping the chamfered side of the hole next to the seal.

4. Cut the packing wick to the required length and saturate with a good quality oil. Install the wick against the inner lip of the leather packing.

5. Install the packing expander ring inside the wick with the gripping point up. Put the notch, at the loop end of the ring, under the clip on the opposite end of the ring. Install the piston retainer with the cutout portion over the loop of the expander ring.

6. Install the nut on the threaded end of the push rod and tighten securely. NOTE: Be careful the piston retainer does not shift when tightening the nut. Also leave the assembly ring in place until ready to install the piston assembly in the cylinder.

7. Install in the center bore of the end plate the O-ring seal, push rod washer, cup retainer, sleeve, spring, snap-ring, piston stop washer and seal O-ring. NOTE: Make sure the snap ring is seated fully, in the groove in the bore of the end plate.

8. Install the valve piston cups, back to back, on the control valve piston. Dip the piston assembly in clean brake fluid and install in the valve fitting with the hole end of the piston first. Install a new O-ring on the valve fitting and insert the fitting into the control valve bore in the end plate. Install the piston stop

washer and snap ring in the bore.

9. Install the piston return spring over the push rod with the small end next to the piston. Slide the end plate over the end of the push rod. Compress the return spring slightly to project the push rod approximately 2 inches through the end plate, and hold in place with two hook type clamps. Install the hydraulic piston on the end of the push rod and attach with the retainer pin. Slide the snap ring into its groove to hold the pin in place.

10. Dip the piston cup in clean brake fluid and install the cup on the piston with the lip away from the end plate. Next dip the piston assembly in clean brake fluid and coat the inside of the hydraulic cylinder with fluid. Guide the hydraulic cylinder over the piston being careful not to turn the lip of the seal cup backwards when installing.

11. Screw the hydraulic cylinder into the end plate until the cylinder bottoms. Then back off the cylinder until the bleeder screw in the end cap aligns with the bleeder screw in the end plate and tighten the lock nut. Compress the return spring and remove the hook clamps.

12. In the groove in the end plate install the large O-ring seal. Coat the inside of the vacuum cylinder with a good quality oil. Remove the assembly ring from the piston and insert the piston into the cylinder. NOTE: Tip the piston 45 degrees or more when sliding it into the cylinder. This will make it easier to install the piston.

Align the scribe marks on the end plate and cylinder shell and install the hook bolts, lock washers and nuts. Tighten the nuts a little at a time to avoid warping the end plate or the cylinder shell.

13. Install the valve diaphragm and spring retainer on the diaphragm plate. Install the valve poppet seal over the end of the valve seal and place the assembly in the valve body.

14. Install the poppet return springs with the small end of the small spring over the button on the valve seal. In the recess in the valve body, install the O-ring seal and attach the tube and cover with the snap ring.

15. In the groove in the control vacuum port of the valve body install the small O-ring seal.

16. Install the valve diaphragm and spring retainer assembly on the end plate flange and position the control valve return spring on the retainer. Position the control valve housing on the spring and secure with the four hold down bolts. NOTE: Be sure to align the scribe marks made on the housing and end plate before assembling the housing to the end plate.

17. Install the O-ring seal on the end of the vacuum tube and install the tube with one end in the control valve body and the other end secured to the rear of the shell with the tube nut.

18. Install the unit on the vehicle and check for vacuum leaks and road test for proper operation of unit.

NOTE: Be sure to bleed all air from the hydraulic cylinder and brake lines before road testing the vehicle.

Bendix Dual Diaphragm Type

This unit features a direct pedal connection to a vacuum unit mounted on the firewall, with the master cylinder directly mounted to booster.

The booster chamber contains two diaphragms and is under constant engine vacuum. When brakes are applied, the control valve is opened to allow atmospheric pressure behind both diaphragms. This provides the power boost to the master cylinder.

This vacuum-suspended system provides reserve against fade. Pedal linkages are eliminated, no additional vacuum storage tanks are needed.

NOTE: Do not attempt to disassemble the booster. It is serviced only by the dealer.

Bendix Tandem Diaphragm Type Frame Mounted

Disassembly

1. Remove all hydraulic and vacuum lines attached to booster and hydraulic cylinder. Then remove the unit from frame brackets and remove from vehicle.

2. Scribe marks across both clamp rings onto the shell surfaces, also across top of hydraulic cylinder flange onto the front shell. Scribe marks across control valve body and housing below hydraulic cylinder.

3. Disconnect the control tube and nut from control valve port and remove the three hose clamps and tee. Remove the seal ring from the control tube.

4. Remove the rear clamping ring and remove the rear shell.

5. Remove the front clamping ring and separate the front, center and rear shells and remove the diaphragm assemblies.

6. Clamp the hydraulic cylinder in a soft jawed vice being careful to avoid damaging cylinder.

7. Press on the spring retainer to compress the diaphragm return spring and remove the three bolts that hold the hydraulic cylinder to the front shell and support plate. Then carefully release the pressure on the return spring and pull the push rod and hydraulic piston from the cylinder.

8. Remove the return spring from the piston end of the push rod. NOTE: Do not remove the spring retainer except to replace damaged parts.

9. Remove the snap ring from the groove in the piston and press plunger pin from the hole in the piston and push rod.

10. Remove the piston, snap ring, seal retainer, push rod cup, push rod bearing and support plate and piston stop from the push rod.

11. Remove the cup from the piston and the O-ring from the groove in the push rod bearing.

12. Remove the end fitting from the hydraulic cylinder and remove the snap ring from the end cap. Disassemble the residual pressure check valve.

13. Remove the end fitting seal from the push rod being careful not to damage the push rod.

14. Clamp the nut, on the push rod seat end of the rear shaft, in a vise and remove by unscrewing the shaft. Remove the assembly

Cutaway view of brake booster and master cylinder
(© Chrysler Corp.)

from the vise and remove the front diaphragm and diaphragm plate from the shaft.

15. Slide center shells off the shaft and remove the O-ring seal from its groove in the hub of the center shells.

16. Clamp the nut on the rear shaft and remove by unscrewing the shaft. Remove the nut, washer, rear diaphragm, diaphragm plate and washer from the shaft.

17. Remove the valve body and control valve from the valve housing.

18. Remove the cups from the control valve piston and slide the control valve diaphragm and retainer off the opposite end of the piston.

Cleaning and Inspection

Clean all metal parts in clean metal parts cleaner. Discard any old parts that are to be replaced with new ones. Clean all hydraulic parts in clean brake fluid. Check the diaphragms for cracks, tears and kinks and replace any diaphragms that are questionable. Inspect all metal and plastic parts for nicks, cracks, scores or burrs and replace any damaged parts. Check the shells for cracked or broken welds, dents or cracks. DO NOT attempt to disassemble the center shell assembly. Inspect the hydraulic cylinder bore and valve body bore for any surface damage. Remove deposits, pitted areas or light scores with crocus cloth. Replace the part if it can not be cleaned up with crocus cloth.

Assembly

1. Install the valve piston cups back to back in the grooves on the control valve piston.

2. Slide the valve diaphragm retainer, with the flange side first, onto the other end of the piston. Wet the inside of the valve diaphragm with alcohol and slide it over the end of the piston and seat it against the retainer. Install the spring retainer on the hub of the valve diaphragm with the flange side away from the diaphragm.

3. Install the control valve piston and diaphragm assembly on the return spring. Position the spring around the vacuum poppet guides in the valve body and press the bead of the diaphragm firmly into the groove on the flange of the valve body.

4. Dip the control valve piston and cups into clean brake fluid and install them into the control valve bore in the hydraulic cylinder. Align the scribe marks on the valve body and housing and attach with four bolts. Tighten the bolts to 40-60 in. lbs.

5. Assemble the washer, rear diaphragm plate, diaphragm and washer onto the rear shaft with the holes in the shaft towards the diaphragm.

6. Install the nut on the end of the shaft and tighten to 10-15 ft. lbs. Stake the nut in two places to prevent any movement.

7. Install the O-ring seal in its groove inside the hub of the center shells. With a silicone lubricant, coat the seal and bearing and the outer surface of the rear shaft.

8. Insert the front end of the rear shaft through the middle of the center shells.

9. Install the washer, front diaphragm and diaphragm plate on the end of the shaft. Screw on retaining nut and tighten to 10-15 ft. lbs. Stake the nut in two places to prevent any movement.

10. To install a new push rod seal, in end of push rod, place new seal face down on a clean block of wood. Place the push rod upright on the seal stem and strike end of rod with a soft mallet to seat the seal. NOTE: Be sure that the shoulders of the seal and push rod are in contact.

11. Dip all hydraulic parts, push rod and push rod bearing in clean brake fluid. Install the support plate and piston stop assembly, push rod bearing, with O-ring in its groove, push rod cup and seal retainer on the push rod.

12. Install the snap ring on the piston but not in its groove. Attach the piston to the push rod with the plunger pin and then slide the snap ring into its groove in the piston.

13. Dip the piston cup in brake fluid and install on the piston with the open flared end away from the piston.

14. Install the residual pressure check valve in the end fitting, then install the check valve spring and washer in the end fitting and secure with the snap ring.

15. Install the gasket onto the end fitting and screw into the hydraulic cylinder and tighten to 50-85 ft. lbs.

16. Install the O-ring seal in groove around the hydraulic cylinder flange.

17. Slide the small end of the diaphragm return spring over the piston end of the push rod. Lubricate the piston and cylinder bore with clean brake fluid.

18. Bottom the small end of the return spring against the spring retainer on the push rod and place the large coil of the spring in the front shell with the piston through the hole in the shell.

19. With the return slightly compressed, guide the piston, seal retainer, push rod cup, and push rod bearing into the cylinder bore. Seat the cylinder flange against the front shell, make sure the O-ring is in place. Place the support plate and stop plate on the opposite side of the shell and secure the stop assembly and front shell to the cylinder with the three securing bolts. Release the pressure on the spring.

20. On the front and rear diaphragm beads put a light coat of talcum powder or silicon lubricant.

21. Guide the rear shaft onto the push rod and align the scribe marks made on the front shell flanges. Press the shells together and seat the bead of the diaphragm all the way around in the shell flanges.

22. Install the clamp ring on the shell flanges and align the scribe marks. Tighten the clamp screw to 30-40 in. lbs.

23. Align the scribe marks on the rear shells and press them together making sure the diaphragm bead is in the shell flange all the way around. Install the clamp ring, aligning the marks, and tighten the clamp bolt to 30-40 in. lbs.

24. Install the hose tee to the control tube on the rear shell and to hose nipple on the center shell.

Midland Diaphragm Type Booster Applied

25. Install the seal ring on the end of the control tube and nut assembly and attach the tube to the hose tee with a hose clamp. Screw the nut onto the control valve port and tighten to 80-120 in. lbs.
26. Install unit on vehicle and test for vacuum leaks and road test for proper operation.

NOTE: Be sure to bleed hydraulic cylinder of all air before attempting to road test vehicle.

Midland Ross Diaphragm Type

The self-contained booster assembly is mounted on the engine side of the firewall. It is connected directly to the brake pedal. This booster is not equipped with a separate vacuum tank.

The master cylinder is attached to the forward side of the booster. The balance of the hydraulic brake system is identical to other standard service brakes.

Booster Repairs

1. Separate master cylinder from booster body.
2. Remove air filter cover and hub and the filter from the booster body.
3. Remove the vacuum manifold mounting bolt, manifold, gaskets and vacuum check valve from the booster body.
4. Disconnect the valve operating rod from the lever by removing its retaining clip, washers, and pivot pin.
5. Disconnect the lever from the booster end plate brackets by removing its retaining clip, washers, and pivot pin.

Checking pushrod screw with gauge
(© Ford Motor Co.)

6. Remove two brackets from the end plate.
7. Remove the rubber boot from the valve operating rod.
8. To remove the bellows, control valve, and diaphragm assemblies, remove large C-ring that holds the rear seal adapter assembly to the booster end plate.
9. Scribe matching lines on the booster body and the end plate. Then remove the ten retaining screws. Tap the outside of the plate with a soft hammer and separate the plate from the booster body.
10. Push the bellows assembly into the vacuum chamber and remove the bellows, control valve, and diaphragm as an assembly from the booster body.
11. Remove the outer O-ring from the control valve hub.
12. To disassemble the bellows, pushrod, and control valve assemblies, remove the large bellows retaining ring, bellows, bellows retainer, and support ring from the diaphragm and valve assembly.

13. Remove the retainer and support ring from the bellows.
14. Remove pushrod assembly, the reaction lever and ring assembly, and the rubber reaction ring from the control valve hub.
15. Remove the reaction cone and cushion ring from the pushrod assembly. Then disassemble the reaction levers from the ring.
16. Remove the two plastic plunger guides from the control valve plunger. Then remove the retainer that holds the reaction load ring and atmospheric valve on the control valve hub.
17. Slide the reaction load ring and atmospheric valve from the control valve hub.
18. Separate the control valve hub and the plunger assembly from the diaphragm by sliding the plunger and rear seal adapter from the rear of the hub. Then

Pushrod gauge
(© Ford Motor Co.)

Disassembled view of booster (© Ford Motor Co.)

remove the hub outer O-ring from the front side of the diaphragm.

19. To disassemble the control valve plunger, remove the hub rear seal adapter from the valve plunger assembly, and remove the seal from the adapter.
20. Remove the O-rings, the seal, and the fiber gaskets from the plunger.
21. If the plunger assembly needs to be replaced, hold the plunger and pull out the valve operating rod with pliers. Do not separate the operating rod and plunger unless the plunger is to be replaced.

Assembly

1. If valve operating rod was removed for replacement of plunger, install a new rubber bumper and spring retainer on the rod before installing it on the replacement plunger. Then push the rod firmly until it bottoms in the plunger.
2. Install fiber gaskets, plunger seal, and the two O-rings on the plunger assembly.
3. Install the valve hub rear seal in the adapter assembly with the sealing lip toward the rear. Then slide the adapter assembly onto the plunger with the small diameter end of the hub toward the rear.
4. To assemble the control valve, pushrod, and bellows assemblies, install the hub outer O-ring. Then install the plunger with the seal adapter and the hub on the diaphragm. To do this, hol the hub on the front side of the

diaphragm and insert the plunger assembly in the hub from the rear side of the diaphragm.

5. Install atmospheric valve and then the reaction load ring onto the plunger and hub. Compress the valve spring, and install the load ring retainer into the groove of the plunger.
6. Install two plastic plunger guides into their grooves on the plunger.
7. Install rubber reaction ring into the valve hub so that the ring locating knob indexes in the notch in the hub, with the ring tips toward the front.
8. Assemble the reaction lever and ring assembly, and install the assembly into the valve hub.
9. Install the reaction cone and cushion ring on the pushrod. Then install the pushrod assembly on the valve hub so that the plunger indexes in the rod.
10. Assemble the bellows, retainer, and support ring. The ring should be positioned on the middle fold of the bellows.
11. Position the bellows assembly on the diaphragm, and secure it with the retaining ring. Make sure the retaining ring is fully seated.
12. Install the bellows, control valve, and diaphragm assemblies with a screwdriver, moving the booster body retaining screw tapping channel just enough to provide a new surface for the self-tapping attaching screws.
13. Install the diaphragm, the control valve components, and the bellows as an assembly into the

booster body. (Be sure the lip of the diaphragm is evenly positioned on the retaining radius of the booster body.) Pull the front lip of the bellows through the booster body, and position it around the outer groove of the body.

14. Install O-ring in the front side of the end plate, and locate the plate on the booster body. Align the scribed lines, compress the two assemblies together with a clamp. Then install all ten self-tapping attaching screws.
15. Install the large C-ring onto the rear seal adapter at the rear side of the end plate.

Pushrod Adjustment

The pushrod has an adjusting screw to maintain the correct relationship between the control valve plunger and the master cylinder piston after the booster is completely assembled. If this screw is not properly adjusted, the brakes may drag.

To check adjustment of the screw, make a gauge to the dimensions shown. Place this gauge against the master cylinder mounting surface of the booster body. The pushrod screw should be adjusted so that the end of the screw just touches the inner edge of the slot in the gauge.

Booster Installation

1. Install rubber boot on the valve operating rod.
2. Position the two mounting brackets on the end plate, and install on retaining nuts.
3. Connect the lever assembly to the lower end of the mounting brackets with its pivot pin. Then

Midland Vacuum Booster (© Ford Motor Co)

install the spring washer and retaining clip.

4. Connect the valve operating rod to the upper end of the lever with its pivot pin, washer, and retaining clip.

5. Install the vacuum check valve, the vacuum manifold, the two gaskets, and the mounting bolt. Torque the mounting bolt to 8-10 ft lbs.

Midland Diaphragm Type Frame Mounted

The Midland frame mounted booster is a remote type, without mechanical operation, utilizing vacuum to boost the hydraulic pressure between master and wheel cylinder.

Removal

1. Remove all hydraulic lines from the booster unit hydraulic cylinder.

2. Remove all vacuum lines from the booster unit and remove the support bracket bolts.

3. Remove the unit from the vehicle and place on a clean work bench.

Disassembly

1. Remove the control tube from the control valve body and the rear body.

2. Scribe marks across the diaphragm body and across the flanges of the slave cylinder body and the control valve body.

3. Remove the body clamp carefully, and remove the rear body and diaphragm with the return spring.

4. Remove the push rod, spring retainer and collar from the return spring.

5. Scribe a line across the valve body cover and the valve body, and remove the valve body cover and gasket.

6. Remove the valve body, spring, and the piston and diaphragm assembly from the slave cylinder.

7. From the end of the slave cylinder remove the end plug, copper gasket, spring, spring seat and spring retainer.

8. Remove the piston cup and piston assembly from the cylinder. NOTE: If the assembly does not fall free from the cylinder it may be pushed out by inserting the push rod through the bushing.

9. From the hydraulic piston remove the check valve, check valve retainer and the return spring.

10. Hold the cylinder in a soft jawed vise and remove the push rod bushing, lockwasher and front body.

11. Remove the gasket, rubber seal and transfer bushing from the slave cylinder body. From the bushing remove the two push rod bushing snap rings, and remove the washer and two seals. From the outside of the push rod bushing remove the O-ring seal.

12. From the lower end of the control valve piston remove the seal, also remove the seal from the piston boss.

13. Remove the retaining nut from the piston boss and remove the diaphragm plate and control valve diaphragm.

14. Remove the screw, lockwasher, spacer, spring, disc., and the seal from the control valve body.

Assembly

1. Install new spring in the control valve body and assemble the spring and spacer in the valve body. Secure with the screw and locknut.

2. Secure the control valve diaphragm and plate in place with the attaching nut.

3. On the control valve piston install the piston seal.

4. In the hydraulic piston install the check valve spring, check valve and retainer, making sure that the valve floats free in the bore and does not bind.

5. On the front end of the slave cylinder body, install the transfer bushing, seal and gasket.

6. In the push rod bushing install the push rod seals, washer and snap rings. NOTE: Install the push rod seals with the open end of the seal towards the slave cylinder body.

Install the lockwasher over the end of the rod bushing and install the bushing seal.

7. With the slave cylinder mounted in a vise, position the front body over the end of the cylinder, inserting the transfer bushing in the front body.

8. Thread push rod bushing in place and tighten securely, making sure the front body seats squarely on the slave cylinder body.

9. Coat the piston bore of the slave cylinder with brake fluid, also the hydraulic piston, seals, spring retainer and spring.

10. With the recessed end towards the push rod bushing, install the hydraulic piston in the slave cylinder bore. On top of the piston, install the piston cup, large spring retainer and spring. Install the spring seat in the spring coils.

11. Install a new copper gasket on the end plug and screw the plug into the cylinder tightening securely.

12. Dip the control valve piston and diaphragm in brake fluid and position the control valve spring on the diaphragm, making sure that the small end of the spring is over the piston boss.

13. With the control valve body positioned over the spring, and with the scribe marks aligned, secure the valve body to the slave cylinder with the four attaching bolts.

14. Install a new gasket on the valve body cover and secure the cover to the valve body with the four attaching bolts.

15. Install the collar over the threaded end of the push rod and position the retainer on the spring. Insert the rod and collar through the coils of the spring and the retainer. Install the diaphragm over the threaded end of the push rod and secure in place with the push rod nut. Coat the push rod with brake fluid.

16. Install the return spring assembly over the push rod bushing.

17. Install the rear body on the diaphragm aligning the scribe marks on the front and rear shells. Making sure that the bead of the diaphragm is properly placed between the body halves, compress the return spring and install and tighten the ring clamp band.

18. Install the by-pass tube and install the unit on the vehicle.

19. Check the unit for vacuum leaks and road test the vehicle for proper operation of the unit.

NOTE: Bleed all air from the hydraulic cylinder and lines before road testing the vehicle.

Kelsey-Hayes Diaphragm Type

Identification

The Kelsey-Hayes power brake unit can be identified by the twistlock method of locking the housing and cover together, plus the white-colored vacuum check valve assembly.

Removal

1. With engine off, apply brakes several times to equalize internal brake pressure.

2. Disconnect hydraulic line from master cylinder.

3. Disconnect vacuum hose from power brake check valve.

4. Disconnect power brake from brake pedal (under instrument panel).

5. Disconnect power brake unit from dash panel.

6. Remove power brake and master cylinder assembly from the vehicle.

Disassembly

1. Separate master cylinder from power brake unit.

2. Remove master cylinder pushrod and air cleaner plate.

Power piston assembly (© G.M. Corp.)

Power brake unit (© G.M. Corp.)

3. Mount the power unit in a vise with the master cylinder attaching-studs up.
4. Scribe an index line across the housing and cover for reassembly reference.
5. Pry out the housing lock. Do not damage the lock, as it must be used at assembly.
6. Remove check valve from cover by prying out of rubber grommet.
7. Place parking brake flange holding tool over the master cylinder mounting studs.
8. Rotate the tool and cover in a counterclockwise direction. Then, separate the cover from the housing. This will expose the power piston return spring and diaphragm.
9. Lift out the power piston return spring. Remove the brake unit from the vise.
10. Remove power piston by slowly lifting the piston straight up.
11. Remove air cleaner, guide seal and seal retainer from the cover.
12. Remove the block seal from the center hole of the housing, using a blunt drift. (Don't scratch the bore of the housing, it could cause a vacuum leak.)

Power Piston Disassembly

1. Remove power piston diaphragm from the power piston. Keep it clean.
2. Remove screws that attach the plastic guide to the power piston. Remove guide and place to one side.
3. Remove the power piston square seal ring, reaction ring insert,

reaction ring and reaction plate.
4. Depress operating rod slightly, then remove the Truarc snapring.
5. Remove control piston by pulling the operating rod.
6. Remove the O-ring seal from the end of the control piston.
7. Remove the filter elements and dust felt from the control piston rod.

Cleaning and Inspection

Thoroughly wash all metal parts in a suitable solvent and dry with compressed air. The power diaphragm, plastic power piston and guide should be washed in a mild soap and water solution. Blow dust and all cleaning material out of internal passages. All rubber parts should be replaced, regardless of condition. Install new air filters at assembly. Inspect all parts for scoring, pits, dents or nicks. Small imperfections can be smoothed out with crocus cloth. Replace all badly damaged parts.

Assembly

When assembling, be sure that all rubber parts, except the diaphragm and the reaction ring are lubricated with silicone grease.
1. Install control piston O-ring onto the piston.
2. Lubricate and install the control piston into the power piston. Install the Truarc snap-ring into its groove. Wipe all lubricant off the end of the control piston.
3. Install air filter elements and felt seal over the pushrod and down past the retaining shoulder on the rod. Install the power pis-

ton square seal ring into its groove.
4. Install the reaction plate in the power piston. Align the three holes with those in the power piston.
5. Install the rubber reaction ring in the reaction plate. Do not lubricate this ring.
6. Lubricate outer diameter of the reacton insert and install in the reaction ring.
7. Install reaction insert bumper into the guide.
8. Place guide on the power piston, align the holes with the aligning points on the power piston. Install retaining screws and torque to 80-100 in. lbs.
9. Install diaphragm on power piston; be sure that the diaphragm is correctly seated in the power piston groove.
10. With the housing blocked to prevent damage, install the block seal in the housing.
11. Install a new cover seal on the retainer and lubricate thoroughly, inside and out, with silicone grease, then install in the cover bore. Install new air filter.
12. Lubricate check valve grommet and install the vacuum check valve.
13. Mount the power unit in a vise, with master cylinder attaching studs up.
14. Apply a light coating of silicone grease to the bead, *outer edge only*, of the power piston diaphragm.
15. Install the power piston assembly in the housing with the operating rod down.
16. Install the power piston return spring into the flange of the guide.
17. Place the cover over the return spring and press down on the cover. At the same time, pilot the guide through the seal.
18. Rotate the cover to lock it to the housing. Be sure the scribe lines are in correct index and that the diaphragm is not pinched during assembly.
19. Install the housing lock on one of the long tangs of the housing.
20. Remove the power unit from the vise.
21. Install the master cylinder pushrod and air cleaner plate, then install the master cylinder on the studs. Install attaching nuts and washers. Torque to 200 in. lbs.

Installation

1. Install firewall to power brake seal.
2. Install power brake unit onto firewall and torque the attaching nuts to 200 in. lbs.

3. Install pushrod to brake pedal attaching bolt. Torque to 30 ft. lbs.

4. Install vacuum hose onto the power brake unit.

5. Attach the hydraulic tube and fill the master cylinder. Bleed hydraulic system.

6. Adjust stop-light switch if necessary.

Floating Caliper Disc Brakes

Dual Piston

This disc brake is a floating caliper design with two pistons on one side of the rotor. It is a two piece unit consisting of the caliper and cylinder housing. The caliper is mounted to the anchor plate on two mounting pins which travel in bushings in the anchor plate. The bushings and pins are protected by boot type seals.

Two brake shoe and lining assemblies are used in each caliper, one on each side of the rotor. The shoes are identical and are attached to the caliper with two mounting pins.

The cylinder housing contains the two pistons. The pistons are fitted with an insulator on the front and a seal on the back lip. A friction ring is attached to the back of the piston with a shouldered cap screw. The pistons and cylinder bores are protected by boot seals which are fitted to a groove in the piston and attached to the cylinder housing with retainers. The cylinder assembly is attached to the caliper with two cap screws and washers.

The anchor plate is bolted directly to the spindle. It positions the caliper assembly over the rotor forward of the spindle.

Floating caliper disc brake (© Ford Motor Co.)

Disc Brake Shoe Adjustment

The front disc brake assembly is designed so that it is inherently self-adjusting and requires no manual adjustment.

Automatic adjustment for lining wear is achieved by the piston and friction ring sliding outward in the cylinder bore. The piston assumes a new position in the cylinder and maintains the correct adjustment.

Front Disc Brake Shoe and Lining

Replace shoe and lining assemblies when lining is worn to a minimum of 1/16″ in thickness (combined thickness of shoe and lining 1/4″ minimum).

Removal

1. Remove the shoe and lining mounting pins, anti-rattle springs and old shoe and lining assemblies.

Installation

1. Remove the master cylinder cover.

2. Loosen the piston housing-to-caliper mounting bolts sufficiently to permit the installation of new shoe and lining assemblies. *Do not move pistons.*

3. Install new shoe and lining assemblies. Install the brake shoe mounting pins and anti-rattle springs. *Be sure that the spring tangs are located in the holes provided in the shoe plates.*

4. Torque the brake shoe mounting pins to 17-23 ft lbs.

5. Reset the pistons to the correct location in the cylinders by placing shims or feeler gauges of .023 to .035″ thickness between the shoe plate of the outboard shoe and lining assembly and the caliper; then, retighten the piston housing-to-caliper mounting bolts. *Keep the cylinder housing square with the caliper.*

6. Loosen the piston housing-to-caliper mounting bolts and remove the shims.

7. Torque the piston housing-to-caliper mounting bolts to 155 to 185 ft lbs.

8. Check the master cylinder reservoirs.

9. Install the master cylinder cover.

Front disc brake disassembled (© Ford Motor Co.)

Disc Brake Caliper

Removal

1. Remove the wheel and tire assembly.
2. Remove the pins and nuts retaining the caliper assembly to the anchor plate.
3. Disconnect the brake hose from the caliper and remove the caliper.

Installation

1. Connect the brake hose to the caliper.
2. Position the caliper assembly to the anchor plate and install the retaining pins and nuts. Torque the nuts to specifications.
3. Install drum and wheel and bleed brake system.

If the caliper assembly is leaking, the piston assemblies must be removed from the piston housing and replaced. If the cylinder bores are scored, corroded or excessive wear is evident, the piston housing must be replaced. *Do not hone the cylinder bores.* Piston assemblies are not available for oversize bores. The piston housing must be removed from the caliper for replacement.

Disassembly

1. Remove the two pins and nuts retaining the caliper to the support. Disconnect the flexible brake hose and plug the end to prevent brake fluid leakage.
2. Remove the boot retainers and remove the dust boots from the pistons and cylinder housing.
3. Position the caliper assembly in a vise.
4. Place a block of wood between the caliper and the cylinders, and apply low pressure air to the brake hose inlet. One piston will be forced out.
5. Reverse the piston and install it by hand pressure back into the cylinder bore far enough to form a seal. Block the reversed piston from moving out of the bore and place the wooden block between the remaining piston and the caliper.
6. Force out the second piston with low pressure air. *Care should be taken as the piston is forced out of the bore.*
7. Remove the two bolts and separate the caliper from the cylinder housing.

Assembly

The piston assembly and dust boots are not to be reused. A new set is to be used each time the caliper is assembled.

1. Apply a film of clean brake fluid in the cylinder bores and on the piston assemblies. *Do not apply brake fluid on the insulators.*
2. Start the piston assemblies into the cylinder bores using firm

Bolt Mounted Caliper (© Chevrolet Div. GM Corp)

hand pressure. *Exercise care to avoid cocking the piston in the bore.*

3. Lightly tapping with a rawhide mallet, seat each piston assembly until the friction ring bottoms out in the cylinder bore.
4. Install the piston dust boots and retainers.
5. Position the piston housing on the caliper and install the piston housing-to-caliper mounting bolts and washers. Torque the piston housing-to-caliper mounting bolts to 155 to 185 ft lbs.
6. Install the flexible brake hose.
7. Bleed the brake system and centralize the pressure differential valve.

Do not move the vehicle after working on the disc brakes until a firm brake pedal is obtained.

Sliding Caliper Disc Brakes

Single Piston

This caliper is a one piece type with a single piston on the inboard side. The piston is made of steel and is plated to resist wear and corrosion. The piston has a square cut seal which provides for a seal between the piston and the caliper cylinder wall. A rubber dust boot located in a groove in the cylinder helps keep contamination from the piston and cylinder wall.

The caliper is mounted on an adapter which is mounted on the steering knuckle.

Disc Brake Adjustment

No adjustment is required on this unit other than applying the pedal several times after the unit has been worked on. This is to seat the shoes and after this is done the hydraulic

pressure maintains the proper clearance between the brake shoes and the rotor.

Brake Shoe Removal

Replace the brake shoes when the linings are worn within 1/32″ of the shoe or the rivets.

Removal

1. Remove the master cylinder cover and if the cylinder is more than 1/3 full remove the fluid necessary to make the cylinder only 1/3 full. This is done to prevent any overflow from the cylinder when the piston is pushed into the bore of the caliper.
2. Raise vehicle on hoise and remove the front wheels.
3. Compress the piston back into the bore by using a large C-clamp and compressing the unit until the piston bottoms in the bore.
4. Remove the two retaining bolts that hold the caliper into the support. If the caliper has retaining clips remove the retaining clips and anti-rattle springs. If the caliper has key type retainers, remove the key retaining screws, and using a hammer and drift, punch drive the key out of the caliper.
5. Slide the caliper off the rotor disc. Be careful not to damage the dust boot on the piston when removing the caliper. NOTE: Do not let the caliper hang with the brake hose supporting the weight. This can cause damage to the hose which could result in a loss of brakes. Set the caliper on the front suspension arm or tie rod.
6. Remove the outer shoe from the caliper. It may be necessary to tap the shoe to loosen it from the

caliper. Remove the inner shoe from the caliper or spindle assembly depending on where the shoe stays.

7. Remove the shoe support spring from the piston.

Cleaning and Inspection

Clean the sliding surfaces of the caliper and clean any dirt from the mounting bolts, clips or keys.

Inspect the boot on the piston for signs of cracks, cuts or other damage. Check to see if there is signs of fluid leaking around the seal on the piston. This will show up in the boot. If there is an indication of a fluid leak, the entire caliper has to be disassembled and the seal replaced.

Installation

1. Make sure that the piston is fully bottomed in the cylinder bore and install the outboard shoe in the recess of the caliper. NOTE: On shoes with anti-rattle springs be sure to install the spring before installing the shoe in the caliper.
2. Place the outer shoe on the caliper and press it into place with finger pressure.
3. Position the caliper on the rotor and carefully slide it down into position over the rotor.
4. Install the caliper mounting bolts and torque them to 35 ft lbs. On models with retaining clips install the anti-rattle springs and the retaining clips and torque the retaining screws to 200 in lbs. On models with key type retainers press down the caliper and install the key in its slot and drive it in place with a hammer and drift. Install the retaining screw and torque to 12-18 ft lbs.
5. Install the wheels and lower the vehicle. Check the master cylinder fluid level and add any fluid necessary to bring it up to the proper level.
6. Pump the brake pedal several times until a firm brake pedal is established. Road test the vehicle to check for proper operation.

Disc Caliper

Removal

1. Remove the cover on the master cylinder and check if the fluid level is 1/3 full. If it is more than 1/3 full remove the necessary amount to bring the level down. This step is necessary to avoid overflow from the master cylinder when the piston is compressed into the cylinder bore.
2. Raise the vehicle and remove the wheel.
3. Compress the piston into the caliper bore and remove the brake

hose from the caliper. Tape the end of the hose to prevent dirt from entering the line.
4. Remove the caliper retaining bolts, clips or wedges and remove the caliper from the vehicle.

Disassembly

1. Clean the outside of the caliper with clean brake fluid and drain any fluid from the caliper.
2. Remove the piston from the caliper by connecting the hydraulic line to the caliper and gently stroking the brake pedal. This will push the piston from the caliper bore.
3. With care remove the boot from the caliper piston bore.
4. Remove the piston seal from the caliper bore using a piece of wood or plastic. NOTE: DO NOT use a metal tool to remove the seal. This can damage the bore or burr the edges of the seal groove.
5. Remove the bleeder valve.

Cleaning and Inspection

1. Clean all the parts with clean brake fluid and blow out all the passages in the caliper. NOTE: When ever the caliper is disassembled discard the boot and piston seal. These parts must not be reused.
2. Inspect the outside of the piston for signs of wear, corrosion,

scores or any other defects. If any defects are detected replace the piston.
3. Check the caliper bore for the same defects as the piston. However, the bore can be cleaned up to a point with crocus cloth. If there are any marks that will not clean up with the cloth the caliper must be replaced.

Assembly and Installation

1. Lube the caliper bore and the piston with clean brake fluid and position the seal for the piston in the cylinder bore groove.
2. Install the dust boot into the groove in the piston with the fold faces toward the open end of the piston.
3. Install the piston in the bore being careful not to unseat the piston seal in the bore.
4. With the piston bottomed in the cylinder position the boot in the groove in the caliper. Make sure that the retaining ring in the seal is pressed down evenly around the cylinder.
5. Install the bleeder screw in the caliper and install the caliper back on the vehicle.
6. Connect the brake hoses and bleed the calipers of air. When bleeding is done pump the pedal several times to develop a firm brake pedal.

Caliper Assembly Retaining Clip Type (© Chrysler Corp)

Disc Brake Caliper Retainer Key Type (© Ford Motor Co)

AIR BRAKES TROUBLE DIAGNOSIS

Condition	Possible Cause	Correction
Insufficient brakes	1. Brakes need adjusting. 2. Low air pressure (below 80 pounds). 3. Brake valve delivery pressure below normal.	1. Adjust brakes. 2. Inspect air compressor and inspect all fittings and lines for leaks. 3. Inspect air compressor and repair or replace.
Brakes apply too slowly	1. Brakes need adjusting or lubricating. 2. Low air pressure (below 80 pounds). 3. Brake valve delivery pressure below normal. 4. Excessive leakage with brakes applied. 5. Restricted tubing or hose.	1. Adjust brakes and lubricate brake anchors and brake support platforms. 2. Inspect compressor and air lines, repair as necessary. 3. Inspect pressure and air lines, repair as necessary. 4. Inspect all lines and fittings and repair as necessary. 5. Clean or replace tubing or hose.
Brakes no not apply	1. No air pressure in brake system. 2. Restricted or broken tubing or hose. 3. Defective brake valve.	1. Inspect air compressor and drive belt. 2. Clean out air system or replace broken hose. 3. Replace brake valve.
Brakes do not release	1. Brake shoes binding. 2. Brake valve not in fully released position. 3. Defective brake valve. 4. Restriction in air lines or hose.	1. Clean and lubricate all brake shoe anchors. 2. Align and adjust valve. 3. Replace brake valve. 4. Clean out all air lines or hoses.
Air pressure will not raise to normal	1. Defective air gauge (registering incorrectly.) 2. Excessive leakage. 3. Air reservoir drain cock open. 4. Governor out of adjustment. 5. No clearance at compressor. 6. Slipping compressor drive belt. 7. Defective or worn compressor.	1. Replace the air gauge. 2. Inspect all joints with soapy water and correct as necessary. 3. Close reservoir drain cock. 4. Inspect and adjust governor. 5. Check and adjust compressor unloading valves. 6. Adjust compressor drive belt. 7. Replace air compressor.
Air pressure raises slowly to normal	1. Excessive leakage. 2. Clogged compressor air filter. 3. No clearance at compressor unloading valves. 4. Compressor discharge valves caking. 5. Slipping compressor drive belt. 6. Worn compressor. 7. Excessive carbon in compressor cylinder head or discharge line.	1. Inspect all lines and fittings, then repair as necessary. 2. Clean and air dry the compressor air filter. 3. Clean, reseat and adjust the compressor valves. 4. Clean the carbon and reseat the valves. 5. Tighten or replace the compressor drive belt. 6. Replace the air compressor. 7. Clean the carbon and reseat the valves.
Air pressure rises above normal	1. Defective air gauge (registering incorrectly). 2. Governor out of adjustment. 3. Defective governor. 4. Restriction in the line between governor and the compressor. 5. Too much clearance at compressor unloader valves. 6. Excessive carbon in compressor cylinder head. 7. Compressor unloader valves stuck closed.	1. Replace the air gauge. 2. Clean and adjust governor. 3. Replace governor. 4. Clean all air lines and recheck fittings for leaks. 5. Adjust unloader valves. 6. Clean the carbon and reseat the valves. 7. Clean and seat the valves.
Air pressure drops quickly with the engine stopped and brakes released	1. Leaking brake valve. 2. Leaking air brake line or hose. 3. Compressor discharge valves leaking. 4. Governor leaking. 5. Excessive leakage in any part of the air brake system.	1. Clean, reseat or replace the brake valve. 2. Test all air brake joints with soap suds and repair as necessary. 3. Reseat or replace the discharge valve. 4. Reseat or replace the governor. 5. Test the air brake joints with soap suds and repair as necessary.
Air pressure drops quickly with engine stopped and brakes fully applied	1. Brake chamber diaphragm leaking. 2. Brake valve leaking. 3. Leakage elsewhere in the system.	1. Recondition or replace the brake booster. 2. Rebuild or replace the brake valve. 3. Repair as necessary.
Compressor knock	1. Drive pulley loose. 2. Back lash in drive gears or drive coupling. 3. Bearings worn or burned out. 4. Excessive carbon in compressor cylinder head.	1. Tighten pulley nut, or install a new pulley if inner diameter of the hub is worn. 2. If drive gears or coupling show back lash replace as necessary. 3. Replace compressor. 4. Clean carbon from cylinder head.

AIR BRAKES TROUBLE DIAGNOSIS

Condition	Possible Cause	Correction
Safety valve blows off	1. Safety valve out of adjustment.	1. Adjust safety valve. Turn adjusting screw clockwise to raise blow-off pressure and counterclockwise to lower blow-off pressure. Adjust blow-off pressure to 150 pounds.
	2. Pressure in air system above normal.	2. Refer to "Air Pressure Rises Above Normal."
	3. Governor out of adjustment.	3. Adjust governor to maintain pressure at 80 to 85 pounds and compression at 100 to 150 pounds.
Excessive oil or water in air brake system	1. Reservoir too full of oil or water.	1. Drain reservoir more frequently.
	2. Compressor passing excessive amount of oil.	2. If condition exists, compressor is worn. Replace the compressor.
	3. Compressor air strainer is dirty.	3. Wash air cleaner in mineral spirits and dry with compressed air.

Air Brakes

Air Supply System

The air supply system is used with the full air brake system. In the full air system, air pressure is applied directly to the shoes through a diaphragm and mechanical linkage.

If the brake system is not operating properly, the air supply system should be checked first.

Operating Tests

Before performing any of the following tests, operate the engine until the air pressure builds up to 90 psi. With the air brake system charged, open the drain cocks in each reservoir. Close the drain cocks after all moisture is drained from the reservoirs. Some models have automatic moisture ejector valves and do not require manual draining.

Low Pressure Indicator

Exhaust the brake system pressure and observe the pressure at which the warning buzzer sounds. The contacts in the indicator should close the circuit to the buzzer, when reservoir pressure is between 58 psi minimum and 65 psi maximum. If the buzzer does not start to sound within this pressure range during discharge, or if a sounding buzzer does not stop within this pressure range during the pressure buildup, the electrical connections are loose or the indicator valve is not operating properly.

Reservoir Safety Valve

To determine if the safety valve is operative, pull the exposed end of the valve stem. If the safety valve does not blow off when the stem is pulled, the valve ball is probably stuck in its seat. In such a case, remove and disassemble the valve for cleaning.

Automatic Moisture Ejector Valve

With the system charged, make several foot valve applications and note each time an application is made if an exhaust of air occurs at the exhaust port of drain valve. If no air comes out, push the wire stem. If no air comes out, the filter is plugged and the valve should be removed and cleaned.

NOTE: Because the automatic moisture ejector valve functions as reservoir pressure is reduced, excessive leakage in the system will cause constant exhausting of the valve.

Governor

With the engine running, build up air pressure in the system, and observe at what pressure reading on the dash gauge the pressure stops climbing. This is the point of governor cutout which should be between 118 and 125 lbs.

With the engine still running, slowly reduce the air pressure in the sytem by applying and releasing the brakes. Observe the pressure reading on the dash gauge at the point where the pressure starts to build up again. This is the point of governor cut-in which should be between 98 and 104 lbs.

If the governor does not cut the compressor in and out according to these specifications, adjust the governor pressure settings. Before adjusting the governor, check the accuracy of the dash gauge with a test gauge.

Check Pressure Build-Up

With the engine running at fast idle speed, observe the time required to raise system pressure from 50 to 90 lbs. If more than five minutes is required, perform the leak tests as outlined in the following paragraphs.

Also check for low engine idle speed, a slipping comperssor drive belt, excessive carbon in the compressor cylinder head, or a worn out air compressor.

Check Stop Light Switch

With all air pressure exhausted from the air brake system, start the engine and move the brake valve to the applied position. Stop lights should light before the dash gauge registers 5 psi. Release the brakes.

Quick Release Valve and Relay Valve

With the air brake system fully charged, apply the brakes. Inspect the brake action on the wheels controlled by the quick release valve or relay valve in question. The brakes should apply promptly. Release the brakes and inspect to be sure that the air pressure is exhausted rapidly from the exhaust port. Be sure the exhaust port is not restricted.

Leak Tests

With the engine stopped and the brakes fully applied, watch the rate of drop in air pressure as registered by the dash gauge. With the engine stopped and the reservoirs charged to the governor cutout pressure (118-125 psi), the rate of drop should not exceed 2 psi per minute. The rate of drop should also not exceed 3 psi per minute after the initial drop with brakes fully applied. If the pressure drops faster than specified, check the items outlined in the following paragraphs.

Compressor

With the engine stopped, discharge valve leakage can be detected by carefully listening at the compressor for the sound of escaping air. With air pressure applied to the unloader cavity (with governor cut-off), remove the air filter or the air pick up tube and check for air leaks by squirting oil around the unloader plunger and stem. If excessive air leaks are found, replace the unloader mechanism.

Governor

With the governor in the cutout position, test for leakage at the exhaust valve by applying soap suds to the exhaust vent in the body.

With the governor in the cut-in position, test for leakage of the inlet valve by applying soap suds to the exhaust vent in the body.

In either of the foregoing tests, leakage in excess of 1" soap bubble in three seconds indicates the governor should be replaced.

Reservoir Safety Valve

Coat the end of the safety valve

with soap suds. Leaks causing not more than a 3" soap bubble in three seconds are permissable.

Automatic Moisture Ejector Valve

With the system charged and pressure stabilized in the system, there should be no leaks at the drain valve exhaust. A constant slight exhaust of air at the drain valve exhaust could be caused by excessive leakage in the air brake system.

Brake Control Valve

With the pedal fully released, coat the exhaust port with soap suds to check for leaks. With the pedal fully applied, coat the exhaust port with soap suds and check for leaks. Leaks

causing not more than a three" soap bubble in three seconds are permissable.

Brake Chambers

With the brakes fully applied, coat the clamp ring and bolt flanges holding the diaphragm in place with soap suds. No leaks are permissable.

Quick Release Valve

With brakes applied, coat the exhaust port with soap suds to detect leakage. Leakage in excess of a 3" soap bubble in three seconds is not permissible.

Relay Valve

With the brakes *released*, coat the exhause port with soap suds and observe the leakage.

With the brakes fully *applied*, coat the exhaust port with soap suds and observe the leakage.

Leakage in either of the foregoing tests should not exceed a 3" soap bubble in three seconds.

Air Brakes
Rockwell Wedge Type

Service Air Chamber Removal

NOTE: Exhaust all air pressure from the system before attempting repair work.
1. Disconnect the air inlet line.
2. Using a drift and a light hammer, loosen the spanner nut.

Rockwell double wedge brake—disassembled view—typical (© Ford Motor Co.)

3. Unscrew the service chamber assembly from the wedge housing.

Installation

1. Check position of the wedge in plunger housing to make certain wedge assembly is properly seated. Be sure to replace automatic adjusting identification ring on service chamber tube. Thread spanner nut onto power unit tube.
2. Screw the service chamber into the plunger housing until it bottoms (spanner nut loose).
3. Align connection ports with brake lines, if necessary, by unscrewing service chamber not more than one full turn.
4. Connect brake lines.
5. Make the hold a full pressure brake application. Drive spanner nut with a drift and hammer until it is tight against the plunger housing. Release the brake pressure.
6. Check for leaks at all connections.

Brake Shoe Removal

1. Remove the wheel, hub, and drum assembly. *If equipped with Fail-Safe units, be sure that the brakes are released (actuating spring compressed by turning the release bolt approximately 18 to 21 turns clockwise.) Do not force.*

Rockwell single wedge brake—disassembled (© Ford Motor Co.)

Bendix wedge brake—disassembled view (© Ford Motor Co.)

2. Remove the brake shoe retracting springs.
3. Remove the shoe hold-down springs on single wedge brakes.
4. Remove the shoes.

Installation

1. Clean, inspect and lubricate the brake actuator and adjuster assemblies.
2. Apply a film of high temperature grease at all shoe contact points.
3. Mount the ends of the brake shoes in the grooves in the actuating plungers. When installing shoes on double wedge brake assemblies, make certain that the end, marked is mounted on a plunger having an adjusting or star wheel. Install the shoe hold-down springs on single wedge brakes.
4. Install new shoe retracting springs.
5. Install the wheel, hub, and drum assembly. *If equipped with Fail-Safe Units, turn the release bolt counterclockwise until the stop is reached (approximately 18 to 21 turns) to release the manual compression of the actuating spring. Do not force the release bolt.*

Wedge Brake Adjustment

The wedge type air brakes are self adjusting.

A preliminary adjustment can be made by rotating the wheels forward and applying air to the brake chambers 25 or 30 times.

Bendix Wedge Type

Service Air Chamber Removal

NOTE: Exhaust all air pressure from the system before attempting repair work.
1. Disconnect the air inlet line.
2. Using a drift and a light hammer, loosen the locknut.
3. Unscrew the service chamber assembly from the wedge housing.

Installation

1. Insert the service chamber assembly into the wedge housing making sure that the wedge shaft mates with the piston or diaphragm shaft seat.
2. Screw the service chamber assembly into the wedge housing until it bottoms, then back out less than one turn to align the unit with the air inlet line.
3. Tighten the locknut, using a drift and hammer.
4. Connect the air inlet line and restore system air pressure. Check for operation.

Brake Shoe Removal

All brake shoes front and rear, are constructed with an adjusting end

and an anchor end. When installing the shoes, make certain that the end marked ADJ. END is mounted correctly in the adjusting plunger link. To remove the brake shoes, follow this procedure:
1. Unhook the two shoe-to-shoe springs.
2. Remove the brake shoes.

Installation

1. Coat the shoe slots in the anchoring plungers with Lubriplate.
2. Clean the shoe guide bosses and the steady rests on the torque spider and coat the rubbing surfaces Lubriplate.
3. Position the shoes in the steady rests and install the shoe-to-shoe springs. On rear brakes, be sure the end of the shoe marked ADJ. END is engaged in the link at the adjuster plunger.
4. Install drum and hub, wheel and tire.
5. Apply the brakes several times before moving the truck, to assure proper seating and adjustment of the brake shoes.

Cam Type Air Brakes

Slack Adjuster Adjustment

Apply the brakes and measure the travel of the brake chamber push rod. If equipped with a Maxi-brake unit, the minimum air pressure should be 90 psi while measuring the travel. The travel should be kept to the minimum possible without causing the brakes to drag. *Adjustment of the yoke on the brake chamber push rod should not be changed.*

When new, the yoke is adjusted so that the slack adjuster brake chamber push rod angle is slightly greater than 90 degrees when the brakes are applied. Brake lining wear will not change this angle as long as the slack adjusters are kept adjusted to compensate for lining wear.

Front

This procedure applies only to trucks equipped with S-cam operated brakes.

A push rod travel, that reaches or exceeds the maximum indicates need of adjustment. Turn the adjusting screw clockwise until the push rod travels ¾" in going from released to fully applied position. When making the adjustment, turn the screw in quarter turns.

Rear

This procedure applies to vehicles equipped with either standard or Maxi-brake S-cam type slack adjusters.

A push rod travel, that reaches or exceeds the maximum indicates need of adjustment. Depress the lock sleeve and turn the hexagon head of the wormshaft clockwise until the push rod travels one inch in going from released to fully applied position. Be sure that the lock sleeve comes back out and engages the hexagon head of the wormshaft sa as to lock the adjustment.

When adjusting either front or rear slack adjusters, raise the wheels and make certain that there is no brake drag.

Front non-servo Bendix wedge brake (© Ford Motor Co.)

Service Air Chamber Removal

1. Release all air from the system, then disconnect the air line at the brake chamber.
2. Disconnect the push rod clevis from the slack adjuster.
3. Remove the attaching nuts and the brake chamber assembly.

Installation

1. Position the brake chamber assembly on the mounting bracket and install the attaching nuts.
2. Install the clevis and cotter pin.
3. Connect the air line to the brake chamber and build up air pressure.
4. Adjust the brakes.

Slack Adjuster Removal

1. Remove the clevis pin attaching the slack adjuster to the brake chamber push rod.
2. Remove the lock ring (front) or cotter pin (rear) attaching the slack adjuster to the camshaft.
3. Mark the position of the slack adjuster on the camshaft, then slide the slack adjuster off the shaft.

Installation

1. Place the slack adjuster on the camshaft, aligning the locating marks. Excessive front camshaft end play may be remedied by installing an additional spacer at the cam end of the camshaft. Install the lock ring or the cotter pin.
2. Connect the brake chamber push rod to the slack adjuster by installing the clevis pin in the upper hole, and install the cotter pin.
3. Lubricate the slack adjuster, and adjust the brakes.

Front Brake Shoe and Camshaft

Removal

1. Remove the brake shoe retracting spring from the brake shoes and the C-washer from each anchor pin.
2. Remove the four brake shoe retaining clips, then slide the brake shoes off the anchor pin.
3. Mark the position of the slack adjuster on the camshaft housing.
4. Disconnect the brake chamber clevis, and remove the slack adjuster from the camshaft.
5. Pull the camshaft out of the camshaft housing.

Installation

1. Install the camshaft in the camshaft housing.
2. Slide the brake shoes on the anchor pins, and install a new C-washer on each anchor pin.

Typical front brake assembly–S-Cam Type © Ford Motor Co.)

Tighten the anchor pin lock nuts. Install the brake shoe hold down clips.
3. Install the brake shoe retracting spring.
4. Install the slack adjuster on the camshaft, lining up the marks. Install the camshaft snap ring.
5. Connect the brake chamber push rod clevis to the slack adjuster by installing the pin in the upper hole of the slack adjuster.
6. Install the hub and drum and wheel.

Rear Brake Shoe and Camshaft—Eaton Type

Removal

1. Remove the axle shaft, wheels, and hub and drum assembly.
2. Remove the retracting springs and anchor springs, then remove the brake shoes and cam roller assemblies.
3. Mark the position of the slack adjuster on the camshaft, then remove the slack adjuster.
4. Remove the camshaft from the backing plate.

Installation

1. Insert the camshaft through the backing plate and into the camshaft housing.
2. Install the brake chamber and bracket assembly.
3. Install the slack adjuster on the camshaft, aligning the locating marks, and install the cotter pin.
4. Lubricate the camshaft, rollers, and pins with Lubriplate. Do not lubricate the cam face.
5. Position the cam rollers and pins in the brake shoes, then place the brake shoes in position on the anchor pin and cam.
6. Install the retracting springs and anchor springs.
7. Install the hub, wheels, and axle shaft.
8. Adjust the brakes and slack adjuster.

Brake Chambers

The brake chamber assembly is used at each wheel and converts the energy of compressed air into mechanical force and motion required to apply the brakes. There are two basic types of brake chambers, one is a standard chamber and the other incorporates an emergency back-up system on top of a service brake chamber.

The emergency system uses a large power spring to apply the brakes when the air pressure falls below a certain level. The spring mechanically applies the brakes.

In the following paragraphs are the repair procedures for several types of brake chambers. Take extreme caution in disassembling the units which have spring applied emergency systems. The power spring is very powerful and one can be severely injured if some of the repair steps are not followed carefully. On some of the chambers it is necessary to use a hydraulic press to help remove the power spring. If a press is not available DO NOT attempt to disassemble the unit.

Stop Master Brake Chambers

Removal

1. Drain all air from the system

Super "Fail-Safe" (© Chevrolet Div. GM Corp)

"Fail-Safe" Air Chamber (© Chevrolet Div. GM Corp)

and disconnect the air lines from the chamber.

2. Using a punch or small chisel, drive the tabs of the lockwasher from the notches in the spanner nut which secures the brake chamber to the spider housing.

3. Using a punch and hammer or a wrench, loosen the spanner nut and remove the brake chamber from the brake housing.

Disassembly

1. Remove the clamping ring nut and bolt.

2. Scribe a mark across the pressure and non-pressure housing to assure proper assembly of the unit.

3. Remove the diaphragm, plate rod, rubber boot and plastic guide from the housing.

Cleaning and Inspection

1. Clean all the metal parts with a good cleaning solvent and wipe dry with a cloth or blow dry with air. CAUTION: Do not use any solvent on the diaphragm.

2. Inspect the diaphragm for any sign of wear or deterioration and replace the diaphragm if necessary.

3. Examine all other parts for wear, cracks, obstructed passageways or dirt and replace parts as necessary.

Assembly

1. In the non-pressure housing, install the boot, rod, guide and diaphragm.

2. Align the scribe marks on the

pressure and non-pressure housings and secure the clamp ring in place with the nut and bolt.

3. Thread the chamber into the brake housing until it bottoms, then back the chamber out, not more than one turn, so the chamber ports are in line with the air lines. Lock the chamber in place by tightening the spanner nut and lock in place by staking the lockwasher tabs in place on the nut and housings.

4. Connect the air lines and check the unit for any air leaks.

Stop Master "Fail Safe" Brake Chambers
Removal and Disassembly

CAUTION: Before attempting to remove the brake chamber, block the

wheels securely because the parking brake will not be applied.

1. With the air pressure up to normal and the brake released, loosen the release bolt lock and set to one side. Compress the power spring by turning the release bolt clockwise as far as it will go. (Approx. 18 turns)

2. Drain the air from the system and disconnect the air lines from the brake chambers.

3. Scribe marks across the pressure and non-pressure housings and loosen the clamping ring. Slide the ring forward and hang on the non-pressure plate tube.

4. Remove the entire cap and spring assembly, pressure housing and diaphragm. The dia-

1 Clevis Assembly
2 Service Brake Housing
3 Service Brake Diaphragm Return Spring
4 Push Rod Assembly
5 Adapter-To-Service Brake Chamber Clamp
6 Service Brake Diaphragm
7 Push Rod Plate
8 Adapter
9 Parking, Brake Chamber-To-Adapter Clamp
10 Pressure Plate
11 Compression Spring
12 Parking Brake Chamber

(Serviced As One Assembly)

13 Release Stud Access Plug
14 Parking Brake Diaphragm
15 Adapter Push Rod
16 Parking Brake Diaphragm Return Spring
17 Release Stud Assembly
18 O-Ring
19 Nylok Screw

Anchorlok Brake Parts (© Ford Motor Co)

Power Spring Compressing Fixture
(© Chevrolet Div. GM Corp)

STUD, NUT, AND
WASHER STOWED
AT SIDE OF CHAMBER

STUD, NUT, AND
WASHER INSTALLED
(SPRING COMPRESSED)

Spring Compressing Assembly (© Chevrolet Div. GM Corp)

phragm plate rod and boot will stay in the non-pressure housing.

5. Hold the pressure housing in a soft jawed vise. NOTE: Do not tighten the vise to tightly for this could distort the housing.

6. Remove the washer and the O-ring seal from the pressure housing.

7. Remove the piston assembly from the cap by pulling the piston straight out from the cap. NOTE: Sometimes when the spring is fully compressed, it will cock slightly making it necessary to loosen the release bolt a few turns so the piston may be removed easily.

8. Rivets hold together the piston, retainer plate, seal and expander. If any part in this assembly is defective the entire assembly must be replaced. The parts in this assembly are not serviced separately.

9. The cap and spring assembly is also serviced as an assembly. If any part in this unit is defective, the entire unit must be replaced. NOTE: DO NOT attempt to disassemble the cap and spring assembly.

Cleaning and Inspection

1. Clean all metal parts with a good parts cleaner and wipe dry with a clean cloth or blow dry with air.

2. Inspect all parts for signs of wear, scratches, pitting, scores, deterioration, dirt or obstructions, and replace any parts as necessary. NOTE: Unless the cap and spring assembly is in bad condition, it should not be replaced. If replacement is necessary, see the procedure in step 9 of the removal section.

3. Discard the old O-ring seal and rubber washer in the housing.

Assembly

1. In the groove in the pressure housing, install a new O-ring seal.

2. Install the piston in the pressure housing.

3. At the bottom of the internal threads in the pressure housing install a new rubber washer. Thread the cap and spring assembly into the pressure housing and tighten securely.

4. Position the piston diaphragm over the plate rod in the non-pressure housing. Install the pressure housing over the assembly, aligning the scribe marks on the housings to ensure alignment of the air lines.

5. Install the clamping ring over the pressure and non-pressure housings and tighten with the nut and bolt.

6. Install the air lines and build up air pressure to the normal level. Push the parking brake knob in to allow air to enter the outer brake chamber.

7. Turn the release bolt counterclockwise as far as it will go to release the spring pressure.

8. Check for air leaks and road test the vehicle to check for proper operation of the unit.

Stop Master "Super Fail Safe" Brake Chambers

Removal and Disassembly

NOTE: Before attempting to remove the brake chamber, block the wheels firmly because the parking brake will not be applied when the chamber is removed.

1. With the air pressure up to a normal level, cage the power spring by turning the release bolt 18 to 21 turns clockwise. Do not force the bolt beyond the stop point.

2. Remove the clamp ring on the pressure and non-pressure housings and remove the pressure housings.

3. Release the foot set screw and

remove the foot from the piston.

4. Remove the piston seal from the back of the housing. Also remove the sealing compound found at the joint between the cap and housing.

5. Remove the lock ring from the housing and separate the cap and the spring piston assembly from the housing.

6. Remove the back-up rings and the O-ring seal from the housing groove.

7. Remove the snap ring and hex nut from the release bolt.

8. Secure the cap and the spring and piston assembly in a spring compressing fixture. NOTE: This fixture is necessary to hold the power spring compressed during disassembly. Without this device it is not possible to disassemble the unit safely. If one of these fixtures is not available or can not be made, DO NOT attempt to disassemble the unit any further. If a fixture is available procede with the following steps:

9. With the unit firmly secured in the compressing fixture, turn the release bolt until the square nut falls free.

10. Release pressure on the fixture until the spring is unloaded and remove the unit from the fixture.

11. Separate the spring and piston from the cap. Remove the back-up ring and O-ring seal from the piston.

12. Remove the two spring bearing washers and remove the "E" ring from the release bolt.

13. Remove the flat washer from the release bolt and remove the bolt from the cap.

14. Remove the O-ring seal and second flat washer from the release bolt.

Cleaning and Inspection

1. Clean and inspect all parts for signs of wear and deterioration.

2. Use clean solvent on all metal parts but DO NOT use any on the rubber back-up rings or O-ring seals.

NOTE: The sealing compound on the cap locking ring must be replaced to prevent contamination from the outside.

Assembly

1. Install the outer flat washer and O-ring seal on the release bolt.
2. Install the release bolt in the hole in the cap, with the head of the bolt towards the outside of the cap.
3. Install the inner flat washer and "E" ring on the release bolt.
4. Take the two spring bearing washers and install one on the piston and the other in the cap.
5. On the piston, install the back-up ring and the O-ring seal.
6. Install the spring and piston in the cap assembly. Install the assembly in the compressing fixture and compress the spring.
7. Install the square nut on the release bolt and tighten enough to hold the spring securely. Remove the assembly from the fixture.
8. Install the hex nut and snap ring on the release bolt.
9. Install the back-up rings and the O-ring seal in the groove in the housing.
10. Install the cap, spring and piston assembly in the housing, with the rubber seal between the cap and housing.
11. Install the lock ring in the housing and seal the joint between the cap and housing with sealing compound.
12. Install the piston in the housing and thread the foot, through the housing, into the piston.
13. Lock the foot in place with the set screw and lock the set screw in place with sealer.
14. Assemble the pressure housing to the non-pressure housing and secure the two housings together with the clamping ring.
15. Connect the air lines and build air pressure up to a normal level and uncage the release spring by turning the release bolt counterclockwise as far as it will go.
16. Check unit for air leaks and road test vehicle for proper operation.

Anchorlok Brake Chambers

NOTE: Before removing the brake chamber, make sure that the wheels of the vehicle are securely blocked against movement. When the chamber is removed the parking brake will not be applied.

Removal and Disassembly

1. Release all air from the system and disconnect the air lines from the brake chamber.

2. Remove the release stud from the carrying pocket in the housing. Remove the plug in the end of the housing and insert the release stud through the hole in the housing and the spring pressure plate. Turn the stud 1/4 turn to engage the tangs on the release stud with the slots in the pressure plate. Install the nut on the stud and tighten with a wrench to compress the spring. Tighten the nut until the spring is completely caged. NOTE: Make sure the tangs on the stud stay engaged with the slot in the plate. DO NOT remove the nut and stud unless the chamber is installed and securely clamped.
3. Disconnect the push rod yoke from the slack adjuster.
4. Remove the securing bolts from the brake chamber and remove the chamber from the vehicle.
5. Remove the parking brake housing-to-adapter clamping ring.
6. Remove the parking brake housing, spring and pressure plate as an assembly. NOTE: The spring, housing and pressure plate are serviced as an assembly and should not be taken apart.
7. Remove the parking brake diaphragm and remove the adapter-to-service chamber clamping ring.
8. Remove the adapter and service brake diaphragm.

Cleaning and Inspection

1. Clean all metal parts with clean solvent and inspect all parts for signs of wear and deterioration. Replace all parts necessary.
NOTE: Do not disassemble the spring, housing and pressure plate assembly. This is to be serviced only as a complete unit.

Assembly

1. Install a new service brake diaphragm on the service brake body. Position the adapter assembly on the service brake body and install the chamber clamping ring and tighten securely.
2. Install a new parking brake diaphragm on the adapter housing. Install the parking brake housing, spring and pressure plate assembly on the adapter housing and secure in place with the clamping ring, tightening the bolt firmly.
3. Install the assembly on the mounting bracket and secure with the attaching nuts.
4. Connect the push rod yoke to the slack adjuster.
5. Connect the air lines to the chamber and build up air pressure to a normal level. Remove the brake release stud from the back of the chamber and replace

it in the storage compartment on the chamber. Install the access plug in the hole in the back of the chamber.
6. Check the unit for air leaks and road test vehicle for proper operation of the unit.

Maxibrake Brake Chambers

Removal and Disassembly

1. Release all air from the system and disconnect the air lines from the brake chamber.
NOTE: Before releasing all air from the system block the wheels securely to guard against movement of the vehicle.
2. Install a Schrader valve in the spring brake chamber and charge the chamber with approximately 100 lbs. of air pressure. This holds the parking brake spring compressed.
3. Disconnect the push rod yoke from the slack adjuster. Remove the mounting nuts from the support bracket and remove the chamber from the vehicle.
4. Scribe marks across the clamp ring, pressure plate and cylinder assembly so they can be reassembled in their proper places.
5. Mount the cylinder assembly in a vise using one of the mounting studs with the nut installed to hold on to. NOTE: Be sure to release the air pressure in the unit before disassembly.
6. Remove the clamping ring and remove the pressure plate and the service brake diaphragm from the cylinder assembly.
7. From the push rod, remove the clevis yoke. Push inward on the face plate of the push rod and remove the flanged nut from the back of the push rod shaft. Remove the push rod, spring retainer and return spring from the cylinder.
8. Using a spring compressing tool, insert the end through the neck of the piston from the back, and remove the push rod bushings.
9. Install the spring compressing tool through the cylinder assembly and loosely install the spacer and nut on the threaded end. The tool is used to compress the parking brake spring so the unit can be safely disassembled.
10. Tighten the nut on the tool shaft until the flat part of the tool is resting firmly against the spring support.
11. Remove the eight screws that hold the support plate in place. Slowly back off the nut on the compressing tool until all the pressure is off of the spring. Remove the tool and the spring from the cylinder.
12. With air, blow any loose dirt from

the cylinder and wipe the walls of the cylinder clean. Drive the piston, for the parking brake, from the cylinder by using a drift or socket of the proper size. Remove the O-ring and wiper ring from the piston grooves.

13. Remove the O-ring, nylon bushing and back-up ring from the cylinder center boss.

Cleaning and Inspection

1. Clean all metal parts in clean solvent and inspect them for signs of wear. Check the diaphragms for signs of deterioration or cracks and replace them as necessary. Replace any seals or parts that may come with a rebuilding kit.
2. Coat the groove inside the center boss with a good quality grease and fill the piston O-ring groove half full. Lightly coat the inside of the cylinder with grease. With a rust inhibitor compound coat the piston safety spring.

Assembly

1. In the groove in the cylinder boss install the back-up ring and then install the nylon bushing. NOTE: The bushing must be installed with the beveled side facing the inside of the cylinder.
2. In the bottom groove of the piston, install the large O-ring seal, saturate the felt wiper ring with a good oil and install it in the top groove of the piston.
3. Install the piston assembly in the cylinder holding the felt ring in place. If it is necessary, use a block of wood and a light hammer to bottom the piston in the cylinder.
4. Install the piston spring on the piston in the cylinder and place the spring support on top of the spring. Install the spring compressing tool through spring and cylinder. Tighten the nut on the tool slightly while centering the spring on the piston hub. Then tighten the nut securely until the holes in the spring support and cylinder are in alignment.
5. Install the eight screws that hold the support plate in place and tighten them securely.
6. Remove the spring compressing tool from the cylinder.
7. Into the piston install the push rod bushing and tap the bushing slightly to make sure it is seated.
8. Install the push rod spring retainer and spring on the push rod and install the assembly in the cylinder. Secure the push rod in place with the flanged nut.
9. Install the service brake diaphragm on the pressure plate, with the crown surface facing the pressure plate.

Maxibrake (© Ford Motor Co)

10. Install the pressure plate and diaphragm on the cylinder assembly making sure that the scribe marks are in alignment. Press on the top of the pressure plate to compress the service return spring and install the clamping ring. Torque the bolt on the clamping ring to 150-175 in lbs.
11. With a Schrader valve installed in the safety chamber air inlet, apply enough air pressure to compress the safety spring and piston assembly.
12. Tighten the flanged nut on the push rod shaft until there is 1/16 inch clearance between the flange of the nut and neck of the piston tube. Lock the nut in place with the jam nut.
13. Install the clevis yoke on the push rod maintaining a clearance of 2 15/16 inches between the centerline of the clevis pin holes and the mounting flanges of the cylinder assembly, on type 24 or 30 units. On type 36 units the clearance should be 3¼ inches.
14. Pressurize the unit with air and check for air leaks. After checking, leave the chamber charged with air and install the brake chamber assembly on the mounting brackets on the vehicle. In-

stall the attaching nuts and torque them to 110-150 ft lbs.
15. Connect the push rod yoke to the slack adjuster and release the air from the unit through the Schrader valve and remove the valve.
16. Connect the air lines to the chamber and build air pressure up to a normal level.
17. Check the unit for leaks again and road test the vehicle to check for proper operation.

MGM Stopgard Brake Chamber

Removal-Complete Unit

1. Release all air from the system and remove the air lines from the brake chamber. NOTE: Block the wheels securely against movement, when the chamber is removed there will be no parking brake.
2. Cage the parking spring by removing the breather cap and unscrewing the release bolt approximately 30 turns until the brake shoes are released from the drum.
3. Remove the cotter pin from the clevis yoke pin and remove the pin.
4. Remove the mounting stud nuts and remove the unit from the vehicle.

Installation—Complete Unit

1. Install the unit on the mounting bracket and install the securing nuts and torque to 150 ft lbs.
2. Position the push rod yoke on the slack adjuster and install the clevis yoke pin and secure it in place with the cotter pin.
3. Release the parking spring by turning the release bolt down until the bolt bottoms on the case and torque the nut to 50 ft lbs.
4. Connect the air lines and build up air pressure to a normal level. Check the unit for air leaks and proper operation.

Removal and Disassembly—Service Brake Diaphragm

NOTE: Before working on vehicle block the wheels against movement. The parking brake will not be applied when the brake chamber is removed.

1. Cage the parking spring as described in step number 2 of the complete unit removal procedures.
2. Release all the air from the system and remove the air lines from the brake chamber.
3. Supporting the chamber with one hand, loosen the retaining bolt on the clamping ring for the service brake chamber and remove the ring. Lift the spring brake chamber away from the service brake chamber and set aside.
4. Remove the service brake diaphragm and inspect it for cracks, signs of wear or signs of deterioration. Inspect the return spring, service piston and the inside of the exposed chambers for signs of wear and replace any parts necessary.

Assembly—Service Brake Diaphragm

1. Install the diaphragm over the service piston and spring and check the alignment of the spring to the chamber and piston while installing.
2. Install the spring brake chamber on the diaphragm in the same position it was removed in and install the clamping ring. Tighten the nuts on the clamp to 25-35 ft lbs. Check around the ring when assembling to make sure of proper alignment and clamp seating. Tap around the clamp ring with a soft hammer to help seat the clamp and re-torque the nuts.
3. Release the parking spring following the procedure described in step number 3 of the Complete Unit Installation section.
4. Connect the air lines to the chamber and build up air pressure to a normal level. Operate the brake several times to check the operation of the unit.
5. With pressure in the chambers, check the unit for leaks with soapy water. Release the air in the service brake section only and retorque the clamping ring to 25-35 ft lbs.

Removal and Disassembly—Parking Brake Diaphragm

NOTE: Before working on the vehicle block the wheels against any movement. The parking brake will not be applied when the brake chamber is removed.

1. To remove the chamber follow steps 1 through 3 in the Service Brake Diaphragm Removal section.

2. Place the spring brake chamber in a hydraulic press using a split tube and a flat plate on top of the assembly for a surface to press on. NOTE: The tube can be made by using a piece of heavy tubing, 5 inches long and having an outside diameter of 4 inches. The press must have a minimum of 8 inches of travel after it comes in contact with the flat plate on top of the chamber.
3. Apply light pressure with the press and remove the clamping ring nuts and the clamping ring.
4. Very slowly and carefully release the pressure on the unit. There should be no pressure on the unit from the inside and press ram and flat plate on the unit should separate almost at once. NOTE: If there is still pressure on the unit after the press has been relaxed a fair amount, either the spring is not fully manually released or the release assembly is damaged. Continue to release pressure on the unit until the parking brake spring is fully released and the parts fall free.
5. Remove the head, spring and piston assembly from the flange case on the press. CAUTION: Be very careful with the head assembly because the parking spring is caged by the release bolt between the head and the piston.
6. Remove the parking brake diaphram and inspect the inside of the flange case for wear or damage. If any parts are damaged see the Parking Brake Air Chamber Disassembly procedures to repair.

MGM Stopgard Brake (© Ford Motor Co)

NOTE: Make sure that the screw holding the push rod is tightened securely.

Assembly—Parking Brake Diaphragm

1. Install the diaphragm on the flange case and place the parking brake spring and piston assembly on the diaphragm.
2. Check all the parts for proper alignment and place the unit in the press with the split tube and flat plate in place.
3. With the press, apply light pressure to the assembly and install the clamping ring and tighten the bolts to 25-35 ft lbs. Tap around the outside edge of the clamping ring with a soft hammer and retorque the clamp to 25-35 ft lbs.
4. Leave the assembly in the press and attach an air line with 100-125 psi of pressure to the spring brake inlet and check the unit for leaks. If any leaks are discovered disassemble the unit and reposition the parts and reassemble. After the unit passes the leak test retorque and clamp nuts to 25-35 ft lbs again.
5. Install the unit on the vehicle following steps 2 through 5 in the Service Brake Diaphragm Assembly section.

Removal and Disassembly—Spring Brake Air Chamber

1. Remove the spring brake section from the vehicle as described in Steps 1 through 3 in the Service Brake Diaphragm Removal section. NOTE: If the power spring is broken, it can usually be confirmed by unscrewing the retaining bolt and shaking the unit. If there is a noticeable rattle from the head end of the unit this usually means that the spring is broken. Further indication of a broken spring is light resistance when the release bolt is screwed into the unit. CAUTION: Even if the spring is broken it is necessary to manually cage the spring before disassembling the unit.
2. From the release bolt remove the lock pin with a small punch.
3. Remove the head, spring and piston assembly from the flange case as described in steps 1 through 5 in the Parking Brake Diaphragm Removal section.
4. Install the head, spring and piston assembly in a hydraulic press using two split tubes. NOTE: A tube 4 inches in diameter and 3 inches long must be placed under the unit supporting the piston and another 4 inches in diameter and 6 inches long

must be placed on top of the assembly between the press ram and the head. A flat metal plate must be placed on top of the top tube to provide a flat surface for the press to press on. Also the press must be able to travel away from the assembly a minimum of 8 inches or the spring will not release completely.

CAUTION: Without the press and tube assembly the unit can not be disassembled safely. If a press is not available, DO NOT attempt to disassemble the unit.

5. Make sure that the assembly is straight in the press and apply light pressure on the unit with the press.
6. Pop the center plug out of the bottom of the piston with a screwdriver, and using a long, broad bladed screwdriver, unscrew the release bolt until it falls free. If the bolt binds, apply a little more pressure to the assembly with the press.
7. When the release bolt is removed, very slowly release the pressure on the head until the press ram separates from the head.
8. Remove the head assembly and remove the spring, thrust washers, and piston from the press. Clean all the parts and inspect for any signs of damage and wear and replace the parts as necessary.

Assembly—Spring Brake Air Chamber

1. Before assembling the head, spring and piston, grease the inside of the head assembly, the outside of the piston shank, the inside of the piston shank and the threads of the release bolt.
2. Position the split tube on the press and install the following parts on top of it: piston, thrust washer (late models use a spring shield cup instead of the washer), spring, thrust washer and head. On top of the head install the second split tube with the flat plate on top of it.
3. Check the parts to make sure they are in alignment straight up and down and slowly apply pressure to the assembly while checking constantly for any misalignment that might occur. CAUTION: Stand to the side of the press when compressing the spring. If misalignment occurs, release the pressure on the unit and start to compress the spring again.
4. When the piston spring is fully compressed and the piston bottoms against the head, install the release bolt through the bottom of the piston and screw the bolt

in until approximately 3 inches of the bolt extend through the top of the head.
5. Relax pressure on the press slowly until the press ram separates from the split tube and flat plate.
6. Remove the head assembly from the press and install the release nut on the release bolt and lock it in place with the lock pin.
7. Install the piston plug in the bottoms against the head, install the place with a light hammer.
8. Follow steps 1 through 5 in the Parking Brake Diaphragm Assembly section to install the unit back on the vehicle.

MGM Shortstop Brake Chamber

Removal—Complete Unit

1. Drain all air from the system and disconnect the air lines from the unit. NOTE: Block the wheels of the vehicle securely. When the brake chamber is removed the parking brake will not be applied.
2. Remove the breather cap and filter and unscrew the release bolt as far as it will go.
3. On the service brake chamber tube, loosen the lock nut with a drift punch and hammer.
4. From the wedge housing unscrew the entire shortstop and service brake chamber assembly and remove from the vehicle.

Installation—Complete Unit

1. Make sure that the release bolt is unscrewed completely and screw the entire unit into the wedge housing until it bottoms against the housing.
2. Back the unit out less than one turn to align the hose connections.
3. Tighten the lock nut securely on the brake chamber tube and connect the air lines to the unit.
4. Charge the unit with air and tighten the release bolt into the unit. Install the cap and filter on the unit.
5. Check the unit for leaks and road test the vehicle for proper operation of the unit.

Removal—Shortstop Unit Only

1. Drain the air from the system and disconnect the air lines from the unit. NOTE: Block the wheels of the vehicle securely. When the brake chamber is removed the parking brake will not be applied.
2. Remove the breather cap and filter and unscrew the release bolt as far as it will go.
3. Remove the clamping ring on the brake chamber and shortstop

unit and remove shortstop unit from the vehicle.

Installation—Shortstop Unit Only

1. Making sure that the release bolt is unscrewed completely, install the unit on the brake chamber and install the clamping ring. Tighten the bolts securely.
2. Connect the air lines and charge the chamber with air. Screw the release bolt into the unit tightly. Install the cap and filter assembly and check the unit for leaks and road test the vehicle for proper operation of the unit.

Disassembly—Shortstop Unit

1. Remove the shortstop unit only from the vehicle and using a sharp, thin bladed knife, remove the soft sealer from the head of the Phillips head screw in the case assembly.
2. Remove the Phillips head screw and the plate under it.
3. From the top of the head remove the release bolt and washer and insert a screw driver through the release bolt hole. Hold the screwdriver against the top of the push rod and charge the spring air chamber with air (minimum 70 psi).
4. Remove the screwdriver and using a drift punch and hammer remove the anti-explosion nut and Delrin washer from the top of the head.
5. Release the air in the chamber and remove the sealer in the groove for the snap ring in the head.
6. Install the assembly in a press with the case side down. The press must have a minimum of 6 inches of travel away from the unit or the head can not be disassembled safely.
7. Apply a little pressure to the head with the press. NOTE: Do not attempt to press the head into the case assembly too far or the case assembly will be damaged.
    Remove the snap ring from the groove in the head with a screwdriver.
8. Relax the pressure of the press very slowly. The spring will push the head out of the case. NOTE: If the assembly has a broken spring use a cage or screen for

MGM Shortstop Brake (© Ford Motor Co)

protection when disassembling.
    When the pressure is off of the head, remove the assembly from the press.
9. Remove the head and spring from the case. Hold the piston by the hub and remove it from the case by pulling straight out.
10. Clean all parts and inspect them for signs of wear and damage. Replace all parts necessary.

Assembly—Shortstop Unit

1. Lubricate the inside of the case assembly with a low temperature moly-type grease. Also lubricate the seal groove of the piston, the collar seal and the push rod seal.
2. Install the seal on the piston if removed and install the piston in the case by tilting the piston to one side and inserting it in the case and slowly bringing it to a straight position in the case bore.
3. Install the push rod in the seal in the piston. Install the spring on the piston and install the head on top of the spring.
4. Place the assembly in the press and using care start to compress the spring into the case. NOTE: Make sure that the spring and

head assembly goes into the case straight, if it does not, stop, release the press and start to compress the assembly again.
    Continue to press the head into the case until the head bottoms against the shoulder in the case.
5. Install the snap ring in the groove in the case and tap the ends of the snap ring to make sure that it is seated properly.
6. Release the pressure on the press and remove the assembly from the press.
7. Insert a screwdriver through the release bolt hole and press down firmly on the push rod. Charge the cylinder with air (minimum 70 psi).
8. Remove the screwdriver and install the Delrin guide washer and the anti-explosion washer and tighten to 30 ft lbs.
9. Install the release bolt and washer in the assembly. Install the plate and Phillips head screw in the push rod and tighten.
10. Release pressure on the unit and apply sealer to the groove over the snap ring.
11. Install the unit back on the vehicle and check for leaks and road test for proper operation.

Bendix Hydraulic Brake Anti-Skid System

NOTE: Before attempting any repair operations on the anti-skid system, determine the problem area by tests outlined at the end of this section.

Pressure Modulator
Removal

1. Disconnect the vacuum hose from the vacuum inlet on the modulator bypass valve.

2. Disconnect the modulator hydraulic lines from the modulator hydraulic cylinder.
3. Disconnect the modulator electrical leads.

4. Loosen the nut that secures the rear of the modulator to the mounting bracket. Loosen the outer nuts on the two lower 'J' bolts, these nuts secure the front of the modulator to the bracket.

5. Lift the modulator upward to disengage the modulator bolts from the slots in the mounting bracket and remove the modulator from the vehicle.

CAUTION: Do not attempt to disassemble the modulator. The heavy-duty diaphragm return spring is compressed inside the modulator, and any attempt to remove the retaining bolts from the end plate could result in injury.

Installation

1. Position the modulator, with the bypass tube up, on the mounting bracket so that the two lower bolts and the stud on the rear of the modulator fit into the slots in the mounting bracket.

2. Tighten the nut on the stud at the rear of the modulator. Tighten the outer nuts on the two lower 'J' bolts.

3. Connect the brake lines to the hydraulic cylinder.

4. Connect the vacuum hose to the vacuum inlet on the bypass valve.

5. Connect the electrical leads to the modulator.

6. Proceed to the "Testing & Trouble Shooting" section to make sure the modulator is operating properly.

Electronic Control Unit (Computer)

Removal

1. Turn off the vehicle power to the control unit.
2. Disconnect and lable the control unit electrical connectors.
3. Remove the control unit mounting screws and remove the control unit.

Typical Bendix system installation (© IHC)

Modulator vacuum and hydraulic lines—Bendix System (© IHC)

Electronic Control Unit—Bendix System (© IHC)

Pressure modulator—Bendix (© IHC)

Pressure modulator-cross section view—Bendix System (© IHC)

Installation

1. Position the control unit over the mounting holes and secure with the retaining screws.
2. Connect the electrical leads.
3. Proceed to the "Testing & Trouble Shooting" section to make sure the control unit is working properly.

Wheel Speed Sensor

Removal

1. Raise the vehicle and secure. Remove the wheel and brake drum assembly.
2. Remove the straps that hold the sensor leads in place. Disconnect the wheel speed sensor leads.
3. Press the wheel speed sensor inward (toward the vehicle), to reduce the pressure on the knarled shaft, and remove the drive ring assembly.
4. Remove the nut which secures the sensor to the brake backing plate and remove the sensor.
5. Loosen the sensor lead grommet in the backing plate, and pull the sensor lead through the hole.

Installation

1. Insert the sensor lead through the hole in the backing plate and seat the grommet.
2. Position the sensor mounting bracket with the lower front brake mounting hole aligned with the lower hole in the sensor bracket. Align the upper sensor bracket hole with the upper forward mounting hole. Hold the bracket in place with the lower nut.
3. Press the speed sensor inward and position the drive ring on the hub.
4. Connect the sensor electrical lead and secure with new strap.

Removing the drive ring—Bendix System (© IHC)

5. Install the wheel and drum assembly. Lower the vehicle.
6. Proceed to the "Testing & Trouble Shooting" section to make sure the sensor is working properly.

Testing & Trouble Shooting Bendix Hydraulic Anti-Skid System

NOTE: The following equipment is required to perform tests on this system:

a. V.O.M. capable of measuring: AC voltage in the .10-5.0 range; DC voltage in the 6-18 range; Resistance accurately in the 0-10 ohm, 100-1,000 ohm, 5,000-100,000 ohm ranges.
b. Vacuum gauge that measures vacuum from 0-25 inches Hg.
c. Pressure gauge capable of measuring hydraulic pressure from 0-1,000 psi.

Test #1—Red Brake Warning Light

1. *If the brake warning light is not on,* turn the ignition switch to the "start" position. The light should come on while the engine is cranking.
   a. If the warning light does not come on when the engine is cranking, replace the bulb and check the warning lamp circuit operation.
   b. If the light stays on after the bulb has been replaced, proceed to Step 2 to determine if the problem is in the anti-skid system or if the trouble is in the basic brake system.
   c. If the light comes on when the engine is cranking and goes off when the engine starts, proceed to Test #3.

Drive ring and speed sensor components—Bendix System (© IHC)

Trouble shooting chart—Bendix System (© IHC)

2. *If the brake warning light is on,* disconnect the lead from the brake warning switch.
   a. If the warning light goes out when the lead is disconnected, the trouble is in the basic brake system. Refer to the "Hydraulic Brake" section.
   b. If the light does not go out when the lead is disconnected, the trouble is in the anti-skid system. Proceed to Test #3.

   After the electrical circuit checks are completed, be sure that all the connectors are properly installed.

Test #2—Green Cycling Indicator

1. Locate and separate the cycling light connector leading from the controller (connector "A"). Apply 12 volts directly from the battery positive terminal to the bulb side of the connector.
   a. If the cycling bulb does not light, replace the bulb and socket assembly.
   b. If the cycling bulb does light reassemble the connector and proceed to Step 2.
2. Test the anti-skid system by driving the vehicle on gravel or other surface with minimal traction. The test must be performed at a minimum speed of 20 mph. Apply the brakes enough to lock the wheels under normal conditions. Watch for the cycling light to flicker. If the cycling light flickers rapidly and the rear wheels appear to roll to low

Electrical circuit diagram—Bendix System (© IHC)

speed and lock, the anti-skid system is working properly. If not, proceed to Test #3.

Test #3—Electrical Circuit Checks

1. *Check at the electronic control unit.*
   NOTE: Make the measurements listed in the chart that follows. These measurements are made at the control unit connectors. The connectors should be disconnected except those measurements indicated by a double asterisk (**). All readings must be made on the terminals on the side of the connector attached to the control unit assembly and the speed sensor

assemblies. If any reading is not as specified, refer to the step indicated for additional readings or corrections.

2. *Modulator switch circuit.* Make the measurements in the sequence listed below to identify the defective component. When it appears that the faulty component has been found, reconnect all connectors except at the control unit and repeat the measurements in step 1 that produced the incorrect reading. *This remeasurement should be made prior to replacing any components to insure that the trouble still exists.*
   a. Disconnect connector "D" (located at the modulator).
   b. On the modulator lead side of the connector, measure the resistance Pin #3 and ground. If zero ohms is measured, the modulator cable is defective and must be replaced. If the measurement is above zero ohms, the modulator or the modulator switch is defective and must be replaced.
3. *Air valve and bypass valve circuits.* Make the measurements in the sequence listed below to identify the defective component. When it appears that the faulty component has been found, reconnect all connectors except at the control unit and repeat the measurements in step 1 that produced the incorrect reading. *This remeasurement should be made prior to replacing any components to insure that the trouble still exists.*
   a. Disconnect connector "D" (located at the modulator).
   b. On the modulator lead side of the connector, measure the

Electrical connectors—Bendix System (© IHC)

resistance between the pin where the incorrect reading was recorded and ground.

c. If the reading is 3.0-5.0 ohms, the modulator cable assembly is defective and must be replaced.

d. If the reading is still incorrect, the modulator must be replaced.

4. *Electronic Control Unit ground circuit.*

a. Disconnect the body ground wire under the instrument panel.

b. Clean the eye on the end of the wire and ground point on wire where the wire is attached.

c. Reinstall the ground wire. Remeasure the resistance between Pin #2, connector 'B', on the brake harness side and ground.

d. If the reading is zero ohms, the ground connection was faulty and the problem has been corrected.

e. If the reading is above zero ohms, the brake harness is faulty and must be replaced.

5. *Power supply circuit.* Make the measurements in the sequence listed below to identify the defective component. When it appears that the faulty component has been found, reconnect all connectors, except at the control unit, and repeat the measurements in step 1 that produced the incorrect reading. *This measurement should be made prior to replacing any components to insure that the trouble still exists.*

a. Check the 10 amp fuse on the fuse panel in line between the ignition switch and the power connector, replace the fuse if defective.

b. If the fuse is good, be sure that the circuit is properly connected at the ignition switch and that battery voltage is present at the ignition switch terminal.

c. If the fuse is good, connections and battery voltage are correct at the switch terminals, but there is no power at Pin #4, Connector "B", with the ignition switch "on", the brake harness is faulty and must be replaced.

6. *Stop light to Electronic Control Unit circuit.* Make the measurements in the sequence listed below to identify the defective component. When it appears that the defective component has been found, reconnect all connectors, except at the control unit, and repeat the measurements in step 1 that produced the incorrect reading. *This measurement*

Electronic Control Unit Checks

Connector	Take Measurement Between	Measure For	Ignition Switch Position	Brake Pedal Position	Reading	Improper Reading Refer to Test #3; Step #
"A" (Three Pins)	Pin #1 -Ground	Ohms	Off	Released	3.0-50	3
	Pin #2 -Ground	Ohms	Off	Released	3.0-5.0	3
	Pin #3 -Ground	Ohms	Off	Released	0	2
	**Pin #2 -Ground	DC Volts	On	Applied	0	8
	**Pin #1 -Ground	DC Volts	On	Applied	0	8
"B" (Four Pins)	Pin #1 -Ground	DC Volts	Off	Applied	12*	6
	***Pin #2 -Ground	DC Volts	Off	Released	0 w/Headlights ON	7
	**Pin #2 Pin #2 -Con. "C"	Ohms	Off	Released	0	8
	Pin #3 -Ground	DC Volts	On	Released	12*	9
	Pin #2 -Ground	Ohms	Off	Released	0	4
	Pin #4 -Ground	DC Volts	On	Released	12*	5
"C" (Three Pins)	Pin #1 -Ground	Ohms	Off	Released	Above-50,000	10
	Pin #1 -Pin #2	Ohms	Off	Released	250-350	10
	Pin #2 -Ground	Ohms	Off	Released	Above-50,000	10
	Pin #3 -Ground	Ohms	Off	Released	Above-50,000	10
	Pin #3 -Pin #2	Ohms	Off	Released	250-350	10

* Measurement should be the same as battery voltage.
** Make the measurement with all electrical connectors installed.
*** Make the measurement with the headlights on.

should be made prior to replacing any components to insure that the trouble still exists.

a. With the brakes applied, measure the DC voltage between the output (stop light) side of the stop light switch and ground.

b. If the reading is correct (battery voltage), the brake harness is defective and must be replaced.

c. If the reading is still incorrect (below battery voltage), measure the DC voltage between the battery side of the stop light switch and ground.

d. If the reading is correct (battery voltage), adjust the switch position or replace the switch as necessary.

e. If the reading is incorrect (below battery voltage), check the wiring to the stop light switch and repair or replace the wiring as necessary.

7. *Voltage feedback.* Make the measurements in the sequence listed below to identify the defective component. When it appears that the faulty component has been found, reconnect all connectors, except at the control unit, and repeat the measurements in step

1 that produced the incorrect reading. *This measurement should be made prior to replacing any components to insure that the trouble still exists.*

a. Depress and release the brake pedal and check the operation of the brake lights.

b. If the stop lights are not functioning normally, refer to the "Hydraulic Brake" section. After the defect has been found and corrected, repeat the measurement of DC voltage between Pin #1 Connector "B" and ground (with the headlights on).

c. If the stop lights function properly and the reading is still above zero volts, check the ground connections in both tail light-stop light assemblies, correct as necessary.

8. *Electronic Control Unit circuits.* If the reading is above zero volts, the electronic control unit is defective and must be replaced.

9. *Warning light circuit.* Make the measurements in the sequence listed below to identify the defective component. When it appears that the defective component has

been found, reconnect all the connectors, except at the control unit, and repeat the measurement in step 1 that produced the incorrect reading. *This measurement should be made prior to replacing any components to insure that the trouble still exists.*

a. Check the circuit connection at the ignition switch.

b. Measure the DC voltage between the circuit terminal on the ignition switch and ground.

c. If the reading is correct (battery voltage) but the battery voltage is not present at Pin #3, Connector "B", the brake harness is defective and must be replaced.

10. *Speed sensor circuit.* Make the measurements in the sequence listed below to identify the defective component. When it appears that the defective component has been found, reconnect all the connectors, except at the control unit, and repeat the measurements in step 1 that produced the incorrect reading. *This measurement should be made prior to replacing any components to insure that the trouble still exists.*

a. Separate the connector at the wheel speed sensor.

b. On the wheel speed sensor side of the connector, repeat the measurement from step 1 that produced the incorrect reading.

c. If the reading is now within limits, the speed sensor cable is defective and must be replaced.

d. If the reading is still incorrect, separate the speed sensor cable connector in the line with the incorrect reading.

e. On the speed sensor side of the connector, measure the resistance of the two terminals and between each terminal and ground.

f. If the readings are within limits (see chart) the speed sensor harness is defective and must be replaced.

g. If any of the readings are incorrect, the corresponding speed sensor is defective and must be replaced.

Test #4 Modulator Operation

1. With the engine running, disconnect the "D" connector. (modulator lead).

2. On the modulator side of the connector, measure the resistance between Pin #3 and ground.

3. If the reading is above zero ohms, replace the modulator.

Test #5 Vacuum and Hydraulic Test

1. Check the vacuum supply as follows

a. Visually inspect all vacuum hoses in the engine compartment for damage. Make sure all hose connections are tight. Replace or tighten all hoses as necessary.

b. Start the engine and listen for a hissing sound indicating a vacuum leak. Repair as necessary.

c. Disconnect all vacuum lines at the modulator, and connect a vacuum gauge between the modulator and the vacuum line.

d. With the engine running, the gauge should read normal engine vacuum. If reading is not within limits, recheck for vacuum leak or tune the engine as necessary.

2. Check the operation of the air valve and the bypass valve as follows:

a. Disconnect connector "D" (modulator electrical lead).

b. Start the engine and note the reading on the vacuum gauge.

CAUTION: The air and bypass valves should not be energized for more than two minutes, with a five minute cooling off period to follow. If the valves are energized longer, the solenoids will overheat and be damaged.

c. Connect a jumper lead from the positive pole of the battery to Pin #1 on the modulator side of the connector.

d. The reading on the vacuum gauge should drop. If the reading remains constant, the modulator is defective and should be replaced.

e. Connect a second jumper wire from the positive side of the battery to Pin #2 on the connector (the jumper wire to Pin #1 must still be in place).

f. The vacuum gauge reading should jump to the reading noted in step 2b above.

g. If the vacuum gauge reading does not increase, the modulator is defective and must be replaced.

h. If the vacuum gauge reading does increase, proceed to step 3.

3. Check the operation of the hydraulic shut-off valve as follows:

a. Install a hydraulic pressure gauge in the modulator output port.

b. Bleed the air from the hydraulic system and the gauge.

c. Start the engine and depress the brake pedal to obtain 500-600 psi on the gauge.

d. With the brake pedal depressed, connect jumper wires from the battery positive terminal to Pins #1 and #2 of the electrical connector, modulator side.

e. The hydraulic pressure should drop to zero. If not, the modulator is faulty and should be replaced.

f. Hold the pedal depressed for two minutes, with the jumper wires connected. The hydraulic pressure must not increase.

g. Release the brake pedal, disconnect the jumper wires from the battery and turn the engine off.

h. If the hydraulic pressure did rise during the two minutes the pedal was depressed, the modulator is defective and must be replaced.

4. If the results of all the steps in this test were normal, the electronic control unit is faulty and must be replaced.

Test #6 Hydraulic Pressure Test

1. Check the output of the hydraulic system as follows:

a. Connect a hydraulic pressure gauge in the output side of the modulator.

b. Bleed the air from the hydraulic gauge and the hydraulic system.

c. Disconnect the modulator electrical lead.

CAUTION: The air and bypass valves should not be energized for more than two minutes, with a five minute cooling off period to follow. If the valves are energized longer, the solenoids will overheat and be damaged.

d. Connect a jumper wire from the positive battery terminal to the #2 pin on the modulator side of the electrical connector.

e. Start the engine and depress the brake pedal to obtain 600 psi on the hydraulic pressure gauge.

f. If the pressure does not rise when the brake pedal is depressed, the modulator is defective and must be replaced.

Test #7 False Cycling Test

1. Inspect each wheel speed sensor as follows:

a. Remove the wheel and drum assembly and check the sensor mounting bracket to be sure that the sensor is held securely against the rubber drive ring. Remove the sensor drive ring.

b. Check the sensor for wear or damage to the tone wheel teeth. Check the sensor bracket and sensor lead for damage. Replace any part if necessary.

c. Inspect the rubber drive band pressed into the drive ring. If the band slips inside the ring or the band is excessively worn, replace.

d. Check the sensor knarled wheel for deposits. If the deposits are excessive or uneven, clean the knarled area with a knife.

e. Install the drive ring and wheel.

f. Repeat the above operations on each wheel.

2. Make the system functional checks as follows:

a. Drive over a rough area (gravel road, brick road, etc.) with a foot resting lightly on the brake pedal. (just enough to turn the brake lights on) until the false cycling occurs. Keep speed below 15 mph.

b. At connector "C" on the control unit, use a short piece of wire as a jumper and connect pins #1 and #3, with the connector joined.

c. Disconnect one wheel speed sensor at a time. Drive over the same rough area that produced the false cycling.

d. When the false cycling stops, the sensor that is disconnected is defective and must be replaced.

NOTE: Be sure to remove the jumper wire when the tests are completed.

3. If the speed sensors are working properly, and the electronic control unit has not been checked out previously, go back to test #1 and check the electronic control unit.

Air Brake Anti-Skid Systems Section

Component Description
Speed Sensor & Rotor

Wheel speed is recorded by the electromagnetic action of the sensor as the rotor revolves. A pulse is generated each time a tooth of the slotted rotor passes the sensor. The sensor is composed of a permanent magnet, coils and an output cable. There is an adjusting spring that maintains the proper clearance between the sensor and the rotor. The rotor is a steel disc with slots or teeth which is secured to the brake drum. As the wheel revolves, the passing of the teeth over the sensor "excites" the sensor and creates an electric signal.

Computer Module/Control Valve

The control valve, in normal operation, performs the relay function of supplying air to the brake chambers.

The pressure is equal to that called for by the vehicle operator with the treadle valve. Service pressure is supplied from the treadle valve, through the solenoid, to the top of the diaphragm. Deflection of this diaphragm downwards forces open the poppet valve supply seat, allowing the supply air to flow through the delivery ports to the brake chamber. When the "anti-skid" action is started by the computer, which has sensed imminent wheel lock from the wheel speed sensors, the pressure to the brake chamber is modulated through the action of a solenoid. When energized by the computer command, the solenoid blocks off air flow from the treadle valve to the top of the diaphragm and directs the existing air to exhaust. This action allows the diaphragm to move upward, which closes the poppet supply seat, opens the exhaust seat and directs the brake chamber air to exhaust.

The computer portion of the valve is a fully solid state unit designed to sense wheel rotation speed and prevent wheel lock-up, through action of the solenoid in the control valve. The computer is attached directly to the control valve. The solid state components are completely sealed to prevent damage from foreign material. These systems operate on 12 volt D.C. current, either positive or negative grounds. These systems have provisions for the following: two wheel speed sensors, a solenoid output, a 12 V.DC input, and a failure warning circuit. The internal failure sensing circuitry monitors the system for proper operation. When a failure is detected, it causes an internal fuse to open and returns the brakes to standard manual control.

Failure Warning System

The Failure Warning Unit is an electronic-mechanical device which

Typical anti-skid brake system (© Ford Motor Co.)

monitors the failure warning signals from the computers. When a computer detects an electrical or electronic malfunction, it will cause a fuse to blow on the warning unit, which in turn energizes an indicator light on the dash panel.

AC Wheel Lock Control System

NOTE: Before attempting any repair operations on the anti-skid system, determine the problem area by the tests outlined at the end of this section.

Control Valve (Modulator) Assembly

Removal

1. Turn off the vehicle power to the modulator assembly.
2. Exhaust the air reservoir that supplies the modulator assembly to be removed.
3. Lable the electrical cables and disconnect.
4. Lable the air lines and disconnect.
5. Remove the modulator assembly mounting bolts, and remove the modulator assembly from the vehicle.

Disassembly

1. Remove the screws securing the controller cover. Separate the cover assembly from the modulator assembly by tapping lightly with a soft faced hammer. Be very careful not to damage the sealing surfaces of the cover.
2. Disconnect the two solenoid leads from the controller terminals.

NOTE: It is not necessary to remove the lower cover unless the entire valve is to be replaced.

3. Remove the screws securing the lower controller cover to the modulator assembly. Separate the lower cover from the valve assembly by tapping lightly with a soft faced hammer.
4. Discard the lower cover gasket and clean all gasket material from the sealing surfaces.
5. Remove the bolts securing the solenoid valve housing to the relay valve housing.
6. Separate the solenoid valve housing and the relay valve housing, and discard the 'O' ring.

NOTE: The relay valve housing includes the following: rate control valve (flow restrictor), relay valve piston, relay valve, and the relay exhaust.

7. Remove the rate control valve from the relay valve housing by pulling the head with pliers, or pry under the head with a suitable tool.

Typical electrical schematic—AC System (© AC Spark Plug Division)

Removing the outer controller cover screws—AC System (© AC Spark Plug Division)

Disconnecting the solenoid leads—AC System (© AC Spark Plug Division)

Removing the lower controller cover screws—AC System (© AC Spark Plug Division)

Removing the solenoid housing to relay valve housing bolts—AC System (© AC Spark Plug Division)

Removing the relay piston valve—AC System (© AC Spark Plug Division)

Relay valve piston spring—AC System (© AC Spark Plug Division)

8. Remove the 'O' ring from the rate control valve and discard.
9. Pull the relay valve piston out of the relay valve housing, discard the 'O' ring.
10. Remove the conical spring from the relay valve housing and discard.
11. Remove the bolt securing the seal to the relay valve piston, separate the components and discard the molded rubber valve assembly.
12. Remove the snap ring and washer holding the exhaust valve body in the relay valve housing.
13. Remove the exhaust valve body, spring, and modulation tube.
14. Remove and discard the exhaust valve body 'O' ring, modulation tube 'O' ring, and the spring.
15. Remove the seal retainer from the modulator tube. Do not distort the seal retainer. Remove and discard the seal.
16. Remove the screw from the exhaust valve body and separate the parts. Discard the rubber exhaust diaphragm.

NOTE: *The solenoid valve housing includes: the solenoid, check valve* cover and check valve, solenoid valve, solenoid exhaust, and the rate control valve (restriction piston).

17. Remove the 1/8 inch allen-head set screw in the solenoid valve housing.
18. Remove the solenoid with a socket suitable for this purpose.

19. Remove the 'O' ring from the solenoid and discard.
20. Remove the tension ball from the solenoid valve housing (the tension ball is located under the allen-head set screw previously removed).
21. Remove the three screws secur-

Modulator assembly—exploded view—AC System (© AC Spark Plug Division)

Removing the relay exhaust valve retaining snap ring—AC System (© AC Spark Plug Division)

ing the check valve cover to the solenoid valve housing.

22. Separate the cover from the housing. Remove the cover 'O' ring and discard.

23. Remove the spring and button check valve in line with the solenoid valve, discard the spring and the button check valve.

24. Remove the metal valve seat retainer from over the other check valve using a heavy piece of wire formed into a hook shape. Be very careful not to damage the check valve seat. Remove and discard the 'O' ring.

25. Remove the spring and check valve and discard.

NOTE: The solenoid valve includes: the valve body, spring, valve cage, valve stem, and diaphragm.

26. Remove all of the solenoid valve components by pushing with a screw driver on the flat surface of the solenoid valve, through the check valve opening toward the solenoid opening. Do not damage the check valve seat on the solenoid valve.

Relay valve components—AC System (© AC Spark Plug Division)

Relay exhaust valve components—AC System (© AC Spark Plug Division)

Removing the check valve cover—AC System (© AC Spark Plug Division)

Removing the solenoid valve tension ball retaining screw—AC System (© AC Spark Plug Division)

Removing the solenoid—AC System (© AC Spark Plug Division)

27. Remove and discard all 'O' rings from the solenoid valve components. Discard the solenoid valve stem, spring and the diaphragm.
28. Pull the rubber solenoid exhaust out of its metal retainer, discard the solenoid exhaust.
29. Working with pliers, remove the restriction piston from the solenoid valve body.
30. Remove the 'O' ring from the restriction piston and discard.

Assembly

NOTE: Lubricate all new rubber seals and 'O' rings with a high quality silicone grease prior to assembly.

1. Install a new 'O' ring on the restriction piston and insert the piston in the solenoid valve body.

Push the piston in until it bottoms in the valve body.
2. Install a new rubber solenoid exhaust in the metal retainer, press it in with a small rod until it "snaps" in place.
3. Install new 'O' rings on the solenoid valve body and press the small end into the solenoid valve housing through the solenoid bore until it bottoms. Make sure the valve assembly is properly seated.
4. Install a new spring on the valve stem, new 'O' ring on the valve cage, and insert the valve stem (end without spring) into the open end of the valve cage. Install a new diaphragm seal on the end of the valve stem protruding from the valve cage.
5. Install the cage and valve spring in the solenoid bore. The spring on the valve stem will seat in the valve body and aid in guiding the stem into the bore of the valve body. When the solenoid valve assembly is properly installed, the valve spring will hold the valve stem slightly above the diaphragm seal in the solenoid bore.
6. Install a new check valve button

Removing the restriction piston from the solenoid valve body—AC System (© AC Spark Plug Division)

Solenoid valve parts—AC System (© AC Spark Plug Division)

Removing the check valve seat-retainer—AC System (© AC Spark Plug Division)

Cut-away view of installed solenoid valve components—AC Systems (© AC Spark Plug Division)

Solenoid valve stem and spring—AC System (© AC Spark Plug Division)

Pushing the solenoid valve components from the solenoid bore—AC System (© AC Spark Plug Division)

Installing the check valve with the conical spring
AC System (© AC Spark Plug Division)

Solenoid valve cage and stem installed in the solenoid bore—AC System (© AC Spark Plug Division)

on the check valve spring. Insert the large end of spring into the largest check valve bore.

7. Install a new 'O' ring on the valve seat retainer and press the retainer into the largest check valve bore. Make sure that it is fully seated.

8. Install a new check valve button on the check valve spring. Insert the rounded end of the check valve button into the remaining check valve bore. The check valve will contact the valve seat on the (solenoid) valve body.

9. Install a new 'O' ring in the groove on the check valve cover. Align the check valve spring with the boss on the check valve cover and install the cover. Tighten the retaining bolts to 55-64 inch-pounds.

10. Install a new 'O' ring on the solenoid.

11. Thread the solenoid into the solenoid bore and tighten with a suitable socket. Torque the solenoid to 66-96 inch-pounds torque.

12. Drop a new tension ball into the hole in the solenoid valve housing. Install the allen-head set screw and tighten to 20-30 inch-pounds.

13. Position a new rubber diaphragm on the exhaust valve body and secure with the screw and concave washer. The concave side of the washer should face toward the head of the screw.

14. Install a new rubber seal on the modulation tube and secure by pressing on the metal retainer.

15. Install a new rubber 'O' ring on the modulation tube and exhaust valve body.

16. Insert the modulation tube, seal end first, into the relay valve housing. Drop the spring over the modulation tube.

17. Press the exhaust valve body into the relay valve housing until the valve is fully seated with the spring nested in the spring seat of the relay valve housing. Secure the assembly with the washer and snap ring. Make sure that the snap ring is fully seated under the lip of the bore, with the bevel side out.

18. Press a new molded rubber valve

assembly into the relay valve piston with the molded rib against the piston. Secure with bolt and tighten to 70-80 inch-pounds.

19. Install a new 'O' ring on the relay valve piston.

20. Position the small end of a new conical spring over the lugs in the piston cavity of the relay valve housing.

21. Insert the relay valve piston into the piston bore of the relay valve housing.

22. Insert the flow restrictor into its bore in the relay valve housing, be sure it is properly seated.

23. Install a new 'O' ring on the solenoid valve housing.

24. Align the rate control valve restriction bores and bolt holes on the solenoid and relay valve housings. Press the two housings together until they are fully seated.

25. Install the bolts holding the solenoid and relay valve housings together and tighten to 110-130 inch-pounds.

26. Position a new lower controller cover gasket on the modulator assembly. Install the lower cover assembly and secure with retaining screws, tighten to 140-160 inch-pounds.

27. Place a new controller cover gasket on the lower cover.

28. Install the solenoid leads on the controller assembly.

Check valve cover boss and long check valve spring—AC System (© AC Spark Plug Division)

Cut-away view of the relay valve housing—AC System (© AC Spark Plug Division)

29. Assemble the controller/cover to the lower controller cover, care must be used so that the solenoid leads are not pinched. Install the retaining screws and tighten to 16-20 foot-pounds.

Installation

1. Install the modulator assembly on the vehicle and tighten the retaining bolts to 18-22 foot-pounds.
2. Connect the air lines to the modulator assembly.
3. Connect the electrical lines to the modulator assembly.
4. Recharge the air reservoir that supplies the modulator assembly.
5. Proceed to the "Testing & Troubleshooting" section at the end of this section, and check the modulator operation, both electrical and air.

Wheel Speed Sensor

Removal

NOTE: It is not necessary to remove the wheel and brake drum assembly for removal or installation of this type of wheel speed sensor.

1. Disconnect the electrical cable from the sensor.
2. Loosen the sensor lock nut.
3. Thread the sensor out of the mounting bracket.

Wheel speed sensor components—exploded view—AC System
(© AC Spark Plug Division)

Installation

Installation
1. Install the sensor as follows:

   a. New sensor; Thread the sensor into the mounting bracket until it is in full contact with the brake drum.

   b. Used sensor; remove the old pad. Thread the sensor into the mounting until it is in full contact with the brake drum, then back out sensor

1½ turns. The gap should be between 0.050-0.100 inch.
2. Secure the sensor assembly in the mounting bracket with the lock-nut, tighten to 30-40 foot-pounds.
3. Install the sensor electrical cable.
4. Recheck the wheel speed sensor gap, the gap should be .050-.100 inch.
5. Proceed to the "Testing & Trouble shooting" section and check the operation of the wheel speed sensor.

PROBLEM	TRACTOR
"WARNING LIGHT OFF" & "NO BULB-CHECK"	

WARNING LIGHT/LIGHTS COME ON FOR UP TO 5 SECONDS WHEN IGNITION SWITCH IS TURNED ON TO CHECK BULB AND WARNING CIRCUIT. THIS IS NORMAL AND IS CALLED THE "BULB—CHECK". WHEN THERE IS NO "BULB—CHECK", TROUBLESHOOTING IS REQUIRED.

VOLT-OHMMETER METHOD

WHEN THERE IS NO "BULB—CHECK", THE MOST PROBABLE CAUSE IS A LOOSE OR BURNED—OUT WARNING LAMP. IF THE LAMP CIRCUIT IS FUNCTIONAL, EVERY AXLE SYSTEM HAS A PROBLEM IN THE POWER CABLE AND/OR MODULATOR.

STEP	PROCEDURE	WARN LIGHT	BULB CHECK	RESULT	NEXT STEP
1 (WARNING LAMP & CAB WIRING TEST)	JUMPER FROM "NEGATIVE SUPPLY" TO LAMP WHERE GREEN WIRES FROM POWER CABLES ARE ATTACHED.	OFF	—	PROBLEM IS IN LAMP, LAMP SOCKET OR CAB WIRING.	1A
		ON	—	LAMP AND LAMP WIRING OK. EVERY AXLE SYSTEM HAS A PROBLEM IN THE POWER CABLE AND/OR MODULATOR.	2

STEP	PROCEDURE	WARN LIGHT	BULB CHECK	RESULT	NEXT STEP
2 AXLE SYSTEM TEST	REPEAT THIS STEP FOR EVERY AXLE SYSTEM. DISCONNECT POWER CABLES FROM ALL MODULATORS. MEASURE D. C. VOLTAGE AT POWER CABLE AS SHOWN — OBSERVE POLARITY. JUMPER	ON	—	VOLTAGE GREATER THAN 10 V.D.C. POWER CABLE IS OK. PROBLEM IS IN MODULATOR.	2A
		OFF	—	PROBLEM IS IN POWER CABLE REGARD-LESS OF VOLTAGE MEASURED.	2B
		ON OR OFF	—	METER POINTER DEFLECTS DOWNSCALE (INDICATING REVERSE POLARITY) PROBLEM IS REVERSE POLARITY IN POWER CABLE OR IN CAB WIRING.	2C
1A WARNING LAMP & CAB WIRING	CORRECT WARNING LAMP AND/OR CAB WIRING PROBLEM BY REPAIRING OR RE-PLACING FAULTY COMPONENTS. TURN IGNITION "ON" AND LOOK FOR "BULB-CHECK".	—	YES	"BULB-CHECK" IS FUNCTIONAL. PUT VE-HICLE BACK IN SERVICE.	—
		—	NO	CONTINUE TROUBLESHOOTING.	1
2A REPLACE MODULATOR	REPLACE MODULATOR. DISCONNECT AND RE-CONNECT ALL HOSES AND CABLES PROPERLY. TURN ON IGNITION AND LOOK FOR "BULB-CHECK".	—	YES	THIS AXLE SYSTEM OK. CONTINUE TROU-BLESHOOTING NEXT AXLE.	2
				IF THIS IS FINAL AXLE SYSTEM, RECON-NECT ALL POWER CABLES AND PUT VE-HICLE BACK IN SERVICE.	
		—	NO	PROBLEM IS STILL IN MODULATOR.	(2A)
2B POWER CABLE	REPLACE POWER CABLE AND RECONNECT TO MODULATOR. TURN IGNITION "ON", AND LOOK FOR "BULB-CHECK"	—	YES	THIS AXLE SYSTEM IS OK. CONTINUE TROUBLESHOOTING NEXT AXLE.	2
				IF THIS IS FINAL AXLE SYSTEM, RECON-NECT ALL POWER CABLES AND PUT VE-HICLE BACK IN SERVICE.	
		—	NO	CONTINUE TROUBLESHOOTING THIS AXLE.	2
2C CAB WIRING	CORRECT REVERSE POLARITY PROBLEM IN POWER CABLE OR IN CAB WIRING, AND RECONNECT POWER CABLE TO MODULA-TOR. TURN IGNITION "ON" AND LOOK FOR "BULB-CHECK".	—	YES	THIS AXLE SYSTEM IS OK. CONTINUE TROUBLESHOOTING NEXT AXLE.	2
				IF THIS IS FINAL AXLE SYSTEM, RECON-NECT ALL POWER CABLES AND PUT VE-HICLE BACK IN SERVICE.	
		—	NO	CONTINUE TROUBLESHOOTING THIS AXLE.	2

TRACTOR WARNING LIGHT/LIGHTS LOCATED IN THE INSTRUMENT PANEL, OPERATE WHEN THE IGNITION SWITCH IS "ON" OR POWER IS APPLIED TO THE WHEEL LOCK CONTROL SYSTEM.

WARNING LIGHT/LIGHTS COME ON FOR UP TO 5 SECONDS WHEN IGNITION SWITCH IS TURNED ON TO CHECK BULB AND WARNING CIRCUIT.

WARNING LIGHT/LIGHTS ARE NORMALLY "OFF" WHEN SYSTEMS ARE FUNCTIONAL.

VOLT-OHMMETER METHOD

WARNING LIGHT/LIGHTS COME ON AND STAY ON WHEN A PROBLEM IS DETECTED IN ONE OR MORE AXLE SYSTEMS.

TROUBLE SHOOTING PROCEDURE LOCATES FAULTY AXLE SYSTEM/SYSTEMS AND ISOLATES PROBLEM TO WARNING LIGHT, POWER CABLE, SENSOR CABLE, SENSOR, MODULATOR, OR VEHICLE WIRING.

	STEP	PROCEDURE	WARN LIGHT	RESULTS	NEXT STEP
LOCATE FAULTY AXLE	1	TURN TRACTOR IGNITION SWITCH "ON". DISCONNECT POWER CABLE FROM EACH MODULATOR ASSEMBLY, ONE AT A TIME, UNTIL WARNING LIGHT GOES "OFF". (DO NOT RECONNECT CABLES UNLESS INSTRUCTED.) POWER CABLE — MODULATOR ASSEMBLY	OFF	WARNING LIGHT WILL GO "OFF" WHEN A FAULTY SYSTEM IS DISCONNECTED. CONTINUE TROUBLE-SHOOTING THAT AXLE SYSTEM.	2
			ON	IF WARNING LIGHT STAYS "ON" WHEN ALL SYSTEMS ARE DISCONNECTED, PROBLEM IS IN WARNING LIGHT CIRCUIT.	1A
POWER CABLE TEST	2	MEASURE D. C. VOLTAGE AT POWER CABLE TERMINALS AS SHOWN.	—	VOLTAGE GREATER THAN 10 V. D. C. MODULATOR IS GETTING POWER. PROBLEM IS IN SENSOR, SENSOR CABLES, OR MODULATOR.	3
			—	VOLTAGE LESS THAN 10 V.D.C. MODULATOR IS NOT GETTING POWER. PROBLEM IS IN POWER CABLE, POWER CABLE CONNECTIONS TO CAB WIRING, OR CAB WIRING.	2A
SENSOR & SENSOR CABLE	3	DISCONNECT SENSOR CABLES FROM BOTH SENSORS. MEASURE RESISTANCE OF EACH SENSOR AS SHOWN:	—	RESISTANCE BETWEEN 1000 & 2000 OHMS.	3A
			—	RESISTANCE NOT BETWEEN 1000 & 2000 OHMS. SENSOR IS BAD – REPLACE & RECHECK PER THIS STEP.	(3)
	3A	MEASURE RESISTANCE OF EACH SENSOR FROM SENSOR TERMINAL TO SENSOR BODY AS SHOWN.	—	RESISTANCE GREATER THAN 100,000 OHMS. SENSOR IS GOOD.	3B
			—	RESISTANCE LESS THAN 100,000 OHMS. SENSOR IS BAD – REPLACE & RECHECK PER STEP 3.	3

	STEP	PROCEDURE	WARN LIGHT	RESULTS	NEXT STEP
SENSOR & SENSOR CABLE	3B	RECONNECT SENSOR CABLES TO BOTH SENSORS. DISCONNECT BOTH SENSOR CABLES FROM MODULATOR & MEASURE RESISTANCE AT TERMINALS OF BOTH SENSOR CABLES AS SHOWN:	—	BOTH CABLES HAVE A RESISTANCE BETWEEN 1000 & 2000 OHMS.	3C
			—	RESISTANCE OF ONE CABLE (OR BOTH CABLES) IS NOT BETWEEN 1000 & 2000 OHMS. RECHECK CONNECTION BETWEEN SENSOR & SENSOR CABLE. IF RESISTANCE IS STILL NOT BETWEEN 1000 & 2000 OHMS, SENSOR CABLE IS BAD — REPLACE CABLE & RECHECK PER THIS STEP.	(3B)
	3C	MEASURE RESISTANCE AT TERMINALS OF BOTH SENSOR CABLES AS SHOWN.	—	BOTH CABLES HAVE A RESISTANCE GREATER THAN 100,000 OHMS. SENSOR & SENSOR CABLES ARE GOOD.	3D
			—	RESISTANCE OF ONE CABLE (OR BOTH CABLES) IS LESS THAN 100,000 OHMS. SENSOR CABLE IS BAD — REPLACE CABLE AND RECHECK PER STEP 3B.	3B
	3D	RECONNECT BOTH SENSOR CABLES TO THE MODULATOR. ALSO RECONNECT THE POWER CABLE.	OFF	SYSTEM IS "OK"	5
			ON	SENSOR & SENSOR CABLES HAVE BEEN CHECKED AND FOUND GOOD. PROBLEM MUST BE IN MODULATOR.	4
REPLACE MODULATOR	4	REPLACE MODULATOR ASSEMBLY, DISCONNECT AND RECONNECT ALL HOSES AND CABLES PROPERLY.	OFF	SYSTEM IS "OK".	5
			ON	THERE IS STILL A PROBLEM WITH THE SYSTEM ON THIS AXLE. CONTINUE TROUBLE-SHOOTING.	3
LOCATE OTHER FAULTY AXLES	5	PLUG IN REMAINING POWER CABLES TO OTHER AXLE/S, ONE AT A TIME, AND CHECK THE WARNING LIGHT AFTER EACH CABLE IS PLUGGED IN. POWER CABLE	OFF	SYSTEM IS "OK".	—
			ON	IF WARNING LIGHT COMES ON AND STAYS ON AFTER PLUGGING IN POWER CABLE, THERE IS SOMETHING WRONG WITH THAT AXLE SYSTEM ALSO.	2

Anti-Skid Systems

	STEP	PROCEDURE	WARN LIGHT	RESULTS	NEXT STEP
LOCATE FAULTY AXLE	1A	DISCONNECT GREEN WIRES AT CAB END OF POWER CABLES, ONE AT A TIME, UNTIL THE WARNING LIGHT GOES "OFF".	OFF	IF WARNING LIGHT GOES "OFF" WHEN A GREEN WIRE IS DISCONNECTED, PROBLEM IS IN POWER CABLE CONTAINING THAT GREEN WIRE.	1B
			ON	IF ALL GREEN WIRES HAVE BEEN DISCONNECTED AND WARNING LIGHT IS STILL "ON", PROBLEM IS SHORT TO NEGATIVE IN THE WARNING LIGHT SOCKET.	1C
	1B	REPLACE POWER CABLE. RECONNECT GREEN WIRES, ONE AT A TIME, MAKING SURE THE WARNING LIGHT REMAINS "OFF"	OFF	WARNING LIGHT CIRCUIT IS "OK".	5
			ON	IF WARNING LIGHT COMES "ON" WHEN A GREEN WIRE IS RECONNECTED, PROBLEM IS IN POWER CABLE CONTAINING THAT GREEN WIRE.	(1B)
	1C	REPAIR OR REPLACE WARNING LIGHT SOCKET TO ELIMINATE SHORT. RECONNECT GREEN WIRES, ONE AT A TIME, MAKING SURE WARNING LIGHT REMAINS "OFF".	OFF	WARNING LIGHT CIRCUIT IS "OK".	5
			ON	IF WARNING LIGHT COMES "ON" WHEN A GREEN WIRE IS RECONNECTED, PROBLEM IS IN POWER CABLE CONTAINING THAT GREEN WIRE.	1B
POWER CABLE	2A	TO INVESTIGATE FURTHER, MEASURE D.C. VOLTAGE AT CAB END OF POWER CABLE AS SHOWN.	—	VOLTAGE GREATER THAN 10V. DC, PROBLEM IS IN POWER CABLE.	2B
			—	VOLTAGE LESS THAN 10 V. DC, PROBLEM IS IN CAB OR VEHICLE WIRING.	2C
	2B	REPLACE POWER CABLE AND CHECK VOLTAGE PER STEP 2 PROCEDURE. IF VOLTAGE IS LESS THAN 10 V. DC, THERE IS STILL A POWER CABLE PROBLEM REPAIR OR REPLACE. IF VOLTAGE IS GREATER THAN 10 V. DC, RECONNECT POWER CABLE TO MODULATOR.	OFF	SYSTEM IS OK.	5
			ON	POWER CABLE PROBLEM HAS BEEN CORRECTED. OTHER PROBLEM IS IN SENSORS, SENSOR CABLES, OR MODULATOR.	3

510

	STEP	PROCEDURE	WARN LIGHT	RESULTS	NEXT STEP
POWER CABLE	**2C**	CHECK AND REPAIR TRUCK ELECTRICAL SYSTEM INCLUDING FUSE OR CIRCUIT BREAKER, BATTERY, AND BATTERY TERMINALS AND ALTERNATOR OR GENERATOR. AFTER REPAIRING PROBLEM IN VEHICLE ELECTRICAL SYSTEM, RECONNECT POWER CABLE TO MODULATOR.	OFF	SYSTEM IS "OK".	5
			ON	THERE IS STILL A PROBLEM WITH THE AXLE BEING EVALUATED.	2

AIRBRAKE - WLC TRACTOR MODULATOR ELECTRICAL SERVICE PROCEDURE
("SOLENOID" AND/OR "CONTROLLER & COVER ASSEMBLY" ONLY)
VOLT-OHMMETER METHOD

	STEP	INSTRUCTIONS		NEXT STEP
DISASSEMBLY	**1**	REMOVE CONTROLLER & COVER ASSEMBLY & DISCONNECT SOLENOID LEADS (REFER TO "MODULATOR OVERHAUL – ELECTRICAL PROCEDURE").		2
SOLENOID	**2**	TAKE SOLENOID LEADS AND MOMENTARILY CONNECT THEM TO A 12 VOLT BATTERY.	SOLENOID IS OK IF YOU HEAR A "CLICK" WHEN LEADS ARE CONNECTED AND ANOTHER "CLICK" WHEN THEY ARE DISCONNECTED. PROBLEM IS IN THE CONTROLLER & COVER ASSEMBLY.	5
			IF "CLICKS" ARE NOT HEARD, PROBLEM IS IN SOLENOID.	3
	3	REPLACE THE SOLENOID (REFER TO "MODULATOR OVERHAUL ELECTRICAL PROCEDURE").		4
	4	TEST NEW SOLENOID IN SAME MANNER AS SHOWN STEP #2.	SOLENOID IS OK IF A "CLICK" IS HEARD WHEN LEADS ARE CONNECTED AND ANOTHER "CLICK" WHEN THEY ARE DISCONNECTED. REASSEMBLE THE CONTROLLER & COVER ASSEM. (REFER TO "MODULATOR OVERHAUL – ELECTRICAL PROCEDURE")	6
			IF NO "CLICKS" ARE HEARD, PROBLEM IS STILL IN SOLENOID.	3

	STEP	INSTRUCTION		NEXT STEP
CONTROLLER	5	INSTALL NEW CONTROLLER & COVER ASSEM (REFER TO "MODULATOR OVERHAUL – ELECTRICAL PROCEDURE")		6
TESTING REPAIRED TRACTOR MODULATOR ASSEMBLY	6	TEST THE REPAIRED MODULATOR BY SIMULATING A VEHICLE INSTALLATION ON THE BENCH AS FOLLOWS: CONNECT TWO SPEED SENSORS, TWO SPEED SENSOR CABLES, A BATTERY, AND A 12 VOLT TROUBLE LIGHT AS SHOWN. WHEN THE LEAD IS CONNECTED TO THE NEGATIVE TERMINAL OF THE BATTERY, A NORMAL "BULB CHECK" SHOULD OCCUR.	NORMAL BULB–CHECK IS OBSERVED. (THE TROUBLE LIGHT COMES ON FOR UP TO 5 SECONDS AND THEN GOES OFF.)	7
			NO "BULB–CHECK" IS OBSERVED OR TROUBLE LIGHT REMAINS ON. DOUBLE CHECK ALL ELECTRICAL CONNECTIONS. IF THE LIGHT REMAINS ON, THERE IS STILL A PROBLEM IN THE MODULATOR ASSEMBLY.	1
	7	DISCONNECT ONE SENSOR CABLE FROM MODULATOR TO SIMULATE A FAULT.	IF THE TROUBLE LIGHT COMES "ON" AND STAYS ON, THE WARNING SYSTEM HAS CORRECTLY DETECTED THE FAULT.	8
			IF THE TROUBLE LIGHT DOES NOT COME "ON", THE WARNING CIRCUIT IS NOT OPERATING.	5
	8	RECONNECT THE SENSOR CABLE TO THE MODULATOR.	IF THE TROUBLE LIGHT GOES "OFF", THE MODULATOR IS OPERATING PROPERLY AND MAY BE RETURNED TO SERVICE.	—
			IF THE TROUBLE LIGHT REMAINS "ON", DOUBLE CHECK ALL TEST CONNECTIONS. IF LIGHT REMAINS "ON", THERE IS A PROBLEM IN THE CONTROLLER & COVER ASSEMBLY.	5

Within step 6 instruction cell figure labels: 12 VOLT TROUBLE LIGHT; BLOW – UP; PWR; TO BATT (+); TO BATT (–); TO TROUBLE LIGHT

B.F. Goodrich Systems

NOTE: Before attempting any repair operations on the anti-skid system, determine the problem area by the tests outlined at the end of this section.

Control Valve
Disassembly (On Vehicle)
1. Turn off vehicle power to the computer.
2. Exhaust the air reservoir that supplies the valve to be removed.
3. Separate the computer from the valve assembly.
4. Disconnect the solenoid leads from the valve assembly. It is not necessary to disconnect the sensor cables or the power cables from the computer module.
5. Lable and disconnect all air lines attached to the valve assembly.
6. Remove the valve assembly mounting bolts and remove the valve assembly from the vehicle.

Assembly

1. Inspect all air lines and cables connected to the computer/valve assembly. If any are in question, replace them.
2. Install the valve assembly on the vehicle, making sure that a good metal to metal contact is achieved.
3. Connect all air lines to their appropriate ports on the valve assembly.
4. Check the supply reservoir by using the tractor power or auxiliary air supply, check the air lines for leaks.
5. Connect the solenoid leads to their terminals on the computer module.
6. Install the computer module on the valve. Care must be taken not to pinch the solenoid leads between the computer and the valve assemblies.
7. Check the operation of the valve by applying the brakes and observing the brake action. There should be no audible leakage during application and air should exhaust rapidly when the brakes are released.
8. Perform the electrical tests as outlined in "Testing & Trouble Shooting" section.

Computer Module Assembly

Disassembly (On Vehicle)

NOTE: If the computer module is being separated on the vehicle, it is not necessary to discharge the air system.

1. Turn off vehicle power to the computer module.
2. Tag the lead wires and disconnect them.
3. Remove the computer to valve retaining bolts and carefully separate the computer from the valve assembly.
4. Tag and disconnect the solenoid lead wires.
5. Remove the computer assembly.

Assembly

1. Connect the solenoid lead wires to their terminals on the computer assembly.
2. Install the computer module on the valve assembly. Care must be taken during installation not to pinch any of the wires between the computer and valve assemblies.
3. Connect the sensor and power lead wires.
4. Perform the electrical operations tests as outlined in the "Testing & Trouble Shooting" section.

Wheel Speed Sensor

Removal

1. Remove the wheel and brake drum assembly.

Service Port 3/8 NPT
Supply Port 3/4" NPT
Delivery Port 1/2" NPT
4-Port Relay Valve

Valve assembly with computer module removed (© B.F. Goodrich)

Computer module seperated from the valve assembly (© B.F. Goodrich)

2. Loosen and remove the sensor assembly mounting bolt.
3. Disconnect the sensor lead wire.
4. Remove the sensor.

Installation

1. If the same sensor is being reinstalled, inspect for damage or wear.
2. Connect the sensor lead wires.
3. Install the wheel speed sensor assembly on the brake spider. Be sure that the sensor is aligned correctly. Secure the sensor lead wires.

Rotor assembly (© B.F. Goodrich)

4. Replace the wheel and brake drum assembly.
5. Check the voltage output of the sensor as outlined in the "Testing & Trouble Shooting" section.

Rotor

Removal

1. Remove the wheel and brake drum assembly.
2. Remove the rotor attaching bolts.
3. Lift the rotor assembly out of the brake drum.

Installation

1. Attach the rotor assembly to the brake drum.
2. Make sure that the wheel speed sensor is correctly positioned.
3. Install the wheel and brake drum assembly.
4. Check the voltage output of the sensor as outlined in the "Testing & Trouble Shooting" Section.

Modulator Operation & Leak Test

1. Block the wheels and fully charge the air system.
2. Apply and release the brakes several times. Check for prompt application and release of brake chambers at all wheels.

Wheel speed sensor assembly (© B.F. Goodrich)

3. Leak test the exhaust port with a soap solution. Slight leakage is permitted as follows:
   a. Brakes Applied—one inch bubble in 3 seconds.
   b. Brakes Released—one inch bubble in 5 seconds.

NOTE: Replace and valve if it does not function properly in step 2 or if excessive leakage is observed.

Warning Lamp Operation Test

1. Turn the ignition key to the "ON" position and observe the warning lamp. It should be on for 3-5 seconds, then go off and stay off.
2. If the lamp stays on, refer to "General Electrical Diagnosis".
3. If the light flashed on and off, locate and correct the loose connection.
4. If the lamp fails to light, replace the bulb and recheck.
5. If the lamp still fails to light, check for good ground connection and check if there is power to the bulb. Repair the circuit as required.
6. If there is power to the "Power" terminal on the monitor, but no power to the "Ind" terminal for 3-5 seconds, after turning the ignition switch "ON", replace the monitor assembly.

NOTE:
P1, P2, P3 POSTS CONNECT TO POWER TERMINAL OF CONTROLLERS.

W1, W2, W3 POSTS CONNECT TO WARNING TERMINAL OF CONTROLLERS.

ON A TWO AXLE INSTALLATION A JUMPER WIRE MUST BE INSTALLED BETWEEN THE W2 AND W3 TERMINALS.

Failsafe monitor unit (© B.F. Goodrich)

General Electrical Diagnosis

The electrical system should be tested out anytime the WARNING LAMP STAYS LIT. This can be caused by:

1. No power to the system. Warning relay is powering the warning lamp circuit.
2. Malfunction of the axle system.

Defective computer module, sensor or solenoid valve.
3. Defective warning monitor assembly.

NOTE: The diagnostic charts that follow will isolate the defective component or sub-system. You will need a VOM (volt-ohm meter) to perform the tests outlined.

△1 If failsafe monitor unit is mounted to a non-conductive surface - a ground wire must be provided to chassis.

△2 On an axle system where less than 3 axles are used to connect unused W terminals with a jumper to the used W terminal.

△3 The left sensor connectors are green and the right sensor connectors are yellow.

△4 The power/warning connectors from the controllers are colored black.

B.F. Goodrich circuit diagram (© B.F. Goodrich)

Anti-Skid Systems

CONDITION 1: FAILSAFE INDICATOR LIGHT DOES NOT COME ON WHEN KEY SWITCH IS TURNED TO "ON" POSITION.

Locate failsafe monitor unit and remove cover (if so equipped). Is battery voltage present between indicator light terminals after key switch has been reset? (Fig. 1)

FIGURE 1. BATTERY VOLTAGE

YES — Check light bulb and bulb socket. Check for open wiring between failsafe monitor and indicator light.

NO — Is there battery voltage present between failsafe monitor's key terminal and ground? (Fig. 2)

NEGATIVE GROUND. FOR POSITIVE GROUND, REVERSE LEADS. FIGURE 2.

YES — Replace failsafe monitor unit and check the operation of the system.*

NO — Check for:
Open wire between key switch and failsafe monitor.
Defective key switch
A poorly grounded failsafe monitor. (Mounting bolt near W3 terminal)
Repair or replace any malfunctioning components and check operation of system.*

*NOTE
After each check, turn key off and then on to reset failsafe circuitry in controller.

CONDITION 2: FAILSAFE INDICATOR LIGHT DOES NOT GO OUT AFTER 3 - 5 SECONDS.

BATTERY VOLTAGE FIGURE 3. NEGATIVE GROUND. FOR POSITIVE GROUND, REVERSE LEADS.

BATTERY VOLTAGE NEGATIVE GROUND. FOR POSITIVE GROUND, REVERSE LEADS. FIGURE 4.

BATTERY VOLTAGE NEGATIVE GROUND. FOR POSITIVE GROUND, REVERSE LEADS. FIGURE 5.

Locate failsafe monitor unit and remove cover (if so equipped). Is battery voltage present between power and ground terminals at failsafe monitor? (Fig. 3).

YES — Are fuses okay?

NO — Check for an open power wire, open circuit breaker, or defective key switch. Repair or replace any malfunctioning components and check oepration of system.

YES — Is there battery voltage between all "P" terminals and ground? (Fig. 4).

NO — Replace fuse and check operation of system.* Should replacement fuse blow, follow procedure as outlined in Condition 4.

YES — Is there voltage at all "W" terminals within 4 volts of battery voltage? On negative ground vehicles, measure between "W" terminals and ground. On positive ground installations, measure between "W" terminals and power. (Fig. 5).

NO — Replace failsafe monitor and check operation of system.*

YES — Replace failsafe monitor if correct voltage is present on all "W" terminals and failsafe light still remains on. Then, check operation of system.*

NO — Lack of voltage on a "W" terminal indicates which axle is malfunctioning. Remove controller on malfunctioning axle and check for voltage between power and common terminals (Fig. 6). Is battery voltage present? See NOTE**.

*NOTE
After each check, turn key off and then on to reset failsafe circuitry in controller.

**NOTE
On controllers that do not use a separate ground wire, but use modulator housing for a ground, it will be necessary to connect a jumper wire between controller and modulator housing during testing.

CONDITION 2 (CONT.)

BATTERY VOLTAGE

NEGATIVE GROUND.
FOR POSITIVE GROUND,
REVERSE LEADS.

FIGURE 6.

VOLTAGE WITHIN 4
VOLTS OF BATTERY
VOLTAGE.

SOLENOID LEADS
CONNECTED, WARNING
WIRE DISCONNECTED.

NEGATIVE GRD.
FOR POSITIVE GRD.
TRUCKS, MEASURE
BETWEEN WARNING
AND POWER TERMI-
NALS.

FIGURE 7.

FIGURE 8.
300 - 600 OHMS.

300 - 600 OHMS.

FIGURE 9.

INFINITE
RESISTANCE

FIGURE 10.

FIGURE 11.

5 - 10 OHMS.

INFINITE
RESISTANCE

FIGURE 12.

YES
Check for voltage between warning and common terminals on negative ground vehicles and between warning and power terminals on positive ground installations (Fig. 7). When making this check, disconnect warning wire at controller and make sure solenoid leads are connected.* Is reading within 4 volts of battery voltage?

NO
Check power wire and connectors between controllers and failsafe monitor for an open circuit. Also, check controller for a proper ground.

YES
Check warning wire and connectors between controller and failsafe monitor for an open or ground. Repair or replace wire as necessary.

NO
Check sensor circuit resistance at controller with key switch turned off. Disconnect "SL" and "SR" wires and measure resistance between disconnected "SL" wire and "SC" terminal. Then, measure resistance between "SR" wire and "SC" terminal (Fig. 8). Do both sensor circuits measure 300 - 600 ohms?

YES
Remove both "SC" sensor wires from controller and check resistance (RX1K scale) between disconnect "SL" wire and common terminal of controller. (Fig. 10). Repeat check between "SR" wire and common. Do both sensor wires measure infinite resistance (high resistance, no needle deflection) to common?

NO
Check sensor resistance at connector closest to wheel on malfunctioning sensor circuit (Fig. 9). Is sensor resistance 300 - 600 ohms?

YES
Repair or replace sensor wire between controller and sensor's connectors.

NO
Remove wheen and drum, and replace sensor.

YES
Check solenoid resistances by disconnecting solenoid leads and measuring between same size spade terminal leads with an ohmmeter (RX1 scale) (Fig. 11). Do both solenoids have 5 - 10 ohms resistance?

NO
Disconnect sensor connector closest to wheel on grounded sensor circuit. Measure resistance (RX1K) between sensor and chassis ground (Fig. 12). Should resistance measure infinite, repair or replace grounded sensor wire between sensor and controller. However, if sensor resistance to ground is not infinite, replace grounded sensor.

YES
Replace controller and check operation of system.*

NO
Replace solenoids and check operation of system. When replacing solenoids, replace them one at a time to avoid mixing them.

*NOTE
After each check, turn key off and then on to reset failsafe circuitry in controller.

CONDITION 3: FAILSAFE INDICATOR LIGHT COMES ON WHEN VEHICLE IS MOVING.

VOLTAGE WITHIN 4 VOLTS OF BATTERY VOLTAGE.

NEGATIVE GROUND. FOR POSITIVE GROUND INSTALLATIONS, MEASURE BETWEEN WARNING AND POWER TERMINALS.

FIGURE 5.

300 - 600 OHMS.

FIGURE 8.

300 - 600 OHMS.

FIGURE 9.

INFINITE RESISTANCE

FIGURE 10.

INFINITE RESISTANCE

FIGURE 12.

Operate vehicle until failsafe light comes on. With vehicle stopped and key switch still on, remove failsafe monitor cover (if so equipped). Check for voltage at all "W" terminals (Fig. 5). On negative ground vehicles, measure between "W" and ground terminals. On positive ground installations, check between "W" and power terminal. Lack of voltage indicates which axle system is malfunctioning.

Turn key switch off, then remove controller and disconnect "SL" and "SR" sensor wires. Measure resistance between "SL" wire and "SC" terminal. Then measure resistance between "SR" wire and "SC" terminal (Fig. 8). Do both sensor circuits measure 300 - 600 ohms?

YES

Remove both "SC" wires from controller and measure resistance between disconnected "SL" wire and common terminal of controller (Fig. 10). Repeat check of "SR" wire and common. Do both sensor wires measure infinite resistance to common?

NO

Disconnect sensor connector closest to wheel on malfunctioning sensor circuit (Fig. 9). Measure sensor resistance. Is it between 300 - 600 ohms?

YES

Repair or replace shorted or grounded sensor cable between sensor connector and controller.

NO

Remove wheel and brake drum, and replace sensor. Then check operation of system.*

YES

Is exciter to sensor engagement correct for both sensors? Exciter should pass between sensor with an equal air gap above and below exciter teeth. Also, inside edge of exciter teeth should be flush with end of sensor (Fig. 13).

To make the check, it will be necessary to remove wheel and brake drum. However, if a BFG test set is available, sensor output can be checked without removing wheel and drum.

NO

Disconnect sensor connector closest to wheel on grounded sensor circuit. Measure resistance between sensor and ground (Fig. 12). If resistance is infinite, repair or replace grounded sensor wire between sensor and controller. Should resistance be less than infinite, replace grounded sensor.

EXCITER

SENSOR ASSEMBLY

EQUAL CLEARANCE

SENSOR AND EXCITER FLUSH

CLEARANCE

FIGURE 13.

YES

Replace controller and check operation of system.*

NO

Loosen sensor bracket and reposition sensor. After making any adjustments, rotate hub and check for any interference between exciter and sensor. Then, check operation of system.*

*NOTE

After each check, turn key off and then on to reset failsafe circuitry in controller.

CONDITION 4: REPLACEMENT FUSE BLOWS.

Turn key switch off and then disconnect "P" and "W" wires in blown fuse circuit at failsafe monitor. Install a new fuse and reapply power. Does replacement fuse blow?

NO
Remove controller on malfunctioning axle system and disconnect power wire. Measure resistance with an ohmmeter RX1K between disconnected power wire and common terminal.** Is resistance infinite?

YES
Replace failsafe monitor and check operation of system.

YES
Disconnect sensor wires ("SL", "SC", "SR") from controller and measure resistance between disconnected sensor wires and common terminal. Is resistance infinite?

NO
Repair or replace grounded power wire between controller and failsafe monitor.

YES
Disconnect solenoid leads from controller and measure resistance RX1K between disconnected solenoids leads and common terminal. Is resistance infinite?

NO
Repair or replace sensor cable or sensor. Then, check operation of system.*

YES
Replace axle's controller and check operation of system.*

NO
Replace solenoids and check operation of system.*

**NOTE
On controllers that do not use a separate ground wire, but use modulator housing for a ground, it will be necessary to connect a jumper wire between controller and modulator housing during testing.

*NOTE
After each check, turn key off and then on to reset failsafe circuitry in controller.

Eaton Skid Control Systems

NOTE: Before attempting any repair operations on the anti-skid system, determine the problem area by the tests outlined at the end of this section.

Control Valve

Disassembly (On Vehicle)

1. Turn off the vehicle power to the computer.
2. Exhaust the air reservoir that supplies the valve to be removed.
3. Separate the computer from the valve assembly.
4. Disconnect the two solenoid leads from the valve assembly. It is not necessary to disconnect the sensor and power cables from the computer.
5. Disconnect and label all air lines attached to the valve assembly.

6. Remove the valve assembly mounting bolts and remove the valve assembly from the vehicle.

Assembly

1. Inspect all air lines and cables connected to the computer/valve

Computer and control valve assembly—Eaton System (© Ford Motor Co.)

assembly. If any are in question, replace them.

2. Install the valve assembly on the vehicle, making sure that a good metal to metal contact is achieved.

3. Connect all air lines to their appropriate ports on the valve assembly.

4. Check the supply reservoir by using the tractor power or auxiliary air supply. check the air lines for leaks.

5. Connect the solenoid leads to the solenoid.

6. Install the computer assembly on the valve. Care must be taken not to pinch the solenoid leads between the computer and the valve assemblies.

7. Check the operation of the valve by applying the brakes and observing the brake action. There should be no audible leakage during application and the air should exhaust rapidly when the brakes are released.

8. Perform the electrical tests as outlined in the "Test & Trouble Shooting" section.

Solenoid

Removal

1. Turn off vehicle power to the computer.

2. Exhaust the air reservoir that supplies the valve with the defective solenoid.

3. Separate the computer from the valve assembly and disconnect the solenoid leads at the solenoid.

4. Remove the solenoid mounting nuts. Remove the solenoid complete with the 'O' rings.

Installation

1. Position the two NEW 'O' rings on the solenoid and lightly coat with lubricant.

2. Carefully push the solenoid into its mounting cavity in the valve assembly. Be sure that no damage occurs during installation.

3. Install the retaining nuts and torque to 125-150 inch lbs.

4. Recharge the brake system and have a helper apply and hold the brakes. Apply a soap solution to the base of the solenoid and to the exhaust valve. No air leakage is permitted.

5. Connect 12 volts to the terminal tabs. The solenoid should exhaust. If a leak develops at the solenoid base, the small "O" ring may have been damaged during installation and should be replaced.

Computer Assembly

Disassembly

NOTE: If the computer module is being separated on the vehicle, it is not necessary to discharge the air system. Remove the terminal cover and identify and tag the wires before removing them from the terminal posts.

1. Remove the through bolts from the front of the computer module.

2. Carefully separate the computer module from the valve assembly.

3. Disconnect the solenoid leads.

4. Identify the wires in the module housing and disconnect.

5. Remove the spring clip and separate the harness from the module housing.

Assembly

1. Connect the lead wires to their respective terminals in the computer module.

2. Install the spring clip.

3. Connect the solenoid lead wires.

4. Install the computer module on the valve assembly. Care must be taken during installation so the wires are not pinched between the computer module and the valve assembly.

5. Place junction box bracket over the computer module cover and install the retaining bolts. Tighten securely.

6. Perform electrical operation tests to be sure that system is working properly.

Wheel Speed Sensor

Removal

1. Remove the wheel and brake drum assembly.

2. Loosen and remove the screw packs and pull the sensor away from the bracket.

3. Disconnect the lead wires at the junction box or modulator.

Installation

1. Inspect the gauge blocks for indicator grooves.

2. Connect the sensor lead wires to junction block or modulator terminals.

3. Place the sensor bracket and install the screw packs. Be sure that the screw pack and lower body are fully engaged in the sensor slot.

4. Slide the sensor to the outermost position on the bracket, toward the brake drum and disc assembly.

5. Tighten the screw packs to 35-50 inch pounds.

6. Replace the wheel and brake drum assembly.

NOTE: To be sure of proper positioning of the sensor, minimize rocking the wheel assembly into position. Put the wheel assembly in place and use the bearings and spindle nut to draw the wheel assembly into position. The rotor assembly will position the sensor and wear it slightly for proper running clearance.

7. Check the voltage output of sensor as outlined in the test section.

Rotor

Removal

1. Remove the wheel and brake drum assembly.

2. Remove the rotor attaching screws.

Solenoid and 'O' ring—Eaton System (© Eaton)

Computer assembly electrical connections—Eaton System (© Ford Motor Co.)

Wheel speed sensor assembly—Eaton System (© Ford Motor Co.)

Monitor test point locations—Eaton System (© Ford Motor Co.)

3. Life the rotor assembly out of the brake drum.

Installation

1. Attach the rotor assembly to the brake drum.
2. Position the wheel speed sensor as described in "Wheel Speed Sensor-Installation".
3. Install the wheel and drum assembly.

NOTE: To be sure of proper positioning of the sensor, minimize rocking the wheel into place. Put the wheel in position and use the bearings and spindle nut to draw the wheel assembly into position. The rotor will push the sensor into its proper position. The rotor will position the sensor and wear it slightly for proper running clearance.

Eaton Skid Control System-Testing & Trouble Shooting

NOTE: To properly diagnose this system the following test procedures MUST be performed in exact order. Do NOT skip any test procedure, follow the procedures as they are outlined in the dignostic charts. When a defect is found, correct as required and complete the remaining tests.

Modulator Operation & Leak Test

1. Block the wheels and fully charge the air system.
2. Apply and release the brakes several times. Check for prompt application and release of brake chambers at all wheels.
3. Leak test the exhaust port with a

soap solution. Slight leakage is permitted as follows:
a. Brakes Applied—one inch bubble in 3 seconds.
b. Brakes Released—one inch bubble in 5 seconds.

NOTE: Replace and valve if it does not function properly in step 2 or if excessive leakage is observed.

Wheel speed sensor assembly location—Eaton System (© Ford Motor Co.)

Wheel speed rotor assemblies—Eaton System (© Ford Motor Co.)

Warning Lamp Operation Test

1. Turn the ignition key to the "ON" position and observe the warning lamp. It should be on for 3-5 seconds, then go off and stay off.
2. If the lamp stays on, refer to "General Electrical Diagnosis".
3. If the light flashed on and off, locate and correct the loose connection.
4. If the lamp fails to light, replace the bulb and recheck.

5. If the lamp still fails to light, check for good ground connection and check if there is power to the bulb. Repair the circuit as required.
6. If there is power to the "Power" terminal on the monitor, but no power to the "Ind" terminal for 3-5 seconds, after turning the ignition switch "ON", replace the monitor assembly.

General Electrical Diagnosis

The electrical system should be tested out anytime the WARNING LAMP STAYS LIT. This can be caused by:

1. No power to the system. Warning relay is powering the warning lamp circuit.
2. Malfunction of the axle system. Defective computer module, sensor or solenoid valve.
3. Defective warning monitor assembly.

NOTE: The diagnostic charts that follow will isolate the defective component or sub-system. You will need a VOM (volt-ohm meter) to perform the tests outlined.

MONITOR TEST

FRONT COVER REMOVED

P W G W³ W¹ P¹
W²

EQUIPMENT NEEDED

DC VOLTMETER
WITH PROBE TIPS
FOR TEST LEADS

TEST POINTS

INSERT TEST LEAD PROBES INTO FEMALE CONNECTOR BESIDE PLUG OR REMOVE COVER TO EXPOSE TEST POINTS.

⏚ = CHASSIS GROUND

TEST	PROCEDURE	RESULTS
A. Power to Monitor	1. Voltmeter: + to P, − to ⏚ 2. Ignition on 3. 11-14 volts required	Not Okay — check power supply circuit and blue wire to power relay. Okay — check ground (B).
B. Monitor Ground	1. Voltmeter: + to P, − to G 2. Ingition on 3. 11-14 volts required	Not Okay — ground monitor and recheck warning lamp. Okay — check power out (C).
C. Power out to Warning Relay	1. Voltmeter: + to PI, − to ⏚ 2. Ignition on 3. 11-14 volts required	Not Okay — replace monitor assembly. Okay — check for warning signal in.
D. Warning Signal In	1. Ignition on 2. Voltmeter: + to W1, W2, W3, − to ⏚ 3. 3-8 volts required for OK signal	Not Okay — test modulator sending not-okay signal. Okay — check warning signal out (D1).
D1. Warning Signal Out	1. Ignition on 2. Voltmeter: + to W − to ⏚ 3. Zero volts required	Voltage Out — replace monitor. Okay (no voltage) — check warning relay (E).
E. Warning Relay	1. Ignition on 2. Voltmeter: + to green wire terminal of relay − to ⏚ 3. 11-14 volts required	Okay — check relay ground. Repair ground or replace relay. Not Okay - repair green wire from monitor PI to relay.

NOTE: Replace monitor assembly if:
(1) Warning relay and W1, W2, W3 signals are okay, but light stays on.
(2) Light doesn't come on momentarily with ignition on (see "Warning Lamp Operation Test").

TEST POINTS

BLUE — POWER
ORANGE
GREEN — COMMON—SENSOR
ORANGE
RED — TO MONITOR
BLACK — GROUND

MODULATOR BOX
TERMINALS

⏚ = CHASSIS GROUND

SOLENOID
LEADS

COMPUTER SEPARATED
FROM VALVE

EQUIPMENT NEEDED

DC VOLTMETER
OHMMETER
AC VOLTMETER
(OR COMBINED VOM)

COMPUTER & WHEEL SPEED SENSOR TEST

TEST	PROCEDURE NOTE: Voltages are DC unless specified AC	RESULTS
F. Warning Signal Out	1. Ignition on 2. Voltmeter: + to RED — to ⏚ 3. 3-8 volts required for okay	Okay — repair red wire to monitor and check warning light. Not Okay — check power in (G).
G. Power in to Modulator	1. Ignition on 2. Voltmeter: + to BLUE — to ⏚ 3. 11-14 volts required	Okay — check modulator ground (H). Not Okay — repair blue wire to splice in harness (if other modulators okay) or check out power supply (Fig. 20).
H. Modulator Ground	1. Ignition off 2. Ohmmeter leads to computer and ⏚ 3. Zero ohms required.	Okay — check solenoid resistance (I) and solenoid terminal resistance (I1). Not Okay — Repair ground.
I. Solenoid Resistance	1. Separate computer from valve 2. Ohmmeter to solenoid terminals 3. 4-6 ohms required	Okay — check lead resistance (I1). Not Okay — replace valve assembly.
I1. Solenoid Lead Resistance (In Computer)	1. Solenoid leads off 2. Ohmmeter: to solenoid leads on computer 3. 10,000 ohms or higher required	Okay — check sensor output voltage (J). Not Okay — reverse ohmmeter leads and recheck Still Not Okay — replace computer module.
J. Sensor Output Voltage (Test both Sensors)	1. Jack up wheels and release brakes. Ignition off. 2. AC voltmeter: + to ORANGE — to GREEN 3. Turn wheel (43 rpm for 20-inch; 56 rpm for 15 inch) 4. 0.3 volts AC required	Okay — check for shorted sensor (L). Not Okay — check sensor resistance (K).
K. Sensor Resistance (Test Low-Output Sensor)	1. Remove orange and green leads 2. Ohmmeter: to wire eyelets 3. 500-1500 ohms required	Okay — remove wheel and re-position sensor. Not Okay — repair open sensor wire or replace sensor.
K1. Computer Sensor Terminal Resistance	1. Green wire off terminal. 2. Ohmmeter: open terminal and ⏚ 3. 10,000 ohms required	Okay — check for shorted sensor or wire (L). Not Okay — replace computer module.
L. Shorted Sensor or Wire	1. Ohmmeter: GREEN wire and ⏚ 2. Both sensors connected 3. 3000 ohms required	Okay — replace computer module if all tests above are okay. Not Okay — repair shorted sensor wire. If not shorted, replace sensor.

OHMMETER
DC VOLTMETER

TEST	PROCEDURE	RESULTS
M. Power out of Breaker	1. Voltmeter: + to A − to ⏚ 2. 12-14 volts required.	Okay — check for power from relay (O). Not Okay — check for short to ground.
N. Short to Ground	1. Circuit breaker open 2. Ohmeter leads: A and ⏚ 3. Should be infinite resistance	Okay — replace breaker. Zero Resistance — trace and repair short circuit
O. Power out from Relay	1. Ignition on 2. Voltmeter: + to C − to ⏚ 3. 11-14 volts required	Okay — check blue wiring to monitor and modulators: tests A and G. Not Okay — check battery power in (P).
P. B+ Power in to Relay	1. Voltmeter: + to B :− to ⏚ 2. 11-14 Volts required	Okay — check ignition power in (Q). Not Okay — repair circuit between relay and breaker.
Q. Ignition Power in to Relay	1. Ignitionon 2. Voltmeter: + to D − to ⏚ 3. 12-14 volts required	Okay — check relay ground. If okay, replace relay and recheck warning lamp. Not Okay — locate and repair open ignition power circuit.

NOTE: Refer to wiring schematics for connector locations.

POWER SUPPLY TEST

Kelsey-Hayes System

NOTE: Before attempting any repair operations on the anti-skid system, determine the problem area by the tests outlined at the end of this section.

Control Valve & Solenoid

Disassembly (On Vehicle)

1. Turn off the vehicle power to the computer.
2. Exhaust the air reservoir which supplies air to the valve to be removed.
3. Remove the cover from the computer module and move the computer and cover away from the valve assembly. Do not stretch the solenoid leads.
4. Remove the solenoid lead terminals and insulator block by sliding terminals off the spade lugs. Use long-nose pliers or pry out with a screwdriver.
5. Pull out dust seal over the solenoid leads.
6. Remove one flat-head screw to separate the computer mounting plate from the valve assembly.

Kelsey-Hayes modulator assembly (© Ford Motor Co.)

523

LONGER SCREWS

LOCKWASHER AND FLAT WASHER

LOCKWASHER AND FLAT WASHER

GROUND STRAP

LOCKWASHER ONLY

COMPUTER MODULE

DUST SEAL

VALVE ASSEMBLY

SOLENOID VALVE WIRES

COMPUTER MOUNTING PLATE

Disassembly of modulator assembly—Kelsey-Hayes (© Ford Motor Co.)

7. Identify all air lines and disconnect.
8. Remove mounting bolts, remove the valve assembly from the vehicle.

NOTE: It may be necessary to remove the mounting bracket from the frame first.

Installation

1. Replace or repair any lines to valve that may be damaged or in questionable condition.
2. Install the mounting bracket and valve on the vehicle.
3. Attach the computer mounting plate to the valve assembly with flat-head screws.

4. Install the dust seal over the solenoid leads and into the pocket in the valve. Make sure that it is firmly seated.
5. Install the solenoid leads to the spade lugs on the computer assembly.
6. Attach the computer assembly and the ground strap with four bolts, lockwashers and flat washers.

NOTE: Use the longer bolts at the top of the valve. Flat washer is not required on ground strap bolt.

7. Tighten the computer mounting bolts to 50 inch pounds torque.
8. Connect all air lines.

9. Perform "Operation & Leak Test" as outlined in "Testing & Trouble Shooting."

Computer

Disassembly (On Vehicle)

NOTE: When only the computer module is being separated from the valve assembly, it is not necessary to discharge the air system.

1. Remove the computer module cover. Identify and remove the electrical lead wires.
2. Remove the four hex bolts that hold the computer to the valve assembly.
3. Carefully separate the computer from the valve. Do not stretch the solenoid lead wires.
4. Remove the solenoid lead terminals and insulator block by sliding the terminals off the spade lugs. Use a long-nose pliers or pry off with a screwdriver.
5. Pull the dust seal out over the solenoid leads.
6. Remove one flat-head screw to separate the computer mounting plate from the valve assembly.

Assembly

1. Attach the computer mounting plate to the valve assembly with a flat-head screw.
2. Install the dust seal over the solenoid leads and into the pocket in the valve. Make sure that it seats firmly.
3. Install the solenoid leads to the spade lugs on the computer assembly.
4. Attach the computer assembly and ground strap with four bolts, lockwashers and flat washers.

NOTE: Use the longer bolts at the top of the valve assembly. A flat washer is not required for the ground strap.

5. Tighten to 50 inch pounds.
6. Attach all electrical leads and perform test operations as outlined in the "Testing & Trouble Shooting" section.

Wheel Speed Sensors Drum Brakes

Removal

1. Remove the wheel and brake drum assembly.
2. Remove the bracket attaching bolts and separate the bracket from the backing plate.
3. Push the sensor out of its bracket.
4. Disconnect the sensor leads at the junction block. Remove the sensor assembly.

Installation

1. Connect the sensor leads to the junction block.

Computer assembly and electrical connections—Kelsey-Hayes (© Ford Motor Co.)

as outlined in the "Testing & Trouble Shooting" section.

Re-Positioning

NOTE: Whenever the brake drum is removed, the sensor must be repositioned in the following manner.

1. Push the sensor to its outermost position.
2. Refer to **NOTE** following step 4 of the Installation procedures.
3. Check the sensor voltage output as outlined in the "Testing & Trouble Shooting" section.

Disc Brakes

Removal

1. Disconnect the sensor leads at the junction block.
2. Remove the clamp behind the spindle.
3. Screw the sensor out of the assembly.
4. Push the sensor out of the assembly screw.

Installation

1. Insert the sensor in the screw assembly and push out far enough to contact the rotor when installed.
2. With hub and brake disc installed, install the sensor assembly.
3. Install the wiring clamp and attaching screw.
4. Attach the sensor leads to the junction block.
5. Check the sensor voltage output as outlined in the "Testing & Trouble Shooting" section.

2. Insert the sensor in the bracket and push out far enough to contact the rotor when the brake drum is installed.
3. Install the bracket and mounting screws.
4. Replace the wheel and brake drum assembly.

NOTE: It is important to minimize rocking of the wheel and drum assembly during installation, as this may cause the sensor to be positioned incorrectly. Put the wheel in place and use the bearings and spindle nut to draw the wheel into position. The rotor assembly will position the sensor for proper running clearance as the bearings are adjusted.

5. Check the sensor voltage output

Wheel speed sensor-drum brakes—Kelsey-Hayes (© Ford Motor Co.)

Anti-Skid Systems

Wheel speed sensor-disc brakes—Kelsey-Hayes (© Ford Motor Co.)

Re-Positioning

NOTE: Whenever the hub and brake disc or the hub and spider assembly are removed, it is necessary to re-position the sensor assembly as follows:

1. Install the hub and brake disc and adjust the wheel bearings.
2. Screw out the sensor assembly two or three turns.
3. Push the sensor against the rotor.
4. Tighten the sensor.

Rotor (Drum Brakes Only)
Removal
1. Remove the wheel and the brake drum assembly.
2. Remove the rotor attaching screws.
3. Lift the rotor out of the brake drum.

Installation
1. Attach the rotor to the brake drum assembly.

2. Reposition the sensor as described in "Wheel Sensor-Re-Positioning."
3. Install the wheel and drum.

NOTE: To be sure that the proper positioning of the sensor is achieved, minimize rocking the wheel assembly into position. Put the wheel in place and use the bearings and spindle nut to draw the assembly into proper position. The rotor assembly will push the sensor into position for proper running clearance as the bearings are adjusted.

4. Check the sensor voltage output as outlined in the "Testing & Trouble Shooting" section.

Kelsey-Hayes System-Testing & Trouble Shooting
Modulator Operation & Leak Test
1. Block the wheels and fully charge the air brake system.

2. Apply and release the brakes several times. Check for prompt application and release of brake chambers at ALL wheels.
3. Leak test exhaust port (under the valve) with a soap solution. Slight leakage is permitted as follows:
   a. Brakes Applied—one inch bubble in 3 seconds.
   b. Brakes released—one inch bubble in 5 seconds.

NOTE: Replace the valve if it does not function properly in step 2 or if excessive leakage is observed.

Warning Lamp Operation Test
1. Turn the ignition key to the "ON" position and observe the warning lamp. It should be on for 2-4 seconds, then go off and stay off.
2. If the lamp stays on, refer to "General Electrical Diagnosis".
3. If light flashes on and off, locate and correct loose connection.
4. If lamp fails to light, replace the bulb and recheck.
5. If lamp still fails to light, check for good ground connection and if there is power to the bulb. Repair the circuit as required.
6. If there is power to the "P" terminal of the monitor, but no power to the "W" terminal for 2-4 seconds, after turning the ignition switch "ON". Replace the monitor assembly.

General Electrical Diagnosis
The electrical system should be tested out anytime the WARNING LAMP STAYS LIT. This can be caused by:
1. No power to the system. Warning relay is powering warning light circuit.

EXCITER NOTCHES

WEDGE BRAKES   CAM BRAKES

Wheel speed sensor rotor assemblies—drum brakes only—Kelsey-Hayes (© Ford Motor Co.)

Monitor test point locations—Kelsey-Hayes (© Ford Motor Co.)

follow will isolate the defective component or sub-system. For a starting point, it may be helpful to ignition-cycle the system to isolate the trouble to one of three areas. Then, you will need a DC voltmeter, AC voltmeter and an ohmmeter (a VOM that combines all these functions is suitable) to make the tests.

Ignition-Cycling

1. Turn the key to the "ON" and "OFF" position several times.
2. Check for a 60 pounds air supply.
3. Hold the brakes applied and again turn the ignition "ON" and "OFF" several times, while checking modulator exhaust.
4. Hold a piece of paper over the exhaust port of each valve. A small amount of air should discharge at each cycle.
5. Results:
   a. All Valves Cycle—test monitor assembly.
   b. No Valves Cycle—test power supply.
   c. One Valve Only Does Not Cycle-test modulator and sensors (at modulator).

2. Malfunction of the axle system. Defective Computer module, sensor or solenoid valve.

3. Defective warning monitor assembly.
NOTE: *The diagnostic charts that*

Monitor Diagnostic Tests

TEST	PROCEDURE	RESULTS
A. Power to Monitor	1. Voltmeter: + to P — to ⏚ 2. Ignition on 3. 11-14 Volts required	Not Okay — check power supply circit (Fig. 20) and blue wire to relay. Okay — check monitor ground (B).
B. Monitor Ground	1. Voltmeter: + to P — to G 2. Ignition on 3. 11-14 volts required	Not Okay — repair ground and check warning light. Okay — check power out (C)
C. Power Out to Warning Relay	1. Voltmeter: + to P¹ — to ⏚ 2. Ignition on 3. 11-14 volts required	Not Okay — replace monitor assembly. Okay — check for warning signal in (D).
D. Warning Signal In	1. Ingition on 2. Jumper from P (or any hot terminal) to W1, W2, W3 in turn. 3. Drive vehicle 15 mph or faster if vehicle speed is involved. 4. Light should go out for terminal receiving a warning signal	Warning Light out — test modulator sending warning signal. Light stays on — check warning signal out(D1).
D1. Warning Signal Out	1. Ignition 2. Voltmeter: + to W — to ⏚ 3. Zero volts required	Voltage out — replace monitor Okay (no voltage) — check warning relay (E).
E. Warning Relay	1. Ignition on 2. Volmeter: + to green wire terminal of relay — to ⏚	Okay — check relay ground. Repair ground or replace relay. Not Okay — repair green wire from monitor PI to relay.

NOTE: Replace monitor assembly if:
(1) Warning relay and W1, W2, W3 signals are okay, but light stays on.
(2) Light doesn't come on momentarily with ignition on (see "Warning Lamp Operation Test").

Anti-Skid Systems

TEST POINTS

EQUIPMENT NEEDED

DC VOLTMETER
OHMMETER
AC VOLTMETER
(OR COMBINED VOM)

⏚ = CHASSIS GROUND

NOTE: VOLTAGES ARE DC UNLESS SPECIFIED AC

Modulator & Sensor Test

TEST	PROCEDURE NOTE: Voltages are DC unless specified AC	RESULTS
F. Warning Signal Out	1. Remove red wire 2. Voltmeter: + to FAIL – to CHASSIS 3. Ignition on 4. Okay signal is 6-14 volts	Less than 6 volts — check power in to modulator (G). Okay — repair red wire from modulator to monitor and check warning light.
G. Power in to Modulator	1. Ignition on 2. Voltmeter: + to HOT – to ⏚ 3. 11-14 volts required	Okay — check ground (H). Not Okay — repair blue wire to splice in harness (if other modulators OK) or check out power supply (Fig. 20).
H. Modulator Ground	1. Ignition on 2. Voltmeter: + to HOT – to CHASSIS 3. 11-14 volts required	Okay — check solenoid resistance (I). Not Okay — repair ground.
I. Solenoid Resistance	1. Ohmmeter leads to solenoid pins 2. 4-6 ohms required	Not Okay — replace valve assembly. Okay — check sensor output voltage (J).

J. Sensor Output Voltage
(Test both Sensors)
	1. Jack up wheels and release brakes.
	   Ignition off.
	2. AC Voltmeter: + to ORANGE
	           – to GREEN
	3. Turn wheel 30 rpm (one turn every
	   2 seconds)
	4. 0.2 volts AC required
		Not Okay — check sensor resistance (K).
		Okay — check for sensor short (L).

K. Sensor Resistance (Test Low-Output Sensor)	1. Remove orange and green wires 2. Ohmmeter leads to wire eyelets. 3. 4000Ω to 6000Ω required	Okay — remove wheel and reposition sensor. Not Okay — repair open sensor wire or replace sensor.
L. Short Sensor or Wire	1. Ohmmeter leads: sensor Wire and ⏚ 2. High resistance (10,000Ω) required	Okay — replace computer module if all other tests are okay. Not Okay — repair shorted sensor wire. If not shorted, replace sensor.

EQUIPMENT NEEDED

CIRCUIT
BREAKER

B+ ○─╮╭─○ ●─── B
      A   IGNITION

────── BLUE ─)<─●
         C   D
      TO
      MONITOR

E

TO MODULATOR
                    POWER RELAY

⊥ CHASSIS GROUND

OHMMETER
DC VOLTMETER

TEST	PROCEDURE	RESULTS
M. Power out of Breaker	1. Voltmeter: + to A – to ⊥ 2. 12-14 volts required.	Okay — check for power from relay (O). Not Okay — check for short to ground.
N. Short to Ground	1. Circuit breaker open 2. Ohmeter leads: A and ⊥ 3. Should be infinite resistance	Okay — replace breaker. Zero Resistance — trace and repair short circuit.
O. Power out from Relay	1. Ignition on 2. Voltmeter: + to C – to ⊥ 3. 11-14 volts required	Okay — check blue wiring to monitor and modulators; tests A and G. Not Okay — check battery power in (P).
P. B+ Power in to Relay	1. Voltmeter: + to B – to ⊥ 2. 11-14 Volts required	Okay — check ignition power in (Q). Not Okay — repair circuit between relay and breaker.
Q. Ignition Power in to Relay	1. Ignition on 2. Voltmeter: + to D – to ⊥ 3. 12-14 volts required	Okay — check relay ground. If okay, replace relay and recheck warning lamp. Not Okay — locate and repair open ignition power circuit.

NOTE: Refer to wiring schematics for connector locations.

Power Supply Test

Rockwell-Standard "Skid-Trol"

NOTE: Before attempting any repair operations on the anti-skid system, determine the problem area by the tests outlined at the end of this section.

Control Valve and Solenoid

Disassembly (On Vehicle)

1. Turn off the vehicle power to the computer.
2. Exhaust air reservoir which supplies the valve to be removed.
3. Remove the six computer cover to upper housing capscrews and pull the computer and cover assembly from the housing.
4. Disconnect the two solenoid leads from the computer; however, it is not necessary to disconnect the power and sensor cables. Set the cover assembly to the side.
5. Disconnect all air lines (service, supply and delivery) from the valve.
6. Separate the valve from the vehicle by removing the valve to vehicle screws and washers at the triangular mounting flange of the lower housing.

Assembly

1. Install the valve and secure with the capscrews and washers at the triangular mounting flange of the lower housing.
2. Connect all the air lines to their appropriate ports on the valve.
3. Check the supply reservoir by using the tractor power or auxiliary air supply and check the air lines for leaks.
4. Inspect the computer cover gasket for any damage. Replace if necessary. Use a suitable adhesive to bond the gasket to the cover.
5. Connect the solenoid leads to the computer.
6. Install the computer and cover assembly into the upper housing and secure the assembly loosely.
CAUTION: Make sure that the solenoid leads are not pinched between the cover assembly and the upper housing.

7. Check the operation of the valve by applying the brakes and observing the brake action. There should be no audible leakage during application and the air should exhaust rapidly when the brakes are released.
8. Perform the electrical tests as outlined in the "Test & Trouble Shooting" section.
9. After the electrical tests have been performed, tighten the cover screws to 100 inch pounds.

Computer

Disassembly (On Vehicle)

1. Turn the vehicle power to the computer OFF.
CAUTION: Failure to turn the power off may cause damage to the computer when it is removed from the valve assembly.
2. Remove all the connectors from the cover. If only the computer fuse is to be replaced. it is not necessary to remove the sensor or power connectors from the cover.
CAUTION: When removing the connectors, do not twist as this will damage the pins and sockets.

SOLENOID

SOLENOID LEADS

COMPUTER FUSE

GASKET

Computer removed from upper housing-Skid-Trol® (© Chrysler Corp.)

SENSOR HOUSING

SENSOR BRACKET

SPRING

RUBBER SUPPORT CAP

LOCATING EAR (ONE PER SIDE)

SENSOR AND CABLE ASSEMBLY

Sensor parts—Skid-Trol® (© Chrysler Corp.)

3. Remove the cover retaining screws and pull cover with computer and gasket from the housing.
4. If replacing computer, disconnect the valve solenoid leads from the computer.
5. Inspect the computer cover gasket for damage, replace if necessary.

Assembly

1. Before installing the computer, and cover assembly, check the fuse to insure that it is placed tight in the fuse holder and that it is not blown.
2. If the computer was replaced, connect the solenoid leads to the computer.
3. Install the computer and cover the assembly into the upper housing and secure loosely with the screws.
CAUTION: Check to make sure that the solenoid leads are not pinched between the cover and upper housing.
4. Install the power cable into the threaded port on the cover, matching the flats of the port and the connectors.
CAUTION: Do not twist the connector into the threaded port as this will damage the pins and sockets.
5. Hand tighten the power cable compression nut until secure. DO NOT USE WRENCH OR PLIERS TO TIGHTEN.
6. Perform the electrical tests as outlined in "Test & Trouble Shooting" which follows in this section.
7. After performing test. tighten the cover to housing screws to 100 inch pounds.
8. Install both sensor cables into the computer cover, matching

flats of connectors to flats of ports. Push connectors straight in. DO NOT TWIST.
NOTE: There are no left or right requirements for the sensor cables, they are interchangeable.
9. Hand tighten both sensor cable compression nuts until secure. DO NOT USE PLIERS OR WRENCH TO TIGHTEN.

Wheel Speed Sensor

Removal

1. Cut off the nylon tie straps which hold the sensor cable to the air delivery hose, only up to the in line connector. Do not cut off straps holding cable leading to the computer.
2. Disconnect the sensor to computer cable at the inline connector by pulling straight apart without twisting. Twisting will damage the pins.
3. Slide the sensor cable and

connector through the hole in the spider or dust shield.
4. Remove the sensor and adjusting spring from the sensor housing by prying out the spring using a twisting motion from side to side.

Installation

1. Slip a new spring over the back and sides of the sensor. A new spring should be used to assure proper operation of the self adjusting mechanism.
2. Inspect the rubber support caps and replace them if necessary. Apply a silicone base lubricant to the rubber caps.
3. Install the sensor and spring over the pins and press in until the spring engages the side of the housing.
4. The initial sensor setting is 0.44 inch out from the housing.
5. Insert the connector through the hole in the brake spider or dust

0.44 (7/16")

PK658

Setting the wheel speed sensor—Skid-Trol (© Chrysler Corp.)

Rotor runout tool with dial indicator—Skid-Trol® (© Chrysler Corp.)

Checking rotor runout Skid-Trol® (© Chrysler Corp.)

shield. The grommet should be used for sealing and relief of strain.

6. Lead the cable along the air delivery hose to the inline connector. Check to be sure that the cable does not interfere with any moving parts. Also check to be sure that the routing of the cable to the in line connector does not come into contact with any suspension or drive line parts. Tie the cable to the air hose at 8 inch intervals.

NOTE: When the wheel is installed, the sensor should be positioned to its maximum extension in the housing. As the wheel is drawn on to the axle, the rotor presses against the sensor face, forcing the sensor back into its correct clearance. Rigs located on the sensor face will wear away during the first few revolutions of the wheel, so there will be no contact between the sensor and the rotor. Make sure that the wheel bearings are properly adjusted.

Rotor

Removal

1. Jack up the vehicle and secure.
2. Remove the hub, drive and tire.
3. Test the rotor fan runout (see test procedures that follow).
4. Remove the rotor from the inside of the brake drum by removing the bolts and washers.

Installation

1. Apply a suitable sealant to the rotor/brake drum contact area.
2. Install the rotor on the brake drum with bolts and washers and tighten.
3. Perform the rotor runout test.

Rotor Runout Test

1. Place the hub and drum on the work bench. Position the inner and outer bearings against their respective cups.

NOTE: To perform this test a special tool is required. The tool is a rotor runout tool with dial indicator

(Chrysler #C-4369). The tool consists of two cones and a shaft which centers the dial indicator and holds the bearings in place.

2. Assemble the runout tool through the hub and position against the bearings. Secure the fixture in position by tightening the jam nut.
3. Position the dial indicator so that the pointer contacts the rotor face and set the dial to zero.
4. Holding the cone clasp handle, pivot the indicator around the complete rotor surface while observing the dial reading. The total indicator reading should not exceed 0.020 inch, if the reading is excessive, the rotor must be replaced.

Skid-Trol Testing & Trouble Shooting

NOTE: To perform a number of the following tests, a special tester is required. This tester is called a Service Aid Tester (S.A.T.) and is Chrysler Special Tool #C-4368.

To properly diagnose this system

the following test procedures MUST be performed in exact order. DO NOT skip any test procedure, follow the test procedures as they are written. When a defect is found, correct as required and complete the remaining tests.

Axle System Failure Determination

1. In order to determine which axle the failure has occurred on, all system components must be properly connected.
2. Working with a suitable ohm meter, check the continuity between the terminals of each relay that have the following wires attached to them:
   Relay #1 Light Green and Brown
   Relay #2 Dark Blue and Green
   Relay #3 Dark Green and Tan
3. The relay that produces the infinite resistance reading (ohms) is the axle where the failure has occurred.
4. If no relay produces an infinite reading, proceed to the "Relay Test," as one of the relays may be defective.

Testing the solenoid and valve with the Service Aid Tester—Skid-Trol® (© Chrysler Corp.)

Failure Warning Light Test

1. Turn the ignition switch to the "Start" position. While the engine is cranking the light should come on.
2. If the light does not come on, check the following:
   a. Make sure the light bulb is in working order.
   b. Inspect and test the continuity of the wiring, connections and the bulb socket.
   c. If none of the above are found to be defective, proceed to the "Relay Test".

Solenoid And Valve Assembly Test Preparation

1. Test the Service Aid Tester battery as instructed by the units instructions. The indicator light must glow brightly to indicate battery is good.
2. Remove the computer from the valve assembly. Replace fuse if necessary. If fuse is not blown, proceed to the "Relay Test."
3. Position the computer in the housing. Secure tightly with 2 or 3 screws and leave the wheel sensor cables disconnected.
4. Connect both remale plugs (double end) of S.A.T. 'Y' cable into the sensor sockets of the computer.
5. Connect the male plug (single end) of the 'Y' cable into the female socket at the top of the S.A.T.
6. Turn the ignition switch to the "Run" position, but do not start engine.

Test With System Not Pressurized

1. Press and release the test button on the S.A.T. to cycle computer. Listen for one set, 3 or 4, of clicks from the computer and valve assembly. Depressing and releasing the test button will not cause the computer to continuously cycle, it will only cycle once.

Test With System Pressurized

1. Have helper apply and hold brakes.
2. Press and release the test button on the S.A.T. to cycle computer. Listen for one short burst of air from the computer and valve assembly. Depressing and releasing the button will not cause the computer to continuously recycle, it will only cycle once.

Results

1. If one set of clicks or one short blast of air is heard, computer and solenoid are operating properly: process to the "Sensor Test."

2. If no clicks is heard or air blast, the computer or solenoid are defective. To determine which component is defective, it will be necessary to do the following:
   a. Turn the ignition switch to the "Off" position, again remove the computer from the valve assembly. disconnect the solenoid leads and replace the fuse.
   b. Turn the ignition switch to the "Run" position but do not start the engine. If the fuse continues to blow, the computer is most likely defective. However, before replacing the computer, make sure that the solenoid is operating properly. Proceed to the next step.
   c. Working with a suitable ohm meter, measure the resistance of the solenoid. If the resistance is not below 3 ohms, the solenoid is defective. If the resistance is within 2 to 3 ohms, replace the computer. However, before replacement, make sure that the wiring and connections are in proper operating condition. Refer to "Testing Wiring and Connections"

Sensor Test

NOTE: in order to perform the following tests, it is very important that the wheel bearings be properly adjusted.

1. Jack up and secure vehicle so that wheels being tested will spin freely.
2. Disconnect the two sensor cables from the computer assembly by first loosening the compression nuts, then pull straight out of computer. DO NOT TWIST AS THIS WILL DAMAGE THE PINS AND SOCKET.
3. Connect the sensor cable to the sensor (male) socket of the S.A.T. If an extension is needed, use the S.A.T. 'Y' cable.
4. Rotate the wheel being tested at a speed not in excess of 25 RPM. Good test results can be achieved by having the wheel revolve at a rate of one revolution per 6 seconds.
5. As the wheel is revolving, press the test button on the S.A.T., while observing the indicator light.
6. If the indicator light flashes uniformly over every complete revolution, the sensor is in good working order. Test the other wheel sensor.
7. If the indicator flashes randomly, one of the following conditions may exist.
   a. Excessive air gap between the sensor and rotor. Remove

the wheel assembly. Proceed to "Sensor Performance Test". If the sensor is found to be defective, remove and replace as outlined in "Wheel Speed Sensor-Removal & Installation."
   b. Loose. intermittent connection at S.A.T. or broken wire in sensor lead. Check sensor connection at the S.A.T. If this is not effective, replace sensor as outlined in "Sensor-Removal & Installation."
8. Indicator flashes only periodically, flashes at same spot each revolution, indicates one of the following conditions
   a. Rotor has excessive runout. Check as outlined in "Rotor Runout Test".
   b. Excessive air gap between sensor and rotor. Refer to step 7a.
9. Indicator light continously off during every wheel revolution.
   a. Loose connection, refer to step 7b.
   b. Excessive air gap, refer to step 7a.
   c. Sensor defective, replace as outlined in "Wheel Speed Sensor-Removal and Installation".

Sensor Performance Test

1. Insert the sensor cable into the S.A.T. Use the 'Y' cable as extension if necessary. (Wheel assembly must be removed for this test.
2. Rub a steel rod across the sensor poles while the test button of the S.A.T. is depressed. Observe the indicator light.
3. If the indicator light flickers, the sensor is good. If the indicator does not light, check the connection at the S.A.T. and repeat the test. If the light still does not flicker, replace the sensor.

Relay Test

1. Ignition switch must be in the "off" position.
2. Disconnect the wires from the relay being tested.
3. Working with a suitable ohm meter, check the resistance between the terminals that had red and purple wires connected to them. Check the resistance between the remaining two terminals.
4. There should be zero resistance between the Red and Purple terminals, if not. or if there is infinite resistance, replace the relay. Resistance between the remaining two terminals should be 50 ohms or less; if there is greater than 50 ohms resistance or if the reading is infinite resistance, replace the relay.

Index

Gasoline Engines Rebuilding

Diesel Engines

Index

Diesel Engines

This section describes, in detail, the procedures involved in rebuilding a typical gasoline engine. The procedures specifically refer to an inline engine. However, they are basically identical to those used in rebuilding engines of nearly all designs and configurations.

The section is divided into two parts. The first, Cylinder Head Reconditioning, assumes that the cylinder head is removed from the engine, all manifolds are removed, and the cylinder head is on a workbench. The camshaft should be removed from overhead cam cylinder heads. The second section, Cylinder Block Reconditioning, covers the block, pistons, connecting rods and crankshaft. It is assumed that the engine is mounted on a work stand, and the cylinder head and all accessories are removed.

Procedures are identified as follows:

Unmarked—Basic procedures that must be performed in order to successfully complete the rebuilding process.

Starred (*)—Procedures that should be performed to ensure maximum performance and engine life.

Double starred (**)—Procedures that may be performed to increase engine reliability. These procedures are usually reserved for extremely heavy-duty usage.

In many cases, a choice of methods is also provided. Methods are identified in the same manner as procedures. The choice of method for a procedure is at the discretion of the user.

The tools required for the basic rebuilding procedure should, with minor exceptions, be those included in a mechanic's tool kit. An accurate torque wrench, and a dial indicator (reading in thousandths) mounted on a universal base should be available. Bolts and nuts with no torque specification should be tightened according to size (see chart). Special tools, where required, all are readily available from the major tool suppliers. The services of a competent automotive machine shop must also be readily available.

When assembling the engine, any parts that will be in frictional contact must be pre-lubricated, to provide protection on initial start-up. Any product specifically formulated for this purpose may be used. NOTE: *Do not use engine oil.* Where semi-permanent (locked but removable) installation of bolts or nuts is desired, threads should be cleaned and coated with a liquid locking compound. Studs may be permanently installed using a stud mounting compound.

Aluminum has become increasingly popular for use in engines, due to its low weight and excellent heat trans-

fer characteristics. The following precautions must be observed when handling aluminum engine parts:
—Never hot-tank aluminum parts.
—Remove all aluminum parts (identification tags, etc.) from engine parts before hot-tanking (otherwise they will be removed during the process).
—Always coat threads lightly with engine oil or anti-seize compounds before installation, to prevent seizure.
—Never over-torque bolts or spark plugs in aluminum threads. Should

stripping occur, threads can be restored according to the following procedure, using Heli-Coil thread inserts:

Tap drill the hole with the stripped threads to the specified size (see chart). Using the specified tap (NOTE: *Heli-Coil tap sizes refer to the size thread being replaced, rather than the actual tap size*), tap the hole for the Heli-Coil. Place the insert on the proper installation tool (see chart). Apply pressure on the in-

TORQUE (ft. lbs.)*

U.S.

Bolt Diameter (inches)	Bolt Grade (SAE)				Wrench Size (inches)	
	1 and 2	5	6	8	Bolt	Nut
1/4	5	7	10	10.5	3/8	7/16
5/16	9	14	19	22	1/2	9/16
3/8	15	25	34	37	9/16	5/8
7/16	24	40	55	60	5/8	3/4
1/2	37	60	85	92	3/4	13/16
9/16	53	88	120	132	7/8	7/8
5/8	74	120	167	180	15/16	1
3/4	120	200	280	296	1-1/8	1-1/8
7/8	190	302	440	473	1-5/16	1-5/16
1	282	466	660	714	1-1/2	1-1/2

Metric

Bolt Diameter (mm)	Bolt Grade				Wrench Size (mm) Bolt and Nut
	5D	8G	10K	12K	
6	5	6	8	10	10
8	10	16	22	27	14
10	19	31	40	49	17
12	34	54	70	86	19
14	55	89	117	137	22
16	83	132	175	208	24
18	111	182	236	283	27
22	182	284	394	464	32
24	261	419	570	689	36

*—Torque values are for lightly oiled bolts. CAUTION: Bolts threaded into aluminum require much less torque.

Heli-Coil Specifications

Heli-Coil Insert			Drill	Tap	Insert. Tool	Extracting Tool
Thread Size	Part No.	Insert Length (In.)	Size	Part No.	Part No.	Part No.
1/2 -20	1185-4	3/8	17/64 (.266)	4 CPB	528-4N	1227-6
5/16-18	1185-5	15/32	Q(.332)	5 CPB	528-5N	1227-6
3/8 -16	1185-6	9/16	X(.397)	6 CPB	528-6N	1227-6
7/16-14	1185-7	21/32	29/64 (.453)	7 CPB	528-7N	1227-16
1/2 -13	1185-8	3/4	33/64 (.516)	8 CPB	528-8N	1227-16

STANDARD SCREW FITS IN . . .

HELI-COIL INSERT IN . . .   HELI-COIL TAPPED HOLE

Heli-Coil installation

Removing the carbon from the cylinder head

sert while winding it clockwise into the hole, until the top of the insert is one turn below the surface. Remove the installation tool, and break the installation tang from the bottom of the insert by moving it up and down. If the Heli-Coil must be removed, tap the removal tool firmly into the hole, so that it engages the top thread, and turn the tool counter-clockwise to extract the insert.

Snapped bolts or studs may be removed, using a stud extractor (un-threaded) or locking pliers (thread-ed). Penetrating oil will often aid in breaking frozen threads. In cases where the stud or bolt is flush with, or below the surface, proceed as follows:

Drill a hole in the broken stud or bolt, approximately ½ its diameter. Select a screw extractor of the proper size, and tap it into the stud or bolt. Turn the extractor counter-clockwise to remove the stud or bolt.

Magnaflux and Zyglo are inspection techniques used to locate material flaws, such as stress cracks. Magna-fluxing coats the part with fine magnetic particles, and subjects the part to a magnetic field. Cracks cause breaks in the magnetic field, which are outlined by the particles. Since Magnaflux is a magnetic process, it is applicable only to ferrous materials. The Zyglo process coats the material with a fluorescent dye penetrant, and then subjects it to blacklight inspection, under which cracks glow brightly. Parts made of any material may be tested using Zyglo. While Magnaflux and Zyglo are excellent for general inspection, and locating hidden defects, specific checks of suspected cracks may be made at lower cost and more readily using spot check dye. The dye is sprayed onto the suspected area, wiped off, and the area is then sprayed with a developer. Cracks then will show up brightly. Spot check dyes will only indicate surface cracks; therefore, structural cracks below the surface may escape detection. When questionable, the part should be tested using Magnaflux or Zyglo.

CYLINDER HEAD RECONDITIONING

Identify the Valves

Invert the cylinder head, and number the valve faces front to rear, using a permanent felt-tip marker.

Checking the valve stem-to-guide clearance

Remove the Rocker Arms

Remove the rocker arms with shaft(s) or balls and nuts. Wire the sets of rockers, balls and nuts together, and identify according to the corresponding valve.

Remove the Valves and Springs

Using an appropriate valve spring compressor (depending on the configuration of the cylinder head), compress the valve springs. Lift out the keepers with needlenose pliers, release the compressor, and remove the valve, spring, and spring retainer.

Check the Valve Stem-to-Guide Clearance

Clean the valve stem with lacquer thinner or a similar solvent to remove all gum and varnish. Clean the valve guides using solvent and an ex-panding wire-type valve guide clean-er. Mount a dial indicator so that the stem is at 90° to the valve stem, as close to the valve guide as possible. Move the valve off its seat, and mea-sure the valve guide-to-stem clear-ance by moving the stem back and forth to actuate the dial indicator. Measure the valve stems using a micrometer, and compare to speci-fications, to determine whether stem or guide wear is responsible for ex-cessive clearance.

De-carbon the Cylinder Head and Valves

Chip carbon away from the valve

heads, combustion chambers, and ports, using a chisel made of hard-wood. Remove the remaining deposits with a stiff wire brush. NOTE: *En-sure that the deposits are actually removed, rather than burnished.*

Hot-Tank the Cylinder Head

Have the cylinder head hot-tanked to remove grease, corrosion, and scale from the water passages. NOTE: *In the case of overhead cam cylinder heads, consult the operator to deter-mine whether the camshaft bearings will be damaged by the caustic solu-tion.*

Degrease the Remaining Cylinder Head Parts

Using solvent, clean the rockers, rocker shaft(s) (where applicable), rocker balls and nuts, springs, spring retainers, and keepers. Do not remove the protective coating from the springs.

Check the Cylinder Head for Warpage

Place a straight-edge across the gasket surface of the cylinder head. Using feeler gauges, determine the clearance at the center of the straight-edge. Measure across both diagonals, along the longitudinal centerline, and across the cylinder head at several points. If warpage exceeds .003″ in a 6″ span, or .006″ over the total length, the cylinder head must be resurfaced. NOTE: *If warpage exceeds the manu-facturers maximum tolerance for material removal, the cylinder head must be replaced.* When milling the cylinder heads of V-type engines, the intake manifold mounting position is altered, and must be corrected by milling the manifold flange a propor-tionate amount.

① ③ CHECK DIAGONALLY
② CHECK ACROSS CENTER

Check the cylinder head for warpage using a straight edge and feeler gauges

Grinding the correct angle on the valve face

Grind the valve seats using a power grinder

Replacing Valve Guides

NOTE: *Valve guides should only be replaced if damaged or if an oversize valve stem is not available.*

Depending on the type of cylinder head, valve guides may be pressed, hammered, or shrunk in. In cases where the guides are shrunk into the head, replacement should be left to an equipped machine shop. In other cases, the guides are replaced as follows: Press or tap the valve guides out of the head using a stepped drift. Determine the height above the boss that the guide must extend, and obtain a stack of washers, their I.D. similar to the guide's O.D., of that height. Place the stack of washers on the guide, and insert the guide into the boss. NOTE: *Valve guides are often tapered or beveled for installation.* Using a stepped installation tool, press or tap the guides into position. Ream the guides according to the size of the valve stem.

Replacing Valve Seat Inserts

Replacement of valve seat inserts which are worn beyond resurfacing or broken, if feasible, must be done by a machine shop.

Resurfacing (grinding) the Valve Face

Using a valve grinder, resurface the valves according to specifications. CAUTION: *Valve face angle is not always identical to valve seat angle.*

Examples of valves ground incorrectly
WRONG   WRONG
CORRECT

A minimum margin of 3/64" should remain after grinding the valve. The valve stem tip should also be squared and resurfaced, by placing the stem in the V-block of the grinder, and turning it while pressing lightly against the grinding wheel.

Resurfacing the Valve Seats Using a Grinder

Select a pilot of the correct size, and a coarse stone of the correct seat angle. Lubricate the pilot if necessary, and install the tool in the valve guide. Move the stone on and off the seat at approximately two cycles per second, until all flaws are removed from the seat. Install a fine stone, and finish the seat. Center and narrow the seat using correction stones, as described above.

Checking the Valve Seat Concentricity

Coat the valve face with Prussian blue dye, install the valve, and rotate it on the valve seat. If the entire seat becomes coated, and the valve is known to be concentric, the seat is concentric.

*Install the dial gauge pilot into the guide, and rest the arm on the valve seat. Zero the gauge, and rotate the arm around the seat. Run-out should not exceed .002".

Lapping the Valves

NOTE: *Valve lapping is done to ensure efficient sealing of resurfaced valves and seats. Valve lapping alone*

Check the valve seat for concentricity using a dial gauge

Lapping the valves by hand

HAND DRILL
ROD
SUCTION CUP
Lapping the valves using a hand drill

is not recommended for use as a resurfacing procedure.

*Invert the cylinder head, lightly lubricate the valve stems, and install the valves in the head as numbered. Coat valve seats with fine grinding compound, and attach the lapping tool suction cup to a valve head (NOTE: *Moisten the suction cup*). Rotate the tool between the palms, changing position and lifting the tool often to prevent grooving. Lap the valve until a smooth, polished seat is evident. Remove the valve and tool, and rinse away all traces of grinding compound.

*Fasten a suction cup to a piece of drill rod, and mount the rod in a hand drill. Proceed as above, using the hand drill as a lapping tool. CAUTION: *Due to the higher speeds involved when using the hand drill, care must be exercised to avoid grooving the seat.* Lift the tool and change direction of rotation often.

Checking the valve springs for correct pressure and height

Check the Valve Springs

Test the spring pressure at the installed and compressed (installed height minus valve lift) height using a valve spring tester. Springs used on small displacement engines (up to 3 liters) should be ± 1 lb. of all other springs in either position. A tolerance of ± 5 lbs. is permissible on larger engines.

Install Valve Stem Seals

Due to the pressure differential that exists at the ends of the intake valve guides (atmospheric pressure above, manifold vacuum below), oil is drawn through the valve guides into the intake port. This has been alleviated somewhat since the addition of positive crankcase ventilation, which lowers the pressure above the guides. Several types of valve stem seals are available to reduce blow-by. Certain seals simply slip over the stem and guide boss, while others require that the boss be machined. Recently, Teflon guide seals have become popular. Consult a parts supplier or machinst concerning availability and suggested usages. NOTE: *When installing seals, ensure that a small amount of oil is able to pass the seal to lubricate the valve guides; otherwise, excessive wear may result.*

Install the Valves

Lubricate the valve stems, and install the valves in the cylinder head as numbered. Lubricate and position the seals (if used, see above) and the valve springs. Install the spring retainers, compress the springs, and insert the keys using needlenose pliers or a tool designed for this purpose. NOTE: *Retain the keys with wheel bearing grease during installation.*

Check Valve Spring Installed Height

Measure the distance between the spring pad and the lower edge of the

spring retainer, and compare to specifications. If the installed height is incorrect, add shim washers between the spring pad and the spring. CAUTION: *Use only washers designed for this purpose.*

Check the valve spring installed height

Inspect the rocker arms, balls, studs, and nuts:

Visually inspect the rocker arms, balls, studs, and nuts for cracks, galling, burning, scoring, or wear. If all parts are intact, liberally lubricate the rocker arms and balls, and install them on the cylinder head. If wear is noted on a rocker arm at the point of valve contact, grind it smooth and square, removing as little material as possible. Replace the rocker arm if excessively worn. If a rocker stud shows signs of wear, it must be replaced (see below). If a rocker nut shows stress cracks, replace it. If an exhaust ball is galled or burned, substitute the intake ball from the same cylinder (if it is intact), and install a new intake ball. NOTE: *Avoid using new rocker balls on exhaust valves.*

Removing the rocker arm stud

Installing the rocker arm stud

Ream the stud bore for oversize studs

Replacing Rocker Studs

In order to remove a threaded stud, lock two nuts on the stud, and unscrew the stud using the lower nut. Coat the lower threads of the new stud with Loctite, and install.

Two alternative methods are available for replacing pressed in studs. Remove the damaged stud using a stack of washers and a nut or use a stud puller. In the first, the boss is reamed .005-.006″ oversize, and an oversize stud pressed in. Control the stud extension over the boss using washers, in the same manner as valve guides. Before installing the stud, coat it with white lead and grease. To retain the stud more positively, drill a hole through the stud and boss, and install a roll pin. In the second method, the boss is tapped, and a threaded stud installed. Retain the stud using a locking compound.

Inspect the Rocker Shaft(s) and Rocker Arms

Remove rocker arms, springs and washers from rocker shaft. NOTE: *Lay out parts in the order in which they are removed.* Inspect rocker arms for pitting or wear on the valve contact point, or excessive bushing wear. Bushings need only be replaced if wear is excessive, because the rocker arm normally contacts the shaft at one point only. Grind the valve contact point of rocker arm smooth if necessary, removing as little material as possible. If excessive material must be removed to smooth and square the arm, it should be replaced. Clean out all oil holes and passages in rocker shaft. If shaft is grooved or worn, replace it. Lubricate and assemble the rocker shaft.

Inspect the Pushrods

Remove the pushrods, and, if hollow, clean out the oil passages using fine wire. Roll each pushrod over a piece of clean glass. If a distinct clicking sound is heard as the pushrod rolls, the rod is bent, and must be replaced.

Check the push rods by rolling them on a flat surface

Checking push rods using a dial indicator

The length of all pushrods must be equal. Measure the length of the pushrods, compare to specifications, and replace as necessary.

Inspect the Valve Lifters

Remove lifters from their bores, and remove gum and varnish, using solvent. Clean walls of lifter bores. Check lifters for concave wear. If face is worn concave, replace lifter, and carefully inspect the camshaft. Lightly lubricate lifter and insert it into its bore. If play is excessive, an oversize lifter must be installed (where possible). Consult a machinist concerning feasibility. If play is satisfactory, remove, lubricate, and reinstall the lifter.

Check for Concave Wear on Face of Tappet Using Tappet for Straight Edge

Check the valve lifter face for concave wear

Testing Hydraulic Lifter Leak Down

Submerge lifter in a container of kerosene. Chuck a used pushrod or its equivalent into a drill press. Position container of kerosene so pushrod acts on the lifter plunger. Pump lifter with the drill press, until resistance increases. Pump several more times to bleed any air out of lifter. Apply very firm, constant pressure to the lifter, and observe rate at which fluid bleeds out of lifter. If the fluid bleeds very quickly (less than 15

Checking the lifter using a tester

seconds), lifter is defective. If the time exceeds 60 seconds, lifter is sticking. In either case, recondition or replace lifter. If lifter is operating properly (leak down time 15-60 seconds), lubricate and install it.

Checking the Main Bearing Clearance:

Invert engine, and remove cap from the bearing to be checked. Using a clean, dry rag, thoroughly clean all oil from crankshaft journal and bearing insert. NOTE: *Plastigage is soluble in oil; therefore, oil on the journal or bearing could result in erroneous readings.* Place a piece of Plastigage® along the full length of journal, reinstall cap, and torque to specifications. Remove bearing cap, and determine bearing clearance by comparing width of Plastigage to the scale on Plastigage envelope. Journal taper is determined by comparing width of the Plastigage strip near its ends. Rotate crankshaft 90° and retest, to determine journal eccentricity. NOTE: *Do not rotate crankshaft with Plastigage installed.* If bearing insert and journal appear intact, and are within tolerances, no further main bearing service is required. If bearing or journal appear defective, cause of failure should be determined before replacement.

Typical hydraulic lifter

Remove Crankshaft from Block

Measure the main bearing journals at each end twice (90° apart) using a micrometer, to determine diameter, journal taper and eccentricity. If journals are within tolerances, reinstall bearing caps at their specified torque. Using a telescope gauge and micrometer, measure bearing I.D. parallel to piston axis and at 30° on each side of piston axis. Subtract journal O.D. from bearing I.D. to determine oil clearance. If crankshaft journals appear defective, or do not meet tolerances, there is no need to measure bearings; for the crankshaft will require grinding and/or undersize bearings will be required. If bearing appears defective, cause for failure should be determined prior to replacement.

Measure the Plastigage to determine the clearance

Engine Rebuilding

Service the Crankshaft

Ensure that all oil holes and passages in the crankshaft are open and free of sludge. If necessary, have the crankshaft ground to the largest possible undersize.

* Have the crankshaft Magnafluxed, to locate stress cracks. Consult a machinist concerning additional service procedures, such as surface hardening (e.g., nitriding, Tuftriding) to improve wear characteristics, cross drilling and chamfering the oil holes to improve lubrication, and balancing.

Clean the crankshaft thoroughly to make sure it is free of dirt and sludge

Removing Freeze Plugs

Drill a hole in the center of the freeze plugs, and pry them out using a screwdriver or drift.

Remove the Oil Gallery Plugs

Threaded plugs should be removed using an appropriate (usually square) wrench. To remove soft, pressed in plugs, drill a hole in the plug, and thread in a sheet metal screw. Pull the plug out by the screw using pliers.

Hot-tank the Block

Have the block hot-tanked to remove grease, corrosion, and scale from the water jackets. NOTE: *Consult the operator to determine whether the camshaft bearings will be damaged during the hot-tank process.*

Check the Block for Cracks

Visually inspect the block for cracks or chips. The most common locations are as follows:
  Adjacent to freeze plugs.
  Between the cylinders and water jackets.
  Adjacent to the main bearing saddles.
  At the extreme bottom of the cylinders.
Check only suspected cracks using spot check dye (see introduction). If a crack is located, consult a machinist concerning possible repairs.

* Magnaflux the block to locate hidden cracks. If cracks are located, consult a machinist about feasibility of repair.

Check the Connecting Rod Bearing Clearance

Connecting rod bearing clearance is checked in the same manner as main bearing clearance, using Plastigage. Before removing the crankshaft, connecting rod side clearance also should be measured and recorded.

* Checking connecting rod bearing clearance, using a micrometer, is identical to checking main bearing clearance. If no other service is required, the piston and rod assemblies need not be removed.

Removing the Crankshaft

Using a punch, mark the corresponding main bearing caps and saddles according to position (i.e., one punch on the front main cap and saddle, two on the second, three on the third, etc.). Using number stamps, identify the corresponding connecting rods and caps, according to cylinder (if no numbers are present). Remove the main and connecting rod caps, and place sleeves of plastic tubing over the connecting rod bolts, to protect the journals as the crankshaft is removed. Lift the crankshaft out of the block.

Remove the Ridge

In order to facilitate removal of the piston and connecting rod, the ridge at the top of the cylinder must be removed. Place the piston at the bottom of the bore, and cover it with a rag. Cut the ridge away using a ridge reamer, exercising extreme care to avoid cutting too deeply. Remove the rag, and remove cuttings that remain on the piston. CAUTION: *If the ridge is not removed, and new rings are installed, damage to rings will result.*

Cylinder bore ridge

Removing the Piston and Connecting Rod

Invert the engine, and push the pistons and connecting rods out of the cylinders. If necessary, tap the connecting rod boss with a wooden hammer handle, to force the piston out. CAUTION: *Do not attempt to force the piston past the cylinder ridge (see above).*

Install the Oil Gallery Plugs and Freeze Plugs

Coat freeze plugs with sealer and tap into position using a piece of pipe, slightly smaller than the plug, as a driver. To ensure retention, stake the edges of the plugs. Coat threaded oil gallery plugs with sealer and install. Drive replacement soft plugs into block using a large drift as a driver.

* Rather than reinstalling lead plugs, drill and tap the holes, and install threaded plugs.

Check the Bore Diameter and Surface

Visually inspect the cylinder bores for roughness, scoring, or scuffing. If evident, the cylinder bore must be bored or honed oversize to eliminate imperfections, and the smallest possible oversize piston used. The new pistons should be given to the machinist with the block, so that the cylinders can be bored or honed exactly

Points to measure to check cylinder bore out-of-round

Points to measure to check cylinder bore taper

to the piston size (plus clearance). If no flaws are evident, measure the bore diameter using a telescope gauge and micrometer, or dial gauge, parallel and perpendicular to the engine centerline, at the top (below the ridge) and bottom of the bore. Subtract the bottom measurements from the top to determine taper, and the parallel to the centerline measurements from the perpendicular measurements to detrmine eccentricity. If the measurements are not within specifications, the cylinder must be bored or honed, and an oversize piston installed. If the measurements are within specifications the cylinder may be used as is, with only finish honing (see below).

NOTE: *Prior to submitting the block for boring, perform the following operation(s).*

Check the Block Deck for Warpage

Using a straightedge and feeler gauges, check the block deck for warpage in the same manner that the cylinder head is checked (see Cylinder Head Reconditioning). If warpage exceeds specifications, have the deck resurfaced. NOTE: *In certain cases a specification for total material removal (Cylinder head and block deck) is provided. This specification must not be exceeded.*

Check the Deck Height

The deck height is the distance from the crankshaft centerline to the block deck. To measure, invert the engine, and install the crankshaft, retaining it with the center main cap. Measure the distance from the crankshaft journal to the block deck, parallel to the cylinder centerline. Measure the diameter of the end (front and rear) main journals, parallel to the centerline of the cylinders, divide the diameter in half, and subtract it from the previous measurement. The results of the front and rear measurements should be identical. If the difference exceeds .005", the deck height should be corrected. NOTE: *Block deck height and warpage should be corrected together.*

Check the Cylinder Block Bearing Alignment

Remove the upper bearing inserts. Place a straightedge in the bearing saddles along the centerline of the crankshaft. If clearance exists between the straightedge and the center saddle, the block must be align-bored.

Clean and Inspect the Pistons and Connecting Rods

Using a ring expander, remove the rings from the piston. Remove the retaining rings (if so equipped) and remove piston pin. NOTE: *If the piston pin must be pressed out, determine the proper method and use the proper tools; otherwise the piston will distort.* Clean the ring grooves using an appropriate tool, exercising care to avoid cutting too deeply. Thoroughly clean all carbon and varnish from the piston with solvent. CAUTION: *Do not use a wire brush or caustic solvent on pistons.* Inspect the pistons for scuffing, scoring, cracks, pitting, or excessive ring groove wear. If wear is evident, the piston must be replaced. Check the connecting rod length by measuring the rod from the inside of the large end to the inside of the small end using calipers. All connecting rods should be equal

Remove the piston rings using a ring expander

length. Replace any rod that differs from the others in the engine.

* Have the connecting rod alignment checked in an alignment fixture by a machinist. Replace any twisted or bent rods.

* Magnaflux the connecting rods to locate stress cracks. If cracks are found, replace the connecting rod.

Fit the Pistons to the Cylinders

Using a telescope gauge and micrometer, or a dial gauge, measure the cylinder bore diameter perpendicular to the piston pin, 2½" below the deck. Measure the piston perpendicular to its pin on the skirt. The difference between the two measurements is the piston clearance. If the clearance is within specifications or slightly below (after boring or honing), finish honing is all that is required. If the clearance is excessive, try to obtain a slightly larger piston to bring clearance within specifications. Where this is not possible, obtain the first oversize piston, and hone (or if necessary, bore) the cylinder to size.

Measure the size of the piston

Measure the cylinder bore with a telescopic gauge

Measure the telescopic gauge to determine the bore diameter

Assemble the Pistons and Connecting Rods

Inspect piston pin, connecting rod small end bushing, and piston bore for galling, scoring, or excessive wear. If evident, replace defective part(s). Measure the I.D. of the piston boss and connecting rod small end, and the O.D. of the piston pin. If within specifications, assemble piston pin and rod. CAUTION: *If piston pin must be pressed in, determine the proper method and use the proper tools; otherwise the piston will distort.* Install the lock rings; ensure that they seat properly. If the parts are not within specifications, determine the service method for the type of engine. In some cases, piston and pin are serviced as an assembly when either is defective. Others specify reaming the piston and connecting rods for an oversize pin. If the connecting rod bushing is worn, it may in many cases be replaced. Reaming the piston and replacing the rod bushing are machine shop operations.

Clean and Inspect the Camshaft

Degrease the camshaft, using solvent, and clean out all oil holes. Visually inspect cam lobes and bearing journals for excessive wear. If a lobe is questionable, check all lobes as indicated below. If a journal or lobe is worn, the camshaft must be reground or replaced. NOTE: *If a journal is worn, there is a good chance that the bushings are worn.* If lobes and journals appear intact, place the front and rear journals in V-blocks, and rest a dial indicator on the center journal. Rotate the camshaft to check straightness. If deviation exceeds .001", replace the camshaft.

* Check the camshaft lobes with a micrometer, by measuring the lobes from the nose to base and again at 90°. The lift is determined by subtracting the second measurement from the first. If all exhaust lobes and all intake lobes are not identical within specs, the camshaft must be reground or replaced.

BEARING JOURNALS

FUEL PUMP DRIVE ECCENTRIC

DISTRIBUTOR DRIVE GEAR

Check the camshaft for alignment using a dial indicator

EXPANDING COLLET

THRUST BEARING

EXPANDING MANDREL

BACK-UP NUT

PULLING NUT

PULLER SCREW

PULLER SCREW EXTENSION

CAMSHAFT BEARING (LOOSE)

PULLING PLATE

Camshaft rmoval and installation tool (typical)

Replace the Camshaft Bearings

If excessive wear is indicated, or if the engine is being completely rebuilt, camshaft bearings should be replaced as follows: Drive the camshaft rear plug from the block. Assemble the removal puller with its shoulder on the bearing to be removed. Gradually tighten the puller nut until bearing is removed. Remove remaining bearings, leaving the front and rear for last. To remove front and rear bearings, reverse position of the tool, so as to pull the bearings in toward the center of the block. Leave the tool in this position, pilot the new front and rear bearings on the installer, and pull them into position. Return the tool to its original position and pull remaining bearings into position. NOTE: *Ensure that oil holes align when installing bearings.* Replace camshaft rear plug, and stake it into position to aid retention.

Finish Hone the Cylinders

Chuck a flexible drive hone into a power drill, and insert it into the cylinder. Start the hone, and move it up and down in the cylinder at a rate which will produce approximately a 60° cross-hatch pattern. NOTE: *Do not extend the hone below the cylinder bore.* After developing the pattern, remove the hone and recheck piston fit. Wash the cylinders with a detergent and water solution to remove abrasive dust, dry, and wipe several times with a rag soaked in engine oil.

Check Piston Ring End-Gap

Compress the piston rings to be used in a cylinder, one at a time, into that cylinder, and press them approximately 1″ below the deck with an inverted piston. Using feeler gauges, measure the ring end-gap, and compare to specifications. Pull the ring out of the cylinder and file the ends with a fine file to obtain proper clearance. CAUTION: *If inadequate ring end-gap exists, ring breakage could result.*

Install the Piston Rings

Inspect the ring grooves in the piston for excessive wear or taper. If necessary, recut the groove(s) for use with an overwidth ring or a standard ring and spacer. If the groove is worn uniformly, overwidth rings, or standard rings and spacers may be installed without recutting. Roll the outside of the ring around the groove to check for burrs or deposits. If any are found, remove with a fine file. Hold the ring in the groove, and measure side clearance. If necessary, correct as indicated above. NOTE: *Always install any additional spacers above the piston ring.* The ring groove must be deep enough to allow the ring to seat below the lands. In many cases, a "go-no-go" depth gauge will be provided with the piston rings. Shallow grooves may be corrected by recutting, while deep grooves require some type of filler or expander behind the piston. Consult the piston ring supplier concerning the suggested method. Install the rings on the piston, lowest ring first, using a ring expander. NOTE: *Position the ring markings as specified by the manufacturer.*

Check the ring side clearance using a feeler gauge

Install the Camshaft

Liberally lubricate the camshaft lobes and journals, and slide the camshaft into the block. CAUTION: *Exercise extreme care to avoid damaging the bearings when inserting the camshaft.* Be careful not to force the shaft toward the rear of the engine block as this can unseat the welch plugs in some engines. Install and tighten the camshaft thrust plate retaining bolts.

Check Camshaft End-Play

Using feeler gauges, determine whether the clearance between the camshaft boss (or gear) and backing plate is within specifications. Install shims behind the thrust plate, or reposition the camshaft gear and retest end-play.

* Mount a dial indicator stand so that the stem of the dial indicator rests on the nose of the camshaft, parallel to the camshaft axis. Push the camshaft as far in as possible

Properly honed cylinder walls should look as shown

Check the ring end gap using a feeler gauge

Measuring the camshaft end play using feeler gauges

Measuring camshaft end play using a dial indicator (6 cyl. engines)

Measuring camshaft end play (8 cyl. engines)

and zero the gauge. Move the camshaft outward to determine the amount of camshaft end-play. If the end-play is not within tolerance, install shims behind the thrust plate, or reposition the camshaft gear and retest.

Install the Rear Main Seal (Where Applicable)

Position the block with the bearing saddles facing upward. Lay the rear main seal in its groove and press it lightly into its seat. Place a piece of pipe the same diameter as the crankshaft journal into the saddle, and firmly seat the seal. Hold the pipe in position, and trim the ends of the seal flush if required.

Install the Crankshaft

Thoroughly clean the main bearing saddles and caps. Place the upper halves of the bearing inserts on the saddles and press into position. NOTE: *Ensure that the oil holes align.* Press the corresponding bearing inserts into the main bearing caps. Lubricate the upper main bearings, and lay the crankshaft in position. Place a strip of Plastigage on each of the crankshaft journals, install the main caps, and torque to specifications. Remove the main caps, and compare the Plastigage to the scale on the Plastigage envelope. If clearances are within tolerances, remove the Plastigage, turn the crankshaft 90°, wipe off all oil and retest. If all clearances are correct, remove all Plastigage, thoroughly lubricate the main caps and bearing journals, and install the main caps. If clearances are not within tolerance, the upper bearing inserts may be removed, without removing the crankshaft, using a bearing roll out pin. Roll in a bearing that will provide proper clearance, and retest. Torque all main caps, excluding the thrust bearing cap, to specifications. Tighten the thrust bearing cap finger tight. To properly align the thrust bearing, pry the crankshaft the extent of its axial travel several times, the last movement held toward the front of the engine, and torque the thrust bearing cap to specifications. Determine the crankshaft endplay (see below), and bring within tolerance with thrust washers.

Measure Crankshaft End-Play

Mount a dial indicator stand on the front of the block, with the dial indicator stem resting on the nose of the crankshaft, parallel to the crankshaft axis. Pry the crankshaft rearward to the full extent of its travel, and zero the indicator. Pry the crankshaft forward and record crankshaft end-play. NOTE: *Crankshaft end-play also may be measured at the thrust bearing, using feeler gauges.*

Checking the crankshaft end play using a dial indicator

Install the Pistons

Press the upper connecting rod bearing halves into the connecting rods, and the lower halves into the connecting rod caps. Position the piston ring gaps according to specifica-

tions, and lubricate the pistons. Install a ring compresser on a piston, and press two long (8″) pieces of plastic tubing over the rod bolts. Using the plastic tubes as a guide, press the pistons into the bores and onto the crankshaft with a wooden hammer handle. After seating the rod on the crankshaft journal, remove the tubes and install the cap finger tight. Install the remaining pistons in the same manner. Invert the engine and check the bearing clearance at two points (90° apart) on each journal with Plastigage. NOTE: *Do not turn the crankshaft with Plastigage installed.* If clearance is within tolerances, remove *all* Plastigage, thoroughly lubricate the journals, and torque the rod caps to specifications. If clearance is not within specifications, install different thickness bearing inserts and recheck. CAUTION: *Never shim or file the connecting rods or caps.* Always install plastic tube sleeves over the rod bolts when the caps are not installed, to protect the crankshaft journals.

Installing the piston and connecting rod

Check Connecting Rod Side Clearance

Determine the clearance between the sides of the connecting rods and the crankshaft, using feeler gauges. If clearance is below the minimum tolerance, the rod may be machined to provide adequate clearance. If clearance is excessive, substitute an unworn rod, and recheck. If clearance is still outside specifications, the crankshaft must be welded and reground, or replaced.

Check the connecting rod size clearance using a feeler gauge

Inspect the Timing Chain

Visually inspect the timing chain for broken or loose links, and replace the chain if any are found. If the chain will flex sideways, it must be replaced. Install the timing chain as specified. NOTE: *If the original timing chain is to be reused, install it in its original position.*

Check the timing chain deflection (typical)

Check the timing gear runout (typical)

Check the timing gear backlash (typical)

Check Timing Gear Backlash and Runout

Mount a dial indicator with its stem resting on a tooth of the camshaft gear. Rotate the gear until all slack is removed, and zero the indicator. Rotate the gear in the opposite direction until slack is removed, and record gear backlash. Mount the indicator with its stem resting on the edge of the camshaft gear, parallel to the axis of the camshaft. Zero the indicator, and turn the camshaft gear one full turn, recording the runout. If either backlash or runout exceed specifications, replace the worn gear(s).

Completing the Rebuilding Process

Following the above procedures, complete the rebuilding process as follows:

Fill the oil pump with oil, to prevent cavitating (sucking air) on initial engine start up. Install the oil pump and the pickup tube on the engine. Coat the oil pan gasket as necessary, and install the gasket and the oil pan. Mount the flywheel and the crankshaft vibrational damper or pulley on the crankshaft. NOTE: *Always use new bolts when installing the flywheel.* Inspect the clutch shaft pilot bushing in the crankshaft. If the bushing is excessively worn, remove it with an expanding puller and a slide hammer, and tap a new bushing into place.

Position the engine, cylinder head side up. Lubricate the lifters, and install them into their bores. Install the cylinder head, and torque it as specified. Insert the pushrods (where applicable), and install the rocker shaft(s) (if so equipped) or position the rocker arms on the pushrods. If solid lifters are utilized, adjust the valves to the "cold" specifications.

Mount the intake and exhaust manifolds, the carburetor(s), the distributor and spark plugs. Adjust the point gap and the static ignition timing. Mount all accessories and install the engine in the car. Fill the radiator with coolant, and the crankcase with high quality engine oil.

Break-in Procedure

Start the engine, and allow it to run at low speed for a few minutes, while checking for leaks. Stop the engine, check the oil level, and fill as necessary. Restart the engine, and fill the cooling system to capacity. Check the point dwell angle and adjust the ignition timing and the valves. Run the engine at low to medium speed (800-2500 rpm) for approximately ½ hour, and retorque the cylinder head bolts. NOTE: *On engines with aluminum heads or block, retorque engine cold.* Road test, and check again for leaks.

Follow the manufacturer's recommended engine break-in procedure and maintenance schedule for new engines.

Measuring Timing Chain Stretch

	Clearance	Location
361 C.I.D.	.005 to .0015 inch	Top of Skirt
413 C.I.D.	.002 to .003 inch	Piston Pin Center Line

THE ELLIPTICAL SHAPE OF THE PISTON SKIRT SHOULD BE .013 TO .015 IN. LESS AT DIAMETER (A) THAN ACROSS THE THRUST FACES AT DIAMETER (B). MEASUREMENT IS MADE ⅛ IN. BELOW LOWER RING GROOVE

DIAMETERS AT (C) AND (D) CAN BE EQUAL OR DIAMETER AT (D) CAN BE .0015 IN. GREATER THAN (C) FOR 413 MEASURE AT (F) AND (D), (D) TOBE .0005 TO .0015 GREATER THAN (F)

Piston Measurements

GENERAL ENGINE SPECIFICATIONS

Engine Model	Number of Cylinders	Bore x Stroke	Piston Cu. In. Displ.	Maximum HP @ RPM	Maximum Torque @ RPM	Firing Order	Gov. No. Load RPM	Low Idle
25000 MK II	6	5¼ x 6½	844	378 @ 2000	1075 @ 1400	1-5-3-6-2-4	2300	550

CRANKSHAFT AND BEARING SPECIFICATIONS

Engine Model	Main Bearing Journal Dia.	Main Bearing Clearance	Rod Bearing Journal Dia.	Rod Bearing Clearance	Crankshaft Endplay
25000 MK II	3.9945-3.9960	.0021-.0048	3.3715-3.3730	.0026-.0056	.007-.015

PISTON AND RING SPECIFICATIONS

Engine Model	Piston-to Liner Clearance	Piston Pin Dia.	Ring End Gap				Liner Inside Dia.
			1st	2nd	3rd	4th	
25000 MK II	.007-.009	2.0015-2.0017	.019-.036	.016-.038	.017-.038	.016-.035	5.871-5.873

TORQUE SPECIFICATIONS

Engine Model	Cylinder Head Capscrews				Main Bearing Cap		Crankshaft Pulley	Flywheel Capscrews	Exhaust Manifold	Connection Rod	
25000 MK II	⅝-11 185	¾-10 390	⅞-9x6⁷⁄₁₆ 400		⅝-11x6 185		325	200	85	⅝-18x3¾ 245	⅝-18 195

Cooling System

Thermostat Removal

1. Remove capscrews from upper end of water by-pass tube and remove it from thermostat cover.
2. Unbolt and remove outlet elbow and gasket.
3. Remove the thermostat cover, and thermostats and gaskets from the manifold.
4. Clean and inspect cover, gaskets and seals.

Thermostat Installation

1. Position gasket on manifold and install thermostats.
2. Position thermostat cover on manifold and secure with capscrews and lockwashers.
3. Place the radiator inlet elbow and gasket in position at the front of the thermostat cover and secure with capscrews and lockwashers.
4. Using a new gasket, position the top of the water by-pass tube on the thermostat cover and secure with capscrews and lockwashers.

Fuel System
Robert Bosch

Injection Pump Removal

1. Make sure the FPI mark on the pump coupling hub is aligned with the timing pointer on the pump.
2. Disconnect the engine stop and speed control linkage from the injection pump.

Thermostat Assemblies

3. Shut off fuel supply.
4. Disconnect fuel inlet and outlet tubes and fuel return and injection lines. Disconnect lube oil feed and drain tubes.
5. Remove capscrews from injection pump drive coupling flange.
6. Remove capscrew which secures hub clamp to the shaft of the accessory drive assembly. Force the hub clamp as far as possible toward the front of the engine. This will facilitate removing the pump from the dowels in the pump mounting bracket.
7. Remove the capscrews and lock-washers that secure the injection pump to the mounting bracket.
8. Lift the injection pump to clear the dowels and remove it and the coupling as an assembly from the mounting bracket.

Injection Pump Installation and Timing

1. Depending on the production date, the timing pointer is located either on the front gear housing cover or in the flywheel housing.
2. If the engine has been rotated since the pump was removed,

Robert Bosch injection pump

position number one piston on TDC compression.

3. Rotate the engine in normal direction of rotation until the timing pointer lines up with the mark denoting 34° BTDC at 2100 rpm.

4. Make certain that all the slack is out of the timing gears and fuel pump drive. If the correct mark is passed, back up several notches past the mark and approach it in the normal direction of rotation. Never back up to the mark for a setting.

5. If coupling was removed from pump:
   a. Position key in injection pump camshaft keyway.
   b. Position hub on camshaft. Install lockwasher and nut; torque nut to 85-90 ft lbs.
   c. Current production couplings have a dust shield which installs in a groove on the flange with the peak of the

shield toward the front of the engine.
   d. Position the two inserts in the flange.
   e) Assemble the flange to the hub with rubber inserts separating the flange and hub fingers.
   f. Work the cover over the rubber inserts and secure to flange with capscrews and lockwashers.

6. Position the FPI mark on the coupling hub, opposite the pointer on the pump.

7. Install the pump and coupling as an assembly on the pump mounting bracket by holding the pump assembly at a slight angle and positioning the bore in the coupling flange on the pilot of the hub clamp and lowering the pump onto the dowels.

8. Loosely install the capscrews and lockwashers that secure the pump.

9. Insert two .010″ feeler gauges between the hub and flange. The gauges should be 180° apart on each side of the coupling.

10. Force the hub clamp toward the pump and secure with capscrews and lockwashers. Do not tighten.

11. Tap the injection pump and hub clamp with a soft mallet until a slight and equal drag is felt on each feeler gauge. Remove feelers.

12. Torque the pump-to-bracket capscrews to 18-23 ft lbs.

13. Torque the clamp-to-accessory drive capscrews to 39 ft. lbs.

14. Align the FPI mark on the flange with the pointer on the pump.

15. Torque the clamp-to-flange capscrews to 29 ft lbs.

16. Install lube oil supply and drain tube assemblies.

17. Install fuel supply and return tube assemblies.

Front end timing pointer
1 Pointer
2 Timing marks

Rear end timing pointer
1 Flywheel timing marks
2 Pointer
3 Flywheel housing

18. Install high pressure lines.
19. Connect the engine stop and control linkages.
20. Install the timing cover, if so equipped.

Governor

Engine Speed Adjustment

1. Run engine to normal operating temperature.
2. If engine is not equipped with a tachometer, one may be installed on the front end of the engine crankshaft.
3. The engine speed may be checked from the tachometer drive at the rear of the accessory drive which is driven at 1½ times the crankshaft speed.
4. Engine speed may also be checked with a stroboscopic tachometer by marking the pump coupling flywheel which is driven at ½ engine speed.
5. Move the accelerator to low and high speeds and make certain the control moves the governor speed control lever through its full arc.
6. Operate engine at low idle, 500-600 rpm. Adjust if necessary.
7. Move the accelerator so the engine operates at high idle, 2250-2350 rpm. Adjust if necessary.

Low Idle Adjustment

1. With engine running, loosen the jam nut on the low idle adjusting screw.
2. Hold the governor speed control lever so the stop contacts the low idle adjusting screw. Turn the idle adjusting screw as necessary to increase or decrease idle speed.
3. When correct idle speed, 500-600 rpm, is achieved, hold the low idle adjusting screw and tighten the jam nut.

High Idle Adjustment

1. Remove the flat head screw seal from the securing link and remove the link to gain access to the high idle adjusting screw.
2. With engine running, loosen jam nut on the high idle screw. Hold governor speed control lever so control lever shaft stop contacts the high idle screw. Turn adjusting screw to increase or decrease high speed.

Injector Nozzles

Removal

1. Remove valve cover.
2. Disconnect and remove fuel return manifold.
3. Using a tubing socket, loosen the injection tube nuts from the top of the injection nozzles.

4. Loosen the injection tube nuts from the fuel line connectors. *CAUTION:* Do not bend lines during removal.
5. Free the nozzle end of the tubes and remove the tubes from the engine.
6. Remove the nut and washer from the clamps; remove the clamps.
7. Carefully pry upward on the nozzle protection cap. Pull nozzles from the cylinders. Cover openings in cylinders.

Testing and Adjusting

1. Open the nozzle tester valve and loosen the filler cap.
2. Connect the nozzle to the tester.
3. Operate the tester handle and observe the tester gauges. The nozzle should pop at 4100-4150 psi.
4. To adjust pop pressure, remove the protection cap from the upper end of the nozzle and loosen the adjusting screw locknut.
5. Operate the tester handle and turn the screw until the proper pop point is reached. Hold the screw and tighten the locknut to 75 ft lbs.
6. Operate the pressure handle until the gauge shows about 3900 psi. Check nozzle tip for leakage. If leakage is observed, relieve the pressure by loosening one of the line nuts and remove the valve and valve body for cleaning and inspection.
7. Operate the handle at about 100 strokes per second and observe the spray pattern. *WARNING:* Do not let spray contact skin. Spray can penetrate skin and cause blood poisoning.
8. If spray is not acceptable, remove nozzle and clean tip.

Nozzle Installation

1. Thoroughly clean the inside of the nozzle holder sleeves before installing the holder.
2. Place a new nozzle holder gasket in position on the holder with the concave face toward the retaining nut. Carefully insert the holder into the sleeve in the head.
3. Install the clamp, washer and nut on each nozzle. Do not tighten.
4. Install the injection tubes by first inserting one end of the tubes into the nozzle holders. Start, but do not tighten, the tube nuts.
5. Install the fuel return manifold.
6. Tighten the nozzle holder clamp nuts to 43-48 ft lbs.
7. Tighten the injection tube nuts and the fuel return manifold nuts.

Flow Timing the Injection Pump

NOTE: A hand primer pump capable of supplying 2-3 psi. to the pump gallery is necessary.

1. Position the engine crankshaft so that the timing marks indicate #1 piston TDC compression.
2. Remove the injection pump top cover and position it out of the way. Clean all external surfaces of the pump and lines.
3. Temporarily position the cover on the pump and remove the #1 injection line.
4. Remove the delivery valve holder from the pump.
5. Remove the fill piece, spring, delivery valve gasket, and delivery valve from the top of the barrel and plunger assembly.

Adjusting nozzle opening pressure

1 Pressure adjusting screw
2 Adjusting screw locknut
3 Nozzle tester
4 Valve handle
5 Tester handle
6 Spray collector
7 Nozzle holder assembly

6. Remove the fluted delivery valve from the valve body and reinstall the valve body and old gasket with the holder.

7. Loosen the capscrews securing the injection pump coupling hub clamp to the coupling flange. Place the stop lever in the run position and the speed control lever in the high speed position. Turn the pump coupling clockwise several degrees. Rotation is determined from pump drive end.

8. Rotate the injection pump camshaft counterclockwise while operating the hand primer. Camshaft should be rotated very slowly. As the #1 plunger starts to close off the intake port of the barrel the fuel flow will be reduced. Continue turning the camshaft until the fuel stops. A bulge of fuel will appear on top of the valve holder. Wipe this away and continue to operate the primer. If the bulge appears again, it means that the fuel inlet port in the barrel is not completely closed. A very slight rotation of the pump camshaft will now cause the plunger to close the inlet port. When the port is completely closed, the FPI mark on the pump coupling will align with the pointer on the injection pump, indicating proper timing of the pump to the engine. Repeat this step several times.

9. Securely tighten the hub clamp-to-injection pump coupling flange retaining capscrews.

10. Remove the delivery valve holder, copper gasket, and valve body from the pump. Wash all components in clean fuel oil.

11. Place the delivery valve into the valve body and position this assembly on top of the plunger and barrel.

12. Place a new copper gasket on the top of the delivery valve assembly and insert the fill piece into the spring. Position this assembly on top of the delivery valve, fill piece up.

13. Lubricate a new O-ring and position it on the valve holder. Screw the holder into the pump and torque to 50-55 ft. lbs. Install the top cover, connect the high pressure line and tighten the nut.

Aneroid Adjustment

NOTE: Prior to adjustments on early models, make certain the stop screw is turned until it bottoms. Current production pumps have the stop screw bottomed. The stop screw is locked in position by a locknut within the aneroid housing. A setscrew is screwed into the stop screw threads. A soft metal seal plug seals the setscrew. This plug can be removed with a sharp instrument.

1. Remove the aneroid housing side cover.

2. Back off the pump shutoff lever stop screw until clearance is obtained between the lever and the stop screw, when the lever is completely in the stopped position.

3. With the injection pump shutoff in the stopped position, check the clearance between the end of the rack and the aneroid lever gap adjustment screw. The current specified clearance is 10-10½ mm.

4. To adjust clearance, loosen the lever adjusting screw locknut and turn the screw to gain specified clearance.

5. Connect shop air to aneroid.

6. Place pump shutoff lever in the run position.

7. Slowly apply air pressure from zero until the linkage begins to move. This movement must occur between 6.3-6.6 psi for all units.

8. Turn the guide bushing with a screwdriver to adjust.

NOTE: It is important that the aneroid lever and gap adjustment screw does not interfere with the movement of the rack to the specified full load position.

9. With the swivel position on the fuel stop, observe the rack end. It must not be contacting the aneroid lever gap adjusting screw.

10. With the shutoff lever held in the stopped position, turn the stop screw until it contacts the shutoff lever. Then continue to turn the screw an additional ½ turn.

Fuel System American Bosch

Injection Pump Removal

1. Align the FPI mark on the pump coupling flywheel and the timing pointer on the pump.

2. Disconnect engine stop and speed control linkage from the pump.

3. Shut off the fuel supply.

4. Disconnect the inlet and outlet hoses. return line and injection lines.

5. Remove capscrews from the pump drive coupling flange, and the capscrews which secure the injection pump to the mounting bracket. Remove the pump and coupling assembly.

Installation and Timing

1. If the engine was rotated, make sure the #1 piston is on TDC compression. Timing marks may be located on the damper or the flywheel depending on engine production date. The timing hole cover must be removed to gain access to flywheel timing marks.

2. Rotate the crankshaft in normal rotation direction until the timing pointer is aligned with the mark indicating 34° BTDC at 2100 rpm. Never back up to the timing mark. If timing is passed, back up past the mark and then forward to align mark and pointer.

3. Install the rubber spacer and

Removing fuel injection tube

1 Hose
2 Diaphragm cover
3 Guide bushing
4 Pin & snap ring
5 Rack
6 Aneroid housing

7 Gap-10mm
8 Gap adjusting screw
9 Stop screw
10 Setscrew
11 Seal plug
12 Lever

Aneroid assembly

drive coupling flange to the coupling flywheel. Sealing lips of the rubber spacer not be forced inward.

4. Install new O-rings and oil drain coupling in the counterbores of the oil passages in the pump mounting bracket.
5. Align the FPI mark on the coupling flywheel with the timing pointer.
6. Position the pump and drive coupling assembly on the mounting bracket. Slide the pump forward and install, but do not tighten the capscrews and washers.
7. Insert two .010″ feeler gauges on the sides between the coupling hub and flange, 180° apart.
8. Tap the pump forward with a soft mallet until a slight and equal drag is felt at each gauge. Torque the mounting bracket capscrews to 44-49 ft. lbs. for 7/16″-14 × 1⅛″ capscrews and 40-45 ft. lbs. for the 7/16″-14 × 1⅝″ capscrews. Remove feeler gauges.
9. Make sure that the FPI timing mark on the coupling flywheel is aligned with the timing pointer. If not, turn the coupling flywheel to obtain proper alignment.
10. Torque the two drive coupling capscrews to 29 ft. lbs.
11. Connect the inlet and outlet hoses, fuel return and injection lines.
12. Install timing cover, if equipped.

Governor

Engine Speed

See engine speed adjustment under Robert Bosch procedures.

Governor Adjustments

1. Disconnect the accelerator linkage from the governor speed control lever so the lever can be moved by hand.
2. Remove the speed adjusting screw access cover from the governor.

Front end timing pointer

─ DRIVE COUPLING ASSEMBLY ─

1 Coupling hub
2 Coupling flange
3 Spider
4 Coupling flywheel
5 Pump timing pointer
6 Hand primer pump
7 Overflow valve
8 Pump
9 Governor
10 Oil drain coupling
11 O-rings
12 Mounting bracket
13 Oil supply hose

American Bosch pump

Injection pump alignment

1 Coupling flywheel
2 Rubber spider
3 Pump timing pointer
4 FPI timing mark
5 Drive coupling flange
6 Drive coupling hub
7 Capscrew
8 Feeler gauge
9 Hub capscrew

Governor speed adjustment points

1 Speed control lever
2 High idle screw
3 Low idle screw
4 Jam nut

3. With engine running, loosen low idle adjusting screw jam nut. Hold governor speed control lever so lever shaft stop plate contacts the low idle adjusting screw. Turn the idle adjusting screw to attain 500-600 rpm. Tighten jam nut.
4. Loosen high idle screw jam nut. Hold governor speed control lever so lever shaft stop plate contacts the high idle screw. Turn screw to attain 2250-2350 rpm. Tighten jam nut.

Injection Nozzle Service

See Injector Nozzle section under Robert Bosch procedures.

Flow Timing the Injection Pump

NOTE: A hand primer pump capable of supplying 2-3 psi to the fuel oil gallery is necessary.

1. Align the FPI timing marks with #1 piston at compression.
2. Clean all external pump and line surfaces.
3. Remove #1 nozzle injection line from the pump.
4. Remove holder, delivery valve spring and delivery valve from the valve body at the top of the plunger and barrel assembly.
5. Reinstall the holder and nut. Tighten nut securely.
6. Loosen the pump coupling hub capscrews, place the stop lever in the run position, place the speed control lever in the high speed position and turn the coupling several degrees clockwise as viewed from the pump drive end.
7. Operate the hand primer pump and rotate the pump camshaft counterclockwise very slowly. As #1 plunger starts to close off the

intake port of the barrel, the fuel volume from the delivery valve holder will be reduced.

8. When the fuel stops flowing a bulge of fuel will appear on top of the delivery valve holder. Wipe off the bulge and continue to operate the primer pump. If the bulge appears again, it indicates that the inlet port in the barrel is not completely closed. A slight rotation of the pump camshaft will now cause the plunger to close the inlet port. At this point the FPI mark on the pump coupling will align with the pointer on the pump.

9. Repeat this procedure several times.

10. Securely tighten the coupling hub-to-coupling flange capscrews.

11. Remove the holder nut and holder, wash all components and reassemble. Torque the holder nut to 60-65 ft. lbs. Connect the injection line.

Lubrication System

Full-Flow Filters

Removal & Installation

1. Clean filter head and bodies.
2. Drain filters.
3. Remove centerbolts, filter bodies and elements.
4. Install new elements and gaskets, position filter bodies and torque center bolts to 45-50 ft lbs.

By-Pass Filter

Removal & Installation

1. Clean the filter cover.
2. Drain filter housing.
3. Remove the cover clamp ring and lift the cover from the filter housing.
4. Unscrew and remove the T-handle hold-down from the center tube. Remove the filter element.
5. Clean interior of housing and install drain.
6. Insert new element and press down firmly. Be sure that the T-handle hold-down orifice plug hole is open. Install hold-down and tighten securely.
7. Install cover gasket and cover.

Lubricating Oil Pump Specifications

Disassemble oil pump and check the following fits and clearances:

Pump driving gear-to-cover, running   .010-.029"
Gear-to-pumpbody radial clearance   .00225-.00325"
Gear side clearance   .005-.007"
Shaft bushings—
I.D.   .7495-.7505"

Oil pump-exploded view

Gear shafts—O.D.   .7475-.7480"
Shaft-to-bushing clearance   .0015-.0030"

Valve Adjustment

1. Operate the engine until normal operating temperature is reached.
2. Remove the rocker cover.
3. Crank the engine until the #6 cyl. intake valves begin to open.
4. Loosen the locknut on #1 cyl. bridge adjusting screw. Back off screw one turn.
5. Press down firmly on the center of the bridge and turn the adjusting screw until it makes contact with the valve stem. Tighten the locknut.
6. Loosen the rocker arm adjusting screw locknut and adjust rocker arm to bridge clearance. Clearance is: intake—.015", exhaust—.020". Tighten lock nut.

Air Compressor

Cylinder Head Removal and Installation

1. Drain coolant from compressor crankcase.
2. Remove discharge valve capnuts, springs and valves from top of air compressor cylinder head.
3. Remove hose assembly from compressor cylinder head.
4. Remove discharge flange and gasket from head.
5. Unbolt and remove cylinder head. It may be necessary to tap cylinder head with a soft mallet

Valve lash adjustment

to loosen.

6. Remove inlet valve springs from head and mark for replacement.
7. Clean loose carbon and foreign matter from head with a safe solvent. Head may be scraped to remove hard deposits.
8. Rinse head in solvent and blow dry.
9. Clean spring and discharge valve parts in solvent and blow dry.
10. Reassemble parts and head in reverse order of removal. Use new gaskets.
11. Refill cooling system.

Engine Disassembly

NOTE: Disassembly procedures are described with engine out of vehicle and mounted on a work stand.

Valve arrangement—front head; rear head identical

Cylinder Head

1. Loosen clamps, remove bracket bolt and remove breather tube from rocker cover and head.
2. Remove rocker covers from heads.
3. Disconnect air inlet elbow from turbocharger and intake manifold.
4. Remove bracket bolts and disconnect and remove oil inlet and outlet lines from turbocharger.
6. Remove high pressure fuel lines and fuel drain line from head covers and pump.
7. Remove exhaust manifold end sections by unbolting and swiveling out of connecting sleeves. Unbolt and remove center section.
8. Disconnect and remove water inlet and outlet hoses from intake manifold and clamp.
9. Remove manifold end caps and carefully slide out intercooler.
10. Unbolt and remove intake manifold.
11. Disconnect and remove fuel lines between cylinder head cover and injectors.
12. Remove bolts and lift off rocker shaft assemblies.
13. Unbolt and remove head covers. Remove pushrods.
14. Remove head bolts and lift off heads.

Cylinder Block

15. Remove fire rings from block.
16. Remove lifter covers from block, unbolt and remove lifter brackets and remove lifters.
17. Remove fan, hub and housing assemblies.
18. Disconnect lines from oil cooler and unbolt and remove cooler and bracket assemblies.
19. Disconnect all lines and hoses, remove water pump pulley, remove pump attaching bolts and remove pump assembly. Remove clamp and idler assembly.
20. Unbolt and remove coolant inlet and outlet manifolds.
21. For injection pump and governor removal, see Fuel Section.
22. Disconnect coolant inlet and outlet lines, and oil inlet line from

1 Head
2 Lifting eye
3 Capscrew
4 Lower cover gasket
5 Head cover
6 Rocker cover gasket
7 Breather tube
8 Clamp
9 Elbow clamp
10 Elbow
11 Rocker cover bolt
12 Sealing washer
13 Rocker cover-rear
14 Rocker cover—front
15 Rocker cover bolt stud
16 Head capscrew
17 Injector sleeve
18 Bridge guide pin
19 Intake valve guide
20 Exhaust valve guide
21 Valve seat spring
22 Damper & spring
23 Stem lock
24 Roto-coil
25 Head capscrew
26 Lifting eye
27 Valve seat
28 Valve seat
29 Intake valve
30 Exhaust valve
31 Head gasket
32 Liner gasket

Rear cylinder head, exploded view

oil compressor. Remove compressor-to-bracket bolts and lift off compressor.

NOTE: Compressor may be either a right or left hand mount.

23. Remove crankshaft pulley bolt

and 6 pulley-to-damper bolts. Using a suitable puller, remove the pulley and damper.
24. Unbolt and remove the timing case cover. Remove the oil pan.
25. Unbolt and remove the accessory

Timing gear housing, exploded view

Water pump, idler and fan and hub mounting

drive unit.

26. Remove camshaft drive gear. Remove camshaft retainer and key; carefully slide camshaft from block.
27. Unbolt and remove timing case and gasket.
28. Remove the eight flywheel capscrews and carefully lift off flywheel.
29. Remove the eight flywheel housing bolts and carefully remove housing.
30. Remove crankshaft rear seal and O-ring. Remove camshaft rear O-ring. Remove the oil pump.
31. Remove connecting rod nuts and lower bearing halves. Remove carbon ridge from liner and push piston and rod assembly out of block.
32. Remove lower main bearing cap bolts and lift out main caps.
33. Lift crankshaft from block with hoist.
34. Using a wood block, drive out the liners.
35. Remove upper main bearing halves.
36. Unbolt and remove piston cooling nozzle jets.

Engine Assembly
1. Push cylinder liners, with new seals into place in the block. Protrusion should be .002-.005".
2. Install piston cooling nozzles making sure that the nozzles spray toward the center of the piston. Torque to 35 ft lbs.
3. Install upper main bearing halves.
4. Carefully lower crankshaft into position.
5. Install lower main bearing halves with a piece of Plastigage to check clearance. Remove caps and check Plastigage width. If satisfactory (.0021-.0048) coat bearings and journals with SAE 30 oil and install caps. Torque 7/8-9 × 6- 7/16 bolts to 400 ft lbs and 5/8-11 × 6 bolts to 185 ft lbs.
6. Install piston and rod assemblies taking care to avoid damage to the cooling nozzles. Position rods on crankshaft journals.
7. Using Plastigage, check rod cap-to-crankshaft clearance. If satisfactory (.0026-.0056") coat journal and bearing with SAE 30 oil and install caps. Torque to 245 ft lb for 5/8-18 × 3¾ socket head and 195 ft lbs for 5/8-18 nut.
8. Install rear oil seal and O-ring, and camshaft O-ring.
9. Install flywheel housing and tighten bolts.
10. Install flywheel and torque bolts to 200 ft lbs.
11. Install timing case and new gasket.
12. Coat camshaft with SAE-30 oil and carefully slide into place. Install retainer, key and gear.
13. Install and secure accessory drive unit.
14. Install timing case cover and gasket.
15. Install oil pump discharge tube and suction tube assemblies.
16. Install oil pan.
17. Using a suitable press, install crankshaft pulley and damper. Torque center bolt to 325 ft lbs.
18. Mount air compressor on bracket. Connect coolant and oil lines.
19. For injection pump and governor installation, see Fuel Section.
20. Install coolant inlet and outlet manifolds.
21. Position water pump assembly in place, install retaining bolts and clamp. Install and secure idler assembly. Connect all hoses and lines.
22. Position oil cooler and secure bracket. Connect lines and hoses.
23. Assemble and secure fan, hub and housing.
24. Install lifters and brackets. Position and secure lifter covers.
25. Install fire rings on block face.

Cylinder Head
26. For injector installation see Fuel Section.
27. Position heads on block with new head gaskets.
28. Torque head bolts in sequence to 185 ft lbs for 5/8-11 capscrews and 390 ft lbs for ¾-10 capscrews.
29. Install head covers and torque to 38-42 ft lbs.
30. Install rocker shaft assemblies and tighten capscrews in order from front cover.
31. Install fuel lines between injectors and head covers.
32. Install air intake manifold. Carefully insert intercooler and install end caps. Connect coolant lines.
33. Install exhaust manifold center section. Insert end section into connector sleeves and bolt to head.
34. Install high pressure fuel lines and drain line between head covers and pump.
35. Position turbocharger on manifold and torque nuts to 18-21 ft lbs.
36. Connect oil inlet and outlet lines to turbocharger.
37. Connect air inlet elbow from turbocharger to manifold.
38. Check valve adjustment as previously described. Install rocker covers.
39. Install breather tube.

1 ¾" dia. by 7¼" long
2 5/8" by 6" long
3 Guide stud location
   All other capscrew locations use 5/8" dia. by 7" long

Head bolt torque sequence

NOTE: If cylinder heads do not have capscrew holes at locations 13 and 14, disregard and continue to follow the numerical sequence.

GENERAL SPECIFICATIONS

ENGINE MODEL	NO. OF CYLINDERS	BORE & STROKE	PISTON DISP. CU. IN.	MAXIMUM HORSEPOWER @ R.P.M.	TORQUE SAE @ R.P.M.	FIRING ORDER RIGHT HAND ROTATION	LOW IDLE R.P.M.	HIGH IDLE R.P.M.
1140	(V)8	4.5 x 4.1	522	150 @ 3200	277 @ 1800	1-2-7-3-4-5-6-8	575	3380
1145	(V)8	4.5 x 4.1	522	175 @ 3200	326 @ 1700	1-2-7-3-4-5-6-8	575	3410
1150	(V)8	4.5 x 4.5	573	200 @ 3000	403 @ 1600	1-2-7-3-4-5-6-8	575	3255
1160	(V)8	4.5 x 5.0	636	225 @ 2800	474 @ 1400	1-2-7-3-4-5-6-8	575	3060
1673C	6	4.75 x 6.0	638	250 @ 2200	690 @ 1600	1-5-3-6-3-4	600	2530
1674	6	4.75 x 6.0	638	270 @ 2200	805 @ 1600	1-5-3-6-2-4	650	1
1693T	6	5.4 x 6.5	893	325 @ 2100	1000 @ 1450	1-5-3-6-2-4	550	2
1693TA	6	5.4 x 6.5	893	425 @ 2100	1275 @ 1400	1-5-3-6-2-4	550	3
3208	(V8)	4.5 x 5	636	210 @ 2800	485 @ 1400	1-2-7-3-4-5-6-8	650	3030
3406	6	5.4 x 6.5	893	4	6	1-5-3-6-2-4	600	5
3408	(V)8	5.4 x 6	1099	7	N.A.	1-5-3-6-2-4	650	3030

1. Serial Numbers and High Idle R.P.M. Settings:
   94B1-94B1060 — 2500 94B1682-94B2557 — 2520
   94B1061-94B1681 — 2480 94B2558-Up — 2505
2. Serial Numbers and High Idle R.P.M. Settings:
   65B1-65B781 — 2190
   65B782-Up — 2305
3. 65B1-65B781 — 2230 65B2918-Up — 2375
   65B782-65B2917 — 2260
4. Precombustion Chamber Models—280 & 325 hp @ 2100
   Direct Injection Models—280 hp @ 2100
   Precombustion Chamber Models w/Aftercooler—360 hp @ 2100

5. 280 PC—2260
   280 DI—2300
   325 PC—2285
   360 PC—2300
6. 280 PC—840 @ 1400
   280 DI—865 @ 1385
   325 PC—970 @ 1400
   360 PC—1080 @ 1400
7. Direct injection—360 & 400 @ 2100
   Precombustion chambers w/aftercooling—450 @ 2100

CRANKSHAFT AND BEARING SPECIFICATIONS

ENGINE SERIES	MAIN BEARING JOURNAL DIAMETER	MAIN BEARING CLEARANCE	SHAFT END THRUST ON BEARING NO.	SHAFT END PLAY	ROD BEARING JOURNAL DIAMETER	ROD BEARING CLEARANCE
1140	3.4995-3.5005	.0015-.0045	4	.003-.009	2.7496-2.7504	.0015-.0045
1145	3.4995-3.5005	.0015-.0045	4	.003-.009	2.7496-2.7504	.0015-.0045
1150	3.4995-3.5005	.0015-.0045	4	.003-.009	2.7496-2.7504	.0015-.0045
1160	3.4995-3.5005	.0015-.0045	4	.003-.009	2.7496-2.7504	.0015-.0045
1673C	3.499-3.500	.0030-.0059	7	.006-.019	2.999-3.000	.0004-.0007
1674	3.499-3.500	.0030-.0059	7	.011-.018	2.999-3.000	.0004-.0007
1693T	4.4995-4.5005	.0035-.0066	7	.006-.018	3.5395-3.5405	.0029-.0060
1693TA	4.4995-4.5005	.0035-.0066	7	.006-.018	3.5395-3.5405	.0029-.0060
3208	3.4990-3.5000	.002-.005	4	.003-.009	2.7496-2.7504	.0015-.0045

PISTONS, PINS, RINGS SPECIFICATIONS

ENGINE SERIES	RING-TO-GROOVE CLEARANCE TOP RING	INTERMEDIATE RING	OIL RING	PISTON PIN DIAMETER	PISTON TO PIN BUSHING CLEARANCE	RING END GAP COMP.	OIL	CYLINDER LINER INSIDE DIAMETER
1140	.0045-.0070	—	.0015-.0035	1.4998-1.5000	.003	.045	.010-.030	4.5000-4.5010
1145	.0045-.0070	—	.0015-.0035	1.4998-1.5000	.003	.045	.010-.030	4.5000-4.5010
1150	.0045-.0070	—	.0015-.0035	1.4998-1.5000	.003	.045	.010-.030	4.5000-4.5010
1160	.0045-.0070	—	.0015-.0035	1.4998-1.5000	.003	.045	.010-.030	4.5000-4.5010
1673C	.0022-.0044	.0025-.0039	.0015-.0033	1.699-1.700	.006	.045	.010-.030	4.750-4.752
1674	.0030-.0044	.0025-.0039	.0015-.0033	1.699-1.700	.006	.017-.023	.013-.023	4.750-4.752
1693T	.0057-.0071	.0030-.0048	.0015-.0030	1.9997-2.0000	.0003-.0010	.019-.029	.015-.025	5.400-5.402
1693TA	.0055-.0073	.0030-.0048	.0015-.0030	1.9997-2.0000	.0003-.0010	.021-.027 [1]	.015-.025	5.400-5.402
3208	.0030-.0055	—	.0015-.0035	1.5009-1.5012	.003	.0225-.045	.0175-.045	4.500-4.5010

1. Applies to top ring. Intermediate ring is .019-.029

ENGINE TORQUE SPECIFICATIONS

ENGINE MODEL	CYLINDER HEAD FT. LBS.	INTAKE MANIFOLD FT. LBS.	EXHAUST MANIFOLD FT. LBS.	CONN. ROD FT. LBS.	MAIN BEARING CAPS FT. LBS.	DAMPER TO CRANKSHAFT BOLT FT. LBS.	FLYWHEEL TO CRANKSHAFT FT. LBS.	OIL PUMP MOUNTING BOLTS FT. LBS.	OIL PAN BOLTS FT. LBS.
1140	①	32	32	30②	③	265	55	18	15
1145	①	32	32	30②	③	265	55	18	15
1150	①	32	32	30②	③	265	55	18	15
1160	①	32	32	30②	③	265	55	18	15
1673	④	—	32	30⑤	175	230	100	—	—
1674	④	—	32	30⑤	175	230	100	—	—
1693	⑥	—	70	⑦	75⑧	148	—	—	—
3208	①	—	32	30②	30⑧	460	55	18	15

① Large bolts: 60 then 95
  Small bolts: 32
② Plus 60°
③ See text under engine assembly
④ Numbered bolts: 115 then 175
  Lettered bolts: 22 then 32
⑤ Plus 90°
⑥ 200 then 330
⑦ 50 plus 180°
⑧ Plus 120°

Caterpillar Diesel Engines

Trouble Diagnosis

Hard Starting or Failure to Start
1. No fuel getting to engine—clogged filters, empty tank, plugged or kinked lines.
2. Fuel shutoff solenoid not energized on 1100 engines, energized on 1673C and 1674 engines.
3. Fuel shutoff solenoid stuck.
4. Fuel transfer pump delivering less than 10 PSI.
5. Injection timing incorrect.
6. Fuel injection pump drive slipping (1100 Series only).

Misfiring
1. Fuel injection lines installed in improper firing order.
2. Defective injection nozzle or pump.
3. Incorrect valve lash.
4. Sticking valves.
5. Incorrect injection timing.
6. Fuel transfer pump delivering less than 10 PSI.
7. Faulty high pressure fuel line.
8. Poor compression.
9. Air in fuel system.

Excessive Black or Gray Smoke
1. Insufficient combustion air—clogged air cleaner or manifold, malfunctioning turbocharger.
2. Faulty fuel nozzle.
3. Incorrect injection timing.
4. Incorrect fuel ratio control setting or injector rack setting.

Excessive White or Blue Smoke
1. Oil consumption due to:
   a. Worn valve guides.
   b. Scored rings or liners.
   c. High crankcase oil level.
   d. Misfiring.

Lack of Power
1. Improperly adjusted accelerator linkage.
2. Failed fuel nozzle.
3. Improper grade of fuel.
4. Turbocharger clogged or dragging.
5. Air induction leaks.
6. Improper injection timing.
7. Excessive valve lash.
8. Fuel supply pressure less than 10 PSI.
9. Faulty timing advance unit.

Low Oil Pressure
1. Lubricating oil diluted with fuel.
2. Excessive clearances in bearings in crankshaft or timing gears.
3. Defective oil pump or relief valve.
4. Crankcase oil level excessive.
5. Oil temperature too high—faulty cooler or cooler relief valve.

Coolant Temperature Too High
1. Combustion gases leaking into coolant.
2. Low coolant level.
3. Faulty water pump.
4. Faulty thermostat.
5. Injection timing incorrect.
6. Pinched shunt line (1100 Series).

Injection valve and pre-combustion chamber

(© Caterpillar Tractor Co.)

Troubleshooting-General Notes

When troubleshooting for misfiring, operate the engine at the speed where missing is most noticeable. Loosen each injector pump fuel line nut, one at a time. That cylinder (or those cylinders) which effect performance the least should be tested for a defective fuel nozzle or pump first.

Fuel transfer pump output should be 10-20 PSI at cranking speed. At full load, the rating is 25 PSI, and at high idle, 30 PSI.

In testing for poor performance or smoke, remember that they can result from either fuel system defects or engine mechanical defects. An air intake restriction across the air cleaner of 30″ of water, or an exhaust system restriction of more than 15″ of water can cause smoke and poor performance because of lack of oxygen and compression. If fuel system inspection reveals no problem on cylinders that misfire, a compression test and measurement of intake and exhaust manifold pressures might be the next step.

Compression Check
1. Remove the fuel injection nozzle of the cylinder to be checked, leaving the pre-combustion chamber in place.
2. Rotate the crankshaft until the piston of the cylinder to be tested is at TDC on the compression stroke.
3. Adapt an air pressure hose to the pre-combustion chamber, using a threaded fitting or rubber adapter.
4. Apply approximately 100 PSI pressure and listen for air leakage at the air cleaner inlet, exhaust outlet, and crankcase breather. On turbocharged engines, it may be necessary to remove the air inlet and exhaust connections to detect leakage. Air through the air intake indi-

Caterpillar • Diesel Engines

cates a leaky intake valve, air through the exhaust indicates a leaky exhaust valve, and air through the crankcase breather indicates problems with piston, rings, or liner. If there is valve leakage, check the valve clearance.

Engine Tune-Up

Valve Adjustments

1100 and 3208 Series Engines

1. Remove valve covers.
2. Rotate the crankshaft in a clockwise direction until the piston of No. 1 cylinder is at TDC on the compression stroke. The TDC-1 mark on the damper or pulley will align with the timing pointer.
3. Adjust the lash for intake and exhaust valves of cylinders No. 1 and 2. Adjust the inlet valve for .015″ lash, and the exhaust for .025″ lash. Lash adjustment is accomplished by loosening the locknut, adjusting the screw to the dimension of the feeler gauge, and then holding the screw while retightening the locknut to 19-25 ft lbs. Recheck the adjustment to ensure it was not disturbed during tightening of the locknut.
4. Rotate the crankshaft 180° clockwise, so the VS mark will align with the pointer. Adjust lash for all valves of cylinders 7 and 3. Rotate the crankshaft 180° clockwise again, until the TDC mark on the damper or pulley aligns with the pointer. Adjust the lash of all valves on cylinders 4 and 5.
5.
6. Again rotate the crankshaft 180° clockwise (the VS mark will again align on engines so equipped). Adjust the lash for cylinders 6 and 8.
7. Replace the valve covers.

1673 Series Engines

1. Remove the valve cover. Rotate the flywheel so the timing pointer is at TC 1-6 cyl. on the flywheel. Observe the positions of the valves for cylinders 1 and 6.
2. If No. 1 cylinder is on compression stroke, adjust the clearances of the inlet valves on cylinders 1, 2, and 4, and the clearances of the exhaust valves on cylinders 1, 3, and 5. If No. 6 cylinder is on compression stroke, adjust the clearances of the inlet valves of cylinders 3, 5, and 6, and the exhaust valve clearances for cylinders 2, 4, and 6. Clearances are: exhaust—.025″, intake—.015″.

I-INLET VALVE
E-EXHAUST VALVE

Locations of cylinders and valves (© Caterpillar Tractor Co.)

3. Following this, rotate the crankshaft 360° so the cylinder at the opposite end of the engine is on compression stroke, and adjust valves as described above.

1674 Series Engines

1. Remove the valve cover. Rotate the flywheel so the timing pointer is at TC 1-6 cyl. on the flywheel. Observe the positions of the valves for cylinders 1 and 6.
2. If No. 1 cylinder is on compression stroke, adjust the clearances of the inlet valves on cylinders 1, 2, and 4, and the clearances of the exhaust valves on cylinders 1, 3, and 5. If No. 6 cylinder is on compression stroke, adjust the clearances of the inlet valves of cylinders 3, 5, and 6, and the exhaust valve clearances for cylinders 2, 4, and 6. Adjustments are made by turning the adjusting screw clockwise until the button just contacts the tip of the valve stem (can no longer be wiggled), and then turning backward 10 clicks (.020″) for exhaust valves, and four clicks (.008″) for intake valves.
3. Following this, rotate the crankshaft 360″ so the cylinder at the opposite end of the engine is on compression stroke, and adjust as described above.

1693 and 3406 Series Engines

1. Follow generally the adjusting procedures given for 1674 Series engines, adjusting the inlet valve cam followers to .018″ and the exhaust cam followers to .030″.

Injection Pump Timing

1100 Series

1. Remove the timing slot plug. Insert a timing pin.
2. Very slowly rotate the crankshaft clockwise until the timing

pin drops into the camshaft timing slot.
3. Remove the timing hole plug. Insert a timing bolt and attempt to thread it into the timing gear. The cover retaining bolt to the right of the timing hole, which is shown in the illustration, may be used.
4. If the bolt threaded into the timing gear in the last step, the engine is in time. Otherwise, proceed as described below.
5. Remove the tach drive adaptor on the front cover.
6. On hydraulically governed engines, remove the tachometer driveshaft with a special deep well socket. Then, with a Puller Group, thread a special bolt assembly into the camshaft, avoiding the use of excessive force. Install another special bolt into the gear carrier or adapter, and tighten it until the gear carrier comes loose.
7. On engines with "max-min" governors, loosen the timing advance retaining bolt with a 9/16″ deep socket. Tighten the bolt until it starts to turn with effort as the taper drive of the carrier starts separating from the camshaft.
8. Turn the crankshaft clockwise until the bolt will thread into the timing gear and is centered in the hole through the front cover.
9. On hydraulically governed engines, torque the gear retaining bolt to 30-34 ft lbs, and on other engines, torque it to 33-37 ft lbs.
10. Recheck the timing by removing the timing pin and bolt, rotating the engine two revolutions, and replacing them, making further adjustments as necessary.
11. Remove the cover retaining bolt from the timing hole, and install it back into the cover. Remove the timing pin from the timing

555

Caterpillar • Diesel Engines

slot. Install the plugs into the timing hole and fuel pump housing opening. Install the tach drive adapter.

Injection Pump Timing—3208 Series

1. Remove the bolt from the timing pin hole.
2. Turn the crankshaft clockwise until the pin drops in the notch in the pump camshaft.
3. Remove the timing hold plug and put a bolt through the front cover and into the threaded hole in the timing gear. The timing should be correct if the bolt threads easily.
4. If not, remove the tachometer drive cover and disconnect the tachometer drive shaft and washer from the camshaft for the injection pumps.
5. Pull the drive gear from the injection pump camshaft.
6. Turn the crankshaft clockwise until the bolt threads into the hole in the timing gear. Timing should now be correct.
7. Install the washer and tachometer drive shaft. Tighten tachometer drive shaft to 80 ft lbs. for early models and 110 ft lbs. for later models.

1673C Series

1. Remove the injection pump housing. Remove the valve and timing pointer covers.
2. Rotate the crankshaft counterclockwise 60 degrees, and then continue rotating until the TC1-6 cyl. mark on the flywheel aligns with the pointer and both valves of No. 1 cylinder are closed.
3. Attempt to install a special timing plate onto the rear face of the accessory drive housing with the dowels aligned and bolts installed as shown.
4. If the plate can be installed as shown, the engine is in time. Otherwise, proceed as described below.
5. Remove the small front cover from the timing gear housing. Loosen, but do not remove, the gear retaining nut.

6. Separate the gear from the accessory drive shaft. Rotate the shaft in either direction as necessary to permit installation of the timing plate, and install it.
7. Torque the gear retaining nut to 90-110 ft lbs.
8. Remove the timing plate and reinstall the valve cover and pump housing.

1674 Series

1. Remove the valve and timing covers. Rotate the crankshaft counterclockwise 30 degrees, and then continue rotating until the TC1 and 6-6 cyl. mark is aligned with the pointer in the flywheel housing. Do not turn the crankshaft backwards anywhere in the procedure.
2. If all four valves on No. 1 cylinder are not closed, turn the

crank another revolution. Install the timing bolt into the flywheel to make sure flywheel and housing are aligned. Also make sure the timing pin will drop into the timing hole between the inlet valves of clynders No. 5 and No. 6.
3. Remove the timing pin and cover shown in the illustration. Insert the timing pin back into the hole it came out of, and determine whether or not it will freely slide into the timing slot. If the pin cannot be inserted, proceed as described below.
4. Remove the accessory drive gear cover. Loosen the four retaining bolts, and rotate the drive shaft until the pin will slide freely into the timing slot in the pump camshaft. Remove the timing pin. Tighten the bolts.

Nozzle spray pattern appearance (© Caterpillar Tractor Co.)

Nozzle testing setup (© Caterpillar Tractor Co.)

Tightening nozzle locknut (© Caterpillar Tractor Co.)

Timing bolt location (without Brakesaver) (© Caterpillar Tractor Co.)

Timing pin location (© Caterpillar Tractor Co.)

Coupling bolt location (© Caterpillar Tractor Co.)

Timing bolt location (with Brakesaver) (© Caterpillar Tractor Co.)

5. Remove all other timing pins from their timing holes.
6. Rotate the flywheel counterclockwise two complete turns, without going backwards. Insert the timing pin into the pump camshaft again, and make sure alignment is correct, repeating the timing procedure, if necessary.
7. Replace valve and timing hole covers and timing pin.

1693 Series

1. Remove the valve cover and rotate the flywheel clockwise 30 degrees.
2. Rotate the flywheel counterclockwise until the timing bolt can be installed into the flywheel. Do not back up during the procedure.
3. Ensure that all valves for No. 1 cylinder are closed, and turn the flywheel exactly another 360 degrees if they are not. Install the timing bolt and plug back into their normal locations.
4. Insert the timing pin into the pump camshaft timing hole and check to see if the pin freely enters the slot in the pump camshaft. If it can be inserted, the pump is timed. Otherwise, proceed as below.
5. Remove the accessory drive housing cover. Loosen the three retaining bolts, and then retighten the front coupling bolt to 10 ft lbs.
6. Rotate the camshaft until the timing pin squarely rides in the pump camshaft slot.
7. Remove the timing pin and tighten the bolts to 66-74 ft lbs. Rotate the flywheel two full

turns counterclockwise and recheck the adjustment, repeating it as necessary.
8. Reinstall the timing pin and cover.

Torquing Head Bolts

1100 and 3208 Series Engines

1. Tighten bolts 1-18, in numerical order, to 50-70 ft lbs.
2. Tighten bolts 1-18, in numerical order, 90-100 ft lbs.
3. Retorque 1-18, in numerical order, to 90-100 ft lbs.
4. Torque 19-22, in numerical order, to 27-37 ft lbs.

1673C Series Engines

1. Tighten numbered bolts, in numerical order to 115 lb ft.
2. Retorque numbered bolts, in numerical order, to 170-180 ft lbs.
3. Retorque all numbered bolts, in numerical order, to 170-180 ft lbs.
4. Tighten all lettered bolts, in alphabetical order, to 22 ft lbs.
5. Retorque all lettered bolts, in alphabetical order, to 27-37 ft lbs.
6. Retorque lettered bolts, alphabetically, to 27-37 ft lbs.

Timing pin location (© Caterpillar Tractor Co.)

1674 Series Engines

1. Torque all bolts, in numerical order, to 135 ft lbs.
2. Retorque, in numerical order, to 180-190 lb.
3. Retorque, in numerical order, to 180-190 ft lbs.

1693 Series Engines

1. Tighten all bolts, in numerical order, to 200 ft lbs.
2. Retorque, in sequence, to 320-340 ft lbs.
3. Retorque, in sequence, to 320-340 ft lbs.

Fuel System

Fuel Injection Pump Housing and Governor

Removal and Installation

1100 Series with Hydraulic Governor

Removal

1. Remove the plug from the timing pin hole in the fuel injection pump housing. Install the timing pin.
2. Rotate the crankshaft clockwise until the timing pin drops into the slot in the pump camshaft.
3. Disconnect the electrical shutoff solenoid wire.
4. Remove the tach drive adapter housing. Remove the adapter shaft with a socket.
5. Thread a special bolt assembly into the camshaft, avoiding the use of force. Then, install another special bolt into the gear carrier, and tighten this bolt with a wrench until the gear car-

Caterpillar · Diesel Engines

1100 Series head bolt torquing pattern
(© Caterpillar Tractor Co.)

1693 Series head bolt torquing sequence
(© Caterpillar Tractor Co.)

1673 Series head bolt torquing pattern
(© Caterpillar Tractor Co.)

1674 Series head bolt torquing pattern
(© Caterpillar Tractor Co.)

rier pops loose. Remove the puller bolts.

6. Remove the timing hole cover from the front cover and insert a 5/16-18 bolt. 2½" long.

7. Rotate the crankshaft in a clockwise direction until the bolt mentioned in the above step can be threaded into the timing gear and is centered in the hole.

8. Remove the injection pump housing retaining bolts, and remove the pump and governor with a hoist.

Installation

1. Position the pump with a hoist and install the mounting bolts.

2. Install the tach drive adapter shaft. Tighten the retaining nut to 30-34 ft lbs.

3. Remove the timing pin and bolt. Rotate the crankshaft, in a clockwise direction, two full revolutions. Install the timing pin and bolt. If both cannot be installed at once, retime the pump as described in "Injection Pump Timing".

4. Remove the timing bolt, and reinstall the timing hole cover.

5. Remove the timing pin from the slot in the injection pump camshaft, and install the plug. Install the tach drive housing, and reconnect the fuel shutoff solenoid wire.

1100 Series with "Max-Min" Governor

Removal

1. Remove the timing hole plug from the injection pump housing and install the timing pin. Rotate the crankshaft clockwise until the pin drops into the timing slot in the pump camshaft.

2. Disconnect the fuel shutoff solenoid wire. Remove the tach drive adapter housing.

3. Back off the retaining bolt for the automatic timing advance unit.

4. Loosen the automatic timing advance drive at the pump camshaft. Back off the retaining bolt well through the area where it turns easily, until the tapered portion starts to separate from the camshaft.

5. Remove the plug from the timing hole in the front cover. Insert a 5/16"-18 bolt about 2½" long.

6. Rotate the crankshaft clockwise until the bolt can be threaded into the timing gear and is centered in the hole.

7. Remove the pump housing retaining bolts, and remove the pump and governor.

Installation

1. Position the governor and pump and install the retaining bolts.

2. Install the retaining bolt for the automatic advance unit, and torque to 33-37 ft lbs.

3. Remove the timing pin and bolt, rotate the crankshaft two revolutions in a clockwise direction, and attempt to reinstall them. If either cannot be reinstalled, retime the pump as described in "Injection Pump Timing".

4. Remove the timing bolt and install the hole plug. Remove the timing pin from the slot in the pump camshaft and install the plug in the hole.

5. Install the tach drive adapter housing, and connect the wire to the fuel shutoff solenoid.

3208 Series

1. Remove the air cleaner, injection lines and intake manifold.

2. Remove the plug from the cover in the pump housing. Turn the engine clockwise until the timing pin drops into the notch in the pump camshaft.

3. Remove the tachometer drive housing and disconnect the tachometer drive shaft.

4. Pull the drive gear free of the camshaft.

5. Remove the plug from the timing hole in the front cover and install a 5/16"-18NC bolt 2½" long. Turn the crankshaft until the bolt can be installed in the timing gear.

6. Remove fuel line and bolts from pump and remove pump and governor assembly.

1600 Series Engines

Removal

1. Rotate the crankshaft clockwise to bring it to the position where No. 1 piston is at TDC on the compression stroke (see Injection Pump Timing).

2. Remove the turbocharger lubrication and oil drain lines.

3. Disconnect the fuel ratio control sensing line, the governor linkage, and the shutoff solenoid wire. If applicable, disconnect the wiring from the Brakesaver switch.

4. Disconnect the fuel injection lines and fuel supply line at the housing.

5. Remove the injection pump mounting bolts, and remove the assembly with a hoist.

Installation

1. Position the assembly on the engine and install the mounting bolts.

2. Install fuel lines and torque retaining nuts to 25-35 ft lbs.

3. Connect the fuel supply line at the housing. Connect the governor control linkage, and, where applicable, the wiring to the Brakesaver switch.

4. Install the turbocharger oil supply and drain lines.

5. Check and, as necessary, correct the pump camshaft timing as described in the section on "Injection Pump Timing".

Air Compressor

Troubleshooting

Insufficient Operating Pressure

1. Slipping drive belt.
2. Excessive leakage in system.
3. Dirty intake strainer.
4. Restriction in system.
5. Leaking valves.
6. Excessive wear.

Excessive Noise

1. Improper lubrication.
2. Loose drive pulley.
3. Damaged oil pump.
4. Loose mounting brackets.
5. Restriction in line.

Compressor Passes Oil

1. Dirty air strainer.
2. Flooded oil return line.
3. Back pressure from engine crank-case.
4. Excessive oil pressure.
5. Worn oil seals.
6. Piston rings improperly installed.

Air Leakage Test

1. Build up pressure in the system until the governor cuts out. Stop the engine.
2. Listen for air escaping at the intake. If air is escaping, squirt some oil around the unloader pistons. If there is no leakage, the air may be escaping at the discharge valves.
3. If the location of the leak has not been determined, disconnect the discharge line and supply air back through the discharge port. If air movement can be heard, the discharge valves are leaking.

Removal

NOTE: Perform these procedures with caution, as only general procedures are available.
1. Carefully block the vehicle's wheels.
2. Drain the entire brake system.
3. If the compressor is water cooled, drain the engine cooling system, and the compressor head and block.
4. Disconnect air, water, and oil lines.
5. Remove the mounting bolts. Remove the compressor.
6. Remove the pulley with a gear puller.

Installation

On compressors lubricated by the engine:
1. Clean the oil supply line. Operate the engine long enough to determine that an adequate oil flow is present.
2. Clean the oil return line or the return passages in the compressor mounts.

On compressors with their own oil supply:
1. Fill the compressor with the proper amount of clean engine oil.

Then, on all units:
1. Install a new gasket, ensuring that oil holes are properly aligned, where applicable.
2. Inspect the pulley. Replace or reinstall.
3. Clean air cleaner. Install properly. Where engine air cleaner is used, make sure connections are tight.
4. Inspect air and water lines. Clean or replace, as necessary.
5. Reconnect air lines, using a new gasket for the discharge line.
6. Align the pulley, install and tension the belt.
7. Tighten mounting bolts securely and evenly.
8. Operate to check for leakage of any kind or noisy operation.

Oil Pan

1100 and 3208 Series Engines

Removal

1. Drain crankcase.
2. Remove oil pan mounting bolts. Remove the pan.

Installation

1. Clean oil pan and cylinder block gasket surfaces thoroughly.
2. Install the new gasket.
3. Put the pan in position and install the mounting bolts, torquing to 14-20 ft lbs.
4. Refill crankcase (12 qts.).

1600 Series Engines

Removal

1. Drain the crankcase.
2. Remove the oil gauge level and its guide. Remove the Brake-saver oil line, where applicable.
3. Remove the pan mounting bolts, and remove the pan.

Installation

1. Position the new gasket on the engine. Install pan and mounting bolts.
2. Install the oil level gauge and its guide. Where applicable, install the Brakesaver oil line.
3. Refill crankcase.

Oil Pump

1100 and 3208 Series Engines

Disassembly

1. Remove the timing gear cover and oil pickup.
2. Remove the cover retaining bolts. Remove the cover.
3. Remove the outer and inner rotors.
4. Check size of bearing to determine whether or not replacement is required. Bearing must be 2.802"-2.806". Remove the bearing if it is not to specifications.

Assembly

1. Clean all parts thoroughly in a safe solvent. Thoroughly lubricate all parts with 30 weight oil.
2. Install the bearing in the timing cover, using a special driver.
3. Install outer and inner rotors.
4. Check the rotor tip clearance to make sure it falls within the permissible range of .002"-.006". Up to .009" is permitted with used parts.
5. Install the cover and mounting bolts and locks, torquing the bolts to 13-23 ft lbs.
6. Check end clearance to ensure that it is within the permissible range of .002"-.006".

1673 C

Disassembly

1. Remove the cover retaining bolts, and remove the cover.
2. Remove the pump drive gear with a puller.
3. Remove rotors and shafts and idler gear and shaft.

Assembly

1. Clean all parts thoroughly in an approved solvent.
2. Check to make sure the edges of the drive shaft bearings are .020" beneath finished surfaces of the pump body.
3. Check to make sure idler gear shaft diameter is 1.2479"-1.2485", with a bearing clearance of .0020"-.0036".
4. Check pump rotor shafts to ensure their diameters are .7404"-

1100 Series oil pump—rotors removed (© Caterpillar Tractor Co.)

Checking rotor tip clearance (© Caterpillar Tractor Co.)

.7410″, and that bearing clearance is .0010″-.0026″. Check that rotor bearings are recessed .030″ from finished gear surfaces.

5. Install rotors and shafts. Install cover, and torque retaining bolts. Install idler gear and shaft.
6. Heat the drive gear to nearly 750°F. and install.
7. When assembling the unit to the engine, make sure the plate on the bottom of the tube assembly is level with the bottom of the cover.

1674 Series

Disassembly

1. Remove the suction bell.
2. Remove cotter pin, nut and washer from the end of driving gear, and pull gear off with a special puller.
3. Remove housing bolts, and remove outer housing and bushings.
4. Separate the two housing halves.
5. Remove shafts and remaining bushings.

Assembly

1. Clean all parts thoroughly in an approved solvent.
2. Check bearings and shafts for a clearance of .002″-.003″.
3. Install shafts and bushings.
4. Assemble the front and rear housing halves.
5. Install housing front cover so the dowel matches the dowel hole in the body. Install housing bolts.
6. Install drive gear and install and torque the mounting nut to 60 ft lbs. Torque nut further to align slots in it for installation of the cotter pin.
7. Install new cotter pin.

1693 Series

Disassembly

1. Remove the suction bell.
2. Remove the cotter pin, nut, and washer from the drive gear shaft. Pull the gear with a puller.
3. Remove housing bolts and separate housing halves.
4. Remove outer gears and separator plate.
5. Remove remaining shafts and gears.

Assembly

1. Clean all parts in an approved solvent.
2. Check all bearings and shafts for a clearance of .005″ or less. Check rotors for a rotor to cover clearance on the drive gear side of .002″-.004″.
3. Install shafts and integral rotors into rear housing half.

Oil pump, 1673C (© Caterpillar Tractor Co.)

4. Install separator plate. Install main pump rotors.
5. Assemble the housings, and install the housing bolts.
6. Install the drive gear, and install the nut, torquing to 100 ft lbs. Continue torquing the nut just until cotter pin grooves are in proper alignment.
7. Install a new cotter pin in the drive gear mounting nut.
8. Install the suction bell.

Intake Manifold

1100 and 3208 Series

Removal

1. Remove the injection lines, and plug or cap all open ends.
2. Disconnect crankcase ventilator hose.
3. Remove intake manifold bolts, and remove the manifold. Tape engine inlet ports.

Installation

1. Remove sealing tape from intake ports. Clean gasket surfaces thoroughly.
2. Install the gaskets. Position the manifold on the engine block.
3. Tighten the bolts numbered 3 and 4 to 10-20 ft lbs.

Oil pump, 1693 (© Caterpillar Tractor Co.)

4. Tighten *all* bolts to 27-37 ft lbs.
5. Reconnect the crankcase ventilation hose.
6. Uncap and reconnect all injector lines, torquing to 25-35 ft lbs.

Aftercooler Core

1693 Series

Removal

1. Drain the cooling system.
2. Remove the turbocharger outlet pipe and elbow.
3. Disconnect the aftercooler vent line.
4. Remove the cover from the front of the aftercooler top cover.
5. Remove the aftercooler top cover.
6. Remove the mounting bolts from the water inlet collar, and pull the collar out of the housing.
7. Remove the core from the housing.

Installation

1. Put the core in position in the housing.
2. Push the water inlet line collar into the housing, and install the mounting bolts.
3. Install the top cover.
4. Install the front cover and mounting bolts.
5. Connect the vent line and install the turbocharger outlet and elbow.
6. Refill the cooling system.

Exhaust Manifold

1100 and 3208 Series

Removal

1. Remove the retaining bolts and locks.
2. Remove the manifold.

Tightening sequence, 1100 intake manifold (© Caterpillar Tractor Co.)

Aftercooler—1693 Series (© Caterpillar Tractor Co.)

Installation

1. Clean the gasket mounting surfaces, and position the gaskets on the block.
2. Install the retaining bolts and torque to 27-37 ft lbs.
3. If necessary, turn manifold bolts up to 30° farther to make one edge parallel to each locking tab.
4. Bend lock tabs over flats.

Crankshaft Pulley and Vibration Damper

1100 and 3208 Series

Removal

1. Remove the retaining bolt and its washer.
2. Remove the pulley with a puller, step plate, washers (2), and two bolts.

Installation

1. Lubricate the lip of the front oil seal and the sealing surface of the crankshaft pulley with engine oil.
2. Start the pulley onto the crankshaft. Install a hardened nut, thrust bearing assembly, and one small and four large washers, as shown.
3. Hold the bolt to prevent turning, and press the pulley onto the crankshaft until it contacts the crankshaft gear.
4. Remove the installation tools, and install the retaining bolt and washer. Torque to 230-300 ft lbs on 1100 series and 400-520 ft lbs on 3208 series.

Removing pulley (1100 Series)
(© Caterpillar Tractor Co.)

1673 C

Removal

1. Remove the pulley mounting bolts. Remove the pulley hub with two ⅜″ NC forcing screws.
2. Remove damper-to-hub fastening bolts, and separate hub, pulley, and damper.

Installation

1. Replace faulty parts and assemble hub, damper, and pulley, aligning bolt holes.
2. Install damper-to-hub fastening bolts.
3. Reposition damper assembly on the crankshaft, and employ mounting bolt to press unit back in place. Lubricating the inside surface of the hub, and tapping the assembly periodically with a hard rubber mallet during tightening of the bolt with facilitate installation.
4. Torque the mounting bolt to 210-250 ft lbs.

1674 Series

Removal

1. Remove the hub mounting bolts, and remove the hub assembly, retaining tab lock and spacer.
2. Remove pulley-to-hub bolts and washers, and damper-to-hub bolts and washers, separate parts, and replace faulty components.

Installation

1. Assemble hub, pulley, and damper, and install pulley-to-hub bolts and washers and damper-to-hub bolts and washers.
2. Install assembly, spacer, tab lock, and mounting bolts, torquing bolts to 130-170 ft lbs.
3. Tap bolt head with a hammer, and retorque. Bend tab locks to retain bolts.

1693 Series

Removal

1. Remove alternator and water pump drive belts.
2. Remove pulley mounting bolts, and remove the pulley.
3. Remove the vibration damper retaining bolts, lock, and plate. Install a suitable spacer using the retaining plate and bolts.
4. Install a hydraulic press, as shown, and remove the assembly.

Installation

1. Position the damper on the crankshaft. Install the retaining plate, bolts, and lock.
2. Torque the retaining bolts to 137-159 ft lbs, tap the bolts with

Installing pulley (1100 Series) (© Caterpillar Tractor Co.)

Crankshaft pulley and vibration damper removal (1693 Series)
(© Caterpillar Tractor Co.)

a hammer, and retorque. Bend the retaining lock.

3. Install the pulley, install and tension the V-belts.

Turbocharger

Removal and Installation

1600 Series

Removal

1. Disconnect the oil supply and drain lines.
2. Remove the air discharge pipe and elbow, and the inlet pipe.
3. Attach a hoist to support the unit, remove the mounting bolts and nuts, and remove the unit with the hoist.

Installation

1. Hoist the unit into place on the engine. Install the mounting bolts and nuts, torquing them to 36-44 ft lbs.

2. Connect air inlet piping, air outlet piping and the outlet elbow.
3. Install oil supply and drain lines.

Water Pump

1673 Series

NOTE: These instructions include an exploded view for ease in assembly and disassembly without step-by-step procedures, and notes on special procedures.

1. In removing bearings:
   a. Remove the bearings and gear with a special push-puller, bearing pulling attachment, step plate, and ratchet box wrench.
2. In removing impeller:
   a. Use a ½" NC forcing screw to remove the impeller.
3. In installing bearings:
   a. Heat the bearings to 300°F. before installation. Then, do not install shaft assembly in

the pump housing until the gear and bearings have cooled to room temperature.
4. In installing the impeller:
   a. Press the unit onto the shaft until it bottoms on the pump shaft shoulder.
5. In installing the seal:
   a. Wet the outside diameter of the rubber cup and ceramic ring assembly, and the seal bore of the pump housing. Use hand pressure only in installation of the rubber and ceramic seats in the pump housing bore. Make sure both seats are square.
   b. Wet the inside diameter of the rubber bellows and carbon washer assembly and the pump shaft. Use hand pressure only in installing the bellows and washer assembly onto the pump shaft, and make sure the carbon washer

Exploded view of water pump (1673C Series) (© Caterpillar Tractor Co.)

1674 Type 1

52 ± 2 LB. FT.
8,6 ± 0,3 M.KG

Exploded view of water pump (1674 Series) (© Caterpillar Tractor Co.)

1674 Type 2

52 ± 2 LB. FT.
8,6 ± 0,3 M.KG

Exploded view of water pump (1674 Series) (© Caterpillar Tractor Co.) Type 2

Installing water pump seal (1693 Series) (© Caterpillar Tractor Co.)

Water Pump Cross Section (1693 Series) (© Caterpillar Tractor Co.)

contacts the ceramic ring.
c. Install the spring and then the impeller.

1674 Series Type 1

NOTE: These instructions include an exploded view for ease in assembly and disassembly without step-by-step procedures, and notes on special procedures.
1. In installing the seals, make sure the spring loaded lip faces away from the bearings.
2. Lubricate the cavity between bearings so it is half full of multipurpose grease.
3. In pressing the impeller onto the shaft, make sure it bottoms on the shaft shoulder.

Type 2
1. In installing the seals, make sure the spring loaded lip faces the bearings.
2. Torque the inner nut to 25-35 ft lbs. Then, tighten further to align the cotter pin hole, and install the cotter pin, bending both legs around the nut.
3. Lubricate the cavity between the bearings until it is full of multipurpose grease.

1693 Series
Removal
1. Loosen the drive belts and remove them.
2. Remove the thermostat bypass line, and disconnect the governor linkage.
3. Disconnect the water inlet line from the bottom of the water pump and the aftercooler water supply line. On Brakesaver engines, disconnect the cooler hose at the elbow.
4. Install a ⅜"-16NC forged eyebolt in the pump and attach a hoist.
5. Remove the attaching bolts and remove the pump.

Disassembly
1. Remove the pulley retaining nut and lock.
2. Install a puller assembly and remove the pulley. Remove the pulley key.
3. Remove the retainer and seal.

4. Remove the seal from the retainer.
5. Remove the cover retaining nuts and bolts, and remove the housing cover.
6. Remove the impeller retaining nut. Remove the impeller, unscrewing it from the shaft in a clockwise direction.
7. Remove the shaft assembly. Remove the bearings and spacer from the shaft. Remove the carbon seal assembly and the lip type seal.

Assembly
1. Install the carbon seal into the housing with a seal installer.
2. Install the lip type seal, with the lip toward the bearings. Lubricate the seal with multipurpose grease.
3. Install the bearings and spacer on the shaft.
4. Install the shaft in the housing.
5. Lubricate the cage seal, and install it in the cage, with the lip toward the bearings.
6. Install the cage onto the housing.
7. Install the pulley, lock, and retaining nut, and torque the nut to 50-55 ft lbs. Bend the lock tab over.
8. Screw the impeller onto the shaft. Adjust the clearance between impeller and housing to .005"-.0015".
9. Install the impeller retaining nut, and torque to 50-55 ft lbs. Strike the pulley end of the shaft, and check impeller clearance while rotating the shaft.
10. Install the cover, retaining bolts, and nuts.

Installation
1. Attach a hoist to the pump and hoist the pump into position on the front of the engine. Install the pump retaining bolts.
2. Connect the aftercooler water supply line and the inlet hose at the bottom of the pump.
3. Install the thermostat bypass line, and connect the governor control linkage.
4. Install the fan and alternator belts, and tension properly.

Temperature Regulator

All Series

Removal
1. Drain the cooling system.
2. Disconnect outlet, bypass, and vent lines.
3. Remove the retaining bolts, and remove the housing.
4. Remove thermostat(s) from the housing.

Installation
1. Install a new seal. On 1673C engines, install the seal with the lip toward the cover. On 1647 engines, the lip faces the front of the engine.
2. On 1673C engines, install the washer, as shown.
3. Install thermostat(s).
4. Put the housing into position and install the retaining bolts.
5. Connect the vent line, and the outlet and bypass hoses.
6. Refill the cooling system.

Engine Disassembly

1100 and 3208 Series
NOTE: The following procedures are performed with the engine out of the vehicle and on a work stand.

Fuel Lines
1. Disconnect the injection lines between pump and heads.
2. Disconnect left fuel return line.
3. Disconnect the inlet and outlet lines from the fuel filter base.
4. Disconnect the inlet and outlet lines from the fuel transfer pump.
5. Disconnect the fuel shutoff solenoid lines.
6. Remove all disconnected lines from engine.
7. Unbolt and remove fuel transfer pump.

Injection Nozzles
8. Remove valve covers, fuel return manifold and rocker arm assembly.
9. Remove fuel injection nozzle clamp.
10. Disconnect injection nozzle and line from adapter.
11. Remove adapter and lift nozzle from head. Do not pry nozzle!
12. Remove carbon seal nozzle dam.

Automatic Timing Advance Unit

13. To remove automatic timing advance unit on engine equipped with hydraulic governor and engine camshaft mounted timing advance nut:
    a. Remove timing slot plug and insert timing pin.
    b. Turn crankshaft clockwise (front view) until timing pin drops into slot in pump camshaft.
    c. Remove retaining screw and washer from engine camshaft and remove timing unit.
14. To remove automatic timing advance unit from engines equipped with hydraulic governor and fuel pump camshaft mounted timing advance unit:
    a. Remove timing slot plug and insert timing pin.
    b. Turn the crankshaft clockwise (front view) until the timing pin drops into slot in pump camshaft.
    c. Remove tachometer drive adapter shaft—a 5/8" deep socket helps.
    d. Using a suitable puller, remove the advance unit from the camshaft.
15. To remove automatic timing advance unit from engines equipped with a "Max-Min" governor:
    a. Remove timing slot plug and insert timing pin.
    b. Rotate engine crankshaft clockwise (front view) until the timing pin drops into slot in fuel pump camshaft.
    c. Loosen retaining bolt, then tighten when the taper drive on the carrier starts to separate from the injection pump camshaft.
    d. Remove the automatic timing advance unit.

Injection Pump and Governor

16. To remove injection pump housing and governor on engines with hydraulic governor:
    a. Remove the plug from the timing pin hole in the fuel injection pump housing. Install the timing pin.
    b. Rotate the crankshaft clockwise until the timing pin drops into the slot in the pump camshaft.
    c. Disconnect the electrical shutoff solenoid wire.
    d. Remove the tach drive adapter shaft with a socket.
    e. Thread a special bolt assembly into the camshaft, avoiding the use of force. Then, install another special bolt into the gear carrier, and tighten this bolt with a wrench until the gear carrier pops loose. Remove the puller bolts.
    f. Remove the timing hole cover from the front cover and insert a 5/16-18 bolt, 2½" long.
    g. Rotate the crankshaft in a clockwise direction until the bolt mentioned in the above step can be threaded into the timing gear and is centered in the hole.
    h. Remove the injection pump housing retaining bolts, and remove the pump and governor with a hoist.
17. To remove injection pump housing and governor on engines with "Max-Min" governor:
    a. Remove the timing hole plug from the injection pump housing and install the timing pin. Rotate the crankshaft clockwise until the pin drops into the timing slot in the pump camshaft.
    b. Disconnect the fuel shutoff solenoid wire. Remove the tach drive adapter housing.
    c. Back off the retaining bolt for the automatic timing advance unit.
    d. Loosen the automatic timing advance drive at the pump camshaft. Back off the retaining bolt well through the area where it turns easily, until the tapered position starts to separate from the camshaft.
    e. Remove the plug from the timing hole in the front cover. Insert a 5/16-18" bolt about 2½" long.
    f. Rotate the crankshaft clockwise until the bolt can be threaded into the timing gear and is centered in the hole.
    g. Remove the pump housing retaining bolts, and remove the pump and governor.

Intake Manifold

18. Remove the injection lines and plug or cap all open ends.
19. Disconnect the crankcase ventilator hose.
20. Remove the intake manifold bolts, and remove the manifold. Tape engine inlet ports.

Exhaust Manifold

21. Remove the retaining bolts and locks.
22. Remove the manifold.

Rocker Shafts

23. On engines with through head adapters:
    a. Remove shaft retaining bolts.
    b. Remove shaft assembly and pushrods.

Cylinder Heads

24. Remove the water sleeve clamps from between the cylinder head and timing gear cover.
25. Using tool 8S6692 or equivalent, move water sleeve into front cover.
26. Attach lifting device to head, unbolt and remove head.

Pistons & Connecting Rods

27. Remove ridge from cylinders.
28. Turn crankshaft so that journal for piston being removed is at top of travel.
29. Remove the rod cap.
30. Remove piston from cylinder.

Crankshaft Pulley

31. Remove pulley bolt and washer.
32. Using a suitable pulley puller, remove the pulley from the crankshaft.

Timing Gear Cover

33. Unbolt and remove the oil pan and oil pump suction bell.
34. Disconnect the water temperature sending unit.
35. Disconnect the tachometer drive cable and remove the drive housing.

Timing pin in housing 3208 series

Removing housing—1100 and 3208, typical

36. Disconnect the heater hoses from the timing gear cover.
37. Remove oil cooler water outlet elbow from rear of timing gear cover.
38. Remove cover bolts and mark each bolt as to location.
39. Attach a hoist to the front cover and pry cover off engine.

Camshaft Gears (on Engines With Fuel Injection Pump Mounted Timing Advance)

40. Using puller 1P2320, or equivalent, remove the small outer gear.
41. Remove the spacer immediately behind the gear.
42. Install puller 1P2321, or equivalent, and remove the large inner gear.

Camshaft (Gear Installed)

43. Remove cam followers with a magnet. Mark location.
44. Turn crankshaft clockwise (front view) and align crankshaft gear timing mark with timing mark on large camshaft gear.
45. Remove camshaft thrust pin from rear of block.
46. Carefully withdraw camshaft from block.
47. Remove bearings with suitable puller.

Flywheel, Rear Oil Seal and Wear Sleeve

48. Unbolt and remove flywheel.
49. Unbolt and remove flywheel housing.
50. Using a puller, remove rear oil seal.
51. Wear sleeve can be removed with an outside puller.

Crankshaft

52. Unbolt and remove main bearing caps.
53. Attach sling to crankshaft and hoist out of block.
54. Remove upper bearing halves.

Oil Pump

55. Remove pump cover.
56. Remove outer rotor and inner rotor. Check bearing size. Bearing should be 2.80″ ± .002″.

Fuel Nozzle Service

1100 and 3208 Series

1. Remove loose carbon from the tip, carbon seal dam groove, and the body below this groove with a special wire brush. Avoid brushing more than the minimum required to remove deposits, and this can remove the protective coating.

   NOTE: Be careful to avoid contact of the fuel spray with clothing or skin. Direct nozzle discharge into the collector, as fuel spray can penetrate the skin and cause infection.

2. Connect the nozzle to a tester, using one hand squeezing two wrenches, in order to avoid damage to the nozzle and tester. Only perfectly clean fuel may be used.
3. Close the gauge protector valve and the on-off valve. Open the isolator valve on the pump. Operate the tester at 60 strokes/minute until the nozzle is adequately flushed.
4. Open the gauge protector valve and raise the pressure slowly until the nozzle valve opens, and note the pressure. The pressure should be 2,400-2,850 PSI with a used valve, and 2,750-2,850 with a new valve.
5. Remove the nozzle from the tester, install it in a special nozzle holding tool, and loosen the adjusting screw locknut. Then reinstall the nozzle into the tester, tip downward.
6. Turn the lift adjusting screw in until it bottoms, and note the fraction of a turn required. If it can be turned more than ¾ of a turn, it is damaged. Back out the screw far enough to prevent bottoming when the pressure adjusting screw is turned.
7. Adjust the opening pressure to 2,550-2,650 PSI with a used nozzle, 2,750-2,950 with a new nozzle, but do not tighten the locknut.
8. Pump fuel through the nozzle and hold the pressure adjusting screw in place. Slowly turn the lift adjusting screw clockwise until the valve ceases to open. Raise the pressure an additional 200 PSI to ensure valve is bottomed.
9. Back out the lift screw ⅝-⅞ of a turn.
10. Remove the nozzle from the tester and place it in a holding tool. Secure the tool in a vise, avoiding clamping any part of the nozzle. Hold the adjusting screw, and tighten the locknut to 70-75 in. lbs.
11. Mount the nozzle in the tester and recheck the opening pressure.
12. Wrap the nozzle body to absorb leakage from the leak-off boot. Point the tip into the fuel collector and operate the pump rapidly. Dry the tip of the nozzle.
13. Raise the pressure to within 200-300 PSI of the opening pressure. The nozzle should leak three drops or less in 15 seconds.
14. Close the gauge protector valve and the on-off valve, and open the pump isolator valve. Point the nozzle tip into the fuel collector.
15. Operate the tester at 60 strokes per minute, and observe the fuel spray. Fuel should be finely atomized, and in four straight, equally spaced streams.
16. Loosen the collector nuts and reposition the nozzle tip slightly above the horizontal. Operate the tester, bringing the pressure to 1400-1600 PSI. Observe the leakage from the return at the top of the nozzle. Leakage should be 1-10 drops in 15 seconds after the first drop fall with No. 2 diesel oil.

Engine Assembly

Oil Cooler

1. Clean block surfaces and install

Oil cooler

| 1 Inlet water line | 3 Retaining bolts |
| 2 Outlet water line | 4 Oil cooler |

Installing wear sleeve

1 Bolts
2 Pilot

oil cooler unit. Torque retaining bolts to 32 ft. lb.

2. Connect inlet and outlet hoses.

Oil Pump

3. Coat parts with SAE 30.
4. Install inner and outer rotors.
5. Check rotor tip clearance .004-.009".
6. Install cover and torque mounting bolts to 18 ft. lbs.
7. Check end clearance .002-.006 in.

Crankshaft and Main Bearings

8. Install upper bearing halves and coat with SAE 30.
9. Lower crankshaft into place.
10. Lubricate lower halves with SAE 30 and install.
11. Oil bolt threads and torque as follows:
1140 (36B1-36B1923) 1145 (97B1-97B6154) 1150 (96B1-96B6580) 1160 (95B1-95B13691) torque from front to rear to 60 ft. lb., then to 175 ft. lb. 1140 (36B1924 and up) 1145 (97B6155 and up) 1150 (96B6581 and up) 1160 (95B13692 and up) and 3208 Series torque from front to rear to 30 ft. lb., then an additional 120°.
12. Check crankshaft end play .006-.012".

Flywheel, Rear Oil Seal and Wear Sleeve

13. Press wear sleeve into place with chamfer outward.
14. With seal installer, first apply gasket cement to the O.D. of the metal shell, lubricate the seal lip with SAE 30, position seal with spring lip inward.
15. Using a new gasket, install flywheel housing and tighten nuts.
16. Position flywheel on crankshaft so that marks are aligned.
17. Coat bolt threads with Permatex Form—A-Gasket.
18. Install retaining bolts and torque to 55 ft. lb.

NOTE: The "V" cut on the lock should align with the mark on the flywheel.

Camshaft

19. Install bearings with pilot type installer.
20. Coat the bearing surfaces with SAE 30.
21. Install camshaft, aligning gear timing mark with mark on crankshaft gear.
22. Install thrust pin and torque to 35 ft. lb.
23. If gears were removed, heat both gears to 600°F and press on shaft; aligning timing marks.

Timing Gear Cover

24. Lubricate water sleeve O-rings.
25. Position new cover gasket on block.
26. Install water sleeves in cover (1140, 145 and 1150 use silver sleeves; 1160 uses gold).
27. Position cover on engine and install retaining bolts.
28. Connect oil cooler water elbow to back of cover.
29. Using tool 8S6692, or equivalent, slide water sleeves into heads and install clamps.
30. Install oil pump suction bell, oil pan gasket and oil pan. Torque pan bolts to 17 ft. lb.
31. Connect water temperature sending unit and install tachometer drive housing and cable.

Crankshaft Pulley

32. Coat pulley sealing surface with SAE 30.
33. With suitable installer press pulley onto crankshaft.
34. Remove installer and tighten retaining bolt to 265 ft. lb. on 1100 Series and 460 ft. lb. on 3208 Series.

Pistons & Connecting Rods

35. Turn crankshaft so that journal worked on is at the top of its travel.
36. Lubricate all parts with SAE 30.
37. Install piston and rod assembly with the piston notch toward engine center.
38. Install rod cap, and torque bolt to 30 ft. lb. +60°.

Cylinder Head

39. If removed, install valves.
40. Install new gasket on block.
41. Lower head into place with a hoist.
42. Use anti-seize on bolt threads and tighten in sequence.
1 thru 18 to 60 ft. lb. then to 95 ft. lb. Tighten bolts 19 thru 22 to 32 ft. lb.
43. Slide water sleeve into head and install clamp.

Rocker Arm Assembly

44. Lubricate all parts with SAE 30.
45. Install pushrods and position shaft assembly on head.
46. Install retaining bolts and nuts and torque to 18 ft. lb.
47. Install fuel return line.
48. Adjust valves to: inlet .015 cold; exhaust .025 cold.
49. Install valve cover. Torque bolts to 120 in. lb.

Exhaust & Intake Manifolds

50. Position new gasket and exhaust manifold on engine and torque bolts to 32 ft. lb. Bend lock tabs over bolts. Position intake manifold and gasket on engine, connect one fuel injection line and torque bolts nearest center to 15 ft. lb., then torque all bolts to 32 ft. lb.

Fuel Injection Pump & Governor (Engines with "Max-Min" Governor)

51. Position pump and governor in place as a unit.
52. Install retaining bolts and tighten.

Fuel Injection Pump & Governor (Engines with Hydraulic Governor)

53. Install injection pump and governor assembly and tighten retaining bolts.
54. Install the tachometer drive adapter shaft and tighten retaining nut to 32 ft. lb.

Automatic Timing Advance Unit (Engines Equipped with "Max-Min" Governor)

55. Lubricate unit through opening in end plates before installing on engine.
56. Position automatic timing advance unit on the fuel injection pump camshaft.
57. Install retaining bolt and torque to 35 ft. lb.

Automatic Timing Advance Unit (Engines Equipped with Hydraulic Governor & Camshaft Mounted Timing Advance Unit.)

58. Align holes in weights with dowels in gear and install the timing unit.
59. Align pin in washer with hole in camshaft and install washer.
60. Install retaining screw and tighten to 108 in. lb. Stake screw in two places.
61. Check gear and weight assembly end clearance .003-.027".

Automatic Timing Advance Unit (Enginess Equipped with Hydraulic Governor and Fuel Pump Camshaft Mounted Timing Advance Unit.)

62. Apply SAE 30 through openings in end plates of the timing unit prior to installation.
63. Position the timing unit on the injection pump camshaft.
64. Install the tachometer drive adapter shaft; tighten nut to 32 ft. lb.

Fuel Return Manifold (Engines Without Through-Head adapters)

65. Position Unit on engine and connect boots to top of injection nozzles.
66. Connect boot to bleed off line.

Fuel Return Manifold (Engines with Through-Head Adapters)

67. Position unit on engine and connect boots to top of injection nozzles.

68. Connect boot to bleed off line. Install clamps and tighten to 18 ft. lb.

Fuel Injection Nozzles (Without Through-head Adapters)

69. Clean nozzle bore, fittings and gasket surfaces.
70. Install a new compression seal and carbon seal.
71. Install a new grommet.
72. Lubricate the exterior surface of the cap, pull grommet over cap. Rotate grommet so the flat surface will face the valve cover when nozzle is installed.
73. Coat grommet groove with 7M7260 Liquid Gasket, or equivalent, remove caps and install nozzle into head with a twisting motion.
74. Assemble and tighten clamp; connect fuel lines to nozzles and hand-tighten nuts.
75. Install rocker assembly. Torque bolts to 18 ft. lb. Tighten fuel line fitting after lines have been purged.

Fuel Injection Nozzles (Engines with Through-head Adapters)

76. Clean nozzle core and fittings.
77. Install a new compression seal and carbon seal dam.
78. Install a new O-ring on the nozzle and adapter.
79. Install the nozzle in the head with a twisting motion.
80. Install adapter and tighten injection nozzle-to-adapter nut to 30 ft. lb. Hand tighten line fitting.
81. Install the nozzle clamp.
82. Install the fuel return manifold and rocker assembly. Install bolts and tighten to 18 ft. lb.

Fuel Transfer Pump

83. Clean pump mounting surface.
84. Position pump, install bolts and tighten to 32 ft. lb.

Fuel Injection Lines

85. Remove caps, lay on lines as a unit and hand tighten fittings. When lines are purged, tighten fittings. On engines with through-head adapter, tighten retaining nuts to 30 ft. lb.

Engine Disassembly 1673

NOTE: Disassembly is performed with engine out of vehicle and on work stand.

1. Disconnect the turbocharger oil supply and drain lines.
2. Remove the air discharge pipe and elbow and the inlet pipe.
3. Attach a hoist to support the unit, remove the mounting bolts and lift off the unit.
4. Remove alternator.
5. Disconnect and remove fuel lines.
6. Remove rocker housing rear cover.
7. Remove rocker housing retaining bolts, and lift off housing.
8. Remove water pipe, and exhaust manifold.
9. Remove fan and pulley mounting bracket assembly.
10. Remove water by-pass line, and air compressor coolant line.
11. Remove air compressor water return line.
12. Remove head bolts and attach lifting fixture to head. Lift head off engine.
13. Unbolt and remove rocker assembly.
14. Compress springs and remove keepers; lift out valves.
15. Remove pushrod and keep in order of removal.
16. Lift tappets out of block with magnet.
17. Remove injectors from head; do not pry.
18. Remove pulley hub bolt and with 2-bolt puller, remove pulley from crankshaft.
19. Remove bolts, attach hoist and pry off front and rear covers.
20. Using suitable pullers, remove auxiliary drive shaft gear and camshaft gear.
21. Remove fuel transfer pump.
22. Remove idler gear.
23. Remove auxiliary driveshaft retainer and seal and carefully slide shaft out of block.
24. Remove camshaft front and rear retainers and carefully slide camshaft out of block.
25. Remove bolts, attach hoist to flywheel and lift off.
26. Unbolt and remove flywheel housing.
27. Using outside puller, remove oil seal and wear sleeve.
28. Remove oil pan.
29. Remove cylinder ridge.
30. Unbolt and remove rod bearing caps.
31. Push piston and rod assemblies out of cylinders.
32. Unbolt and remove main bearing caps, attach a hoist and lift out crankshaft. Remove liners with a puller.
33. Remove governor cover, plate and housing.
34. Remove injection pump bolts and using extractor 8S2244 or equivalent, remove pump.
35. Pull off oil pump drive gear and remove pump.
36. Unbolt and remove oil cooler.
37. Remove attaching bolts and lift off water pump.

Engine Assembly

1. Install water pump and tighten bolts.
2. Install oil cooler taking care to avoid damaging element.
3. Install oil pump and tighten mounting bolts. Heat gear to 750°F before installing.
4. Check end clearance—.0015-.0035". The edges of the shaft bearings should be .020" below surface of pump body and cover.
5. When installing fuel pump, sight down pump and align notches in bonnet and barrel with the mark 180" from the pump gear segment center tooth. Position the pump so that the notches align with the guide pins in the housing bore. Align the pump gear segment center tooth with the fuel rack center notch. Keep a downward force on the pump and install the bushing until it's flush with the housing.
6. Install fuel transfer pump and tachometer drive.
7. Assemble and install governor on engine front.
8. Check orifice in piston cooling nozzles with a .090 drill rod.
9. Install upper main bearing halves, coat with SAE 30 and in-

1 Water pipe	3 Water by-pass line
2 Fan and pulley mounting bracket	4 Compressor water return line

5 Turbocharger-to-inlet manifold air pipe
6 Turbocharger lubricating oil supply line

7 Turbocharger oil drain line
8 Exhaust elbow
9 Turbocharger
10 Fuel lines (six)
11 Valve cover
12 Cylinder head

567

1 Fuel injection nozzles
2 Fuel lines
3 Fuel priming pump
4 Governor
5 Injection pump housing
6 Fuel filter
7 Transfer pump
8 Tachometer drive

1 Fuel injection lines (six)
2 Exhaust pipe connection
3 Fuel priming pump
4 Governor
5 Inject on pump housing

stall thrust plates with words "Block Side" next to block.

10. Install upper lower caps and torque bolts to 175 ft. lb.
11. Install cylinder liners coating seals and bore with liquid soap prior to insertion. Drive liner into place with a hammer and block of wood. Attach push-puller and torque to 50 ft. lb. Liner protrusion must be .001-.005".
12. Install piston and rod assembly, with crankshaft journal up.
13. Install rod bearing cap and torque to 30 ft. lb. +90°.
14. Install oil seal and wear sleeve with a seal installer.
15. Assemble flywheel housing and flywheel torque all bolts to 100 ft. lb. Trim housing gasket square with bottom of block.
16. Install front plate and gasket. Trim gasket.
17. Install camshaft and tighten fasteners.
18. Install camshaft gear aligning "C" on gear with "C" on crankshaft gear.
19. Install idler gear; bearing must be centered in hub.
20. Install accessory drive shaft and gear.
21. Rotate the shaft in the direction necessary to install the 8S5417 Timing Plate. Tighten the gear retaining nut to 100 ft. lb. and remove the timing plate. The fuel injection pump camshaft will be in time with the engine crankshaft when the pump housing is installed.

22. Install the fuel transfer pump.
23. Install front and rear covers. Tighten bolts, trim gaskets.
24. Install shim between trunnion hub and support halves to obtain a .002" fit. New bushing must be heated to 250° in oil for 2 hrs. before installing.
25. Install pulley and tighten bolt to 230 ft. lb. Tap bolt head with hammer and re-torque.
26. Install damper.
27. Assemble valves and rocker assemblies in head.
28. Install tappets in block.
29. Install injectors in head, torque to 150 ft. lb. Coat mating surfaces with liquid soap.
30. Position gasket on head. Lower head into place. Install head bolts and torque large numbered bolts as follows:
    Step 1—115 ft. lb.
    Step 2—175 ft. lb.
    Tighten small lettered bolts as follows:
    Step 1—22 ft. lb.
    Step 2—32 ft. lb.
31. Install pushrods in order as removed.
32. Install following parts: valve cover—torque to 6 ft. lb., fuel lines, turbocharger oil drain line, exhaust elbow, turbocharger oil supply line, turbocharger-to-inlet manifold air pipe, air compressor water return line, water bypass line, fan and pulley mounting bracket, water pipe.
33. Install exhaust manifold and torque to 32 ft. lb.

Engine Disassembly—1674

NOTE: Disassembly is performed with engine out of vehicle and on workstand.

1. Remove alternator.
2. Remove turbocharger oil drain line.
3. Remove camshaft housing rear cover.
4. Remove camshaft housing retaining bolts, attach hoist and lift off housing.
5. Unbolt retainers and remove camshaft gears.
6. Remove stake mark and drive out retaining pin. Slide camshafts out of heads.
7. Disconnect and remove fuel injection lines.
8. Disconnect turbocharger exhaust pipe.
9. Remove air compressor coolant line.
10. Remove cylinder head bolts, attach hoist and lift off head.
11. Compress springs, remove keepers and lift out valves.
12. Remove precombustion chambers.
13. Remove pulley and damper bolts; lift off as an assembly. Remove trunnion hub retainer and pull off hub.
14. Unbolt support halves, unbolt and pry off front cover.
15. Unbolt flywheel and remove with hoist.
16. Unbolt and remove flywheel housing.
17. Remove rear cover.

Securing top plate to block around one liner

1 Air sensing line
2 Retaining bolts
3 Cover

Fuel ratio control

Aftercooler

18. Remove ridge in cylinder.
19. Remove rod caps and push piston and rod assemblies out of block.
20. Remove lower main bearing halves and hoist crankshaft out of block. Remove upper bearing halves.
21. Remove cylinder liners with a puller.
22. Remove cylinder block top plate.
23. Remove fuel lines from governor, remove attaching bolts and lift off.
24. Attach hoist to injection pump, remove bolts and lift off unit.
25. Remove bolts, locks and plate and remove variable timing unit.
26. Remove attaching bolts and lift out oil pump.
27. Remove water temperature regulator cover from head.
28. Remove aftercooler from head.

Engine Assembly—1674

1. Install aftercooler on head; tighten bolts.
2. Install water temperature regulator with seal lip toward engine.
3. Install oil pump by aligning dowel in cover with dowel hole in body, tighten nut to 60 ft lbs., back off and retighten to align cotter pin.
4. When installing injection pump, sight down pump to align notches in the bonnet and barrel with the pump gear segment cen-

ter tooth. Position the pump to align notches with the guide pins in the housing bore. Align the pump gear segment center tooth with the fuel rack center notch. Install pump keeping a downward force on the pump and install bushing until flush with the housing. Torque pump retaining bolts to 150 ft lbs.
5. Remove injection pump camshaft timing pin, rotate camshaft to TDC #1 and install pin.
6. Install governor and automatic advance unit.
7. Install upper main bearing halves in block and coat with SAE 30. Lower crankshaft into position.
8. Install lower bearing caps and torque to 175 ft lbs.
9. Install top plate and gasket. Install liners by coating seals, liners and bores with liquid soap and driving liners into place with a hammer and wood block.
10. Install piston and connecting rod assemblies, coat bearing surfaces with SAE 30 and install caps. Torque to 30 ft lbs. = 90°.
11. Install rear cover and new gasket; cut gasket flush with bottom of block.
12. Install flywheel housing and flywheel; torque bolts to 100 ft lbs.

13. Install front cover and new gasket; cut gasket flush with bottom of block.
14. Install shims between trunnion hub and upport halves to obtain a .002-.003″ fit. Install hub bolts and tighten to 150 ft lbs., tap with hammer and retighten.
15. Install pulley and damper.
NOTE: Support bushing must be heated in oil at 250° for 2 hrs.
16. Install precombustion chambers in head and torque to 150 ft lbs. Zinc coated washer is installed first, then glow plug. Tighten glow plug to 120 in lbs.
17. Install valves and injectors; assemble valve springs. Injector nozzle nut torque is 105 ft lbs. Nozzle should be finger tight in body.
18. Position new head gasket on block and lower head into place. Install bolts and torque in sequence, to 135 ft lbs.; then to 185 ft lbs.
NOTE: If cylinder block top plate was removed, install a new gasket between the plate and block.
19. Install air compressor coolant line.
20. Install exhaust manifold and exhaust pipe-to-turbocharger pipe.
21. Install turbocharger and make all connections. Torque mounting bolts to 40 ft lbs. and clamp bolts

Fuel shut-off solenoid

Accessory drive housing

to 120 in lbs.
22. Install fuel injection lines and torque connections to 30 ft lbs.
23. Install camshafts in housing. Shafts are not interchangeable and are markeed "IN" and "EX."
24. Install camshaft gears and retainers.
25. Install camshaft housing and rear cover.
26. Install turbocharger oil drain line.
27. Install alternator.

Engine Disassembly—1693

NOTE: Disassembly is performed with engine out of vehicle and mounted in work stand.
1. Remove oil cooler water outlet elbow.
2. Remove oil outlet line.
3. Disconnect oil inlet line.
4. Unbolt and remove unit.
5. Remove alternator and water pump drive belts.
6. Remove water temperature regulator bypass line.
7. Disconnect governor control linkage.
8. Disconnect water pump inlet hose and after cooler water supply line. Remove mounting bolts and lift off water pump.

NOTE: On engines with Brakesaver do not disconnect the cooler elbow. Disconnect the cooler hose from the elbow.
9. Disconnect air sensing line from the fuel ratio control.
10. Remove the bolts and use the cover to turn the adjusting bolt 5 turns.
11. Remove the two mounting bolts and pull out and down on the unit to remove.
12. Disconnect the wiring from the fuel shut-off solenoid.
13. Unbolt and remove the unit.
14. Rotate the crankshaft clockwise (front view) to #1 TDC.
15. Remove the turbocharger oil supply line and drain line.
16. Disconnect the Brakesaver wiring where applicable.
17. Disconnect the fuel injection lines from the pump housing.
18. Disconnect the fuel inlet line from the pump housing.
19. Unbolt and remove the pump and governor.
20. Disconnect the fuel supply line and fuel transfer pump drain line from the accessory drive housing.
21. Remove the oil level gauge guide mounting bolt from the fuel priming pump.
22. Remove the accessory drive housing cover and loosen coupling bolts. Remove the tachometer drive assembly.
23. Attach a hoist and remove the accessory drive housing mounting bolts. Remove the unit.
24. Unbolt and remove the oil pan. On Brakesaver engines, remove the oil line.
25. Remove oil pump.
26. Remove lines from water temperature regulator.
27. Unbolt and remove unit.
28. Remove turbocharger air outlet pipe and elbow, and air inlet pipe.
29. Remove mounting bolts and lift off unit.
30. Disconnect aftercooler vent line.
31. Remove front and top covers from aftercooler.
32. Remove water inlet collar from aftercooler.
33. Remove the aftercooler core from housing.
34. Remove the valve cover.
35. Bring #1 to TDC compression.
36. Remove the camshaft driveshaft cover and pull out drive shaft.

NOTE: On Brakesaver engines it is necessary only to remove the two rear plugs to remove driveshaft.
37. Remove the flow plug wiring harness and all inner fuel injection lines.
38. Remove all 15 bolts and locks, pry camshafts off of dowels and lift out.
39. Remove outer fuel injection lines.
40. Remove valve cover base.
41. Remove the air compressor water line.
42. Remove the oil filter base mounting plate.
43. Remove all cylinder head mounting bolts.
44. Attach a hoist and lift off cylinder head.
45. Pry off spacer plate using 6 forcing screws 2/8-16 NC.
46. Remove rod bearing caps.
47. Push piston and rod assemblies out of block.
48. Using a puller, remove liners.
49. Unbolt and remove pulley and vibration damper spacer.
50. Using a hydraulic puller, remove the damper.
51. Pry out front seal.
52. Unbolt and remove front cover.
53. Remove crankcase breather tube.
54. Disconnect all lines from air compressor.
55. Remove mounting bolts and lift off unit.
56. Attach hoist to flywheel and lift off.

NOTE: On engine with Brakesaver, make two holes in metal part of seal and remove seal. Remove rotor housing bolts, housing and rotor. Remove ring seal from rotor. Remove seal carrier and wear ring from rotor.
57. Remove baffle retaining bolts and locks and remove the baffle and rear seal. On engines with Brakesaver, remove seal ring and carrier from crankshaft.
58. Remove fuel filter housing assembly.
59. Remove the tachometer drive and starter.
60. Unbolt and remove flywheel housing. On engines with Brakesaver, remove Brakesaver control valve, oil filter mounting base, starter and flywheel housing.
61. Remove camshaft idler gear, auxiliary drive idler gear, cluster idler gear, pump idler gear, camshaft drive gear and injection pump drive gear.
62. Unbolt and remove timing plate.
63. Remove main bearing caps and hoist out the crankshaft. Remove the upper main halves.

Engine Assembly

1. Install upper mains, coat with SAE 30 and lower crankshaft into place.
2. Install lower main halves, coated with SAE 30 and torque to 75 ft lbs. plus 120°.
3. Install new timing plate gasket and plate. Trim gasket.
4. Install camshaft drive gear and align plug with master spline on

Camshaft alignment

Installing flywheel rotor seal with tool (A)

camshaft drive collar.

5. Install camshaft gear drive shaft.
6. Install camshaft idler gear with V aligned with V on camshaft idler gear.
7. Install cluster idler gear and align V with camshaft.
8. Install accessory drive idler gear and line up V marks on camshaft idler gear and small cluster gear.
9. Install accessory drive gear and scavenge pump drive gear.
10. Position flywheel housing and install bolts. Torque to 100 ft lbs.
11. Install starter and tachometer drive.
12. Install fuel filter assembly.

NOTE: On engines with Brakesaver: position and install flywheel housing, starter, oil filters, Brakesaver control valve and tachometer drive. Install rear seal and wear ring, rotor and rotor housing.

13. Position flywheel and torque bolts to 100 ft lbs.
14. Position air compressor and drive gear assembly and install mounting bolts. Connect water and air lines.
15. Install the crankcase breather tube.
16. Install front cover, lubricate front seal lip with SAE 30 and coat O.D. of seal with Locktite. Install seal, lip first.
17. Position the damper on the crankshaft. Install retaining plate, bolts and lock. Torque bolts to 148 ft lbs., tap with hammer and retorque.
18. Install pulley.
19. Coat underside of liner flange with Form-A-Gasket. Coat seals with liquid soap.
20. Install liners and drive into position with hammer and wood block.
21. Check liner protrusion—.002-.0076 in four places.
22. Lubricate rings, pistons, liner and rod bearings with SAE 30.
23. Install piston and rod assembly with piston mark front.
24. Install bearing cap and torque nuts to 60 ft lbs. plus 120°.
25. Install spacer plate and gasket.

Liner installation

26. Install head gasket and water seals.
27. Lower head into position, lubricate and install bolts.
28. Torque head bolts in sequence to 200 ft lbs., then to 330 ft lbs., back off and retighten to 330 ft lbs.
29. Install aftercooler inlet and outlet lines.
30. Install oil filter base plate.
31. Connect the air compressor water line. Connect the fuel ratio control sensing line.
32. Connect the turbocharger supply and drain lines.
33. Connect the outer fuel injection lines to the valve cover base and install base on head. Connect glow plug wiring harness. Torque fuel lines to 30 ft lbs.
34. Adjust all camshaft followers to maximum clearance.
35. Align camshaft phasing gear timing marks and install camshafts on engine.

NOTE: #1 piston must be at TDC when installing camshafts.

36. Install inner fuel injection lines and torque to 30 ft lbs.
37. Install camshaft driveshaft and cover. Camshaft driveshaft should have blind spot on top.
38. Install timing bolt in cover.
39. Adjust valves: inlet .018" exhaust .030".
40. Install valve cover.
41. Install aftercooler core, push water inlet collar into housing and install mounting bolts. Install top cover and front cover. Connect vent line to front cover.
42. Install air outlet pipe to front cover.
43. Position turbocharger on engine and torque bolts to 40 ft lbs.
44. Connect inlet pipe and outlet pipe and elbow. Connect supply and drain lines.
45. Install temperature regulators in housing. Attach housing to engine. Connect vent and water lines.
46. Install oil pump.
47. Install oil pan and oil level gauge and guide. On engines with Brakesaver, connect the oil line.
48. Position accessory drive and install mounting bolts. Connect fuel transfer pump drain and supply lines.
49. Position fuel injection pump and governor and install mounting bolts. Connect injection lines and torque to 30 ft lbs. Connect fuel inlet line.
50. Connect fuel ratio control sensing line. Connect Brakesaver wiring.
51. Position fuel shutoff solenoid and install nuts. Connect wire.
52. Install fuel ratio control. Connect air sensing line.
53. Attach hoist and position water pump. Install bolts. Connect aftercooler supply line and inlet hose. Install temperature regulator bypass line and governor control linkage.
54. Install oil cooler and make oil connections.

VALVE ADJUSTMENT

Cummins Diesel Engines

GENERAL SPECIFICATIONS

ENGINE MODEL	BORE & STROKE	PISTON DISP. CU. IN.	MAXIMUM HORSEPOWER @ R.P.M.	TORQUE @ R.P.M.	FIRING ORDER RIGHT HAND ROTATION	LEFT HAND ROTATION	LUBE OIL PRESSURE @ GOVERNED SPEED
V6-140	4⅝ x 3½	352	140 @ 3300	247 @ 1900	1-4-2-5-3-6	—	55 @ 3300
V-352-C	4⅝ x 3½	352	140 @ 3300	247 @ 1800	1-4-2-5-3-6	—	55 @ 3300
V-352-HT	4⅝ x 3½	352	134 @ 3000	264 @ 1800	1-4-2-5-3-6	—	55 @ 3300
V6-140-HT	4⅝ x 3½	352	140 @ 3300	268 @ 1800	1-4-2-5-3-6	—	55 @ 3300
V6-155	4⅝ x 3¾	378	155 @ 3300	289 @ 1900	1-4-2-5-3-6	—	55 @ 3300
V8-185	4⅝ x 3½	470	185 @ 3300	329 @ 1900	1-5-4-8-6-3-7-2	—	55 @ 3300
V-470-C	4⅝ x 3½	470	185 @ 3300	325 @ 1800	1-5-4-8-6-3-7-2	—	55 @ 3300
V-470-HT	4⅝ x 3½	470	178 @ 3000	354 @ 1800	1-5-4-8-6-3-7-2	—	55 @ 3300
V8-185-HT	4⅝ x 3½	470	185 @ 3300	354 @ 1800	1-5-4-8-6-3-7-2	—	55 @ 3300
V8-210	4⅝ x 3¾	504	210 @ 3300	387 @ 1900	1-5-4-8-6-3-7-2	—	55 @ 3300
V-555-225	4⅝ x 4⅛	555	225 @ 3300	425 @ 1800	1-5-4-8-6-3-7-2	—	40 @ 3300
V-555-240	4⅝ x 4⅛	555	240 @ 3300	445 @ 1900	1-5-4-8-6-3-7-2	—	40 @ 3300
VT-555-225	4⅝ x 4⅛	555	225 @ 3300	425 @ 1800	1-5-4-8-6-3-7-2	—	40 @ 3300
VT-555-240	4⅝ x 4⅛	555	240 @ 3300	445 @ 1900	1-5-4-8-6-3-7-2	—	40 @ 3300
NHE-225	5½ x 6	855	225 @ 1950	668 @ 1463	1-5-3-6-2-4	1-4-2-6-3-5	50 @ 1950
NH-250	5½ x 6	855	250 @ 2100	690 @ 1575	1-5-3-6-2-4	1-4-2-6-3-5	50 @ 2100
Super-250	5½ x 6½	927	250 @ 2100	710 @ 1575	1-5-3-6-2-4	1-4-2-6-3-5	50 @ 2100
NTC-230	5½ x 6	855	230 @ 2100	805 @ 1600	1-5-3-6-2-4	1-4-2-6-3-5	50 @ 2100
NH-230	5½ x 6	855	230 @ 2100	625 @ 1600	1-5-3-6-2-4	1-4-2-6-3-5	50 @ 2100
NTC-250	5½ x 6	855	250 @ 2100	855 @ 1575	1-5-3-6-2-4	1-4-2-6-3-5	40 @ 2100
NHC-250	5½ x 6	855	250 @ 2100	685 @ 1575	1-5-3-6-2-4	1-4-2-6-3-5	40 @ 2100
NTE-235	5½ x 6	855	235 @ 2100	650 @ 1575	1-5-3-6-2-4	1-4-2-6-3-5	50 @ 2100
NT-6	5½ x 6	855	250 @ 2100	695 @ 1575	1-5-3-6-2-4	1-4-2-6-3-5	50 @ 2100
NHHTC-250	5½ x 6	855	250 @ 2100	830 @ 1575	1-5-3-6-2-4	1-4-2-6-3-5	50 @ 2100
NHH-250	5½ x 6	855	250 @ 2100	658 @ 1575	1-5-3-6-2-4	1-4-2-6-3-5	40 @ 2100
NHCT-270	5½ x 6	855	270 @ 2100	740 @ 1575	1-5-3-6-2-4	1-4-2-6-3-5	40 @ 2100
Power Torque-270	5½ x 6	855	270 @ 1950	825 @ 1575	1-5-3-6-2-4	1-4-2-6-3-5	40 @ 2100
NT-280	5½ x 6	855	280 @ 2100	780 @ 1575	1-5-3-6-2-4	1-4-2-6-3-5	50 @ 2100
NTC-290	5½ x 6	855	290 @ 2100	825 @ 1575	1-5-3-6-2-4	1-4-2-6-3-5	40 @ 2100
NTCC-290	5½ x 6	855	290 @ 2100	835 @ 1575	1-5-3-6-2-4	1-4-2-6-3-5	40 @ 2100
NHTCC-290	5½ x 6	855	290 @ 2100	845 @ 1575	1-5-3-6-2-4	1-4-2-6-3-5	40 @ 2100
NHHTC-290	5½ x 6	855	290 @ 2100	855 @ 1575	1-5-3-6-2-4	1-4-2-6-3-5	40 @ 2100
Power Torque-300	5½ x 6	855	300 @ 2300	875 @ 1600	1-5-3-6-2-4	1-4-2-6-3-5	40 @ 2100
NT-310	5½ x 6	855	310 @ 2100	855 @ 1575	1-5-3-6-2-4	1-4-2-6-3-5	40 @ 2100
NT-320	5½ x 6	855	320 @ 2100	900 @ 1575	1-5-3-6-2-4	1-4-2-6-3-5	40 @ 2100
Power Torque-330	5½ x 6	855	330 @ 2300	930 @ 1500	1-5-3-6-2-4	1-4-2-6-3-5	40 @ 2100
NT-335	5½ x 6	855	335 @ 2100	925 @ 1575	1-5-3-6-2-4	1-4-2-6-3-5	40 @ 2100
NTC-335	5½ x 6	855	335 @ 2100	930 @ 1575	1-5-3-6-2-4	1-4-2-6-3-5	50 @ 2100
NTCC-335	5½ x 6	855	335 @ 2100	930 @ 1500	1-5-3-6-2-4	1-4-2-6-3-5	50 @ 2100
NHHTC-335	5½ x 6	855	335 @ 2100	838 @ 1575	1-5-3-6-2-4	1-4-2-6-3-5	40 @ 2100
NHHTCC-335	5½ x 6	855	335 @ 2100	945 @ 1500	1-5-3-6-2-4	1-4-2-6-3-5	40 @ 2100
NTC-350	5½ x 6	855	350 @ 2100	975 @ 1575	1-5-3-6-2-4	1-4-2-6-3-5	40 @ 2100
NTCC-350	5½ x 6	855	350 @ 2100	990 @ 1600	1-5-3-6-2-4	1-4-2-6-3-5	40 @ 2100
NTA-370	5½ x 6	855	370 @ 2100	1015 @ 1575	1-5-3-6-2-4	1-4-2-6-3-5	50 @ 2100
NT-380	5½ x 6	855	380 @ 2300	855 @ 1600	1-5-3-6-2-4	1-4-2-6-3-5	40 @ 2300
NTA-380	5½ x 6	855	380 @ 2300	855 @ 1500	1-5-3-6-2-4	1-4-2-6-3-5	40 @ 2300
NTA-400	5½ x 6	855	400 @ 2100	1000 @ 1575	1-5-3-6-2-4	1-4-2-6-3-5	40 @ 2100
NTA-420	5½ x 6	855	420 @ 2300	1045 @ 1725	1-5-3-6-2-4	1-4-2-6-3-5	40 @ 2300
V-903	5½ x 4¾	903	280 @ 2600	700 @ 1575	1-5-4-8-6-3-7-2	—	50 @ 2600
VT-903	5½ x 4¾	903	300 @ 2400	795 @ 1600	1-5-4-8-6-3-7-2	—	50 @ 2400
V-903-C	5½ x 4¾	903	307 @ 2600	706 @ 1800	1-5-4-8-6-3-7-2	—	50 @ 2600
VT-903-C	5½ x 4¾	903	350 @ 2600	848 @ 1800	1-5-4-8-6-3-7-2	—	50 @ 2600
N-927	5½ x 6½	927	280 @ 2100	775 @ 1500	1-5-3-6-2-4	1-4-2-6-3-5	40 @ 2100
KT-450	6¼ x 6¼	1150	450 @ 2100	1350 @ 1500	1-5-3-6-2-4	1-4-2-6-3-5	50 @ 2100
KTA-600	6¼ x 6¼	1150	600 @ 2100	1650 @ 1600	1-5-3-6-2-4	1-4-2-6-3-5	50 @ 2100

CRANKSHAFT AND BEARING SPECIFICATIONS

ENGINE MODEL	PART NUMBER	MAIN BEARING JOURNAL DIAMETER	MAIN BEARING CLEARANCE	ROD BEARING JOURNAL DIAMETER	ROD BEARING CLEARANCE	CRANKSHAFT END PLAY
V-6	159970	3.249-3.250	.0015-.0045	2.499-2.50	.0015-.0045	.004-.014
	176760	3.499-3.500	.0015-.0045	2.499-2.50	.0015-.0045	.004-.014
	181130	3.249-3.250	.0015-.0045	2.499-2.50	.0015-.0045	.004-.014
	183570	3.499-3.500	.0015-.0045	2.499-2.50	.0015-.0045	.004-.014
	195240	3.499-3.500	.0015-.0045	2.499-2.50	.0015-.0045	.004-.014
V-8 378, 504	156340	3.249-3.250	.0015-.0045	2.499-2.50	.0015-.0045	.004-.014
	175050	3.499-3.500	.0015-.0045	2.499-2.50	.0015-.0045	.004-.014
	181140	3.249-3.250	.0015-.0045	2.499-2.50	.0015-.0045	.004-.014
	182360	3.499-3.500	.0015-.0045	2.499-2.50	.0015-.0045	.004-.014
	194840	3.499-3.500	.0015-.0045	2.499-2.50	.0015-.0045	.004-.014
V-8 555	All	3.499-3.500	.0015-.0050	2.749-2.750	.0015-.0050	.004-.014
6-855, 927	All	4.4985-4.50	.0015-.0050	3.1235-3.125	.0015-.0045	.007-.017
V-8 903	All	3.749-3.750	.0015-.0050	3.124-3.125	.0015-.0050	.005-.015
KT-1150	All	5.4985-5.5000	.0026-.0065	3.9985-4.0000	.0020-.0050	.004-.016

PISTON SPECIFICATIONS

ENGINE SERIES	PART NO. PISTON	PART NO. LINER	PISTON TO LINER CLEARANCE	PISTON PIN DIAMETER
V6 352, 378 V8 470, 504, 555	173800, 185310, 200800	179710	.0085-.0110	1.3738-1.3740
6-855, 927	All	All	.0125-.013	1.9988-1.9990
V8-903	All	All	.0095-.0120	1.7488-1.7490
KT-1150	All	All	.0115-.0120	2.3988-2.3990

PISTON RING GAP

ENGINE SERIES	RING PART NO.	GAP
V6-352, 378 V8-470, 504, 555	154700	.013-.023
	171690	.013-.023
	171700	.010-.020
	201645	.010-.030
	201650	.013-.023
	208990	.025-.035
6-855, 927	147670	.023-.033
	132880	.019-.029
	168680	.028-.038
	194610	.010-.020
V-8 903	216981	.017-.027
	194600	.013-.023
	194610	.010-.020
KT-1150	Top Ring	.025-.040
	Center Ring	.025-.040
	Oil Ring	.015-.030

TORQUE SPECIFICATIONS

V6—140	V6—155	V8—555
V8—185	V8—210	

For each step, tighten in specified pattern to the figure indicated. All figures are in ft./lbs. unless indicated inch/lbs. or degrees of rotation. Degrees of rotation refers to rotation of nut or capscrew.

MAIN CAPSCREWS	SIDE CAPSCREWS	CON ROD NUTS	HEAD BOLTS	FLYWHEEL HOUSING	OIL PAN
1. 55-65	35-40	25-30	25	70-75	
2. 115-125	F, G 110-120,	50-55	50-55		$\frac{5}{16}$"—15-17
3. 175-185	Others 100-110	loosen fully	75-80		$\frac{3}{8}$"—25-30
4. loosen fully		20-25	110-115		
5. repeat 1, 2, 3.		30°			
6.		30°			

FLYWHEEL	INTAKE MANIFOLDS	CRANKSHAFT PULLEY	VIBRATION DAMPER	FAN HUB (LOW MOUNTING)	FAN HUB (HIGH MOUNT)
1. 30-35	10	20	90-100	with spacer 20-22	50
2. 60-70	20	40		w/o spacer 30-32	60°
3. 100-105	30-32	60			
4. #195198 caps		80			
only—140-145①		90-100			
5.					

FAN HUB (INTERMEDIATE MOUNT)	FAN HUB (ECCENTRIC)	INJECTOR PLUNGER ADJUSTMENT	VALVE CROSSHEAD ADJUSTMENT LOCKNUT	VALVE CLEARANCE LOCKNUTS
78-85	300	60 inch/lbs.	25-30	40-45

① Serial #F040000 and later.

TORQUE SPECIFICATIONS- Cont'd.

6—855, 927

For each step, tighten in specified pattern to the figure indicated. All figures are in ft./lbs. unless indicated inch/lbs. or degrees of rotation. Degrees of rotation refers to rotation of nut or capscrew.

MAIN CAPSCREWS	CONNECTING ROD NUTS	CYLINDER HEAD BOLTS 4⅞" & 5⅛" BORES	CYLINDER HEAD BOLTS 5½" BORES
1. 150	60	25	25
2. 300-310	120	125	125
3. loosen completely	140	325	225
4. 140	loosen completely	425	280-300
5. 30°	25	460-480	
6.	50-55		
7.	60°		

CAM FOLLOWER HOUSINGS	INJECTOR HOLD DOWN CAPSCREWS	INJECTOR INLET & DRAIN CONNECTIONS 4⅞"—5⅛" BORES	INJECTOR INLET & DRAIN CONNECTIONS 5½" BORES
1. 15-20	4-5	20-25	4-5
2. 30-35	7-8		7-8
3.	10-12		NEWER TYPE (PT TYPES D, A, OR B)
4.	NYLOCK CAPSCREWS 12-14		10-12

VALVE CROSSHEAD ADJUSTING NUTS 25-30	ROCKER LEVER HOUSING 4⅞"—5⅛" 65-75	5½" BORE 55-75	OIL FILTER 20-35	FUEL FILTER 20-25

KT, KTA—1150

MAIN CAPSCREWS	CONNECTING ROD NUTS	CYLINDER HEAD BOLTS (CADMIUM PLATED)	CYLINDER HEAD BOLTS (LUBRITED)	FLYWHEEL
1. 190	70	40	40	40
2. 440	140	110	140	100
3. Loosen Completely	210	180	240	140
4. 190	Loosen Completely	250	350	200
5. 440	70			
6.	140			
7.	210			

EXHAUST MANIFOLDS 40-45	CRANKSHAFT ADAPTER 320-340	VIBRATION DAMPER 65-75	INJECTOR HOLDDOWN BOLTS 4-5 7-8 10-12	VALVE CROSSHEAD ADJUSTING NUTS 25-30

6—855, 927 (CONT)

SECOND ORDER COUNTERBALANCER (4 CYL.) HOUSING	DRIVE ASSEMBLY	FLYWHEEL HOUSING 150	OIL PAN 50-60	FLYWHEEL		CRANKSHAFT FLANGE
1. 50-55	30-35			Snug	180-200	IF CAST IRON PART #139145
2.				190-200		90-100
3.						

VIBRATION DAMPER 60	ACCESSORY DRIVE PULLEY 90-100	FAN HUB SHAFT TO BRACKET NUT 400-500	EXHAUST MANIFOLD WITH LOCKPLATE 25	WITHOUT LOCKPLATE 40	OIL COOLER-FILTER ASSEMBLY 40-45

INJECTOR PLUNGER ADJUSTING SCREW	INJECTOR PLUNGER ADJUSTING NUT 30-40	VALVE ADJUSTMENT LOCKNUTS 30-40	ROCKER COVER 75-95
1. 15° beyond contact			
2. Loosen 1 Turn			
3. 48 inch/lbs.			

V—903

For each step, tighten to the figure indicated. All figures are in ft./lbs. unless indicated inch/lbs. or degrees of rotation. Degrees of rotation refers to rotation of nut or capscrew.

	PIPE PLUGS		MAIN CAPSCREWS	SIDE CAPSCREWS	CON ROD NUTS	CAMSHAFT THRUST PLATE 30-32
	⅛"	⅜"	½"				
1.	5-15	30-45	45-55	50	50-55	50-55	
2.				100	100-110	105-115	
3.				150-160	140-150	loosen completely	
4.				250		30-32	
5.				300-350		60-65	
6.				loosen completely		30-32	
7.				45-50		60-65	
8.				85-90		30°	
9.				135-140		30°	
10.				170-180			
11.				30°			
12.				30°			

TORQUE SPECIFICATIONS- Cont'd.

V—903

INJECTOR HOLD DOWN CAPSCREWS	VALVE CROSSHEAD ADJUSTING SCREWS	CYLINDER HEAD	GEAR HOUSING	CRANKSHAFT ADAPTER	FLYWHEEL HOUSING	OIL PAN 5/16"	OIL PAN 3/8"
1. 30-35	25-30	Snug	30-32	75	Snug	16-18	25-30
2.		50		150	50-55		
3.		100		225			
4.		150		300			
5.		200		330-350			
6.		250					
7.		280-300					

FLYWHEEL	INTAKE MANIFOLDS	WATER PUMP	VIBRATION DAMPER	FAN HUB	ALTERNATOR PULLEY	WATER HEADER COVER PLATE
1. 50-60	10	30-35	200-205	50	60	30-35
2. 100-110	20					
3. 150-165	30-32					
4. 200-210						

LUBE OIL COOLER/FILTER	EXHAUST MANIFOLDS	VALVE ADJUSTING SCREWS	INJECTOR ROCKER LOCKNUT
1. 30-35	15	40-45	25-30
2.	30		
3.	45-50		

Description and Operation

The PT (pressure-time) fuel pump is driven by the air compressor at engine speed. The engine speed governor is incorporated in the fuel pump. The tachometer is coupled to the fuel pump main shaft. The fuel pump supplies fuel under high pressure to the injectors; one for each cylinder.

The fuel injectors meter and inject fuel into the cylinders. The injectors are operated and timed by push rods actuated by the camshaft and cam followers. Engine timing can be varied by changing the injector lifter adjustments.

The variable-speed, mechanical governor has two purposes: it maintains sufficient fuel delivery to the injectors for idling with the throttle control in idling position, and it cuts off fuel to the injectors above maximum rated rpm.

Trouble Diagnosis

The satisfactory performance of a Diesel engine depends on two items of foremost importance, (1) Sufficiently high compression pressure, and (2) The injection of the proper amount of fuel at the right time.

The first one of these items depends mainly on pistons, piston rings, valves and valve operating mechanism; the second item depends on injectors and their operating mechanism, and fuel system.

Lack of engine power, uneven running, excessive vibration, and tendency to stall when idling may be caused by either a compression loss or faulty injector operation.

The causes of trouble symptoms may be varied; therefore a hit-and-miss search should be avoided. A proper diagnosis of symptoms is an orderly process. An "orderly process" means to check the most probable common cause first; then proceed with the n xetmost probable cause.

Hard Starting or Failure To Start

1. Fuel shut off valve closed or fuel tank empty.
2. Inferior quality fuel.
3. Restricted fuel lines.
4. Fuel pump pressure regulation faulty.
5. Plugged injector spray holes.
6. Broken fuel pump drive shaft.
7. Gear pump gears scored or worn.
8. Injector inlet or drain connections loose.
9. Water in fuel.
10. Air leaks in fuel suction line.
11. Incorrect injector timing.
12. Valve leakage.
13. Restricted air intake.
14. Engine in need of overhaul.
15. Incorrect valve timing.

Engine Runs but Misses

1. Restricted fuel lines.
2. Water in fuel or poor quality fuel.
3. Air leaks in fuel suction line.
4. Injectors improperly adjusted or plugged.
5. Low compression, intake or exhaust valves leaking.
6. Leaking supercharger air connection.
7. Restricted drain line.
8. Stuck injector plunger.
9. Improper valve and injector adjustments.

Excessive Smoke

1. Restricted fuel system drain lines.
2. Plugged injector spray holes.
3. Inferior quality fuel.
4. Engine fuel rate too high.
5. Injectors improperly adjusted.
6. Intake manifold or cylinder head gasket leak.
7. Restricted air intake.
8. High exhaust back pressure.
9. Broken or worn piston rings.
10. Engine in need of overhaul.
11. Incorrect valve timing.
12. Worn or scored cylinder liners or pistons.
13. Engine overloaded.

Low Power or Loss of Power

1. Inferior quality fuel.
2. Water in fuel.
3. Fuel suction line leaking.
4. Restricted fuel lines.
5. Low fuel pressure.
6. Plugged injector spray holes.
7. Dirty fuel filters or screens.
8. Improper valve and injector adjustments.
9. Improperly adjusted throttle linkage.
10. High speed governor set too low.
11. Air in system.
12. Sticking stop control (fuel shut off).
13. Restricted air intake.
14. High exhaust back pressure.
15. Intake manifold or cylinder head gasket leakage.
16. Low compression—intake or exhaust valve leakage.
17. Broken or worn piston rings.
18. Incorrect bearing clearances.
19. Worn or scored cylinder liners or pistons.
20. Engine in need of overhaul.
21. Incorrect valve timing.
22. Dirty air cleaner.
23. Overheating engine.

Excessive Fuel Consumption

1. Inferior quality fuel.

2. Restricted fuel system drain lines.
3. Fuel rate set too high.
4. Fuel leaks—external or internal.
5. Plugged injector spray holes.
6. Injectors not adjusted properly.
7. Cracked injector body or cup.
8. Restricted air intake.
9. High exhaust back pressure.
10. Engine overloaded.
11. Incorrect bearing clearances.
12. Engine in need of overhaul.

Excessive Oil Consumption
1. External or internal oil leaks.
2. Cylinder oil control not working.
3. Wrong grade oil for climatic conditions.
4. Broken or worn piston rings.
5. Engine in need of overhaul.
6. Worn or scored cylinder liners or pistons.

Low Lubrication Oil Pressure
1. Oil suction line restricted.
2. Oil pump or pressure regulator valve not working properly.
3. Crankcase oil level too low.
4. Wrong grade of oil for conditions.
5. Insufficient coolant.
6. Worn water pump.
7. Coolant thermostat not working.
8. Loose fan belts.
9. Clogged coolant passages.
10. Clogged oil cooler.
11. Radiator core openings restricted.
12. Air in cooling system.
13. Insufficient radiator capacity.
14. Leaking coolant hoses, connections or gaskets.
15. Incorrect bearing clearances.
16. Engine in need of overhaul.
17. Engine overloaded.

Coolant Temperature Too High
1. Low coolant level.
2. Air leaks in suction line.
3. Low oil level.
4. Engine overloaded.

5. Injectors not properly adjusted.
6. Injector pipe partially clogged.
7. Faulty injectors.
8. Injector timing too early.
9. Worn or scored cylinder liners or pistons.
10. Broken valve springs.
11. Crankshaft vibration damper faulty.
12. Excessive crankshaft end clearance.
13. Flywheel loose or unbalanced.
14. Broken or worn piston rings.
15. Incorrect bearing clearances.
16. Engine in need of overhaul.
17. Broken tooth in engine gear train.
18. Loose mounting bolts.

Fuel System

Description and Operation
The Cummins PT fuel system delivers fuel to each cylinder of the engine in equal, pre-determined amounts; thus PT is an abbreviation for pressure-time. The fuel system consists of the supply tank(s), fuel filter, fuel pump, governor, injectors, fuel shut-off valve, and the fuel supply and drain lines.

The fuel pump is coupled to the air compressor which is driven from the engine gear train. The fuel pump main shaft turns at engine crankshaft speed, and drives the gear pump, governor and tachometer shaft.

The fuel pump consists of a gear pump to draw fuel from the supply tank and deliver it to the injectors under pressure, and a governor and throttle to control fuel pressure to the injectors. A pulsation damper prolongs gear pump life, as it

C-160 naturally aspirated diesel engine
(© Cummins Engine Co.)

Cummins V6 diesel engine
(© Cummins Engine Co.)

C-180 supercharged diesel
(© Cummins Engine Co.)

smoothes the flow of fuel through the pump.

The gear pump receives fuel from the supply tank and pumps the fuel under pressure, varying with engine speed, through the filter screen and governor to the throttle and to the injectors. The filter screen, mounted in the top of the fuel pump, prevents damage to the fuel pump and injectors by filtering from the fuel any foreign particles that may be present. To provide fuel pump cooling a small amount of fuel is bled from the fuel pump and returned to the fuel tank. Thus, a circulation of cooling fuel is provided.

At idle speed, the main throttle shaft passage is closed, allowing fuel to flow around the throttle shaft to the idle port in the governor barrel. At engine speeds above idle, the fuel flows through the main throttle shaft hole and enters the main fuel port in the governor barrel.

When the throttle lever is moved to the idle position and the vehicle is moving in excess of idle speed, a small amount of throttle leakage is provided to purge the injectors of air. The PT fuel pump governor controls both idle and high speed. On the 855 CID engines except the NH-250, the fuel manifold is a tube mounted externally on the engine, with equal length branches (tubing) to the injectors. On the V-6, V-8, and NH-250 engines the manifolds are drilled passages, one in each cylinder head, that are aligned with a passageway in the injector body. These fuel manifolds are connected to the pressure side of the fuel pump by a common fuel line.

Fuel circulates through the injector at all times, except during a short period following injection into the cylinder. From the inlet fuel flows down the inlet passage of the injector, around the injector plunger, between the body end and cup, up the drain passage to the drain connections and manifold and back to the supply tank.

As the plunger comes up the injector feed passage is opened and fuel flows through the metering orifice into the cup. At the same time, fuel flows past the cup and out the drain orifice. The amount of fuel which enters the cup is controlled by the fuel pressure against the metering orifice. Fuel pressure is controlled by the fuel pump.

The plunger, during injection, comes down until the metering orifice is closed and the fuel in the cup is injected into the cylinder. While the plunger is seated in the cup, all fuel flow in the injector is stopped.

On the earlier 855 CID engines, except the NH-250, a flanged injector is used. The fuel mainifold is connected to the inlet port of the injector flange.

V6 engine fuel system
(© Cummins Engine Co.)

NH series fuel system
(© Cummins Engine Co.)

Flanged and cylindrical injectors
(© Cummins Engine Co.)

A removable inlet screen is installed in each inlet port for final fuel filtration. The drain port is located adjacent to the inlet port. The drain ports are connected by a drain mainfold to return surplus fuel to the supply tank.

The V-6, V-8, NH-250 and later 855 CID ANT 1150 cid engines utilize a cylindrical injector. Two radial grooves (annuli) on the injector body index with two drilled passagesin each cylinder head, which serve as fuel inlet and drain mainifolds. The inetls annulus contains a fine mesh screen for final fuel filtration. A fule crossover drain tube, at the flywheel end of the engine connects the two cylinder head drain passages and a common line returns the unused fuel to the fuel tank.

The fuel grooves around the cylindrical injectors are separated by O-rings which seal against the cylinder head injector bore. This forms a leak-proof passage between the injectors and the cylinder head injector bore surface. The injectors contain an orifice plug which can be varied in inside diameter to achieve identical fuel delivery through all injectors.

Ether quick start unit
(© Cummins Engine Co.)

Adjustments and Repairs

Before Making Adjustments

NOTE: The following applies only to in-vehicle adjustment.

1. Run engine to operating temperature; fuel temperature should be above 110° F. (43° C).
2. Engine parts should be in good condition; timing, valves and injectors properly adjusted.
3. Guages and tachometers should be of known accuracy.
4. Throttle control linkage should be adjusted so that full throttle is obtained and when released,

Fuel pump adjustments
(© Cummins Engine Co.)

the throttle is stopped by the front throttle adjusting screw.

NOTE: Pump should be properly adjusted and calibrated prior to installation on vehicle engine. Very little adjustment should be required after installation. The most often made adjustment is the idle setting since this depends on vehicle load.

Adjustments

Idle Speed

1. Remove pipe plug from spring pack cover.
2. The adjusting screw is held in place by a spring clip.
3. Turn screw in to increase or out to decrease speed.
4. If spring pack sealing tool is not used, some air will collect in the spring pack causing a temporary

Preheater operation
(© Cummins Engine Co.)

Fuel pump gauge connections
(© Cummins Engine Co.)

Manifold Pressure Gauge—ST-435 Connection   FUEL SUPPLY LINE   *Vacuum Gauge—ST-434*

Vacuum Gauge Adapter

rough idle condition. This will stabilize when the housing fills with fuel.

5. Replace pipe when idle speed is correct.

NOTE: *The following are factory recommended idle speeds intended as reference points. Some deviations can be made as long as extreme care is taken to avoid causing related problems.*

N and NH—600 ± 20
V6 and V8-185 & 210—625 ± 25
V, VT-903—550 ± 20-30
KT450, KTA 600—

High Idle

1. Operate engine to purge all air from fuel system.
2. With transmission in neutral, open throttle and hold fully open.
3. Add or remove shims under the governor high speed spring until high idle is 10-12% greater than governor cutoff speed.

Throttle Leakage

1. Operate engine to purge all air from system.
2. Adjust throttle control linkage so that pump throttle just contacts the front throttle stop screw when throttle is closed.
3. Place transmission in neutral, open throttle fully and let engine run at high idle—no load.
4. Using a stop watch, check the time required for throttle release to 1000 rpm movement. Repeat several times.
5. If engine begins to stall upon deceleration, increase throttle leakage.
6. Note position of leakage adjusting screw. Turn screw in while checking engine operation until deceleration time is increased 1 to 2 seconds.

7. If engine decelerates too slowly, it may be necessary to decrease leakage.
8. Note position of adjusting screw. Back out screw as engine decelerates until engine tends to stall. Turn screw in until deceleration time is increased 1 to 2 seconds.

Typical chassis mooted fuel filter V6 engine
(© Cummins Engine Co.)

Engine mounted fuel filter NH series
(© Cummins Engine Co.)

Fuel Pump Screen

Remove the retainer cap from the fuel pump. Remove the spring and lift out the filter screen assembly.

Remove the top screen retainer from the filter screen assembly. Wash the screen and magnet in cleaning solvent and dry with compressed air. Install the top screen retainer.

Install the filter screen, *with the hole down*, in the fuel pump.

Install the spring and retainer cap. Torque the retainer cap to specifications.

Fuel Pump Removal

In-Line 6 Cyl. Series Engines

1. Disconnect the accelerator return spring. Disconnect the hand throttle control, tachometer cable and accelerator rod at the fuel pump. Disconnect the lead to the fuel shut-off valve.
2. Disconnect the primer fuel pump line and fuel supply line at the full pump. Remove the fuel outlet line from the shut-off valve and fuel manifold. Disconnect the fuel bleed line.
3. Remove the fuel pump mounting bolts. Remove the fuel pump, gasket and pump drive rubber buffer.

Installation

1. Clean the gasket surfaces of the fuel pump and air compressor.
2. Install the pump, drive rubber buffer. Position a new fuel pump gasket on the air compressor and install the fuel pump. Torque the mounting bolts to specifications.
3. Connect the primer fuel pump line and fuel supply line to the fuel pump. Connect the fuel outlet line to the fuel manifold and fuel shut-off valve. Connect the fuel bleed line.
4. Connect the accelerator rod, hand throttle control and tachometer cable to the fuel pump. Connect the fuel shut-off valve lead. Connect the accelerator return spring.
5. Check the accelerator linkage and adjust if necessary.
6. Start the engine and check for leaks.

FILTER SCREEN

FUEL PUMP

Fuel filter screen removal
(© Cummins Engine Co.)

Cummins Diesel Engines

FUEL OUTLET LINE — FUEL SHUT-OFF VALVE — PRIMER PUMP FUEL LINE

FUEL PUMP LEVER — FUEL SUPPLY LINE

Typical fuel pump installation NH series
(© Cummins Engine Co.)

ACCELERATOR ROD — INLET SCREEN CAP — FUEL SHUT-OFF VALVE — FUEL OUTLET LINES

HAND THROTTLE CONTROL — FUEL SUPPLY LINE

Typical fuel pump installation V6 engines
(© Cummins Engine Co.)

Fuel Pump Removal

V-6 and V-8 Engines

1. Disconnect the air cleaner inlet air tube from the air intake connection on the right intake manifold. Remove the air intake connection and air cross-over connection from the intake manifolds.
2. Disconnect the fuel shut-off valve lead. Disconnect the hand throttle control, accelerator rod and tachometer cable from the fuel pump.
3. Disconnect the fuel supply line and the fuel outlet line(s) from the fuel pump and shut-off valve. Disconnect the fuel bleed line.
4. Remove the fuel pump to air compressor mounting bolts, and remove the fuel pump. Remove the gasket and the pump drive rubber buffer.

Installation

1. Clean the gasket surfaces of the fuel pump and air compressor.
2. Install the pump drive rubber buffer. Use a new gasket and install the fuel pump on the air compressor. Torque the mounting bolts to specifications.
3. Connect the fuel outlet line(s) to the fuel shut-off valve. Connect the fuel supply line to the fuel pump. Connect the fuel bleed line.
4. Connect the accelerator rod, hand throttle control and tachometer cable to the fuel pump. Connect the fuel shut-off valve lead. Check the accelerator linkage and adjust if necessary.
5. Install the air cross-over connection and air intake connection on the intake manifolds. Torque the retaining bolts to specifications. Connect the air cleaner inlet air tube to the air intake connection.
6. Start the engine and check for air and fuel leaks.

Fuel Pump Hydraulic Governor Drive

The fuel pump/hydraulic governor drive is used whenever a hydraulic governor is needed for a particular engine application. The governor mounts atop the housing and the fuel pump is coupled behind the housing.

Disassembly

1. Remove governor drive assembly from governor reservoir. Remove and discard gasket.
2. On governors with 2:1 gear ratio, press out governor drive shaft from gear end. Remove snap ring, ball key and collar.
3. On governors with 3:1 gear ratio, press on shaft from gear end to separate all units from housing.
4. Remove snap ring and ball key; then press out shaft.
5. Remove capscrews and lockwashers and separate drive gear and support assembly from reservoir.

$\frac{.890}{.900}$ DIA.

$\frac{.520}{.540}$

$\frac{.875}{.876}$ DIA.

Bearing and retainer assembly
(© Cummins Engine Co.)

6. Remove drain plug, dipstick, vent plug and elbow.
7. Remove shaft locknut and washer from drive shaft.
8. Use puller to remove coupling, spacer and governor drive gear.
9. Press on small end of shaft to remove shaft from support.
10. Press on large end of shaft to remove drive gear. Remove keys from shaft key way.
11. Remove snap ring from support. Invert housing and press out rear bearing and oil seal. Discard oil seal.

Cleaning and Inspection

1. Clean all parts in approved cleaning solvent and dry thoroughly with clean cloth or air jet.
2. Check bearing for worn race or rough action.
3. Check gears for chipped or broken teeth or uneven wear.
4. Check governor shaft housing oil holes. Make certain they are open.
5. Inspect support and reservoir for cracks, breaks, or rough mating surfaces.

Assembly

1. Lubricate outside of oil seal and press into housing from large end. Open end of seal must be down. Check to see that oil holes in housing are open.
2. Invert housing. Coat outside of rear bearing with lubricant and press bearing into housing to shoulder. Insert snap ring, flat side down.
3. Lubricate large end of shaft. Place key in shaft and press shaft into gear against shoulder. Place flat side, not beveled side, of gear hub against shoulder.
4. Press small end of shaft assembly into large end of housing. Coat shaft first with lubricant so that oil seal will not be damaged.

5. Lubricate shaft and press governor drive gear on small end against bearing in housing.

6. Insert key; then press on coupling. Shoulder of coupling goes against gear.

7. Install flat washer and shaft lock nut.

8. Place reservoir in vise with governor drive studs up. Install dipstick, vent plug, weatherhead fitting, and drain plug.

9. Place gaskets and install drive gear and housing assembly to serial number side of reservoir with four capscrews and lockwashers. Large oil hole in housing must be at top.

10. On governors with 2:1 gear ratio:
    a. Drop thrust washer into housing.
    b. Lubricate ball key and insert in drive shaft; install snap ring.
    c. Line up ball key with thrust washer, invert assembly, and press on gear. Allow .003/.006 inch end play. Check with feeler gauge.

11. On governor with 3:1 gear ratio:
    a. Press governor drive shaft into washer flush with bottom side. Note relief in washer to start shaft.
    b. Press shaft assembly into cylinder until shoulder on shaft is flush with end of cylinder.
    c. Slide this assembly into governor drive housing so that flatwasher rests on bronze bushing.
    d. Invert assembly and install ball key, collared washer and snap ring.
    e. Press on end of cylinder until flat washer is against bronze bushing.
    f. Press gear into position allowing .003/.006 inch end play. Check with feeler gauge.

Fuel Injectors

Removal

Early 855, 927 CID Series Engines (except NH-250) Flange Type

1. Remove the rocker housing cover(s).

2. Disconnect the fuel manifold and fuel return line from the injector inlet and drain connections. Remove the fuel inlet screen (Fig. 13). Remove the fuel inlet and drain connections from the injector.

3. Loosen the injector rocker lever lock nut and unscrew the adjusting screw until the push rod can

be disengaged. Disengage the push rod and tip the rocker lever away from the injector.

4. Remove the injector retaining screws and lift the injector from the cylinder head. *Do not bruise the injector tip. Do not turn the injector bottom side up or the plunger will fall out. Leave the plunger in the injector as the plungers are not interchangeable.*

Installation

1. Insert the injector in the cylinder head. *Be sure the plunger is*

INLET CONNECTION SCREEN

Removing injector inlet screen
(© Cummins Engine Co.)

INJECTOR

DRAIN CONNECTION

FUEL MANIFOLD

Injector fuel inlet and drain connections
(© Cummins Engine Co.)

INJECTOR

Screwdriver

Typical cylindrical injector removal
(© Cummins Engine Co.)

positioned with the plunger class mark centered between the inlet and drain connections.

2. Lubricate the retaining screw threads. Start, *but do not tighten*, the retaining screws. Align the injector by installing the inlet and drain connections 2 turns in the injector. Torque the retaining screws alternately to specifications.

3. Torque the inlet and drain connections to specifications. Install the fuel inlet screen and connect the fuel manifold and fuel return line.

4. Position the push rod under the rocker lever and adjust the injector rocker lever lash to specifications.

5. Install the rocker housing cover(s). Partially tighten the cover screws.

6. Operate the engine until the oil temperature is 140°F, and adjust the injector lash to specifications.

Fuel Injectors Removal

V-6, V-8, and Later in-line 6 Cyl. Cylindrical Type

1. On some model trucks, it will be necessary to remove the **right** side air cleaner for right cylinder bank operations.

2. On some model trucks, it will be necessary to disconnect the brace rod from the left side of the transmission remote control mounting support and position it aside. Disconnect the accelerator pedal rod at the cross-shaft on the engine.

3. Remove the valve covers.

4. Remove the power steering pump and drive bolts from the engine. Leave the hoses attached and position the power steering pump out of the way.

5. Loosen the lock nut and back-off the injector rocker lever adjusting screw until the push rod can be disengaged. Hold the push rod aside and tip the rocker lever away from the injector to clear the injector link.

6. Remove the injector clamp retaining screws and the clamps. Pry the injector from the cylinder head. Remove the O-rings. *Avoid bruising the injector tip. Do not turn the injector upside down as the plunger might fall out. Injector plungers are not inter-changeable.*

Installation

1. Clean the injector sleeve with a cloth-wrapped stick.

2. Install new O-rings on the injector, and coat the O-rings with lubricant.

3. Install the injector in the cylin-

der head. *Be sure the fuel inlet hole is toward the camshaft.* Seat the injector in the sleeve by giving it a quick, hard push with a wooden hammer handle. A snap should be heard as the injector cup seats in the sleeve.

4. Install the hold-down clamp and torque the retaining screws to specifications.

5. Depress the injector springs with a screwdriver (use as a lever with blade under rocker lever shaft), and engage the injector plunger link with the rocker lever. At the same time engage the push rod with the rocker lever adjusting screw.

6. Adjust the injector lash to specifications. Tighten the lock nut. Install the cylinder head cover valve cover if removed and partially tighten the cover screws.

7. Install the right air cleaner, if removed.

8. Operate the engine until the oil temperature is 140°F. Remove the valve cover or cylinder head cover and adjust the injector lash to specifications.

9. Install the power steering pump and drive belts. Adjust the belt tension to specifications.

10. Connect the accelerator pedal rod to the cross shaft. Connect the brace rod to the transmission remote control mounting support.

Injector Adjustment (Exc. 903 Cid V-8)

1. Turn engine, in direction of rotation, to No. 1 top-center firing position. In this position, intake and exhaust valves for No. 1 cylinder are closed.

2. Continue rotating crankshaft until valve set mark on accessory drive pulley aligns with timing marks on gear case cover. (1-6 VS on 6 cylinder, 1-4 VS on 4-cylinder engines.) When these

Alignment of crosshead-stem and guide
(© Cummins Engine Co.)

marks align, the engine is in position to adjust valves and injector plunger for No. 1 cylinder.

3. Check intake and exhaust valve position of cylinder to be adjusted. See that valves are closed and rocker levers free.

4. Check threads on adjusting screw and nut. See that they are clean, well-oiled and free-turning.

5. Turn injector adjusting screw down until plunger contacts cup. Turn adjusting screw an additional 15° to squeeze oil from cup.

6. Slack off adjusting screw one turn.

7. Tighten adjusting screw to 70°F. setting. Use a torque wrench equipped wtih a screwdriver adaptor, graduated in inch-pound divisions, and having a maximum capacity of 150 inch-pounds.

   Setting at 70°F. 48 inch-pounds.
   Setting at 140°F. 60 inch-pounds.

8. Lock screw in place with jam nut.

9. Make final adjustment when en-

gine is at operating (140°F.) temperature.

Injector Torque Settings (in.-lbs.)

	60°-70°F.	140°F.
855, 927 CID	48	72
V6, V8 exc. 903	60	60
KT-1150 CID	48	72

Injector Adjustment V-903 and VT-903

NOTE: Engine oil must be 140-160°F. for this adjustment.

1. Turn the engine until the proper "VS" mark on the vibration damper lines up with the pointer. Make sure both valve rockers for each of the cylinders to be adjusted are free. If rockers are not loose, the engine must be turned over 360 degrees.

2. Support a dial indicator on the engine so that the indicator extension just sits on the top of the injector plunger flange for the cylinder to be adjusted. Make sure the indicator extension is not against the rocker lever.

3. Turn the rocker lever forward until the injector plunger is bottomed in the cup, and all oil is squeezed out.

4. Allow the injector to rise, and then bottom it again. Set the indicator to zero. Again, allow the injector to rise, and bottom it. Make sure the indicator still reads zero.

5. Release the injector completely, and note the reading; .179-.182 is desirable.

6. After adjusting the cylinders listed by each "VS" mark on the vibration damper, turn the engine over to the next mark, adjust those cylinders as described above, and continue in this manner until all eight have been adjusted.

Valve set marks
(© Cummins Engine Co.)

Adjusting injector plunger
(© Cummins Engine Co.)

Injector and Valve Set Positions for V-504, V-555, VT-555 Series Engines					
Bar In Direction Of Rotation		Pulley Position		Set Cylinder	
		Old	New	Valve	Injector
Start		8 & 2 VS	B	—	5
Advance	To	1 & 6 VS	A	—	4
Advance	To	5 & 3 VS	C	5	8
Advance	To	4 & 7 VS	D	4	6
Advance	To	8 & 2 VS	B	8	3
Advance	To	1 & 6 VS	A	6	7
Advance	To	5 & 3 VS	C	3	2
Advance	To	4 & 7 VS	D	7	1
Advance	To	8 & 2 VS	B	2*	—
Advance	To	1 & 6 VS	A	1*	—

* denotes valves are to be set at end of sequence.

Injector and Valve Set Positions For the Left Hand V-8 Engine					
Bar in Direction Of Rotation		Pulley Position		Set Cylinder	
		Old	New	Valve	Injector
Start		2 & 8 V.S.	B	—	3
Advance	To	7 & 4 V.S.	D	—	6
"	"	3 & 5 V.S.	C	3	8
"	"	1 & 6 V.S.	A	6	4
"	"	2 & 8 V.S.	B	8	5
"	"	7 & 4 V.S.	D	4	1
"	"	3 & 5 V.S.	C	5	2
"	"	1 & 6 V.S.	A	1	7
"	"	2 & 8 V.S.	B	2	—
"	"	7 & 4 V.S.	D	7	—

Crosshead Adjustment

It is necessary to adjust the crossheads before making valve adjustments. Some crossheads pilot over a solid guide while others pilot within a tubular guide.
1. Loosen valve crosshead adjusting screw locknut and back off screw one turn.
2. Use light finger pressure at the rocker lever contact surface to hold crosshead in contact with valve stem nearest the push rod.
3. Turn adjusting screw down until it contacts its mating valve stem.
4. For new crossheads and guides, advance adjusting screw one-third of one hex (20 degrees) to straighten the stem in its guide and to compensate for slack in threads. With worn crossheads and guides, it may be necessary to advance the screw as much as 30 degrees in order to straighten the stem in its guide.
5. Hold the adjusting screw in this position and tighten locknut to 25/30 foot-pounds torque.
6. Check clearance between crosshead and valve spring retainer with wire gauge. There must be a minimum of .025 inch clearance at this point.

Valve Adjustment

1. Warm engine until oil temperature is 140-160 degrees F. For each two cylinders, turn the engine over and position it at the proper "VS" mark. If the rockers are not loose at this position, turn the engine another 360 degrees.
2. Adjust crossheads as described above.
3. Adjust valves in the standard manner, to the following clearances: Valve Clearance Setting in Inches

Engine Series	Intake	Exhaust
855/927 cid V6, V8 exc	.014	.027
903 cid	.010	.020
V-903 cid	.012	.025

NOTE: Adjust valves in firing order, except on small V6 and V8. On those engines, follow chart below.

Supercharger

Preliminary Inspection

Before disassembling the supercharger the following inspection procedures must be observed.
1. Check for excessive oil at the air outlet port indicating broken piston ring oil seals.
2. Check radial clearance in bearings:
   a. Remove pump-end cover and force fuel oil through the oil inlet to flush *all* lubricating oil from bearings.
   b. Install an indicator gauge on the rotor timing gear outer diameter.
   c. Check total radial movement by moving gear from side to side. If movement exceeds .003 inch, disassemble unit for a complete bearing inspection.
3. Check rotor shaft end play.
   a. Install a dial indicator at end of rotor shaft.
   b. Push shaft back and forth and note indicator reading.
   c. If total end play exceeds .005 inch, disassemble supercharger and inspect thrust faces.
   d. Perform this operation on both rotor shafts.
4. Check timing gear backlash.
   a. Install an indicator gauge to supercharger housing and check rotor timing gear backlash.
   b. If backlash exceeds .004 inch, a new set of gears must be installed.
5. Insert a feeler gauge into the inlet port between the housing and rotor lobe. Minimum clearance is .005 inch.
6. Check clearance between rotor lobes through the air inlet port. Minimum clearance is .006 inch.

If the preliminary inspection does not indicate any of the above wear

Adjusting valves
(© Cummins Engine Co.)

conditions, the supercharger may be reinstalled on the engine.

NOTE: Use a new gasket when replacing the pump-end cover.

If one or more of the above wear conditions are noted, disassemble the supercharger for a complete inspection or return to factory for a complete rebuild.

Disassembly of Supercharger

1. Raise the lockwasher flange clear of slot in the shaft nut and remove shaft nut with a shaft nut wrench.
2. Wedge a piece of soft metal between timing gear teeth to lock gears while loosening shaft nuts.
3. Remove shaft nut lockwashers from the rotor shafts and slide the outboard bearing journal from the drive rotor shaft. Remove expansion plugs if damaged.
4. Pull the water pump coupling half from the driven rotor shaft with a gear puller.
5. Remove capscrews and lock washers securing end cover and gasket. Discard gasket. Tap cover with a rubber mallet to loosen from housing dowels.
6. Remove capscrews and lockwires securing bearing cages to end plate. Remove bearing cages by rotating and prying.

Supercharger layout
(© Cummins Engine Co.)

7. Remove bearing cage seal rings and press bearings from bearing cages. *Mark bearing cages to assure replacement in identical position from which removed.*

8. If damaged, pry oil collector rings from end plate and remove dowels from end plate.

9. Remove capscrews from front end plate and remove end plate and rotor assembly from housing.

10. Remove oil pressure ferrules and "O" rings.

11. Press drive gear and timing gears from the rotors and end plate assembly and extract the rotors from the end plate assembly. NOTE: The rotors must be rotated into position so the lobe of the rotor being pressed out does not catch on the shaft of the other rotor.

12. Remove lockwires and capscrews securing bearing cages to the gear end plate.

13. Turn the bearing cages sufficiently to clear the end plate and pry them free. Remove shims and bearing cage seal rings from bearing cages and press out bearings. Mark bearing cages to assure identical replacement.

14. Remove thrust washers from the gear end plate.

15. Remove oil collector rings and dowels, if damaged.

16. Remove and discard all shaft seal rings.

Inspection

1. Clean all parts in approved cleaning solvent.

2. Check housing for cracks, nicks, obstructed oil passages and stripped threads. Remove nicks or scratches with a handstone. Be sure all mating surfaces are smooth.

3. Inspect rotors for undue wear, burrs, pits, scratches, or other damage. Check threaded ends, shoulders, spline bearing surfaces, and seal ring grooves for wear. Small burrs and imperfections on the rotor lobes can be dressed down with a handstone. If the lobe surfaces or rotor shafts are badly scored or damaged, discard rotor set.

4. Inspect timing gears, drive gear and all gear hubs for cracks and broken or worn teeth, damaged splines and excessive wear. CAUTION: Rotors, timing gears and the driven gear are not interchangeable. If one of these components is worn or damaged, it must be replaced as part of a complete set of rotors and gears. Do not attempt to replace a single component that is not a part of the original or a completely new set.

5. Examine end plates for cracks or damaged seal ring bores. Check for snug dowel fits. Ex-

.003 MAXIMUM RADIAL MOVEMENT

Checking radial bearing clearance
(© Cummins Engine Co.)

END PLATE PUMP END OIL PRESSURE LINE SEAL RING END PLATE GEAR END
PISTON RING OIL SEALS THRUST WASHER SHIMS BEARING CAGE
WATER PUMP COUPLING
END COVER
BEARING CAGE SEAL RING
COVER GASKET OIL DRAIN LINE SEAL RING
LOCKNUTS
BEARING JOURNAL
DRIVE GEAR
ROTOR TIMING GEAR

Supercharger—cross section
(© Cummins Engine Co.)

Checking end play
(© Cummins Engine Co.)

Checking gear backlash
(© Cummins Engine Co.)

cessive wear and roughness in the seal ring bores will not allow the seal rings to seat properly, thus the end plates must be discarded and replaced with new parts.

6. Check end cover for cracks. End cover *must* have a smooth mating surface.

7. Inspect bearing cages for cracks or excessive wear. Discard defective bearing cages. Bearing cage assemblies are also available in .010 and .020 inch *under-size*.

8. Inspect bearings for scratches or scoring. Check bearing bores with inside micrometers. If bore exceeds 1.3765 inch, discard bearings.

9. Examine thrust washers for burrs, cracks and wear. Discard damaged or worn thrust washers.

10. Check outboard bearing journal for nicks, scoring or excessive wear.

11. Inspect water pump drive coupling half for excessive wear.

12. Check end thrust by measuring bearing cage width and distance from thrust face of gear to end of gear hub. Bearing cage width must be .002/.005 inch less than length of gear hub. If difference between these dimensions is greater than .005 inch, install new gears, thrust washers, and bearing cages.

Assembly of Supercharger

1. Use new shaft nut lockwashers, expansion plugs, seal rings, oil collector rings and gaskets during reassembly.

2. Install shaft seal rings on new rotors.

3. Install new bearing cage seal rings on bearing cages.

4. Press bearings into bearing cages and oil collector rings into end plates. Press in new end plate dowels, if removed.

5. Install oil pressure ferrules, drain ferrules and ferrule seal rings in housing.

6. Position thrust washers, shims, and bearing cages into gear end plate; secure with capscrews and lockwires. NOTE: If old bearing cages are reused, replace in same hole from which removed. Use same shims as originally removed from respective cages. Use .005 inch total shim thickness under each bearing cage. Shim thickness may have to be adjusted when rotor end clearance is checked.

7. Press water pump coupling on the driven rotor shaft extension so that the shaft end is flush with the water pump coupling counterbore.

8. Lubricate the gear end plate seal ring seats and bearings with clean, light engine oil and insert splined shaft end of drive rotor in the bottom hole in the gear end plate. NOTE: Do not damage seal rings while pressing into gear end plate.

9. Position timing gear on drive rotor shaft and press into position.

10. Insert driven rotor shaft through the second hole in the gear end plate and press on timing gear making sure rotors are positioned *exactly* 90° apart as the timing gears mesh.

11. Press drive gear on drive rotor shaft snugly against timing gear and install outboard bearing journal on drive rotor shaft.

12. Install shaft nut lockwashers and shaft nuts on the rotor shaft and tighten securely. Wedge a piece of soft metal or rag between the gear teeth to lock gears while tightening locknuts.

13. Position the expansion plugs on locknuts and tap into place.

14. Push rotors towards gear end plate and check end clearance. End clearance should be .003/.004 inch. Add or remove

Installing idler leaf springs
(© Cummins Engine Co.)

Assembling supercharger idler gears
(© Cummins Engine Co.)

Checking rotor end clearance
(© Cummins Engine Co.)

Removing rotor shaft locknuts
(© Cummins Engine Co.)

Cummins Diesel Engines

Supercharger idler gear and hub layout
(© Cummins Engine Co.)

shims under bearing cage mounting flange to obtain correct end clearance. If shims must be changed, remove locknuts and gears as described in disassembly instructions.

15. Position housing over rotors against end plate and secure with lockwashers and capscrews.
16. Lubricate bearings and seal rings in end plate and position end plate to housing. *Do not damage shaft seal rings.* Tap into place.
17. Position end cover and new gasket to end plate; secure with lockwashers and capscrews.
18. Turn drive gear by hand to check for smooth, free operation.

Supercharger Idler Gear Assembly

It should not be necessary to rebuild this unit unless it has become noisy or loose, thus indicating broken leaf springs or worn bushings.

If disassembly is necessary, proceed as follows:
1. Remove capscrews and idler drive hub, blower gear, thrust washer, and spring retaining cover from assembly.
2. Carefully pry and remove idler leaf springs, 4 spring retaining rings, and separate idler driven gear from spring retainer.

Repair
1. Replace all broken or damaged idler leaf springs.
2. Check two supercharger idler gear bushings and three idler hub bushings.
   a. New idler gear bushings are 1.501/1.500 inside diameter, bushings pressed in place.
   b. New idler hub bushings are 1.501/1.500 inside diameter, idler bushings pressed in place.
   c. Idler gear shaft is 1.4985/1.4975 outside diameter.
3. Check thrust washer for wear. Replace as needed.

Assembly
1. Place spring retainer over idler

Supercharger mounting fixture
(© Cummins Engine Co.)

driven gear cam and drive idler leaf springs and four pins in place. CAUTION: Idler leaf springs are made from spring steel and will cause a serious injury if allowed to fly loose as they are forced between gear cam and spring retainer.
2. Assemble thrust washer to idler gear hub.
3. Mount retainer plate, blower gear and idler gear hub and fasten with six capscrews.
4. Peen capscrews in place.

Gear Train
1. Check all drive and driven gears, crankshaft, camshaft, and idler gears for cracks, chipping or signs of wear.
2. Replace all gears showing visible deep wear pattern or other tooth damage.
NOTE: The extent of gear wear can be determined by checking gear backlash after all gears are assembled.

Gear Case Cover

Disassembly
1. Remove crankshaft oil seal and fuel pump and compressor drive oil seal.
2. Remove bearing race at fuel pump drive, if used.

Inspection and Repair
1. Check bearings, if used; replace

if rough or worn. This is a two piece bearing, one-half remains on drive shaft with outer race only in gear cover.
2. Check fuel pump and compressor drive shaft bushing in cover. If replacement is necessary knock out old bushing and press in new one with suitable driver.
3. A replaceable steel trunnion bushing, may be used to repair worn trunnions. To use bushing:
   a. Machine gear case trunnion to 4.747/4.750 inches outer diameter.
   b. Press bushing over machined trunnion with chamfered side of bushing toward gear case cover.

Assembly
Do not install oil seals until gear case cover is ready to be installed on engine.

Turbocharger

The information listed below covers procedures for cleaning turbocharger compressor wheels and checking bearing clearances.

T-35 and T-50 Turbochargers

Disassembly of Turbocharger
1. Clean the turbocharger exterior, and mark compressor casing, turbine casing, bearing housing and clamps to facilitate assembly.
2. Remove fittings from the lube oil inlet and outlet ports.
3. Unbolt turbocharger V-clamps, discarding nuts, washers, and bolts. Remove V-clamps.
4. Remove compressor casing and O-ring from bearing housing, and discard O-ring.
5. Remove the turbine casing from the bearing housing. If necessary, the turbine casing may be pressed off by supporting the casing at the center, and putting pressure on the turbine end of the shaft, while heating the tur-

Removing front cover plate
(© Cummins Engine Co.)

586

Removing compressor wheel

Installing sealing ring

Installing compressor wheel

bine casing evenly with a torch. Be careful not to drop the bearing housing assembly.

6. Place the bearing housing and rotor assembly on a press, supporting the housing in a specially designed bearing support. Put cardboard or soft wood under the support. Press the rotor shaft through the compressor wheel, using a rod small enough to enter the bore of the wheel. Be careful not to drop any parts.

7. Remove the compressor wheel from the housing. On T-50, remove the heat shield and insulation pad from the rotor shaft. Discard the insulation pad if it is damaged.

8. Seat a soft mandrel against the floating bearing, and drive the oil seal plate from the bearing housing.

9. Remove the oil seal plate from the bearing housing, and remove the seal plate O-ring, and discard it.

10. On T-35, remove the thrust washer and floating bearing from the bearing housing. On T-50, remove the floating bearing and Teflon insert, and discard the insert. Discard the thrust washer if it is scored.

11. Remove the sealing rings from the grooves in the rotor shaft, and discard them.

Cleaning

1. Immerse parts, so they do not touch each other, in a carburetor solvent that *will not damage aluminum, or Ni-Resist alloys*. A soft brush may be used to help remove carbon.

2. Flush out oil passages in the bearing housing from the drain end, to remove dirt loosened by the solvent.

3. Continue to soak parts for at least 12 hours, and as long as 24 hours if possible. Then, repeat the flushing of oil passages.

4. Steam clean all parts, especially oil passages. Dry with compressed air.

Inspection

Inspect all parts for cracks, burning, distortion, scoring, burrs, chips, etc. If compressor or turbine wheels have rubbed the casing, they must be replaced, although the casing can be cleaned up if the scratches are light.

Make the specific checks of various dimensions listed below. Figures are in inches.

1. Measure the sealing ring and bearing bores in the bearing housing. Limits are 3.527-3.533 for the T-35, and 5.049-5.055 for the T-50.

3. On T-35, check distance from oil seal plate stop to turbine stop on casing surface.
T-35   2.239-2.241

4. On T-50 make the measurement from the compressor stop to the bearing stop.
T-50   2.989-2.992

5. Check bearing flange for wear:

	Thickness	Width
T-35	.199-.201	1.97-2.00
T-50	.138-.142	1.920-1.950

6. Check bearing dimensions:

	I.D.	O.D.
T-35	.533-.5335	.873-.874
T-50	.752-.7525	1.272-1.273

Assembly

1. Hold thrust washer on shoulder of shaft with a piece of tubing. Check floating bearing end clearance on slaft.
T-35   —   .001-.007

2. Position sealing ring in groove on turbine end of rotor shaft.

3. Lubricate bearing housing bore on T-50 and install insulation pad, heat shield and insert rotor shaft in housing.

4. Lubricate rotor shaft and floating bearing. Insert floating bearing over shaft and into bearing housing bore. On T-50, position Teflon bearing insert over flange of floating bearing.

5. On T-35 position new thrust washer over turbine shaft with lapped side toward compressor end of shaft and against floating bearing flange. Align mark on thrust washer with balance mark on end of rotor shaft. Balance mark on washer must face outward.

6. Lubricate oil seal bores and insert sealing sleeve assembly.

7. Lubricate and install new O-ring housing with vaseline and place in seal plate. Coat bearing bore oil seal plate over shaft. Align so that retainer of oil seal plate straddles sides of floating bearing flange. Push oil seal plate in bearing housing until plate seats on shoulder. Stops on oil seal plate should be turned so they seal on bearing flange 90° from disassembled position.

CAUTION: On T-35, check alignment mark of thrust washer with mark on end of rotor shaft before installing sleeve.

8. Support rotor and position assembly in a press.

9. Lubricate rotor shaft and position compressor wheel on shaft. On T-35, align the balance mark of compressor wheel with balance mark on shaft end. Press wheel onto shaft down to shoulder. A clearance of .0007" is acceptable on T-50.

10. On T-35, install self-locking nut on shaft. Tighten to 120-130 in. lb.

11. On T-50, install self-locking nut on shaft. Tighten to 20-24 ft. lb.

12. Coat turbine casing bore with anti-seige compound. Insert bearing housing and rotor in bore. Align scribed marks. Assembly seats on shoulders.

13. Install new O-ring in bearing housing and coat lightly with engine oil.

14. Position compressor casing over bearing and shaft. Align marks.

15. Position V-bands around casings. Center V-band openings over oil supply and drain ports. Secure bands; torque nuts to 30 in. lb. It is helpful to tap V-

Checking bearing clearance
(© Cummins Engine Co.)

bands while torquing nuts. Clearance between V-band clamp and casing should be .035″ MIN. *CAUTION:* Do not over-torque or re-tighten clamp.

16. Check radial clearance at turbine end and compressor end by:
    a. Push shaft toward side of bore.
    b. Check minimum distance between tip of vanes & bore.

	Compressor end	Turbine end
T-35	.0011-.0409	.0023-.0397
T-50	.005-.033	.011-.043

17. Check total end clearance with a dial indicator.

T-35	-.004-.015
T-50	-.006-.017

18. Turn rotor by hand to check for interference.

T-506 Turbocharger

Currently, T-506 turbochargers utilize a universal main casing which can be rotated 360° to simplify mounting arrangement and facilitate positioning oil drain.

Formerly, a stationary front cover was used.

1. Clean exterior of turbocharger.
2. Attach turbocharger to Assembly Stand.

Cleaning and Inspection

1. Clean compressor wheel.
   a. Use Bendix cleaner or equivalent; NEVER use a caustic solution which will attack aluminum.
   b. Use nylon or hog bristle brush; NEVER use wire brush.
   c. Immerse compressor wheel end in cleaning solution.
   d. Dry thoroughly with compressed air.
2. Check bearing clearances. Use a dial indicator to indicate side and end-play of rotor shaft. Check as follows:
   a. Fasten a dial indicator to turbine casing.
   b. Place indicator point against hub of turbine wheel.

c. Force turbine wheel up and down, or sideways; note total indicator reading.
   d. Remove one capscrew from front plate (compressor wheel end) and replace with a long stud bolt.
3. Remove capscrews and lock-plates from exhaust casing on turbine end; remove universal main casing or front cover plate.
   e. Attach an indicator to long stud bolt and register indicator point against flat on end of rotor shaft.
   f. Push shaft sideways, noting total indicator reading.
   g. Move indicator point to end of shaft.
   h. Check end-play of rotor assembly.
   i. Compare readings with limits shown in following table.

Type	Min. Radial Clearance	Rotor End Play
T-506	.008	.003/.011
T-350	.0135	.003/.008

If radial or end clearance exceeds the maximum limits, send turbocharger to a factory approved rebuild station for bearing replacement.

T-350 Turbocharger

Disassembly of Turbocharger

Before disassembling, clean exterior thoroughly. Mark housing position with a scribe mark.

1. Attach turbocharger to Assembly Stand.
2. Remove capscrews and lock-plates from the exhaust outlet connection. Remove connection and gasket.
3. Remove capscrews, lockwashers and flatwashers from bearing housing to compressor casing. Lift off compressor casing.
4. Remove capscrews and lock-plates from the bearing or main housing to turbine casing. Lift bearing housing assembly from turbine casing.

Cleaning

1. Immerse parts in Turco Super-Carb or similar solvent. CAUTION: Never use a caustic solution or solvent that may attack aluminum, stellite or ni-resist alloys.
2. Allow parts to soak to remove carbon. A soft bristle brush may be used to remove heavy deposits. *Never use wire or stiff bristle brush.*
3. Steam clean thoroughly to remove all carbon and grease. Apply steam liberally to oil passages in the bearing housing.
4. Blow off excess water and dry with compressed air.

Cleaning aneroid control air filter
(© Cummins Engine Co.)

Inspection and Assembly of Turbocharger

1. Place a new "O" ring on compressor end of bearing housing and coat with oil.
2. Install compressor casing aligning scribe marks made at disassembly.
3. Check impeller radial clearance between impeller vanes and compressor casing. Impeller wheel must be pushed to side and minimum clearance checked. See Table for clearance.
4. Check turbine wheel radial clearance between turbine wheel vanes and turbine casing. Turbine wheel must be pushed to side and minimum clearance checked. It should be .0135.
5. Use a dial indicator and check rotor end play. See Table for end play.
6. Turn rotor by hand to be sure no internal interference is present.
7. Install pipe fittings in bearing housing as required.
8. Install exhaust connection using Never-Seez anti-gall compound on the capscrew threads.
9. Cover all inlets and outlets to prevent dirt entry.

Aneroid Control

Cleaning and Lubrication

1. Clean air filter assembly by reverse flushing with compressed air.
2. Fill aneroid control cavity with clean lubricating oil.

Fuel Pressure Setting

1. Attach a pressure gauge into the injector supply line.
2. Operate engine until oil is 140 F.
3. Disconnect the air line between aneroid bellows and intake manifold.
4. Operate engine at full throttle at BHP setting speed and adjust bottom screw in aneroid until fuel pressure is reduced as needed for the particular altitude.

①	DELCOTRON	⑤	AMMETER	
②	BAT.	⑥	LOAD RHEOSTAT	
③	JUMPER LEAD	⑦	BATTERY	
④	GRD.	⑧	VOLTMETER	

Alternator Output—Bench Test
(© Cummins Engine Co.)

① STEEL FRAME MEMBER
② BODY GROUNDED TO ENGINE
③ GENERATOR
④ CUTOUT RELAY
⑤ AMMETER
⑥ BATTERY
⑦ CLAMP
⑧ TINNED

Basic Generator Wiring Cut-Out Relay
(© Cummins Engine Co.)

Alternator

Self-rectifying A.C. generators are designed and constructed to give long periods of trouble-free service with a minimum amount of maintenance. The rotor is mounted on ball bearings, and each bearing has a grease reservoir which eliminates the need of periodic lubrication. Only two brushes are required to carry current through the two slip rings to the field coils which are wound on the four pole rotor. The brushes are extra long and under normal operating conditions will provide long periods of service.

The stator windings are assembled on the inside of a laminated core that forms the generator frame. Six rectifier diodes are mounted in the slip ring end frame, and are connected to the stator windings through connectors mounted internally in two nylon holders, or a separately mounted rectifier, and they act to change the generator A.C. voltages to a D.C. voltage which appears at the "BAT" terminal on the generator.

Even though the generator is constructed to give long periods of trouble-free service, a regular inspection procedure should be followed to obtain the maximum life from the generator.

Inspect the generator as follows:

1. Inspect the terminals for corrosion and looseness.
2. Inspect the wiring for frayed insulation.
3. Check mounting bolts for proper tension.
4. Inspect the belt for excessive wear and replace if necessary.
5. Check belt tension and alignment.
6. Inspect slip rings and brushes through the end frame assembly. If the slip rings are dirty, clean them up with a 400 grain or finer polishing cloth. To clean, hold the cloth on the rings with engine turning alternator rotor. Blow dust away thoroughly. Rings that are worn or out of round must be trued on a lathe. Brushes worn close to the holder must be replaced.
7. Check the output of the alternator on a test bench, making electrical connections as shown in the illustration. Operate it at the specified speed and check for specified output, adjusting the field rheostat as necessary.

Alternator Safety Precautions

1. Make sure that type, polarity, and part numbers of alternator and regulator are matched according to manufacturer's specifications before installation.
2. Make sure battery and alternator polarity are correct (+to + and − to −). Make sure polarity is correct when installing a booster battery, also.
3. Never operate an alternator when the circuit is open (without a load).
4. Never attempt to polarize an alternator.

Generator

The shunt generator converts mechanical energy to electrical energy, supplying current for electrical equipment by replacing electricity consumed from the battery.

The shunt generator requires external current regulation in the form of a current regulator, voltage regulator, and cut-off relay, which control generator output under all operating conditions.

If the generator produces no output, check for sticking brushes, a gummed or burned commutator, or weakened brush springs. If output is low, check for sticking brushes, low spring tension, or a rough, out of round, dirty, or burned commutator. If necessary, turn down the commu-

Basic generator wiring cut-out relay
(© Cummins Engine Co.)

Basic generator wiring-leece-neville
(© Cummins Engine Co.)

Removing belt driven generator
(© Cummins Engine Co.)

tator in a lathe, and undercut mica if the unit has carbon brushes.

If the generator's output is excessive, the problem is that the field circuit is grounded or the field is shorted. If terminal insulation is not defective, the problem is internal.

Removal

1. Disconnect wiring leads from generator.
2. On belt driven models, remove drive belt. On some C and J models it may be necessary to disconnect No. 1 cylinder injector inlet and drain manifolds to remove generator.
3. Remove belts from generator bracket and lift off generator and bracket.
4. Remove bracket from generator.

Installation

1. Mount bracket to generator, checking that the bracket is mounted to generator so that oil cup and passages are in proper position.
2. On gear driven generators, install rubber buffer between generator coupling and drive coupling and connect the two units.
3. Mount generator and bracket to block.
4. On belt driven models, install drive belt.
5. Connect generator wiring leads to proper terminals.

Leece neville current and voltage regulator wiring
(© Cummins Engine Co.)

Alternator output—bench test
(© Cummins Engine Co.)

Starter Motors

Air Starter

An improved air starting system with increased starting motor torque is now used on current production engines without increasing required air pressure above 120 psi. The air piping system reduces the drive torque engagement of starter drives and flywheel ring gears, therefore, improving service life.

A specially hardened flywheel ring gear is now used and is available for service. On all new installations make sure the letter "W" appears on the ring gear near the part number. This indicates the ring gear is especially hardened.

Air Starter Removal

1. Relieve air system before disconnecting air supply to starter.
2. Depress starter handle to bleed off air in starter.
3. Disconnect main union between starter handle and motor.
4. Unbolt starter from flywheel housing.
5. Support starter and slide it back to disengage starter drive from flywheel ring gear.

Installation

1. Start one capscrew in mounting flange to hold starter during installation.
2. Some applications use a spacer between mounting flange and flywheel housing. Be certain spacer is in place.
3. Slide starter into flywheel housing opening, engaging the drive with flywheel ring gear.
4. Install remaining mounting bolts and tighten securely.
5. Connect air supply line to starter.

Electric Starter

The starter motor used on Cummins engines is a special overload motor capable of delivering high horsepower. In order to obtain this power, it is necessary to build the cranking motor with a minimum of resistance so a large current will be taken through it. The starter motor should be used for short periods only—30 seconds maximum to avoid the possibility of burning out.

Troubleshooting Cranking Motor Problems

1. If cranking is poor, turn on headlights and close starter switch. If lights go out, the problem is most likely a bad connection, while if they dim but still burn, the battery is run down or the starter or engine is mechanically defective. If the lights do not dim at all, the cranking motor or switch may be open.
2. To make a more thorough analysis, check the specific gravity of each battery cell, and, if gravities are satisfactory, check the battery connections and cables and cranking motor switch. If supply of current to the motor is satisfactory, inspect the brushes and commutator. The brushes should contact the commutator snugly, and the commutator should be clean and smooth. Remove the unit for turning down of the commutator or further testing and examination if required.

Removal

1. Disconnect battery cable and all electrical leads from starter.
2. Unbolt and remove starter motor and spacer (if used).

Installation

1. Before installation starter should be checked for type used. There are several different type drives used that must be matched with flywheel ring gears.
2. Place the spacer (if used) on starter.
3. Install starter to flywheel mounting bolts and tighten securely.

Series parallel switch cross section
(© Cummins Engine Co.)

Ingersoll rand air starter piping
(© Cummins Engine Co.)

Bendix westinghouse air starter piping
(© Cummins Engine Co.)

4. Connect wires and cables to starter and battery.

Starter Motor Controls

1. Because of extremely high current flow during cranking, a positive means of connecting and disconnecting the battery and cranking motor must be used. The switch used must have contacts heavy enough to carry the current without burning. A manually operated switch mounted on the floor board or cranking motor frame is the simplest type.
2. Some applications with Bendix drive use a magnetic switch which when energized draws in a plunger and causes a contact disc to make contact between two terminals to complete the circuit from the battery to cranking motor. The magnetic switch winding is usually energized by a push button.
3. Some applications with the overrunning clutch, or Dyer type drive, use a somewhat larger magnetic switch called a solenoid switch. Here, the plunger not only thrusts against a contact disc to close the battery-to-cranking motor circuit, but is also linked to the shift lever so that the drive pinion is shifted into mesh with the flywheel teeth by the solenoid action.
4. Cummins engines require a comparatively high voltage to assure adequate cranking. The series-parallel system is designed to provide a means of connecting two batteries in series to provide increased voltage for cranking, and reconnecting the two batteries in parallel for normal operation of electrical equipment after starting has been accomplished.

Friction Clutch Type Bendix Drive

This type of drive performs in much the same manner as other Bendix drives except it uses a series of spring-loaded clutch plates which slip momentarily during the shock of engagement to relieve the shock and prevent it from being carried back through the cranking motor. The slipping stops as engagement is completed so that cranking torque is transmitted from the cranking motor armature through the drive pinion to the flywheel ring gear.

Overrunning Clutch Drive

1. The overrunning clutch is designed to provide positive meshing and disengagement of the drive pinion and flywheel ring gear. It uses a shift lever which slides the clutch and drive pinion assembly along the armature shaft so it can be meshed and disengaged as required. The clutch transmits cranking torque from cranking motor to the engine flywheel but permits the drive pinion to overrun, or run faster than, the armature after the engine is started. This protects the armature from excessive speed during the brief interval that the drive pinion remains in mesh.
2. The overrunning clutch consists of a shell and sleeve assembly which is splined internally to match splines on the armature shaft. Thus, both the shell and sleeve assembly and armature shaft must turn together. A pinion and collar assembly fit loosely into the shell, and the collar is in contact with four matched steel rollers which are assembled into notches cut in the inner face of the shell. These notches taper inward slightly so that there is less room in the end away from the rollers than in the end with the rollers. The rollers are spring loaded by small plungers.
3. When the shift lever is operated, the clutch assembly is moved endways along the armature shaft so the pinion meshes with the flywheel ring gear. If the teeth should butt instead of mesh, the clutch spring compresses so the pinion is spring loaded against the ring-gear teeth. When the armature begins to rotate, meshing takes place at once. Completion of the shift lever movement closes the cranking motor switch so the armature begins to rotate so.
4. When the engine begins to operate, it attempts to drive the cranking motor armature through the pinion, faster than the armature is rotating. This causes the pinion to rotate with respect to the shell so that it overruns the shell and armature. The rollers are turned back toward the larger section of the shell notches where they are free, and thus, permit, the pinion to overrun. This protects the armature until the automatic controls take over so that the shift lever is released, causing the shift lever spring to pull the overrunning clutch drive pinion out of mesh from the engine flywheel ring gear. This shift lever movement also opens the cranking motor switch so that the armature stops rotating.
5. The overrunning clutch pinion requires the same ring gear as the Bendix pinion.

Series-Parallel Switch

The series-parallel switch makes it possible to use two 12-volt batteries which are connected in parallel for normal operating conditions after the engine is started, but which are connected in series by means of the series-parallel switch to provide 24 volts for the cranking motor. Likewise, two 6-volt batteries can be connected either in parallel or in series to provide a 6-12 volt system.

The switch uses a heavy copper contact disk and heavy tungsten-faced main terminals, which resist the effects of the arcs that occur when the circuits are broken. The main cranking current is carried

591

through these contacts and terminals. In addition, there are contacts in the terminal plate assembly which complete the parallel connections between the batteries for normal operation and also complete the connections that energize the cranking motor solenoid in the cranking position.

After cranking has been accomplished and the series-parallel switch is released, the two batteries again become connected in parallel to provide 12-volt operation of the equipment. In the mechanically operated switch a quick-break mechanism, consisting of a pair of triggers and a cam, causes the contact disk to be snapped away from the stationary contacts very quickly so that there is a very small amount of arcing.

Due to the high voltage of the starting circuit and the great amount of power available from the two batteries, it is essential that every precaution be taken to avoid short circuits or grounds. All wires should be of sufficient size to carry the electrical load to which they are subjected without overheating. Stranded wire and cable should be used throughout to reduce the possibility of breakage because of vibration. All connections should be clean and tight and all terminal clips should be soldered to the wires or cables. Only rosin flux should be used to solder electrical connections. All wires should be adequately insulated and supported at enough points to prevent movement and consequent chafing through of the insulation. Rubber boots, rubber tape or friction tape and shellac should be applied to cover all exposed terminals and clips. This will prevent accidental grounding of an exposed terminal which could cause serious damage to the system.

Cooling System

Water Pump Removal

855, 927 Cid Engines

1. Drain the cooling system.
2. Remove the fan. Remove the alternator drive belt.
3. Remove the water pump retaining ring capscrews, and disengage the water pump drive belts. Remove the retaining ring and water pump body. Remove and

discard the gasket. *On some engines, the fan hub bracket is an integral part of the water pump retaining ring.*

Installation

855, 927 Cid Engines

1. Clean the gasket surfaces on the engine and the water pump.
2. Position the retaining ring and a new copper gasket on the pump. Position the pump in the engine block, and install, but do not tighten, the pump retaining ring bolts.
3. Install the alternator and water pump drive belts on the water pump pulley. Tighten the water pump drive belt and tighten the pump retaining ring bolts alternately starting on side away from belts.
4. Place the alternator drive belt on the alternator pulley and adjust. Tighten the alternator adjusting arm and mounting bolts.
5. Install the fan.
6. Fill and bleed the cooling system. Operate the engine and check for coolant leaks.

Water Pump Removal

V-6 & V-8 Engines

1. Drain the cooling system.
2. Remove the alternator drive belt. Loosen the fan drive belt adjusting screw, and remove the drive belts from the fan and water pump pulleys.
3. Loosen the radiator lower hose at the water pump. Loosen the hose clamps on the by-pass hose connecting the water pump to the thermostat housing. Disconnect the heater and corrosion resistor hoses at the water pump.
4. Disconnect the temperature and warning light sending unit leads at the sending units on the thermostat housing. Disconnect the radiator upper hose and the radiator supply tank vent line at the thermostat housing. *Leave the heater hose and shutterstat air hoses connected.*
5. Remove the thermostat housing from the cylinder head and position it out of the way.
6. Remove the water pump from the engine and radiator lower hose. Discard the pump gasket.

Installation

V-6 & V-8 Engines

1. Clean the gasket surfaces of the thermostat housing, water pump, cylinder head and cylinder block.
2. Apply water-resistant sealer to a new water pump gasket and position it on the water pump housing. Insert the water pump lower elbow in the radiator lower hose, and install the water pump on the engine block. Torque the pump attaching screws to specifications.
3. Use water-resistant sealer and position a new thermostat housing gasket on the cylinder head. Install the thermostat housing; be sure the thermostat housing to water pump by-pass hose and clamps are in place. Tighten the by-pass hose clamps and the mounting bolts.
4. Connect the radiator upper hose and the radiator supply tank vent line to the thermostat housing. Connect the temperature and warning light sending unit leads.
5. Connect the heater and corrosion resistor hoses to the water pump. Tighten the radiator lower hose clamp.
6. Install the fan and water pump drive belts and the alternator drive belt.
7. Fill and bleed the cooling system. Operate the engine and check for coolant leaks.

1150 cid Engines

1. Close valve above water filter, remove and discard filter.
   NOTE: Valve is closed when plunger is down and locked.
2. Remove tube assembly connecting water pump to cooler housing.
3. Remove by-pass tube between pump and thermostat.
4. Unbolt pump and pull straight back, parallel with engine to remove.
5. Install in reverse of above.

Water Pump—Overhaul

Supercharger Driven

Disassembly

1. Remove mounting capscrews, lockwashers, gasket and cover from water pump body.
2. Pull drive coupling from shaft.
3. Remove outer snap-ring from coupling end of pump body.
4. Support pump body on its mounting flange in an arbor press and press out bearing and shaft assembly from impeller and pump housing.
5. Press shaft seal out of pump body.

COVER · GASKET · IMPELLER · SEAL · SLINGER · BODY · SNAP RING · SHAFT AND BEARING · SNAP RING · COUPLING · GASKET

Supercharger driven water pump
(© Cummins Engine Co.)

PULLEY SHEEVE
PULLEY
BEARING
BEARING
SNAP RING
CARBON FACE SEAL
SPACER
IMPELLER
DRIVE SHAFT
BODY
COVER
GASKET
GASKET
INLET CONNECTION

Belt driven water pump
(© Cummins Engine Co.)

5. Support pump on shaft and install slinger over shaft until flange is 1.805/1.825 from end of shaft.
6. Apply sealer to the bottom side or seat of seal driving flange.
7. Press seal in place, apply force on driving lip only. Check carbon for damage before going further.
8. Clean seal with lint free cloth to remove dirt, oil or grease.
9. Press impeller on shaft. Face of impeller hub should be .872/.878 inch below cover mounting face on body. CAUTION: Use extreme care when pressing impeller to prevent damaging ceramic seal.
10. Assemble lockwashers, capscrews and new gasket to water pump cover.
11. Mount cover to pump body and turn shaft to be sure that it is free.

Thermostats

1. Using new gasket, install new or tested thermostat in thermostat housing. NOTE: If thermostat with "V" notch is used, plug vent hole in thermostat housing.
2. If water-cooled turbocharger is used, install new "O" ring on water by-pass coupling.
3. Install thermostat with vent hole *at top.* Failure to do so may result in air lock and incomplete coolant circulation.
4. Install thermostat housing with washers and capscrews.
5. Connect air compressor and turbocharger water outlet lines, if used.
6. Connect water outlet hose. NOTE: The by-pass to water pump hose connection on supercharged engines must be assembled with a shield to protect it from exhaust manifold heat. Four cylinder engines use a small thermostat. Always replace same type thermostat as removed.

Water Pump Overhaul
V-6 and V-8 (470 and 504)

Disassembly

1. Pull the impeller from the shaft with a suitable puller.
2. If there is a grease fitting in the end of the shaft, remove it. Remove the drive pulley with a suitable puller.
3. Remove the large pump housing snap ring with snap ring pliers.
4. Press on the impeller end of the shaft and remove the assembly from the pump body. Remove the rubber boot/ceramic seal from the shaft and discard it, if the pump is so equipped.

6. Remove inner snap-ring from housing.

Inspection

1. Inspect water pump bearing(s). Replace bearing(s) with rough or worn races.
2. Inspect water pump impeller. Replace if cracked or corroded to extent that it will interfere with circulation.
3. Measure impeller bore and shaft outer diameter. There must be a minimum of .0015 inch press-fit between shaft and impeller; replace if necessary.
4. Inspect water pump body seal face.
5. Inspect water pump mounting parts for cracks. Replace as necessary.
6. Examine carbon seal carefully to make sure it is not cracked or chipped.
7. Inspect ceramic seat.

Replacing Ceramic Seat

1. Strike damaged seat with a sharp tool perpendicular to axis of impeller.
2. Scrape adhesive from counterbore, be careful not to damage counterbore surface.
3. Check counterbore of impeller. It must be 1.042/1.046 in diameter and square to the axis of .624/.625 inch bore and within .002 inch total indicator runout.
4. Wash and de-grease impeller in an approved cleaning solvent and air dry. *The bore must be chemically clean to insure a good strong water tight bond.*
5. Apply Bonding Film in counterbore. Care must be used to prevent contamination of film by dust, dirt, oil, moisture or finger-

prints or use of film more than six months old.
6. Remove bonding film liner, it may be necessary to pick liner to start separation.
7. Place ceramic seat in counterbore with identification mark (dimple) against adhesive. Rotate seat to insure a continuous bond.
8. Apply a 15 pound weight on ceramic seat and place assembly in temperature controlled oven at 345°/355°F. for 55 to 65 minutes. NOTE: The temperature and time must be closely controlled to obtain proper bond.
9. Check ceramic seat after curing for squareness to the axis of the .625/.625 inch bore. It must be within .004 inch total indicator reading. Check for scratches, holes, chips or cracks. All unusable parts must be discarded and usable assemblies protected against further damage.

Assembly

1. Install inner snap-ring.
2. Support pump body on its cover mounting face and press bearing and shaft assembly in place against inner snap-ring. When pressing bearings onto shaft, apply load on bearing inner race only.
3. Install outer snap-ring. NOTE: Current production water pump bodies are machined for beveled snap-rings. Older models use flat snap-rings. Use correct body and snap-ring combination. Flat and beveled snap-rings are not interchangeable.
4. Press drive coupling onto shaft and flush with end of shaft.

Removing Impeller
(© Cummins Engine Co.)

5. If the bearing is still in the pump body, press it out.
6. Remove the carbon face seal from the pump body. Remove the flinger from the shaft. Then, remove the shaft from the large bearing, pressing on the inner race of the bearing. If the assembly uses a double row bearing and spacer, use a suitable puller to pull the spacer and bearing from the shaft.
7. Remove the small snap ring from the shaft.
8. Press the single row bearing, if the assembly is so equipped, from the shaft over the pulley end, pressing on the inner race as much as possible.

Inspection
1. Inspect the water pump bearings and replace if they do not appear to be capable of lasting until the next overhaul.
2. Inspect the impeller, and replace if cracking or corrosion will interfere with circulation.
3. Measure impeller bore and shaft outside diameter for proper fit. There must be a minimun .001" press fit between them.
4. Inspect the pump mounts for cracks, and replace as necessary.
5. Examine the carbon face seal for cracks or chipping. Replace if necessary. If the seat requires replacement, it is recommended that the impeller be machined to permit installation.

Assembly
1. Lightly lubricate the pump shaft with clean engine oil.
2. Press the bearing onto the shaft, shielded side toward impeller, until the inner race seats against the shoulder.
3. Apply sealant to the inside diameter of the pump housing at the small bearing seat.
4. Fill the cavity of the bore about 60% with an approved grease.
5. Press the shaft and small bearing into the housing until the bearing seats.

6. Then, press the large bearing over the shaft and into the housing until it seats against the shoulder on the shaft.
7. Install a snap ring in the bore of the body to secure the bearings.
8. Slide the slinger downward until it seats on the shaft bearing shoulder.
9. Press the carbon face seal into the housing with a mandrel until it seats.
10. Support the shaft on the impeller end. Press the pulley onto the shaft until it rests snugly against the bearing inner race.
11. Lubricate the inside diameter of the rubber seat with a water soluble lubricant. No lube must touch the seal face of the ceramic ring. Install the seat assembly over the pump shaft until the polished side of the ceramic ring bottoms against the pump seal.
12. Supporting the shaft on the pulley end, press the impeller on until there is .010"-.020" clearance between the vanes and the pump body. Turn the shaft to check for free rotation.

Right Hand NH Series

Disassembly
1. Remove the hugnut and washer (if used) which hold the pulley in place on the shaft.
2. Using a special puller, remove the pulley from the shaft.
3. Compress and remove the snap ring.
4. Place the pump body and shaft in a press and press the shaft and bearing assembly from the body by exerting force on the impeller end of the shaft.
5. Drive the carbon face seal out of the body with a suitable mandrel.
6. Install the halves of a bearing removal tool around the bearing spacer in the grease channel, press the shaft through the bearing and spacer.
7. Remove the inner bearing snap ring.
8. Remove the inner bearing by supporting it and pressing the shaft out of it.

Inspection
1. Inspect the bearings for worn races or damaged shields, and replace as necessary.
2. Inspect the bearing spacer and replace if worn or damaged.
3. Inspect the impeller and replace if cracks or corrosion are likely to retard the flow of coolant.
4. Inspect the ceramic seat, and replace if damaged.
5. Measure the impeller bore and shaft diameter to check for the presence of a minimum .001"

press fit between them. Replace parts as necessary.
6. Inspect the straightness of the shaft, check for galling on the press fit surfaces, and worn threads, and replace or repair as necessary.
7. Inspect the pulley grooves for wear by installing a new belt in the grooves. The belt should protrude 1/16-"1/8", and should not bottom in the groove. Replace the pulley if the belt does not fit properly or if the groove is chipped or cracked.
8. Measure the pulley bore and shaft diameter to check for the minimum required .001" clearance. Replace the pulley as necessary.
9. Inspect the pump body, checking for cracks, damage from a spun bearing, or stopped up weep holes, and clean, repair, or replace as necessary.

Assembly
1. Lubricate the shaft and bearings with an approved grease.
2. Press the inner bearing over the shaft until it bottoms on the shoulder, using a suitable mandrel pressing on the inner race.
3. Install the snap ring and the bearing spacer.
4. Using a mandrel as described in step 2, press the outer bearing onto the shaft until it seats against the bearing spacer.
5. Check to see that both bearings turn freely, and then press the shaft assembly into the pump body, supporting the body on the seal surface of the impeller end. Press on the outer races of the bearings until they seat within the body.
6. Press the carbon face seal into the pump body until it bottoms, using a special mandrel. Make sure to keep grease off the face of the seal.
7. With the pump supported on the pulley end of the shaft, press the impeller onto the end of the shaft.
8. Place the pump on the impeller end of the shaft and measure the clearance between impeller vanes and the water pump bodly. Clearance should be .0015"-.035".
9. Install the snap ring in the pump body in front of the outer bearing.
10. Support the assembly on the impeller end of the shaft (not on the impeller) and press the pulley onto the shaft until the hub contacts the outer bearing inner race.
11. Install the washer (if used), and install and tighten the nut.

12. Grease the pump bearings before installation.

855 and 927 NTA Series Engines

Disassembly

1. Remove inlet housing to water pump housing mounting bolts.
2. Remove the inlet housing and discard the O-ring.
3. Using a suitable puller, remove the pulley and wear sleeve assembly. Remove the idler pulley assembly.
4. Remove the large snap ring which secures the large bearing in the water inlet housing.
5. Using a special puller, pull the pump impeller off the shaft. Then remove the ceramic seat and rubber seal and discard them.
6. Support the housing, and press the shaft bearing assembly on the impeller end from the inlet housing. Remove the bearings from the shaft.
7. Remove the carbon face seal and the small oil seal from the housing with a suitable mandrel.
8. Remove the large pipe plug from the idler pulley. Remove the small snap ring, and pulley assembly from the shaft.
9. Remove the oil seal, snap ring, and the bearing from the idler pulley.

Inspection

1. Check the impeller for cracks and corrosion which would interfere with coolant flow, and replace if necessary.
2. Inspect bearings for wear or roughness and replace as necessary.
3. Measure the impeller bore, pulley bore, and shaft diameter. There should be a minimum .001" press fit, and the shaft should be straight and smooth. Replace the shaft if necessary.
4. Inspect the pulley grooves for wear and the wear sleeve for wear or grooves.
5. Inspect the housings for cracks, bearing spin damage, and cleanliness of the weep hole. Clean or replace as necessary.
6. Inspect the bypass valve retainer disc and spring.
7. Replace any unserviceable parts.

Assembly

1. Press the bearing into the pulley with a special mandrel. Install the snap ring (flat side toward bearing) and press the seal in until it is flush with the surface of the pulley, using a special seal driver.
2. Now press the pulley assembly onto the shaft and install the snap ring.

3. Install the pipe plug into the pulley. Remove the small pipe plug and install a grease fitting. Fill the unit 1/2 to 2/3 full with an approved grease.
4. With a mandrel and press, press the small bearing onto the impeller end of the shaft and the large bearing onto the pulley end of the shaft. Bearings should be pressed on until they seat against the shoulders.
5. Using a special mandrel, press the small seal into the water inlet housing until it is flush with the bore to .015" indented.
6. Insert the shaft assembly into the water inlet housing. With a suitable mandrel, apply pressure to the outer race of the large bearing to press the assembly in until it seats. Install the retaining ring.
7. Support the impeller end of the shaft and, using a seal driver, press the large oil seal into the inlet housing.
8. Mount the idler pulley bracket onto the pump assembly and secure it.
9. Support the impeller end of the shaft, and press the drive pulley all the way onto the end of the shaft.
10. Use a special mandrel to press the carbon face seal into the inlet housing until it seats. Place the ceramic seat and rubber seal onto the shaft.
11. Support the drive end of the shaft and install the impeller. Press the impeller on until there is .020"-.040" clearance between the impeller and cavity.
12. Install new grease and relief fittings where required, and fill the cavity 1/2 to 2/3 full with an approved type of grease.
13. Lubricate a new O-ring with clean oil, and then install it in the groove of the water housing inlet.
14. Install the water housing inlet onto the main pump housing, carefully aligning the capscrew holes to avoid damaging the O-ring. Install the lockwashers and capscrews.

V-903 and VT-903

Disassembly

1. If there is a grease fitting on the end of the shaft, remove it.
2. With an appropriate puller, remove the impeller and drive pulley from the shaft.
3. Using a special puller with the puller jaws reversed, remove the oil seal from the body of the pump, and discard it. Remove the snap ring from the pump housing with snap ring pliers.

4. Support the body of the pump on the side opposite from the impeller, and press on the impeller end of the shaft to remove the bearing and shaft assembly from the pump body. If the small bearing remains in the body, press it out.
5. Remove the carbon face seal from the pump body. Press the oil seal out of the body and discard it.
6. Press the shaft out of the large bearing. Support it on the inner race of the bearing during the operation.

Inspection

1. Inspect the bearings for roughness or worn races.
2. Inspect the impeller for cracks or corrosion that might interfere with circulation.
3. Measure the impeller bore and the outside diameter of the shaft. There must be .0015" clearance.
4. Inspect the pump body parts for cracking.
5. Examine the carbon face seal carefully for cracks or chips.
6. Inspect the ceramic ring and rubber seat for damage.
7. Replace all unsatisfactory or questionable parts.
8. If there is a wear sleeve on the drive pulley, remove it as follows:
   a. Procure a 3/16" straight shank round punch and grind a 15 degree angle on the end.
   b. Secure the pulley in a vise (exercise care in tightening, to prevent cracking the pulley).
   c. Use the punch to drive the sleeve from the pulley hub by placing the punch through the puller holes in the pulley. Discard the sleeve.

Assembly

1. Lubricate the shaft outside diameter and the inside diameter of the bearings with an approved grease. Then, pack the bearings with grease.
2. If a small bearing is used, press it onto the shaft, with the shielded side toward the impeller end of the shaft, until the inner race seats against the shoulder. Press on the inner race of the bearing.
3. Press the large bearing onto the shaft via the inner race, with the shielded side toward the impeller end of the shaft, until the inner race seats against the shoulder.
4. Press a new oil seal into the body (steel face toward impeller end of body) with a special seal driving mandrel, making sure the seal is not pressed in below the face next to the small bearing.

5. Apply a liquid lead sealer to the press fit area of the seal outside diameter. Then, press the new carbon face seal into the body using a special mandrel, or applying force on the driving lip of the seal.

6. Press the shaft assembly into the pump body bore via the outer bearing race until the race seats in the body. Install the snap ring.

7. Using a special mandrel, press a new oil seal into the pump body until it seats.

8. Press a new wear sleeve into the drive pulley with a sleeve driving mandrel until there is .000″-.015″ indentation.

9. Support the impeller end of the shaft. Press the pulley on until it seats against the inner race of the bearing.

10. Lightly coat the inside diameter of the rubber seat with a water soluble lubricant. Then, slide the seat assembly over the pump shaft, with the polished side of the ring toward the carbon face, until the ring contacts the face.

11. Support the pulley end of the shaft, and press the impeller on until there is .010″-.020″ clearance between the impeller vanes and pump body.

12. Install the grease fitting and fill the cavity about 60% full of an approved lubricant.

NOTE: When installing the pipe plug, use sealant and reduce torque on the ¾″ plug to 25-30 ft-lbs.

1150 cid Engines

Disassembly

1. Inspect driveshaft for wear.
2. Remove inlet assembly and discard O-ring.

---

3. If impeller shroud insert is eroded or worn, replace by:
   a. Pull insert from roll pin in inlet housing; discard insert.
   b. Insert new roll pin in inlet housing.
   c. Lubricate O-ring and position in groove in inlet mating surface.
   d. Install insert over roll pin, press to mating surface of inlet housing.

4. Pull impeller from shaft, remove and discard seal seat.

5. Remove retaining ring, support drive end of pump body, and press out bearing and shaft.

6. Pull carbon face seal and oil seal from body.

7. Inspect bearings and shafts. Remove retaining ring to replace outer bearing.

8. Check impeller bore and shaft diameter. A minimum .00.″ press fit should exist between shaft and bore.

Assembly

1. Lubricate shaft and press bearings onto shaft to shoulders. Secure with retaining ring.

2. Support body at inlet end and press seal into bore until flush within .030″ below shoulder. Seal lip is toward bearing surface area.

3. Lubricate shaft seal mating surface, position bearing and shaft in bore and press outer bearing into bore until seated.

4. Support body at drive end, press carbon face seal into position and install seal seat over shaft.

5. Press impeller onto shaft; impeller-to-body clearance.

6. Lubricate O-ring with clean engine oil, install on inlet housing and secure housing to body.

NOTE: Until filter is installed, inlet housing shut-off valve should be "OFF."

Coolant Manifold

Coolant Manifold—Removal

In-line Engines

Remove engine compartment covers or tilt cab whichever be the case.

1. Drain the engine cooling system.
2. Disconnect the high temperature warning light and the coolant temperature sending unit leads at the coolant manifold.
3. Close the shut-off valve at the shutterstat, and disconnect the air hoses at the shutterstat.
4. Disconnect the heater hose from the coolant manifold. Disconnect the radiator upper hose and the air compressor coolant line from the thermostat housing. Loosen the hose clamps on the cooler coolant elbow.
5. Remove the retaining bolts; then, remove the coolant manifold as an assembly, or in sections if necessary. Discard the gaskets.
6. If the coolant manifold was removed as an assembly, separate the sections. Remove the coupling O-ring seals.

Installation

1. Clean the gasket surfaces of the coolant manifold and cylinder heads. Clean the O-ring seal surfaces on the coolant manifold and couplings.
2. Apply lubricant to new coupling O-ring seals, and assemble the coolant manifold sections, couplings and seals.
3. Position new gaskets coated with water-resistant sealer on the coolant manifold. Position the manifold on the cylinder heads, and install and tighten the retaining bolts.
4. Position the hose on the oil cooler coolant elbow and the thermostat housing, and tighten the hose clamps. Connect the radiator upper hose and the air compressor coolant line to the thermostat housing. Connect the heater hose to the coolant manifold.

Typical coolant manifold
(© Cummins Engine Co.)

1	Drive shaft	8	Body
2	Retainer ring	9	Seal
3	Retainer ring	10	Seal seat
4	Outer bearing	11	Impeller
5	Shaft assembly	12	O-ring
6	Inner bearing	13	Inlet assembly
7	Oil seal	14	Impeller insert
		15	Water filter

Water pump—1150 cid engines

Testing thermostat
(© Cummins Engine Co.)

5. Connect the air hoses to the shutterstat.
6. Connect the high temperature warning light and the coolant temperature sending unit leads at the coolant manifold.
7. Fill and bleed the cooling system. Operate the engine and check for coolant and air leaks.

Lubricating Oil Cooler

855, 927 Cid

Disassembly

1. Remove top exposed "O" ring under the brass retainer being careful not to scratch or mar the sealing surface on the element.
2. Clean out lube oil and contaminants trapped in housing by forcing cleaner through the oil ports.
3. Remove the element from housing, by inserting two 7/32 inch rods 8 inches long into the outside row of tubes opposite each other. NOTE: The rods should not drag bottom of housing.
4. Place a flat bar on top of housing and bundle faces between rods and rotate element in housing to unseal lower "O" ring. NOTE: While turning element lift up gradually on rods to free "O" rings. When up about 5/32 inch, element should be free to lift out of housing.

5. Discard "O" rings and retainer.

Cleaning and Inspection

1. Clean cooler core immediately after removal with approved cleaning solvent that will not harm non-ferrous metal.
2. Inspect element for corrosion or cracks where tubes are welded to end plates.
3. Clean housing in approved cleaning solvent and inspect for cracks or damage.
4. Clamp the cooler assembly in a fixture and connect an air hose.
5. Immerse in a water tank and apply 1-4 psi to the water side. Check for air bubbles.
6. Apply 35-40 psi to the oil side, and repeat the inspection for air leaks.

Repair

1. To repair damaged tubes insert a smaller outside diameter tube inside damaged tube. Cut and flare ends, then solder securely. CAUTION: Do not damage adjacent tubes with heat while soldering.
2. Do not restrict more than 5% of total number of tubes in this manner. If more than 5% of tubes are defective, discard element.

Assembly

1. Lubricate rubber "O" ring and place in groove at bottom of housing.
2. Push element into housing, aligning index marks on housing and element.
3. Press second "O" ring around top of element with a wooden block to assure equal pressure around ring circumference.
4. Place new retainer ring over rubber "O" ring.
5. Assemble new gasket and front cover to housing.
6. Check for oil leaks.

Installing oil cooler element
(© Cummins Engine Co.)

V6 and V8

Disassembly

1. Remove the cooler head and gasket from the housing.
2. Remove the retainer ring from the housing.
3. Remove the top O-ring carefully, avoiding damage to the sealing surface.
4. Use mineral spirits to clean out the lube oil and contaminants. Force the cleaner through the oil ports to accomplish this.
5. Insert two 7/32" x 8" rods into outside tubes opposite each other. Do not insert the rods far enough for them to rub the inside of the housing.
6. Place a flat bar between the rods and rotate the element, while lifting on the rods, to free the lower O-ring.
7. After the tube bundle has risen up about 5/32", lift the element out of the housing. If resistance is encountered, a special puller may be made for pulling the unit out using the two threaded holes in the end of the tube bundle. Discard the O-rings and retainer.

Testing

1. Clamp a rubber gasketed plate to either end of the tube bundle. In-

Shutterstat and thermostat housing connections N series
(© Cummins Engine Co.)

Shutterstat and thermostat housing connections H series
(© Cummins Engine Co.)

Cummins Diesel Engines

Lubricating oil cooler layout
(© Cummins Engine Co.)

stall an air connection in one of the plates.
2. Attach an air hose to the connection. Immerse the tube bundle and apply about 40 psi air pressure.
3. Check for the presence of air bubbles. Repair as described below if they are present.
4. Inspect the support for broken or cracked welds, and repair or replace as necessary.

Repair
1. Damaged tubes may be repaired by inserting a smaller diameter tube into the damaged tube, cutting and flaring the ends, and then soldering securely. No more than 5% of the tubes may be restricted in this manner. If more than 5% of the tubes require such a repair, discard the unit.

Assembly
1. Lubricate a new O-ring with engine oil and install it in the groove at the bottom of the housing. Make sure the ring is fully seated, and that it seats in the groove without being damaged or twisted. Make sure the sealing area on the element is not scratched.
2. Push the element carefully into the housing, aligning the index marks on the housing and element. If unusual resistance is felt, check the O-ring to make sure it has not come out of the groove.
3. Carefully install the other O-ring around the top of the element. Install the retainer ring.
4. Place a new gasket on the cooler/filter head, and secure the head snugly with the capscrews and lockwashers.
5. With the assembly on a flat work surface, and the inlet and outlet flat on top of the plate, check to make sure that inlet and outlet are on exactly the same plane. Torque the capscrews to 28-31 ft-lbs.

Suction Tube
1. Remove the mounting capscrews

from flange mounted suction tube to lube pump body.
2. Remove retaining clip and screen from suction bell.
3. Clean screen and tube; soak in solvent, dry with compressed air.
4. Inspect parts for damage and replace as needed.
5. Reassemble screen.
6. When "O" rings are used on the suction tubes, install new ones.

Corrosion Resistor

Disassembly
1. Remove capscrews and washers from resistor cover. Remove cover, gaskets, and upper plate.
2. Lift element from resistor body.
3. Lift out lower plate (sacrificial metal plate), and spring.
4. Remove drain plug and sump plate from body.

Inspection and Repair
1. Buff or polish sacrificial plate to remove scale and expose metal. Discard plate if less than 50% of metal surface can be exposed by polishing.
2. Inspect resistor body and cover for cracks or leaks.
3. Inspect spring, drain plug and capscrews for wear. Replace as necessary.

Corrosion resistor—layout
(© Cummins Engine Co.)

Assembly
1. Install sump plate and install spring in resistor housing.
2. Remove transparent bag from new element. Install lower plate, new element and upper plate.
3. Install new gasket to resistor cover. Secure cover to housing with capscrews and washers.
4. Install pipe plug.

1150 cid Engines

Disassembly and Inspection
1. Remove capscrews from elements and remove elements from housing.
2. Clean elements immediately with a safe solvent.
3. Inspect all parts for wear or cracks.
4. Plug openings in elements and place elements in water tank. Apply 60 psi air to check for leaks.

Assembly
1. Lubricate O-rings and install elements in housing.
2. If hold-down clamps are used, snug-tighten the cap screws.
3. Install cooler to block and tighten capscrews to 30-35 ft. lb.

Manifolds

Intake Manifold Removal

V-6 Engines
1. Remove the power steering pump mounting bolts and position the pump out of the way where necessary.
2. Loosen the clamp and remove the inlet air flex tube from the air cross-over manifold. Disconnect the air compressor supply line at the air-cross-over manifold. Loosen the hose clamps on the cross-over manifold connection hose and remove air manifold.
3. On the right intake manifold, remove the alternator bracket rear bolt and loosen the 2 front bolts.
   On the left intake manifold, remove the alternator adjusting arm to left intake manifold bolt.
4. Remove the intake manifold(s).

Intake Manifold Removal

855, 927 cid—Engines
1. Open the air reservoir drain cock and exhaust the system. Disconnect the inlet and outlet lines from the shutterstat.
2. On a right intake manifold, remove the corrosion resistor from the air cleaners support frame, and attach it to the cowl with wire. Disconnect the air compressor supply line from the

right air cleaner. For one intake manifold, remove the support frame braces from the air cleaner support. For both intake manifolds, remove the air cleaners and support frame as an assembly. Remove the air cleaner(s), support frame and inlet air tube(s) assembly from the intake manifold.
3. Remove the power steering pump mounting bolts and tie the pump out of the way where necessary.
4. On the right intake manifold, remove the alternator bracket rear bolt and loosen the 2 front bolts. On the left intake manifold, remove the alternator adjusting arm to left intake manifold bolt.
5. Remove the intake manifold(s).

Intake Manifold Removal

V-8 Engines
1. Release the cab locks, tilt the cab forward and lock it in place.
2. Remove the inlet air tube and hoses from the air cleaner and air cross-over manifold. Disconnect the air compressor supply line from the air cross-over manifold. Loosen the hose clamps on the cross-over manifold connection hose.
3. Remove the air cross-over manifold(s) and gasket(s). Remove the intake manifold(s).

Intake Manifold Installation

V-6 Engines
1. Clean the gasket surfaces of the cylinder head(s), intake manifold(s) and air cross-over manifold.
2. Using new gaskets, install the intake manifold(s). On the right intake manifold, install the alternator mounting bracket rear bolt. Tighten the intake manifold bolts and alternator mounting bracket bolts in alternate steps. Position a new gasket on the inlet port flange of the intake manifold(s), and install the air cross-over manifold. On the left intake manifold, attach the alternator adjusting arm.
3. Connect the air compressor supply line to the air cross-over manifold. Connect the inlet air flex tube to the air cross-over manifold and tighten the hose clamp.
4. Install the power steering pump. Adjust the alternator and power steering pump drive belt.
5. Operate the engine and check for air leaks.

Intake Manifold Installation

855, 927 Cid Engines
1. Clean the gasket surfaces of the cylinder head(s), intake manifold(s), inlet air tube adapter(s) and air cleaners support frame.
2. Using new gaskets, install the intake manifold(s). On the right intake manifold, install the alternator mounting bracket rear bolt. Tighten the intake manifold bolts and alternator mounting bolts in alternate steps. On the left intake manifold, attach the alternator adjusting arm.
3. Position new gasket(s) on the inlet port flange of the intake manifold(s). Place new gasket(s) between the inlet air tube adapter(s) and the base of the air cleaner support(s). Install the air cleaner(s) and support frame assembly(ies) on the intake manifold(s).
4. Connect the air compressor supply line to the right air cleaner. Install the corrosion resistor on the air cleaners support frame. Connect the inlet and outlet lines to the shutterstat.
5. Install the power steering pump on the left intake manifold. Adjust the alternator and power steering pump drive belt.
6. Operate the engine and check for air leaks.

Intake Manifold Installation

V-8 Engines
1. Clean the gasket surfaces of the cylinder head(s), intake manifold(s) and air cross-over manifold(s).
2. Using new gasket(s), install the intake manifold(s) and tighten the retaining bolts in alternate steps. Use new gasket(s) and install the air cross-over manifold(s). Tighten the clamps on the manifold connection hose.
3. Connect the air compressor supply line to the air cross-over manifold. Install the inlet air tube and hoses on the air cleaner and air cross-over manifold.
4. Operate the engine and check for air leaks.
5. Lower the cab and lock it in position.

Intake Manifold Removal

In-Line Engines
1. Drain the cooling system.
2. Disconnect both coolant hoses from the radiator supply tank. Remove the radiator overflow tube from the retaining clamps. Disconnect the windshield washer hose at the "Y" connection.
3. In most cases it is necessary to

remove the engine hood to cowl retaining screws. Remove the engine hood to grille retaining bolts. Use a hoist to remove the engine hood assembly.
4. Loosen the hose clamps, and remove the air inlet tube from the air cleaner to the intake manifold.
5. Disconnect the glow plug lead and the primer fuel line from the intake manifold preheater, if so equipped.
6. Disconnect the compressor air inlet line from the compressor, and remove it from the intake manifold. Disconnect the air compressor coolant line from the compressor and the engine coolant manifold. Remove the retaining clip from the rocker cover; then remove the compressor coolant line.
7. Remove the engine compartment covers from the cab floor.
8. Remove the retaining bolts; then remove the intake manifold.

Intake Manifold Removal

Tilt Cab Models
1. Release the cab locks and tilt the cab forward.
2. Loosen the hose clamps, and remove the air inlet tube from the intake manifold and air cleaner. Remove the air cleaner assembly.
3. Disconnect the glow plug lead and the primer fuel line from the intake manifold preheater, if so equipped.
4. Remove the air compressor air inlet line from the intake manifold and air compressor. Remove the parking brake retaining clip from the intake manifold.
5. Remove the retaining bolts; then remove the intake manifold.

Intake Manifold Installation

In-line Engines
1. Clean the gasket surfaces on the intake manifold and cylinder heads.
2. Using new gaskets, install the intake manifold and tighten the manifold bolts in sequence.
3. Install the compressor coolant line on the air compressor and the engine coolant manifold. Attach the retaining clip to the front rocker cover. Install the compressor air inlet line on the compressor and intake manifold.
4. Connect the primer fuel line and glow plug lead to the intake manifold preheater, if so equipped.
5. Install the air inlet tube on the intake manifold and air cleaner, and tighten the hose clamps.
6. If removed, use a hoist to posi-

tion the engine hood assembly on the cowl and grille. Install and tighten the hood to cowl screws and hood to grille bolts.

7. Position the radiator overflow tube in the retaining clamps, and tighten the clamps. Connect the coolant hoses to the radiator supply tank. Connect the windshield washer hose.
8. Install the engine compartment covers on the cab floor.
9. Fill and bleed the cooling system.
10. Start the engine and check for coolant and air leaks.

Intake Manifold Installation

Tilt Cab Models

1. Clean the gasket surfaces on the intake manifold and cylinder heads.
2. Using new gaskets, install the intake manifold. Tighten the manifold bolts in sequence.
3. Install the parking brake retaining clip on the intake manifold. Install the air compressor air inlet line on the compressor and the intake manifold.
4. Connect the primer fuel line and glow plug lead to the intake manifold preheater, if so equipped.
5. Install the air cleaner assembly. Install the air inlet tube on the intake manifold and air cleaner, and tighten the hose clamps.
6. Lower the cab and lock it in position.

Cylinder Head

Cylinder Head Removal

855, 927 Cid Engines

1. Remove the fuel manifold, coolant manifold, exhaust manifold, intake manifold, and rocker housing(s).
2. Remove the injector and valve push rods in order, and place them in a rack for installation in

Removing injector drain connection
(© Cummins Engine Co.)

Installing grommets and retainers
(© Cummins Engine Co.)

the same position from which they were removed.

3. Remove the compression release lever return spring and retaining bolt.
4. Remove the injector inlet and drain connections.
5. Remove the injector hold-down bolts and lift or pry the injectors from the cylinder heads. *Do not turn the injectors upside down, thus avoiding dropping the plungers.*
6. Loosen and remove the cylinder head bolts. Using a lifting eye and a hoist, remove the cylinder head(s), and place them on a bench, with the valves horizontal. Remove the grommet retainers. Remove and discard the grommets, O-rings and gaskets.

Installation

855, 927 Cid Engines

1. Carefully remove excess carbon deposits from the cylinder head(s). *Do not use a scraper or wire brush in the injector sleeve area, to prevent distortion or mutilation of the copper injector sleeves.* Clean the O-ring, grommet and gasket surfaces of the cylinder head(s) and cylinder block. Clean the gasket surfaces of the intake and exhaust manifolds.
2. Check the cylinder liner protrusion of all liners.
3. Press new grommet retainers, with the small end up, in the coolant passages of the cylinder block. Position a new cylinder head gasket on the engine block and cylinder head dowels so that the gasket side marked "TOP" is facing up. Use a gasket with white water hole grommets if block water holes are free of erosion. Use a gasket with black water hole grommets where there is evidence of water hole erosion, if sleeves have not been installed. Install the grommets on the grommet retainers, and press the grommets into the gasket holes. *Avoid all contact be-*

Checking cylinder liner protrusion
(© Cummins Engine Co.)

Cylinder head bolt torque sequence
(© Cummins Engine Co.)

tween grommets and fuel or lubricating oil to prevent damage due to swelling. The optional installation of the grommet retainer above the grommet may become necessary when the cylinder head as 15/32 inch coolant holes or when the holes are eroded.

4. Using lifting eye and a hoist, install the cylider head(s).
5. Lubricate the cylinder head bolt threads and washers with rust preventive. Install the head bolts or caps and torque, in sequence, as specified in the specifications charts.
6. Install the injectors, following the procedures described in this section. *Screw the inlet and drain connections into the injectors about 3 turns to align the injectors before tightening the injector hold-down bolts.*
7. Install the compression release lever return spring and retaining bolt.

Typical cylindrical injector removal
(© Cummins Engine Co.)

8. Install the injector and valve push rods in the same position from which they were removed.
9. Install the rocker housing(s), intake manifold, exhaust manifold, coolant manifold and fuel manifold, and adjust the valve cross-heads and injector and valve lash.
10. Fill and bleed the cooling system. Operate the engine and check for fuel, oil and coolant leaks. When the engine reaches normal operating temperature (140°F oil temperature), remove the rocker housing cover(s), and adjust the injector and valve lash to specifications. Install the rocker housing cover(s).

Cylinder Head Removal

V-6 & V-8 Engines (Exc 903 Cid)

1. Drain the cooling system and exhaust the air reservoir. Disconnect the battery cables.
2. Remove the engine hood assembly where necessary.
3. Disconnect the headlamp wiring harness and remove the grille and headlamp assembly(ies). Remove the front fender(s) where necessary.
4. Loosen the clamps and remove the steering gear shaft to steering wheel shaft universal joint. Position the steering gear shaft out of the way where necessary.
5. Remove the radiator brace rod from the left side of the radiator support and frame rail where necessary.
6. Remove the alternator mounting and adjusting bolts. Leave the leads attached and position the alternator out of the way.
7. On the left cylinder head, remove the power steering pump and drive belts from the engine. Leave the hoses attached and position the power steering pump out of the way. On the right cylinder head, remove only the steering pump drive belts.

8. Loosen the fan drive belts. Remove the cooling fan and hub assembly, spacers and drive belts from the engine.
9. On a right cylinder head, disconnect the shutterstat air hoses at the shutterstat. Disconnect the heater hoses at the thermostat housing and the water pump. Disconnect the coolant temperature and warning light sending unit leads. Loosen the water pump to thermostat housing by-pass hose clamp. Remove the thermostat housing and shutterstat assembly.
10. On the right cylinder head, remove the dipstick tube assembly. Remove the air inlet duct from the air cleaner and air cross-over manifold.
11. Disconnect the accelerator rod and the tachometer cable at the fuel pump. Disconnect the service brake air hose at the brake treadle valve. Remove the air hose from the brake treadle valve to the air reservoir line.
12. On some models it may be necessary to disconnect the grille to cab brace rods at the cab. Remove the cab front support to chassis bolts and nuts. Attach a sling and hoist to the cab supports and raise the cab approximately 4 inches.
13. On the left cylinder head, disconnect the air compressor, supply line at the left air cross-over manifold. Loosen the hose clamps and remove the air cross-over manifold(s) and gasket(s).
14. Remove the valve cover(s) and gasket(s) and cylinder head cover(s) and gasket(s.
15. On the right cylinder head, remove the alternator mounting bracket. Remove the intake manifold(s) and gasket(s).
16. Disconnect the fuel supply line at the front of the cylinder head(s). Disconnect the fuel return line at the rear of the cylinder head(s).

Injector removal
(© Cummins Engine Co.)

17. On the right cylinder head, disconnect the air compressor coolant line at the coolant cross-over tube. Remove the coolant cross-over tube(s) from the cylinder head(s).
18. Remove the push rod cover(s) and gasket(s).
19. Remove the exhaust manifold bolts and separate the exhaust manifold(s) from the cylinder head(s). Leave the manifold(s) attached to the resonator inlet pipe(s).
20. Loosen the lock nuts and back off all of the injector and valve rocker lever adjusting screws. Remove the rocker lever support screws. Remove the injector and valve push rods and place them in a rack for installation in the same position from which they were removed. Remove the rocker lever assembly(ies) with the cylinder head(s). Loosen the crosshead adjusting screw nuts and remove the crossheads, on four valve engines.
21. Remove the injector hold-down clamp screws and clamps. Pry the injectors loose from the cylinder head. *It may be necessary to use a tool such as for removal of the rear injectors.* Remove the injectors and O'rings. *Do not remove the injector plunger, since they are not interchangeable between injectors.*
22. Remove the remaining cylinder head bolts. If the rear bolts cannot be removed due to interference with the cab supports, split a 1½-inch length of rubber hose and install it around the bolt. This will hold the bolt above the bottom of the cylinder head.
23. Install a lifting bracket on the cylinder head, and use a hoist to remove the cylinder head(s). Mark heads "left" or "right".
24. Remove the cylinder head gaskets, grommets, grommet retainers and O-rings. Remove the exhaust manifold gasket(s).

Cylinder Head Installation

V-6 & V-8 Engines (Exc 903 Cid)

1. Carefully remove excess carbon deposits from the cylinder head. *Do not use a scraper or wire brush in the injector sleeve area. to prevent distortion or mutilation of the copper injector sleeves.* Clean all gasket surfaces. Clean the injector bores of the cylinder head with a clean rag and stick. Remove all liquid and dirt from capscrew holes. Make sure cylinder walls are clean and well lubricated. Make sure breather vent tube assemblies (if used) are in place. Coat short capscrews with rust pre-

ventive and install until just snug in the sequence shown.

2. Position new head gasket(s) on the cylinder block and dowels with the side marked "TOP" up. Press new grommet retainers, with the small end up, in the coolant passages of the cylinder block. Install the grommets on the grommet retainers, and press the grommets into the gasket holes. *Avoid all contact between grommets and fuel or lubricating oil to prevent damage due to swelling.* The optional installation of the grommet retainer above the grommet may be necessary when the cylinder head has 15/32-inch coolant holes or when the holes are eroded. With a lifting bracket secured to the head with capscrews, hoist the head in position over the block and lower it in place over the ring dowels. Coat the short capscrews with rust preventive and install. Tighten in the proper sequence until snug.

3. Make sure the injectors are clean and that the button screen around the inlet is in place. Use a clean cloth and clean the injector sleeves. Install new O-rings on injector bodies and lubricate with clean engine oil. Start each C type injector into the bore so the ball check retainer plug is at one o'clock position and guide it by hand until alignment and lack of binding are ensured. Place a clean, blunt object on each injector and snap it onto its seat. In the case of type D injectors, align the injector so the button screen is toward the center of the Vee. Seat D injectors with a T-handle made from 5/8" bar stock with a 5/16" hole 1/2" deep drilled in the bottom and a type D injector link braised into the hole. Apply force with the T handle apparatus positioned on top of the injector plunger. Install type D injector links, if removed. Both types of injectors then require installation of hold-down clamps, washers, and capscrews torqued to 30-35 ft-lbs. Make sure the injector plunger moves freely after installation of clamps.

4. Install crosshead retainers where used, and insert crossheads over crosshead guides. Run adjusting screws down until they touch valve stems, and torque locknuts to 25-30 ft-lbs.

5. Install the push rods in the same position from which they were removed. Lubricate the bolts with rust preventive. Install the bolts and tighten them until snug. Then torque all head bolts

Cylinder Head Tightening Sequence
(© Cummins Engine Co.)

according to the specifications charts in the proper sequence.

6. Adjust the crossheads and the injector and valve lash. See Injector section for injector lash adjustment instructions. Valve clearance at room temperature is .012 intake, .022 exhaust.

7. Using new gaskets, install the exhaust manifold(s). Torque the bolts in 15 ft-lb increments to specifications.

8. Use new gasket(s) and install the push rod cover(s).

9. Install the coolant cross-over tube(s) on the cylinder head(s). On the right cylinder head, connect the air compressor coolant line to the coolant cross-over tube.

10. Connect the fuel return line at the rear of the cylinder head(s). Connect the fuel supply line at the front of the cylinder head(s).

11. Using new gasket(s), install the intake manifold(s). On the right cylinder head, install the alternator mounting bracket.

12. Coat the upper surface of new gaskets and position the gaskets on the cylinder head cover(s) and valve cover(s). Install the cylinder head cover(s) and valve cover(s). *Partially tighten the valve cover screws.*

13. Install the air cross-over manifold(s) with new gasket(s). Tighten the screws and hose clamps. On the left cylinder head, connect the air compressor supply line to the left air cross-over manifold.

14. Install the inlet air duct on the air cross-over manifold, and tighten the hose clamp. On the right cylinder head, install the dipstick tube assembly.

15. Install the thermostat housing and shutterstat assembly. Tighten the hose clamps. Connect the coolant temperature and warning light sending unit leads. Connect the radiator

upper hose and heater hoses to the thermostat housing and water pump. Connect the shutterstat air hoses to the shutterstat.

16. Install the cooling fan and hub assembly, spacers and drive belts.

17. Install the alternator, but do not install the drive belt at this time.

18. Connect the battery cables. Fill and bleed the cooling system. Operate the engine until the oil temperature is 140°F. Remove the valve cover(s) and adjust the injector and valve lash to specifications. Install the valve cover(s) and tighten the screws in alternate steps.

19. Install the alternator drive belt.

20. Lower the cab. Install and tighten the cab front support to chassis bolts, insulators and nuts. Connect the grille to cab brace rods to the cab.

21. Install the air hose to the brake treadle valve and the air reservoir line. Connect the service brake air hose to the brake treadle valve. Connect the tachometer cable and accelerator rod to the fuel pump. Adjust the accelerator linkage.

22. On the left cylinder head, install the power steering pump. Install the drive belts and adjust the belt deflection to specifications.

23. Install the radiator left brace rod.

24. Connect the steering gear shaft to the steering wheel shaft.

25. Install the front fender(s). Install the headlamp and grille assembly(ies). Connect the headlamp wiring harness.

26. Install the engine hood assembly.

27. Operate the engine and check for air, oil and coolant leaks.

Cylinder Head Removal
V-903 and VT-903 Engines

1. Label cylinder head covers as to which side of the engine they are

Cylinder Head Torquing Sequence
(© Cummins Engine Co.)

mounted on, and remove capscrews, lockwashers and flatwashers holding the covers on the heads. Remove the covers, discarding the gaskets.
2. Remove capscrews and associated parts from the push rod cavity covers, remove the covers and discard the gaskets.
3. Loosen all rocker lever adjusting nuts and back out all the adjusting screws.
4. Secure all the rocker levers together with rubber bands or a similar device.
5. Remove the rocker assembly mounting capscrews and washers.
6. Lift off the rocker assemblies.
7. Remove the pushrods.
8. Loosen all crosshead adjusting screw nuts and lift the crossheads off the guides.
9. Remove the injector hold down yoke capscrews, and remove the yokes.
10. Remove the injectors with a special tool. Place injectors in a clean rack carefully, wtih the injectors labeled as to which cylinder they belong in.
11. Attach a special lifting fixture to the head. Remove all remaining capscrews and flatwashers.
12. Insert guide studs in the block for easiest removal. Lift the heads off the block with an adequate hoist via the lifting fixture.
13. Tag heads as to which side of the engine they belong on, remove guide studs, and discard gaskets and grommets.

Cylinder Head Installation

V-903 and VT-903 Engines

Valve guides, valves, and springs should be installed on heads and all liquid and dirt should be removed from the capscrew holes before installation.
1. Plug breather vent tube holes if heads are used on a turbocharged engine. Clean the mating surfaces and make sure cylinders are clean and coated with lubricating oil. Make sure there are no lime deposits in the water passages that could interfere with installation of grommet retainers.
2. Install head gasket, "Top" side up, and install a new O-ring over each ring dowel. Install an oversize gasket if head has been resurfaced.
3. Install new grommets in water passages.
4. Install a new ring dowel and O-ring in the oil passage.
5. Lower the head with the lifting bracket and a hoist until it moves down into place over the ring dowels.
6. Lubricate the capscrews and washers with clean oil, position the washers over the capscrews with the chamfered edge down, and position the O-rings, coated with engine oil, over the threads.
7. Install the capscrews and tighten just until snug in the sequence shown.
8. Make sure the injector sleeves are free of chips or carbon particles. If cleaning is required, perform it with a rag wrapped around a ¾" wooden dowel soaked in solvent.
9. Lubricate the O-rings with engine oil.
10. Lower the injector into the head, aligned so the button screen faces the center of the Vee.
11. With a clean, blunt object, push each injector down into place by exerting pressure on the body. The injector will snap into place.
12. Install links, hold down rings, and clamps, flatwashers, and capscrews. Torque the capscrews to 30-35 ft-lbs. Make sure the hold down clamps do not contact the crosshead stems. Make sure the injector plunger moves freely.
13. Install the crossheads on their guides.
14. Adjust the crossheads by holding each firmly down on the mating valve stem and turning the adjusting screw down until it just touches the other stem. Torque all adjusting screw locknuts to 25-30 ft-lbs.
15. Position both rocker assemblies to the cylinder heads. Coat the capscrews with rust preventive and install in the heads, tightening just until snug.
16. Torque all the cylinder head capscrews in the sequence shown according to the specifications charts.
17. Install push rods and engage adjusting screws with the push rod sockets.
18. Position the pushrod cavity covers onto the heads with new gaskets. Install flatwashers, lockwashers, and capscrews.

Cylinder Head Removal
1150 cid

1. Remove intake manifold.
2. Remove rocker lever covers.
3. Loosen valve and injector adjusting screw locknuts and back out adjusting screws one or two turns.
4. Remove rocker lever capscrews and pull straight up on lever to clear ring dowels.
5. Remove valve crossheads.
   NOTE: Mark push rods, injector links, rocker levers, and all such parts which establish a wear pattern.
6. Remove injector plunger links and push rods.
7. Remove water transfer tube retaining ring between #5 and #6 cylinders.
8. Drive transfer tube into #5 housing far enough to clear #6.
9. Remove capscrews from rocker housing and lift off housing.
10. Remove transfer tube from #5; discard O-rings.
11. Repeat this procedure for the remaining housings.
   NOTE: The thermostat must be removed before #1 housing is removed.
12. Remove by-pass tube, turbocharger supply line and air compressor drain tube from housing.
13. Remove housing support bracket.
14. Remove thermostat-to-gear housing capscrews.
15. Cock thermostat housing clear of fan hub support.
16. Pull thermostat housing and transfer tube from rocker housing.
17. Remove remaining housings.

Removing injector plunger links

Cummins Diesel Engines

Removing thermostat housing

Rolling Injector Sleeve—Upper Portion
(© Cummins Engine Co.)

18. Remove injector hold-down plate.
19. Remove injectors with suitable tool.
20. Remove cylinder head capscrews; lift heads straight up.

Installation

1. Place new head gasket over dowels in block. Gaskets are marked "TOP".
2. Place water, oil, and push tube grommets into position in each cylinder head gasket, on the camshaft side of the engine, requires a gasket.
3. Fix head in hoist and position over block.
4. Lower head onto block, taking care not to disturb grommets.
5. Lubricate head bolts with rust-proof oil. Before snugging capscrews, coat underside of capscrew head with SEA 140 w.
   NOTE: Washers must be placed under capscrews with rounded side up.
6. Tighten capscrews to recommended torque.

Rebuilding Cylinder Head

Valve Guides V6 and V8

1. Where replacement is required, drive out valve guides from underside of cylinder head. Clean new guides sonically, or with a 45 caliber piston cleaning brush. All sealer must be removed. Then, flush with solvent to remove residue.
2. Install new valve guides with special mandrel. Oil mist hole (if used) must face exhaust manifold. If proper mandrels are unavailable, press guides in until protrusion is .775"-.800" above surface (.695"-.710" on 903).
3. If reaming of valve guide is necessary to install valves ream valve guide from bottom side of cylinder head, using a drill press and floating tool holder. Use lu-

bricating oil or soluble oil and water solution for a good finish. CAUTION: Special care must be used to avoid breaking carbide tips. Sharpen carbide tipped tools on a diamond impregnated wheel. New guides are to be reamed to .3800"-.3817" (.4520"-.4532" on 903).

Valve Guides 855 and 927

1. Drive out faulty guides from the bottom of the head. If reaming is required to clean up guide bore, use a special reamer to ream the bore to .760"-.761". Make sure all burrs are removed, and that the corner break does not exceed .015".
2. If a damaged guide bore does not clean up, use a special oversize reamer, and ream to .765"-.766". Install an oversize guide, and make sure that all burrs are removed, and that the corner break does not exceed .015". If necessary, ream valve spring guide hole to .768"-.773".
3. If a special mandrel is unavailable, press the guide in until it protrudes 1.315"-1.325".
4. If guide must be reamed for insertion of valve stem, ream the guide from the bottom with a special reamer using lube oil or soluble oil and water solution. Do not ream beyond .445".

Valve Guides 1150 cid

1. Drive out guides from bottom.
2. Drive in new guide with guide driver.
3. Check guide dimensions:
Installed diameter—inside .4961-.4971
Assembled height   1.325-1.340

Valve Crosshead Guides

1. Remove guides to be replaced, using Puller which contains different size collets to fit the various guides. NOTE: After Engine Serial No. 298655, engines are equipped with "solid" pin-type crosshead guides and crossheads with hollow stems.

Old and new-style crossheads and guides may be used in the same cylinder head.
2. Press in new guides.
   NOTE: *A special solid guide has been released to permit the new hollow crossheads in cylinder heads machined for the larger diameter hollow guide. If no spacers are available, press in the new guide until it protrudes 2.040"-2.060" on V6 and small V8, 2.090"-2.110" on 903. On 855 and 927 engines, if the special installation mandrel is not available, press the new guides in until they protrude 1.860"-1.880".*

Replace Injector Sleeves
Removal

1. Remove worn sleeves by cutting them from cylinder head with a 3/8 inch gouge chisel (sometimes called a muffler sleeve cutting tool) and driving out from lower end. Remove O-ring, if used.
   NOTE: Remove all foreign material from injector sleeve sealing area.

A special sleeve remover tool may be used as follows:

a. Install tool into sleeve bore *with teeth of forming collar resting on sleeve and inside bore.* Do not allow hammer to strike underside of knob.
b. Hold down knob and hammer on nut until forming collar bottoms out.
c. Hold up on the rod, and turn down nut until it bottoms on forming collar.
d. Slide hammer a light blow against the knob to raise and seat the extractor tip within the injector sleeve.
e. Retighten the nut against the top of the forming collar.
f. Repeatedly strike the knob with a hammer and pull the injector sleeve from the head.
g. Back the nut out all the way.
h. Tap the end of the injector sleeve until the forming collar is free or touches the nut.

604

Item	Inch.	[mm]	Item	Inch	[mm]
1.	0.375	[9.5250]	10.	*0.010	[0.2540]
2.	1.250	[31.7500]	11.	0.0937	[2.3812]
3.	0.3136	[7.9654]	12.	0.969	[24.6126]
4.	0.199	[5.0546]		0.971	[24.6634]
	0.209	[5.3086]	13.	0.0034	[0.0863]
5.	0.304	[7.7216]		0.0054	[0.1371]
	0.306	[7.7724]	14.	0.0015	[0.0381]
6.	0.3250	[8.2550]		0.0025	[0.0635]
	0.3300	[8.3820]	15.	0.040 R	[1.0160] R
7.	0.020	[0.5080]		0.060	[1.5240]
			16.	15 deg. Angle Relief	
8.	0.250	[6.3500]	17.	30 deg. Angle Relief	
9.	0.0937	[2.3812]	*Land		

ST-920 Grinding Specifications

i. Rotate the sleeve ⅓ turn until the indentations match the flats on the extractor tip. Remove the sleeve.

Installation—V6 and V8 (exc 903 cid)

1. Lightly lube a new O-ring with engine oil.
2. Install the O-ring in the groove. Installation may be facilitated by sitting the head on one edge so the injector bore is horizontal and using two small rods to feed the seal ring through the bore to the groove.
3. Support the head adequately around the injector opening to avoid cracking it during the following operations. Place the sleeve in the injector bore and drive it in until it bottoms, using a special driver.
4. Remove the driver and install a special hold-down tool. Torque the nut to 35-40 ft-lbs.
5. Install a special sleeve driver into the sleeve over the hold down tool. Apply two light blows to the driver to embed the beads into the sleeve. Retighten the hold-down tool nut to 35-40 ft-lbs.
6. Seal the upper portion of the injector sleeve area with a special expanding roller until 75 in/lbs of torque are required.
7. Remove all the tools and install a special driver. Reseat the sleeve with two light blows of a 2 lb. lead hammer.
8. Seal the sleeve in the lower, tapered seating area with a special angle roller tool.
9. Cut the seat with a special sleeve cutter. Cutter must conform to dimensions shown in illustration. Provide a solid stream of cutting oil during the operation. A special pilot is available for adapting this tool to a drill press. Alternately insert injector to measure tip protrusion (from flat head surface) and cut the head. Final protrusion should be .095"-.115" on V6 and small V8, .075"-.090" on 903, and .060"-.070" on 855 and 927 engines.
10. Install the injector and determine seating surface with Prussian Blue. A band .060" wide must appear all the way around the injector beginning about .275" from the bottom of the head surface.
NOTE: The manufacturer suggests a water pressure test of the cylinder head to check the seal of injector sleeves.

Replace Valve Seat Inserts

1. Remove loose or excessively worn valve seat inserts.
2. Enlarge counterbore to next oversize. Inserts are available in standard .010, .020, .030, and .040 inch oversizes.
3. Use Valve Seat Insert Tool to hold and drive cutters which come in sets. This tool must be driven by an electric motor. On all V6 and V8 engines, restore counter bore and pocket depth at the valve counterbore area (see chart). Restore chamfer by grinding with a 35° stone. Chamfer should be 2.0000"-2.0200" on V6 and small V8, and 2.3000"-2.3200" on 903 V8.
4. Machine counterbore .006/.010 inch deeper than insert height to permit peening of head to hold insert.
5. Install valve seat insert.
6. Peen insert in head with peening tool. A ¼-inch diameter round-end punch may be used.

Grind Valve Seats

1. Check condition of grinding equipment.
   a. Mandrels must be straight and of proper size to fit in reamed valve guides.
   b. Bushings in the grinder must be clean and must fit properly on guide mandrel.
   c. Bearings of drive unit must be in good condition.
2. Dress stone to 30° from horizontal.
3. Grind valve seats, holding seating motor as nearly vertical as possible. A severe angle will cause the seat to be out-of-true depending upon the amount of wear in the grinder bearings, mandrel bushines, etc., even though the grinder has a universal joint.
4. Check valve seat width which should be .063"-.125".
   a. If ground seat is wider than the maximum ⅛ inch, stock can be removed from points "A" and "B" with specially dressed valve seat grinder stones.
   b. Narrowing should not extend beyond chamfer on seat insert. Chamfer provides for peen metal.
5. Dress wheel for final finish.
6. Finish grind with light touches of stone against face.
7. Check guide alignment with eccentrimeter.
   a. Run-out should not exceed .002 inch total indicator reading.
   b. The gauge must be a perfect fit on pilot mandrel.

Grind Valves

1. Check valve grinder setting by using a new valve and an indicator gauge.
   a. Chuck valve on guide area of stem. Relieved portions on both ends of guide area are not necessarily concentric to guide area of stem.
   b. Indicate on ground face of valve.
   c. Turn valve and mark high spot on head of valve.
   d. Rechuck the valve 180° from first position.
   e. Repeat "b" and "c". If the high spots are same for both "a" and "d" positions, the valve is warped. If high spots occur in different positions, chuck is out of alignment. Runout should not exceed .001 inch.
2. Check bearings of machine.
3. The grinding wheel must be the proper grade and properly dressed to avoid chatter and grind marks.
4. Wet grind valves to an exact 30° angle from horizontal.
5. Valves and seats properly ground with precision equipment should not require lapping to effect an airtight seal; however, a small amount of lapping is permissible if necessary in order to pass vacuum test.
6. Check rim thickness. If rim is thinner than specified, valve is not suitable for use because of the danger of burning and cupping.

Cummins Diesel Engines

	Intake	Exhaust
V6, V8	.130"	.130"
In-line	.105"	.105"

7. Check valve in a finish reamed guide and against a newly ground valve seat face. Pencil mark valve as shown in illustration, drop into position and rotate 10 degrees.
8. A true seat will be indicated if all pencil marks are broken. If pencil marks are not broken, the valve seat tools need dressing or the machine has not been properly adjusted. A good seat must:
   1. Have no grinding marks.
   2. Be at a true 30° angle.
   3. Have a grind width within limits.
   4. Have proper guide-to-stem clearance.

Assemble Valves and Springs

1. Lubricate valve stems. Insert valves.
2. Place cylinder head face down on a wooden bench to prevent marring milled surface.
3. Place plastic sleeve over valve stem, and then install seal. Press seal into place with a special driver until it is properly seated.

Valve Seat Insert Data — Inch [mm]

Insert Part No.	ST Cutter	Oversize Diameter	Thickness	Insert Outside Diameter	Cylinder Head Inside Diameter	Insert Thickness	Counterbore Depth In Head
154390	ST-258	Std.	Std.	1.690/1.691 [42.9260/42.9514]	1.687/1.688 [42.8498/42.8752]	0.196/0.201 [4.9784/5.1054]	0.351/0.356 [8.9154/9.0424]
154395	ST-258	0.005 [0.1270]	Std.	1.695/1.696 [43.0530/43.0784]	1.692/1.693 [42.9768/43.0022]	0.196/0.201 [4.9784/5.1054]	0.351/0.356 [8.9154/9.0424]
154391	ST-258-1	0.010 [0.2540]	Std.	1.700/1.701 [43.1800/43.2054]	1.697/1.698 [43.1038/43.1292]	0.196/0.201 [4.9784/5.1054]	0.351/0.356 [8.9154/9.0424]
154392	ST-258-2	0.020 [0.5080]	0.005 [0.1270]	1.710/1.711 [43.4340/43.4594]	1.707/1.708 [43.3578/43.3832]	0.201/0.206 [5.1054/5.2324]	0.356/0.361 [9.0424/9.1694]
154393	ST-258-3	0.030 [0.7620]	0.010 [0.2540]	1.720/1.721 [43.6880/43.7134]	1.717/1.718 [43.6118/43.6372]	0.206/0.211 [5.2324/6.3594]	0.361/0.366 [9.1694/9.2964]
154394	ST-258-4	0.040 [1.0160]	0.015 [0.3810]	1.730/1.731 [43.9420/43.9674]	1.727/1.728 [43.8658/43.8912]	0.211/0.216 [5.3594/5.4864]	0.366/0.371 [9.2964/9.4234]

Caution: Be sure to measure insert before machining head or installing insert in head.

Intake Valve Seat Insert Data (If Swirl Plates Are Used) — Inch [mm]

Insert Part No.	ST Cutter	Oversize Diameter	Thickness	Insert Outside Diameter	Cylinder Head Inside Diameter	Insert Thickness	Counterbore Depth In Head
195000	ST-258	Std.	Std.	1.690/1.691 [42.9260/42.9514]	1.687/1.688 [42.8498/42.8752]	0.176/0.181 [4.4704/4.5974]	0.351/0.356 [8.9154/9.0424]
195001	ST-258-1	0.010 [0.2540]	Std.	1.700/1.701 [43.1800/43.2054]	1.697/1.698 [43.1038/43.1292]	0.176/0.181 [4.4704/4.5974]	0.351/0.356 [8.9154/9.0424]
195002	ST-258-2	0.020 [0.5080]	0.005 [0.1270]	1.710/1.711 [43.4340/43.4594]	1.707/1.708 [43.3578/43.3832]	0.181/0.186 [4.5974/4.7244]	0.356/0.361 [9.0424/9.1694]
195003	ST-258-3	0.030 [0.7620]	0.010 [0.2540]	1.720/1.721 [43.6880/43.7134]	1.717/1.718 [43.6118/43.6372]	0.186/0.191 [4.7244/4.8514]	0.361/0.366 [9.1694/9.2964]
195004	ST-258-4	0.040 [1.0160]	0.015 [0.3810]	1.730/1.731 [43.9420/43.9674]	1.727/1.728 [43.8658/43.8912]	0.191/0.196 [4.8514/4.9784]	0.366/0.371 [9.2964/9.4234]

Caution: Be sure to measure insert before machining head or installing insert in head.

Valve Seat Insert Data — Inch [mm]

Insert Part No.	ST Cutter	Oversize Diameter	Thickness	Insert Outside Diameter	Cylinder Head Inside Diameter	Insert Thickness	Counterbore Depth in Head
127930	ST-662	Std.	Std.	2.0025/2.0035 [50.8635/50.8889]	1.9995/2.0005 [50.7873/50.8127]	0.277/0.282 [7.0358/7.1628]	0.437/0.442 [11.0998/11.2268]
127935	ST-662	0.005 [0.1270]	Std.	2.0075/2.0085 [50.9905/51.0159]	2.0045/2.0055 [50.9143/50.9397]	0.277/0.282 [7.0358/7.1628]	0.437/0.442 [11.0998/11.2268]
127931	ST-662-1	0.010 [0.2540]	Std.	2.0125/2.0135 [51.1175/51.1425]	2.0095/2.0105 [51.0413/51.0667]	0.277/0.282 [7.0358/7.1628]	0.437/0.442 [11.0998/11.2268]
127932	ST-662-2	0.020 [0.5080]	0.005 [0.1270]	2.0225/2.0235 [51.3715/51.3969]	2.0195/2.0205 [51.2953/51.3207]	0.282/0.287 [7.1628/7.2898]	0.442/0.447 [11.2268/11.3538]
127933	ST-662-3	0.030 [0.7620]	0.010 [0.2540]	2.0325/2.0335 [51.6255/51.6509]	2.0295/2.0305 [51.5493/51.5747]	0.287/0.292 [7.2898/7.4168]	0.447/0.452 [11.3538/11.4808]
127934	ST-662-4	0.040 [1.0160]	0.015 [0.3810]	2.0425/2.0435 [51.8795/51.9049]	2.0395/2.0405 [51.8033/51.8287]	0.292/0.297 [7.4168/7.5438]	0.452/0.457 [11.4808/11.6078]

Caution: Be sure to measure insert before machining head or installing insert in head.

Cylinder head bolt torque sequence
(© Cummins Engine Co.)

4. Assemble lower valve spring guides on valve guides.
5. Assemble springs. NOTE: *Reground valve heads seat deeper in cylinder head causing valve stem to protrude further above the guide. This allows valve spring to extend beyond length limits and causes weak spring action. Therefore, up to two spacers may be used to reduce valve spring length.* CAUTION: Too many spacers will cause the compressed spring to become a solid sleeve.
6. Assemble upper valve spring guide. Insert half-collets.
7. Use Valve Spring Compressor to compress valve spring. Use new half-collets.

Test Valves and Seats for Leakage

A vacuum tester to check valves and seats for leakage is available. It consists of a vacuum pump, vacuum gauge and suction cup. Use with any

Checking for loose valve seat inserts
(© Cummins Engine Co.)

6-volt battery source or 110-volt electrical outlet as required. Follow manufacturers procedures for operation.

CAUTION Never vacuum test cylinder head with injectors installed. Installation of injectors while head is removed from block could cause misalignment of valves in valve seat and result in leakage during the vacuum test which would not necessarily occur during actual engine operation.

Valves and seats must be dry and clean.

NOTE: It is possible to mistake leakage around the valve seat insert for valve seat leakage. If this type of leakage is suspected apply grease around the outside edge of the insert to make a grease seal. Perform the vacuum test and inspect the grease seal for a break indicating air leakage between the wall of counterbore and valve seat insert. If a leak around valve seat insert is found,

correction is required before continuing with the test.

Install Crossheads

1. Insert valve crossheads in crosshead guides, or assemble valve crossheads over crosshead guides, depending upon design.
2. Install crosshead retainer to keep crosshead in position and insure correct valve-to-crosshead and rocker lever contact.

Check Vent Holes

Check the vent hole at the top of the cylinder head and at the front of every other rocker shaft bearing. *On all supercharged and turbocharged engines the vent holes must be plugged with a ⅛ inch pipe plug. On naturally aspirated engines, a vented plug must be installed.*

Compression Release

Disassembly

1. Remove mounting stud nuts and lockwashers.
2. Lift compression release housing, shaft, lever and spring from cylinder head.
3. Inspect and install a new packing gland, if necessary.

Assembly

1. Reassemble compression release to cylinder head, being careful to let one end of spring ride

Check fuse plug for overheating
(© Cummins Engine Co.)

Measuring injector tip protrusion
(© Cummins Engine Co.)

Sealing lower end of injector sleeve
(© Cummins Engine Co.)

Sealing upper end of injector sleeve
(© Cummins Engine Co.)

against housing with other end held against upper stud bolt.
2. Clamp lever in place so that open position will lift valves 1/16 inch maximum.

Regrooving cylinder head with special tool
(© Cummins Engine Co.)

Refacing valve seats
(© Cummins Engine Co.)

Minimum valve head rim thickness
(© Cummins Engine Co.)

Rocker Assembly and Housing

Rocker Removal

855, 927, 1150 Cid In-line Engines
1. Remove the rocker housing covers. Remove the lubricating oil pipe caps and gaskets.
2. Loosen the locknuts and back off the adjusting screws two or three turns on all rocker levers.
3. Remove the rocker housing retaining bolts and lift the rocker housing assemblies from the engine by grasping the ends of the injector rocker. Leave the compression lever attached to the linkage on No. 1 cylinder.

Installation

855, 927, 1150 Cid Engines
1. Clean the gasket surfaces of the cylinder heads, rocker housings and covers.
2. Using a new housing gasket, position the rocker housing(s) on the cylinder heads with the ball-ends of the rocker levers fitting into their respective push rod sockets. Install and torque the housing bolts in sequence to specifications. Install the compression release arm with the front rocker housing assembly.
3. Using new gaskets, install the lubricating oil pipe caps and torque to specifications.
4. Adjust the valve crossheads and the injector and valve lash.
5. Coat a new cover gasket with oil-resistant sealer and position it on the rocker housing covers. *Care must be taken in positioning the gasket to the rocker cover to prevent covering the crankcase vent or leaving a gap which would permit oil leakage.* Position the cover and gasket on the rocker housing, and install the retaining bolts and washers.
6. Operate the engine and check for leaks. When engine oil temperature is 140°F. remove the rocker housing covers and adjust the injector and valve lash.

Removing oil pipe cap
(© Cummins Engine Co.)

Rocker Lever Assembly Removal

V-6 & V-8 Engines
Remove the valve cover.
Loosen the lock nuts and back off all of the valve and injector rocker lever adjusting screws. Hold the rocker levers together with rubber bands. Remove the rocker lever support screws and remove the rocker lever assembly(ies).

Installation

V-6 & V-8 Engines
Clean all parts before reassembly.
1. Back off the rocker lever adjusting screws. Lubricate the valve and injector rocker lever pads and adjusting screws with engine oil. Install the rocker lever assembly(ies) and torque the mounting screws to specifications (cylinder head bolt torque).
2. Adjust the crossheads and injector and valve rocker lash.
3. Install the valve cover(s), *and partially tighten the cover screws.*
4. Connect the accelerator rod to the fuel pump. Operate the engine until the oil temperature is 140°F. *Be sure the air reservoir drain cock is open.* Remove the valve cover(s) and adjust the injector and valve rocker lash. Install the valve cover(s) and cover screws. Tighten the cover screws in alternate steps.

Cam Follower Housing Assembly Removal

In-line Engines
Remove the rocker housing assembly(ies).
1. Remove the valve and injector push rods, and place them in a rack for installation in the proper sequence.
2. Remove the cam follower housing assembly for cylinders Nos. 5 and 6. Discard the gasket.
3. Remove the fuel pump. Remove the cam follower housing assembly for cylinders Nos. 3 and 4. Discard the gasket.
4. Remove the air compressor.
5. Remove the cam follower housing assembly for Cylinders Nos. 1 and 2. Discard the gasket.
Inspect and clean all parts before assembly.
NOTE: Do not discard metal spacer used with gasket on some models.

Installation

In-line Engines
1. Clean the gasket surfaces of the cam follower housings and cylinder block. Using new gaskets, in-

Pencil marks on valves
(© Cummins Engine Co.)

Vacuum testing valves for leaks
(© Cummins Engine Co.)

stall the cam follower housing assembly(ies), and tighten the retaining screws.

2. Install the valve and injector push rods in the same sequence that they were removed.

3. Remove the fuel injectors from Nos. 1, 3 and 5 cylinders and time the engine.

Valve Adjustment

The same crankshaft position used in setting the injectors is used for setting the intake and exhaust valves. Set valves after injectors are adjusted.

1. Loosen the locknut and adjusting screw. Insert a feeler gauge between the rocker lever and top of the valve stem or crosshead and turn screw down until the lever just touches the feeler gauge.

Valve clearances all except 1150 cid:

Valve	70°F	140°F
Intake	.014	.014
Exhaust	.027	.027

Valve clearances—1150 cid:

Valve	70°F	140°F
Intake	.014	.014
Exhaust	.027	.027

2. Lock adjusting screw in position with jam nut. Recheck valve clearance after tightening jam nut.

3. Continue turning crankshaft in direction of rotation, performing adjustments, until all valves are adjusted correctly.

4-7/8'' AND 5-1/8'' BORE ENGINES
Rocker housing torque sequence
(© Cummins Engine Co.)

4. Make final adjustment when engine is at operating (140°F.) temperature.

5. Continue adjustments, each cylinder in firing order, until all cylinders are adjusted. This will require two complete revolutions of the crankshaft.

Time the Engine

855, 927, Engines

1. Install the special timing tool in injector sleeve. The short rod is engaged with the injector tube push rod, and the long rod rests on top of the piston.

2. Turn engine in normal direction of rotation until piston stops rising. Install indicator above piston so it is compressed to within .010'' of full compression and zero the dial. Continue turning engine until the rod reaches the 90° mark on the left side of the tool.

3. Install the indicator above the

push tube using the procedure described in 2.

4. Turn engine backwards to about 45° before top dead center.

5. Turn engine in direction of normal rotation until the indicator above the piston reads .2032''. The indicator above the push tube should match the figures shown in the table for 19°.

6. Continue turning the engine until the indicator above the piston reads .0816''. The indicator above the push tube should match the reading for 12°.

7. Continue the procedure for a reading of .0143'' and 5°.

8. If downward travel of pushtube is greater than limits, timing is slow. Correct by adding gaskets between follower housing and block on engines with right hand rotation, or by changing the camshaft key.

V6 and V8 Engines

Follow procedures described above, with figures modified as in the appropriate chart. On these engines, timing is varied with the camshaft key only.

Install the rocker housing(s) and adjust the injector and valve lash. Install the rocker housing covers.

Install air compressor and fuel pump.

Injection Timing Procedure
(© Cummins Engine Co.)

Rocker lever removal
(© Cummins Engine Co.)

Operate the engine and check for leaks. When the engine reaches normal operating temperature (140°F oil temperature), adjust the valve and injector lash to specifications.

Time the Engine
1150 cid Engines

1. Adjustments to timing are made by changing camshaft keys.

Timing fixture ST-593 or equivalent and support block ST-593-40 or equivalent are used to obtain precise timing of push tube and piston travel.

2. Position timing fixture in injector well. Engage push rod indicator in injector push tube socket. Hand tighten hold-downs evenly.
3. If adaptor block is used, attach block to housing then secure rod indicator to block. Mount tools straight in cylinder and over push rod tube. Loosen indicators in their supports to prevent damage when barring engine.
4. Turn crankshaft in direction of rotation to bring piston to be checked to TDC firing position.
5. Position piston indicator to compress stem within .010" of inner travel stop. Secure indicator.

Camshaft Key Data — Inch [mm]

Current Key Part Number	Replaces Key Part Number	Amount Of Offset	Push Rod Indicator Travel	Assembly Instructions	Timing Change	Relative Timing Affect
S-313	—	0.000 [0.0000]	0.0000 [0.0000]	—	—	—
200715	162055 & 172363	0.007 [0.1778]	0.0025 [0.0635]	Arrow toward rear of engine Arrow toward front of engine	Adv. Ret.	1/2° 1/2°
200716	162056 & 172364	0.013 [0.3302]	0.0046 [0.1168]	Arrow toward rear of engine Arrow toward front of engine	Adv. Ret.	1° 1°
200717	161154 & 172365	0.019 [0.4826]	0.0068 [0.1727]	Arrow toward rear of engine Arrow toward front of engine	Adv. Ret.	1-1/2° 1-1/2°
200718	162057 172366	0.025 [0.6350]	0.0089 [0.2260]	Arrow toward rear of engine Arrow toward front of engine	Adv. Ret.	2° 2°
200719	162058 172367	0.031 [0.7874]	0.0110 [0.2794]	Arrow toward rear of engine Arrow toward front of engine	Adv. Ret.	2-1/2° 2-1/2°
200721	162059 172368	0.037 [0.9398]	0.0132 [0.3352]	Arrow toward rear of engine Arrow toward front of engine	Adv. Ret.	3° 3°

Injection Timing Specifications

Model	Crank Angle	Piston Travel Inch [mm]	Push Rod Travel — Inch [mm] Nominal	Fast	Slow
V-903	21.0 deg BTC	−0.2032	−0.049	−0.046	−0.052
	13.5 deg BTC	−0.0816	−0.025	−0.022	−0.028
	5.5 deg BTC	−0.0143	−0.007	−0.004	−0.010
VT-903	21.0 deg BTC	−0.3032	−0.054	−0.051	−0.057
	13.5 deg BTC	−0.0816	−0.0295	−0.027	−0.032
	5.5 deg BTC	−0.0143	−0.0115	−0.0095	−0.0135

Injection Timing

Engine Model	Crank Angle (Degrees)	Piston Travel (Inches)	Push Tube Travel (Inches) Nominal	Fast	Slow
HRC-4, NHC-4, H-6, HR, HRF, NH-180, NH-195, NH-220	19° BTC 12° BTC 5° BTC	− 0.2032 − 0.0816 − 0.0143	− 0.0295 − 0.0150 − 0.0037	− 0.0275 − 0.0130 − 0.0020	− 0.0315 − 0.0165 − 0.0050
NHE-180, NHE-195	19° BTC 12° BTC 5° BTC	− 0.2032 − 0.0816 − 0.0143	− 0.0285 − 0.0140 − 0.0028	− 0.0275 − 0.0130 − 0.0020	− 0.0295 − 0.0150 − 0.0037
NH-250, NHE-225, NHD-230 NHC-250, NHCT-270-1,2,3 (before Serial No. 569212)	19° BTC 12° BTC 5° BTC	− 0.2032 − 0.0816 − 0.0143	− 0.0305 − 0.0160 − 0.0044	− 0.0295 − 0.0150 − 0.0037	− 0.0335 − 0.0185 − 0.0062
NT, NT-265, NT-280, NT-280 NT-200, NFT, HS, HRS, NHS, NHRS, NT-310 (Automotive and Marine)	19° BTC 12° BTC 5° BTC	− 0.2032 − 0.0816 − 0.0143	− 0.0335 − 0.0185 − 0.0062	− 0.0315 − 0.0165 − 0.0045	− 0.0355 − 0.0200 − 0.0075
NTO, NRT, NRTO, NTC-260, NTC-280, NTC-300, NTC-320, NTC-335, NT-380, NHCT-270-4* (Automotive and Marine)	19° BTC 12° BTC 5° BTC	− 0.2032 − 0.0816 − 0.0143	− 0.0360 − 0.0205 − 0.0080	− 0.0340 − 0.0190 − 0.0065	− 0.0380 − 0.0220 − 0.0095
NRT, NRTO, NT-335, NT-380 (Off-Highway)	19° BTC 12° BTC 5° BTC	− 0.2032 − 0.0816 − 0.0143	− 0.0415 − 0.0250 − 0.0115	− 0.0395 − 0.0230 − 0.0100	− 0.0435 − 0.0265 − 0.0130

Note: Procedures and values for timing horizontal engines are identical with corresponding standard models.

*NHCT-270 and NHCT-270HT after Serial No. 569212.

Rocker levers, shafts and bearings
(© Cummins Engine Co.)

Tappets and push rods
(© Cummins Engine Co.)

6. Check for exact O TDC with dial indicator.
7. Turn crankshaft in direction of rotation to 90 ATDC. Position pushrod indicator on follower to .020″ from inner travel stop. Secure indicator.
8. Turn crankshaft back to a position 40 B TDC.
9. Slowly turn engine in direction of rotation until piston indicator is positioned at .0032″ before 0. This is equivalent to .2032″ BTC.
10. Pushrod travel indicator should read:

Timing Code	Piston Travel	Push rod travel
AE	-.2032	.107-.109
AM	-.2032	.124-.128

Gear Case Cover and Seal

Gear Case Cover Removal

In-line Engines

1. Drain the cooling system and the crankcase.
2. When necessary release the cab locks and tilt the cab forward.
3. Remove the radiator and shutter assembly. Remove the front crossmember (radiator support) from the frame where necessary.
4. Remove the oil pan.
5. Remove the cooling fan. Remove all drive belts. Remove the fan hub and bracket assembly. Remove the fan drive pulley from the compressor crankshaft.
6. Remove the power steering pump bracket to engine bolts and position the pump and bracket assembly out of the way.
7. Remove the crankshaft damper capscrews, and pull the damper off the crankshaft. It may be necessary to tap the damper with a soft hammer in order to loosen it from the crankshaft. Remove the crankshaft flange capscrew and retainer, or nut and lock-

plate on some engines, and use puller to remove the flange.
8. Use a jack and wood block under the front of the engine to support it. Remove the engine front support retaining bolts, spacers and insulators. Remove the support bracket cap bolts and bracket cap. Raise the engine and remove the support bracket and insulators as an assembly.
9. Remove the compressor crankshaft pulley nut. Remove the compressor crankshaft pulley. Remove the crankshaft key.
10. If the gear case cover has an outboard camshaft bearing, remove it from the cover. Install guide studs in two of the capscrew holes. Remove the gear case retaining bolts. Using a soft hammer, loosen the gear case cover from the cylinder block, and remove the cover. Remove the seals from the cover. Remove the camshaft thrust-plate, O-ring seal and spacers, if so equipped.

Installation

1. Clean the oil pan and gear case cover with solvent. Be sure all gasket surfaces and oil seal recesses are clean. Remove and clean the oil pump inlet screen.
2. Apply oil-resistant sealer to the OD of the new cover seals (crankshaft and compressor shaft) and install the seals in the gear case cover. Use oil-

Installing camshaft thrust plate
(© Cummins Engine Co.)

resistant sealer to cement a new gasket to the gear case cover.
3. Apply lubricant to the oil seal lips and the seal surface of the compressor shaft. Install the gear case cover and tighten the retaining bolts.
4. Install the crankshaft and fuel pump-compressor drive shaft oil seals with special mandrels. Make sure crankshaft oil seal bore is concentric with shaft within .010″. Relocate cover, if necessary, to ensure concentricity, clearance between seal and shoulder on gear case must be at least .030″. Front face of seal must be square with crankshaft axis within .010″ to 45-50 ft-lbs. Make sure bottom surface is within .004″ of flush with bottom of block.
5. Position the engine front support and insulator assembly on the frame crossmember, and lower the engine onto the support bracket. Install the support bracket cap, lower insulators, spacers, and retaining bolts. Torque the bracket to frame bolts, and then the bracket cap bolts to specifications.
6. If equipped with a camshaft thrust plate, install it as follows: Hold the thrust plate, without spacers, in position against the camshaft, and use feeler gauges to check the clearance between the thrust plate and the gear case cover. Using micrometers, select enough spacers to bring the camshaft end clearance within specifications (.001″-.005″ on engines with thrust plates, .008″-.013″ on engines with outboard bearing supports). Place the spacers on the thrust plate. Apply Lubriplate to a new O-ring and install it on the thrust plate. Install the thrust plate on the gear case cover and tighten the screws.
7. Coat the seal surfaces of the crankshaft flange wtih lubricant and install the flange on the crankshaft. Install the flange

Installing crankshaft seal in gear case cover
(© Cummins Engine Co.)

Installing gear case cover
(© Cummins Engine Co.)

lockplate and lock nut and torque to specifications. Bend the lockplate to secure the nut. Install the crankshaft damper on the crankshaft flange and tighten the retaining screws.

8. Install the fan drive pulley on the compressor crankshaft.

9. Install the power steering pump and bracket assembly on the engine.

10. Install the fan hub and bracket assembly. Torque the screws to specifications. Position the cooling fan, alternator and power steering pump drive belts in the proper pulleys. Install the cooling fan.

11. Install the oil pan.

12. Install the front crossmember, and install the radiator and shutter assembly if removed.

13. Fill and bleed the cooling system. Fill the crankcase. Operate the engine and check for oil and coolant leaks.

Cylinder Front Cover Oil Seal Removal

V-6 & V-8 Engines

1. Drain the cooling system. Disconnect the battery cables.

2. Remove the shutter and radiator.

3. Remove the alternator, cooling fan and power steering pump drive belts.

4. Remove the cooling fan. Remove the crankshaft damper and the crankcase pulley.

5. Punch two holes in the cylinder front cover oil seal. Install a self-tapping screw in each

punched hole, and pry against the screws to remove the oil seal.

Installation

Apply oil-resistant sealer to the OD of a new oil seal. Lubricate the oil seal lips and the crankshaft with engine oil. Install the seal.

Reverse the removal procedure.

Camshaft

For best operation we do not recommend camshaft lobe regrinding.

Journal Wear

New camshaft journal diameter is 1.996"-1.997" on V-6 and small V-8, 2.496"-2.497" on V8 903, and 1.997"-1.998" on in-line engines.

1. Replace camshaft if journals are smaller than specified.

Tightening camshaft retaining bolts
(© Cummins Engine Co.)

Checking clearance between thrust washer
(© Cummins Engine Co.)

RETARD FROM STRAIGHT   STRAIGHT   ADVANCE FROM STRAIGHT

FROM GEAR CASE END OF CAMSHAFT

Camshaft gear keys from gear case end
(© Cummins Engine Co.)

Removing camshaft
(© Cummins Engine Co.)

2. Replace any camshaft with scuffed, scored or cracked injector or valve lobes. Check by magnetic inspection for possible cracks.

Camshaft Gear and Thrust Bearing

The interference fit camshaft gear is keyed to the camshaft. The type of keys used are shown in illustration. The key controls engine timing limits, it may be straight or offset as shown.

The current camshaft thrust bearing is mounted with two instead of three capscrews; interchangeable with older bearing mounted with three capscrews.

Do not remove camshaft gear unless absolutely necessary. If inspection shows it is necessary to remove gear, do so by one of two following methods:

Camshafts with three capscrews mounted thrust bearing.

Removal

1. Heat gear to 300°-400°F.
2. Insert gear puller jaws through access holes in gear.
3. Tighten puller bolt until gear is free of camshaft.
4. Camshafts with two capscrew mounted thrust bearing.
   a. Place camshaft and gear in press. Support gear as near

a. Pin Bore Area
b. Area Below Ring Groove
c. Piston Skirt

Piston Check Points (N20171)
(© Cummins Engine Co.)

Piston Dimensions Check Points (V10167)
(© Cummins Engine Co.)

Piston Dimensions Check Points (V50125)
(© Cummins Engine Co.)

hub as possible by using short bars laying parallel with thrust bearing.
   b. Press camshaft from gear.
NOTE: Care must be taken to prevent gear breakage due to improper use of press and support bars.

Installation

1. Note type of key used. Replace key.
2. Coat gear hub area of camshaft with Lubriplate.
3. Install camshaft thrust bushing on camshaft with grooves in bushing toward gear.
4. Heat gear evenly to 400°/500°F. with heating torch (not a cutting torch).
5. Press on new camshaft gear, aligning gear keyway with camshaft key.
6. Check between camshaft flange and camshaft gear for .0015″ maximum clearance for new thrust bearing. Check timing.

Pistons and Connecting Rods

Pistons and Connecting Rods Removal

Typical of All Engines

1. Drain the cooling system and the crankcase and remove the exhaust manifold(s), intake manifold(s), cylinder head or valve cover (s), cylinder head(s), oil pan, and oil pump.
2. Scrape all of the carbon from the top of the cylinder liners. Polish with a fine emery cloth.
3. Remove the connecting rod cap.
4. Push the connecting rod and piston assembly out of the top of the cylinder. *Avoid damage to the crankshaft journal or the cylinder liner when removing the piston and connecting rod.*
5. Remove the bearings and identify them with the cylinder numbers. Assemble the connecting

Checking piston ring gap
(© Cummins Engine Co.)

Checking ring groove wear
(© Cummins Engine Co.)

rod, cap, bolts and nuts as each rod and piston assembly is removed.

Disassembly

1. Using piston ring expander, remove the piston rings.
2. Remove the piston pin retaining rings. *Heat the pistons in hot water; then remove the piston pins. Do not use any force but pressure from the fingers to remove piston pins.*
3. Remove carbon deposits from the piston surfaces. Clean gum or varnish from the piston pins, piston skirt and piston rings with solvent. *Do not use a caustic cleaning solution or a wire brush to clean pistons.* Make sure the oil ring holes are clean. *Do not use a ring groove cleaning tool or a broken piston ring to clean the ring grooves. Use a soft bristle brush and cleaning solvent.*
4. Consult parts catalog for use of proper pistons and rings. Chrome plated compression rings are used only in the top groove, and should never be filed or used with chrome plated liners. Inspect the pistons, piston pins and piston rings as follows:
   a. Insert each ring into its cylinder liner, positioning it with the head of the piston. Measure the ring gap with a feeler gauge, and ensure that gap compares with figures in specifications section.
   b. Check the top and second ring grooves with the special gauge for each type piston. The shoulders of the gauge must not touch ring groove lands, or piston is not reusable. If the proper gauge is not available, use a segment of a new ring and a .006" feeler gauge. If gauge does not require force, do not use the piston.
   c. With pistons at 70-90°F., measure the skirt diameter at right angles to the pin bore. Measure at points shown in the appropriate illustration, and compare with specifications. Pistons must not be worn to less than 6.235" on 1150 cid engines, 5.483" on in-line 855, 927 engines, 5.4850" on V8-903 engines. Use the chart below for V6 and small V8 engines.

Piston
Part #	Check Points:	Wear Limit
173800	1	4.6130
185310	2, 3	4.6110
200800	2, 3	4.6110

   d. Check the piston pin bore at 70°F. It should be 2.3990 on 1150 1.999" on 855, 927 engines, 1.750" on V8-903 engines, and 1.3479" on other engines.
5. Check piston pin diameter. It should be 2.398 on 1150 1.9978 on 855, 927 engines, 1.7478" on V8-903 engines and 1.3733" on V6 and small V8 engines. Permissible out of round limit is .001" on in-line engines, .0005" and V6 and V8 engines.

Assembly

1. Install one piston pin retaining ring in the piston. Heat the piston in hot water at 210°F for 15 min. and install the piston pin. Install the remaining piston pin retainer.
2. Install the piston rings on the piston, using a piston ring, expander. The side of the piston ring marked "TOP" must be toward the top of the piston. If new piston rings are installed, fit them to the piston and the cylinder bore. *Never use chrome-plated piston rings in a chrome-plated cylinder liner.*

Installation

1. Oil the piston rings, pistons and cylinder walls with clean engine oil. *Be sure to install the pistons in the same cylinders from which they were fitted. The numbers on the connecting rod and bearing cap must be on the same side when installed in the cylinder bore. If a connecting rod is ever transposed from one block or cylinder to another, new bearings should be fitted and the connecting rod should be numbered to correspond with the new cylinder number. On V6 and small V8 engines, install piston with cylinder or piston number, or word "out," toward exhaust side of engine.*
2. Make sure the ring gaps are properly spaced around the circumference of the piston but not in line with the piston pin. Install the piston ring compressor on the piston and push the piston in with a hammer handle until it is slightly below the top of the cylinder liner. *If a band-type ring compressor is used, make certain the inner band does not slip down and bind the piston, or ring breakage will occur. Be sure to guide the connecting rods to avoid damaging the crankshaft journals. Install the piston with the number on the rod toward the camshaft on in-line engines, or outside of block on V type engines.*
3. Turn the crankshaft throw to the bottom of its stroke. Install the connecting rod bearings, and check the clearance of each bear-

ing following the procedure under "Connecting Rod Bearing Replacement."
4. After the bearings have been checked and found satisfactory, apply a light coat of engine oil to the journals and bearings. Install the connecting rod cap. Torque the bolts to specifications. Lock the tab washers.
5. After the piston and connecting rod assemblies have been installed, check the connecting rod bearing side clearance.
6. Install the oil pump, oil pan, cylinder head(s), cylinder head cover(s), intake manifold(s), and exhaust manifold(s).
7. Adjust the valve crossheads; then adjust the injector and valve lash. Torque the rocker lever lock nuts to specifications.
8. Fill the cooling system and crankcase. Operate the engine until the oil temperature is 140°F. Remove the cylinder head covers and adjust the injector and valve lash. Check for oil, air, fuel and coolant leaks. Install the cylinder head covers.

Cylinder Liners

Cylinder Liner Removal

Typical—All Engines

1. Drain the cooling system and the crankcase.
2. Remove the following: coolant manifold, exhaust manifold, fuel manifold, intake manifold, rocker housing assembly(ies), cylinder head(s), oil pan and piston(s) and connecting rod(s).
3. Remove the cylinder liner, using liner puller (or equivalent). If more than one liner is removed, identify them for installation in the same position as removed.

Inspection and Repair

Inspect the cylinder liners and cylinder liner counterbore (crankcase) and repair as necessary. *Before dis-*

Removing cylinder liner
(© Cummins Engine Co.)

Measuring cylinder liner counterbore depth
(© Cummins Engine Co.)

Checking cylinder liner protrusion
(© Cummins Engine Co.)

Aligning cylinder liner valve recess
(© Cummins Engine Co.)

carding a cylinder liner worn beyond the maximum wear limit, determine if it can be ground oversize for use with the next oversize piston. If it is necessary to grind the ID of one liner, inspect all liners for conformance to wear limits.

Check the diametrical clearance of the cylinder liner to cylinder bore in the liner O-ring seal area. *It must be within specifications.*

Installation

1. Check the cylinder liner protrusion by measuring the liner flange and liner counterbore. If necessary, install shims around the liner to provide the specified protrusion.

ENGINE	Protrusion
V6, V8	To eng. "F" .004-.007; After eng. "F" .006-.009
855, 927	.003-.006"
V8-903	.003-.0065"
K-1150	.003-.006"

2. Lubricate new cylinder liner O-rings with clean engine oil, and install them in the liner seal grooves. Be sure the O-rings are not twisted in the grooves.
3. Use engine oil to lubricate the machined portions of the liner bore in the cylinder block.
4. Carefully position the cylinder liner in the same cylinder bore from which it was removed. *Do not use beaded liners with steel-asbestos type head gasket.* Align valves as follows: Install one cylinder head capscrew. Align tool locators with the liner valve recesses and index the notch in tool with the capscrew. Push the liner in place. *Be sure O-rings are not displaced as the cylinder liner passes the top counterbore.*
5. Drive the press-fit liner into the cylinder block bore with liner driver and a hammer.
6. Check the liner protrusion at 4 equidistant points; it must be within specifications. Use a dial bore gauge to check the cylinder liner bore for roundness at several points within range of the piston travel. If the liner bore is

more than 0.002 inch out-of-round, remove the liner and check for possible binding condition which would cause distortion of the liner.

7. Using news gaskets, install the piston(s) and connecting rod(s), cylinder head(s), oil pan and rocker housing assembly(ies), and perform the necessary adjustments for the valve crossheads and injector and valve lash. Install the intake manifold, exhaust manifold, coolant manifold and fuel manifold.
8. Fill the cooling system and crankcase. Operate the engine and check for fuel, oil, coolant and air leaks. When the engine reaches normal operating temperature, check and adjust the injector and valve lash. Use the following specifics for liner counterbore.

Check Cylinder Liner Counterbore

1. Remove all corrosion and carbon deposits. These would affect readings obtained from block gauge.
2. Set gauge on block and depress indicator stem until indicator point touches block. Set dial to "0".
3. Position indicator in gauge block so stem moves about .10 inch to reach "0" on gauge. This leaves

Installing cylinder liner
(© Cummins Engine Co.)

maximum amount of indicator travel available.

4. With indicator at "0", position gauge on deck so that indicator stem is over liner ledge.
5. Depress indicator stem till its point contacts liner ledge.
6. Read depth of counterbore shown on indicator.
7. Check each liner edge at four or more equi-distant locations. NOTE: The liner ledge must not be "cupped" more than .00075 inch. ("Cupped" refers to the condition where that part of the cylinder liner ledge next to the liner is the highest point of the ledge surface). The depth must not vary more than .001 inch.
8. The counterbore at top of a new block is .30925/.31050 inch deep. If counterbore exceeds these limits oversize liners are available. *Only top 1/8 inch of counterbore provides press-fit.*
9. An installed cylinder liner must protrude .003-.006 inch above milled surface of block on in-line engines, .003-.006 inch on V8-903 engines, and .004-.007 inch on V6 and small V8 engines. To check protrusion *without* pressing liner into block:
   a. Measure liner flange outside bead with micrometer. *Do not include bead on top of liner flange in measurement.*
   b. Measure counterbore depth with dial indicator depth gauge.
   c. If measurement difference between two is not in proper range, add shims or counterbore block as necessary to achieve correct cylinder liner protrusion. CAUTION: The following operation must be preceded by careful counter-bore depth measurement and calculation of shim thickness to be used after counterboring. The .007 inch thick shim is the thinnest available. *Always check shim thickness before installing shim.* Use as few shims as possible. Use one thick

Checking counterbore depth
(© Cummins Engine Co.)

Measuring cylinder liner flange
(© Cummins Engine Co.)

shim in place of two thinner shims. Never use shims thinner than .007 inch.

Counterbore Cylinder Liner Ledge

(A special tool for this is available from Cummins)

1. Loosen adjustable tool head lock collar and remove tool holder.
2. Place upper adapter in position and fasten with capscrews.
3. Reposition tool holder, tightening adjustable tool head lock collar finger tight.
4. Install lower adaptor plate on tool with capscrews.

Installing Tool in Block

1. Raise tool bit until tip is flush with tool holder. *Tool bit set screws are not to be loosened to raise or lower tool bits.*
2. Make sure top and bottom adjustable locating pins are retracted and flush with housing before inserting tool in bore. The socket head screws on upper adaptor plate, above pins control this movement.
3. Insert tool into block bore so locating surfaces are on water jacket side of block. Position top of upper adaptor plate 1/32 inch below counterbore.
4. Tighten adjustable locating pins against bore with socket head wrench and extension.
5. Insert wooden block between capscrews inserted in block to prevent tool head from rotating counter-clockwise.
6. Insert handle in socket and rotate counterclockwise to loosen adjustable tool head lock collar.
7. Move tool head out until tool bit contacts counterbore edge.
8. Rotate collar clockwise, by hand, to lock.
9. Lower tool bit until it engages counterbore and remove wooden block. Rotate head clockwise to see if it binds.
10. Replace wooden block between capscrews. Check tool head posi-

FOR STANDARD LINERS

FOR OVER-SIZE LINERS

Oversize press-fit liner counterbore
(© Cummins Engine Co.)

Cross section of new block counterbore
(© Cummins Engine Co.)

tion then lock in place by turning handle clockwise.

Counterbore block

1. Screw tool bit down until it touches counterbore seat.
2. Insert handle and rotate slowly, clockwise, until tool bit stops cutting.
3. If necessary, continue cutting by feeding tool bit down. Feed dial graduations are approximately .002 inch. Cut only ½ graduation at a time. Remove only enough metal to clean up counterbore.
4. Check counterbore depth with dial indicator depth gauge. Measure cylinder liner flange.

Do not include head on liner.

5. Subtract flange thickness from counterbore depth and calculate thickness of shim needed to provide proper liner protrusion above block.

Lapping Counterbore in Block

(Non-Press-fit liners only)

If the cylinder liner flanges and counterbore are not perfectly smooth, the counterbore may be lapped.

1. Place Grade A grit lapping compound on counterbore ledge.
2. Insert cylinder liner.
3. Apply light and even pressure while lapping. Rotate liner one complete revolution, then lap in 30° strokes. Add a few drops of lube oil each 2 or 3 revolutions to keep lapping compound moist.
4. *Remove all lapping compound from counterbore and liner flange.*
5. Apply light coat of prussian blue and check seat. *A full seat must be indicated on both counterbore and liner flange.*
6. Repeat lapping operation as necessary.

Crankshaft

Journals

Crankshafts which are scored or scratched should be reground to standard undersize to fit available standard main bearings and connecting rod bearings. Main bearings are available in .010, .020, .030, and .040 inch undersize. Undersize connecting rod bearings are available in corresponding undersizes.

Oil Passages

1. Use a rod and rag, just as you would to clean a rifle barrel, to check and completely clean oil passages in crankshaft.
2. Replace pipe plugs.
   a. Coat threads with sealer.
   b. Tighten to 5 ft. lbs.
   c. Stake to prevent loosening.

Thrust Flange—V6, Small V8

If crankshaft thrust flange is worn as much as .005 inch or grooved as deep as .005 inch, build up by welding and regrind to size. Oversize thrust rings may also be installed. Installed end clearance must be .014" or less. Mark shaft rear counterweight as required.

Thrust Rings

Measure crankshaft end clearance. Use oversize rings as necessary to create .022"-.035" clearance on 855 engines, .005"-.015" clearance on 903 engines, and .022"-.030" clearance on 927 engines. Mark ring size and location on rear counterweight.

Crankshaft Gear In-Line Engines

If it is necessary to remove crankshaft gear:
1. Attach puller to gear.
2. Apply 75/100 ft. lbs. on puller screw.
3. Heat gear with a heating torch—not a cutting torch—to 300°/400°F. The gear will expand, making it easier to pull.

To assemble gear:
1. Heat gear evenly to 400°/500°F with a heating torch (not a cutting torch).
2. Drive onto crankshaft with tubing.

Crankshaft Gear V-Type Engines

If the gear is damaged, remove it with a hammer and chisel. Place end of chisel between teeth above the key-way and strike several times to loosen the gear.

General Inspection

1. Inspect journals and thrust flange for scoring or scratching and have the shaft reground if they are present.
2. Gauge crankshaft journals for conformity to specifications.
3. Check all journals for out-of-round exceeding .002". Regrind to correct excessive out-of-round.

Checking crankshaft end clearance
(© Cummins Engine Co.)

Removing rear cover
(© Cummins Engine Co.)

Crankshaft Rear Oil Seal

All Engines—The rear cover has a braided asbestos seal around the crankshaft. When the rear cover is assembled to the cylinder block its bore must be in line with the main bearing bore. Cement a new gasket over the dowel pins on the rear of the cylinder block. Assemble the upper cover plate over the dowel pins and tighten the four cup screws. With crankshaft pushed toward the cover plate, check the clearance between the crankshaft flange and the opposing face of the cover place.

Clearance should be a minimum of .004". The clearance of .004" to .006" can be obtained by using gaskets between the cover plate and the cylinder block.

The clearance between the crankshaft and bore of the cover plate should be .009 to .011" (.006" on in-line) around the entire circumference. This clearance is provided when the original rear cover is installed at the factory and maintained by locating dowels. This can be checked after the old asbestos seal has been removed by using a .009" feeler gauge between the shaft and upper cover.

Remove the cover plate and install new asbestos seals into the recess of both upper and lower cover plates. New seals must be beveled on three sides of each end 13/20" by 45°, leaving the inside edge square. The ends of the seals should extend 1/32" above the joining surfaces of the cover plates. Seals should be soaked in lubricating oil an hour or more before installing. Make sure they are well seated in their grooves.

Cement new connecting gaskets to the lower cover plate. Assemble the lower plate to the upper plate and bolt together tightly. Install capscrews to cover plates and pull up evenly to the cylinder block over the dowel pins.

Main and Connecting Rod Bearings

All Cummins main and connecting rod bearings are precision parts with shell thickness, bearing material and bearing crush accurately calculated and held to close tolerances. Both standard and undersized bearings are provided with recommended clearance for the oil film. *Under no circumstances should any attempt be made to scrape or ream these bearings nor should they be lapped or filed to increase oil clearances.*

A properly fitted bearing, after a reasonable period of service, will appear dull gray; indicating it is running on an oil film. Bright spots indi-

Checking thrust flange wear
(© Cummins Engine Co.)

Cleaning oil passages
(© Cummins Engine Co.)

Installing connecting rod gap
(© Cummins Engine Co.)

cate metal-to-metal contact; black spots excessive clearance.

CAUTION: Never use shims with main or connecting rod bearing shells.

Main Bearings

All current engines have grooveless lower main bearing shells and grooved upper shells. Grooveless lower main bearing shells can be installed in engines with serial numbers previous to Serial No. 113353 provided the crankshaft journals do not have prominent ridges formed from wear with the grooved type lower shells. If the ridge is higher than .001 inch, it will be necessary to install grooved shells until the crankshaft is reground.

Main bearing shells are held in place by a locking tang or lip on each shell which mates with milled recesses in the block and cap opposite the camshaft side of the engine.

NOTE: If grooved shells are to be reused, they must be installed in the same position as removed.

Inspection

Inspect connecting rod and main bearing shells for the following defects:

1. Fatigue, corrosive damage, or pitting in the loaded area.
2. Evidence of overheating, i.e., badly discolored or burnished surface.
3. Excessive lead wiping.
4. High spot due to dirt behind bearing.
5. Cracks on the bearing surface or on back of shell.
6. Excessive edge loading or fretting.

Check scratches on the bearing surface. Scratches deep enough to result in ridges on either side of scratch will cause contact during operation and lead to engine failure.

It is not necessary to discard shells due to *minor* discoloration, eroded

lead plate, slight scratches or imperfection outside the load area.

Gauge bearing shells with a ball point micrometer or equivalent. Replace if worn beyond limit shown below.

855, 927	.1215"
903	.15300"
1150	.1690"
V6, V8	
Serial Prefix D	.12275"
Serial Prefix F, G	.12250

Connecting Rod Bearing Replacement

Typical—All Engines

Bearing clearance can be checked by using micrometers or by using Plastigage as outlined in the following procedure. If the Plastigage method is employed, use new standard-size bearings.

Worn limits on bearing shell thickness are as shown below:

855	.071"
1150	.1230"
927	.093"
903	.09295"
V6, V8	.007"

1. Drain the crankcase. Remove the oil pan; if necessary, remove the oil pump.
2. Remove the cap from the connecting rod to which new bearings are to be fitted. Push the piston part way up the cylinder.
3. Remove the bearings from the connecting rod and cap. Clean the crankshaft journal, connecting rod and bearing cap.
4. Install new bearings in the connecting rod and cap. Pull the connecting rod assembly down firmly on the crankshaft journal.
5. Place a piece of Plastigage on the lower bearing surface, the full width of the cap and about ¼ inch off-center.
6. Install the cap and torque the connecting rod nuts to 140 ft-lbs. *Do not turn the crankshaft while the Plastigage is in place.*
7. Remove the cap, then using the Plastigage scale, check the width of the Plastigage. When checking the width of the Plastigage, check at the widest point in order to get the minimum clearance. The difference between the two readings is the taper.
8. Check the bearing side clearance; it must be to specifications. After the bearing clearance has been checked and found to be within the specified limits, clean the Plastigage from the crankshaft journal. *If standard-size bearings or the next under-size bearing does not provide the specified clearance, then crankshaft grinding or replacement is indicated.*

9. Apply Lubriplate to the journal and bearings, then install the connecting rod cap. Install new lock plates and torque the rod nuts to specifications. Bend the tabs on the lock plates to secure the nuts.
10. Repeat the procedure for the remaining connecting rods that require new bearings.
11. Install the oil pump. Install the oil pan.
12. Fill the crankcase. Operate the engine at fast idle and check for oil leaks.

Main Bearing Replacement

In-line Engines

Bearing clearance can be checked by using micrometers or by using Plastigage as outlined in the following procedure. If the Plastigage method is employed, use new standard-size bearings.

1. Drain the crankcase. Remove the oil pan.
2. Remove the main bearing cap to which new bearings are to be installed. *Replace one bearing at a time, leaving the other bearings securely fastened.*
3. Remove the thrust washers. Rotate the crankshaft with barring tool, and force the upper bearing out of the block.
4. Remove the bearing from the cap. Clean the crankshaft journal and bearing inserts.
5. All upper main bearings are grooved and drilled for lubrication. On 855,927 engines, numbers 1, 3 and 5 are alike and Nos. 2, 4 and 6 are alike. Number 7 has the oil groove off center, and it must not be interchanged with the other bearings. On 1150 engines, nos. 2, 3, 4, 5, 6 are interchangeable; nos. 1 & 7 are interchangeable. The wide portion of the bearing is installed toward the flywheel end.
6. Apply lubricant to the upper main bearing, and insert it between the crankshaft journal and crankcase web. Rotate the crankshaft until the bearing seats itself. *The groove on each bearing for the dowel ring must match with the counterbore at the capscrew hole on the exhaust manifold side of the block.*
7. Install the upper thrust rings with the babbit sides *next to the crankshaft flanges.* The upper thrust rings are not doweled to the block. The doweled lower halves prevent them from turning.
8. Replace the cap bearing. The lower main bearings are plain with no grooves or drillings.
9. Support the crankshaft so that its weight will not compress the

Checking rod to crankshaft clearance
(© Cummins Engine Co.)

Laying upper main bearing shells
(© Cummins Engine Co.)

Plastigage and provide a false reading. Position the support so that it will bear against the counterweight adjoining the bearing which is being checked.

10. Place a piece of Plastigage on the bearing surface the full width of the bearing cap and ¼ inch off-center.
11. On the No. 7 (rear) main bearing, install the lower thrust rings. *The lower thrust rings must be held by the dowels in the main bearing cap.*
12. Install the cap and torque the bolts to 150 ft-lbs. *Do not turn the crankshaft while the Plastigage is in place.*
13. Remove the cap, then using the Plastigage scale, check the width of the Plastigage. When checking the width of the Plastigage, check at the widest point in order to get the minimum clearance. Check at the narrowest point in order to get the maximum clearance. The difference between the two readings is the taper.
14. After the bearing clearance has been checked and found to be within the specified limits, clean off the Plastigage. *If standard-size bearings or the next under-size bearing does not provide the specified clearance, then crank-*

shaft grinding or replacement is indicated.

15. Apply lubricant to the bearing and journal. Install the bearing cap, using new lock plates.
16. Torque the bolts to specifications. Bend the tabs on the lock plates to secure the bolts.
17. Repeat the procedure for the remaining bearings that require replacement.
18. Install the oil pan.
19. Fill the crankcase. Operate the engine at fast idle and check for oil leaks.

Main Bearing Replacement

V-6 & V-8 Engines

Bearing clearance can be checked by using micrometers or by using Plastigage as outlined in the following procedure. If the Plastigage method is employed, use new standard-size bearings.

1. Drain the crankcase. Remove the oil pan and oil pump.
2. Remove the main bearing cap side bolts from both sides of the engine block.
3. Remove the cap bolts from the main bearing to which new bearings are to be installed. Use a small pry-bar to loosen the bearing cap. Remove the bearing cap. *Replace one bearing at a time,*

leaving the other bearings securely fastened.

4. Rotate the crankshaft with the barring tool and force the upper bearing out of the block. On the rear main bearing, remove the upper thrust half-rings from the block. On the rear main bearing, remove the thrust half-rings cap.
5. Remove the bearing from the from the bearing cap dowels. Clean the crankshaft journal and bearing inserts.
6. Only the upper main bearings are grooved and drilled for lubrication. Numbers 1 and 4 are alike and Nos. 2 and 3 are alike.
7. Apply Lubriplate to the upper main bearing, and insert it between the crankshaft journal and crankcase web. Rotate the crankshaft until the bearing seats itself. *The groove on each bearing for the dowel ring must match with the counterbore at the capscrew hole on the exhaust manifold side of the block.*
8. Install the upper thrust rings with the *grooved side next to the crankshaft flange.* The upper thrust rings are not doweled to the block; the doweled lower halves prevent them from turning.
9. The lower main bearings are plain with no grooves or drill-

Measuring main bearing shells
(© Cummins Engine Co.)

Installing thrust rings
(© Cummins Engine Co.)

Main bearing side cap screw torque sequence
(© Cummins Engine Co.)

Lubricating oil pump—layout
(© Cummins Engine Co.)

ings. Numbers 1 and 4 are alike and Nos. 2 and 3 are alike.

10. Support the crankshaft so that its weight will not compress the Plastigage and provide an erroneous reading. Position the support so that it will bear against the counterweight adjoining the bearing which is being checked.

11. Place a piece of Plastigage on the bearing surface the full width of the bearing cap and ¼ inch off-center.

12. On the rear main bearing, install the lower thrust rings on the dowels in the main bearing cap.

13. Install the cap and torque the bolts to 180 ft-lbs. *Do not turn the crankshaft while the Plastigage is in place.*

14. Remove the cap, then using the Plastigage scale, check the width of the Plastigage. When checking the width of the Plastigage, check at the widest point in order to get the minimum clearance. Check at the narrowest point in order to get the maximum clearance. The difference between the two readings is the taper.

15. After the bearing clearance has been checked and found to be within the specified limits, clean off the Plastigage. *If standard-size bearings or the next undersize bearing does not provide the specified clearance, then crankshaft grinding or replacement is indicated.*

16. Apply Lubriplate to the bearing and journal. Install the bearing cap, using new lock plates.

17. Torque the bolts to specifications. Bend the tabs on the lock plates to secure the bolts.

18. Repeat the procedure for the remaining bearings that require replacement.

19. Torque the main bearing side capscrews to specifications, following the sequence.

20. Install the oil pump and oil pan.

21. Fill the crankcase. Operate the engine at fast idle and check for oil leaks.

Engine Oil Pump

In-Line Engines

The standard oil pump in these engines is of the two-gear type. In servicing these pumps, note the following:

1. The ball bearing outer race must not turn in the ball bearing cage.

2. The gears must show no excessive wear, or be scored or otherwise damaged.

3. The drive shaft must be replaced if it has been turning in the inner race of the ball bearing; if it is worn smaller than .8735″ where it bears against the bracket bushing, or if it is worn smaller than .8705″ on the body end.

4. The bracket bushing should not be used if its inside diameter is worn larger than .887″.

5. Idler pins should be replaced if worn smaller than .873″.

6. Replace bracket or cover if finished surfaces are scored or visibly worn larger than 2.301″ inside diameter. Maximum gear to pocket clearance should never exceed .008″ or .004″ on a side.

7. The by-pass valve in the body should not open below 75 lbs.

8. When assembling the pump, the pump gear should be pressed on the shaft so there is a clearance of .0015″ between the gear and bracket.

Typical oil filter and luber-finer installation
(© Cummins Engine Co.)

Crankcase Breather Element Replacement

The crankcase breather contains a chemically-treated paper element that must be changed at the specified interval. *Do not attempt to clean the element.*

Remove the wing nut, washer and gasket. Lift out the cover and element. Discard the element. Clean the breather housing and cover with a clean cloth. Install a new element and the cover on the housing. Install the gasket, washer and wing nut.

Oil Filter Replacement

The standard full-flow oil filter is remote-mounted. The optional by-pass oil filter (Luber-Finer) is also remote-mounted.

Full-Flow Oil Filter

To change the standard oil filter element, remove the element from the case and wipe it with clean cloths. *Do not wash the filter bag.*

Reverse the bag and inspect it. If bearing metal or grit is found, immediately inspect the connecting rod and main bearings. Thoroughly wash all parts, except the bag. Install new gaskets and filter bag. If the filter bag is incorrectly installed, the studs may pierce the filter bag.

By-Pass Filter

To change the by-pass filter element (Luber-Finer): Drain the oil, remove the cover, unscrew the T-handle pack hold-down assembly and lift out the pack(s). After cleaning the housing, replace the drain plug, install new pack(s), and replace the hold-down assembly.

Check the O-ring gasket for cleanliness and correct position. Replace the O-ring if it is damaged. Replace the cover and clamping ring. Tighten the capscrew until the clamping lugs come together.

Add an extra 3¼ gallons of oil to the crankcase to fill the filter case and element. Loosen the cover vent plug and start the engine. When the oil reaches the vent, close the plug.

GENERAL SPECIFICATIONS

ENGINE MODEL	BORE & STROKE	PISTON DISP. CU. IN.	HORSEPOWER @ R.P.M.	TORQUE @ R.P.M.	FIRING ORDER* RIGHT HAND ROTATION	LEFT HAND ROTATION	GOVERNOR SPEED NO LOAD	IDLE R.P.M. SPEED
4-53	3.875 x 4.5	212	122 @ 2500	271 @ 1500	1-3-4-2	1-2-4-3	①	450
6V-53	3.875 x 4.5	318	171 @ 2500	423 @ 1500	③	③	①	450
6-71E	4.250 x 5.00	426	219 @ 2100	574 @ 1600	1-5-3-6-2-4	1-4-2-6-3-5	2150	385-400
6-71N	4.250 x 5.00	426	218 @ 2100	605 @ 1200	1-5-3-6-2-4	1-4-2-6-3-5	2340	400
6-71SE	4.250 x 5.00	426	210 @ 2100	575 @ 1600	1-5-3-6-2-4	1-4-2-6-3-5	2150	385-400
6-71T	4.250 x 5.00	426	235 @ 2100	630 @ 1600	1-5-3-6-2-4	1-4-2-6-3-5	2150	385-400
6V-71	4.250 x 5.00	426	210 @ 2100	565 @ 1200	③	③	2340	550
6V-71N	4.250 x 5.00	426	218 @ 2100	605 @ 1200	③	③	2340	550
8V-71	4.250 x 5.00	568	280 @ 2100	750 @ 1200	③	③	2340	550
8V-71N	4.250 x 5.00	568	290 @ 2100	800 @ 1200	③	③	2340	550
8V-71TT	4.25 x 5.0	568	305 @ 1950	1038 @ 1300	③	③	2300	550
12V-71	4.25 x 5.0	852	420 @ 2100	1130 @ 1200	③	③	2300②	550
6V-92TT	4.84 x 5.0	552	270 @ 1950	958 @ 1200	③	③		500④
8V-92TT	4.84 x 5.0	736	365 @ 1950	1223 @ 1400	③	③		500④

① See service plate
② 1973 engines—2100
③
④ City buses—400

CRANKSHAFT AND BEARING SPECIFICATIONS

ENGINE SERIES	MAIN BEARING JOURNAL DIAMETER	MAIN BEARING CLEARANCE	SHAFT END THRUST ON BEARING NO.	SHAFT END PLAY	ROD BEARING JOURNAL DIAMETER	ROD BEARING CLEARANCE
53	2.999-3.000	.0013-.0042	Rear	.004-.011	2.449-2.500	.0015-.0046
V-53	3.499-3.500	.0025-.0057	Rear	.004-.011	2.749-2.750	.0016-.0046
71(T)	3.499-3.500	.0014-.0044	Rear	.004-.014	2.749-2.750	.0014-.0044
V-71(T)	4.499-4.500	.0012-.0046	Rear	.004-.011	2.999-3.000	.0014-.0044
6V-92TT	4.499-4.500	.0016-.0050	Rear	.004-.011	2.999-3.000	.0010-.0040
8V-92TT	4.499-4.500	.0016-.0050	Rear	.004-.011	2.999-3.000	.0010-.0040

PISTONS, PINS, RINGS SPECIFICATIONS

ENGINE SERIES	PISTON CLEARANCE TOP OF SKIRT	BOTTOM OF SKIRT	PISTON PIN DIAMETER	PISTON TO PIN BUSHING CLEARANCE	RING END GAP COMP.	OIL	CYLINDER LINER INSIDE DIAMETER
53, V53	.0052-.0083	.0052-.0083	1.3746-1.3750	.0025-.0034	.020-.046	.010-.025	3.8752-3.8767
71, V71	.004-.0078	.004-.0078	1.4996-1.5000	.0025-.0034	.018-.043	.008-.025	4.2495-4.2511
71T, V71T	.006-.0098	.006-.0098	1.4996-1.5000	.0025-.0034	.018-.043	.008-.025	4.2495-4.2511
6V-92TT	.0055-.0093	.0055-.0093	1.4996-1.5000	.0025-.0034	.025-.040	.025-.040	4.8395-4.8411
8V-92TT	.0055-.0093	.0055-.0093	1.4996-1.5000	.0025-.0034	.025-.040	.025-.040	4.8395-4.8411

ENGINE TORQUE SPECIFICATIONS

ENGINE SERIES	CYLINDER HEAD FT. LBS. CAST IRON BLOCK NUTS	CAST IRON BLOCK BOLTS	MAIN BEARING BOLTS FT. LBS.	CONN. ROD NUTS FT. LBS.	ROCKER SHAFT FT. LBS.	VALVE BRIDGE GUIDE FT. LBS.	CRANKSHAFT END BOLT FT. LBS.
53	——	170-180	120-130	50-55	50-55	——	200-220
V-53	——	170-180	120-130	24-28	50-55	——	200-220
71(T)	175-185①	175-185	180-190②	60-70③	90-100	46-50	290-310
V-71(T)	175-185	175-185	180-190	65-75	90-100	46-50	290-310
6V-92TT		230-240	230-240	60-70	90-100④	46-50	290-310
8V-92TT		230-240	230-240	60-70	90-100④	46-50	290-310

①—Aluminum block nuts 140-160.
②—Aluminum block 120-140.
③—Castellated nut 65-75.
④—Load limit or power control bolts—75 to 85

GMC (Detroit 2-cycle) Diesel Engines

FIRING ORDER AND ROTATION

Trouble Diagnosis

The satisfactory performance of a Diesel engine depends on two items of foremost importance, (1) Sufficiently high compression pressure, and (2) The injection of the proper amount of fuel at the right time.

The first one of these items depends entirely on pistons, piston rings, valves and valve operating mechanism; the second item depends on injectors and their operating mechanism, and fuel system.

Lack of engine power, uneven running, excessive vibration, and tendency to stall when idling may be caused by either a compression loss or faulty injector operation.

The causes of trouble symptoms may be varied; therefore a hit-and-miss search should be avoided. A proper diagnosis of symptoms is an orderly process of diagnosing the symptoms. An "orderly process" means to check the most probable common cause first; then proceed with the next probable cause.

Low Starting R.P.M.
1. Poor or shorted electrical connections.
2. Undercharged or defective battery.
3. Faulty starter or loose starter connections.
4. Infrequent oil changes—change oil.

Low Compression
1. Exhaust valves sticking or burned.
2. Compression rings worn or broken.
3. Cylinder head gasket leaking.
4. Improper valve clearance adjustment.
5. Blower not functioning.
6. Emergency shutoff valve partially or completely closed.

Fuel Problems
1. Injector racks not in full position.
2. Fuel tank or fuel filter empty.
3. Improper grade and type fuel.
4. Diluted fuel.
5. Improperly filtered or restricted fuel flow.
6. Air in fuel system.
7. Faulty fuel pump.

Uneven Running or Frequent Stalling
1. Cylinders cutting out due to incorrect valve adjustment.
2. Insufficient fuel supply.
3. Faulty injectors.
4. Improper injector timing.
5. Incorrect rack setting.
6. Injector tip spray leaks.
7. Cylinder pressures low.
8. Governor instability.
9. Binding injector rack.
10. Faulty adjustments—perform tune up.

11. Improper grade and type of fuel.
12. Diluted fuel.
13. Improperly filtered or restricted fuel flow.
14. Below normal cooling system temperature.

Detonation
1. Oil picked up by air stream.
2. Oil level too high in oil cleaners.
3. Oil accumulation in air box.
4. Defective blower to cylinder block gasket.
5. Leaking blower oil seals.
6. Low coolant temperature.
7. Faulty injectors.
8. Improper injector timing.
9. Injector check valve leaking.
10. Injector spray tip holes enlarged.
11. Broken injector spray tip.

Lack of Power
1. Governor gap setting incorrect.
2. Rack setting incorrect.
3. Injector timing incorrect.
4. Valve clearance incorrect.
5. Insufficient fuel.
6. Air cleaners damaged or clogged.
7. Cylinder liner air inlet ports clogged.
8. Low engine compression.
9. Blower air intake obstructed.
10. Excessive exhaust rack pressure.

General Information

The Diesel engine is an internal combustion power unit, in which the heat of fuel is converted into work in the cylinder of the engine.

Diesel engines differ from gasoline engines principally in the method used to introduce and ignite the fuel. Gasoline engines draw a mixture of fuel and air through the carburetor into the combustion chamber, where it is compressed, then ignited by an electric spark. In the Diesel engines, air alone is compressed in the cylinder; then, a charge of fuel is sprayed into the cylinder, after the air has been compressed, and ignition is accomplished by the heat of compression.

The 2-Cycle Engine

In the two-cycle engine, intake and exhaust take place during part of the compression and power strokes as shown in illustrations. A two-cycle engine, therefore, does not function as an air pump, so an external means of supplying the air is provided. A specially designed blower, on the top of the engine, forces cleaned air into the cylinders to expel the exhaust gases and fill the cylinders with fresh air for combustion.

A series of ports cut into the circumference of the cylinder wall (liner), above the piston, in its lowest position, admits air from the blower into the cylinder when top face of piston uncovers the ports.

The swirling flow of air toward the exhaust valve produces a scavenging effect, leaving the cylinders full of clean air when the piston rises and covers the inlet ports.

As piston continues on upward stroke, exhaust valves close and the charge of fresh air is subjected to the final compression. Air in cylinder is heated to approximately 1000°F. while being compressed.

Shortly before the piston reaches its highest position, the required amount of fuel is sprayed into the combustion space by the unit fuel injector. The intense heat generated during the high compression of the air ignites the fine fuel spray immediately, and the combustion continues as long as the fuel spray lasts. The resulting pressure forces the piston downward to provide a power stroke.

As piston nears the bottom of the downward stroke, exhaust valves are opened and burnt gases are released. Still further downward movements of piston uncovers liner ports and cycle is repeated.

This entire combustion cycle is completed in each cylinder for each revolution of the crankshaft, or, in other words, two strokes; hence, the "two stroke cycle."

Diesel Engine Data

On in-line 53 Series engines, the model and serial numbers are stamped on the right side of the block at the upper rear corner. On V-type 53 Series engines, the model and serial numbers are located on the top right-hand front corner of the block, as viewed from the rear.

On in-line 71 Series engines, serial and model numbers are stamped on a pad located on the block directly in front of the blower and below the exhaust manifold. On V-71 Series engines, engine model and serial numbers are stamped on the block at the right side near the rear end plate.

On 92 Series engines, the engine serial number and engine model number are stamped on the rear of the cylinder block.

When ordering engine parts, order by part number and description, and refer to engine model and serial numbers.

Right and left rotation of engine is indicated by the letters "R" or "L" in the model designation. Truck engines are "R" and coach engines are left "L" rotation.

Certain arrangement of standard accessories are indicated by the letters "A," "B," "C" or "D." Both truck and coach engines are identified by the letter "C," indicating that the starter is on the left and oil cooler on the right as indicated in figure.

Right and left side of engine is determined by standing at rear (trans-

AIR ENTERING COMBUSTION CHAMBER THROUGH CYLINDER LINER PORTS

AIR BEING COMPRESSED WITH THE EXHAUST VALVE CLOSED

Operation of GM Detroit two cycle diesel engine (© G.M.C.)

CHARGE OF FUEL BEING INJECTED INTO COMBUSTION CHAMBER

EXHAUST TAKING PLACE AND CYLINDER ABOUT TO BE SWEPT WITH CLEAN SCAVENGING AIR

Operation of GM Detroit two cycle diesel engine (© G.M.C.)

mission) end.

Right and left rotation of engine is determined by standing at front (opposite transmission) end. If crankshaft rotates clockwise engine is right-hand rotation and is indicated by the letter "R" in model, or if rotation is anti-clockwise engine is left-hand rotation and is indicated by the letter "L" in model.

Minimum and Maximum Engine RPM

The following information is the approved minimum and maximum full-load governor setting for current engines used in truck models. Do not permit engine operation with governor settings higher than indicated for full load setting.

92 Series

Maximum (Full Range) ......See Emission Sticker
Maximum (Dual Range Reduced Speed ....See Emission Sticker
Minimum ....500 (EPA)

71 Series

Maximum (Full Range) 2100
Maximum (Dual Range Reduced Speed) 1900
Minimum 400

53 Series

Maximum 2600-2800
(see nameplate)
Minimum 500-600
NOTE: Above RPM are taken from blower using tachometer head —1549207 which is corrected to compensate for 2.05 to 1 ratio of blower to crankshaft. When corrected tachometer is not available, above RPM can be increased by 5%, or 50 RPM per thousand.

Tune Up and Adjustments

Engine Tune-Up

NOTE: Before tune-up procedure is started it is important that air cleaners and fuel filters are serviced as described in applicable maintenance manuals. Crankcase breather tube and air box drains must be clean and unobstructed. Air box drains may be cleaned with compressed air.

CAUTION: Remove or at least loosen air box hand hole cover, otherwise blower or end plate gaskets may be damaged by excessive air pressure.

Tune-Up Procedures

To completely tune-up an engine, all adjustments except bridge balancing adjustment and exhaust valve cold setting must be performed only after engine has reached its normal operating temperature.

MODEL RC (TRUCK)
Engine rotation and accessory location
(© G.M.C.)

Results obtained from an engine tune-up are usually unsatisfactory, unless a step-by-step, systematic, and orderly approach is used. Proceed in the following sequence:

53 Series

1. Adjust exhaust valve clearance.
2. Time fuel injectors.
3. Adjust the governor gap.
4. Position the injector rack control levers.
5. Adjust maximum no-load speed.
6. Adjust idle speed.
7. Adjust the buffer screw.

71 Series

1. Bridge Balancing Adjustment
2. Exhaust Valve Lash Adjustment
3. Time Fuel Injectors
4. Back-out Buffer Screw
5. Loosen Throttle Delay Cylinder
6. Adjust Idle Speed-Preliminary
7. Adjust Low Speed Gap
8. Adjust Injector Control Racks
9. Adjust Maximum No-Load Speeds
10. Adjust Idle Speed—Final
11. Adjust Buffer Screw
12. Adjust Throttle Delay Cylinder (Coach)

92 Series

1. Adjust exhaust valves.
2. Time fuel injectors.
3. Adjust governor gap.
4. Position rack control levers.
5. Adjust maximum no-load speed.
6. Adjust idle speed.
7. Adjust bumper screw.
8. Adjust throttle booster spring— variable speed governor only.

NOTE: Whenever a push rod has been disconnected from the clevis, the push rod must be screwed back into place until end of push rod appears through the clevis. If this is not done, the piston may hit the head of the valve when the engine is being turned, due to the small clearance, between the valves and piston head at the piston's upper position, or an injector plunger may "Bottom" before being properly adjusted.

Clearance between exhaust valve stem and bridge with engine at operating temperature is important and should be maintained. Too little clearance causes a loss of compression, misfiring of cylinders and eventual burning of valves and valve seats. Too much clearance results in noisy operation of the engine, especially in the low speed range.

Bridge Balancing Adjustment

The exhaust valve bridge assembly is adjusted and the adjustment screw locked securely at the time the cylinder head is installed on the engine. Until wear occurs with the operation of the engine, no further adjustment is required on the exhaust valve bridge.

1. Remove injector fuel jumper lines, then remove rocker arm shaft brackets. Lift rocker arms and swing back to provide access to valve bridge.
2. Remove bridge and spring (when used) from guide. NOTE: Use of bridge springs has been discontinued on latest engines.
3. Loosen adjusting screw lock nut.
4. Install bridge on bridge guide without spring.
5. Press straight down on the pallet surface of bridge. Turn adjusting screw until it just touches the valve stem, then turn screw an additional 1/8 to 1/4 turn and tighten lock nut finger tight.
6. Remove bridge and place in a vise. With screwdriver, hold screw from turning and tighten lock nut on the adjusting screw. Complete the operation by tightening the lock nut to 25 ft. lbs. torque, being sure that screw does not turn. IMPORTANT: Do not tighten while on engine, as binding may damage bridge, guide, and valve.
7. Apply engine oil to bridge and bridge guide.
8. Reinstall the bridge in its original position without the bridge spring.
9. Place a .0015" feeler under each end of the bridge. NOTE: Feeler used at inner end of bridge must be narrow enough to fit in bridge locating groove. Pressing down on the pallet surface of the bridge, both feelers must be tight. If both feelers are not tight, readjust the screw as previously instructed.
10. Remove the bridge and reinstall in its original position with the bridge spring (when used) in place.
11. Adjust remaining bridges as instructed in previous paragraphs.
12. If cylinder head has been removed, reinstall on the engine.

Valve bridge adjustment check
(© G.M.C.)

Adjusting valve bridge
(© G.M.C.)

Tighten cylinder head stud nuts to their specified torque before assembling the rocker shaft brackets to the head. Otherwise valves may be damaged.

13. Install the rocker arm assemblies, *being sure valve bridges are properly positioned on the inner valve stems.*

14. Tighten rocker shaft bracket bolts to their recommended torque.

15. Reconnect fuel jumper lines to injectors and connectors.

Valve Lash Adjustment

Valve lash adjustment must always be made with the engine COLD.

All valves may be lashed in firing order sequence during one full revolution of the crankshaft.

Valve lash must always be adjusted at the push rod. Do not disturb bridge adjusting screw.

1. Place governor throttle control lever in the NO FUEL position.

2. Rotate crankshaft until the injector follower is fully depressed on the cylinder being adjusted.

3. Loosen valve push rod lock nut.

4. On 71 and 92 Series engines, place a .017″ feeler gauge between valve stem and valve bridge adjusting screw on engines with bridge spring, or between bridge and rocker arm on engines not using bridge spring. Adjust push rod to obtain a smooth "pull" on the feeler gauge.

   On 53 Series engines, place a .027″ feeler gauge between the rocker arm bridge. Adjust push rod to obtain a smooth pull on the feeler gauge.

5. Remove feeler gauge. Hold push rod with wrench and tighten push rod lock nut.

6. Check and adjust remaining valves in manner described in previous paragraphs.

7. With engine at operating temperature (160°F. to 180°F.), recheck clearances. At this time, on 71 Series engines, a .013″ feeler gauge should pass between the end of the valve stem and the adjusting screw on the bridge (or between rocker arm and the bridge), and a .015″ feeler gauge should not pass through. On 53 Series engines, the figures are .023″ and .025″. Readjust push rod if necessary.

Injector Timing

To properly time the injector, the injector follower-guide must be adjusted to a definite height.

1. Set governor control lever in the NO FUEL (off) position.

2. Turn engine crankshaft manually or by means of the starter, until the exhaust valve rocker arms are fully depressed, for that particular cylinder.

3. The injector is identified by a colored tab stamped onto the injector body. Injector is timed with 1.460″ gauge. With 9290 injectors and turbocharger and 9295 injectors use a 1.484″ gauge.

4. Place the injector timing gauge

Timing fuel injector
(© G.M.C.)

Engine idle speed adjustment
(© G.M.C.)

in the hole provided on top of the injector body with one of the "flats" toward the injector.

5. Adjust the injector rocker arm by loosening lock nut and turning the push rod with an end wrench, until the bottom of the timing gauge head will just pass over (drag lightly) the top of the injector follower guide.

6. Hold push rod from turning and tighten lock nut. Recheck adjustment with injector timing gauge and readjust if necessary.

7. Repeat the adjustment for all other injectors.

Governor Adjustments—

The governor used on these engines is a limiting speed double weight type, which controls the inejctor control racks.

The following adjustments must be performed in the sequence given, but not until the valves and injectors are in proper adjustment as previously described.

IMPORTANT: Tachometer drive ratio at blower is 2.05 times engine speed and rotation is counterclockwise. Make allowances accordingly or use corrected tachometer head when performing engine tune-up procedures.

Buffer Screw Adjustment

1. Adjust buffer screw so it extends at least 5/8" beyond the locknut.

Idle Speed Adjustment

1. Remove governor high speed spring cover to governor housing.

2. Start engine and operate at idle speed while observing RPM at tachometer.

3. To adjust, loosen lock nut and turn idle adjusting screw IN to increase or OUT to decrease speed. Lock adjusting screw with lock nut when idling speed is approximately 15 RPM below desired setting.

Low Speed Spring Gap Adjustment

When necessary to adjust, proceed as follows:

1. Remove governor control housing cover.

2. Start engine and run engine at 800-1000 RPM by manual operation of the differential lever or injector control tube lever. WARNING: Do not overspeed engine.

3. Measure gap between low speed spring cap and plunger. If gap is not between .001" to .002", loosen lock nut and turn adjusting screw as necessary to obtain desired gap. Tighten lock nut, then recheck gap.

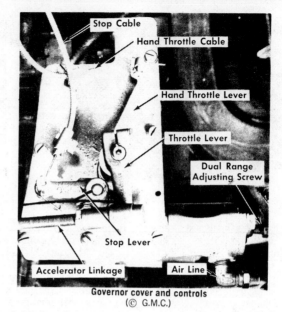

Governor cover and controls
(© G.M.C.)

(Image labels: Stop Cable, Hand Throttle Cable, Hand Throttle Lever, Throttle Lever, Dual Range Adjusting Screw, Stop Lever, Accelerator Linkage, Air Line)

4. Stop engine, then reinstall governor control housing cover and lever assembly to governor housing.

Positioning Injector Racks

The position of the injector control racks must be properly adjusted in relation to the governor.

The letters R or L indicate injector location in right or left cylinder bank when viewed from rear of engine. Cylinders are numbered starting at front of the engine.

NOTE: These instructions cover V-type engines, primarily. The same basic procedure applies to in-line engines, however.

1. Disconnect any linkage attached to the governor throttle control lever.

2. Loosen idle speed adjusting screw until 1/2" of threads project from lock nut.

3. Remove rocker covers from cylinder heads.

4. Loosen all inner and outer injector control rack adjusting screws in right and left cylinder bank. Be sure all injector rack control levers are free on the injector control tubes. NOTE: On coaches equipped with Hydraulic transmission, loosen two nuts attaching throttle delay clamp to injector control tube.

5. Move governor throttle control lever to FULL FUEL position and hold in that position with light finger pressure. Turn *inner* adjusting screw of #1L injector rack control lever until clevis pin binds, then tighten *outer* adjusting screw. NOTE: When the setting is correct, the injector rack will be snug on the pin of the rack control lever and still maintain a snug (not loose or

tight) fit at clevis pin, while throttle is in FULL FUEL position and inner and outer adjusting screws are tight.

6. At right bank, repeat procedure previously described in paragraph 5 for left bank.

7. Set #2 and #3 injector racks to #1 rack for their respective heads.

8. Turn idle speed adjusting screw in until it projects 3/16" from the lock nut to permit starting the engine.

High Speed No-Load Adjustment

Some governors are equipped with a device for reducing the engine RPM when in transmission or rear axle high speeds. These governors are referred to as "Dual Range Type" and are used on some truck engines.

Except Dual Range—71 and 92 Series Engines

1. Loosen the high speed spring retainer lock nut using a spanner wrench.

2. Start engine and operate at maximum speed, while observing engine RPM at tachometer.

3. Turn high speed adjuster IN to increase or OUT to decrease speed until desired no-load setting is obtained.

4. Hold adjuster, then tighten lock nut, using spanner wrench.

5. Recheck and if necessary readjust after tightening lock nut.

53 Series Engines

1. With engine at normal operating temperature, and no load, place the speed control lever in the maximum speed position. Note the engine speed.

Adjusting No. 3L injector rack control lever
(© G.M.C.)

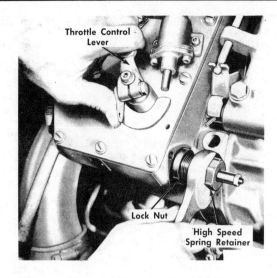

Engine high speed no-load adjustment
(except dual range)
(© G.M.C.)

2. Stop the engine. If it is necessary to adjust the speed, remove the high speed spring retainer with a special tool and withdraw the high speed spring and plunger assembly. Perform the operation very carefully to avoid causing the low speed spring and, cap to fall into the governor.

3. Separate the spring and plunger and add or remove shims as required to correct the no-load speed. Adding .010″ in shims will increase engine speed about 10 rpm.

4. Operate the engine and recheck the no-load speed.

Dual Range

Two types of pistons have been used on Dual Range governors. Early type incorporated a piston with a threaded sleeve, while latest type sleeve is positioned in piston by a shim pack.

Maximum High Speed Adjustment

(Early Type)

1. Start engine and operate at full speed. Be sure air is supplied to governor. No load speed is 125-150 RPM above full load speed.

2. Remove two bolts attaching piston housing to governor control housing. Then remove housing and piston assembly.

3. Remove piston and sleeve assembly with seal ring from piston housing.

4. Measure distance from end of piston to end of sleeve. This dimension should be approximately 25/32″.

5. Should it be necessary to increase engine RPM the dimension should be increased. Also, when necessary to decrease engine RPM the dimension should

be decreased. NOTE: Each full turn of piston and sleeve will change engine approximately 100 RPM.

6. Install piston and sleeve assembly in piston housing, then install piston housing to governor control housing.

7. Check for proper setting and readjust as necessary.

Reduced High Speed Adjustment

(Early Type)

1. Disconnect wire at governor air supply solenoid so as to prevent air reaching governor.

2. Start engine and operate at full speed while observing RPM at tachometer. Proper adjustment is approximately 200 RPM below maximum no-load speed.

3. Loosen lock nut and turn adjusting screw as necessary to obtain proper reduced high speed RPM. Lock screw with nut when proper adjustment is obtained.

4. Should it be necessary to increase engine RPM turn adjusting bolt in to increase, or out to decrease engine RPM.

5. Reconnect wire at solenoid when adjustment is completed.

Maximum High Speed Adjustment

(Late Type)

1. Start with a pack of four .100″ and then .010″ shims. Turn low maximum speed screw out until it extends 1¼″.

2. Disconnect air line so as to prevent air reaching governor piston.

3. Start engine and operate at full speed. No load speed is 125-150 RPM above full load speed.

Dual range governor (early type)
(© G.M.C.)

4. Turn the low maximum speed adjusting screw inward until the desired high maximum no-load speed is obtained.
5. Stop engine, then remove spring housing and piston assembly.
6. Measure distance from inner edge of piston to inner edge of housing, when piston is against adjusting screw.
7. Remove sleeve from piston, then remove shims equal to the distance the piston is from the edge of housing.
8. Install sleeve in the piston, then install piston assembly in spring housing. Install spring housing assembly onto the governor.
9. Start engine and operate at full throttle with air applied at governor. Observe tachometer.
10. Remove air pressure from governor and stop engine. Remove or install shims as required to obtain desired high maximum no-load speed. Remove shims to decrease or add shims to increase engine speed. Each .010″ of shims removed or added will change engine speed approximately 10 RPM.

Reduced High Speed Adjustment

(Late Type)

1. Disconnect air line to prevent air reaching governor piston.
2. Start engine and operate at full throttle while observing RPM at tachometer. Proper adjustment is approximately 200 RPM below maximum no-load speed.
3. Turn low maximum speed adjusting screw as necessary to obtain proper reduced high speed. Turn screw in to increase, or out to decrease engine RPM.
4. Reconnect air line when adjustment is completed.

Idle Speed Adjustment

Final

The engine must be at operating temperature when making the final idle speed adjustment.
1. Start engine and operate at idle speed while observing RPM at tachometer.
2. If necessary to adjust, loosen lock nut and turn idle adjusting screw IN to increase or OUT to decrease. Lock adjusting screw with lock nut when idle speed is approximately 15 RPM below desired setting.
3. Install governor spring housing assembly to governor housing.

Buffer Spring Adjustment

With the idle speed adjusted, and engine at operating temperature adjust buffer spring screw as follows:
1. Turn buffer screw IN until "surge" or "roll" is eliminated and engine idles evenly. NOTE: Do not increase engine idle speed more than 15 RPM with the buffer screw. On 53 Series engine, buffer spring may increase idle speed up to 25 rpm.
2. Hold buffer screw and tighten lock nut.

Throttle Delay Adjustment

The following instructions outline a procedure to follow when adjusting the throttle delay cylinder, used on coaches having hydraulic transmission.
1. Adjustment is made with the engine stopped.
2. Loosen two bolts attaching clamp to injector control tube.
3. Temporarily install a gauge between injector body and shoulder on injector rack. Gauge is .404″ (approx. 13/32″) thick and can be made locally.
4. Position gauge as shown and exert a light pressure on the con-

trol tube in the direction of FULL FUEL.
5. Align the piston so it is flush with the cylinder edge.
6. Tighten the two clamps bolts. then remove gauge.
7. Rotate the injector control rack from "OFF" to "FULL" position to be sure it does not bind.
NOTE: Each time the injector racks are set the throttle delay must be first taken out of adjustment; injector racks are then set and the throttle delay readjusted.

Blower

Description And Operation

In the scavenging process employed in GM two cycle engines, air is forced into cylinders by blower which thoroughly sweeps out all of the burnt gases through the exhaust valve ports, and also helps to cool internal engine parts, particularly exhaust valves. At the beginning of compression stroke, therefore, each cylinder is filled with fresh, clean air, which permits highly efficient combustion.

The blower designed especially for efficient diesel operation, supplies the fresh air needed for combustion and scavenging. Its operation is similar to that of a gear-type pump. On V type engines, two hollow three-lobe rotors revolve with very close clearances in a housing bolted to the top deck of the cylinder block, between the two banks of cylinders. On in-line engines, the blower is mounted on the side of the block. To provide continuous and uniform displacement of air, the rotor lobes on 71 and 92 Series engines are made with a helical (spiral) form.

Two timing gears, located on the drive end of the rotor shafts, space the rotor lobes with a close tolerance; therefore, as the lobes of the two rotors do not touch at any time, no lubrication is required. However, build-up of oil and carbon deposits on the rotor lobes improves the sealing

Governor springs—dual range
(© G.M.C.)

Buffer spring screw adjustment
(© G.M.C.)

GMC (Detroit 2-cycle) Diesel Engines

clearance and tends to increase the air flow.

Oil seals located in the blower end plates prevent air leakage and also keep the oil, used for lubricating the timing gears and rotor shaft bearings from entering the rotor compartment.

Blower Removal—92 Series Engines

The engine governor components are assembled in a combination governor housing and blower front end plate cover. The fuel pump is also attached to the front end of the blower. When removing the blower the governor and fuel pump will also be removed.

1. Disconnect tubing between air cleaner and shutdown housing or turbocharger.
2. Disconnect the exhaust manifold from the turbocharger.
3. Disconnect the air inlet hose from the compressor.
4. Remove the oil inlet line from the top of the center housing and the oil outlet line from the bottom.
5. Unbolt and lift off the turbocharger.
6. Disconnect the shutdown wire from the air shutoff cam pin handle.
7. Remove the air shutdown housing.
8. Remove the adapter and blower screen.
9. Disconnect the oil pressure line from the blower.
10. Loosen the hose clamp on the blower drive support-to-blower seal.
11. Disconnect the tachometer drive cable from the adapter at the rear of the blower.
12. Remove the flywheel housing cover at the blower drive support.
13. Remove the blower drive shaft.
14. Drain engine.
15. Remove thermostat by-pass tube.
16. Disconnect fuel pump lines and fuel return crossover.
17. Remove breather pipe.
18. Disconnect throttle control rods from governor.
19. Remove rocker covers.
20. Remove governor cover.
21. Remove fuel rods.
22. Slide fuel rod cover tube hoses out of way.
23. Remove blower retaining bolts.
24. Attach a hoist to the blower, lift it slightly and move it forward to detach it from the seal at the drive end.

Blower Removal—V-71 Engines

The engine governor components are assembled in a combination governor housing and blower front end

Blower mounting 92 series engine

plate cover. The fuel pump is also attached to the front end of the blower. Therefore, when removing the blower assembly from the engine, the governor and fuel pump will also be

removed at the same time.

1. Remove the manifold and blower screen.
2. Loosen oil pressure line fitting from rear of blower to blower drive support and slide fitting back on tube.
3. Loosen hose clamp on blower drive support-to-blower seal.
4. Remove flywheel housing cover at blower drive support.
5. Remove snap ring and withdraw blower drive shaft from blower.
6. Remove by-pass tube between thermostat housings.
7. Remove fuel inlet and outlet lines to fuel pump. Also, remove the fuel return cross-over tube between cylinder heads.
8. Remove rocker cover(s).
9. Remove governor cover.

2. Housing--Blower
3. Rotor Assy.--R. H. Helix
4. Rotor Assy.--L. H. Helix
6. Plate--Blower Front End
7. Plate--Blower Rear End
9. Seal--Oil
10. Retainer--Blower Bearing
11. Lockscrew-Retainer
13. Bearing--Blower Rotor Front (Roller)
14. Bearing--Blower Rotor Rear (Ball)
15. Screw--Fillister Head
16. Gear--R. H. Helix Rotor
17. Gear--L. H. Helix Rotor
18. Shim--Blower Gear
19. Bolt--Blower Gear
20. Washer
21. Strainer--End Plate Oil Passage
22. Plug--Oil Passage
23. Orifice--Oil Passage
25. Gasket--Cover
27. Cover--Rear End Plate
30. Clamp--Hose
31. Bolt--Cover
32. Lock Washer
33. Washer--Special Flat
35. Hose--Blower Drive Cover
45. Bolt--Blower Mounting
46. Lock Washer
50. Gasket
51. Shaft--Blower Drive
53. Drive Hub
55. Plate--Flexible
59. Bolt
60. Spacer
70. Disc--Fuel Pump Drive
71. Spacer--Fuel Pump Drive Disc
72. Bolt--Drive Disc
73. Lock Washer
81. Collar--Blower End Plate
82. Carrier--Seal Ring
83. Ring--Seal (Piston Type)
84. Spacer

Exploded view of governor

10. Disconnect and remove fuel rods.
11. Loosen hose clamps and slide governor fuel rod cover hose back on each side of governer.
12. Remove bolt and washer through top of each end plate which secures blower to cylinder block.
13. Remove two blower-to-block bolts, retaining lugs and washers on each side of blower.
14. Check to make sure any other tubing or accessories are disconnected which may interfere with removal of blower.
15. Thread eyebolts in diagonally opposite air inlet manifold-to-blower tapped holes and attach lifting sling.
16. Lift blower up slightly and move forward to detach blower from seal at drive end. Then lift blower up and away from engine. Remove blower gasket.

Blower Removal—In-Line
71 Series Engines
1. Drain the cooling system.
2. Disconnect governor linkage.
3. Remove the breather pipe.
4. Remove the governor cover from the housing.
5. Disconnect the fuel rod from the differential lever and injector control tube lever.

Governor Details
(© G.M. Corp)

6. Disconnect the oil supply tube at the housing.
7. Remove the two governor mounting bolts.
8. Remove the bolts holding the control housing to the weight housing, and remove the control housing.
9. Disconnect the fuel lines at the fuel pump.
10. Loosen the water pump connections at the inlet and block.
11. If equipped with a shutdown solenoid, tag the wires, remove them from the solenoid, and remove the solenoid. If equipped with a manual shutdown, disconnect the Bowden cable from the lever and remove the bolt which holds the wire clip to the shutdown housing.
12. Remove the air cleaner and air inlet housing, gasket, striker plate, and air inlet screen from the blower.
13. Remove the bolts securing the flywheel housing small hole cover.
14. Remove the snap ring, and pull the drive shaft out of the drive assembly.
15. Loosen the blower drive shaft cover seal at the blower drive gear hub support.
16. Remove the bolts and washers that secure the blower to the

1. Retainer Lock Nut
2. High Speed Spring Retainer
3. Lock Nut
4. Idle Speed Adjusting Screw
5. High Speed Spring Plunger
6. High Speed Spring
7. Low Speed Spring Seat
8. Low Speed Spring Cap
9. Low Speed Spring
10. Buffer Screw
11. Lock Nut
12. Bolt
13. High Speed Spring Retainer Cover
14. Speed Control Lever
15. Stop Lever
16. Fuel Rod
17. Lock Nut
18. Gap Adjusting Screw
19. Operating Shaft Bearing
20. Operating Shaft
21. Bushing
22. Gasket
23. Plug
24. Bearing Retaining Screw
25. Shaft End Bearing
26. Riser Thrust Bearing
27. Riser
28. Weight Housing
29. Weight Carrier
30. Governor Drive Shaft
31. Low Speed Weight
32. High Speed Weight
33. Operating Shaft Fork
34. Control Housing
35. Operating Shaft Lever
36. Differential Lever
37. Cover

Limiting Speed Governor
(© G.M. Corp)

block. Slide the blower slightly forward, pull the drive shaft cover off the seal, and lift the blower away from the block.

Blower Removal—53 Series Engines

1. Disconnect the governor control linkage. Remove the governor cover screws and washers and remove the cover.
2. Remove the screws and washers which attach the governor cover, and remove the cover and gasket.
3. Remove the mounting bolts and remove the spring housing and gasket from the governor.
4. Remove the spring assembly from the governor. Loosen the hose clamps and slide the hoses back on the fuel rod covers.
5. Remove both rocker covers.
6. Disconnect the lower fuel rod from each injector control tube lever and from each upper fuel rod.
7. Remove the threaded pins which connect the fuel rods to the control link lever.
8. Remove the upper fuel rods.
9. Remove the blower drive cover plate. Remove the snap ring and then pull the blower drive shaft out.
10. Remove the blower drive support assembly bolts and remove the support assembly as shown in the illustration.
11. Remove the blower mounting bolts, and lift the blower off the block.
12. Remove the governor housing attaching bolts, and remove the governor housing.

Blower Disassembly—71 and 92 Series Engines

1. Remove bolts and washers securing rear end plate cover to blower, including tachometer drive adaptor. Remove gasket.
2. Remove six bolts and lock washers which secure flexible blower drive coupling to right-hand helix blower timing gear. Remove retainer and coupling.
3. Remove bolts and washers which secure the combination front end

plate cover and governor housing to blower. Remove housing and gasket. Fuel pump may be removed with governor housing. Remove fuel pump driving disc, spacer and driving fork.
4. Place a clean cloth between rotors, then remove the Allen head bolts and spacers which secure the timing gears to the blower rotor shafts.
5. Remove timing gears, using pullers installed as shown in illustration. Both gears must be pulled at the same time.
6. Secure pullers to gears with 5/16"-24 x 1½" bolts (two bolts on L.H. helix gear and three bolts on R.H. helix gear).
7. Remove shims from rotor shafts, after gears have been removed. Note the number and thicknss of shims on each rotor shaft to ensure identical replacement when assembling blower.
8. Remove bolts and lock washers that secure rotor shaft bearing retainers to both front and rear end plates. Remove retainers.
9. Remove the two special screws that secure the rear end plate to the blower housing, and loosen the two special screws securing the front end plate to housing approximately three turns.
10. Install two pullers on blower end plate as shown in illustration. Align holes in each puller flange with tapped holes in end plate and secure pullers to the end plate with six ¼"-20 x 1¼" or longer bolts. NOTE: Be sure that the ¼"-20 bolts are threaded all the way into the tapped holes in the end plate to provide maximum anchorage for the pullers and to eliminate possible damage to the end plate.
11. Turn the two puller screws uniformly clockwise to withdraw end plate and bearings from blower housing and rotors as shown in illustration.
12. Remove blower front end plate in the same manner as described above for rear plate.
13. Remove rotors from blower housing.

14. New seals should be installed. The seals may be removed from the end plates at the same time the individual bearings are removed.
15. Insert long end of remover through seal and bearing and bring ram of press down on opposite end, forcing bearing and seal out of end plate.

Blower Disassembly 53 Series Engines

1. Remove the bolts, washers, and reinforcement plates which retain the front end plate and cover. Remove the end plate cover and gasket from the end plate.
2. Place a clean rag between the rotors. Remove the bolts which hold the blower drive cam retainer and blower drive spring support to the rotor gear. Separate the retainer and support from the gear.
3. Remove the governor drive plate from the opposite rotor gear.
4. Remove the bolts and blower drive cam pilots from both gears.
5. Install pullers, and remove both drive gears simultaneously. Mark the left hand rotor for identification during reassembly. Remove the shims and rotor gear spacers, and place each part with the proper gear for proper positioning at reassembly.
6. Remove the three bolts from the front end plate and remove the thrust plate and spacers. Remove the bolts that retain the thrust washers. Tap the end plate lightly with a soft mallet to remove it from the dowel pins on the blower housing.
7. Remove the rotors from the housing and then remove the rear end plate as the front end plate was removed.
8. Remove the oil seals from the end plates.
9. Drive the cam from the blower drive spring support with a brass drift. This permits the drive springs and spring seats to fall free.

Blower Mounting 6-53
(© G.M. Corp)

Removing Blower Drive Support
(© G.M. Corp)

Removing oil seal and bearing
(© G.M.C.)

Installing oil seal in end plate
(© G.M.C.)

Blower Inspection

After the blower has been disassembled, wash all parts thoroughly in clean fuel oil, blow dry with compressed air, and inspect as follows:

1. Races and balls or rollers of bearings for indications of corrosion or pitting.
2. Lip type oil seals for scoring, charring, or hardening. Replacement is recommended in all cases.
3. Blower rotor lobes and sealing rib for burrs or scoring.
4. Rotor shaft serrations and bearing surfaces for wear or burrs. On 53 Series engines, rotor shaft bearing surface outside diameter should be .8595″-.8600″.
5. Inside of blower housing for burrs and scoring.
6. The finished inside face of end plates must be smooth and flat. On 53 Series engines, end plate shaft bore inside diameter should be .8610″-.8615″.
7. Blower timing gears must be replaced as a set when worn or damaged to the point where the backlash exceeds .004″.
8. Replace blower drive shaft if bent or serrations are worn

badly.
9. Make sure blower drive coupling springs (pack) and cam are intact and not worn.
10. Clean out all oil holes and cavities.
11. If blower timing gear serrations are worn, replace gears.

Blower Assembly—71 and 92 Series Engines

1. Place the end plate, finished side up, on wood blocks on the bed of the arbor press.
2. Start the oil seal straight into the bore with sealing edge downward. Insert short end of seal installer into seal and use ram of press to press seal down until the flange of the tool contacts the end plate. Repeat for remaining seals.
3. The front end plate may be identified by the fact that the dowel pins extend on either side. The bottom of the plate has six holes. Start the plate dowels into the dowel holes in the front end of the blower. Then, tap the end plate lightly with a rawhide hammer to fit the plate to the housing. Install the special screws.

4. In installing rotors, remember the following points:
   a. The lobes and gear teeth for the driving rotor form a right-hand helix.
   b. The lobes and gear teeth for the driven rotor form a left-hand helix.
   c. Serrations omitted on the gear end of the rotor shaft and in the gear should be in alignment.
   d. Rotors must be installed in the housing with both serrations pointing toward the left when viewing blower from gear end (see illustration).
5. Install the rotors into the housing and front end plate using the oil seal pilot tools as shown in the illustration. Be sure to place rotors as in d. above. The right hand helix rotor is marked "gear end" on one end, while the left hand helix rotor should be positioned so the serrated shaft is at the gear end.
6. Remove the oil seal pilot tools.
7. Install the oil seal pilots over the serrated ends of the rotor shafts.
8. Within the six holes at the bottom, start the end plate dowels

Installing roller bearings in front end plate
(© G.M.C.)

Add Shims Behind
R. H. Gear to Increase
"C" Clearance Here

Air Inlet
Side

Trailing Side

Leading Side

L. H. Rotor

Leading Side

R. H. Rotor

Trailing Side

Add Shims Behind
L. H. Gear to Increase
"CC" Clearance Here

VIEW FROM GEAR END OF BLOWER

Proper location of shims for correct rotor clearances
(© G.M.C.)

Removing or installing bearing retainers
(© G.M.C.)

Removing blower end plate
(© G.M.C.)

into the dowel holes of the housing. Tap the end plate lightly to bring it into position.

9. Install the special screws snugly and remove the oil seal pilot tools.

10. Lube the inside diameter of each front roller bearing with light engine oil. Start the bearings straight onto the rotor shaft with the numbered face facing out.

11. Tap each bearing into the end plate with the installer as shown in the illustration.

12. Install bearing retainers with bolts and lockwashers, and torque the bolts to 7 to 9 ft-lb.

13. Install the rear bearings in the same manner, using the special tool designed for their installation. Install the retainers in exactly the same manner.

14. Follow all applicable precautions listed in step 4 in performing this step. The punch mark on the end of each rotor shaft will assist in aligning the gears on the shafts.

15. Reposition in their original positions any shims removed from the back side of the gears. Rotate the two rotors until the two omitted serrations are in alignment and facing to the left.

16. Mesh the teeth of the rotor gears so that the omitted serrations are aligned and face in the same direction.

17. With the gears in mesh, start them onto the rotor shafts with the omitted serrations in line with those on the rotors. Make sure the right hand helix gear is on the right hand helix rotor, etc. Use 1/2"-20x1 1/4" bolts and plain washers, install and turn the bolts uniformly to pull the gears onto the shaft.

18. Remove the bolts and washers used in drawing the gears onto the shafts. Install the special spacers and Allen head gear retaining bolts and tighten the re-

taining bolts to 55–65 ft lbs. Lubricate the bolts before installation.

Rotor Timing and Clearances —71 and 92 Series Engines

At this stage of the blower assembly, the blower rotors must be timed.

NOTE: Before timing blower, install four 5/16"-18 x 2 1/2" bolts and 3/8" spacers temporarily at each end to secure end plates to housing. After timing, remove spacers and bolts.

1. The blower rotors, when properly positioned in the housing, run with a slight clearance between the lobes. This clearance may be varied by moving one of the helical gears in or out on the shaft relative to the other gear.

2. If the right-hand helix gear is moved out, the right-hand helix rotor will turn counterclockwise when viewed from the gear end. If the left-hand helix gear is moved out, the left-hand helix rotor will turn clockwise when viewed from the gear end. This positioning of the gear, to obtain the proper clearance between the rotor lobes, is known as blower timing.

3. Moving the gears OUT or IN on the rotors is accomplished by adding or removing shims between the gear hub and the bearing.

Removing blower gears
(© G.M.C.)

4. The clearance between rotor lobes may be checked with various thickness feeler ribbons 1/2" wide. When measuring clearances of more than .005", laminated feelers that are made up of .002", .003" or .005" feeler stock are more practical and suitable than one single thick feeler gauge. Clearances should be measured from both the inlet and outlet sides of the blower.

5. Time rotors to have from .002" to .006" clearance between the TRAILING edge of the right-hand helix rotor and the LEADING edge of the left-hand helix rotor ("CC" clearance) measured from both the inlet and outlet sides as shown in illustrations. if possible, keep this clearance to the minimum (.002"). Then check clearance between LEADING edge of right-hand helix rotor and TRAILING edge of left-hand helix rotor ("C" clearance) for the minimum clearance of .012". Rotor-to-rotor measurements should be taken 1" from each end and at center of blower.

6. Having determined the amount one rotor must be revolved to obtain the proper clearance, add shims back of proper gear to produce the desired result. When

more or fewer shims are required, both gears must be removed from the rotors.

7. Placing a .003" shim in back of a rotor gear will revolve the rotor .001".

8. Install the required thickness of shims back of the proper gear and next to the bearing inner race and reinstall both gears. Recheck clearances between rotor lobes.

9. Determine minimum clearances at points "A" and "B" shown in illustration. Insert feelers, between end plates and ends of rotors. This operation must be performed at both ends of each lobe, making 12 measurements in all.

Blower Assembly 71 and 92 Series (Cont.)

1. After blower rotors are timed, complete assembly of blower as follows:

   a. Set drive coupling support on two wood blocks as shown in illustration.

   b. Install spring seats in grooves of coupling support.

   c. Apply grease to springs to hold the leaves together and slide the two spring packs, consisting of 21 leaves per pack, into support.

   d. Place blower drive cam over end of tool, insert tool between

Using pilot tools to install rotors
(© G.M.C.)

spring packs and press cam into place.

2 Attach flexible blower drive coupling and retainer to right-hand helix gear and secure with six bolts and lock washers.

3. Place gasket on blower rear end plate.

4. Attach rear end plate cover and secure with bolts and lock washers.

5. Attach tachometer drive adaptor, if used.

6. Install fuel pump driving disc and spacer.

7. Place gasket on blower front end plate.

8. Install governor assembly (combination governor and front end plate cover) on front end plate and secure with bolts and washers.

NOTE: Make certain that fuel pump driving fork is in registration with fuel pump driving disc. Governor weight shaft is splined to front left-hand helix rotor shaft.

Blower Assembly—53 Series Engines

1. Using an installing tool, install new oil seals in both blower end plates. Install the seals so the lip of the seal faces the inside of the counterbore.

2. Place the front end plate (the front plate has tapped holes for the thrust washer plate bolts and thrust washer lube oil holes) on two wood blocks. Install the rotors with the lobes meshed and the gear ends upward.

3. Install the blower housing (see illustration).

4. Place the rear end plate over the rotor end shafts (see illustration). Then, bolt the end plates in place.

5. Attach the two thrust washers to the front end of the blower with the two retaining bolts. Tighten 5/16"–24 bolts to 24–30 ft lbs, and ⅜"–24 bolts to 54–59 ft lbs.

6. Attach the three spacers and the thrust plate to the front of the blower with the thrust plate bolts, torquing the bolts to 7 to 9 ft lbs. Check the clearance between the thrust plate and the

Measuring "CC" and "C" clearances (© G.M.C.)

Installing blower timing gears
(© G.M.C.)

Measuring end clearance between rotor and end plate ·
(© G.M.C.)

GMC (Detroit 2-cycle) Diesel Engines

Installing inner and outer seals in pump body
(© G.M.C.)

Inserting blower drive cam between springs—
using spreader tool
(© G.M.C.)

1 Wood blocks
2 Drive spring support
3 Blower drive cam
4 Blower drive spring
5 Spring seat
6 Spring spreader tool
7 Spring seat

washers. It should be .001"–.003".

7. Position the rotors so the missing serrations where the gears fit are 90° apart. See the illustration.
8. Install shims and spacers in the counterbores of the rear faces of the rotor gears. Place the gears on the ends of the shafts with the missing serrations aligned with those in the shafts. Tap the gears lightly with a soft hammer to seat them. Rotate the gears until the punch marks line up. Reposition the gears as necessary if the marks do not line up.
9. Wedge a cloth between the rotors. Install the gear retaining bolts and plain washers and turn the bolts in uniformly until the gears are fully installed. Then, remove the bolts and washers.
10. Place the pilot in the counterbore of the gears, install the 12 point

bolt in the right hand rotor shaft, and install the hex head bolt in the left hand rotor shaft. Tighten the bolts to 20-25 ft lbs.
11. Check the backlash between the blower gears. It should be .0005"–.0025" with new gears. Gears must be replaced if backlash exceeds .0035".
12. Check the blower rotor timing and other clearances with a feeler gauge. If necessary, change the rotor-to-rotor clearance by moving one of the gears in or out on its shaft through addition or removal of shims. Measurements should be made using two or three gauge blades combined so as to prodce the proper size gauge. Take measurements from both the inlet and outlet sides of the blower, and across the entire length of each rotor lobe. Measure rotor-to-rotor clearance with the rotors at

a 90° angle to each other.
The clearance between rotors should be at least .010". Rotor-to-housing clearance should be .004" on the outlet side and .010 on the inlet side.
NOTE: During measurement of front and rear rotor end clearances, push the rotor toward the appropriate end plate to make the clearance as tight as possible.
13. Remove the bolts and washers from the front end plate. Secure the front end plate cover and gasket with the bolts, special washers, and reinforcement plates. Tighten the bolts to 20-25 ft lbs.
14. Place the drive spring support on two wood blocks (see illustration) and position the drive spring seats in the support. Apply grease to hold the spring packs together, and then slide the two springs into the drive

NOTE: Time rotors to dimensions on above chart for clearance between trailing side of R.H. Helix Rotor and leading side of L.H. Helix Rotor (cc) from both inlet and outlet side of blower.

VIEWS FROM GEAR END OF BLOWER

	A	B	C	CC	D	E
MIN.	.007"	.014"	.012"	.002"	.016"	.004"
MAX.				.006"		

Chart of minimum blower clearances (© G.M.C.)

GMC (Detroit 2-cycle) Diesel Engines

Measuring Lobe to Housing Clearance
(© G.M. Corp)

Measuring Lobe to End Plate Clearance
(© G.M. Corp)

	A	B	C
3-53	.0075"	.004"	.010"
4-53	.0075"	.004"	.010"
6V-53	.010"	.004"	.010"

Minimum Blower Rotor Clearance
(© G.M. Corp)

Inserting Blower Drive Cam
(© G.M. Corp)

BLOWER ROTOR END CLEARANCES (Minimum)		
Engine	Front End Plate	Rear End Plate
3-53	0.006"	0.008"
4-53	0.006"	0.009"
6V-53	0.008"	0.012"

spring seats.

15. Place the blower drive cam over the end of a special tool, and insert the tool between the springs. Then, press the cam into place between the springs.
16. Install the drive spring support coupling on the left-hand gear of the blower. Secure the cam retainer to the coupling with the four bolts, torquing them to 8–10 ft lbs.
17. Remove the bolts from the rear end plate, and then secure the governor and gasket with bolts and special washers, tightening the bolts to 20–25 ft lbs.

Blower Installation

1. After blower is assembled and timed, and end plate cover and accessories are installed in place, blower is ready to be installed.
2. Place a new blower gasket on top of cylinder block, using a good grade of non-hardening cement to prevent gasket from shifting.
3. Lower the blower into position, reversing the removal procedure.
4. Secure the blower to the block with bolts, retaining lugs, and washers. Tighten the bolts uniformly to 25 ft-lbs. in 5 ft-lb increments on V-71 and 92 Series engines, 16-20 ft lbs on in-line 71 Series and 53 Series engines.

Fuel Pump

Tests

If engine operation indicates insufficient supply of fuel to the injectors and the fuel level is not low in the supply tank, check the fuel flow between the restricted fitting in the fuel return passage in the cylinder head and the fuel supply tank.

Fuel Flow Check

1. Disconnect the fuel return line from the fitting at the fuel tank

and hold the open end of the pipe in a convenient receptacle.

2. Start and run the engine at 1200 r.p.m. and measure the fuel flow return for a period of one minute. Approximately one half gallon of fuel should flow from the return tube per minute.

3. Be sure all connections are tight so that no air will be drawn into the fuel system; then immerse the end of the fuel line in the fuel container. Air bubbles rising to the surface of the liquid will indicate a leak on the suction side of the pump.

4. Whenever the fuel flow check indicates there is insufficient flow for satisfactory engine performance, proceed as follows:

a. Renew the element in the strainer as outlined in respective applicable vehicle manual.

b. Start the engine and run it at 1200 r.p.m. to check the fuel flow. If the fuel flow is still unsatisfactory continue as follows.

c. Renew the element in the fuel filter. If the fuel flow is still unsatisfactory continue as follows.

d. Substitute another fuel pump that is known to be in good condition and again check the flow. When changing a fuel pump, clean all fuel lines with compressed air and be sure all fuel line connections are tight.

Check Fuel Pump

If the fuel pump fails to function satisfactorily, check for broken pump shaft, or dirt in relief valve.

1. Insert the end of a wire through one of the pump body drain holes, then crank the engine momentarily and see if wire vibrates. Vibration will be felt if pump shaft rotates.

2. Without removing the pump from the engine, remove relief valve screw, then remove spring, pin, and valve. Wash parts and blow out valve cavity with compressed air. Install valve parts.

Fuel Pump Removal

1. Disconnect fuel lines from inlet and outlet openings of the fuel pump.

2. Disconnect drain line from fuel pump, if used.

3. Unscrew three pump attaching bolt and washer assemblies and withdraw pump.

4. Check drive coupling and if broken, replace.

Fuel Pump Disassembly

With the fuel pump removed from the engine, disassemble the pump as follows:

1. Remove eight cover bolts, then withdraw the pump cover away from the pump body and off the

Fuel pump assembly
(© G.M.C.)

1 Pump cover	8 Dowel pin
2 Valve plug	9 Drive gear
3 Gasket	10 Drive shaft
4 Valve spring	11 Retaining ball
5 Relief valve	12 Driven shaft
6 Pump body	13 Driven gear
7 Oil seals	

two cover dowels.

2. Withdraw drive shaft, drive gear and gear retaining ball as an assembly from the pump body.

3. Remove drive gear, if necessary, from shaft being careful not to misplace the locking ball.

4. Remove driven gear and shaft as an assembly from pump body.

5. Remove valve screw, holding hand on screw to relieve valve spring tension.

6. Remove spring, pin, and valve from valve cavity in pump body.

7. If inspection indicates oil seals require replacing, remove in manner illustrated, by clamping pump body in a bench vise and screwing threaded end of tool shaft into outer oil seal (seal nearest to bolting flange). Then tap pilot end of shaft with hammer thus removing seal. Repeat this operation to remove the inner seal.

Inspection

1. When the fuel pump has been disassembled, all parts should be washed in clean fuel oil, blown dry with compressed air and inspected.

2. Oil seals once removed from the pump body should be discarded and replaced with new seals. Lips of oil seals must fit snug around the pump shaft.

3. Pump gear teeth should be checked for scoring or chipping. If gear teeth are scored or chipped, they should be replaced.

4. Mating faces of the pump body and cover must be flat and smooth and fit tightly together.

5. The relief valve must be free from score marks and must fit its seat in the pump body. If the relief valve is scored and cannot be cleaned up with crocus cloth, the valve must be replaced.

Fuel Pump Assembly

1. Place inner oil seal on pilot of installer with lip of seal facing shoulder on handle.

2. With pump supported on wood blocks, insert pilot of installer into pump body so seal starts straight into pump flange, then drive seal into place in counterbore of flange until it bottoms.

3. Place adaptor on pilot end of installer with shorter end of adaptor against shoulder on installer. Position outer oil seal on adaptor with lip of seal facing adaptor, then insert pilot of installer into pump so seal starts straight in pump flange and drive seal into pump body until the shoulder of adaptor contracts body.

4. Clamp pump body in soft jaws of bench vise with relief valve cavity up. Lubricate the outside diameter of relief valve and place valve in cavity with hollow end up. Insert spring inside the valve and pin inside of spring. With gasket in place next to head of valve screw place screw over spring and thread into pump body.

5. Install fuel pump drive gear, if removed, over plain end of drive shaft with slot in gear facing plain end of shaft. This operation is very important. Press gear beyond locking ball retain-

ing hole. Then place ball in hole and press gear back until end of slot contacts ball.

6. Lubricate pump shaft and insert square end of shaft into opening at gear side of pump body and through the two oil seals.

7. Place driven gear shaft and gear assembly in pump body with chamfered end of gear teeth facing pump body.

8. Lubricate gears and shafts with clean engine oil.

9. Apply a thin coat of reputable sealer on face of pump cover outside of gear pocket area, then place cover against pump body with two dowel pins in cover entering holes in pump body. The cover can be installed in only one position over the two shafts.

10. Secure cover in place.

11. After assembly, rotate pump shaft by hand to make certain that parts rotate freely. If binding exists, it may be necessary to tap corner of pump cover with a hammer to relieve binding.

Fuel Pump Installation

1. Affix a new gasket to pump body and locate pump drive coupling over square end of fuel pump drive shaft.

2. Install fuel pump on engine and secure.

3. Connect inlet and outlet fuel lines to the fuel pump.

4. Connect drain tube, if used, to pump body.

Crown Valve Fuel Injectors

Description and Operation

The cross section of the injector illustrated, shows the various fuel injector parts. Fuel oil supplied to injector enters the dropforged steel body at the top through the filter cap. After passing through the filter element inlet passage, the fuel oil fills the supply chamber between bushing and spill deflector. The plunger operates up and down in this bushing, the bore of which is connected to fuel supply by two funnel-shaped ports.

Motion of injector rocker arm is transmitted to plunger by follower which bears against plunger spring. Follower is positioned in body by a follower stop pin. In addition to up and down motion, the plunger can be rotated, in operation, around its axis by gear, which is in mesh with the control rack. The fuel is metered by an upper helix and lower helix which are machined into lower end of plunger. The relation of these helixes to the two ports changes with the rotation of the plunger. As plunger moves downward, fuel oil in high-pressure cylinder or bushing is first

displaced through the ports back into supply chamber until lower edge of plunger closes the lower port. Remaining oil is then forced upward through center passage in plunger into recess between upper helix and the lower cut-off from which it can still flow back into supply chamber until helix closes upper port. Rotation of plunger, by changing position of helix, retards or advances the closing of the ports and beginning and ending of injection period, at the same time increasing or decreasing desired amount of fuel which remains under plunger for injection into the cylinder.

Illustration shows the various plunger positions from NO INJECTION to FULL INJECTION.

Illustration shows four positions for downward travel of plunger, rack fixed. On downward travel of plunger, the metered amount of fuel is forced through center passage of the valve assembly, through check valve, and against spray tip valve. When sufficient fuel pressure is built up, valve is forced off its seat and fuel is forced through small orifices in spray tip and atomized into the combustion chamber.

Constant circulation of fresh, cool fuel through the injectors, which renews the fuel supply in the chamber, helps to maintain even operating temperatures of injectors, and also effectively removes all traces of air which might otherwise accumulate in system and interfere with accurate metering of fuel.

The fuel injector outlet opening, which returns the excess fuel oil supplied by fuel pump, is directly adjacent to inlet opening.

Refer to illustration for injector identifying marks. The correct injector must be used and type can be determined by checking injector in engine for number which appears on color tag pressed into body.

Injector Mounting

The injectors are mounted in the cylinder heads, with their spray tips projecting slightly below top of inside surface of combustion chambers. A clamp, bolted to cylinder head and fitting into a machined recess in each side of injector body, holds injector in place in a water-cooled copper tube which passes through cylinder head. A dowel pin in injector body registers with a hole in cylinder head for accurately locating injector assembly.

A copper tube is installed in cylinder head with a seal ring at flanged upper end. The lower end is peened into a recess of the cylinder head. The tapered lower end of injector seats in copper tube, forming a tight seal to withstand the high pressure inside combustion chamber.

Injector Removal

If it becomes necessary to remove one of the fuel injectors for inspection or replacement, follow the procedure given below:

1. Remove valve rocker cover.

2. Remove fuel lines from both the injector and the fuel connectors. *Immediately after removal of fuel lines from an injector, the two fuel feed fittings should be protected to prevent dirt entering injector.*

3. If necessary, crank engine with the starter or a bar at flywheel ring gear until the three rocker arm clevis pins, at outer end of arms, are in line.

4. Loosen two rocker arm bracket bolts holding brackets to cylinder head and swing rocker arm assembly over away from valves and injector.

5. Remove injector hold-down bolt, special washer, and injector clamp.

6. Using tool as illustrated, pry injector from its seat.

7. Lift injector from seat, at the same time disengage control rack linkage.

Injector Tests

Tests using a popping fixture and a comparator may be made if the injector shows no external damage. If these tests and a visual inspection of the plunger show satisfactory condition and performance, the injector may be put back into service without further disassembly and work. Perform all the tests without disassembling the unit. Then, evaluate the test results, and repair the unit as necessary. Rebuilt injectors must pass all tests before being returned to service.

NOTE: Fuel injectors operate at extreme pressure for efficient atomization. Fuel leaving an injector nozzle is moving so fast that it will easily penetrate the skin and cause severe infection. Therefore, extreme care must be taken to ensure that fuel spray is discharged well away from any portion of the skin.

1. Place the upper end of the injector against a bench, as shown in the illustration, and move the rack back and forth while fully depressing the follower. Any binding indicates that internal parts are dirty or damaged.

2. Mount the injector in a testing and popping fixture, as shown in the illustration, with the injector dowel in the proper slot. An adaptor plate must be used for offset body injectors. Position the support plate and popping handle so they are at the proper height.

3. Close the clamp with the inlet tube on the injector. Operate the

pump handle until all air has been purged, and close the outlet clamp.

4. Put the rack in the full fuel position and pump the handle of the test fixture with smooth, even strokes until the injector pops (sprays fuel). Take note of and record the pressure at which this occurs. The pressure must be 450–850 psi, or the unit is faulty.

5. With the pressure just below the pop off point, close the fuel shut off valve and note and time the pressure drop. A drop from 450 to 250 psi must not take less than 40 seconds.

6. If the time for the pressure drop is less than 40 seconds, thoroughly dry the outside of the injector with compressed air, and then open the fuel valve and operate the pump to maintain test pressure. A leak at the injector rack opening indicates a poor bushing-to-body fit. A leak around the spray tip or seal ring indicates a loose injector nut, damaged seal ring, or a brinneled surface on the nut or spray tip. A leak at the filter cap indicates that the cap is loose or a damaged filter cap gasket. A dribble of fuel (if more than a drop or two) indicates a damaged surface or dirt.

7. Thoroughly dry the injector with compressed air and check and tighten the fuel connections.

8. Put the rack in the FULL FUEL position and lock the popping handle with the lock provided. Operate the pump to maintain full test pressure.

9. Adjust the screw in the popping handle so it will depress the plunger just far enough to close both ports in the injector bushing (at this point, the injector spray decreases appreciably and the pressure will rise).

Fuel injector assembly showing fuel flow (© G.M.C.)

1 Follower	14 Filter element
2 Follower spring	15 Filter spring
3 Follower stop pin	16 Gasket
4 Gear	17 Filter cap
5 Gear retainer	18 Identification tag
6 Plunger	19 Valve seat
7 Spill deflector	20 Valve
8 Injector nut	21 Valve spring
9 Plunger bushing	22 Valve cage
10 Seal ring	23 Valve stop
11 Dowel	24 Check valve
12 Rack	25 Spray tip
13 Injector body	

10. Pump up and maintain 1400–2000 psi. Check for leaks and refer to the "Insufficient Injector Holding Time Chart" for evaluation of the causes.

11. Loosen the adjusting screw in the popping handle, pump up pressure to near the pop pressure, and operate the popping handle several times while watching the spray pattern very carefully. Fuel should be discharged from every orifice and should form an even spray pattern. Otherwise, the spray tip requires cleaning.

12. Remove the plunger from the injector as follows:
    A. Mount the injector, right side up, in a holding fixture. Compress the follower spring and, with a screwdriver, raise the spring above the stop pin and withdraw the pin. Allow the plunger spring to rise gradually.
    B. Remove the injector, turn it upside down, and catch the spring and plunger.

13. Inspect plunger, comparing it with plungers shown in the illustration. Check for a chip in

Injector Testing Fixture
(© G.M. Corp)

Pumping Up Test Fixture
(© G.M. Corp)

Checking the Freeness of the Rack and Plunger
(© G.M. Corp)

SCREW DRIVER

Removing Follower Stop Pin
(© G.M. Corp)

the area of the bottom helix and lower portion of the upper helix. Reinstall the plunger and go on with the following test. If the plunger is chipped, replace the plunger and bushing after performing the last test.

14. Install the injector in a GM Diesel injector comparator and seal it firmly. Pull the rack out to the NO FUEL position.

15. Turn on the comparator operating switch. Then, move the rack to the FULL FUEL position.

16. Wait 30 seconds, and then press the fuel flow starting button.

17. After fuel flow stops (after 1000 strokes), pull the rack to the NO FUEL position, turn the comparator off, and reset the counter.

18. Observe the reading on the vial, and refer to the chart on the comparator to see if the volume of fuel falls within specified limits.

Injector Disassembly

If required, the injector may be disassembled in the following manner:

1. Support injector upright in injector assembly fixture, and remove filter caps, springs, filter elements and gaskets. NOTE: Whenever injector is disassembled, filter elements and gaskets should be discarded and replaced with new filters and gaskets.

2. Compress follower spring. Then, using a screwdriver, raise spring above stop pin and withdraw pin. Allow follower spring to rise gradually.

3. Refer to illustration for details and remove plunger follower, spring and plunger as an assembly.

4. Reverse the injector in the fixture and loosen nut from injector body.

5. Remove the spray tip and valve parts off bushing and place in a clean receptacle until ready for assembly.

6. When an injector has been in use for some time, the spray tip, even though clean on the outside, may not be pushed readily from the nut with the fingers. In this event, support the nut on a wood block and drive the tip down through the nut, as shown in illustration.

7. Remove spill deflector, and seal ring from injector nut.

8. Remove plunger bushing, gear retainer, and gear from injector body.

9. Withdraw injector control rack from injector body.

Injector Service

1. Wash all injector parts in clean fuel oil or another suitable solvent. Dry them with filtered compressed air. Use extra care when cleaning passages, drilled holes, etc.

2. Clean out the spray tip with a reamer, as shown in the illustration. Turn the reamer clockwise during cleaning. Wash the spray tip, dry it with compressed air, and then clean the spray tip orifices with a .005" diameter wire. *Note: The wire must be honed until it is smooth and free of burrs, using a stone, before using it for cleaning purposes.* After orifice cleaning, again wash the spray tip in fuel oil or solvent and dry it.

3. Clean fuel and rack holes with appropriate cleaning brushes, and then blow all passages dry with compressed air.

5. When handling the injector

A. Tight rack causing binding in up and down movement.

B. Dirt in fuel. This shows advanced stages of abrasive matter in fuel.

C. Chipped at lower helix.

D. High pressure scoring caused by a plugged tip or wrong size tip being installed.

E. The condition shown can be caused by either lack of fuel at high speeds or water in fuel.

Damaged and Usable Plungers
(© G.M. Corp)

plunger, never touch the finished surfaces with the fingers. Wash the plunger and its bushing in clean fuel oil and dry it with compressed air. Wrap tissue paper around the bushing cleaner tool and out the bushing bore, as shown in the illustration. Then, submerge the parts in clean fuel oil to protect them from corrosion during the remaining steps of injector service.

6. Inspect the control rack and rack gear teeth for excessive wear or damage, and check for excessive wear in the bore of the gear. Replace damaged or worn parts.

7. Inspect the ends of the spill deflector for sharp edges. Remove sharp edges with a medium stone.

8. Inspect the plunger spring for defects and check in a spring tester for a free length of 1.659" (1.504"-92 Series), and compression to 1.028" with a load of 53-59 lbs (70 lbs-92 Series). Replace the spring if less than 49 lbs. will bring it to the 1.028" length.

9. Check the seal ring area of the injector body for burrs and scratches. Check the surface which contacts the injector bushing for scratches or scuff marks. Lap this surface as described below if necessary.

10. Inspect the plunger or any damage like that shown in the illustration. Replace it and the bushing as a set if such damage exists. Inspect the plunger for damage at the portion which rides inside the gear. If sharp edges are found, remove them with a 500 grit stone. Wash the plunger after stoning.

11. Inspect the plunger bushing for cracks or chipping. Slip the

Injector Comparator
(© G.M. Corp)

plunger into the bushing and check for free movement. If wear or scoring prevents free movement, replace the plunger and bushing with a new set.

12. Examine the spray tip seating surface of the injector nut for nicks, burrs, or brinelling. Reseat the surface if damage is mild, or replace the nut if it is severe.

Reaming Spray Tip
(© G.M. Corp)

13. Inspect the injector valve spring for wear or breakage, and replace if either is evident. When the spring is compressed to length of 240", the load should be 4¾-5¾ lbs. If compression to .240" requres less than 4¼ lbs., replace the spring.

14. Inspect the sealing surfaces of the spray tip and valve parts shown in the illustration. Inspect the parts for any imperfection whatever with a magnifying glass, and replace as necessary.

15. Inspect the injector body, bushing, spray tip, and valve assembly seating surfaces, and, if necessary, lap them as described below. Whenever reinstalling used valve parts, all the sealing surfaces must be lapped as described below except those on the crown valve. This is also good practice on new parts.

16. Clean the lapping blocks, using compressed air only. Spread 600 grit dry lapping powder on one of the blocks.

17. Place the part to be lapped flat on the block. Move the part back and forth in a figure eight motion, applying just sufficient pressure to keep the part flat on the block. Draw the part across a clean piece of tissue paper placed on a flat surface every four or five passes to clean it. Inspect it after each cleaning to ensure that it is lapped just enough to ensure production of a flat surface.

18. Wash the part in cleaning solution and dry it with compressed air.

19. Apply lapping powder to a second lapping block and move the part lightly across the block just a few times to give it a smooth surface. Wash the part

CLEANING BUSHING

POLISHING PLUNGER WITH TISSUE

DRYING BUSHING WITH FILTERED AIR

TESTING FIT OF PLUNGER IN BUSHING

CLEANING BUSHING WITH TISSUE AND TOOL

CLEANING VALVE NUT

Cleaning Plunger, Bushing, and Nut
(© G.M. Corp)

Fuel Metering From No Injection To Full Injection, Produced By Rotating Plunger with Control Rack

Fuel metering produced by rotating plunger
(© G.M.C.)

Phases of Injector Operation By Vertical Travel of Plunger

Injector operation by vertical travel of plunger
(© G.M.C.)

in cleaning solution and dry it with compressed air.

20. Place the part on a third lapping block and, without lapping powder, repeat the process very lightly just a few times.

21. Inspect the edge of the hole in the crown valve seat. Use a magnifying glass and check to make sure the seat is a true circle and has a perfectly smooth surface. If the edge is imperfect, lap it as described below:

Mount a deburring tool in a drill motor and place a small amount of lapping powder and oil in a mixture on the tool. Place the valve seat over the pilot of the tool and start the motor. Gently grab the valve seat with the fingers and touch it lightly against the rotating tool. When the seat is uniform, flat lap the seat slightly. Clean the part and examine the width of the edge. The width of the chamfer at the edge of the hole should be .002″-.005″. A greater width will lower the pop pressure of the injector.

22. Wash all parts that have been lapped in a suitable solvent and dry with compressed air. Clean the inside of the injector bushing by wrapping clean tissue around a bushing cleaner tool and rotating it inside the bushing as shown in the illustration.

Injector Assembly

Before starting to assemble an injector, it is necessary to have an extremely clean bench on which to work and place the parts. Refer to illustrations for proper relative positions of the injector parts and the methods for their assembly prior to proceeding with assembly. Since the plunger and bushing are matched parts, they must be considered as one piece and, if one is replaced, both must be replaced.

Assemble Injector Filters

New filters and gaskets should always be used when reassembling injectors.

1. Holding the injector body right side up, place a filter in each of the fuel cavities in the top of the

injector body. Note that the fuel filters have a dimple in one end. When assembling the filters, always have the dimple at the bottom.

2. Place a spring above each filter, a new gasket up against the shoulder of each filter cap, lubricate the threads, and tighten the filter cap in place in the injector body to a torque of 65 to 75 ft.-lbs., using a 9/16″ deep socket wrench. It is important that the filter caps be tightened securely so as to compress the gaskets and effect a good seal with the injector body. Also, when the caps are tightened, they compress the filter springs which hold the filters securely in place so all fuel entering the injector is properly filtered.

3. Install covers on injector filter caps to prevent any dirt particles from entering injector. Be sure covers are clean.

Assemble Rack and Gear

When rack and gear are assembled, the marked tooth of the gear must be engaged between the two marked teeth on the rack.

1. Hold the injector body bottom end up and slide the rack through the proper hole in the body. The two marked teeth can then be observed when looking into the bore for the gear from the bottom of the injector body. The injector rack can be placed in the injector body in only one position and have the tooth marks show in the opening for the gear.

2. Holding the rack in position so the tooth marks show, slide the

gear into proper engagement with the rack.

3. Slide gear retainer down on top of gear; then place plunger bushing down onto retainer with locating pin in bushing guided into slot of injector body.

Assemble Injector Valve Parts

Refer to the illustration and assemble as described below.

1. Support the body of the injector in an injector assembly fixture with the bottom end up.

2. Locate the seal ring on the shoulder of the body. Slide the spill deflector over the barrel of the bushing.

3. Place the valve seat on the end of the bushing. Insert the stem of the valve into one end of the valve spring and the valve stop into the opposite end. Lower the valve cage over the assembly so that the stop seats in the cage. Position the valve cage on the valve seat.

4. Locate the check valve on the center of the cage. Place the spray tip over the check valve and against the cage. Then, lubricate the threads and carefully pilot the nut over the spray tip and check valve assembly. The tip will slide through the hole in the small end of the nut.

5. Screw the nut into place, making sure the valve assembly doesn't shift. If they do shift, turn the end of the spray tip with the fingers while screwing the nut onto the body by hand. A wrench must not be used to tighten the nut at this time!

Assemble the Plunger and Follower

1. Slide the head of the plunger onto the follower. Insert the assembly through the plunger spring and onto the injector.

Sealing Surfaces Which Require Lapping
(© G.M. Corp)

Injector installed
(© G.M.C.)

1 Camshaft
2 Cam follower assy.
3 Push rod
4 Hold-down clamp
5 Rocker arm
6 Injector assy.
7 Cylinder head

Injector removal
(© G.M.C.)

2. Invert the injector in the fixture, so the connector is upward, and push the rack all the way in. Insert the free end of the plunger into the top of the injector body.

3. Start the stop pin into position in the injector body so the bottom coil of the follower spring rests on the flange on the stop pin (see illustration). With the follower slot and the injector body hole in alignment, and the flat side of the plunger positioned to engage the flat side of the gear, press down on the top of the follower and press the follower stop pin into position. The follower will have to be pressed down until the slot and hole are aligned and allow the pin to go in.

4. Again invert the injector assembly, and, using a socket and torque wrench drive, tighten the nut to 55-56 ft lbs. (75-85 on 92 Series).

Check Spray Tip Concentricity

This step must be performed to ensure that the spray tip and injector nut are concentric within .008" for correct alignment of the tip in the spray tip hole of the cylinder head.

1. Mount the injector in a concentricity gauge as shown in the illustration.

2. Zero the dial indicator. Rotate the injector one full turn and note the highest reading on the dial.

3. If the run out exceeds .008", remove the injector from the gauge, loosen the injector nut, re-center the spray tip, and re-torque the nut.

4. If repeated attempts fail to center the tip within the specified runout, the assembly of the injector is unsatisfactory.

Injector Testing

Before placing a reconditioned injector in service, all of the tests (except the visual inspection of the plunger) previously outlined in this section under "Injector Tests" must be performed again.

If an injector is not to be used immediately, caps should be installed on the injector caps. The injector test oil remaining in the injector after the fuel output test will serve as a rust preventive while the injector is in storage.

Injector Installation

Before installing a new or reconditioned injector in an engine, the carbon deposits must be removed from the beveled seat of the injector hole tube in the cylinder head. If not, the injector may be cocked resulting in a fractured spray tip.

Injector tube bevel seat reamer should be used to clean the carbon out of the tube before installing the injector. Refer to "Reaming" in "CYLINDER HEAD" section. Care must be exercised to remove ONLY the carbon so that the proper clearance between the injector body and cylinder head is maintained. Pack the flutes of the reamer with heavy grease.

1. Insert the injector into the injector tube with the locating dowel registering with the locating hole in the cylinder head and with the pin on the injector control tube lever registering with the injector control rack lever.

2. Place injector clamp in position, then install washer and bolt.

Injector body, filters, springs and cap
(© G.M.C.)

Cap
Gasket
Spring
Filter
Body

Injector, plunger follower and spring
(© G.M.C.)

Follower
Plunger
Spring
Body
Stop Pin
Rack
Nut
Tip

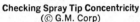

Checking Spray Tip Concentricity
(© G.M. Corp)

Installing Follower Stop Pin
(© G.M. Corp)

Tighten bolt to 20-25 ft.-lbs. NOTE: Check injector rack for free movement. Excess torque will cause the injector control rack to stick or bind. Also, make sure clamp does not interfere with operation of valve or injector springs.

3. Move rocker arm assembly into position and secure rocker arm bracket bolts to torque of 90 to 100 ft.-lbs.

4. Connect fuel pipes to injector fuel connectors, torquing the connections to 12-15 ft.-lbs.

5. As a precautionary measure against any possibility of scoring injector parts upon initial installation due to lack of lubrication, any entrapped air should be bled from the injector before tightening the connections on the fuel outlet side of the injector. This may be accomplished by cranking the engine briefly with the injector rack in the NO FUEL position and then tightening the fuel pipe connection.

6. When installing injector fuel lines, connections should be tightened only enough to prevent leakage of fuel. Excess tightening may result in the flared end of the fuel line being twisted or fractured. A torque wrench adapter is essential to properly tighten fuel line connector nut to 12-15 ft. lbs. torque. Use of this adapter and torque wrench is highly recommended.

7. When all injector lines are installed, the engine should be run long enough (during tune-up procedure) to check for leaks. Should leaks occur, the connections should be tightened only enough to stop the leak.

8. Following installation of the injectors in the engine, a complete engine tune-up should be performed. However, if only one injector has been removed and replaced, and other injectors and the governor adjustment have

not been disturbed, it will only be necessary to adjust the clearance of the valves, valve bridge, and time the injector for the one cylinder, and position the control rack on the cylinder involved to correspond with that of the other racks.

Needle Valve Fuel Injectors

The injectors used in Detroit Diesel Engines are of the unit type, which means that the injector requires only that fuel be supplied to it under pressure, and performs all metering, injection, and atomization functions without the help of a complex distributor type injector pump and the accompanying high pressure fuel lines. This type of design insures a minimum of problems with leakage and uneven fuel distribution.

The injector plunger is operated by a follower, rocker lever, pushrod, and tappet which are similar to those used to operate the engine's exhaust valves, and which are operated by the same camshaft. A fuel rack positions the injector plunger according to the load placed on the engine. While the cylinder is being filled with fresh air and going through the compression stroke, the plunger is in the fully raised position. This permits various passages in the injector unit to be filled with fuel and allows fuel circulation through the unit for removal of excess heat and any air that may have accumulated. When the injector rocker depresses the plunger, the fuel trapped under the plunger is forced down through the check valve. Pressure then builds up in the passages to the needle valve, lifts that valve off its seat, and allows fuel to be injected through the spray tip in atomized form.

The injector plunger contains passages which allow fuel to pass between the area below the plunger and the helical cutout on the upper part of the plunger. Since both the upper and lower ports in the plunger bushing connect with the low pressure fuel supply system, injection will only

occur during that portion of the plunger stroke during which both ports are covered. Rotation of the plunger via the injector rack and gear changes the portion of the helical cutout which effects opening and closing of the ports (see illustration), thus controlling the amount of fuel injected. The high pressure required to force fuel through the needle valve insures that injection will occur only when both ports are fully blocked off. Thus, metering is precise, and plenty of pressure is available for efficient atomization.

Injector body, nut, rack, bushing and spray tip details
(© G.M.C.)

The injectors are mounted in the heads so their spray tips will protrude through the lower surface of the head and into the combustion chamber. A water cooled copper tube surrounds the injector and permits it to be removed without draining the cooling system. A mounting clamp is bolted to the head and fits into a machined recess located on either side of the injector body. A dowel pin in the body of the injector registers with a hole in the head for accurately locating the assembly.

Injector Removal

1. Remove the valve cover. Remove the fuel lines from the injector(s) to be removed, immediately covering the two fuel feed fittings with shipping caps.
2. Crank the engine over until the three clevis pins at the outer ends of the rocker arms are in line.
3. Loosen the bracket bolts holding the brackets to the head and swing the rocker assembly over, away from the valves and injector.
4. Loosen the injector clamp bolt, and remove the bolt, washer, and clamp.
5. Loosen both injector rack control lever adjusting screws and slide the lever away from the injector.
6. Free the injector from its seat and lift it from the head.
7. Cover the injector holes to keep dirt out of the head. Clean the outside of the injector and dry it with compressed air.

Injector Tests

Inspect the exterior of the injector. If there is no damage, the tests following should be performed to determine whether or not the injector re-

1	Follower
2	Follower Spring
3	Follower Stop Pin
4	Plunger
5	Gear
6	Gear Retainer
7	Seal Ring
8	Plunger Bushing
9	Spill Deflector
10	Check Valve
11	Valve Spring
12	Spring Seat
13	Needle Valve
14	Spray Tip
15	Spring Cage
16	Body Nut
17	Check Valve Cage
18	Dowel
19	Control Rack
20	Fuel Filter
21	Injector Body
22	Gasket
23	Filter Cap

Needle Valve Type Fuel Injector
(© G.M. Corp)

quires overhauling. If the injector passes all these tests and examination of the plunger shows no damage, it may be returned to service. If the plunger is visibly damaged or the unit fails to pass any of the tests, the unit requires overhaul. All tests should be performed before an overhauled injector is put back into service.

1. Mount the injector in the tester, locating the dowel in the proper slot in the adaptor plate. Position the injector support and the handle support at the proper height.

2. Place the handle on top of the injector follower and then close the inlet and outlet clamps to hold the injector in the tester. With the control rack in the NO FUEL position, push the handle down to depress the follower as far as it will go. Then, release the pressure on the handle. Begin moving the control rack back and forth and continue doing so while gradually allowing the follower to rise to its fully raised position. Any binding in the rack indicates internal damage or dirt.

Injector Removal
(© G.M. Corp)

Checking the Freeness of the Rack and Plunger
(© G.M. Corp)

Injector Comparator
(© G.M. Corp)

3. Dry the injector thoroughly with compressed air. Pump up the tester, maintaining a pressure of 1600–2000 psi. Inspect for leaks at the filter cap gaskets, body plugs, injector nut seal ring, and rack hole and spray tip orifices.

4. Mount the injector valve parts on a tool body mounted in the adapter in the tester. Operate the pump handle until the spray tip valve has opened several times. Then, operate the handle smoothly at about 40 strokes per minute and note the opening pressure of the needle valve. The pressure should be 2000-3200 psi, the action should be sharp, and a finely atomized spray should be produced. If the opening pressure is low or the atomization is poor, the needle valve and tip assembly must be replaced.

5. Actuate the pump handle several times and then maintain 1500 psi for 15 seconds. Inspect the spray tip for leakage. There should be no fuel droplets, although a very slight wetting is permissible.

6. Cease pumping and time the pressure drop from 1500 to 1000 psi. The drop should require at least five seconds, timed with a watch. If the pressure drop takes less than five seconds, replace the valve and tip assembly.

7. Put the injector rack in FULL FUEL position, and pump the handle to obtain 200-250 psi. Close the fuel shut-off valve. Operate the tester handle at a rate of about 40 times per minute and observe the spray pattern. All spray orifices should be open and injecting evenly. The beginning and ending of injection should be sharp and all the fuel should be well atomized. Sluggish action, dribbling, or plugging of orifices indicate that disassembly and inspection are required.

8. Remove the injector from the tester and support it in a holding fixture. Compress the follower spring and, with a screw driver, raise the spring above the stop pin and withdraw the pin. Gradually release the spring.

9. Lift the follower and plunger from the injector body as an assembly. Inspect the plunger for chipping like that shown in figure 41 C. If plunger is chipped, the injector should be reconditioned before going on to the next test.

10. Invert the injector in the assembly fixture, and push the control rack all the way in. Place the follower spring and stop pin on the injector body so the bottom coil of the spring rests on the narrow flange of the pin. Slide the head of the plunger into the slot in the follower as shown in the illustration. Position the follower and plunger over the injector body and align the slot in the follower with the stop pin hole in the body. Align the flat side of the plunger with the flat in the gear and lower the plunger and follower into the injector body until the follower rests on the spring. Press down on the follower and press the stop pin into the slot in the follower until the spring drops into the slot in the stop pin.

11. Mount the injector in the comparator and turn the wheel to clamp it and the adaptor in position. Make sure the counter is preset to 1,000 strokes.

12. Put the rack in the NO FUEL position. Turn the power switch on.

13. Push the injector rack to the FULL FUEL position. Allow the unit to run for about 30 seconds for purging of air. Then, push the fuel flow start button.

14. After the fuel flow stops (1,000 strokes), pull the rack out to the NO FUEL position. Then turn the unit off and reset the counter.

15. Note the reading on the fuel collection vial and compare it with the chart on the comparator. If the quantity is not within specified limits, the unit requires servicing.

Injector Disassembly

1. Support the injector in the assembly fixture and remove the filter caps, gaskets, and filter elements. Discard used filters and gaskets.

2. Compress the follower spring and use a screwdriver to raise the spring above the stop pin, and withdraw the pin. Release the follower spring gradually.

Removing the Spray Tip from the Injector Nut
(© G.M. Corp)

Fuel Metering From No Injection To Full Injection, Produced By Rotating Plunger with Control Rack

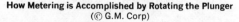

How Metering is Accomplished by Rotating the Plunger
(© G.M. Corp)

Installing the Follower Stop Pin
(© G.M. Corp)

Removing Follower Spring and Plunger
(© G.M. Corp)

Withdraw the rack and the seal ring.

Injector Service

1. Wash all the parts in clean fuel oil or a suitable solvent and dry them with compressed air. Clean the passages, drilled holes, and slots in all parts with extra care.
2. Clean the spray tip with a special reamer, as in the illustration, turning the reamer in a clockwise direction. Wash the spray tip and dry it with compressed air. Clean the orifices with a pin vise using .005" diameter wire for tips with .005"-

Cleaning Injector Body Ring
(© G.M. Corp)

Cleaning the Spray Tip
(© G.M. Corp)

Checking Spray Tip Concentricity
(© G.M. Corp)

.0055" diameter holes, and a .006" wire for tips with .006" diameter ho'es. Hone the end of the wire to remove burrs and taper the end 1/16" back from the tip with a stone. Allow the wire to protrude 1/8" from the holder. After cleaning, wash the spray tip in clean fuel oil and dry it with compressed air. Note: During reaming of the spray tip, avoid contacting the needle valve seat.

3. Clean and brush all injector body passages with an appropriate brush. Dry all passages with compressed air.
4. Insert a reamer into the top of the injector body, turning it clockwise a few turns. Then, remove the reamer and check the face of the ring to make sure the reamer has been contacting it. Repeat the procedure until the

3. Remove the plunger follower and plunger assembly from the body. Remove the follower spring.
4. Reverse the position of the injector in the fixture and, with a socket wrench, loosen the body nut. Remove the nut by carefully lifting it straight up to avoid dislodging the spray tip and valve parts. Remove the spray tip and valve parts and place them in a clean recepticle.
5. If you can't easily push the spray tip off the nut, support the nut on a wood block and drive the tip down through the nut using a special tool, as shown in the illustration.
6. Remove the spill deflector. Lift the bushing straight out of the body.
7. Remove the body from the holding fixture. Invert the body and catch the gear and its retainer.

CLEANING BUSHING

DRYING BUSHING WITH FILTERED AIR

CLEANING BUSHING WITH TISSUE AND TOOL

POLISHING PLUNGER WITH TISSUE

TESTING FIT OF PLUNGER IN BUSHING

CLEANING VALVE NUT

Cleaning plunger, bushing and nut
(© G.M.C.)

647

reamer makes contact over the entire surface of the ring. Clean up the opposite side of the ring similarly.

5. Insert a .375″ straight fluted reamer inside the ring bore in the injector body. Turn the reamer clockwise to remove any burrs inside the ring bore. Then, wash the injector body in clean fuel and dry with compressed air.

6. Use the two types of carbon removing tools to remove carbon deposits from the spray tip seat and the lower end of the injector nut. The tool to be used should be inserted carefully and turned clockwise. Be careful not to remove metal or set up burrs.

7. Wash the injector nut in clean fuel oil and dry with compressed air. Wash the plunger and bushing with clean fuel oil and dry with compressed air, avoiding contact with the finished plunger surfaces.

8. Submerge all parts in a receptacle containing clean fuel oil. Keep all parts of each injector assembly together.

9. Inspect the teeth on the control rack and control rack gear for excessive wear or damage. Check for excessive wear in the bore of the gear. Replace any damaged or worn parts.

10. Inspect the ends of the spill deflector for sharp edges or burrs which could create burrs on the injector body or nut. Remove burrs with a medium stone.

11. Inspect the follower spring and check it with a spring tester. Free length should be approximately 1.659″. Load should be at least 48 lbs. when compressed to 1.028″. Replace the spring if it does not pass both of these tests.

12. Check the seal ring area for burrs or scratches. Check the surface which contacts the injector bushing for scratches, scuff marks, etc. Lap this surface if it is faulty.

13. Inspect the plunger for scoring, chipping, or excessive wear. Check for sharp edges where the plunger rides in the gear. If sharp edges exist, remove them with a 500 grit stone. Wash the plunger after stoning. Inspect the plunger bushing for cracks or chipping. Check the locating pin in the bushing and replace it if it is damaged or sheared off. Check the plunger and bushing for free movement. Replace badly worn, chipped, or scored plungers and bushings with a new assembly.

14. Examine the spray tip seating surface of the injector nut for nicks, burrs, or brinelling. Reseat the seating surface, if neces-

sary, or replace the nut if it is severely damaged.

15. Inspect the injector valve spring and replace it if it is worn or broken.

16. Inspect the arrowed sealing surfaces shown in figure 53. Examine the surfaces under a magnifying glass for burrs, nicks, erosion, cracks, chipping, or excessive wear, and replace as necessary. Check the spray tip for enlarged orifices and replace it if necessary.

17. Examine the needle valve for wear, scoring, or damage to the quill where it contacts the spring seat. If the needle valve is scored or damaged, replace the spray tip assembly. Lap all surfaces indicated by arrows as described below. Lap also the sealing surfaces of new parts to remove burrs or nicks picked up during handling.

18. Clean three lapping blocks with compressed air only. Spread 600 grit dry lapping powder on two of the blocks.

19. Place each part flat on the block. Using a figure eight motion, move the part back and forth across the block, maintaining just sufficient pressure to keep the part completely in contact with the block.

20. After each five passes, clean the part with tissue paper by placing the paper on a flat surface and drawing the part across it. Lap the part just until it is flat—avoid excessive lapping. When the part is flat, wash it in solvent and dry with compressed air.

21. Repeat the lapping process very briefly on the second block. Then, wash and dry the part as before.

22. Lap the part very, very lightly on the third block without the use of powder. Wash again and dry with compressed air.

Injector Assembly

1. Insert the new filters, slotted end up, in each of the two fuel cavities. Place new gaskets on the filter caps, coat the threads with oil, and install the caps, torquing them to 65-75 ft-lbs. Install clean shipping caps on the filter caps.

2. With the injector body bottom end up, slide the rack through the hole in the body. Look into the bore and slide the rack back and forth until you can see the two drill marks shown in the illustration. Hold the rack in this position while placing the gear in the injector body and meshing the teeth of the gear so the drill marks align as shown. Place the gear retainer on top of the gear, align the bushing locating pin

with the slot in the injector body, and slide the end of the bushing into place.

3. Mount the injector in a holding fixture with the bottom end up. Install a new seal ring on the shoulder of the body, and then position the spill deflector over the barrel of the bushing. Place the check valve on top of the center of the bushing, and then place the check valve cage over the valve and against the bushing.

4. Insert the spring seat inside the valve spring, and insert the assembly into the spring cage with the spring seat going first. Place the spring cage, spring seat, and valve spring assembly, with the valve spring down, on top of the check valve cage. Insert the needle valve (tapered end down) into the spray tip.

5. Place the spray tip and needle valve on top of the spring cage with the small end of the needle valve in the hole in the spring cage. Lube the threads of the injector nut, and then carefully position the nut and screw it in place by hand, watching carefully to make sure the valve assembly does not shift. If the valve parts are not centrally located, assembly may be eased by turning the end of the spray tip while screwing the nut onto the body.

6. Invert the injector in the fixture, and push the control rack all the way in. Place the follower spring and stop pin on the body so the bottom coil of the spring rests on the narrow flange of the pin. Slide the head of the plunger into the slot in the follower, and then position the plunger and follower over the injector body and align the slot in the follower with the stop pin hole in the body. Align the flat side of the plunger with the flat in the gear, and lower the plunger and follower straight into the gear and injector body until the follower rests on the spring.

7. Press down on the follower and press the stop pin into the slot in the follower until the spring drops into the stop pin slot. Invert the injector and use a special socket wrench and torque drive to tighten the nut to 75-85 ft.-lbs.

8. Place the injector in a concentricity gauge .Zero the dial indicator. Rotate the injector 360° and note the total run-out indicated. If the run-out exceeds .008″, attempt to recenter the spray tip by removing the injector from the gauge and loosening the nut. After retorquing the nut

and placing the unit back into the gauge, recheck the concentricity. If several attempts fail to bring the concentricity within specifications, check the entire injector assembly.

Injector Testing

Before placing a reconditioned injector in service, all of the tests (except the visual inspection of the plunger) previously outlined in this section under "Injector Tests" must be performed again.

If an injector is not to be used immediately, caps should be installed on the injector caps. The injector test oil remaining in the injector after the fuel output test will serve as a rust preventive while the injector is in storage.

Injector Installation

Before installing a new or reconditioned injector in an engine, the carbon deposits must be removed from the beveled seat of the injector hole tube in the cylinder head. If not, the injector may be cocked resulting in a fractured spray tip.

Injector tube bevel seat reamer should be used to clean the carbon out of the tube before installing the injector. Refer to "Reaming" in "CYLINDER HEAD" section. Care must be exercised to remove ONLY the carbon so that the proper clearance between the injector body and cylinder head is maintained. Pack the flutes of the reamer with heavy grease.

1. Insert the injector into the injector tube with the locating dowel registering with the locating hole in the cylinder head and with the pin on the injector control tube lever registering with the injector control rack lever.
2. Place injector clamp in position, then install washer and bolt. Tighten bolt to 20-25 ft.-lbs. NOTE: Check injector rack for free movement. Excess torque will cause the injector control rack to stick or bind. Also, make sure clamp does not interfere with operation of valve or injector springs.
3. Move rocker arm assembly into position and secure rocker arm bracket bolts to torque of 90 to 100 ft.-lbs.
4. Connect fuel pipes to injector and fuel connectors, torquing the connectors to 12-15 ft.-lbs.
5. As a precautionary measure against any possibility of scoring injector parts upon initial installation due to lack of lubrication, any entrapped air should be bled from the injector before tightening the connections on the fuel outlet side of the injector. This may be accomplished by cranking the engine briefly with the

ONE TOOTH RETARDED   CORRECTLY TIMED   ONE TOOTH ADVANCED

Injector rack to gear timing
(© G.M.C.)

injector rack in the NO FUEL position and then tightening the fuel pipe connection.

6. When installing injector fuel lines, connections should be tightened only enough to prevent leakage of fuel. Excess tightening may result in the flared end of the fuel line being twisted or fractured. A torque wrench adapter is essential to properly tighten fuel line connector nut to 12-15 ft.-lbs. torque. Use of this adapter and torque wrench is highly recommended.
7. When all injector lines are installed, the engine should be run long enough (during tune-up procedure) to check for leaks. Should leaks occur, the connections should be tightened only enough to stop the leak.
8. Following installation of the injectors in the engine, a complete engine tune-up should be performed. However, if only one injector has been removed and replaced, and other injectors and the governor adjustment have not been disturbed, it will only be necessary to adjust the clearance of the valves, valve bridge, and time the injector for the one cylinder, and position the control rack on the cylinder involved to correspond with that of the other racks.

Governor Service

Description

The limiting speed governor uses two high speed and two low speed weights; each set of weights having a fixed stop for the inner and outer positions. A high and low speed spring is also used in this governor; the former works with the high speed weights to limit the maximum engine speed, the latter works with both the low and high speed weights to control the engine idling speed.

The travel of the governor weights, between their inner and outer positions, is transferred to the injector racks by a system of cams and levers over which a manual control can be used.

The governor, which is mounted at front of blower is divided into two main assemblies in separate hous-

ings. These assemblies are: Governor control housing and governor weight and lower housing, and the cover.

The two sets of weights are carried on a horizontal weight shaft inside the governor weight housing. The weight carrier shaft is mounted on an annular ball bearing at one end and opposite end is supported inside and driven by hollow blower rotor shaft. The blower end of governor shaft is serrated and engages with corresponding serrations inside blower shaft, which drives the governor shaft and weights.

Control mechanism transfers motion of governor weights to the injector racks. This mechanism consists of a vertical shaft mounted inside a housing, with a fork or yoke fixed at lower end, an operating lever fixed at upper end, and a high and low speed governing spring with suitable adjustments. The vertical shaft is mounted on annular ball bearings at upper and lower ends.

The motion of the governor weights is transferred to the vertical shaft through a movable riser on the weight carrier shaft and the fork on the lower end of the vertical shaft. This motion is, in turn, transferred to the injector control tube by means of the operating and differential levers on the upper end of the vertical shaft.

The cover assembly serves as a carrier for the throttle control lever, stop lever, and covers the top of the control housing.

The lower portion of governor is lubricated by means of a slinger attached to front end of blower lower rotor shaft. This slinger dips into a well of oil dammed up in blower housing cover and throws the oil onto all parts within governor weight housing. The upper portion of the governor, including the vertical shaft bearings and the control mechanism, is lubricated partly by splash from oil slinger on weight carrier shaft and partly by return oil through the vertical housing from cylinder head.

Limiting Speed Governor Removal—92 Series

1. Remove all accessories attached to the head, governor or engine front, which may interfere with removal.
2. Disconnect governor linkage.
3. Remove the governor housing cover.
4. Remove the fuel rods from the control link operating lever assembly and the injector control tube levers as follows:
   a. Remove the rocker covers.
   b. Remove the right bank fuel rod by removing the control link operating lever pin and the control tube lever clevis pin.

Limiting speed governor (© G.M.C.)

c. Remove the left bank fuel rod by removing the clevis pin in the control tube lever and lift the connecting pin up out of the control link operating lever about ¾".
5. Loosen water by-pass tube clamps and remove tube.
6. Remove fuel lines from injection pump and crossover line from heads.
7. Remove fuel rod cover tube hoses.
8. Note washer locations and remove the bolts securing the governor and fuel pump to the blower.
9. Tap to loosen and remove governor and fuel pump.

Governor Removal—In-Line 71 Engines

1. Disconnect governor control lever linkage.
2. Remove the breather pipe.
3. Remove the screws and lockwashers and pull the governor cover and gasket off the housing.
4. Disconnect the fuel rod from the differential lever (see illustration) and the injector control

tube lever.
5. Disconnect the oil tube where it enters the weight housing.
6. Remove the governor-to-cylinder head bolts.
7. Remove the bolts and lock washers attaching the control housing to the weight housing and remove the control housing from the cylinder head and weight housing.
8. Remove the governor weight housing bolts, and pull the housing off the blower.

Governor Removal—V-71 Models

1. Remove injector and rocker arm covers.
2. Remove cover and gasket from governor housing.
3. Remove the right bank fuel rod by removing the screw type pin, in the control link operating lever, and the clevis pin at the control tube lever and withdraw the fuel rod across cylinder head while rotating rod.
4. Remove the left bank fuel rod by removing the governor operating lever link connecting pin

from the control link operating lever after removing the spring retainer that holds the governor operating lever to the differential lever, then lift upwards on the governor operating link. Remove the clevis pin at the control tube lever and withdraw fuel rod across cylinder head while rotating rod.
5. Loosen the hose clamps on the fuel rod covers and slide each hose and clamp toward the governor.
6. Loosen hose clamps on water by-pass tube. Slide hoses and clamps onto by-pass tube and remove tube from engine.
7. Disconnect and remove the fuel lines from the fuel pump.
8. Remove retaining bolts and slide the governor and fuel pump assembly straight forward, from the blower dowels. Remove governor-to-blower gasket. NOTE: The fuel pump drive coupling may stay with either the fuel pump or the blower rotor shaft. Remove the drive coupling.
9. Remove three bolts and remove the fuel pump and gasket from the governor housing.

Governor Disassembly 71 & 92 Series Engines

Cover

With cover removed from the control housing, disassemble the governor as follows:

1. Loosen governor throttle control lever retaining bolt, and lift control lever from throttle shaft.
2. Remove tapered pin from spacer. Lift lever spacer and seal ring retainer from throttle shaft. Withdraw shaft from cover.
3. Remove seal ring from governor cover.
4. Remove fuel shut-off lever.
5. Remove lock ring from shaft and seal ring retainer (two flat washers).
6. Slide shaft from cover and remove seal ring.
7. At this stage of disassembly, wash cover assembly (containing needle bearings) thoroughly in clean fuel oil and inspect needle bearings for wear or damage. If bearings are satisfactory for further use, removal is unnecessary.
8. Inspect fuel shut-off shaft bushing. If bushing is damaged, replace governor cover.
9. If needle bearing removal is necessary, then press both bearings out of cover.

Spring (Except Dual Range)

1. Place control housing in soft jaw vise.
2. Remove two bolts attaching high speed spring retainer cover to housing, then remove cover.
3. Loosen lock nut. Remove high speed spring· retainer, idle adjusting screw, high speed spring, spring plunger, low speed spring, spring seat, and spring cap as an assembly.

Spring (Dual Range)

1. Remove two bolts and withdraw spring housing, cover, piston, sleeve, and low maximum speed adjustment screws as an assembly.
2. Remove high speed spring retainer, and withdraw high and low speed springs and related parts as an assembly.

Weights

1. Remove the governor weight housing cap, and gasket.
2. Remove bearing retaining bolt.
3. Thread a 5/16"-24 x 3" bolt into tapped end of weight shaft, and press shaft from bearing.
4. Slide riser thrust bearing and governor riser from shaft. This bearing is specially designed to absorb thrust load; therefore looseness between the mating

Location and size of governor housing retaining bolts
(© G.M.C.)

Location	Washer	Bolt
4	Copper	5/16"-18 x 5-¼"
10	Copper	5/16"-18 x 4"
1	Lock	5/16"-18 x 3-¾"
2-3-5-6-7-8-9	Lock	5/16"-18 x 2-¼"

parts does not indicate excessive wear.
5. Remove weight shaft bearing from governor housing.
6. Mark low and high speed weights and carrier with a center punch for identification, also note position of flat washers so that the parts can be replaced in original position.
7. Using a 3/32" Allen wrench remove Allen set screw from low speed weights. Withdraw pins and governor weights. NOTE: If necessary the bushings in the high speed weights may be removed at this time.

View of governor weights
(© G.M.C.)

8. If required, the weight carrier may be pressed from governor weight shaft and a new carrier installed.

Operating Shaft

1. Lift differential lever off of pin of operating shaft lever after removing retainer clip and washer.
2. Remove bearing retaining screw, flat washer, and lock washer.
3. Remove expansion plug from bottom of control housing.
4. Loosen operating fork set screw.
5. Support control housing bottom side up on bed of press and insert a 9/16" open end wrench between operating fork and governor housing. Using a brass rod, press operating shaft from operating fork. Withdraw operating shaft, operating lever, and upper bearing as an assembly from control housing.
6. Support operating shaft lever and upper bearing on bed of arbor press. Using a brass rod, press operating shaft from operating lever and upper bearing.

Link Operating Lever

1. Remove retaining screw from governor housing and withdraw governor control lever shaft lock clip.
2. Slide governor control link operating lever shaft from governor housing. Remove governor control link operating lever assembly and two flat washers.
3. Remove the needle bearings, if necessary.

Governor Inspection

Inspect all bearings to be sure that they are satisfactory for further use.

Inspect spring seats, plungers, adjusting screws, lock nuts, and other parts of control housing for defects that might affect governor operation.

Inspect operating shaft and shaft bearing for excessive wear. If excessive wear is noted, a new bearing or shaft must be installed.

Examine riser thrust bearing for excessive wear, flat spots or corrosion. If any of these conditions exist, a new thrust bearing assembly must be installed.

Inspect roller bearings and throttle shaft for excessive wear or flat spots. If one or both conditions exist, new bearings and throttle shaft must be installed.

If new bearings are installed in the governor cover, the lower bearing should be flush with the lower end of the bearing boss. The upper bearing must be pressed in approximately ⅛″ below the top surface of the upper bearing boss.

Examine weight carrier pins and bushings for excessive wear and flat spots. If either of these conditions exist, new parts must be installed.

Weights should be assembled and checked for free movement.

Governor Assembly

Cover

1. Place the cover on the bed of an arbor press with the inner face of the cover facing down. Start upper needle bearing straight into bearing bore of cover with number on bearing up. Then press bearing into cover.
2. Reverse cover on bed of press (inner face of cover up). Start second bearing straight into bearing bore of cover with number on bearing up. Place a flat washer over pilot of remover tool, insert pilot of tool into bearing and under ram of press, then press bearing down into cover until washer contacts cover.
3. Lubricate throttle shaft needle bearings with multi-purpose grease. Then insert throttle shaft through bearings.
4. Insert seal ring over shaft and
6. Press spacer down on shaft until holes in spacer are in line with shaft and against seal ring.
5. Start spacer over throttle shaft bearing. Place retainer over with holes in lever and shaft for hole in shaft.
   into counterbore against upper tapered pin in alignment.
7. Insert tapered pin in hole of spacer, then drive pin into place.
8. Position throttle control lever on throttle shaft and tighten retaining bolt.
9. Slide fuel shut-off lever shaft through bushing and place lever, under governor cover, on right side of pin (viewed from blower end of governor.)
10. Place seal ring on fuel shut off

NON-TURBOCHARGED ENGINES

INTERNAL STARTING AID SCREW

Limiting speed governor

2. Housing-Governor	27. Weight-High Speed
3. Gasket-Housing to Blower	29. Pin-Weight
4. Bolt-Housing to Blower	30. Flat Washer
5. Lock Washer	31. Screw-Weight Pin Set
8. Shaft-Governor Operating	40. Shaft-Weight Carrier
9. Lever-Operating Shaft	41. Riser-Governor
10. Pin-Shaft Lever	42. Bearing-Riser Thrust
11. Bearing-Operating Shaft (Upper)	43. Bearing-Weight Carrier Shaft End
13. Fork-Operating Shaft	44. Bolt-Bearing Retainer
14. Bearing-Operating Shaft (Lower)	45. Lock Washer-Special
15. Plug-Expansion	46. Flat Washer
16. Screw-Bearing Retaining	47. Plug-Governor Housing
17. Lock Washer	48. Gasket-Housing Plug
18. Flat Washer	53. Lever-Control Link Operating
19. Screw-Starting Aid Adjusting (Internal)	54. Bearing-Operating Lever
20. Screw-Gap Adjusting (Internal)	55. Shaft-Operating Lever
21. Spacer-Operating Shaft	56. Washer-Operating Lever Shim
25. Carrier-Governor Weight	57. Pin-Fuel Rod Connecting (Short)
26. Weight-Low Speed	58. Pin-Fuel Rod Connecting (Long)
	59. Clip-Operating Lever Shaft Lock
	60. Screw-Lock Clip

61. Lock Washer	88. Snap Ring-Speed Control Shaft
65. Screw-Buffer	89. Shaft Stop Lever
66. Lock Nut-Buffer Screw	90. Spring-Stop Lever Shaft Return
67. Lever-Governor Differential	91. Ring-Stop Shaft Seal
68. Pin-Differential Lever	92. Washer-Seal Ring Retainer
69. Washer-Differential Lever and Connecting Link Flat	93. Snap Ring-Stop Shaft
70. Retainer-Spring	94. Gasket-Governor Housing Cover
71. Link-Operating Lever Connecting	95. Screw-Housing Cover
80. Cover-Governor Housing	96. Lock Washer
81. Bearing-Speed Control Shaft	97. Carrier-Governor Weight
82. Bushing-Stop Lever Shaft	98. Weight-Low Speed
83. Shaft-Speed Control Lever	99. Weight-High Speed
84. Pin-Fulcrum Lever	100. Pin-Weight
85. Spacer-Speed Control Shaft	101. Ring-Weight Pin Retainer
86. Ring-Control Shaft Seal	102. Shaft-Weight Carrier
87. Washer-Seal Ring Retainer	103. Locknut
	104. Screw, Gap Adjusting (External)
	105. Screw, Starting Aid Adjusting (External)
	106. Locknut

lever shaft and seal ring retainer (two flat washers) and retain with lock ring.

11. Install fuel shut-off lever on shaft and secure with clamping bolt.

Installation

1. Place gasket on fuel pump and mount fuel pump on governor housing.
2. Place fuel pump drive fork on fuel pump shaft. Rotate pump shaft until fork aligns with drive on blower rotor.
3. Slide governor and fuel pump assembly straight on dowels of blower housing. Align splines of weight shaft with splines in blower rotor and fuel pump coupling with drive while assembling governor to blower.
4. Insert bolts and washers at locations as indicated and tighten alternately and evenly.
5. Reconnect fuel lines at fuel pump.
6. Install water by-pass tube between thermostat housing with the use of hoses and hose clamps.

7. Slide each hose on the fuel rod covers and tighten hose clamps.
8. Assemble the governor operating lever link connecting pin to the governor operating lever connecting link as follows:
   a. Insert one control link operating lever retaining ring on inner groove of pin.
   b. Insert connecting link over end of pin and against retaining ring.
   c. Insert one control link operating lever retaining ring on outer groove of pin.
9. Insert fuel rods between cylinder heads and governor as follows:
10. Install right fuel rod:
    a. Insert fuel rod through fuel rod cover and into control link operating lever.
    b. Align rod end with opening in the control link operating lever and insert pin. Screw pin into postion and tighten securely.
11. Install left fuel rod:
    a. Place on shim on differential lever.
    b. Slide the operating lever link connecting pin into the control link operating lever and at the same time slide the connecting link over the pin of the differential lever.
    c. Secure the assembly by placing shim over pin of differential lever and retain with the spring retainer.
12. Place governor housing cover-gasket on housing and install governor cover. Be sure governor control lever assembly enters slot of differential lever and shut down lever, on under side of cover, is between the stop pin and the differential pin. Tighten screws securely.
13. Reconnect control linkage to throttle and stop control levers at top of cover.
14. Perform tune-up.

Governor Service—53 Series

1. Disconnect the governor control linkage.
2. Remove the attaching screws and washers, pull the governor cover and lever assembly off the governor, and remove the cover gasket.
3. Remove the two bolts and washers, and remove the spring housing and gasket from the governor.
4. Referring to the illustration, remove the spring retainer with a special wrench and pull the spring assembly out of the governor.
5. Loosen the clamps on the fuel rod cover hoses, and then slide the hoses back.
6. Remove the rocker covers.
7. Disconnect the lower fuel rods at the injector control tube levers and at the threaded portions where they connect with the upper fuel rods.
8. Remove the threaded pins that connect the fuel rods to the control link lever. Then, remove the upper fuel rods.
9. Remove the blower drive support as described in the blower removal instructions.
10. Check the clerance between the drive gear and each weight, with the weight fully extended, as shown in the illustration. Clearance must be .10″.
11. Remove the governor weight shaft and carrier from the drive support, prying if necessary.
12. Remove the blower as described in the appropriate section. Remove the attaching bolts, and pull off the governor housing and gasket.

Disassembly

1. Remove the pipe plug from the throttle shaft.
2. Loosen the bolt, and remove the speed control lever.
3. Remove the throttle shaft retaining ring and retaining washers. and pull the throttle shaft out of the cover. Remove the cover seal ring.
4. Loosen the clamp, and remove the speed control lever.
5. Remove the retaining ring and two retaining washers and withdraw the stop lever shaft.
6. Remove the seal ring from the cover.
7. Use the fuel oil to clean the governor cover. Inspect the needle bearings for wear. If the bearings are badly worn, use an arbor press to remove them with a special bearing remover.
8. Remove the low speed spring cap, spring, and spring seat.
9. Depress the high speed spring and remove the idle speed adjusting screw locknut. Then, pull the high speed spring and shims from the assembly. Remove the idle speed adjusting screw from the spring plunger.
10. Remove the buffer screw and spring.
11. Remove the spring pin and washer from the control link lever, and pull off the control link lever and washer.
12. Inspect the bearings. If replacement is required, place the control link lever on an arbor press supported by a sleeve. Press the bearings out of the lever with a special tool, as shown in the illustration.
13. Remove the spring pin and washer from the operating shaft lever, and remove the differential lever.
14. Remove the plug from the bottom of the governor housing. If applicable, remove the set screws from the governor operating fork.
15. Remove the retaining screw and washer from the operating shaft upper bearing. Invert the governor housing and place it on wooden blocks on the bed of an arbor press. Using a rod small enough to pass through the bearing, press down on the shaft until the bearing is free, and remove the bearing.
16. Place an open end wrench between the operating fork and the housing, and a rod on the end of the operating shaft, as shown in the illustration. Press the shaft out of the fork. Then, withdraw

Governor Spring Assembly
(© G.M. Corp)

Minimum Clearance Between Drive Gear and Weights
(© G.M. Corp)

653

Removing the Governor Cover Bearing
(© G.M. Corp)

the shaft, operating shaft lever, and bearings.

17. Press the shaft off the operating shaft and upper bearing.
18. Remove the governor weight pin retaining rings. Drive the pins out with a punch held against the grooved end of each pin. Remove the governor weights.
19. Press the shaft from the weight carrier as shown in the illustration.
20. Slide the riser and bearing assembly from the shaft.
21. Remove the snap ring and thrust washer from the blower drive gear shaft. Slide the shaft and gear off the blower drive support.
22. Press the drive gear off the shaft and remove the key.
23. Tap the governor weight shaft bearing to remove it from the blower drive support. If the bearing will not move, drive the plug from the support and, with a spacer against the outer race of the bearing, tap the bearing off the support.

Inspection

1. Clean all parts in fuel oil and dry them with compressed air.
2. Inspect all bearings and replace if they are pitted or corroded. Check ball bearings by revolving them slowly by hand, and replace any that have rough or tight spots.
3. Examine the riser thrust bearing for wear, flat spots, or corrosion. Install a new assembly if any are indicated.
4. Inspect the control link lever, needle bearings, and control link lever pin. The pin must project 1.055"-1.060" above the boss. Replace worn parts.
5. Examine the weight carrier, weights, and pins. Replace any worn parts.
6. Inspect the governor springs, spring seat, spring cap, plunger, spring retainer, adjusting screws, and housing for wear,, and replace parts as necessary.

Assembly

1. Place the cover on the bed of an arbor press, inner face down. Start a needle bearing, number side up, into the bearing bore in the cover. Then, insert a special bearing installer and press the bearing in until the shoulder of the tool touches the cover. *Do not use an impact tool for installation.*
2. Invert the cover and install the second bearing in precisely the same way.
3. Install the pipe plug in the throttle shaft.
4. Pack the needle bearings with grease. Slide the throttle shaft assembly through the bearings. The fulcrum lever pin must be seated in the slot on the underside of the cover.
5. On the top of the upper bearing, install a new seal ring, two seal retaining washers, and the retaining ring.
   NOTE: A seal ring back up washer is used in place of the lower washer on some governor covers.
6. Install the stop lever and speed control lever, and tighten the clamping bolts.
7. Start the upper operating shaft bearing, with the numbered side up, onto the end of the shaft. Support the lower end of the shaft on an arbor press, and then place a sleeve on the inner race and press the bearing on until it contacts the shoulder on the shaft.
8. Start the operating shaft lever, pivot pin up, onto the end of the

Governor Details
(© G.M. Corp)

Removing Bearings from Control Link Lever
(© G.M. Corp)

shaft with the flat on the shaft registering with the flat in the lever bore. Then, use a sleeve to press the lever until it rests tightly against the bearing.

9. Insert the lever and shaft through the top of the governor housing. Position the operating fork so it is over the lower end of the shaft, with the finished cam surfaces facing the rear of the governor.
10. Support the operating shaft and governor housing on the bed of an arbor press with the upper end of the shaft resting on a steel block (see illustration) Align the flat on the fork with the flat on the shaft. Place a sleeve over the shaft and against the fork. Press the fork until it rests against the shoulder on the shaft. Install the set screw and, if necessary, the lock screw.
11. Start the lower operating shaft bearing, with the number up, onto the end of the shaft. Place a sleeve on the inner race and press the bearing down until it rests against the shoulder in the housing.
12. Lubricate both bearings with engine oil.
13. Apply sealant around a new expansion plug and install it in the housing.
14. Install the upper operating shaft bearing retaining screw and washer.
15. Place the differential lever over the pivot pin in the operating shaft lever. Install the washer and spring pin.
16. Install the gap adjusting screw and locknut in the operating shaft lever.
17. Place a steel spacer on the bed of an arbor press, and position the control link lever on top of the spacer.
18. Install bearings on either side of the lever, number side up, with a special tool, as shown in the illustration.
19. Place the washer on the control link lever pin in the housing.

Removing Governor Operating Fork
(© G.M. Corp)

Removing Shaft from Weight Carrier
(© G.M. Corp)

Pack the needle bearings with grease and install the lever, tapped end of the link pin holes down, over the pin in the governor housing. Install the washer and spring pin.

20. Install the buffer screw so it extends 9/16"-5/8" out of the housing and lock it in place with the lock nut.

21. Lube the governor weight shaft with engine oil and slide the riser assembly over the shaft, bearing end toward the serrated end of the shaft. Pack the bearing with grease.

22. Use an installer as illustrated and press the shaft into the weight carrier.

23. Position the low speed weights (longer cam arm) on opposite sides of the weight carrier. Install the weight pins and retaining rings. The grooved end of the weight pins should be pushed through the smaller hole in the carrier and through the weight, and the knurled end should then be driven in just until the retaining ring can be installed. Install the high speed weights similarly.

24. Place the blower drive support, inner face up, on the bed of an arbor press. Start the governor weight shaft bearing, numbered side up, into the bore of the support. Place a suitable sleeve against the outer race and press the bearing against the shoulder of the blower drive support.

25. Install the steel thrust washer and snap ring on the end of the blower drive gear shaft.

26. Lubricate the blower drive gear shaft with engine oil and install it in the blower drive support.

27. Install the key in the shaft. Install the blower drive support in an arbor press.

28. Lubricate the inner surface of the blower drive gear. Start it onto the shaft, with the keyway in the gear properly aligned with the shaft key. Place a spacer on the gear and then press it onto the shaft until the clearance between the lower surface of the gear and the blower drive support is .005".

29. Support the inner race of the bearing in the blower drive support. Start the weight end of the governor weight shaft onto the bearing. Press the shaft straight in until the shoulder contacts the inner race of the bearing.

30. Apply sealant to the cup plug, and press the plug in until it is flush with the blower drive support.

31. Check the clearance between the fully extended governor weights and the blower drive gear. It must be at least .100".

Installation

1. Position a new gasket on the governor housing, and then put the housing in position against the blower rear end plate. Secure the housing with the bolts and lock washers.

2. Install the blower and governor assembly as described in the appropriate section.

3. Install the blower drive support assembly as described in the appropriate section.

4. Insert the upper fuel rods through the fuel rod covers, hoses, and clamps. Attach the fuel rods to the governor control link lever. Thread the link pins into the lever.

5. Attach the lower fuel rods to the injector control tube levers and upper fuel rods.

Installing Governor Cover Bearings
(© G.M. Corp)

Installing Governor Operating Fork
(© G.M. Corp)

Installing Bearings in Control Link Lever
(© G.M. Corp)

Installing Weight Carrier
(© G.M. Corp)

6. Slide the fuel rod cover hoses into position and secure them with the clamps.
7. Assemble the governor spring as follows:
   a. thread the idle adjusting screw into the spring plunger.
   b. Install the original shims over the spring plunger.
   c. Place the high speed spring over the spring plunger.
   d. Lube the spring and plunger with engine oil. Place the spring retainer over the plunger and secure it with a locknut when about ¼″ of the idle adjusting screw extends beyond the locknut.
   e. Lube and then insert the spring seat, low speed spring, and spring cap into the open end of the spring plunger.
   f. Start the retainer and spring assembly into the governor housing.
8. Position a new gasket on the governor housing and install the cover and lever assembly. The control link lever must engage the pin on the differential lever, the pin in the stop lever shaft must enter the slot in the differential lever, and the pin in the stop lever shaft must engage between the stop on the underside of the cover and the vertical extension of the control link lever.
9. Secure the cover with the screws and lockwashers.
10. Perform a complete engine tune up. Then, connect the linkage to the governor control linkage.

Cooling System

Description

Control of engine temperature is accomplished by means of two thermostats controlling the flow of cool-

Installing Drive Gear
(© G.M. Corp)

ing liquid within a sealed cooling system. A sealed system utilizes a pressure valve which maintains a slight pressure within the system when engine is running at normal operating temperature, thus raising the efficiency of the system.

Coolant is drawn from the lower portion of the radiator by the water pump and is forced through the oil cooler housing and into the cylinder block. From the cylinder block the coolant passes up through the cylinder head and, when the engine is at normal operating temperature, through the thermostat housing and into the upper portion of the radiator. Then the coolant passes down a series of tubes, where the coolant temperature is lowered by the air stream created by the revolving fan.

During the engine warm-up period, action of thermostats directs flow of cooling liquid back to the water pump. This arrangement permits circulation of liquid within the engine, warming the engine and shortening the warm-up period. As engine reaches normal operating temperature, thermostats open gradually, allowing cooling liquid to flow through radiator, thus maintaining an efficient operating temperature.

Water Pump Service—71 Series
Water Pump Seal Replacement

The water pump seal can be replaced by removing the impeller without removing the pump from the engine.
1. Remove the water pump cover and gasket.
2. Remove nut and washer securing impeller to pump shaft.
3. Remove the impeller from the shaft with a special puller.
4. Pry the seal from the housing with a pair of pliers.
5. Using a hollow tool placed over the outer casing, tap the new seal into the pump housing.
6. Inspect the ceramic seat for cracks and for a good bond to the impeller. Replace impeller if necessary.
7. Apply oil to the ceramic seat and mount the impeller on the shaft, installing and torquing the locknut to 30-35 ft-lbs.
8. Measure impeller to pump housing clearance. It must be at least .015″ as measured by a feeler gauge placed in the water inlet opening.
9. Position a new gasket and locate the pump cover on the studs. Install the mounting nuts.

Water Pump Removal

1. Drain cooling system by opening drain cocks at corners of cylinder block.
2. Remove hose clamps and slide hoses off the pump body.
3. Remove the three bolts that secure the pump to the balance weight cover, then lift the pump away from the engine being careful not to damage teeth of water pump drive gear.

Disassembly

1. Remove the cover and impeller.
2. Remove bearing retaining snap ring by placing pliers through

Water pump components (© G.M.C.)

Removing retaining ring
(© G.M.C.)

Removing water pump seal
(© G.M.C.)

Pressing drive gear from shaft
(© G.M.C.)

one of the holes in the water pump drive gear.

3. Push the pump shaft, bearings and gear from housing.
4. Press gear from shaft.
5. Inspect the pump seals and remove only if cracked or worn. New seals should be used for replacement.

Inspection

1. Wash all the pump parts thoroughly in clean fuel oil and blow dry with compressed air, then inspect.
2. Ball bearings and races should be examined for indications of corrosion or pitting.

Assembly

1. Apply a film of lube oil to the outside diameter of the seal and place it so the lip is facing the bearings. Tap the seal into the pump housing.
2. Mount pump body in an arbor press with impeller side upward. Using a suitable hollow tool (to

slide over seal face and spring) place on outer casing and press water seal into pump housing.

3. Apply film of lube oil to shaft, then slide shaft and bearings in pump housing. Install bearing retaining ring. NOTE: Early engines have pump gear and camshaft gear with 59 and 42 teeth respectively. Latest pump gear and camshaft gear have 92 and 66 teeth respectively. Early and latest type gears are not interchangeable.
4. Place water pump in arbor press. Support shaft on impeller end and press the drive gear onto shaft, against the inner race of bearing. CAUTION: Support should be placed directly between shaft and base of press. Pump housing or studs should not be allowed to touch press while gear is being installed.
5. Apply a thin film of oil to the ceramic seat of impeller and place on tapered shaft. Place the washer and lock nut on shaft and tighten to 30-35 ft-lbs. torque.
6. Measure the clearance between the impeller and pump housing. There should be a minimum clearance of .015". This can be checked by placing a feeler

gauge in the water outlet opening.

7. Using a new gasket between cover and body tighten nuts securely.

Water Pump Installation

1. Mount the pump on the engine and tighten the three bolts.
2. Slide the hose into position on the pump and tighten the clamps.
3. Fill the cooling system with clean fresh water.

Water Pump Service—92 Series

Water Seal Replacement— On Vehicle

1. Remove pump cover and gasket.
2. Remove the lock nut and washer and pull the impeller.

NOTE: Prevent damage to the ceramic insert by positioning the impeller with the insert up.

GMC (Detroit 2-cycle) Diesel Engines

3. Place seal puller over the seal and into the two slots.
4. Position the sleeve over the puller. Insert the slotted end of the arm through the seal puller and position the cover stud in the slot of the arm.
5. Finger-tighten the set screw to hold the arm in position.
6. Pull the seal by turning the screw clockwise.
7. Press a new seal into place in the seal cavity.
8. Inspect the ceramic impeller insert. If damaged, replace as follows:
   a. Bake the used insert and impeller at 500° F for one hour to remove insert. Clean the bond area with a wire brush and alcohol. Dry thoroughly.
   b. Place the adhesive washer in the bond area with the insert on top.
   c. Clamp the insert and impeller together with a ⅜″ bolt and nut and two smooth ⅛″ bolt and nut and two smooth ⅛″ thick washers.
   d. Place the assembly in an oven and bake at 350°F for 1 hour.
   e. Remove from oven and allow to cool at room temperature before removing bolt.
9. Apply sealer to the threads of the pump shaft, place the impeller, washer and nut on the shaft. Torque the nut to 45-50 ft. lb.
10. Check the impeller-to-housing clearance: .015″ min.

Water Pump Removal— 92 Series

1. Remove radiator, fan and shroud.
2. Remove hoses.
3. Unbolt and remove pump.

Removing water pump seal
(© G.M.C.)

Water Pump Disassembly —92 Series

1. Position the pump gear so that the slot is over the ends of the bearing retaining ring. Remove the ring.
2. Remove the pump cover and gasket.
3. Remove the impeller lock nut.
4. Pull the impeller.
5. Press out the shaft, bearings and pump gear assembly.
6. Press the shaft out of the gear.
7. Press the shaft out of the large bearing.
8. Press the shaft out of the small bearing.
9. Remove the water seal as described in the on-vehicle operation.
10. Remove the oil seal.

Water Pump Assembly— 92 Series

1. Lubricate bearing bores and shaft. Install bearings.
2. Press the shaft into the housing.
3. Install the retaining ring.

4. Press the gear flush on the shaft end.
5. Coat the oil seal lip with SAE 30 and insert into the pump housing. Tap into place.
6. Install the water seal as described in the on-vehicle operation.
7. Install impeller and check impeller-to-housing clearance: .015″ minimum.

Water Pump Installation— 92 Series

1. Fit the seal ring to the housing and mount the pump on the engine. Install and tighten mounting bolts.
2. Check gear lash at impeller puller holes: .0015-.0045″. Lash is adjusted by repositioning the pump.
3. Install water pump cover and new gasket. Check nylon bolt inserts to prevent leaks. Never substitute an ordinary bolt for the cadmium plated bolts used.

Removal of Pulley
(© G.M. Corp)

Removing Shaft from Impeller
(© G.M. Corp)

Pressing Shaft into Pump
(© G.M. Corp)

Thermostat Housing Details
(© G.M. Corp)

Water Pump Service—53 Series
Removal
1. Drain the cooling system by opening all drain cocks. Loosen the adjustment and then remove the water pump belts.
2. Loosen the hose clamps and then slide the water by-pass tube.
3. Remove the water pump mounting bolts and remove the pump.

Disassembly
1. Note the position of the pulley and then remove it with a puller as shown in the illustration.
2. Remove the water pump cover.
3. Press the shaft and bearing, seal, and impeller out of the pump housing by applying pressure *on the outer race of the bearing* with a special remover.
4. Press the end of the shaft out of the impeller, as shown in the illustration, using special plates and a holder.
5. Remove the seal assembly from the pump shaft.

Inspection
1. Clean all parts in fuel oil, with the exception of the bearing and shaft assembly, and dry with compressed air.
2. Examine the impeller for damage and for excessive wear on the face contacting the seal, and replace it if it is faulty.
3. Check the bearing for a feeling of roughness when rotated, and for pitting, corrosion or other evidence of damage. Replace if faulty.

Assembly
1. Using a special installer as shown in the illustration, applying pressure to the *outer bearing race*, press the shaft and bearing into the pump body until the race is flush with the outer face of the body.
2. Coat the outside diameter of a new seal with sealing compound. Support the face of the body and the outer race of the bearing, apply pressure to the outer seal flange only to force the flange on until it contacts the body. Wipe the face of the seal with a chamois.
3. Place the pulley end of the shaft on the bed of an arbor press. Press the impeller onto the shaft until it is flush with the large end of the body.
4. Place the pulley on the bed of an arbor press. Using a heavy rod between the press ram and the impeller end of the shaft, press the shaft into the pulley until the pulley is in its original position.
5. Bolt the cover and a new gasket onto the pump body, tightening the bolts to 6-7 ft lbs.
6. Run the pump dry at 1,200 rpm for at least 30 seconds to seat the seal.

Installation
1. Position a new gasket onto the body flange, and bolt the water pump to the oil cooler housing.
2. Install the water-pump-to-by-pass-hose and clamps.
3. Install and adjust the drive belts.
4. Close all drains, refill the system. and operate the engine to check for leaks.

Thermostat

Description
The temperature of the coolant is controlled by two thermostats, one for each cylinder head. On truck engines, thermostats are installed in separate housing attached directly to cylinder head. On coach engines both thermostats are installed in a single housing attached to right cylinder head.

Removal
1. Drain cooling system to necessary level.
2. On 71 Series engines, remove the hose connections from the thermostat housing cover. On 53 and 92 Series engines, remove the cross-over by-pass tube and disconnect the by-pass tube that goes to the water pump.
3. On 71 and 92 Series engines, remove the bolts which secure the cover to the thermostat housing. On 53 Series engines, remove the bolts and the thermostat housings.
4. Remove the thermostat and clean seat for thermostat in housing.
5. Inspect seal pressed in thermostat housing. Remove if necessary.

Installation
1. Place new gasket on the thermostat housing. If the seal was removed, replace the seal with the closed end toward the thermostat.
2. Set the thermostat in housing and replace the cover or housing and hoses.
3. Fill cooling system and check for leaks.

Engine Repair Section
Cylinder Head

The cylinder head and/or gasket at either right-hand or left-hand cylinder bank may be replaced in manner described below:

Cylinder Head Removal
1. Drain cooling system. Remove engine access cover from inside cab.
2. Disconnect battery. Remove air cleaners.

3. Disconnect exhaust pipe from exhaust manifold.

4. Remove exhaust manifold.

5. At front of cylinder head remove thermostat housing and accessory brackets (when used).

6. Disconnect fuel lines from fittings at front of cylinder head. When removing left-hand head, disconnect fuel return line from fitting at rear of head.

7. Remove rocker arm cover from head.

8. Remove cover from governor housing. Remove nut from fuel rod, then remove pin attaching link to tube lever and remove link.

9. Inside governor housing, remove fuel rod.

10. Loosen hose clamps, then move hoses as necessary to permit removal of rod cover (tube).

11. Remove injector rack control tube and bracket assembly.

12. If the cylinder head is to be overhauled, remove the injectors at this point. Remove cylinder head bolts in gradual stages to relieve spring pressure. When bolts have been removed, lift cylinder head assembly off cylinder block. Remove seals and gaskets from cylinder liners and from recesses in block.

CAUTION: When resting the cylinder head assembly on a bench protect the cam follower rollers and injector spray tips by resting the valve side of the head on wooden blocks approximately 2 inches thick.

Cylinder Head Installation

1. Clean carbon from tops of pistons and, if necessary, remove any deposits found in groove and counterbores in top of cylinder block.

2. Install new cylinder head compression gaskets and seals as follows:

   a. Install a new compression gasket on each cylinder liner.

   b. Place new seal rings in the counterbores of water and oil holes in cylinder block.

   c. Install a new oil seal in milled groove near the outer edge of area covered by cylinder head.
   NOTE: Oil seals, and compression gaskets should never be re-used.
   CAUTION: Compression gaskets and/or seals which are jarred out of their proper location will allow leaks and "blow-by" which will result in poor performance and damage to engine.

3. Make sure each pushrod is screwed far enough into its clevis that the end projects all the way through.

4-53 CYLINDER HEAD

3-53 AND 6V-53 CYLINDER HEAD

Cylinder Head Bolt Tightening Sequence
(© G.M. Corp)

4. Wipe bottom of cylinder head clean, then lower cylinder head onto guide studs and down into contact with block. Lubricate threads and pressure area of bolt heads with S.A.E. #30 engine oil, then start all cylinder head bolts. Beginning at camshaft side of cylinder head tighten head bolts lightly to overcome tension of cam follower springs.

5. Tighten cylinder head bolts about one-half turn in sequence. Use torque wrench for final tightening of cylinder head bolts. Correct torque is 230-240 foot-pounds on 92 Series, 175 to 185 foot-pounds on 71 Series engines, 170-180 on 53 Series engines. Do not tighten bolts beyond specified torque.

6. Cover oil drain holes in head to prevent foreign objects from falling into holes. Install injectors (if removed). Check push rods to see that each one is threaded completely through clevis, then tip rocker arms into position with valve bridges squarely positioned at valve stems. Install rocker arm shaft bracket bolts and tighten to 50 foot-pounds torque.

7. Set injector control tube and lever assembly in place and install attaching bolts finger tight. Check injector control tube levers for engagement with slots in injector control racks. Also, be sure ends of rack control tube return springs are properly hooked; i.e., one end hooked around adjacent control tube bracket. Tighten bracket to head bolts and torque to 10 to 12 foot-pounds.

8. Try operating the injector control tube to determine if return spring rotates tube back to "No-Fuel" position after tube is manually moved to "Full-Fuel" position. If there is binding present, strike the control tube brackets lightly with soft hammer to correct any misalignment of tube bearings.

9. Install fuel rod through opening in top of governor housing; pass rod through hoses, clamps, and tubular cover (used at left-hand head). Attach fuel rod to governor lever with screw inside governor housing. Install governor housing cover with new gasket. Assemble hose and clamps to secure fuel rod cover.

10. Install fuel link between fuel rod and lever on control tube.

11. Connect fuel line at fitting at rear of left-hand cylinder head.

Governor cover housing removed
showing fuel rod connecting screws
(© G.M.C.)

1 Fuel rod to R.H. cylin-
  der head
2 Governor springs
3 Fuel rod-to-lever screws
4 Governor housing
5 Fuel rod to L.H. cylinder
  head
6 Fuel rod operating lever

V6-engine with rocker arm cover removed
(© G.M.C.)

12. Mount thermostat housing on front of cylinder head.
13. Install exhaust manifold. Tighten manifold stud nuts to 25 to 40 foot-pounds.
14. Connect exhaust pipe. Fill cooling system and check for leaks.
15. Adjust exhaust valve clearance. Set injector timing.
16. Start engine and operate until normal operating temperature is reached, then recheck cylinder head bolt torque and make final check of exhaust valve clearance.
17. Install rocker arm cover on cylinder head.

Valve Seats

Inspect valve seats to determine if they are fit for further use. Inspection should include cleanliness, concentricity, flatness, and presence of cracks. If exhaust valve seat inserts are loose in cylinder head, or if for any reason due to wear pitting, etc., replacement of valve seat is necessary, oversize (.010") exhaust valve seat inserts are available.

Valve Seat Insert Counterbore Dimensions

	Diameter	Depth
53 Series	1.159-1.160	.300 -.312
71 Series	1.260-1.261	.338 -.352
92 Series	1.440-1.4410	.3395-.3505

The valve seat inserts are shrunk into the cylinder head and, therefore, must be replaced as outlined in the following procedure to avoid damage to the cylinder head:

Valve Seat Removal

1. Place cylinder head on its side on workbench.
2. Place collet of tool inside valve insert so that bottom of collet is flush with bottom of insert.
3. Hold the collet handle and turn the T handle to expand collet cone and insert is held securely by the tool.
4. Insert drive bar of tool through valve guide.

5. Tap the drive bar once or twice to move the insert about 1/16" away from its seat in the cylinder head.
6. Loosen the collet cone and move the tool into the insert slightly so that the narrow flange at the bottom of the collet is below the valve seat insert.
7. Tighten the collet cone and continue to drive the insert out of the cylinder head.

Valve Seat Installation

1. Wash the counterbores in the cylinder head for the valve seat inserts with trichloroethylene or other good solvent. Also, wash the valve inserts with the same solvent. Dry the counterbores and inserts with compressed air.
2. Inspect the counterbores for cleanliness, concentricity, flatness and cracks.

3. Immerse the cylinder head for at least 30 minutes in water heated to 180°F. to 200°F. At the same time, cool the valve seat insert as much as possible (dry ice may be used for this purpose).
4. Rest the cylinder head, bottom side up, on bench and lay an insert in counterbore—valve seat up. If the temperature of the two parts are allowed to become nearly the same, installation may become difficult and damage to the parts may result.
5. Using tool, drive insert down tight into counterbore.
6. Grind the valve seat insert and check it for concentricity in relation to the valve guide.

Recondition Valve Seat

Exhaust valves which are to be reused may be refaced, if necessary, using standard refacing procedure.

Fuel rod and link installation
(© G.M.C.)

1 Governor housing
2 Hose and clamp
3 Control rod cover
4 Fuel control rod
5 Rod Nut
6 Lower link
7 Link pin
8 Injector control tube lever
9 Control tube spring
10 Control tube
11 Cylinder head (L.H.)

Exhaust Valve, Insert, and Seat Dimensions
(© G.M. Corp)

Before installing either a new or used valve, examine the valve insert in the cylinder head for proper valve seating. The proper angle for the seating face of both the valve and valve insert is 30°. The angle of the valve seat insert must be exactly the same as the angle of the valve face so as to provide proper seating of the valve.

Grind the inserts as follows:

1. First apply a 30° grinding wheel on valve seat insert.
2. Use a 60° grinding wheel to open the throat of the insert.
3. Then grind top surface with a 15° wheel to narrow width of the seat from 1/16″ to 3/32″ (71 and 92 Series), or 3/64″- 5/64″ (53 Series). The 30° face of the insert may be adjusted relative to the center of the valve face with the 15° and 60° grinding wheels.
   CAUTION: Do not permit grinding wheels to contact the cylinder head when grinding the inserts.
4. After valve inserts have been ground, the cylinder head should be thoroughly cleaned. Then check the concentricty of the valve seats relative to the valve guides. Total runout for a good valve seat should not exceed .002″. If total runout exceeds .002″ check for bent valve guide before regrinding insert.
5. After valve seats have been ground, the position of the contact area between the valve and valve insert should be determined in the following manner:
   a. Apply a light coat of Prussian Blue or similar paste to the valve seat insert.
   b. Lower stem of valve in the valve guide and "bounce" valve on seat. *Do not rotate valve.*

Installing cylinder head on engine
(© G.M.C.)

This procedure will show (on the valve face) the area of contact. The most desirable area of contact is at the center of the valve face.

Injector Tube

Whenever inspection indicates that

Cylinder head tightening sequence V6-engine
(© G.M.C.)

injector copper tube in cylinder head requires replacement, the operation must be performed with the greatest of care and with special tools in the manner following:

Injector Tube Removal

1. Attach cylinder head holding plates to the cylinder head or support the cylinder head on its side with exhaust ports down. Place the injector tube installer into injector tube.
2. Insert pilot through the small opening in injector tube and thread pilot into hole in end of installer.
3. Tap end of pilot with hammer to loosen injector tube. Lift tube, pilot, and installer from cylinder head.

Inspection

Installation of the injector tube re-

Cylinder head tightening sequence in-line 4 cyl. and V8 engines
(© G.M.C.)

Cylinder head tightening sequence in-line 6 cyl. engine
(© G.M.C.)

Reaming Injector Tube Bevel Seat
(© G.M. Corp)

1 Spray Tip
2 Orifice - Injector
   Spray Tip
3 Cylinder Head
4 Straight Edge - Steel

Checking Spray Tip Location in Relation to Head Surface
(© G.M. Corp)

quires careful preparation and inspection to make sure that the area of the cylinder head is clean so that when tube contacts the cast iron cylinder head, foreign material will not prevent tube seating at bottom or sealing at top.

Injector Tube Installation

1. Place injector tube sealing ring in cylinder head injector tube counterbore.
2. Place drive in injector tube, insert pilot through the small opening of injector tube and thread pilot tapped end of driver.
3. Slip the injector tube into injector bore and drive into place. The flange at upper end of tube will seat on the seal ring and into the counterbore of cylinder head when the injector tube is properly positioned.
4. With the injector tube properly positioned in cylinder head, flare lower end of injector tube, as follows:
   a. Turn cylinder head bottom side up, remove pilot and thread flaring tool into tapped end of driver.
   b. Then, using a socket and torque wrench, apply approximately 30 ft.-lb. torque on flaring tool.
   c. Remove injector tube installing tools and proceed to ream the injector tube.

Injector Tube Reaming

After an injector tube has been installed in a cylinder head, it must be hand reamed, spot faced, and hand reamed again, each step using its own special tool, as described below:
1. Place cylinder head right side up and clean out the injector tube.
2. Place a few drops of cutting oil on the reamer flutes and carefully position the reamer in the injector tubes.
3. Turn the reamer clockwise, withdrawing it frequently for removal of chips until its lower

shoulder contacts the injector tube. Clean out all the chips.
4. Turn the head upside down, insert the pilot of the cutting tool into the small hole of the injector tube, and attach a socket drive.
5. Rotate the tool clockwise until enough stock has been removed that the lower end of the tube is from flush to .005″ below the finished surface of the head.
6. Wash the interior of the injector tube with clean fuel oil and dry with compressed air.
7. Lubricate the bevel seat of the tube with light cutting oil. Seat the reamer into the tube so it contacts the bevel seat.
8. Turn the reamer steadily without any downward force, and then remove it. Blow out the chips and observe the cutting pattern.
9. Continue reaming carefully, removing the reamer, blowing out the chips, and inspecting the cut frequently. Test the reaming job by installing the injector after each inspection of the cutting. The job is complete when the shoulder of the spray tip is flush to .015″ on 53 and 71 Series and .005″ on 92 Series below the fire deck of the cylinder head.

Valve Guides

Cleaning And Inspection

After cleaning, inspect the valve guides for fractures, scoring or excessive wear and replace if necessary. The inside diameter of a new valve guide is .3125″ to .3135″ which will produce a valve stem-to-guide clearance, with a new valve, of .002″ to .004″. If the clearance exceeds .005″, install a new guide and/or valve.

Valve Guide Removal

1. Support the cylinder head (bottom side up) on wood blocks 2″ above the workbench.
2. Drive valve guide out of cylinder head.

Valve Guide Installation

Rest the bottom of the cylinder head on a workbench, and install guide as follows:
1. Remove exhaust valve bridge guides.
2. Insert the threaded end of the valve guide into installer. Valve guides must be installed with internal threads toward top to provide for lubrication of valve stems.
3. Locate the valve guide squarely in the top of cylinder head and tap gently to start it into place.
4. With the guide properly started, drive in until its upper end projects .88″ on 53 and 71 Series and .67-.71″ on 92 Series above the top of the cylinder head. This dimension is automatically provided by the valve guide installer tool.
   NOTE: Service valve guides are "pre-finished" and, therefore, do not require reaming.
5. Install threaded valve bridge guides. Tighten to 45-50 ft. lbs. Latest type guides are pressed into cylinder head.

Valve Bridge and Guide

Early engines used an exhaust valve bridge guide which was threaded into cylinder head. Threaded bridge guides were superseded by a straight guide which is pressed into cylinder head. Valve bridge springs have now been eliminated on latest engines.

A combination of soft steel guide and a soft steel bridge must be avoided, otherwise premature wear will occur.

Valve bridge springs can be removed and discharged on any engine whenever desirable; however, it is suggested that they be removed at time of overhaul. On engines used in trucks and parlor coaches heavier exhaust valve springs must be used when bridge springs are removed.

Removing valve seat insert
(© G.M.C.)

MAX. VALVE .021″ ABOVE HEAD

MAX. VALVE .007″ BELOW HEAD

VALVE SEAT INSERT

¹⁄₁₆″ TO ³⁄₃₂″   VALVE

30°

CYLINDER HEAD

NEW VALVE AND NEW INSERT

Installation of valve and valve seat insert
(© G.M.C.)

Bridge Guide Removal

1. Threaded guide can be identified by the hexagon section at the base of the guide and can be removed by using a thin wall socket.
2. On pressed guides, file or grind two notches 1/16″ deep on opposite sides of the guide and about 1¼-1½″ from upper end on 92 Series engines, ¾″ from upper end on 71 Series engines, and about 1½″ from upper end on 53 Series engines.
3. Place tool spacer over end of guide, then place remover tool over guide with two screws in alignment with two notches. Tighten set screws securely on 53 Series engines, place the other spacer required for the operation over the guide remover.
4. Thread nut onto remover tool and turn to pull guide from cylinder head.
5. Should guide be broken, drill a hole about ½″ deep in end of guide with #3 (.2130″) drill. Tap the guide with ¼″-28 bottoming tap. Thread adapter into guide, then attach slide hammer to adapter and pull guide.

Bridge Guide Installation

1. Threaded bridge guide may be installed, using thin wall socket.
2. Start pressed guide into cylinder head (undercut end first).
3. Use installer tool to drive guide into place.
4. Use of installer tool will properly position guide to its proper height of 2.04″ above cylinder head.

Cylinder Head Assembly

New service replacement cylinder heads are equipped with valve guides, bridge guides, valve seat inserts, exhaust manifold studs, water nozzles, injector hole tubes and necessary plugs.

CAUTION: When installing plugs in fuel manifolds, apply a small amount of sealant to threads of plugs only. Work sealant into threads and wipe off excess with clean, lint-free cloth so that sealant will not be washed into the fuel system and result in serious damage to the injectors.

When a new cylinder head is to be used, the parts listed above should be removed from the old head and installed in the new head. If the old cylinder head is to be reused, the parts listed below should be installed in the old head prior to installation of the head to the cylinder block.

1. Exhaust valves and springs, cam followers and springs, valve and injector rocker arms and shafts should be assembled to cylinder head.
2. Using new steel washers, install fuel connectors and tighten to 35-40 ft.-lbs. torque.
3. Install fuel injectors as described in the appropriate section.

Valve and Injector Mechanism

Description

Rocker Arms

Valve and injector rocker arms for each cylinder operate on a separate shaft supported by two cast iron brackets. A single bolt fastens each bracket securely to top of cylinder head.

Checking valve seat concentricity
(© G.M.C.)

Cam Followers

Contact between cam followers and cam is made by a hardened steel roller. The roller is equipped with a steel-backed bronze bushing running directly on a pin in lower end of cam follower. A separate coil spring, located inside of the hollow cam follower, is held in place in cylinder head by a spring seat retainer. A dropforged steel guide is provided for each set of three cam followers. This guide, located on bottom of cylinder head, keeps the rollers in line with cams and also serves as a retainer during assembly and disassembly.

Maintenance

Some service operations may be accomplished on cylinder head, valves, and injectors assembly without removing the cylinder head assembly from the block. These operations are:

1. Valve Lash.
2. Valve Spring Replacement.
3. Valve Bridge Adjustment.
4. Rocker Arm, Shaft or Shaft Bracket Replacement.
5. Injector Replacement.
6. Cam Follower Spring Replacement.
7. Cam Follower Replacement.
8. Push Rod Replacemet.

Valve Lash and Bridge Adjustment

CAUTION: Whenever a push rod has been disconnected from the push rod clevis, the rod must be screwed back into the clevis, flush with the top of the threaded portion of the clevis before valve lash is checked. *If this is not done, before engine is turned, the piston may hit head of valve due to the small clearance between valves and piston head at the piston upper position.*

Correct valve lash is important due to high compression pressures. Too little clearance causes a loss of compression, missing cylinder, and eventual burning of valves and valve seats. Too much clearance between valve stem and valve rocker arm results in noisy operation of engine, especially in idling range.

NOTE: It is recommended when lashing valves to set them first cold; then start engine and warm up to normal operating temperature. Reset valve lash after engine has warmed up to operating temperature.

Valve Spring

It is possible, if occasion requires, to remove or replace the exhaust valve springs without removing cylinder head. The springs, however, are normally removed when the head is off the engine. Both methods are covered in paragraph following.

Valve Spring Removal

(Head installed)

Procedure for removing exhaust valve springs while cylinder head is installed is as follows:
1. Remove rocker cover.
2. Bring valve and injector rocker arms in line horizontally.
3. Remove fuel lines from injectors and fuel connectors.
4. Remove the two bolts holding rocker arm shaft brackets to cylinder head then remove brackets and shaft. Lift rocker arms up and away from the valves.
5. Remove exhaust valve bridges and bridge springs.
6. Remove cylinder block air box cover so that piston travel may be observed, then turn crankshaft until piston is at top of stroke.
7. Thread valve spring compressor adaptor into rocker shaft bolt hole in cylinder head. Apply pressure to end of valve spring compressor handle to compress valve spring. Remove the two-piece tapered spring lock.
8. Release tool and remove valve spring cap, valve spring and spring seat.

Valve Spring Removal

(Head removed)

To remove the exhaust valve spring with the cylinder head removed from the engine, use the following procedure:
1. Support the cylinder head on wood blocks 2″ above the workbench so as to keep the cam followers clear of workbench.
2. Remove fuel lines from injector and fuel connectors.
3. Remove the two bolts holding rocker arm shaft brackets to cylinder head. Lift rocker arms and brackets up and away from injector.
4. Remove fuel injector.
5. Remove exhaust valve bridges and bridge springs.

Valves, injector and operating mechanism
(© G.M.C.)

1 Bracket bolt	11 Valve spring cap	20 Cam follower guide
2 Rocker shaft bracket	12 Valve spring	21 Cam follower
3 Valve rocker arm	13 Bridge spring (Early models)	22 Push rod
4 Injector rocker arm	14 Valve spring seat	23 Spring seat—lower
5 Rocker shaft	15 Bridge guide (Pressed Type)	24 Push rod spring
6 Valve bridge	16 Valve seat insert	25 Spring seat—Upper
7 Screw nut	17 Exhaust valve	26 Spring seat retainer
8 Adjusting screw	18 Guide bolt	27 Lock nut
9 Injector assembly	19 Lock washer	
10 Valve spring lock		

6. Remove exhaust valve spring from cylinder head as previously outlined. In addition, use a block of wood under cylinder head to support exhaust valve.

Inspection

After removing valve spring, clean with fuel oil and dry with compressed air. Check spring for pitted or fractured coils. Then, using spring tester, test spring load.

Valve Spring Testing Specifications

Valve Removal

With the cylinder head removed

Valve Spring Testing Specifications
53 Series	25 lbs. @ 1.93″
71 Series-2 valve	135 lbs. @ 1 49/64″
71 Series-4 valve	79 lbs. @ 1.416″
92 Series	25 lbs. @ 1.80″

from the engine and valve springs removed, number each valve and adjacent area prior to removal to facilitate later assembly to the same seat.

Then withdraw valves from cylinder head.

Inspection
1. Scrape the carbon from the valve stem, wash with clean fuel

BRIDGE IMPROPERLY POSITIONED   BRIDGE PROPERLY POSITIONED

Relationship of Exhaust Valve Bridge and Stems on 53 Series Engines
(© G.M. Corp)

oil, and check for scratches or scuff marks.

2. Valve faces should be smooth, and free from ridges and pits. Carbon on the face of the valve indicates a faulty seat and a resultant leak or "blow-by." If any of these conditions exist, a new valve should be installed or the valve refaced to an angle of 30°. NOTE: The valve face angle must be identical to the valve seat angle.

3. Valve heads should be square with the valve stem and should not be warped.

Valve Installation

With the cylinder head thoroughly cleaned, the valve guides checked or replaced and the valves and valve inserts ground, install the valves as follows:

1. Apply a light coat of engine oil to the valve stems and install them in the cylinder head.

2. Secure the valves in place temporarily with masking tape. Then turn head over, resting valve heads on wood block or board and install spring seats, valve springs, valve spring caps and locks by reversing the procedure for removal.

NOTE: After valves have been installed, check to make sure the heads of the valves do not project more than .021″ beyond surface of cylinder head.

Rocker Arms and Shaft Removal

1. Remove valve rocker cover.
2. Remove fuel lines from injector and fuel connectors.

Checking location of injector spray tip in relation to surface of cylinder head
(© G.M.C.)

1 Spray tip
2 Orifice—injector spray tip
3 Cylinder head
4 Straight edge-steel

3. Bring push rod ends—outer ends—or injector and valve rocker arms in line horizontally.

4. Remove the two bolts which hold the rocker arm shaft brackets to the cylinder head. Remove brackets and shaft.

5. Loosen the lock nut at upper end of push rod, next to clevis, and unscrew the rocker arm from the push rod.

Inspection

1. Make certain that oil passages in rocker arm shaft and bracket bolts are open and clean.

2. Inspect rocker arm shaft and bushings inside the rocker arms for excessive wear. Clearance should be .001″ to .0025″ with new parts. A maximum clearance of .004″ is allowable with worn parts.

3. Check push rod clevis to rocker arm bushings and pins for excessive wear. The clearance between the steel clevis pin bushing and the bronze rocker arm bushing is .0015″ to .003″. The side clearance between the clevis and rocker arm should be from .008″ to .017″.

Reaming injector tube bevel seat for injector body nut
(© G.M.C.)

Installing exhaust valve guide
(© G.M.C.)

Removing injector tube
(© G.M.C.)

Compressing valve spring
(© G.M.C.)

4. Examine the injector rocker arm pallet (contact face) for wear. The rocker arm pallet may be refaced up to .010″ by grinding. However, proceed with caution when surface grinding so rocker arms are not overheated. All radii and finish should be as close to original grind as possible.

Installation

1. Install cylinder head, if removed.
2. Apply clean engine oil to outer surface of rocker arm shaft and install rocker arm shaft and/or rocker arms by reversing the sequence of operations for removal.
3. Tighten rocker arm bracket bolts to 90-100 ft lb. torque on 71 and 92 Series engines, 50-55 ft lb. on 53 Series engines. Then check position of exhaust valve bridges. Valve stem on camshaft side of cylinder head should register with recess in bridge guide.
4. Connect fuel lines from injectors to fuel connectors, torquing them to 12-15 ft lbs.
5. Adjust exhaust valve clearances and time fuel injectors.
6. Start engine. While engine is running in preparation for final tune-up, inspect the fuel lines for leaks. If leaks at the connections are discovered, tighten connecting nuts carefully. Should fuel oil leak into the crankcase and dilute the lubricating oil, the engine bearings will be seriously damaged.
7. Perform final engine tune-up after engine reaches normal operating temperature.

Cam Follower

Cam followers may be removed from either the top or bottom of the cylinder head. When followers are removed from the bottom, removal of the cylinder head will be necessary; when they are removed from the top, cylinder head removal is unnecessary. If the cylinder head is off the engine for any reason, the cam followers can best be removed from the bottom of the head.

Cam Follower Removal

(Head removed)

1. Remove cylinder head.
2. Rest cylinder head on its side and remove the two bolts that secure cam follower guide to cylinder head. Remove guide.
3. Pull the cam followers from the bottom of the cylinder head.
4. Remove fuel lines from injector and fuel connectors.
5. Loosen the lock nuts at upper end of push rods, and unscrew push rods from the rocker arm clevises.
6. Pull push rod and spring assemblies from bottom of cylinder head.
7. Remove push rod lock nut, upper spring seat, spring and lower spring seat from each push rod for cleaning and inspection.
8. The upper push rod spring seat retainers remain in the cylinder head. If the head is to be changed, these retainers must be removed, if not, they may be left in place.

Cam Follower Removal

(Head installed)

A push rod, push rod spring, spring seats and cam follower may be removed from the top of the cylinder head.

1. Remove rocker cover.
2. Remove fuel lines from injector and fuel connectors.
3. Remove rocker arm brackets and rocker arm shaft.
4. Loosen lock nut at upper end of push rod, next to clevis, and unscrew rocker arm from push rod

EARLY TYPE   INTERMEDIATE TYPE   CURRENT TYPE
Exhaust valve bridge and guide (© G.M.C.)

to be removed.

5. Run nut out on push rod so that remover may be inserted between the nut and the upper spring seat, with lower end of tool resting on upper spring seat. On 53 Series engines, remove the locknut and install a flat washer under it.

6. Screw nut down on upper end of push rod, thus compressing push rod spring, relieving spring seat retainer.

7. Remove retainer from cylinder head with a screwdriver or similar tool.

8. Unscrew nut at outer end of push rod, thus releasing spring.

9. Pull push rod, spring, spring seats and cam followers out through top of cylinder head.

Replace Roller And Pin

1. Lock holding tool securely in vise and place cam follower in the groove in top of tool with follower pin resting on top of corresponding size plunger.

2. With suitable drift, drive pin from follower. Exercise caution in removing cam follower body and roller from holder, as follower pin is seated on top of spring loaded plunger.

3. Position follower body in groove of holding tool with the proper size tool plunger extending through roller pin hole in one of the legs of the follower body.

4. Coat new roller bushing and pin with engine oil.

5. With roller assembly placed properly on tool, align pin with hole in follower and carefully drive pin into the assembly until end of pin is centered in legs of follower.

6. Check side clearance between roller and follower body. This clearance should be .015" to .023".

Cam Follower Inspection

1. Clean the cam follower carefully and inspect it and the cam for excessive wear or scoring. Replace parts as necessary.

2. Check the cam follower spring for a free length of 2.62" on 53 Series engines, and 2⅝" on 71 and 92 Series engines. Replace if free length is not approximately correct.

3. Using a spring tester and torque wrench, check 92 series springs for a load of 250 lbs @ 2.1406", 71 Series springs for a load of 172 lbs. @ 2.116", 53 Series springs for a load of 250 lbs. @ 2-9/64". Replace springs which do not meet these minimum specifications.

4. Check the cam follower-to-head clearance, which must be .006"

Cam follower and guide location
(© G.M.C.)

Labels: Cylinder Head · Cam Follower Assembly · Cam Follower Guide · Lock Washer · Retainer Bolt

maximum, and replace followers as necessary.

5. Measure the clearance between roller bushing and pin (.010" maximum) and the side clearance between the roller and follower (.015"-.023") and replace parts which do not meet specifications.

Cam Follower Installation

(Head removed)

To assemble the cam follower and push rod assembly through the bottom of the cylinder head proceed as follows:

1. Assemble over the push rod, in order listed, lower spring seat, push rod spring, upper spring seat, and push rod lock nut. On 53 Series engines, replace lower spring seats with the newer, serrated design.

2. With the upper spring seat retainer in place in the cylinder head, slide the push rod assemblies into position from bottom of cylinder head.

3. Screw push rod lock nut down on upper end of push rod as far as possible, and screw push rod into clevis until end of rod is flush with or above inner side of clevis.

4. Note the oil hole in the bottom of the follower. With this oil hole pointing away from the valves, so that the hole is not covered by the follower guide, slide the followers into position from bottom of head. NOTE: To insure initial lubrication of the follower roller pin, immerse cam follower assemblies in clean lubricating oil for at least five minutes before installing them in cylinder head.

5. Secure follower guide to bottom of cylinder head to hold group of cam followers in place. Tighten guide bolts to 12-15 ft lbs. Then check to be sure there is clearance between the cam follower legs and the cam follower guide. Clearance is .005" on 53 Series engines.

Cam Follower Installation

(Head installed)

1. With the oil hole in the bottom of the follower over the trailing side of roller (cam follower oil hole toward outside of cylinder head), insert follower into bore in head. NOTE: To insure initial lubrication of the follower roller pin, immerse cam follower assemblies in clean lubricating oil for at least five minutes before installing them in cyclinder head.

2. Install lower spring seat, push rod spring and upper spring seat on push rod in the order listed and set the assembly down into the cam follower. Use serrated lower spring seats on 53 Series engines.

3. Start nut on outer end of push rod, and install tool beneath nut on push rod and against upper spring seat. Then screw nut down on push rod until spring is compressed sufficiently to permit retainer to be inserted in cylinder head. Partially collapse retainer and install in groove in the cylinder head.

4. Unscrew nut at outer end of push rod and remove tool.

5. Screw lock nut as far as possible down on push rod, then screw rocker arm clevis down on push rod until the end of the push rod is flush with or above inner side of clevis.

6. Observe that the injector rocker arm (the center arm of the group) is slightly different from the exhaust valve rocker arms; the boss for the shaft on the valve rocker arms is longer on one side of the arm than on the other. The extended boss of valve rocker arms must face the injector rocker arm.

Camshaft

Camshaft Removal

Whenever an engine is being completely reconditioned or the cam-

Cam roller wear clearance
(© G.M.C.)

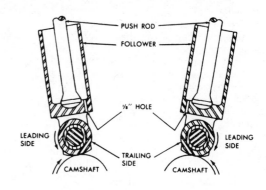

Installation of cam followers
(© G.M.C.)

shafts, camshaft gears, bearings or thrust washers need replacing, the camshafts must be removed from the engine in the following manner:

Camshaft Removal

1. Drain engine and mount in overhaul stand.
2. Remove heads.
3. Remove flywheel and housing.
4. Remove water pump.
5. Remove from balance weight cover.
6. Remove the retaining plate bolts and plates.
7. Wedge on a clean rag between the gears and remove the gear retaining nut from each shaft. On left hand rotation engines, remove the lock bolt and washer from the right camshaft.
8. Pull the camshaft vibration damper and hub.
9. Remove the water pump drive gear from the right camshaft.
10. Remove the key and spacer from each shaft.
11. Remove intermediate bearing lock screws from the block.
12. Remove end bearing retaining bolts.
13. Pull each shaft assembly from the block.

71 Series

1. Remove all accessories and assemblies with their attaching parts necessary to mount engine on overhaul stand.
2. Remove cylinder head.
3. Remove flywheel and flywheel housing.
4. Remove water pump.
5. Remove balance weight cover.
6. Remove bolts securing retainer plates to camshaft timing gears. Then remove retainer plates.
7. Wedge a clean rag between gears. Using a socket wrench, remove nuts from both ends of each camshaft.
8. Attach puller to camshaft pulley. Use adaptor between end of camshaft and puller screw to protect end of camshaft.

9. Remove water pump drive gear from front end of right bank camshaft.
10. Remove Woodruff key and spacer from forward end of both camshafts.
11. Remove lock screw from the top of cylinder block at each camshaft intermediate bearing.
12. Remove three bolts which secure each camshaft end bearing assembly to rear of engine. Rotate camshaft gear as required to reveal bearing bolts through hole in web of gear.
13. Withdraw camshaft, bearings, and gear as an assembly from rear end of cylinder block.
14. Remove three bolts from each camshaft front end bearing. Then, withdraw bearings from cylinder block and front end plate. If the bearings cannot be withdrawn readily by hand, remove by prying under bearing flange.

53 Series

1. Drain the cooling system.
2. Remove accessories and assemblies and their attaching parts as required to permit mounting the engine in an overhaul stand. Mount the engine securely in the stand, and release the lifting sling.

Removing the Camshaft Gear
(© G.M. Corp)

3. Remove the cylinder head(s) as described in the appropriate section.
4. Remove the flywheel and housing as described in the appropriate section.
5. Remove the gear nut retainer plate bolts (if used) and remove the retainer plates.
6. Wedge a clean rag between the camshaft gears, and then remove the gear mounting nuts.
7. Force the balance weight off the end of each shaft, using heavy screwdrivers between the weight and upper front cover.
8. Remove the upper front cover-to-block attaching bolts. Tap the cover and dowel assembly away from the block, remove the woodruff keys and oil seal spacers, and clean all traces of old gasket material off the block.
9. Remove the oil slingers from the front ends of both shafts.
10. Remove the thrust washer retaining bolts securing the shaft thrust washers to the block by inserting a socket through the hole in the web of the gear.
11. Withdraw the shaft, thrust washer, and gear from the rear of the block.

Disassembly—92 Series

1. Pull camshaft gear.
2. Remove rear end bearing and thrust washers.
3. Remove intermediate bearing lock rings.
4. Remove end plugs. This is accomplished by drilling and tapping the plugs.

Disassembly—71 Series

1. Remove gear from camshaft.
2. Slide camshaft rear end bearing and thrust washers off camshaft
3. Remove lock rings from camshaft intermediate bearings then separate and remove two halves of each bearing.

Disassembly—53 Series

1. Place the assembly in an arbor

GMC (Detroit 2-cycle) Diesel Engines

press, with the gear suitably supported. Place a wood block under the lower end of the shaft.

2. Place a short piece of ¾" O.D. brass rod between the end of the camshaft and the ram of the press. Force the camshaft out of the gear.

3. Remove the thrust washer, key and spacer.

Inspection

Be sure that oil holes in camshaft end bearings are clean.

Inspect cams and journals and replace the camshaft if scored or worn. Inspect cam followers.

Examine both faces of camshaft rear end bearing and thrust washers. If either face is scored or if thrust washers are worn excessively, replace washers. New standard size thrust washers are .120" to .122" thick. Examine surfaces of gear and camshaft which the thrust washers contact; if these surfaces are scratched but not severely scored, they may be smoothed down with an oil stone. However, if score marks are too deep to be removed or parts are badly worn, new parts must be used.

Clearance between the thrust washer and thrust shoulder of the camshaft, using new parts, is from .004" to .012", or a maximum of .018" with used parts. Thrust washers are available in .005" and .010" oversize and may be used to reduce excessive clearance within the specified limits of .004" to .012".

On 71 and 6V-92 Series engines, the clearance between new camshaft end journals and their respective new bearings is from .0025" to .004", or a maximum of .006" with worn parts. On 8V-92 Series engines the clearance is .0035 to .005" or a maximum of .006" On 53 Series engines, clearance is .0045"-.006" with new parts, or .008" with worn parts. End bearings are available in .010" or .020" undersize for use with shafts which have worn or been reground and the clearances exceed the specified limits.

On 71 and 92 Series engines, the clearance between the camshaft journals and the intermediate bearings is from .0025" to .005" with new parts, or a maximum of .009" with worn parts. Camshaft intermediate bearings are available in .010" and .020" undersize for use with worn or reground shafts in which the clearances exceed the .0025" to .005" limits. Bushings must be finished bored to a 20 R.M.S. finish after installation.

Also inside diameter of bushing must be square with rear face of bearing within .0015" total indicator reading. Camshaft rear end bearing bushings must project .045" to .055" from each end of bearing. Bushings in camshaft front end bearing do not project from bearing. End of inner bushing in front end bearing should be installed flush with end of bearing; end of outer bushing should be flush with counterbore in bearing.

If necessary, replace oil seal in left bank camshaft front end bearing.

Examine teeth of water pump drive gear and camshaft gears for evidence of scoring, pitting and wear. Replace gears if necessary.

On 53 Series engines, oversize camshaft and balance shaft bearings are available in sets .010" oversize on the outside diameter to permit re-use of a block having scored bearing bores. To use the oversize bearings, camshaft and balance shaft bores must be line bored to the dimensions shown below:

End Bearings   2.385"-2.386"
Intermediate Bearings   2.375"-2.376"

In removal and installation of bearings, end bearings must be removed prior to removal of intermediate bearings. Reverse this procedure during installation.

Removing camshaft gear retaining nut
(© G.M.C.)

Removing camshaft bearing bolts
(© G.M.C.)

Camshaft components (© G.M.C.)

1 Gear retaining nut
2 Lock washer
3 Water pump drive gear
4 Balance weight
5 Spacer
6 Weight bolt
7 Woodruff key
8 Camshaft—right
9 Timing gear-right
10 Retainer bolt and lock washer
11 Nut retainer
12 Timing gear-left
13 Retainer bolt and lock washer
14 Thrust washer
15 Rear bearing
16 Camshaft—left
17 Intermediate bearing
18 Lock ring
19 Set screw
20 Gasket
21 Front bearing
22 Oil seal
23 Camshaft pulley

GMC (Detroit 2-cycle) Diesel Engines

Camshaft Assembly— 92 Series

1. Install new end plugs.
2. Apply heavy grease to the steel face of each thrust washer and place a thrust washer against each end of the two camshaft rear end bearings. The steel face of each washer must be against the bearing.
3. Lubricate the rear camshaft bearing journal and slide a rear end bearing on each shaft.
4. Install the camshaft gear with a press.
5. Lubricate the intermediate bearing journals and place the two halves of each bearing on a camshaft journal and lock halves together with two lock rings.

Camshaft Installation— 92 Series

1. Install and align the right camshaft and gear. Secure the rear end bearing with 3 bolts and lock washers. Torque bolts to 35-40 ft. lb.
2. Turn intermediate bearings until the holes line up with the tapped holes in the block. Install screws and torque to 15-20 ft. lb.
3. Install the left camshaft the same way.
4. Fix a new gasket to the front end bearing and seal. Lubricate the journal and slide the bearing on the left bank with the bolting flange toward the outer end. Install the bolts and torque to 35-40 ft. lb.
5. Install the right bank camshaft front end bearing, without the oil seal. Secure the bearing and torque to 35-40 ft. lb.
6. Install the spacers—polised one

Removing or installing camshaft assembly
(© G.M.C.)

on the left.
7. Install both keys.
8. Install the pulley on the left shaft and the water pump drive gear and external weight on the right gear.
9. Attach vibration damper and hub to water pump drive gear. Torque to 30-35 ft. lb.
10. Insert gear and pulley retaining nuts and washers.
11. Wedge a clean rag between the gears and torque each nut to 300-325 ft. lb.
12. Install the nut retainers and torque to 35-39 ft. lb.
13. Thrust washer-to-shoulder clearance should be .004-.012″ when checked. Gear backlash is .003-.008″.

Camshaft Assembly—71 Series

Assemble parts on camshaft as follows:

1. Apply heavy cup grease to the steel face of camshaft thrust washers and install thrust washers against each end of camshaft rear bearing. Be sure steel face of washer is next to bearing.

2. Lubricate the camshaft rear bearing journal and slide rear bearing onto camshaft journal with bolting flange of bearing toward outer (gear) end of shaft.
3. Install timing gear on camshaft.
4. Lubricate the camshaft intermediate bearing journals, then place the two halves of each intermediate bearing on camshaft journal and lock halves together with two lock rings. Assemble lock rings with gap in upper bearing and ends equal distance (approximately ½ inch) above split line of bearing.

Camshaft Installation— 71 Series

1. Insert forward end of assembled camshaft through opening in rear end plate until the first intermediate bearing enters bore. Continue to work the camshaft and bearings into the cylinder block until gear teeth are about to engage the teeth of mating gear. Use care not to damage cam lobes when installing shaft.
2. Then, with the timing marks on the mating gears in alignment, slide camshaft gear into mesh.
3. Secure camshaft rear bearing to cylinder block. Rotate camshaft gear as required to install bearing bolts through hole in web of gear. Tighten bolts to 35-40 ft.-lb. torque.
4. Turn camshaft intermediate bearings so that locking holes in bearings align with holes in top of cylinder block and secure in place with lock screws.
5. Install opposite camshaft as out-

LEFT-HAND ROTATION ENGINES   RIGHT-HAND ROTATION ENGINES

Gear train and timing marks (© G.M.C.)

lined in preceding paragraphs.

6. Using a new bearing to end plate gasket, install left bank camshaft front end bearing—the one with the oil seal—in the cylinder block. Secure bearing in place. Tighten bolts to 35-40 ft.-lbs. torque.

7. Install right bank camshaft front end bearing—the one without the oil seal—in the cylinder block. Tighten bearing retaining bolts to 35-40 ft.-lb. torque.

8. Lubricate outside diameter of camshaft front spacer and slide spacer onto front end of left bank camshaft.

9. Install camshaft front spacer on right bank camshaft.

10. Install Woodruff keys in keyways in front end of each camshaft.

11. Install pulley on front end of left bank camshaft and water pump drive gear on right bank camshaft.

12. Slip an internal tooth lock washer over front end of each camshaft. Star nuts on forward end of both camshafts. NOTE: Early engines have water pump gear, and camshaft gear with 59 and 42 teeth respectively. Latest pump gear and camshaft gear have 92 and 66 teeth respectively. Early and latest type gears are not interchangeable.

13. Start nuts on rear end of each camshaft.

14. Wedge a clean rag between the camshaft gears to prevent their rotation; then, using a 1½″ socket wrench, tighten nut on each end of both camshafts to 300-325 ft.-lb. torque.

15. Secure camshaft timing gear nuts with gear nut retainers, bolts and lock washers. Tighten gear nut retainer bolts to 35-39 ft.-lb. torque.

16. Check clearance between thrust washer and thrust shoulder of camshaft. Clearance should be .004″ to .012″, or a maximum of .018″ with used parts.

17. Check backlash between mating

Camshaft gear installed
(© G.M.C.)

gears. Backlash should be .003″ to .008″, and should not exceed .010″ between worn gears.

18. Install flywheel housing and other parts or assemblies, that were removed from the engine.

Camshaft Installation—53 Series

1. Identify the timing gear end of the camshaft, stamped "R.H.-R. BANK" and "V7" or "R.H.-L. BANK" and "V7". The gear must be installed on this end of the camshaft.

2. Place the rear spacer over the timing gear end of the shaft and install the key.

3. Lube the thrust washer with engine oil and install it over the gear end of the shaft and spacer.

4. Start the camshaft gear over the end of the shaft with the key and keyway in line.

5. Support the shaft in an arbor press and place a sleeve between the gear and the ram of the press. Press the gear on until it is tight against the spacer.

6. Measure the clearance between the camshaft thrust washer and the camshaft. It should be .008″-.015″ with new parts, with a maximum used parts figure of .021″.

7. Install the gear retainer nut finger tight.

8. Lubricate the bearings and

shafts with engine oil and slide the shaft assemblies into the block. Align the timing marks on the gears.

9. Install the oil slinger.

10. Put a new gasket onto the engine front cover, install the cover onto the engine, and secure it with bolts and lock washers. Torque the bolts to 35 ft lbs.

11. Apply cup grease to the outside diameters of the oil seal spacers and slide them onto the shafts.

12. Secure the thrust washers in place and tighten the bolts to 30-35 ft lbs.

13. Install the keys and then install the pulleys, tightening the retaining nuts to 300-325 ft lbs. If a balance pulley does not slip easily onto the end of the shaft, loosen the thrust washer retaining bolts, support the rear end of the shaft, and place a hollow sleeve over the end of the shaft to permit the pulley to be tapped into position.

14. Install the gear nut retainer plates (if used) and torque the bolts to 35-39 ft lbs.

15. Check the clearance between the thrust washer and gear. The clearance should be .008″-.015″ with new parts, or up to .019″ with used parts.

16. Check the backlash between mating gears. It must be .003″-.005″, or up to .007″ with used parts.

17. Replace cylinder heads and flywheel housing as described in the appropriate section.

Gear Train

Description

The gear train consists of a crankshaft gear, an idler gear, two camshaft gears and a blower drive gear.

The crankshaft gear is bolted to a flange at the rear end of the crankshaft. The idler gear is mounted on a stationary hub on either the right or left side of the engine depending upon the engine rotation. The camshaft gears are pressed on and keyed to their respective shafts and each

Camshaft gears installed
(© G.M.C.)

Retaining Nut

Locking Plate

Pressing gear off camshaft
(© G.M.C.)

Press

Gear

Camshaft

is secured by a nut and gear nut retainer.

The two camshaft gears mesh with each other and run at the same speed as the crankshaft gear. Since the former two gears must be in time with each other, and the two as a unit, in time with the crankshaft gear, timing marks have been stamped in the face of the gears to facilitate correct gear train timing. When assembling the engine, it is important to remember engine rotation. Then line up the appropriate timing marks on the gears as each gear is installed on the engine.

Crankshaft Gear

The crankshaft timing gear is bolted to a flange at the rear end of the crankshaft and drives the camshaft gears, as well as the blower drive gear, through an idler gear. One gear attaching bolt hole is offset so that the gear can be attached in only one position.

Crankshaft Gear Removal —71 and 92 Series

1. Remove six bolts retaining gear to crankshaft.
2. Remove gear using a suitable gear puller.

Installation

1. Position gear on rear end of crankshaft with all six bolt holes in gear aligned with tapped holes in the crankshaft flange. Since one bolt hole is offset, the gear can be attached in only one position on the crankshaft.
2. Align timing mark on crankshaft gear with corresponding mark on the idler gear.
3. Install gear to crankshaft bolts, then tighten bolts to specified torque (35-39 ft.-lb.)
4. Check backlash between mating gears. Backlash should be .003" to .008", and should not exceed .010" between worn gears.

Crankshaft Gear Removal— 53 Series

1. Attach a bar type puller with plates to the crankshaft gear with long bolts. Adjust the lengths of the bolts so they are even.
2. Turn the center screw of the puller and pull the gear off the crankshaft.

Installation

1. Start the gear over the end of the crankshaft with the timing marks aligned and the gear keyway aligned with the key in the shaft.
2. Hold a heavy hammer against the head of the bolt in the front end of the crankshaft. Place an installer against the rear face of the timing gear. Use a heavy hammer to drive the gear up against the shoulder on the crankshaft.

Camshaft Gears

Since the two camshaft gears must be in time with each other, timing marks are stamped on the rim of both gears. Also, since these two gears as a unit must be in time with the crankshaft, timing marks are located on the idler and crankshaft gears.

Camshaft Gear Removal

1. Remove camshafts from engine.
2. Place one of the camshaft and gear assemblies in arbor press with gear suitably supported. Lay a wood block under the lower end of the camshaft.
3. Then, using a short piece of one inch (¾" on 53 Series) O.D. brass rod beween end of camshaft and ram of press, force

Idler gear and hub details (© G.M.C.)

Pressing hub from idler gear bearing (© G.M.C.)

Idler gear installed (© G.M.C.)

GMC (Detroit 2-cycle) Diesel Engines

Checking idler gear bearing pre-load
(© G.M.C.)

Pressing hub into idler gear bearing
(© G.M.C.)

camshaft out of camshaft gear.
4. If necessary, remove Woodruff key from camshaft. Remove the thrust washer and spacer on 53 Series engines.

Installation

NOTE: On 53 Series engines, install gear on end marked "R.H.-R Bank" or "R.H.-L Bank."
1. Install camshaft rear end bearing and thrust washers on camshaft. Apply heavy cup grease to the steel face of camshaft thrust washers and place a washer on each end of camshaft rear bearing. Steel face of washer is next to bearing. On 53 Series engines, install the rear camshaft spacer and key.
2. Lubricate the camshaft rear bearing journal and slide rear bearing onto camshaft journal with bolting flange of bearing toward outer (gear) end of shaft.
3. Start camshaft gear over end of camshaft with key in shaft registering with keyway in gear.
4. Press gear tight against shoulder on shaft in manner illustrated in Fig. 5. If available, camshaft gear installer may be used for this purpose. On 53 Series engines, measure the thrust washer-to-camshaft clearance. It should be .008″-.0015″ with new parts, or up to .021″ with used

Installing idler gear assembly
(© G.M.C.)

parts.
5. Start camshaft gear retaining nut on camshaft. Tighten nut after shaft is installed in cylinder block.
6. Install camshaft in cylinder block.

Idler Gear

The idler gear is mounted on a double row, tapered roller bearing, which in turn is supported on a stationary hub. A bolt passes through the hub and rear end plate. A dowel in the hub correctly positions the hub and prevents the hub from rotating.

The idler gear bearing cup has a light press fit in the gear and is held in place by a retainer. The idler gear

bearing cones are pressed onto the gear hub and do not rotate. A spacer separates the two bearing cones.

A left-hand helix gear is provided for right-hand rotation engines, and a right-hand helix gear is provided for left-hand rotation engines.

An idler gear hole spacer (dummy hub) is used on the side opposite the idler gear.

Idler Gear Removal —71 and 92 Series

1. Remove bolt and special washer. Then remove idler gear, hub and bearing assembly from the engine.
2. Remove idler gear hold spacer (dummy hub) from the opposite side in the same manner.
3. Remove bearing retainer. NOTE: Component parts of idler gear bearing are mated; therefore, match-mark the parts during disassembly to assure they will be reassembled in their original positions.
4. Place idler gear and bearing assembly in arbor press. While rotating the idler gear to prevent brinelling of bearing, press the hub out of the bearing.
5. Tap bearing cup (outer race) from idler gear by using a brass drift alternately at four notches provided in shoulder of gear.

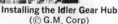

Installing the Idler Gear Hub
(© G.M. Corp)

Installing the Idler Gear
(© G.M. Corp)

1	Support to plate bolt
2	Copper washer
3	Blower drive gear support
4	Gasket
5	Blower drive gear
6	Thrust bearing
7	Thrust washer
8	Lock plate
9	Drive gear support nut
10	Plate to hub bolt and lockwasher
11	Spring plate
12	Plate to gear bolt and lockwasher
13	Gear hub
14	Snap ring

Blower drive gear and support components (© G.M.C.)

Assembly

Pay attention to matching marks previously made on parts to assure their reassembly in same positions from which they were removed and proceed as follows:

1. Support idler gear, with shoulder down, on bed of arbor press, locate bearing cup (outer race) at bearing bore of gear, and press cup into place tight against shoulder in gear.
2. Support one bearing cone, numbered side down, on bed of arbor press and lower idler gear and bearing cup assembly down over the bearing cone.
3. Lay spacer ring on face of bearing cone.
4. Place second bearing cone, numbered side up, in idler gear and bearing cup assembly and against spacer ring.
5. Position the idler gear hub over the bearing cones so that the oil hole in hub is 180° from gap in spacer ring.
6. Press hub into idler gear bearing cones, while rotating the gear to seat rollers properly between cones, until face or hub which will be adjacent to cylinder block end plate is flush with the corresponding face of bearing cone. Bearing cones should be supported so as not to load the bearing rollers during this operation.
7. Prior to installing and securing

the bearing retainer, check the pre-load of the bearing assembly as outlined below.

Then, when the torque required to rotate the idler gear is within specified limits, secure bearing retainer to the idler gear with three bolt locks.

Pre-Load Check

If the mating crankshaft and camshaft gears are not already mounted on the engine, the torque required to rotate the idler gear may be checked by mounting the idler gear in position on the engine, using a steel plate 4″ square and ⅜″ thick against the hub and cone as follows under heading "Engine Mounted Method."

However, if the crankshaft and camshaft gears are on the engine, a suitable fixture, which may be held in a vise, can be made locally to accomplish a "Bench Test Method" of determining torque. Three plates, a ½″-13 x 1-¾″ bolt and a plain washer are used with a ½″-13 nut and plain washer for mounting. One of the plates is used to take the place of a flywheel housing, and the other two plates, the cylinder block. "Engine-mounted" conditions are simulated by tightening the nut to 80-90 ft.-lb. torque and tightening the three plate-to-hub attaching bolts to 25-40 ft.-lb. torque. The components of the fixture may be made from steel stock.

The idler gear bearing should be cleaned and lubricated with clean light engine oil prior to the pre-load test. Idler gear assemblies which in-

clude new bearings should be "worked in" by grasping the gear firmly by hand and rotating the gear back and forth several times.

Idler Gear Installation— 71 and 92 Series

1. Position the crankshaft gear and camshaft gear so that the match marks will align with those on the idler gear.
2. With these marks in alignment, start the idler gear into mesh with the crankshaft gear and the camshaft gear, and simultaneously rotate the gear hub so that the hollow pin at the inner face of the hub nearly registers with the hole in the end plate.
3. Then simultaneously roll the idler gear into position, and align the hollow dowel with the hole in the end plate. Gently tap the hub until the hub seats against the end plate.
4. After making sure that the hub is tight against the end plate, secure the idler gear assembly in place with a ½″-13 bolt and special washer. Tighten bolt to 80-90 ft.-lb. torque.
5. Lubricate the idler gear and bearing liberally with clean engine oil.
6. Check backlash between mating gears. Backlash should be .003″ to .008″, and should not exceed .010″ between worn gears.

Blower drive gear assembly installed (© G.M.C.)

Checking clearance between thrust washer and thrust bearing (© G.M.C.)

675

Removal—53 Series

1. Remove the idler gear thrust washer from the hub.
2. Slide the idler gear straight back off the hub.
3. Remove the bolt securing the idler gear hub to the block. Remove the hub and idler gear thrust washer assembled.

Installation—53 Series

1. Place the inner thrust washer on the forward end of the idler gear hub with the flat in its inner diameter over the flat on the end of the hub. Make sure the oil grooves face the idler gear.
2. Place the small end of the idler gear hub through the end plate and into the counterbore of the block.
3. Insert two 3/8"-16 bolts through the idler gear hub and thread them into the block to ensure alignment of the holes when installing the flywheel housing.
4. Insert the special bolt through the center of the idler gear hub and thread it into the block. Torque it to 40-45 ft lbs., and then remove the two bolts installed in the step above.
5. Lubricate the idler gear hub and idler gear bearings with clean oil.
6. Position the crankshaft gear and camshaft or balance shaft gear so they will align with the marks on the idler gear. Then, install the idler gear.
7. Apply a thin layer of cup grease to the inner face (with oil grooves) of the outer idler gear thrust washer. Place the washer over the hub with the oil grooves facing the gear and the flat over the flat on the end of the hub.
8. Check the backlash between the mating gears. It should be .003"-.005" between new gears, with a maximum clearance of .007" between used gears.

Blower Drive Gear and Support Assembly —71 and 92 Series

The blower drive gear, is mounted on the blower drive gear support, which is attached to the cylinder block rear end plate. This gear is driven by the right cylinder bank camshaft gear.

Removal

1. Remove blower.
2. Remove two blower drive support-to-cyclinder block rear end plate attaching bolts with copper washers and tap the assembly away from the end plate, using care not to damage the gear teeth.

Disassembly

1. Clamp blower drive gear support in soft jaws of bench vise.
2. Remove three spring plate to gear bolts and lock washers.
3. Remove spring plates and blower drive gear hub as an assembly from gear. If necessary, spring plates may be removed from hub.
4. Straighten lugs on blower drive gear support nut lock plate, then remove nut.
5. Remove lock plate, blower drive gear thrust washer, thrust bearing and gear from support.

Inspection

Examine faces of thrust bearings and thrust washer and, if scored or worn excessively replace.

Check inside diameter of blower drive gear bearings for wear; also check outside diameter of support hub on which gear bearings ride. The inside diameter of new bearings in 1.6260" to 1.6265". The clearance between bearings and support should be .001" to .0025" with new parts and a maximum of .005" with used parts. Install new parts, whenever clearance exceeds the maximum.

If new bearings are installed in blower drive gear, outer end of bearings must be pressed in flush with sides of gear and bore of bearings should be square with bolt boss faces and pitch diameter of teeth of gear within .003" total indicator reading, after reaming bushings to twenty micro-inches.

Assembly

1. With blower drive support clamped in soft jaws of bench vise, position one of the blower drive gear thrust bearings on support so that tangs on bearing register with holes in support.
2. Lubricate hub of support, bearings in gear, both thrust bearings and the blower drive gear, support thrust washer with clean engine oil.
3. Slide gear on hub with flat side of gear down.
4. Install second thrust bearing on support with tangs on bearing facing up.
5. Position blower drive support thrust washer on support so that slots in thrust washer register with tangs on bearing.
6. Install gear on support with lock washer and nut. Tighten nut to 50-60 ft.-lb torque and bend lugs on lock washer against flats on nut to secure nut.
7. Check clearance between blower drive gear support thrust washer and blower drive gear

thrust bearing. Clearance should be .005" to .010", and should not exceed .012" between worn parts.
8. If spring plates were removed from blower drive gear hub, attach spring plates to hub with three bolts and lock washers. Tighten bolts to 35-39 ft.-lb. torque.
9. Assemble spring plates and hub to gear with three bolts and lock washers. Tighten bolts to 35-39 ft.-lb. torque.

Blower Drive Gear and Support Assembly Installation

1. Using a new gasket, attach gear and support assembly to cylinder block rear end plate with two bolts and copper washers. Tighten bolts to 25-30 ft.-lb. torque.
2. Check backlash between blower drive gear and camshaft gear. Backlash should be .003" to .008" with worn parts.
3. Remove four fly-wheel housing-to-blower drive support bolts. Then install blower.

NOTE: Refer to appropriate sections of Governor Service—53 Series for Blower Drive Gear and Support Assembly service for that series.

Piston and Piston Rings

Inspection

Excessively worn or scored pistons, rings and cylinder liners indicate improper maintenance or operating conditions which should be corrected as quickly as possible.

Piston

1. A careful examination of the piston should be made for scoring, cracks, worn or damaged ring grooves, plugged oil drain holes, or indications of excessive heat such as may melt the tin coating on the pistons. Pistons which are heavily scored, overheated, cracked or have excessively widened ring grooves should be discarded. Pistons which are only slightly scored may be cleaned up and reused.
2. Examine the inside of the piston closely for cracks across the struts and discard piston if such cracks are present. The pistons may be checked for cracks for use of the various methods of magnetic particle inspection.
3. Inspect the top of the piston crown for burned spots or other indications of overheating such as carbon formation in the underside of the piston crown. Such spots or carbon coating on underside of piston may indicate a lack of sufficient oil spray on

Reaming piston pin bushing
(© G.M.C.)

Removing or installing piston rings
(© G.M.C.)

the underside of piston via the drilled passage in the connecting rod.

Piston Pin Bushing

1. Inspect and measure the inside diameter of the piston pin bushings in each piston and, also inspect and measure the piston pin. With new parts, the piston pin-to-bushing clearance should be from .0025″ to .0034″. However, with worn parts, a maximum clearance of .010″ is allowable.

A .010″ oversize piston pin is available to aid in obtaining the proper clearance with worn bushings.

Piston Pin Bushing Removal

1. Place piston in holding fixture.
2. Drive bushing out of piston.
3. Revolve piston 180° in fixture and remove the second piston pin bushing in the same manner.

Installation

1. When installing bushings in a piston, locate the split or joint at the bottom, that is away from the piston head.
2. Insert spacer in hole in fixture and place piston on fixture so that spacer protrudes into bushing bore.
3. Insert installer in a bushing; then slide the bushing and installer inside piston and position over inside edge of lower bushing bore.
4. Insert handle through upper bushing bore and into installer.
5. Using hammer on upper end of handle, drive bushing into piston bushing bore until bushing bottoms on spacer.
6. Turn piston over in fixture and install second bushing in a similar manner.

Piston and ring assembly
(© G.M.C.)

1 Compression rings	5 Retainer
2 Piston	6 Expander
3 Bushing	7 Oil ring
4 Piston pin	

Reaming

The bushing must be reamed after pressing into place.

1. Clamp piston bushing reaming fixture in vise, then insert guide bushing in fixture and secure with set screw.
2. Place piston assembly in fixture and insert pilot end of reamer, through clamping bar, piston pin bushings, and into guide bushing.
3. With piston, fixture and reamer in alignment, tighten wing nuts securely.
4. Turning reamer in a clockwise direction only, with uniform motion, both when reaming and withdrawing reamer, ream the piston pin bushings.
5. Remove piston from fixture. Blow out chips resulting from reaming and check bushings for

correct reamed inside diameters, as below:

71 and
92 Series—1.5025″-1.5030″
53 Series—1.3773″-1.3780″

Piston Ring Installation

With the connecting rod assembly inspected and assembled to the piston, be certain to check proper location of piston rings assembled on the piston.

1. Assemble compression rings on piston, and stagger ring gaps around piston. When installing compression or oil control rings, do not spread the rings more than is necessary to slip them on piston to avoid overstressing rings. CAUTION: The top compression ring is a tapered face ring. Therefore, this ring must be installed with the side marked "T or "TOP" facing up.
2. Install oil control rings by hand with the scraping edge down. First install expander being careful not to overlap ends of expander. Second, install top oil ring with gap 180° from gap in expander. Check to be sure expander ends are not overlapped. Third install bottom oil ring with gap 45° from gap of top oil ring. Recheck to be sure ends of expander are not overlapped. NOTE: Upper oil control ring, used on "N'" series truck and all coach engines, has chrome plated wiping edge, and must be installed on top of other rings.
3. Install the second set of oil control rings and their expander as above.

Fitting Pistons

1. Measurements of pistons and bore for pistons in cylinder liners should be taken at room temperature (70°F.).

GMC (Detroit 2-cycle) Diesel Engines

2. Measurements should be taken on the piston skirt lengthwise and crosswise of the piston pin. On 92 Series engines, piston diameter is 4.4650"-4.4750" above and below the seal ring groove. On 71 Series engines, piston diameter is 4.2428"-4.245", and the piston taper should not exceed .0005" from bottom compression ring groove to bottom of piston. On 53 Series engines, the diameter is 3.8693"-3.8715" measured 1.750" or more from the piston top.

3. On 92 Series engines, piston-to-liner clearance should be .0055-.0093" with a .012" clearance allowable. On 71 Series engines piston-to-liner clearance should be from .004" to .0078". With used parts, a maximum clearance of .012" is allowable. On 53 Series engines, piston-to-liner clearance is .0037"-.0074", not to exceed .010". This clearance should be checked at four places, 90° apart, around the circumference of the piston.

4. Cylinder liner bores should be round within .002" and straight within .001" when fitted into the cylinder block. Measure cylinder liner bores with a suitable gauge, both lengthwise and crosswise of the piston pin throughout the entire length of the cylinder liner.

5. Check the piston-to-liner clearance while the piston is held upside down in the liner. The liner should be in place in the cylinder block, otherwise inaccurate readings will be obtained. This clearance should always be checked when installing either new or used pistons and liners.

6. A feeler gauge set may be used for this purpose. The set consists of a feeler gauge pack, spring scale, and swivel connection. The spring scale, attached to the feeler gauge pack by means of the

Installing piston assembly in ring compressor and cylinder assembly
(© G.M.C.)

Installing piston assembly and liner in cylinder block
(© G.M.C.)

swivel connection, is used to measure the force in pounds required to withdraw the feeler from between the piston and liner.

7. Select the feeler ribbon with a thickness that will require approximately six pounds pull to remove. The clearance will be .001" greater than the thickness of the feeler used, i.e., a feeler .004" thick indicates a clearance of .005" when withdrawn at a pull of six pounds. Feeler

ribbon used for checking this clearance must be perfectly flat and free of nicks and scratches.

8. If any bind between the piston and liner is detected, remove the piston and liner and inspect them for burrs.

9. Service pistons are available in standard size, and in .010", .020", and .030" oversize. These within very close limits. Therefore, pistons all weigh the same fore, one or more oversize pistons may be installed in an engine without causing damage to the engine. Since cylinder liners are furnished in standard inside diameter only, the installation of oversize pistons becomes necessary only when cylinder liners have been rehoned.

10. All new piston rings must be installed whenever a piston is removed, whether or not a new liner and/or piston is installed.

Fitting Piston Rings

1. Insert one ring at a time inside the liner and far enough down in the bore to be on the wiping area of the rings when piston is installed. To assure that the ring is parallel with top of liner, use a piston to crowd the ring into liner bore; then measure gap with a feeler gauge.

2. If the piston ring gap is below the specified limits, it may be increased by stoning the ends of the ring. Stone both ends of the piston ring in such a direction that the stone will cut from the outside (chrome plated) surface of ring toward the inside surface. This will prevent any chipping or peeling of the chrome plate. The ends of the ring must remain square and chamfer must be approximately .015" on outer edge.

3. Check ring clearances in the piston grooves. Nominal ring groove widths, which may vary

Fitting piston in cylinder liner
(© G.M.C.)

Measuring piston ring gap
(© G.M.C.)

± .001″, and ring clearances in grooves are given below

Ring-to-Groove-Clearance—92 Series
#1	.001″-.005″
#2	.010″-.013″
#3	.004″-.007″

Ring-to-Groove-Clearance—71 Series
#1	.004″-.007″
#2—N Series	.010″-.013″
#2—Others	.0095″-.013″
#3, #4—N Series	.004″-.007″
#3—Others	.0075″-.011″
#4—Others	.055″-.009″
Oil Rings	.0015″-.0055″

Ring-to-Groove Clearances—53 Series
#1	.0026″-.0049″
#2	.0070″-.0100″
#3, #4	.0050″-.0080″
Oil Rings	.0015″-.0055″

When an oversize piston is installed, piston rings of the same oversize must also be installed.

Cylinder Liners

Description

The cylinder liners used in Detroit Diesel engines are of the replaceable dry type, made of hardened alloy cast iron and are a slip fit in the cylinder block.

A flange at the top of each liner fits into a counterbore in the cylinder block and rests on a cast iron insert to provide accurate alignment and positioning of the liners. Compression is sealed with an individual laminated compression gasket for each cylinder.

Cylinder Liner Removal

1. Remove the cylinder head assembly. Remove the oil pan.
2. Remove oil pickup suction pipe and screen, if necessary.
3. Remove the cylinder liner compression gasket.
4. Remove the piston and connecting rod assembly.
5. Loosen the liner with the tool shown in the illustration. Slip

Cylinder liner measurement diagram
(© G.M.C.)

the lower puller clamp upward on the puller rod and slip it off the tapered cone. Cock the lower clamp on the rod so it will slide down through the liner. Lower the rod down through the liner so the clamp will drop back onto the tapered cone in a horizontal position.

6. Slide the upper clamp down against the top edges of the liner.
7. Strike the upset head on the upper end of the puller rod sharply with the puller weight. thus releasing the liner from the cylinder block.

Honing Liner

Cylinder liners are available in standard size inside diameter only, therefore installation of oversize pistons becomes necessary when liners are honed oversize. Also, liners are available in oversize outside dimensions which must be used whenever cylinder block bores are honed.

1. Liners should not be honed in the cylinder block, but should be removed and placed in a honing fixture (a scrap cylinder block makes an excellent honing fixture). If it is necessary to hone liners in the cylinder block that is to be used in building up the engine, the engine must be dismantled, and then, after honing, the block must be thoroughly cleaned.
2. Honing should be done, with a 120 grit stone, in such a manner as to produce a crisscross pattern with hone marks on a 45° axis. This operation may be performed using emery cloth if a hone is unavailable.
3. When cylinder liner has been honed, inspect to be sure liner is free of burrs over its entire area.
4. After honing, the liners must conform to the same limits on taper and out-of-round as a standard size liner, and the piston-to-liner clearance must be the same as that specified for standard parts.

Taper and Out-of-Round

If a liner is worn to such an extent that the taper or out-of-round limits have been exceeded, the liner must be honed out for oversize pistons or the liner must be replaced. Permissible taper is .001″, out of round .002″.

Remove Ridge

The inside diameter of a used liner measured just below the top of the ring travel must not exceed the unworn diameter at the top by more than .004″. A larger step than this may cause interference with new compression rings. In order to pre-

Honing bore of cylinder block
(© G.M.C.)

vent ring breakage caused by this difference in diameter, hone the liner just enough to remove this ridge.

Break Glaze

Never install new piston rings in a used liner unless the glaze in the liner is broken.

Even though the liner taper and out-of-round are within specifications, the glaze must be removed by working a hone up and down the full length of the liner a few times.

Honing Cylinder Block

The fit of a liner depends to a great extent upon the condition of the bore before honing. Distortion may cause low spots that will clean up. A low spot is not objectionable above the ports if it does not exceed 1¼″ or the size of a half dollar. Below the ports, larger spots are permissible.

Roughing and finishing stones should be fairly coarse. A No. 80 grit stone may be used for roughing, and a No. 120 grit stone is satisfactory for finishing.

The following inspection should be made before honing cylinder block:
1. Clean bore and inlet port opening.
2. Measure the bore for high spots and the most narrow section.
3. Liners are fitted from .0005″ to .0025″ loose. A clearance of .0005″ produces a slip fit and .0024″ clearance allows the liner to slide freely into place. Refer to chart for standard and oversize cylinder liner bore in cylinder block.

Rough Honing

Insert hone in bore and adjust stones snugly to the most narrow section.

Start hone and "feel out" bore for high spots. These will cause an increased drag on the stone. Move hone up and down bore with short overlapping strokes about 1″ long: Concentrate on the high spots in the first cut. Do not hone as long at the ports as in the rest of the bore—this area,

Cylinder liner removal
(© G.M.C.)

Checking bore at cylinder block
(© G.M.C.)

as a rule, cuts away more rapidly.

When bore is fairly clean, remove hone to inspect the stones and measure bore. Decide carefully which spots must be honed most. To move the hone from top to bottom of bore will not correct an out-of-round condition. To remain in one spot too long may cause bore to become tapered. Where and how much to hone can be judged by feel. A heavy cut in distorted bore produces a more steady drag on the hone than a light cut and so makes it difficult to feel the high spots. Therefore, use a light cut with frequent stone adjustment.

Finish Honing and Fitting Liner

Rough hone cylinder bore until the liner can be pushed from 3″ to 4″ into the bore, or until bore is within approximately .005″ of the diameter of the liner. Do not expect finishing stones to remove more than .001″ of stock, or to true up the bore to any extent.

Work the finish hone with short, rapid strokes up and down the bore. Use light tension on the stones and hone only enough to allow the liner to enter the bore either with a light push fit or a free slip fit.

Cylinder Liner Installation

Install the cylinder liner in the block and measure the distance from top of liner flange to top of block to assure proper sealing of the cylinder head compression gaskets as follows:
1. Clean liner and be sure bore and counterbore in block is clean.
2. Check cylinder liner counterbore depth.

92 Series
  Depth ....4755″-.4770″
  Variation ....none

71 Series
  Depth ....4770″-.4795″
  Variation ....0015″*

53 Series
  Depth ....300″-.302″
  Variation ....0015″

Adjacent liners to vary no more than .001″ gauged on longitudinal cylinder centerline.
3. Place a cylinder liner insert in counterbore in cylinder block. NOTE: Cylinder liner inserts are available in .004″ and .008″ thinner sizes as well as standard size for both standard to .005″ oversize and .010″, .020″ and 030″ oversize outside diameter cylinder liners. Matching oversize inserts should be installed whenever oversize (O.D.) liners are used.
4. Push liner into cylinder block by hand, until liner flange rests on insert. If the liner does not slide freely into place, withdraw, turn 90° and insert liner again. Each liner should slide freely into place to assure there will be no distortion.
5. Clamp liner in place with cylinder liner hold-down clamps.
6. Measure the distance from the top of liner flange to top of block, using a dial indicator. When in place, top of liner flange should be from .045″ (.0465″ on 53 Series) to .050″

below top of cylinder block, and there must not be over .001″ (.0015″ on 53 Series) difference in height below top of block between any two adjacent liners when gauged on longitudinal cylinder centerline.
6. Install new cylinder liner compression gaskets.

Connecting Rod and Bearings

Bearing Removal

(Connecting Rod Installed)

When removal of connecting rod bearing shells becomes necessary, they may be removed as follows:
1. Remove the oil pan.
2. Disconnect and remove the lubricating oil pump suction pipe and screen assembly from main bearing cap.
3. Remove one connecting rod bearing cap. Push connecting rod and piston assembly up into cylinder liner far enough to permit removal of upper bearing shell.

Installing cylinder liner in block
(© G.M.C.)

4. Install bearing shells before another cap is removed.

Bearing Installation

1. Rotate crankshaft until connecting rod journal is at the bottom of its travel, wipe the journal clean and lubricate with clean engine oil.
2. Install upper bearing shell—the one without an oil groove (on 53 Series engines, this shell has a short groove and a hole at each parting line.)
3. With tang of upper bearing shell in groove of connecting rod, pull piston and rod assembly down until upper rod bearing seats firmly on crankshaft journal.
4. Place lower bearing shell—the one with the oil groove—in bearing cap, with tang of shell in groove of cap, and lubricate with clean engine oil.
5. Note identifying marks on cap and rod and assemble cap to rod. Tighten connecting rod bolt nuts to 60-70 ft lbs. on 92 Series engines, 65-75 ft lbs. torque on 71 Series engines, 50-55 ft lbs. on 53 Series engines.
6. Install lubricating oil pump suction pipe and screen assembly.
7. Install oil pan and fill crankcase with recommended lubricating oil to "FULL" mark on dipstick.
8. If new bearings were installed, operate engine on run-in schedule.

Assembly of Rod and Piston

(Conecting Rod to Piston)

Apply clean engine oil to the piston pin and bushings and proceed with assembly of the rod to piston in the following manner:

1. Rest piston in holding fixture. Place a new piston pin retainer in either side of piston. Position installer tool over retainer and strike tool just hard enough to cause a deflection in the piston pin retainer and even seating of retainer. Driving too hard against the tool may force the piston bushing inward, thus reducing the piston pin end clearance.
2. Place upper end of connecting rod between piston pin bosses in line with piston pin holes and slide pin into position. The piston pin should slip readily into position without forcing if clearances are correct.
3. Install second piston pin retainer as outlined above. After piston pin retainers have been installed, it is advisable to visually check for piston pin end clearance by cocking rod on pin and shifting pin in its bushings.

Piston and Rod Installation

1. With piston assembled to connecting rod and piston ring in place, apply clean engine oil to piston, rings, and inside of piston ring compressor.
2. Place compressor on wood bench or table with tapered side of compressor up.
3. Stagger the piston ring gaps properly on the piston, being careful that oil ring expanders are not overlapped.
4. Start the top of the piston straight into compressor, then push piston down until it contacts wood block.
5. Place the ring compressor, piston, and connecting rod assembly on the liner. On 53 Series engines, align numbers on rod and cap with the match-mark on the liner. Replacement connecting rods must be stamped with number stamped on original rod. Carefully push the piston and rod assembly down into the liner until piston is free of the ring compressor, using care to avoid ring breakage. Remove the compressor. Install hold-down clamps to keep other liners in place on 53 Series engines.
6. Rotate the crankshaft until connecting rod journal is at bottom of its travel, wipe the journal clean and lubricate journal with clean engine oil.
7. Lubricate and install upper bearing shell—the one without an oil groove—in the connecting rod. On 53 Series engines, this shell has a short groove at each parting line.
8. Note that each connecting rod and its cap are stamped on one side—1L, 1R, 2L, 2R, etc. These numbers and letters are for identification purposes and indicate the particular cylinder in which each is used. These positions should always be maintained when rebuilding an engine. On 53 Series engines, apply permanent anti-freeze to the inner surface of the seal ring and install it.
9. Position the piston, rod and liner assembly in its proper location according to marks on liner and with connecting rod numbers and letters toward outside of the cylinder block. Slide the liner, pistons, and rod assembly straight into the block bore until the flange of liner seats on the insert in cylinder block counterbore. CAUTION: The centerline of the connecting rod is slightly offset. Therefore, when installing to crankshaft, be sure that the narrow side of the two connecting rods on the crankshaft journal are together to avoid cocking the rod.
10. Lubricate and place lower bearing shell—the one with the oil groove—in connecting rod cap with tang of shell in groove of cap.
11. Assemble cap to rod with identifying marks on cap and rod adjacent to each other. Tighten connecting rod bolt nuts to 60-70 ft lbs. on 92 Series engines, 65-75 ft.-lbs. torque on V71 Series engines, or 50-55 ft.-lbs. on 53 Series engines. Phosphate coated, 53 Series nuts should be torqued to 45-50 ft.-lbs.

Crankshaft and gears (© G.M.C.)

12. Check connecting rod side clearance. The clearance between each pair of connecting rods should be .008″ to .016″ with new parts with V-type engines, .008″-.012″ on In-line engines.
13. Remove cylinder liner hold-down clamps.

Crankshaft and Main Bearings

Crankshaft Removal

When necessary to remove crankshaft the operation may be performed as follows:

1. Drain oil, then remove the oil pan.
2. Remove the lubricating oil pump screen and suction pipe assembly.
3. Remove hydraulic fan assembly.
4. Remove flywheel and flywheel housing.
5. Remove crankshaft front cover. On 53 Series engines, remove the crankshaft pulley.
6. Remove connecting rod bearing caps. Note that each cap and rod is stamped with a number corresponding with the cylinder number.
7. Remove main bearing caps. Note that each cap is stamped with a number which corresponds with number stamped on cylinder block.
8. Lift crankshaft, timing gear, oil pump drive spline as an assembly from crankshaft.
9. Remove main bearing inserts from crankcase and bearing caps, also thrust washers at rear main bearing. Carefully identify each bearing so that it can be replaced in its original location.

Main Bearings Removal

(Crankshaft Installed)

When removal of main bearing shells becomes necessary, and the removal of the crankshaft is not required or undesirable, this operation may be performed by using the following procedure.

NOTE: Remove bearing shells one at a time, inspect, and reinstall or replace, replacing all shells if only one or more need replacing.

All crankshaft main bearing journals except the rear are drilled for an oil passage.

1. Remove the oil pan to expose the main bearing caps.
2. Remove the lubricating oil pump intake pipe assembly. NOTE: In text following, main bearing stabilizers are mentioned in several instances. Early model engines used these parts which have since been discontinued and any reference made to stabilizers

Removing main bearing cap
(© G.M.C.)

Removing rear main bearing upper shell
(© G.M.C.)

should be disregarded on latest engines.

3. Remove only one main bearing cap stabilizer at a time, then place washers on main bearing bolts just removed, equal to thickness of stabilizer and reinstall bolts. Remove remaining stabilizer(s) in a like manner.
4. Remove main bearing caps using temporarily installed cap screws and pinch bars.
5. To remove all except rear main bearing shell, insert a 5/16″ x 1″ bolt with a 1/2″ diameter and a 1/16″ thick head (made from a standard bolt) into the crankshaft journal oil hole, then revolve the shaft to the right (clockwise) and roll the bearing shell out of position. The head of the bolt should not extend beyond the outside diameter of the shell.
6. Two-piece thrust washers are used each side of the rear main bearing. The lower half of these washers will be removed when removing the rear main bearing cap; upper half can be removed upon removal of bearing cap by

pushing on end of washer with a small rod, thus forcing washer around and out on opposite side of bearing.

7. Remove rear main bearing upper shell by driving on the edge of the bearing shell with a small curved rod, at the same time revolving the crankshaft, thus rolling the shell from its position.

Main Bearings Installation

(Crankshaft Installed)

Make sure parts are clean. Apply clean engine oil to each crankshaft journal and install main bearing shells by reversing the sequence of operations given for removal.

Upper and lower main bearing shells are not alike; the upper shell is grooved and drilled for lubrication—the lower shell is not. Be sure to install the grooved and drilled shells in the cylinder block and plain shells in the bearing caps, otherwise the oil feed to the upper end of the connecting rods will be blocked off.

1. When installing the upper main bearing shells with crankshaft in place, start the end of the

shell having no tang around the crankshaft journal, so that when shell is in place the tang will fit into groove in the shell support.

2. Assemble crankshaft thrust washer before installing rear main bearing cap. Clean both halves of thrust washer carefully, removing any burrs from the seats—*the slightest particle of dirt between washers and crankshaft may decrease clearance beyond limits.*

Slide upper halves of thrust washers into place in their grooves; then assemble lower halves over dowel pins in bearing cap. NOTE: Main bearing caps are bored in position and marked 1, 2, 3, etc. They must be replaced in their original positions.

3. With lower bearing shell installed in bearing cap, install cap and draw bolts up snug. Then rap cap sharply with soft hammer to seat cap properly and draw cap bolts uniformly tight, 230-240 ft lbs. on 92 Series engines, to 180-190 ft lbs. torque on 71 Series engines, 120-130 ft lbs. on 53 Series engines.

NOTE: If the bearings have been installed properly, the crankshaft will turn freely with all main bearing caps bolted tightly.

4. Install main bearing cap stabilizers by reversing their removal procedure. Tighten main bearing bolts to specified torque and 7/16"-14 x 1⅛" stabilizer cylinder block bolts, if used, to 70-75 ft-lbs. torque.

5. Check crankshaft end play at thrust washers. This clearance should be from .004" to .011" with new parts or a maximum of .018" with used parts. Insufficient clearance will usually denote misalignment of the rear main bearing. In such case, loosen and retighten the rear main bearing cap. If lack of clearance is still present, dirt or a burr on inner face of one or

1 Main bearing cap bolts
2 Main bearing caps
3 Main bearing—lower
4 Rear main bearing thrust washer
5 Main bearing—upper
6 Crankcase

Upper and lower main bearings, thrust washers and seals
(© G.M.C.)

more of the thrust washers may be the cause.

6. Install lubricating oil pump intake pipe assembly.

7. Install oil pan with new gasket. Fill crankcase to proper level.

Crankshaft Installation

If shells previously used are to be used again, install them in the same locations from which they were removed.

When a new crankshaft is installed, all new main and connecting rod (upper and lower) bearing shells

should also be installed.

With oil pump drive gear, and crankshaft timing gear, assembled on the front and rear ends respectively of the crankshaft, the crankshaft may be installed as follows:

1. Install upper grooved bearing shells in the cylinder block.

2. Apply clean engine oil to all crankshaft journals and set crankshaft in place so that timing marks on the crankshaft timing gear and the gear train idler gear match.

3. Install the upper halves of the rear main bearing thrust washers on each side of the bearing, and the doweled lower halves on each side of the rear main bearing cap.

4. With lower main bearing shells installed in bearing caps, install caps and stabilizers in their original position and draw bolts up snug. Then rap caps sharply with a soft hammer to seat them properly, and draw bearing cap bolts uniformly tight, starting with center cap and working alternately towards both ends of block, to 230-240 ft lbs. on 92 Series engines, 180-190 ft-lbs. torque on 71 Series engines, 120-130 ft-lbs. on 53 Series engines. Tighten 7/16"-14" x 1⅛" stabilizer to cylinder block bolts,

Checking crankshaft end play
(© G.M.C.)

GMC (Detroit 2-cycle) Diesel Engines

Crankshaft rear oil seal installed
(© G.M.C.)

Use of oil seal spacer and sleeve
on grooved crankshaft
(© G.M.C.)

if used, to 70-75 ft-lbs. torque.

NOTE: If bearings have been installed properly, the crankshaft will turn freely with all main bearing cap bolts drawn to specified torque.

5. Check crankshaft end play at thrust washers. This clearance should be .004″ to .011″ with new parts or a maximum of .018″ with used parts. Insufficient clearance will usually denote misalignment of the rear main bearing. In such case, loosen the bearing cap, then retighten as described above. If lack of clearance is still present, either dirt or a burr on the inner face of one or more of the thrust washers may be the cause.
6. Lubricate and install connecting rod bearings.
7. Install flywheel housing and flywheel.
8. Install crankshaft front cover and oil pump assembly.
9. Affix new gasket to bolting flange and secure oil pan in place with bolts and lock washers.
10. Fill crankcase to the proper level with recommended oil.

Oil Seal Removal

If inspection reveals a worn or damaged oil seal, it must be replaced. Remove the oil seal as follows:

1. Remove flywheel housing as directed in respective section of this manual.
2. Support crankshaft flywheel housing on wood blocks. Then drive out old oil seal.

Oil Seal Sleeve Installation

When the oil seal spacer can no longer be used, an oil seal sleeve may be pressed on the crankshaft to provide a replaceable wear surface at the point of contact with the rear oil seal. The oil seal sleeve may be used with either the single lip or double lip type oil seal, and can also be used in conjunction with the seal spacer. However, oversize oil seals must be used with the oil seal sleeve. Installation of the oil seal sleeve is performed as follows:

1. Stone all high spots off the circumference of the crankshaft.
2. Coat the area of the shaft where the seal will be positioned with shellac or equivalent sealer.
3. Press the sleeve onto the shaft. The sleeve must be *pressed squarely on the shaft.*
4. Wipe off all excess sealer.

Rear Oil Seal Installation

1. Support inner face of flywheel housing on a flat surface.
2. Install rear oil seal spacer, if used, against shoulder in oil seal counterbore in housing.
3. Apply a non-hardening sealant to the outer edge of the oil seal and position the seal with the lip pointing toward the inner face (toward shoulder in counterbore) of the housing.
4. Drive oil seal against seal spacer or shoulder in oil seal counterbore of housing.
5. If flywheel housing has not been removed from engine, lubricate lip of seal with Lubriplate or equivalent. Slip seal over crankshaft and start squarely into counterbore of housing. Using a hardwood block and hammer, tap seal alternately around edge of casing until seal is in place.
6. Remove all excess sealant from housing and oil seal.
7. Coat lip of oil seal lightly with Lubriplate or equivalent.
8. When installing flywheel housing on engine, use oil seal expander to avoid damage to lip of seal.

Engine Lubrication System

Illustrations show the flow of oil through engine lubricating system including the various components such as the oil pump, full flow oil filter, oil cooler, pressure regulator, and by-pass valve.

The oil pump is placed in the crankshaft front cover and consists of a pair of spur gears, one large and one small, which mesh together and ride in a cavity inside the crankshaft front cover. The large gear is concentric with and splined to a pump drive hub on the front end of the crankshaft. The pump idler gear is much smaller and runs on a bushing and hardened steel shaft pressed into the crankshaft cover.

Oil is drawn by suction from the oil pan through the intake screen and pipe to the oil pump where it is pressurized. The oil then passes from the pump into a short gallery in the cylinder block to the oil cooler adaptor plate. At the same time, oil from the pump is directed to a spring-loaded pressure relief valve mounted on the cylinder block. This valve discharges excess oil directly to the oil sump when the pump pressure exceeds 100 p.s.i.

From the oil cooler adaptor plate, the oil passed into the full flow filter through the oil cooler (truck engines only) and then back into the cylinder block where a short vertical oil gallery and a short diagonal oil gallery carry the oil to the main longitudinal oil gallery through the middle of the block. On engines used in coaches, oil filter is mounted at crankcase front cover and oil from pump goes directly to filter and returns to cylinder block. Valves are also provided to by-pass the oil filter and oil cooler should either one become plugged.

Stabilized lubricating oil pressure is maintained within the engine at all speeds, regardless of the oil temperature, by means of a pressure regulator valve located at the end of a vertical oil gallery connected to the main oil gallery. This vertical gallery is located at the front of the cylinder block on the side opposite the cooler. When the oil pressure at the valve exceeds 50 p.s.i., the regulator valve opens, discharging excess oil back into the sump.

From the main oil gallery, the pressurized oil flows through drilled passages to each main bearing then passes to an adjacent pair of connecting rods by means of grooves in the unloaded halves of the main and connecting rod bearings and drilled passages in the crankshaft. The rifle drilled connecting rods carry oil from the rod bearings to the piston pin bushings and to the nozzle at the upper end of each connecting rod which provides the cooling oil spray for the piston crowns.

At the rear of the block, two diagonally drilled oil passages which intersect the main oil gallery, carry oil to the two rear camshaft end bearings. Oil is then conducted through the rifle drilled camshaft to the intermediate and front end bearings. Oil from the camshaft intermediate bearings is directed against the camshaft lobes and cam rollers which run in an oil bath. This oil from the intermediate bearings provides lubrication of the cam lobes immediately after starting the engine when the oil is cold and before camshaft bearing oil flow and oil drainage from the cylinder head have had time to build up.

The diagonally drilled oil passage on the right side at the rear of the block intersects with a vertical passage to carry oil to the right bank cylinder head. A short gallery also intersects with this diagonal passage to lubricate the idler gear bearing. Another gallery intersecting the diagonal passage at the front of the block supplies oil to the left bank cylinder head.

Drilled passages, intersecting longitudinal galleries which parallel the camshafts, lead to the blower and supply oil for the blower drive gears and bearings.

Oil from the right-hand camshaft pocket is directed through a tube to lubricate the water pump drive gear and bearings and the front camshaft gear.

The gear train is lubricated by the overflow of oil from the camshaft pockets spilling into the gear train compartment and by splash from the oil pan. A certain amount of oil also spills into the gear train compartment from both camshaft rear end bearings, the blower drive gear bearing, and the idler gear bearing. The blower drive gear bearing is lubricated through an external pipe from the blower rear end plate to the blower drive support.

The valve and injector operating mechanism is lubricated from a longitudinal oil passage, on the camshaft side of each cylinder head, which connects to the main oil gallery in the cylinder block. Oil from this passage enters the drilled rocker arm shafts through the lower end of the rocker shaft bolts and rocker shaft brackets. Excess oil from the rocker arms lubricates the exhaust valves and cam followers.

Oil Cooler Testing

Pressure Check Core

After the oil cooler core has been cleaned, it may be checked for leaks as follows:

1. Make a suitable plate and attach to flanged side of cooler core. Use a gasket made from rubber to assure a tight seal. The plate should be drilled and tapped to permit an air hose fitting to be attached at the inlet side of the cooler core.

2. Attach air hose and apply approximately 75 p.s.i. air pressure and submerge cooler core and plate assembly in a container of water. Any leaks will be indicated by air bubbles in the water. If leaks are indicated, replace cooler core.

3. After pressure check is completed, remove plate and air hose from cooler core and dry with compressed air.

By-Pass Spring

Inspect valve and spring for wear and replace if necessary. The by-pass valve spring has a free length of approximately 2-1/64". A force of $13\frac{3}{8}$ to $14\frac{5}{8}$ pounds is required to compress the spring to a length of 1.793" when new. When a force of 12 lbs. or less will compress the spring to 1.793", replace the spring. The spring may be checked in spring tester.

Diagram of engine lubrication system (© G.M.C.)

GENERAL SPECIFICATIONS

ENGINE MODEL	BORE AND STROKE	HORSEPOWER @ R.P.M.	TORQUE FT. LBS. @ R.P.M.	COMPRESSION PRESSURE @ 600 R.P.M.	FIRING ORDER	GOVERNED SPEED R.P.M.	IDLE SPEED
D-351-V6	4.56 x 3.58	130 @ 3200	234 @ 2000	500	1-6-5-4-3-2	3200	625-650
D-478-V6	5.125 x 3.86	150 @ 3200	275 @ 2000	500	1-6-5-4-3-2	3200	625-650
DH-478-V6	5.125 x 3.86	170 @ 3200	310 @ 2000	500	1-6-5-4-3-2	3200	625-650
D-637-V8	5.125 x 3.86	195 @ 2600	——	500	1-8-4-3-6-5-7-2	2600	625-650
DH-637-V8	5.125 x 3.86	220 @ 2600	——	500	1-8-4-3-6-5-7-2	2800	625-650

PISTONS, PINS, RINGS, CRANKSHAFT AND BEARINGS

ENGINE MODEL	PISTON CLEARANCE	PISTON RING END GAP MINIMUM COMP.	PISTON RING END GAP MINIMUM OIL	PISTON PIN DIAMETER	ROD BEARINGS SHAFT DIAMETER	ROD BEARINGS BEARING CLEARANCE	MAIN BEARING SHAFT DIAMETER	MAIN BEARING BEARING CLEARANCE	SHAFT END PLAY	THRUST ON BEARING NO.
D-351-VP	.0062-.0068	.015	.013	1.6148-1.6150	2.8112-2.8122	.001-.0031	3.1237-3.1247	.0013-.0039	.003-.008	3
478-V6	.0067-.0073	.017	.017	1.6148-1.6150	2.8112-2.8122	.001-.0031	3.1237-3.1247	.0013-.0039	.003-.008	3
637-V8	.0067-.0073	.017	.017	1.6148-1.6150	2.8112-2.8122	.001-.0031	3.1237-3.1247	.0013-.0039	.003-.008	4

VALVE SPECIFICATIONS

ENGINE MODEL	VALVE LASH (HOT) IN.	VALVE LASH (HOT) EXH.	VALVE FACE ANGLE (DEG.)	VALVE STEM CLEARANCE INTAKE	VALVE STEM CLEARANCE EXHAUST	VALVE STEM DIAMETER INTAKE	VALVE STEM DIAMETER EXHAUST	VALVE SPRINGS FREE LENGTH INNER	VALVE SPRINGS FREE LENGTH OUTER
D351-V6	.010	.018	45	.0015-.003	.002-.0035	.3407-34.12	.3402-.3407	2.46	2.67
478-V6	.010	.018	45	.0015-.003	.0025-.004	.3725-.3730	.4340-.4345	2.46	2.67
637-V8	.010	.018	45	.0015-.003	.0025-.004	.3725-.3730	.4340-.4345	2.46	2.67

ENGINE TORQUE SPECIFICATIONS

ENGINE MODEL	CYLINDER HEAD FT. LBS.	INTAKE MANIFOLD END BOLTS FT. LBS.	EXHAUST MANIFOLD END BOLTS FT. LBS.	MANIFOLD CLAMP BOLTS	CONN. ROD FT. LBS.	MAIN BEARING CAPS FT. LBS.	DAMPER TO CRANKSHAFT BOLT FT. LBS.	FLYWHEEL TO CRANKSHAFT FT. LBS.	CAMSHAFT GEAR BOLT FT. LBS.	OIL PUMP TO BLOCK BOLTS FT. LBS.	OIL PAN BOLTS FT. LBS.
D351-V6	130-135	20-25	15-20	20-25	55-65	——	200-210	100-110	50-60	30-35	10-15
478-V6	130-135	20-25	15-20	20-25	55-65	——	240-260	100-110	50-60	30-35	20-25
637-V8	130-135	20-25	15-20	20-25	55-65	——	240-260	100-110	50-60	30-35	10-15

Trouble Diagnosis

The satisfactory performance of a Diesel engine depends on two items of foremost importance, (1) Sufficiently high compression pressure, and (2) The injection of the proper amount of fuel at the right time.

The first one of these items depends, mainly on pistons, piston rings, valves and valve operating mechanism; the second item depends on injectors and their operating mechanism, and fuel system.

Lack of engine power, uneven running, excessive vibration, and tendency to stall when idling may be caused by either a compression loss or faulty injector operation.

The causes of trouble symptoms may be varied; therefore a hit-and-miss search should be avoided. A proper diagnosis of symptoms is an orderly process of diagnosing the symptoms. An "orderly process" means to check the most probable common cause first; then proceed with the next most probable cause.

Hard Starting

1. Improper oil viscosity.
2. Low battery output.
3. Defective starter or solenoid.
4. Low temperature.
5. Burned or warped valves.
6. Improper valve lash.
7. Worn or broken piston rings.
8. Defective cylinder head gasket.
9. Fuel line shut off valve closed.
10. Engine stop mechanism not released.
11. Low fuel supply.
12. Clogged vent in fuel tank cap.
13. Clogged fuel filters.
14. Broken fuel line allowing air leak into system.
15. Air trapped in system.
16. Water or ice in fuel system.
17. Defective fuel supply pump.
18. Overflow valve stuck or leaking.
19. Low fuel delivery.
20. Improper grade or type fuel.

Abnormal Engine Operation

1. Idle speed set too low.
2. Cylinder misfiring.
3. Burned or sticking valves.
4. Engine temperature too hot or too cold.
5. Fuel system deficiencies.
6. Detonation due to improper injector timing.
7. Defective injection nozzles.
8. Lack of power due to improper valve adjustment.
9. Insufficient fuel.
10. Insufficient air due to clogged air cleaner or intake system.
11. Excessive exhaust back pressure.
12. Low cylinder compression.

Excessive Black or Gray Smoke

1. Insufficient combustion air.
2. Exhaust pipe or muffler clogged.
3. Injection pump improperly timed to engine.
4. Incorrect engine valve timing.
5. Injector nozzles leaky, worn or improper opening pressure.
6. Wrong grade and type of fuel.
7. Engine overheating.
8. Poor cylinder compression.
9. Damaged or worn piston rings and/or pistons.
10. Cylinders overfueled.

High Lubricating Oil Consumption

1. Oil lines or connections leaking.
2. Leaking gaskets.
3. Crankcase oil level too high.
4. Pistons and/or rings worn or damaged.

Excessive White or Blue Smoke

1. Oil level in air cleaner too high.
2. Injection pump improperly timed to engine.
3. Engine crankcase oil level too high.
4. Engine running too cool.
5. Poor cylinder compression.
6. Damaged or worn pistons and or rings.
7. Wrong grade or type of fuel.
8. Improper or dirty oil in use.

Low Engine Oil Pressure

1. Defective oil gauge or sending unit.
2. Oil viscosity too low.
3. Oil diluted with fuel oil.
4. Suction loss.
5. Weak or broken relief valve spring in oil pump.
6. Worn oil pump.
7. Excessive clearance at crankshaft, camshaft or balance shaft bearings.
8. Overheating.

NOTE: In case of no oil pressure the oil pump drive shaft or drive gear teeth could be worn to the point where oil pump is not driven. Inspection can be made by removing the oil pump and tachometer drive housing and gear at rear of engine.

Engine Overheats

1. Scale deposits in cooling system.
2. Air flow thru radiator restricted or clogged.
3. Loose fan drive belt.
4. Low coolant level.
5. Hoses collapsed.
6. Defective thermostats.
7. Combustion gases in coolant water.
8. Incorrect injection pump to engine timing.

Engine Tune-Up

Description

GMC Toro-Flow Diesel truck engines are four stroke cycle type of 60-degree, V-6 and V-8 design. Fuel for combustion is injected directly into combustion area through hole-type nozzles—one nozzle for each cylinder. Fuel injection pump has a single plunger with distributor type hydraulic head. Pump is mounted between cylinder heads and is driven from drive gear bolted to engine camshaft gear.

Illustrations show D478 engine with typical accessories installed, and typical V-8 engine, model D637.

The descriptions of the various components are applicable to all of the engines in the Toro-Flow Diesel series: namely, D351, D and DH478, and D and DH637 unless otherwise indicated.

Engine Tune-Up

Before performing other tune-up procedure, check battery electrolyte specific gravity at each cell to be sure battery is fully charged.

Check Cylinder Compression

1. Start engine and run until normal operation temperature is reached.
2. Stop engine and remove high pressure line clamps. Remove

Typical D478 Toro flow diesel engine

Views of D637 Toro flow diesel engine (© G.M.C.)

Gauge and adapter for checking compression (© G.M.C.)

1 Fuel leak-off hose
2 Injection nozzle bolts and lock washers
3 Compression gauge and hose
4 Leak-off hose connector
5 Adapter
6 Fuel injection pump assembly
7 Adapter and fuel hose assembly
8 Overflow valve
9 Fuel receptacle
10 Fuel return line (hose)
11 Fuel supply pump assembly
12 Fuel secondary filter

the high pressure line between injection pump and nozzle holder at cylinder to be checked. Remove the nut at each end from the threads at pump and nozzle holder and lift the line away from both units without bending.

3. Disconnect leak-off hoses from tee or elbow on injection nozzle holder. Remove nozzle holder retaining bolts and pull the holder assembly out of well in cylinder head. Clean nozzle holder cavity and gasket seat in cylinder head, then turn engine over with starter to blow loose carbon out of combustion chamber and nozzle holder cavity. Use a nozzle holder copper gasket at bottom of well and install the compression gauge adapter in place of nozzle holder as shown, using the nozzle holder bolts to hold the adapter in place. Connect gauge to the adapter. Be sure all connections are tight.

4. If a rear cylinder is being checked, insert plug in the disconnected leak-off hose. When other cylinders are being checked, join the disconnected leak-off hoses with a two-way or three-way connector, as required.

5. Install adapter and hose in outlet port in hydraulic head on injection pump and place hose in receptacle to catch fuel oil while

running the engine. CAUTION: Under no condition should the high pressure outlet port on the injection pump be plugged to prevent the escape of fuel.

6. Start the engine and allow engine to idle at 625 rpm. Observe and record the compression pressure shown on compression gauge. NOTE: Do not attempt to obtain compression pressure by cranking engine with starter.

7. Perform this operation on each cylinder. The compression pressure in any one cylinder should be not less than 500 psi at 625 rpm. Also, there should not be

more than a 30 psi difference between cylinders.

Cylinder Head Bolts

Check cylinder head bolts for proper torque. Normally head bolts should not need tightening at tune-up intervals.

Manifold Bolts

Check manifold bolts for proper torque and be sure end bolts have been securely locked.

Valve Clearance

Engine must be at normal operat-

Adjusting valves (© G.M.C.)

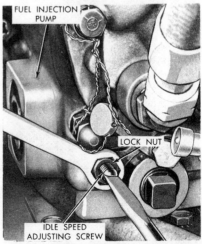

Adjusting engine idle speed (© G.M.C.)

ing temperature. Check and set exhaust valves to .018 and intake to .010 inch clearance.

Inspect Fuel System

1. Check all fuel lines for evidence or leaking.
2. Check and service fuel and air filters as directed in "owner's and driver's manual."
3. Check accelerator controls and linkage for binding. Check proper operation of stop control. (manual or solenoid type)
4. Check engine idle speed which should be 625 RPM. To adjust, remove lower acord nut at rear of injection pump. With engine running, loosen lock nut and turn adjusting screw. Retighten lock nut and install acorn nut.

NOTE: In instances where engine still does not perform properly, it may be necessary to remove the fuel injection nozzles and check the nozzle opening pressure and spray pattern.

Fuel System

Description

The fuel system used with Toro-Flow Diesel engines includes the various components schematically illustrated.

Fuel Injection Pump Assembly

The fuel injection pump assembly is of the PSJ series manufactured by American Bosch Arma Corporation.

Injection pump assembly is mounted on machined rear face of engine front cover assembly. Pump assembly is held in place by three studs and nuts.

The high pressure pump is the single plunger type, which distributes equal amounts of fuel to the fuel injection nozzles, at the cylinders, in the proper firing sequence.

Injection pump is gear driven from a pump drive gear bolted to front face of engine camshaft gear. Pump input shaft, on which the pump driven gear is mounted, rotates at engine crankshaft speed. The cam lobes on input shaft actuate the pump plunger to inject fuel to cylinders for each revolution of the engine crankshaft.

Included in the fuel injection pump assembly are the following units or devices:

1. Fuel supply pump.
2. Hydraulic head assembly.
3. Timing advance mechanism.
5. Governor and fuel control unit.
5. Excess fuel device for starting.

An overflow valve assembly is installed on the hydraulic head housing and incorporates a valve assembly which maintains proper fuel pressure within the fuel chamber to assure an adequate supply of fuel to the pump

plunger at all times.

Seal wires are installed by the manufacturer and in no case are the seals to be removed or the pump disassembled except by authorized personnel.

Complete replacement pumps are available through G.M.C. Truck dealers.

Fuel Injection Nozzle

Holder Assemblies

The fuel injection nozzle and holder assemblies are utilized to carry the high pressure fuel through the cylinder head to nozzle tip and deliver it to the combustion chamber.

The nozzle holder consists of a forged body which houses the spindle and spring, and has a high pressure fuel duct. The spindle bore and spring chamber are utilized as a passage for leak-off fuel which seeps past and lubricates the nozzle valve.

The nozzle valve and body are a closely matched pair which must always be used together as a unit. *Valves and valve bodies are not interchangeable*; however, matched nozzle and valve assemblies are available. Nozzle and valve assembly is located on nozzle holder by dowel pins and the assembly is firmly seated at lapped mating surfaces on body and nozzle holder by the nozzle cap nut. A high pressure duct in nozzle valve body aligns with duct in nozzle holder to carry high pressure fuel to the valve seat area. Pressure spring at upper part of holder seats at a flange on spindle, and spring is retained by the pressure adjusting nut.

Spring pressure is transferred through the spindle to the nozzle valve. Spring holds the valve on its seat in nozzle body.

A perfect seal is necessary at valve seat to prevent fuel dribble as well as to prevent any of the combustion gases in cylinder from entering the spray nozzle interior chamber.

The cap nut at upper end of nozzle holder assembly serves to lock the spring adjusting nut and is threaded to accept a leak-off tee of elbow to which is attached the leak-off hose.

A high pressure fuel line from outlet port in injection pump hydraulic head is connected to threaded portion on nozzle body forging.

The fuel injection nozzle holder assemblies are held in place in cylinder heads by two bolts; and a copper gasket is used at bottom of each nozzle well in head.

Fuel Injection Nozzles and High Pressure Lines

Fuel Injection Nozzle Operation

Fuel under pressure is fed from the rotary single plunger injection pump to the appropriate nozzle via the high pressure pipe line and finds its way through the ducts in the nozzle holder and valve body to the lower end of valve. When the pressure reaches 3000 psi, the valve will lift, and fuel is injected through holes in nozzle tip and into combustion chamber. Nozzle valve closes again when the line pressure drops. Any leakback through the leak-off line fitting is passed back to the junction fitting on injection pump overflow valve.

1 Nozzle valve and body
2 Nozzle valve spring
3 Fuel leak-off line
4 Hydraulic head assembly
5 Fuel metering sleeve
6 Pump plunger
7 Pump face gear
8 Lubricating oil line
9 Fuel return line
10 Tappet and roller
11 Cam
12 Governor gears
13 Governor weights
14 Stop lever
15 Supply pump gears
16 Fulcrum lever
17 Governor stop plate

Arrangement of fuel system units (8 cyl. engines) (© G.M.C.)

GMC Toro-Flow Diesel Engines

Locating a Misfiring Cylinder

This procedure will not serve to detect a nozzle with incorrect popping pressure within a moderate range. Such a malfunction can only be determined by removal of nozzle assembly from engine and checking on test stand.

1. Connect an accurate tachometer at the tachometer drive fitting on engine.
2. With engine idling, loosen a high pressure line nut at injection nozzle holder. When a high pressure line nut is loosened, the pressure build-up will not be great enough to cause the nozzle to deliver fuel to the cylinder being tested and no power will result. If there is little or no drop in engine rpm when the line nut is loosened, the nozzle may be at fault and it should be removed for cleaning and inspection.

NOTE: Nut at high pressure line must remain loose only long enough to observe the tachometer reading, since fuel will spill from the loosened nut with each discharge from the injection pump port.

Nozzle and Holder Assembly Maintenance

Normally, unless engine performance, or other trouble diagnosis symptoms indicate a malfunction of fuel injection nozzles, the nozzle and holder assemblies should not be removed from engine.

When it becomes necessary to remove nozzle and holder assemblies, follow the procedures given to remove, clean, and test the units.

Removing Nozzle and Holder Assemblies

1. Disconnect the high pressure line nut at the fuel injection nozzle holder and at fuel injection pump hydraulic head.
2. Remove the clamp assembly from line being removed then remove the high pressure line. IMPORTANT: High pressure line must be disconnected at both ends and clamp must be removed so line can be removed without bending. Install dust caps at injection pump outlet port and at nozzle holder when line is removed.
3. Force leak-off hose off fitting in top of nozzle holder. Remove the two nozzle holder bolts and lock washers, then pull nozzle holder assembly out of cylinder head, meanwhile using air hose to blow away any dirt particles which may be loosened as the nozzle holder is lifted out.
4. Remove copper gasket, and then plug the opening in cylinder head

1 Spring
2 Cap gasket
3 Pressure adjusting nut
4 Cap nut
5 Leak-off line tee
6 Spindle
7 Nozzle holder
8 Valve
9 Valve body
10 Nozzle cap nut
11 Gasket (copper)

Nozzle holder and valve assembly components (© G.M.C.)

to prevent objects from being accidentally dropped into nozzle well.

Inspection Before Disassembly

NOTE: It is recommended that each nozzle assembly be tested for leakage and valve opening pressure as well as for spray pattern before disassembly. If nozzle assembly is found to be in good condition, it should not be disassembled, but should only be cleaned externally. If the holes in nozzle tip are clogged as indicated by unsatisfactory spray pattern, the components should be disassembled before attempting to clean the holes.

Disassembly

1. With nozzle holder mounted on fixture or held in vise, loosen cap nut and remove nut and gasket from spring pressure adjusting nut.
2. With Allen wrench, remove spring pressure adjusting nut from nozzle holder. Remove spring and spindle. IMPORTANT: Do not proceed with step 3 unless pressure adjusting nut has been loosened to relieve spring pressure.
3. Invert nozzle holder and remove the nozzle cap nut from nozzle holder, then separate valve body from the nozzle holder.

Cleaning and Inspection

The nozzle tip should be cleaned with a brass wire brush before disassembling the valve body from nozzle holder. The nozzle tip orifices should be cleaned using orifice needle and holder. Care must be used when cleaning orifices to avoid breaking orifice cleaning needle in hole. After

disassembly, all parts should be carefully cleaned. If lapped surfaces on holder and mating surface on valve body are scratched, remove dowel pins from nozzle holder and polish the surface on lapping block using special fine lapping compound. Also polish the mating surface on valve body. Install new dowel pins after nozzle holder surface has been lapped.

Assembling Injection Nozzle Parts

1. Dip valve and body in clean fuel and insert valve in body. NOTE: The valve must be free in the body. By lifting the valve about one-third of its length out of the body, the valve should slide back to its seat without aid when the assembly is held at a 45 degree angle.
2. Mount nozzle holder in holding fixture, then set valve body in place on nozzle holder dowel pins and screw nozzle cap nut onto nozzle holder. Before tightening cap nut, use centering sleeve over nozzle tip to locate the nozzle valve body in center of opening in cap nut. After nut has been tightened sufficiently to seat parts, remove centering sleeve and tighten cap nut (10) to 50 to 55 foot-pounds.
3. Set nozzle holder upright in holding fixture or vise and insert spindle into holder. Place spring on spindle, then thread spring pressure adjusting nut into threads in nozzle holder. Place cap nut gasket over nut, then install cap nut on threads on adjusting nut.
4. Check nozzle on test fixture for spray pattern and valve opening pressure.

5. Setting Injection Nozzle Valve Opening Pressure. Using test pump, proceed as instructed below to set the valve opening pressure and test for leaks.

With nozzle holder assembly connected to tester, actuate the test stand handle rapidly (about 25 strokes per minute) to expel air from nozzle and holder and to "settle" the spring and nozzle loading column.

Depress operating handle slowly to raise pressure. Continue to depress handle and note the gauge pressure at which the nozzle valve opens. If opening pressure is not as specified, remove the leak-off tee and loosen cap nut so Allen wrench can be used to adjust spring pressure.

Use Allen wrench to turn pressure adjusting nut and change spring pressure. Turning nut clockwise increases pressure. Repeat valve opening pressure test each time adjusting nut is changed until correct opening pressure is obtained.

NOTE: When new pressure adjusting spring is installed, adjust the opening pressure 10% higher than specification to allow for spring set.

After correct valve opening pressure is obtained, tighten cap nut firmly to lock the adjustment. Recheck for valve-opening pressure after cap nut is tightened.

Operate test pump handle with several fast sharp strokes, meanwhile observing spray pattern. Spray should be in the nature of finely atomized sprays indicating that all holes are open. D351 engines have five orifices in each nozzle tip. Nozzle tips on other engines have only four orifices.

Stroke pump slowly (approx. 3 seconds). Some degree of "chatter" should occur, indicating that nozzle valve is free and component parts are correctly assembled.

Depress the pump handle slowly with a 10-second stroke and hold the pressure slightly (approx. 100 lbs.) below nozzle valve opening pressure to check for valve seat leakage. No fuel droplets should appear. Occasionally a slight wetting of the tip

(2) may be noticed. This is permissible since it is caused from hydraulically balancing the spring and nozzle valve.

Remove the nozzle holder assembly from test stand and if nozzle holder is not to be installed immediately, it should be wrapped in clean paper.

If nozzle does not operate properly, replace valve and body or install rebuilt nozzle holder assembly.

Nozzle Holder Assembly Installation

Use seat cleaner and wrench handle first to clean seat, and the bore in cylinder head through which the injection nozzle valve body extends, then use brush to finish cleaning the well cavity.

1. Use new copper gasket at lower end of injection nozzle assembly and insert the nozzle holder assembly into place in cylinder head.
2. Gradually tighten nozzle holder bolts alternately to avoid any tendency to bend the holder assembly.
3. Final tension on two nozzle holder bolts should be equal to seat the assembly squarely on copper gasket. Correct torque reading is 17 to 20 foot-pounds.
4. Connect leak-off lines at tee or elbow on nozzle holder. Place the high pressure line in place so that fittings on both ends line up squarely with respective threads at both the injection pump and the nozzle holder. Use torque wrench and adapter to tighten nut at hydraulic head to 16 to 19 ft.-lbs. Tighten nuts at injector nozzle holders to 22 to 26 foot-pounds.

Injection Timing

The fuel injection pump assembly is timed to the engine when pump assembly is installed, and should not require any subsequent alteration if the installation is done properly.

In the event there is reason to suspect that fuel injection is not properly timed, the following procedure is necessary to check the timing.

Same procedure is used both on the 6-cylinder and 8-cylinder engines except as indicated in text.

Checking Injection Timing (With All Fuel Units Installed)

1. Remove the cover and gasket from right side of fuel injection pump to expose the alignment mark in the opening below the control unit lever.
2. On 6-cylinder engines, remove the access cover from top of engine front cover assembly to expose pointer and mark on injection pump hub. On 8-cylinder engines, remove the inspection plate from top of advance mechanism housing to expose the pointer and timing mark.
3. Remove left hand rocker arm cover, then crank engine to place No. 1 piston on compression stroke—(both valves will then be closed and push rods can be turned with fingers). Slowly crank the engine until the "INJ" mark on crankshaft damper is aligned with pointer in engine front cover. At this point pump should be injecting fuel into No. 1 cylinder.
4. If 6-cylinder engine is correctly timed, the mark and pointer will be indexed and mark on face gear viewed through cover opening in pump housing will be in the position shown in the illustration. If 8-cylinder engine is correctly timed, the mark and pointer will be indexed and mark on pump face gear viewed through cover opening in pump housing will be in the position shown in the illustration.
5. If the mark on pump drive hub is not indexed with pointer, or if the mark on face gear is not visible in opening, the injection timing is not correct. However, before proceeding to reset the injection timing, recheck to make sure No. 1 piston is on compression stroke and "INJ" mark on damper is aligned with pointer.

V-6 FIRING ORDER 1-6-5-4-3-2

Firing order and mated cylinders
6 cyl. Toro flow engines
(© G.M.C.)

V-8 FIRING ORDER 1-8-4-3-6-5-7-2

Firing order and mated cylinders
8 cyl. Toro flow engines
(© G.M.C.)

1 Cup
2 Spray tip
3 Nozzle holder
  assy.
4 Pressure gauge
5 Fuel high
  pressure line
6 Allen wrench
7 Cap nut
8 Box end wrench
9 Fixture
10 Pump handle
11 Test stand

Test stand for checking
injection nozzle operation
(© G.M.C.)

Using special needle to clean spray holes
in nozzle valve body
(© G.M.C.)

Setting Injection Timing

The elongated holes in injection pump driven gear make possible the setting of injection timing when installing the fuel injection pump assembly as well as for making correction of timing when necessary.

With engine crankshaft positioned for firing on No. 1 cylinder use special wrench and box end wrench to loosen the driven gear mounting bolts.

Bring engine back to firing position on No. 1 cylinder before loosening the last bolt.

With bolts loose, use special wrench to turn injection pump shaft and hub as necessary to align mark on hub with pointer for 6-cylinder engines or to index and mark pointer

Using centering sleeve to locate valve body
while tightening cap nut
(© G.M.C.)

when viewed through opening on 8-cylinder engines. Hold the shaft with wrench and tighten driven gear mounting bolts.

Recheck to make sure of exact indexing of marks.

Fuel Injection System

Illustrations show cut-away views of fuel injection pump for 6-cylinder engines. Same construction is used on pumps for 8-cylinder engines.

Service Operations

The service operations contained herein can be accomplished without removing the fuel injection pump assembly from the engine. WARNING: Do not attempt to work on the fuel injection pump, nozzles, or high pres-

Cylinder head nozzle well cleaning equipment (© G.M.C.)

Tightening nuts on high pressure lines
(© G.M.C.)

1 Injection pump assy.
2 Lock wire
3 Face gear
4 Mark on face gear
5 Mark on ledge
6 Pump driven gear
7 Pump drive hub
8 Pointer (in pump body)
9 Mark on drive hub
10 Engine front cover

Timing marks at face gear and at injection pump
gear flange (6 cyl. engines)
(© G.M.C.)

sure lines in a dusty area. Extreme precautions must be taken to prevent any dust particles from entering the fuel passages in lines and nozzles. Any dirt or abrasive material permitted to enter the fuel supply port on fuel injection pump could quickly cause extensive damage to, or possible ruin of the pump hydraulic head mechanism.

Fuel Delivery Valve

Removal

Wash off top of the head assembly and blow dry with air hose.

Remove delivery valve cap, then remove spring from cavity. Remove the valve from its seat.

Using special wrench adapter, remove the delivery valve retainer from head assembly.

Use needle-nose pliers or tweezers to reach into cavity and remove the delivery valve seat.

Installation

CAUTION: Use utmost care to keep delivery valve and retaining parts absolutely clean during installation.

Place fuel delivery valve and seat assembly in position in hydraulic head cavity, then install the retainer. Use adapter and torque wrench to tighten valve retainer to 65 to 70 foot-pounds torque; then loosen the retainer and retorque to 65-70 foot-pounds. Tightening the retainer twice positively seats the parts to prevent any fuel leakage.

Place delivery valve spring over pilot on delivery valve and install cap using torque wrench to tighten cap once to 55 to 60 foot-pounds.

Control Unit Assembly

Removal

Remove the four control unit cover attaching screws, then remove cover and gasket.

Place a clean lint-free cloth in opening so parts cannot fall into pump interior as they are removed.

On early type pumps, remove the retainer ring which secures control rod to lever on control unit. Late production pumps have a different design at control rod and the retainer plate prevents disengagement of rod from lever.

Remove lock wire from plate screws. Remove screws, plate, and the spacers which retain the control unit, then disengage the control rod from lever.

Mark the parts is necessary so the control unit can be installed in original location without changing the pump calibration.

Carefully withdraw the control unit assembly from bore in housing, using two thin screwdrivers diagonally across from each other to start the unit out of bore.

Remove O-ring seal from control unit. Hold the control unit level so the pin will not fall out of place.

Installation

Using a clean screwdriver, carefully insert it through the control unit opening in the pump housing and carefully move the metering sleeve downward to its lowest-position on plunger.

Lubricate the control unit O-ring and assemble it to the control unit.

Holding the control unit, pin, and O-ring assembly, with the control

Installing fuel injection nozzle assembly
(© G.M.C.)

Tightening nozzle holder bolts
with torque wrench
(© G.M.C.)

693

1 "INJ" mark on hub
2 Advance mechanism housing
3 Pointer
4 Fuel injection pump assembly
5 Pointer in front cover
6 Crankshaft damper assembly

POINTER AND MARK AT PUMP ADVANCE COVER OPENING

POINTER AND MARKS AT CRANKSHAFT PULLEY

Timing marks at advance mechanism and crankshaft damper (8 cylinder engines) (© G.M.C.)

Timing marks (6 cylinder engine)
(© G.M.C.)

1 Pump shaft holding wrench (special tool)
2 Fuel injection pump assembly
3 Pointer
4 Driven gear mounting hub
5 Injection pump driven gear
6 Driven gear mounting bolts
7 Hub retaining nut

Using special wrench to hold pump shaft
while tightening driven gear bolts
(© G.M.C.)

unit arm horizontal and pointing toward the rear of the pump and with the pin horizontal and the identification dot up, insert the assembly into the pump housing.

If the pin is not properly positioned, the control unit arm can not be rotated 360 degrees.

Rotate the control unit bushing, which was marked so the screw scallops in the control unit bushing are aligned with the holes for the retainer plate attaching screws and the control unit bushing flange in the same position as before removal.

On early pump, engage the control rod with hole in control unit lever, then install new retainer ring which secures rod to lever.

Assemble control unit retaining plate, screws (with lock washers), and spacers then install parts to re-

View of hydraulic head showing internal components
(© G.M.C.)

EXCESS FUEL STARTING DEVICE — GOVERNOR COVER — DROOP SCREW — FUEL SUPPLY PUMP — CONTROL ROD — FUEL DELIVERY VALVE — HYDRAULIC HEAD ASSEMBLY — OVER FLOW VALVE — CONTROL UNIT COVER — FACE GEAR — GOVERNOR SPRINGS — GOVERNOR HOUSING — FULCRUM LEVER — GOVERNOR SLEEVE — GOVERNOR WEIGHTS — "C" CLAMP — PUMP HOUSING — TIMING ADVANCE MECHANISM

Cut away view of fuel injection pump (6 cyl. engines) (© G.M.C.)

tain the control unit. Tighten screws to 18 to 33 inch-pounds. Install lock wire through screw heads. On late production pumps, the retaining plate retains the control unit and also prevents control rod from becoming disengaged from lever.

Using new gasket, install control unit cover and secure with screws and lock washers.

Overflow Valve

NOTE: Parts of latest type injection pump overflow valve assembly are shown in illustration. The complete valve assembly may be installed or the valve and/or spring shown may be installed.

Overflow Valve Removal

1. Disconnect leak-off lines from fitting at valve and disconnect fuel return line.
2. Using wrench on hex-shaped portion of valve assembly remove the assembly from injection pump body.

Disassembly

Grip the overflow valve body in vise fitted with soft jaws, then screw the valve seat out of valve body. Remove valve and spring. Some assemblies may have spacer washers which are used in manufacture to provide correct setting.

Assembly

Place spring, (spacers, if removed), and valve in valve body; then after positioning the valve seat

over valve, thread the valve seat into body. Tighten the valve seat securely. NOTE: Overflow valve spring may be shimmed, if necessary, to provide 40 psi at governed speed.

Overflow Valve Installation

Screw the overflow valve assembly into threaded port in injection pump body, using wrench on the hex-shaped portion of valve.

Install fittings and connect return line and leak-off lines to overflow valve body.

Fuel Supply Pump

Fuel Supply Pump Removal

Disconnect the fuel lines and

HEAD RETAINING PLATE — DELIVERY VALVE SPRING — RETAINER — CAP — HYDRAULIC HEAD ASSEMBLY

Injection pump cap, spring and valve retainer (© G.M.C.)

remove fittings from supply pump.

Remove the three supply pump attaching bolts and lock washers, then remove the supply pump and gasket. CAUTION: As supply pump is removed the governor inner spring guide and spring spacers are free to fall out of place. Exercise necessary care to prevent loss of these parts. Plug the fuel inlet and outlet line openings to prevent dirt from entering.

Fuel Supply Pump Disassembly

Remove governor outer spring guide from pump assembly.

Remove the five screws and lock washers which attach cover to insert. Tap the insert lightly with plastic hammer to separate insert from cover. Remove gears from insert.

Remove relief valve retainer screw and remove spring and relief valve assembly.

Supply Pump Component Inspection

Inspect for wear in gear cavities in pump insert. Also look for evidence of worn surface or scoring on cover area at which contact is made with gears.

Note condition of the oil seal in pump insert.

Examine relief valve parts. Use new parts when assembling pump if any of the components are defective. Relief valve should pass fuel through center in only one direction.

Inspect idler gear shaft which is a press fit in bore in insert. If pin is worn, scored, or loose in bore, obtain a new insert and pin assembly.

Installing fuel delivery valve retainer with adapter and torque wrench (© G.M.C.)

Fuel control unit assembly
(© G.M.C.)

Fuel injection pump hydraulic head assembly replacement
(© G.M.C.)

Control unit retaining parts and alignment marks
(© G.M.C.)

Assembling Fuel Supply Pump

Dip each of the gears in clean fuel oil and place gears in cavity in insert assembly.

Use new gasket. Screws with lock washers must be tightened evenly and firmly.

Dip relief valve and spring in fuel oil, then install valve with the spring pilot engaged with spring. Install spring retainer cap and tighten firmly.

Fuel Supply Pump Installation

Check governor, inner and outer springs to make certain the inner spring guide and original spacers are in place. Outer spring guide must be in place at pump insert.

Place gasket on cover flange with bolt holes aligned.

Observe through opening in oil seal the position of flat in pump gear bore. A clean screwdriver may be used to turn the gear so as to align the gear with flat on shaft.

Move supply pump assembly into position at injection pump housing using care to engage drive gear with flat on shaft. Install and tighten supply pump attaching bolts.

Connect fuel lines to fittings at supply pump, remove vent plug from top of secondary fuel filter and bleed air from pump and lines.

Replacing Hydraulic Head Assembly

In cases where the hydraulic head is in satisfactory operating condition, but it becomes necessary to remove the head assembly to replace the O-ring seals or other parts of the pump, it is possible to remove and install the hydraulic head without removing the pump assembly from the engine; and recalibrating is not required.

Hydraulic Head Removal

Disconnect and remove fuel high pressure lines, then plug or cap the

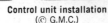

Control unit installation
(© G.M.C.)

Overflow valve (typical)
(© G.M.C.)

openings in the hydraulic head and nozzles.

Remove injection pump control unit assembly.

Turn engine crankshaft to place No. 1 piston in firing position with the marking on crankshaft damper aligned with pointer, and the mark on face gear (visible in inspection window in pump housing) indexed with mark on housing. Make sure the No. 1 piston is on compression stroke.

NOTE: Mark on gear face should be indexed with housing mark, even though the damper mark may not be exactly registered with pointer.

Remove the head assembly locating screw and gasket. Remove retaining plate. Tap the hydraulic head assembly lightly with plastic or lead hammer or slightly rotate the assembly with a wrench on the delivery valve cap to loosen it in housing bore. Raise the hydraulic head assembly up out of the pump housing. Remove upper seal ring from groove in head assembly. Remove the head lower seal ring from bottom of bore in pump housing. *Do not turn engine crankshaft while hydraulic head is removed from pump.*

Hydraulic Head Installation

Lubricate the hydraulic head O-ring seals, then place lower ring in position at bottom of bore in pump body.

Place upper O-ring seal in groove in hydraulic head.

Position the hydraulic head assembly so the locating slot in head block is aligned with head locating screw; and turn face gear so that timing mark on gear is aligned with mark on housing. Insert head assembly into housing bore. Teeth on face gear must mesh with drive gear teeth.

Install head locating screw with copper washer (gasket) and if necessary, rotate head assembly so the locating screw can be turned freely—indicating no interference. Tighten locating screw to 10 to 11 foot-pounds torque.

Place head retaining plate over the head assembly with word "UP" on top, and install bolts in diagonally opposite corners. Gradually tighten

plate bolts until sure the gear teeth are properly meshed, then install remaining two bolts and tighten all bolts to 13 to 15 foot-pounds.

Install the control unit assembly.

Install the fuel lines between hydraulic head oulet ports and fuel injection nozzles.

Prime the fuel system.

Install equipment which may have been removed to gain access to the injection pump assembly. After engine is started, inspect for fuel leakage at hydraulic head, and high pressure fuel lines.

Internal Governor Spring Pack Adjustment (Without Special Tool)

Break the fuel injection pump seal

Fuel supply pump and injection pump assembly
(© G.M.C.)

(if used), back out idle adjusting screw, and remove three bolts attaching the fuel supply pump to the governor housing.

Remove the governor cover and gasket.

Remove fuel supply pump. Remove inner and outer governor springs and adjusting spacers (noting the position of spacers and spring guides. The inner spring is the high speed spring and must have a gap. The outer spring is the low speed spring and must be precompressed. Determine the proper shim pack behind the governor springs with supply pump gasket in place as follows: NOTE: The flat on the fuel pump drive shaft must engage with the gear in the supply pump.

1 Governor inner (high speed) spring guide
2 Flat on pump drive shaft
3 Governor outer (low speed) spring
4 Pump insert
5 Pump cover
6 Insert to cover screws and lock washers
7 Relief valve retainer screw
8 Gasket
9 Oil Seal
10 Pump idler gear pin
11 Outer (low speed) spring guide

Fuel supply pump components
(© G.M.C.)

1 Insert assembly
2 Pin (pressed into Item 1)
3 Drive gear
4 Idler gear
5 Screws with lock washers
6 Gasket
7 Valve spring retainer cap
8 Valve spring
9 Relief valve assembly
10 Pump cover

Inner Spring: Position governor sleeve assembly in forward position as shown in illustration. Then, place adjusting spacers between inner spring and the spring guide so that when supply pump with gasket is held in installed position (flush with governor housing), inner spring can be turned but has no end play. This can be checked with a finger through governor cover opening. Remove supply pump and remove adjusting spacers to obtain proper gap of 0.089 to 0.108 inch on both the 6-cylinder engines and the 8-cylinder engines.

Outer Spring: Place adjusting spacers between governor sleeve and outer spring so that when supply pump with gasket is held in installed position, the outer spring can be turned but has no end play. Then, remove supply pump and add adjusting spacers with total thickness of 0.059 to 0.079 inch to give proper precompression on outer spring.

NOTE: Do not install outer spring when checking spacer pack for inner spring or install inner spring when checking spacer pack for outer spring.

Reinstall the inner and outer governor springs with their respective spacers as previously determined.

Reinstall the fuel supply pump and new gasket, taking care that the inner and outer spring guides do not fall off the supply pump insert. The flat on the fuel pump drive shaft must engage with the gear in the supply pump. Exercise care so that seal is not damaged.

Reinstall governor cover. Turn the idle speed adjustment screw until seven or eight threads are visible, then install screw lock nut.

Start engine and adjust idle speed to 625-675 spm with full accessory load. Set high speed at 3440 rpm no-load on 6-cylinder engine, or to 3250 rpm on 8-cylinder engines.

NOTE: Range of idle screw adjustment after setting by above method is approximately one turn. More adjustment than this may allow droop screw to rest against excess fuel piston stop plate and give erratic idle.

Connect the accelerator linkage and stop linkage, making sure that full travel of the accelerator lever can be obtained.

Internal Governor Spring Pack Adjustment (Using Special Tool)

A special tool is available for use to accurately select injection pump governor spring spacers. The tool serves in determining the required spacers, both for the inner (high speed) and the outer (low speed) spring. Refer to illustration for loca-

Fuel injection pump with hydraulic head removed
(© G.M.C.)

tion of spacers. Whenever occasion arises for checking either of the governor springs, the other spring should also be checked. Tool may be used without removing the injection pump assembly from engine.

Assembly and Adjustment After Governor Spring Spacer Selection

Place inner and outer governor springs and their respective spacers in position in governor housing, then install fuel supply pump. The flat on governor shaft must engage drive gear in supply pump. Tighten supply pump mounting bolts to 5 to 6 foot-pounds torque.

Connect fuel lines at fittings in supply pump cover. Install cover on top of governor housing. Connect controls if they have been disconnected; and adjust controls for full travel in both directions.

Check and, if necessary, adjust high speed with no-load. Tighten the adjusting screw lock nuts immediately after making the adjustment.

NOTE: The normal idle and maximum speeds depend almost entirely on the characteristics of the governor springs, hence the speeds can only be varied to a limited degree by the adjusting screws at rear of governor housing.

Checking for Air Leaks in Fuel Supply (Suction) Line

CAUTION: Exercise necessary care to prevent any dirt from entering the fuel system when fuel lines are disconnected in making following tests.

Disconnect outlet line from fuel supply pump and install sight glass, or plastic line so that fuel may be observed while engine is running.

Start engine, then look for air bubbles in the pump discharge line.

If a leak is apparent in the suction lines, filter or fittings, a sight glass or section of plastic line may be installed at inlet fitting on supply pump to determine if air is reaching pump through suction side of system. If no bubbles are observed at inlet connection, but continue to be present at outlet line, a defective supply pump is indicated.

NOTE: Be sure the fuel filter between fuel tank and pump is not clogged, and that filter gaskets are in good condition.

Checking for Inadequate Fuel Pump Delivery and/or Overflow Valve Malfunction

Make necessary inspection to determine that fuel filters are not clogged.

Remove, clean, and inspect the supply pump relief valve assembly and spring. Also, disconnect lines from overflow valve and remove the valve assembly from the fuel injection pump. Disassemble the overflow valve, inspect parts. Replace overflow valve or parts as required.

Check supply pump pressure as follows:

Install pressure gauge in line between supply pump outlet and secondary filter.

Remove overflow valve and install

Governor spring and spacer arrangement
(© G.M.C.)

1 Supply pump
2 Outer spring guide
3 Outer spring
4 Outer spring spacer
5 Inner spring guide
6 Inner spring spacer
7 Inner spring
8 Governor sleeve

a fuel shut-off valve, connecting the fuel return line to the valve discharge opening.

Open the valve slightly and then start the engine. While running the engine a 2400 rpm momentarily close the fuel shut-off valve. The pressure gauge should show between 55 and 65 psi.

CAUTION: Keeping the shut-off valve closed for any period of time can cause the injection pump plunger to overheat and seize.

If pressures are appreciably lower than specified the supply pump should be overhauled or the unit should be replaced with a new supply pump assembly.

Remove shut-off valve and pressure gauge, and reinstall overflow valve assembly.

Fuel Injection Pump Assembly

NOTE: The fuel injection pump assembly is available for service replacement as a complete assembly. In most instances the required repairs may be made without removing the injection pump assembly from the engine.

Fuel Injection Pump Replacement

Replacement should only be made if it is definitely indicated that the fuel injection pump assembly is at fault and is not repairable without removing the unit from the engine.

Fuel Injection Pump Removal

CAUTION: Do not attempt to work on the fuel injection pump, nozzles, or high pressure lines in a dusty area. Extreme precautions must be taken to prevent any dust particles from entering the fuel passages in lines and nozzles. Any dirt or abrasive material permitted to enter the fuel supply port on fuel injection pump could quickly cause extensive damage to, or possible ruin of the pump hydraulic head mechanism.

1 Inner (high speed) spring
2 Fulcrum lever assy.
3 Governor housing
4 Excess fuel starting device
5 Control rod
6 Governor sleeve
7 Outer (low speed) spring
8 Outer spring guide

Governor mechanism
(© G.M.C.)

Fuel high pressure line installation
(6 cyl. models)
(© G.M.C.)

Preliminary Operations (All Engines)

Depending on type of vehicle and accessory equipment, remove the necessary equipment to provide access to fuel injection pump assembly, high pressure fuel lines and engine controls. Carefully observe the arrangement of accelerator control linkage, and the engine stop mechanism. A stop solenoid or an engine stop air cylinder is mounted on the injection pump assembly. Disconnect wire from stop solenoid terminal (when used). Disconnect stop control cable and disconnect accelerator linkage

from lever at left side of injection pump assembly.

Remove tubing clamps which are shown in illustration. Use the adapters shown and loosen high pressure tubing nuts at fuel injection nozzles and at pump hydraulic head. Use air hose to blow away any loose dirt particles at hydraulic head and at nozzles. Remove the high pressure tubing using care not to bend tubing.

NOTE: To facilitate installation, each line may be tagged with identification number corresponding with cylinder numbers.

Insert plugs in pump ports and cap the fittings at injection nozzles as soon as lines are removed. The importance of cleanliness cannot be over-emphasized.

Illustrations show caps at injection nozzles and plugs in hydraulic head ports.

Disconnect fuel leak-off lines from overflow valve.

Replacing Fuel Injection Pump on 6-Cylinder Engine

Disconnect fuel lines from fittings on supply pump at rear end of injection pump assembly. Also disconnect the fuel line at left side of injection pump housing. Cap or plug all openings to prevent entrance of dust.

At right side of pump assembly, disconnect lubricating oil line and the fuel return line at the overflow valve assembly.

TIGHTENING NUT AT NOZZLE HOLDER

TIGHTENING NUT AT HYDRAULIC HEAD

Torque wrench adapter for tightening nuts on high pressure lines
(© G.M.C.)

Fuel high pressure line installation (8 cyl. engines)
(© G.M.C.)

1 Injection pump
   assembly
2 Fuel supply line fitting
3 Drive gear
4 Mounting studs
5 Seal ring
6 Overflow valve
7 Lubricating oil fitting
8 Pointer
9 Mark on adapter hub
10 Engine front cover
11 Stop lever

Installing fuel injection pump assembly (6 cyl. engines) (© G.M.C.)

Remove the gear access cover from top of engine front cover to provide access to injection pump driven gear and attaching bolts. The driven gear must be removed from hub on pump shaft before the injection pump assembly can be removed from engine.

CAUTION: To prevent accidental dropping of bolt washers into engine front cover and out of reach, pack clean shop rags into cavity below the gear attaching bolts. Do not crank engine until the rags have been removed.

When removing the last of the three pump driven gear bolts, hold the pump shaft from turning with special wrench.

Remove the stud nuts and washers which secure the fuel injection pump assembly to engine front cover, then remove the pump assembly. Remove the sealing ring from pump mounting flange.

Remove pump driven gear from opening in front cover.

Installation

Preliminary Operations

If a new fuel injection pump assembly is being installed, it will be necessary to transfer the fuel line and oil line fittings from the removed pump assembly to the new pump. Observe the position of each fitting as it is removed, and install it in same position on new pump assembly.

CAUTION: Carefully clean any accumulated dirt from fittings before installing in replacement pump assembly and install dust caps to exclude any foreign material when the fittings are installed.

Inspect gear teeth on injection pump drive gear and driven gear before installing pump. Be sure the mounting surface on pump flange and the mating surface at engine front cover are clean.

Remove the cover from right-hand side of injection pump so alignment

marks on gear face and ledge can be seen.

Fuel Injection Pump Installation

Set fuel injection pump driven gear in place through access opening in top of engine front cover. Driven gear teeth must engage teeth on pump drive gear and flat side of gear must be toward rear.

Check position of rocker arms at No. 1 cylinder to be sure No. 1 piston is on compression stroke. Observe "INJ" mark on crankshaft damper assembly which must be indexed with the pointer on front cover.

Through opening in right-hand side of fuel injection pump assembly, look for mark on edge of gear face. If mark is not visible, turn the pump shaft until mark comes into view, then set the mark on hub in alignment with pointer in pump housing.

Install seal ring on pilot at forward side of pump mounting flange, then lift the injection pump assembly

1 injection pump
   assembly
2 Plugs to seal
   openings
3 Seal ring
4 Adapter hub
5 Pump mounting
   studs
6 Drive gear
7 Engine front
   cover

Installing fuel injection pump assembly (8 cyl. engines) (© G.M.C.)

into position on mounting studs.

Install plain washer and nut on each of the three pump mounting studs and tighten the nuts evenly to seat pump flange firmly on cover.

Check the position of threaded hole in pump hub in relation to elongated slot in driven gear. If necessary, change the position of gear so threaded hole in hub is approximately centered in slot in gear. The gear teeth can be lifted out of mesh with drive gear to change gear position.

Start one of the driven gear mounting bolts with plain washer through driven gear slot and into mounting hub, then using special wrench hold pump hub timing mark in alignment with pointer and tighten gear mounting bolt firmly.

Crank the engine as necessary to bring other driven gear bolt holes into position for installing remaining two bolts; install bolts and plain washers, then tighten bolts to 35 to 40 foot-pounds.

Install pump side cover and gear access cover connect oil supply line, and fuel return to overflow valve.

Mount a new secondary filter on filter bracket and connect fuel lines.

Connect accelerator control linkage and engine stop mechanism.

CAUTION: The fuel injection nozzles should be inspected and repaired as necessary, or replaced with new nozzles whenever a new or rebuilt fuel injection pump is installed on engine. Attempting to start an engine having defective injection nozzles can damage or ruin a fuel injection pump assembly.

Install high pressure fuel lines.

Prime the fuel system, before attempting to start engine. During priming procedure, the supply line should remain disconnected from fitting on left side of pump assembly until all air has been purged from fil-

Injection pump rear support and lubricating oil drain (8 cyl. engines)
(© G.M.C.)

1 Bolt with lock washer and plain washer
2 Bolt with lock washer and plain washer
3 Injection pump support
4 Fuel injection pump assembly
5 Nipple
6 Oil drain hose
7 Hose clamp
8 Pump support bracket
9 Hose connector elbow
10 Grommet
11 Lifter compartment cover

ters, supply pump, and lines; then continue to flush fuel through open end of line to avoid the possibility of any loose particles entering the fuel chamber surrounding the hydraulic head assembly.

Start engine and inspect all fuel line and lubricating oil line connections for leakage.

Check and adjust engine idle speed if required.

Replacing Fuel Injection Pump on 8-Cylinder Engine

Removal

Disconnect fuel lines from fittings on supply pump at rear end of injection pump assembly. Also disconnect the fuel supply line at left side of injection pump housing. Cap or plug all openings to prevent entrance of dust.

Disconnect and remove lubricating oil lines.

At rear end of injection pump loosen clamps on oil drain hose. Pull hose connector elbow out of grommet

in valve lifter cover; then remove connector and hose.

Remove two bolts and washers which hold pump support and bracket together; then remove the two bolts and washers at lifter compartment cover. Remove the pump support bracket.

Remove the gear access cover from top of engine front cover to provide access to injection pump driven gear and attaching bolts. The driven gear must be removed from hub on pump shaft before the injection pump assembly can be removed from engine.

When removing the last of the three pump driven gear bolts hold the pump shaft from turning with special wrench.

Remove the two lower mounting bolts and washers, first, then place a suitable wood block under rear of injection pump to support the assembly while two upper bolts and washers are removed from mounting studs.

Remove the fuel injection pump from engine; then remove driven

Injection pump driven gear and pump mounting studs (© G.M.C.)

gear from front cover. Remove sealing ring from pilot at pump mounting flange.

Installation

Preliminary Operations

If a new fuel injection pump assembly is being installed, it will be necessary to transfer the fuel line and oil line fittings from the removed pump assembly to the new pump. Observe the position of each fitting as it is removed, and install it in same position on new pump assembly.

CAUTION: Carefully clean any accumulated dirt from fittings before installing in replacement pump assembly and install dust caps to exclude any foreign material when the fittings are installed.

Inspect gear teeth on injection pump drive gear and driven gear before installing pump. Be sure the mounting surface on pump flange and the mating surface at engine front cover are clean.

Remove the cover from right-hand side of injection pump so alignment marks on face gear and ledge can be seen.

Fuel Injection Pump Installation

Set fuel injection pump driven gear in place through access opening in top of engine front cover. Driven gear teeth must engage teeth on pump drive gear and flat side of gear must be toward rear.

Check position of rocker arms at No. 1 cylinder to be sure No. 1 piston is on compression stroke. Observe "INJ" mark on crankshaft damper assembly which must be indexed with the pointer on front cover.

Through opening in right-hand side of fuel injection pump assembly, look for mark on edge of face gear. If mark is not visible turn the pump shaft until mark comes into view. Through inspection plate opening in top of advance mechanism housing check the position of mark in relation to pointer. If necessary turn pump shaft to index mark with pointer.

Install injection pump support on bottom of pump housing using two bolts with lock washers.

Install seal ring on pilot at forward side of pump mounting flange, then lift the injection pump assembly into position on mounting studs.

Install plain washer and nut on each of the four pump mounting studs and tighten the nuts evenly to seat pump flange firmly on cover.

NOTE: A suitable block may be inserted between rear of pump and lifter compartment cover to support pump while installing nuts and washers at mounting flange.

Place injection pump support

bracket in place on valve lifter cover with holes for bolts aligned with threaded holes in cylinder block and weld nuts on injection pump support. Install two bolts with lock washers and plain washers but tighten these bolts only enough to bring support and bracket into contact with each other. Install two bolts with lock washers and plain washers to secure the pump support bracket, then tighten· the bolts which clamp the bracket to the pump support. Install nipple in threaded hole in pump housing, insert grommet in hole in lifter cover; then assemble oil drain hose and elbow. Hose must be clamped at nipple and end of elbow must be inserted into grommet.

Check the position of threaded hole in pump hub in relation to elongated slot in driven gear. If necessary, change the position of gear so threaded hole in hub is approximately centered in slow gear. The gear teeth can be lifted out of mesh with drive gear to change gear position.

Start one of the driven gear mounting bolts with plain washer through slot in driven gear and into drive hub on pump shaft. Use special wrench to hold pump shaft so timing mark is indexed with pointer while tightening gear mounting bolt firmly.

Crank the engine as necessary to bring other driven gear bolt holes into position for installing remaining two bolts, then install bolts and plain washers and tighten bolts to 35 to 40 foot-pounds.

Install cover on pump housing. Install inspection plate and gasket on top of advance mechanism housing. Install gear access cover on engine front cover assembly.

Connect lubrication oil supply lines at fittings on housings. Connect the fuel return line to overflow valve assembly.

Thoroughly clean and inspect the fuel lines to be used in connecting the secondary filter. Mount a new secondary fuel filter on filter bracket with the fuel lines connected.

Connect accelerator control linkage and engine stop mechanism.

CAUTION: The fuel injection nozzles should be inspected and/or repaired as necessary, or replaced with new nozzles, whenever a new or rebuilt fuel injection pump is installed on engine. Attempting to start an engine having defective injection nozzles can damage or ruin a fuel injection pump assembly.

Install high pressure fuel lines.

Prime the fuel system before attempting to start engine. During priming procedure the supply line should remain disconnected from fitting in left side of pump assembly until all air has been purged from filters, supply pump, and lines; then

continue to flush fuel through open end of line to avoid the possibility of any loose particles entering the chamber surrounding the hydraulic head assembly.

Start engine and inspect all fuel line and lubricating oil line connections for leakage.

Check engine idle speed and, if necessary, adjust to proper setting.

Water Pump

General

The engines covered are equipped with either of two water pumps shown in illustrations.

Type 1 pump is used on all 6-cylinder engines except DH478, unless engine is in vehicle equipped with air conditioning, in which case type 2 pump is used.

Type 2 is the standard water pump used on all 8-cylinder engines and DH478, 6-cylinder engines. Overhaul procedure for each type of pump is given separately under appropriate headings below.

Type 1 Water Pump Overhaul

Disassembly

1. Support the hub and press shaft out.
2. Support pump body on press and press on front end of shaft to force shaft bearing, and impeller assembly out of body toward rear.
3. Support impeller as near as possible to hub at forward side, then press on rear end of shaft to remove impeller from shaft. With impeller removed from shaft, re-

Water pump (6 cyl. engines exc. DH 478)
(© G.M.C.)

move seal assembly.

4. Shaft and bearing assembly and seal must be replaced whenever pump is disassembled. Surface contacted by seal on impeller hub must be smooth and flat. Late pumps do not have slinger.

Assembly

1. Be sure bore through pump body is clean and free from burrs.
2. Install shaft and bearing assembly in pump body, pressing on bearing outer race. Proper location of bearing and shaft assembly is shown in illustration. Measure from rear face of body to bearing as shown.
3. Coat outer surface of seal which fits into pump body with sealing compound, then press seal assembly into body.
4. Press fan hub on front end of pump shaft to dimension shown in illustration. Hub front face must be located 2-7/8 inches from rear surface of pump body.
5. Install impeller on rear end of pump shaft, using pressure at rear face of impeller hub while supporting front end of shaft. Locate impeller so a space of 3/8 inches exists between impeller and pump body.

Type 2 Water Pump Overhaul

Disassembly

1. Support water pump pulley hub at rear surface and press shaft out of hub.
2. Insert spacers between pump body and impeller, then while supporting pump body with shaft in vertical position, press the pump shaft out of impeller

1 Pulley hub   3 Seal assembly
2 Slinger   4 Seal seat
     5 Impeller
     6 Pump body
     7 Shaft and bearing assembly

**Water pump
(6 cyl. DH 478 and all 8 cyl. engines)**
(© G.M.C.)

and force bearing out of body.

3. Remove seal assembly from pump body. If seal seat in impeller is not in good condition, use a thin blade to pry the seal seat out of impeller. Thoroughly clean the counterbore in impeller.

Assembly

1. On early production pumps, the slinger should be 1.470 inches from end of shaft as shown. Late pumps do not have slinger.
2. Apply sealer in seal cavity in body, then press new seal assembly squarely into place with seal flange seated against body.
3. Support pump body solidly on press bed and press on shaft bearing outer housing to install shaft and bearing assembly in body. Bearing housing must bottom in pump body.
4. Place neoprene seal on ceramic seat, then install seat in the recess in impeller with neoprene seal bottomed in counterbore.
5. Support front end of pump shaft and press impeller onto rear end of shaft until rear face of impeller hub is 1.330 inches from body mounting flange as shown in illustration.
6. While supporting rear end of pump shaft, press pulley hub on front end of shaft to dimension shown.

Manifolds

Manifold Removal

NOTE: With engine in vehicle, the exhaust pipes must be disconnected from exhaust manifold flanges before removing exhaust manifolds. Air intake hoses and any brackets bolted to intake manifolds must also be removed. On V-8 engines, the balance tube and connecting hoses must be removed.

Bend lock away from each of the exhaust manifold end bolts, then

1 Exhaust Manifold
2 Clamp
3 Air Intake Elbow (Rubber)
4 Intake Manifold
5 Balance Tube
6 Manifold Clamp
7 Clamp Bolt
8 Balance Tube Hose and Clamps
9 Manifold End Bolt
10 Exhaust Pipe Bolts

Manifolds and attaching parts on 8 cyl. engines (right side) (© G.M.C.)

remove the short bolt attaching intake manifold to cylinder head.

Remove the bolts and clamps holding manifolds to cylinder head, then remove the intake manifold.

Remove the short bolt attaching exhaust manifold to cylinder head, and remove the exhaust manifold and gaskets.

Manifold Installation

Manifolds are attached in similar manner at both cylinder heads. In some instances accessory support brackets must be removed to gain access to manifold bolts, if engine is installed in vehicle. Clean the manifold gasket surfaces and cylinder head mating surfaces.

Place bolt lock on exhaust manifold short end bolt, then insert bolt through hole in end of exhaust manifold. Place clamp on clamp bolt and insert clamp bolt through hole in exhaust manifold flange. Place manifold gasket at exhaust manifold so it is held in proper position by bolts.

Hold exhaust manifold and gasket against cylinder head and start the two bolts into tapped holes.

Place lock on long end bolt and insert bolt through hole in intake manifold. Position intake manifold at cylinder head and start end bolt into tapped hole in head. Install a clamp bolt with clamp through hole in intake manifold flange and thread bolt into cylinder head to properly locate intake manifold. Tighten clamp bolts with the respective clamps bridging bosses at intake and exhaust manifolds sufficiently to hold intake and exhaust manifolds in place.

Install remaining clamps and clamp bolts and position the clamps to contact manifold bosses squarely.

Manifold balance tube installation (8 cyl. engines)
(© G.M.C.)

Tighten exhaust manifold end bolt to 15 to 20 foot-pounds torque. Tighten intake manifold end bolt to 20 to 25 foot-pounds, and tighten intake and exhaust manifold clamp bolts to 20 to 25 foot-pounds. Bend locks to secure the exhaust manifold end bolts.

Install balance tube between intake manifolds.

Engine Repairs

Cylinder Head Overhaul

General

The two cylinder heads on each engine are identical except for position of water outlet sleeve and core hole plug, and procedure is same to repair either head.

Cylinder heads for D/DH478 and D/DH637 engines are constructed as shown in sectional view of engines. D351 engine cylinder heads are similar to heads on D/DH478 and D/DH637 except that they do not have exhaust valve seat inserts.

Unless otherwise noted, the cylinder head repair procedures apply to all Toro-Flow Diesel engines. Illustration shows cylinder head components and associated parts for 8-cylinder engines.

1 End bolt
2 Bolt lock
3 Cylinder head
4 Intake manifold
5 Crankcase ventilation cap
6 Exhaust manifold
7 Clamp bolts
8 Gasket
9 Manifold clamps
10 Dip stick tube
11 Tube clamp and bracket

Manifolds and attaching parts on 6 cyl. engines (right side) (© G.M.C.)

Cylinder head components and associated parts (8 cyl. engine) (© G.M.C.)

1 Bolt lock
2 End bolt
3 Clamp
4 Clamp bolt
5 Exhaust manifold
6 Intake manifold
7 Manifold gasket
8 Cylinder head bolts
9 Lifting bracket
10 Valve keys
11 Intake valve seal
12 Spring cap
13 Valve outer springs
14 Valve inner springs
15 Valve rotators
16 Cylinder head
17 Water tube
18 Push rods
19 Intake valve
20 Valve lifters
22 Exhaust valve seat insert
23 Cylinder head gasket

Cleaning

Flush out water passages, and clean oil drain-back holes and hole at bottom of end rocker arm shaft bracket which supplies oil to valve overhead mechanism.

Disassembling Cylinder Head

1. Using valve spring compressor, relieve pressure of valve springs against retaining parts.
2. Remove valve keys, release the spring compressor, then at intake valve, remove springs and spring cap. After springs and retaining parts are removed from intake valve stem. Remove intake valve from cylinder head.
3. After releasing spring compressor at exhaust valves, remove springs and spring cap, then remove exhaust valve from cylinder head.
4. Remove valve rotators from cylinder head.

Cleaning and Inspection of Cylinder Head Components

1. Clean deposits from valve stems, and ports in cylinder head.
2. Use injection nozzle well cleaning tools to remove any carbon deposits from nozzle wells.
3. Test valve springs for tension with valve spring tester.
4. Check valves for burned or pitted faces and for wear or corrosion at valve stems. NOTE: Valves with oversize stems are available for use when guide bores in cylinder head are excessively worn. Guides are integral with head and must be reamed out to provide proper fit with oversize valve stem.
5. On cylinder heads with replaceable exhaust valve seat rings, inspect rings which must be tight in head and seats must be in good condition.
6. Inspect all plugs for evidence of leakage.
7. Visually inspect valve spring retaining parts. Also examine valve rotators for evidence of wear and damage.

Repair of Cylinder Head Components

Reaming Valve Guides

If clearance between valve stems and guides is excessive, select service valve with oversize stem for use in rebuilding cylinder head. Intake and exhaust valves are available with 0.020, 0.030, and 0.040 inch oversize stems.

Reamers are of proper dimensions to provide correct clearance for valve stem with corresponding oversize.

Replacing Exhaust Valve Seat Rings (All Except D351 Engines)

In cases where exhaust valve seat ring is damaged, the ring may be replaced as follows:

Assemble special exhaust valve seat insert remover in cylinder head as shown. Press tool firmly against ring, then while holding tool with handle, tighten screw to expand tool which will engage inner edge of ring.

Attach slide hammer to threaded end of tool screw, then slide weight sharply to end of rod to remove seat ring.

Clean cylinder head.

Pack new inserts in dry ice for minimum of 15 minutes.

Preheat cylinder head by immersion in water at a temperature of 180°F., to 200°F. Place cylinder head on bench, blow out each insert counterbore with air, then lay chilled insert in counterbore with valve side toward installer.

Use of valve spring compressor (© G.M.C.)

Using valve seat installer, insert pilot end of tool into guide, then drive insert down tight into counterbore. This operation must be done quickly while the valve seat inserts are cold. Due to extreme hardness of material, exhaust valve seats must be finished with special grinding equipment.

Reconditioning Valve Seats

Reconditioning of valve seats on high compression engines is very important because seating of valves must be as near perfect as possible in order to obtain the maximum power and performance built into the engine.

IMPORTANT: Before attempting to grind any seat, valve port and valve seat must be free from any foreign deposits such as carbon, grease, etc. Valve guide must be thoroughly cleaned of carbon or dirt with a wire brush.

Use a valve seat grinder pilot which fits snugly in valve guide.

Seat-grinding stone must be accurately dressed to 45-degree angle for grinding intake and exhaust valve seats. After grinding, use dial indicator to check concentricity of valve seat with pilot hole. Seat should be concentric with pilot within 0.002 inch (Total Indicator Reading).

NOTE: When installing new valve seat inserts and/or new valves in cylinder head, measure distance from cylinder head surface to top of valve head with valve contacting seat. Intake valves must not project more than 0.050 inch above head; and exhaust valves must not project more than 0.045 inch. Grind necessary amount of stock from valve face to obtain proper dimension.

Test valve for perfect contact with seat in cylinder head.

Refacing Valves

Valves that are slightly pitted or burned can be refaced to the proper angle.

Set chuck at a 45 degree angle for both the intake and the exhaust valves.

Take light cut from face of valve by passing grinding wheel across valve until valve face is true and smooth.

NOTE: Care must be taken while grinding not to remove too much stock from valve face. If it should be necessary to reduce thickness of intake valve head to 0.055 inch or less at outer edge of valve head to obtain smooth face, discard valve. Exhaust valves should not be used if head at outer edge is less than 1/16 inch after refacing.

Test valves for contact with seats in cylinder head.

1	Exhaust valve
2	Cylinder head
3	Valve rotator
4	Spring cap
5	Valve keys
6	Outer springs
7	Inner springs
8	Intake valve oil seal
9	Intake valve
10	Exhaust valve seat insert

Sectional view through cylinder head and valves
(© G.M.C.)

Assembling Cylinder Head Components

Lubricate valve rotators with engine oil before assembling to cylinder head. Keep all components clean and apply SAE 90 hypoid gear lubricant for at least 1½ inches at tip of all valve stems prior to installation.

Set valve rotator in place at cylinder head and insert valve through guide.

Set inner and outer springs in place on rotator with close-wound coils toward cylinder head and place spring cap (4) on springs.

Use spring compressor to hold valve in place and at same time compress springs. On intake valves install oil seal in lower groove in intake valve stem. Place two valve keys in valve stem groove, then release the spring compressor.

Valve Operating Mechanism

General

Mechanism for operating the intake and exhaust valves consists of mechanical lifters at camshaft, tubular push rods, and rocker arms mounted on hardened steel shaft.

Each rocker arm is equipped with a self-locking screw for adjusting valve lash.

On 6-cylinder engines, the rocker arm shafts are each supported on five cast aluminum brackets. Construction on 8-cylinder engines is similar to that on 6-cylinder models but there are two more rocker arms and six brackets support the rocker arm shafts.

Inspection of Rocker Arms and Shafts

1. Wash rocker arms, shaft, and bracket assemblies in solvent. Oil holes in rocker arms must not be clogged.
2. Check torque required to turn adjusting screw in rocker arm. If screw turns with less than 5 foot-pounds, or if screw threads are not in good condition, replace screw.
3. Examine shaft for evidence of wear. Replace worn parts when assembling.

IMPORTANT: When installing new adjusting screws in rocker arms, lubricate screw threads and threads in rocker arm with engine oil prior to assembly.

Removing exhaust valve seat ring with special tool
(© G.M.C.)

Using special driver to install exhaust valve Seat rings
head
(© G.M.C.)

Cylinder head tightening sequence (6 cylinder engine)
(© G.M.C.)

Damper and Crankshaft Pulley

General

Latest engines have a counterbore in damper hub to accomodate a seal ring which seals against oil leakage. When installing crankshaft damper look for counterbore at rear edge of hub bore and install new seal ring on crankshaft as instructed below. The special installer may not be required on some (late) engines on which the oil seal ring is used but must be used on all other engines. Whenever a new damper assembly is being installed, the late type with counterbore and seal ring should be used.

1. Place the seal ring over end of crankshaft and position the ring squarely on crankshaft at inner end of damper key. *Do not place seal ring against slinger.* The seal must roll into hub counterbore when damper is installed.
2. Apply engine oil on damper hub at seal surface, then start damper onto crankshaft with keyway aligned with key. Assemble installer, screw, and thrust bearing and tighten screw firmly into threaded hole in crankshaft. Turn the nut on screw to force damper into place on crankshaft. Installer is not required on late engines.
3. Assemble cone, retainer and damper retainer bolt. Tighten bolt to specified torque with torque wrench.

Engine Front Cover Removal

NOTE: The thermostat housing and engine water pump assembly may remain on front cover during cover removal.

1. At rear side of engine front cover, remove bolts which attach cap to cylinder block and front cover, then remove cap and gasket.
2. At front side of front cover assembly, remove the bolts and washers which attach cover to cylinder block.
3. Jar the cover loose with a lead hammer, and remove the cover. Cover assembly must be lifted upward sufficiently to clear the injection pump drive gear before it can be moved forward.

Gear Train Removal

1. Remove four bolts attaching injection pump drive gear to camshaft gear, then remove drive gear.
2. Bend lock plates away from plate retaining bolts. Remove bolts and gear retainer plates from idler gear shafts. Remove idler gears.
3. Gears are keyed to respective shafts and may remain on shafts until shafts are removed from cylinder block. Crankshaft gear can be removed from crankshaft with special puller, with crankshaft either installed or removed. An arbor press should be used to replace camshaft gear or balance shaft gear. Before the gear can be removed from V-8 engine balance shaft, the balance weight must be removed.

Gear Train Installation

1. Turn crankshaft so "O" mark on gear is at 12 o'clock position. Turn camshaft gear so "X" mark is at 6 o'clock position.
2. Lubricate bushing in camshaft idler gear, then install idler gear on idler gear shaft so "X" marks are indexed and "O" marks are indexed.
3. Using two bolts and lock plate, install gear retaining plate at idler gear shaft. Tighten bolts to 15 to 20 foot-pounds, then bend corners of lock plate to secure bolts.
4. Lubricate bushing in balance shaft idler gear then position gear so alignment marks are indexed with marks on gears.
5. Retain idler gear with retainer plate and bolts in same manner

as described in step 3 above.
6. Using narrow feeler gauge, check gear back lash between gear sets. Make backlash check at several points at each gear; there must be no tight spots in any position.
7. Install injection pump drive gear on camshaft gear with self-locking bolts. Tighten bolts with torque wrench to 35 to 40 foot-pounds with bolt threads oiled.
8. Check torque on camshaft gear retainer bolt. With bolt threads oiled the proper torque is 50 to 60 foot-pounds.

Engine Front Cover Installation

1. Locate front cover gasket at front of cylinder block with bolt holes in gasket aligned with holes in cylinder block.
2. Carefully guide front cover over injection pump drive gear and over end of crankshaft. Oil seal in cover and gear teeth may be damaged if care is not used in positioning cover assembly.
3. Install four short bolts with lock washers, then install long bolts with lock washers on all except the one bolt which passes through water passage which requires a copper washer. Copper washer serves as a gasket to prevent water leakage. Tighten front cover to cylinder block bolts to 22 to 27 foot-pounds torque.
4. At top of cylinder block, behind front cover, install cylinder block cap using new cap gasket.

Checking Engine Valve Timing

Valves must open and close in rect relationship to upper dead center of cranksh check of valve timi following proced ferring to r damper f center

707

Crankshaft damper retaining parts
(© G.M.C.)

2. Turn engine clockwise (viewed from front of engine) to "UDC" mark at crankshaft damper on compression stroke. Both the intake and the exhaust valve on No. 1 cylinder will then be closed.
3. Adjust valve lash on No. 1 exhaust valve (front valve) to exactly 0.054 inch on 6-cylinder engines; or to 0.057 inch on 8-cylinder engines.
4. Turn engine clockwise until No. 1 exhaust valve opens and begins to close, then with fingers try turning push rod of No. 1 exhaust valve as engine is cranked slowly. When push rod rotates with finger pressure, the "UDC" mark on damper should be at pointer. This will be about 1 revolution from starting point. If push rod starts to rotate at any point within one-quarter inch either side of "UDC" mark, the valve timing is correct. Be sure

to adjust exhaust valve clearance to 0.018 inch after performing the foregoing check.
5. If when checking valve timing, the push rod starts to rotate at a point more than three-quarters inch either side of the "UDC" mark, the camshaft can be considered "out of time." NOTE: When valve timing has been corrected, it will be necessary to re-time the fuel injection pump.

Balance Shaft, Gear and Thrust Plate

Balance Shaft Removal

NOTE: Balance shaft cannot be removed from cylinder block until bolts which secure weights to the balance shaft have been removed. Self-locking bolts secure the weights on V-8 engines. Locks under weight bolt heads are used on V-6 engines. Special wedges are required to expand weights and relieve clamping action so balance shaft can be removed.

1. Remove balance shaft weight bolts from all weights.
2. Insert wedges in slots in balance shaft weights and tap each wedge lightly to just relieve clamping pressure of weights on shaft.
3. At front of cylinder block, remove the two bolts and washers which secure balance shaft thrust plate to block, then remove balance shaft, by pulling shaft forward through bearings and removing weights from crankcase as each one drops off shaft.

4. On V-8 engine remove spacer plate from balance shaft and gear assembly.

The balance shaft, gear, and thrust plate may be inspected without removing gear from shaft. Clean all parts thoroughly before beginning inspection. Be sure oil passages in shaft are unobstructed and clean.

Inspection

1. Check balance shaft bearing surfaces for evidence of scoring and for wear. Use micrometer to measure shaft diameter at bearing areas. There are four bearing areas on V-6 balance shafts, and five bearing areas on V-8 balance shafts. Diameter of new balance shaft is 1.4705 to 1.4695 inches at bearing areas.
2. On 6-cylinder engines, measure clearance between thrust plate and balance shaft gear hub using feeler gauge. Clearance (endplay) should be 0.003 to 0.005 inch.
3. On 8-Cylinder engines use feeler gauge in manner similar to that shown in figure 45 to measure clearance between thrust plate, and gear. Correct clearance between these parts if 0.002 to 0.006 inch.
4. Mount balance shaft in Vee blocks and use dial indicator to measure shaft runout. With shaft supported at ends, runout should not exceed 0.002 inch for 6-cylinder engines or 0.003 inch for 8-cylinder engines (total indicator reading).

Removing gear from camshaft
(© G.M.C.)

sing special tools)

Checking timing gear backlash
(© G.M.C.)

Balance Shaft Gear and Thrust Plate Replacement (D351 and D, DH478 Engines)

Removal

Using suitable press plates, support the balance shaft gear while applying pressure on front end of shaft with arbor press. Press shaft out of gear, then remove gear key from slot in shaft and remove thrust plate.

Installation

1. Place thrust plate on balance shaft with the trade mark and part number facing forward.
2. Drive key into place in slot.
3. While supporting rear end of balance shaft, start gear squarely onto shaft with keyway in gear aligned with key in shaft. Extended hub on gear must be toward thrust plate. Timing mark on gear is at front side of gear.
4. Complete the gear installation by using a hollow driver between press and gear hub. Slowly press gear into position while using feeler gauge to measure the space between gear hub and thrust plate.

Balance Shaft Weight, Gear, and Thrust Plate Replacement (D, DH637 Engines)

General

In the event it should be necessary to replace balance shaft on 8-cylinder

engines the balance weight pin hole must be drilled and taper reamed at assembly.

Balance Shaft Weight and Gear Removal

1. Use a suitable punch and hammer to drive tapered pin out of weight and shaft.
2. Support rear side of thrust washer on arbor press plate, then press on front end of balance shaft and force the shaft out of gear and weight. CAUTION: When pressing balance shaft out of gear and weight, press plate used to support the thrust washer, must be positioned so as to allow gear and weight keys to clear the plate without interference. Support

the thrust washer close to shaft to avoid bending the thrust washer.

Balance Shaft, Weight, and Gear Assembly Procedure

General Information

1. The procedure for installing gear and weight on a new balance shaft differs from procedure required when the original balance shaft is used. Each procedure is covered separately under 2. and 3. following:
2. Assembling Parts Using Original Balance Shaft
   a. With keys installed in respective keyways, place thrust washer over keys and into place against shoulder on

Front cover bolt arrangement and torquing instructions
(© G.M.C.)

Bolt Location	Length (Inches)	Ft. Lb. Torque
A	4-1/4	25-30
B	4-1/2	10-15
C	2	35-45
D	2-7/8	10-15
E	2-7/8	25-30
F	3-3/4	25-30
G	1	25-30

Gear train and timing marks (V6 engine)
(© G.M.C.)

1 Camshaft gear
2 Injection pump drive gear
3 Drive gear bolts
4 Self locking bolt
5 Camshaft gear retainer
6 Lock plates
7 Balance shaft idler gear
8 Balance shaft thrust plate
9 Balance shaft gear
10 Gear retainer plate
11 Plate retaining bolts
12 Crankshaft balancer key
13 Cylinder block
14 Camshaft idler gear

Gear train and timing marks (V8 engine)
(© G.M.C.)

1 Drive gear bolts
2 Camshaft gear
3 Injection pump drive gear
4 Camshaft idler gear
5 Lock plates
6 Plate retaining bolts
7 Gear retainer plate
8 Crankshaft gear
9 Crankshaft
10 Balance shaft gear
11 Balance shaft
12 Hole plug (ball)
13 Balance shaft front weight
14 Thrust plate
15 Balance shaft idler gear

GMC Toro-Flow Diesel Engines

balance shaft.

b. Lubricate the front area on balance shaft and the bore through gear and weight with engine oil. Then start balance shaft gear onto front end of shaft with keyway aligned with keys and gear extended hub toward thrust washer. Support rear end of balance shaft and press the gear into place. Hold the thrust plate so it does not catch between gear hub and thrust washer as gear is pressed into place.

c. Press balance shaft weight onto balance shaft until solidly seated against gear.

d. Use No. 5 tapered reamer to clean up tapered hole in weight and shaft, then use air hose to blow into drilled oil passage and blow out any cuttings which may be in oil holes. Also flush out oil passages with clean solvent.

e. Drive in new tapered pin to secure balance shaft front weight to balance shaft referring to illustration for pin installation views. Stake the pin hole in weight to secure tapered pin.

3. Assembling Parts Using New Balance Shaft and Weight

a. Accomplish the procedure as instructed under steps 2. a., b., and c. to assemble thrust plate gear and weight on balance shaft.

b. Using drill press and 0.25 inch, long shank drill piloted in pin hole in balance weight, drill squarely through balance shaft. NOTE: If a previously-used balance weight is used, pilot the drill from the thick side of weight. If a

new weight is used a straight pilot hole is provided for use in drilling pin hole in shaft.

c. After pin hole has been drilled in balance weight shaft, use No. 5 tapered reamer to ream the pin hole in weight and shaft. Ream the pin hole sufficiently to allow new pin to enter freely until only 3/32-inch of pin is above weight surface. When reaming is completed and before pin is driven into place, use air hose and blow all cuttings out of oil hole at center of balance shaft. Also flush out the oil passages with clean solvent.

d. Using punch and hammer, drive tapered pin into place until large end of pin is just below surface of weight, then use staking tool and stake edge of pin hole to secure the pin.

e. Plug oil hole in each end of balance weight shaft with 11/32-inch diameter steel ball. Drive each ball in 0.030 inch below surface of shaft.

Balance Shaft Bearings

Inspect balance shaft bearings for scoring. Also use inside micrometer to determine inside diameter at each bearing. If damage to bearings is apparent, or if extensive wear is indicated, the balance shaft bearings should be replaced.

Balance Shaft Bearing Replacement

Pre-sized balance shaft bearings are available for service replacement for both the 6-cylinder and 8-cylinder engines. The bearings provide proper fit without reaming. Four bearings

are used on 6-cylinder engines and five are used on 8-cylinder engines.

Cylinder block must be stripped and flywheel housing removed to permit use of special tools in replacing balance shaft bearings. Crankshaft should also be removed for easy access to balance shaft bearing area.

Since the outside dimension of each bearing is different than other bearings, the balance shaft bearings will fit only their respective bores. Smallest diameter bore is at rear and bore sizes increase progressively toward front. Bearings have a chamfer at outer edge to facilitate installation.

Be sure all oil supply passages in cylinder block are clean before installing new balance shaft bearings. Use suitable tool to provide smooth chamfer at forward edge of each balance shaft bearing bore. Dip bearing assemblies in light engine oil prior to installation.

Notice that two of the bearings have oil holes and oil grooves. When installing these bearings, *an oil hole must be aligned with hole in block.*

IMPORTANT: Be sure to remove from cylinder block any shavings or metal particles which have resulted from the bearing installation procedure. Also recheck each bearing position to see that split in bearing is at top of bore and that oil hole in intermediate bearings registers with oil hole in cylinder block. Plug should be driven in slightly below surface of block.

Piston, Rod, and Bearing Cleaning and Inspection

Cleaning

Immerse all parts in dry-cleaning solvent to loosen and remove accumulated oil, sludge, or other deposits.

Valve timing diagram (all Toro flow diesel engines)
(© G.M.C.)

A—BALANCE SHAFT AND FRONT WEIGHT IN POSITION

B—FRONT WEIGHT AND THRUST PLATE SECURED
Balance shaft and weight installation
(© G.M.C.)

1 Cylinder block
2 Balance weight
3 Bolt with lock
4 Notch in balance shaft
5 Thrust plate
6 Balance shaft gear
7 Thrust plate bolt with lock washer

1	Drain plug and gasket	42	Camshaft bearing hole plug
2	Oil pan	43	Camshaft rear (no. 5) bearing
3	Pan gasket	44	Camshaft no. 4 bearing
4	Oil inlet screen and pipe assembly	45	Camshaft no. 3 bearing
5	Pipe flange bolt	46	Camshaft no. 2 bearing
6	Gasket	47	Camshaft no. 1 bearing
7	Engine oil pump	48	Camshaft gear key
8	Pump to block gasket	49	Spacer
9	Plug	50	Camshaft thrust plate
10	Bearing cap rear bolt	51	Camshaft gear
11	Rear bearing cap side bolt	52	Fuel injection pump gear
12	Cap side bolts (except rear)	53	Washer
13	Bearing cap bolt and washer	54	Pump gear bolt
14	No. 1 bearing cap	55	Spacing washer
15	No. 2 bearing cap	56	Fuel injection pump drive gear
16	No. 3 bearing cap	57	Gear retainer washer
17	No. 4 bearing cap	58	Self-locking bolt
18	Rear bearing cap side seal	59	Idler gear shaft
19	Rear bearing cap	60	Balance shaft idler gear
20	Crankshaft no. 1, 2, 3, and 5 lower bearing	61	Gear retainer plate
21	Crankshaft no. 1, 2, 3, and 5 upper bearing	62	Lock plates
		63	Plate retaining bolts
22	No. 4 lower bearing	64	Balance shaft front (no. 1) weight
23	Crankshaft	65	Balance shaft gear
24	No. 4 upper bearing	66	Thrust plate
25	Balance shaft	67	Weight key
26	Crankshaft rear bearing seal	68	Gear key
27	Flywheel bolts	69	Thrust washer
28	Bolt lock plates	70	Spacer
29	Flywheel assembly	71	Camshaft idler gear shaft
30	Oil pump drive shaft	72	Crankshaft gear key
31	Balance shaft weight bolt	73	Crankshaft damper key
32	Balance shaft front (No. 1) bearing	74	Camshaft idler gear
33	Balance shaft no. 2 weight	75	Gear retainer plate
34	Balance shaft no. 2 bearing	76	Balance shaft weight pin
35	Balance shaft no. 3 bearing	77	Crankshaft gear
36	Balance shaft no. 3 weight	78	Oil slinger
37	Balance shaft no. 4 bearing	79	Oil seal assembly
38	Balance shaft no. 4 weight	80	Oil seal ring
39	Balance shaft rear (no. 5) bearing	81	Damper
		82	Damper cone
40	Hole plug	83	Damper retainer
41	Camshaft	84	Retainer bolt
		85	Pulley bolt
		86	Crankshaft pulley

Crankshaft, camshaft, balance shaft and associated parts (8 cyl. engine) (© G.M.C.)

Remove piston rings and tag rings to identify them with respective piston. If there is a possibility that same rings will be installed at assembly, mark the top of top ring and oil ring so they can be reinstalled with same side upward. Clean ring grooves with groove cleaner. Use suitable tool to clean oil drain holes in oil ring groove.

Checking Piston Ring Fit

After thoroughly cleaning piston rings and ring grooves in pistons, try fit of piston rings in respective cylinder bore.

1. Place piston rings in cylinder one at a time and push ring at least half-way down cylinder bore, using head of piston to position ring squarely in bore. Measure ring gap with feeler gauge. If gap is too small, remove ring and dress off ends of ring with fine cut file or other tool designed for this purpose.
2. If piston ring gap is within specified dimensions, as determined in step 1. above, the rings should be checked for fit in grooves in piston.
   a. Using piston ring spreader

tool install rings in respective grooves.
   b. On all except turbo-charged engines, use feeler gauge to measure clearance between 2nd compression ring and piston ring land.
   c. On all engines, use feeler gauge to measure clearance between oil control ring and ring land.
   d. At top compression ring and 2nd compresssion ring on turbo-charged engines check fit of each compression ring in groove. Because of normal taper to the keystone and one-half keystone rings, feeler gauges cannot be used to check ring fit.

Clamp piston firmly in horizontal position so piston rings will hang downward with tapered surfaces seated in tapered groove.

Using dial indicator, check position of top ring surface "A" and 2nd compression ring surface "C" in relation to surface on piston ring land "B".

Surface "A" on top compression ring should normally be 0.002 to 0.012 inch below ring land surface,

while surface "C" on 2nd compression ring used with turbo-charged engines should normally be 0.000 to 0.014 inch below ring land.

IMPORTANT: When checking position of piston rings, do not use for reference any area on piston other than the surface and do not indicate from surface of steel insert since this is below the surface of piston.

Piston and Pin Inspection

Remove piston pin retainers and push out piston pin.

Measure each piston at 7/8 inch above bottom of skirt at right angle to pin bore and compare dimension with diameter at bottom of cylinder bore in which piston was installed.

Inspect piston ring lands and grooves for wear and other damage. Measure piston pin bores in piston bosses, and compare with diameter of pins. Piston pins should have clearance of 0.005 to 0.007 inch in respective pistons (oversize pins are available).

NOTE: New service pistons are fitted with piston pins.

Connecting Rod and Bearing Inspection

Connecting Rod Inspection

1. With bearing halves removed from rod and cap, install cap

711

1 No. 3 bearing
2 Balance weight bolt
3 No. 1 (front) bearing
4 Thrust washer
5 Spacer plate
6 Thrust plate
7 Balance shaft gear

8 No. 1 (front) weight
9 Weight key
10 Steel ball (plug)
11 Weight pin
12 Idler gear
13 Gear retainer plate
14 Plate retaining bolts
15 Lock plate
16 Gear bushing
17 Idler gear shaft
18 Dowel pin
19 Cylinder block assembly
20 Gear key
21 No. 2 weight
22 No. 2 bearing
23 No. 3 weight
24 No. 4 (rear) weight
25 No. 5 bearing
26 Balance shaft hole plug
27 No. 4 bearing

Balance shaft, weight and idler gear installed (V8 engines) (© G.M.C.)

and tighten rod bolt nuts to 60 foot-pounds torque. Check bore at lower end for elongation. If bore is out-of-round, the rod should be replaced or reconditioned. Examine surfaces in rod and cap which are contacted by bearing halves. If there is evidence of fretting of metal at these surfaces, the surfaces must be polished to provide a smooth surface for bearing halves to seat against. If bore is round and within specifications, make careful visual inspection of piston pin bushing for evidence of wear. Test fit of piston pin in bushing by measuring pin O.D. and bushing I.D. At 70°F., there should be a clearance of 0.008 to 0.0014 inch.

Connecting Rod Alignment

2. Connecting rod assembly should be placed in suitable aligning fixture to determine if rod is twisted or bent. Piston pin hole must be parallel with axis of crankpin hole in all planes within .002 inch in 7 inches.

Bearings

3. Carefully inspect connecting rod bearing halves for evidence of scores, chipping, or flaking out of bearing metal. If a visual inspection reveals any of these defects, replace with new parts. Measure each bearing half with accurate reading tube micrometer. Take measurement at right angle to split line.

Connecting Rod Repair

If inspection indicates that connecting rod piston pin bushing requires replacement, install new bushing which is furnished for service as follows:

1. Remove old bushing, using driver and arbor press.
2. Inspect bore in upper end of connecting rod. Measure bore I.D. which must be 1.802 to 1.803 inches to assure satisfactory fit of new bushing. Clean oil hole at top of rod.
3. Support connecting rod and press new bushing into place, using care to align oil hole in bushing with hole in top of connecting rod.
4. Diamond bore and hone bushing to provide 0.008 to 0.0014 inch clearance of pin in bushing at normal room temperature of 70°F. Suitable fixture should be used to assure finished hole alignment.
5. Dress bushing edges to remove any portion of bushing extending beyond edge of rod. Be sure oil passage in top of rod is free from cuttings.
6. With connecting rod alignment fixture, check connecting rod for bent or twisted condition.

Piston and Ring Fitting

General

Pistons must be fitted to cylinder bores by measuring to assure correct clearance between piston skirt and cylinder wall. Pistons and piston rings are available in oversize dimensions. The pistons must be assembled on respective connecting rods and installed in original positions in block. Pistons should be stamped with corresponding cylinder number. Number 1 cylinder is at front of left bank and cylinder Number 2 is at front of right bank, thus left bank cylinders are numbered from front to rear as shown for 6-cylinder engine.

Checking clearance between thrust plate and balance shaft gear (V6 engine)
(© G.M.C.)

1 No. 1 (front) balance weight
2 Thrust plate
3 Weight key
4 Balance shaft
5 Tapered pin
6 Balance shaft gear

Balance weight shaft weight pin installation (8 cyl. engines)
(© G.M.C.)

REAMING PIN HOLE THRU WEIGHT AND SHAFT

INSTALLING TAPERED PIN

Installing balance shaft weight pin (8 cyl. engines) (© G.M.C.)

Balance shaft bearing installation (© G.M.C.)

Fitting Pistons in New or Reconditioned Cylinder Block

1. When necessary to select replacement pistons for new block or for original bore in block which does not have a ring-travel ridge, refer to selection size number stamped on top of block adjacent cylinder bore. number is used to indicate bore size to permit selection of standard size piston for proper fit. Selection numbers range from 1 through 7 for production. For service use, three standard size pistons are available: Size 1 for use in cylinders marked either 1 or 2; size 3 for cylinders marked 3 or 4; and size 5 for cylinders marked 5 or 6; and size 7 for cylinders marked 7.

2. Oversize pistons are available and do not have selection numbers. Cylinders must be rebored and honed to proper dimensions to provide correct fit when installing oversize pistons. CAU-

TION: Whenever possible, remove crankshaft when reboring or honing cylinder bores. If crankshaft is not removed, it must be covered to keep abrasive away from crankshaft bearings. Wash cylinder bores after honing and wipe dry before checking piston fit.

3. As new piston is fitted to each cylinder, stamp cylinder number on top of piston to assure installation of pistons on corresponding connecting rod and in proper cylinder. Refer to figure for cylinder numbering arrangement.

Preparing Cylinder Bores When Re-Ringing Pistons

Ridge must be removed completely. Use polishing hone to break glaze. At end of honing operation allow hone to work free in bore. Do not remove while hone is still cutting. Clean cylinder walls with soap and water and stiff scrub brush, then wipe with clean cloth or absorbent paper. Apply

engine oil to cylinder walls to prevent rusting.

Assembly of Connecting Rod and Piston

1. If original pistons and connecting rods are to be installed, refer to marks (numbers) on connecting rods and assemble rods to pistons from which they were removed. When new pistons are installed, assemble pistons on rods bearing the numbers of cylinders for which pistons were fitted.

2. Apply engine oil on piston pin, rod bushing and pin bosses; then hold rod between pin bosses in piston and push piston pin through piston and connecting rod. Always use a new retainer ring in groove at each end of piston.

3. Check alignment of piston and connecting rod on alignment fixture.

Cleaning oil holes in oil ring groove in piston
(© G.M.C.)

Measuring piston ring gap
(© G.M.C.)

Measuring piston ring clearance in groove
(© G.M.C.)

Checking for wear at piston and rings
(© G.M.C.)

1 Top piston ring insert
   (integral with piston)
2 Straightedge
3 Oil control ring
4 2nd compression
   ring (½ keystone
   type, see text)
5 Top compression ring
   (keystone type)

Removing Crankshaft and Bearings

1. Remove plugs which seal rear bolt holes in rear bearing cap.
2. Remove the bearing cap side bolts, the heads of which are located at outer sides of cylinder block.
3. Remove balance of bearing cap bolts and washers. Then at thrust bearing cap, use bearing cap remover tool and slide hammer to remove the bearing cap. This must be pulled straight out of block to avoid bending or loosening dowel pins as well as to prevent damage to thrust faces on main bearing halves.
4. At other bearing caps, if necessary, use a round bar in bolt hole to work cap out of block; or the tool and slide hammer may be employed at all except rear bearing cap.
5. Lift crankshaft straight out of cylinder block assembly to prevent any binding which could damage thrust faces on thrust bearing.
6. Remove bearing upper halves from cylinder block and lower halves from bearing caps. Tag each pair of bearing halves, so they may be reinstalled in origi-

Cross section view of piston and connecting rod
(© G.M.C.)

1 Piston
2 Top compression
   ring (keystone
   type)
3 2nd compression
   ring (tapered
   face)
4 Oil control ring
5 Expander spring
6 2nd compression
   ring (taper face,
   reverse twist)
7 Oil control ring
8 Expander
9 Piston pin
10 Connecting rod
11 Oil hole in rod and
    bushing
12 Bushing
13 Piston pin retainer
14 Oil groove

nal positions.

Crankshaft Rear Bearing Oil Seal

Crankshaft rear bearing oil seal consists of two pieces of special packing. One piece is installed in groove in rear bearing cap and the other piece is installed in similar groove in cylinder block. Crankshaft is knurled and polished at area used to prevent oil leakage at sides of crankshaft rear bearing cap and plugs are used to seal rear bolt holes.

Seal Installation

1. Apply cement in seal groove in cylinder block and in crankshaft rear bearing cap.

2. Position seal in groove in block and pack seal firmly into place in groove.

3. In similar manner, install seal in bearing cap.

4. Using a sharp knife; cut off both ends of each seal which project out of grooves.

Installing Crankshaft and Bearings

Thoroughly clean to remove all cuttings and abrasive material.

1. Place crankshaft bearing upper halves in respective bearing bores in crankcase, then apply engine oil on each bearing. Apply sealer on cylinder block area contacted by crankshaft rear bearing cap.
2. Lower crankshaft into place in crankcase, and with bearing lower halves in place, position all crankshaft bearing caps. Each cap has the word "FRONT" cast at front edge of cap and caps are numbered from front to rear with numerals 1, 2, 3, etc.
3. Lubricate all bearing cap bolts and bolt washers. Insert the ⅝-11 bolts with washers into holes in bearing caps and start bolts into threads in cylinder block, but do not tighten bolts until side (½-13) bolts have been started into threads in bearing caps.
4. Insert the side bolts from outer sides of crankcase and start each bolt into threads in bearing caps. Insert two ½-13 rear bearing cap (vertical) bolts and start threads into block.
5. Tighten the ⅝-11 bearing cap-to-cylinder block bolts to 170 to 180 foot-pounds.
6. Tighten all ½-13 bolts to 90 to 100 foot-pounds.
7. Apply Diesel fuel oil on the two bearing cap side seals, then insert a seal in groove at each side of rear bearing cap chamfered end first. Chamfer must be toword outer side of crankcase to mate with radius at broached bearing cap seat in block. The narrow edge of side seals must mate with narrow side of grooves in cap. NOTE: When side seals are fully inserted, exposed end will protrude approximately 0.045 inch beyond surface of bearing cap. *Do not cut off side seals.*
8. Install two bolt hole plugs in bearing cap to seal the holes and prevent oil leakage.
9. Crankshaft must turn freely with all cap bolts tightened.

Camshaft, Gear and Thrust Plate

Camshaft Removal

Remove thrust plate attaching bolts and lock washers at front end of camshaft. Turn gear as necessary to align holes in gear with bolts.

Carefully pull camshaft assembly forward to remove from cylinder block. Do not damage bearings.

1. Check camshaft for general con-

Cylinder numbering arrangement and size selection numbers (6 cylinder engine)
(© G.M.C.)

dition. Bearing journals should not be scored or burred.
2. Support camshaft at end journals, then with dial indicator, check camshaft for straightness.
3. Inspect thrust plate for wear at thrust surfaces. Replace plate and spacer if worn. NOTE: If the camshaft gear has not been removed from camshaft, the extent of wear on thrust plate may be determined with feeler gauge by measuring space between thrust plate and shoulder on camshaft. Correct clearance is 0.0045 to 0.0085 inch.
4. Inspect camshaft gear for wear and damage at teeth. If gear teeth are not in good condition: gear must be replaced.

Camshaft Gear Replacement

1. Remove bolt, retainer, and spacer washer from camshaft.
2. Position camshaft and gear assembly in arbor press, and press the camshaft out of gear. A bolt tightened ino tapped hole in camshaft may be used to apply pressure to camshaft.
3. Remove key from slot in camshaft, then remove spacer and thrust plate.

Measuring bearing thickness
(© G.M.C.)

4. Position spacer on camshaft with chamfered side toward camshaft shoulder. Place thrust plate over spacer and install key in keyway.
5. Position camshaft in arbor press with support plate clamped below front journal. Place gear at camshaft with the keyway in gear aligned with key in camshaft. Use hollow tubing as shown to apply pressure on gear hub, and press gear onto camshaft until hub bottoms solidly at spacer.
6. Install the spacer washer at camshaft gear hub, then install thick retaining washer and self-blocking bolt. Final tightening of bolt may be deferred until camshaft and gear train are installed.

Camshaft Bearings

Inspect each camshaft bearing for scoring, wear, or looseness.

Measure I.D. of camshaft bearings and compare with O.D. of corresponding camshaft journal. If excessive wear is indicated, replace camshaft bearings.

Pre-sized camshaft bearings are available for service replacement for all engines.

Although these bearings provide proper fit without reaming no attempt should be made to replace them without first obtaining the required special tool set.

All camshaft bearings can be pulled forward through the block. It is recommended that all bearings be removed before installing any new camshaft bearings. Replacement procedures vary to some degree between the 6 and 8 cylinder engines.

NOTE: That when installing bearings, split must be on top and chamfered end must be toward the rear.

1 Starter
2 Piston
3 Manifolds
4 Valve rotator
5 Fuel injection nozzle assy.
6 Fuel injection pump assy.
7 Camshaft
8 Push rod
9 Connecting rod assy.
10 Balance shaft and weight assy.
11 Oil filter assy.
12 Engine oil pump assy.
13 Oil inlet screen and tube assy.
14 Main bearing cap bolts

Sectional view of Toro flow diesel engine (© G.M.C.)

This will properly position oil holes.

IMPORTANT: Make sure all shavings and metal particles which may have resulted from bearing installation, are removed from block. Also recheck each bearing position to insure the split is properly located at top.

Engine Oil Pump and Drive

The engine oil pump assembly is located in the engine crankcase. The pump assembly is bolted to the cylinder block and driven from a gear on the rear portion of the camshaft. Oil intake is through a screen at bottom of oil pan. Illustrations show installed view of oil pump and inlet screen assembly.

Overhauling Oil Pump

Disassembly

1. Remove spring and valve from pump body.
2. Remove pump cover from body.
3. Remove inner rotor and shaft assembly, then remove outer rotor from cavity in body.

Cleaning and Inspection

1. Be sure screen and suction pipe assembly is clean.
2. Inspect ends of drive shaft which engage drive sockets in oil pump shafts. Replace drive shaft

1 Damper (in screen support)
2 Oil inlet screen and pipe assy.
3 Rod identification numbers (2, 4 and 6)
4 Rod identification numbers (1, 3 and 5)
5 Gaskets
6 Engine oil pump assy.
7 Bearing cap side seal (2 used)
8 Oil pan stud (1 used)
9 Hole plug (2 used)

Crankcase ready for Oil pan installation
(© G.M.C.)

if excessively worn or damaged.
3. Check fit of inner rotor shaft in body. If excessive wear is indicated at either the shaft or body, replace worn parts.
4. Place the outer rotor in body and insert inner rotor and shaft assembly in operating position. Check clearance between outer rotor and body and clearance between edge of inner rotor lobe and outer rotor with feeler gauge. If clearances are greater than specified in "Specifications," replace parts as necessary. Inner rotor and shaft are furnished for service as an assembly. With rotors in pump body, place straightedge across rotors and body, then with feeler

gauge, measure clearance between rotors and straightedge. Clearance should be 0.0011 to 0.0039 inch.
5. Use straightedge to check rotor side of pump cover for flatness. Also look for grooves and other evidence of wear on pump cover. Replace cover if not in good condition.
6. Inspect relief valve and valve spring. On 6-cylinder engines without turbo-charger spring should have 14.7 to 16.3 pounds pressure when compressed to 1.69 inches. Spring free length should be 2.72 inches.

On turbo-charged 6-cylinder engines and 8-cylinder engines, free length of relief valve spring is 2.72

inches; and spring pressure is 17.8 to 19.4 pounds when compressed to 1.69 inches.

Assembling Oil Pump

1. Coat all oil pump parts with engine oil, then place outer rotor in pump body. Insert inner rotor shaft through bore in oil pump body and move inner rotor into mesh with outer rotor.
2. Install cover on pump body and retain with four cover screws. Try turning pump shaft which should turn freely without drag through six or more revolutions. If shaft cannot be turned or if binding occurs when shaft is turned, disassemble pump and make necessary corrections.
3. Insert relief valve and spring into body, then install spring cap.

Oil Pump Drive Shaft and Housing

The shaft and housing which drives the engine oil pump are installed at rear of cylinder block. The shaft has an attached gear which meshes with spiral gear teeth on camshaft. When tachometer is used, the cap is omitted and tachometer drive shaft housing is connected to threaded housing.

Inspection

Check oil passages in housing and check clearance between shaft and bushing in housing. If bushing is worn, a new bushing may be installed.

If drive gear or shaft is worn or otherwise damaged, a new shaft and gear assembly must be installed at assembly.

Housing Bushing Replacement

1. Drive worn bushing out of housing and discard bushing.
2. Inspect edge of bore in housing and remove any sharp edges.

Removing crankshaft No. 3 bearing cap with special tool
(© G.M.C.)

Removing or installing crankshaft rear main bearing side bolts
(© G.M.C.)

3. Press new bushing into housing to dimension shown.
4. If necessary to provide free fit of drive gear and shaft assembly in bushing, ream the bushing. Apply engine oil on shaft and bushing and insert shaft into place in housing.

Flywheel Housing and Flywheel Inspection

Cast iron flywheel housing is bolted to rear face of cylinder block and is located by two dowel pins. Some D351 engines have an apron type housing with pressed metal under-pan. These housings have a small pilot opening in which the transmission drive gear retainer fits. Bosses are provided on these housings for attaching engine rear mounting brackets.

Other housings have a large SAE type opening to which the transmission bell housing is attached; inspection to determine squareness of housing rear face and concentricity of pilot opening should be made with housings bolted to cylinder block.

Apron Type Housing Inspection

Check housing for damaged threads, and for cracked or broken flanges. Bolt the housing to cylinderblock and check pilot hole for concentricity and rear face for squareness with dial indicator supported at crankshaft flange or flywheel. Illustrations show typical use of dial indicator for checking pilot hole concentricity and rear face squareness. When checking for squareness at housing rear face, care must be used to prevent endwise float of crankshaft as this would result in false reading.

SAE Type Housing Inspection

Make inspection of flywheel housing for fracture and other damage. Examine all threads in tapped holes. Inspection to determine squareness

1 Side Seal
2 Crankshaft Oil Seal
3 Rear Bearing Cap
4 Bearing Cap Rear Bolts
5 Bolt Hole Plugs
6 Cylinder Block

Cross section at seals and bearing cap bolts
(© G.M.C.)

Installing crankshaft rear bearing oil seal with special tool
(© G.M.C.)

Installing camshaft gear
(© G.M.C.)

Install Front Bearing 0.010-0.030 Inch
Beyond Front Face of Block. Locate Other
Bearings Flush With Front of Bore.

Camshaft bearing installation (V6 engine)
(© G.M.C.)

Flywheel Repair

Replacing Starter Gear

1. To remove damaged starter ring gear, heat ring gear with torch, then drive gear off flywheel.
2. Inspect ring gear surface of flywheel. Surface must be free of nicks and burrs. Uniformly heat flywheel ring gear to faint straw color below blue range (400°F.)

CAUTION: *Do not heat metal to red heat as metal structure will be changed.* Install ring gear on flywheel as soon as possible after ring is heated. Make certain that chamfered edge of ring gear teeth are installed toward engine side of flywheel.

Machining Clutch Surface on Flywheel

When flywheel surface contacted by clutch facing is found to be scored, burned or worn, the flywheel can be restored to serviceable condition by machining to provide a smooth, flat surface. Do not remove more than 1/32-inch of stock in machining. After machining friction surface on recessed type flywheel, remove a corresponding amount of stock from surface to which clutch cover is bolted.

Checking for concentricity of flywheel housing pilot bore
(© G.M.C.)

Checking for squareness of bolting flange on flywheel housing
(© G.M.C.)

Checking location of pilot hole in apron type housing
(© G.M.C.)

Checking flywheel housing for squareness (apron type)
(© G.M.C.)

Engine component installation at crankcase (8 cyl. engines) (© G.M.C.)

A - Rod identification numbers (2, 4, 6, 8)
B - Rod identification numbers (1, 3, 5, 7)
1 Hole plug
2 Oil pan stud
3 Rear bearing cap side seal
4 Bearing cap side bolts
5 Crankshaft thrust bearing
6 Oil slinger
7 Weight clamp bolts
8 Balance shaft

Flat End of Seals Should Protrude Beyond End of Bearing Cap Approximately .045"

Dip Side Seals in Diesel Fuel Oil Prior to Installation

Assemble Side Seals Into Slots in Bearing Cap With Chamfer on End of Seal to Outside and Top (Bearing End) of The Bearing Cap

Bearing Cap

Bearing cap side seal installation
(© G.M.C.)

PRESS
BOLT
CAMSHAFT GEAR
SUPPORT PLATE
CAMSHAFT

Removing camshaft gear
(© G.M.C.)

of rear face is made after housing is installed on cylinder block. Illustration shows dial indicated to determine concentricity and squareness at SAE type flywheel housing. Repair of broken or cracked housings is not recommended.

Flywheel Inspection

Inspect flywheel surface which is contacted by clutch facing. Surface must be smooth and should not be grooved or show deep heat checks. On flywheels having notches which drive clutch plate, inspect for wear at notches. Inspect starter ring gear which is shrunk on flywheel.

Correcting Flywheel Housing Misalignment

If flywheel housing is misaligned as indicated by check, cause of misalignment must be determined if possible and necessary measures must be taken to remedy the condition.

1. Remove housing from cylinder block and look for dirt or burrs on mating surfaces which may prevent housing from seating against cylinder block.
2. If misalignment is due to distor-

tion, or combination of tolerances, try installing another housing from service stock.
3. When a selection of housings is not available, housing bore may be aligned by removing dowel pins from cylinder block, then align housing by shifting housing while held loosely in place by mounting bolts. If necessary, enlarge the mounting bolt holes to permit additional movement.
4. When aligned, tighten housing bolts firmly, then ream dowel pin holes to a convenient oversize and install overside dowel pins.

719

GENERAL SPECIFICATIONS

ENGINE MODEL	BORE & STROKE	PISTON DISP. CU. IN.	HORSEPOWER @ R.P.M.	TORQUE @ R.P.M.	FIRING ORDER* RIGHT HAND ROTATION	LEFT HAND ROTATION	GOVERNOR SPEED FULL LOAD	IDLE SPEED R.P.M.
DV-462B	$4\frac{1}{8}$ x $4\frac{5}{16}$	461	160 @ 3000	—	1-8-7-3-6-5-4-2	—	3000	550-600
DV-550B	$4\frac{1}{2}$ x $4\frac{5}{16}$	549	200 @ 3000	—	1-8-7-3-6-5-4-2	—	3000	550-600
DVT-573	$4\frac{1}{2}$ x $4\frac{1}{2}$	573	240 @ 2600	—	1-8-7-3-6-5-4-2	—	2600	575-625
V-800	$5\frac{5}{16}$ x $4\frac{1}{2}$	798	350 @ 2600	820 @ 1800	1-8-7-3-6-5-4-2	—	2600	625-675

CRANKSHAFT AND BEARING SPECIFICATIONS

	MAIN BEARING JOURNAL DIAMETER	MAIN BEARING CLEARANCE	SHAFT END THRUST ON BEARING NO.	SHAFT END PLAY	ROD BEARING BORE DIAMETER	ROD BEARING CLEARANCE
DV-462B	3.123-3.124	.0026-.0059	Inter.	.004-.010	2.9455-2.9460	.0019-.0044
DV-550B	3.123-3.124	.0026-.0059	Inter.	.004-.010	2.9455-2.9460	.0019-.0044
DVT-573	3.477-3.490	.0018-.0048	Rear	.004-.010	3.200-3.201	.0018-.0051
V-800	3.7477-3.7490	.0026-.0059	Rear	.003-.011	3.200-3.201	.0026-.0056

PISTONS, PINS, RINGS SPECIFICATIONS

ENGINE SERIES	PISTON CLEARANCE	PISTON PIN DIAMETER	PISTON TO PIN BUSHING CLEARANCE	RING END GAP COMP.	OIL	CYLINDER LINER INSIDE DIAMETER
DV-462B	.0055-.0065	1.4998-1.5000	.0005-.009	.013-.023	.013-.028	1
DV-550B	.006-.007	1.4998-1.5000	.0002-.0006	.013-.023	.013-.028	1
DVT-573	.0042-.006	1.6248-1.6250	.0001-.0003	.013-.023	.010-.030	4.5008-4.5016
V-800	.0060-.0090	2.0000-2.0002	.0011-.0005	.018-.028	.008-.018	5.3125-5.3135

1—Check piston-to-liner clearance with a .006" x ½" gauge.
Tension on spring scale must be 8-12 lbs.

ENGINE TORQUE SPECIFICATIONS

ENGINE SERIES	CYLINDER HEAD FT. LBS. CAST IRON BLOCK BOLTS	MAIN BEARING BOLTS FT. LBS.	CONN. ROD BOLTS FT. LBS.	CAMSHAFT THRUST PLATE BOLTS FT. LBS.	FLYWHEEL CAPSCREWS FT. LBS.	CRANKSHAFT END BOLT FT. LBS.
DVB-462B	110	130	55	25-30	210-230	325-375
DV-550B	110	130	55	25-30	210-230	325-375
DVT-573	300-320	275-300	100-110	40	110	325
V-800	220	390	35	30	235	220

The International Harvester DV-8 Series Diesels are all V-8, 90 degree, direct injection, open chamber engines with 5 main bearing crankshafts. All engines use wet cylinder liners, replaceable valve seats, and valve rotators.

A special combustion chamber design is employed in the normally aspirated engines. Virtually the entire air charge is forced into a compact, spherical chamber located in the top of the piston. This raises temperatures and pressures to very high levels before injection, improving combustion efficiency. In all DV-8 engines, a special oil spray nozzle system provides for efficient piston cooling. As long as oil pressure is 55 psi, oil is sprayed onto the bottom surfaces of the pistons. At extremely low rpm, oil pressure is too low to provide piston cooling, thus preventing overcooling at idle.

In all the engines, right and left side cylinder heads are interchangeable. All the engines employ gear driven injector pumps which meter and pressurize the fuel charge. The injectors provide for proper atomization and distribution within the chamber through the configuration of

The International DV-8 diesel engine
(© International Harvester Co.)

their nozzles and the operation of heavily sprung check valves. An electrically driven pump pulls fuel through the primary fuel filter, and forces it through the secondary filter and to the injector pump.

Engine Fails to Start
1. Tank empty, tank valve closed.
2. Plugged filter or fuel lines.
3. Defective damper valve.
4. Defective transfer pump.
5. Plugged injector line.
6. Defective pump plunger.

Engine Starts Hard
1. Cranking speed too slow (below 250 rpm).
2. Swirl destroyer stuck open (except DVT-573).
3. Accelerator fails to reach full fuel position.
4. Improper fuel.
5. Water in fuel.
6. Improper injection timing.
7. Poor compression.

Erratic Engine Operation
1. Improper fuel.
2. Inadequate transfer pump pressure.
3. Injection lines leaking.
4. Incorrect injector timing.
5. Faulty injector nozzle.
6. Poor compression.

Low Power Without Smoke
1. Accelerator linkage travel restricted.
2. Governor high idle adjustment incorrect.
3. Low transfer pump pressure.
4. Low fuel supply pressure.
5. Improper maximum fuel setting.
6. Injector plungers worn.
7. Exhaust system restricted.
8. Swirl destroyer in "on" position (except DVT-573).
9. Air cleaner slightly restricted.
10. Faulty injector nozzles.
11. Improper injection timing.

Engine Smokes, but with No Loss in Power
1. Faulty Nozzles.
2. Faulty maximum fuel setting.

Lube Oil Diluted with Fuel
1. Faulty nozzles.
2. Incorrect delivery valve torque.
3. Faulty pump plunger.
4. Damaged pump barrel seat.
5. Cracked pump housing.

Engine Smokes and Lacks Power
1. Swirl destroyer on (except DVT 573).
2. Air cleaner restricted.
3. Faulty nozzles.
4. Injector pump out of time.
5. Loss of compression in one cylinder.
6. Maximum fuel setting substantially too high.

DVT-573 nozzle assembly
(© International Harvester Co.)

Engine Tune-up

Injector Pump Timing— DV-462B, DV-550B
1. Put engine shutoff control in "shut-off" position.
2. Remove the cap from the timing

Timing mark and pointer
(© International Harvester Co.)

The injection pump timing pin
(© International Harvester Co.)

Injection pump with fuel lines removed
(© International Harvester Co.)

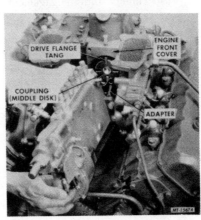

Removing the injection pump
(© International Harvester Co.)

pin on the left side of the injector pump.
3. Loosen No. 1 injector nozzle in its bore. Rotate the engine. When the nozzle pops up, start watching the timing mark and pointer on the front of the engine. NOTE: Nozzle hold-down bolts must be threaded in at least two turns.
4. Stop rotating the engine when the pointer indicates 34 degrees BTDC on 550B engines, or 32 degrees on 462B engines. If damper is turned beyond the proper mark, turn the engine backwards until it has passed at least ¼ of a turn beyond the mark.
5. Attempt to insert the timing pin into the slot in the pump camshaft. If the pin cannot be inserted, repeat steps 3-5. If the pin can be inserted, adjust timing as described below.
6. Remove upper and lower halves of the air cleaner, and, where necessary, the manifold crossover adapter. Cover manifold openings.
7. Disconnect the accelerator rod and control cable at the governor.
8. Clean the pump and connections with diesel fuel. Disconnect the low pressure and the injector lines, and the pump lube oil line. Cap all openings.
9. Remove the pump stabilizing brackets. Remove the adapter mounting bolts which hold the adapter and housing to the front cover.
10. Pull the pump rearward, freeing the drive flange tangs from the middle disc, and remove it.

DV-462, 550 nozzle assembly
(© International Harvester Co.)

Cleaning the nozzle pressure chamber
(© International Harvester Co.)

11. Install the coupling onto the tangs of the drive shaft, with the blind holes in the center of the coupling facing the pump.
12. Position the drive flange of the pump so that its tangs are horizontal and the timing pin can be engaged with the pump camshaft.
13. Locate the pump on the engine, carefully engaging the drive flange tangs with the coupling. Secure the adapter and pump to the rear of the engine front cover with the mounting bolts.
14. Install the stabilizing brackets.

V-800

1. Remove pump from engine.
2. Remove the cover from the rear of the mounting adapter.
3. Reach through the opening with a deep socket and loosen the pump drive capscrews. Rotate the pump camshaft to bring each of the six capscrews around into view.
4. Remove the timing pin cover.
5. Rotate the pump camshaft while holding in on the notch in the camshaft. Install the timing pin holding tool to keep the pin depressed.
6. Scribe timing marks on gear and align with scribe mark on advance unit.
7. Install and lubricate a new O-ring on the flange of the pump mounting adapter.

Testing the nozzle
(© International Harvester Co.)

Polishing the valve seat
(© International Harvester Co.)

Cleaning the valve seat
(© International Harvester Co.)

Timing pin tool

8. Push pump into place on engine, engaging camshaft gear and compressor idle gear.
9. Visually check, through the adapter opening, that the injection pump gear bolt is near the center of the slotted hole in the advance unit. If not, the pump is out of time one tooth in either direction.
10. Push pump into engagement

Cleaning the nozzle tip
(© International Harvester Co.)

Loosening the nozzle retainer nut
(© International Harvester Co.)

Injection timing marks aligned

with the camshaft gear and air compressor idler gear. Before O-ring enters bore, align the mounting holes in the pump flange with those in the front plate.

NOTE: When the pump is installed, the gear should have rotated far enough clockwise to allow the gear bolts to be positioned in the middle of the slots in the advance unit. If alignment is not correct, remove the pump, rotate the gear one tooth and reinstall.

11. Install all pump mounting bolts.
12. Using a deep socket, reach in through the access hole and tighten the first gear bolt to 50 ft lbs.
13. Remove the timing pin holding tool. Make sure that the timing pin is completely released.
14. Torque the five remaining bolts to 50 ft lbs. each, by rotating the crankshaft through two revolutions, stopping each 120° to tighten the next bolt.
15. Recheck static timing at the vibration damper. It should be 22°BTDC at #1 compression.

Cleaning the orifice holes
(© International Harvester Co.)

Fast idle adjustment location
(© International Harvester Co.)

16. Install the access cover and gasket and the timing pin cap.

Injector Nozzle Service

The injector nozzles direct a metered amount of fuel into the combustion chamber in finely atomized form. The nozzle valve is lifted off its seat by high pressure fuel and is returned to its seat by spring pressure while fuel pressure is still extremely high, thus ensuring the production of a high velocity stream of fine fuel particles of precisely controlled size.

The fuel enters the nozzle holder through the inlet fitting and passes to the pressure chamber just above the nozzle valve seat. When the injector pump plunger has raised the fuel pressure to the specified level, the pressure in the pressure chamber lifts the valve off its seat. The process is reversed as the pump nears the end of its stroke.

Nozzle Troubleshooting

Excessive Leak-off

1. Dirt between pressure face or spring retainer and nozzle holder.
2. Loose retainer nut.
3. Defective nozzle.

Nozzle Blueing (Excessive Heat)

1. Faulty installation or improper torquing of hold-down nuts.
2. Faulty engine cooling system.

Opening Pressure Too High

1. Incorrect shim adjustment.
2. Dirty valve.
3. Sticking or seized valve.
4. Clogged nozzle.

Opening Pressure Too Low

1. Shim adjustment incorrect.
2. Valve spring broken.
3. Worn seat.

Nozzle Drips

1. Carbon deposits.
2. Sticking valve.
3. Faulty nozzle.

Distorted Spray Pattern

1. Carbon deposits on nozzle tip.
2. Partially blocked nozzle hole.
3. Defective nozzle.

Nozzle Service

1. Using kerosene or diesel fuel, clean the fuel line connections very thoroughly.
2. Remove the high pressure and leak-off lines, and cover all openings with caps.
3. Remove the mounting bolts.
4. Pull the nozzles out of the engine, rotating them slightly to break it loose of carbon deposits, if necessary.
5. Cover the openings in the block, and ensure that the nozzle tips are protected.
6. With a clean, lint free cloth, wipe all dirt and carbon from each nozzle assembly.
7. Procure or make a holding fixture similar to that shown in the illustration.
8. Using a 12 point, deep well socket, remove the nozzle retainer nut. Remove the spray nozzle and spring retainer or plate, being careful not to drop any parts. If disassembly is difficult, the assembly may first be soaked in any good carbon solvent.
9. Thoroughly soak all disassembled parts in a pan of solvent.
10. Hold the nozzle valve stem in a revolving chuck, and use mutton tallow on a soft cloth to clean it. An oil soaked piece of wood or a fine wire brush will help in cleaning. *Do not use any hard tools in cleaning.*
11. Clean the inside of the nozzle body, and the valve seat, with special brass scrapers.
12. Using cleaning tallow on a wooden stick, polish the valve seat.
13. Extend the cleaning needle 1/32" out from the pin vise. Clean the orifice holes. Clean the sac hole (inside tip) with .050" reamer on 462-550, .047" on 573-800.
14. Clean the nozzle tip with a wire brush or soft cloth, but avoid scraping carbon from the surface around the orifices, or damage may result.
15. Rinse all parts of the assembly very thoroughly in clean fuel. Remove all carbon from the retainer nut.

Head bolt tightening sequence DVT-573
(© International Harvester Co.)

Head bolt tightening sequence for DV-462, 550
(© International Harvester Co.)

16. Mount the nozzle holder in a fixture and clamp the assembly in a vise with the lapped face of the holder upward.
17. Install the spring retainer or plate, noting proper location of locating dowels.
18. Install the nozzle retaining nut hand tight, noting that the nozzle is concentric with the holder.
19. Tighten the retainer nut with a 12 point deep socket to 50-60 ft lbs. on 462 and 550 engines, 60-70 ft. lbs. on 573 engines, and 35 ft lbs. on 800 engines.
20. Fill a test fixture with fuel oil, and bleed the test pump of air.
21. Connect the nozzle to the test pump and operate the handle several times to remove all air from the whole system. *During this and all procedures involving actual operation of the nozzle and valve, avoid contact with the high velocity spray from the nozzle, as it will penetrate the skin.*
22. Operate the handle and check the nozzle opening pressure. Specifications are:

New
DV-462, 550—2250-2350
DV-462B, 550B—2225-2375
DVT-573—3100-3200
Rebuilt
DV-462, 550—2000
DV-462B, 550B—2150-2375
DVT-573—2850

The nozzle should operate so as to produce a fine, atomized mist and a high pitched squeak. The atomized streams must not be streaked.

23. Pump up the pressure again to a level just below the pop pressure. Be sure there is no leakage at the the nozzle, spring retainer, and holder. Leakage may be seen at the retainer nut (external) or at the leak-off outlet (internal). If leakage occurs, disassemble and clean again.
24. Change the opening pressure, if necessary, by adding shims to increase it, or subtracting them to decrease it. Place shims at the top of the spring, and ensure that the dark, hardened wear shim is next to the top of the spring.
25. Raise the nozzle to the point where it pops three times to expel air. Wipe the tip to make it perfectly dry. Then, raise pres-

sure to within 500 psi of pop pressure, and hold it. If the tip remains dry or is not wet enough after five seconds to produce a droplet, it is satisfactory.

26. *Carefully* clean the nozzle bore in the cylinder head, using an appropriately shaped round piece of brass or brush. Pay particular attention to the seating surfaces, as even a tiny particle of carbon on them will prevent proper sealing.

27. Carefully install each nozzle into the bore it was removed from, avoiding contact of the tip with the recess wall, and using a new O-ring.

28. Tighten mounting bolts evenly, in gradual stages, to 15 ft lbs. (462,550), or 8-12 ft lbs (573). The manufacturer suggests that, where nylock bolts are used, they be replaced.

Lo-Idle Adjustment

DV-462B, DV-550B

1. Bring engine to operating temperature. Note tachometer reading. Lo-idle speed is 550-600.

2. If necessary to adjust the lo-idle, loosen the locknut and turn clockwise to reduce rpm, or counterclockwise to increase it. Tighten the locknut.

3. Operate the engine up to hi-idle three times, and allow it to return to lo-idle. If the adjustment is not correct, repair binding in the linkage.

Valve Adjustment

All Engines

1. Remove valve covers. Allow engine to cool down until all parts are at uniform temperature. Intake valves are adjusted to .014″, exhaust to .016″ except on V-800 which is intake .013″, exhaust .025″.

2. Rotate the engine in the normal direction of rotation until the No. 1 intake valve just starts to open. Adjust both valves on No. 6 cylinder.

3. Continue rotating the engine until No. 8 intake valve is just opening, and adjust valves on No. 5 cylinder.

4. Rotate the engine until No. 7 intake valve is just opening, and adjust the valves on No. 4 cylinder.

5. Rotate the engine until No. 3 intake valve is just opening, and adjust the valves on No. 2 cylinder.

6. Rotate the engine until No. 6 intake valve is just opening, and adjust the valves on No. 1 cylinder.

7. Rotate the engine until No. 5 intake valve is just opening, and adjust

the valves on No. 8 cylinder.

8. Rotate the engine until No. 4 intake is just opening, and adjust the valves on No. 7 cylinder.

9. Rotate the engine until No. 2 intake is just opening, and adjust the valves on No. 3 cylinder.

Torquing Cylinder Heads

DV-462B, DV-550B

1. Torque all bolts in the pattern shown to 30 ft lbs.

2. Torque, in the same pattern, to 60 ft lbs.

3. Torque, in pattern, to 110 ft lbs.

DVT-573

1. Torque all bolts, in the sequence shown, to 100 ft lbs.

2. Torque, in sequence, to 190 ft lbs.

3. Torque, in sequence, to 320 ft lbs.

4. Loosen each bolt one half turn and retorque to 320 ft lbs, one bolt at a time. NOTE: After torquing head bolts, valve adjustment *must* be performed.

V-800

1. Torque bolts in sequence shown to 100 ft lbs.

V-800 head bolt torque sequence

2. Torque in sequence to 160 ft lbs.

3. Torque in sequence to 185 ft lbs., loosen ¼ turn and torque to 205 ft lbs.

4. After run-in, back off ¼ turn and torque to 220 ft lbs.

FUEL SYSTEM

Injector Pump

DV-462B, DV-550B
Removal

1. Remove upper and lower halves of the air cleaner, and, where necessary, the manifold crossover adapter. Cover manifold openings.

2. Disconnect the accelerator rod and control cable at the governor.

3. Clean the pump and connections with diesel fuel. Disconnect low pressure and injector lines, and the pump lube oil line. Cap all openings.

4. Remove the pump stabilizing brackets. Remove the adapter mounting bolts which hold the adapter and housing to the front cover.

5. Pull the pump rearward, freeing

the drive flange tangs from the middle disc, and remove it.

Inspection

1. Inspect pump mounting flange and the bosses of the rear mounting bracket.

2. Inspect the drive flange for damage, wear, or loose mounting.

3. Torque the securing nut to 75 ft lbs.

Installation

1. Install the coupling onto the tangs of the drive shaft, with the blind hole in the center of the coupling facing the pump.

2. Position the drive flange of the pump so that its tangs are horizontal and the timing pin can be engaged with the pump camshaft.

3. Locate the pump on the engine, carefully engaging the drive flange tangs with the coupling. Secure the adapter and pump to the rear of the engine front cover with the mounting bolts.

4. Install the stabilizer brackets.

DVT-573

Removal

1. Remove air compressor.

2. Remove the front cover plates and gaskets from the heads.

3. Remove all leak-off lines at the injector nozzles. Cap all openings.

4. Remove the injector lines and dampers assembled. Cap all openings.

5. Remove the mounting caps and lockwashers.

6. Lift the injection pump and shaft off the engine. Pull the gasket off the drive housing.

Installation

1. Install a new gasket onto the drive housing.

2. Put the pump in place on the engine.

3. Install the mounting screws and lockwashers.

4. Uncap openings, and install the injector lines and dampers.

5. Uncap and install the leak-off lines.

6. Install the front cover plates and gaskets.

7. Install the air compressor.

V-800

1. Disconnect and remove injection pump oil supply and return lines. Remove oil pressure tube.

2. Remove two accelerator rod-to-pump control bolts. Remove three accelerator rod bracket-to-cylinder head bolts.

3. Remove accelerator rod and bracket.

Injection pump oil lines

Location for checking the fuel
transfer pressure
(© International Harvester Co.)

4. Remove pump bracket-to-engine bolt.
5. Support pump and remove the five attaching bolts.
6. Slide the pump rearward clear of the drive gear.
7. To install, follow instructions under INJECTOR PUMP TIMING.

Fuel System Priming

DV-462B, DV-550B

1. Check to make sure that there is plenty of fuel in the tank.
2. Turn the starting switch to "on" position. Turn and hold the primer switch to the "on" position.
3. Open the vent valve on top of the primary filter. When fuel flows without bubbles, close the valve.
4. Open the vent valve on top of the secondary filter. Close the valve after fuel flows out bubble-free.
5. Open the vent valve at the right front of the injection pump. Close the valve when the discharge is free of bubbles.
6. Allow primer switch to return to "off" position.

Electric Fuel Pump Pressure Check

DV-462B, DV-550B

1. Install an adapter at the priming vent and run a hose to a special test kit.
2. Operate the engine under load, and read the fuel pressure. It should be 3-5 psi.
3. If reading is not to specifications, look for a damaged or plugged supply line or faulty pump.

Transfer Pressure Check

1. Connect an adapter to the priming outlet at the right front of the injection pump. Connect a test gauge, located in the cab, to the adapter.
2. Operate the engine under load, and observe the pressure. It must be 16 psi or more on pumps, and 21 psi or more on C92 pumps.
3. If pressure is low, check for

clogged filters. Otherwise, the transfer pump is defective.

ENGINE REMOVAL

DV-462B, DV-550B

1. Drain the cooling system by opening drain cocks on either side toward the rear of the block, at the rear of the oil cooler, and at the lower left portion of the radiator. Drain the engine oil.
2. Disconnect the battery ground cable. Tape thoroughly the end of the terminal.
3. Remove the secondary fuel filter with a strap wrench. Remove both oil filter assemblies from the cooler.
4. Raise the hood assembly, and block upward with slack in the stop cables.
5. Disconnect the headlight wiring harness from the junction block at right front of the hood. Remove the harness from the clips at the right front fender.
6. Disconnect the hood stop cable yokes at the radiator support.
7. Remove the hood hinge pins, removing the cotter pin and flat washer on either side and then either pin.
8. Remove the hood and fender assembly (which requires two persons). Remove the front bumper.
9. Remove the upper radiator hose. Loosen the lower radiator hose clamp at the engine water inlet and, where heater equipped, remove heater hoses.
10. Release both splash panel latches on either side, and remove both panels.

Location of splash panel latches for removal
of DV series engines
(© International Harvester Co.)

DVT-573 Cover plates
(© International Harvester Co.)

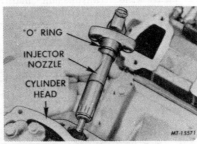

Location of injector nozzle O-ring
(© International Harvester Co.)

Heater and coolant hose locations
on DV series engines
(© International Harvester Co.)

Removal of DV series engines
(© International Harvester Co.)

11. Disconnect the shutterstat hose where it connects at the engine water outlet.
12. Disconnect both radiator stay rods at either end.
13. Disconnect the thermostat bleed hose where it enters the upper radiator tank.
14. Disconnect windshield washer hose and wiring harness from the stay rods and radiator support.
15. If the truck is equipped with a shutterstat, disconnect the linkage and spring at the actuating cylinder. Remove the shutter or radiator grille. Remove the radiator shell side panels.
16. Remove the radiator core and tanks.
17. Remove the air cleaner intake elbow and the radiator support assembly.
18. Disconnect the:

   a. fuel supply and return hoses at the rear of the engine.
   b. left and right exhaust pipes at the manifolds (and remove seals).
   c. armature and field wires at the alternator.
   d. temperature indicator wire at the front of the right cylinder head.
   e. oil pressure sending wire.
   f. wiring harness at all clips along the right side of the intake manifold and the rear of the left of the intake manifold.
   g. main air supply line at the compressor
   h. flexible air line at the compressor governor.
   i. throttle and control cable, swirl destroyer cable, and engine shutoff cable at their points of connection on the injection pump.
   j. accelerator linkage at the

bellcrank and at the injection pump.
   k. tachometer cable at the rear of the block.
   l. wiring and battery cable at the starter solenoid.
   m. alternator mounting strap. Loosen the alternator mounting bolts, remove the belts, and pull the alternator away from the thermostat housing.
   n. water line at the thermostat housing and air compressor, and remove it.

19. Remove the:
   a. thermostat housing, thermostat, and gasket.
   b. governor line from the air compressor and governor.
   c. air compressor governor from its mounting bracket.
   d. leak-off line and clip from the rear of the right cylinder head.
20. Disconnect both power steering lines at the pump.
21. Install an engine lifting plate to the thermostat mounting surface on the front cover with four $\frac{3}{8}$" x $1\frac{1}{4}$" hex head bolts and flat washers. Bolts should be turned exactly $\frac{1}{4}$ turn beyond finger tight position.
22. Route a special cable under the flywheel housing and attach both ends to a special lifting hoist. Make sure cable does not contact the timing indicator pin on the flywheel housing.
23. Remove the front mount bolts and self locking nuts. Lower the insulator retainer and the insulator from the mounting.
24. Remove the dust shield from the clutch cross shaft.
25. Disconnect the vertical link on the clutch release linkage.
26. Disconnect the clutch cross shaft linkage and nut on the end of the cross shaft. Remove the bearing retainer caps and pull the shaft outward.
27. Remove the rear engine mounts on either side of the flywheel housing.
28. Remove all (12) bell housing to flywheel housing caps. Make sure the engine ground strap is pulled free when the cap is removed.
29. Pull the engine forward until it clears the transmission main drive gear and clutch driven disc, and then raise it out of the chassis.

DVT-573

1. Drain the cooling system by opening cocks on either side toward the rear of the block, at the rear of the oil cooler, and on the lower radiator tank. Drain the crankcase.
2. Disconnect the battery ground

Exhaust manifold removal
(© International Harvester Co.)

cable, and thoroughly tape the end.
3. Disconnect and/or remove the following:
   a. the radiator hoses and pipes.
   b. all wiring at all connection points on the engine assembly.
   c. exhaust pipe at the turbocharger.
   d. the air cleaner pipe cleaner pipe at the turbocharger and air cleaner (and remove).
   e. throttle linage at the throttle cross-over shaft
   f. the throttle return spring at the clip at the left-front of the engine.
   g. the fuel line at the final fuel filter.
   h. air supply line at the air compressor (and remove).
   i. control cable at the other cable unit.
   j. heater hoses.
   k. engine ground strap at the engine.
   l. tachometer cable at the air compressor.
   m. power steering lines at the pump.
   n. air compressor governor line.
   o. fuel leak-off line at the tee at the rear of the front cover plate.
   p. transmission remote control shift lever housing.
   q. air conditioner compressor lines, *after a complete discharge of the system.*
   r. hose at the shutterstat.
   s. crankcase breather tube.
   t. oil filler tube hose.
4. Securely attach an oversize chain at both engine lifting brackets (front and rear).
5. Attach the chain to a hoist and raise just enough to hold engine in position.
6. Remove the front engine mounts and their insulators and retainers.
7. Remove the rear mounts and auxiliary parts.
8. Raise the engine from the chassis, using extreme care to avoid damage to wiring and piping.

Location of engine crossover tube clip
(© International Harvester Co.)

V-800

Due to various chassis designs and equipment, disconnect points will vary from vehicle to vehicle.

1. Drain the cooling system and engine oil.
2. Disconnect the battery ground.
3. Remove radiator hoses and pipes.
4. Disconnect all electrical wiring.
5. Disconnect the exhaust pipe at the turbocharger.
6. Remove the air cleaner pipe from the turbocharger and air cleaner.
7. Disconnect the throttle linkage at the throttle shaft and return spring from clip at the left front of the engine.
8. Disconnect the fuel inlet line at the final filter.
9. Remove the air supply line at the compressor.
10. Disconnect the other control cable.
11. Remove the heater hoses.
12. Disconnect the engine ground strap.
13. Disconnect the tachometer cable at the air compressor.
14. Disconnect the power steering line.
15. Remove the air compressor governor line.
16. Disconnect the fuel leak-off line at the front cover plate.
17. Remove the remote control shaft lever housing.
18. Remove the refrigerant compressor lines.
19. Disconnect the shutterstat hose.
20. Remove oil filler tube hose.
21. Rig-up lifting equipment and take up the engine weight.
22. Remove engine mount bolts,

Using a screwdriver as a stop during fan removal
(© International Harvester Co.)

Location of oil cooler lines
(© International Harvester Co.)

front first, and lift out engine.
NOTE: Use extreme care to avoid damage to pipes and wires.

ENGINE DISASSEMBLY

DV-462B, DV-550B

NOTE: The disassembly procedures below are intended for disassembly operations using an engine stand. The sequence of disassembly would vary slightly if different equipment were used, although the following serves as a general guide, even where in-chassis work is to be accomplished.

Preliminary Parts Removal

1. Remove both exhaust manifolds.
2. Remove two screws in the oil pan flange, and remove the exhaust manifold heat shield.
3. Remove the starting motor and adapter.
4. Remove the oil cooler return line from the cooler and engine water outlet.
5. Remove the oil cooler water inlet line, disconnecting it at the oil cooler and crossover tube. Remove the water line connecting the crossover tube to the air compressor. Remove the water line clip from the power steering pump mounting bracket bolt.
6. Remove the oil line running from the oil cooler base to the tee at the base of the air compressor mounting. Disconnect the clip from the engine crossover tube clip extension and remove the oil line.

Air cleaner air and oil line locations
(© International Harvester Co.)

Location of the exhaust manifold heat shield
(© International Harvester Co.)

7. Remove the crossover tube and gaskets from the water pump and crankcase.
8. Loosen both fuel filter line nuts at the top of the filter base, loosen the mounting capscrews, and remove the base.

The engine may be mounted on an overhaul stand at this time.

Major Disassembly

1. Remove the power steering belt, loosening the mounting bracket capscrews and adjusting bolt locknut to permit easy accomplishment of the operation. Remove the pump mounting stud nuts and lockwashers, and remove the pump.
2. Remove the mounting bracket capscrews and lockwashers. Remove the mounting bracket.
3. Loosen the air conditioner compressor mounts, slide the unit inward, and remove the drive belt.
4. Remove the compressor mounting capscrews, lockwashers, and flatwashers, and remove the compressor.
5. Remove the mounting bracket capscrews and lockwashers, and remove the bracket.
6. Remove the oil sending unit from the cooler base.
7. Remove the oil cooler capscrews, and pull the cooler and gasket off the engine.
8. Remove the oil filters from the cooler base.
9. Remove the capscrews from the cooler and filter base, and remove the entire unit and gasket.
10. Remove the alternator mounting bolts, disengage the belts, and re-

Location of compressor mounting capscrews
(© International Harvester Co.)

Location of fuel injection line clips
(© International Harvester Co.)

Injector mounting bracket capscrews
(© International Harvester Co.)

Lifting sling
(© International Harvester Co.)

Injector pump oil feed line clip
(© International Harvester Co.)

move the alternator from the engine.

11. Using a special wrench and with a heavy duty screwdriver blade against the lug on the water pump body forming a stop against one pulley hub spoke, remove the fan drive assembly. NOTE: Do not permit the screwdriver to become wedged between the water pump body and pulley hub spoke (see illustration).

12. Push the idler pulley toward the center of the engine and remove the main and accessory drive belts.

13. Remove the capscrews and washers from the alternator mounting bracket, and remove the unit from the engine.

14. Disconnect the air line from the air compressor to the crossover or air cleaner adapter plate. Disconnect the oil line at the adapter plate.

15. On models equipped with an intake manifold crossover, remove the unit's capscrews and lift it off the manifolds or air cleaner adapter plate.

16. Remove the crossover or adapter mounting gaskets and screens. Tape the intake manifold openings to prevent the entrance of dirt.

17. Remove the air compressor mounting capscrews and their lockwashers. Remove the compressor and gasket from the engine.

18. Remove the mounting capscrews and washers from the compressor adapter plate, and remove the adapter plate. Remove the adapter plate O-ring from the underside of the plate.

19. Remove the ventilator pipe connecting the right cylinder head cover and intake manifold.

20. Remove clips and grommets from the fuel injection lines. Disconnect the lines from the pump and nozzles, and immedi-

ately cap all openings.

21. Disconnect the leak-off lines at the injection pump, at either end of the lines running between manifolds, and between manifold and injection pump. Remove grommets and plug or cap all fittings.

22. Remove the fuel supply line clip from the front of the right valve cover, and disconnect fittings at either end and remove the line.

23. Remove the two clips holding the primary to secondary filter line in place, disconnect fittings at either end, and remove the line. Cap or plug all openings.

24. Remove the clip attaching the injector pump oil feed line to the left intake manifold, disconnect fittings at either end of the line, remove the line, and cap the opening in the pump.

25. Remove the capscrews holding the horizontal bracket to the injector pump, and the pump-to bracket screw, and remove the bracket.

26. Remove the capscrews securing the brace to the injector pump, and those securing it to the intake manifold. Remove the brace.

27. Remove the injector pump adapter capscrews and lockwashers, and remove the pump and its gasket from the engine. Remove the drive disc from the pump or flange.

28. Unsnap the swirl destroyer linkage ball studs at the manifolds.

29. Remove the intake manifold capscrews and lockwashers, and remove the manifolds and gaskets.

30. Remove the right bank water

outlet mounting caps and lockwashers. Remove the dipstick tube, and water outlet and gasket.

31. Repeat the operation on the left bank water outlet (there is no dipstick tube to remove on this side).

32. Remove all cylinder head cover screws and washers, and remove covers and gaskets.

33. Remove the nozzle assemblies from the heads, keeping them in order so each can be reinstalled in the same cylinder at reassembly.

34. Remove the rocker assemblies from the heads.

35. Remove valve tips and pushrods.

36. Install a lifting sling similar to that shown in the illustration, using ⅜"NC × ¾" capscrews. The tab should be made of ⅜" × ¾" cold rolled stock.

37. Remove all head bolts and lift each head off the two dowel sleeves. Remove the gaskets. Proceed carefully and avoid prying, which could damage the gasket surface.

38. Compress the clutch plate with the three capscrews "A" in the illustration. These screws are ⅜"-16NC × 2, and flatwashers should be used under them.

39. Remove the clutch back plate-to-flywheel retaining capscrews, and remove the clutch assembly.

40. Remove the clutch pilot bearing with a slide hammer and puller.

41. Remove the flywheel mounting bolts, and remove the flywheel from the crankshaft flange.

42. Remove the flywheel housing capscrews, and remove the housing, being careful not to damage the roll pins.

43. Remove the capscrews and washers from the camshaft cover plate, and remove the plate and gasket.

44. Disconnect the water crossover pipe at the rear of the crankcase, and remove it.

45. Remove all tappets with a mag-

International • Diesel Engines

Locating crankshaft for removal of piston cooling nozzles
(© International Harvester Co.)

Location of oil pump screenbrace and related parts
(© International Harvester Co.)

Removing piston and connecting rod assembly
(© International Harvester Co.)

netic remover. If necessary, use only a small amount of carburetor solvent to loosen the tappets.

46. Remove oil pan mounting caps. Remove the pan and gasket.
47. Remove the oil pump screenbrace mounting nuts, bolts, and washers, and remove the brace and clamp.
48. Remove the oil pump mounting capscrews, and remove the pump. It may be necessary to turn crankshaft rear counterweight away from the oil pump shaft.
49. Disconnect and remove the idler arm spring from the front cover and idler arm.
50. Remove the idler arm capscrew and remove the arm and spacer from the bracket.
51. Remove the water pump pulley capscrews, and remove the pulley.
52. Remove the water pump mounting caps, and remove the front portion of the pump and the gasket from the pump body. Remove the remaining pump body screws, and remove the body and lift the body and gasket off the front cover.

Removing the camshaft, gear, and spacer
(© International Harvester Co.)

53. Remove the injector pump drive flange nut, and then remove the drive flange with retainer and grip springs using a special puller.
54. Remove the injector pump drive gear mounting caps and washers. Remove the drive gear by inserting a screwdriver into the injection pump oil return hole in back of the gear housing and pushing the drive gear off the shaft.
55. Remove the snap ring from the front bearing of the injector pump drive.
56. Tap the drive shaft and bearing assembly from the front cover, using a hammer and brass drift.
57. Mount the injector pump drive shaft in a press and use an adaptor to force the bearing from the shaft.
58. Remove the drive shaft rear bearing from the front cover with a special remover and handle.
59. Position a wood block between a crankshaft counterweight and the crankcase to prevent shaft rotation. Remove the crankshaft pulley with a special puller.

60. Remove the crankshaft pulley with a special puller.
61. Remove the two Nylock capscrews and lockwashers from the rear of the front cover.
62. Remove all but two of the front cover caps. Support the front cover, remove the remaining caps, and lift the cover and gasket off the dowel pins.
63. Remove the oil seal from the front cover with a hammer and drift.
64. Remove the spring, nuts, and lockwashers from the swirl destroyer mounting plate, and remove the plate and control rod assembly. Remove the flatwashers from the mounting studs.
65. Remove the tappet cover mounting capscrews and washers, and remove the cover from the engine. Pull off the gasket and discard it.
66. Remove the camshaft thrust plate capscrews and camshaft nut, and remove the camshaft, gear and spacer with a special remover.
67. Rotate the crankshaft to the position shown in the illustration.

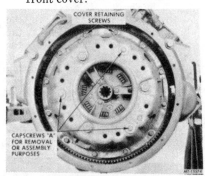

Installation locations for capscrews used in compressing the clutch plate
(© International Harvester Co.)

Removing the clutch pilot bearing
(© International Harvester Co.)

Location of injection pump drive gear
(© International Harvester Co.)

Removing the connecting rod cap
(© International Harvester Co.)

Removing the drive shaft rear bearing
(© International Harvester Co.)

729

Locations of mounting bolts for the oil cooler
and accessories
(© International Harvester Co.)

Location of power steering pump mounting
capscrews
(© International Harvester Co.)

68. Remove the piston cooling nozzles from both sides of the crankcase.
69. Remove all ridges from upper cylinder bores.
70. For each cylinder, remove the connecting rod cap, push the rod and piston assembly out of the cylinder bore at the top, and replace the cap and bearing inserts on the rods so the numbered sides match.
71. Remove the self locking bolts, tie bolts, and seal washers from each cap.
72. Remove the front four main caps with a remover and slide hammer by inserting the hook end of the remover into the horizontal hole toward the center line of the crankshaft.
73. Remove the rear main cap with a special puller and adapter.
74. Remove the rear main cap oil seal.
75. Lift the crankshaft straight upward to remove it from the crankcase.

ENGINE DISASSEMBLY

DVT-573

NOTE: The disassembly procedures below are intended for disassembly operations using an engine stand. The sequence of disassembly would vary slightly if different equipment were used, although the following serves as a general guide, even where in-chassis work is to be accomplished.

Removing rear oil seal using a special remover
(© International Harvester Co.)

Preliminary Parts Removal

1. Remove the front oil filter body and element.
2. Loosen alternator adjusting and mounting bolts, and remove the belt.
3. Loosen the fan pulley and bracket mounting bolts and the bracket adjusting screw, and remove the main drive belts.
4. Loosen and remove hose clamps, and remove the hoses from the water pump.
5. Remove the water pump body mounting bolts and oil outlet tube mounting bolts. Remove the three bolts mounting the oil filter base, and remove the inlet tube, base, oil cooler, and water pump assembly. Be careful not to lose oil cooler O-rings.
6. Remove the breather pipe hose clamp, clip (at manifold extension), and nut and washer holding the unit to the right cylinder head cover, and remove the unit.

Major Disassembly

1. Remove the starting motor mounting bolts, and remove the motor from the flywheel housing.
2. Remove the alternator adjusting strap screw, flat washer, lockwasher, and all mounting bolts and nuts. Remove the unit from the bracket.
3. Remove the fan blade mounting

Removing the rear main cap with puller
and adapter
(© International Harvester Co.)

bolts and washers from behind the fan. Remove the blade and adapter.
4. Remove the fan pulley hub mounts and washers, and loosen the adjusting screw. Remove the fan pulley hub and bracket assembly.
5. Loosen the cross-over tube hose clamp at the left thermostat housing. Remove the tube and hose.
6. Remove the capscrews and washers from the front cover access plate, and remove the plate and O-ring.
7. Disconnect water and air lines at the air compressor, and at the left side thermostat housing and cylinder head.
8. Remove both thermostat housings, and remove both thermostats and gaskets.
9. Loosen, but do not fully remove, the crankshaft pulley nut. In this position, pulley will be restrained if it is forced suddenly off the shaft.
10. Install a puller, and pull the crankshaft pulley free of the shaft taper. Then, remove the bolt and pulley.
11. Remove the front mounting bracket.
12. Remove the remaining alternator mounting capscrews, and remove the bracket.
13. Loosen the capscrews which fasten the power steering pump to the front cover, and remove the pump and adapter.

Removing the main caps with a slide hammer
(© International Harvester Co.)

14. Remove capscrews and washers holding the air compressor and the cover plate to the front cover.
15. Remove all remaining front cover capscrews and washers, and remove the front cover and gasket.
16. Remove the front cover oil seal with a drift and hammer.
17. Disconnect the oil level gauge tube clip, and remove the gauge tube.
18. Remove all remaining oil pan capscrews and lockwashers, and remove the oil pan and gasket.
19. Disconnect the throttle rod at the injection pump, and remove the throttle cross shaft, and bracket assembly.
20. Disconnect the oil feed line at the air compressor elbow.
21. Remove the remaining capscrew holding the air compressor to the cover plate, and remove the compressor and gasket.
22. Remove the compressor oil feed line from the crankcase.
23. Disconnect the fuel filter and by-pass hoses at the injection pump.
24. Disconnect the leak-off lines at the junction block, and the aneroid control valve hose at the elbow on the right head. Seal off all ends with plastic caps, and

plug all openings.
25. Disconnect the hose at the final filter, remove the filter's mounting bolts, and remove the filter from the bracket.
26. Where applicable, remove the oil filler tube and gasket from the flywheel housing.
27. Remove the capscrew and washer from the turbocharger elbow bracket on the flywheel housing. Remove the elbow, bracket, and gasket from the turbocharger, plug or tape the opening.
28. Lift the exhaust sleeve and seal rings out of the turbocharger.
29. Remove the mounting capscrews and washers from the turbocharger exhaust inlet elbow, and remove the elbow and gaskets.
30. Bend back the locking tabs on the rear manifold section rear mounting washer, and remove the capscrews and washers, and manifold and gasket.
31. Bend back the locking tabs on the front manifold section front mounting washer, and remove the capscrews and washers, and manifold and gasket.
32. Remove the capscrews and washers from the center section, and remove the manifold and gasket.
33. Repeat steps 30-32 on the oppo-

site cylinder head.
34. Disconnect the turbocharger oil pressure line at the crankcase and the vent line at the access hole cover.
35. Remove the capscrews from the oil pressure line fitting at the turbocharger and remove the oil line with the fitting and gasket.
36. Disconnect the vent line at the turbocharger, and remove it.
37. Remove the turbocharger capscrews and washers, and the capscrew and plastic washer from the left rear access hole cover. Lift the turbocharger and oil return as an assembly off the cylinder heads.
38. Remove the turbocharger adapters and their O-rings, and the access hole cover and adapter gaskets.
39. Remove the oil pressure line, including safety switch tee, from the cylinder head.
40. Remove the cylinder head front cover plates and gaskets.
41. Remove injector leakoff lines from the injectors, and cap or plug all openings.
42. Remove all injector lines and dampers as an assembly, and cap or plug all openings.
43. Remove the injector pump mounting bolts and washers. Lift

Location of remaining front cover capscrews
(© International Harvester Co.)

Lifting the exhaust sleeve and seal rings out of the turbocharger
(© International Harvester Co.)

Turbocharger oil pressure and vent lines
(© International Harvester Co.)

Injector leak-off lines
(© International Harvester Co.)

Location of spacer blocks required in clutch plate removal
(© International Harvester Co.)

Location of flywheel setscrews and locating pins
(© International Harvester Co.)

the pump and drive shaft from the housing. Remove the housing gasket.

44. Remove the oil inlet pipe mounting clip capscrew, disconnect the inlet pipe at the regulator valve housing, and remove the assembly.

45. Remove the oil pressure regulator housing mounting capscrews and washers, and remove the housing, gasket, and valve.

46. Remove the injection nozzle mounting capscrews. Carefully use a prybar to loosen each injector, and then lift each injector with its gasket and O-ring from the head. Place injectors in a stand so as to identify their position in the engine for reassembly.

47. Remove valve cover capscrews and washers, and lift covers and their O-ring seals off the heads.

48. Install a valve cover capscrew in either end of each rocker arm assembly (a total of four per head), tightening just enough to hold the assemblies together for removal. Remove rocker assembly mounting caps, and remove the assemblies.

49. Remove all pushrods from the heads.

50. Remove all but the center head bolt on either side, and collect all loose washers.

51. Install a lifting eye on the front of the head to be removed first. Attach a sling to the lifting eyes, and use a hoist to apply tension to the sling. Remove the center bolt and washer, and lift the head and gasket off the block.

52. Repeat the removal operation for the other head.

53. Remove the capscrews and their washers from the remaining access hole covers, and remove the covers and gaskets.

54. Remove all tappets through the access hole.

55. Place two wood spacer blocks between $\frac{1}{2}'' \times \frac{3}{4}'' \times 3\frac{1}{2}''$ between the clutch plate and throwout bearing.

56. Remove the clutch plate mounting capscrews and washers, and remove the plate assembly.

57. Remove the rear disc and facings. Remove the intermediate pressure plate and front disc with facings.

58. Remove flywheel setscrews and intermediate pressure plate locating pins.

59. Remove the clutch pilot bearing

with a special puller and slide hammer.

60. Mark the position of the flywheel bore and crankshaft flange, and the position of the lock plates on the flywheel.

61. Flatten out the tabs on the lock plates, and remove the flywheel mounting capscrews.

62. Install guide pins and puller screws and remove the flywheel. Guide pins may be made by cutting the hex head off $\frac{5}{8}$-18NF $\times$ 4'' capscrews. Puller screws are $\frac{1}{2}$-13NC $\times$ 2''.

63. Remove the mounting capscrews from the rear oil seal plate, and lift the plate and gasket off the flywheel housing.

64. Remove the crankshaft rear oil seal by working around it in a clockwise direction with a special remove and slide hammer.

65. Remove the flywheel housing mounting capscrews and washers, and remove the housing. Remove the housing gasket from the rear of the crankcase.

66. Remove the mounting bolts from the injection pump drive gear, and remove the gear. Remove the

Removing rocker assemblies
(© International Harvester Co.)

Removing the cylinder head with a lifting sling
(© International Harvester Co.)

Forcing the cylinder sleeves out of the block
(© International Harvester Co.)

Forcing the Woodruff key off the crankshaft
(© International Harvester Co.)

Using a special remover to pull the camshaft
(© International Harvester Co.)

housing mounting bolts and washers, and remove the drive assembly, including bearings, shaft spring, and O-ring.

67. Straighten the tabs on the camshaft thrust plate capscrew locks with a hammer and chisel, and remove the capscrews and locks.

68. Put the crankcase in a vertical position with camshaft gear upward. Lift the camshaft, thrust plate, and gear assembly out of the crankcase.

69. Remove the power steering pump idler gear mounting bolt, and remove the idler gear, bearing adapter, and spacer from the front cover plate.

70. Remove the oil pump outlet tube bracket capscrews and washers, and the oil pump mounting capscrews and washers.

71. Lift the oil pump from the front bearing cap, disengaging the oil outlet tube from the crankcase transfer sleeve.

72. Force the Woodruff key from the crankcase with a hammer and chisel.

73. Block the crankshaft from turning with a wood block inserted between the crankcase and one of the crankshaft throws, and remove the crankshaft nut.

74. Remove the crankshaft gear with a special puller.

75. Unbolt the front cover plate, and remove it and the gasket.

76. Use a ridge reamer to remove ridges in the tops of all cylinder bores.

77. Remove the connecting rod caps, and push each rod and piston assembly from its cylinder bore. Replace caps and bearing inserts into the rods so the numbered sides match.

78. Remove the main cap bolts and washers, and remove the caps from the crankcase.

79. Lift the crankshaft straight up and out of the upper main bearing halves.

80. Remove the upper main bearing halves from the crankcase.

81. Remove the piston cooling nozzles from the crankcase, and place in order for installation in the same positions.

82. Locate a hardwood block on the bottom of each cylinder sleeve, and hammer it to force the sleeve upward and out of the block. Mark each sleeve as it is removed for reinstallation in the same bore.

V-800

1. Remove engine and mount in work stand SE-1962 or equivalent. Before mounting in work stand it will be necessary to remove the following:
   a. unbolt and remove the fan.
   b. remove the two alternator bolts.
   c. remove the three main drive belts.
   d. unbolt and remove the water pump and O-ring.
   e. remove the volute housing from the oil cooler.
   f. remove oil delivery tube from the filter base.
   g. remove the oil filters.
   h. remove oil filter base.
   i. remove oil transfer sleeve.
   j. remove breather pipe.
   k. remove air inlet elbow from turbocharger.
   l. remove fuel bleed-off line from "T" at right cylinder head and "T" at intake manifold.
   m. disconnect oil delivery tube nut at front of engine and position tube so that it won't interfere with the stand.

2. Mount engine in stand.
3. Check timing before disassembly. Timing is 22 BTDC.
4. Remove starter.
5. Remove alternator and mounting bracket.
6. Remove fan pulley hub and bracket.
7. Remove cross-over tube and hose.

Aligning timing marks
(© International Harvester Co.)

Installing the wear sleeve with a special installer
(© International Harvester Co.)

Installing rear main cap side oil seals
(© International Harvester Co.)

International · Diesel Engines

V-800 oil transfer sleeve

V-800 injection pump connections

8. Remove refrigerant compressor and bracket.
9. Disconnect water hose from left cylinder head thermostat housing and air compressor. Disconnect oil supply line from compressor and injection pump.
10. Unbolt and lift off air compressor. A sling hoist is helpful in

The crankshaft roll pin
(© International Harvester Co.)

that the compressor must be moved straight back, carefully, to disengage gears before lifting.
11. Remove left and right thermostat housings and thermostats.
12. Remove vibration damper from crankshaft.
13. Back the crankshaft pulley nut off about ½″ and using a suitable puller, remove the pulley. Leaving the nut in place prevents the pulley from snapping out.
14. Disconnect the fuel delivery hose, supply hose and bleed line. Lift the assembly from the head.

15. Remove the final filter reservoir.
16. Remove high pressure fuel lines between pump and right cylinder head.
17. Remove high pressure fuel lines between pump and left cylinder head. Remove two forward lines first.
18. Remove oil filler tube.
19. Remove turbocharger elbow and sleeve.
20. Remove oil return line from hose. Disconnect oil feed line at engine "V."
21. Remove oil feed and return lines from turbocharger.

Checking rod end clearance
(© International Harvester Co.)

Checking gear backlash
(© International Harvester Co.)

Enlarging the flywheel housing to dowel pin holes
(© International Harvester Co.)

Aligning the flywheel housing with the crankcase
(© International Harvester Co.)

Turn the crankshaft as necessary to insure that the counterweights are positioned away from the oil pump shaft
(© International Harvester Co.)

734

Power steering pump

22. Loosen turbocharger inlet and outlet hose clamps.
23. Remove the four turbocharger-to-support manifold lock nuts and lift unit from support manifold.
24. Remove hose between air outlet and intake manifold.
25. Remove modulator-to-intake manifold crossover air line.
26. Remove left cylinder head and injection pump leak-off lines.
27. Unbolt (6) and remove intake manifold crossover.
28. Unbolt and remove the turbocharger support manifold.
29. Remove the exhaust manifold adapters.
30. Unbolt (3) and remove the oil regulator valve housing.
31. Lift cartridge type valve assembly from engine.
32. Disconnect and remove injection pump oil supply and return lines. Remove oil pressure tube.
33. Unbolt (2) and remove accelerator rod lever from injection pump control. Unbolt (3) and remove accelerator rod bracket from left cylinder head.
34. Remove injection pump bracket-to-engine bolt.
35. Support pump in a sling hoist and remove the five retaining bolts.
36. Slide pump rearward to disengage gears.
37. Unbolt and remove fuel filter mounting adapter from right cylinder head.
38. Loosen nut at the base of the oil level gauge tube, unbolt the extension and remove the oil level gauge.
39. Loosen capscrews and remove power steering pump and

Torquing the injection pump drive hub
(© International Harvester Co.)

V-800 injection pump lower bracket

adapter from front cover plate.
40. Unbolt (4) the exhaust manifold front section and remove along with gasket.
41. Remove the three rear section bolts and remove manifold and gasket.
42. Unbolt (3) and remove the center section.
43. Repeat above three steps for opposite manifold.
44. Unbolt and remove cylinder head covers.
45. Disconnect and remove fuel return manifold.
46. Disconnect fuel supply lines at nozzle and head.

V-800 injection nozzle retainers

47. Remove injection nozzle capscrews and hold-down retainers. Remove nozzle heads.
48. Unbolt and remove rocker arm assemblies. Lift out pushrods.
49. Remove all head bolts and washers except lower center bolt. Loosen this bolt.
50. Attach lifting device to head, and take up all slack. Remove

Install the drive shaft rear bearing in the front cover
(© International Harvester Co.)

Positioning the pump drive flange
(© International Harvester Co.)

V-800 tappet removal

center bolt and lift off head.
51. Remove access hold covers and gaskets, and injection pump support bracket. Remove oil inlet tube.
52. Remove tappets through access holes.
53. Remove clutch assembly from flywheel.
54. Remove six flywheel mounting bolts, install guide pins and puller screws and remove flywheel. Guide pins can be made from $5/8$-18NF $\times$ 4″ bolts, by cutting off head.
55. Remove crankshaft rear seal.
56. Remove wear sleeve with a cold chisel.
57. Unbolt and remove oil pan.
58. Unbolt and remove a flywheel housing.
59. Remove engine front cover.
60. At this time, it is a good procedure to check camshaft end play.
61. Straighten the camshaft thrust plate capscrew locks, unbolt and remove the camshaft. This is

Installing a special locating fixture onto the pump drive flange
(© International Harvester Co.)

best done with the engine in a vertical position.

62. Remove the air compressor idler gear assembly from the front cover plate.

Removing rocker arm assembly

Removing wear sleeve

Removing main bearing caps

63. Remove the power steering pump idler gear mounting bolt. Remove idler gear and adapter.
64. Remove the oil pump inlet tube and gasket.
65. Unbolt and remove the oil pump.
66. Remove the crank pulley woodruff key with a chisel.
67. Remove the crankshaft nut.
68. Pull off crankshaft gear.
69. Remove the front cover plate.
70. Remove ridge from each cylinder.
71. Remove and mark connecting rod caps.
72. Remove pistons taking care to avoid damaging spray nozzles.
73. Unbolt and remove main bearing

caps. Mark caps for installation.
74. Using a sling hoist, lift crankshaft out of block.
75. Remove upper main halves.
76. Using a wood block and hammer, drive sleeves from block. Mark sleeves for installation.

ENGINE ASSEMBLY

DV-462B, DV-550B

1. Install the water drain cocks into the block and turn the block upside down.
2. Coat the camshaft lobes, bearing surfaces and bores, and gears with a heavy duty hypoid lubricant.
3. Use a special installer to insert the camshaft into the front of the block.
4. Install the camshaft rear bearing cover plate and gasket with the capscrews and washers.
5. Use a dial indicator, as shown, and check the camshaft end play. It should be .0035"-.0115". If end play is not to specifications, the thrust flange must be replaced.
6. Wipe and then lubricate with engine oil the cylinder block halves of the main bearings.
7. Place the bearing shell halves in position in the bores of the block, making sure that they are fully seated, that the shell oil holes line up with those in the block, and that the tangs fit snugly into the recesses.
8. Place the lower bearing shell halves in the main bearing caps, following the procedures described in step 7.
9. Relubricate all bearing surfaces, and lift the crankshaft into position, aligning the timing marks.
10. Install the bearing caps with the number toward the right side of the crankcase. Install new self locking bolts and flatwashers and tighten slightly.
11. With a soft mallet, tap each bearing cap to bring its rear machined face flush with the rear machined face on the portion of the block adjacent to it. Bearing must be flush on both left and right sides. Torque bolts to 130 ft lbs.
12. Install the bearing tie bolts and torque to 50 ft lbs.
13. Install the aligner studs of a special oil seal installer into the end of the crankshaft flange.
14. Place the seal over the end of the crankshaft aligning it with the crankcase bore.
15. Drive the seal into the bore until the outer edge is flush with the crankcase. Remove the installer and aligner studs from the crankshaft flange.
16. Insert the rear main cap side oil seals, using an installer made

Right side intake manifold
(© International Harvester Co.)

from a piece of 1/8" welding rod. Such a tool may be made from welding rod by puddling a ball on the end of the rod and filing it to about 5/32" diameter. If excess material protrudes above the crankcase after installation of the seal, cut the excess off flush with the bottom of the rear main cap mating surface.

17. Rotate the crankshaft to ensure that there is no binding between it and the camshaft. Then, hook up a dial indicator as shown and check the backlash, which should be .0005"-.0045".
18. Turn the block so the front end faces upward. Rotate the crankshaft so the crankpin for number 1 cylinder is at TDC. Lubricate the cylinder bores, crankshaft journals, pistons, pins, and rings with engine oil. Insert each piston into the ring compressor and install the assembly into the cylinder bore with the word "Top" toward the centerline of the block.
19. Lubricate each connecting rod bearing shell on both sides with engine oil, and install bearings and caps with the number matching and on the numbered side of the rod.
20. Install new bolts, caps, and lockwashers, and torque to 55 ft lbs. Release all torque load, and retorque to 55 ft lbs. Then, turn each nut an additional flat (1/6 turn).
21. Check connecting rod and play

Swirl destroyer linkages
(© International Harvester Co.)

as shown, and ensure that it is within .008"–.018".

22. Rotate the engine so the bottom of the crankcase faces upward.

23. On DV-550 engines, install the piston cooling nozzles with the locating pin engaging the hole in the crankcase. Install bolts and washers finger tight. Lower each piston in its bore to make sure the nozzle is centered in the slot in the skirt. After this is verified for each nozzle, tighten its mounting bolt to 12 ft lbs.

24. Make sure the crankshaft counterweights are positioned away from the oil pump shaft, rotating the crank as necessary. Install the oil pump, with the capscrews and lockwashers. Make sure the pump is correctly aligned in order to avoid binding.

25. Install the screen to the pump body. Place a straightedge across the pan rails of the pump body, and measure the distance from the bottom of the straightedge to the top of the pump screen at both sides. The screen should be checked and positioned so that both dimensions are 6½". Then, tighten the pump screen tube locknut to 20 ft lbs.

26. Install the screen clamp and brace, tightening the bolts evenly to avoid disturbing the screen.

27. Place the flywheel housing over the roll pins, and tap into place with a soft hammer. Install cap screws and washers, and tighten in sequence shown to 150 ft lbs. The two lower mounting capscrews require two turns of Teflon thread sealing tape. If new crankcase or flywheel housing is used, check runout as shown. It must not exceed .010". If necessary, ream roll pin holes with a tapered ½" reamer and install oversize roll pins. Align the housing with the engine mounted with the rear end upward.

28. Position the flywheel on the crankshaft flange roll pin. Install the self-locking bolts and torque to 110 ft lbs.

29. Coat the outside diameter of the clutch pilot bearing and the inside diameter of the flywheel bore with a locking compound and install the pilot bearing into the flywheel. Keep the compound from getting onto the inside of the bearing or between the flywheel and crankshaft. Allow two hours curing time.

30. Position the driven disc against the flywheel with the long portion of the hub to the rear. Position the clutch onto the flywheel over the driven disc. Locate the clutch so that the inspection mark (white paint) on the flange of the backing plate or cover is as near as possible to the "L" on the flywheel. Install the two or three mounting capscrews and lockwashers loosely.

31. Insert a clutch aligning arbor or transmission main gear shaft through the hub of the driven disc and into the pilot bearing.

32. Hold the driven disc in position while installing the mounting capscrews and lockwashers in the flange of the clutch backing plate or cover. Tighten the capscrews alternately and evenly until secure. Remove the capscrews installed to keep the clutch in a compressed position.

33. Position the gasket on front, rear, and sides of the tappet cover, and install the tappet cover with the gasket onto the crankcase with bolts and lockwashers.

34. Put a new gasket for the front cover over the dowel pins on the crankcase. Coat the right water outlet gasket with grease and position it to the crankcase, making sure the tab will not block the water passage. Install the front cover and the idler arm mounting bracket. NOTE: The second set of mounting bolts from the bottom of the front cover, and the two on the back side of the cover are Nylock bolts. It is a good practice to replace these bolts, but if a careful inspection indicates they are in good condition, they may be reused.

35. Position the front cover oil seal and a small pilot of a special installer with the wiping lip toward the outer end of the pilot. Make sure the crankshaft pulley key is removed from the end of the crankshaft, and then place the installer over the outer end of the crankshaft and drive the seal into the cover. Make sure the inner shoulder of the tool contacts the machined surface of the cover before removing the tool.

36. Assemble a retaining screw through the bore of the installer and place a ⅝" diameter adapter over the threaded end of the screw. Install the handle on the retaining screw.

37. Position the injection pump drive shaft rear bearing on the pilot of the installer and install the bearing. The bearing is properly installed on the front cover when the 5⅜" diameter adapter contacts the machined injection pump mounting surface on the front cover.

38. Mount the injection pump drive shaft into a press and use a suitable adapter to press the front bearing onto the shaft until it bottoms on the shaft flange.

39. Position the shaft and bearing into the front cover. Install the snap ring.

40. Align the pump drive gear teeth with the camshaft gear teeth. Rotate the pump drive shaft until the holes in the shaft are aligned with the holes in the drive gear. Tap the gear onto the drive shaft with a soft hammer. Install the capscrews and lockwashers and torque.

Minimal clearance exists between crankshaft
and piston cooling nozzles
(© International Harvester Co.)

Checking crankshaft endplay
(© International Harvester Co.)

Installation of drive plate, washer, and nut
(© International Harvester Co.)

(© International Harvester Co.)

41. Assemble the injection pump drive hub, grip springs, retainer, and nut, and torque the nut to 75 ft lbs.

42. Install the idler pulley arm to the mounting bracket with the spacer between the arm and the boss on the front cover. Secure the arm with a bolt and lockwasher.

43. Install the woodruff key in the front of the crankshaft and install the pulley with a special installer. Install the nut and washer, and tighten the nut.

44. Rotate crankshaft until No. 1 piston is on compression stroke, and position the shaft so that the timing point aligns with 32 degrees BTDC on 462 engines, or 34 degrees BTDC on 550 engines.

45. Position the pump drive flange so that tangs are vertical with the marked tang up. Install a special locating fixture onto the flange and engage the pin in the roll pin hole at the rear of the front cover. Install the locating fixture mounting bolts.

46. Tighten the drive shaft nut to 75 ft lbs. Remove the injection pump drive flange locating fixture.

47. Install a new gasket and the water pump body, and secure with screws and lockwashers.

48. Position the O-ring in the water pump housing, and install the pump assembly and flat head screws. Install the water pump housing, using a new Nylock screw in the lower mounting case, leaving the second and hole.

49. Install a new gasket and the oil pan to the bottom of the crank-third bolts on the right pan rail

Checking connecting rod end clearance
(© International Harvester Co.)

Checking flywheel housing runout
(© International Harvester Co.)

Installation of special adapter and sleeve
(© International Harvester Co.)

Checking flywheel housing concentricity
(© International Harvester Co.)

Rear engine mount
(© International Harvester Co.)

DVT series front mount
(© International Harvester Co.)

out for later securing of the exhaust manifold heat shield.

50. Using a special tappet installer install each tappet into its original bore.

51. Position new head gaskets over aligning dowel sleeves, making sure all gasket bolt holes are in line with crankcase holes.

52. With a special holding sling, mount each head, aligning it carefully with the crankcase dowel sleeves. Install head bolts and washers hand tight.

53. Torque head bolts alternately and evenly, in the sequence shown, to 110 ft lbs.

54. Insert each pushrod in its original position.

55. Install a valve cup on each valve stem.

56. Loosen rocker arm locknuts and back off adjusting screws.

57. Install the rocker arm assemblies, aligning rockers and valves. Install all mounting bolts loosely, check for interference at all rockers and pushrods, and then tighten the mounting bolts.

58. Position each pushrod under its rocker adjusting screw and tighten adjusting screws until they just contact the pushrods, rotating the engine as necessary.

59. Adjust the valves as described in Engine Tune-Up section.

60. Using new O-rings and gaskets, install each injector nozzle into its original bore, torquing hold-down capscrews to 15 ft lbs. Use a new Nylock screw unless careful inspection reveals the tab is in perfect condition.

61. Install valve covers with new gaskets, and secure with screws and washers.

62. Position new O-rings on the right side water outlet pipe and install it in the water outlet. Position a new O-ring in the water outlet in the front cover. Insert the end of the outlet pipe into the front cover and secure it to the right side head with capscrews and lockwashers.

63. Repeat this operation to install the opposite water outlet pipe.

64. Install the swirl destroyer mounting plate over the tappet cover studs, and secure it with the mounting nuts and lockwashers.

65. Mount bushings on the swirl destroyer shaft, placing the larger four bushings over the sleeves on the shaft.

66. Position the shaft and plates in the manifold ports with the plates in closed position, and slide the shaft over until one of the plates contacts the manifold. Back off .005″ and adjust the collars against the manifold, being careful to prevent binding, and tighten setscrews and locknuts.

67. Install a rubber band as shown in the illustration on swirl destroyer linkage, and install intake manifolds and gaskets. Install capscrews and lockwashers.

68. Connect the actuating rods to swirl destroyer linkages on both sides, adjust rod length so that plates are closed at "Start" position, and tighten locknuts.

69. Turn the injection pump drive coupling until the punch mark on the coupling tang is pointed toward the transfer pump mount-

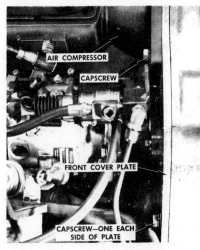

Installation of capscrews on either side of the cover plate (© International Harvester Co.)

ing flange. Rotate the crankshaft so the injection pump drive shaft flange tang which is punch marked is on top and flanges are vertical. Engage the timing indicator pin with the hole in the flywheel.

70. Install the coupling disc over the tangs of the pump drive flange.

71. Place a gasket on the pump mounting flange, and make sure the swirl destroyer flaps are in an open position.

72. Install the pump, ensuring that the coupling drive tangs engage with the holes in the coupling disc and that the pump adapter housing indexes with the roll pins. Install mounting capscrews and washers.

73. Install the injection pump support braces and bracket with capscrews, lockwashers, and flat washers.

74. Connect the fuel supply line to the secondary fuel filter.

75. Remove all dust caps, and install injection nozzle leak-off lines and grommets, and injector pump to manifold leak-off line. Install the leak-off line at the rear of the intake manifolds.

76. Put O-ring in place, and install the air compressor adapter plate to the front cover with the capscrews and lockwashers.

77. Connect the oil line located at the compressor adapter plate to the injector pump.

78. Remove all dust caps, and install the fuel supply line to the transfer pump.

79. Remove all dust caps, and install fuel injection lines, and secure them to the manifold with grommets, clips, and capscrews.

80. Remove dust caps, and install the crankcase ventilator pipe between the right cylinder head cover and intake manifold.

81. Install the water crossover pipe to the rear of the crankcase.

82. Install the water pump pulley to the hub and secure it with capscrews and lockwashers.

83. Install the oil dipstick tube.

International • Diesel Engines

84. Install the air compressor gasket, and install the air compressor onto the adapter plate.
85. Install the alternator bracket, and install the alternator.
86. Install the air conditioner compressor mounting bracket, and install the compressor.
87. Install the power steering pump mounting bracket, using a class "4" bolt in the lower mount, and install the pump to the mounting bracket.
88. Install accessory drive belts, and adjust each set by moving the compressor or pump on its mounting bracket and tightening when tension is correct.
89. Push the idler pulley inward, and install main drive belts over crankshaft, water pump, and idler pulleys. Then, tension belts and tighten idler pulley mount.
90. Insert two capscrews into either end and the middle of the oil filter and cooler base. Position the gasket against the base and start the threads of the capscrews into the gasket.
91. Place the assembly against the crankcase, and tighten the capscrews alternately to an even torque.
92. Install a new gasket and the oil cooler to the cooler base. Install the oil pressure sending unit into the cooler base.
93. Remove tape from intake manifold openings, and install gaskets and screens with "Air Cleaner Side" marking up.
94. Install the air cleaner adapter to the intake manifold.
95. Install the crankcase ventilator pipe to the right cylinder head cover and intake manifold.
96. Connect the air line from the compressor to the air cleaner adapter.
97. Install the fan to the modulated fan drive. Install the assembly to the pump hub with a special wrench. Use a heavy screwdriver against the lug on the pump body to stop one of the pulley hub spokes from turning during tightening. Tighten the nut to 40 ft lbs (left hand thread).
98. Install a lifting plate to the thermostat mounting surface and a cable affixed under the flywheel housing, attach suitable hoisting equipment and remove the engine from the overhaul stand. The steps which follow involve installing units to the engine while on the hoist:
    a. Install the crossover tube and its gasket, making connections at the water pump body and crankcase.
    b. Install the water line that runs from the crossover tube to the air compressor.
    c. Install the starting motor and its adapter to the flywheel housing.
    d. Install the exhaust manifold heat shield.
    e. Install the gasket and base for the secondary fuel filter, and connect the fuel supply lines.
    f. Install the exhaust manifolds and gaskets, torquing bolts to 30 ft lbs.
    g. Connect the water inlet line to the oil cooler and engine crossover tube.
    h. Connect the water return line from the oil cooler to the water outlet on the odd-numbered bank.
    i. Connect the oil feed line from the filter base to the tee on the air compressor adapter plate.

ENGINE ASSEMBLY
DVT-573
1. Install the water drain cocks into the block, and turn the block upside down.
2. Apply a non-hardening sealant to one side of the front plate gasket, and position the gasket on the block. Position the front plate over the gasket and dowel pins.
3. Apply a drop of thread locking compound to the threads of each capscrew, and install capscrews and washers, torquing to 30-35 ft lbs.
4. Position each cooling nozzle in its original position and install the capscrew and lockwasher.
5. Coat the lobes, bearing surfaces, gear, and bearing bores of the camshaft, and insert it into the front of the crankcase, taking care not to damage the bearings.
6. Install the capscrews and lock plates for the camshaft thrust flange, and torque the capscrews to 25-30 ft lbs. Bend lock tabs back against capscrew heads.
7. Install the camshaft gear key, and heat the camshaft gear to 250°F. Then, position the gear, timing marks outward, onto the end of the camshaft. Installation will be facilitated if the key is started before starting the gear onto the camshaft. Start the gear by tapping with a soft hammer and then using the mounting capscrews and flat washers to draw it on the shaft.
8. Remove the mounting capscrews, discard the flatwashers, replace them with external tooth lockwashers, and torque the capscrews to 25-30 ft lbs.
9. Check the camshaft end play with a dial indicator. If it is not .005"-.013", replace the camshaft thrust plate.
10. Wipe the backs of the cylinder block halves of the main bearings, and then lubricate lightly on both sides with engine oil.
11. Position each shell in the cylinder block bore, seating it fully and making sure the oil holes in the bearing shells line up with those in the block. Make sure, also, that the locking tangs on the bearings fit into the recesses.
12. Repeat steps 11 and 12 for the lower shells, and install them into the caps.
13. Lubricate all bearing surfaces with engine oil, and install the crankshaft, aligning the timing marks (two dots) on the camshaft gear with the dot on the crankshaft gear.
14. Install the bearing caps in numbered order, starting at the front of the engine. Use self locking bolts and lockwashers, and torque to 275-300 ft lbs. Check crankshaft end play for conformance to .003"-.011" specifications.
15. Rotate the crankshaft to check that there is no binding of the gears . Check gear backlash with a dial indicator (.007"-.013").
16. Position the block so the front end faces upward. Turn the crank so the No. 1 crankpin is at TDC. Coat the cylinder bore, crankshaft journal, piston, pin and rings for No. 1 cylinder with engine oil. Insert the piston into the ring compressor, and install the assembly into No. 1 cylinder with the "CAMSIDE" marking facing the centerline of the block. Avoid damage to the piston cooling nozzle during this operation, as there is minimal clearance. Coat all connecting rod bearing surfaces with engine oil. Install the cap with the numbered side matching and on the numbered side of the rod. The large chamfer side of the rod and cap will be to the fillet side of the crankpin. Install new connecting rod cap bolts, and torque to 100-110 ft lbs. Repeat this procedure for all remaining cylinders.
17. Check the conecting rod end play, as shown. End play must be .008"-.020".
18. Wipe off the rear face of the crankcase and flywheel housing, apply a thin film of a non-hardening sealer, and install a new gasket.
19. Put the housing in position over the two dowel pins, install capscrews and lockwashers, and torque evenly.
20. Attach a flywheel housing aligner and a dial indicator to the crankshaft flange, and place the indicator pointer against the fly-

wheel housing flange. Remove the crankshaft end play, record the indicator reading, and then rotate the assembly around the housing, reading it at four points, 90 degrees apart. Keep the end play at zero throughout the operation. Runout must not exceed .008″.

21. Position the indicator needle against the inside bore of the flywheel housing (see illustration). Read the indicator, and then rotate the crankshaft slowly and record the greatest variation. It must not exceed .008″.

22. Install a new rear oil seal with a special installer (do not drive the seal onto the crankshaft), as follows:
    a. Clean the crankshaft seal surface, and inspect it to ensure that it is free of burrs or nicks.
    b. Inspect the surface of the flywheel housing where the oil seal face plate is installed, remove burrs with a stone, and thoroughly clean the area.
    c. Fasten an adapter to the crankshaft flange with two special bolts. Remove the protective cover from the oil seal and place the seal on the cover, teflon surface outward.
    d. Position the sleeve on the adapter.
    e. Install the drive plate, washer, and nut.
    f. Carefully tighten the nut until the drive plate legs seat on the flywheel housing.
    g. Remove the installing tool.
    h. Lube the seal face of the oil seal face plate with engine oil. Install the face plate and gasket. Torque the capscrews to 18-20 ft lbs.

23. Install the guide pins into the crankshaft flange. Position the flywheel over the pins, lining up all holes. Draw the flywheel onto the dowel pins using four of the capscrews.

24. Remove the four capscrews and the guide pins. Install the six flywheel capscrews and their locks, torque to 210-230 ft lbs, and bend the locks over the capscrew heads.

25. Install the clutch pilot bearing. Install the front driven disc (the disc whose hub protrudes approximately an equal distance on either side) with the riveted hub flange toward the transmission.

26. Place four square headed driving pins in the flywheel square with the flywheel face. Install two Allen setscrews to secure each drive pin. Install the intermediate plate in the flywheel, and index it with the driving pins.

27. Install the rear driven disc with the longer toward the rear of the transmission. Install the clutch assembly, aligning the splines of the driven discs with the pilot bearing through use of a main drive gear shaft or aligning bar.

28. Tighten the capscrews around the flywheel ring uniformly. Remove the spacer blocks and aligning bar from the clutch assembly.

29. Position the oil outlet pipe in the oil pump cover, and bolt the oil pump to the No. 1 main bearing cap. Bolt the outlet pipe to the No. 2 main cap, making sure that the end is engaged with the opening in the right side of the crankcase. Check the backlash of the gears with a dial indicator, as shown. Limits are .004″-.014″.

30. Lubricate the transfer tube O-rings with engine oil and install it in the opening on the right side of the crankcase, checking for proper engagement with the oil outlet tube.

31. Mount the injection pump drive assembly, including bearings, shaft, spring, and O-ring, to the back of the front cover plate with the four capscrews and lockwashers.

32. Slide the injection pump drive gear onto the shaft, aligning its timing mark with the two marks on the camshaft gear, as shown. Install the capscrews and external tooth lockwashers, and torque to 21-24 ft lbs.

33. Insert the power steering pump idler gear spacer into the front cover plate. Place the adapter and bolt in the idler gear bearing, and install the gear to the front of the crankcase. Torque the bolt to 140-160 ft lbs.

34. Install each tappet in its bore through the access openings in the crankcase.

35. Lubricate the cylinder head contacting surfaces, bolts, and lockwashers with engine oil. Check that threaded crankcase holes are free of oil to prevent hydraulic lock.

36. Install one of the cylinder head gaskets, and hoist the head for that side onto the engine, fitting it over the crankcase dowels. Install, but do not torque, the 12 short bolts.

37. Install the pushrods. Install the rocker arm assembly, applying an inward pressure to each bracket in order to hold the assembly until the end brackets locate on the cylinder head dowels.

38. Back off all rocker adjustments, and insert each into its pushrod. Then, install the four long head bolts.

39. Torque the cylinder head bolts, as described under "Torquing Cylinder Heads, DVT-573".

40. Repeat steps 35-39 for the other cylinder head.

41. Clean the nozzle sleeves using a *soft* object, such as a cloth wrapped around a stick.

42. Install a new O-ring on each nozzle assembly, install each in its original bore, and torque the hold-down bolts alternately as follows:
    a. First Bolt: 3-4 ft lbs.
    b. Second Bolt: 3-4 ft lbs.
    c. First Bolt: 5-8 ft lbs.
    d. Second Bolt: 5-8 ft lbs.
    e. First Bolt: 8-12 ft lbs.
    f. Second Bolt: 8-12 ft lbs.
    g. Recheck torque of first bolt.

43. Install all but the left-rear access hole cover, making sure each has a gasket and plastic washers under all capscrews.

44. Install the oil pressure regulator valve and housing, using a new gasket.

45. Rotate the oil pump drive shaft until the blind shaft spline matches that inside the pump drive assembly on the rear of the front cover plate. Install the pump into the pump drive assembly. Install the mounting capscrews, and secure the adapter plate to the flange of the pump drive housing.

46. Install the oil inlet line to pressure regulator valve housing, securing the clip on the line to the front of the right head with capscrew, lockwasher, and flat washer.

47. Apply a non-hardening sealer to one side of the front cover gasket, and install the gasket onto the front cover. Trim the gasket so it is flush with the bottom of the front cover.

48. Lift the front cover onto the locating dowels, and carefully tap it into place. Install the capscrews, lockwashers, and flatwashers to the locations arrowed in the illustration. Install one capscrew, and related lockwasher and flat washer, on each side, from the back side of the cover plate.

49. Mount the fan pulley and bracket assembly onto the front cover with the two lower mounting capscrews and their lockwashers and flat washers. Do not torque the capscrews. Install the adjusting screw and its flatwasher.

50. Mount the alternator mounting bracket to the front cover plate with the two upper mounting capscrews, lockwashers, and flatwashers, and nuts. The leak-off line junction block must be on the uppermost capscrew.

51. Install the capscrew (with flatwasher installed) through the

fan pulley and bracket assembly, front cover, and alternator bracket. Install the nut and lockwasher.

52. Remove all plastic caps and plugs, and install the fuel injection lines and damper.
53. Install the leak-off lines, connecting to nozzles and junction block.
54. Connect the appropriate hose between the elbow on the right head and the aneroid control valve.
55. Install the leak-off line that runs between the injection pump and the elbow at the junction block.
56. Install the accelerator cross shaft bracket and gasket to the left head with the three capscrews and lockwashers. The final line damper must be under the head of the rear capscrew.
57. Install the final fuel filter bracket, with gasket, to the right head. Install the capscrews and lockwashers, making sure the fuel line damper is installed under the head of the rear screw, and the safety switch tee is under the front screw.
58. Install the oil line to the galley fitting in the V of the block, and to the safety switch tee.
59. Install the final filter to its mounting bracket with four capscrews and lockwashers.
60. Connect the fuel line to the final filter and injection pump.
61. Position thermostats into their housings and install each housing into its position on the appropriate head with capscrews and lockwashers.
62. Mount the air compressor and gasket to the front cover plate, engaging the compressor gear with the injection pump drive gear, with the capscrews, flatwashers, lockwashers, and nuts. The alternator adjusting strap goes under the top right capscrew on the front cover.
63. Connect the water inlet and outlet lines between the air compressor and left thermostat housing.
64. Connect the air inlet pipe between the compressor and left cylinder head.
65. Connect the compressor oil feed line between the oil gallery fitting in the V of the block and the compressor.
66. Install the accelerator cross shaft to the bracket, and connect the throttle rod between the cross shaft and injection pump.
67. Install the accelerator mounting bracket to the bracket on the front cover plate.
68. Position the alternator on its bracket, and install the capscrews and nuts, but do not tighten. Attach the adjusting

strap with the capscrews, flatwasher, and lockwasher, and tighten finger tight.

69. Apply an anti-seize compound to the slip joint of each exhaust manifold section and, using new gaskets and bolt locks, install the manifold, one section at a time, starting at the front. Apply anti-seize to the bolts, and leave the bolts slightly loose until all sections are in place. Then, torque the bolts to 100-120 ft lbs. Bend the lock tabs.
70. Install the Woodruff key into the crankshaft, and then install the crankshaft pulley and nut, and torque to 325-375 ft lbs.
71. Position the power steering pump gasket onto the front cover plate, and insert the pump into the plate, engaging the drive and idler gears. Install capscrews, flat washers, lockwashers, and nuts.
72. Check that the oil drain line O-ring is in its groove in the left hand rear tappet access cover, and position the access cover on the drain line.
73. Inspect the turbocharger compressor mounting pads on the cylinder head for flatness and complete removal of old gasket material. Position the adapters with O-rings installed onto the turbocharger compressor housing.
74. Position the turbocharger on the mounting pads. Insert the gaskets between the adapters and heads, and install the adapter and bracket mounting capscrews and lockwashers finger tight.
75. Loosen the compressor and turbine clap bolt nuts, and tighten the adapter and bracket mounting capscrews.
76. Coat the joints of the turbocharger inlet exhaust elbows with anti-seize compound, and install elbows and gaskets to the turbine housing. Install mounting capscrews, coating the threads with anti-seize compound. Torque both clamp bolt nuts to 8-12 ft lbs.
77. Insert the exhaust sleeve, with seal rings installed, into the turbine housing. Install the exhaust elbow and bracket, connecting it to the turbocharger and flywheel housing.
78. Slide the access hole cover down on the oil drain line, and mount it onto the crankcase.
79. Force 4-5 oz. of engine oil into the turbocharger bearing housing.
80. Install the turbocharger oil inlet filter screen, gaskets, and a special break-in oil pressure line to the turbocharger. Connect the other end of the oil line to the oil

galley. After 5-25 hrs. of operation, the screen and run-in line are replaced with a regular line.

81. Install the vent line, making connections at the bearing housing and the right rear access hole cover.
82. Attach the oil filler elbow and its gasket to the flywheel housing.
83. Install the oil pan and gasket.
84. Install the starting motor to the flywheel housing, and torque capscrews to 105-120 ft lbs.
85. Connect the dipstick tube to the oil pan and clip it to the exhaust manifold.
86. Adjust the valve tappets as described in Engine Tune-Up section.
87. Install the valve covers with new gaskets.
88. Mount the engine front mounting bracket to the front cover. Install the rear mounting brackets to the flywheel housing.
89. Hoist the engine out of the overhaul stand, using a chain fastened to both lifting eyes. Proceed with the steps below with the engine on the hoist.
90. Assemble the oil filter base, cooler, and water pump assembly to the crankcase, using a new gasket between the filter base and crankcase.
91. Install the elbow between the transfer sleeve and oil filter base, using a new O-ring.
92. With a new O-ring in the flange, install the oil inlet line to the oil cooler.
93. Install new oil filters and gaskets, and mount filter cases, torquing mounting bolts to -5-20 ft lbs.
94. Install the hose and clamps between the right thermostat housing and water pump connection.
95. Install the crossover pipe, and its hoses and clamps between the left thermostat housing and the water pump connection.
96. Install the main drive and accessory belts, and tension so that 1/2" deflection is possible halfway between pulleys.
97. Connect the hose elbow and clamp to the breather on the right rear cylinder head cover.
98. Position the breather pipe in the elbow, and clip the pipe to the right valve cover rear stud with the clip, flat washer, and lockwasher.

V-800

1. Apply Permatex #2 or equivalent to one side of the front plate gasket and install front plate. Torque bolts to 35 ft lbs. Use Loctite "B" on threads.
2. If removed, install piston cooling nozzles in crankcase.
3. Coat camshaft and bore with

Aligning camshaft timing marks

MT-16633

Piston in holding tool

heavy duty hypoid axle oil and insert camshaft into place.

4. Install and torque thrust plate to 30 ft lbs.

5. If camshaft gear was removed, heat gear to 250°F and install on shaft over key using a soft hammer. As soon as retainer plate clears a few threads, press the gear on with the retainer capscrews. Torque capscrews to 30 ft lbs.

6. Lubricate and install upper main valves. Position crankshaft in block, oil the journals and install the lower halves and caps. Make certain the timing marks align. Use new cap bolts; check bearing fit with Plastigage. Torque main caps to 390 ft lbs.

7. Rotate crankshaft and camshaft to check for binding and backlask. Backlash should be .002"-.014".

8. Coat pistons, pins, rings, bores and journals with engine oil. Position respective crank pin on top of travel and insert piston assembly. Number on piston is toward center of engine. Take care to avoid damage to the piston cooling nozzles. There is very little clearance between the bottom of the rod and the nozzle.

9. Coat bearing surfaces with engine oil and install bearing caps. Numbered sides of rod and cap should match. Use new cap bolts and torque to 130 ft lbs.

10. Check connecting rod end play—.008"-.020".

11. Install flywheel housing and gasket. Tighten capscrews evenly.

12. Check flywheel housing runout with a dial indicator adapted off of the crankshaft flange. The indicator pointer should rest on the housing flange. Check reading at four 90° opposed points. Crankshaft endplay should be held at zero. T.I.R. = .008".

13. Check housing concentricity in the same manner with indicator pointer on the inside flange surface. T.I.R. = .008".

14. Install crankshaft rear wear sleeve and oil seal. Do not at-

tempt to install the seal and sleeve without installer tool SE-2205 or its equivalent. Do not drive the seal or sleeve into place. Lip on oil seal faces inward.

15. Install guide pins into crankshaft flange and position flywheel so that attaching bolts can be started. Draw up bolts evenly and torque to 235 ft lbs.

16. Install pilot bearing.

17. Position the oil inlet pipe and gasket on the oil pump cover.

18. Install the oil pump by bolting the pump to the #1 main bearing cap; the outlet pipe to the #2 main bearing cap, and the inlet pipe to the #3 and 4 main bearing caps.

19. Check gear backlash: between pumping gears—.008"-.012"; between idler gears and crankshaft gear: .004"-.014".

20. Lubricate and install the transfer tube in the right side of the block.

21. For injection pump installation, see the section entitled "Injector Pump Timing."

22. Insert power steering pump idler gear spacer in front cover plate. Position adapter and bolt in idler gear bearing. Install gear in front of block. Torque bolt to 150 ft lbs.

23. Install tappets in their bores as marked.

24. Connect oil delivery tube between oil filters and regulating valve.

25. Lubricate cylinder head mating surfaces, position new head gaskets on the block and install heads with the aid of a hoist.

26. Lubricate the bolt threads and flat washers with Nolykote "G" or equivalent; install and snug the eleven short bolts.

27. Install pushrods.

28. Lubricate and install valve bridges.

29. Install valve lever assembly by applying inward pressure on each end bracket until brackets are located on cylinder head.

30. Back-off adjusting screws and seat lever balls in pushrod sockets and valve lever bridges. Install and snug the nine long head bolts.

31. Torque the head bolts in sequence in the following four steps: 100, 160, 185, back-off ¼ turn then go to 205 ft lbs. After run-in, torque to 220 ft lbs.

32. Clean nozzle sleeves, place new O-rings and gaskets on nozzles, install nozzles in bores with retainers and bolts. Torque bolts to 35 ft lbs.

33. Install access hole covers.

34. Install pressure regulating valve and housing with gasket.

35. Connect oil delivery tube loosely to housing.

36. Install new gasket on front cover and install cover over dowels. Tap into place. Install capscrews.

37. Position the two machined blocks behind the engine front plate (the 3-hole block to the left). Position the bracket and pulley assembly and thread in the adjusting bolt to support the weight of the assembly. Install the four capscrews but don't tighten until belts are installed.

38. Install the fuel filter mounting adapter and gasket to the right cylinder head.

39. Install the alternator mounting bracket.

40. Install the alternator adjusting strap and lifting eye.

41. Flush and install high pressure fuel lines. Torque connections to 20 ft lbs.

42. Install leak-off manifold to injection nozzles.

MT-16643

Valve lash adjustment

RIGHT BANK

E CYL. I No.2	E CYL. I No.4	E CYL. I No.6	E CYL. I No.8 E

FRONT OF ENGINE

E CYL. I No.1	E CYL. I No.3	E CYL. I No.5	E CYL. I No.7 I

LEFT BANK

E - EXHAUST VALVE   I - INTAKE VALVE   MT-16642

Valve arrangement

43. If front cover oil seal was replaced. install new wear sleeve.
44. Install crankshaft pulley and torque nut to 425 ft lbs.
45. Install vibration damper and torque nuts evenly.
46. Install oil pan and new gasket. Torque capscrews to:
    3/8 NC—25-30 ft lbs.
    1/2 NC—65-75 ft lbs.
47. Adjust valves cold as follows:
    a. Bring no. 1 to TDC compression.
    b. Adjust intakes 1, 2, 4, 5; exhausts 1, 3, 7, 8.
    c. Turn crankshaft one revolution and bring #6 to TDC compression.
    d. Adjust intakes 3, 6, 7, 8; exhausts 2, 4, 5, 6.

To Perform An Adjustment:

a. Loosen the bridge adjusting screw nut and back out screw several turns.
b. Hold bridge firmly against guide to contact cam side valve. There should be no contact between the opposite valve and bridge adjusting screw.
c. Set the lash on the cam side valve. Leave feeler in place, hold bridge firmly against rocker adjust rocker screw so that feeler is snug and torque nut to 35 ft lbs.
d. Set lash on opposite side in the same manner. Torque nut to 25 ft lbs.
48. Install head covers and torque capscrews to 25 ft lbs.
49. Install lube oil return line between the injection pump and tappet access cover.
50. Install injection pump linkage and bracket.
51. Install lube line between engine "V" and alternator bracket.
52. Install lube line between rear of alternator bracket and injection pump.
53. Install power steering pump, adapter and gasket into front cover. Install and tighten capscrews and washers.
54. Install intake manifold and gaskets. Tighten capscrews carefully. Install the aneroid sensing tube.

55. Connect all fuel return piping at the intake manifold.
56. Using a sling, install air compressor and new gasket. Torque capscrews to 45 ft lbs.
57. Connect the oil supply line between the compressor and the injection pump.
58. Install thermostats and housings.
59. Connect air compressor hoses to the left thermostat housing.
60. Install the refrigerant compressor and brackets to the front cover and left thermostat housing.
61. Cost exhaust couplings with anti-seize compound and insert into manifolds.
62. Place the turbocharger support manifold on the block and loosely install the four bolts.
63. Starting from the front, install the exhaust manifold one section at a time.
64. Torque all bolts *after* all sections are in place. Torque to 85 ft lbs. and retorque after run-up.
65. Lower the turbocharger into place, guiding the oil return pipe and air outlet into their hoses.
66. Carefully align unit and tighten mounting nuts. Tighten hose clamps to 45 ft lbs.
67. Install the turbocharger oil supply line.
68. Install idler pulley bracket and turnbuckle to front cover.
69. Install starter. Torque bolts to 110 ft lbs.
70. Install oil dipstick tube.
71. Install final filter-reservoir assembly.
72. Install the bleed line to the tee on the cylinder head.
73. Connect the hoses from the fuel reservoir to the forward injection pump fitting and from the final filter to the rear of the transfer pump.
74. Install the alternator; do not tighten bolts.
75. Install fan and spacer.
76. Install the front engine mount bracket to the front cover.
77. Install the rear engine mount brackets to the flywheel housing.
78. Install the oil fill tube.
79. Attach hoist and remove engine from stand.
80. Remove the forward filter body

and install the oil cooler and filter assembly.
81. Install filter body and drain plugs.
82. Connect oil delivery tube to the oil regulating valve housing and filter assembly.
83. Using a new oiled O-ring install the water pump.
84. Install the by-pass hoses and pipe from the thermostat to the water pump.
85. Install turbocharger air inlet elbow.
86. Install and adjust drive belts.
87. Close all drain plugs and petcocks.
88. Check all hoses and fittings for tightness.

ENGINE INSTALLATION

General

1. Check to be sure that all lines, cables, and similar parts removed from the engine assembly are properly reinstalled. Check all visible connections on units removed.
2. Exercise care throughout reinstallation to avoid pinching the wiring harness.

DV-462B, DV-550B

1. Lower the engine and align the main drive gear spline of the transmission with the clutch driven disc. Install flywheel housing to bell housing bolts and torque to 150 ft lbs. Install front mount components, and torque locknuts to 95-105 ft lbs. Install the rear mount components, and torque the locknuts to 95-105 ft lbs. Torque mounting bracket to fllywheel housing bolts to 150 ft lbs.
2. Connect the wiring, pipes, hoses, and linkages that were disconnected at removal.
3. Remove the lifting plate and cable.
4. Install the thermostats into the front cover. Position the gasket over the thermostats, checking that the air compressor return line hole or cooling system bleeder hole is open, and install the housing. Connect the air compressor water return line to the engine water outlet.
5. Install the compressor governor and governor line.
6. Install the secondary fuel filter as described on the filter body.
7. Install new O-rings on the oil filter base, lubricate them with engine oil, and insert the mounting bolt into the filter body. Place a new element in the body bearing the description "DIESEL LUBE FILTER."
8. Mount the oil filter body to the base, and torque the bolt to 25-35 ft lbs.

9. Repeat 7 and 8 for the other filter.
10. Install the radiator support assembly. Install the radiator into the support. Install the radiator side panels.
11. Install the grille or shutter, and connect the shutter linkage to the cylinder.
12. Install the radiator stay rods.
13. Install the upper and lower radiator hoses and their clamps.
14. Latch both splash panels into position. Install hood and fenders, and attach the hood stop cables to the supports at the radiator. Attach the front bumper to the frame.
15. Connect the battery ground strap and fill the cooling system.
16. If possible, prime the engine lubricating system. DO NOT ROTATE CRANKSHAFT.
17. Fill the crankcase with the proper quantity of oil.
18. Start the engine and operate to determine that all controls are functioning properly. Check for air, water, and oil leaks.

DVT-573

1. Lower the engine into the frame and align front and rear mountings. Install front mount components, and torque locknuts to 80-100 ft lbs. Assemble the rear mounts and note that the insulators are in the carriers. Lower the rear mounting brackets, check that the insulators are still properly located, and install and tighten bolts and nuts.
2. Connect wiring, lines, hoses, and linkage disconnected during removal.
3. Remove the hoisting equipment and lifting chain.
4. Connect transmission and controls.
5. Connect exhaust and air intake lines to the turbocharger.
6. Connect the battery ground strap.
7. Fill the cooling system.
8. Prime the engine lubricating system, if possible. DO NOT ROTATE CRANKSHAFT.
9. Fill the crankcase to the proper level.
10. Start the engine and operate it to determine that all controls are functioning properly. Check for air, water, and oil leaks.

V-800

1. Install in reverse of removal instructions. Take note of the following:
2. Install transmission and controls *after* removing hoisting equipment.
3. Connect exhaust and air induction systems to turbocharger.
4. Connect battery ground; fill cooling system.
5. Fill crankcase and prime engine. Inspect all hose connections.

Turbocharger-exploded view

Key	Description	Key	Description
1	HOUSING, Turbine	13	RING, Plate Seal
2	CLAMP, Housing (3)	14	COLLAR, Thrust
3	PLATE, Lock (3)	15	BEARING, Inboard Thrust
4	SCREW, Hex Hd Cap (6)	16	BEARING, Shaft (2)
5	CLAMP, V-Band	17	RING, Retaining (3)
6	HOUSING, Compressor	18	HOUSING, Rotating
7	CORE ASSEMBLY	19	RING, Piston Seal
8	NUT, Impeller Lock	20	WHEEL and SHAFT, Turbine
9	WHEEL, Impeller	21	SCREW, Hex Hd Cap (4)
10	PLATE, Back	22	PLATE, Bolt Lock (4)
11	RING, Piston	23	WASHER, Bearing (2)
12	SPACER, Thrust	24	SHROUD, Turbine Wheel

Turbocharger AiResearch Units

Pre-Disassembly Checks

1. Check free-spin of wheels.
2. Position a magnetic dial indicator on a vise, clamp and support the unit and measure the axial end play at the shaft end. T.I.R. should be .003-.008".
3. Remove oil drain cover and position dial indicator pointer on shaft and check radial shaft movement. T.I.R. should be .003-.007".

Disassembly

1. Cover intake and exhaust ports; wash unit in safe solvent.
2. Mark all components prior to disassembly.
3. Remove the clamp and lift the turbine housing, with center housing attached, from the compressor housing.
4. Remove the capscrews and lockplates securing the center housing to the turbine housing. Separate housings by tapping with a rubber mallet.
   CAUTION: Never rest the center housing on either the compressor or turbine wheel.
5. Support the center housing in an oil filled container with the compressor wheel submerged. Heat the oil to 350°F for ten minutes.
6. Support the hot unit in a press and force the shaft from the wheel.
7. Loosen, but don't remove the bolts securing the center housing to the back plate.
8. Invert the center housing and remove the bolts and lock plates.
9. Remove the spacer, collar and bearing from the center housing.
10. Remove the seal ring from its groove.

Position of related parts

Bearing removal

11. Remove the bearing and washer from the compressor side.
12. Invert the center housing and remove the retainer ring, bearing and washer from the turbine end.
13. Remove the piston ring from the thrust spacer and shaft.

Assembly

1. Install new inboard retainers into grooves in the center housing bore. Round edge of retainer is to be toward bearing.
2. Install the washers in the center housing bore and install lubricated bearings until they bottom on washers.
3. Install new bearing retainer in the turbine end of the center housing.
4. Install a new piston ring into the groove on the shaft.
5. Place the shroud over the turbine end of the center housing. Insert the shaft through the shroud and center housing. A gentle rocking and pushing action should suffice.
6. Slip the bearing over the shaft. The hole and cutout must engage the anti-rotating pins in the center housing.
7. Install a new seal ring onto the spacer. Install the spacer into the bore of the thrust collar.
8. Install the collar, with spacer, over the shaft and on to the bearing.

9. Install a new seal ring in the compressor side.
10. Align the marks and install the back plate over the shaft and thrust spacer. Install capscrews and torque to 80-100 in lbs.
11. Using the same heating process as for disassembly, press the compressor wheel onto the shaft. Tighten the lock nut, using two wrenches to 120 in lbs. hot. When assembly has cooled below 150°F remove the lock nut. Reinstall the locknut and torque to 18-20 in lbs. and $\frac{1}{3}$ turn.
12. Check wheel free spin.
13. Align marks and install center housing into turbine housing.
14. Install clamps, lockplates and bolts. Torque bolts to 160-190 in lbs.
15. Align marks and install the compressor housing. Install clamps and torque nut to 100-130 in lbs.
16. Check for free rotation.

ENGINE LUBRICATION SYSTEM

GENERAL SPECIFICATIONS

ENGINE MODEL	BORE & STROKE	PISTON DISP. CU. IN.	HORSEPOWER @ R.P.M.	TORQUE @ R.P.M.	FIRING ORDER*	GOVERNOR SPEED NO LOAD	IDLE SPEED R.P.M.
END 465	4⁷/₁₆ x 5	464	110 @ 2600	253 @ 1600	1-5-3-6-2-4	2800	500-575
END 465B	4⁷/₁₆ x 5	464	140 @ 2600	325 @ 1600	1-5-3-6-2-4	2800	500-575
END 465C	4⁷/₁₆ x 5	464	155 @ 2600	350 @ 1600	1-5-3-6-2-4	2800	500-575
END 475	4.53 x 4.92	475	140 @ 2400	350 @ 1300	1-5-3-6-2-4	2600	450
ENDT 475	4.53 x 4.92	475	190 @ 2400	470 @ 1500	1-5-3-6-2-4	2600	500
END 673	4⁷/₈ x 6	672	176 @ 2100	496 @ 1200	1-5-3-6-2-4	2270	500-575
END 673B	4⁷/₈ x 6	672	176 @ 2100	496 @ 1200	1-5-3-6-2-4	2270	500-575
END 673A	4⁷/₈ x 6	672	155 @ 2100	426 @ 1400	1-5-3-6-2-4	2270	500-575
END 673C	4⁷/₈ x 6	672	187 @ 2100	527 @ 1400	1-5-3-6-2-4	2270	500-575
END 673P	4⁷/₈ x 6	672	187 @ 2100	527 @ 1400	1-5-3-6-2-4	2270	500-575
END 673E	4⁷/₈ x 6	672	180 @ 2100	540 @ 1400	1-5-3-6-2-4	2270	500-575
ENDT 673	4⁷/₈ x 6	672	225 @ 2100	653 @ 1500	1-5-3-6-2-4	2265	500-575
ENDT 673A	4⁷/₈ x 6	672	225 @ 2100	653 @ 1600	1-5-3-6-2-4	2320	500-575
ENDT 673B	4⁷/₈ x 6	672	250 @ 2100	704 @ 1500	1-5-3-6-2-4	2310	500-575
ENDT 673C	4⁷/₈ x 6	672	250 @ 2100	704 @ 1500	1-5-3-6-2-4	2310	500-575
ETAZ 673A	4⁷/₈ x 6	672	315 @ 1900	1050 @ 1450	1-5-3-6-2-4 .		
ENDT 675	4⁷/₈ x 6	672	237 @ 1700	906 @ 1200	1-5-3-6-2-4	2270	500-575
ENDT 676ESI	4⁷/₈ x 6	672	285 @ 2100	1080 @ 1200	1-5-3-6-2-4	2310	525-575
END 711	5 x 6	707	211 @ 2100	602 @ 1350	1-5-3-6-2-4	2270	500-575
END 711A	5 x 6	707	211 @ 2100	602 @ 1350	1-5-3-6-2-4	2270	500-575
END 707	5 x 6	707	195 @ 1950	550 @ 1600	1-5-3-6-2-4	2280	500-575
ENDD 711	5 x 6	707	200 @ 2100	602 @ 1350	1-5-3-6-2-4	2185	500-575
END 864	5 x 5½	864	255 @ 2300	639 @ 1700	1-5-4-8-6-3-7-2	2500	500-575
END 864B	5 x 5½	864	270 @ 2300	672 @ 1600	1-5-4-8-6-3-7-2	2500	500-575
ENDD 864	5 x 5½	864	237 @ 2000	686 @ 1400	1-5-4-8-6-3-7-2	2190	550-575
ENDT 864	5 x 5½	864	300 @ 2300	788 @ 1600	1-5-4-8-6-3-7-2	2500	550-575
ENDT 865	5¼ x 5	866	325 @ 2100	1100 @ 1350	1-5-4-8-6-3-7-2	2650	600-650
ENDT 866	5¼ x 5	866	375 @ 2200	1040 @ 1600	1-5-4-8-6-3-7-2	2500	600-650

CRANKSHAFT AND BEARING SPECIFICATIONS

ENGINE SERIES	MAIN BEARING JOURNAL DIAMETER	MAIN BEARING CLEARANCE	ROD BEARING JOURNAL DIAMETER	SHAFT END PLAY	ROD BEARING CLEARANCE
END 465	3.4970-3.4980	.002-.004	2.7470-2.7480	.0040-.0110	.0010-.0035
END 475	3.3465	.002-.0045	2.9510	.0020-.0100	.0020-.0040
END(T) 673, 711, ETAZ 673	3.9980-3.9990	.002-.0045	2.9970-2.9980	.0040-.0110	.0011-.0036
ENDT 675, 676	3.9980-3.9990	.002-.005	2.9970-2.9980	.0040-.0110	.0011-.0036
END(T) 864	3.9980-3.9990	.0025-.0055	3.4970-3.4980	.0040-.0110	.0015-.0045
ENDT 865, 866	3.9980-3.9990	①	3.747-3.748	.0040-.0110	.002-.005

① Engines after Nov. 15, 1974—.0026-.0056
Engines before Nov. 15, 1974—.0016-.0046

PISTONS, PINS, RINGS SPECIFICATIONS

ENGINE SERIES	PISTON CLEARANCE	PISTON PIN DIAMETER	PISTON TO PIN BUSHING CLEARANCE	RING END GAP COMP.	RING END GAP OIL
END 465	.0060-.0070	1.4366	.0001-.0003	.0130-.0250	.0130-.0250①
END 475	.0060	1.6538-1.6540	.0001-.0003	.0200-.0280②	.0120-.0240
END(T) 673, 711, ETAZ 673	.0050-.0070①	1.8742-1.8743⑥	.0001-.0002	.0130-.0250③	.0130-.0250④
ENDT 675, 676	.0050-.0070	1.9988-1.9990	.0001-.0002	.0130-.0250	.0130-.0250
END(T) 864	.0081-.0099	1.8744-1.8743	.0001-.0002	.0150-.0320	.0150-.0320⑤
ENDT 865, 866	.0080	2.1240-2.1241	.0002-.0005	.0150-.0320	.0150-.0320

① Figures apply to 673 engines only. For 711 engines, figures are: .008"-.010".
② Figure refers to #1 ring. #2 and #3 are .0120"-.0240".
③ Figures are for 673 engines. For 711 engines, figures are: .008"-.010".
④ One piece U-shaped ring requires no end gap. Figures are for 673 engines. For 711 engines, figures are: .008"-.010".
⑤ One piece U-shaped ring requires no end gap.
⑥ ENDT 673—1.9988-1.9989

R.H. Side of ENDT475

L.H. Side of ENDT475

CYLINDER HEAD BOLT TIGHTENING SEQUENCE

Cylinder Head Nut Torquing
Sequence END465 Series

Cylinder Head Nut Torquing
Sequence END, T673 and 711 (5/8 in. Stud)

Cylinder Head Nut Torquing
Sequence END475 Series

Cylinder Head Nut Torquing
Sequence END, T, 864 Series

Cylinder Head Nut Torquing
Sequence END673 and 711 (3/4 in. Stud at
15 & 18 Locations)

ENGINE TORQUE SPECIFICATIONS

ENGINE SERIES	CYLINDER HEAD FT. LBS.	MAIN BEARING BOLTS FT. LBS.	CONN. ROD BOLTS FT. LBS.	ROCKER BRACKET CAPS FT. LBS.	FLYWHEEL MOUNTING NUTS FT. LBS.	CORE PLUGS FT. LBS.
465	150	150①	150①	40①	150-175②	40-50
475	140①	150	80①	40	149	—
673, 711	150③	150④	150①	55①	150-175	40-50
675, 676	175	200	150①	55①	150-175	40-50
864	175①⑤	240①⑥	150①	55①	150①	40-50
865, 866	225①	350①⑦	175①	35	150①	40-50

① Oiled
② Nylock—150
③ 5/8" nuts—175, 3/4"—300
④ 1 1/16"—200
⑤ 1 1/16"—235 oiled
⑥ Turbocharged—275 oiled
⑦ Buttress Screw—100 oiled

Trouble Diagnosis

Engine Cranks, Will Not Start

1. Emergency Shutoff Valve Closed
2. Air Intake Manifold Closed
3. Fuel Tank Vent Plugged
4. Temperature Too Low (Use Starting Aid)
5. Fuel Pump Inoperative, Leaks
6. Injection Pump Rack Stuck
7. Governor Problems
8. Injection Pump Worn, Incorrectly Adjusted
9. Poor Compression

Engine Runs, All Cylinders Fire Erratically

1. Low Fuel Pressure
2. Improper Governor Idle Adjustment
3. Air Intake Manifold Valve Partly Closed
4. Restricted Air Intake, Clogged Air Cleaner

5. Injection Pump Worn, Improperly Adjusted
6. Low Compression
7. Leaky Head Gasket
8. Valve Adjustment Improper
9. Plugged Fuel Tank Vent
10. Fuel Supply Pump Faulty
11. Fuel Lines Leaky or Restricted
12. Governor Shaft Binding
13. Governor Internal Malfunction
14. Improper Governor Adjustments
15. Faulty Injection Pump Overflow Valve

Engine Runs, Some Cylinders Fire Erratically

1. Improper Governor Idle Adjustment
2. Poor Compression (on some cylinders)
3. Injection Pump Condition or Adjustments Improper
4. Improper Valve Clearance, Worn Valve Train
5. Faulty Injector Nozzle

6. Injection Pump Plunger Rack Stuck
7. Improper Valve Clearance, Worn Valve Train

Engine Lacks Power

1. Emergency Shutoff Cock Partly Closed
2. Inadequate Fuel Pressure—Poor Pump, Clogged, Leaky Lines
3. Injection Pump Faulty or Adjustments Improper
4. Governor Improperly Adjusted, Governor Linkage Binding
5. Faulty, Improperly Adjusted Injector Nozzle
6. Poor Compression
7. Improper Valve Clearance
8. Turbocharger Passing Oil
9. Turbocharger Impeller Binding
10. Air Intake Clogged
11. Leaky Head Gasket
12. Worn or Broken Rings
13. Scuffed Pistons or Liners
14. Turbocharger Passing Oil

General Description

All Mack Diesel engines are of water cooled, four cycle, open combustion chamber design, in either in-line six cylinder or 90° V-8 configuration. All in-line engines have dry type cylinder liners, while all V-8 engines use wet type sleeves. All in-line engines employ two cylinder heads which cover three cylinders each. V-8 heads cover 2 cylinders each.

Large in-line engines and V-8 engines employ water-cooled oil coolers, in addition to the sump, to control lubricant temperature. Turbocharged engines employ a special piston cooling system consisting of nozzles located in the crankcase which spray oil over the entire inner surface of each piston. Oil is supplied, in most cases, directly from the oil pump. Nozzles are sized so that oil flow will be eliminated at idle speed to prevent over-cooling.

Some turbocharged engines also employ an anti-lag valve which supplies the turbocharger with oil directly routed from the pump at start-up. Once oil pressure is established, the anti-lag closes off the direct supply line, and sends oil that has been cooled and filtered to the turbocharger.

Series 465, 475, 673, 711, 707, and 864 engines are relatively conventional in design, and operate efficiently only within a relatively narrow range of rpm. The Maxidyne 675, 676, 865, and 866 engines are different, however, in having a much wider operating range with especially high torque output a relatively low rpm. Combustion chamber and manifold design that produces high turbulence at low speeds combined with variable rates of fuel injection at different engine speeds produce these torque characteristics. The 675 and 676 engines feature taper top piston design and corresponding connecting rod design for distribution of combustion pressure over a greater area

of the wrist pin, piston, and rod. The combustion chambers are also sealed by a special fire ring which reduces the temperatures and pressures to which the head gaskets are subjected.

The 676 engine features an air to air intercooler. This system reduces engine inlet air temperature, allowing for the introduction of a greater mass of cooler air to the combustion chamber.

The 865 and 866 engines also features an oversquare or short-stroke design for higher maximum speeds, and pressure regulated oil supply to the piston cooling nozzles.

The 865 engine also features an oversquare or short-stroke design for higher maximum speeds, and pressure regulated oil supply to the piston cooling nozzles.

Troubleshooting—Compression Testing

It should be remembered that Diesels are compression ignition engines which employ only the heat generated during compression of the intake air charge to initiate combustion. While fuel or ignition system problems are most often the cause of actual misfiring in gasoline engines, a Diesel can misfire because of a basic mechanical malfunction such as a burned valve or clogged air intake, as well as fuel system problems. It should also be remembered that engine temperature has such a great effect on compression heating effect that a perfectly maintained engine may fail to fire when cold, requiring use of ether to initiate combustion. Finally, it should be remembered that adequate cranking speed is necessary for full compression temperatures to be generated. If the cranking system is performing even slightly below par, a good engine may not start when cold.

Because low compression is a most common cause of operating problems, compression testing has been included in the Troubleshooting section. The Tune-Up and Fuel System sections which follow should also be consulted in case the engine operates poorly. Because of the importance of efficient atomization in burning the relatively non-volatile Diesel fuel, and because of the importance of proper breathing and compression, these sections are placed adjacent to the Troubleshooting section. Before attempting troubleshooting, it is wise to check for sufficient fuel and oil of the proper types, restricted air intakes, and loose or restricted fuel lines or fittings.

Where misfiring of some cylinders is suspected, the problem cylinder(s) may be identified by loosening the high pressure fitting on top of the fuel injection pump 1/2 turn for each cylinder, one at a time. Faulty cylinders will produce no additional firing impulses when the fitting is retorqued.

If referral to the chart indicated low compression could be the cause of the malfunction, test the compression of each cylinder as described below:
1. Operate the engine at fast idle until it reaches operating temperature. Stop the engine.
2. Disconnect the fuel line at the nozzle of the cylinder to be checked. Place a container near the open end of the line to catch the fuel.
3. Remove the injection nozzle and holder assembly. Clean carbon from the nozzle tip with a special wire brush.
4. Remove carbon from the cylinder head nozzle hole with a special reamer and wire brush. Use an air gun to remove loose carbon. Crank the engine a few times with the starter to remove any remaining loose material.

5. Install a special adapter onto the gauge, place a copper gasket on the adapter, and insert the assembly into the nozzle hole. Secure the assembly with the injector hold-down nuts.
6. Start the engine, and set the throttle for 1,000 rpm. Compare the reading with the figures on the chart below.

Engine Series	Minimum	Normal
END 465	486	540
END 475	490	540
ENDT 475	430	470
END 673	500	530
END 711	500	530
ENDT 673	525	575
ENDTL 673	525	575
ENDLT 673B	415	460
END 864	490	525
ENDT 864	450	485
END 707	500	530
END 675, 676	—	460
ENDT 865	—	485
ENDT 866	—	*

* Prior to Eng. #7WO515—485
After Eng. #7WO515—540

7. Remove the gauge. Reinstall the injection nozzle and holder with a new gasket washer and holder dust seal. *Make sure only one gasket washer is used.*
8. Repeat the test for the remaining cylinders.
9. Compare readings with each other. They should be within 50 psi.
10. Check all nozzle holder and fuel line fittings for proper torque. Start the engine and make sure there are no fuel leaks.

Tune-Up

1. Adjust valve clearance as follows:

a. Run the engine at fast idle long enough to normalize it. This takes about 1/2 hour with a cold engine, 15 minutes with an engine which has just come off the road.
b. Stop the engine, remove rocker covers, and restart the engine, running it at normal idle.
c. Using the specified gauge (see General Specifications), check valve clearance. If necessary, loosen the locknut, rotate the adjusting screw with a screwdriver, and resecure locknut.
d. Recheck clearance, making sure a light pull will move the gauge between the rocker shoe and valve stem.
e. Repeat steps C and D for all valves. Shut down engine.
f. Replace rocker cover gaskets, reinstall rocker covers, and run the engine to check for leaks.
2. Check the injection pump timing as described in the following sections.

Injection Pump Timing to Engine END(T) 465, 673, 711-PSJ-PSM Pump

1. Rotate engine in the normal direction of rotation until no. 1 cylinder is on compression stroke and the flywheel timing mark indicates the timing in degrees specified on the data plate on the pump. Remove the timing gear inspection hole capscrews, cover, and gasket. Remove control lever cover and timing device cover.
2. Rotate the injection pump drive shaft by turning the hub coun-

Aligning pointer and scribe mark on type PSJ, PSM pumps

terclockwise until the place bolts bottom lightly at the ends of the elongated slots. Then, slowly rotate the shaft clockwise until the pointer in the timing device housing and the scribe mark on the timing device spider flange line up. See the illustration. If this cannot be accomplished, shift the position of the driving gear one tooth in the appropriate direction and repeat the procedure.

3. Torque the place bolts on the driven gear to the pump shaft hub. Torque the injection pump drive shaft gear hub nut.

4. Rotate the engine over until no. 1 cylinder is again on the compression stroke and the flywheel timing mark again indicates the specified timing setting.

5. Recheck the timing marks in the control lever window and timing device housing, and on the spider flange and ensure all marks align correctly.

6. Reinstall the control lever cover, timing device cover, and timing gear inspection hole gasket cover. Tighten the capscrews on the timing gear cover evenly to avoid oil leaks.

Injection Pump Timing to Engine END(T) 673, 675, 711-APE and PE Pump

1. Rotate the engine in normal direction of rotation until no. 1 cylinder is on compression stroke and the flywheel timing mark is approaching the setting in degrees which is specified on the valve cover escutcheon plate.

2. Remove no. 1 delivery valve holder and its retaining nut from the injection pump.

3. Install a suitable air line, equipped with a separator and pressure regulator, onto the IN fitting of the injector pump. Failure to equip the line properly may cause serious pump damage because of the admission of moisture.

4. Attach a fixture, fabricated as shown in the illustration, to the delivery valve holder.

5. Turn on the air supply and adjust the regulator so that a steady flow of bubbles exists within the fixture.

6. Slowly rotate the crankshaft, watching the bubbles, just until the flow of bubbles stops.

7. If bubbles do not stop at precisely the right point, loosen the four bolts which secure the hub to the timing gear. Make sure bolts are loose enough to permit the gear to rotate to the fully retarded position.

8. Bar the engine in the normal direction of rotation until no. 1 cylinder is on the compression stroke and the flywhel timing mark indicates the specified timing.

9. Very slowly turn the hub nut with an 11 16″ box wrench toward the advanced position. Watch the air bubbles and stop cranking the hub when the bubbles stop. Tighten two capscrews which are opposite each other to secure the hub for the next step.

10. Bar the engine over in the normal direction of rotation, stopping the instant when bubbles stop flowing. If the timing is correct, tighten the other two hub capscrews. Otherwise, repeat steps nine and 10 until timing is correct.

11. Shut off the air supply, disconnect the air line, remove the fixture from the injection pump, and then install the delivery valve and spring, torquing the holder to specification.

Injection Pump Timing to Engine END 475

1. Bar the engine in the normal direction of rotation until no. 1 cylinder is on compression stroke and the flywheel timing mark corresponds with the recommended setting in degrees shown on the pump data plate.

2. Check the port closing marks on pump and coupling. If they are not aligned, loosen the two coupling adjustment bolts, adjust the coupling until it is aligned, and tighten the bolts.

3. Bar the engine over in normal direction of rotation until crankshaft is again in timing position and check for proper alignment of marks. Repeat the adjustment if necessary.

Position of drive coupling tangs and timing marks at No. 1 piston TDC.

Position of drive coupling tangs and timing marks just prior to pump installation.

APE injection pump air flow testing device

Injection pump closing mark on END475 engine

Injection Pump Timing to Engine
END(T) 864, 865, 866

1. Turn the engine in the normal direction until no. 1 cylinder is on compression stroke, and the flywheel timing mark is lined up with the specified mark.
2. Remove the inspection covers on top of the injection pump and auxiliary drive housing.
3. Check to see if the timing mark aligns with the pointer which is visible through the hole on top of the injection pump. If it does not align, leave the coupling screw adjacent to the timing marks tight, but loosen the other two screws, rotating the crankshaft as necessary to accomplish this. Then, repeat step 1.
4. Loosen the third screw as necessary, align the timing marks, and then tighten all three screws. Repeat step 1, check the timing, readjust and recheck as necessary, and reinstall all covers.

Injection Timing

All engines
High Pressure Method:

1. Cap or connect injection lines on all except #1 delivery valve outlet.
2. Remove all fuel return lines at overflow relief valve union fitting, and cap valve port connections.
3. Connect the high pressure line from the portable PC stand to the fuel pump inlet of the pump gallery.
4. Connect return line from the #1 cylinder delivery valve holder to the portable PC stand.
5. Loosen the engine-to-pump coupling bolts and move the injection pump drive counterclockwise (rear view-8 cyl; front view—6 cyl) until pump drive is at end of adjusting slots. Hand tighten bolts.
6. Turn engine crankshaft clock-

wise (front view) until #1 cylinder is coming up on its compression stroke. Stop at the recommended static port closing degrees BTC for the particular engine involved.

7. Remove control rack cap plug and insert correct timing plunger gauge—MACK # J-24345-1 for American Bosch and J-24345-2 for Robert Bosch.

NOTE: If pump does not have retard start, a plug gauge is not required. If pump has a torque limiter, a plug gauge is not required when setting static timing; 80-120 psi air pressure must be applied and held to the torque limiter.

8. Secure stop level in running position.
9. Work throttle lever several times and secure in the full load position.
10. Apply fuel pressure to the gallery.
11. Turn pump drive clockwise (rear view-8 cyl; front view—6 cyl) until the fuel flow from #1 delivery outlet changes from a solid stream to drops.
12. Lock the drive gear bolts securely. Do not disturb the relative position of the gear shaft.
13. Turn engine crankshaft clockwise a minimum of 45° followed by clockwise rotation to check port closing at desired timing on damper or flywheel.
14. Torque the drive gear bolts: 35 ft. lb.—6 cyl, 26 ft. lb.—8 cyl.
15. Remove the timing plug gauge and replace the control rack cap plug.
16. Remove caps from the overflow relief valve union port connections and reconnect all fuel return lines.

Alternate Low Pressure Method:

1. Remove #1 delivery valve holder from injection pump and remove delivery valve and spring. On Robert Bosch pumps, remove the shim.
2. Install a suitable air line onto the "in" fitting of the pump gallery. CAUTION: Equip air line with a separator & regulator. Moisture will damage pump parts.
3. Rig up a fixture and attach to the delivery valve holder.
4. Secure stop lever in the running position.
5. Activate throttle lever several times and secure in full load position.
6. Remove control rack cap plug and insert timing plug gauge— MACK # J-24345-1 for American Bosch and J-24345-2 for Robert Bosch.

NOTE: Pumps without retard start and those with torque limiter do not require plus gauge. Those with

torque limiter do need 80-120 psi air applied and held to torque limiter.

7. Apply air and just crack regulator so that a steady flow of air bubbles is seen in the fixture jar.
8. Rotate crankshaft slowly in direction of normal rotation. At the instant bubbles stop, stop rotating shaft.
9. Timing indicator must register recommended degrees BTC.
10. Repeat steps 8 & 9 to ensure accuracy.

If timing is not correct:

11. Loosen the engine-to-pump drive coupling bolts and move the pump drive counterclockwise (rear view—8 cyl; front view—6 cyl (until pump drive is at end of adjusting slots. Snug tighten bolts.
12. Turn engine in direction of normal rotation until #1 cylinder is on compression stroke & timing mark indicates correct degrees BTC.
13. Turn pump drive clockwise (rear view) while checking bubbles in fixture jar. Stop when bubbles cease.
14. Tighten two opposite bolts to secure hub, and rotate crankshaft and check timing.
15. When timing is correct, tighten two remaining bolts.
16. Remove timing plug gauge and replace control rack plug.
17. Replace delivery valve and spring. Torque the delivery valve holder nut.

Engine Auxiliaries

Fuel System

NOTE: Mack fuel injection pumps are factory sealed. No adjustments should be made by other than Mack authorized repair stations, or the engine warranty may be voided. Therefore, these adjustments are not covered here.

Fuel Injector Service

The fuel injectors in Mack diesel engines receive metered fuel at injection pressure from the injector pump. The nozzles are used to provide effective atomization of the fuel through use of a nozzle valve and discharge nozzle, which insure sharp start-up and cutoff of fuel flow and production of four high velocity streams which will effectively penetrate to all parts of the combustion chamber.

The nozzle body at the lower end of the injector consists of the hole type nozzle, the seat for the nozzle valve, and the fuel passage. The nozzle valve spindle extends upward to the top of the nozzle holder, where there is an adjustable spring for maintenance of precise injector pop

High pressure port closing system diagram.

Adjusting injection pump coupling on END864 engine

INDEXING HOLE

Removing carbon from nozzle tip

pressure. Controlled clearance between the nozzle body and the nozzle valve lubricates the mechanism. A leak-off fitting at the top of the injector returns excess fuel to the fuel tank.

Injector nozzles should be removed and checked after 50,000 to 75,000 miles, or if troubleshooting reveals poor performance. *Extreme* care must be taken to ensure absolute cleanliness during nozzle service. It must also be remembered that oil leaving an injector nozzle is moving at extreme speed. Contact with the skin will usually result in penetration. Therefore, testing must be carried out in a manner that will protect the skin from nozzle discharge.

Removal

1. Clean the cylinder head around the nozzles and the tubing connections with solvent. Blow dry with compressed air.
2. Remove the leak-off lines, carefully recovering the copper gaskets.
3. Remove the high pressure fuel lines, and install protector plugs in their open ends.
4. Remove the nuts from the hold down studs. Use a small pry bar to remove nozzles, gripping them under the hold-down flanges at a point near to the nozzle body. Use penetrating oil to aid removal if the nozzle is especially tight.
5. Place nozzles in a rack in order of removal so they may be installed in the engine in original order. Plug the nozzle ports in the cylinder head(s).

Testing

1. Clean carbon from the nozzle with a special wire brush as shown in the illustration.
2. Mount the nozzle holder assembly in a tester. Make sure the tester is filled with clean fuel.
3. Close the pressure gauge valve (to protect the gauge). Operate the actuating lever at about 25 strokes per minute to expel air and settle the spring and nozzle loading column.
4. Open the pressure gauge valve one half turn and slowly operate the actuating lever to raise the pressure to the point where the nozzle opens. Carefully watch the gauge, and note the exact pressure at which the nozzle opens. Also check the characteristics of the flow to ensure that no leakage or dripping course occurs after the end of injection.
5. Compare the opening pressure with the figure specified in the nozzle opening pressure chart and adjust the nozzle to specifications if necessary.
6. Wipe the nozzle tip dry. Operate the actuating lever slowly to bring pressure to within 100 psi

LEAK OFF FITTING

OPENING PRESSURE ADJUSTING SCREW

UPPER CAP NUT

LOCKNUT

BLEED HOLE

SPRING RETAINING CAP NUT

SPRING

HIGH PRESSURE FUEL INLET

NOZZLE HOLDER

SPINDLE

VALVE LIFT

DOWEL PIN

NOZZLE CAP NUT

NOZZLE VALVE

NOZZLE BODY

FUEL DISCHARGE HOLES

CENTERING SLEEVE

Typical fuel injection nozzle and holder

of opening pressure (20 psi with END 475 nozzles) and maintain the pressure for five seconds. If drops of fuel form or if the nozzle sprays slightly, reject it.
7. Close the gauge valve (to protect the gauge) and operate the lever at about 15 strokes per minute. The spray pattern formed should be sharp, solid, and with uniform quantities and angles between orifices. Use short, rapid strokes on END 475 nozzles to produce a good spray pattern. Reject a nozzle with a poor spray pattern.
8. On all but 475 series nozzles, test the nozzle to make sure it makes a chattering sound. Operate the actuating handle so the stroke takes about two seconds. Close the pressure gauge valve. A distinct and regular chattering sound must be produced, although an occasional variation is acceptable. Reject a nozzle which does not pass the chatter test.

Disassembly

1. Loosen the opening pressure adjusting screw all the way to relive *all* downward pressure.
2. Position the nozzle assembly on a suitable block in a vise. Remove the upper cap nut.
3. Loosen the locknut, if the nozzle is equipped with one, and loosen the opening pressure adjusting screw all the way to relieve *all* downward pressure.
4. Use a special wrench to remove the spring retaining capnut. Remove the pressure adjusting spring and spindle assembly.
5. Invert the holder assembly in a soft-jawed vise and remove the nozzle capnut. Remove the nozzle body and valve assembly. Keep these two parts together as they are a mated assembly. Reinstall nozzle cap nut loosely.

Inspection

1. Wash all parts in a safe solvent

Testing nozzle opening pressure

Loosening locknut on pressure adjusting screw

and inspect for wear as described below:

a. Check the spring for corrosion and pitting and replace if they are evident.
b. Check spindle for straightness within .010" T.I.R.
c. Check the lapped surfaces of the nozzle body and holder for cracks and scratches. Replace parts that are cracked, and lap parts which are slighly scratched. If the holder lapped surface is spalled more than .003" deep in the needle valve area, it must be replaced rather than resurfaced.
d. Remove the locating dowels from the holder very carefully to prevent damaging the lapped surface. Check the spring retaining cap nut to make sure the bleed hole is open.
e. Clean the pressure chamber of the nozzle body with a special scraper, as shown in the illustration.

ACCEPTABLE   NON–ACCEPTABLE

Nozzle spray pattern

Removing spring retaining cap nut

f. Using a special needle and vise, clean the nozzle body holes, as in the illustration. Be careful to avoid breaking the needle inside the discharge holes, as fragments may prove to be impossible to remove.
g. Lift the valve about 1/3 of its length out of the nozzle body, hold the body at 45 degrees from the vertical, and release the valve. It should slide back freely. If the valve is not free, work the valve in the nozzle body using a special polishing tallow. Clean the nozzle valve and body in solvent and blow dry.
h. Check the nozzle valve lift using a straightedge and dial indicator as shown in the illustration. See the injection Nozzle Opening Pressure Chart for specifications. Place the nozzle in a fixture and run a straightedge across the top of the nozzle body. Mount a dial indicator right

INJECTION NOZZLE OPENING PRESSURE CHART

END	Normal PSI	Valve Lift	Inj. Pump	Holes	Dia. Inch
465A, B, C	3000 to 3050	0.012 to 0.014	PSJ, PSM	5	0.010
475	1985 to 2035	0.012 to 0.014	CAV	4	0.011
T475	2840 to 3130	0.010 to 0.012	CAV	5	0.011
673A, B, C, D	3000 to 3050	0.012 to 0.014	PSJ, PSM	4	0.0128
673, T673	2300 to 2350	0.012 to 0.014	APE	4	0.0128
T673A, B	3000 to 3050	0.012 to 0.014	PSJ, PSM	4	0.0132
T675	3000 to 3050	0.012 to 0.014	APE	5	0.0126
T673C	3000 to 3050	0.012 to 0.014	APE	5	0.0126
707	3000 to 3050	0.012 to 0.014	APE	4	0.0138
673E	3000 to 3050	0.012 to 0.014	APE	4	0.0138
711A, B	3000 to 3050	0.012 to 0.014	PSJ, PSM	4	0.0138
711	2300 to 2350	0.012 to 0.014	APE	4	0.0128
864	2300 to 2350	0.012 to 0.014	PSJ, PSM	4	0.0138
D864	2300 to 2350	0.012 to 0.014	PSJ, PSM	4	0.0128
T864	3000 to 3050	0.012 to 0.014	PSJ, PSM	4	0.0147
T864	3000 to 3050	0.012 to 0.014	APE	5	0.0126
T865	3000 to 3050	0.012 to 0.014	APE	5	0.0126

IF A NEW SPRING IS USED, OPENING PRESSURE IS TEN PERCENT HIGHER above the needle valve and zero it. While holding the straightedge, raise the needle valve with a pair of tweezers just until the lower portion of the valve contacts the straightedge. Hold the valve in position while reading the dial indicator. If the valve lift is not to specification, the assembly must be replaced.

i. If the injector uses a filter in the fuel inlet connection, clean it by reverse flushing it with compressed air.

j. Check the ends of the high pressure fuel tubes to make sure they are open. Ream ENDT 864 lines to .085″ and all others to .078″. Flush out the chips.

Assembly

1. Place the injection nozzle holder in a soft jawed vise.
2. Position the nozzle body and valve onto the holder, aligning dowel pins and holes carefully.
3. Install the nozzle cap nut, using a special centering sleeve during the initial tightening. Remove the centering sleeve and torque the cap nut to specification, using a special adapter.
4. Invert the holder and install the spindle and pressure adjusting spring. Tighten the pressure adjusting screw and lock it in position with the locknut.
5. Install the injector in a test stand and adjust opening pressure as described in the section on service.
6. Install the nozzle holder with a new gasket and install and tighten upper capnuts.

Installation

1. Remove copper nozzle tip gasket from the hole in the cylinder head. Clean the nozzle cavity with a special reamer and wire brush. Check the gasket seat for trueness and cleanliness. Crank the engine over by hand to blow loose carbon from the cavity.
2. Apply an anti-seize compound to the outside diameter of nozzle and holder, and position the assembly in the head with a new nozzle tip gasket and dust seal O-ring. The nozzle tip gasket may be held in place with a small amount of grease.
3. Seat the nozzle squarely and then install and tighten hold down nuts evenly.
4. Install the high pressure fuel lines and torque nuts carefully so that tubing will not be distorted.
5. Install the leak-off lines with their copper gaskets.
6. Operate the engine and check for leaks. Retighten fittings as necessary.

Checking nozzle valve lift

Removing carbon from nozzle body

Cleaning nozzle body fuel discharge holes

Fuel Filter Service

Because of the close clearances employed in fuel injection systems, extremely efficient filtration of fuel is an absolute necessity. In-line, full flow primary and secondary filters make up the filtration system. The secondary filter incorporates an air bleed valve which returns bleed air and fuel to the vent valve on the fuel tank.

Primary Filter

Both types of primary filters contain a wire mesh filter which is cleaned by manually rotating a blade around the element. Every 2,000 miles, the cap nut should be rotated approximately two revolutions. Elements with the high type cap nut require that the cup nut be removed and installed upside-down on the shaft in order for it to be rotated. At this time, the cup nut gasket should be inspected. Replace it, if necessary, before reinstalling the nut. Torque the nut sufficiently to prevent leakage.

Both types of primary filters should be drained every 6,000 miles, or sooner, if fuel is of poor quality. To perform this operation, remove the drain plug until clean fuel appears. Replace the plug carefully, tightening it sufficiently to ensure that there will be no leakage.

On the type of filter with the low cap nut, the shaft o-rings should be replaced every 6,000 miles, or sooner if a leak develops. Replacement may be performed as follows:

1. Remove the shaft circlet and unscrew the shaft nut.
2. Remove the filter housing retain-

1. Cap nut
2. Cap nut gasket
3. Cover
4. Cover gasket
5. Retaining ring
6. Cleaning blade
7. Housing
8. Drain plug
9. Cotter pin
10. Filter element
11. Shaft
12. O-Ring

Primary fuel filter

1. Shaft circlet
2. Nut
3. O-ring
4. Cover
5. Gasket
6. Housing retaining ring
7. Cleaning blade
8. Filter housing
9. Shaft
10. Drain plug
11. Cotter pin
12. Filter element

Primary fuel filter

ing ring bolts and nuts, and remove the housing.

3. Remove the cotter pin from the end of the shaft, and then withdraw the shaft.
4. Remove the old o-rings and install new ones from the unthreaded end of the shaft.
5. Lubricate the rings and then insert the shaft from the bottom.
6. Install the shaft nut, circlet and cotter pin.
7. Install a new gasket, fill the housing with clean fuel, place the housing in position, and install the retaining ring bolts and nuts.
8. Tighten the nuts evenly, and then prime the filter from the IN side with clean fuel. Operate the engine and check for leaks.

Secondary fuel filter

Secondary Filter

The element of the cartridge type fuel filter may be replaced as follows:

1. Remove the filter housing drain plug and allow the filter to drain.
2. On filters with constant air bleed, remove the air bleed line from the filter cover.
3. Remove the housing cover, gasket, and element.
4. Wash the interior of the housing with clean fuel oil. Replace the drain plug.
5. Install a new element. New gaskets should be employed at top and bottom of the new element in the constant air bleed type of unit. The element in the manually vented type of unit should be kept in the protective plastic bag until right before installation.
6. Fill the housing with clean fuel. Install the cover securely with a new gasket.
7. Install the air bleed line on constant air bleed filters.
8. On manually vented type filters, close the bleed valve by turning it in, and pump the hand priming pump 150-200 strokes. Immediately after pumping stops, open the bleed valve, turning it outward all the way. Then, pump the primer 50 more strokes to pressurize the system.
9. Start the engine, and operate it while checking for leaks.
10. Replacement should again be performed after 6,000 miles on constant air bleed filters, 8,000 miles on manually vented filters. Replacement should also be made if fuel pressure drops below 10

psi with constant bleed filters, or 12 psi with manually vented filters.

Spin On Filters

Spin on type primary and secondary fuel filters are provided on some engines. The filters should be replaced every 16,000 miles, or sooner, if fuel pressure drops below 15 psi with PSJ/PSM pump, or 10 psi with the APE pump.

The filter may be replaced as described below:

1. Bleed valve
2. Cover retaining screw
3. Washer
4. Spring
5. Gasket
6. Plastisol end cap
7. Drain plug
8. Center tube
9. Housing
10. Cover

Secondary fuel filter

1. Clean the adapter, line connections, and adjacent area with solvent spray. Dry with compressed air.
2. Use a special wrench to unscrew the filter from the adapter, remove and save the dust cap, and discard the used filter.
3. Clean the dust cover with solvent and blow dry with compressed air.
4. Install the dust cover on the new filter.
5. Apply a small amount of clean engine oil to the gasket sealing surface.
6. Screw the filter onto the adapter, and turn it by hand one full turn after the gasket contacts the adapter.
7. Loosen the secondary filter to injector pump fuel line at the pump on APE pumps, or the line at the filter bleed shutoff valve (with valve open) on PSJ/PSM pumps.
8. Operate the hand primer through about 200 strokes or until fuel flows, free of bubbles, from the open fitting.
9. Tighten the fuel line fitting on APE type pumps.
10. On APE pumps operate the primer through 20 more strokes, and secure the handle. On PSJ/PSM pumps, operate the primer until bubble-free fuel flows from the filter bleed valve, then close the valve and continue pumping until fuel flows from the filter bleed line. Retighten the bleed line and secure the pump handle.
11. Start the engine and operate it while checking for leaks. Open the filter bleed valve on PSJ/PSM fuel systems.

Air Compressor

Inspection

Inspect the compressor flange for straightness, lack of cracking, and proper condition of mounting holes. Check the coupling teeth and ensure the shaft nut is tight and the tab is bent to the locknut.

END 465, END(T) 673, 711

Installation

Current production engines do not require compressor phasing, but many older models require that the coupling and drive be in proper mesh. Check to make sure mesh is proper if problems occur.
1. Position the adapter ring in the auxiliary housing counterbore.
2. Place the gasket in position on the compressor and position the compressor on the auxiliary housing.
3. Install retaining capscrews with proper torque.

Spin-on secondary filter

END 475

1. Position key in the compressor shaft and install the drive gear.
2. Install the gear lockwasher and nut.
3. Install a new o-ring seal on the inner flange of the compressor, and then install the compressor on the rear of the timing gear housing.
4. Install lockwashers and torque nuts to specification.
5. Check the backlash between compressor and camshaft gear.
6. Install the timing gear inspection cover.

ENDT 864, 865, 866

1. Position the gasket on the compressor flange and position the compressor on the auxiliary drive housing.
2. Install the capscrews loosely. Adjust the position of the compressor until the backlash is correct.
3. Torque capscrews to specification.

Oil Pan

All Engines Except END 475 Series

Inspection

Inspect the pan for dents, cracks or other such damage. Check to make sure the flange is in good condition and that the bolt holes are not elongated. Make sure the baffle is securely mounted and that the drain hole threads are not damaged.

Installation

1. Position the gasket on the pan. Position the pan up against the block with all bolt holes properly lined up.
2. Install the capscrews, and tighten in rotation to the specified torque.

END 475

Inspection

Inspect the pan for dents, cracks or other such damage. Check to make sure the flange is in good condition and that the bolt holes are not elongated. Check the oil pressure relief valve mounting pad to make sure it is flat and that the mounting hole threads are in good condition. Check the oil screen for holes, cracks, and broken welds, and check the oil passages to make sure they are not obstructed. Check that the mounting surface of the screen cover is clean and that the pick up tube hole is in good condition.

Installation

1. Position a spacer on the stud in the center of the pan. Install the screen assembly over the stud, locating the crimped section on the lug. Install the lockwasher and nut.
2. Mount the baffle in the pan with capscrews and lockwashers.
3. Position the new gasket in place on the flange. Position a new o-ring on the pressure relief valve tube. Install a new felt washer on the oil pick up tube.
4. Position the pan on the crankcase and install the capscrews, torquing them evenly.

Oil Sump

END 475 Inspection

Inspect the sump casting and oil screen for dents, cracks or other damage. Make sure the mounting cover is clean and that the mounting surface and holes are not damaged.

Installation

1. Place the space on the stud in the center of the cover.
2. Position the sump over the stud. Install the lockwasher and nut. Torque the nut to specification.
3. Install the magnetic drain plug in the cover.
4. Position a new felt washer on the suction line and a new gasket on the pan.
5. Install the assembly. Install the capscrews and torque them evenly.

Oil pan sump, END475 engine

OIL PUMP SPECIFICATIONS IN INCHES

	END 465	END 475	END(T) 673	END(T) 711	END 864	ENDT 675, 676	ENDT 865, 866
Bushings to Inner Rotor Shaft	.0015-.0025	0015-.0025					
Driven Gear to Idler Gear Backlash		.0020-.0040		.0020-.0060	.0020-.0060		.0050-.0070
Idler Gear to Crankshaft Gear Backlash	.0020-.0040	.0020-.0040			.0050-.0070		.004-.009
Gear O.D. to Cavity Side			.0025-.0045	.0035-.0060	.0035-.0060	.0035-.0060	.0035-.0070
Gear to Cover End			.0015-.0035	.0015-.0035	.0015-.0035	.0025-.0050	.0015-.0060①
Gear Backlash In Pump	.0250-.0290		.0250-.0290	.0250-.0290	.0250-.0290	.0295-.0235	.0250-.0290

① with 2" Gears—.0015-.0095"

Checking oil pump gear end clearance, END465. 673. T, and 711 engines

Oil Pump
ENDT 465, 673, 675, 676, 711

Inspection

1. Inspect the oil pump drive gear to make sure the gear teeth are in good condition and worn in a normal pattern. Check to make sure the journal wear is not excessive and that the splines are in good condition. Make sure oil

Spirolox retainer ring installation on END465 engine

holes are not obstructed.

2. Check the pump housing flanges and gear cavity for scoring or other damage. Make sure the idler shaft is not tight in the housing.
3. Check the oil pressure regulator body and cap to make sure they are clean and that all holes and threads are in good condition. Check regulator spring for proper tension and good condition of the ends.

Assembly

1. Apply a small amount of oil to the drive gear shaft and position the gear in a vise.
2. Install the housing over the shaft and position the drive gear on the shaft splines.
3. On END 465 Series engines, secure the drive gear with the Spirolox retaining ring.
4. Lubricate the idler gear shaft and install the idler gear.
5. Check the end clearance, side clearance, and backlash of the gears as shown in the illustrations. See the Oil Pump Specifications Chart.
6. Mount the oil pump cover in a vise and install the tab lock, pressure relief valve plunger, spring and cap. Torque the cap down and then bend the tab lock.
7. Remove the cover from the vise and position it on the oil pump body. Install the capscrews. Rotate the oil pump shaft to check for free rotation.
8. Lubricate the drive shaft gear and position the assembly on the block. Install the retaining capscrews, and torque and lockwire them.
9. Make sure the oil pick up pipe and shield assembly are clean and unobstructed. Place a gasket on the pump flange and install the oil pick up line. Torque the screws and lockwire them together.
10. Install the oil screen, support, and inlet pipe.

Checking oil pump gear side clearance on END465, 673, T, and 711 engines

END 475 Series

Inspection

1. Inspect the housing for cracks, the condition of the holes and flanges (flanges should be flat) and fully open passages.
2. Check the idler and driven gear to make sure they are worn in a regular pattern and that the teeth are in good condition. Make sure the idler shaft ball bearings rotate easily and are not excessively worn. Check the rotor to make sure it is not worn or scored.
3. Check the bushing for wear. If

Checking oil pump gear backlash on END465, 673, T, and 711 engines

Installing oil pump on END465, 674, T, and 711 engines

Installing oil pump

they must be replaced, use a special tool to install them and ream to provide the required running clearance.

Assembly

1. Install the lock ring in the groove in the idler gear bore of the housing.
2. Install the rear ball bearing and stub shaft into the housing from the rear, as shown in the illustration.
3. Install the spacer washer over the stub shaft and install the front ball bearing.
4. Position the idler with the dish toward the housing, and install the capscrew to retain the idler gear and ball bearings (the capscrew is reverse threaded). Check the idler gear for freedom of rotation.
5. Install the rotor and shaft assembly into the housing. Position the cover on the housing and install the capscrews and lockwashers.
6. Put the key into the shaft, and then position the oil pump drive gear onto the shaft. Install the retaining washer and nut.

Oil pump idler gear END465, 674, T, and 711 engines

7. Check the backlash between idler and driven gear.

Installation

1. Install the new o-ring at the pump outlet and position the assembly on the engine. Install the capscrews and lockwashers.

END 864

Inspection

1. Inspect the housing for cracks, damaged screw holes, bent flanges, or clogged passages.

2. Inspect idler and driven gears for damaged teeth or an improper wear pattern. Check the oil pump pressure and scavenge gears for damaged teeth, an improper wear pattern, or improper fit in the housing.

Assembly

1. Install the idler gear shaft into the housing. Install the pressure pump shaft and gear into the housing and put the driven idler gear onto the shaft.
2. Install the scavenge housing over both shafts and install the scavenge drive and driven gears onto their shafts. Put the scavenge pump cover into position, install and torque the capscrews, and check the gears for proper end float and side clearance.
3. Position the shield onto the inlet housing and install the capscrews. Push the screen into its proper position in the shield assembly.

Installation

1. Install the locating plate on the pump and position the assembly on the block with the forward

Installing oil pump pressure relief valve plunger on END465, 673, T, and 711 engines

Oil pump END864 engines

Checking oil pump idler gear backlash ENDT864 engine

Drilling new guide pin holes in oil pump, ENDT864 engine

face of the mounting legs flush with the block and the guide pin through the locating plate.

2. Check the backlash between idler and drive gears. Tap the housing lightly to obtain the correct backlash, as shown in the illustration. Then, torque the mounting bolts.

3. If the oil pump gears have been replaced or a replacement pump is to be installed, guide pins may have to be realigned in locating plate as follows:

   a. Install the pump with the mounting screws lightly torqued. Make sure both forward faces of the legs are flush with the front face of the block.

   b. Install the locate plate with two lightly torqued capscrews.

   c. Install the guide pin into the recess in the block, going through the locating plate.

   d. Lightly tap the pump housing to adjust the idler gear to drive gear backlash. When proper lash is established, tighten the locating plate screws.

   e. Remove the assembly from the engine without loosening locating plate screws.

   f. Drill two holes, .186"-194" in diameter, .188" deep through the locating holes in the locating plate into the housing leg.

   g. Install two locating pins into the pump housing. Then, reinstall the pump assembly as previously outlined.

4. Position new gaskets on the block and pump outlet hole. Install the outlet tube with flat washers and nylock capscrews.

5. Install the scavenger tube clamp with the loop toward the centerline of the engine and secure it on the inner side of the bracket toward the center of the engine using a capscrew and elastic stop nut.

Oil pump outlet tube, END864 engine

Oil pump scavenge tube, END864 engines

ENDT 865, 866

Inspection

1. Check pump gear for pattern and wear.
2. Check pump shaft for wear.
3. Clear all oil passages.
4. Check housing, flanges and cavity for scoring and cracks.
5. Check idler shaft for scoring and binding.
6. Check safety valve plunger, body and cap for wear and dirt.
7. Check safety valve spring tension.

Installation

1. Align hole in driven gear with driven shaft and press on gear.

1. Install roll pin.
2. Press idler shaft in flush with housing.
3. Lubricate gear and shaft assembly and install in housing.
4. Install pumping gear on splined end of shaft.
5. Press one idler gear bushing from each end into gear.
6. Install idler gear on shaft. Check backlash (.004-.009"), end float (.0015-.0040") and side clearance (.0035-.0070").
7. Install cover on housing. Torque capscrews (30 ft. lb.).
8. Rotate pump shaft to check for binding.
9. Install safety valve plunger, spring, cap, and retainer in cover.
10. Lubricate pump drive shaft gear and install on engine.

Intake Manifold
All Engines

Inspection

1. Inspect the manifold for restrictions.
2. Check the mounting flanges for erosion, cracks, and straightness.

Installation

1. Put new gaskets into position on the block.
2. Put the manifold in position on the block.
3. Install capscrews and tighten to the proper torque.
4. On 864 Series engines, position the O-rings and install the inlet manifold crossover tubes and connecting hose (see illustration).

865, 866 oil pump idler gear.

Intake manifold crossover tube END864 engines

Installing thermostat END465 engines

Exhaust Manifold

Inspection

1. Inspect the manifold for erosion or restrictions.
2. Check mounting flanges for erosion, cracks, and straightness.

Installation

1. Put new gaskets in position on the head.
2. Install and tighten the attaching washers and nuts or the capscrews to the proper torque.

Water Outlet Manifold

Inspection

1. Inspect the manifold for restrictions.
2. Check the mounting flanges for cracks or warping.
3. On END (T) Series engines, check the thermostat seal in the water outlet fitting for looseness and erosion.

Water manifold and thermostat assembly END, T, 864 engines

Installation

1. Place new hose and clamps or a new tube and o-ring between front and rear halves of the manifold, as applicable. Put new gaskets into position on the cylinder head.
2. Install capscrews and tighten to the proper torque. Position the hoses and clamps on engines em-

ploying them.
3. Install the thermostat and by-pass fitting and the housing cover as appropriate. See illustrations. On END T 864, install a new thermostat seal, if necessary. See illustration.

Crankshaft Pulley and Vibration Damper

Crankshaft Hub-END 475 Series

Inspection

1. Inspect the hub for scoring, or damage to the threaded holes, or keyway.

Installation

1. Place the hub key in the crankshaft keyway.

Installing thermostat seal END, T, 864 engines

Installing thermostat END465 engines

Installing crankshaft hub END475 engines

Installing crankshaft hub all engines except END475

2. Align the keyway slot in the hub with the key and start the hub onto the crankshaft. Drive the hub into position with a special tool. See illustration.

3. Install the wedge cone, bolt, and lockwasher. Torque the bolt.

Crankshaft Vibration Damper Hub

All Engines Except END 475

Inspection

1. Inspect the hub for scoring, or damage to the flange, threaded holes, or keyway.

Installation

1. Place the hub key in position in the keyway in the crankshaft.

2. Heat the vibration damper hub to 250° F. in hot oil, unless the damper is an integral part of the hub. In this case, heat the unit in a solution of one to two percent soluble oil and water at 200-225° F. for 13-14 minutes.

3. Wipe the bore with a dry rag, and position the unit onto the crankshaft with the keyway and key aligned. Drive the unit into position.

4. Install the washer and retaining bolt, and torque the bolt to specifications.

NOTE: On ENDT 865, 866 the TDC mark must align with the timing indicator 30 degrees to the left of the engine center line. On 6 cyl engines exc. MB chassis, a spun steel pulley replaces the cast iron original. Spacer 537GC215 must be used.

Combination Pulley and Vibration Damper END 475

Inspection

1. Inspect the v-belt channels, mounting holes, and flanges for excessive wear. Make sure the housing and rubber bond are sound.

Installation

1. Position the pulley and damper assembly on the crankshaft hub. Secure it with hardened washers and capscrews, torquing capscrews to specification. Where pulley and damper parts are separate, torque capscrews which hold them together to specification also.

Engine Disassembly

Mack diesels are easily disassembled with a minimum of special tools. Rather than detail a disassembly procedure, take note of the following helpful hints:

1. Always remove injection nozzles and holders before removing heads.

2. To remove PSJ or PSM pumps from END 465, 673 or 711 series, remove the access plate on timing gear cover. The pump driven gear must be removed before the pump can be removed.

3. Always remove the pump, governor and adapter as an assembly.

4. On ENDT 864, 865, 866 series, be sure to remove buttress screws at main bearings before attempting to remove caps.

5. Use new capscrews on connecting rods at overhaul.

6. When removing piston and rod assemblies on engines with oil-cooled pistons, carefully guide connecting rod end to avoid damage to oil spray nozzles.

Engine Assembly

Cylinder Head

1. If new nozzle holder sleeves are used, use a 7/8-14NF thread, tap at the large end and remove the old sleeve with a puller.

2. To install new nozzle sleeves, heat to 180°F, apply a light coat of sealer to each end of the sleeve, position sleeve, small end first, in hole and press into place.

3. To install new valve guides, chill guides in dry ice and safe solvent, or in freezer for approximately 30 minutes. Install guide from top of head until it extends the required distance.

Engine Series	Guide Protrusion
465	$1^{9}/_{16}$
475	$^{63}/_{64}$
673	$1^{35}/_{64}$
711	$1^{35}/_{64}$
864	$1^{7}/_{8}$
865	$1^{7}/_{8}$
866	$1^{7}/_{8}$
675	—
676	—

4. Chill new valve seats in dry ice to −112°F and position in head using press. Hold seat in position while it warms up.

5. Grind seats to 30° 30'. END 475 uses a 30° angle.

6. Grind valves to 30° 30' angle; 29° 30' for END 475.

7. Install valves and check valve to piston head clearance.

Engine Series	Gauge
465	J-22149
673	17-T-11324
675	.014" min
676	.014" min
711	17-T-11486
864	J-22099
865	—
866	—

8. Valve spring installation.
   a) END 465
      1. Position inner spring centering washers, inner and outer valve springs, oil shields, and retainer washers (O-ring in intake) over stems.
      2. Install keys.
   b) END 475
      1. Position lower guide washers, inner and outer valve springs and upper guide washers over valve stems.
      2. Install keys.
      3. Install stem wear caps.
   c) END (T) 673, 675, 676, 711
      1. Position inner and outer valve springs over the exhaust and intake valves.
      2. Position the oil shield, O-ring and retainer washers over the intake valve stems and install keys.
      3. Position roto cap washers over the exhaust valve stems and install keys.
   d) END (T) 864, 865, 866
      1. Position lower guide washers, inner and outer valve springs, oil shields, O-rings and retainer washers over the intake valve stems and install keys.
      2. Position the roto coil washers, inner and outer valve springs and retainer washers over the exhaust valve stem and install keys. ENDT engines use roto coil on both intake and exhaust valves.

9. On "T" engines with piston spray coolers, be sure spray fittings are clean and unobstructed. On 673, 675, 677 engines, position the cooling nozzle on the inside crankcase wall. On 864, 865, 866 engines the spray fitting is installed from outside the crank-

Positioning rod in piston cooling oil nozzle.

case and is located by the positioning sleeve.

10. Cylinder lines—Dry type
   a. Check liner for out-of-round. Take reading in two directions at each of three different levels.
   b. Insert liner in bore. If liner enters bore ½ to ⅔ of the way, a light press should force liner into position.
   c. If liner does not enter ½ to ⅔ of bore and is within tolerance, shrink liner for 25 min. in dry ice and alcohol.
   d. Check liner shoulder protrusion: .0005 below to .0035 above.

11. Cylinder Sleeves—Wet type
   a. Check sleeves for out of round or taper. Take readings in three directions at each of three levels.
   b. Measure bore at upper and lower locations for sleeve fit.
   c. Position new sleeve in cylinder block, without O-rings to check sleeve-to-deck fit. Shims will adjust this fit.
   d. Check liner-above deck dimensions.
   e. Remove sleeve and install O-rings.
   f. Lubricate sleeve O.D. at ring locations.
   g. Insert sleeve until it contacts the O-rings.
   h. Push down with palms of hands in a quick motion to bottom sleeve. A light tap with a soft mallet is permissable.

NOTE: If, for any reason, the liner must be moved back out, for any distance, the O-rings will be damaged.

END 475 sleeves have a dot at the top which must face forward.

Crankshaft Installation

1. Inspect crankshaft for wear. Check oil passages.
2. Check pattern on crankshaft gear.
3. On END 865, ENDT 865, 866, check condition of wear ring. The wear ring can be removed by splitting it with a cold chisel. To install a new wear ring:
   a. Heat new ring to 400°F.

Cylinder sleeve fit **END 864**

   b. Position heated ring on crankshaft with arrow on I.D. pointing toward center of shaft.
   c. Press wear ring on shaft to shoulder.
4. Install crankshaft gear aligning key in crankshaft.
5. Heat gear to 400°F (212°F—END 475).
6. Align key way and position gear on shaft with larger chamfer toward engine.
7. Drive gear into place using suitable driver.
8. Insert upper half of main bearing shells in cylinder block. Insert the lower half in the cap.
9. Apply a light coat of oil to the shell surfaces and journals and lower the crankshaft into position.
10. Align dots on timing gears. On END 475 engines, the number of teeth on the idler gear provides the timing location. When the alignment marks are indexed, the idler gear will align only

once every 54 revolutions with the other three gears. The three timing marks on the idler gear are located so that the crankshaft, camshaft and injection pump drive gears are all indexed on #1 cylinder compression.

On 673, 675, 676 and 711 series align the dots on the auxiliary drive gear with those on the injection pump drive gear. On engines without auxiliary drive gear timing marks:
   a. Install the gears with the mating numbers outward.
   b. Align the dots on the crankshaft and camshaft gears.
   c. Align the dots on the injection pump gears.
   d. Rotate the camshaft clockwise to align it with the dots on the auxiliary shaft drive gear.
11. Install front and rear thrust washers at center main bearing.
12. Force crankshaft fore and aft to align thrust washers.
13. Check end play.
14. Check main bearing clearance with plastigage.
15. Torque main bearing caps. Check crankshaft free rotation. Use oversize thrust washer or undersize main bearings to correct binding.
16. On 864 engines, buttress screws are used at the 2, 3 and 4 main bearing locations. On 865, 866 engines, buttress screws are used at all main bearing locations. On these engines the short buttress screws are located at the 2 and 4 locations. Torque buttress screws *after* main bearing capscrews are torqued.

Pistons and Connecting Rods exc. V8 Engines

1. Heat piston to 200°F. Position piston on connecting rod and install pin. Arrow on piston crown faces front.
2. Install pin retainers.
3. Install rings on pistons with staggered gaps.
4. Coat piston, rings and liner with light oil.
5. With respective crankpin at bot-

Installing crankshaft wear ring—V8

Timing gear alignment CAV pump—END 475

Timing gear alignment APE pump END 673, 711

Timing gear alignment PSJ-PSM pump—END 673, 711

tom center and rod number on auxiliary side, install piston and rod assemblies in their bores with arrows toward front.

6. Guide large end of rod into position. Mack tool #J-21480 is used for this purpose.

CAUTION: If engine is turbocharged, use extreme care to avoid damage to piston spray cooler or rod bearings.

7. Check bearing clearance with plastigage.

8. Coat journals and bearings with oil, install caps and capscrews, check rod and cap side clearance (.007"), and torque capscrews.

9. On turbocharged engines, check skirt to spray nozzle clearance (.062-.025"):

   a. Position #1 and 6 at BDC.

   b. Sight along nozzle. Nozzle should be pointing midway between connecting rod and inside face of piston boss when nozzle is square with engine center line. Bend to adjust.

   c. Slide go (.062) and no-go (.125) wires between nozzle tube and skirt.

   d. Repeat for other pistons.

Piston and Connecting Rods—V8 Engines

1. Heat pistons to 200°F.

Timing gear alignment BSJ-PSM pump—END 864

2. Position pistons on crowns with arrows toward right.

3. Install rods 1, 2, 3 and 4 in pistons with the numbers toward you.

4. Install rods 5, 6, 7 and 8 with the numbers away from you.

5. Install pins and retaining rings.

6. Install rings on pistons—stagger gaps.

Buttress screws—V8

Positioning connecting rod on crankshaft.

7. Coat the pistons, rings and liner with light oil.
8. With the crankpin at BDC and rod number toward center of engine, install piston and rod assemblies.
CAUTION: On turbocharged engines, take care that the rod doesn't damage the piston spray nozzle.
9. Check rod bearing clearance with plastigage.
10. Oil the capscrews, install the caps, finger-tighten the capscrews and check side clearance between paired rods (.007-.015").
11. A tapered brass wedge may be used to force rods against crankshaft cheeks to align rod with cap.
12. Torque bearing caps and check crankshaft for free rotation.
13. Check piston-to-cylinder block deck height (.018").

Turbocharger
ENDT 673, 675, 676 Series
Troubleshooting

If turbochargr trouble is suspected, check the unit out carefully as outlined in order to avoid unnecessary removal of a functional unit.

1. Start the engine and operate it while listening carefully for an unusual type of noise or vibration from the unit. Unusual noise indicates that the unit is out of balance, or that there is damage to the compressor or turbine wheels.
2. Check for leaks in turbocharger-to-manifold or manifold-to-block plumbing. Make sure clamps and bolts are tight and that all hoses and gaskets are in good shape.
3. Check the air cleaner and lines supplying the turbocharger for restrictions.
4. Check the exhaust plumbing between block and turbine inlet for loose bolts or connections or blown gaskets. Check for restrictions in the exhaust pipe downstream of the turbine.
5. Check the radial and axial play of the unit. If either is excessive, the unit will have to be removed

for overhaul. These are .0230" and .0040" respectively.

Disassembly

1. Clean the exterior of the unit with a pressurized spray of cleaning solvent and air blow dry.
2. Mark the alignment of the turbine housing and compressor housing with the bearing housing, using a center punch or small chisel.
3. Remove the Vee clamp and separate the compressor housing from the bearing housing. Be careful not to damage compressor wheel.
4. Remove the o-ring from the groove in the bearing housing, if the unit is equipped with one.
5. Position the turbocharger in a vise. Mount a dial indicator so the contact point is on the side of the compressor wheel retaining nut. Move the compressor wheel away from the indicator while pressing the turbine wheel in the opposite direction, and zero the indicator.
6. Press the compressor wheel toward the indicator while pressing the turbine wheel in the opposite direction and read the indicator. If the measurement exceeds the maximum, the turbocharger must be overhauled.
7. Mount the indicator so the end contacts the end of the turbine shaft. Move the shaft toward the indicator and zero it. Then move the shaft to the opposite extreme of end-to-end travel, and record the reading. If this reading is greater than specifications, overhauling is necessary.
8. Remove the vee clamp and separate the turbine housing from the bearing housing. If force is required, use a soft mallet only.
9. Place the bearing housing on a bench and hold the turbine wheel at the hub with a ⅜" eight point or ⅝" 12 point socket. With a ⅝" box wrench, loosen and remove the compressor wheel retaining nut.
10. Slide the compressor wheel off the shaft. Remove the turbine

wheel and shaft from the housing. Remove the piston ring from the shaft.
11. Remove the large snap ring from the bearing housing. Use two screwdrivers to carefully pry the compressor insert from the bearing housing. Remove the o-ring from the compressor insert.
12. Remove the finger sleeve, oil deflector, thrust ring, thrust bearing, and spacer from the bearing housing.
13. With tru-arc pliers, remove the snap ring from the compressor end of the bearing housing. Remove the compressor bearing. Then, using tru-arc pliers, remove the rear bearing snap ring. Remove the snap rings and bearings from the turbine end of of the bearing housing in the same way.
14. Remove the oil control sleeve, which is located between the snap ring and the turbine bearing.
15. Soak the turbine wheel and housing (avoid wetting the shaft) in an appropriate carbon removing solvent for 25 minutes. Then, remove carbon with a brush. Clean the remaining parts in a solvent spray and dry with compressed air.

Inspection

1. Inspect the turbine and compressor housing for wear due to contact with rotating parts. Make sure the mounting flange is flat and free from erosion.
2. Check the bearing housing for warped flanges, worn bearing bores or snap ring grooves, and loose groove pins. Make sure all oil passages are clean. Make sure threaded holes and oil inlet and outlet pads are in good condition.
3. Inspect bearings and replace if tin plating is worn off either the inside or outside diameter, or if bearings show signs of imbedment of foreign matter.
4. Make sure the shaft is not scored or worn at bearing locations. Make sure oil seal ring grooves and threads on the ends of the shaft are in good condition.

Removing compressor insert

Compressor bearings and snap rings

Loosening locknut on compressor wheel

Compressor bearing housing and thrust assembly

5. Check turbine and compressor wheels for signs of rubbing or vanes worn to a feather edge. Make sure the compressor wheel bore is not galled.

6. Make sure the thrust bearing is worn evenly, and that the drilled hole is clean.

Preparation for Reassembly

1. Discard all parts that show excessive wear, rubbing, scoring, or galling.

2. Where there is minor surface damage, polish it out using silicon carbide cloth on aluminum parts and crocus cloth on steel parts.

2. Discard piston rings, seal rings, bearing retainers and the compressor retaining nut at reassembly.

Reassembly

Before reassembling each part, check it to ensure it is clean. Lubricate all moving parts with engine oil.

1. Mount the bearing housing on a bench with the compressor end down. Install the tru-arc bearing retainer into the inner snap ring groove. Make sure rounded surface is positioned toward bearing.

2. Install the bearing in the housing bore and seat it against the tru-arc ring.

NOTE: AiResearch turbochargers feature an anti-wear washer in-board of the bearing.

3. Install the oil control sleeve, flat surface toward the bearing, and then install the bearing retainer in the outer groove.

4. Invert the bearing housing so the turbine is down and the compressor up. Install the inner bearing retainer, force the bearing in until it seats, and install the outer retainer.

5. Install the piston ring on the turbine wheel shaft, and, with the ring centered, insert the shaft through the bearing so the turbine wheel is firmly seated against the bearing housing. Avoid forcing the ring, and be sure it is centered.

6. Position the housing with the turbine wheel down. Install the first thrust ring on the shaft and position it against the bearing housing.

7. Install the thrust bearing over the shaft and groove pins, and press it into position against the bearing housing.

8. Install the thrust bearing over the shaft. Install the groove pins and press them into position against the bearing housing.

9. Install the spacer sleeve over the shaft and into the inside diameter of the thrust bearing.

10. Install the second thrust ring. Engage the oil deflector over the groove pins in the same position as the thrust bearing with the baffle downward.

11. Install the piston ring in the groove of the flinger sleeve. Center the ring. Install the flinger sleeve into the compressor insert.

12. Position the o-ring in the groove of the compressor insert and install the compressor insert over the shaft and press into position. The insert must be pressed in until it clears the large retaining ring groove.

13. Insert the compressor insert retaining ring with tru-arc pliers. Make sure the ring is properly positioned in the groove.

14. Install the compressor wheel, pushing it down until it bottoms.

15. Coat the threads of the shaft and the face of the washer with graphite grease. Install the locknut onto the shaft, and torque

Adaptor for turbocharger dial indicator

Compression tester

USE 24ST ALUMINUM OR EQUIVALENT

Turbocharger assembly and disassembly device

the locknut while holding the turbine wheel with a ⅜″ eight point or ⅝″ 12 point socket.

16. Spin the compressor wheel to check for absolute freedom from binding.

17. Install the o-ring in the bearing housing compressor flange.

18. Position the compressor and vee clamp onto the bearing housing. Align the marks and torque the vee clamp nut. AiResearch TEO6A & THO8A—50 in. lb. others—120 in. lb.

19. Following the same procedure, install the turbine housing.

20. Spin the compressor wheel to ensure freedom from binding.

21. Inspect the air intake system to ensure cleanliness, and make sure no foreign material has found its way into the exhaust manifold.

22. Inspect the oil supply line and drain line to make sure no clogging or leakage has occurred and that any check valves operate freely.

23. Inspect the turbocharger mounting pad to ensure it is not eroded and is flat.

24. Position a new gasket on the exhaust manifold, position the turbocharger, and install the mounting bolts. Torque to 30 ft. lb.

25. Connect the oil supply line, and compressor inlet and outlet piping, torquing all clamps snugly.

26. Pull engine stop button out so engine will not start, and crank the engine until a steady flow of oil comes from the drain line

connection. Then, connect the drain line. Make sure the drain line slopes downward along its entire length, with no kinks.

ENDT 864, 865, 866 Series

Preliminary Inspection

1. Remove the compressor housing, force the compressor toward the turbine end of the unit, and spin the compressor. Check for binding, rubbing, or unusual noises.

2. Remove the turbine exhaust outlet and check the end play of the turbine shaft and the radial float of the bearings. Move the shaft with equal pressure on both ends.

3. If there is binding or rubbing, or end play or radial float is excessive, remove the unit for repairs.

Disassembly

1. Clean the exterior of the unit with a spray of cleaing solvent and blow dry.

2. Mount the turbocharger on a bench. Install a locally fabricated dial indicator holder, like that shown in the illustration, to the oil drain mounting pad.

3. Install a plunger type dial indicator, with a one inch travel and three inch extension, to the indicator holder.

4. Zero the indicator. Move the shaft back and forth, applying equal pressure at both ends. The unit must be overhauled if end play exceeds .0070″.

5. Check the end float with the indicator mounted to the center housing and its tip on the end of

the shaft. Hold the shaft toward the indicator and zero it. Then, move the shaft back and forth and read the total indicator movement. If it exceeds .0070″, the unit must be overhauled.

6. Mark the turbine and compressor housings with a center punch to permit correct alignment at reassembly.

7. Remove the vee clamp and pull off the compressor housing, carefully avoiding damage to the compressor.

8. Unlock the tabs and remove the capscrews, which secure the turbine housing. Remove the turbine housing carefully, using only a soft mallet if force is required.

9. Mount the bearing housing in a specially fabricated fixture like that shown in the illustration. Then mount the fixture in a vise so the turbine wheel will be pointed downward. Remove the turbine wheel retaining nut with a socket and t-handle.

10. Heat the bearing housing at 325-375° F. for a maximum of 10 minutes.

11. Remove the bearing housing from the oven. Press the turbine wheel shaft out of the compressor wheel with an arbor press. Keep the shaft centered within the bearing housing until the shaft is clear of the housing.

12. Remove the assembly from the holding fixture, and remove the piston ring from the turbine wheel shaft.

13. Unlock the locking tabs and remove the thrust plate retaining capscrews and the thrust plate. Remove the thrust spacer, and then remove the piston ring from the spacer.

14. Remove the inboard thrust bearing, thrust collar, and seal ring, and bearing from the bearing housing.

15. Use special pliers to remove the two tru-arc rings, and then remove the rear bearing.

Cleaning

1. Soak the turbine housing and wheel in a carbon removing solvent for 25 minutes. Do not immerse the shaft.

2. Remove the assembly from the solvent and use a bristle brush to remove remaining carbon.

3. Clean all parts with a solvent spray and blow dry.

Inspection

1. Inspect turbine and compressor housings for signs of contact with rotating parts. Make sure the mounting flange is flat, and without erosion. Check the condition of the threaded holes and

parting surfaces.

2. Check the condition of the bearing housing to ensure the bearing bores are in good condition and that the inboard thust bearing positioning pins are securely in position. Make sure oil holes and threaded holes are in good condition.

3. Check the condition of the inboard thrust bearing and thrust collar, and make sure that thrust collar holes are not obstructed.

4. Check the condition of the thrust plate mating surfaces. Check the condition of the thrust spacer bore.

5. Check the condition of the bearings—especially for the imbedment of foreign matter.

6. Check the turbine wheel shaft for wear or scoring at the journal locations. Check the condition of the oil seal ring groove and threads on the end of the shaft.

7. Inspect the turbine and compressor wheels for signs of rubbing or vanes worn to a feather edge. The compressor wheel bore must not be galled.

8. Check the condition of the turbine wheel shroud. Make sure the mating surface is clean and flat.

9. Reject all parts that show damage. New piston rings, seal ring, bearing retainers, compressor retaining nut, and lock plates should always be used at reassembly.

10. Polish areas showing minor surface damage with silicon carbide cloth on aluminm or crocus cloth on steel.

Reassembly

1. Coat all moving parts with clean engine oil prior to reassembly. Make sure all parts are absolutely clean.

* AiResearch TE06A & TH08A—50 in. lb.

2. Install the piston ring in the groove in the turbine wheel shaft. Posiion the turbine wheel in the holding fixtue.

3. Install the rear bearing, and then insert the tru-arc retaining ring with the rounded side toward the bearing.

NOTE: AiResearch turbochargers feature an anti-wear washer inboard of the bearing.

4. Install the front bearing tru-arc retaining ring in the groove in the center housing, with the rounded side toward the bearing. Install the bearing.

5. Position the shroud on the rear end of the center housing and install it over the turbine wheel shaft. Gentle rocking while carefully forcing the shroud on will allow the ring to seat and permit the housing to bottom on the shaft. If necessary, a dental pick or similar tool may be used to seat the ring.

6. Make sure the front bearing is in proper location. Then, install the inboard thrust washer over the shaft. Make sure the holes in the washer align with the pins in the center housing, and that the washer is seated flat.

7. Install the thrust collar so it will be positioned next to the inboard thrust washer.

8. Install the square cut oil ring in the groove in the center housing.

9. Position the thrust plate over the shaft and align the oil holes. Install the center housing to the thrust plate retaining capscrews and lock tabs. Torque the capscrews (40 in. lb.) and bend the tab locks.

10. Install the piston ring in the groove in the thrust spacer. Install the spacer over the shaft with the ring up, sliding it down until it is positioned in the thrust plate. Bottom the ring in the groove in the spacer and push the spacer into position.

11. Heat the compressor wheel in an oven at 325-375° F. for 10 minutes or less.

12. Remove the compressor wheel from the oven and install it over the turbine wheel shaft. Install and torque the compressor wheel retaining nut to 120 in-lbs while the compressor is hot, using a t-handle.

13. Allow the compressor to come to room temperature. Remove the compressor wheel retaining nut. Check the surface of the nut which bears against the washer and the compressor wheel for

pick-up. They must be smooth and clean.

14. Lightly oil the shaft threads and install the nut, torquing to 18-20 in-lbs. Tighten it about 1/3 of a turn farther. Remove the holding fixture and check the unit for free rotation.

15. Put the turbine housing into position on the bearing housing, aligning the marks made during disassembly. Install the housing clamps, lock plates, and capscrews, coating the threads of the screws with anti-seize compound before installation. Torque the capscrews (120 in. lb.*) and bend over the tabs. Make sure the turbine still rotates freely.

16. Put the compressor housing into position, align marks made during disassembly, and install the vee clamp. Torque the vee clamp bolt nut.

17. Check the assembly for free rotation by pushing the turbine toward the compressor and turning the shaft. Repeat the check while pushing the compressor end of the shaft.

18. Inspect the air intake system to ensure cleanliness, and make sure no foreign material has found its way into the exhaust manifold.

19. Inspect the oil supply line and drain line to make sure no clogging or leakage has occurred and that any check valves operate freely.

20. Inspect the turbocharger mounting pad to ensure it is not eroded and is flat.

21. Position a new gasket on the exhaust manifold, position the turbocharger, and install the mounting bolts. Torque to 35 ft. lb.

22. Connect the oil supply line, and compressor inlet and outlet piping, torquing all clamps snugly.

23. Pull engine stop button out so engine will not start, and crank the engine until a steady flow of oil comes from the drain line connection. Then, connect the drain line. Make sure the drain line slopes downward along its entire length, with no kinks.

Engine Series	Altitude Feet							
	0	2,000	4,000	6,000	8,000	10,000	12,000	14,000
END673E	530	500	460	430	390	360	340	310
ENDT673C ENDT675, ENDT676	475	445	415	385	355	325	295	275
ENDT(B)865, 866 14.95:1 *	485	455	425	385	355	335	305	285
ENDT(B)865, 866 15.7:1 *	540	510	480	440	410	380	350	330

* Compression Ratio   Minimum Compression Pressure PSI

GENERAL SPECIFICATIONS

ENGINE MODEL	CUBIC IN. DISP.	HORSEPOWER @ R.P.M.—SAE	TORQUE @ R.P.M.—SAE	FIRING ORDER	GOVERNED SPEED	OIL PRESSURE	VALVE CLEARANCE INTAKE	EXHAUST	BORE & STROKE
OM352A	346	144 @ 1800	318 @ 2000	1-5-3-6-2-4	2800	35.5 @ 2800	.007	.011	3.82 x 5.04
OM352	346	120 @ 1800	257 @ 1800	1-5-3-6-2-4	2800	35.5 @ 2800	.007	.011	3.82 x 5.04

CRANKSHAFT AND BEARING SPECIFICATIONS

(INCHES)

ENGINE MODEL	MAIN BEARING JOURNAL DIA.	MAIN BEARING CLEARANCE	SHAFT ENDPLAY	ROD BEARING JOURNAL DIA.	ROD BEARING CLEARANCE
OM352	3.4696	.0019-.0035	.0074	2.3641	.0019-.0035

PISTON ASSEMBLY SPECIFICATIONS

(INCHES)

ENG. MODEL	RING SIDE CLEARANCE 1st	2nd	3rd	4th	5th	PISTON SKIRT DIA.	RING END GAP 1st	2nd	3rd	4th	5th	CYLINDER LINER INSIDE DIA.
OM352	.0017-.0031	.0021-.0032	.0028-.0032	.0013-.0024	.0009-.0020	3.815	.013-.021	.013-.012	.013-.021	.009-.014	.009-.014	3.819

ENGINE TORQUE SPECIFICATIONS

(FT. LB.)

ENGINE MODEL	CYLINDER HEAD	ROCKER SUPPORT	EXHAUST MANIFOLD	CONN. ROD	MAIN BRG. CAP	DAMPER TO CRANKSHAFT	FLYWHEEL	NOZZLE HOLDER	OIL PAN	ROCKER COVER
OM352	①	80	36	72 + 90°	②	362-398	22+90°	50	5	18

① Three Steps
43, 65, 80

② To eng. 100 HP/009386 M14 ⎫
110 HP/006010 M14 ⎬ 86
126 HP/020157 M14 ⎭
From above engines—101
Type Suffix M15—36+90°

Engine Disassembly

NOTE: Disassembly procedure is done with engine removal from vehicle and mounted in a work stand.

1. Remove all hoses and lines from clips on cylinder head.
2. Unbolt and remove cover and gasket.
3. Remove fuel filter.
4. Remove upper cooling line.
5. Remove injection high pressure lines.
6. Remove rocker arm assemblies.
7. Lift out pushrods and mark order for re-installation.
8. Disconnect pull rod on throttle valve lever.
9. Unbolt exhaust pipe from manifold.
10. Attach lifting device and remove head bolts in reverse order of installation. Lift off head. Place head on its side to avoid damage to nozzles.
11. Remove injection leak-off pipe.
12. Remove nozzle holder pressure screw and remove nozzle holder with a slide hammer or puller.
13. Unscrew nozzle sleeve with slotted socket.
14. Compress valve springs, remove keepers and disassemble valves and springs.
15. Remove flywheel attaching bolts and remove flywheel by tapping with a plastic hammer in a downward direction.
16. Remove alternator and belt.
17. Remove damper bolt and remove damper from crankshaft with puller.
18. Unbolt and remove front cover and timing housing bottom.
19. Remove oil pan.
20. Remove oil pump.
21. Remove cylinder liner ridge.
22. Unbolt and remove rod bearing caps. Mark cap.
23. Push piston and rod assemblies from block.
24. Remove piston cooling nozzles.
25. Unbolt and remove lower main bearing caps.
26. Remove crankshaft from block.
27. Remove upper main halves.
28. Remove oil filler connection from timing housing.
29. Set engine to injection delivery beginning: 18° BTC.
30. Remove fuel lines from injection pump.
31. Remove oil supply line.
32. Unbolt and remove injection pump.
33. Remove pushrod chamber cover.
34. Remove valve tappets.
35. Unbolt and remove air compressor.
36. Unscrew thrust washer from camshaft.

NOTE: Locking plate is only used on engines up to 130 HP/115816.

37. Remove camshaft.
38. Remove starter.
39. Remove electric line from oil pressure transmitter or oil pressure gauge line.
40. Unscrew exchanger from crankcase.
41. Remove upper cooling pipe and thermostat.
42. Remove coolant hoses from water pump.
43. Remove fan and pulley assembly.
44. Unbolt and remove water pump.

Mercedes Benz Diesel Engines

Service Procedures

Pistons

1. Remove rings from pistons.
2. Remove piston pin locks and separate rod, pin, and position.
3. Clean ring grooves and check width:
   Groove 1—.118"
   Groove 2—.118"
   Groove 3—.118"
   Groove 4—.216"
   Groove 5—.216"
4. Assemble rings in grooves.
5. Assemble piston, pin and rod. Install locks.
6. Install bearing halves in rod and cap.

Valve Guides

1. Force guide out of head with mandrel driver.
2. Ream guide bore to next highest step: 1, .2 or .5MM over.
3. Coat new guide with graphited oil and drive into head with suitable mandrel driver. Ream guides to .3551" for intake and .3945" for exhaust valves.

Injection Nozzles—Testing

1. Remove carbon from nozzle.
2. Install nozzle in tester 000589142700.
3. Push pump lever slowly until reading is $20 Kp/cm^2$ (284 psi) below opening pressure ($200 \pm 10 Kp/cm^2 + 2,844 \pm 142$ psi).
4. The nozzle should show no signs of leakage for at least 10 seconds.
5. Move hand lever at the rate of about one stroke per second and read opening pressure: 2844 psi.
6. Disconnect pressure gauge and operate lever at about 4 to 6 strokes per second. The nozzle should buzz softly. No lateral diffusion of the spray should occur.

Injection Nozzles—Repair

1. Insert nozzle holder into mounting fixture 403489 003100 and remove pressure nut. Disassemble nozzle.

Piston dia.	77
Stroke	30
Total displacement	140 cm^3
Delivery lits/min at rpm	209,54/3000
Max. operating pressure	7,35 kp/cm^2 (104.5 psi)
Filling time from 3 to 4 kp/cm^2 using a 40 lits. air tank and 1 500 rpm of air compressor	18^1) sec

^{1}) During repairs max. 23 sec.

Cylinder Liner and Piston

CYLINDER LINER	BORE DIA.	PISTON DIA.	PISTON CLEARANCE
Normal	77,010 / 76,990	76,980 / 76,970	
Normal I	77,085 / 77,065	77,055 / 77,045	
Rep.-St. I	77,260 / 77,240	77,230 / 77,220	0,010-0,020 wear limit max. 0,03
Rep.-St. II	77,510 / 77,490	77,480 / 77,470	
Rep.-St. III	77,760 / 77,740	77,730 / 77,720	

Piston Rings

GROOVE	PISTON RING DESIGNATION (PART NO.)	WIDTH OF RING GROOVE	SIDE CLEARANCE	GAP CLEARANCE
I	Angular compression ring (900282 077000) 12 f 77 x 70,2 x 2,5 x KE 54 N 282	2,5+0,012	0,010-0,034	0,30-0,45
II	Angular compression ring (900282 077000) 12 f 77 x 70,2 x 2,5 x KE 54 N 282	2,5+0,012	0,010-0,034	0,30-0,45
III	Slotted chamfered oil control ring (900282 077000) 42 f 77 x 70,2 x 4 KE 54 N 283	4,0+0,012	0,010-0,034	0,25-0,40
IV	Slotted chamfered oil control ring (900278 077000) 30 f 77 x 70,2 x 3 KE 54 N 278	3,0+0,012	0,010-0,034	0,30-0,45

Note: The designation of the piston rings refers only to normal stage of piston.

Loosening vibration damper bolt

Rod cap removal

Main cap removal

Pointer on timing housing at beginning of delivery

Piston Pins

COLOR CODE	PISTON PIN OD	BORE IN PISTON
yellow	16,0135 / 16,0110	16,0435 / 16,0410
green	16,0160 / 16,0136	16,0460 / 16,0435
Piston pin clearance in connecting rod bushing		0,009-0,024
Piston pin clearance in piston		0,027-0,032

Connecting Rod

Basic bore in connecting rod		35,016 / 35,000
Basic bore for connecting rod bushing		19,021 / 19,000
Distance from center of camshaft lifting pin to center of piston pin bore		92,000 / 91,950
Perm. deviation of parallel axle alignment for length of 100 mm		0,03
Width of connecting rod on	connecting rod eye	21,935 / 21,883
	piston pin eye	22,3 / 22,2
Radial play of crankpins		0,030-0,066
Axial play (end play) of crankpins		0,065-0,317

Camshaft Lifting Pin and Connecting Rod Bearing

STAGES	LIFTING PIN DIA.	BEARING BORE IN INSTALLED CONDITION	WALL THICKNESS FOR BEARING SHELLS READY FOR INSTALLATION
Normal	32,000 / 31,984	32,066 / 32,026	1,475-1,487
Normal I	31,900 / 31,884	31,966 / 31,926	1,525-1,537
Rep.-St. I	31,750 / 31,734	31,816 / 31,776	1,600-1,612
Rep.-St. II	31,500 / 31,484	31,566 / 31,526	1,725-1,737
Rep.-St. III	31,250 / 31,234	31,316 / 31,276	1,850-1,862

Connecting Rod Bushing

OD	19,048 / 19,035
ID	16,035 / 16,025
Overlap of connecting rod bushing in connecting rod	0,014-0,048

2. Clean nozzle in fuel oil. Injection holes can be cleaned with tool 00589006800 or equivalent.
3. Place nozzle needle and body in diesel fuel and check slidability by means of a drop test: pull needle 1/3 way out of body and release. Needle should slide back to its seat under its own weight.
4. Assemble nozzle and place in holder. Torque pressure nut to 57 ft. lbs.

Air Compressor—Disassembly

1. Remove head, unscrew liner and pull off over piston.
2. Unlock and force out piston pin. Remove piston.
3. Unbolt and remove connecting rod, bearing and cap.
4. Unscrew suction valve cap from cylinder head.
5. Remove valve spring, valve disc and suction valve seat.
6. Unscrew pressure valve seat from cylinder head and remove together with valve disc, valve spring and spring housing.
7. Remove piston rings.
8. Clean all parts in alcohol. Check the following specifications: ALL MEASUREMENTS IN MILLIMETERS.

Air Compressor—Assembly

1. Insert bearing shells into connecting rod and cap.
2. Bolt connecting rod cap to rod and measure bore at 3 places.
3. Remove cap and measure ID of rod bushing.
4. Attach rod assembly to camshaft lifting pin.
5. Install rings on piston and assemble piston and pin onto connecting rod. Install pin locks.
6. Install liner over piston and screw liner into block.
7. Install suction valve components into head.
8. Insert pressure valve components into head and screw on pressure valve seat with socket wrench.
9. Screw cylinder head to liner using new gasket.
10. Install suction and brake hose.

1 Compressed air outlet duct
2 Intake duct
3 Cylinder head
4 Head gasket
5 Liner
6 Piston
7 Connecting rod
8 Engine Crankcase

Piston

9 Camshaft lift pin
10 Camshaft oil duct
11 Rod bearing cap
 A With liner screwed on, piston projects 0.1-0.3mm
 B Gasket 0.25 and .05 mm thick

Oil Pump—Disassembly

1. Clamp pump in soft jaw vise.
2. Pull helical gear.
3. Unscrew housing cover.
4. Unscrew oil pressure relief valve plug and remove along with spring and piston.
5. Unscrew valve housing.
6. Remove oil pump gear wheel and drive shaft.
7. Pull gear wheel from shaft.
8. Remove strainer and force shaft from housing.

Oil Pump Assembly

1. Heat oil pump drive gear to 175° F and install on shaft.
2. Press pump shaft into housing.
3. Install pump shaft into housing.
4. Check end play of oil pump gear wheel.
5. Heat helical gear to 175° F and install on drive shaft.
6. Check drive shaft end play.
7. Install relief valve, strainer and housing cover.

Water Pump Disassembly

1. Pull hub from pump shaft.
2. Unscrew and remove sealing ring holder.
3. Remove grease cup.
4. Push shaft and bearing from impeller end.
5. Force small bearing and seal from housing.
6. Remove sliding ring seal from housing.
7. Pull bearing from shaft.
8. Remove counter ring from impeller.

Water Pump—Assembly

1. Press radial seal into housing.

Tightening Torques in kpm (Ft. lb.)

Connecting rod	1,5+0,2 (10.8)
Cylinder liner on crankcase	3,5— 4 (25.3-28.9)
Cylinder head on liner	3,5— 4 (25.3-28.9)
Inlet and exhaust valve on cylinder head	12 — 14 (86.7-101.2)

Oil Pump—Dimensions in M.M.

Radial play of drive shaft	0,016-0,042
Radial play between oil pump gear wheel and oil pump shaft	0,011-0,040
Overlap between oil pump shaft and housing	0,010-0,039
Radial play of oil pump gear wheels between housing and gear wheel	0,030-0,105
End play of oil pump gear heels between housing cover and gear wheel	0,025-0,089
Backlash of oil pump gear wheels	0,15-0,25
Backlash of oil pump drive gears (helical gears)	0,096-0,128
Number of teeth of oil pump gear wheels	7/7
Test torque of oil pump helical gear	7 kpm (50 ft. lb.)
Test torque of oil pump gear wheel (driving)	

DIMENSION A	Dia. in housing	17,018 / 17,000
	Dia. of drive shaft	16,984 / 16,976
Dimension B = Dia. of oil pump shaft		15,039 / 15,028
DIMENSION C	Height of gear wheel housing	40,025 / 40,000
	Height of oil pump gear wheel	39,975 / 39,936
DIMENSION D	Perm. play between driving helical gear and upper edge of pump housing with driving gear at upper edge of pump housing	0,04
Dimension E = Installation height of drive shaft		0,5-0,8

a Reference dimension 143.5 ± 0.5 MM
A Water pump shaft
B Hub
C Holder with front oil seal ring
D O-ring
E Large grooved ball bearing

F Small grooved ball bearing
G Rear seal ring
H Sliding ring seal
J Impeller
K Impeller-to-housing .08 mm

Timing mark alignment

Oil Pump Test

Delivery rate measured with SAE 10 oil Oil temperature 50° C	300 rpm	6,2 lits/min
Oil counter pressure 6,0 kp/cm²	1 400 rpm	43,5 lits/min

Springs for oil pressure relief valves

	OD MM	WIRE DIA. MM	ADJUSTED TO KP/CM²	UN-LOADED SPRING LENGTH MM	SPRING PRELOAD		SPRING FINAL LOAD	
					LENGTH MM	LOAD KP	LENGTH MM	LOAD KP
In oil pump	9,3	1,7	5,2±0,5	49,4	45,4	4,39	36,2	14,5

Tightening Torques in kpm (Ft. lb.)

Cover to oil pump	3,5 (25.2)
Strainer to cover	2-2,5 (14.4-18)
Oil pressure relief valve to cover	6 (43.3)

Dimensions in M.M.

Water pump shaft dia.		on impeller seat	15,039 / 15,028
	Bearing seat	large bearing	30,009 / 29,996
		small bearing	17,008 / 16,997
Shaft dia. for hub			29,054 / 29,041
Bore dia. in hub			29,021 / 29,000
Hub dia. for sealing ring front			42,000 / 41,840
Shaft dia. for rear sealing ring			17,008 / 16,997
Bore dia. in impeller			15,018 / 15,000
Press impeller on water pump shaft			Flange surface—impeller flush with housing, flange
Lubrication of water pump			Grease approx. 80 grams

2. Press sliding ring seal into housing.
3. Press bearings onto shaft.
4. Fit seal on hub and around bearing.
5. Press hub on shaft.
6. Press shaft into housing.
7. Install seal holder to housing.
8. Install counter ring and seal on impeller.
9. Press impeller onto shaft.
10. Check clearances.

Engine Assembly

1. Bolt water pump and gasket to engine. Torque pump bolts to 35 ft. lbs.
2. Install thermostat and fan. Torque thermostat housing bolts to 21 ft. lbs. and fan-to-hub bolts to 25 ft. lbs.
3. Coat heat exchanger cover with grease and position new gasket on cover.
4. Position sealing discs on holes of oil outlet and inlet duct.
5. Place heat exchanger plates, one on top of another in position. Place sealing rings under bolt heads and hand-tighten bolts.
6. Attach heat exchanger to engine. Torque bolts to 25 ft. lbs. Insert bypass valve.
7. Install starter.
8. Connect oil pressure sending unit line.
9. Carefully slide camshaft into block. Align timing marks with idler gear.
10. Attach thrust washer.
11. Insert valve tappets in order as marked.
12. Install pushrod chamber cover.
13. Install injection pump into timing hosing so that mark on pump gear is aligned with arrow in timing housing.
14. Attach fuel supply, oil, and injection lines.
15. Clean all crankshaft bearing surfaces; insert upper main halves in block. Coat with SAE 30. Attach main caps and check bore. Remove caps.
16. Install crankshaft into block.

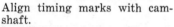

Pointer on timing housing at beginning of delivery

Rod cap alignments

Align timing marks with cam-shaft.

17. Install caps and torque to specifications.
18. Install piston cooling nozzles.
19. Assemble piston and rod, coat all parts with SAE 30 and install piston with notch forward. Assemble rod caps and torque to specifications.
20. Install oil pump and new gasket.
21. Install oil pan and gasket.
22. Install front cover and timing housing.
23. Heat vibration camper to 175°F and install on crankshaft with key. Install and torque bolt.
24. Install alternator.
25. Set engine to #1 compression at 18° BTDC. Remove oil supply line from injector timing housing. Remove #1 injection line from pump. Remove pipe connection from #1 pump cylinder and remove filler piece, compression spring and valve cone. Reinstall pipe connection and overflow pipe. Unscrew fuel supply line from pump and attach reservoir. Fill reservoir with clean fuel and open shut-off valve. Set control valve on pump to full load. When adjusted **ONE DROP** of fuel should come out of overflow pipe every 15-20 sec. If flow is greater or less, unbolt pump in swivel until adjustment is correct. Reconnect pump. Reinstall parts.
26. Position flywheel on crankshaft and align bolt holes. Oil bolt threads and tighten in a cross pattern.

27. Assembly valves in head.
28. Install sleeves in head and torque to 43 ft. lbs.
29. Install holder seals in sleeves.
30. Insert holders into sleeves. Tighten pressure nut to 43-50 ft. lbs.
31. Install oil drain pipe and new seals.
32. Place new head gasket on block.
33. Lower head into position, lubricate bolt threads and install bolts. Tighten bolts in pattern shown to 43, then 65 then 80 ft. lbs.
34. Install pushrods as marked.
35. Mount rocker arm assembly and torque to 80 ft. lbs.
36. Install injection lines.
37. Attach exhaust manifold (36 ft. lbs.) and exhaust pipe.
38. Attach and secure pull rod to throttle valve.
39. Install upper cooling line with new seals.
40. Attach fuel filter.
41. Install dipstick.
42. Adjust valves.
43. Install cylinder head cover and attach all lines and hoses clipped to cover.

Fuel reservoir in place

Head bolt torque sequence

Removing filler from #1 injection port

Removing #1 injection line

GENERAL SPECIFICATIONS

ENGINE MODEL	BORE AND STROKE	HORSEPOWER @ R.P.M.	TORQUE FT. LBS. @ R.P.M.	COMPRESSION PRESSURE CRANKING SPEED	FIRING ORDER	NO LOAD R.P.M.	GOVERNED SPEED FULL LOAD R.P.M.	IDLE SPEED
354D	3.875 x 5	120 @ 2800	260 @ 1450	430	153624	3000	2800	525

PISTONS, PINS, RINGS, CRANKSHAFT AND BEARINGS

ENGINE MODEL	PISTON CLEARANCE	PISTON RING END GAP MINIMUM COMP.	OIL	PISTON PIN DIAMETER	ROD BEARING SHAFT DIAMETER	ROD BEARING CLEARANCE	MAIN BEARING SHAFT DIAMETER	MAIN BEARING CLEARANCE	SHAFT END PLAY	THRUST ON BEARING NO.
354D	.0059	.015	.011	1.375	2.499-2.4995	.0015-.003	2.9985-2.999	.0025-.0045	.006-.014	4

VALVE SPECIFICATIONS

ENGINE MODEL	VALVE LASH (HOT)	VALVE FACE ANGLE	VALVE STEM INTAKE	CLEARANCE EXHAUST	VALVE GUIDE BORE	VALVE STEM DIAMETER INTAKE	VALVE STEM DIAMETER EXHAUST	VALVE SPRINGS TEST LENGTH INNER	TEST LENGTH OUTER	TEST PRESS. LBS. INNER	TEST PRESS. LBS. OUTER
354D	.010	45°	.001-.003	.002-.004	.3750-.3760	.373-.374	.3720-.3730	1⁹/₁₆″ @ 15 lbs.	1²⁵/₃₂″ @ 40 lb.	1⁹/₁₆″ @ 15 lb.	1²⁵/₃₂″ @ 40 lb

ENGINE TORQUE SPECIFICATIONS

ENGINE MODEL	CYLINDER HEAD FT. LBS.	INTAKE MANIFOLD FT. LBS.	EXHAUST MANIFOLD FT. LBS.	CONN. ROD FT. LBS.	MAIN BEARING CAPS FT. LBS.	CRANKSHAFT END NUT FT. LBS.	FLYWHEEL CRANKSHAFT TO FT. LBS.	CAMSHAFT GEAR BOLT FT. LBS.	FUEL INJECTOR NUTS FT. LBS.	OIL PAN BOLTS FT. LBS.
354D	1	31-36	41-45	65-70	145-150	250-275	75-80	45-50	23-26	10-15

1—⁷/₁₆″ studs 55-60 lbs. ½″ studs 80 lbs.

Trouble Diagnosis

The satisfactory performance of a Diesel engine depends on two items of foremost importance, (1) Sufficiently high compression pressure, and (2) The injection of the proper amount of fuel at the right time.

The first one of these items depends entirely on pistons, piston rings, valves and valve operating mechanism; the second item depends on injectors and their operating mechanism, and fuel system.

Lack of engine power, uneven running, excessive vibration, and tendency to stall when idling may be caused by either a compression loss or faulty injector operation.

The causes of trouble symptoms may be varied; therefore a hit-and-miss search should be avoided. A proper diagnosis of symptoms is an orderly process of diagnosing the symptoms. An "orderly process" means to check the most probable common cause first; then proceed with the next most probable case.

Hard Starting

1. No fuel at injectors.
   a. No fuel in tank.
   b. Stop control in "stop" position.
   c. Air in fuel system.
2. Oil in crankcase too heavy.
3. Wrong type fuel oil.

4. Injection pump timing wrong.
5. Injectors in need of service.
6. Cold starting aid inoperative.
7. Poor compression in one or more cylinders.

No Power (Exhaust Clean)

1. Restricted fuel supply.
   a. Restriction on suction side of fuel pump.
   b. Air leak on suction side of fuel pump.
   a. Blocked fuel filter.
   d. Faulty low pressure fuel pump.
2. Incorrect fuel injection pump delivery.

Low Power, Max R.P.M. Low (Clean Exhaust)

1. Throttle lever not reaching wide open position.
2. Air in fuel system.

Low Power, Engine Misfires (Clean Exhaust)

1. One or more broken or cracked fuel lines.

Low Power, Engine Smooth (Smoky Exhaust)

1. Blocked air cleaner.
2. Wrong injector settings.

3. Incorrect valve lash.
4. Wrong grade fuel oil.
5. Injection pump timing late.

Low Power (Engine and Exhaust Overheat)

1. Injection timing late.

Low Power, Engine Misfires (Dirty Exhaust)

1. One or more injectors faulty.
2. Injection pump timing late.
3. Broken parts in fuel injection pump.
4. Valves bad in one or more cylinders.

Low Power, Engine Misfires, Engine Has Metallic Knock (Dirty Exhaust)

1. Exhaust valves badly carboned.
2. Needle stuck in injector.
3. One or more rocker levers broken.
4. One or more push rods bent.

Blow-By From Breather Tube

1. One or more pistons and/or liners scored.

Power Good, Poor Fuel Mileage (Exhaust Smoky and Black)

1. Fuel pump delivery too high due

Trouble Diagnosis

to unauthorized adjustment.

Fuel Oil in Oil Pan
1. Diaphragm on low pressure pump leaking.
2. "O" ring on fuel injection pump leaking.

3. Bad injectors.

Water in Oil Pan or Oil in Radiator
1. Cracked head or block.
2. Blown head gasket.

Fuel System

General Description

The Perkins-6-354 Diesel engine is a vertical four stroke cycle power unit.

The Perkins-6-354 Diesel engine is a six-cylinder direct injection unit havng a 3⅞" bore and 5" stroke.

The efficient operation of a diesel engine depends on the correct amount of fuel being injected into the cylinder at exactly the right time in the operating cycle. It also depends upon each cylinder being fully charged with air that has been compressed to the correct pressure and temperature in order to provide the necessary oxygen for complete and efficient combustion of the injected fuel oil.

Trouble shooting the fuel system becomes basically a process of elimination of the various components to ascertain which one is not functioning as it should. From this it follows that any malfunction in the combustion cycle will result in inefficient and/or incomplete burning of the fuel and air mixture, therefore, the most common complaint is likely to be "No Power."
—The causes of "No Power" fall into two major categories which are fairly easy to diagnose, the Key being the condition of the exhaust gas.

If the *correct* amount of fuel is being injected but power is low, the exhaust gasses will be heavy and generally black, brown or whitish brown in color due to incomplete combustion in the cylinders.

If too much fuel is being injected the exhaust will be black in color but the power will be good.

If insufficient fuel is being injected and power is low, the exhaust gasses will be hardly visible due to complete burning of the mixture in the cylinders.

Other associated complaints will be in the nature of:
1. Hard starting.
2. Flames in exhaust pipe.
3. Rough idle and missing at light loads.
4. Noisy and vibrating.
5. Overheating (especially the exhaust).
6. Low governed speed.

Fuel Filters

Always be careful to keep dirt of any kind from the fuel system. Within the system itself much has been done to be sure that only clean fuel oil reaches the fuel injection pump and nozzles. Fuel oil filters are provided as follows:

The *primary filter* is a screen unit located in the upper half of the fuel supply pump.

It should be removed for cleaning, every 12,000 miles or oftener as conditions warrant. The primary filter may be removed by unscrewing the bolt which secures the domed cover to the top of the fuel supply pump.

When reassembling after cleaning, make sure that a good joint is made between cover and fuel supply pump body. Any leakage of air here may cause air locks in the fuel system.

The *secondary* or *final filter* contains a paper element, this element being located between top and bottom covers the filter. Do not attempt to clean the paper element, it should be *replaced* every 20,000 miles.

Fuel Filter Replacement

1. Unscrew bolt in center of top cover.
2. Remove filter bottom cover.
3. Remove paper element and discard.
4. Clean filter top and bottom covers.
5. Replace the gaskets and rubber O-ring.
6. After reassembling, prime fuel system.

Fuel Supply Pump

The fuel supply pump is of the diaphragm type similar to the type used on gasoline engines. It is located on the right side of the engine and driven by an eccentric cam on the camshaft. A hand primer is an integral part of the fuel supply pump. Use the hand primer to pump fuel from tank until supply pump, filters, pipes, and injection pump are filled with fuel.

Priming System

Whenever an attempt is made to start a new or rebuilt engine, an engine on which the fuel lines have been disconnected (fuel filter change, service of injection pump, etc.), or an engine which has been standing idle for some time, the fuel system must be primed or bled. The procedure for priming the fuel system is as follows:

1. Loosen air vent screw on top of governor control housing.
2. Loosen vent screw in hydraulic head locking screw on side of fuel pump body.
3. Operate priming lever of fuel supply pump and when fuel, free from bubbles, flows from around each venting point, tighten head locking screw vent first and then vent screw on governor housing. If priming lever does not operate, rotate engine until operation is possible.
4. Loosen pipe union fitting at injection pump fuel inlet and

1 Tank
2 Supply pump
3 Filter
4 Injection pump
5 Injection nozzles
A Vent screw—governor housing
B Vent screw—head locking screw
C Fitting—pump fuel inlet
D Unions—Nozzle fuel inlet

Fuel system with C.A.V. hydraulic governed injection pump
(© Chrysler Corp.)

1 Bolt, fuel pump cover
2 Washer
3 Cover, fuel pump
4 Gasket, cover
5 Screen, fuel filter
6 Body, pump, upper half
7 Sleeve
8 Nut
9 Gasket, inlet & outlet valve
10 Valve, inlet & outlet
11 Retainer, valve
12 Screw, retainer
13 Diaphragm
14 Spring, diaphragm
15 Retainer, oil seal
16 Seal, oil
17 Body, pump lower half
18 Gasket, pump mounting
19 Spring, lever
20 Washer, rocker arm pin
21 Arm, rocker
22 Lever
23 Retainer
24 Pin, rocker arm
25 Washer, lock
26 Bolt
27 Washer
28 Screw

Fuel pump
(© Chrysler Corp.)

carefully to avoid bending or damaging. Dirt or chips should not be allowed to enter fuel lines. Do not disassemble injector line assembly unless one or more of the lines are to be replaced. Cover or tape fuel openings on the injection pump to prevent dirt from entering the pump.

Disconnect the accelerator and stop cable, remove the three injection pump attaching stud nuts and lift out the injection pump.

Fuel Injection Pump Repairs

Disassembly or repair of the fuel injection pump should never be attempted by anyone other than an authorized C.A.V. dealer, since special equipment is needed to properly service and repair this assembly. Satisfactory repair and adjustment are impossible without proper test equipment and procedures.

Fuel Metering

Apart from small losses which occur during the injection stroke, the total volume of fuel introduced into the element is passed on to the nozzle. Metering is effected, therefore, by regulating the volume of fuel which enters the element at each charging stroke. The volume of the charge is governed by two principal factors—the fuel pressure at the inlet port, and the time available for fuel to flow into the element while the inlet ports in the rotor and the hydraulic head are in register. It is by controlling the pressure at the inlet port that accurate metering is achieved.

Fuel Injector Pump Installation and Timing

The correct static injection pump timing (engine stopped) is 24° before top dead center. If the procedure we are covering here is followed carefully, the correct specified timing will result.

The fuel injection pump adapter plate has a slot, approximately 1/8" wide in its inside diameter. Also, on the edge of the adapter plate flange, adjacent to one of the bolt holes a

supply pump. When fuel, free from air bubbles, flows from threads, retighten fitting.

5. Loosen unions at nozzle ends of two of high pressure fuel injection pipes.
6. Set accelerator at full open position and make sure "stop" control is in "run" position.
7. Crank engine until fuel oil, free from air bubbles, flows from both fuel pipes.
8. Retighten unions on fuel injection pipes. The engine is now ready for starting.

Fuel Injection Pump

The C.A.V. Model DPA fuel injection pump is a distributor type pump incorporating an all speed governor and an automatic advance.

Pumping is effected by a single pumping element, having twin opposed plungers, situated transversely in a central rotating member which also acts as a distributor. The rotor revolves in a stationary member, known as the hydraulic head. The pump plungers are operated by contact with cam lobes on a stationary internal cam ring. The fuel is metered before entering the pumping element, and the accurately metered high pressure charges are distributed to the engine cylinders in correct firing order and at the required timing intervals through a system of ports in the rotor and the hydraulic head.

A simple hydraulic type governor is embodied in the pump to give accurate control of engine speed throughout the complete speed range of the engine and under all conditions of engine loading. An automatic advance mechanism is also provided to vary the point of commencement of injection.

Fuel Injection Pump Removal

Disconnect the fuel injector lines at the injectors and at the injector pump. Unbolt the mounting clamp from the cylinder head and remove the six injector lines as an assembly. Injector lines must be handled

Removing fuel pump from engine
(© Chrysler Corp.)

Installing fuel filter
(© Chrysler Corp.)

Removing injection pump
(© Chrysler Corp.)

Alignment of timing slots
(© Chrysler Corp.)

scribed line will be found.

Set the adapter plate in position on the three mounting studs with the scribe line next to the stud which is farthest from the center of the engine.

The timing mark for top dead center is located on the front face of flywheel. A pointer is located on flywheel housing.

To check timing, make certain the number one piston is at exact top dead center, and is on the compression stroke as follows: With valve cover removed rotate the crankshaft with the flywheel. When the number six exhaust valve is just seating, align the mark on the flywheel with the pointer. Number one cylinder will be at T.D.C.

A slot approximately ⅛″ wide can be seen on the top edge of the fuel injection pump drive hub on the vertical shaft.

Rotate the auxiliary shaft and fuel injection pump drive shaft in the direction of engine rotation, to where the ⅛″ slot in injector pump drive hub exactly aligns with the ⅛″ slot in inside diameter of adapter plate.

Place the auxiliary drive shaft gear on front of the shaft with chamfered side in, and so when it is against the mounting flange on shaft, the bolt holes in the flange are at center of slotted holes in the gear. If the bolt holes will not center in the slotted holes, turn the gear 120 degrees (one bolt hole). One of the three possible positions will allow the bolt holes to be centered. Install the retaining washer and the three recessed head retaining screws, with lock washers on each screw.

Check to make sure that the ⅛″ slot in fuel injection pump drive hub

is exactly aligned with corresponding slot in adapter plate. If some slight correction is necessary, bring the slots into alignment by turning injection pump vertical drive shaft. Then tighten the three gear retaining screws securely.

With the gasket positioned on the studs, align the master spline on the fuel injection pump shaft with the master spline in the vertical shaft, and set injection pump on adapter plate.

Align scribed line on injection pump mounting flange with scribed line on adapter plate, and tighten the three retaining nuts securely.

With Gasket Sealer on each side of gaskets, install camshaft gear cover and auxiliary drive shaft gear cover and tighten the bolts.

Install the vibration damper and

1 Shaft, splined
2 Tube, pilot
3 Seals, oil
4 Ring, snap
5 Lever, control
6 Shaft, pinion
7 Housing, governor
8 Screw, idle
9 Washer
10 Spring, idle
11 Rack
12 Spring, governor
13 Plate, dished (dashpot)
14 Plate, roller to roller adjusting
15 Valve, metering
16 Chamber, metering
17 Port, charging
18 Head, hydraulic
19 Rotor, distributing
20 Liner, transfer pump
21 Seal, "O" ring
22 Rotor, transfer pump
23 Plate, end
24 Bolt, end plate
25 Vane, sliding
26 Port, distributor
27 Hole, radial
28 Connector, nozzle pipe
29 Fitting, head locating with damper
30 Shoe, roller
31 Screw, cam advance
32 Ring, cam
33 Plunger
34 Plate, roller to roller adjusting
35 Plate, drive
36 Roller, cam
37 Housing, pump

C.A.V. fuel injection pump (© Chrysler Corp.)

Removing nozzle assembly
(© Chrysler Corp.)

Nozzle valve and body (removed from holder)
(© Chrysler Corp.)

pulley assembly, retaining washer and nut, tightening the nut to 250 foot-pounds.

Injector Nozzles

General Information

The performance of the high speed diesel engine depends largely on the proper function of its fuel injection system. For maximum efficiency it is essential the engine be not only provided with metered amounts of fuel at exactly timed intervals, but also that it receives each charge of fuel in the proper condition so it can be completely consumed without causing smoke in the exhaust. This briefly is the function of the injection nozzle assembly. The complete assembly consists of a nozzle and a nozzle holder.

Nozzle Maintenance

All nozzles should be removed from the engine at regular intervals. Just how long these intervals should be, depends on the different conditions under which the engine will operate. Where ideal conditions of good combustion, adequate cooling, and absolutely clean fuel are realized, the nozzles will need little attention. Since the efficiency of the nozzles vitally affects the performance and economical operation of the diesel engine, no engine should be allowed to run with

Injection nozzle
(© Chrysler Corp.)

nozzles that are defective. 18,000 miles is a good standard interval between inspections.

Nozzle trouble is usually indicated by one or more of the following symptoms:
1. Cylinder knock.
2. Engine overheating
3. Loss of power
4. Smoky exhaust (black)
5. Increased fuel consumption.
While the above faults may be

caused by defective nozzles, it should also be determined that they are not caused by other engine troubles such as wrong fuel, water in fuel, dirty or damaged filters, incorrect maximum fuel setting, defective engine lubrication, incorrect pump timing, incorrect engine valve timing, or faulty valves.

If everything else is in order and the nozzles are still suspected, the nozzle causing the trouble can often be found by releasing the pipe union nut on each nozzle in turn, with engine running and listening to the idling performance of each of the cylinders.

Nozzle Testing

To test a doubtful nozzle, loosen injection pipe at both ends and remove nozzle holder from cylinder head. A *blast of compressed air around each nozzle before loosening the holder will help prevent dirt or moisture from entering the combustion chamber when nozzle is removed.* Turn the nozzle and holder around the injection pipe so that nozzle points away from engine. Retighten both ends of injection line. Next, loosen pipe unions at the other nozzles to prevent fuel oil from being sprayed into cylinders. Turn engine with starter until the removed nozzle sprays fuel into the air. If spray is "wet," or "streaky," or to one side, or if the

Alignment of scribed line on injector pump and adapter plate
(© Chrysler Corp.)

Timing mark on flywheel and pointer
(© Chrysler Corp.)

Cleaning nozzle with brass wire brush
(© Chrysler Corp.)

Cleaning valve tip with brass wire brush
(© Chrysler Corp.)

Pressure faces of nozzle and holder
(© Chrysler Corp.)

Cleaning nozzle body channel bores
(© Chrysler Corp.)

nozzle "dribbles," remove and install a complete new or reconditioned unit.

WARNING: Keep hands away from spray. The working pressure will cause oil to penetrate the skin.

After making a nozzle replacement, the faulty unit should be sent to a test bench for cleaning and testing.

Nozzle Cleaning, Inspection

Nozzle maintenance like injection pump maintenance should be performed in a clean dust-free place where no other work is performed. A work bench with a holding fixture or small vise with soft jaws is essential for making the disassembly. A hand test pump with a good supply of clean diesel fuel or test oil should also be provided.

1. Attach injecton nozzle to hand test pump and check completely for spray pattern nozzle opening pressure setting, and back leakage.
2. If nozzle is faulty secure nozzle assembly in holding fixture or vise. Release pressure on nozzle valve spring by loosening lock nut and adjusting screw. Remove nozzle retainer nut and nozzle.
3. Inspect nozzle for carbon and note whether valve lifts out freely. Brush all carbon from outside with a brass wire brush. Place body and valve in clean fuel oil or cleaning solvent to soak and soften carbon. *The nozzle should be free from all damage and not "blued" from overheating. All polished surfaces should be relatively bright without scratches or dull patches. All pressure surfaces must be clean since these must mate to form a high pressure joint between nozzle holder and nozzle.*

4. Clean small feed channel bores with drill or wire of .066 inch diameter. These bores are rarely choked and insertion of drill or wire by hand will be sufficent.
5. Insert probe or groove scraper in fuel gallery and press against side of cavity to clear all carbon deposits from this area.
6. Clean all carbon from valve seat area by rotating and pressing probe on to seat.
7. Clear spray holes with appropriate size cleaning wire. Do not break wire in holes since such particles are almost impossible to remove (Hole Dia-.0126 in.).
8. Install nozzle in a flushing tool that can be coupled to a nozzle hand test pump and wash out all carbon particles. Force fuel or test oil through nozzle vigorously since this is best way to remove loosened particles that may still be present both in body cavities and spray holes.
9. Clean nozzle valve tip by brushing away carbon with a brass wire brush. To assemble valve into nozzle, immerse both items in clean fuel oil and fit them together under surface so as to prevent closely fitting lapped surfaces from being touched by hand. *If nozzle is blued or seat has a dull ring indicating wear or pitting, complete unit should be set aside. No attempt should be made to lap nozzle valve and body unless special training and equipment are available.*
10. Make sure lapped pressure faces on both nozzle and holder are clean and free from metalic particles. If holder has been disassembled, all parts should be thoroughly washed in fuel oil or cleaning solvent.

Injector Installation

Before installing injectors, make certain that all of the old copper sealing washers have been removed from the recesses in the cylinder head and have been discarded. Use only new copper sealing washers of the correct replacement part number. Old copper sealing washers can be removed with a piece of bent wire.

The recess in cylinder head, the faces of the copper washer, and corresponding face on injector must be thoroughly clean to avoid possible combustion leakage.

Place copper washer in position, and then injector. Make sure injector is an easy fit in the recess and on attaching studs, and that it can be placed down on copper washer without any force of any kind.

The nuts on attaching studs should then be tightened down evenly in order to prevent the injector nozzle from becoming cocked and bound in cylinder head.

This is very important, since any unevenness in tightening down may cause distortion and eventual failure of the injector nozzle, and will most certainly result in faulty sealing at copper washer.

Governor

The hydraulic governor is of simple design, the working parts being contained in a small housing. The control lever is carried on a pinion shaft, the pinion meshing with a rack which is free to slide on the metering valve stem.

The metering valve slides in a chamber in the hydraulic head, into which bore the diagonally drilled metering port opens.

A self-centering damping washer is carried on the valve stem against a shoulder, the governor spring being held between the plate and the rack. The plate slides in a cylindrical bore

Installing injector assembly

Details of motoring valve and shut-off spindle of hydraulic governor
(© Chrysler Corp.)

1 Nut, cap
2 Gasket, cap nut
3 Nut, lock
4 Washer, locknut tab
5 Screw, valve spring adjusting
6 Washer, adjusting screw
7 Spring, valve
8 Spindle, valve
9 Holder, nozzle
10 Gasket, connector
11 Connector, inlet
12 Pin, dowel
13 Nozzle, body and valve assy.
14 Nut, nozzle retainer

Nozzle and holder parts
(© Chrysler Corp.)

filled with fuel, and acts as a dashpot to damp out any violent movement of the metering valve.

An idling spring is located between the rack and the washer fitted at the top of the valve spindle and known as the shut-off washer. A screw is placed so as to form an idling stop.

The governor is operated by fuel at transfer pressure which is fed from the annular groove surrounding the pump rotor. The fuel passes through the metering valve, which is hollow, and via transverse holes to an annular space around the valve.

End wise movement of the metering valve varies the area of the metering port which registers with the annulus around the valve; the effective area of the port is that part which is uncovered by the inner edge of the groove or annulus.

The metering valve is loaded by the governor spring and this load may be manually adjusted by moving the control lever.

As the engine control is operated to give increased speed, the valve is pushed to the full open position by the governor spring. When engine speed increases, transfer pressure increases also, and this pressure forces

the valve back against the spring pressure until a balance is reached.

When the engine control is moved towards the idling stop, the idling spring is compressed, and the compression of the main governor spring is reduced. Equilibrium is reached when the forces exerted on the metering valve by the idling spring and fuel at transfer pressure are balanced by compression of the main spring. The latter becomes progressively less as the engine control is moved towards the idling stop, thus enabling the reduced transfer pressure at low speeds to operate the metering valve and perform the governing function throughout the idling range.

Details of the valve and the shut-off mechanism are shown in illustration. The shut-off spindle is carried in the governor housing, and carries a half-round end or "cam," which contacts the underside of the shut-off washer. Rotation of the spindle by the shut-off lever lifts the metering valve to a position where the metering port is blanked off, and thus stops the engine.

Automatic Advance

Under full load conditions, the maximum amount of fuel is introduced into the element, and the plungers and actuating rollers are forced outwards to the limit of their travel. As the rotor turns, the rollers are brought into contact with cam lobes on the cam ring. The point of contact is near the base of the cams.

Under lightly loaded conditions, fueling is decreased and the plunger travel is proportionally reduced. Contact between roller and cam is now made at a point near the cam peak.

The advance device corrects the tendency of the pump to retard timing under varying load conditions at constant speed.

The device illustrated provides progressive advancement of injection timing as engine speed is increased.

The piston is free to slide in a cylinder machined in the body of the device. Movement of this piston is transmitted to the cam ring by the ball-ended lever, causing the cam ring to rotate within the pump housing.

Pressure exerted on the piston by the springs, tends to hold the piston and the cam ring in the fully retarded position.

Fuel oil at transfer pressure enters the device through a fuel passage in the screw which secures the device to the pump housing. Transfer pressure acts upon the piston and tends to move the cam ring towards the fully advanced position.

Transfer pressure increases progressively as the engine speed is raised, and the piston is moved along the cylinder to compress the springs and move the cam ring towards the fully advanced position. When engine speed is decreased, transfer pressure falls, and the piston and cam ring are moved towards the retarded position by spring pressure.

The impact of the actuating rollers on the cam lobes at commencement of injection tends to move the cam ring towards the retarded position. Such movement is prevented by a non-

Automatic advance mechanism
(© Chrysler Corp.)

return valve situated in the fuel passage in the screw securing the device to the pump housing. Normal leakage between the piston and the cylinder permits the device to return to the retarded position when the engine speed falls.

Any desired timing advance up to a maximum of 9° (pump) is obtainable, and the engine speed at which this is attained can be varied by fitting stronger or weaker springs. The stronger the spring the higher will be the engine speed at which maximum timing advance is attained. Fine adjustment is made by shims fitted between the springs and the spring cap.

Governor No-Load Speed Setting

1. Warm engine to normal operating temperature.
2. Use accurate tachometer for checking engine speed.

3. Increase engine speed until governor control is apparent; this should be 3600-3700 rpm. If necessary, break seal and readjust by changing tension on governor spring. Increasing tension increases speed 50 rpm per turn of nut.

Water Pump

Removal and Installation

1. Drain cooling system and remove fan belt and fan.
2. Use a suitable puller and remove pump pulley.
3. Remove the pump to block mounting bolts and remove the pump.
4. Install by reversing the removal procedures.

Servicing Water Pump

Remove the self-locking nut and

Water pump (disassembled view) (© Chrysler Corp.)

Removing water pump pulley
(© Chrysler Corp.)

Installing bearing retainer snap ring
(© Chrysler Corp.)

flat washer which secure water pump pulley to pump shaft.

Using remover, pull the pulley from pump shaft. Remove key.

Press water pump shaft, complete with impeller, out through the rear of pump body. Press impeller off shaft.

Using snap ring pliers, remove bearing retaining snap ring from front of pump body.

With a suitable tool, press the two bearings and spacer out through front of pump body.

To complete disassembly of water pump, remove front seal, retainer, and flange.

Inspection of Water Pump Parts

Examine pump body for cracks, damage or corrosion.

Examine pump shaft for wear. If pump bearing inner races rotate on shaft, shaft must be replaced.

Clean all rust and scale from impeller, and inspect it for cracks and damage. Examine impeller hub sealing surface for wear or scoring. If impeller shows any damage, cracks or wear at seal surface, it should be replaced.

Wash bearings in thin lubricating oil, and replace them if any evidence of wear is found.

Assemble Water Pump

Press rear bearing onto front of shaft, and against shoulder, with sealed end of bearing toward rear of shaft.

Position bearing spacer on shaft, and press front bearing against spacer with sealed end of bearing toward front end of shaft.

Place front seal retaining flange in position against rear face of rear bearing. This dished flange must be positioned so the center of flange is not in contact with bearing.

Position first the front seal, and then seal retainer against retainer flange.

Half fill the space between the two bearings with short fibre water pump grease, or multi-purpose chassis grease and press the complete assembly into pump body through front end. Then position bearing snap ring firmly in groove, using snap ring pliers.

Place a new rear seal in pump on rear end of pump shaft with carbon face to rear so it will contact the impeller hub. Make sure seal is resting squarely, and is not cocked in any way.

At this point, the shaft should be rotated by hand to be sure it turns without binding.

Some of the attaching bolts must be entered in the holes in the pump body before pressing on the pump pulley, since it is not possible to position them after the pulley is installed

With key in position in shaft and with necessary attaching bolts in their holes, support shaft at its rear end, and press pulley onto shaft, with keyway aligned. Make sure shaft does not move rearward.

Checking impeller to pump body clearance

Install flat washer and self-locking nut on front of pump shaft and tighten nut to 50 to 55 foot-pounds.

Press impeller onto shaft to where clearance between pump body and inner edge of impeller vanes is between .012″ and .019″.

Engine Section

Engine Removal and Installation

1. Disconnect battery.
2. Drain cooling system and engine oil.
3. Disconnect fuel in-line and return line, and exhaust pipe. Remove air cleaner.
4. Disconnect wiring for alternator, gauges, switches, etc.
5. Bleed air booster brake and disconnect line.
6. Disconnect hydraulic clutch line, stop control cable accelerator and hand throttle, coolant and heater hoses.
7. Remove radiator.
8. Remove driveshaft and transmission.
9. Install engine lifting sling.
10. Remove front engine support bolts, rear engine support nuts and lift the engine assembly from the chassis. *When removing Perkins Diesel Engines it may be necessary to shift lifting hook from one notch to another to lift engine at required angle for clearance.*
11. Reverse procedure for installing.
12. Check for oil, air, water or vacuum leaks.

Cylinder Head

Removal

1. Disconnect battery cables, drain radiator and block.

2. Remove air cleaner, and disconnect breather pipe.
3. Remove cylinder head cover from head.
4. Remove rocker arm support stud nuts. The rocker arm assembly complete with lubrication tube and "O" ring can now be removed as an assembly.
5. Carefully lift valve push rods out of engine. CAUTION: It is possible to drop No. 2, 3, 10 and 11 push rods down into oil pan and if this occurs, they cannot be retrieved without removing oil pan.
6. Disconnect fuel injector lines at both ends. Unbolt mounting clamp from cylinder head and remove six injectors lines as an assembly. *Injector lines must be handled carefully to avoid bending or damaging, and dirt or chips should not be allowed to enter fuel lines.*
7. Remove cylinder head to water pump by-pass tube.
8. Remove fuel lines.
9. Remove six injectors and copper sealing washers. *If injectors stick, tap them sideways carefully with a soft hammer to loosen them. Place injectors where tips will not be damaged, do not use a wire brush or other abrasive on injectors.*
10. Remove upper radiator hose and heater hoses.
11. Disconnect exhaust pipe at manifold flange and fuel return line bracket.
12. Remove 32 cylinder head stud nuts.
13. Remove voltage regulator to prevent possible damage. *Avoid damage to cylinder head and block surfaces by careless prying under cylinder block.*
14. Remove No. 4 and 5 rocker shaft studs, install lifting fixture on cylinder head and remove.

Installation

1. Install intake and exhaust manifolds, using new gaskets. Use the short bolts for the third manifold bolt from each end to avoid bolt interference with the push rods.
2. The mating surfaces of cylinder head and cylinder block must be

Cylinder head assembly (typical)
(© Chrysler Corp.)

clean. A cracked head, must, of course, be renewed.

3. If the longitudinal bow in the head is more than 0.006", or the transverse boy exceeds 0.003", then machining of the head joint face is necessary. Machining is also necessary if the head has deep scratches, scores, nicks, or fret marks, in particular, across the areas where the gasket bore eyelets seal, or, where they run into water or oil apertures. *No more than 0.010" should ever be removed from the gasket face of the head* and if the head cannot be cleaned by removing 0.010" then it must be renewed. The surface finish of the head should be of a medium ground finish of 60/100 micro inches, or equivalent to the top face of the cylinder block. *Only the minimum amount of metal should ever be removed from the head face* and the amount removed should be stamped on the head face in case further resurfacing becomes necessary. Care should be taken in selecting the area for stamping.
4. If the head bottom face has been machined, check that the valve heads are recessed below the head face by not less than 0.029". If the valve heads are recessed less than 0.029" then the valve seats must be ground until the valve heads are recessed at least 0.029" and not more than 0.049". After machining of the head the atomizer nozzle protru-

sion must not be greater than 0.2165" and this figure *must not* be achieved by the use of additional atomizer seating washers as these may be inadvertently removed at a later date and result in a loss of power.

5. The cylinder head studs and nuts must be examined for damaged threads or other signs of wear. Studs must fit snugly into the cylinder block. With a light smear of oil on the threads screw the studs into the block tightening to 10 ft/lbs, when they should not be slack or wobble. Any suspect studs should be renewed as should any loose fitting nuts.
6. IMPORTANT: The relief counter-bore between the block and the top of the sleeve *must* be free of carbon deposits. The gasket cannot seal properly unless the counter-bore is perfectly clean.
7. Place gasket on block face, using gasket as supplied, *dry, with no jointing compound.*
8. Fit cylinder head carefully so as not to damage threads on studs, or, gasket. Lightly oil threads and working face of cylinder head nuts and fit nuts.
9. The head must be tightened as follows: Using an accurate torque wrench, with the engine cold and rocker assembly removed from engine:

a. Pull down to 80 ft/lbs (½" studs) or 55 ft/lbs (7/16" studs) following the sequence shown.
b. Pull down to 85 ft/lbs (½" studs) or 60 ft/lbs (7/16" studs) following the same sequence.
c. Pull down to 85 ft/lbs (½" studs) or 60 ft/lbs (7/16" studs) *again,* following same sequence. This final tightening of the nuts should be carried

Cylinder head tightening sequence
(© Chrysler Corp.)

HELI-COIL INSERT CHART

Heli-Coil Insert			Drill	Tap	Inserting Tool	Extracting Tool
Thread Size	Part No.	Insert Length	Size	Part No.	Part No.	Part No.
1/2-20	1185-4	3/8"	17/64(.266)	4 CPB	528-4N	1227-6
5/16-18	1185-5	15/32"	Q(.332)	5 CPB	528-5N	1227-6
3/8-16	1185-6	9/16"	X(.397)	6 CPB	528-6N	1227-6
7/16-14	1185-7	21/32"	29/64(.453)	7 CPB	528-7N	1227-16
1/2-13	1185-8	3/4"	33/64(.516)	8 CPB	528-8N	1227-16

out to ensure that no loss of tension has occurred on studs earlier in the tightening sequence.

10. Install all push rods, being careful not to drop any of them into the crankcase.

11. Replace rocker assembly. The oil feed pipe to the rockers locates in a hole in the cylinder head and a rubber "O" ring should fit around the stem of the pipe when the rockers have been fitted. In order to ensure the new seal locates correctly, fit it immediately below the lower convolution and as the pipe is inserted into the cylinder head the "O" ring will roll up and over the lower convolution and locate itself correctly between the two convolutions. If, before inserting the pipe in the cylinder head, the "O" ring is fitted *between* the convolutions then it will roll up and over the upper convolution when inserting the pipe and fail to make an effective seal. Always fit a new "O" ring.

12. Rocker assembly shaft pillar securing nuts should be tightened to 29-32 ft/lbs.

13. Adjust valve lash (clearance)—Inlet and Exhaust to 0.012"—engine cold.

14. Using new copper gaskets, install the fuel injectors in cylinder head.

15. Install fuel lines.

16. Install six injector lines as an assembly.

17. Install cylinder head to water pump by-pass tube, upper radiator hose, heater hoses and voltage regulator.

18. Connect exhaust pipe to manifold flange. Install fuel return line bracket.

19. Fill cooling system. Connect battery cables.

20. Start engine and idle (550 r.p.m.) for a few minutes, checking that the valve action is satisfactory and lubricating oil is reaching the rockers.

21. Run engine at 1200/1500 r.p.m. for at least *one hour*, or until coolant temperature is, at least, 180°F or higher. If necessary, a radiator blind should be used to achieve this.

STANDARD SCREW FITS IN . . .
HELI-COIL INSERT IN . . .
HELI-COIL TAPPED HOLE.

Heli-coil installation
(© Chrysler Corp.)

22. Stop engine. Remove rocker assembly. Check head nut tightness quickly before engine loses temperature, following diagram sequence as before. AGAIN check head nut tightness following same sequence.

23. Replace rocker assembly. Check fit of "O" ring as at item 9 and tighten rocker assembly securing nuts to 29-32 ft/lbs. Adjust valve lash (clearance) to 0.010"—engine hot.

24. Restart engine and idle at 550 r.p.m. Check the oil feed to the rockers and check for leak at the "O" ring around the rocker feed pipe. Check that the valve lash (clearance) is correct and that no valve is sticking. IMPORTANT: A retightening of cylinder head nuts must be made approximately 250 miles or at the end of two weeks after the gasket change.

25. Use special adapter wrench to tighten nuts underneath the rocker arms. Readjust tappets to .010" clearance "hot."

Repair of Damaged or Worn Threads

Damaged or worn threads can be repaired by the use of Heli-Coils. Essentially, this repair consists of drilling out worn or damaged threads, tapping the hole with a special Heli-Coil Tap, and installing a Heli-Coil Insert into the tapped hole. This brings the hole back to its original thread size (See Fig. 1).

The following chart lists the threaded hole sizes which are used in the engine block and the necessary tools and inserts for the repair of damaged or worn thread. Heli-Coil tools and inserts are readily available from automotive parts jobbers.

Servicing Cylinder Head

In the Perkins 354 Diesel Engine,

carbon rarely, if ever, forms in the combustion chambers in sufficient quantity to require periodic decarbonizing of the engine. Valve ports require cleaning at every head service.

Due to high thermal efficiency and other characteristics, the valves in this engine are relatively free from trouble due to overheating.

As noted in the maintenance schedule for this engine, it is recommended that tappet clearances be checked at 18,000 mile intervals. Both intake and exhaust should be adjusted to .010" hot.

Disassembly of Cylinder Head

Remove manifolds.

Note that on this diesel engine no heat riser connection is required between intake and exhaust manifolds.

Clean gasket material from manifolds or cylinder head.

Remove thermostat and housing assembly.

Pry out retaining snap ring, and remove thermostat from housing.

All intake and exhaust valves are numbered consecutively from one to 12, commencing at the front of the engine.

The cylinder head is marked with corresponding numbers opposite the valve seats.

Using a valve spring compressor, remove the valve locks, spring retainers, inner and outer springs, and the intake valve stem seals.

Remove valves from cylinder head, and remove spring seats from top end of valve guides.

A complete new set of valve springs should be installed whenever the engine undergoes a major overhaul.

Valve stem to guide clearance (new): Intake—.0015" to .0035". Exhaust—.002" to .004".

If valve stem to guide clearance is excessive, the worn parts should be replaced. Valve guide bore diameter

Adjusting tappet clearance
(© Chrysler Corp.)

(new) for intake and exhaust valve guides is .375″ to .376″.

Stem diameters for new valves are .3725″ to .3735″ for intake valves and .372″ to .373″ for exhaust valves.

With a new head and valves, the top surface of all valves should be recessed not less than .029″ and not more than .039″ below the surface of the cylinder head.

Clean the valves thoroughly, and examine them carefully.

Any new valves used should be stamped with the same number as the discarded valve, which the replaced.

Remove any carbon deposits from the cylinder head combustion chambers and valve ports.

Thoroughly clean water passages in cylinder head. If excessive scale is present, a proper cleaning solution should be used.

Grind Valves

Valves and valve seats should be reconditioned in the conventional way, either using grinding compound or accepted valve and seat refacing equipment. Valve seat and valve face angle are both 45 degrees.

After valves and seats have been reconditioned, the valve head depth must be checked. Use a straight edge and feeler gauge to check this dimension. It must be between the limits of .029″ and .060″.

Valve seat counterbore dimensions
(© Chrysler Corp.)

Intake	
A	.283 to .288 in.
B	2.0165 to 2.0175 in.
C	Radius .015 in. (max.)
Exhaust	
A	.375 to .380 in.
B	1.678 to 1.679 in.
C	Radius .015 in. (max.)

It is essential that valve heights be held within these limits to provide clearance between valve and piston, and to maintain correct combustion chamber volume.

Valve seat inserts are not installed in these engines in production. However, if a seat is worn or damaged to such an extent that reconditioning places the valve depth beyond the limits of .029″ to .060″, a counterbore can be machined into the cylinder head and a valve seat insert can be installed.

Before you can install a valve seat insert, a new valve guide must be installed.

Valve Guides

Press out old valve guide, and thoroughly clean bore in cylinder head.

Press in a new valve guide, to where the top of the guide protrudes ⅝″ above the spring seat machined surface on the cylinder head. Coat valve guides with engine oil to reduce friction during installation.

Using valve guide bore as a pilot, machine a counterbore in the cylinder head to the required dimensions.

Remove all chips and thoroughly clean insert counterbore, removing any burrs which may be present.

Again using valve guide bore as a pilot, press insert home with an installing tool.

Use a steady pressure with either a hand or hydraulic press. The tool will insure squareness. Under no circumstances should the insert be hammered in. Also, do not use lubrication when pressing in the insert. Chill seats with dry ice to reduce interference while installing them.

Visually inspect to make sure that insert has been pressed in squarely, and that it is flush with bottom of counterbore.

Using valve guide bore as a pilot, machine "flare" in insert to dimensions shown. Remove any chips or burrs from seat.

Grind insert seat to a 45° angle (90° included angle), and to where valve head depth below cylinder head face is within limits of .029″ to .039″.

It is advisable to work as closely as possible to the minimum figure in order to allow for reseating at a later date if required.

An existing insert may also be replaced in the same manner, except that it will not be necessary to machine a counterbore.

The gasket face of cylinder head may be resurfaced to eliminate score marks, warpage, etc. No more than .010″ should ever be removed from the gasket face of the cylinder head however.

Checking valve head depth
(© Chrysler Corp.)

Relieve seat at 30 degrees
to dimension A .094 to .099 inch
(© Chrysler Corp.)

Rocker shaft assembly
(© Chrysler Corp.)

Layout of valve parts
(© Chrysler Corp.)

To replace valve guides, press out old guides. Clean bores in cylinder head, and remove all burrs.

Coat new guides with oil, and press them into where they protrude 5/8" above the cylinder head. Care should be exercised, since the guides are made of cast iron and are, therefore, very brittle.

Rocker Arm Assembly

Remove retaining snap rings and end washers from ends of rocker shaft, and slide off rocker arms and springs.

Remove rocker shaft oil feed pipe locating screw, and slide oil feed pipe off rocker shaft. Remove the small "O" ring from pipe.

Assemble Cylinder Heads and Valves

Install valves in their proper positions as numbered, place valve seat washers in position, and install new valve stem seals (open end to valve guides) on the intake valves.

Position inner and outer valve springs so close coils are next to the cylinder head, and install valve retainers and locks.

All valve springs on this engine incorporate a damper coil (close coil). Care must be taken to assure that this damper coil is replaced nearest to the cylinder head.

Install gasket, thermostat and tapered snap ring in the thermostat housing, and using a new gasket, install the assembly on the cylinder head.

Using a new gasket, install rear cover on cylinder head.

Install intake and exhaust manifolds using new gaskets. Use short bolts for third manifold bolt from each end to avoid bolt interference with push rods.

Timing Gears and Camshaft

Removal

1. Remove vibration damper retaining screw and lock.
2. Slide the vibration damper assembly off the splined end of the crankshaft.
3. Remove camshaft gear cover and auxiliary drive gear cover or tachometer drive adapter from timing gear case.
4. Remove auxiliary shaft drive gear by unscrewing three recessed head retaining screws and the retaining plate.
5. Remove camshaft retaining screw, washer and lock plate.
6. Pull camshaft gear. *Avoid driving the camshaft back against the plug in the rear wall of the cylinder block, since an oil leak could develop if this plug is disturbed.*
7. Remove bolts and remove the timing gear case.
8. Remove two self-locking nuts and remove camshaft idler gear and auxiliary shaft idle gear.

Note that the camshaft idler gear can be identified as having a timing mark (punch mark), while the auxiliary shaft idler gear has no timing mark.

The two idler gear hubs are doweled, and can be readily removed from the hub mounting studs by gripping the end of the rolled pin and tapping hub with a soft hammer.

Camshaft and Auxiliary Drive Shaft

The camshaft is supported by **four** pressure fed bearings and is driven by helical type gears. The thrust washers used to control end thrust of both the camshaft and auxiliary drive shaft are fitted in machined recesses in the front of the cylinder block and are located by dowel pins. Before the thrust washers, camshaft

Valve numbering (© Chrysler Corp.)

Removing auxiliary drive gear
(© Chrysler Corp.)

Removing auxiliary drive shaft (© Chrysler Corp.)

Removing idler gear hub (© Chrysler Corp.)

or auxiliary drive shaft can be removed, the timing gear case must be removed.

Camshaft Removal
(with Gear Case and Gears Removed)

1. Remove the rocker arm cover.
2. Remove the six rocker arm support stud nuts and flat washers. The rocker arm assembly complete with lubrication tube and "O" ring can now be removed as an assembly.
3. Lift the push rods out of the engine. Do this carefully since it is possible to drop No. 2, 3, 10 and 11 push rods down into the crankcase.
4. Disconnect the fuel lines, remove the pump attaching screws and remove the fuel pump from the engine.
5. Remove the alternator.
6. Remove push rod inspection covers.
7. Lift tappets to full travel and hold in full position with clothes pins, carefully remove camshaft and thrust washer.

Auxiliary Drive Shaft Removal
(Gear Case and Gears Removed)

Disconnect the fuel injector lines at the injectors and at the injector pump. Unbolt the mounting clamp from the cylinder head and remove the six injector lines as an assembly.

Injector lines must be handled carefully to avoid bending or damaging. Cover or tape fuel openings on the injection pump to prevent dirt from entering the pump.

1. Disconnect the accelerator and stop cable, remove the three injection pump attaching stud nuts and lift out the injection pump.
2. Remove the three attaching stud nuts and lift the injection pump adapter from the engine.
3. Disconnect the coupling and lines and remove the vacuum pump or air compressor.
4. Loosen the coupling clamp bolt, and remove the coupling from rear end of auxiliary drive shaft.
5. Remove the woodruff key from the rear end of the auxiliary shaft.
6. Pull out the auxiliary drive shaft and the two half moon shaped thrust washers.

If a suitable puller is available the injector and engine oil pump vertical drive shaft assembly can be removed from the top. If tool is not available the following steps are necessary:

Remove the dipstick and dipstick tube.

Remove the attaching screws and remove the oil pump assembly.

Disconnect the oil delivery housing from the crankcase by removing the two attaching bolts.

Loosen the locknut, and unscrew the oil pump locating set screw. This screw is located outside the cylinder block. Now remove the oil pump and oil delivery housing assembly.

The two parts of this assembly are connected by a short pipe which is a push fit in each component.

Inspect the short pipe for wear.

Tap out the injector pump and engine oil pump vertical drive shaft assembly from inside the crankcase.

Remove the seal from the rear end of the auxiliary drive shaft bore in the crankcase. This can be done by prying behind the lip extension of the seal retainer.

The engine oil pump and injector pump vertical drive shaft can be removed with a suitable puller, if the engine oil pan and oil pump are not to be removed.

Injector Pump Vertical Drive Removal

Use a suitable puller with fine jaws to remove the bearing, being careful not to damage the bronze gear.

Remove the four recessed screws, support the gear carefully, and press the shaft out of the gear.

Removing camshaft gear
(© Chrysler Corp.)

Removing idler gear (© Chrysler Corp.)

Removing auxiliary drive gear (© Chrysler Corp.)

Auxiliary drive and injection pump
vertical drive parts
(© Chrysler Corp.)

To reassemble, press the bronze gear onto the injection pump vertical drive shaft with holes in gear and flange aligned, and with counterbored side away from flange and secure it with the retaining screws. Then press a new bearing on the shaft. Use a new gear if necessary.

Insert the vertical shaft, gear and bearing assembly in the cylinder block, and push it down into position.

On a few engines, one or more steel shim .002″ thick is fitted beneath the bearing. Fit the shim (shims) into the block first and then slide complete vertical drive assembly into block on top of shim (shims). Always replace shim (or shims) into block from which they came. *Do not* fit shims into a block which did not have them in the first place.

The vertical shaft and gear must be installed before installing the horizontal positioned auxiliary drive shaft.

Auxiliary Drive Shaft Removal

Place the two thrust washer halves in the groove on the auxiliary drive shaft immediately behind the timing gear mounting flange on the auxiliary drive shaft, and with the chamfer to the rear. Then enter the shaft into the cylinder block bore so the two thrust washer halves straddle the small locating dowel in the recess at the front of the cylinder block. Do this carefully so as not to damage the bronze gear or the worm gear on the auxiliary shaft.

With the key in place in front end of crankshaft, place crankshaft gear on shaft with timing mark on gear toward front of engine, and using a suitable driver, drive gear into place on shaft.

Turn crankshaft until number one and number six pistons are at top dead center. The timing mark on flywheel can be used to accurately determine this position. Also, the line on front face of crankshaft is vertical in respect to engine when number one and number six are at top dead center.

Install Camshaft and Tappets

Examine camshaft for wear or pitting on cam lobes. If condition is not satisfactory, a new camshaft must be installed.

Oil camshaft lightly, and carefully slide it into place in cylinder block.

Do not drive on front end of camshaft for any reason, since this will dislodge the camshaft plug in the rear of the cylinder block, and an oil leak will result.

Do not install camshaft gear until timing gear case has been installed. The timing case must be installed first.

Place camshaft thrust washer in place, chamfered side in, and so small dowel in cylinder block is entered in hole provided in thrust washer.

Idler Gears

Place the two idler gear hubs on

Vertical drive parts
(© Chrysler Corp.)

their mounting studs at front of cylinder block, so ends with largest chamfer are toward cylinder block and their hollow dowels are aligned with holes provided. Tap hubs into place with a soft hammer.

The hollow dowels in idler gear hubs also serve as oil feed passages for idler gears.

The two idler gears are different. The timing marks are on camshaft idler gear. The auxiliary drive idler gear is plain.

Place camshaft idler gear on its hub, engaging it with crankshaft gear so the two adjacent teeth with timing marks on idler gear straddle the one tooth on crankshaft gear which has a timing mark.

Secure camshaft idler gear with retaining washer and self-locking nut. Tighten nut to 45 to 50 footpounds.

Install auxiliary drive idler gear in exactly the same way, except that there are no timing marks to be concerned with on the auxiliary drive idler gear.

Pistons and Rings

Piston and Rod Removal

1. Remove cylinder head assembly as outlined earlier in the engine section.
2. Remove oil dipstick and tube.
3. Remove oil pan attaching bolts and remove oil pan and pump assembly.
4. Disconnect oil delivery housing from crankcase.
5. Loosen the locknut and unscrew the oil pump locating screw.
6. Remove oil pump and oil delivery housing assembly.
7. Remove top ridge of cylinder bores with a ridge reamer before removing pistons from cylinder block.
8. Turn crankshaft so that two connecting rod journals are at bottom center.
9. Remove connecting rod caps and inserts, and remove rod and pis-

Installing camshaft (© Chrysler Corp.)

Installing camshaft thrust washer
(© Chrysler Corp.)

Toroidal cavity in piston note markings
(© Chrysler Corp.)

ton assemblies from cylinder bores.

10. Keep related parts of each assembly together for convenience when matching for reassembly.

Disassemble Piston and Rod Assemblies

Remove five piston rings.

Remove the piston pin retaining rings from both ends of pin bore in piston.

Make sure the ends of the pin bores are clean, and remove any burrs around the retainer grooves.

Warm the piston up to about 120°F. This can be done by immersing the pistons in clean liquid of that temperature for a short period of time. Do not use a torch.

After warming the piston to 120°F., it should be possible to remove pin by pushing it out of bore.

If the piston pin bushings are worn, they can be replaced.

Replacing Piston Pin Bushings

Using a suitable pressing tool, press the pin bushing out of the connecting rod.

Piston pins and bushings are supplied in standard size only. Standard pin diameter is 1.375″.

Position a new bushing so the oil hole will align with the oil hole at the top of the connecting rod, and press the bushing into the connecting rod bore.

Ream the bushing to provide pin clearance of .0007″ to .0017″.

Connecting rod alignment should be checked on a reliable fixture. The piston pin should be parallel and in the same plane with the bearing bore centerline within .001″.

Cleaning and Inspecting Pistons

Use a ring groove cleaning tool to clean the ring grooves, being careful not to gouge or damage the groove surfaces.

A power wire brush should never be used to clean pistons.

Examine the piston carefully for cracks or other defects.

If a piston ring groove has been damaged by a broken ring, or if ring grooves have been worn excessively wide, due to high mileage, or if piston skirt is scored, the piston should be replaced.

When a new piston is being installed, stamp it for the cylinder position number in which it is to be installed.

All pistons in any one engine must be of same size.

Fitting New Piston Rings

New rings should be checked in the cylinder bore for correct ring gap.

To check ring gap in worn cylinder liners the ring should be positioned at the bottom of the bore, below the ring travel area, where minimum wear has occurred.

With the ring positioned squarely in the cylinder, check the gap with a feeler gauge.

The ring can be positioned squarely in the cylinder bore by using a piston to push it down into the bore.

Ring gap at the top compression ring should be .015″ to .019″. The second and third compression rings, and also the upper and lower oil rings should have a gap of .011″ to .016″.

New rings are available in standard size for installation in new liners and worn liners which have not been rebored. They are also available in .030″ oversize for use *only* in rebored liners.

New rings must be thoroughly washed before installation.

Assembling Piston and Connecting Rod Assembly

Heat piston to 120°F. before installing piston pin.

Coat the pin with light engine oil.

Position the piston and connecting rod so the word "front" on the piston will be toward the front of the engine when the stamped numbers on the connecting rod are toward the side of the engine opposite the camshaft.

Alignment of timing marks on drive gears
(© Chrysler Corp.)

Connecting rod numbering (© Chrysler Corp.)

Push the piston pin through the piston pin hole and rod bushing, and center the pin between the two retainer ring grooves in the piston.

Make sure the piston is centered between the grooves, and install both retaining rings.

Assure that both pin retaining rings are perfectly seated in their grooves.

When installing the piston pin, *do not* have one of the retaining rings in place, and drive the pin against it to permit installation of the second retaining ring.

This practice can result in damage to the groove or ring, and result in the ring eventually coming out of the groove, permitting the pin to seriously damage the cylinder liner.

Install the two oil rings.

Note that the 2nd and 3rd compression rings are tapered, and are marked "T" for top side.

In current production, the second and third compression rings are internally stepped. These rings must be assembled to the piston so that the step faces the crown of the piston.

The number one (top) compression ring is chrome plated, and can be installed either side up. Install this ring last.

Space the piston ring gaps equally around the piston, and so they are not in line with one another.

Connecting rod bearing upper and lower inserts are both alike. Also note that the parting faces of the rod and cap are serrated to ensure accurate positioning of the cap, and under no circumstances should they be filed.

Connecting rod bolts should be carefully inspected for possible damage, and should be replaced if they are not in excellent condition.

The original self-locking nuts must be replaced with new ones, since they will have lost some of their prevailing torque.

When replacing connecting rod bolts or nuts, use only the correct factory supplied replacement parts.

Connecting rod bearings are available in standard size, and in .010″, .020″, and .030″ undersizes.

Place upper and lower connecting rod bearing inserts in position in the rod bore.

Make sure the piston and rod assembly and the cylinder bore are perfectly clean, and oil them with engine oil.

Piston and Rod Installation

1. Position the crankshaft so the throw for the rod and piston being installed is at bottom center.
2. Install the piston and rod assembly in the cylinder. Use an installing tool, and make sure the

Installing piston (© Chrysler Corp.)

Measuring cylinder liner height (© Chrysler Corp.)

Measuring piston height (© Chrysler Corp.)

Installing connecting rod cap (© Chrysler Corp.)

rings do not catch on the top of the block during installation.

3. Make sure the assembly is in the cylinder for which it is marked and that the word *front* on the piston is toward the front of the engine, and that the numbered side of the connecting rod is opposite from the camshaft side of the engine.
4. Pull the rod into position at the crankshaft journal, and making sure the bearing inserts are both properly positioned, install the connecting rod cap and bearing in place.
5. Install the two connecting rod bolts with new self-locking nuts. Connecting rod bolt heads have two flats. The largest flat must be positioned toward the connecting rod. Tighten to 65 to 70 foot-pounds.

With a properly fitted piston and rod assembly, the piston should protrude above the top of the cylinder block no less than .003, and no more than .0095″ when at top dead center. This can be checked by placing a straightedge across the top of the liner and with a feeler gauge, measure the liner protrusion above the top surface of the cylinder block and the gap between the piston top and the straight edge (the smallest height must be to the piston).

The difference between the two dimensions is the height of the piston above the block. If the piston height is excessive, the piston must be removed from the engine and the top machined to bring the height within the specified limits. Should the piston height be too low at top dead center, it must be replaced.

Piston protrusion above the top of the block is most important and should always be checked at TDC. Service pistons should not require machining if they are stamped with the letter "L" on the crown.

Cylinder Liners

Servicing Cylinder Liners

The Dry type cylinder liners are pressed into cylinder block with a .003″ to .005″ interference fit. Pressing force required is approximately ten tons.

Liners must be bored and honed after they have been pressed into the cylinder block. For a standard piston, the finished honed inside diameter of the liner must be between 3.877″ and 3.8785″.

If liners are worn or scored, they can be rebored to .030″ oversize. Finished inside diameter must be between 3.907″ and 3.9085″.

All pistons in any one engine must be of the same size. *Liners should be carefully inspected for cracks or* other damage before making a decision whether to rebore or replace a liner.

During reboring, it is most important that true alignment of the bores relative to the crankshaft centerline be maintained.

If cylinder liners are not acceptable for reboring to .030″ oversize, they must be pressed out, and new liners pressed into the cylinder block.

The first step when installing new liners is to remove all cylinder head attaching studs from the top of the cylinder block.

With cylinder block placed in a suitable press, cylinder liners must be pressed out through top of cylinder block, using the proper tool to adapt the press ram to the bottom of the cylinder liner.

Make sure the outside of liners are clean and well oiled before pressing them into the cylinder block.

When pressing in liners, the press load should be released several times during the first inch to allow the liner to centralize itself in the cylinder block parent bore. *Cylinder liners can be removed and installed with engine in truck. Also chilling liners with dry ice may reduce pressing effort required.*

The latest type of cylinder liner (Engine No. 8039047 and later) protrudes .030″ to .035″ above the block face. This liner should be bored and honed to size in the same manner as the earlier recessed-block type liner. *The earlier-type liner must not be pulled up above the top surface of the block.*

After they are pressed in, the liners should be finish bored to 3.877″ to 3.878″.

When work on the cylinder liners has been completed, reinstall cylinder head attaching studs, replacing any which have been weakened by corrosion, or damaged.

Crankshaft and Bearings

Crankshaft Removal

1. Remove oil dipstick and tube.
2. Remove oil pan attaching bolts and remove oil pan and sump assembly.
3. Disconnect oil delivery housing from crankcase.

Location of crankshaft thrust washers
(© Chrysler Corp.)

4. Loosen the locknut and unscrew the oil pump locating screw.
5. Remove oil pump and oil delivery housing assembly.
6. Remove two vertical bolts which attach lower half of rear main bearing oil seal retainer to cylinder block.
7. Remove upper and lower halves of seal retainer.
8. Remove attaching screws from front and rear main bearing bridge pieces and lift both bridge pieces out of cylinder block.
9. Bend down tabs on main bearing bolt locks and remove main bearing bolts.
10. Remove center (no. 4) main bearing cap along with the two lower half crankshaft thrust washers.
11. Remove six remaining main bearing caps and lift out the crankshaft. NOTE: Identification marks on main bearing caps are positioned away from camshaft side.

Servicing Crankshaft and Bearings

Bearing clearance at the seven main bearings is .0025″ to .0045″. Specified clearance at connecting rod bearings is .0015″ to .003″.

Main and connecting rod bearings are both available in standard, .010″, .020″, and .030″ undersize.

Crankshaft end clearance is specified .002″ to .014″, and is controlled by four semi-circular thrust washers, two on each side of the center (No. 4) main bearing. These thrust washers are available in .0075″ oversize to overcome end thrust wear. Lower

thrust washers have locating tabs, while upper thrust washers do not.

.0075″ oversize thrust washers, can be used on both sides of No. 4 main bearing to reduce end play by .015″ when required. If two standard thickness thrust washers are used on one side of No. 4 main bearing, and two oversize washers are used on the other side, crankshaft end play will be reduced by .0075″.

Care must be taken to avoid placing one standard and one oversize thrust washer on the same side of No. 4 main bearing.

Specified end play at connecting rod bearings is .0095″ to .0135″.

Under normal circumstances, by the time the main bearings and thrust washers require replacing, the crankshaft will need to be removed for regrinding. However, if for any reason, one or more of bearings or thrust washers have to be removed for inspection or replacement, this can be done without removing crankshaft from engine.

Main Bearings

To remove a main bearing without removing the crankshaft, take off the cap of the bearing involved, and loosen the remaining main bearing bolts one or two turns.

Before No. 1 or No. 7 main bearing caps can be removed, it is necessary to remove the main bearing bridge piece at the end involved.

To remove front main bearing bridge piece, it is necessary to remove two recessed screws attaching it to cylinder block, as well as the two lower timing case attaching screws.

When removing the rear main bearing bridge, it is necessary to remove the two recessed screws attaching it to the cylinder block, and the two lower rear main bearing oil seal housing attaching screws.

To remove the top half of a main bearing, using a suitable piece of wood or tool, apply pressure to the end of the bearing opposite from the locating tab, and rotate bearing around crankshaft.

Locating tabs are on camshaft side

View of crankshaft and bearings
(© Chrysler Corp.)

Removing main bearing upper half
(ⓒ Chrysler Corp.)

Aligning bridge piece
(ⓒ Chrysler Corp.)

of engine.

When installing a new bearing shell start the upper half, plain end first, and rotate the shell around the crankshaft and into position.

Crankshaft Thrust Washers

To replace crankshaft thrust washers with the crankshaft in place, remove the center (No. 4) main bearing cap, and remove the two bottom half thrust washers from the recesses in the cap.

The two top half thrust washers can now be removed by sliding them around from one side, using a piece of wood or similar tool, and rotating them until they can be removed.

After replacing individual main bearings or thrust washers, make sure all main bearing bolts which have been loosened are tightened to 145 to 150 foot-pounds and secured with new lock tabs.

Main bearing cap bolts now have a steel shim between cap and lock tab to prevent the bolt head from biting into the lock tab.

Crankshaft Installation

Before the crankshaft and bearings are installed, all oil passages in the cylinder block and crankshaft must be thoroughly clean. Inspect the main bearing bolts, and replace as necessary.

CAUTION: In no case should bolts other than the specified main bearing bolts be used, since they are of special heat treated high grade steel.

Make sure the bearing shells and the main bearing bores in the block and caps are free of all foreign matter, and place the main bearing upper halves in position in the cylinder block.

No. 4 main bearing is wider than the others. Also, upper main bearings have large slotted oil holes, which are not found in the lower halves.

1. Oil the upper bearings lightly, and place the crankshaft in position.
2. Lightly lubricate the two upper thrust washers (no locating tabs) and slide them into places in the recesses provided on each side of No. 4 main bearing in the cylinder block.
3. Place lower main bearings in bearing caps. Place the two lower thrust washers on the No. 4 main bearing cap so their locating tabs are positioned in the slots provided in the cap.
4. The main bearing caps are numbered as to their positions, No. 1 being at the front of the engine, and must be installed accordingly.
5. Install caps with bearings so bearing locating tabs are on the same side of the engine as tabs on upper halves.
6. When caps are properly installed, their stamped serial numbers will be in line on the same side of the engine. Check main bearing clearances, using shim stock or plasti-gage. Clearance at all seven main bearings should be .0025″ to .0045″.

When using plasti-gage to measure main bearing clearances with engine in truck, support the crankshaft to take up clearance between the upper bearing and the crankshaft journal. This can be done by snugging bearing caps of the adjacent bearings with a strip of .005″ to .015″ cardboard between lower bearing and journal. When doing this, avoid unnecessary strain on crankshaft and bearing, or false reading may be obtained. Do not rotate crankshaft while plasti-gage is installed. Be sure to remove cardboard before installing oil pan.

7. Use new tab locks on the main bearing bolts, and tighten evenly to 145 to 150 foot-pounds.
8. Check crankshaft end play. It should be .006″-.014″. Use oversize thrust washers to correct excessive end play.
9. Bend lock tabs to secure the main bearing bolts. Check crankshaft for free rotation.

Installing Main Bearing Bridge Pieces

Make sure front and rear main bearing bridge pieces are clean, coat attaching surfaces with Gasket Sealer, and place them in position. Place new end seals in grooves provided.

Start recessed attaching screws, and using a straight-edge to align the bridge pieces so they are flush with front and rear faces of cylinder block, tighten screws securely.

Crankshaft Rear Oil Seal

The crankshaft rear oil seal is composed of two rubber cored woven asbestos strips which are inserted in the upper and lower halves of the seal retainer.

The seal surface around the rear of the crankshaft has a shallow spiral oil return groove recessed to a depth of .004″ to .008″.

The seal stripes come cut to length, and they must never be shortened.

Place one half of seal retainer in a smooth jawed vise with seal groove facing upward.

Imbed about one inch of each end of a seal strip into ends of groove so each end projects .010″ to .020″ beyond retainer parting face. Allowing middle portion of seal strip to bulge out of groove will enable you to do this.

With thumb or fingers, press the remainder of strip into groove, working from center. Then use any convenient smooth round bar to further imbed the seal strip by rolling and pressing its inner diameter.

This procedure results in compression of the seal material near each end, to prevent the seal ends from pulling away and leaving a gap when the assembly is tightened around the crankshaft.

Install the remaining seal strip in the other half of the seal retainer, using the same methods to position

Removing rear main bearing oil seal
(© Chrysler Corp.)

Engine oil pan and sump assembly
(© Chrysler Corp.)

and seat the seal material.

Make sure gasket faces are clean and apply Gasket Sealer, to both sides of new upper and lower retainer gaskets. Also, apply a light coat of sealer to the parting faces between upper and lower seal retainers.

Spread a film of graphited grease over the inside diameter of the upper and lower seals.

Assemble seal retainer halves around crankshaft, drawing the halves together squarely with two bolts.

Make certain upper and lower halves pull completely together, with no ragged edges of the seal ends caught between the parting faces, and are aligned.

Rotate the seal and retainer assembly around crankshaft to make sure it turns freely on the shaft. (This can be done if clutch housing has been removed).

With upper and lower gaskets in place, bolt the seal and retainer assembly to the rear of the engine.

With the retainer to cylinder block attaching bolts pulled up snugly, loosen the two bolts which hold the upper and lower retainer halves together. Make sure the retainer to cylinder block attaching bolts are all tight (Do not back them off). Then retighten the two bolts which attach the upper retainer half to the lower retainer bolt.

Align the index hole in the flywheel with the index hole in the crankshaft flange and install the flywheel. Tighten the bolts to 75 footpounds.

Engine Lubrication

Oil Pan Removal

1. Remove dipstick and dipstick tube.
2. Remove oil pan attaching screws and remove oil pan and sump assembly.

Oil Pump Removal

Disconnect oil delivery housing from crankcase by removing two attaching bolts. Loosen the locknut and unscrew the oil pump locating screw. This screw is located outside cylinder block below fuel injection pump.

Remove oil pump and oil delivery housing assembly. The oil pump and oil delivery housing are connected by a short pipe which is a push fit in each component.

Oil Pump and Oil Delivery Housing

The oil pump and oil delivery housing are both a push fit on the connecting pipe. Pull them both loose from the pipe and remove the two "O" rings from their internal grooves in the two assemblies and discard them. Whenever these seals are disturbed, they must be replaced. Inspect the connecting pipe for wear at "O" ring seal surfaces.

Servicing Relief Valve

Remove cotter key, spring retain-er, spring and plunger from relief valve bore in oil delivery housing. *Do not* stretch or distort spring.

Wash housing and relief valve parts thoroughly, and replice any worn or damaged parts.

Lubricate bore in delivery housing, and install plunger with small end outward.

Install relief valve spring and retainer, and secure them in place with cotter key.

Servicing Oil Pump

Remove two attaching screws, and remove pump intake tube.

Remove four pump cover to pump body attaching screws and remove cover.

Remove pump shaft and inner rotor and outer rotor.

Thoroughly clean all parts and inspect rotors for cracks and scores.

Install inner and outer rotor in pump body, making sure chamfered edge of outer rotor enters pump body first.

Check clearance between maxi-

Removing engine oil pump
(© Chrysler Corp.)

Checking end clearance of rotors
(© Chrysler Corp.)

Checking clearance between rotors
(© Chrysler Corp.)

mum diameter of inner rotor and minimum diameter of outer rotor at all points, using a feeler gauge. This clearance between inner and outer rotor should be between .004″ and .008″.

The clearance between outer rotor and body must fall between .005″ and .010″. A clearance of .002″ to .005″ must be maintained between top of rotor and end plate.

If pump rotors or body show excessive scoring or other damage, or if the above mentioned clearances are exceeded, the oil pump assembly must be replaced.

The oil pump parts are not available individually. The pump must be replaced as an assembly.

Thoroughly lubricate interior surfaces of pump and rotors. Make sure outer rotor is positioned in pump body chamfered end first, and install pump cover, securing it with four attaching screws.

Clean pump intake tube, and attach it to oil pump, using a new gasket. Tighten the two bolts firmly.

Install new "O" rings in the recesses in the pipe bores in the oil pump and oil delivery housing. Lubricate the "O" rings and connector pipe with engine oil, and place one end of the pipe in the oil pump body and the other end in the oil delivery housing. Be careful not to dislodge the "O" rings from their grooves.

Place oil pump and delivery housing assembly in position in the engine crankcase, while engaging the splines of oil pump shaft with splines in the pump vertical drive shaft.

Install oil pump retaining screw through side of the engine so it engages the oil pump to hold it in position. *Do not* tighten screw at this time.

Place a new gasket between the oil delivery housing and engine, and attach housing with two bolts.

Tighten oil pump retaining screw and lock it in place with locknut.

Oil Pan, Sump Well and Screen

Place a new gasket on the oil pan, with Gasket Sealer, on both sides and install the pan on the engine, tightening the bolts firmly. Avoid tightening the bolts too tightly, since this can distort the oil pan sealing surface.

Clean the pump well and screen thoroughly, and using a new gasket and Sealer, attach the sump well to engine pan. Make sure oil pickup tube is properly positioned in the screen as sump well and screen assembly are placed in position.

Installing Rear Main Bearing Lower Oil Seal

Trimming Rear Main Bearing Lower Oil Seal

Turbocharger

TROUBLESHOOTING

Trouble and Symptoms	Probable Causes Check causes given in sequence shown.
Noisy	9, 10, 11, 12, 13, 14, 15, 17, 20, 23, 25, 26, 27, 28, 29, 30
Low turbocharger speed	1, 3, 4, 7, 8, 13, 15, 16, 20, 23, 25, 26, 27, 29, 30, 34
Low turbocharger pressure	1, 3, 5, 7, 14, 11, 12, 13, 15, 16, 23
Cracked turbocharger housings or flanges	1, 3, 5, 7, 30, 11, 12, 13, 15, 16, 19, 20, 23, 26, 27, 28, 31, 32, 33

Engine lacks power
    Black smoke
    Blue smoke
	
	1, 2, 3, 5, 16, 24, 7, 19, 15
	24, 2, 7, 4, 22, 34

Lubrication oil consumption excessive	19, 21, 22, 3, 1, 5, 18, 24, 25, 34
Lubrication oil leakage	21, 19, 18, 22, 24, 25, 34
Insufficient lubrication	19, 21, 17, 31

Oil in Air Inlet System
    Before turbocharger
    After turbocharger
	
	1, 2, 3, 4, 5, 7, 18, 19, 34
	1, 2, 3, 4, 7, 5, 22, 24, 25, 28, 34

Oil in Exhaust System
    Before turbocharger
    After turbocharger
	
	12
	22, 24, 25

Unbalance of rotating assembly	25, 23, 9, 3, 11, 12, 13, 18, 19, 20
Drag or bind in rotating assembly	9, 26, 27, 28, 30, 25, 18, 19, 20, 17, 13, 22, 29, 11, 12, 31, 32, 33, 34
Damaged turbine wheel	12, 13, 15, 25, 27, 28, 30, 32, 33
Damaged compressor impeller	6, 9, 11, 13, 25, 26, 27, 28, 30, 33
Worn bearings or journals	17, 18, 19, 20, 21, 26, 27, 28, 30, 31, 32, 33

Probable Causes

1. Air inlet snorkel cap or screen restricted.
2. Oil "pull over" from oil bath type air cleaner.
3. Dirty air cleaner.
4. Oil bath air cleaner oil viscosity too low.
5. Oil bath air cleaner oil viscosity too high.
6. Dry type air cleaner element missing, leaking, not sealing correctly.
7. Collapsed or restricted air inlet line before turbocharger.
8. Restricted air inlet line turbocharger to engine.
9. Loose, chafed or open air inlet line from air cleaner to turbocharger.
10. Loose, chafed or open air inlet line from turbocharger to inlet manifold.
11. Foreign object in inlet system air cleaner to turbocharger.
12. Foreign object in exhaust system (from engine, check engine).
13. Turbocharger flanges, clamps or bolts loose.
14. Inlet manifold cracked or flange gaskets loose or missing.
15. Exhaust manifold cracked or flange gaskets loose, blown or missing.
16. Restricted exhaust system.
17. Oil lag (delay in oil supply to turbocharger at start up).
18. Lubricating oil contaminated with dirt or other material.
19. Improper type lubricating oil used.
20. Insufficient lubrication.
21. Restricted or leaking oil feed line.
22. Restricted oil drain line.
23. Nozzle ring damaged or restricted.
24. Turbocharger seal leakage.
25. Worn shaft bearings.
26. Excessive dirt build-up behind compressor impeller.
27. Excessive carbon build-up behind turbine wheel.
28. Unbalance of rotating assembly.
29. Bearing seizure.
30. Improper mounting, brackets or supports.
31. Too fast acceleration at initial start (oil lag).
32. Too little warm-up time.
33. Insufficient time allowed for temperature stabilization before engine shut-down.
34. Air compressor passing oil.

Index

Carter

YEAR	MODEL OR TYPE	FLOAT LEVEL (IN.)	FLOAT DROP (IN.)	Pump Travel Setting	CHOKE SETTING Unloader (IN.)	Housing	Idle Screw Turns Open	Idle Speed (RPM)	Fast Idle Speed (RPM)	Dashpot Plunger Clearance (IN.)
Dodge/Plymouth										
				MODEL BBS						
1970-71	4658S	1/4	—	—	—	—	1-2	550	2600	—
	4659S	1/4	—	—	3/16	2 R	1-2	550	700	—
	4629S	1/4	—	—	—	—	1-2	650	2800	—
	4630S	1/4	—	—	3/16	2 R	1-2	650	1550	—
	4730S	1/4	—	—	—	—	1-2	550	—	—
1972-73	6395S	1/4	—	—	.190	—	1-2	800	2000	—
	6396S	1/4	—	—	.190	—	1-2	800	1800	—
	6219S	1/4	—	—	.190	—	1-2	700	2000	—
	6218S	1/4	—	—	.190	—	1-2	700	1800	—
	6220S	1/4	—	—	—	—	1-2	700	2800	—
1974	7044S	1/4	—	—	3/16	—	1-2	800	2000	—
	7045S	1/4	—	—	3/16	—	1-2	800	1800	—
				MODEL BBD						
1970-71	4613S	5/16	—	1.00	1/4	2 R	1 1/2	700	1600	—
	4748S	5/16	—	1.00	1/4	2 R	1 1/2	700	1600	—
	4614S	5/16	—	1.00	1/4	2 R	1 1/2	600	1600	—
1972-73	6316SA	1/4	—	.280	1/4	—	—	750	1700	—
	6317SA	1/4	—	.280	1/4	—	—	700	1700	—
	6343SA	1/4	—	.280	1/4	—	—	750	1700	—
	6344SA	1/4	—	.280	1/4	—	—	700	1700	—
	6221S	1/4	—	.310	1/4	—	—	750	1600	—
	6222S	1/4	—	.310	1/4	—	—	750	1900	—
	6363S	1/4	—	.310	1/4	—	—	750	1600	—
	6364S	1/4	—	.310	1/4	—	—	750	1700	—
	6365S	1/4	—	.340	—	—	—	700	1900	—
	6224S	1/4	—	.340	—	—	—	700	1900	—
	6228S	1/4	—	.340	—	—	—	600	1600	—
	6368S	1/4	—	.310	—	—	—	600, 700 Calif.	1600	—
	6229S	1/4	—	.390	—	—	—	600	1600	—

YEAR	MODEL OR TYPE	FLOAT LEVEL (IN.)	FLOAT DROP (IN.)	Pump Travel Setting (IN.)	CHOKE SETTING Unloader (IN.)	Housing	Idle Screw Turns Open	ON THE TRUCK ADJUSTMENTS Idle Speed (RPM)	Fast Idle Speed (RPM)	Dashpot Plunger Clearance (IN.)
Dodge/Plymouth, Continued										
				MODEL BBD						
1974	6610S	1/4	—	1/2	.28	—	—	750	1700	—
	6611S	1/4	—	1/2	.28	—	—	750	1500	—
	8008S	1/4	—	1/2	.28	—	—	750	1700	—
	6613S	1/4	—	1/2	.28	—	—	750	1600	—
	6536S	1/4	—	1/2	.28	—	—	750	1700	—
	6537S	1/4	—	1/2	.28	—	—	750	1500	—
	6585S	1/4	—	1/2	—	—	—	700	1900	—
	6586S	1/4	—	1/2	—	—	—	700	1900	—
1975-76	8019S	1/4	—	1/2	.28	—	—	800	1500	—
	8020S	1/4	—	1/2	.28	—	—	750	1500	—
	8022S	1/4	—	1/2	.31	—	—	750	1500	—
	8024S	1/4	—	1/2	.28	—	—	750	1500	—
	8025S	1/4	—	1/2	.31	—	—	750	1500	—
	6536S	1/4	—	1/2	.28	—	—	750	1700	—
	6537S	1/4	—	1/2	.31	—	—	750	1500	—
	8013S	1/4	—	1/2	.31	—	—	700	1500	—
	8014S	1/4	—	1/2	.31	—	—	700	1500	—
	6585S	1/4	—	1/2	—	—	—	700	1900	—
	8016S	1/4	—	1/2	.31	—	—	700	1500	—
	8026S	1/4	—	1/2	.31	—	—	700	1500	—
	6586S	1/4	—	1/2	—	—	—	700	1900	—
				MODEL TQ						
1973	6446	1.0	—	31/64	.19	—	—	700	1700	—
	6518	1.0	—	31/64	.19	—	—	700	1700	—
1974	9022S	1.0[1]	—	35/64	.31	—	—	750	1800	—
	9025S	1.0[1]	—	31/64	.31	—	—	700	1700	—
	9017S	1.0[1]	—	15/32	.31	—	—	700	1700	—
	6545S	1.0[1]	—	31/64	.31	—	—	700	1700	—
1975-76	9034S	29/32	—	1/2	.31	—	—	700	1700	—
	9035A	29/32	—	1/2	.31	—	—	700	1700	—
	6545S	29/32	—	1/2	.31	—	—	700	1700	—
	9036S	29/32	—	1/2	.31	—	—	700	1700	—

Note[1]—Brass float, 29/32 with plastic float

Ford

YEAR	MODEL OR TYPE	FLOAT LEVEL (IN.)	FLOAT DROP (IN.)	Pump Travel Setting (IN.)	CHOKE SETTING Unloader (IN.)	Housing	Idle Screw Turns Open	Idle Speed (RPM)	Fast Idle Speed (RPM)	Dashpot Plunger Clearance (IN.)
				MODEL YF						
1970	D0TF-J	7/32	1 1/4	—	.28	Index	—	—	—	7/64
	D0TF-E	7/32	1 1/4	—	.28	Index	—	—	—	Solenoid
	D0TF-L	7/32	1 1/4	—	.28	Index	—	—	—	Solenoid
	D0TF-K	7/32	1 1/4	—	.28	1 L	—	—	—	7/64
	D0TF-F	7/32	1 1/4	—	.28	1 L	—	—	—	Solenoid
	D0TF-G	7/32	1 1/4	—	.28	Index	—	—	—	Solenoid
1971	D1TF-VA	3/8	1 1/4	—	.28	Index	—	—	—	Solenoid
	D1TF-XA	3/8	1 1/4	—	.28	Index	—	—	—	—
	D1TF-YA	3/8	1 1/4	—	.28	Index	—	—	—	7/64
	D1TF-ABA	7/32	1 1/4	—	.28	1 L	—	—	—	7/64
	D1TF-ZA	7/32	1 1/4	—	.28	1 L	—	—	—	Solenoid
	D1TF-AAA	7/32	1 1/4	—	.28	Index	—	—	—	Solenoid
1972	D2TF-MA	3/8	1 1/4	—	.28	Index	—	—	—	Solenoid
	D2TF-LA	3/8	1 1/4	—	.28	1 L	—	—	—	Solenoid
	D2TF-FA	3/8	1 1/4	—	.28	1 L	—	—	—	Solenoid
	D2TF-VA	3/8	1 1/4	—	.28	1 L	—	—	—	Solenoid
	D2TF-SA	3/8	1 1/4	—	.28	1 L	—	—	—	7/64

YEAR	MODEL OR TYPE	FLOAT LEVEL (IN.)	FLOAT DROP (IN.)	Pump Travel Setting (IN.)	CHOKE SETTING Unloader (IN.)	Housing	ON THE TRUCK ADJUSTMENTS Idle Screw Turns Open	Idle Speed (RPM)	Fast Idle Speed (RPM)	Dashpot Plunger Clearance (IN.)
Ford Continued										
				MODEL YF						
1973	D3TF-TA	3/8	1¼	—	.28	Index	—	—	—	Solenoid
	D3TF-KA	3/8	1¼	—	.28	1 L	—	—	—	Solenoid
	D3TF-AAA	3/8	1¼	—	.28	1 L	—	—	—	Solenoid
	D3TF-ABA	3/8	1¼	—	.28	Index	—	—	—	Solenoid
	D3TF-LA	3/8	1¼	—	.28	1 R	—	—	—	.1
1974	D4TE-ZA	3/8	1¼	—	.28	1 L	—	—	—	Solenoid
	D4TE-YC	3/8	1¼	—	.28	Index	—	—	—	.1
1975	D5TE-ALA	3/8	1¼	—	.28	Index	—	—	—	—
	D5TE-APA	3/8	1¼	—	.28	Index	—	—	—	—
	D5TE-ADA	3/8	1¼	—	.28	Index	—	—	—	—
	D5TE-AKA	3/8	1¼	—	.28	Index	—	—	—	—
	D5TE-AMA	3/8	1¼	—	.28	1 R	—	—	—	—
	D5TE-AGA	3/8	1¼	—	.28	1 R	—	—	—	—
	D5TE-ANA	3/8	1¼	—	.28	1 R	—	—	—	—
1976	D5TE-ADA	3/8	1¼	—	.28	Index	—	—	—	—
	D5TE-ADB	23/32	1¼	—	.28	Index	—	—	—	—
	D5TE-AKA	3/8	1¼	—	.28	Index	—	—	—	—
	D5TE-AKB	23/32	1¼	—	.28	Index	—	—	—	—
	D5UE-EA	3/8	1¼	—	.28	Index	—	—	—	—
	D5TE-BSB	23/32	1¼	—	.28	Index	—	—	—	—
	D5TE-CBA	3/8	1¼	—	.28	Index	—	—	—	—
	D5UE-FA	3/8	1¼	—	.28	Index	—	—	—	—
	D5TE-APB	23/32	1¼	—	.28	Index	—	—	—	—
	D5TE-CAB	23/32	1¼	—	.28	Index	—	—	—	—
	D6TE-HA	23/32	1¼	—	.28	Index	—	—	—	—
	D5UE-AAB	23/32	1¼	—	.28	Index	—	—	—	—
	D5UE-HB	23/32	1¼	—	.28	Index	—	—	—	—
	D6TF-DA	23/32	1¼	—	.28	Index	—	—	—	—
	D5UE-GB	23/32	1¼	—	.28	Index	—	—	—	—
	D5TE-AGA	3/8	1¼	—	.28	1 R	—	—	—	—
	D5TE-AGB	3/8	1¼	—	.28	1 R	—	—	—	—
	D5TE-AFA	3/8	1¼	—	—	—	—	—	—	—
	D5TE-AFB	3/8	1¼	—	—	—	—	—	—	—
	D5TE-AJA	3/8	1¼	—	—	—	—	—	—	—
	D5TE-AJB	3/8	1¼	—	—	—	—	—	—	—
Jeep										
				MODEL YF						
1972	6287S	29/64	1¼	—	19/64	Index	—	—	1600	3/32
	6288S	29/64	1¼	—	19/64	Index	—	—	1600	3/32
1973	6299S	29/64	1¼	—	9/32	1 R	—	—	1600	3/32
	6300S	29/64	1¼	—	9/32	1 R	—	—	1600	3/32
	6401S	29/64	1¼	—	9/32	1 R	—	—	1600	—
1973	64013	29/64	1¼	—	9/32	1 R	—	—	1600	3/32
1974	6431	.48	1⅜	—	.28	1 R	—	—	1600	.095
	6511	.48	1⅜	—	.28	1 R	—	—	1600	.095
	7001	.48	1⅜	—	.28	1 R	—	—	1600	—
	7029	.48	1⅜	—	.28	1 R	—	—	1600	.095
1975	7043	.48	1⅜	—	.28	1 R	—	—	1600	—
	7041	.48	1⅜	—	.28	1 R	—	—	1600	.075
	7040	.48	1⅜	—	.28	1 R	—	—	1600	.075
1976	7088	.48	1⅜	—	.28	1 R	—	—	1600	—
	7084	.48	1⅜	—	.28	1 R	—	—	1600	.075
	7109	.48	1⅜	—	.28	2 R	—	—	1600	.075
	7083	.48	1⅜	—	.28	2 R	—	—	1600	.075
	7085	.48	1⅜	—	.28	1 R	—	—	1600	.075

YEAR	MODEL OR TYPE	FLOAT LEVEL (IN.)	FLOAT DROP (IN.)	Pump Travel Setting (IN.)	CHOKE SETTING Unloader (IN.)	Housing	Idle Screw Turns Open	ON THE TRUCK ADJUSTMENTS Idle Speed (RPM)	Fast Idle Speed (RPM)	Dashpot Plunger Clearance (IN.)
International										
	6591S, 6550S	1.06	—	.34/.14[1]	.28-.32	1 R	—	800	1600	.06/.08[2]
	6590S, 6592S, 6551S	1.06	—	.34/.14[1]	.28-.32	1 R	—	700	1600	.06/.08[2]

MODEL TQ

Note [1]—Primary/secondary.
Note [2]—Manual/automatic.

SINGLE BARREL—YF TYPE

Single barrel YF carburetor—exploded View

SINGLE BARREL—YF TYPE

YF fast idle adjustment

YF metering rod adjustment

YF unloader adjustment

YF float level adjustment

YF float drop adjustment

SINGLE BARREL—BBS TYPE

BBS float adjustment

BBS pump adjustment

BBS dashpot adjustment

BBS fast idle adjustment

BBS unloader adjustment

Carter Carburetors

SINGLE BARREL—BBS TYPE

SCREW (3)

HOUSING AND SPRING

GASKET

BAFFLE PLATE

CHOKE SHAFT AND LEVER

FAST IDLE CAM AND SPRING

HOUSING RING

UNLOADER ARM AND TRIP LEVER

PISTON PIN

CHOKE PISTON

SCREW (2 SHORT)

SCREW (4 LONG)

CHOKE VALVE

SCREW (2)

ROCKER ARM

SCREW

AIR HORN

GASKET

FAST IDLE LINK

CUP WASHER

STEP-UP PISTON RETAINER SCREW

PUMP SPRING

STEP-UP PISTON

STEP-UP ROD

ACCELERATOR PUMP PLUNGER

MAIN METERING JET

STEP-UP PISTON SPRING

IDLE ORIFICE TUBE

FLOAT FULCRUM PIN RETAINER

STEP-UP PISTON GASKET

FLOAT

DISCHARGE PASSAGE CHECK BALL

FLOAT FULCRUM PIN

SPRING

PLUG

FAST IDLE ADJUSTING SCREW

ACCELERATOR PUMP JET

MAIN BODY

CLIP

FUEL INLET NEEDLE VALVE SEAT AND GASKET

CHOKE CONNECTOR ROD

THROTTLE LEVER AND SHAFT

PLUG

GASKET

ACCELERATOR PUMP ROD

SCREW (2)

HAIRPIN CLIP

THROTTLE VALVE

THROTTLE BODY

IDLE MIXTURE ADJUSTING SCREW

SPRING

Carter BBS single barrel—typical

TWO BARREL—BBD TYPE

HOLD LIP TO VALVE

GAUGE

BBD float adjustment

FROM AIR HORN TO TOP OF PUMP SHAFT (NOT ARM)

FAST IDLE SCREW OFF CAM

BEND HERE TO ADJUST

THROTTLE VALVE CLOSED

BBD pump adjustment

802

TWO BARREL—BBD TYPE continued

BBD fast idle adjustment

ADJUST SCREW ON INDEX TO PROPER SPEED

GAUGE

BBD fast idle index adjustment

INDEX MARK

BEND TANG TO ADJUST

THROTTLE VALVE HELD CLOSED

BBD unloader adjustment

GAUGE

BEND TANG TO ADJUST

HOLD THROTTLE WIDE OPEN

SCREW — CHOKE HOUSING — GASKET — PLATE — PIN — PISTON

RETAINER — CHOKE VALVE — SCREW — SCREW — AIR HORN — LOOSE LEVER — CHOKE LEVER — WASHER — SCREW — FAST IDLE ROD

CHOKE SHAFT — SCREW — GASKET — ROCKER ARM — SCREW — HAIRPIN CLIP — SPRING — PLUNGER — RETAINER — CHECK BALL — MAIN JETS — WASHER — SCREW — STEP UP RODS — STEP UP PISTON — SPRING — GASKET — SCREWS

VENTURI CLUSTER — GASKET — RETAINER — GASKET — FLOATS — DISCHARGE CHECK BALL — FULCRUM PIN — MAIN BODY — NEEDLE VALVE AND SEAT — FAST IDLE CAM — SCREW — GASKET — HAIRPIN CLIP — SCREW — THROTTLE VALVES — THROTTLE BODY — IDLE SPEED SCREW — FAST IDLE SCREW — MIXTURE SCREWS AND SPRINGS — SPRING — SCREW — WASHER — WASHER — PUMP ROD — LOOSE LEVER — THROTTLE SHAFT — HAIRPIN CLIP

Carter—BBD two barrel—typical

FOUR BARREL—TQ

1 Fuel Inlet Nut and Gasket
2 Idle Compensator Screw
3 Idle Compensator
4 Idle Compensator Gasket
5 "E" Retainer
6 Primary Diaphragm Choke Pull-Off Rod Washer
7 Primary Diaphragm Choke Pull-Off Rod
8 Auxiliary Diaphragm Choke Pull-Off Rod (if equipped)
9 Choke Lever Screw
10 Choke Lever
11 Choke Connector Rod
12 Countershaft Lever Screw
13 Countershaft, Lever, Outer
14 Countershaft Lever Spring
15 Countershaft Lever, Inner
16 Fast Idle Cam Rod
17 Throttle Connector Rod
18 Cover Plate Screw
19 Metering Rod Cover Plate (opposite pump)
20 Metering Rod Cover Plate (pump side)
21 Step-Up Piston Cover Plate
22 Step-Up Piston & Hanger Assembly
23 Metering Rod
24 Step-Up Piston Spring
25 Bowl Cover Screw
26 IH Part Number Location
27 Bowl Cover Assembly
28 Float Pin
29 Float Assembly
30 Needle, Seat, and Gasket
31 Pump Passage Tube
32 Bowl Cover Gasket
33 Secondary Metering Jet
34 Primary Metering Jet
35 Quad Rings
36 Pin Spring Retainer
37 Bowl Vent Valve Lever, Upper
38 Bowl Vent Valve Lever Spring
39 Bowl Vent Valve Arm

40 Bowl Vent Valve Grommet
41 Rivet Plug
42 Pump Housing Screw
43 Pump Housing
44 Pump Housing Gasket
45 Discharge Check Needle
46 Pump Arm Screw
47 Pump Arm
48 Pump "S" Link
49 Air Valve Lock Plug
50 Air Valve Adjustment Plug
51 Air Valve Spring
52 Pump Intake Check Assembly
53 Plunger Assembly
54 Plunger Spring
55 Main Body
56 Main Body Gasket
57 Step-Up Piston Lifter
58 Step-Up Piston Lifter Lever Pin
59 Solenoid & Diaphragm Choke Pull-Off

Bracket Screw
60 Solenoid
61 Solenoid Operating Lever Screw
62 Curb Idle Speed Screw & Lever
63 Bowl Vent Lever, Lower
64 Throttle Shaft Washer
65 Hose
66 Primary Diaphragm Choke Pull-Off Bracket
67 Auxiliary Choke Pull-Off and Dashpot
68 Auxiliary Choke Pull-Off and Bracket (if equipped)
69 Dashpot and Bracket
70 Limiter Cap
71 Idle Mixture Screw
72 Idle Mixture Screw Spring
73 Throttle Body Assembly
74 Carter Part Number Location
75 Low Idle Speed Screw

Exploded view of typical Carter Thermo-Quad®

FAST IDLE SCREW ON SECOND STEP AGAINST SHOULDER OF FIRST STEP

Carter TQ fast idle speed adjustment cam position

SCALE

TOP OF FLOAT

BEND HERE TO ADJUST

GASKET IN PLACE

Carter TQ float height measurement

Carter TQ accelerator pump stroke adjustment

Carter TQ choke unloader adjustment

Ford/Autolite/Motorcraft Carburetors

YEAR	MODEL OR TYPE	FLOAT LEVEL (IN.)	FLOAT DROP (IN.)	Pump Travel Setting (IN.)	CHOKE SETTING Unloader (IN.)	Housing	Idle Screw Turns Open	Idle Speed (RPM)	Fast Idle Speed (RPM)	Dashpot Plunger Clearance (IN.)
Ford										
				MODEL 2100[1]						
1970	D0UF-B	13/16	—	hole 2	.06	2 R	—	—	—	Solenoid
	D0UF-C	13/16	—	3	.06	Index	—	—	—	5/64
	D0UF-E	13/16	—	2	.06	Index	—	—	—	Solenoid
	D0TF-B	7/8	—	3	.06	Index	—	—	—	1/8
	D0TF-N	7/8	—	3	.06	Index	—	—	—	Solenoid
	D0TF-C	13/16	—	3	.06	Index	—	—	—	1/8
	D0TF-M	13/16	—	3	.06	Index	—	—	—	Solenoid
	D0TF-R	13/16	—	3	.06	Index	—	—	—	1/8
	D0TF-S	7/8	—	3	.06	Index	—	—	—	1/8
1971	D1TF-AMA	13/16	—	3	.06	Index	—	—	—	Solenoid
	D1TF-EA	13/16	—	3	.06	Index	—	—	—	1/8
	D1TF-HA	7/8	—	3	.06	Index	—	—	—	1/8
	D1TF-ALA	7/8	—	3	.06	2 R	—	—	—	1/8
	D1TF-NA	13/16	—	3	.06	1 R	—	—	—	1/8
	D1TF-AKA	13/16	—	3	.06	2 R	—	—	—	1/8
1972	D2TF-EA	13/16	—	2	.06	2 R	—	—	—	Solenoid
	D2TF-CA	13/16	—	3	.06	2 R	—	—	—	1/16
	D2TF-DB	13/16	—	3	.12	2 R	—	—	—	1/16
	D2TF-AA	7/8	—	3	.16	1 L	—	—	—	1/8
	D2TF-AB	7/8	—	3	.16	1 L	—	—	—	1/8
	D2TF-FC	7/8	—	2	.14	1 L	—	—	—	Solenoid
	D2TF-AAA	7/8	—	2	.14	1 L	—	—	—	Solenoid
	D2TF-JA	7/8	—	3	.14	2 R	—	—	—	1/8
	D2TF-GA	13/16	—	3	.14	Index	—	—	—	1/8
	D2TF-KA	13/16	—	3	.14	2 R	—	—	—	1/8
1973	D3TF-NR	13/16	—	2	—	2 R	—	—	—	Solenoid
	D3TF-NA	13/16	—	2	—	2 R	—	—	—	Solenoid
	D3TF-BE	29/32	—	2	—	2 R	—	—	—	Solenoid
	D3TF-DD	7/8	—	3	—	Index	—	—	—	Solenoid
	D3TF-MC	13/16	—	3	—	Index	—	—	—	Solenoid
	D3TF-GC	7/8	—	3	—	Index	—	—	—	—
	D3TF-HC	13/16	—	3	—	Index	—	—	—	.065
	D3TF-DE	7/8	—	3	—	Index	—	—	—	Solenoid

D2BFEA SEE NEXT PAGE

YEAR	MODEL OR TYPE	FLOAT LEVEL (IN.)	FLOAT DROP (IN.)	Pump Travel Setting (IN.)	CHOKE SETTING Unloader (IN.)	CHOKE SETTING Housing	Idle Screw Turns Open	ON THE TRUCK ADJUSTMENTS Idle Speed (RPM)	ON THE TRUCK ADJUSTMENTS Fast Idle Speed (RPM)	Dashpot Plunger Clearance (IN.)
Ford, Continued										
			MODEL 2100[1]							
1973	D3TF-UA	13/16	—	3	—	Index	—	—	—	Solenoid
	D3TF-MC	13/16	—	3	—	Index	—	—	—	Solenoid
	D3TF-VA	7/8	—	3	—	Index	—	—	—	Solenoid
	D3TF-XA	13/16	—	3	—	1 L	—	—	—	Solenoid
1974-75	D4TE-EA	13/16	—	2	—	2 R	—	—	—	—
	D4TE-CAA	13/16	—	2	—	2 R	—	—	—	—
	D4TE-LA	13/16	—	2	—	2 R	—	—	—	—
	D4TE-AZA	13/16	—	2	—	2 R	—	—	—	—
	D4TE-GA	13/16	—	3	—	2 R	—	—	—	—
	D4TE-TA	7/8	—	3	—	Index	—	—	—	—
	D4TE-BAA	7/8	—	3	—	1 R	—	—	—	—
1976	D5TE-ABA	.81	7/16[2]	4	—	—	—	—	—	—
	D5TE-ASA	.88	31/64[2]	4	—	Index	—	—	—	—
	D5TE-ATA	.88	31/64[2]	4	—	Index	—	—	—	—
	D5TE-BYA	7/8	31/64[2]	3	—	2 R	—	—	—	—
	D5TE-AAF	7/8	31/64[2]	3	—	3 R	—	—	—	—
	D5TE-YF	7/8	31/64[2]	3	—	2 R	—	—	—	—
	D5TE-ZB	7/8	31/64[2]	3	—	2 R	—	—	—	—
			MODEL 2150[1]							
1975	D5TE-BHA	7/8	—	hole 2	—	Index	—	—	—	—
	D5TE-LA	7/8	—	2	—	Index	—	—	—	—
	D5TE-PA	7/8	—	2	—	3 R	—	—	—	—
	D5TE-BCA	7/8	—	3	—	2 R	—	—	—	—
	D5TE-BCB	7/8	—	3	—	2 R	—	—	—	—
	D5TE-BFA	7/8	—	3	—	2 R	—	—	—	—
	D5TE-BFB	7/8	—	3	—	2 R	—	—	—	—
	D5TE-VA	7/8	—	3	—	2 R	—	—	—	—
	D5TE-AUB	7/8	—	3	—	2 R	—	—	—	—
	D5TE-BGA	7/8	—	3	—	3 R	—	—	—	—
	D5TE-ZA	7/8	—	3	—	3 R	—	—	—	—
	D5TE-YD	7/8	—	3	—	3 R	—	—	—	—
	D5TE-AAD	7/8	—	3	—	3 R	—	—	—	—
	D5TE-BDA	7/8	—	3	—	2 R	—	—	—	—
	D5TE-BDB	7/8	—	3	—	2 R	—	—	—	—
	D5TE-BEA	7/8	—	3	—	2 R	—	—	—	—
1976	D5TE-BEB	7/8	31/64[2]	3	—	2 R	—	—	—	—
			MODEL 4300							
1974	D4TE-BB	3/4	—	hole 1	—	Index	—	—	.20[3]	—
			MODEL 4350							
1975	D5TE-ARC	15/16	—	hole 1	.30	Index	—	—	.17[3]	—
	D5TE-ARD	1.0	—	1	.30	Index	—	—	.17[3]	—
	D5TE-BBA	15/16	—	1	.30	Index	—	—	.17[3]	—
	D5TE-BBB	59/64	—	1	.30	Index	—	—	.17[3]	—
	D5TE-BBC	1.0	—	1	.30	Index	—	—	.17[3]	—
1976	D6UE-KA	1.0	—	3	.30	Index	—	—	.17[3]	—
	D6UE-LA	1.0	—	3	.30	Index	—	—	.17[3]	—
	D6TE-NA	1.0	—	3	.30	Index	—	—	.17[3]	—
	D6TE-UA	1.0	—	3	.30	Index	—	—	.17[3]	—

Note [1]—Fuel level in bowl given for float level.
Note [2]—Dry float setting.
Note [3]—Fast idle cam setting.

YEAR	MODEL OR TYPE	Float Level (IN.)	Fuel Level (IN.)	Fast Idle Cam (IN.)	Pump Travel Setting	Choke Setting	Idle Screw Turns Open	ON THE TRUCK ADJUSTMENTS Idle Speed (RPM)	Fast Idle Speed (RPM)	Dashpot Plunger Clearance (IN.)
Jeep										
				MODEL 2100						
1972	2DM2	3/8[1]	—	—	13/64	1 R	—	—	1600	1/8
1973	3DM2	3/4[2]	—	—	1/4	1 R	—	—	1600	1/8
1974	4DMJ2	25/32[2]	—	—	1/4	2 R	—	—	1600	—
	4DM2	25/32[2]	—	—	1/4	2 R	—	—	1600	9/64
	4RA2	25/32[2]	—	—	1/4	1 R	—	—	1600	—
	4RHD2	3/4[2]	—	—	1/4	2 R	—	—	1600	—
1975	5DM2J	25/32[2]	—	—	1/4	2 R	—	—	1600	1/8
	5DM2	25/32[2]	—	—	1/4	2 R	—	—	1600	1/8
1976	6DM2J	15/16[2]	—	—	1/4	1 R	—	—	1600	1/8
	6DM2	15/16[2]	—	—	1/4	2 R	—	—	1600	1/8
	6DA2J	15/16[2]	—	—	1/4	1 R	—	—	1600	1/8
	6RHM2	.93[2]	—	—	1/4	2 R	—	—	1600	—
	6RHA2	.93[2]	—	—	1/4	2 R	—	—	1600	—
				MODEL 4300						
1971-73	—	13/16	—	—	9/32	—	—	—	1600	9/64
1974	4TA4	.82	—	—	.33	2 R	—	—	1600	9/64
	4THD4	.82	—	—	.33	2 R	—	—	1600	—
				MODEL 4350						
1975	5THA4	.90	—	—	.33	2 R	—	—	1600	—
	5THM4	.90	—	—	.33	2 R	—	—	1600	—
1976	6THA4	.90	—	—	.33	2 R	—	—	1600	—
	6THM4	.90	—	—	.33	2 R	—	—	1600	—
	6THA4C	.90	—	—	.33	2 R	—	—	1600	—

Note [1]—Dry.
Note [2]—Wet fuel level, measured on vehicle.

[handwritten notes:]
CHOKE HOUSING - 1R
CHOKE UNLOADER - 1/16
FAST IDLE - 1400
CURB IDLE - 800/500
FUEL LEVEL - 13/16
CHOKE PULLDOWN - 9/64

[handwritten notes:]
MOTORCRAFT D2BFEA 2BBL
FAST IDLE CAM - 1/8
ACCEL. PUMP - 2
FLOAT LEVEL - 7/16

TWO BARREL

ADJUSTING NEEDLES

Idle speed adjustment

CHOKE PLATE
AIR HORN ASSEMBLY
MAIN BODY
FUEL BOWL VENTS
ACCELERATING PUMP ASSEMBLY

Float shaft retainer removal

TWO BARREL

BOOSTER VENTURI SCREW

DISCHARGE CHECK BALL AND WEIGHT

GASKET

NOZZLE BAR AND BOOSTER VENTURI ASSEMBLY

GASKET

ACCELERATING PUMP INLET BALL CHECK

ACCELERATING PUMP OVER-TRAVEL SPRING

THROTTLE SHAFT AND LEVER

RETURN SPRING

PUMP DIAPHRAGM

PUMP COVER

PUMP LEVER

THROTTLE PLATES

PUMP ROD

IDLE MIXTURE NEEDLE AND SPRING

ACCELERATING PUMP OVER-TRAVEL LEVER

LEFT FRONT VIEW

AIR HORN

CHOKE PLATE

CHOKE PLATE SHAFT

GASKET

FLOAT SHAFT

CHOKE PLATE ROD

FLOAT

SHAFT RETAINER

DAMPER SPRING

FUEL INLET NEEDLE

MAIN JETS

FUEL INLET NEEDLE SEAT

FUEL INLET FITTING

SPRING

GASKET

IDLE SPEED ADJUSTING SCREW

FILTER SCREEN

MAIN BODY

DISTRIBUTOR VACUUM FITTING

FAST IDLE ADJUSTING SCREW

GASKET

HAND THROTTLE LEVER

POWER VALVE

GASKET

COVER

CHOKE PLATE CAM AND LEVER

RIGHT REAR VIEW

HAND THROTTLE CABLE BRACKET AND CHOKE CABLE BRACKET

Ford two barrel—disassembled view

Straight Edge REFER TO SPECIFICATIONS

Fuel level adjustment

Fast idle adjustment

FLOAT HINGE

FLOAT

FUEL INLET NEEDLE, CLIP, AND ANTI-SPLASH WASHER

GUIDE

FUEL INLET SEAT

FLOAT SHAFT

RETAINER

TORSION SPRING

Float assembly installed

FOUR BARREL

HIGH-SPEED BLEED
METERING ROD YOKE
AND LIFT ROD

BOOSTER
VENTURI

SPRING

RETAINER

BOOSTER
VENTURI
SCREW

GASKET

WEIGHT

ACCELERATING PUMP
DISCHARGE BALL CHECK

NOZZLE BAR, HIGH-SPEED
BLEED AND BOOSTER
VENTURI ASSEMBLY

GASKET

MAIN BODY

IDLE
MIXTURE
NEEDLE

ELASTOMER
VALVE

IDLE
LIMITER
CAP

ACCELERATING
PUMP DIAPHRAGM

ACCELERATING
PUMP COVER

VENT VALVE
ACTUATING
LEVER

RETURN SPRING

SPRING

THROTTLE SHAFT
LEVER ASSEMBLY

KICKDOWN
ADJUSTMENT
SCREW

KICKDOWN
LEVER

THROTTLE
PLATES

ACCELERATING PUMP
OVER-TRAVEL SPRING

THROTTLE SOLENOID
POSITIONER
(SOLENOID-DASHPOT)

UPPER BODY

FUEL BOWL VENT VALVE

ACCELERATING
PUMP ROD

RETAINING
CLIP

CHOKE PLATE

CHOKE PLATE
SHAFT

CHOKE PLATE LEVER

CHOKE PLATE
ROD

DUST SHIELD

RETAINER

CURB IDLE RPM
ADJUSTING NUT

CHOKE CLEAN
AIR TUBE

GASKET

FLOAT

MAIN JETS

SOLENOID OFF
IDLE (HOT ENGINE)
SPEED ADJUSTING
SCREW

SPRING

DIAPHRAGM
LINK

HOT IDLE
COMPENSATOR

CHOKE PULLDOWN
DIAPHRAGM
ASSEMBLY

PULLDOWN
VACUUM SUPPLY
TUBE

GASKET

ENRICHMENT
VALVE

GASKET

COVER

FAST IDLE
ADJUSTING
SCREW

SPRING

FLOAT SHAFT
SHAFT RETAINER

FUEL INLET NEEDLE

FUEL INLET NEEDLE SEAT

SHIELD

FILTER SCREEN

CHOKE
LINKAGE

FLOAT DAMPER SPRING
(IF SO REQUIRED)

FAST IDLE CAM

RETAINER

LINK

SHIELD

CHOKE HOUSING

CHOKE LEVER

GASKET

THERMOSTATIC
SPRING HOUSING

RETAINER

SCREW

FAST IDLE
ADJUSTING
LEVER

Motorcraft 2150 carburetor, typical exploded view

PUMP SHAFT

ACCELERA-
TING PUMP
SPRING
RETAINER

PIN

PUMP
SPRING

NO. 1
NO. 2
NO. 3

PIN
RETAINER

PUMP PISTON

**Setting accelerator pump stroke,
Motorcraft 4350**

DRILL TWO 3/16'' HOLES
6'' BETWEEN CENTERS

1/8''

1/8''

1-1/2''

NO. 12 - 32 x 2'' SCREWS (2 REQ'D.)
NO. 12 NUTS (6 REQ'D.)

1/2''

ADJUST BOTH NUTS TO FLOAT
HEIGHT SPECIFICATIONS

Fabricating float gauge, Motorcraft 4350

FOUR BARREL

Motorcraft 4350 carburetor, typical exploded view

Checking float level with fabricated gauge, Motorcraft 4350

Chevrolet

Year	Model or Type	Float Level (IN.)	Fuel Level (IN.)	Bowl Vent Valve (IN.)	Pump Travel Setting (IN.)	Choke Setting Unloader (IN.)	Housing	Idle Screw Turns Out	On the Truck Adjustments Air Bypass Turns Open	Idle Speed (RPM)	Fast Idle Speed (RPM)	Dashpot Plunger Clearance (IN.)
					MODEL 4150G							
1970	R4199A	1	2	.060	.015	—	—	3	—	—	2000	—
	R4200A	1	2	.060	.015	—	—	3	—	—	2000	—
1971-72	4772-1	3	2	.060	.015	—	—	3	—	—	1800-2400	—
	4773-1	3	2	.060	.015	—	—	3	—	—	1800-2400	—
1973	R6510A	2	4	.060	.015	—	—	3	—	—	1800-2400	
	R6521A	2	4	—	.015	—	—	3	—	—	1800-2400	
	R6511A	2	4	.060	.015	—	—	3	—	—	1800-2400	
	R6522A	2	4	—	.015	—	—	3	—	—	1800-2400	
1974	R6742A	2	4	.060	.015	—	—	—	—	—	2200	
	R6743A	2	4	.060	.015	—	—	—	—	—	2200	
	R6744A	2	4	—	.015	—	—	—	—	—	2200	
	R6745A	2	4	—	.015	—	—	—	—	—	2200	
1975-76	R6928A, R7264A	5	—	.060	hole 1	—	—	—	—	—	2200	
	R6929A, R7266A	5	—	.060	1	—	—	—	—	—	2200	
	R6930A	5	—		1	—	—	—	—	—	2200	
	R6931A	5	—		1	—	—	—	—	—	2200	

Note 1—Float Level. Primary—.195". Secondary—.250".
Note 2—Float adjustment: Fuel level should be plus or minus 1/32 in. with threads at bottom of sight holes.
  To adjust turn adjusting nut on top of bowl clockwise, to lower, counterclockwise to raise.
Note 3—Adjust float parallel to bowl floor.
Note 4—Bottom of sight plug.
Note 5—Primary—.197, Secondary—.166.

Dodge/Plymouth

Year	Model or Type	Float Level (IN.)	Fuel Level (IN.)	Bowl Vent Valve (IN.)	Pump Travel Setting (IN.)	Choke Setting Unloader (IN.)	Housing	Idle Screw Turns Out	Air Bypass Turns Open	Idle Speed (RPM)	Fast Idle Speed (RPM)	Dashpot Plunger Clearance (IN.)
					MODEL 1920							
1971-73	6593A	.26	—	.015	—	.065	—	1½	—	750	2000	—
	6594A	.26	—	.015	—	.065	—	1½	—	750	1700	—
	6595A	.26	—	.015	—	.065	—	1½	—	750	2000	—
	6596A	.26	—	.015	—	.065	—	1½	—	750	1700	—
					MODEL 1945							
1974	6725A	3/64	—	—	2 7/32	¼	—	—	—	800	1600	—
	6921A	3/64	—	—	2 7/32	¼	—	—	—	800	1600	—
	6875A	3/64	—	—	2 11/32	¼	—	—	—	750	1800	—
1975-76	7074A	3/64	—	—	2 7/32	¼	—	—	—	800	1600	—
	7209A	3/64	—	—	2 7/32	¼	—	—	—	800	1600	—
	7076A	3/64	—	—	2 21/64	¼	—	—	—	750	1700	—
	7210A	3/64	—	—	2 21/64	¼	—	—	—	750	1700	—
	7078A	3/64	—	—	2 7/32	¼	—	—	—	800	1600	—
	7079A	3/64	—	—	2 21/64	¼	—	—	—	750	1700	—
	7080A	3/64	—	—	2 7/32	¼	—	—	—	700	1600	—
	7081A	3/64	—	—	2 21/64	¼	—	—	—	700	1700	—
	7082A	3/64	—	—	2 7/32	¼	—	—	—	700	1600	—
	7083A	3/64	—	—	2 21/64	¼	—	—	—	700	1700	—
					MODEL 2210							
1970-73	6484A	.18	—	.015	¼	.25	—	—	—	750	1900	—
	6484A	.18	—	.015	¼	.17	—	—	—	700	1900	—
	6575A	.18	—	.015	¼	.17	—	—	—	750	1900	—
	6485	.18	—	.015	¼	.17	—	—	—	750	1900	—
	6486A	.18	—	.015	¼	.17	—	—	—	700, 750 Calif.	1800	—
	6454A	.18	—	.015	¼	.17	—	—	—	700	1800	—
	6472A	.18	—	.015	¼	.17	—	—	—	700	1800	—
	6487A	.18	—	.015	¼	.17	—	—	—	700	1800	—
	6488A	.18	—	.015	¼	.17	—	—	—	700	1800	—

Holley Carburetors

Year	MODEL OR TYPE	Float Level (IN.)	Fuel Level (IN.)	Bowl Vent Valve (IN.)	Pump Travel Setting (IN.)	CHOKE SETTING Unloader (IN.)	Housing	Idle Screw Turns Out	ON THE TRUCK ADJUSTMENTS Air Bypass Turns Open	Idle Speed (RPM)	Fast Idle Speed (RPM)	Dashpot Plunger Clearance (IN.)
Dodge/Plymouth												
					MODEL 2210							
1974	6764A	.18	—	—	.27	.17	—	—	—	750	1700	—
	6765A	.18	—	—	¼	.17	—	—	—	750	1800	—
	6886A	.18	—	—	¼	.17	—	—	—	750	1800	—
	7052A	.18	—	—	¼	.17	—	—	—	750	1800	—
1975-76	6764A	.18	—	—	.26[1] .31	.17	—	—	—	750	1700	—
	6765A	.18	—	—	.26[1] .31	.17	—	—	—	750	1800	—
					MODEL 2245							
1974	6762-1A	.18	—	.015	.26	.22	—	—	—	750	1700	—
	6860A	.18	—	.015	.26	.17	—	—	—	750	1800	—
	6990A	.18	—	.015	.26	.17	—	—	—	750	1600	—
1975-76	7187A	.18	—	—	.26[1] .31	.17	—	—	—	700	1600	—
	7188A	.18	—	—	.26[1] .31	.17	—	—	—	700	1600	—
	7103A	.18	—	—	.26[1] .31	.17	—	—	—	750	1600	—
	7088A	.18	—	—	.26[1] .31	.17	—	—	—	750	1600	—
	7089A	.18	—	—	.26[1] .31	.17	—	—	—	750	1600	—
	7090A	.18	—	—	.26[1] .31	.17	—	—	—	700	1600	—
	7091A	.18	—	—	.26[1] .31	.17	—	—	—	750	1600	—
	7092A	.18	—	—	.26[1] .31	.17	—	—	—	750	1600	—

Note 1—from curb idle/from closed throttle

Year	MODEL OR TYPE	Float Level	Fuel Level	Bowl Vent	Pump Travel	Unloader	Housing	Idle Screw	Air Bypass	Idle Speed	Fast Idle	Dashpot
					MODEL 2300G							
1970-71	2951107	1	1	—	.015-.063	—	—	1.0	—	500	—	—
1972-73	6277A	1	1	—	.015-.063	—	—	1.0	—	700	—	—
	6278A	1	1	—	.015-.063	—	—	1.0	—	600, 700 Calif.	—	—
1974	6769-1A	1	1	—	.015[a]	—	—	1.0	—	700	—	—
	6770A	1	1	—	.015[a]	—	—	1.0	—	700	—	—
1975-76	6719-1A	1	1	—	.015[a]	—	—	—	—	700	—	—
	7137A	1	1	—	.015[a]	—	—	—	—	700	—	—
					MODEL 4150G							
1970-72	2951109	1	1	—	.015-.063	—	—	1.0	—	500	—	—
1975-76	6771A	1	1	—	.015[a]	—	—	—	⸱	700	—	—
	7138A	1	1	—	.015[a]	—	—	—	—	700	—	—

Note 1—Float setting. (Dry) Float parting line parallel with floor of bowl.
(Wet) Fuel level with bottom of sight plug hole.
Note 2—Setting at full throttle.

Ford

Year	MODEL OR TYPE	Float Level	Fuel Level	Bowl Vent	Pump Travel	Unloader	Housing	Idle Screw	Air Bypass	Idle Speed	Fast Idle	Dashpot
					MODEL 4150							
1976	D5TE-CB	3	1	—	hole 2	—	—	—	—	—	—	—
	D4TE-EAA	3	1	—	2	—	—	—	—	—	—	—
	D4HE-BA	3	1	—	1	—	—	—	—	—	—	—
	D4HE-CA	3	1	—	1	—	—	—	—	—	—	—
	D5HE-CA	3	1	—	1	—	—	—	—	—	—	—
	D4HE-DA	3	1	—	1	—	—	—	—	—	—	—
	D5HE-BA	3	1	—	1	—	—	—	—	—	—	—

Year	MODEL OR TYPE	Float Level (IN.)	Fuel Level (IN.)	Bowl Vent Valve (IN.)	Pump Travel Setting (IN.)	CHOKE SETTING Unloader (IN.)	Housing	Idle Screw Turns Out	ON THE TRUCK ADJUSTMENTS Air Bypass Turns Open	Idle Speed (RPM)	Fast Idle Speed (RPM)	Dashpot Plunger Clearance (IN.)
Ford												
					MODEL 4160							
1975	D5TE-DA	3	1	—	—	.32	Index	—	—	—	top step	—
	D5TE-EA	3	1	—	—	.32	Index	—	—	—	—	—
	D5TE-FA	3	1	—	—	.32	Index	—	—	—	—	—
	D5TE-GA	3	1	—	—	.32	Index	—	—	—	—	—
GMC												
					MODEL 4150G							
1972	R-6292A	1	2	—	.015	—	—	—	—	500	—	—
	R-6293A	1	2	—	.015	—	—	—	—	500	—	—
1973	R6510A	2	4	.060	.015	—	—	3	—	—	1800-2400	—
	R6521A	2	4	—	.015	—	—	3	—	—	1800-2400	—
	R6511A	2	4	.060	.015	—	—	3	—	—	1800-2400	—
	R6522A	2	4	—	.015	—	—	3	—	—	1800-2400	—
1974	R6742A	2	4	.060	.015	—	—	—	—	—	2200	—
	R6743A	2	4	.060	.015	—	—	—	—	—	2200	—
	R6744A	2	4	—	.015	—	—	—	—	—	2200	—
	R6745A	2	4	—	.015	—	—	—	—	—	2200	—
1975-76	R-6928A, R7264A	3	—	.060	hole 1	—	—	—	—	—	2200	—
	R-6929A, R7266A	3	—	.060	1	—	—	—	—	—	2200	—
	R-6930A,	3	—	—	1	—	—	—	—	—	2200	—
	R-6931A,	3	—	—	1	—	—	—	—	—	2200	—

Note 1—Float level. A—Primary—.195. B—Secondary—.250.
Note 2—Lower edge of sight plug hole.
Note 3—Primary—.197, Secondary—.166.
Note 4—Bottom of sight plug.

CARB. MODEL	CARB. PART NO.	Float Level	Pump Link Position	Fuel Level	Idle Mix. Screw Turn Out	Fast Idle Setting	Dashpot Clearance	Choke Setting
International								
1920	4405	1	hole 2	$^{27}/_{32}$	3.0	½-1 turn	.11-.14	—
	4542-1	1	2	$^{27}/_{32}$	3.0	½-1 turn	—	—
	6286	1	2	$^{27}/_{32}$	2.0	½-1 turn	.05-.08	—
	6266	1	2	$^{27}/_{32}$	2.0	½-1 turn	.11-.14	—
	3993-1	1	2	$^{27}/_{32}$	3.0	½-1 turn	.13-.16	—
	4487	1	2	$^{27}/_{32}$	3.0	½-1 turn	.13-.16	—
	4591	1	2	$^{27}/_{32}$	3.0	½-1 turn	.08-.11	—
1940C	6442	2	$^{25}/_{32}$	$^{11}/_{16}$	—	2000 rpm	.07-.09	1 R
2110G	4326	1$^{11}/_{32}$	—	¾	1½-2	—	—	—
2210C	6443	.2	.7	½	—	2200 rpm	.07-.09	Index/2 R[3]
	6443-1	.2	.7	½	—	2200 rpm	.07-.09	Index/2 R[3]
	6776	.2	.7	½	—	2200 rpm	.07-.09	Index
	6620	.2	.7	½	—	2200 rpm	—	1 R
	6674-1	.2	.7	½	—	2200 rpm	.07-.09	—
2300	2997-2, 2976-2	—	—	⅜	3.0	.00	.09-.12	—
	3991-1, 4079-1	—	—	⅜	3.0	.00	.09-.12	—
	4306, 4308	—	—	⅜	3.0	.00	.09-.12	—
	4574	—	—	⅜	3.0	.00	—	—
	4594	—	—	⅜	3.0	.00	.09-.12	—
	4081-1, 4083-1	—	—	⅜	3.0	.00	.09-.12	—
	6379	—	—	⅜	3.0	.00	.08-.11	—
	6391	—	—	⅜	1½-2	.11	—	—

Holley Carburetors

CARB. MODEL	CARB. PART NO.	Float Level	Pump Link Position	Fuel Level	Idle Mix. Screw Turn Out	Fast Idle Setting	Dashpot Clearance	Choke Setting
International								
2300G	2979	—	—	3/8	3.0	.02	—	—
	2980, 2975	—	—	3/8	3.0	.02	—	—
	4310-1, 4311-1	—	—	3/8	1½-2	.02	—	—
2300C	3679-3, 2520-3	—	—	3/8	3.0	—	.09-.12	1 L
	3937-2, 3936-2	—	—	3/8	3.0	—	.09-.12	Index
	4078-1, 4080-1	—	—	3/8	3.0	—	.09-.12	1 L
	4082-1, 4084-1	—	—	3/8	3.0	—	.09-.12	1 L
	4307, 4309	—	—	3/8	3.0	—	.09-.12	1 L
	4593	—	—	3/8	3.0	—	—	Index
	4595	—	—	3/8	3.0	—	.09-.12	Index
	6393	—	—	3/8	1½-2	2000 rpm	—	1 L
	6394	—	—	3/8	1½-2	2000 rpm	.09-.12	1 L
	6380	—	—	3/8	3.0	2000 rpm	.08-.11	4 L/1 L[3]
	6386	—	—	3/8	3.0	2000 rpm	.08-.11	4 L/1 L[3]
4150	4318	—	—	½ 5/8[4]	3.0	.025	—	—
	4237	—	—	½ 5/8[4]	3.0	.025	—	—
	4572	—	—	½ 5/8[4]	3.0	.025	—	—
	4320	—	—	½ 5/8[4]	3.0	.025	.06-.09	—
	4264	—	—	½ 5/8[4]	3.0	.025	.06-.09	—
	4601	—	—	½ 5/8[4]	3.0	.025	.09-.12	—
4150C	4319	—	—	½ 5/8[4]	3.0	.025	—	3 L
	4312	—	—	½ 5/8[4]	3.0	.025	—	2 L
	4599	—	—	½ 5/8[4]	3.0	.025	—	Index
	4313	—	—	½ 5/8[4]	3.0	.025	.06-.09	2 L
	4602	—	—	½ 5/8[4]	3.0	.025	.09-.12	Index
	4321	—	—	½ 5/8[4]	3.0	.025	.06-.09	3 L
4150G	4323	—	—	3/8 5/8[4]	3.0	.025	—	—
	4324	—	—	3/8 5/8[4]	3.0	.025	—	—
4160C	6444	2	.015	½ 5/8[4]	—	.09-.12	.07-.09	Index/2 R[3]
852-FFG	4329, 4330	1¼	—	5/8	1½-2	—	—	—
	6398, 6398-1, 6438	1¼	—	5/8	1½-2	—	—	—
	4438, 4679, 4378	1¼	—	5/8	1½-2	—	—	—
	4331, 4338, 4377, 4332	1¼	—	5/8	1½-2	—	—	—

Note 1—Use special gauge.
Note 2—Flush with top of bowl.
Note 3—Summer/winter.
Note 4—Primary/secondary.

HOLLEY MODEL 1920

Checking float setting

Measuring wet fuel level

Fast idle cam adjustment

Choke vacuum kick setting

HOLLEY MODEL 2300G

Fast idle speed adjustment

Fuel level sight plug location

HOLLEY MODEL 2300G continued

LOCK SCREW

METERING BODY

CHOKE VALVE

FAST IDLE CAM

FUEL LEVEL ADJUSTING NUT

FAST IDLE ADJUSTING SCREW

CURB IDLE ADJUSTING SCREW

GOVERNOR DIAPHRAGM

THROTTLE OPERATING HOUSING

FUEL INLET FITTING

THROTTLE LEVER

FUEL BOWL

ACCELERATING PUMP COVER

ACCELERATING PUMP LEVER

ACCELERATING PUMP OPERATING LEVER

Holley model 2300G carburetor

LOCKNUT

ADJUSTING NUT

GAUGE

ACCELERATING PUMP LEVER

Checking accelerating pump lever clearance

SCREWDRIVER

SIGHT PLUG

WRENCH

GASKET

Adjusting fuel level

HOLLEY MODEL 4150G

Power system

Model 4150G four barrel

Pump system

Fuel inlet system

Idle system

Secondary idle system (idle and low speed)

Main metering system

Secondary throttle operating system

Holley Carburetors

HOLLEY TWO BARREL

Holley two barrel—typical

HOLLEY FOUR BARREL

Holley four barrel—typical

HOLLEY MODEL 852 FFG

THROTTLE VALVE

AIR HORN

CHOKE CABLE BRACKET

CHOKE LEVER

GOVERNOR DIAPHRAGM COVER

MAIN BODY

ACCELERATOR PUMP LINK

THROTTLE OPERATING HOUSING

THROTTLE LEVER

IDLE LIMITER CAPS

THROTTLE BODY

CURB IDLE SPEED ADJUSTING SCREW

THROTTLE OPERATOR SHAFT HOUSING ASSEMBLY

RETAINER SCREWS

Throttle operating housing—removal

PLUGS AND GASKET

Main jet passage plugs

PUMP LINK

Accelerator pump link

FLOAT

MEASURE FLOAT LEVEL HERE

AIR HORN AND FLOAT BOWL COVER ASSEMBLY

X

Setting float level

HOLLEY MODEL 2110 AND 2110G

HOLLEY MODEL 2300

Rochester Carburetors

YEAR	MODEL OR TYPE	FLOAT LEVEL (IN.)	FLOAT DROP (IN.)	PUMP ROD	IDLE VENT
Chevrolet					
		MODEL 2G, 2GC, 2GV			
1970	7040125	$2^3/_{32}$	$1^3/_4$	$1^3/_8$	.027
	7040405	$2^3/_{32}$	$1^3/_4$	$1^3/_8$	.027
	7040108	$2^7/_{32}$	$1^3/_4$	$1^3/_8$	.027
	7040123	$2^3/_{32}$	$1^3/_4$	$1^{17}/_{32}$	.020
	7040124	$2^3/_{32}$	$1^3/_4$	$1^{17}/_{32}$	.020
	7040105	$2^3/_{32}$	$1^3/_4$	$1^3/_8$	.027
	7040425	$2^3/_{32}$	$1^3/_8$	$1^{17}/_{32}$	.020
1971	7041105	$2^1/_{32}$	$1^3/_4$	$1^3/_{64}$	——
	7041111	$2^1/_{32}$	$1^3/_4$	$1^3/_{64}$	——
	7041125	$2^1/_{32}$	$1^3/_4$	$1^3/_{64}$	——
	7041126	$2^1/_{32}$	$1^3/_4$	$1^3/_{64}$	——
	7041138	$2^3/_{32}$	$1^1/_4$	$1^5/_{32}$	——
	7041139	$2^3/_{32}$	$1^1/_4$	$1^5/_{32}$	——
1972	7042102	$2^1/_{32}$	$1^9/_{32}$	$1^5/_{16}$	——
	7042103	$2^1/_{32}$	$1^9/_{32}$	$1^5/_{16}$	——
	7042104	$2^1/_{32}$	$1^9/_{32}$	$1^5/_{16}$	——
	7042105	$2^1/_{32}$	$1^9/_{32}$	$1^5/_{16}$	——

Rochester Carburetors

Chevrolet Truck, Continued

MODEL—2G Cont.

YEAR	MODEL OR TYPE	FLOAT LEVEL (IN.)	FLOAT DROP (IN.)	PUMP ROD	IDLE VENT
	7042108	$2^5/32$	$1^9/32$	$1^1/2$	—
	7042109	$2^5/32$	$1^9/32$	$1^1/2$	—
	7042123	$2^3/32$	$1^9/32$	$1^1/2$	—
	7042124	$2^3/32$	$1^9/32$	$1^1/2$	—
	7042822	$2^1/32$	$1^9/32$	$1^5/16$	—
	7042823	$2^1/32$	$1^9/32$	$1^5/16$	—
	7042824	$2^1/32$	$1^9/32$	$1^5/16$	—
	7042825	$2^1/32$	$1^9/32$	$1^5/16$	—
1973	7043103	$2^1/32$	$1^9/32$	$1^5/16$	—
	7043105	$2^1/32$	$1^9/32$	$1^5/16$	—
	7043108	$2^1/32$	$1^9/32$	$1^7/16$	—
	7043123	$2^3/32$	$1^9/32$	$1^7/16$	—
	7043124	$2^3/32$	$1^9/32$	$1^7/16$	—
	7043424	$2^3/32$	$1^9/32$	$1^7/16$	—
	7047796	$2^3/32$	$1^9/32$	$1^7/16$	—
1974	7044113	$1^9/32$	$1^9/32$	$1^9/32$	—
	7044114	$1^9/32$	$1^9/32$	$1^3/16$	—
	7044123	$1^9/32$	$1^9/32$	$1^9/32$	—
	7044124	$1^9/32$	$1^9/32$	$1^3/16$	—
	7044133	$1^9/32$	$1^9/32$	$1^9/16$	—
	7044134	$1^9/32$	$1^9/32$	$1^7/16$	—
	7044434	$1^9/32$	$1^9/32$	$1^7/16$	—
1975	7045115	$2^1/32$	$3^1/32$	$1^5/8$	—
	7045116	$2^1/32$	$3^1/32$	$1^5/8$	—
	7045123	$2^1/32$	$3^1/32$	$1^5/8$	—
	7045124	$2^1/32$	$3^1/32$	$1^5/8$	—
1975-76	7044133	$1^9/32$	$1^9/32$	$1^9/16$	—
	7044134	$1^9/32$	$1^9/32$	$1^7/16$	—
	7044434	$1^9/32$	$1^9/32$	$1^7/16$	—

MODEL—M & MV

YEAR	MODEL OR TYPE	Float Level (IN.)	Idle Speed Screw Setting	Metering Rod	Choke Rod	Fast Idle (Running)	Idle Vent
1970	7040011	$1/4$	1	.070	.150	2400	—
	7040012	$1/4$	1	.070	.150	2400	—
	7040021	$1/4$	1	.070	.190	2400	—
	7040025	$1/4$	1	.070	.180	2400	—
	7040022	$1/4$	1	.070	.275	2400	—
	7040026	$1/4$	1	.070	.275	2400	—
	7040002	$1/4$	1	.070	.190	2400	—
	7040008	$1/4$	1	.080	.200	2400	—
	7040014	$1/4$	1	.070	.170	2400	—
	7040017	$1/4$	1	.090	.190	2400	—
1971	7041021	$1/4$	1	.080	.180	2400	—
	7041022	$1/4$	1	.070	.300	2400	—
	7041023	$1/16$	1	—	.120	2400	—
	7041024	$1/16$	1	—	.080	2400	—
	7041025	$1/4$	1	.070	.180	2400	—
	7041026	$1/4$	1	.070	.275	2400	—
1972	7042011	$1/4$	1	.070	.150	2400	—
	7042012	$1/4$	1	.070	.150	2400	—
	7042021	$1/4$	1	.078	.150	2400	—
	7042022	$1/4$	1	.079	.125	2400	—
	7042025	$1/4$	1	.070	.180	2400	—
	7042026	$1/4$	1	.070	.275	2400	—
	7042991	$1/4$	1	.076	.150	2400	—
	7042992	$1/4$	1	.078	.125	2400	—

MODEL—M & MV

YEAR	MODEL OR TYPE	Float Level (IN.)	Idle Speed Screw Setting	Metering Rod	Choke Rod	Fast Idle (Running)	Idle Vent
1973	7043021	1/4	1	.080	.275	2400	——
	7043022	1/4	1	.080	.245	2400	——
	7043025	1/4	1	.070	.350	2400	——
	7043026	1/4	1	.070	.375	2400	——
	7043026	1/4	1	.070	.375	2400	——
	7043009	1/4	1	.070	——	1800-2400	——
	7043012	1/4	1	.070	——	1800-2400	——
	7043312	1/4	1	.070	——	1800-2400	——
1974	7044021	.295	——	.080	.275	1800	——
	7044022	.295	——	.080	.245	1800	——
	7044321	.295	——	.080	.300	1800	——
	7044025	1/4	——	.070	.245	2400	——
	7044026	1/4	——	.070	.275	2400	——
	7044011	1/4	——	.070	.150	——	——
	7044012	1/4	——	.070	.150	——	——
1975	7045002	11/32	——	.080	.260	1800	——
	7045003	11/32	——	.080	.275	1800	——
	7045004	11/32	——	.080	.245	1800	——
	7045005	11/32	——	.080	.275	1800	——
	7045302	11/32	——	.080	.245	1800	——
	7045303	11/32	——	.080	.275	1800	——
	7045304	11/32	——	.080	.245	1800	——
	7045305	11/32	——	.080	.275	1800	——
1975-76	7044012	1/4	——	.070	.150	——	——

Note 1—Adjust idle speed screw until it just contacts the lever tang. For automatic transmission add another 1¼ turns and 2 turns for standard transmission.

MODEL—4 MV, 4QJ, M4MC, M4MCA

YEAR	MODEL OR TYPE	Float Level (IN.)	Air Valve Dashpot	Secondary Metering Rod	PUMP ROD Adj.	PUMP ROD Hole	Idle Vent	Fast Idle (Bench)	Choke Rod	Vacuum Break	Choke Unloader	Air Valve Spring Wind-up
1970	7040511	1/4	.020	——	5/16	Inner	——	2 Turns	.100	.245	.450	7/16
	7040513	1/4	.020	——	5/16	Inner	——	2 Turns	.100	.245	.450	7/16
	7040208	1/4	.020	——	5/16	Inner	——	2 Turns	.100	.245	.450	7/16
	7040509	1/4	.020	——	5/16	Inner	——	2 Turns	.100	1	.450	13/16
	7040206	1/4	.020	——	5/16	Inner	——	2 Turns	.100	.245	.450	13/16
1971	7041206	1/4	.020	——	——	——	——	——	.100	.260	.450	——
	7041208	1/4	.020	——	——	——	——	——	.100	.260	.450	——
	7041209	11/32	.020	——	——	——	——	——	.100	.260	.450	——
	7041211	1/4	.020	——	——	——	——	——	.100	.260	.450	——
1972	7042206	7/32	.020	——	——	——	——	——	.100	.250	.450	——
	7042207	5/16	.020	——	13/32	——	——	——	.100	.250	.450	——
	7042208	3/16	.020	——	13/32	——	——	——	.100	.260	.450	——
	7042210	3/16	.020	——	3/8	——	——	——	.100	.215	.450	——
	7042211	3/16	.020	——	3/8	——	——	——	.100	.215	.450	——
	7042218	1/4	.020	——	3/8	——	——	——	.100	.250	.450	——
	7042219	5/16	.020	——	3/8	——	——	——	.100	.260	.450	——
	7042910	3/16	.020	——	3/8	——	——	——	.100	.215	.450	——
	7042911	3/16	.020	——	3/8	——	——	——	.100	.215	.450	——
1973	7043202	7/32	——	——	13/32	——	——	——	——	.215	.450	1/2
	7043203	7/32	——	——	13/32	——	——	——	——	.215	.450	1/2
	7043210	7/32	——	——	13/32	——	——	——	——	.215	.450	1/2
	7043211	7/32	——	——	13/32	——	——	——	——	.215	.450	1/2
	7043208	5/16	——	——	13/32	——	——	——	——	.215	.450	1/2
	7043215	5/16	——	——	13/32	——	——	——	——	.215	.450	1/2
	7043200	1/4	——	——	13/32	——	——	——	——	.250	.450	11/16
	7043216	1/4	——	——	13/32	——	——	——	——	.250	.450	11/16
	7043207	1/4	——	——	13/32	——	——	——	——	.250	.450	11/16
	7043507	1/4	——	——	13/32	——	——	——	——	.275	.450	11/16

MODEL—4 MV, 4QJ, M4MC, M4MCA

YEAR	MODEL OR TYPE	Float Level (IN.)	Air Valve Dashpot	Secondary Metering Rod	PUMP ROD Adj.	PUMP ROD Hole	Idle Vent	Fast Idle (Bench)	Choke Rod	Vacuum Break	Choke Unloader	Air Valve Spring Wind-up
1974	7044202, 7044502	1/4	—	—	13/32	—	—	—	.430	.230	.450	1/8
	7044203, 7044503	1/4	—	—	13/32	—	—	—	.430	.230	.450	7/8
	7044218, 7044518	1/4	—	—	13/32	—	—	—	.430	.215	.450	7/8
	7044219, 7044519	1/4	—	—	13/32	—	—	—	.430	.215	.450	7/8
	7044213, 7044513	11/32	—	—	13/32	—	—	—	.430	.215	.450	7/8
	7044223, 7044227	.675	—	—	13/32	—	—	—	.430	.220	.450	7/16
	7044212, 7044217	.675	—	—	13/32	—	—	—	.430	.230	.450	7/16
	7044512, 7044517	.675	—	—	13/32	—	—	—	.430	.230	.450	7/16
	7044500, 7044520	.675	—	—	13/32	—	—	—	.430	.250	.450	7/16
	7044224	11/32	—	—	13/32	—	—	—	.430	.215	.450	7/8
	7044214, 7044514	11/32	—	—	13/32	—	—	—	.430	.215	.450	7/8
	7044215, 7044515	11/32	—	—	13/32	—	—	—	.430	.215	.450	7/8
	7044216, 7044516	11/32	—	—	13/32	—	—	—	.430	.215	.450	7/8
1975	7045212	3/8	.015	—	.275	Inner	—	—	.430	.225	.450	7/16
	7045213	11/32	.015	—	.275	Inner	—	—	.430	.210	.450	7/8
	7045214	11/32	.015	—	.275	Inner	—	—	.430	.215	.450	7/8
	7045215	11/32	.015	—	.275	Inner	—	—	.430	.215	.450	7/8
	7045216	11/32	.015	—	.275	Inner	—	—	.430	.210	.450	7/8
	7045217	3/8	.015	—	.275	Inner	—	—	.430	.225	.450	7/16
	7045225	11/32	.015	—	.275	Inner	—	—	.430	.200	.450	3/4
	7045229	15/32	.015	—	.275	Inner	—	—	.430	.200	.450	3/4
	7045583	11/32	.015	—	.275	Inner	—	—	.430	.230	.450	7/8
	7045584	11/32	.015	—	.275	Inner	—	—	.430	.230	.450	7/8
	7045585	11/32	.015	—	.275	Inner	—	—	.430	.230	.450	7/8
	7045586	11/32	.015	—	.275	Inner	—	—	.430	.230	.450	7/8
	7045588	11/32	.015	—	.275	Inner	—	—	.430	.230	.450	3/4
	7045589	11/32	.015	—	.275	Inner	—	—	.430	.230	.450	3/4
	7045202	15/32	.015	—	.275	Inner	—	—	.300	.180/.170[2]	.325	7/8
	7045203	15/32	.015	—	.275	Inner	—	—	.300	.180/.170[2]	.325	7/8
	7045218	15/32	.015	—	.275	Inner	—	—	.325	.180/.170[2]	.325	3/4
	7045219	15/32	.015	—	.275	Inner	—	—	.325	.180/.170[2]	.325	3/4
	7045220	17/32	.015	—	.275	Inner	—	—	.300	.200/.550[2]	.325	9/16
	7045512	17/32	.015	—	.275	Inner	—	—	.300	.180/.550[2]	.325	9/16
	7045517	17/32	.015	—	.275	Inner	—	—	.300	.180/.550[2]	.325	9/16

Note 1—Vacuum Break   Auto. Trans.—.245. Stand. Trans.—.275.
Note 2—Front/Rear

YEAR	Carb. Model	Fuel Level (Wet)	Float Level (Dry)	Float Drop	Pump Setting	Idle Vent Setting	Hot Idle Speed (RPM)	Idle Mix Screw Setting	Choke Setting
GMC									
			MODEL—2G						
1970	7040123	—	23/32	1 3/8	1 7/16	—	—	—	—
	7040124	—	23/32	1 3/8	1 7/16	—	—	—	—
1971	7041123	—	23/32	1 3/4	1 5/32	.025	—	—	—
	7041124	—	23/32	1 3/4	1 5/32	.025	—	—	—
1972	7042123	—	23/32	1 9/32	1 1/2	—	—	—	—
	7042124	—	23/32	1 9/32	1 1/2	—	—	—	—

YEAR	Carb. Model	Fuel Level (Wet)	Float Level (Dry)	Float Drop	Pump Setting	Idle Vent Setting	Hot Idle Speed (RPM)	Idle Mix Screw Setting	Choke Setting
GMC, Continued									
			MODEL—2 G						
1973	7043123	——	23/32	19/32	17/16	——	——	——	——
	7043124	——	23/32	19/32	17/16	——	——	——	——
	7043424	——	23/32	19/32	17/16	——	——	——	——
	7047796	——	23/32	19/32	17/16	——	——	——	——
1974-76	7044133	19/32	19/32	19/16	——				
	7044134	19/32	19/32	17/16	——				
	7044434	19/32	19/32	17/16	——				
			MODEL—2GV, 2GC						
1970	7040105	——	23/32	1¾	——	.027	——	——	——
	7040405	——	23/32	1¾	——	.027	——	——	——
	7040108	——	23/32	1¾	——	.027	——	——	——
	7040125	——	23/32	1¾	——	.027	——	——	——
	7040425	——	23/32	1¾	——	.027	——	——	——
1971	7041105	——	21/32	1¾	——	——	——	——	.040
	7041125	——	21/32	1¾	——	——	——	——	.040
	7041138	——	23/32	1¼	——	——	——	——	.100
	7041139	——	23/32	1¼	——	——	——	——	.100
1972	7042102	——	21/32	19/32	15/16	——	——	——	.080
	7042104	——	21/32	19/32	15/16	——	——	——	.080
	7042822	——	21/32	19/32	15/16	——	——	——	.080
	7042824	——	21/32	19/32	15/16	——	——	——	.080
	7042103	——	21/32	19/32	15/16	——	——	——	.110
	7042105	——	21/32	19/32	15/16	——	——	——	.110
	7042823	——	21/32	19/32	15/16	——	——	——	.110
	7042825	——	21/32	19/32	15/16	——	——	——	.110
	7042108	——	25/32	19/32	1½	——	——	——	.170
	7042113	——	23/32	19/32	1½	——	——	——	.100
	7042833	——	23/32	19/32	1½	——	——	——	.100
	7042114	——	23/32	19/32	1½	——	——	——	.100
	7042834	——	23/32	19/32	1½	——	——	——	.100
	7042100	——	25/32	131/32	15/16	——	——	——	.040
	7042820	——	25/32	131/32	15/16	——	——	——	.040
	7042101	——	25/32	131/32	15/16	——	——	——	.075
	7042821	——	25/32	131/32	15/16	——	——	——	.075
1973	7043105	——	21/32	19/32	15/16	——	——	——	.150
	7043103	——	21/32	19/32	15/16	——	——	——	.150
	7043108	——	21/32	19/32	15/16	——	——	——	.200
1974	7044113	19/32	19/32	19/32	——				
	7044114	19/32	19/32	13/16	——				
	7044123	19/32	19/32	19/32	——				
	7044124	19/32	19/32	13/16	——				
1975	7045115	21/32	31/32	1⅝	——				
	7045116	21/32	31/32	1⅝	——				
	7045123	21/32	31/32	1⅝	——				
	7045124	21/32	31/32	1⅝	——				
			MODEL M, MV						
1970 (MV)	7040007	——	¼	——	——	——	——	——	.190
	7040021	——	¼	——	——	——	——	——	.190
	7040022	——	¼	——	——	——	——	——	.275
	7040025	——	¼	——	——	——	——	——	.180
	7040026	——	¼	——	——	——	——	——	.245
1971 (M)	7040011	——	¼	——	——	——	——	——	.100
	7040012	——	¼	——	——	——	——	——	.100
(MV)	7041021	——	¼	——	——	——	——	——	.180
	7041022	——	¼	——	——	——	——	——	.300
	7041025	——	¼	——	——	——	——	——	.180

Rochester Carburetors

YEAR	Carb. Model	Fuel Level (Wet)	Float Level (Dry)	Float Drop	Pump Setting	Idle Vent Setting	Hot Idle Speed (RPM)	Idle Mix Screw Setting	Choke Setting
GMC, Continued									
1971	7041026	—	¼	—	—	—	—	—	.275
1972 (MV)	7042011	—	¼	—	—	—	—	—	.150
	7042012	—	¼	—	—	—	—	—	.150
	7042014	—	¼	—	—	—	—	—	.125
	7042021	—	¼	—	—	—	—	—	.150
	7042022	—	¼	—	—	—	—	—	.125
	7042025	—	¼	—	—	—	—	—	.180
	7042026	—	¼	—	—	—	—	—	.275
	7042991	—	¼	—	—	—	—	—	.150
	7042992	—	¼	—	—	—	—	—	.125
	7042984	—	¼	—	—	—	—	—	.125
	7042987	—	¼	—	—	—	—	—	.150
1973 (M)	7043009	—	¼	—	—	—	—	—	.100
	7043012	—	¼	—	—	—	—	—	.100
	7043312	—	¼	—	—	—	—	—	.100
(MV)	7043021	—	¼	—	—	—	—	—	.275
	7043022	—	¼	—	—	—	—	—	.245
	7043025	—	¼	—	—	—	—	—	.350
	7043026	—	¼	—	—	—	—	—	.375
1974 (MV)	7044021	—	.295	—	—	—	—	—	.275
	7044022	—	.295	—	—	—	—	—	.245
	7044321	—	.295	—	—	—	—	—	.300
	7044025	—	¼	—	—	—	—	—	.245
	7044026	—	¼	—	—	—	—	—	.275
(M)	7044011	—	¼	—	—	—	—	—	.150
	7044012	—	¼	—	—	—	—	—	.150
1975 (MV)	7045002	—	¹¹⁄₃₂	—	—	—	—	—	.260
	7045003	—	¹¹⁄₃₂	—	—	—	—	—	.275
	7045004	—	¹¹⁄₃₂	—	—	—	—	—	.245
	7045005	—	¹¹⁄₃₂	—	—	—	—	—	.275
	7045302	—	¹¹⁄₃₂	—	—	—	—	—	.245
	7045303	—	¹¹⁄₃₂	—	—	—	—	—	.275
	7045304	—	¹¹⁄₃₂	—	—	—	—	—	.245
	7045305	—	¹¹⁄₃₂	—	—	—	—	—	.275
1975-76 (M)	7044012	—	¼	—	—	—	—	—	.150

MODEL 4MV, 4QJ, M4MC, M4MCA

YEAR	Carb. Model	Fuel Level (Wet)	Float Level (Dry)	Float Drop	Pump Setting	Idle Vent Setting	Hot Idle Speed (RPM)	Idle Mix Screw Setting	Choke Setting
1970 (4MV)	7040511	—	¼	—	—	⅜	—	—	—
	7040208	—	¼	—	—	⅜	—	—	—
	7040206	—	¼	—	—	⅜	—	—	—
	7040509	—	¼	—	—	⅜	—	—	—
1971 (4MV)	7041208	—	¼	—	—	—	—	—	.100
	7041211	—	¼	—	—	—	—	—	.100
	7041206	—	¼	—	—	—	—	—	.100
	7041209	—	¹¹⁄₃₂	—	—	—	—	—	.100
1972 (4MV)	7042202	—	¼	—	⅜	—	—	—	.100
	7042203	—	¼	—	⅜	—	—	—	.100
	7042206	—	¼	—	¹³⁄₃₂	—	—	—	.100
	7042207	—	¹¹⁄₃₂	—	¹³⁄₃₂	—	—	—	.100
	7042208	—	³⁄₁₆	—	⅜	—	—	—	.100
	7042210	—	³⁄₁₆	—	⅜	—	—	—	.100
	7042211	—	³⁄₁₆	—	⅜	—	—	—	.100
	7042215	—	¼	—	⅜	—	—	—	.100
	7042218	—	¼	—	⅜	—	—	—	.100
	7042219	—	¹¹⁄₃₂	—	⅜	—	—	—	.100
	7042220	—	¼	—	⅜	—	—	—	.100
	7042902	—	¼	—	⅜	—	—	—	.100
	7042903	—	¼	—	⅜	—	—	—	.100

YEAR	Carb. Model	Fuel Level (Wet)	Float Level (Dry)	Float Drop	Pump Setting	Idle Vent Setting	Hot Idle Speed (RPM)	Idle Mix Screw Setting	Choke Setting
GMC, Continued									
MODEL 4MV, 4QJ, M4MC, M4MCA									
1972 (4MV)	7042910	—	$3/16$	—	$3/8$	—	—	—	.100
	7042911	—	$3/16$	—	$3/8$	—	—	—	.100
1973 (4QJ)	7043200	—	$1/4$	—	$13/32$ [6]	—	—	—	.430
	7043202	—	$7/32$	—	$13/32$ [6]	—	—	—	.430
	7043203	—	$7/32$	—	$13/32$ [6]	—	—	—	.430
	7043207	—	$1/4$	—	$13/32$ [6]	—	—	—	.430
	7043208	—	$5/16$	—	$13/32$ [6]	—	—	—	.430
	7043210	—	$7/32$	—	$13/32$ [6]	—	—	—	.430
	7043211	—	$7/32$	—	$13/32$ [6]	—	—	—	.430
	7043215	—	$5/16$	—	$13/32$ [6]	—	—	—	.430
	7043216	—	$1/4$	—	$13/32$ [6]	—	—	—	.430
	7043507	—	$1/4$	—	$13/32$ [6]	—	—	—	.430
1974 (4QJ)	7044202, 7044502	—	$1/4$	—	$13/32$	—	—	—	.430
	7044203, 7044503	—	$1/4$	—	$13/32$	—	—	—	.430
	7044218, 7044518	—	$1/4$	—	$13/32$	—	—	—	.430
	7044219, 7044519	—	$1/4$	—	$13/32$	—	—	—	.430
	7044213, 7044513	—	$11/32$	—	$13/32$	—	—	—	.430
	7044223, 7044227	—	.675	—	$13/32$	—	—	—	.430
	7044212, 7044217	—	.675	—	$13/32$	—	—	—	.430
	7044512, 7044517	—	.675	—	$13/32$	—	—	—	.430
	7044500, 7044520	—	.675	—	$13/32$	—	—	—	.430
	7044224	—	$11/32$	—	$13/32$	—	—	—	.430
	7044214, 7044514	—	$11/32$	—	$13/32$	—	—	—	.430
	7044215, 7044515	—	$11/32$	—	$13/32$	—	—	—	.430
	7044216, 7044516	—	$11/32$	—	$13/32$	—	—	—	.430
1975 (4MV)	7045212	—	$3/8$	—	.275	—	—	—	.430
	7045213	—	$11/32$	—	.275	—	—	—	.430
	7045214	—	$11/32$	—	.275	—	—	—	.430
	7045215	—	$11/32$	—	.275	—	—	—	.430
	7045216	—	$11/32$	—	.275	—	—	—	.430
	7045217	—	$3/8$	—	.275	—	—	—	.430
	7045225	—	$11/32$	—	.275	—	—	—	.430
	7045229	—	$15/32$	—	.275	—	—	—	.430
	7045583	—	$11/32$	—	.275	—	—	—	.430
	7045584	—	$11/32$	—	.275	—	—	—	.430
	7045585	—	$11/32$	—	.275	—	—	—	.430
	7045586	—	$11/32$	—	.275	—	—	—	.430
	7045588	—	$11/32$	—	.275	—	—	—	.430
	7045589	—	$11/32$	—	.275	—	—	—	.430
(M4MC)	7045202	—	$15/32$	—	.275	—	—	—	.300
	7045203	—	$15/32$	—	.275	—	—	—	.300
	7045218	—	$15/32$	—	.275	—	—	—	.325
	7045219	—	$15/32$	—	.275	—	—	—	.325
	7045220	—	$17/32$	—	.275	—	—	—	.300
(M4MCA)	7045512	—	$17/32$	—	.275	—	—	—	.300
	7045517	—	$17/32$	—	.275	—	—	—	.300

Note 6—Pump rod location: Inner.

ROCHESTER MODEL 2G

GAUGE FROM GASKET SURFACE TO BOTTOM OF FLOAT

BEND TANG TO ADJUST

Float drop adjustment

BEND HERE TO ADJUST

GAUGE FROM TOE OF FLOAT AT SHARP EDGE OF SEAM TO AIR HORN GASKET

Float level adjustment

ACCELERATOR PUMP LEVER

CHOKE ROD

THROTTLE LEVER

IDLE SPEED SCREW

ROCHESTER model 2G carburetor

GAUGE FROM TOP OF AIR HORN RING TO TOP OF PUMP ROD

BEND PUMP ROD TO ADJUST

THROTTLE VALVES FULLY CLOSED

Accelerator pump rod adjustment

ROCHESTER MODELS M AND MV

IDLE SPEED SCREW

IDLE MIXTURE SCREW

Rochester monojet carburetor

TURN VALVE TO ADJUST

GAUGE BETWEEN BOTTOM OF VALVE AND TOP OF AIR HORN

Idle vent adjustment

ROCHESTER MODELS M AND MV

Fast idle adjustment

Float level adjustment

ROCHESTER MODEL 4MV

Rochester 4MV carburetor

ROCHESTER MODEL 4MV continued

HOLD RETAINER FIRMLY IN PLACE

GAUGE FROM TOP OF CASTING TO TOP OF FLOAT AT TOE.

PUSH FLOAT DOWN LIGHTLY AGAINST NEEDLE

BEND FLOAT UP OR DOWN TO ADJUST

Float level adjustment

CAM FOLLOWER ON HIGH STEP OF FAST IDLE CAM

PRIMARY THROTTLE VALVE CLOSED

AFTER SCREW MAKES CONTACT ON LEVER, TURN SCREW TO ADJUST.

Fast idle adjustment

GAUGE FROM TOP OF CHOKE VALVE WALL, NEXT TO VENT STACK, TO TOP OF PUMP STEM

BEND PUMP LEVER TO ADJUST

ROD IN SPECIFIED HOLE OF PUMP LEVER.

THROTTLE VALVES COMPLETELY CLOSED

Pump rod adjustment

ROD IN BOTTOM OF SLOT

GAUGE BETWEEN AIR HORN WALL AND LOWER EDGE OF CHOKE VALVE

DIAPHRAGM SEATED

BEND TANG TO ADJUST

PUSH UP LIGHTLY ON VACUUM BREAK LEVER UNTIL TANG CONTACTS ROD

Vacuum break adjustment

ROD IN BOTTOM OF SLOT

SPECIFIED GAUGE BETWEEN WALL AND LOWER EDGE OF CHOKE VALVE

BEND CHOKE ROD TO ADJUST

ROTATE VACUUM BREAK LEVER DOWNWARD

CAM FOLLOWER ON SECOND STEP OF CAM

Choke rod adjustment

OPEN PRIMARY THROTTLE UNTIL ACTUATING LINK CONTACTS TANG

BEND TANG TO ADJUST

.070 GAUGE

LINK SHOULD BE IN CENTER OF SLOT

Secondary opening adjustment

ROCHESTER MODEL 4MV continued

WITH LOCK SCREW LOOSENED AND WITH AIR VALVE CLOSED, TURN ADJUSTING SCREW SPECIFIED NUMBER OF TURNS AFTER SPRING CONTACTS PIN. TIGHTEN LOCK SCREW.

LOCK SCREW

ADJUSTING SCREW

Air valve spring adjustment

CHOKE VALVE WIDE OPEN

LEVER AGAINST TANG

.020 GAUGE

SCREW MUST BE SET AT PROPER R.P.M.

BEND TANG TO ADJUST

Secondary closing adjustment

HOLD CHOKE VALVE WIDE OPEN BY ROTATING VACUUM BREAK LEVER TOWARDS OPEN CHOKE *(clockwise)*

.015 CLEARANCE

BEND LEVER TO ADJUST

CHOKE VALVE CLOSED

BEND PIN TO ADJUST

.015 MAX. CLEARANCE

SECONDARY LOCKOUT OPENING CLEARANCE
①

SECONDARY LOCKOUT LEVER SIDE CLEARANCE
②

Secondary lockout adjustment

MEASURE FROM CASTING SURFACE NEXT TO AIR CLEANER STUD HOLE TO TOP OF METERING ROD

BEND HANGER AT THIS POINT TO ADJUST

Secondary metering adjustment

VENT VALVE ARM MUST CONTACT BI-METAL STRIP AT THIS POINT.

GAUGE FROM TOP OF CHOKE VALVE WALL, NEXT TO VENT STACK, TO TOP OF PUMP STEM AS SPECIFIED.

VENT VALVE CLOSED

BEND WIRE TANG TO ADJUST

OPEN PRIMARY THROTTLE TO A POINT WHERE IDLE VENT VALVE ARM JUST CONTACTS BI-METAL STRIP AT VALVE.

Idle vent adjustment

AIR VALVE COMPLETELY CLOSED

BEND HERE FOR SPECIFIED CLEARANCE BETWEEN ROD AND END OF SLOT

DIAPHRAGM SEATED

Air valve dashpot adjustment

Dodge/Plymouth

MODEL WW3

YEAR	Model or Type	Float Level	Fast Idle Cam Position	Vacuum Kick	Choke Setting	Bowl Vent	Choke Unloader	Fast Idle Speed	Idle Mix. Screw Adjust
1970-72	310	7/32	—	—	—	—	—	—	1 1/8
	308	7/32	—	—	—	—	—	—	1 7/8
	283	7/32	—	—	—	.060	—	—	1 1/4
	287	7/32	.089	.221	2 R	.060	15/64	700	1 1/4
	298	7/32	.089	.094	2 R	.060	15/64	700	1 1/4
	300	7/32	—	—	—	.050	—	—	1 1/2
	302	7/32	—	—	—	.050	—	—	1 1/2
	303, 304	7/32	—	—	—	—	5/16	1400	1 1/4-1 3/8 1 1/2
	299	7/32	.161	—	Index	.050	5/16	1400	1 1/2
	301	7/32	.161	—	Index	.050	5/16	1400	1 1/2

Chevrolet

MODEL WW, WWC

YEAR	Carb. Model	Fuel Level (Wet)	Float Level (Dry)	Float Drop	Hot Idle Speed (RPM)	Pump Setting	Idle Mix. Screw Setting	Idle Vent Setting	Choke Setting
1973	23-257	—	3/16	—	—	.97	—	—	—
	23-258	—	3/16	—	—	.97	—	—	—
	23-259	—	7/32	—	—	.28	—	—	—
	23-260	—	7/32	—	—	.28	—	—	—
1974	23-264	—	.22	—	—	.97	—	—	—
	23-265	—	.22	—	—	.68	—	—	—

GMC

MODEL WW

1970-71	671829	—	.190	—	—	.420-.450	—	—	—
1972	23-244	—	.190	—	—	.420-.450	—	—	—
	23-248	—	.190	—	—	.420-.450	—	—	—
1973	23-257	—	3/16	—	—	.97	—	—	—
	23-258	—	3/16	—	—	.97	—	—	—
1974	23-264	—	.22	—	—	.97	—	—	—

MODEL WWC

1973	23-259	—	7/32	—	—	.28	—	—	—
	23-260	—	7/32	—	—	.28	—	—	—
1974	23-265	—	.22	—	—	.68	—	—	—

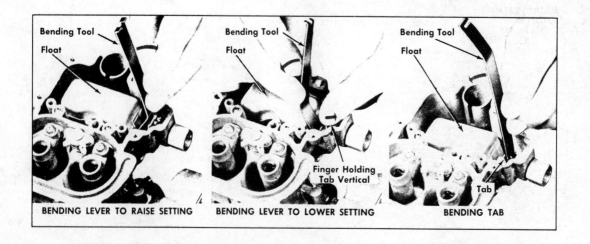

Float level adjustment Type WW-3 carburetor

STROMBERG TYPE—WW3

ACCELERATOR PUMP PLUNGER STEM

CHOKE LEVER

ACCELERATOR PUMP ROCKER ARM

FAST IDLE LINK

CHOKE LEVER RETAINING SCREW

ACCELERATOR PUMP ROD

IDLE SPEED ADJUSTING SCREW

THROTTLE LEVER

CHOKE VALVE

AIR HORN

MAIN BODY

VACUUM ADVANCE TUBE FITTING

THROTTLE BODY

CLOSED CRANKCASE VENT TUBE FITTING

Type WW-3 carburetor

FLOAT LEVEL GAUGE

Checking float setting

LIGHT CLOSING PRESSURE AGAINST CHOKE VALVE

FAST IDLE ROD (BEND AT ANGLE)

FAST IDLE CAM

DRILL OR GAUGE

FAST IDLE SPEED ADJUSTING SCREW

CAM

SCREW

FAST IDLE SPEED ADJUSTING SCREW ON LOWEST STEP OF FAST IDLE CAM

Fast idle cam adjustment

LIGHT CLOSING PRESSURE AGAINST CHOKE VALVE

DRILL OR GAUGE

THROTTLE AT WIDE OPEN POSITION

BEND THROTTLE LEVER TANG

Unloader adjustment (wide open kick)

CHOKE VALVE WIDE OPEN

FAST IDLE SPEED ADJUSTING SCREW ON THE SLOWEST SPEED STEP ON THE CAM

CAM

FAST IDLE CAM

SCREW

Fast idle speed adjustment (on vehicle)

Diagnosis Guide

Symptoms—Rough Idle
Fuel System

1. Leak in vacuum system (lines, connections, diaphragms, etc.).
2. Engine idle too low.
3. Idle fuel mixture incorrect.
4. Air leaks at manifold, carburetor, etc.
5. Power valve leaking fuel.
6. Idle fuel system air bleeds or fuel passages restricted.
7. Secondary throttle not closing (4-V carburetor).
8. Float setting incorrect.
9. Hot and cold air intake system stuck in Heat On position.

Ignition System

1. Defective or poorly adjusted points.
2. Poorly functioning spark plugs.
3. Incorrect ignition timing.
4. Insufficient secondary voltage at plug wires.

Exhaust System

1. Exhaust control valve inoperative (if so equipped).

Engine

1. Leak in vacuum system (lines, connections, diaphragms, etc.).
2. Air leaks at manifold, carburetor, etc.
3. Poor compression (head gasket, exhaust or intake valve leaks, failure of rings, cracked or broken piston, etc.).

4. Inoperative crankcase ventilator (PCV) valve, or restricted tubing.
5. Improperly adjusted valve tappets.
6. Worn camshaft lobes.
7. Incorrect valve timing.

Overheating at Idle

With engine operating, check warning light, or temperature gauge. Trouble could develop in the distributor vacuum control valve (temperature sensing valve).

Engine Stalls
Fuel System

1. Idle speed too low.
2. Idle mixture out of adjustment.
3. Carburetor fast idle too low.
4. Choke out of calibration or adjustment.
5. Choke mechanism binding.
6. Float level too high.
7. Interference with fuel flow.
8. Bad fuel pump.
9. Obstructed fuel lines or tank vent.
10. Carburetor icing.
11. Vapor lock.
12. Inoperative carburetor dashpot.

Engine Noises
Thermactor Pump

The thermactor pump, like any air pump, may produce a detectable sound. This noise should not, however, be of a level audible to anyone within the passenger compartment.

A new air pump, until broken in, may produce a slight squealing or chirping sound.

If pump noise is objectionable, check the following:

1. Drive belt alignment and tension.
2. Loose mounting.
3. Hoses disconnected or leaking.
4. Interference of hoses and body.
5. Defective centrifugal filter fan.
6. Defective relief valve.
7. Improper pressure-setting plug, broken spring, or plug missing. If, after checking the above noise factors, the trouble still persists, replace or repair the pump.

Ignition

1. Ignition, initial timing, too far advanced.
2. Poor engine mounting.
3. Leaking cylinder head gasket.
4. Crankcase ventilator circuit inoperative (stuck open or closed).
5. Poor compression, valves, tappet clearance, or piston and ring assemblies.
6. Worn camshaft lobes.
7. Incorrect valve timing.

Exhaust System

1. Air by-pass valve vacuum line collapsed, plugged, disconnected or leaking, causing backfire.
2. Malfunctioning air by-pass valve, causing backfire.
3. Malfunctioning distributor vacuum advance control valve, causing backfire.
4. Exhaust system leak.

General

With emission level maintenance standards getting stricter on both the State and Federal levels, proper testing and adjustment of emission control systems are becoming increasingly important. Much confusion results from the many types and combinations of emission control systems currently in use.

This section covers testing and adjustment of the emission control systems and their individual components. Many of the components are similar (or the same) from one manufacturer to another and therefore the testing procedures are the same. Thus, one test may be used for several different manufacturers or models. Where components, although similar, differ significantly the tests are different.

For the sake of added clarity, a general description of the various types of emission control systems follows.

Positive Crankcase Ventilation (PCV) Systems

A simple valve, operated by intake manifold vacuum, is used to meter the flow of air and vapors through the crankcase. Air is drawn in through the carburetor air cleaner. When the vehicle is decelerating or the engine is idling, high manifold vacuum closes the valve; this restricts the flow of crankcase vapor into the intake manifold. During acceleration or at a constant speed, the intake manifold vacuum drops, the valve spring forces the valve open and more vapors flow into the intake manifold from the crankcase. If a backfire occurs the valve closes, preventing the vapor in the crankcase from being ignited. If the vapor is ignited, an explosion will result.

Air Injection System

A belt-driven air pump supplies air to an injection manifold which has a nozzle positioned behind each exhaust valve. Injection of air at this point causes combustion of any unburned hydrocarbons in the exhaust manifold rather than allowing them to escape into the atmosphere. An antibackfire valve controls the flow of air from the pump to prevent backfires resulting from an overly rich mixture under closed throttle conditions. A check valve, sometimes an integral part of the air injection manifold, functions to prevent hot exhaust gas backflow into the pump and hoses in case of pump failure or when the antibackfire valve is working.

Thermostatically Controlled Air Cleaner

Thermostatically controlled air cleaners are used to improve operation of the engine and to prevent carburetor icing during warm-up in cold weather.

A movable door in the air cleaner snorkle allows air to be drawn in from either a manifold heat stove (cold operation) or from under the hood (normal operation). The door may be operated by a bimetallic spring or a vacuum motor. Doors of both types may use a vacuum override to provide cold air intake during periods of hard acceleration when stove-heated air is normally being supplied.

Distributor Controls

There are three basic types of distributor controls:

1. Engine vacuum controls
2. Transmission-controlled spark —transmission gear selected and/or temperature.
3. Speed-controlled spark—vehicle speed and/or temperature.

It is easier to consider these three types separately, although some of them perform similar functions and may be used in conjunction with one another.

Engine Vacuum Controls

Many small valves and solenoids fall into this class of emission controls. Some distributors are equipped with a dual-diaphragm vacuum unit which retards the spark during closed throttle deceleration and idle. On some distributors, solenoids may be used to either advance or retard the timing under predetermined conditions.

A deceleration valve may be used to provide maximum vacuum advance when the car is slowing down, by sending intake manifold vacuum to the distributor vacuum unit. By doing this, emissions may be better controlled during deceleration.

Because emission-controlled engines run hotter, it is often necessary to use a coolant temperature vacuum valve to provide additional vacuum advance when the engine is overheated. The valve is threaded into an engine coolant passage. If the engine overheats, the additional vacuum advance causes the engine speed to increase; allowing it to cool down quite rapidly. A similar valve may also be used to determine the temperature at which a TCS, SCS, or EGR system operates (see below).

A spark delay valve is installed on some engines to prevent the vacuum advance from working immediately under heavy acceleration.

Transmission-Controlled Spark (TCS) System

Many variations of transmission-controlled spark (TCS) systems are used to control vehicle emissions. The basic components of these systems are: a transmission switch, which is operated either by oil pressure (automatic transmissions) or by the gear selected (manual transmission); and a vacuum solenoid. The solenoid allows vacuum to be supplied to the distributor vacuum unit or ports it into the atmosphere. Usually vacuum is supplied only in high gear and is ported in the lower gears. However, few TCS systems are quite this simple.

For example, most TCS systems use some type of temperature switch to control their operation, i.e., the system will not function below a specified air or engine temperature. In some cases it will not work above a specified temperature either. Some cars use a coolant temperature-operated vacuum valve in conjunction with the TCS system.

Various reversing and time delay relays may also be used, depending upon the needs of the engine and transmission.

Speed-Controlled Spark (SCS) Systems

Speed-controlled spark (SCS) systems perform a similar function to the transmission-controlled systems above. Many of the components are the same and used in similar way in both of the systems. The major difference lies in the switch which is activated by the speed, rather than the gear.

In its simplest form, this switch is nothing more than a centrifugal switch, connected to the speedometer drive, which completes the SCS circuit at or above a predetermined speed. A more complicated type of switch uses a small speedometer gear (or speedometer cable) driven pulse generator to send a signal to an amplifier, which, in turn, completes the SCS system circuit at predetermined speed.

Once the circuit has been completed, vacuum is allowed to flow to the distributor vacuum unit. When the circuit is not energized, vacuum is ported into the atmosphere.

Like the transmission-controlled spark systems, SCS systems use temperature switches and various relays.

Road Speed-Controlled Vacuum Spark Advance System (SCS)

This is a vacuum operated, speedometer cable actuated spark delay system. Distributor spark advance is controlled by a road speed sensor driven in line by the speedometer cable. Advance is delayed until the vehicle reaches 23 mph, with manual transmission and 31 mph, with automatic transmission.

Prior to advance cut-in, a control valve in the speed sensor is held by spring pressure allowing air from the air cleaner to pass through the sensor by way of a connecting hose and through another hose into the intake manifold. This air flow blocks the vacuum advance which must pass through the sensor by means of connecting hoses.

Carburetor Controls

Because of the increase in engine speed necessary to control emissions at idle, dieseling has become a problem. As a result, many carburetors use a solenoid to allow the throttle to close when the ignition is shut off, thus reducing engine speed which, in turn, prevents dieseling.

To prevent dieseling on some air-conditioned cars, a signal from an amplifier engages the A/C compressor clutch momentarily when the engine is shut off. This puts a load on the engine, thus slowing it down.

Evaporative Emission Control Systems

To control emissions resulting from fuel evaporation, all trucks made after 1971 use a closed fuel supply system. Instead of fuel vapor being vented into the atmosphere, it goes into a vapor/liquid separator and is routed from there, either directly through a charcoal storage canister, or into the crankcase. To prevent vapor loss at other points, the carburetor has controlled vents and a PCV system (see above) is used along with the evaporative emission control system.

Exhaust Gas Recirculation (EGR)

Exhaust gas recirculation (EGR) systems are used to reduce NO_x emissions by lowering peak flame temperature during combustion. Exhaust gases are routed into the intake manifold via floor jets, intake manifold passages, and/or an EGR control valve. This valve may be located either on the intake manifold or on a special carburetor spacer.

Some EGR systems use coolant temperature-operated vacuum valves or air temperature-operated valves to determine when they function. In addition, a vacuum amplifier (mechanical) may be provided if a weak vacuum signal is being supplied to the EGR valve.

Catalytic Converters

Starting 1975, all trucks rated under 6000 lb GVW, sold in California are equipped with catalytic converters, as are some of the trucks sold in the rest of the U.S. The converters are used to oxidize hydrocarbons (HC) and carbon monoxide (CO). They are necessary because of even stricter emission standards for the 1975-76 models.

The catalysts are made of noble metals (platinum and palladium) which are bonded to either a monolithic (one-piece) element or to individual pellets. The catalyst causes the HC and CO to break down without taking part in the reaction; hence, a catalyst life of 50,000 miles is expected.

Vacuum-Operated Heat Risers

Starting 1975, some Ford and GM engines have a vacuum-operated heat riser (manifold heat valve). These valves replace the bimetallic spring operated valves which have been previously used.

Positive Crankcase Ventilation (PCV) System

Valve Tests

1. See if any deposits are present in the carburetor passages, the oil filler cap, or the hoses. Clean these as required.
2. Connect a tachometer, as instructed by its manufacturer, to the engine.
3. With the engine idling, do one of the following:
   a. Remove the PCV valve hose from the crankcase or the oil filler connection.
   b. On cars with the PCV valve located in a grommet on the valve cover, remove both the valve and the grommet.
   NOTE: If the valve and the

PCV valve (typical)

hoses are not clogged-up, a hissing sound should be present.
4. Check the tachometer reading Place a finger over the valve or hose opening (a suction should be felt).
5. Check the tachometer again. The engine speed should have dropped at least 50 rpm. It should return to normal when the finger is removed from the

opening.
6. If the engine does not change speed or if the change is less than 50 rpm, the hose is clogged or the valve is defective. Check the hose first. If the hose is not clogged, replace, do not attempt to repair, the PCV valve.
7. Test the new valve in the above manner, to make sure that it is operating properly.
   NOTE: There are several commercial PCV valve testers available. Be sure that the one used is suitable for the valve to be tested, as the testers are not universal. Follow the manufacturer's instructions.

air injection systems

Air Pump Tests

CAUTION: Do not hammer on, pry, or bend the pump housing while tightening the drive belt or testing the pump.

Belt Tension and Air Leaks

1. Before proceeding with the tests, check the pump drive belt tension to see if it is within specifications.
2. Turn the engine by hand. If it has seized, the belt will slip, producing noise. Disregard any chirping, squealing, or rolling sounds from inside the pump; these are normal when it is turned by hand.
3. Check the hoses and connections for leaks. Hissing or a blast of air is indicative of a leak. Soapy water, applied lightly around the area in question, is a good method for detecting leaks.

Air Output Tests

1. Disconnect the air supply hose at the antibackfire valve.
2. Connect a vacuum gauge, using a suitable adaptor, to the air supply hose. NOTE: If there are two hoses plug the second one up.
3. With the engine at normal operating temperature, increase the idle speed and watch the vacuum gauge.
4. The air flow from the pump should be steady and fall between 26 psi. If it is unsteady or falls below this, the pump is defective and must be replaced.

Pump Noise Diagnosis

The air pump is normally noisy; as

Air Injection Systems

Air injection reactor pump

engine speed increases, the noise of the pump will rise in pitch. The rolling sound the pump bearings make is normal, however, if this sound becomes objectionable at certain speeds, the pump is defective and will have to be replaced.

A continual hissing sound from the air pump pressure relief valve at idle, indicates a defective valve. Replace the relief valve.

If the pump rear bearing fails, a continual knocking sound will be heard. Since the rear bearing is not separately replaceable, the pump will have to replaced as an assembly.

Antibackfire Valve Tests

There are two different types of antibackfire valves used with air injection systems. A by-pass (diverter) valve is used on most current engines, while most older engines use a gulp type antibackfire valve. Test procedures for both types are given below.

Gulp Valve

1. Detach the air supply hose which runs between the pump and the

gulp valve.
2. Connect a tachometer and run the engine between 1,500-2,000 rpm.
3. Allow the throttle to snap closed. This should produce a loud sucking sound from the gulp valve.
4. Repeat this operation several times. If no sound is present, the valve is not working or the vacuum connections are loose.
5. Check the vacuum connections. If they are secure, replace the gulp valve.

By-pass (Diverter) Valve (except 1975-76 Ford)

1. Detach the hose, which runs from the by-pass valve to the check valve, at the by-pass valve hose connection.
2. Connect a tachometer to the engine. With the engine running at normal idle speed, check to see that air is flowing from the by-pass valve hose connection.
3. Speed the engine up, so that it is running at 1,500-2,000 rpm. Allow the throttle to snap shut.

The flow of air from the by-pass valve at the check valve hose connection should stop momentarily and air should then flow from the exhaust port on the valve body or the silencer assembly.

4. Repeat step three several times. If the flow of air is not diverted into the atmosphere from the valve exhaust port or if it fails to stop flowing from the hose connection, check the vacuum lines and connections. If these are tight, the valve is defective and requires replacement.

5. A leaking diaphragm will cause the air to flow out both the hose connection and the exhaust port at the same time. If this happens, replace the valve.

By-Pass Valve—1975-76 Ford

1. Allow the engine to reach normal operating temperature. Put the transmission in Neutral (N) or Park (P) and apply the parking brake.

2. Stop the engine. Remove the by-pass valve-to-check valve hose from the by-pass valve. On V6s and V8s, remove both hoses.

3. Install a tachometer and start the engine.

4. Hold your hand over the by-pass valve hose connection(s) and increase the engine speed to 1500 rpm. Air should flow from the hose connection(s).

5. Remove and plug the by-pass valve vacuum hose. Increase the engine speed to 1500 rpm. No air should flow from the hose connections. Instead, air should flow out the exhaust ports in the silencer cover.

6. If the by-pass valve fails the preceeding tests, replace it.

AIR INJECTION SYSTEM DIAGNOSIS CHART

Problem	Cause	Cure
1. Noisy drive belt	1a Loose belt	1a Tighten belt
	1b Seized pump	1b Replace
2. Noisy pump	2a Leaking hose	2a Trace and fix leak
	2b Loose hose	2b Tighten hose clamp
	2c Hose contacting other parts	2c Reposition hose
	2d Diverter or check valve failure	2d Replace
	2e Pump mouting loose	2e Tighten securing bolts
	2g Defective pump	2g Replace
3. No air supply	3a Loose belt	3a Tighten belt
	3b Leak in hose or at fitting	3b Trace and fix leak
	3c Defective anti-backfire valve	3c Replace
	3d Defective check valve	3d Replace
	3e Defective pump	3e Replace
4. Exhaust backfire	4a Vacuum or air leaks	4a Trace and fix leak
	4b Defective anti-backfire valve	4b Replace
	4c Sticking choke	4c Service choke
	4d Choke setting rich	4d Adjust choke

7. Stop the engine. Remove the tachometer and reconnect all hoses. If you are going to perform the air injection decel valve test, leave the tachometer in place.

Check Valve Test

1. Before starting the test, check all of the hoses and connections for leaks.

2. Detach the air supply hose(s) from the check valve(s).

3. Insert a suitable probe into the check valve and depress the plate. Release it; the plate should return to its original position against the valve seat. If binding is evident, replace the valve.

4. Repeat step three if two valves are used.

5. With the engine running at normal operating temperature, gradually increase its speed to 1,500 rpm. Check for exhaust gas leakage. If any is present, re-

place the valve assembly.

NOTE: Vibration and flutter of the check valve at idle speed is a normal condition and does not mean that the valve should be replaced.

International Harvester

A.I.R. Function Test

1. Inspect filter for clogging. Replace if necessary.

2. Disconnect one air hose from anti-backfire valve.

3. Operate engine at 1,500 rpm.

4. If no air flow is felt at the anti-backfire valve, check for air at the pump exhaust valve silencer. If air exhausts continuously, replace the anti-backfire valve. If no air proceeds from the pump with the anti-backfire valve removed and the engine running, replace the pump.

5. If air flow was felt in the first part of step 4, remove the vacuum hose from the anti-backfire

Air injection reactor system

Air injection tubes

IN LINE

AIR MANIFOLD ASSEMBLY

CHECK VALVE

INJECTION TUBE

CHECK VALVE

V-8

AIR MANIFOLD ASSEMBLY

ENGINE EXHAUST VALVES

COMBUSTION PIPE ASSEMBLY

CHECK VALVE

PIPE EXTENSION (THRU MANIFOLD OR CYLINDER HEAD)

CARBURETOR

MUFFLER

FRESH AIR

AIR PUMP

DIVERTER VALVE (IN OPEN POSITION)

Schematic of A.I.R. system

valve. If no vacuum is felt in the hose, stop the engine and check for restrictions in the hose or fittings.

6. Resume the 1,500 rpm idle speed and reconnect the vacuum hose to the anti-backfire valve. Air flow should momentarily stop at the outlet and occur for a brief time at the silencer, then resume, after a few seconds, at the outlet. If not, replace the valve.

1975-76 Ford Differential Vacuum Valve Test

The differential vacuum valve is only used on air injection systems on models with catalytic converters.

Perform the by-pass valve test prior to this test.

1. Allow the engine to reach normal operating temperature. Put transmission in Park (P) or Neutral (N) and apply the parking brake.
2. Stop the engine. Remove the by-pass valve-to-check valve hose at the by-pass valve end. On V8s, remove both hoses.
3. Install a tachometer and start the engine.
4. Hold your hand over the by-pass valve hose connections(s) and in-

COMBUSTION PIPE ASSEMBLY

ENGINE EXHAUST VALVES

PIPE EXTENSION (THRU MANIFOLD OR CYLINDER HEAD)

CHECK VALVE

CARBURETOR

MUFFLER

FRESH AIR

DIVERTER VALVE (IN OPEN POSITION)

AIR PUMP

Schematic of AIR system
(© G.M. Corp.)

OUTLET

DIVERTED AIR OUTLET

INLET

DIAPHRAGM ASSEMBLY

SIGNAL LINE CONNECTION

VALVE IN OPEN POSITION

Diverter valve

crease engine speed to 2500 rpm. Release the throttle. Air flow from the hose connections should stop momentarily and then start again. When the hose connection air flow stops, air should start coming out the by-pass valve silencer ports.

5. If the by-pass valve isn't working correctly in step 4, check to see that the decel valve is getting a vacuum signal.
6. If the decel valve is getting vacuum, and the by-pass valve is known to be working OK, replace the decel valve.
7. Stop the engine. Remove the test equipment and reconnect the hoses.

1975-76 Ford Air Injection System Solenoid Vacuum Valve Tests

Air injection system solenoid vacuum valves are used only on models with catalytic converters. There are two types of solenoid vacuum: type I is normally closed and type II is normally open. Check the vehicle's tune-up specifications decal to determine which type is used.

Type I (Normally Closed)

1. Allow the engine to reach normal operating temperature. Be sure that the air cleaner temperature is above 65°F.
2. Allow the engine to idle, Detach the vacuum hose from the by-pass valve. Air should flow from the by-pass valve silencer exhaust ports. Connect the by-pass valve vacuum hose.
3. If the air is exhausted out the silencer cover exhaust ports, the solenoid vacuum hose connections are OK. The vacuum supply hose should always go to the bottom solenoid fitting (type I).
4. Detach the vacuum supply hose from the solenoid. Place your finger over the end of the hose. Vacuum should be felt. It not, check the hose and manifold vacuum fitting. Reconnect the vacuum hose.
5. Unfasten the solenoid vacuum valve wiring.

6. Connect one terminal of the solenoid vacuum valve to a 12V power source. Ground the other terminal. Air should *not* come out the by-pass valve exhaust ports.

7. Disconnect the 12V power source and ground wires. Reconnect the solenoid valve wiring.

8. Air still should not come out of the by-pass valve exhaust ports.

9. If the solenoid vacuum valve doesn't operate as outlined, replace it.

Type II (Normally Open)

1. Do steps 1 through 3 of the type I solenoid vacuum valve test.
NOTE: The vacuum supply hose should be connected to the black nozzle on type II valves.

2. Unfasten the wiring from the solenoid vacuum valve.

3. Connect one terminal of the vacuum valve to a 12V power source. Ground the other terminal.

4. Air should flow from the by-pass valve exhaust ports.

5. Disconnect the 12V power source and ground wires. Reconnect the solenoid vacuum valve wiring.

6. Air should *stop* flowing out of the by-pass valve exhaust ports. If it doesn't operate as outlined replace the solenoid vacuum valve.

1975-76 Ford Vacuum Reservoir Check

A vacuum reservoir is required on some air injection systems when used with a catalytic converter. To check it:

1. Detach the solenoid vacuum valve-to-reservoir hose from the reservoir fitting.

2. Connect a vacuum gauge to the reservoir fitting.

3. Disconnect the manifold vacuum hose from the reservoir and connect an external vacuum source in its place.

4. Apply a 14 in. Hg vacuum to the reservoir and trap it. The vacuum should not drop more than 1 in. Hg in 1 min.

5. Remove the test equipment and reconnect the vacuum lines.

Thermostatically Controlled Air Cleaner

Air Door Tests

Non-Vacuum-Operated and 1970-71 Ford Vacuum-Operated

1. Unfasten the temperature sensing valve and snorkle assembly from the air cleaner. Place it in a container of cold water. Make sure that the thermostat is completely covered with water.

2. Place a thermometer, of known accuracy, in the water. Heat the water slowly and watch the temperature.

3. At 105°F, or less, the door should be closed (manifold heat position).

4. Continue heating the water until it reaches 130°F. The door should be fully open to the outside air position.

5. If the door does not open at or near this temperature, check it for binding or a detached spring. If neither of these situations exist, the sensor is defective and must be replaced.
NOTE: This usually means that the entire snorkle assembly must be replaced.

Vacuum-Operated Door— Except 1970-71 Ford

1. Either start with a cold engine or remove the air cleaner from the engine for at least half an hour. While cooling the air cleaner, leave the engine compartment hood open.

2. Tape a thermometer, of known accuracy, to the inside of the air cleaner so that it is near the temperature sensor unit. Install the air cleaner on the engine but do not fasten its securing nut.

3. Start the engine. With the engine cold and the outside temperature less than 90°F., the door

Components of the thermostatically controlled air cleaner
(© G.M. Corp)

should be in the "heat on" position (closed to outside air).
NOTE: Due to the position of the air cleaner on some cars, a mirror may be necessary when observing the position of the air door.

4. Operate the throttle lever rapidly to ½-¾ of its opening and release it. The air door should open to allow outside air to enter and then close again.

5. Allow the engine to warm up to normal temperature. Watch the door. When it opens to the outside air, remove the cover from the air cleaner. The temperature should be over 90°F; 115°F is about normal. If the door does not work within these tempera-

ture ranges, or fails to work at all, check for linkage or door binding.

If binding is not present and the air door is not working, proceed with the vacuum tests, given below. If these indicate no faults in the vacuum motor and the door is not working, the temperature sensor is defcetive and must be replaced.

Vacuum Motor Tests

1970-71 Ford

1. Detach the hose from the vacuum override motor. Connect a vacuum gauge to the hose.

2. With the engine at idle, the vacuum gauge should read 15 in. Hg or better. If it is less than this, check the vacuum lines and connections for leaks.

3. If the vacuum is at specification, install the hose back on the vacuum motor.

4. With the underhood temperature below 100°F, check the air door position. If the air door is less than halfway to the "heat on" position and no components are binding, remove the vacuum

THERMOSTAT

TO AIR CLEANER

MANIFOLD VACUUM

HOT AIR

Duct and valve assembly in "heat on" position — warm-up

motor for bench-testing.

5. Connect the motor to an *alternate* vacuum source. If the rod on the motor moves at least ½ in., reinstall it and check for a defective thermostat bulb.
6. If the rod does not move at all or if it moves less than ½ in., the motor is defective and should be replaced.

GM, Chevrolet, Jeep and Ford (1972-on)

NOTE: Be sure that the vacuum hose that runs between the temperature switch and the vacuum motor is not pinched by the retaining clip under the air cleaner. This could prevent the air door from closing.

1. Check all of the vacuum lines and fittings for leaks. Correct any leaks. If none are found, proceed with the test.
2. Remove the hose which runs from the sensor to the vacuum motor. Run a hose directly from the manifold vacuum source to the vacuum motor.
3. If the motor closes the air door, it is functioning properly and the temperature sensor is defective.
4. If the motor does *not* close the door and no binding is present in its operative, the vacuum motor is defective and must be replaced.

NOTE: If an alternate vacuum source is applied to the motor, insert a vacuum gauge in the line by using a T-fitting. Apply at least 9 in. Hg of vacuum in order to operate the motor.

Chrysler Corp.

1. Remove the air cleaner from the carburetor and allow it to cool to 90°F. Connect a vacuum source to the sensor as well as a vacuum gauge.
2. Apply 20 in. Hg to the sensor, the door should be in the "heat on" (up) position. If it remains

Testing the vacuum motor — Chrysler heated air intake system
(© Chrysler Corp)

in the "off" position, test the vacuum motor.

3. Connect the motor to a vacuum source. In addition to the vacuum gauge, a hose clamp and a bleed valve are necessary. Connect them in the following order:
   a. Vacuum source
   b. Hose clamp (or shut-off valve)
   c. Bleed valve
   d. Vacuum gauge
   e. Vacuum motor
4. Appy 20 in. Hg vacuum to the motor. Use the hose clamp to block the line, so that the motor will retain the vacuum. The door operating motor should retain this amount of vacuum for five minutes. Release the hose clamp.

NOTE: If the vacuum cannot be built up to the specified amount the diaphragm has a leak and the valve will require replacement.

5. By slowly closing the bleed valve, check the operation of the door. The door should start to raise at not less than 5 in. Hg and should be fully raised at no more than 9 in. Hg.
6. If the vacuum motor fails any of the tests in steps 3-5, it is defective. Replace it with a new unit.
7. If the door works properly but fails to pass step two, the sensor is a fault and should be replaced.

NOTE: If the engine has a dual snorkle air cleaner, check the right

side as in steps 3-5, above. However, there is no temperature sensor in the right-side door.

Cold Weather Modulator Tests 1975-76 Ford

Some 1975-76 Ford models use a cold weather modulator to prevent the air door from being opened under hard acceleration, when the temperature is below 55°F.

Check the vehicle's tune-up specifications decal, to see if the cold weather modulator is used, before beginning this test:

1. Stop the engine.
2. Cool the modulator unit in the air cleaner to below 40°F with aerosol circuit test spray or equivalent.

CAUTION: Do not spray the modulator with the engine running. If the spray is drawn into the carburetor, poisonous PHOSGENE gas will come out the tailpipe. Perform this test only in a well ventilated area.

3. Apply at least 16 in. Hg with an external vacuum source to the vacuum motor side of the modulator. Trap the vacuum.
4. The modulator must hold at least 14 in. Hg vacuum for one minute. If it doesn't, replace the modulator.
5. Use a heat gun or run the engine to warm the modulator to at least 70°F.
6. Perform step 3. This time the modulator should not hold the vacuum. Replace it, if it does.

Distributor Controls

Dual Diaphragm Distributor Tests

1. Connect a timing light to the engine. Check the ignition timing.
   NOTE: Before proceeding with the tests, disconnect any spark control devices, distributor vacuum valves, etc. If these are left connected, inaccurate results may be obtained.
2. Remove the retard hose from the distributor and plug it. Increase the engine speed. The timing should advance. If it fails to do so, then the vacuum unit is faulty

and must be replaced.

3. Check the timing with the engine at normal idle speed. Unplug the retard hose and connect it to the vacuum unit. The timing should instantly be retarded from 4-10°. If this does not occur, the retard diaphragm has a leak and the vacuum unit must be replaced.

Timing Retard Solenoid Test

A timing retard solenoid is used on some Chrysler Corp. products up to, and including the 1971 model year.

1. Connect a timing light to the engine and check the timing.

2. Detach the solenoid ground lead near its carburetor end. Timing should advance at least 5° and there should be an increase in engine speed.
3. Reconnect the ground lead. Timing should be retarded to the original position noted and the engine should slow down. Repeat the test several times.
4. If the timing does not behave in the manner indicated, the solenoid is defective and must be replaced; it cannot be adjusted or repaired.

Carburetor/control valve/distributor relationship

Timing Advance Solenoid Test

NOTE: A timing advance solenoid is used on Chrysler products starting in 1972. It should not be confused with the retard solenoid above.

1. Attach a tachometer to the engine.
2. Detach the vacuum advance line from the distributor advance unit.
3. Run the engine at normal idle and check engine rpm with the tachometer.
4. Detach the solenoid lead wire at its connection, which is about 6 in. away from it. Run a jumper wire from the battery to the disconnected lead from the solenoid.
5. When the two leads are touched, the engine speed should increase by 50 rpm or, if a timing light is used, the timing should advance 7-8°. NOTE: Do not touch the jumper wire to the solenoid lead for more than 30 seconds, or the solenoid will overheat.
6. If the engine speed does not increase or the timing advance, the solenoid is defective and must be replaced. Remember to reconnect it when through testing.

Deceleration Valve Tests

NOTE: Timing, idle speed and air/fuel mixture should be at proper specifications before starting this test.

1. Connect a vacuum gauge to the distributor vacuum advance line, by using a T-connection which has about the same inside diameter as the line. Do not clamp the line shut.
2. If the carburetor is equipped with a dashpot, tape its plunger down so that it cannot touch the throttle lever at idle.

3. Speed the engine up to about 2,000 rpm and retain this speed for about five seconds.
4. Release the throttle, allowing the engine to return to normal idle.
5. The vacuum reading should rise to about 15-16 in. Hg and stay there for one second. It should take about three seconds for the vacuum to return to its normal 6 in. Hg reading. These specifications do not apply to Jeeps. See note under "Deceleration Valve Adjustment for Jeep trucks."
6. If the valve does not retain its high reading for about one second or if it takes over three seconds for the reading to return to normal, the valve should be adjusted, as outlined below.

To check for a leaking valve diaphragm, proceed as follows:
1. Remove the vacuum gauge and connect it to the manifold vacuum line with a T-connection.
2. Clamp the valve-to-distributor vacuum line and, with the engine at normal idle speed, check the vacuum reading.
3. Clamp the line shut between the deceleration valve and the T-

Distributor vacuum advance control valve

Typical distributor modulator installation (© Ford Motor Company)

Dual diaphragm vacuum advance mechanism

connection. Check the vacuum gauge reading again.

4. If the second reading is higher than the first, the valve diaphragm is leaking and the valve should be replaced.

Deceleration Valve Adjustments

If the deceleration valve test indicated a need for adjustments, proceed as follows:

1. Remove the cover to gain access to the adjusting screw.
2. If an *increase* in valve opening time is desired, turn the adjusting screw counterclockwise.
3. If a *decrease* in time is desired, turn the adjusting screw clockwise. NOTE: Each complete turn of the adjusting screw equals ½ in. Hg. Thus, if the vacuum reading at the end of three seconds if 7½ in. Hg, it will take three turns of the screw to return it to the proper 6 in. Hg reading.
4. After finishing the adjustments, retest the valve, as outlined above. If the valve cannot be adjusted to proper specifications, it is defective and must be replaced.

NOTE: On 1970 Jeep trucks equipped with a deceleration valve, the test and adjustment procedures are the same, but the specifications are different. Operate the engine at 2,000 rpm for ten seconds; the vacuum reading range should fall between 4 (low)—20 (high) in. Hg.

Coolant Temperature Operated Vacuum Valve Tests

NOTE: On some vehicles equipped with distributor control systems, this valve also is used to override the control system under overheating conditions. If a malfunction of the distributor control system occurs, remember to check the vacuum valve.

1. Check all of the vacuum hoses

Distributor with dual-diaphragm vacuum advance

for proper installation and routing.

2. Connect a tachometer to the engine.
3. Run the engine until it reaches normal operating temperature

but do not allow it to overheat. Be sure that the choke is open.

4. On Chrysler Corp., trucks, detach the distributor solenoid ground lead at the carburetor (if so equipped).
5. Check engine rpm with the carburetor at curb idle.
6. Detach the vacuum line from the intake manifold at the valve end. Plug this hose.
7. Check the idle speed; there should be no change. If the idle speed drops 100 rpm or more, the valve is defective and must be replaced.
8. Check the coolant level and radiator cap. Reconnect the intake manifold hose to the temperature valve.
9. Cover the radiator to increase the coolant temperature. Then do one of the following:
   a. If the vehicle is equipped with a temperature gauge, run the engine until the gauge registers near the top of the "Normal" range.
   b. On vehicles equipped with warning lights, run the engine until the red temperature light comes on. CAUTION: Do not run the engine at an abnormal high temperature for any longer than is required to test the valve. It is not necessary, nor desirable, to overheat an engine when the car uses a tempera-

Distributor modulator details (© Ford Motor Company)

ture gauge, i.e., t he gauge should never be allowed to register "H" (Hot) when testing the valve.

10. If the engine speed has increased by at least 100 rpm, the valve is functioning properly. If there is little or no increase in engine speed, the valve is faulty and must be replaced.

11. Uncover the radiator and allow the car to cool by running the engine at idle.

12. On Chrysler products, remember to connect the distributor solenoid wire.

Ford Spark Delay Valve Tests

NOTE: If the distributor vacuum line contains a cut-off solenoid, it must be open during this test.

1. Detach the vacuum line from the distributor at the spark delay valve end. Connect a vacuum gauge to the valve, in its place.

2. Connect a tachometer to the engine. Start the engine and rapidly increase its speed to 2,000 rpm with the transmission in neutral.

3. As soon as the engine speed is increased, the vacuum gauge reading should drop to zero.

4. Hold the engine speed at a steady 2,000 rpm. It should take longer than two seconds for the gauge to register 6 in. Hg. If it takes less than two seconds, the valve is defective and must be replaced.

5. If it takes longer than the number of seconds specified in the chart below for the gauge to reach 6 in. Hg, disconnect the vacuum gauge from the spark delay valve. Disconnect the hose which runs from the spark delay valve to the carburetor at the valve end. Connect the vacuum gauge to this hose.

6. Start the engine and increase its speed to 2,000 rpm. The gauge should indicate 10-16 in. Hg. If it does not, there is a blockage in the carburetor vacuum port or else the hose itself is plugged or broken. If the gauge reading is within specification, the valve is defective.

7. Reconnect all vacuum lines and remove the tachometer, once testing is completed.

Typical GM coolant temperature-operated vacuum valve
(© G.M. Corp)

DISTRIBUTOR ADVANCE IS CONTROLLED BY CARBURETOR VACUUM

DISTRIBUTOR RETARD IS CONTROLLED BY MANIFOLD VACUUM

Typical Ford coolant temperature-operated vacuum valves (© Ford Motor Co)

Testing the Ford Spark Delay Valve—the black side should be connected to the vacuum source.

Check Valve Test

If the spark delay valve is working properly, but vacuum still is not present when it should be, test the check valve for proper operation:

1. Remove the hoses from either side of the check valve, being careful to note the proper valve installation direction.

2. Connect the BLACK side of the valve to a vacuum source and the colored side to a vacuum gauge.

3. The gauge should show a vacuum reading, as soon as vacuum is applied to the valve.

4. Reverse the connections to the check valve; the vacuum gauge should read zero.

5. Replace the valve if it fails either of the above tests.

Spark Delay Valve Color Code (Ford)

Color (With Black)	1972 Time Delay Maximum (sec)	1973 Time Delay Maximum (sec)
Green	20	20
Blue	15	16
Red	40	28
White	5	12
Yellow	10	14
Orange	—	24

Chrysler Orifice Spark Advance Control (OSAC) Valve

NOTE: Air temperature around the car must be above 68°F for this test because the OSAC valve has a

Ford Spark delay valve circuit
(© Ford Motor Co.)

Ford transmission controlled spark system
(© Ford Motor Co)

CIRCUIT ENERGIZED
TRANSMISSION NOT IN HIGH GEAR
TEMPERATURE ABOVE 55° F

Testing the transmission-controlled spark system with the circuit energized
(© Ford Motor Co)

CIRCUIT DE-ENERGIZED
TRANSMISSION IN HIGH GEAR (OR REVERSE-AUTOMATIC)
TEMPERATURE SWITCH CAN BE OPEN OR CLOSED DEPENDING ON TEMPERATURE

Testing the transmission-controlled spark system with the circuit de-energized
(© Ford Motor Co)

temperature sensor in it. Valves produced from around 1 March 1973 do not have an ambient temperature sensor built into them. They may be identified by their white gasket (old OSAC valves had a black one) and a pasted-on label with the part number (3755499) on it. 1974-75 models have the OSAC valve located in the air cleaner, rather than on the firewall.

1. Check the vacuum hoses and connections for any signs of leaks or plugging.
2. Detach the vacuum line which runs from the distributor to the OSAC valve at the distributor end. Connect a vacuum gauge to this line.
3. Connect a tachometer to the engine. Rapidly open the throttle and then stabilize the engine speed at 2,000 rpm in neutral. When the throttle is rapidly opened the vacuum gauge reading should drop to zero.
4. With the engine speed at a steady 2,000 rpm, it should take about 15 seconds for the vacuum level to rise and then stabilize. NOTE: The length of time may vary slightly with different engines; 15 seconds is an approximate figure.
5. If the vacuum level rises immediately, the valve is defective and must be replaced.
6. If there is no increase in vacuum at all, disconnect the hose which runs from the carburetor to the OSAC valve at the valve and connect a vacuum gauge to this hose. Speed the engine up to 2,000 rpm.
7. If there is no vacuum reading on

Using a test lamp to check the temperature of the transmission switch
(© Ford Motor Co)

NOx (TCS) system schematic manual transmission
(© Chrysler Corp)

the gauge, check for a clogged carburetor port, filters or hoses.
8. If three is a vacuum reading, the valve is defective and must be replaced.

9. Reconnect the vacuum hoses, after disconnecting the vacuum gauge. Disconnect the tachometer.

Transmission Controlled Spark System Tests

Ford

NOTE: When performing the following tests, be sure that the temperature switch is kept above 65°F, except as noted. On models equipped with a spark delay valve, the spark delay valve must be remove for this test to be valid.

Manual Transmission System Test
1. Connect a vacuum gauge between the distributor and the distributor modulator valve, using a T-connector.
2. Start the engine. With the transmission in neutral, the vacuum gauge should read zero.
3. Increase engine speed to between 1,000-1,500 rpm with the clutch

The two types of distributor modulator valve used on Ford products

pedal depressed. The vacuum reading should remain at zero.

4. With the clutch still depressed, place the transmission in high gear. Increase engine speed, as before. The vacuum gauge should now read at least 6 in. Hg. If it does not, proceed further with testing. Remember to shift into neutral or stop the engine before engaging the clutch.

5. Unfasten the transmission switch lead from the distributor modulator terminal. Connect the lead in series with a low amperage test lamp and the positive side of the battery.

6. Move the gear shift lever through all of the gears. The test lamp should remain on until high gear is entered.

7. If the lamp stays on when the transmission is in high, either the switch is defective or the circuit is grounded. If it fails to come on at all, the switch is defective or the circuit has a loose wire.

8. If the transmission switch is functioning properly but the system check indicates that something is still wrong, proceed with the temperature switch test below.

Automatic Transmission System Test

1. Connect a vacuum gauge between the distributor and the distributor modulator valve using a T-connection. Start the engine.

2. When the transmission is in Park or neutral, the vacuum gauge should read zero.

3. Apply the brakes and shift into Reverse. Increase the engine speed. The gauge may or may not register a vacuum.

4. If no vacuum is present, detach a wire from the distributor modulator valve and shift into neutral. Increase engine speed to between 1,000-1,500 rpm. This time the gauge should definitely show a vacuum reading.

5. If vacuum still is not present, disconnect the two vacuum lines from the distributor modulator valve and join them, using a nipple, to bypass the valve. Repeat step four.

6. If there is vacuum now, proceed with the rest of the tests. If no vacuum is present, check for loose, pinched, or plugged hoses. When finished, reconnect the wire to the valve.

7. Detach the transmission switch lead from the distributor modular valve. Connect the lead in series with a test lamp and the positive terminal of the battery.

8. Start the engine and apply the brakes. Move the transmission

NOx (TCS) system components—manual transmission (© Chrysler Corp)

selector through all of the positions on the quadrant.

9. The lamp should go out only when Reverse is selected. If it stays on in Reverse or fails to come on at all, either the switch is defective or the wiring is faulty.

10. If the transmission switch and wiring are in proper order, but vacuum still is not present, it will be necessary to test the temperature switch.

Temperature Switch Tests

NOTE: Vehicles made from 15 March 1973 do not use the ambient temperature switch with the TCS system.

1. Detach the temperature switch lead from its terminal or the distributor modulator valve. Connect the lead to a grounded test lamp.

2. Remove the temperature switch from either the right or left door pillar. Warm the switch by holding it in the palm of the hand. The lamp should come on once 65°F is reached.

3. Using ice, or an aerosol spray circuit cooler, cool the switch to below 49°F. The test lamp should go out.

4. If the lamp fails to go on or off when it should, the switch is defective and must be replaced.

5. If the temperature switch is functioning properly, and no vacuum was present in the system test, the distributor modula-

tor valve is defective.

Distributor Modulator Valve Test

1. Perform the above system test.

2. If the other components, i.e., the transmission switch and the temperature switch, are functioning properly and vacuum is present when it should not be, or vice versa, the fault probably lies in the distributor modulator valve.

3. Before replacing the valve, however, remember to check for clogged, pinched, or loose vacuum hoses, as these could result in similar symptoms.

American Motors Jeep

NOTE: All 1973 V8s and 1973 sixes from 15 March on, as well as all 1974 engines with TCS, use a coolant temperature operated vacuum valve to shut the TCS system off below 160°F.

Manual Transmission Test

The transmission-controlled spark (TCS) system used on Jeep vehicles equipped with manual transmissions is similar to the one used by Ford for their cars with manual transmissions.

The major difference is in the temperature switch. The American Motors switch is located on the front upper crossmember and closes at 63°F. Also, American Motors refers to the "distributor modulator valve" (Ford) as the "solenoid vacuum valve."

NOTE: Vehicles made from 15 March 1973 do not use the ambient temperature switch with the TCS system.

Bearing these differences in mind, test the American Motors system in the same manner as outlined under "Ford—Manual Transmission."

1973½-74 Automatic Transmission

NOTE: The spark control system used on AMC vehicles equipped with automatic transmissions and made after 15 March 1973, is controlled by a switch which operates on transmission governor oil pressure. Test procedures for cars made before this date may be found in the "Speed Controlled Spark Systems" section.

1. Disconnect the electrical lead from the terminal of the governor pressure switch. NOTE: The switch may easily be reached

A typical transmission controlled spark system (© General Motors Corp)

TCS system installation (© G.M. Corp)

with the hood opened. On sixes, the switch is located on the right rear of the cylinder block; on V8s, it is attached to a bracket at the rear of the right-hand rocker cover.

NOTE: The switch may easily be reached with the hood opened. On sixes, the switch is located on the right rear of the cylinder block; on V8s, it is attached to a bracket at the rear of the right-hand rocker cover.

2. Connect a 12V test light in series, between the lead and the terminal on the switch. CAUTION: Use a low amperage test light, so that the switch contacts will not be damaged.
3. Raise the truck, block the front wheels (if they are not off the ground), and securely support it so that the rear wheels are free to turn.
4. Apply the service brakes. Start the engine. The test light should glow.
5. Place the gear selector in Drive (D), release the brake pedal and slowly depress the gas pedal.
6. Watch the speedometer and the test light; between 33-37 mph the switch should open and the test light should go out.

7. If the light does not go out within this speed range, adjust the switch by turning the 1/16 in. allen screw on the switch terminal. Turn the screw clockwise to increase or counterclockwise to decrease the switch cut-out speed. The switch should be adjusted to open at 35 mph.
8. If the switch cannot be adjusted to specification, replace it.
9. If the switch is working properly, but the TCS system is not working, the solenoid vacuum valve is probably defective.

Chrysler

Manual Transmission

NOTE: For testing procedures to be used on Chrysler products that are equipped with an automatic transmission, see Speed Control Spark.

1. Turn the ignition switch to the "on" position. Place the transmission selector lever in the "neutral" position.
2. Disconnect the wire from the B+ terminal on the ignition system ballast resistor while holding the solenoid vacuum valve.
3. When the wire is disconnected, the valve should be felt to de-energize.
4. Reconnect the wire to the ballast resistor, the valve should be felt to energize. If the solenoid vacuum valve does not react this way, either the vacuum valve or the transmission switch is defective, or voltage is not present at the ballast resistor. Connect a test light to the B+ terminal of the resistor to check for voltage.
5. To test the solenoid vacuum valve, disconnect the wiring connector from the solenoid. Run a jumper wire from the piggy-back connector on the ballast re-

DISTRIBUTOR LEAD

Chevrolet vacuum advance solenoid — other GM cars similar
(© G.M. Corp)

The combination vacuum advance solenoid and coolant temperature-operated vacuum valve sistor to one of the terminals on the solenoid vacuum valve. Connect another jumper wire from the other terminal on the solenoid vacuum valve to a good ground. When the ignition switch is turned to the "on" position, the vacuum valve should be felt to energize. If the vacuum valve does not energize, it is defective. If the vacuum valve does energize, but did not energize in Steps 2-4, proceed to Step 6. Connect the lead wires to the vacuum valve.

6. Disconnect the lead wire from the transmission switch. Connect a jumper wire from the just disconnected switch lead to a good ground. When the ignition switch is turned to the "on" position the solenoid vacuum valve should be felt to energize. If the switch does energize when the lead wire to the switch was connected to ground, but failed to energize in Steps 2-4, the transmission switch is either defective or it has a bad ground. If the transmission switch is attached to the transmission with 180 in. lbs torque, it is correctly grounded.

7. If the vacuum valve energized in Step 5, but did not energize in Step 6, the lead wire from the ballast resistor to the vacuum valve is defective.

GM and Chevrolet
SYSTEM TEST

1. Connect a vacuum gauge to the vacuum source for the vacuum solenoid. With the transmission in neutral and the engine idling, vacuum should be present.

2. If there is no vacuum present,

1970-71 CEC System
(© G.M. Corp)

check for a clogged vacuum port, damaged vacuum lines or loose hose connections.

3. Disconnect the vacuum gauge and reconnect the vacuum line.

4. Detach the vacuum line from the distributor vacuum unit and connect it to the vacuum gauge. This is the line which contains the vacuum advance solenoid or CEC solenoid.

5. With engine temperature above 95°F and the transmission in neutral, run the engine for at least 25 seconds. The vacuum gauge should read zero.

6. Do one of the following:
   a. Manual transmission—Depress the clutch pedal and move the shift lever through the gears. Increase engine speed in each gear, enough to cause vacuum advance. A

vacuum should be present only in High gear. NOTE: On 1970-71 models with four-speed transmissions, vacuum should also be present in third gear.

   b. Automatic transmission—Raise the rear wheels of the car off the ground. Support the car and block the front wheels, so that it cannot roll forward. Place the transmission in Drive and speed the engine up enough so that the transmission will shift into high gear; vacuum should only be present when the transmission enters high gear, and not while it is in lower gears. NOTE: Some vehicles are equipped with a time-delay device, so it may take 20-25 seconds before vacuum is present once the proper gear has been reached: Do not run the engine any longer than necessary to complete the test.

7. If no vacuum is present when it should be or if it is present when it should not be, first check the TCS system fuse (if so equipped) and then proceed with the individual tests outlined below.

VACUUM ADVANCE SOLENOID TESTS

NOTE: There are several different types of vacuum advance solenoids used on GM vehicles; look at the chart below to determine proper model usage.

   Type A—Normally Opened

1. Disconnect the vacuum line from the vacuum advance solenoid to the distributor vacuum unit, at the distributor end. Connect a vacuum gauge to the line after

1972-73 CEC system without the reversing relay (© G.M. Corp)

making sure that it is not broken or clogged.

2. Detach the electrical leads from the solenoid. With the engine running, the vacuum gauge should register a vacuum. If it does not, the solnoid is faulty and must be replaced.

3. Using care to observe the proper polarity, connect one solenoid terminal to a 12 V power source. Using a jumper wire, connect the transmission switch terminal on the vacuum solenoid to ground. The solenoid should energize and the vacuum gauge reading should return to zero. If vacuum is still present, the solenoid is jammed and should be replaced.

4. If the solenoid is not defective, connect it in the original manner and go on to the next appropriate test.

Type B—Normally Closed

1. Disconnect the line which runs from the vacuum advance solenoid to the distributor vacuum unit. Connect a vacuum gauge to this line, after making sure that it is neither plugged nor broken.

2. Detach both electrical leads from the solenoid. The gauge should indicate zero vacuum. If it does not, the solenoid is defective and must be replaced.

3. Using care to observe proper polarity, connect the "hot" lead of the solenoid to a 12 V power source. Ground the other lead. Vacuum should now be present in the line. If it is not, the solenoid is defective and needs to be replaced.

4. If the solenoid is not defective, connect it in the original manner and go on with the next applicable test.

Type C—CEC Solenoid and Relays

The test for the CEC solenoid is similar to that for the Type B vacuum advance solenoid, above, except that a vacuum gauge is not needed. With 12 V applied to the CEC solenoid, its plunger should extend. With no power applied to the solenoid, the plunger should retract. If it fails to do either properly, the solenoid is defective and must be replaced. If it

TCS SWITCH TERMINAL

DETENT TERMINAL

The terminals on the Turbo-Hydramatic 400 Transmission Switch
(© G.M. Corp.)

VACUUM ADVANCE SOLENOID AND TRANSMISSION SWITCH USAGE

| Make | Year | Model | Test Section Used For: | |
			Vacuum Advance Solenoid	Transmission Switch
Chevrolet, G.M.	1970	All	A	E, F
	1971	L6, V8	C	E, F
	1972-73	L6, V8	C	D
	1974	L6, V8	B	D

is not defective, reconnect it.

NOTE: A defective CEC solenoid will also affect the operation of the throttle. For further details, see *"Carburetor Modifications."*

Models made prior to 1972 which are equipped with a CEC solenoid, use a reversing relay to provide proper switching action for the solenoid. To test relay operation:

1. Bypass the relay by grounding its single wire connector.

2. If the CEC solenoid plunger will now extend, and it did not extend in the above test, the reversing relay is defective.

A time-delay relay is used on some models equipped with a CEC solenoid to provide vacuum advance for 15-20 seconds after the ignition is switched on. To check its operation, proceed as follows:

1. Disconnect the electrical lead from the temperature switch.

2. Allow the relay to cool. Turn the ignition on. The CEC solenoid should energize (plunger extend) for about 15-20 seconds and then go off.

3. If it fails to go off, detach the blue lead from the time-delay relay. If the CEC solenoid now de-energizes, then the relay is faulty and must be replaced.

If none of the CEC system components which were tested are defective, go on to the next applicable test.

VACUUM DELAY RELAY TEST

This relay is a solid-state unit which is used on some 1972 models. (It is not used with the CEC solenoid and should not be confused with the *time*-delay relay, above.) It is located underneath the dashboard, inside the passenger compartment. To test it proceed in the following manner:

1. Turn the ignition on. Then, using a lower amperage test lamp, check to see that the relay is getting power. If it is not, check its wiring.

2. Disconnect and ground the black lead.

3. Wait for 26 seconds. The vacuum advance solenoid should then energize. If it does not, the relay is faulty and must be replaced. If it does, reconnect the vacuum delay relay and proceed with the next applicable test.

TEMPERATURE SWITCH TEST

1. Connect a vacuum gauge to the vacuum advance solenoid to the distributor vacuum unit.

2. Allow the engine to cool to around 75°F and then start it. The gauge should indicate the presence of a vacuum.

3. If it does not, ground the lead from the cold terminal of the temperature switch.

4. On temperature controls with an additional hot terminal, repeat step 3—this time grounding the hot terminal.

5. If vacuum is not present when either terminal is grounded, the temperature switch is defective. If vacuum still is not present, reconnect the temperature switch leads and vacuum line. Proceed with the next applicable test.

TRANSMISSION SWITCH TESTS

NOTE: There are several different types of transmission switches used on GM vehicles. Check the chart below for proper model usage and then proceed with the applicable test.

Type D—Normally Opened

This test should be performed last, once all the other TCS system components are known to be in proper working order.

1. Repeat steps 4-6 of the "System Test." There should be vacuum to the distributor in high gear.

2. If there is none, disconnect the lead from the transmission switch and ground it.

3. If vacuum is now present, i.e., the vacuum advance solenoid has energized, then the transmission switch is faulty and must be replaced.

Type E—Manual Transmission Normally Closed

NOTE: Some models with manual transmissions use a two-terminal transmission switch. Before proceeding with the test, ground the extra terminal.

1. Detach the switch connector at the side of the transmission.

2. Connect a test lamp in series with the switch and 12 V power source. CAUTION: Do not use a bulb any larger than 0.8 amp (no. 1893); the switch contacts will be damaged at a higher am-

perage.

3. With the engine and ignition off, move the gear shift lever through all of the gears. The test lamp should remain lighted in every gear except third and fourth (if so equipped). NOTE: On 1972 models with four-speed transmissions, the lamp should remain lighted in third gear and not go out until fourth is selected.

4. If the test lamp fails to go out when it should, the switch is defective.

5. If the test lamp fails to come on at all, the switch is broken or the wiring is faulty.

6. If the switch is not defective, reconnect it when finished testing.

Type F—Automatic Transmission Normally Closed

1. Connect a test lamp as detailed in steps 1-2 of the test for type E switch above. Pay particular attention to the "Caution."

2. Raise the rear wheels of the car so they are off the ground and support the car so that it cannot move forward.

3. Start the engine. Shift the transmission into Drive. Increase engine speed so that the transmission shifts into high gear, the test lamp should go out when the transmission enters high gear.

4. Allow the engine to return to idle and apply the brakes. Shift into Reverse. The light should go out again, except on vehicles equipped with Powerglide.

5. In all other gears the lamp should remain on. If it does not

or if it fails to go out when it should, replace the switch.

Speed Controlled Spark Systems

Ford Distributor Modulator System—1970-71

System Tests

Check the distributor vacuum advance on an analyzer (distributor modulator system bypassed if distributor is left in engine for test). If it is functioning correctly, proceed with the tests outlined below.

1. Disconnect the distributor vacuum advance line from the carburetor and connect a vacuum gauge to vacuum line fitting on the carburetor. Run the engine at 1,500 rpm and take a vacuum reading. Make a note of the result. Disconnect the vacuum gauge and attach the vacuum line back on the carburetor.

2. Using a short length of rubber hose to bypass the distributor modulator control box, connect the distributor vacuum advance unit directly to the carburetor. Disconnect the vacuum line from the distributor vacuum advance unit and connect it to the vacuum gauge.

3. Run the engine at 1,500 rpm again. The vacuum gauge reading should be similar to that obtained above. If it is zero or much less than in step one, check for pinched or leaking vacuum lines.

4. Remove the hose used to bypass the distributor modulator and reconnect the vacuum lines as originally found. Leave the vacuum gauge connected to the distributor vacuum line, however.

5. Raise the rear wheels off the ground and support the vehicle so that it cannot roll forward. Run the engine at idle until normal operating temperature is reached.

6. Remove the thermal switch from the door pillar. Hold the switch in the palm of the hand long enough to bring its temperature above 60° F.

7. Place the transmission selector in Drive. Accelerate to 35 mph. By the time this speed is reached, the vacuum gauge should show a reading.

8. If the vacuum gauge shows a reading below 20-35 mph, or if it does not show a reading above 35 mph, proceed with the individual component tests as required. NOTE: Remember to check the coolant temperature operated vacuum valve, if so equipped, as possible cause of trouble. The test procedures may be found above.

Power Supply Test

1. Switch the ignition on. Take a voltage reading at the red lead which runs to the control module.

2. If the voltmeter reads zero, check for a blown system fuse or faulty wiring.

Typical distributor modulator installation (© Ford Motor Co)

3. If the voltmeter registers normal battery voltage, the module is getting the proper power. Proceed with the next test.

Thermal Switch Test

1. Disconnect the thermal switch at its multiconnector.
2. Connect an ohmmeter to the grey (or white) and black leads coming from the switch.
3. Warm the switch by holding it in the palm of the hand until it is above 68° F. There should be no reading (zero) on the ohmmeter. If there is a reading the switch is defective and needs to be replaced.
4. Chill the switch, using ice or cold water, to below 50° F. There should now be a reading (resistance indicated) on the meter. If there is no reading, the switch is defective and should be replaced.
5. If the temperature switch is functioning properly, proceed with the next test.

Control Module Test

1. Disconnect the thermal switch multiconnector from the module. Use a jumper lead to connect the two red wires leading from the two halves of multiconnector.
2. Attach a vacuum gauge to the distributor vacuum line fitting on the carburetor. Run the engine at fast idle and note the reading. Disconnect the gauge and reconnect the vacuum line to the port.
3. Connect the vacuum gauge to the vacuum hose that runs to the distributor vacuum advance unit.
4. Use another jumper lead to connect the grey (or white) wire, which runs from the control module to the thermal switch connector, to ground.
5. Run the engine at fast idle again and note the vacuum reading. It should be almost the same as that taken at the carburetor port.
6. If the reading is zero or lower than that at the carburetor port, the module is defective and must be replaced.
7. If the module is functioning properly, reconnect it and go on with the next test.

Speed Sensor Test

1. Detach the speed sensor leads at its multiconnector. Connect the test prods of an ohmmeter to them.
2. With the sensor at room temperature, the meter should read between 40-60 ohms.
3. Test for continuity between the black lead and the speed sensor case. There should be no meter reading.

DISTRIBUTOR MODULATOR SYSTEM TROUBLESHOOTING CHART

4. The speed sensor is defective if the reading in step 2 does not fall within specifications or if a reading is obtained between the case and the black lead.

Ford Electronic Spark Control (ESC)—1972-73

This system replaces the distributor modulator system, above. The test procedures for the two systems are somewhat different and should not be interchanged, except as noted.

NOTE: Vehicles made on or after 15 March 1973 do not use a temperature switch.

System Test

1. Raise the rear wheels off the ground and support the truck so it cannot roll forward.
2. Detach the vacuum hose on the

Components of the Ford ECS system
(© Ford Motor Co)

Using an ohmmeter to see if the speed sensor is grounded to the case
(© Ford Motor Co)

Checking the impedance of the speed sensor with an ohmmeter
(© Ford Motor Co)

primary side of the distributor vacuum advance unit. Connect a vacuum gauge to the hose.

3. Warm the temperature sensor in the palm of the hand, after removing it from its location on the door pillar (left or right, depending upon model). Be sure it is heated to above 65°F.

4. Start the engine. Place the transmission selector in Drive. Accelerate until the speed specified in the chart is reached (see below) This speed is determined by the color of the amplifier case. Wait for 40 seconds; this allows the time delay valve to work (if so equipped). At this point vacuum should be present.

Amplifier Case Color	Vacuum Advance Cut-in Speed (mph)
Black	23
White	28
Blue	33
Grey	35

5. If there is no vacuum, first check for a clogged carburetor vacuum port.

6. Then check the vacuum lines to see if they are pinched, clogged or misrouted. NOTE: Remember to check the coolant temperature-operated vacuum valve, if so equipped, as a possible source of the malfunction. The test procedures for it are given above.

7. If the above checks indicate that the problem does not lie in the vacuum supply system, proceed with the ESC individual component tests.

Distributor Modulator Solenoid Test

1. Disconnect the electrical leads from the distributor modulator solenoid.

2. Increase engine speed. If there is no vacuum reading, with the gauge connected as in the System Test, the solenoid is defective and must be replaced. Reconnect the electrical leads to the distributor modulator solenoid and allow the engine to slow down.

3. If vacuum occurs below the spec-

ified cut-in speeds (see the chart in step 4, above), the solenoid is not being energized and the trouble lies elsewhere in the system. Proceed with the next test.

Temperature Switch Tests

1. Disconnect the temperature switch at the multiconnector. Connect an ohmmeter to the switch terminals.

2. Warm the switch by placing it in the palm of the hand. The ohmmeter should show a reading. If it does not, the switch is defective.

3. Chill the switch to 49°F or below, by using ice or cold water. There should be no reading (zero) on the ohmmeter. If a resistance is indicated, the temperature switch is defective.

4. Replace the switch if defective. If it is not, proceed with the next test.

Power Supply Test

1. Ground one side of a low-amperage test lamp and connect the other side to the temperature switch connector of the instrument panel wiring (red/yellow hash lead).

2. Turn on the ignition. The lamp should light. If it fails to do so, check the wiring to the ignition switch or check the ignition switch itself.

3. If the ESC system is getting

power, proceed with the next test.

Speed Sensor Test

This test is exactly the same as that for the speed sensor used in the distributor modulator system.

Perform the speed sensor test as outlined in the "Distributor Modulator" section, above.

Amplifier

If everything else in the ESC system is functioning properly, the fault lies with the amplifier module. Replace the amplifier and repeat the "System Test".

Chrysler Corp.

Automatic Transmission System Test

1. Warm the engine to normal operating temperature. Be sure the ambient temperature is well above 70°F.

2. T-connect a vacuum gauge between the distributor and the solenoid vacuum valve.

3. Raise the vehicle on a lift, with the wheels hanging free.

4. Disconnect the vacuum line at the vacuum switch on the control unit.

5. Start the engine and run at a speed above 850 rpm. Vacuum gauge should read zero.

6. Disconnect the wire from the control unit. The vacuum gauge should read normal advance unit

NOx (SCS) system—automatic transmission
(© Chrysler Corp)

TO VOLTAGE REGULTOR

CONTROL UNIT ASSEMBLY

BALLAST RESISTOR

TEMPERATURE SWITCH

TO IGNITION 1

TO IGNITION 2

TO COIL

GROUND AT MOUNTING BOLT

VACUUM SWITCH

SPEED SWITCH

NOTE: TORQUE TO 150 IN. LBS. AT INSTALLATION.

CONTROL MODULE

SOLENOID VACUUM VALVE

NOx (SCS) system schematic—automatic transmission
(© Chrysler Corp)

operating vacuum. Reconnect the wire. The gauge should drop to zero.

7. Unplug and reconnect the vacuum line to the vacuum switch. Disconnect the wire from the control unit to the speed switch. The gauge should read normal advance unit operating vacuum.

8. Place transmission in Drive. Sharp acceleration should cause the gauge reading to drop sharply to zero. Do not exceed 40 mph.

9. Accelerate above 30 mph. The gauge should read normal vacuum advance unit operating vacuum.

10. If solenoid valve did not operate during the tests, repace control unit.

American Motors Jeep 1972-73

NOTE: Although American Motors calls all of their spark control systems "Transmission-Controlled Spark" (TCS), the one used with automatic transmissions is really a speed-controlled spark system (SCS). American Motors vehicles made on or after 15 March 1973 do not use an SCS system, but have, instead, a transmission controlled spark (TCS) system. Consult the appropriate section above for system testing.

System Test

This test should be performed with the air temperature above 65°F and the coolant temperature above 160°F.

1. Raise the rear wheels off the ground and support the truck so it cannot roll forward.

2. Disconnect the vacuum hose which runs between the distributor vacuum unit or the coolant temperature vacuum override valve and the vacuum advance solenoid at the distributor or valve end. Connect a vacuum gauge to the hose.

3. Start the engine and shift into Drive Accelerate until the speedometer registers the speed specified in the chart at the end of this section.

4. Until the specified speed is reached, the vacuum reading should be zero. Once this speed is reached, vacuum should be present.

5. If no vacuum is registered at or above the specified speed, check the vacuum lines and connections first. Examine the carburetor port to be sure that it is not clogged. NOTE: Remember to check the coolant temperature vacuum override valve, if so equipped, as its failure could cause a loss of vacuum. Test procedures for it are given earlier in this section.

6. If there is nothing wrong with the vacuum supply, disconnect the gauge, reconnect the hose and proceed with the next test.

Transmission Switch Tests

1. Leave the rear wheels of the car off the ground as in the system test above.

2. Disconnect the transmission switch leads. Connect a low-amperage test lamp in series with the switch and the positive side of the battery.

3. Accelerate to the specified speed (see chart below) and watch the test lamp. It should remain on until the specified speed is reached. If the lamp fails to go out or if it does not light at all, the switch is defective and must be replaced.

4. If the switch is working properly, reconnect it and go on with the next test.

Vacuum Advance Solneoid Test

1. Disconnect the vacuum advance solenoid leads. Connect a vacuum gauge to the solenoid hose as in the system test.

2. Place the transmission in neutral and start the engine. Increase engine speed. The gauge should indicate the presence of a vacuum.

3. Connect the hot lead to a 12 V power source. Ground the other lead. Increase the engine speed again. The solenoid should energize, resulting in a vacuum reading of zero.

4. Replace the vacuum advance solenoid if it is faulty. If it is not, reconnect the wiring and go on with the next appropriate test.

Ambient Temperature Override Switch

1. Disconnect the ambient temperature switch leads.

2. Replace the switch in the circuit with a jumper wire.

3. Repeat the system test. If the vacuum gauge now reads zero or below the specified speed, i.e., the solenoid energizes, the temperature switch is defective.

4. If the switch proves not to be defective when tested in step 3, reconnect if after removing the jumper lead.

5. Cool the switch, using either ice, cold water, or an aerosol spray circuit tester, to below 63°F. Repeat the system test. If there is no vacuum below the specified speed, the switch is stuck closed and must be replaced.

International Harvester

System Test

1. Disconnect the advance hose from the distributor and plug open end. Apply parking brake. Check and adjust, if necessary, timing and idle to specifications.

2. Connect vacuum gauge between distributor and advance hose.

3. Idle engine. If vacuum is high— full manifold vacuum—check for restrictions in air bleed hoses, speed sensor control and high temperature vacuum valve (V-8). Air should flow freely in one direction through each valve.

4. If vacuum is low, disconnect vacuum line from sensor on 4 cyl. models, vacuum line from sensor and vacuum line from throttle modulator on 6 cyl. models, and vacuum line from high temperature control valve on V-8 models. NOTE: disconnections should be made at Tee connectors. Idle engine and hold finger over Tee. Engine should speed up and vacuum should rise to full manifold vacuum level. If not, check for a leaky or restricted vacuum hose, restricted vacuum port at carburetor, or leaky advance unit. If vacuum increases as it should:

5. Jack up rear and secure vehicle on jack stands so that wheels are

free of ground.

6. Place transmission in second gear—manual or automatic—and accelerate lightly. Vacuum should be 6-8″ Hg at 23 mph manual, or 31 mph automatic. Both readings have a leeway of plus or minus 2 mph. If the proper vacuum reading is not attained, check for leaks in the hoses or throttle modulator. If they check out okay, replace the speed sensor control. NOTE: modulator should extend when vacuum is applied.

7. If vacuum is attained in the above step, accelerate to 12 mph above cutoff. Vacuum should exceed 12″ Hg on 4 and 8 cyl. engines and 17″ Hg on 6 cyl. engines. If so, the system is functioning normally; if not, replace the sensor.

1973 Ford Temperature Activated Vacuum System (TAV)

System Test

1. Disconnect the vacuum line from the primary port of the distributor. Connect a vacuum gauge to the line by means of a T-fitting. Connect the other end of the T-fitting to the distributor.

2. Be sure that the air temperature is above 65°F. Hot water may be used to warm the temperature switch, which is located in the front door pillar.

3. Place the transmission in Park or Neutral. Start the engine.

4. Run the engine at idle; the vacuum gauge should read zero.

5. Increase the engine speed to 1,500 rpm or slightly more. The gauge should read 5 in. Hg or better.

6. If there is no vacuum reading, check for leaking, plugged, or pinched lines and fittings.

7. Detach the EGR port hose and plug up the carburetor line. The vacuum gauge should read zero.

8. If it does not, check the lines and then proceed with the three-way vacuum valve test, below. If it does, go on Step 9.

9. Next, detach one of the power leads from the three-way vacuum valve.

10. Speed the engine up to 1,500 rpm or more. The vacuum gauge should now read 6 in. Hg or better.

11. If the system fails to function as outlined, check the ambient temperature switch, the EGR valve, or the three-way vacuum valve.

12. If everything is functioning properly, reconnect the leads and vacuum lines after disconnecting the vacuum gauge.

SCS VACUUM ADVANCE

Make	Year	No vacuum advance below	With engine temperature (deg F)
American Motors	1971	30 mph	All temperatures①
	1972-73	34 mph	above 160①②

①—Air temperature above 63°F

②—V8 only

Temperature Switch Test

Test the ambient temperature switch, as outlined under "Ford Electronic Spark Control—1972-73," above. The switch is in either the left or right front door pillar.

Three-Way Vacuum Valve Test

1. Remove the three-way vacuum valve from the car.

2. Connect a vacuum gauge to the horizontal port at the *bottom* of the valve.

3. Apply a vacuum source to the horizontal port at the *top* of the valve.

4. Ground one of the valve terminals while connecting the other terminal to a 12V power supply. The vacuum gauge should read zero.

5. With the valve energized connect the vacuum source to the bottom *vertical* port. The vacuum gauge should now indicate an amount of vacuum equal to the output of the vacuum source.

6. Disconnect the leads from the valve. The vacuum gauge reading should return to zero.

7. If the valve fails to function as outlined, replace it. If it is functioning correctly, check the EGR valve operation as detailed in the appropriate section below.

1973½-75 Ford Cold Temperature Activated Vacuum System (CTAV)

The cold temperature activated vacuum (CTAV) system is similar to the temperature activated system used on 1973 vehicles made before 15 March (see the previous section). On CTAV equipped vehicles, the temperature sensor has been moved from the door pillar to the air cleaner housing, and a latching relay has been added. The latching relay prevents variations in ambient temperature from affecting the system; once the CTAV system has been activated it cannot recycle until the ignition system has been shut off.

The CTAV system is tested in the same way as the TAV system. (except for the air cleaner mounted temperature switch). Follow the test procedure outlined in the TAV section. If all of the CTAV system components are working properly, then the latching relay must be defective;

replace it and repeat the "System Test".

Air Cleaner-Mounted Temperature Switch—Normally Closed

The normally closed temperature switch may be identified by its rectangular connector.

1. Disconnect the temperature switch connector and remove the switch from the air cleaner.

2. Warm the switch in the palm of your hand.

3. Connect a self-powered test light between the terminals of the switch connector. The test light should glow.

4. Cool the switch with ice or aerosol circuit testing spray. The light should go off.

5. If the switch doesn't work as outlined, replace it.

Air Cleaner-Mounted Temperature Switch—Normally Opened

The normally opened temperature switch may be identified by its round connector.

1. Perform steps 1 and 2 of the test for the normally closed switch.

2. Connect a self-powered test light between the terminals on the switch connector. The test light should stay off.

3. Cool the switch with ice or aerosol circuit testing spray. The test light should come on.

4. If the switch doesn't work as outlined, replace it.

1975 Ford Cold Start Spark Advance (CSSA) System

System Test

1. Allow the engine to reach normal operating temperature. Stop the engine.

2. If the engine is equipped with a spark delay valve (SDV), remove it and test it separately. Use a fitting to connect the two halves of the vacuum hose together where the SDV was mounted.

3. Using a T-fitting, connect a vacuum gauge to the distributor vacuum unit.

4. Block the wheels, set the parking brake, place the transmission in Neutral (N), and start the engine. Open the throttle halfway and then allow it to close.

5. The vacuum gauge should register a rise and then a fall in vacuum. If it doesn't, check for plugged vacuum fittings, and/or

Antidieseling Solenoid Tests

NOTE: Antidieseling solenoids are also referred to as, "throttle stop" or "idle stop" solenoids.

1. Turn the ignition key on and open the throttle. The solenoid plunger should extend (solenoid energize).
2. Turn the ignition off. The plunger should retract, allowing the throttle to close. NOTE: With the antidieseling solenoid de-energized, the carburetor idle speed adjusting screw must make contact with the throttle shaft to prevent the throttle plates from jamming in the throttle bore when the engine is turned off.
3. If the solenoid is functioning properly and the engine is still dieseling, check for one of the following:
   a. High idle or engine shut off speed;
   b. Engine timing not set to specification;
   c. Binding throttle linkage;
   d. Too low an octane fuel being used.
   Correct any of these problems, as necessary.
4. If the solenoid fails to function as outlined in steps 1–2, disconnect the solenoid leads; the solenoid should de-energize. If it does not, it is jammed and must be replaced.
5. Connect the solenoid to a 12V power source and to ground. Open the throttle so that the plunger can extend. If it does not, the solenoid is defective.
6. If the solenoid is functioning correctly and no other source of trouble can be found, the fault probably lies in the wiring between the solenoid and the ignition switch or in the ignition switch itself. Remember to reconnect the solenoid when finished testing.

NOTE: On some 1970–71 Ford models, dieseling may occur when the engine is turned off because of feedback through the alternator warning light circuit. A diode kit is available from Ford to cure this problem. A failure of this diode may also lead to a similar problem.

A/C Operated Antidieseling Device Tests

1. Run the engine and turn off all

loose or misrouted hoses. If everything else checks out OK, then test the two coolant temperature operated vacuum valves

Carburetor Controls

Ford and AMC electrically assisted choke hook-up (© Ford Motor Co)

of the air conditioning controls.
2. Turn the engine off. The air conditioner compressor clutch should engage for several seconds to slow the engine down.
3. If the compressor clutch engagement does not occur, check the wiring for a loose connection, at either the compressor or the antidieseling relay.
4. Check to see that the relay is properly grounded to its mounting. Examine the air conditioner fuse(s) to see that they are not blown.
5. Start the engine and turn on the air conditioner. The clutch should engage. If it does not, the problem lies in the air conditioner circuit.
6. If the truck is equipped with a blocking relay, remove it for bench-testing. Connect a 12V test lamp between the two outboard connectors. Ground the mounting bracket. Connect a 12V power source to the center terminal. The lamp should come on. If it does not, the blocking relay is defective and must be replaced.
7. If all of the other components are functioning properly, the antidieseling relay is defective and requires replacement.

CEC Solenoid Operation

The CEC solenoid is used on some GM models. It has two functions; one is to regulate distributor vacuum and the other is operate as a throttle positioner. When the solenoid is energized, the throttle blade is held off its seat by a plunger located at one end of the CEC solenoid. This provides higher engine rpm during deceleration, thus reducing exhaust emissions.

Because of its dual function, failure of this valve can lead to higher

(PVS) as outlined elsewhere in this section.
6. Remove the T-fitting and vacuum gauge. Install the SDV, if so equipped.

emission levels or an idle which is considerably faster than normal. If the CEC solenoid is suspected of not working properly, follow the complete set of test procedures for it in "Distributor Controls," above.

Electrically Assisted Choke

Ford and AMC Jeep

1. Detach the electrical lead from the choke cap.
2. Use a jumper lead to connect the terminal on the choke cap and the wire terminal, so that the electrical circuit is still completed.
3. Start the engine.
4. Hook up a test light between the connector on the choke lead and ground.
5. The test light should glow. If it does not, current is not being supplied to the electrically assisted choke.
6. Connect the test light between the terminal on the alternator and the terminal on the choke cap. If the light now glows, replace the lead, since it is not passing current to the choke assist. CAUTION: Do not ground the terminal on the alternator while performing Step 6.
7. If the light still does not glow, the fault lies somewhere in the electrical system. Check the system out.

If the electrically assisted choke receives power but still does not appear to be functioning properly, reconnect the choke lead and proceed with the rest of the test.

8. Tape the bulb end of the thermometer to the metallic portion of the choke housing.
9. If the electrically assisted choke operates below 55°F, it is defective and must be replaced.
10. Allow the engine to warm up to

between 80 and 110°F; at these temperatures the choke should operate for about 1½ minutes.

11. If it does not operate for this length of time, check the bi-metallic spring to see if it is connected to the tang on the choke lever.

12. If the spring is connected and the choke is not operating properly, replace the cap assembly.

Chrysler Corp.

CAUTION: Do not immerse the choke heating element in any type of liquid, especially solvent, for any reason.

NOTE: A short circuit in the choke wiring or in the heater will show up as a short in the ignition system.

1. Disconnect the electrical leads from the choke control switch before starting the engine.

2. Connect a test light between the smaller of the two terminals on the choke control switch and a ground.

3. Start the engine and run it until it reaches normal operating temperature.

4. Apply power from a 12V source to the terminal marked "BAT" on the choke control switch.

5. The test light should light for at least a few seconds or for as long as five minutes. If the light does not come on at all or if it stays on longer than five minutes, replace the switch.

6. Disconnect the test light and reconnect the electrical leads to the choke switch, if it is functioning properly.

7. Detach the lead from the choke switch which runs to the choke heating element.

8. Connect the lead from an ohmmeter to the crimped section at the choke end of the wire, which was removed in Step 7. CAUTION: Do not connect the ohmmeter to the metallic heater housing.

9. Ground the other ohmmeter test lead to the engine manifold.

10. The meter should indicate a resistance of 4–6 ohms.

11. If the reading is not within specifications, or if it indicates an opened (zero resistance) or a shorted (infinite resistance) heater coil, replace the heater assembly.

NOTE: The electrically assisted choke does not change any carburetor service procedures. If any parts of the electrically assisted choke are defective, they must be replaced. Adjustment is not possible.

1975 GM and Chevrolet Secondary Choke Break Systems

System Test—L6 And V8 (4-bbl)

If the engine temperature is above 70°F, a timer starts as soon as the ignition switch is turned on. If you turn the ignition on but do not start the engine within 35 seconds, you will be attempting to start the engine with a wide-opened choke. To start the engine now, it will be necessary to turn the ignition off and start the engine immediately.

1. With the engine warmed-up and running, shut the ignition off.

2. Start the engine. It should take about 35 seconds for the secondary vacuum break to operate. If it doesn't the system is defective.

3. To simulate a cold engine, ground the temperature switch lead. Disconnect the lead from the temperature switch; there should be two terminals. Ground each terminal individually until you find the one that operates the red, "HOT" warning light on the dash. The *other* terminal is the timer terminal.

4. Ground the timer terminal with a jumper lead. Start the engine and watch the secondary vacuum break, for at least one minute. The break should not operate. If it does, proceed with the component tests.

5. Leave the engine running and disconnect the ground wire. About 35 seconds later the vacuum break should operate. If, not, proceed with the component tests.

6. The simulated cold test will not check temperature switch operation. The temperature switch will either have to be checked on a cold engine or by removing it, as outlined below.

Temperature Switch Test—L6 and V8 (4-bbl)

1. Turn the ignition switch on.

2. Remove the connector from the temperature switch and ground each terminal. One terminal will cause the red "HOT" warning light to come on; the *other* terminal works the timer.

3. With the engine temperature below 70°F, connect a self-powered

5. With the engine running and the solenoid energized, the gauge should read zero.

6. Disconnect the jumper wires and the gauge should show full manifold vacuum.

7. Replace the solenoid if it is defective.

Chrysler electrically assisted choke system components :© Chrysler Corp)

Timer Test—L6 and V8 (4-bbl)

If the secondary choke break vacuum solenoid and temperature switch are OK, and the system is not working, the problem is probably in the timer. Replace it and perform the system test again.

Adjusting the Secondary Choke Vacuum Diaphragm—L6 and V8 (4-bbl)

1. Disconnect the vacuum hose from the secondary choke break vacuum diaphragm.
2. Connect a hand-operated vacuum pump with a gauge to the diaphragm.
3. Cover the diaphragm bleed hole with your finger. Apply vacuum to the diaphragm. It should hold vacuum and not leak down. If it leaks it is defective.
4. Note the position of the choke cover and then remove it. Put the follower lever on the highest step of the fast idle cam.
5. Tape the bleed hole in the diaphragm. Use a hand pump to apply vacuum to the diaphragm. Apply enough vacuum to pull the diaphragm in all the way. It may take a few seconds for the diaphragm to make a full stroke.
6. Push the lever on the inside of the choke coil housing toward the closed position (up).
7. The choke rod should be in the bottom of the slot in the choke lever, and the choke plate wide-open.
8. If not, bend the rod at the first bend (next to the vacuum break diaphragm), until the choke plate is wide-open.
9. Remove the tape, install the hose and put the choke cover back in its original position.
test light between the temperature switch timer terminal and ground. The light should come on.
7. With the engine temperature above 70°F, the light should go off.
NOTE: If necessary, remove the temperature switch to cool it. Re-

lieve cooling system pressure first.
8. Replace the temperature switch if it doesn't work as outlined.

Vacuum Solenoid Test—L6 and V8 (4-bbl)

The solenoid for the secondary choke break system is the one next to the choke vacuum diaphragm. The one on the heat valve bracket is for the EFE system.
1. Remove the connector from the choke vacuum solenoid.
2. Connect one of the solenoid terminals to a 12 volt power source and ground the other terminal.
3. If the solenoid doesn't "click" on (energize) when the connection is made in step 2, the solenoid is defective. Replace it.
4. Leave the solenoid connected as in step 2. Disconnect the hose from the choke secondary vacuum break and connect a vacuum gauge to it.

1975 Chrysler Coolant Control Idle Enrichment (CCIE) System

California System Test

NOTE: The engine coolant temperature must be below 80°F for this test.
1. Disconnect the vacuum line, which runs from the two-nozzle coolant temperature operated vacuum valve to the CCIE valve on the carburetor, at the air bleed (on the vacuum valve side).
2. Connect a vacuum gauge to this line and start the engine.
3. The vacuum gauge should register manifold vacuum. If it does not, check the lines and fittings to see if they are pinched or plugged.
4. If everything is in good condition, replace the coolant temperature operated vacuum valve.
5. If the valve is OK, then run the engine until the coolant temperature goes above 90°F. Above this temperature, the vacuum

gauge should read zero; if it does not, replace the vacuum valve.
6. Check the air bleed and the vacuum line which runs from it to the carburetor. Replace either if it is plugged.
7. Remove the vacuum gauge and connect the vacuum lines.

Federal (except California) System Test

NOTE: The engine coolant temperature must be below 150°F for this test.
1. Disconnect the vacuum line which runs from the two-nozzle coolant temperature operated vacuum valve to the CCIE valve on the carburetor, at the air bleed (on the vacuum valve side).
2. Connect a vacuum gauge to the disconnected line.
3. Start the engine, the gauge should register manifold vacuum for about 35 seconds, and then drop to zero.
4. If there is no vacuum, stop the engine. Check the vacuum lines and fittings. If these are in good shape, check the EGR delay timer and solenoid as detailed in the appropriate section.
5. If the delay timer, solenoid, fittings, and lines check out OK, then replace the two-nozzle coolant temperature operated vacuum valve.
6. If there was vacuum present long after 35 seconds in Step 3, then check the EGR delay timer and solenoid.
7. Start the engine and allow the coolant to warm-up to above 150°F, then stop the engine.
8. Start the engine again; there should be no vacuum reading on the gauge. If there is, replace the coolant temperature operated vacuum valve.
9. Check the air bleed and the vacuum line from it to the carburetor. Replace either if it is plugged.
10. Remove the vacuum gauge and connect the vacuum lines.

Evaporative Emission Control System

There are several things to check for if a malfunction of the evaporative emission control system is suspected.
1. Leaks may be traced by using an infrared hydrocarbon tester. Run the test probe along the lines and connections. The meter

will indicate the presence of a leak by a high hydrocarbon (HC) reading. This method is much more accurate than a visual inspection which would indicate only the presence of a leak large enough to pass liquid.
2. Leaks may be caused by any of

the following, so always check these areas when looking for them:
a. Defective or worn lines;
b. Disconnected or pinched lines;
c. Improperly routed lines;
d. A defective filler cap.

NOTE: If it becomes necessary to replace any of the lines used in the evaporative emission control system, use only those hoses which are fuel resistant or are marked "EVAP."

3. If the fuel tank has collapsed, it may be the fault of clogged or pinched vent lines, a defective vapor separator, or a plugged or incorrect fuel filler cap.

4. To test the filler cap, clean it and place it against the mouth. Blow into the relief valve housing. If the cap passes pressure with light blowing or if it fails to release with hard blowing, it is defective and must be replaced.

NOTE: Replace the cap with one marked "pressure/vacuum" only. An incorrect cap will render the system inoperative or damage its components.

Vapor emission control system components

Exhaust Gas Recirculation (EGR) Systems

All 1973-76 GM EGR Valve Tests

1. Start the engine. Allow it to warm up and reach normal idle speed. NOTE: Be sure that under-hood temperature is above 50-60°F, before testing the EGR valve.
2. Increase the engine speed to 1,200–1,500 rpm and watch the EGR valve shaft. The shaft should move upward at this speed.
3. Allow the engine to return to normal idle; the valve shaft should go down.
4. If the shaft fails to raise in step two, check the vacuum line which runs from the carburetor port to the valve. Make sure that it is not loose, clogged, or pinched. If the EGR valve now works, replace the ambient temperature switch. If none of these conditions are present, proceed with the next step.
5. Test the valve diaphragm by disconnecting the vacuum line and applying an outside vacuum source to the valve. The shaft should raise between 8–10 in. Hg. It should retain the pressure and not leak down. On dual diaphragm valves, repeat this test, applying 8–10 in. Hg. vacuum to the tube at the center of the valve. This portion of the valve should also retain the vacuum reading (not leak down).
6. If the valve shaft is frozen in the raised position, the valve is defective.
7. If the valve fails any of the above tests, it is defective. Re-

place it as an assembly; the valve cannot be disassembled and repaired.

8. In some cases the valve may be cleaned with a wire brush or in a spark plug cleaning machine, to loosen deposits which may cause the valve to stick.

NOTE: If the engine is to be tested by "shorting out" the cylinders when it is equipped with an EGR valve, first disconnect the vacuum hose at the valve and plug it. Failure to do this will cause uneven idling and indicate false test results. Do not short cylinders on models equipped with a catalytic converter.

1974 GM and Chevrolet Dual Diaphragm EGR Valve

A dual diaphragm EGR valve is

used on some V8s which are sold in California. The dual diaphragm valve may be identified by the two vacuum hoses which run to it. To test, proceed as follows:

1. Shut the engine off.
2. Disconnect the *lower* vacuum line from the EGR valve.
3. Connect a hand-operated vacuum pump, which has a built in vacuum gauge, to the lower port on the EGR valve.
4. Draw about 14 in. Hg with the pump. There should be no drop in the gauge reading for at least 30 seconds.
   If the vacuum gauge shows a drop within 30 seconds, replace the EGR valve.
   If the valve is good, disconnect the pump and connect the vacuum line to the lower port.

Floor jet location in Chrysler Corp V8s — sixes use only one jet (© Chrysler Corp)

Typical hose routing and component layout of a Chrysler Proportional EGR system

1974-75 GM and Chevrolet Backpressure Transducer Valve (BPV)

1. Take the air cleaner off of the carburetor and plug the manifold vacuum fitting.
2. Block the drive wheels, place the transmission in Park, and turn the air conditioner off.
3. Start the engine and allow it to reach normal operating temperature. Place the cam follower on the high step of the fast idle cam.
4. Connect a vacuum gauge to the carburetor side of the BPV. Note the reading. Reconnect the vacuum line.
5. Connect a vacuum gauge to the EGR valve side of the BPV with a T-fitting. The gauge should read 1.7-3.2 in. Hg; if it does not, replace the BPV.
6. With the vacuum gauge still connected, remove the vacuum line from the EGR valve and plug it; the gauge should read the same as in Step 4. If it does not read within 2-3 in. Hg of the figure obtained in Step 4, replace the BPV.
7. Remove the vacuum gauge, connect the vacuum lines, and replace the air cleaner.

Chrysler Corp. Floor Jet Service—1972-73

All six-cylinder engines have one floor jet, while all V8s have two.

1. Turn the engine off. Remove the air cleaner assembly from the carburetor.
2. Hold the choke and throttle valves open. Shine a flashlight through the carburetor to inspect the floor jet(s). The jet(s) is/are in satisfactory condition if the passage shows an open path to the orifice.
3. If the jet(s) is/are clogged, completely remove the carburetor. Withdraw the jet and clean it. CAUTION: Use care when handling the jets. They have very thin walls and are, therefore, easily damaged. Because they are made out of stainless steel, they are not magnetic and cannot be retrieved readily if dropped into the manifold.
4. Install the jet(s) and tighten to 25 ft lbs. Install the carburetor and attach the air cleaner.

NOTE: "Shorting out" cylinders on engines equipped with floor jets is not a reliable test procedure. The unburned mixture is circulated to the other cylinders, causing the engine speed to fluctuate. Because of this false test results may be obtained.

Chrysler Corp. 1973 (early) Proportional EGR System Tests

NOTE: Air temperature should be above 68°F for this test.

1. Check all of the vacuum hoses which run between the carburetor, intake manifold, EGR valve, and the vacuum amplifier (if so equipped). Replace the hoses and tighten the connections, as required.
2. Allow the engine to warm up. Connect a tachometer to it. Start with the engine idling in neutral and rapidly increase the engine speed to 2,000 rpm.
3. If the EGR valve stem moves (watch the groove on the stem), the valve and the rest of the system are functioning properly. If the stem does not move, proceed with the rest of the EGR system tests.
4. Disconnect the vacuum supply hose from the EGR valve. Apply a vacuum of at least 10 in. Hg to the valve with the engine warmed-up and idling and the transmission in neutral.

NOTE: A source of more than adequate vacuum is the intake manifold vacuum connection. Run a hose from the EGR valve directly to the connection.

5. When vacuum is applied to the EGR valve, the engine speed should drop at least 150 rpm. In some cases the engine may even stall. If the engine does not slow down and the EGR valve does not operate, the valve is defective or dirty. Replace it or remove the deposits from it. NOTE: Always replace the EGR valve gasket with a new one when the valve is removed for service, even if the valve itself is not replaced.
6. If the EGR valve is functioning properly, reconnect its vacuum line and test the temperature control valve.
7. Disconnect the vacuum hose which runs to the temperature control valve and plug it. Repeat steps 2-3. If the EGR valve now functions, the temperature control valve is defective and must be replaced.

8. If everything else is functioning properly, the EGR system does not work and the engine is equipped with a vacuum amplifier (see the chart below), the amplifier is at fault. Replace it and repeat the system test.

NOTE: Before replacing the amplifier, check the vacuum port in the carburetor. If it is clogged, clean it with solvent; do not use a drill.

Engine	*Vacuum amplifier used on:*
225—6	All
318—V8	California only
360—V8	All
440—V8	All non-high-performance engines

Chrysler Corp. 1973 (late)—75 Proportional EGR System Tests

NOTE: This system is used starting with trucks made on or after 15 March 1973. It replaces the system tested in the above section.

1. Perform steps 1–6 of the 1973 proportional EGR system tests, detailed in the above section.
2. Depressurize the cooling system. Remove the coolant temperature operated EGR vacuum valve (CCEGR) from the top tank of the radiator. On 1975 360-V8 2-bbl engines, remove the CCEGR valve from the front of the block.
3. Place the CCEGR valve in an ice bath so that its threaded portion is covered. Cool it to less than 40°F.
4. Connect a hand-operated vacuum pump and gauge to the valve nipple which had blue or yellow striped hose attached to it.
5. Apply at least 10 in. Hg vacuum to the valve. The gauge should show no more than a 1 in. Hg drop in vacuum in 1 minute.
6. If the reading drops off more than this, replace the CCEGR valve.
7. Proceed with step 8 in the preceding section.

Chrysler Corp. 1974-75 EGR Delay System

NOTE: Not all engines use an EGR delay timer; some 1975 engines also used the EGR delay timer to control the coolant control idle enrichment (CCIE) system as well.

1. Unfasten the distributor-to-coil lead.
2. Disconnect the vacuum line which runs from the delay solenoid to the vacuum amplifier at the amplifier end.
3. Turn the car's ignition switch to "START" and then release it, so that it returns to "RUN".
4. Suck on the end of the disconnected hose; the hose should be blocked.
5. After about 35 seconds from the

The 1973½ EGR temperature control valve is located on the top tank of the radiator on Chrysler Products

Temperature sensing valve used on the Chrysler EGR system

time that the ignition switch was turned to "START", the solenoid should open, allowing air to flow through the line that you are sucking on.
6. If the system isn't working, disconnect the solenoid and connect it directly to a 12-volt power source, making and breaking the circuit several times. If the solenoid works, replace the delay timer.
7. If the solenoid doesn't work, replace the solenoid.
8. Reconnect the vacuum lines and the coil after completing the test.

Chrysler Corp. 1975 EGR Reminder Light

NOTE: This light is designed to remind the driver that regularly scheduled service is due; it does not mean that the EGR system is not working properly.

1. After checking the EGR system for proper operation, slide the rubber boot on the EGR reminder odometer up, out of the way.
2. Reset the odometer with a small screwdriver.
3. Slide the boot back down over the odometer. The light will come on again when the next 15,000 mile check-up is due.

1973 Ford EGR System Tests

1. Allow the engine to warm up, so that the coolant temperature has reached at least 125°F.
2. Disconnect the vacuum hose which runs from the temperature cut-in valve to the EGR valve at the EGR valve end. Connect a vacuum gauge to this hose with a T-fitting.
3. Increase engine speed. The gauge should indicate a vacuum. If no vacuum is present, check the following:
   a. The carburetor—look for a clogged vacuum port.
   b. The vacuum hoses—including the vacuum hoses to the transmission modulator.
   c. The temperature cut-in valve—if no vacuum is present at its outlet with the engine temperature above 125°F and vacuum available from the carburetor, the valve is defective.
4. If all of the above tests are positive, check the EGR valve itself.
5. Connect an outside vacuum source and a vacuum gauge to the valve.
6. Apply vacuum to the EGR valve. The valve should open at 3–10 in. Hg, the engine idle speed should slow down, and the idle quality should become more rough.
7. If this does not happen, i.e., the EGR valve remains closed, the EGR valve is defective and must be replaced.
8. If the valve stem moves but the idle remains the same, the valve orifice is clogged and must be cleaned.

NOTE: If an outside vacuum source is not available, disconnect the hose which runs between the EGR valve and the temperature cut-in valve and plug the hose connections on the cut-in valve. Connect the EGR valve hose to a source of intake manifold vacuum and watch the idle. The results should be the same as in steps 6–7, above.

Vacuum Modulator—Bench Test

NOTE: The vacuum modulator is used only with an automatic transmission.

1. Remove the vacuum modulator from the truck.
2. Connect the modulator to an outside vacuum source: a distributor tester, for example. NOTE: The vacuum source should be adjusted to supply 18 in. Hg, with the end of the vacuum line blocked off.
3. Connect the vacuum line from the vacuum source to the EGR port on the vacuum modulator.
4. The vacuum modulator should hold the 18 in. Hg reading. If it does not, then the diaphragm is leaking and must be replaced.

Temperature Cut-In Valve— Bench Test

1. Remove the valve from the engine.
2. Connect an outside source of vacuum to the top port on the valve. Leave the bottom port vented to the atmosphere.
3. Use ice or an aerosol spray to cool the valve below 60°F.
4. Apply 20 in. Hg vacuum to the valve. The valve should hold a minimum of 19 in. Hg vacuum for five minutes without leaking down.
5. Leave the vacuum source connected to the valve and place it, along with a high temperature thermometer, into a non-metallic, heat-resistant container full of water.
6. Heat the water. The vacuum in the valve should drop to zero once the temperature of the water reaches about 125°F.
7. Replace the valve if it fails either of the tests.

1973 Ford High Speed EGR Modulator—System Tests

NOTE: Before beginning this test, check the EGR valve and the other related components as outlined in the section above.

1. Detach the line from the EGR valve. Connect a vacuum gauge to the line, using a T-fitting, and reconnect the EGR valve. NOTE: Position the vacuum gauge so that it can be seen from the driver's seat.
2. Raise the rear wheels of the car off the ground, supporting it so that it cannot roll forward.
3. Start the engine and allow it to warm up at *fast* idle for 3–4 minutes.
4. Return the engine to normal idle; the vacuum gauge reading should return to zero.

5. Place the transmission in Third gear (manual) or Drive (automatic). Increase the engine speed; vacuum should also increase.
6. At an indicated speed of approximately 67 mph, the vacuum gauge reading should drop to zero.

If the system is functioning properly, lower the car, disconnect the vacuum gauge, and reconnect the vacuum lines. If the system is malfunctioning, proceed with the tests below.

Power Supply Tests

CAUTION: Do not use a self-powered test light; damage to the amplifier could result.

1. Check the electrical leads which run to and from the vacuum solenoid valve with a low-amperage test light. The car should be running so that power is being supplied to the system.
2. If there is no current at the valve, trace the wiring back to its power source to determine the reason for the failure.
3. If there is current at the valve, remove the power connector from the amplifier and check for current at the connector. If there is none, replace the wiring between the amplifier and the vacuum valve.

Speed Sensor Tests

1. Check the resistance of the speed sensor by touching its leads with the test prods of an ohmmeter. The ohmmeter should read 40–60 ohms.
2. Replace the speed sensor if its resistance is not within specifications.
3. Check the connector on the speed sensor to be sure that it is tight. If the ground interlock loop between the connectors is loose, the circuit will not be grounded and the speed sensor will appear not to be functioning.

Vacuum Solenoid Valve Tests

1. Disconnect the leads from the vacuum solenoid valve which run to the amplifier. CAUTION: Never connect a jumper lead or a self-powered test light to the valve while it is still connected to the amplifier; damage to the amplifier could result.
2. Connect a vacuum gauge to the EGR valve port on the vacuum valve.
3. With the valve disconnected from the amplifier, connect the valve directly to a 12V power source (the battery) with jumper leads.
4. With the transmission in Neu-

tral and current flowing to the valve, increase the engine speed to 1,500 rpm. The vacuum gauge should read zero. If it does not, replace the valve.

5. Disconnect the 12V power source from the valve. The gauge should show a vacuum reading with the engine speed at 1,500 rpm.

If the valve is not functioning properly, replace it. If it is functioning properly and the system still is not, the only other possible source of trouble is the amplifier; replace it.

NOTE: There is no way to test amplifier operation other than by process of elimination or by substitution. Attempts to check it will probably lead to its failure, if it is not already defective.

1974-75 Ford EGR System— Component Tests

1. Perform Steps 5-8 of the "1973 Ford EGR System Test". Replace the EGR valve and gasket, if necessary.
2. Connect a vacuum gauge to the EGR port on the carburetor, after disconnecting the EGR vacuum hose.
3. With the engine running (warmed-up), quickly open the throttle halfway. Allow the throttle to close.
4. If the vacuum gauge shows a quick rise and fall in vacuum, the EGR port is not clogged. No reading indicates a clogged port; if there is no reading, clean the port.
5. Check the coolant temperature operated vacuum valve (PVS) which controls the EGR system vacuum, when the engine is cold, as outlined in the appropriate section. Check the vacuum hoses for correct routing.

If everything else is in good working order, proceed with the vacuum amplifier tests (if so equipped):

6. Run the engine until normal operating temperature is reached.
7. Check the vacuum amplifier connections to be sure that they are tight and that the hoses are routed properly.
8. Remove the hose which runs from the EGR valve to the vacuum amplifier at the EGR valve end. Connect a vacuum gauge to this hose; the gauge *must* read in increments of 1 in. Hg or less.
9. Disconnect the venturi vacuum hose at the carburetor port.
10. With the engine at curb idle, the vacuum gauge should read either zero or show a small reading.
11. Increase the engine speed to 1500-2000 rpm, then allow it to return to idle.
12. If the vacuum reading increases more than 1 in. Hg or if it does

not return to the same figure indicated in Step 10, replace the amplifier.

13. Reconnect the venturi hose to the carburetor port.

14. With the engine at curb idle, there should be no great increase in vacuum above the figure obtained in Step 10 (more than 0.5 in. Hg). If the vacuum increases greatly, check the idle speed, it is probably too high.

15. Unfasten the external reservoir hose from the amplifier and plug it.

16. Rapidly increase the engine speed to 1500-2000 rpm. The vacuum gauge reading should increase by at least 4 in. Hg; if it does not, replace the amplifier.

17. After completing the tests, remove the gauge and connect the vacuum hoses.

18. Check the external vacuum amplifier reservoir, if so equipped, by following the procedure outlined below.

External Amplifer Reservoir

Without Check Valve

1. Disconnect the reservoir-to-amplifier hose. Connect a vacuum gauge to it.

2. Using an external vacuum source, apply at least 14 in. Hg to the reservoir.

3. Trap the vacuum in the reservoir.

4. The vacuum should drop no more than 1 in. Hg in 1 minute. If it does, replace the reservoir.

With External Check Valve

1. Connect an external vacuum source and gauge to the amplifier side of the T-fitting in the reservoir-to-check valve hose.

2. Apply and trap 15 in. Hg to the line. Vacuum should leak down no more than 1 in. Hg in 1 minute. If it doesn't the system is OK. If it does, proceed with the rest of the test.

3. Remove the reservoir hose at the T-fitting and apply 15 in. Hg to the reservoir. Trap the vacuum in the reservoir.

4. The vacuum should drop no more than 1 in. Hg in 1 minute. If it does, replace the reservoir.

5. Remove the check valve hose. Apply 15 in. Hg vacuum to the check valve and trap it.

6. The vacuum should drop no more than 1 in. Hg in 1 minute. Replace the check valve if it does otherwise.

7. Remove the vacuum pump, and gauge. Reconnect the hoses.

Two-Nipple EGR/PVS

1. Disconnect the hoses from the EGR coolant temperature operated vacuum valve (PVS).

2. Connect a vacuum gauge to one of the nipples and an external vacuum source to the other (it doesn't matter which).

3. If the engine is cold, start it and allow the coolant temperature to reach at least 135°F.

4. If the vacuum doesn't indicate vacuum with the engine warm when vacuum is applied, the PVS is defective. Replace it.

5. If vacuum is indicated, the PVS is OK.

Three-Nipple EGR/PVS

1. Disconnect the EGR vacuum hose, from the carburetor port. Connect the hose to either manifold vacuum or an auxiliary vacuum source.

2. Remove the vacuum hose from the EGR valve and connect a vacuum gauge to the hose.

3. If the engine is cold, start it and allow the coolant temperature to reach at least 135°F.

4. If the gauge doesn't indicate vacuum the PVS is defective and should be replaced.

5. If the gauge indicates vacuum the PVS is OK. Remove the gauge and reconnect the vacuum lines.

1973 American Motors Jeep EGR System Test

NOTE: Start the test with the engine cold.

1. Disconnect the vacuum line at the EGR valve. Connect a vacuum gauge to the vacuum line.

2. Heat the low ambient compensator (located in front of the radiator) in the palm of the hand, until it is above 60°F.

3. Start the engine; increase engine speed. There should be no vacuum reading on the gauge. Allow the engine to warm up to at least 125°F (160°F—304 V8/manual). With the ambient temperature compensator above 60°F and the engine coolant temperature above 125°F (160°F), vacuum should be present when the engine speed is increased.

4. Using a trouble light or some other suitable heat source, heat the *high* temperature compensator (mounted on the firewall) to above 155°F. Speed the engine up; the vacuum reading should be zero or quite low.

5. Cool the *high* temperature compensator to below 115°F, using ice; the gauge should now show a strong vacuum reading.

6. Using ice, cool the *low* ambient compensator to below 60°F; the vacuum reading should decrease.

7. If vacuum is present when it should not be, while one of the components is being tested, re-

place the component and repeat the system test.

8. If *no* vacuum is present when it should be, check the vacuum lines. If the lines are satisfactory, replace the suspect component and repeat the system test. Disconnect the vacuum gauge when the tests are completed.

9. Connect the EGR valve directly to the carburetor port or some other source of vacuum. Speed up the engine; the valve stem should move upward (8–10 in. Hg). Allow the engine to slow down; the valve stem should move down. If the valve is defective, replace it. Reconnect the vacuum lines.

NOTE: The following components were dropped from the EGR system on, or after 15 March 1973:

1. High temperature compensator—All engines.

2. Low temperature compensator—All engines.

3. Coolant temperature override switch—Six-cylinder engines only.

Those steps of the test procedure which deal with these components are not required on models made after 15 March 1973.

1974-75 American Motors Jeep EGR System

EGR Valve Tests—All Engines

1. Start the engine and allow it to reach normal operating temperature.

2. Compress the EGR valve diaphragm by hand; the engine speed should drop by about 200 rpm.

CAUTION: Be careful when depressing the valve diaphragm, the area around the valve gets very hot.

3. If the engine speed doesn't drop, but the engine is idling smoothly, the EGR passage to the intake manifold is plugged and must be cleaned.

4. If the engine idle is poor, and lifting the diaphragm has no effect on its speed, the EGR valve is probably plugged or defective. Clean or replace it, as necessary.

5. Insert a T-fitting in the EGR valve vacuum line and connect a vacuum gauge to the fitting.

6. Increase the engine speed slowly, while watching the vacuum gauge; at the same time either watch or feel the valve diaphragm.

7. The valve should start to open between 1.8-3.2 in. Hg and be fully opened at 3.8-7.3 in. Hg.

8. At wide-open throttle, the diaphragm should be fully depressed with no sign of leakage. Replace the valve if it is defective.

Emission Control Systems

EGR Coolant Temperature Operated Vacuum Valve—All Engines

NOTE: Engine coolant temperature must be below 100°F before beginning this test.

1. Be sure that the lines are routed correctly and are not pinched, plugged, or leaking.
2. Unfasten the vacuum line from the EGR valve. Connect a vacuum gauge to this line.
3. Start the engine and increase its speed to 1500 rpm. The vacuum gauge should read zero; if it does not, replace the coolant temperature operated vacuum valve.
4. Allow the engine to run until the coolant temperature reaches 115°F or more.

NOTE: At 115°F, the needle on the car's temperature gauge should be halfway between "C" and the beginning of the band.

5. Increase the engine speed to 1500 rpm again. The vacuum gauge should show ported vacuum; if it doesn't, replace the vacuum valve.

Exhaust Backpressure Sensor Test—California Engines

1. Check all vacuum lines and fittings. Make sure that the vacuum line to the EGR valve is connected to the coolant temperature operated vacuum valve nipple with the 0.030 in. restriction.
2. Install a vacuum gauge, using a T-fitting, in the line which runs from the EGR valve to the backpressure sensor.
3. Start the engine and allow it to warm-up. With the engine at curb idle the vacuum gauge should read zero.
4. If vacuum is present, check the vacuum lines to be sure that manifold vacuum is *not* being used instead of carburetor ported vacuum. If the correct ported vacuum is being used, check to be sure that the throttle plate isn't sticking opened.
5. Increase the engine speed to 2000 rpm, while watching for one of the following:
   a. If the coolant temperature is less than 115°F, the gauge should read zero.
   b. If the coolant temperature is less than 115°F, the gauge should show ported vacuum.
6. If vacuum is not shown when it should be, or vice versa, check the coolant temperature operated vacuum valve, as previously outlined.
7. If everything else is in good working order, remove the backpressure sensor. Check to see that the spacer port and tube are not blocked. Clean them with a spiral wire brush, as necessary. If this doesn't solve the problem, replace the backpressure sensor.

Catalytic Converters

Testing the Converter

At the present time there is no known way to reliably test catalytic converter operation in the field. The only reliable test is a 12 hour and 40 minute "soak test" (CVS) which must be done in a laboratory.

An infrared HC/CO tester is not sensitive enough to measure the higher tailpipe emissions from a partially-failed converter. Thus, a bad converter may allow enough HC and CO emissions to escape, so that the car is not in compliance with Federal (or state) standards, but still will not cause the needle on the HC/CO tester to move off zero.

You can check a converter for physical damage, such as a ripped skin or crushed shell. You can test for a plugged converter the same way you test for a plugged muffler. You can look for pellets coming out of the tailpipe, which means the pellets are breaking up. All such physical damage means the converter must be repaired, replaced, or recharged. But when it comes to testing the actual efficiency of the converter, or measuring the amount of HC and CO that it removes from the exhaust, forget it.

If you have a vehicle with high HC or CO coming out the tailpipe, the problem has to be in the engine. If you took the converter off most 1975 vehicles, they would still be as clean as the 1974 cars. The converter removes so little HC and CO from the exhaust that even with the converter taken off, the car would still pass state or city emission control laws. The converter was put on the 1975 vehicles so they would pass the EPA and California laboratory test, which is much more severe than any state or city used car standards, including California.

If you discover the vehicle has high tailpipe emissions, or if the vehicle gets a citation for high emissions, it's easy to jump to the conclusion that the converter is to blame. *Do not replace or recharge a converter because of high tailpipe emissions.* The problem is in the engine, not the converter.

Following are the most common causes of high tailpipe emissions, as measured on an infrared tester.

High HC	Missing cylinder Lean mixture screws Extreme flooding
High CO	Rich mixture screws Dirty air cleaner High float level

The only domestic manufacturer who gives idle CO settings is Chrysler. The mixture screws are set with the air pump disconnected, which reduces the efficiency of the converter and causes enough CO to go through that you get a reading. American Motors and General Motors use the lean drop method of setting idle mixture, and Ford uses the speed increase method of adding propane.

Recharging or Changing Converters

Because the converter cannot be tested in the field, many people wonder what should be done to it. We have established the following guidelines.

1. The manufacturer requires it.
2. The converter is damaged beyond repair.
3. The law requires it.
4. The catalyst doesn't work.

So far, there is no requirement by either the car manufacturer or the law to change or recharge the converter according to mileage or time. General Motors and American Motors converters can be repaired if the bottom cover is damaged by installing a replacement cover.

We know of only two ways to tell if the catalyst isn't working. If *you* see pellets or pieces of the catalyst coming out the tailpipe, the catalyst is breaking up, and the converter must be recharged or changed. The other indication is the catalyst that melts and plugs the exhaust. In that case, you have to do something immediately, because the car probably won't run.

Leaded fuel will reduce the efficiency of the converter while the leaded fuel is being used. After the leaded fuel has been used up, and the car runs again on non-leaded fuel, the converter will recover its efficiency to a degree. How much the converter recovers depends on how long it was run on leaded fuel. How much efficiency is reduced you have no way of knowing.

Converter Removal

A new car dealer is prohibited by federal law from tampering with emission controls. If the catalyst melts or breaks up, he must replace or recharge the converter. An independent shop's work on emission controls is regulated by state and local laws. Before you remove a converter

862

Layout of Catalytic Converter Ramcharger/Trailduster—2 w/Drive top, 4 w/Drive Bottom
(© Chrysler Corp.)

make sure that you are not breaking any state or local laws.

Catalyst Damage

Converters operate best at an internal temperature of 600-1500°F. At 1700°F or higher, the catalyst begins to melt or break up. The converter generates its own heat, according to how many hydrocarbons are fed through it. Hydrocarbons are nothing more than raw, liquid fuel, so any excess of fuel will cause the converter to overheat. The following conditions will cause extra fuel to go through the converter, and may damage it.

1. Fast idle for a long time.
2. A missing plug or plugs, for a long time.
3. An extremely rich mixture for a long time.

How long is a long time? Only the converter knows. Garage testing may overheat the converter if carried on too long. Any testing that requires shorting out one or more cylinders will put raw fuel through the converter.

There is nothing wrong with these tests, as long as they are done quickly. The same applies to dynamometer tests. It isn't necessary to hold the engine at full throttle for more than a few seconds. There is no reason for changing normal dynamometer procedures. However, if you are doing experimental work that requires a lot of dyno running, the converter could overheat. For extensive experimental work, we suggest removing the converter temporarily and putting a length of empty tubing in its place. On the dyno, you can remove the converter (if it isn't welded) and put your exhaust collector over the end of the exhaust pipe.

The following check list shows possible causes for catalyst damage:

Excessive vibration
Rich mixtures
Leaded fuel
Spark plug misfire
Excessive fast idle
Running out of gas (causes misfire)
Fuel additives
Carbon solvents

Misuse of engine (turning key off at speed)
Total ignition failure at speed

Catalyst Protection System Testing

Chrysler Corp.

1. Start the engine and allow it to warm up.
2. Connect a tachometer to the engine.
3. Increase the engine speed to 2,500 rpm; the solenoid plunger should extend.
4. Release the throttle, once the engine speed has dropped below 2,000 rpm; the plunger should retract.
5. If the solenoid doesn't work properly, disconnect it from the speed switch and connect it to a 12 volt power source. If the plunger extends, the solenoid is working and the speed switch is defective. Replace the speed switch.
6. If the plunger does not extend, the solenoid is defective and must be replaced.
7. With the solenoid connected to the 12 volt power source (energized) so that its plunger is out,

Emission Control Systems

adjust the engine speed to 1,500 rpm.

CAUTION: Do not adjust the curb idle speed with the catalyst protection system solenoid. This is not an antidieseling solenoid. If the curb idle speed is adjusted with this solenoid, it will be far above 2,000 rpm once the solenoid has been energized, creating a hazardous driving situation. The only way to stop an engine which has been adjusted in this manner, is to shut it off and not restart it until the solenoid has been correctly adjusted.

8. Reconnect the solenoid to the speed switch and disconnect the tachometer, once the proper setting has been obtained.

Replacing the Catalyst

Chrysler and Ford

The catalyst used in Ford and Chrysler products is the monolithic (one-piece) type which cannot be removed from the converter for replacement.

If the catalyst fails, it will be necessary to replace the entire converter assembly with a new one. To do so, proceed as follows:

CAUTION: Allow the converter assembly to cool completely before attempting to service it; catalyst temperatures can reach 1500°-1600°F.

1. If a grass shield is used, remove the bolts which secure it and lower the shield from underneath the vehicle.
2. Unbolt the converter assembly at the mounting flanges, just as you would a normal exhaust pipe from the manifold.

NOTE: Support the exhaust pipe while the converter is removed.

3. Replace the old converter with a new unit which is the exact same size, part number, and type (or its *exact* equivalent) as was originally installed.
4. Remove the plastic plugs from the ends of the converter (if used) and install it in the reverse order of removal, being sure to use new gaskets to ensure a leakfree fit.
5. Install the grass shields.

GM and AMC Jeep

General Motors and American Motors vehicles use pellets in their converters, which may be replaced without replacing the whole catalytic converter assembly.

To replace the pellets, proceed as follows:

CAUTION: Allow the converter assembly to cool completely before attempting to service it; catalyst temperatures can reach 1500°F.

1. Using a ¾ in. allen wrench, loosen, but do not remove the converter fill plug.
2. Remove the four nuts and bolts at each converter flange. Lower the converter being careful to note the position of, and saving any gaskets used.
3. Loosely install the upper rear flange nuts and bolts, to secure the exhaust system to the hanger while the converter is removed.
4. Place the converter on the workbench and remove the fill plug. Drain the old pellets into a container and discard them.
5. Inspect the converter housing for signs of damage. Replace the assembly, if necessary.
6. Clamp the special vibrator to the converter flange on the opposite end from the fill plug, with the mounting nuts and bolts.
7. Place the converter on a 30° angle with the fill plug end up.

Layout of Catalytic Converter Ford F100 Trucks (© Ford Motor Co.)

IGNITION SWITCH
TO BATTERY

START

RUN

BALLAST RESISTOR

THROTTLE POSITION
SOLENOID

ELECTRONIC CONTROL UNIT

BATTERY

ELECTRONIC SPEED SWITCH

Fill the converter with new catalyst pellets through a funnel.
8. When it appears that the converter is full, connect the air supply to the vibrator and continue to add pellets in small amounts. Pack the pellets in tightly with your fingers.
9. Once the pellets are flush with

Catalyst Protection System

the fill plug, remove the air supply from the vibrator. Coat the fill plug with an anti-seize compound and tighten it 50 ft lbs (GM) or 40 ft lbs (AMC).
10. Remove the vibrator.
11. Install the converter assembly on

the car in the reverse order of removal, being sure to use all necessary gaskets. Tighten the flange nuts and bolts.
NOTE: GM makes a kit to replace the bottom converter cover should it become torn or damaged.

Vacuum-Operated Heat Risers

These valves are similar to the spring-operated heat risers used on American cars for many years. The old valve was operated by a bimetal spring. The type of valve is operated by a vacuum motor (diaphragm) which, in turn, is controlled by a vacuum valve that is temperature-sensitive. In some applications the vacuum is controlled by a solenoid that is hooked up to a temperature switch.

1975 Ford Vacuum Exhaust Heat Valve

Valve Test

1. With the engine off, look at the rod which connects the diaphragm with the valve lever. The rod should be fully extended (no vacuum applied).
2. Connect a hand-operated vacuum pump with a gauge to the diaphragm unit.
3. Apply vacuum. Check the results against the chart below:

Engine	Valve starts to close (*in. Hg*)	Valve Closed (*in. Hg*)
302, 351W	1-3	6 or less
315M, 400	3-6	10 or less

4. If the valve rod doesn't extend fully when no vacuum is applied and doesn't close fully when vacuum is applied, tap the valve and apply heat riser lubricant to free it.
5. Apply 15-20 in. Hg vacuum to the diaphragm and trap it. If the vacuum leaks down more than 2 in. Hg in one minute, replace the valve assembly.

Coolant Temperature Operated Vacuum Valve

1. Start with the engine cold.
2. Remove the vacuum line from the top nipple. Connect a hand-operated vacuum pump to the nipple.
3. Plug the middle nipple. Apply vacuum. The valve should hold the vacuum without leaking down.
4. With the engine at normal operating temperature, leave the middle nipple open and apply vacuum. The valve should hold vacuum and not leak down.
5. With the engine hot, remove the vacuum pump and connect the hose. Attach a hose to the middle

nipple and blow through it. Air should come out through the valve vent.
6. If the valve doesn't work as outlined, replace it with a new one.

GM Early Fuel Evaporation (EFE) System

Starting in 1975, all L6 and most GM V8 engines use a vacuum-operated heat riser valve. GM calls this system "Early Fuel Evaporation" or "EFE" for short.

With the exception of the 250-6 and the 454-V8, all engines use a coolant temperature operated vacuum valve (EFE/TVV) to control vacuum to the EFE valve vacuum motor. The 250-6 and 454-V8 use an oil temperature switch and vacuum solenoid, instead.

EFE Valve Test—All Engines

1. Inspect the manifold heat riser valve and linkage for damage and binding. Check for plugged, cracked, or misrouted vacuum hoses.
2. Connect external vacuum source and vacuum gauge to the EFE valve vacuum motor, after dis-

connecting the vacuum hose from it.

3. Apply at least 10 in. Hg vacuum to the motor. The valve should move freely. The motor should hold the plunger in the retracted position for 1 minute without the application of additional vacuum.

4. If the vacuum motor leaks down in less than 1 minute or fails to operate the EFE valve (linkage not binding), replace it.

5. If the valve or linkage binds, use heat riser lubricant on it. If the valve can't be freed by tapping it loose and lubricating it, replace the assembly.

EFE Vacuum Solenoid Test—250-6 and Chevrolet 454-V8

1. Disconnect the engine harness wiring plug from the solenoid. Use a short jumper wire to connect one of the solenoid terminals to ground. Run a hot wire from the positive battery terminal to the other terminal.

2. The solenoid should click when the wire is connected. If not, the solenoid is defective.

3. To check for correct vacuum switching of the solenoid, connect an engine manifold vacuum hose to the nozzle that points straight down in the opposite direction from the wire terminals. Connect a vacuum gauge to the nozzle that points out to the side of the solenoid.

4. With the engine running, energize the solenoid as described above. Full manifold vacuum should appear on the gauge.

5. De-energize the solenoid and the vacuum should drop to zero. If not, the solenoid is defective.

6. The manifold vacuum hose must connect to the bottom and nozzle, not to the side nozzle. If the hoses are hooked up backwards, the EFE valve may stay closed after the engine warms up.

7. Repairs are limited to replacement. Test the new solenoid to be sure it sends vacuum to the EFE actuator when energized. If it allows vacuum through when de-energized it's the wrong solenoid.

Oil Temperature Switch Test—250-6 and Chevrolet 454-V8

1. Disconnect the oil temperature switch harness wiring.

2. Connect a self-powered test light between the switch terminal and ground.

3. If the engine is cold (below 150°—250-6 or 100°F—454-V8), the test light should come on.

4. Run the engine. When it reaches normal operating temperature, the light should go out.

5. Replace the switch if it doesn't work as outlined.

EFE Coolant Temperature Operated Vacuum Valve Tests

5-nozzle Valve

This valve may be identified by the nozzle on top and four nozzles down the side. A vent is also located on the other side.

1. Remove the vacuum hose from the top (vertical) nozzle and cap it.

2. Connect a hand-operated vacuum pump to the top nozzle on the side and a vacuum gauge to the next lower nozzle.

3. On a cold engine vacuum should register on the gauge.

4. Allow the engine to warm up to about 120°F.

5. The gauge should register zero. The valve should hold vacuum and not leak down.

6. Remove the vacuum gauge from the lower nozzle and blow through it. Air should come out of the vent.

7. Replace the valve if it doesn't work as outlined.

4-Nozzle Valve

This valve may be identified by the one vertical nozzle on top and the three nozzles down the side. There is also a vent on the side opposite the three nozzles.

1. Remove the hose from the top (vertical) nozzle. Connect a hand-operated vacuum pump to it.

2. Connect a vacuum gauge to the top nozzle on the side (marked "HV").

3. On a warm engine, about 120°F., the vertical nozzle should be

closed and you should be able to get a reading on the hand pump gauge. The gauge connected to the "HV" nozzle should read zero.

4. Remove the vacuum gauge and blow through the "HV" nozzle; air should come out the vent.

5. Relieve the cooling system pressure and remove the coolant temperature operated vacuum valve.

6. Cool the valve in an ice bath. Below 120°F, you should get a reading on the gauge attached to the HV nozzle. The vacuum should not leak down.

7. Replace the valve if it doesn't work as outlined.

2-Nozzle Valve

This valve may be identified by the two nozzles on the one side with a vent on the opposite side.

1. Disconnect the vacuum hose from the top nozzle. Connect a hand-operated vacuum pump to the nozzle.

2. Connect a vacuum gauge to the lower nozzle.

3. On a cold engine the vacuum gauge on the lower nozzle should register when the vacuum is applied to the upper nozzle. The vent should be closed.

4. Warm the engine up, so that the coolant is above one of the following:
   Chevrolet V8—180°F
   Cadillac V8—150°F
   All other V8—120°F

5. Apply vacuum to the upper nozzle. The gauge on the lower nozzle should register zero.

6. Remove the vacuum gauge from the lower nozzle. Blow through the nozzle, air should come out the vent.

7. Replace the valve if it doesn't work as outlined.

EFE Check Valve Test

Some engines have a check valve in the EFE vacuum line.

1. Remove the vacuum hose from the tapered end of the check valve.

2. Connect a hand-operated vacuum pump with gauge to the check valve. Apply vacuum and trap it.

3. The vacuum should not leak down. Replace the check valve if vacuum leaks down more than 0.5 in. Hg in one minute.

Diesel Engine Emission Control Systems

PERIODIC MAINTENANCE

1. Injector Nozzles: Remove and test spray pattern, clean, and adjust opening pressure, if necessary, when smoke or poor performance are present.

2. Puff Limiter: Mack puff limiters are either of the piston or diaphragm design with sealed, internal governor control and are connected to the inlet manifold by a flexible tube. Service consists of checking the tube for

chafing, connections for tightness, and the unit for stroke and boost pressure.
American Bosch injector pump
   Pump Limiter Stroke—.095-.105″
Robert Bosch injector pump
   Puff Limiter Stroke—.080″

American Bosch injector pump
Boost Pressure (PSI) —12
Robert Bosch injector pump
Boost Pressure (PSI) —5.9-8.9
3. Injector Pump: Timing should be checked and set every 50,000 mi. See service section for specifications.
4. Lubrication System: Check crankcase level daily before starting engine. Except END&T 475: EO-H: Change oil and filters at 16,000 mi. EO-G: Change oil and' filters at 8,000 mi. END&T 475: These models have no filter element. A centrifugal type oil filter is located on the left side of the engine. It should be cleaned every 4,000 mi. See service section for filter disassembly. ENDT 475 Turbocharger Oil Filter: Change every 6,-000 mi.
5. Turbocharger: Remove end housings and clean compressor and turbine impellers at 50,000 mi. using a commercial solvent.
6. Valves: Check and adjust to specifications every 50,000 mi.
7. Inter-cooler: Blow out fins in reverse direction of airflow every 50,000 mi. Remove end cover from tip turbine fan and wash with solvent every 50,000 mi.
8. Crankcase vent cap: clean every 50,000 mi.
9. Overboard breather tube: Clean and inspect every 50,000 mi.
10. Cooling system: Check level daily.
11. Air Cleaner: Dry—Change element when indicator show red. Oil bath—Clean and refill every 8,000 mi. Clean upper element every 24,000 mi.

TROUBLESHOOTING

Smoke and Erratic Engine at Idle
1. Fuel filters clogged.
2. Injection pump overflow valve faulty.
3. Injection pump internal adjustment incorrect.

Smoke and Erratic Engine at Idle and High Speed
1. Air intake manifold valve closed.
2. Restricted air intake or clogged air cleaner.
3. Injection pump internal adjustment incorrect.

Smoke and Missing at Idle and High Speed
1. Injection pump internal adjustment incorrect.
2. Worn injection pump shaft bearings.
3. Loose injection pump drive assembly.

Blow-by at Crankcase Breather
1. Rings stuck or worn.
2. Rings broken or improperly fitted.
3. Scuffed pistons or sleeves.

Black Smoke and Stalling
1. Defective governor parts.
2. Turbocharger passing oil.
3. Restricted air intake, clogged air cleaner.

Black or Brown Smoke and Power Loss
1. Air intake manifold valve closed.
2. Fuel tank vent plugged.
3. Faulty nozzle spray, leaking, or incorrect opening pressure.

Blue or White Smoke and Power Loss
1. Leaky Cylinder head gasket.
2. Rings stuck or worn.
3. Rings broken.

Engine Puffs Excessively
1. Improper governor setting.
2. Defective puff limiter hose.
3. Defective puff limiter diaphragm or piston.

Detroit Diesel Emission Control
Continuous research and development, and the inherent operating efficiency of a diesel engine, make most modern, commercial designs very clean powerplants. Because of the severity of pollution resulting from automotive sources, efforts have been made to make the diesel engine still more clean and odor free than ever before. These modifications include:
1. Provision of the new "C" type injector, whose low sac volume reduces the amount of oil left under the needle valve after the end of injection, thus assuring that a larger proportion of the fuel enters the chamber in properly atomized form.
2. Redesign of the injector plunger to provide retarded injection timing at part throttle, which reduces peak temperatures and nitrous oxides.
3. Slightly retarded timing through a change in the external timing dimension.
4. Use of a throttle delay system on all turbocharged engines. This system slows the movement of the injector rack toward full fuel, thus compensating for the gradual increase in airflow due to the inertia of the turbocharger. Thus, excessively rich mixtures are avoided.

Required Maintenance Services
1. Replace fuel filters or filter elements every 10,000 miles or at the first sign of plugging.
2. Check injector timing as described in the Detroit Diesel service section every 40,000 miles in city service, or 80,000 miles in highway service, and adjust as necessary.
3. Check the idle and no load speeds as described in the service section every 40,000 miles.
4. Inspect the throttle delay adjustment (the initial location of the cylinder) every 80,000 miles, and adjust as necessary.
5. Inspect a dry type air cleaner and service it every 20,000 miles. Clean and or repair as necessary, checking the gaskets and aspirator (where so equipped) along with the element. Intake restriction must not exceed 20 inches of water for turbocharged engines, or 25 inches of water for normally aspirated engines.
6. Clean and refill the oil cup on oil bath air cleaners every 4,000-6,-000 miles, depending on operating conditions. Remove and steam clean the element and baffles annually. Increased frequency of service is necessary if dusty conditions are encountered. Intake restriction must not exceed 25 inches of water on normally aspirated engines, or 20 inches of water on turbocharged engines.
7. Engine oil and filters must be changed at 3,000 miles, and every 4,000-6,000 miles thereafter.
8. The turbocharger air intake, exhaust ducts, and mountings should be checked daily. Check also the lubricant lines for restricted flow, and listen for any unusual noises or vibration. Any turbocharger malfunction whatsoever will result in overly rich mixtures and excessive smoke and carbon monoxide emissions.
9. The cooling system should be checked for proper coolant level daily. Thermostats and seals should be checked annually. The barrel of the thermostat should be lightly polished if the seals are working effectively. The thermostat should be checked for operating temperature within limits, as too low a temperature will cause excessive smoke emissions.
10. The blower and screen should be inspected annually. The screen should be cleaned in fuel oil and dried with compressed air (failure to dry can cause the engine to run away when started). Install the screen and gasket assembly with the screen toward the blower. Check for evidence of seal leakage, and repair as necessary.

Index

Manual Steering

Power Steering

STEERING TROUBLE DIAGNOSIS

Condition	Possible Cause	Correction
	Steering Gear	
Excessive Play or Looseness in the Steering	(1) Steering gear shaft adjusted too loose or shaft and/or bushing badly worn.	(1) Replace worn parts and adjust according to instructions.
	(2) Excessive steering gear worm end play due to bearing adjustment.	(2) Adjust according to instructions.
	(3) Steering linkage loose or worn.	(3) Replace worn parts.
	(4) Front wheel bearings improperly adjusted.	(4) Adjust wheel bearings.
	(5) Steering arm loose on steering gear shaft.	(5) Inspect for damage to the gear shaft and steering arm, replace parts as necessary.
	(6) Steering gear housing attaching bolts loose.	(6) Tighten the attaching bolts to specifications.
	(7) Steering arms loose at steering knuckles.	(7) Tighten according to specifications.
	(8) Worn king pins or bushings.	(8) Replace king pins and bushings.
	(9) Loose spring shackles.	(9) Adjust or replace parts as necessary.
Hard Steering	(1) Low or uneven tire pressure.	(1) Inflate the tires to recommended pressures.
	(2) Insufficient lubricant in the steering gear housing or in steering linkage.	(2) Lubricate as necessary.
	(3) Steering gear shaft adjusted too tight.	(3) Adjust according to instructions.
	(4) Improper caster or toe-in.	(4) Align the wheels.
	(5) Steering column misaligned.	(5) See "Steering Gear Alignment."
	(6) Loose, worn or broken pump belt.	(6) Adjust or replace belt.
	(7) Air in system.	(7) Bleed air from system.
	(8) Low fluid level in the pump reservoir.	(8) Fill to correct level.
	(9) Pump output pressure low.	(9) See "Pressure Test."
	(10) Leakage at power cylinder piston rings. (Linkage type).	(10) Replace piston rings and repair as required.
	(11) Binding or bent cylinder linkage. (Linkage type).	(11) Replace or repair as required.
	(12) Valve spool and/or sleeve sticking. (Linkage type).	(12) Free-up or replace as required.
Pull to One Side (Tendency of the Vehicle to Veer in one Direction Only)	(1) Incorrect tire pressure or tire sizes not uniform.	(1) Check tire sizes and inflate the tires to recommended pressures.
	(2) Wheel bearings improperly adjusted.	(2) Adjust wheel bearings.
	(3) Dragging brakes.	(3) Inspect for weak, or broken brake shoe spring, binding pedal.
	(4) Improper caster, camber or toe-in.	(4) Adjust to specifications.
	(5) Grease, dirt, oil or brake fluid on brake linings.	(5) Inspect, replace and adjust as necessary.
	(6) Broken or sagging rear springs.	(6) Replace the rear springs.
	(7) Bent front axle, linkage or steering knuckle.	(7) Replace the parts as necessary.
	(8) Worn or tight king pin bushings.	(8) Lubricate or replace as necessary.
Wander or Weave	(1) Improper caster, camber or toe-in.	(1) Adjust to specifications.
	(2) Worn king pin and bushings.	(2) Replace parts as required.
	(3) Worn or improperly adjusted front wheel bearings.	(3) Adjust or replace parts as necessary.
	(4) Loose spring shackles.	(4) Adjust or replace parts as necessary.
	(5) Incorrect tire pressure or tire sizes not uniform.	(5) Check tire sizes and inflate tires to recommended pressure.
	(6) Loose steering gear mounting bolts.	(6) Tighten to specifications.
	(7) Tight king pin bushings.	(7) Lubricate or ream to proper fit.
	(8) Tight king pin thrust bearings.	(8) Adjust to .001 to .005 inch clearance.
Wheel Tramp (Excessive Vertical Motion of Wheels)	(1) Incorrect tire pressure.	(1) Inflate the tires to recommended pressures.
	(2) Improper balance of wheels, tires and brake drums.	(2) Balance as necessary.
	(3) Loose tie rod ends or steering connections.	(3) Inspect and repair as necessary.
	(4) Worn or inoperative shock absorbers.	(4) Replace the shock absorbers.
	(5) Excessive run-out of brake drums, wheels or tires.	(5) Repair or replace as required.
Shimmy	(1) Badly worn and/or unevenly worn tires.	(1) Rotate tires or replace if necessary.
	(2) Wheels and tires out of balance.	(2) Balance wheel and tire assemblies.
	(3) Worn or loose steering linkage parts.	(3) Replace parts as required.
	(4) Worn king pins and bushings.	(4) Replace king pins and bushings.
	(5) Loose steering gear adjustments.	(5) Adjust steering gear as necessary.
	(6) Loose wheel bearings.	(6) Adjust wheel bearings.
	(7) Improper caster setting.	(7) Adjust caster to specifications.
	(8) Weak or broken springs.	(8) Replace as required.
	(9) Incorrect tire pressure or tire sizes not uniform.	(9) Check tire sizes and inflate tires to recommended pressure.
	(10) Faulty shock absorbers.	(10) Replace as necessary.
	(11) Power cylinder loose at bracket.	(11) Tighten or replace bushings as necessary.
	(12) Power cylinder not aligned in same plane as tie rod.	(12) Correct the alignment.
	(13) Improper valve spool nut adjustment allowing control valve end play.	(13) Adjust according to instructions.
	(14) Loose steering gear mounting bolts.	(14) Tighten to specifications.

STEERING TROUBLE DIAGNOSIS

Condition	Possible Cause	Correction
Intermittent or No Power Assist	(1) Belt slipping and/or low fluid level.	(1) Adjust or replace belt. Add fluid as necessary.
	(2) Piston or rod binding in power cylinder. (Linkage type).	(2) Repair or replace piston and rod.
	(3) Sliding sleeve stuck in control valve. (Linkage type).	(3) Free-up or replace sleeve.
	(4) Improper pump operation.	(4) Refer to "Power Steering Pump."
Poor or No Recovery from Turns	(1) Improper caster setting.	(1) Adjust to specifications.
	(2) Steering gear adjustments too tight.	(2) Adjust according to instructions.
	(3) Improper spool nut adjustment. (Linkage type).	(3) Adjust according to instructions.
	(4) Valve spool installed backwards. (Linkage Type).	(4) Install valve spool correctly.
	(5) Low tire pressure.	(5) Inflate tires to recommended pressure.
	(6) Tight steering linkage.	(6) Lubricate as necessary.
	(7) King pins frozen.	(7) Lubricate as necessary.

POWER STEERING PUMP

Condition	Possible Cause	Correction
Intermittant Assist	(1) Flow control valve sticking.	(1) Pressure test pump and service as necessary.
	(2) Slipping belt.	(2) Adjust belt.
	(3) Low fluid level.	(3) Inspect and correct fluid level.
	(4) Low pump efficiency.	(4) Pressure test pump and service as necessary.
No Assist	(1) Pump seizure.	(1) Replace pump.
	(2) Broken slipper spring(s).	(2) Recondition pump or replace as necessary.
	(3) Flow control bore plug ring not in place.	(3) Replace snap ring. Inspect groove for depth.
	(4) Flow control valve sticking.	(4) Pressure test pump and service as necessary.
No Assist When Parking Only	(1) Wrong pressure relief valve.	(1) Install proper relief valve.
	(2) Broken "O" ring on flow control bore plug.	(2) Replace "O" ring.
	(3) Loose pressure relief valve.	(3) Tighten valve. DO NOT ADJUST.
	(4) Low pump efficiency.	(4) Pressure test pump and service as necessary.
Noisy Pump	(1) Low fluid level.	(1) Inspect and correct fluid level.
	(2) Belt noise.	(2) Inspect for pulley alignment, paint or grease on pulley and correct. Adjust belt.
	(3) Foreign material blocking pump housing oil inlet hole.	(3) Remove reservoir, visually check inlet oil hole and service as necessary.
Pump Vibration	(1) Pump hose interference with sheet metal or brake lines.	(1) Reroute hoses.
	(2) Belt loose.	(2) Adjust belt.
	(3) Pulley loose or out of round.	(3) Replace pulley.
	(4) Crankshaft pulley loose or damaged.	(4) Replace crankshaft pulley.
	(5) Bracket pivot bolts loose.	(5) If unable to tighten, replace bracket.
Pump Leaks	(1) Cap or filler neck leaks.	(1) Correct fluid level.
	(2) Reservoir solder joints leak.	(2) Resolder or replace reservoir as necessary.
	(3) Reservoir "O" ring leaking.	(3) Inspect sealing area of reservoir. Replace "O" ring or reservoir as necessary.
	(4) Shaft seal leaking.	(4) Replace seal.
	(5) Loose rear bracket bolts.	(5) Tighten bolts.
	(6) Loose or faulty high pressure ferrule.	(6) Tighten fitting to 24 foot-pounds or replace as necessary.
	(7) Rear bolt holes stripped or casting cracked.	(7) Repair, if possible, or replace pump.

Manual Steering Gear

Manual Steering Gear Service

Steering Gear Alignment

Before any steering gear adjustments are made, it is recommended that the front end of the truck be raised and a thorough inspection be made for stiffness or lost motion in the steering gear, steering linkage and front suspension. Worn or damaged parts should be replaced, since a satisfactory adjustment of the steering gear cannot be obtained if bent or badly worn parts exist.

It is also very important that the steering gear be properly aligned in the truck. Misalignment of the gear places a stress on the steering worm shaft, therefore a proper adjustment is impossible. To align the steering gear, loosen the steering gear-to-frame mounting bolts to permit the gear to align itself. Check the steering gear to frame mounting seat, if there is a gap at any of the mounting bolts, proper alignment may be obtained by placing shims where excessive gap appears. Tighten the steering gear-to-frame bolts. Alignment of the gear in the truck is very important and should be done carefully so that a satisfactory, trouble-free gear adjustment may be obtained.

Gemmer Worm and Double Roller Tooth Type

With Screw Adjusted Mesh

The steering gear is of the worm and roller type with a 24 to 1 gear ratio. The cross shaft is straddle mounted with a bearing surface at the top and bottom points of the shaft mounting areas. The three tooth cross shaft roller is mounted in ball bearings. The proper lubricant used in the gear box is S.A.E. 90 Extreme Pressure Lubricant.

The external adjustments given below will remove all play from the steering gear.

Worm Bearing Adjustment

1. Turn the steering wheel about one full turn from straight ahead and secure it so it doesn't move.
2. Determine if there is any worm gear end-play by shaking the front wheel sideways and noting if there is any end movement that may be felt between the steering wheel hub and the steering jacket tube. (Be sure any movement noted is not looseness in the steering jacket tube.)
3. If end play is present, adjust the worm bearings by loosening the four cover cap screws about 1/8". Separate the top shim, using a knife blade, and remove it. Do not damage the remaining shims or gaskets.
4. Replace the cover and recheck the end-play again. If necessary, repeat steps 2 and 3 until the end-play movement is as small as possible without tightening the steering gear too much. NOTE: Adjustment may be done with the Pitman arm disconnected. With the steering

Typical gemmer steering gear
(© Ford Motor Co.)

wheel turned about one full turn from straight ahead, using a spring scale tool, adjust with the shims as given above until the spring scale pull is between 1/4 and 5/8 ft. lbs.

Cross Shaft Roller and Worm Mesh Adjustment

1. Turn the steering wheel to the middle of its turning limits with the Pitman arm disconnected. The steering gear roller should be on the worm high spot.
2. Shake the Pitman arm sideways to determine the amount of clearance between the worm cross shaft roller. Movement of more than 1/32" indicates that the roller and worm mesh must be adjusted.
3. Loosen the adjusting screw lock nut and tighten the external cross shaft adjusting screw a small amount. Recheck the clearance by shaking the Pitman arm. Repeat until the clearance is correct. (Do not overtighten.) NOTE: The cross shaft roller and worm mesh adjustment may be done, using a spring scale tool, by measuring the amount of wheel pull as the external cross shaft adjusting screw is tightened. When the spring scale pull is between 7/8 and 1 1/8 ft. lbs., the adjustment is correct.
4. Tighten the Pitman arm attaching nut to 100-125 ft. lbs. The steering wheel nut (if loosened) should be tightened to 15-20 ft. lbs. torque.

Steering Gear

Disassembly

1. Remove steering gear oil seal, using a suitable puller.

2. Remove cross shaft, using an arbor to prevent bearings from dropping out.
3. Remove cover, shims and cover gasket.
4. Remove worm gear, thrust bearings and bearing cups.

Assembly

1. Clean and inspect all parts, replace as necessary. NOTE: If either thrust bearing is excessively worn, replace them both.
2. Reassemble steering gear, using new oil seal.
3. Perform worm bearing and cross shaft roller and worm mesh adjustments.
4. Lubricate to specifications.

Ford Steering Gear— Recirculating Ball Type

Steering Worm and Sector Gear Adjustments

The ball nut assembly and the sector gear must be adjusted properly to maintain a minimum amount of steering shaft end play and a minimum amount of backlash between the

WORM BEARING PRELOAD SHIMS

WORM AND ROLLER MESH ADJUSTMENT

Steering gear adjustments
(© Ford Motor Co.)

Inch-Pounds Torque Wrench

Checking steering gear preload
(© Ford Motor Co.)

sector gear and the ball nut. There are only two adjustments that may be done on this steering gear and they should be done as given below:

1. Remove the steering gear from the vehicle.
2. Loosen the locknut on the sector shaft adjustment screw and turn the adjusting screw counterclockwise about three turns.
3. Measure the worm bearing preload by attaching an in. lbs. torque wrench to the input shaft. Note the reading required to rotate input shaft about 1½ turns either side of center. If the torque reading is not about 4-5 in. lbs., adjust the gear as given in the next step.
4. Loosen the steering shaft bearing adjuster lock nut and tighten or back off the bearing adjusting screw until the preload is within the specified limits.
5. Tighten the steering shaft bearing adjuster lock nut, and recheck the preload torque.
6. Turn the input shaft slowly to either stop. Turn gently against the stop to avoid possible damage to the ball return guides. Then rotate the shaft three turns to center the ball nut.
7. Turn the sector adjusting screw clockwise until the proper torque (9-10 in. lbs.) is obtained that is necessary to rotate the worm gear past its center (high spot).
8. With the input shaft centered, hold the sector shaft and check the lash between the ball nuts, balls, and worm shaft by applying 15 lbs. torque to the steering input shaft in both right and left turn directions. The total travel of the wrench should not exceed 1¼".
9. Tighten the sector adjusting screw locknut, and recheck the backlash. Install the steering gear.

Steering Gear

Disassembly

1. Rotate the steering shaft three turns from either stop.
2. Remove the sector shaft adjusting screw locknut and loosen the screw one turn. Remove the steering shaft bearing adjuster, and the housing cover bolts and remove the sector shaft. Remove the shaft by turning the screw clockwise. Keep the shim with the screw.
3. Remove the sector shaft from the housing.
4. Carefully pull the steering shaft and ball nut from the housing, and remove the steering shaft lower bearing. Do not run the ball nut to either end of the worm gear to prevent damaging

the ball return guides. Disassemble the ball nut only if there are signs of binding or tightness.

5. To disassemble the ball nut, remove the ball return guide clamp and the ball return guides from the ball nut. Keep ball nut clamp side up until ready to remove the ball bearings.
6. Turn the ball nut over and rotate the worm shaft from side to side until all 50 balls have dropped out into a clean pan. With all balls removed, the nut will slide off the wormshaft.
7. Remove the upper bearing cup from the bearing adjuster and the lower cup from the housing. It may be necessary to tap the housing or the adjuster on a wooden block to jar the bearing cups loose.

Inspection

1. Carefully clean and inspect all parts. If the inspection shows bearing damage, the sector shaft bearing and the oil seal should be pressed out.
2. If the sector shaft bearing and oil seals were removed, press new bearings and oil seals into the housing. Do not clean, wash, or soak seals in cleaning solvent.
3. Apply the recommended steering gear lubricant to the housing and seals, filling the pocket between sector shaft bearings.

Assembly

1. Install the bearing cup in the lower end of the housing and a bearing cup in the adjuster nut. Install a new seal in the bearing

adjuster if the old seal was removed.

2. Apply gear lube to the outside of the worm shaft and the inside of the ball nut. Lay the steering shaft down, and position the ball nut on the shaft with the guide holes upward and the shallow end of the teeth to the left of the steering wheel position. Align the grooves in worm and ball nut by sighting through the guide holes.
3. Insert the ball guides into the holes in the ball nut, lightly tapping them, if necessary, to seat them.
4. Insert 25 balls into the hole in the top of each ball guide. If necessary, rotate the shaft slightly to distribute the balls evenly in the circuit.
5. Install the ball guide clamp, tightening the screws to the proper torque. Check that the worm shaft rotates freely.
6. Coat the threads of the steering shaft bearing adjuster, the housing cover bolts, and the sector adjusting screw with a suitable oil-resistant sealing compound. Do not apply sealer to female threads and do not get sealer on the steering shaft bearings.
7. Coat the worm bearings, sector shaft bearings, and gear teeth with steering gear lubricant.
8. Clamp the housing in a vise, with the sector shaft axis horizontal, and place the steering shaft lower bearing in its cup. Place the steering shaft and ball nut assemblies in the housing.

Steering shaft and related parts—Ford recirculating ball gear
(© Ford Motor Co.)

Sector shaft and housing—Ford recirculating ball gear
(© Ford Motor Co.)

9. Position the steering shaft upper bearing on top of the worm gear and install the steering shaft bearing adjuster, adjuster nut, and the bearing cup. Leave the nut loose.
10. Adjust the worm bearing preload according to the instructions given earlier.
11. Position the sector adjusting screw and adjuster shim, and check for a clearance of not more than 0.002" between the screw head and the end of the sector shaft. If the clearance exceeds 0.002", add enough shims to reduce the clearance to under 0.002" clearance.
12. Start the sector shaft adjusting screw into the housing cover. Install a new gasket on the cover.
13. Rotate the steering shaft until the ball nut teeth mesh with the sector gear teeth, tilting the housing so the ball will tip toward the housing cover opening.
14. Lubricate the sector shaft journal and install the sector shaft and cover. With the cover moved to one side, fill the gear with lubricant (about 0.97 lb.). Push the cover and the sector shaft into place, and install the two top housing bolts. Do not tighten the bolts until checking to see that there is some lash between the ball nut and the sector gear teeth. Hold or push the cover away from the ball nut and tighten the bolts to the proper torque (30-40 ft. lbs.).
15. Loosely install the sector shaft adjusting screw lock nut and adjust the sector shaft mesh load as given earlier. Tighten the adjusting screw lock nut.

Saginaw Recirculating Ball Type

The steering gear is of the recirculating ball nut type. The ball nut, mounted on the worm gear, is driven by means of steel balls which circulate in helical grooves in both the worm and nut. Ball return guides attached to the nut serve to recirculate the two sets of balls in the grooves. As the steering wheel is turned to the right, the ball nut moves upward. When the wheel is turned to the left, the ball nut moves downward.

The sector teeth on the pinion shaft and the ball nut are designed so that they fit the tightest when the steering wheel is straight ahead. This mesh action is adjusted by an adjusting screw which moves the pinion shaft endwise until the teeth mesh properly. The worm bearing adjuster provides proper preloading of the upper and lower bearings.

Before doing the adjustment

Steering gear assembly—Saginaw recirculating (© Ford Motor Company)

procedures given below, ensure that the steering problem is not caused by faulty suspension components, bad front end alignment, etc. Then, proceed with the following adjustments.

Steering Worm and Sector Adjustment

1. Tighten the worm bearing adjuster plug until all end play has been removed, then loosen ¼ turn.
2. Use an 11/16 in. 12 point socket to carefully turn the wormshaft all the way into the right corner then turn back about ½ turn.
3. Tighten the adjuster plug until the proper thrust bearing preload is obtained (5-8 in. lbs.). Tighten the adjuster plug locknut to 85 ft. lbs.
4. Turn the wormshaft from one stop to the other counting the number of turns. Then turn the shaft back exactly half the number of turns to the center position.
5. Turn the lash (sector shaft) adjuster screw clockwise to remove all lash between the ball nut and sector teeth. Tighten the locknut to 25 ft. lbs.
6. Using an 11/16 in. 12 point socket and an in. lb. torque wrench, observe the highest reading while the gear is turned through tht center position. It should be 16 in. lbs. or less.
7. If necessary repeat steps 5 and 6.

Disassembly

1. Place the steering gear in a vise, clamping onto one of the mounting tabs. The wormshaft should be in a horizontal position.
2. Rotate the wormshaft from stop to stop and count the total number of turns. Turn back exactly halfway, placing the gear on center.

3. Remove the three self locking bolts which attach the sector cover to the housing.
4. Using a plastic hammer, tap lightly on the end of the sector shaft and lift the sector cover and sector and sector shaft assembly from the gear housing.

Removing sector shaft assembly—Saginaw recirculating ball (© Ford Motor Company)

NOTE: It may be necessary to turn the wormshaft by hand until the sector will pass through the opening in the housing.

5. Remove the locknut from the adjuster plug and remove the adjuster plug assembly.
6. Pull the wormshaft and ball nut assembly from the housing.

NOTE: Damage may be done to the ends of the ball guides if the ball nut is allowed to rotate to the end of the worm.

Removing bearing retainer from adjuster—Saginaw recirculating ball (© Ford Motor Co)

Manual Steering Gears

7. Remove the worm shaft upper bearing from inside the gear housing.
8. Pry the wormshaft lower bearing retainer from the adjuster plug housing and remove the bearing.
9. Remove the locknut from the lash adjuster screw in the sector cover. Turn the lash adjuster screw clockwise and remove it from the sector cover. Slide the adjuster screw and shim out of the slot in the end of the sector shaft.
10. Pry out and discard both the sector shaft and wormshaft seals.

Inspection

1. Wash all parts in cleaning solvent and blow dry with an air hose.
2. Use a magnifying glass and inspect the bearings and bearing caps for signs of indentation, or chipping. Replace any parts that show signs of damage.
3. Check the fit of the sector shaft in the bushings in the sector cover and housing. If these bushings are worn, a new sector cover and bushing assembly or housing bushing should be installed.
4. Check steering gear wormshaft assembly for being bent or damaged.

Shaft Seal Replacement

1. Using a screwdriver, pry out the old seal.
2. Install the new seal by pressing the outer diameter of the seal with a suitable size socket.

NOTE: Make sure the socket is large enough to avoid damaging the external lip of the seal.

Sector Shaft Bushing Replacement

1. Place the steering gear housing in an arbor press.
2. Insert tool T75P3527A in the lower end of the housing and press the sector shaft bushing from the housing.

NOTE: Service bushings are bored to size and require no further reaming.

Removing sector shaft bushing—Saginaw recirculating ball (© Ford Motor Company)

Removing wormshaft lower bearing cup from the adjuster plug—Saginaw recirculating ball (© Ford Motor Company)

Sector Cover Bushing Replacement

1. The sector cover bushing is not serviced separately. The entire sector cover assembly including the bushing must be replaced as a unit.

Ball Nut Service

If there is any indication of binding or tightness when the ball nut is rotated on the worm the unit should be disassembled, cleaned and inspected as follows:

Ball Nut Disassembly

1. Remove the screws and clamp retaining the ball guides in the ball nut. Pull the guides out of the ball nut.
2. Turn the ball nut upside down and rotate the wormshaft back and forth until all the balls have dropped out of the ball nut. The ball nut can now be pulled endwise off the worm.
3. Wash all parts in solvent and dry them with air. Use a magnifying glass and inspect the worm and nut grooves and the surface of all balls for signs of indentation. Check all ball guides for damage at the ends. Replace any damaged parts.

Ball Nut Assembly

1. Slip the ball nut over the worm with the ball guide holes up and the shallow end of the ball nut teeth to the left from the steering wheel position. Sight through the ball guide to align the grooves in the worm.
2. Place two ball guide halves together and insert them in the

upper circuit in the ball nut. Place the two remaining guides together and insert them in the lower circuit.
3. Count out 25 balls and place them in a suitable container. This is the proper number of balls for one circuit.
4. Load the 25 balls into one of the guide holes while turning the wormshaft gradually away from that hole.
5. Fill the remaining ball circuit in the same manner.
6. Assemble the ball guide clamp to the ball nut and tighten the screws to 18-24 in. lbs.
7. Check the assembly by rotating the ball nut on the worm to see that it moves freely.

NOTE: Do not rotate the ball nut to the end of the worm threads as this may damage the ball guides.

Assembly

1. Coat the thrtads of the adjuster plug, sector cover bolts and lash adjuster with a non-drying oil resistant sealing compound.

NOTE: Do not apply compound to the female threads. Use extreme care when applying compound to the bearing adjuster so that it does not come in contact with the wormshaft bearing.

2. Place the steering gear housing in a vise with the wormshaft bore horizontal and the sector cover opening up.
3. Make sure that all seals, bushings and bearings cups are installed in the gear housing and that the ball nut is installed on the wormshaft.

Filling the ball circuits—Saginaw recirculating ball (© Ford Motor Company)

Manual Steering Gears

4. Slip the wormshaft upper bearing assembly over the wormshaft and insert the wormshaft and ball nut assembly into the housing, feeding the end of the shaft through the upper ball bearing cup and seal.
5. Place the wormshaft lower bearing assembly in the adjuster plug bearing cup and press the stamped retainer into place with a suitable size socket.
6. Install the adjuster plug and locknut into the lower end of the housing while carefully guiding the end of the wormshaft into the bearing until nearly all end play has been removed from the wormshaft.
7. Position the lash adjuster including the shim in the slotted end of the sector shaft.

NOTE: End clearance should not be greater than .002. If the end clearance is greater than .002 a shim package is available with thicknesses of .063, .065, .067, .069.

8. Lubricate the steering gear with 11 oz. of steering gear grease. Rotate the wormshaft until the ball nut is at the other end of its travel and then pack as much new lubricant into the housing as possible without losing out the sector shaft opening. Rotate the wormshaft until the ball nut is at the other end of its travel and pack as much lubricant into the opposite end as possible.
9. Rotate the wormshaft until the ball nut is in the center of travel. This is to make sure that the sector shaft and ball nut will engage properly with the center tooth of the sector entering the center tooth space in the ball nut.
10. Insert the sector shaft assembly including lash adjuster screw and shim into the housing so that the center tooth of the sector enters the center tooth space in the ball nut.
11. Pack the remaining portion of the lubricant into the housing and also place some in the sector cover bushing hole.
12. Place the sector cover gasket on the housing.

13. Install the sector cover onto the sector shaft by reaching through the sector cover with a screwdriver and turning the lash adjuster screw counterclockwise until the screw bottoms, then back the screw off one-half turn. Loosely install a new lock nut onto the adjuster screw.
14. Install and tighten the sector cover bolt to 30 ft. lbs.

Chrysler Recirculating Ball Type

The steering gear is of the recirculating ball nut type. The ball nut, mounted on the worm gear, is driven by means of steel balls which circulate in helical grooves in both the worm and nut. Ball return guides attached to the nut serve to recirculate the two sets of balls in the grooves. As the steering wheel is turned to the right, the ball nut moves upward. When the wheel is turned to the left, the ball nut moves downward.

The sector teeth on the pinion shaft and the ball nut are designed so that they fit the tightest when the steering wheel is straight ahead. This mesh action is adjusted by an adjusting screw which moves the pinion shaft endwise until the teeth mesh properly. The worm bearing adjuster

Chrysler recirculating ball type steering gear (© Chrysler Corp.)

provides proper preloading of the upper and lower bearings.

Worm Bearing Pre-load Adjustment

1. Remove the steering gear arm and lockwasher from the sector shaft, using a suitable gear puller.
2. Remove the horn button or horn ring.
3. Loosen the cross-shaft adjusting screw locknut, and back out the adjusting screw about two turns.
4. Turn the steering wheel two complete turns from the straight ahead position, and place an in. lb torque wrench on the steering shaft nut.
5. Rotate the steering shaft at least one turn toward the straight ahead position while measuring the torque on the torque wrench. The torque should be between $1\frac{1}{8}$ and $4\frac{1}{2}$ in. lbs. to move the steering wheel. If torque is not within these limits, loosen the worm shaft bearing adjuster locknut and turn the adjuster clockwise to increase the preload or counterclockwise to decrease the preload. When the preload is correct, hold the adjuster screw steady and tighten the locknut. Recheck preload.

Ball Nut Rack and Sector Mesh Adjustment

NOTE: this adjustment can be accurately made only after proper preloading of worm bearing.

1. Turn steering wheel gently from one stop to the other, counting the number of turns. Turn the steering wheel back exactly half way, to the center position.
2. Turn the cross-shaft adjusting screw clockwise to remove all lash between ball nut rack and the sector gear teeth, then

Checking lash adjuster end clearance—Saginaw recirculating ball (© Ford Motor Company)

875

Steering gear adjustment locations (© Chrysler Corp.)

FILLER PLUG

SECTOR SHAFT ADJUSTMENT

WORM SHAFT BEARING ADJUSTMENT

HOLDING FIXTURE

tighten adjusting screw locknut to 35 ft. lbs.

3. Turn the steering wheel about ¼ turn away from the center or high spot position. With the torque wrench on the steering wheel nut measure the torque required to turn the steering wheel through the high spot at the center position. The reading should be between 8 and 11 in. lbs. This is the total of the worm shaft bearing preload and the ball nut rack and sector gear mesh load. Readjust the cross-shaft adjustment screw if necessary to obtain a correct torque reading.

4. After completing the adjustments, place the front wheels in a straight ahead position, and with the steering wheel and steering gear centered, install the steering arm on cross-shaft. Tighten the steering arm retaining nut to 180 ft. lbs.

Steering Gear Disassembly and Assembly

1. Attach the steering gear assembly to a holding fixture and put the holding fixture in a bench vise. Thoroughly clean the outside surface before disassembly.
2. Loosen the cross-shaft adjusting screw locknut, and back out the adjusting screw about two turns to relieve the mesh load between the ball nut rack and the sector gear teeth. Remove the cross-shaft seal as given in the procedure for cross-shaft seal replacement.
3. Position the steering gear worm shaft in a straight ahead position.
4. Remove the attaching bolts from the cross-shaft cover and slowly remove the cross-shaft while sliding arbor tool into the housing. Remove the locknut from the adjusting screw and remove the screw from the cover by turning it clockwise. Slide the adjustment screw and its shim out of the slot in the end of the cross-shaft.
5. Loosen the worm shaft bearing adjuster locknut with a brass drift (punch) and remove the locknut. Hold the worm shaft steady while unscrewing the adjuster. Slide the worm adjuster off the shift.

CAUTION Handle the adjuster carefully to avoid damaging the aluminum threads. Also, do not run the ball nut down to either end of the worm shaft to avoid damaging the ball guides.

6. Carefully remove the worm and ball nut assembly. This assembly is serviced as a complete assembly only and is not to be disassembled or the ball return guides removed or disturbed.
7. Remove the cross-shaft needle bearing by placing the gear housing in an arbor press; insert a tool in the lower end of the housing and press both bearings through the housing.

The cross-shaft cover assembly, including a needle bearing or bushing, is serviced as an assembly.

8. Remove the worm shaft oil seal from the worm shaft bearing adjuster by inserting a blunt punch behind the seal and tapping alternately on each side of the seal until it is driven out of the adjuster.
9. Remove the worm shaft in the same manner as that given in step 8. *Be careful not to cock the bearing cup and distort the adjuster counter bore.*
10. Remove the lower cup if necessary by placing the locking head jaws of remover tool C-3868 behind the bearing cup and expanding the remover head by pressing down on the center plunger of the tool. Pull the bearing cup out by turning the

WORMSHAFT AND BALL NUT ASSEMBLY

Removing the wormshaft and ballnut assembly (© Chrysler Corp.)

SECTOR SHAFT BEARING TOOL

SECTOR SHAFT

Removing the cross shaft (© Chrysler Corp.)

WORM SHAFT ADJUSTER

TOOL C-3884

Removing the wormshaft adjuster (© Chrysler Corp.)

TOOL C-3868

Removing the lower bearing cup
(© Chrysler Corp.)

PRESS RAM

SECTOR SHAFT BEARING TOOL

Removing the cross shaft inner and outer bearings (© Chrysler Corp.)

remover screw clockwise while holding the center screw steady.

11. Wash all parts in clean solvent and dry thoroughly. Inspect all parts for wear, scoring, pitting, etc. Test operation of the worm shaft and ball nut assembly. If ball nut does not travel smoothly and freely on the worm shaft or if there is binding, replace the assembly.

NOTE: extreme care must be taken when handling the aluminum worm bearing adjuster to avoid thread damage. Also, be careful not to damage the threads in the gear housing. Always lubricate the worm bearing adjuster before screwing it into the housing.

12. Inspect the cross-shaft for wear and check the fit of the shaft in the housing bearings. Inspect the fit of the shaft pilot bearing in the housing. Be sure the worm shaft is not bent or damaged.

13. Install the cross-shaft lower needle bearing. Press the bearing into the housing about 7/16 in. below the end of the bore to leave space for the new oil seal.

14. Install the upper needle bearing in the same manner and press it into the inside end of the housing bore flush with the inside end of the bore surface.

15. Install the worm shaft bearing cups (upper and lower) by placing them and their spacers in the adjuster nut and press them into place.

PRESS RAM

BEARING CUP INSTALLER

WORMSHAFT BEARING ADJUSTER

Installing the wormshaft upper bearing cup (© Chrysler Corp.)

16. Install the worm shaft oil seal by placing the seal in the worm shaft adjuster with the metal seal retainer up. Drive the seal into place with a suitable sleeve until it is just below the end of the bore in the adjuster.

NOTE: apply a coating of steering gear lubricant to all moving parts during assembly. Also, put lubricant on and around oil seal lips.

17. Clamp the holding fixture and housing in a bench vise with the bearing adjuster opening upward. Place a thrust bearing in the lower cup in the housing.

18. Hold the ball nut from turning and insert the worm shaft and ball nut assembly into the housing with the end of the worm shaft resting in the thrust bearing. Place the upper thrust bearing on the worm shaft. Thoroughly lubricate the threads on the adjuster and the threads in the housing.

19. Place a protective sleeve of tape over the splines on the worm shaft to avoid damaging the seal. Slide the adjuster assembly over the shaft.

20. Thread the adjuster into the housing and, with Tool wrench C-3884 and the splined nut set, tighten the adjuster to 50 ft. lbs. while rotating the worm shaft to seat the bearings.

21. Loosen the adjuster so no bearing preload exists. Tighten the adjuster for a worm shaft bearing preload of 1⅛ to 4½ in. lbs. Tighten the bearing adjuster locknut and recheck the preload.

22. Before installing the cross-shaft, pack the worm shaft cavities in the housing above and below the ball nut with steering gear lubricant. A good grade of multi-purpose lubricant may be used if steering gear lubricant is not available. *Do not use gear oil.* Pack enough lubricant into the worm cavities to cover the worm.

23. Slide the cross-shaft adjusting screw and shim into the slot in the end of the shaft. Check the end clearance for no more than 0.004 in. clearance. If the clearance is not within the limit, remove old shim and install a new shim, available in three different thicknesses, to get the proper clearance.

SECTOR SHAFT

SHIM

ADJUSTING SCREW

Measuring the cross shaft adjusting screw and clearance (© Chrysler Corp.)

24. Start the cross-shaft and adjuster screw into the bearing in the housing cover. Using a screwdriver through the hole in the cover, turn the screw counterclockwise to pull the shaft into the cover. Install the adjusting screw locknut, but do not tighten at this time.

25. Rotate the worm shaft to center the ball nut.

26. Place a new gasket on the housing cover and install the cross-shaft and cover assembly into the steering gear housing. *Be sure to coat the cross-shaft and sector teeth with steering gear lubricant before installing the cross-shaft in the housing.* Allow some lash between the cross-shaft sector teeth and the ball nut rack. Install and tighten the cover bolts to 25 ft. lbs.

27. Place the cross-shaft seal on the cross-shaft with the lip of the seal facing the housing. Press the seal in place.
28. Turn the worm shaft about ¼ turn away from the center of the high spot position. Using a torque wrench and a ¾ in. socket on the worm shaft spline, check the torque needed to rotate the shaft through the high spot. The reading should be between 8 and 11 in. lbs. Readjust the cross-shaft adjusting screw until the proper reading is obtained. Tighten the locknut to 35 ft. lbs. and recheck cross-shaft torque.

Cross-Shaft Oil Seal Replacement

1. Remove the steering gear arm retaining nut and lockwasher.
2. Remove seal with a seal puller or other appropriate tool.
3. Place a new oil seal onto the splines of the cross-shaft with the lip of the seal facing the housing.
4. Remove the tool, and install the steering gear arm, lockwasher, and retaining nut. Tighten the nut to 180 ft. lbs. torque.

Ross Cam and Twin Lever Type

The cam and lever steering gear consists of a spiral cam and a cross shaft and lever assembly with two lever studs. When the steering wheel is turned, the cam moves the studs, causing the cross shaft to rotate and the steering arm to move. There are two adjustments that must be done: end play of the steering shaft, and backlash adjustment of the lever studs (tapered pins).

Steering Gear End-Play Adjustment

The steering gear is adjusted for the cam groove. Loosen the cover enough to remove one or more shims as required. As each shim is removed, retighten the cover and check the end-play. Adjustment should leave a slight drag in the steering gear but still allow it to turn easily. Replacement shims are available in three thicknesses: 0.002″, 0.003″, and 0.010″. (0.0508, 0.0762, and 0.254 mm).

Steering Gear Backlash Adjustment

The steering gear lever studs (tapered pins) backlash adjustment is done by turning the adjusting screw in until a slight drag is felt through the mid-position when turning the steering wheel slowly from one stop to the other. This adjustment is done when the steering wheel is centered in the straight ahead driving position. The cam groove is cut shallow in this area to provide a close adjustment of the pins. Do not adjust the screw in any other position of the steering gear.

Steering Gear Disassembly

Disassembly

NOTE: When disassembling early production models, the line across the face of the steering arm and the end of the shaft should match. On later production models, blind splines on the lever shaft and in the steering gear arm engage, allowing correct positioning of the arm.

1. Remove the steering gear arm.
2. Loosen the adjusting screw lock nut and unscrew the adjusting screw two turns.

3. Remove the side cover screws and washers. Remove the side cover and gasket.
4. Remove the lever shaft.
5. Remove the upper cover plate screws, the upper cover, and gasket. Remove the cam, wheel tube, and bearing assembly.

Assembly

1. Inspect all bearings, seals, cam grooves, etc. for wear, chipping, scoring and other damage. Replace all worn parts.
2. Assemble all parts to the wheel tube in the reverse order of disassembly. Assemble the cam, wheel tube, and bearing assembly and install in the housing, seating the lower bearing ball cup correctly in the housing. NOTE: New plastic retainer type cam bearings are available for Ross steering gears that replace, and are interchangeable with, the lock ring type cam bearings on gears equipped with early type cams.
3. With the adjusting shims installed in the housing, install the upper cover and adjust the cam bearings.
4. Install the lever shaft, gasket, and side cover on the housing. Set the adjusting screw for a minimum backlash of the studs in the cam groove, with the steering gear at the center point of travel.
5. Assemble the upper bearing spring and spring seat in the jacket tube, being sure the spring seat is positioned correctly. Install it with the long flange down against the bearing and not up inside the spring coil.
6. Install the steering gear assem-

Ross cam & lever steering gear (© Chrysler Corporation)

bly in the truck, reversing the removal procedure.

7. After installing the steering gear assembly in the truck, install the steering wheel temporarily and position the steering gear in the midposition (straight ahead). Do this by slowly turning the steering wheel from one stop to the other, then turning it to the middle of its range.

8. With the steering wheel held steady and the front wheels facing straight ahead, install the steering arm on the lever shaft, with the ball end down. If properly installed, the line across the face of the arm and the end of the shaft should match.

Ross Worm and Roller Steering Gear

Bearing preload adjustment

1. Loosen the four capscrews which fasten the end cover to the steering gear housing.
2. Alternately tighten the capscrews evenly and rotate the worm gear shaft. Tighten the screws to 18 to 22 ft. lbs.
3. If necessary, remove the end cover and either add or subtract from the number of shims, and repeat steps 1 and 2 to obtain the correct bearing preload.

Worm Gear and Roller Gear Backlash Adjustment

1. Loosen the locknut and turn the adjustment at the side cover counterclockwise until the worm gear shaft turns freely through its entire range of travel.
2. Count the number of turns necessary to rotate the worm gear shaft through its entire range of travel.
3. Turn the shaft back exactly half the number of turns to the center position.
4. Turn the shaft back and forth through its center of travel and tighten the adjustment screw to obtain a rolling torque requirement of 7 to 12 inch lbs.

5. Hold the adjustment screw in position and torque the locknut to 16-20 ft. lbs.
6. Recheck the rolling torque and repeat the above procedure if necessary.

Disassembly

1. Drain the lubricant from the gear.
2. Make index marks on the roller gear and shaft assembly and on the steering arm to assure correct alignment during reassembly.
3. Remove the nut and lockwasher from the shaft.
4. Using a puller remove the arm from the shaft.

NOTE: Do not use a hammer or wedge to remove the steering arm or damage to the gear and shaft assembly may result.

5. Remove the four side cover attaching screws and remove the cover and roller gear and shaft assembly as a unit.
6. Remove the locknut from the adjustment screw and turn the screw clockwise until it is completely unthreaded from the side cover, then remove the roller gear and shaft assembly from the cover.
7. Remove the four end cover attaching screws and remove the cover from the housing.
8. Withdraw the worm gear and shaft assembly from the housing.
9. Remove the lower and upper bearing cups and ball bearings from the shaft.
10. Remove and discard both the worm gear shaft and roller gear shaft housing oil seals.

Inspection

1. Clean all parts with a suitable cleaning solvent and blow dry with an air hose.
2. Check the steering gear housing for cracks, leaks or breaks and replace if damaged.
3. Examine the roller gear to assure that it has proper freedom of movement and does not have

excessive lash or roughness. Replace if necessary.

4. Check the adjustment screw of the roller gear and shaft assembly for excessive end play. If end play exceeds 0.015 inch, remove the retaining ring, thrust washer and screw from the gear and shaft assembly and replace with new parts.
5. Inspect the roller gear and shaft needle bearings for wear or damage. Insert a shaft through each bearing and check for clearance. If clearance exceeds 0.010 inch, replace the bearings. Either needle bearing may be removed by pressing out with a piloted mandrel. When pressing in a new bearing make sure that the face of the bearing is flush with the bearing boss of the cover or housing.
6. Inspect the worm gear and shaft assembly for wear, scoring or pitting. Polish the assembly with a fine abrasive cloth or replace if necessary.
7. Check the upper and lower ball bearings and cups of the worm gear and shaft assembly for wear and damage. Replace the ball bearings as a full set if worn or damaged.

Assembly

1. Press new oil seals into the worm gear shaft and roller gear shaft oil seal bores of the housing with the longer lip of each seal facing into the housing.
2. Lubricate the worm gear and shaft assembly and upper ball bearing and cup with SAE 80 gear lubricant.
3. Install the bearing and cup on the shaft.
4. Carefully install the shaft assembly into the steering gear housing.
5. Lubricate the lower end of the worm gear and shaft assembly and lower ball bearing and cup with SAE 80 gear lubricant.
6. Install the bearing, cups and spacer on the shaft.

Ross worm and roller steering gear (© Chrysler Corp.)

7. Position the shims and end cover on the steering gear housing and install the four capscrews loosely.
8. Adjust the bearing preload.
9. Position the tapped hole of the side cover to the adjustment screw of the roller gear and shaft assembly and thread the adjustment screw counterclockwise into the cover until the end of the shaft just touches the inner face of the cover.
10. Install a locknut loosely on the adjustment screw.
11. Install a new side cover gasket.
12. Lubricate the roller gear with SAE 80 gear lubricant.
13. Carefully insert the gear and shaft assembly into the steering gear housing. The roller gear and worm gear must mesh to seat the side cover to the housing.
14. Tighten the side cover capscrews to 18-22 ft. lbs.
15. Make a worm gear and roller gear backlash adjustment.
16. Clamp the exposed section of the roller gear and shaft assembly firmly into a soft jaw vise.
17. Align the index marks made during disassembly and position the steering arm to the splined end of the shaft.
18. Install the lockwasher and nut on the shaft threads and tighten the nut to draw the arm into position on the spine.
19. Fill the steering gear housing to the required level with SAE 80 gear lubricant.

Power Steering Gear

General Information

The procedures for maintaining, adjusting, and repairing the power steering systems and components discussed in this chapter are to be done only after determining that the steering linkages and front suspension systems are correctly aligned and in good condition. All worn or damaged parts should be replaced before attempting to align the power steering systems. After correcting any condition that could affect the power steering, do the preliminary tests of the steering system components.

Preliminary Tests

Lubrication

Proper lubrication of the steering linkage and the front suspension components is very important for the proper operation of the steering systems of trucks equipped with power steering. Check the steering gear box for sufficient lubricant by removing the filler plug and checking the level. Add enough fluid gear oil S.A.E. 90 to bring the oil level to the filler plug hole if necessary.

CAUTION: Do not use a pressure gun to add fluid gear oil because the pressure will force the oil out of the steering gear box.

NOTE: The Dodge power steering systems use the same lubricant in the steering gear box and in the power steering pump reservoir.

Air Bleeding

Air bubbles in the power steering system must be removed from the fluid. Be sure the reservoir is filled to the proper level and the fluid is warmed up to the operating temperature. Then, turn the steering wheel through its full travel three or four times until all the air bubbles are removed. Do not hold the steering wheel against its stops. Recheck the fluid level.

Fluid Level Check

1. Run the engine until the fluid is at the normal operating temperature. Then, turn the steering wheel through its full travel three or four times, and shut off the engine.
2. Check the fluid level in the steering reservoir. On trucks built before 1968, the fluid level is checked by removing the reservoir cap and looking in the filler tube for the fluid level. On 1968 and later trucks, a dipstick is provided in the filler tube that shows the proper fluid level. If the fluid level is low, add enough fluid to raise the level to the Full mark on the dipstick or filler tube.

Pump Belt Check

1. Inspect the pump belt for cracks, glazing, or worn places. Using a belt tension gauge, check the belt tension for the proper range of adjustment. The amount of tension varies with the make of truck and the condition of the belt. New belts (those belts used less than 15 minutes) require a higher figure. The belt deflection method of adjustment may be used only if a belt tension gauge is not available. The belt should be adjusted for a deflection of 3/8" to 1/2".

Fluid Leaks

Check all possible leakage points (hoses, power steering pump, or steering gear) for loss of fluid. Turn engine on and rotate the steering wheel from stop to stop several times. Tighten all loose fittings and replace any defective lines or valve seats.

Turning Effort

Check the turning effort required to turn the steering wheel after aligning the front wheels and inflating the tires to the proper pressure.

1. With the vehicle on dry pavement and the front wheel straight ahead, set the parking brake and turn the engine on.
2. After a short warm-up period for the engine, turn the steering wheel back and forth several times to warm the steering fluid.
3. Attach a spring scale to the steering wheel rim and measure the pull required to turn the steering wheel one complete revolution in each direction. The effort needed to turn the steering wheel should not exceed the limits specified.

NOTE: This test may be done with the steering wheel removed and a torque wrench applied on the steering wheel nut.

Power Steering Pump Flow

Since the power steering pump

Power steering pump test circuit diagram (© Ford Motor Co.)

provides all the power assist in a power steering system, the pump must operate properly at all times for the system to work. After performing all the checks given above, the power steering pump may be tested for proper flow by the following procedure:

1. Disconnect the pressure and return lines at the power steering pump and connect the test pressure and return lines. The test lines are connected to a pressure gauge and two manual valves.
2. Open the two manual valves, connect a tachometer to the engine, and start the engine. Run the engine at idle speed until the reservoir fluid temperature reaches about 165-175 degrees Fahrenheit. This temperature must be maintained during the test. Manual valve B may be partially opened to create a back pressure of no more than 350 psi to aid the temperature rise. Reservoir fluid must be at the proper level.
3. After the engine and the reservoir fluid are sufficiently warmed up, close the manual valve B. Note the pressure gauge reading. It must be a minimum of 620 psi.
4. If the pressure reading is below the minimum acceptable pressure, the pump is defective and must be repaired. If the pressure reading is at or above the minimum value, the pump is normal. Open manual valve B and proceed to the pump fluid pressure test.

Power Steering Pump Fluid Pressure Test

1. Keep the lines and pressure gauge connected as in the Pump Flow Test.
2. With manual valve A and B opened fully, run the engine at the proper idle speed. Then, close manual valve A and manual valve B, in that order. CAUTION: Do not keep both valves closed for more than 5 seconds since the fluid temperature will increase abnormally and cause unnecessary wear to the pump.
3. With both manual valves closed, the pressure reading should be as given in the specifications. If the pressure is below the minimum reading, the pump is defective and must be repaired. If the pressure reading is at or above the minimum reading, the pump is normal and the power steering gear or power assist control valve must be checked.

Checking the Oil Flow and Pressure Relief Valve in the Pump Assembly

When the wheels are turned hard right, or hard left, against the stops, the oil flow and pressure relief valves come into action. If these valves are working and are not stuck there should be a slight buzzing noise.

CAUTION: Do not hold the wheels in the extreme position for over three or four seconds because, if the pressure relief valve is not working, the pressure could get high enough to damage the system.

Power Steering Hose Inspection

1. Inspect both the input and output hoses of the power steering pump for worn spots, cracks, or signs of leakage. Replace hose if defective, being sure to reconnect the replacement hose properly. Many power steering hoses are identified as to where they are to be connected by special means, such as fittings that will only fit on the correct pump fitting, or hoses of special lengths.

Test Driving Truck to Check the Power Steering

When test driving to check power steering, drive at a speed between 15 and 20 mph. Make several turns in each direction. When a turn is completed, the front wheels should return to the straight ahead position with very little help from the driver.

If the front wheels fail to return as they should and yet the steering linkage is free, well oiled and properly adjusted, the trouble is probably due to misalignment of the power cylinder or improper adjustment of the spool valve.

The power steering oil pump supplies all the power assist used in power steering systems of all designs. There are various designs of oil pumps used by the truck manufacturers but all pumps supply power to operate the steering systems with the least effort. All power steering pumps have a reservoir tank built onto the oil pump. These pumps are driven by belts turned by pulleys on either the engine, the rear of the generator, or the front of the crankshaft.

During operation of the engine at idle speed, there is provision for the power steering pump to supply more fluid pressure. During driving speeds or when the truck is moving straight ahead, less pressure is needed and the excess is relieved through a pressure relief and flow control valve. The pressure relief part of the valve is inside the flow control and is basically the same for all pumps. The flow control valve regulates, or controls, the constant flow of fluid from the pump

as it varies with the demands of the steering gear. The pressure relief valve limits the hydraulic pressure built up when the steering gear is turned against its stops.

During pump disassembly, make sure all work is done on a clean surface. Clean the outside of the pump thoroughly and do not allow dirt of any kind to get inside. Do not immerse the shaft oil seal in solvent.

If replacing the rotor shaft seal, be extremely careful not to scratch sealing surfaces with tools.

Pump Overhaul

Vane Type Power Steering Pump

The vane type power steering pump is used in Saginaw steering systems. The operation is basically the same as that of the roller type pumps. Centrifugal force moves a number of vanes outward against the pump ring, causing a pumping action of the fluid to the control valve.

Removal

1. Disconnect hoses at the pump, securing them in a raised position to prevent oil drainage. Cap or cover the ends of the hoses to keep dirt out.
2. Install two caps on the pump fittings to prevent oil drainage.
3. Loosen the bracket-to-pump mounting nuts, move pump toward engine slightly, and remove the pump drive belt.
4. Remove the bracket-to-pump bolts and remove the pump from the truck.
5. While holding the drive pulley steady, loosen and remove the pulley attaching nut. Slide the pulley off the shaft. NOTE: Do not hammer the pulley off the shaft.

Installation

1. To install the pump on the truck, reverse the removal procedure. Always use a new pulley nut, tightening it to 25-45 ft. lbs. torque.
2. After reconnecting the hoses to the pump, fill the reservoir with fluid and bleed the pump of air by turning the drive pulley counterclockwise (as viewed from the front) until air bubbles do not appear.
3. Install the pump drive belt over the pulley, move the pump against the belt until tight enough, then tighten the mounting bolts and nuts.
4. Bleed the air from the system.

Disassembly

1. Clean the outside of the pump in

Vane type power steering pumps (© G.M.C.)

1 Union
2 Union "O" ring seal
3 Mounting studs
4 Reservoir
5 Dip stick and cover
8 End plate retaining ring
9 End plate
10 Spring
11 Pressure plate

12 Pump ring
13 Vanes
14 Drive shaft retaining ring
15 Rotor
16 Thrust plate
17 Dowel pins
18 End plate "O" ring
19 Pressure plate "O" ring
20 Mounting stud square ring

21 Flow control valve
22 Flow control valve spring
23 Flow control valve square ring seal
24 Pump housing
25 Reservoir "O" ring seal
26 Shaft seal
27 Shaft

a non-toxic solvent before disassembling.

2. Mount the pump in a vise, being careful not to squeeze the front hub too tight.
3. Remove the union and seal.
4. Remove the reservoir retaining studs and separate the reservoir from the housing.
5. Remove the mounting bolt and union O-rings.
6. Remove the filter and filter cage; discard the element.
7. Remove the end plate retaining ring by compressing the retaining ring and then prying it out with a screwdriver. The retaining ring may be compressed by inserting a small punch in the 1/8" diameter hole in the housing and pushing in until the ring clears the groove.
8. Remove the end plate. The end plate is spring-loaded and should rise above the housing level. If it is stuck inside the housing, a slight rocking or gentle tapping should free the plate.
9. Remove the shaft woodruff key and tap the end of the shaft gently to free the pressure plate, pump ring, rotor assembly, and

thrust plate. Remove these parts as one unit.
10. Remove the end plate O-ring. Separate the pressure plate, pump ring, rotor assembly, and thrust plate.

Inspection

Clean all metal parts in a non-toxic solvent and inspect them as given below:

1. Check the flow control valve for free movement in the housing bore. If the valve is sticking, see if there is dirt or a rough spot in the bore.
2. Check the cap screw in the end of the flow control valve for looseness. Tighten if necessary being careful not to damage the machined surfaces.
3. Inspect the pressure plate and the pump plate surfaces for flatness and check that there are no cracks or scores in the parts. Do not mistake the normal wear marks for scoring.
4. Check the vanes in the rotor assembly for free movement and that they were installed with the radiused edge toward the pump ring.

5. If the flow control valve plunger is defective, install a new part. The valve is factory calibrated and supplied as a unit.
6. Check the drive shaft for worn splines, breaks, bushing material pick-up, etc.
7. Replace all rubber seals and O-rings removed from the pump.
8. Check the reservoir, studs, casting, etc. for burrs and other defects that would impair operation.

Assembly

1. Install a new shaft seal in the housing and insert the shaft at the hub end of housing, splined end entering mounting face side.
2. Install the thrust plate on the dowel pins with the ported side facing the rear of the pump housing.
3. Install the rotor on the pump shaft over the splined end. Be sure the rotor moves freely on the splines. Countersunk side must be toward the shaft.
4. Install the shaft retaining ring. Install the pump ring on the dowel pins with the rotation arrow toward the rear of the

Removing end plate ring (© G.M.C.)

Correct vane assembly (© G.M.C.)

pump housing. Rotation is clockwise as seen from the pulley.

5. Install the vanes in the rotor slots with the radius edge towards the outside.

6. Lubricate the outside diameter and chamfer of the pressure plate with petroleum jelly so as not to damage the O-ring and install the plate on the dowel pins with the ported face toward the pump ring. Seat the pressure plate by placing a large socket on top of the plate and pushing down with the hand.

7. Install the pressure plate spring in the center groove of the plate.

8. Install the end plate O-ring. Lubricate the outside diameter and chamfer of the end plate with petroleum jelly so as not to damage the O-ring and install the end plate in the housing, using an arbor press. Install the end plate retaining ring while pump is in the arbor press. Be sure the ring is in the groove and the ring gap is positioned properly.

9. Install the flow control spring and plunger, hex head screw end in bore first. Install the filter cage, new filter stud seals and union seal.

10. Place the reservoir in the normal position and press down until the reservoir seats on the housing. Check the position of the stud seals and the union seal.

11. Install the studs, union, and drive shaft woodruff key. Support the shaft on the opposite side of the key when tapping the key into place.

Roller Type Power Steering Pump

The roller type power steering pump is designed similar to other constant flow centrifugal force pumps. A star-shaped rotor forces 12 steel rollers against the inside surface of a cam ring. As the rollers follow the eccentric pattern of the cam ring, oil is drawn into the inlet ports and exhausted through the discharge ports while the rollers are moved into vee shaped cavities of the rotor, forcing oil into the high pressure circuit. A flow control valve permits a regulated amount of oil to return to the intake side of the pump when excess output is produced during high speed operation. This reduces the power needs to drive the pump and minimizes temperature build-up.

The flow control valve used in one make of pump is a two-stage valve. Oil under high pressure passes through two holes into a metering circuit located in a sealed oil passage. At low speed, about 2.7 gpm. passes to the gear. As speed increases and the valve moves, excess oil is bypassed to the inlet and the valve blocks flow through one hole. This drops the oil flow to about 1.6 gpm. at high speeds.

When steering conditions produce excessive pressure needs (such as turning the wheels against the stops), the pressure built up in the steering gear exerts force on the spring end of the flow control valve.

This end of the valve contains the pressure relief valve. High pressure lifts the relief valve ball from its seat, allowing oil to flow through a trigger orifice located in the front land of the flow control valve. This reduces pressure on the spring end of the valve which then opens and allows the oil to return to the intake

HOLE FOR REMOVING END PLATE RING

Installing end plate retaining ring (© G.M.C.)

Installing flow control valve (© G.M.C.)

Power Steering Gears

side of the pump. This action limits the maximum pressure output of the pump to a safe level. Normally, the pressure needs of the pump are below the maximum limits, causing the pressure relief ball and the flow control valve to remain closed.

Removal

1. Loosen the pump mounting and locking bolts and remove the belt.
2. Disconnect both hoses at the pump. Cap and tie the hoses out of the way. Cap the hose fittings on the pump.
3. Remove the mounting and locking bolts, the pump and brackets from the truck.

Installation

1. Position the pump and brackets on the engine and install the mounting and locking bolts.
2. Install the drive belt and adjust for the proper tension.
3. Connect the pressure and return hoses, using a new pressure hose O-ring.
4. Fill the pump reservoir to the top of the filler neck with power steering fluid.
5. Start the engine and turn the steering wheel several times from stop to stop to bleed the pump of air. Check the oil level and add fluid if necessary.

NOTE: When checking the oil level, see that the level is as follows: engine cold-bottom of filler tube; engine hot-half way up filler tube.

Disassembly

1. Remove pump from engine, drain reservoir, and clean outside of pump. Clamp the pump in a vise at the mounting bracket.
2. Remove the drive pulley.
3. Remove the shaft seal by installing the seal remover adapter over the end of the drive shaft with the large end toward the pump. Place the seal remover tool over the shaft and through the adapter. Then, screw the ta-

Removing shaft seal (© Chrysler Corp.)

884

pered thread well into the metal portion of the seal. Tighten the large drive nut and remove the seal.

4. Remove the pump from the vise and remove the bracket mounting bolts. Remove the bracket.
5. Remove the reservoir and place the pump in a soft-faced vise with the shaft down. Discard the mounting bolt and the reservoir O-rings.
6. Move the end cover retaining ring around until one end of the ring lines up with the hole in the pump body. Insert a small punch in the hole and push it in far enough to bend the ring so a screwdriver can be inserted between the ring and the housing. Remove the ring.
7. Remove the end cover and spring from the housing. It may be necessary to tap the cover gently to loosen it in the housing.
8. Remove the pump from the vise and turn the pump over so the rotating group may come out of the housing. Tap the end of the drive shaft to loosen these parts. Lift the pump body off the rotating group. Check that the seal plate is removed from the bottom of the housing bore.
9. Discard the O-rings from the pressure plate and end cover.
10. Remove the snap-ring, bore plug, flow control valve and spring from the housing. Discard the O-ring. If necessary to dismantle the flow control valve for cleaning, see the procedure for disassembly.

Inspection

1. Remove the clean out plug with an Allen wrench.
2. Wash all metal parts in clean, non-toxic solvent. Blow out all passages with compressed air and air dry all cleaned parts.
3. Inspect the drive shaft for excessive wear and the seal area for nicks or scoring. Replace if necessary.
4. Inspect the end plates, rollers, rotor and cam ring for nicks, burrs, or scratches. If any of the components are damaged enough to cause poor operation of the pump, all the interior parts may have to be replaced to prevent later failures.
5. Inspect the pump body drive shaft bushing for excessive wear. Replace the pump body and bushing as one assembly.

Assembly

1. Install the 1/8" pipe clean out plug, tightening it to 80 in. lbs. torque.
2. Place the pump body on a clean

flat surface and install a **new** shaft seal into the bore.

3. Install a new end cover O-ring into the groove in the pump bore. Be sure to lubricate the O-ring with power steering fluid before installing it.
4. Lubricate and install a new O-ring in the groove on the pump body where the reservoir fits snugly.
5. Install the brass seal plate to the bottom of the housing bore. Align the notch in the seal plate with the dowel pin hole in the housing.
6. Carefully install the front plate with the chamfered edge down in the pump bore. Align the index notch in the plate with the dowel pin hole in the housing. CAUTION: Be extremely careful to align the dowel pin hole properly. Pump can be completely assembled with the dowel pin not seated properly in the hole.
7. Place the dowel pin in the cam ring and position the cam ring inside the pump bore. Notch in the cam ring must be facing up (away from the pulley end of pump housing). If the cam ring has two notches, one machined and one cast, install the cam ring with the machined notch up. Check the amount of dowel pin extending above the cam ring surface. If more than 3/16" is showing, the dowel pin is not seated in the index hole in the housing.
8. Install the rotor and shaft in the cam ring and carefully install the 12 steel rollers in the cavities of the rotor. Lubricate the rotor, rollers, and the inside surface of the cam ring with power steering fluid. Rotate the shaft by hand to be sure all the rollers are seated parallel with the shaft and are not sticking or binding.
9. Position the pressure plate by carefully aligning the index notch on the plate with the dowel pin and inserting a clean drill (number 13 to 16) in the cam ring oil hole next to the dowel pin notch until it bottoms on the housing floor.
10. Lubricate and install a new O-ring on the pressure plate. Position the pressure plate in the pump bore so that the dowel pin is in the index notch on the plate and the drill extends through the oil passage in the pressure plate. Seat the pressure plate on the cam ring using a clean 1 1/8" socket and a soft-faced hammer to tap it gently. Remove the drill and inspect the plate at both oil passage slots to be sure that the

OIL SEAL
PUMP BODY
SEAL PLATE
"O" RINGS
FRONT PLATE
ROTOR ROLLERS (12)
CAM RING
DRIVE PULLEY
ROTOR
PRESSURE PLATE
FIBRE GASKET
MOUNTING BRACKETS
FILLER CAP
FLOW CONTROL VALVE ASSEMBLY
"O" RINGS
RESERVOIR
DOWEL PIN
END COVER SPRING
END COVER
RETAINER RING
MOUNTING SCREW
MOUNTING SCREW

Roller type power steering pump (© Chrysler Corp.)

plate is squarely seated on the cam ring.

11. Place the large coil spring over the raised portion of the installed pressure plate.

12. Place the end cover, lip edge facing up, over the spring. Press the end cover down below the retaining ring groove. Install the retaining ring in the groove. Be sure the end cover chamfer is squarely seated against the snap-ring.

13. Replace the reservoir mounting bolt seal.

14. Lubricate the flow control valve assembly with power steering fluid and insert the valve spring and valve in the bore. Install a new O-ring on the bore plug, lubricate with fluid, and carefully install in the bore. Install the snap-ring with the sharp edge up. Do not depress the bore plug more than 1/16″ below the snap-ring groove.

15. Place the reservoir on the pump body and visually align the mounting bolt hole. Tap the reservoir down on the pump with a plastic-faced hammer.

16. Remove the pump from the vise and install the mounting brackets with the mounting bolts on the pump. Tighten the bolts to 18 ft. lbs. torque.

17. Install the drive pulley by using the installer tool as follows: place the pulley on the end of the shaft and thread the installer tool into the 3/8″ threaded hole in the end of the shaft. Put the installer shaft in a vise and

tighten the drive nut against the thrust bearing, pressing the pulley on the shaft until it is flush. Do not try to press the pulley on the shaft without the special installer tool since the pump interior will be damaged by any other installation procedure. A small amount of drive shaft end play will be seen when the pulley is installed. This end play is necessary and will be minimized by a thin coat of oil between the rotor and the end plates when the pump is operating.

18. Install the pump assembly on the engine, install the drive belt and hoses (use new O-ring on pressure hose), and check for leaks.

Flow Control Valve Disassembly

1. After removing the pump from the engine and the reservoir from the pump, remove the snap-ring and plug from the flow bore. Discard the O-ring.

2. Depress the control valve against the spring pressure and allow the valve to spring out of the bore. If the valve is stuck in the bore or it did not come out of the bore far enough, it may be necessary to tap the housing lightly to remove it.

3. If the valve has dirt or foreign particles on it or in its bore, the rest of the pump needs cleaning. The hoses should be flushed and the steering gear valve body reconditioned. If the valve bore is badly scored, replace the pump body and the flow control valve.

4. Remove any nicks or burrs by

gently rubbing the valve with crocus cloth. Clamp the valve land in a vise with soft-jaws and remove the hex head ball seat and shims. Note the number and gauge (thickness) of the shims on the ball seat. They must be re-installed for the same shim thickness to keep the same value of relief pressure.

5. Remove the valve from the vise and remove the pressure relief ball, guide, and spring.

Flow Control Valve Assembly

1. Insert the spring, guide and pressure relief ball in the end of the flow control valve.

2. Install the hex head plug using the exact number and thickness shims that were removed. Tighten the plug to 80 in. lbs. torque.

3. Lubricate the valve with power steering fluid and insert the flow control valve spring and valve in the housing bore. Install a new O-ring on the bore plug, lubricate with fluid and carefully install into the bore. Install the snap-ring. Do not depress the bore plug more than 1/16″ beyond the snap-ring groove.

Slipper Type Power Steering Pump

The slipper type power steering pump is a belt-driven constant displacement assembly that uses a number of spring-loaded slippers in the pump rotor to force oil from the inlet side to the flow control valve. Openings in the metering pin allow a flow of about two gpm. of fluid to the steering gear before the flow control valve directs the excess fluid to the inlet side of the pump again. Maximum pressure in the pump is limited by the pressure relief valve which opens when the oil pressure exceeds the maximum limits.

The slipper type power steering pump discussed in this section is used on Ford trucks and is called the Ford-Thompson power steering pump.

Removal

1. Drain the fluid from the pump reservoir by disconnecting the fluid return hose at the pump. Then, disconnect the pressure hose from the pump.
2. Remove the mounting bolts from the front of the pump. On eight cylinder engines, there is a nut on the rear of the pump that must be removed. After removing all the mounting bolts and nuts from the pump, move the unit inward to loosen the belt tension and remove the belt from the pulley. Then remove the pump from the truck.

Installation

1. Position the pump on the mount-

Flow control valve (© Chrysler Corp.)

ing bracket and loosely install the mounting bolts and nuts. Put the drive belt over the pulley and move the pump outward against the belt until the proper belt tension is obtained. Measure the belt tension with a gauge for the proper adjustment. Only in cases where a belt tension gauge is not available should the belt deflection method be used. If the belt deflection method is used, be sure to check the belt with a tension gauge at the earliest time since the deflection method is not accurate.

2. Tighten the mounting bolts and nuts to the specified torque limits.
5. Tighten the pressure hose fitting hex nut to the proper torque. Then connect the pressure hose to the pump and tighten the hose nut to the proper torque.

4. Connect the fluid return hose to the pump and tighten the clamp.
5. Fill the pump reservoir with power steering fluid and bleed the air bubbles from the system.
6. Check for leaks and recheck the fluid level. If necessary, add fluid to raise the level properly.

Disassembly

1. Drain as much fluid from the pump as possible after removing the pump from the truck.
2. Install a $\frac{3}{8}$-16″ capscrew in the end of the pump shaft to avoid damaging the shaft end with the pulley remover tool. Install the pulley remover tool on the pulley hub and place the pump and remover tool in a vise. Hold the pump steady and turn the tool nut counterclockwise to draw the pulley off the shaft. The pulley must be removed without in

Removing end cover retaining ring (© Chrysler Corp.)

Installing cam ring (© Chrysler Corp.)

Installing pressure plate (© Chrysler Corp.)

Seating pressure plate (© Chrysler Corp.)

Ford Thompson power steering pump, sectional view
(© Ford Motor Co.)

and out pressure on the pump shaft to avoid damaging the internal thrust washers.

3. Remove the pump reservoir by installing the pump in a holding fixture with an adapter plate in a vise with the reservoir facing up.

4. Remove the outlet fitting hex nut and any other attaching parts from the reservoir case.

5. Invert the pump so the reservoir is now facing down. Using a wooden block, remove the reservoir by tapping around the flange until the reservoir is loose. Remove the reservoir O-ring seal and the outlet fitting gasket from the pump.

6. Again invert the pump assembly in the vise, remove the pump housing holding bolts and the pump housing.

7. Remove the housing cover, the O-ring seal and the pressure springs from inside the pump housing. Remove the pump cover gasket and discard it.

8. Remove the retainer end plate and upper pressure plate. In some pumps, the end plate and the upper pressure plate are made as one unit.

9. Remove the loose fitting dowel pin. Be careful not to bend the fixed dowel pin which remains in the housing plate assembly.

10. Remove the rotor assembly being careful not to let the slippers and springs fall out of the rotor. It may not be necessary to disassemble the rotor assembly unless the lower pressure plate, housing plate, rotor shaft and/or seal is to be replaced. However, the rotor assembly may be disassembled by removing the slippers and springs from the cam ring.

11. Remove any rust, dirt, burrs, or scoring from the pulley end of the rotor shaft before removing the shaft from the housing plate. The shaft must come out without restrictions to avoid scoring or damaging the bushing. Remove the pump rotor shaft.

12. Remove the lower pressure plate.

13. Remove the rotor shaft seal after first wrapping a piece of 0.005″ shim stock around the shaft and pushing it into the inside of the seal until it touches the bushing. With a sharp tool, pierce the seal body and pry the seal out. Do not damage the bushing, housing, or the shaft. Install a new seal using a soft-faced hammer.

14. If the pump has a flow control valve, disassemble according to instructions given in the section on the roller type power steering pump.

Inspection

1. Wash all metal parts in clean, non-toxic solvent. Blow out all oil passages with compressed air and air dry all cleaned parts.

2. Inspect the drive shaft for excessive wear and seal area for nicks or scoring. Replace if necessary.

3. Inspect the pressure plates, slippers, rotor, and cam ring for nicks, burrs, or scratches. If any of the parts are damaged enough to cause poor operation or binding of the pump, replace the defective part.

4. Inspect the pump body drive shaft bushing for excessive wear. Replace if necessary.

Assembly

1. With the pump assembly positioned on the adapter plate in the holding fixture, install the lower pressure plate on the anchor pin with the chamfered slots at the center hole facing up.

Ford Thompson power steering pump disassembled (© Ford Motor Co.)

Lower pressure plate installed
(© Ford Motor Co.)

FLATS ON LEFT

DOUBLE STEP

Correct slipper installation—Ford
(© Ford Motor Co.)

2. Lubricate the rotor shaft with power steering fluid and insert the shaft into the lower pressure and housing plates.

3. Assemble the rotor, slippers, and springs by wrapping a piece of wire around the rotor, installing the springs, and sliding a slipper in each groove of the rotor over the springs. Then, insert the assembly into the cam ring. Be sure the flat side of the slippers are toward the left side. Be sure that the springs are installed straight and are not cocked to one side under the slippers.

4. Install the cam ring and rotor assembly on the drive shaft with the fixed dowel passing through the first hole to the left of the cam notch when the arrow on the cam outside diameter is pointing toward the lower pressure plate. If the cam and rotor assembly does not seat properly, turn the rotor shaft slightly until the spline teeth mesh, allowing the cam and rotor to drop into position.

5. Insert the looser fitting dowel through the cam insert and lower pressure plate into the hole in the housing plate assembly. When both dowels are installed properly, they will be the same height.

6. Install the upper pressure plate so the tapered notch is facing down against the cam insert. The fixed dowel should pass

through the round dowel hole and the loose dowel through the long hole. The slot between the ears on the outside of the pressure plate should match the notch on the cam insert.

7. Install the retainer end plate so the slot on the end plate matches the notches on the upper pressure plate and the cam insert.

8. Install the pump valve assembly O-ring seal on the pump valve assembly. Do not twist the seal.

9. Place the pump valve assembly on top of the retainer end plate with the large exhaust slot on the pump valve in line with the outside notches of the cam, upper pressure plate, and retainer end plate. All parts must be fully seated. If correctly installed, the relief valve stem will be in line with the lube return hole in the pump housing plate.

10. Put small amounts of vaseline on the pump housing plate to hold the cover gasket in place. Install the cover gasket in place.

11. Insert the pressure plate springs into the pockets in the pump valve assembly.

12. Plug the intake hole in the housing.

13. Lubricate the inside of the housing and the housing cover seal with power steering fluid. Install two studs for use as positioning guides, one in the bolt hole nearest the drain hole and the other in the bolt hole on the opposite side of the housing plate.

14. Align the small lube hole in the housing rim and the lube hole in the housing plate. Install the housing, using a steady, even,

FIXED DOWEL   DOUBLE STEP

ARROW POINTING DOWN
Cam and rotor installation
(© Ford Motor Co.)

FIXED DOWEL   EARS

Upper pressure plate installation
(© Ford Motor Co.)

FIXED DOWEL   EARS

Retainer end plate installation
(© Ford Motor Co.)

O-RING SEAL
LUBE RETURN HOLE
EXHAUST SLOT
EARS

Valve and pressure spring installation
(© Ford Motor Co.)

downward pressure. Do not jar the pressure spring out of position. Remove the guide studs and loosely install the housing retaining bolts finger tight.

15. Tighten the retaining bolts evenly to 28-32 ft. lbs. until the housing flange contacts the gasket.

16. Install a 3/8-16 hex head screw into the end of the rotor shaft and put a torque wrench on it. Check the amount of torque needed to rotate the rotor shaft. If the torque is more than 15 in. lbs., loosen the retaining bolts

SLIPPER SPRINGS

Correct slipper installation—Dodge
(© Chrysler Corp.)

slightly and rotate the rotor shaft. Then, retighten the retaining bolts evenly. Do not use the pump if the shaft torque exceeds 15 in. lbs.

17. Release the pin in the bench holding fixture and shake the pump assembly back and forth. If there is a rattle, the pressure springs have fallen out of their seats and must be reinstalled.

18. Install the reservoir O-ring seal on the housing plate without twisting it. Lubricate the seal and install the reservoir, aligning the notch in the reservoir flange with the notch in the outside edge of the pump housing plate and bushing assembly. Using only a soft-faced hammer, tap at the rear outer corners of the reservoir. Inspect the assembly to be sure the reservoir is fully seated on the housing plate.

19. Install the identification tag (if one was removed) on the outlet valve fitting. Install the outlet valve fitting nut and tighten to 43-45 ft. lbs. torque.

20. Turn the pump assembly over and install the pulley using the tool used to remove the pulley. Turn the tool nut clockwise to draw the pulley on the shaft until it is flush with the shaft end. Do not exert inward and outward pressures on the shaft to avoid damaging the internal thrust areas. Remove the tool.

Bendix Linkage—Type Power Steering System

The Bendix linkage-type power steering is a hydraulically controlled system composed of an integral pump and fluid reservoir, a control valve, a power cylinder, connecting fluid lines, and the steering linkage. The hydraulic pump, which is driven by a belt turned by the engine, draws fluid from the reservoir and provides pressure through hoses to the control valve and the power cylinder. There is a pressure relief valve to limit the pressures within the steering system to a safe level. After the fluid has passed from the pump to the control valve and the power cylinder, it returns to the reservoir.

In-Truck Adjustments

Control Valve Centering Spring Adjustment

1. Raise the truck and remove the spring cap attaching screws and remove the spring cap. CAUTION: Be very careful not to position the hoist adapters of two post hoists under the suspension and/or steering components. Place the hoist adapters under the front suspension lower arms.

2. Tighten the adjusting nut snug (about 90-100 in. lbs.); then, loosen the nut 1/4 turn (90 degrees). Do not turn the adjusting nut too tight.

3. Place the spring cap on the valve housing. Lubricate and install the attaching screws and washers. Tighten the screws to 72-100 in. lbs. torque.

4. Lower the truck and start the engine. Check the steering effort using a spring scale attached to the steering wheel rim for a pull of no more than 12 lbs.

Power Steering Control Valve

Removal

1. Raise the truck on a hoist. If a two post hoist is used, be sure to place the hoist adapters under the front suspension steering arms. Do not allow the hoist adapters to contact the steering linkage.

2. Disconnect the four fluid line fittings at the control valve and drain the fluid from the lines. Turn the front wheels back and forth to force all the fluid from the system.

3. Loosen the clamping nut and bolt at the right end of the sleeve.

4. Remove the roll pin from the steering arm-to-idler arm rod through the slot in the sleeve.

5. Remove the control valve ball stud nut.

6. Remove the ball stud from the sector shaft arm.

7. After turning the front wheels fully to the left, unthread the control valve from the center link steering arm-to-idler arm rod.

Installation

1. Thread the valve on the center link until about four threads are still visible.

2. Position the ball stud in the sector shaft arm.

3. Measure the distance between the grease plug in the sleeve and the stud at the inner end of the left spindle connecting rod. If the distance is not correct, disconnect the ball stud from the sector shaft arm and turn the valve on the center link until the correct distance is obtained.

4. When the distance is correct and the ball stud is positioned in the sector shaft arm, align the hole in the steering arm-to-idler arm rod with the slot near the end of the valve sleeve. Install the roll pin in the rod hole to lock the valve in place on the rod.

5. Tighten the valve sleeve clamp bolt to the proper torque.

13. Install the ball stud nut and tighten to the proper torque. Install a new cotter pin.

7. Connect all fluid lines to the control valve and tighten all fittings securely. Do not over-tighten.

8. Fill the fluid reservoir with power steering fluid to the full mark on the dipstick.

9. Start the engine and run it for a few minutes to warm the fluid in the power steering system. Turn the steering wheel back and forth to the stops and check the system for leaks.

10. Increase the engine idle speed to about 1000 rpm. Turn the steering wheel back and forth several times, then stop the engine. Check the control valve and hose connections for leaks.

11. Recheck the fluid level and add fluid if necessary.

12. Start the engine again, and

Power steering installation—typical
(© Ford Motor Co.)

Control valve—typical (© Ford Motor Co.)

check the position of the steering wheel when the front wheels are straight ahead. Do not make any adjustments until toe-in is checked.

13. With engine running, check front wheel toe-in.

14. Check steering wheel turning effort which should be equal in both directions.

Power Steering Power Cylinder Removal and Installation

1. Disconnect the two fluid lines from the power cylinder and drain the fluid.

2. Remove the pal nut, attaching nut, washer and the insulator from the end of the power cylinder rod. Remove the cotter pin and castellated nut holding the power cylinder stud to the center link.

3. Disconnect the power cylinder stud from the center link.

4. Remove the insulator sleeve and washer from the end of the power cylinder.

5. Inspect the tube fittings and seats in the power cylinder for nicks, burrs, or other damage. Replace the seats or tubes if damaged.

6. Install the washer, sleeve and the insulator on the end of the power cylinder rod.

7. While extending the rod as far as possible, insert the rod in the bracket on the frame and then, compress the rod so the stud may be inserted in the center link. Secure the stud with the

castellated nut and a new cotter pin.

8. Install the insulater, washer, nut, and a pal nut on the power cylinder rod.

9. Connect the two fluid lines to their proper ports on the power cylinder.

10. Fill the reservoir with power steering fluid to the full mark on the dipstick. Start the engine and run for a few minutes to warm the fluid. Turn the steering wheel back and forth to the stops to fill the system. Stop the engine.

11. Recheck the fluid level and add fluid if necessary. Check for fluid leaks.

12. Start the engine again, turn the steering wheel back and forth, and check for leaks while the engine is running.

Control Valve

Disassembly

1. Clean the outside of the control valve of dirt and fluid.

2. Remove the centering spring cap from the valve housing. The control valve should be put in a soft-faced bench vise during disassembly. Clamp the control valve around the sleeve flange only to avoid damaging the valve housing, spool, or sleeve.

3. Remove the nut from the end of the valve spool bolt. Remove the washers, spacer, centering spring, adapter, and the bushing from the bolt and valve housing.

4. Remove the two bolts holding the valve housing and the sleeve

together. Separate the valve housing and the sleeve.

5. Remove the plug from the sleeve. Push the valve spool out of the centering spring end of the valve housing, and remove the seal from the spool.

6. Remove the spacer, bushing and valve housing.

7. Drive the pin out of the travel regulator stop with a punch and hammer. Pull the head of the valve spool bolt tightly against the travel regulator stop before driving the pin out of the stop.

8. Turn the travel regulator stop counterclockwise in the valve sleeve to remove the stop from the sleeve.

9. Remove the valve spool bolt, spacer, and rubber washer from the travel regulator stop.

10. Remove the rubber boot and clamp from the valve sleeve. Slide the bumper, spring, and ball stud seat out of the valve sleeve and remove the ball stud socket from the sleeve.

11. Remove the return port hose seat and the return port relief valve.

12. Remove the spring plug and O-ring. Then remove the reaction limiting valve.

13. Replace all worn or damaged hose seats by using an Easy-Out screw extractor or a bolt of proper size as a puller. Tap the existing hole in the hose seat, using a starting tap of the correct size. Remove all metal chips from the hose seat after tapping. Place a nut and washer on a bolt of the same size as the tapped hole. The washer must be large

enough to cover the hose seat port. Insert the bolt in the tapped hole and remove the hose seat by turning the nut clockwise and drawing the bolt out. Install a new hose seal in the port, and thread a bolt of the correct size in the port. Tighten the bolt enough to bottom the seal in the port.

Assembly

1. Coat all parts of the control valve assembly with power steering fluid. Seals should be coated with lubricant before installation.
2. Install the reaction limiting valve, spring and plug. Install the return port relief valve and the hose seat.
3. Insert one of the ball stud seats (flat end first) into the ball stud socket, and insert the threaded end of the ball stud into the socket.
4. Place the socket in the control valve sleeve so that the threaded end of the ball stud can be pulled out through the slot.
5. Place the other ball stud seat, spring, and bumper in the socket. Install and securely tighten the travel regulator stop.
6. Loosen the stop just enough to align the nearest hole in the stop with the slot in the ball stud socket and install the stop pin in the ball stud socket, travel regulator stop, and valve spool bolt.
7. Install the rubber boot, clamp, and the plug on the control valve sleeve. Be sure the lubrication fitting is turned on tightly and does not bind on the ball stud socket.
8. Insert the valve spool in the valve housing, rotating it while installing it.
9. Move the spool toward the centering spring end of the housing,

and place the small seal bushing and spacer in the sleeve end of the housing.
10. Press the valve spool against the inner lip of the seal and, at the same time, guide the lip of the seal over the spool with a small screwdriver. Do not nick or scratch the seal or the spool during installation.
11. Place the sleeve end of the housing on a flat surface so that the seal, bushing and spacer are at the bottom end; then push down the valve spool until it stops.
12. Carefully install the spool seal and bushing in the centering spring end of the housing. Press the seal against the end of the spool, guiding the seal over the spool with a small screwdriver. Do not nick or scratch the seal or the spool during installation.
13. Pick up the housing, and slide the spool back and forth in the housing to check for free movement.
14. Place the valve sleeve on the housing so that the ball stud is on the same side of the housing as the ports for the two power cylinder lines. Install the two bolts in the sleeve, and torque them to the proper torque.
15. Place the adapter on the centering spring end of the housing, and install the bushing, washers, spacers and centering spring on the valve spool bolt.
16. Compress the centering spring and install the nut on the bolt. Tighten the nut snug (about 90-100 in. lbs.); then, loosen it not more than $\frac{1}{4}$ turn. Do not over-tighten to avoid breaking the stop pin at the travel regulator stop.
17. Move the ball stud back and forth to check for free movement.

18. Lubricate the two cap attaching bolts. Install the centering spring cap on the valve housing, and tighten the two cap bolts to the proper torque.
19. Install the nut on the ball stud so that the valve can be put in a vise. Then, push forward on the cap end of the valve to check the valve spool for free movement.
20. Turn the valve around in the vise, and push forward on the sleeve end to check for free movement.

Power Cylinder Seal Removal and Installation

Removal

1. Clamp the power cylinder in a vise and remove the snap-ring from the end of the cylinder. Do not distort or crack the cylinder in the vise.
2. Pull the piston rod out all the way to remove the scraper, bushing, and seals. If the seals cannot be removed in this manner, remove them by carefully prying them out of the cylinder with a sharp pick. Do not damage the shaft or seal seat.

Installation

1. Coat the new seals with power steering fluid and place the parts on the piston rod. Coat with grease or lubricant.
2. Push the rod in all the way, and install the parts in the cylinder with a deep socket slightly smaller than the cylinder opening.

Power Steering Pump

Removal and Replacement

To remove or install the power steering pump, see the section on the slipper type pump.

Saginaw Linkage—Type Power Steering System

Control Valve

Removal

1. Raise front of vehicle and place on stands.
2. Remove relay rod to control valve clamp bolt.
3. Disconnect two pump to control valve hose connections and allow fluid to drain into a container, then disconnect the valve to power cylinder hoses.
4. Remove ball stud to pitman arm retaining nut and disconnect control valve.
5. Turn steering gear so that pitman arm is away from valve, to allow working room, and un-

screw control valve from relay rod.
6. Remove control valve from vehicle.

Disassembly

1. Place valve assembly in vise with dust cap end up, then remove dust cap.
2. Remove adjusting nut.
3. Remove valve to adapter bolts then remove housing and spool from adapter.
4. Remove spool from housing.
5. Remove spring, reaction spool, washer, reaction spring and seal. O-ring may now be removed from reaction spool.
6. Remove annulus spacer, valve

shaft washer and plug-to-sleeve key.
7. Carefully turn adjuster plug out of sleeve. Use care not to nick the top surface.
8. If necessary to replace a connector seat, tap threads in center hole using a 5/16-18 tap. Thread a bolt with a nut and a flat washer into the tapped hole so the washer is against the face of the port boss and the nut is against the washer. Hold the bolt from turning while backing the nut off the bolt. This will force the washer against the port boss face and back out the bolt, drawing the connector seat

Chevrolet side mounted power cylinder
(© G.M.C.)

G.M.C. power steering system—tilt cab—typical
(© G.M.C.)

from the top cover housing. Discard the old connector seat and clean the housing out thoroughly to remove any metal tapping chips. Drive a new connector seat against the housing seat, being careful not to damage either seat.

9. Remove adapter from vise and turn over to allow spring and one of the two ball seats to drop out.

10. Remove ball stud with other ball seat and allow sleeve to fall free.

Inspection

1. Wash all parts in non-toxic solvent and blow dry with air.

2. Inspect all parts for scratches, burrs, distortion, excessive wear and replace all worn or damaged parts.

Power cylinder—typical (© Ford Motor Co.)

3. Replace all seals and gaskets.

Assembly

1. Install sleeve and ball seat in adapter, then the ball stud and then the other ball seat and spring (small end down).

2. Place adapter in vise. Put the shaft through the seat in the adjuster plug and screw adjuster plug into sleeve.

3. Turn plug in until tight, then back off until slot lines up with notches in sleeve.

4. Insert key. Be sure small tangs on end of key fit into notches in sleeve.

5. Install valve shaft washer, annu-

lus spacer, reaction seal (lip up), spring retainer, reaction spring and spool, then washer and adjustment spring. Install O-ring seal on reaction spool before installing spool on shaft. Install washer with chamfer up.

6. Install seal on valve spool with lip down. Then install spool, being careful not to jam spool in housing.

7. Install housing with spool onto adapter. The side ports should be on the same side as the ball stud. Bolt the housing to the adapter.

8. Depress the valve spool and turn the locknut into the shaft about four turns. Use a clean wrench or socket.

NOTE: Always use a new nut.

Installation and Balancing

1. Install the control valve on the relay rod so that control valve bottoms, then back off enough (if necessary) to install the clamp bolt. Do not back off more than two turns. There should be approximately 1/16-1/8″ gap.

2. Tighten control valve clamping-bolt and install ball stud to pitman arm.

3. Reconnect the four hoses to the valve.

4. Fill system with type A fluid and bleed air by running engine, then slowly turning wheels from lock to lock with engine idling. Be sure to keep reservoir full during this process. Do not replace dust cover before the following balancing procedure is completed.

5. Disconnect the piston rod from frame bracket if not already separated.

6. If piston rod is retracted, turn adjusting nut clockwise until rod begins to move out. Then turn nut counterclockwise until rod just begins to move in. Now,

Balancing control valve (© G.M.C.)

G.M.C. power steering system—conventional cab—
typical
(© G.M.C.)

turn the nut clockwise exactly half the rotation needed to change the direction of piston rod movement. If piston rod is extended before starting, reverse the above to get the midpoint in piston movement. CAUTION: Do not turn the nut back and forth more than is absolutely necessary to balance the valve.

7. With valve properly balanced it should be possible to move the rod in and out manually.

8. Shut off engine and connect piston rod to frame bracket.

9. Restart engine with front wheels still off ground. If the wheels do not turn in either direction from center, the valve has been properly balanced. Correct the condition by rebalancing the valve if necessary.

10. After proper adjustment, grease the end of valve and install dust cap.

Power Cylinder

Removal

1. Remove the two hoses which are connected to the cylinder and drain fluid into a container.

2. Remove power cylinder from frame bracket.

3. Remove cotter pin and nut and pull stud out of relay rod.

4. Remove cylinder from vehicle.

Inspection

1. Check seals for leaks around cylinder rod. If leaks are found, replace seals.

2. Check hose connection seats for damage and replace if necessary.

3. For service other than seat or seal replacement, it is necessary to replace the power cylinder.

4. The ball stud may be replaced by removing snap-ring.

Disassembly and Assembly

1. To remove piston rod seal, remove snap-ring and pull out on rod. Remove back-up washer, piston rod scraper and piston rod seal from rod.

2. To remove the ball stud, depress the end plug and remove the snap-ring. Push on the end of the ball stud and the end plug, spring, spring seat, ball stud and seal may be removed. If the ball seat is to be replaced, it must be pressed out.

3. Reverse disassembly procedure. Be sure snap-ring is properly seated.

Installation

1. Install power cylinder on vehicle in reverse of removal procedure.

2. Reconnect the hydraulic lines, fill system and bleed out air as described in the installation and balancing section of control valve servicing.

Power Steering Hoses

Carefully inspect the hoses. When installing, be sure to place in such a position as to avoid all chafing or other abuse when making sharp turns.

Chevrolet power steering control valve (© G.M.C.)

1 Dust cover	15 Annulus spacer	22 Ball seat spring
2 Adjusting nut	16 Gasket	23 Ball seat
3 Vee block seal	17 Valve shaft washer	24 Ball seat
4 Valve spool	18 "O" ring seal	25 Sleeve bearing
5 Valve mounting bolts	19 Plug to sleeve key	26 Adapter housing
6 Lock washer	20 Ball adjuster nut	27 Lubrication fitting
7 Valve housing	21 Valve shaft	28 Ball stud
8 Valve adjustment		29 Cover
9 "O" ring seal		
10 Valve reaction spool		
11 Spring thrust washer		
12 Valve spring		
13 Spring retainer		
14 Annulus seal		

Saginaw Rotary Type Power Steering

1 Snap ring	6 Ball stud	12 Scraper element
2 End plug and lube fitting	7 Ball seat	13 Piston rod scraper
3 "O" ring	8 Ball stud seal	14 Snap ring
4 Spring	9 Piston body	15 Piston rod
5 Spring seat	10 Piston rod seal	
	11 Backup washer	

Power cylinder components (©) G.M.C.)

The rotary type power steering gear is designed with all components in one housing.

The power cylinder is an integral part of the gear housing. A double-acting type piston allows oil pressure to be applied to either side of the piston. The one-piece piston and power rack is meshed to the sector shaft.

The hydraulic control valve is composed of a sleeve and valve spool. The spool is held in the neutral position by the torsion bar and spool actuator. Twisting of the torsion bar moves the valve spool, allowing oil pressure to be directed to either side of the power piston, depending upon the directional rotation of the steering wheel, to give power assist.

On many trucks of the General Motors Corporation, a modified version of the rotary valve power steering system provides variable ratio steering to assist the driver to steer the truck easier and safer. The steering gear ratio will vary from a high ratio of about 16:1 while steering straight ahead to a lower gear ratio of about 12.1:1 while making a full turn to either side.

Roller Pump Removal

Remove the reservoir cover and use a suction gun to empty the reservoir. Disconnect the hoses from the pump and tie them in a raised position to prevent oil drainage. Loosen the pump adjusting screw and remove the pump belt, then take out the retaining bolts and remove the pump and reservoir.

Installation

Position the pump assembly and install the retaining bolts. Be sure

1 Locknut	28 Side cover	42 "O" ring
2 Retaining ring	29 "O" ring	43 Plug
3 Dust seal	30 Adjuster retainer	44 "O" ring
4 Oil seal	31 Shim	45 Housing end cover
5 Bearing	32 Adjuster screw	46 Retainer ring
6 Adjuster plug		
7 "O" ring		
8 Thrust washer (large)		
9 Thrust bearing		
10 Thrust washer (small)		
11 Spacer		
12 Retainer		
13 Spool valve spring		
14 "O" ring		
15 Spool valve		
16 Teflon oil rings		
17 "O" rings		
18 Valve body		
19 Stub shaft	33 Thrust washer	
20 "O" ring	34 Spring	
21 Wormshaft	35 Pitman shaft	47 Needle bearing
22 Thrust washer	36 Screws and lock washers	48 Oil seal
23 Thrust bearing	37 Clamp	49 Back up washer
24 Thrust washer	38 Ball return guide	50 Oil seal
25 Housing	39 Balls	51 Back up washer
26 Locknut	40 Rack-piston	52 Retaining ring
27 Attaching bolts and washers	41 Teflon oil seal	

Power steering gear—light duty trucks (©) G.M.C.)

Power steering gear—medium duty trucks (© G.M.C.)

1 Sector	11 Adjuster plug needle bearing	21 Ring back-up seal
2 Wormshaft	12 Adjuster plug shaft seal	22 Torsion bar
3 Body drive pin	13 Adjuster plug	23 Spool valve pin
4 Valve body	14 Adjuster plug snap ring	24 Valve body pin
5 Cap assembly	15 Adjuster plug dust seal	25 Top cover (valve) seal
6 Valve spool	16 Bearing race	26 Back-up washer
7 Spool dampener "O" ring	17 Upper thrust bearing	27 Top cover (valve) bearing
8 Thrust bearing spacer	18 Bearing race	28 Ball nut and balls
9 Spool spring	19 Spacer	29 Bearing retainer
10 Adjuster plug "O" ring seal	20 Valve body ring	30 Lower thrust bearing

there is clearance between the pump bracket and the engine front support bracket. Install the hoses and place the pump belt on the pulley. Adjust the belt to 1/2" deflection, then tighten the adjusting screw.

Connect the hoses to the pump assembly.

Fill the reservoir to within 1/2" of the top with automatic transmission fluid type A.

Start the engine and rotate the steering wheel several times to the right and left to expel air from the system, then recheck the oil level and install the reservoir cover.

Power Steering Unit

Fluid Used

This unit uses automatic transmission fluid type A. The fluid capacity is 4½ pints.

Bleeding the System

Fill the pump reservoir to within 1/2" of the top. Start and run the engine to attain normal operating temperatures. Now, turn the steering wheel through its entire travel three or four times to expel air from the system, then recheck the fluid level.

Checking Steering Effort

Run the engine to attain normal operating temperatures. With the wheels on a dry floor, hook a pull scale to the spoke of the steering wheel at the outer edge. The effort required to turn the steering wheel should be 3½-5 lbs. If the pull is not within these limits, check the hydraulic pressure.

Pressure Test

To check the hydraulic pressure, disconnect the pressure hose from the gear. Now connect the pressure gauge between the pressure hose from the pump and the steering gear housing. Run the engine to attain normal operating temperatures, then turn the wheel to a full right and a full left turn to the wheel stops.

Hold the wheel in this position only long enough to obtain an accurate reading.

The pressure gauge reading should be within the limits specified. If the pressure reading is less than the minimum needed for proper operation, close the valve at the gauge and see if the reading increases. If the pressure is still low, the pump is defective and needs repair. If the pressure reading is at or near the minimum reading, the pump is normal and needs only

an adjustment of the power steering gear or power assist control valve.

Worm Bearing Preload and Sector Mesh Adjustments

Disconnect the pitman arm from the sector shaft, then back off on the sector shaft adjusting screw on the sector shaft cover.

Center the steering on the high point, then attach a pull scale to the spoke of the steering wheel at the outer edge. The pull required to keep the wheel moving for one complete turn should be 1/2-2/3 lbs.

If the pull is not within these limits, loosen the thrust bearing locknut and tighten or back off on the valve sleeve adjuster locknut to bring the preload within limits. Tighten the thrust bearing locknut and recheck the preload.

Slowly rotate the steering wheel several times, then center the steering on the high point. Now, turn the sector shaft adjusting screw until a steering wheel pull of 1-1½ lbs. is required to move the worm through the center point. Tighten the sector shaft adjusting screw locknut and recheck the sector mesh adjustment.

Install the pitman arm and draw the arm in position with the nut.

Removing adjuster plug (© G.M.C.)

Removing adjuster plug seal retaining ring
(© G.M.C.)

Removing thrust bearing retainer
(© G.M.C.)

1 Retaining ring
2 Dust seal
3 Oil seal
4 Needle bearing
5 Adjuster plug
6 "O" ring
7 Thrust washer (large)
8 Thrust bearing
9 Thrust washer (small)
10 Spacer
11 Retainer

Adjuster plug (© G.M.C.)

Service Operations

Adjuster Plug and Rotary Valve Removal

1. Thoroughly clean exterior of gear assembly. Drain by holding valve ports down and rotating worm back and forth through entire travel.
2. Place gear in vise.
3. Loosen adjuster plug locknut with punch. Remove adjuster plug with spanner.
4. Remove rotary valve assembly by grasping stub shaft and pulling it out.

Adjuster Plug Disassembly & Assembly

1. Remove upper thrust bearing retainer with screwdriver. Be careful not to damage bearing bore. Discard retainer. Remove spacer, upper bearing and races.
2. Remove and discard adjuster plug O-ring.
3. Remove stub shaft seal retaining ring (Truarc pliers will help) and remove and discard dust seal.
4. Remove stub shaft seal by prying out with screwdriver and discard.
5. Examine needle bearing and, if

required, remove same by pressing from thrust bearing end.
6. Inspect thrust bearing spacer, bearing rollers and races.
7. Reassemble in reverse of above.

Rotary Valve Disassembly

Repairs are seldom needed. Do not disassemble unless absolutely necessary. If the O-ring seal on valve spool dampener needs replacement, perform this portion of operation only.

1. Remove cap-to-worm O-ring seal and discard.
2. Remove valve spool spring by prying on small coil with small screwdriver to work spring onto bearing surface of stub shaft. Slide spring off shaft. Be careful not to damage shaft surface.
3. Remove valve spool by holding the valve assembly in one hand with the stub shaft pointing down. Insert the end of pencil or wood rod through opening in valve body cap and push spool until it is out far enough to be removed. In this procedure, rotate to prevent jamming. If spool becomes jammed it may be necessary to remove stub shaft, torsion bar and cap assembly.

Rotary Valve Assembly

CAUTION: All parts must be free

and clear of dirt, chips, etc., before assembly and must be protected after.

1. Lubricate three new back-up O-ring seals with automatic transmission oil and reassemble in the ring grooves of valve body. Assemble three new valve body rings in the grooves over the O-ring seals by carefully slipping over the valve body. NOTE: If the valve body rings seem loose or twisted in the grooves, the heat of the oil during operation will cause them to straighten.
2. Lubricate a new dampener O-ring with automatic transmission oil and install in valve spool groove.
3. Assemble stub shaft torsion bar and cap assembly in the valve body, aligning the groove in the valve cap with the pin in the valve body. Tap lightly with soft remainder of assembly. Valve body pin must be in the cap groove. Hold parts together during the remainder of assembly.
4. Lubricate spool. With notch in spool toward valve body, slide the spool over the stub shaft. Align the notch on the spool with the spool drive pin on stub shaft and carefully engage spool

Installing balls in rack position (© G.M.C.)

Separating valve spool from valve body
(© G.M.C.)

in valve body bore. Push spool evenly and with slight rotating motion until it reaches the drive pin. Rotate slowly, with some pressure, until notch engages pin. Be sure dampener O-ring seal is evenly distributed in the spool groove. CAUTION: Use extreme care because spool to valve body clearance is very small. Damage is easily caused.

5. With seal protector over stub shaft, slide valve spool spring over shaft, with small diameter of spring going over shaft last. Work spring onto shaft until small coil is located in stub shaft groove.

6. Lubricate a new cap to O-ring seal and install in valve body.

Adjuster Plug and Rotary Valve Installation

1. Align narrow pin slot on valve body with valve body drive pin on the worm. Insert the valve assembly into gear housing by pressing against valve body with finger tips. Do not press on stub shaft or torsion bar. The return hole in the gear housing should be fully visible when properly assembled. CAUTION: Do not press on stub shaft as this may cause shaft and cap to pull out of valve body, allowing the spool dampener O-ring seal to slip into valve body oil grooves.

2. With seal protector over end of stub shaft, install adjuster plug assembly into gear housing snugly with spanner, then back plug off approximately one-eighth turn. Install plug locknut but do not tighten. Adjust preload as de-

scribed in the adjustment section.

3. After adjustment, tighten locknut.

Pitman Shaft Removal and Installation

1. Completely drain the gear assembly and thoroughly clean the outside.

2. Place gear in vise.

3. Rotate stub shaft until pitman shaft gear is in center position. Remove side cover retaining bolts.

4. Tap end of pitman shaft with soft hammer and slide shaft out of housing.

5. Remove and discard side cover O-ring seal.

6. The seals, washers, retainers and bearings may now be removed and examined.

7. Examine all parts for wear or damage and replace as required.

8. Install in reverse of above. Make proper adjustment as described in adjustment section.

Rack-Piston Nut and Worm Assembly Removal

1. Completely drain the gear assembly and thoroughly clean the outside.

2. Remove pitman shaft assembly as previously described.

3. Rotate housing end plug retaining ring so that one end of ring is over hole in gear housing. Spring one end of ring so screwdriver can be inserted to lift it out.

4. Rotate stub shaft to full left turn position to force end plug out of housing.

5. Remove and discard housing end plug O-ring seal.

6. Remove rack-piston nut end plug with ½" square drive.

7. Insert special tool in end of worm. Turn stub shaft so that rack-piston nut will go into tool and then remove rack-piston nut from gear housing.

8. Remove adjuster plug and rotary valve assemblies as previously described.

9. Remove worm and lower thrust bearing and races.

10. Remove cap O-ring seal and discard.

Rack-Piston Nut and Worm Disassembly and Assembly

1. Remove and discard piston ring and back-up O-ring on rack piston nut.

2. Remove ball guide clamp and return guide.

3. Place nut on clean cloth and remove ball retaining tool. Make sure all balls are removed.

4. Inspect all parts for wear, nicks, scoring or burrs. If worm or rack-pinion nut need replacing, both must be replaced as a matched pair.

5. In reassembling reverse the above.

NOTE: When assembling, alternate black and white balls, and install guide and clamp. Packing with grease helps in holding during assembly. When new balls are used, various sizes are available and a selection must be made to secure proper torque when making the high point adjustment.

Rack-Piston Nut and Worm Assembly Installation

1. Install in reverse of removal procedure.

2. In all cases use new O-ring seals.

3. Make adjustments as previously described.

Chrysler Full-Time Power Steering (Constant Control Type)

Chrysler power steering disassembled view (© Chrysler Corp.)

The Chrysler Corporation Constant Control Type Power Steering Gear System consists of a hydraulic pressure pump, a power steering gear and connecting hoses.

The power steering gear housing contains a gear shaft and sector gear, a power piston with gear teeth milled into the side of the piston which is in constant mesh with the gear shaft sector teeth, a worm shaft which con-

nects the steering wheel to the power piston through a coupling. The worm shaft is geared to the piston through recirculating ball contact.

A pivot lever is fitted into the spool valve at the upper end and into a drilled hole in the center thrust bearing race at the lower end. The center thrust bearing race is held firmly against the shoulder of the worm shaft by two thrust bearings, bearing

races and an adjusting nut. The pivot lever pivots in the spacer which is held in place by the pressure plate.

When the steering wheel is turned to the left the worm shaft moves out of the power piston a few thousandths of an inch, the center thrust bearing race moves the same distance since it is clamped to the worm shaft. The race thus tips the pivot lever and moves the spool valve down, allowing

Chrysler power steering gear (© Chrysler Corp.)

Removing valve body assembly (© Chrysler Corp.)

Removing pilot lever (© Chrysler Corp.)

oil under pressure to flow into the left-turn power chamber and force the power piston down. As the power piston moves, it rotates the cross-shaft sector gear and, through the steering linkage, turns the front wheels.

On a right turn the worm shaft moves into the power piston, the center thrust bearing race thus tips the pivot lever and moves the spool valve up, allowing oil under pressure to flow into the right power chamber and force the power piston up.

Pressure Test

Connect the pressure test hoses with the pressure gauge installed between the pump and steering gear.

Now, fill the reservoir to the level mark, then start the engine and bleed the system. Allow the engine to idle until the fluid in the reservoir is between 150° F. and 170° F. Now turn the steering wheel to the extreme right and check the pressure reading, then turn to the extreme left and check the reading again. The gauge reading should be equal in each direction. If not, it indicates excessive internal leakage in the unit.

The pressure should agree with the specifications in Pump Section for satisfactory power steering operation.

Reconditioning

1. Drain gear by turning worm shaft from limit to limit with oil connections held downward. Thoroughly clean outside.
2. Remove valve body attaching screws, body and three O-rings.
3. Remove pivot lever and spring. Pry under spherical head with a screwdriver.

CAUTION: Use care not to collapse slotted end of valve lever as this will destroy bearing tolerances of the spherical head.

4. Remove steering gear arm from sector shaft.
5. Remove snap-ring and seal back-up washer.
6. Remove seal, using proper tool to prevent damage to relative parts.
7. Loosen gear shaft adjusting screw locknut and remove gear shaft cover nut.
8. Rotate wormshaft to position sector teeth at center of piston travel. Loosen power train retaining nut.
9. Insert tools into housing until both tool and shaft are engaged with bearings.
10. Turn worm shaft either to full left or full right (depending on car application) to compress power train parts. Then remove power train retaining nut as mentioned above.
11. Remove housing head tang washer.
12. While holding power train completely compressed, pry on piston

teeth with screwdriver, using shaft as a fulcrum, and remove complete power train.

CAUTION: Maintain close contact between cylinder head, center race and spacer assembly and the housing head. This will eliminate the possibility of reactor rings becoming disengaged from their grooves in cylinder and housing head. It will prohibit center spacer from separating from center race and cocking in the housing. This could make it impossible to remove the power train without damaging involved parts.

13. Place power train in soft-jawed vise in vertical position. The worm bearing rollers will fall out. Use of arbor tool will hold roller when the housing is removed.
14. Raising housing head until wormshaft oil shaft just clears the top of wormshaft and position arbor tool on top of shaft and into seal. With arbor in position, pull up on housing head until arbor is positioned in bearing. Remove when the housing is removed.
15. Remove large O-ring from housing head groove.
16. Remove reaction seal from groove in face of head with air pressure directed into ferrule chamber.
17. Remove reactor spring, reactor

Removing worm shaft oil seal (© Chrysler Corp.)

Removing cylinder head oil seal (© Chrysler Corp.)

Removing reaction seal from wormshaft support (© Chrysler Corp.)

Retaining bearing rollers with arbor tool (© Chrysler Corp.)

ring, worm balancing ring and spacer.

18. While holding wormshaft from turning, turn nut with enough force to release staked portions from knurled section and remove nut.

NOTE: Pay strict attention to cleanliness.

19. Remove upper thrust bearing race (thin) and upper thrust bearing.
20. Remove center bearing race.
21. Remove lower thrust bearing and lower thrust bearing race (thick).
22. Remove lower reaction ring and reaction spring.
23. Remove cylinder head assembly.
24. Remove O-rings from outer grooves in head.
25. Remove reaction O-ring from groove in face of cylinder head. Use air pressure in oil hole located between O-ring grooves.
26. Remove snap-ring, sleeve and rectangular oil seal from cylinder head counterbore.
27. Test wormshaft operation. Not more than 2 in. lbs. should be required to turn it through its entire travel, and with a 15 ft. lb. side load.

Removing reaction seal from cylinder head (© Chrysler Corp.)

NOTE: The worm and piston is serviced as a complete assembly and should not be disassembled.

28. Shaft side play should not exceed 0.008 in. under light pull applied 2 5/16 in. from piston flange.
29. Assemble in reverse of above, noting proper adjustments and preload requirements following.
30. When cover nut is installed, tighten to 20 ft-lbs. torque.
31. Valve mounting screws should be tightened to 200 in.-lbs. torque.
32. With hoses connected, system bled, and engine idling roughly, center valve unit until not self-steering. Tap on head of valve body attaching screws to move valve body up, and tap on end plug to move valve body down.
33. With steering gear on center, tighten gear shaft adjusting screw until lash just disappears.
34. Continue to tighten 3/8 to 1/2 turn and tighten locknut to 50 ft. lbs.

Ford Integral Power Steering Gear

The Ford integral power steering unit is a torsion-bar type.

The torsion bar power steering unit includes a worm and one-piece rack piston, which is meshed to the gear teeth on the steering sector shaft. The unit also includes a hydraulic valve, valve actuator, input shaft and torsion bar assembly which are mounted on the end of the worm shaft and operated by the twisting action of the torsion bar.

The torsion-bar type of power steering gear is designed with the one piece rack-piston, worm and sector shaft in one housing and the valve spool in an attaching housing. This makes possible internal fluid passages between the valve and cylinder, thus eliminating all external lines and hoses, except the pressure and return hoses between the pump and gear assembly.

The power cylinder is an integral part of the gear housing. The piston is double acting, in that fluid pressure may be applied to either side of the piston.

A selective metal shim, located in the valve housing of the gear is for the purpose of tailoring steering gear efforts. If efforts are not within specifications they can be changed by increasing or decreasing shim thickness as follows:

Efforts heavy to the left—Increase shim thickness.

Efforts light to the left—Decrease shim thickness.

Steering Gear Adjustments

The only adjustment which can be performed is the total over center position load, to eliminate excessive lash between the sector and rack teeth.

1. Disconnect the Pitman arm from the sector shaft.
2. Disconnect the fluid return line at the reservoir, at the same time cap the reservoir return line pipe.
3. Place the end of the return line in a clean container and cycle the steering wheel in both directions as required, to discharge the fluid from the gear.
4. Turn the steering wheel to 45 degrees from the left stop.
5. Using an in-lb torque wrench on the steering wheel nut, determine the torque required to rotate the shaft slowly through an

Removing worm bearing race nut (© Ford Motor Co.)

Installing worm bearing race nut (© Ford Motor Co.)

approximately 1/8 turn from the 45 degree position.

6. Turn the steering gear back to center, then determine the torque required to rotate the shaft back and forth across the center position. Loosen the adjuster nut, and turn the adjuster screw until the reading is 11-12 in-lb greater than the torque 45 degrees from the stop. Tighten the lock nut while holding the screw in place.

7. Recheck the readings and replace the Pitman arm and the steering wheel hub cover.

8. Correct the fluid return line to the reservoir and fill the reservoir with specified lubricant to the proper level.

Valve Centering Shim

Removal and Installation

1. Hold the steering gear over a drain pan in an inverted position and cycle the input shaft several times to drain the remaining fluid from the gear.

2. Mount the gear in a soft-jawed vise.

3. Turn the input shaft to either stop then, turn it back approximately 1¾ turns to center the gear.

4. Remove the two sector shaft cover attaching screws, the brake line bracket and the identification tag.

5. Tap the lower end of the sector shaft with a soft-faced hammer to loosen it, then lift the cover and shaft from the housing as an assembly. Discard the O-ring.

6. Remove the four valve housing attaching bolts. Lift the valve housing from the steering gear housing while holding the piston to prevent it from rotating off the worm shaft.

7. Remove the valve housing and the lube passage O-rings and discard them.

8. Place the valve housing, worm and piston assembly in the bench mounted holding fixture with the piston on the top.

9. Rotate the piston upward (back off) 3½ turns.

10. Insert Tool T66P-3553-C (with the arm facing away from the piston) into a bolt hole in the valve housing. Rotate the arm into position under the piston.

11. Loosen the Allen head race nut set screw from the valve housing.

12. Using Tool T66P-3553-B, loosen the worm bearing race nut.

13. Lift the piston-worm assembly from the valve housing. During removal hold the piston to prevent it from spinning off at the shaft.

14. Change the power steering valve centering shim.

15. Install the piston-worm assembly into the valve housing. Hold the piston worm to prevent it from spinning off of the shaft.

16. Install the worm bearing race nut and torque to 2-8 in-lbs using Tool T66P-3553-B.

17. Install the race nut set screw (Allen head) through the valve housing.

18. Rotate the piston upward (back off) ½ turn and remove Tool T66P-3553-C.

19. Remove the valve housing, worm, and piston assembly from the holding fixture.

20. Position a new lube passage O-ring in the counterbore of the gear housing.

21. Apply vaseline to the teflon seal on the piston.

22. Place a new O-ring on the valve housing.

23. Slide the piston and valve into the gear housing being careful not to damage the teflon seal.

24. Align the lube passage in the valve housing with the one in the gear housing, and install but do not tighten the attaching bolts.

25. Rotate the ball nut so that the teeth are in the same place as the sector teeth. Tighten the four valve housing attaching bolts to 35-45 ft-lbs.

26. Position the sector shaft cover O-ring in the steering gear housing. Turn the input shaft as required to center the piston.

27. Apply vaseline to the sector shaft journal; then, position the sector shaft and cover assembly in the gear housing. Install the brake line bracket, steering gear identification tag and the two sector shaft cover attaching studs.

28. Position an in-lb torque wrench on the gear input shaft and adjust the meshload to approximately 4 in-lbs. Then, torque the sector shaft cover attaching studs to 55-70 ft-lbs.

29. After the cover attaching bolts have been tightened to specification, adjust the mesh load to 17 in-lbs with an in-lb torque wrench.

Steering Gear Disassembly

1. Hold the steering gear over a drain pan in an inverted position and cycle the input shaft several times to drain the remaining fluid from the gear.

2. Mount the gear in a soft-jawed vise.

3. Remove the lock nut from the adjusting screw.

4. Turn the input shaft to either stop then, turn it back approximately 1¾ turns to center the gear.

5. Remove the two sector shaft cover attaching studs, the brake line bracket and the identification tag.

6. Tap the lower end of the sector shaft with a soft-hammer to loosen it, then lift the cover and shaft from the housing as an assembly. Discard the O-ring.

7. Turn the sector shaft cover counterclockwise off the adjuster screw.

8. Remove the four valve housing attaching bolts. Lift the valve housing from the steering gear housing while holding the piston to prevent it from rotating off the worm shaft. Remove the valve housing and the lube passage O-rings and discard them.

9. Stand the valve body and piston on end with the piston end down. Rotate the input shaft counterclockwise out of the piston allowing the ball bearings to drop into the piston.

10. Place a cloth over the open end of the piston and turn it upside down to remove the balls.

11. Remove the two screws that attach the ball guide clamp to the ball nut and remove the clamp and the guides.

12. Install the valve body assembly in the holding fixture (do not clamp in a vise) and loosen the race nut screw (Allen head) from the valve housing and remove the worm bearing race nut.

13. Carefully slide the input shaft, worm and valve assembly out of the valve housing. Due to the close diametrical clearance between the spool and housing, the slightest cocking of the spool may cause it to jam in the housing.

14. Remove the shim from the valve housing bore.

Valve Housing

1. Remove the dust seal from the rear of the valve housing and discard the seal.

2. Remove the snap-ring from the valve housing.

3. Turn the fixture to place the valve housing in an inverted position.

4. Insert special tool in the valve body assembly opposite the seal end and gently tap the bearing and seal out of the housing. Discard the seal. Caution must be exercised when inserting and removing the tool to prevent damage to the valve bore in the housing.

5. Remove the fluid inlet and outlet tube seats with an EZ-out if they are damaged.

6. Coat the fluid inlet and outlet tube seats with vaseline and position them in the housing. Install and tighten the tube nuts to press the seats to the proper location.

7. Coat the bearing and seal surface of the housing with a film of vaseline.

8. Seat the bearing in the valve housing. Make sure that the bearing is free to rotate.

9. Dip the new oil seal in gear lubricant; then, place it in the housing with the metal side of the seal facing outward. Drive the seal into the housing until the outer edge of seal does not quite clear the snap-ring groove.

10. Place the snap-ring in the housing; then, drive on the ring until the snap-ring seats in its groove to properly locate the seal.

11. Place the dust seal in the housing with the dished side (rubber side) facing out. Drive the dust seal into place. The seal must be located behind the undercut in the input shaft when it is installed.

Worm and Valve

1. Remove the snap-ring from the end of the actuator.

2. Slide the control valve spool off the actuator.

3. Install the valve spool evenly and slowly with a slight oscillating motion into the flanged end of valve housing with the valve identification groove between the valve spool lands outward, checking for freedom of valve movement within the housing working area. The valve spool should enter the housing bore

Ball nut and valve housing (© Ford Motor Co.)

VALVE HOUSING

BEARING

OIL SEAL

DUST SEAL

INLET TUBE SEAT

OUTLET TUBE SEAT

SNAP RING

Valve housing disassembled (© Ford Motor Co.)

freely and fall by its own weight.

4. If the valve spool is not free, check for burrs at the outward edges of the working lands in the housing and remove with a hard stone.

5. Check the valve for burrs and if burrs are found, stone the valve in a radial direction only. Check for freedom of the valve again.

6. Remove the valve spool from the housing.

7. Slide the spool onto the actuator making sure that the groove in the spool annulus is toward the worm.

8. Install the snap-ring to retain the spool. The beveled ID of the snap-ring must be assembled toward the spool.

9. Check the clearance between the spool and the snap-ring. The clearance should be between .0005-.035 inch. If the clearance is not within these limits, select a snap-ring that will allow a clearance of .002 inch.

Piston and Ball Nut

1. Remove the teflon ring and the O-ring from the piston and ball nut.

2. Dip a new O-ring in gear lubricant and install it on the piston and ball nut.

3. Install a new teflon ring on the piston and ball nut being careful not to stretch it any more than necessary.

Steering Gear Housing

1. Remove the snap-ring and the spacer washer from the lower end of the steering gear housing.

2. Remove the lower seal from the housing. Lift the spacer washer from the housing.

3. Remove the upper seal in the same manner as the lower seal. Some housings require only one seal and one spacer.

4. Dip both sector shaft seals in gear lubricant.

5. Apply lubricant to the sector shaft seal bore of the housing and position the sector shaft inner seal into the housing with the lip facing inward. Press the seal into place. Place a spacer washer (0.090 inch) on top of the seal and apply more lubricant to the housing bore.

6. Place the outer seal in the housing with the lip facing inward and press it into place. Then,

place a 0.090 inch spacer washer on top of the seal.

7. Position the snap-ring in the housing. Press the snap-ring into the housing to properly locate the seals and engage the snap-ring in the groove.

Steering Gear Assembly

Do not clean, wash, or soak seals in cleaning solvent.

1. Mount the valve housing in the holding fixture with the flanged end up.

2. Place the required thickness valve spool centering shim in the housing.

3. Carefully install the worm and valve in the housing.

4. Install the race nut in the housing and torque it to 42 ft-lbs.

5. Install the race nut set screw (Allen head) through the valve housing and torque to 20-25 in-lbs.

6. Place the piston on the bench with the ball guide holes facing up. Insert the worm shaft into the piston so that the first groove is in alignment with the hole nearest to the center of the piston.

7. Place the ball guide in the piston. Place the 27 to 29 balls, depending on the piston design, in the ball guide turning the worm in a clockwise direction as viewed from the input end of the shaft. If all of the balls have not been fed into the guide upon reaching the right stop, rotate the input shaft in one direction and then in the other while installing the balls. After the balls have been installed, do not rotate the input shaft or the piston more than 3½ turns off the right stop to prevent the balls from falling out of the circuit.

8. Secure the guides in the ball nut with the clamp.

9. Position a new lube passage

Tool–T65P-3524-A2   Tool–T65P-3524-A3

Tool–
T57L-500-A

Removing bearing and oil seal
(© Ford Motor Co.)

STEERING GEAR HOUSING

INNER SEAL

SPACER WASHER

SNAP RING

OUTER SEAL

SPACER WASHER

Steering gear housing (© Ford Motor Co.)

O-ring in the counterbore of the gear housing.

10. Apply vaseline to the teflon seal on the piston.

11. Place a new O-ring on the valve housing.

12. Slide the piston and valve into the gear housing being careful not to damage the teflon seal.

13. Align the lube passage in the valve housing with the one in the gear housing and install but do not tighten the attaching bolts.

14. Rotate the ball nut so that the teeth are in the same plane as the sector teeth. Tighten the four valve housing attaching bolts to 35-45 ft-lbs.

15. Position the sector shaft cover O-ring in the steering gear housing. Turn the input shaft as required to center the piston.

16. Apply vaseline to the sector shaft journal then position the sector shaft and cover assembly in the gear housing. Install the brake line bracket, the steering identification tag and two sector shaft cover attaching bolts. Torque the bolts to 55-70 ft-lbs.

17. Attach an in-lb torque wrench to the input shaft. Adjust the mesh load to 17 in-lbs.

Ross HF-54 and HF-64 Integral Power Steering Gear

Adjustments

Unloader Valve Adjustment

This unloader valve adjustment is for right turn only on HF-54 Model gears and for both turns on HF-64 Model gears. Prior to performing the following procedure, obtain the vehicle's straight ahead position by driving the vehicle with hands off the steering wheel thus allowing the unit to find its own center. Now mark the steering column to steering wheel with chalk or masking tape.

1. Check the front wheel turning angles and adjust as required with the wheels off the ground.

2. Position the wheels straight ahead and lower the vehicle.

3. RIGHT TURN—HF-54 OR HF-64 GEARS: With the engine at idle, the vehicle standing still and the fluid at normal operating temperature, rotate the steering wheel to the right the prescribed number of turns.

   H-54 .... 1¾
   H-64 - 2 port 1¼
   H-64 - 4 port 1½

Hold in this position.

4. Loosen the locknut and turn the unloader valve pressure adjusting screw until an audible hiss is heard. Tighten the locknut.

5. Return the wheel to a straight ahead position while the vehicle is moving. With the vehicle standing still, again rotate the steering wheel the prescribed turns; then, check for the audible hiss. Readjust if necessary as in Step 4 and check once more as in this step. It is important to remember that the HF-64 gear has a pitman arm stop for the right turn cast on the gear housing. The pitman arm must not contact this stop prior to contacting the unloader valve. When the hiss is heard during the adjustment, the clearance between the pitman arm and the cast stop should be 1/16 to 1/8-inch minimum.

6. *Left turn—HF-64 gear only:* Repeat Steps 3, 4, and 5 while rotating the steering wheel to the left 1¾ turns.

Sector Shaft Adjustment

1. Disconnect the drag link from the Pitman arm.

2. Center the steering wheel. Grasp the Pitman arm and check it for free movement (lash) between the sector shaft and the rack piston.

3. If free movement is noted (lash), remove the steering gear from the vehicle.

4. Loosen the sector shaft adjustment screw locknut on the side cover.

5. After rotating the input shaft through its full travel for a minimum of five cycles, adjust the sector shaft adjusting screw to provide 15-20 in-lb torque as the input shaft is rotated 90 degrees each side of center.

6. Back out the adjusting screw one turn and note the torque required to move the input shaft 90 degrees each side of the center position. Move the adjusting screw in to provide an increase in torque of 2-4 in-lb at a point within 45 degrees each side of

Input shaft seals and retainers (© Ford Motor Co.)

center after the adjusting screw jam nut is first tightened snug. Now torque to a final 20-25 ft-lb. The input torque of the completely assembled gear, minus hydraulic oil, should not exceed 15 in-lb for the full travel of the output shaft.

7. Install the steering gear in the vehicle.
8. Connect the drag link to the Pitman arm.
9. Connect the pump lines and refill the system with the specified fluid.

Disassembly

1. Rotate the input shaft so the index mark on the end of the sector shaft is perpendicular to the center-line of the gear (straight-ahead position).
2. Remove the side cover attaching screws and washers.
3. Tap lightly on the end of the sector shaft with a soft hammer to disengage the side cover seal and allow the housing to drain.
4. Remove all nicks, burrs, rust and paint before removing the shaft. Lift the side cover and

sector shaft from the housing as an assembly.
5. Remove the sector shaft seal adapter attaching screws and remove the adapter from the housing.
6. Remove the four screws that attach the control valve adapter to the housing.
7. Remove the control valve and rack piston from the housing as an assembly.
8. Remove the sector shaft adjustment screw lock nut. Turn the adjustment clockwise until free of the side cover.

Ross model H-54 steering gear (© Ford Motor Co.)

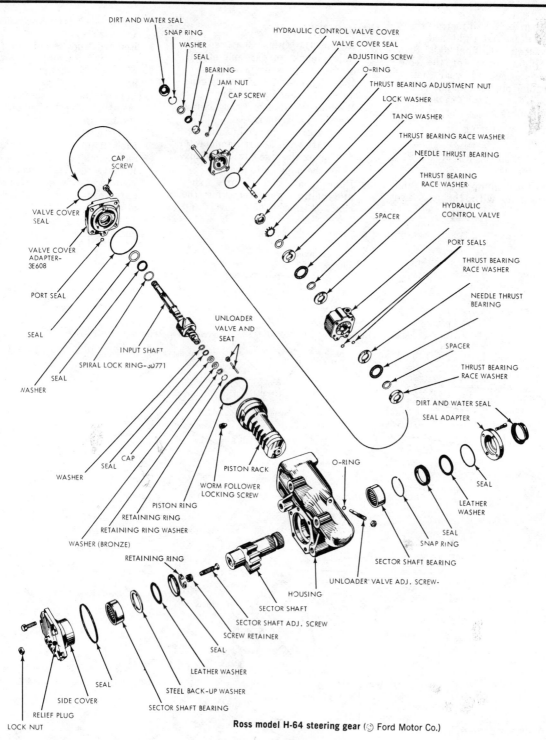

DIRT AND WATER SEAL
SNAP RING
WASHER
SEAL
BEARING
JAM NUT
CAP SCREW

HYDRAULIC CONTROL VALVE COVER
VALVE COVER SEAL
ADJUSTING SCREW
O-RING
THRUST BEARING ADJUSTMENT NUT
LOCK WASHER
TANG WASHER
THRUST BEARING RACE WASHER
NEEDLE THRUST BEARING
THRUST BEARING RACE WASHER
HYDRAULIC CONTROL VALVE
SPACER
PORT SEALS
THRUST BEARING RACE WASHER
NEEDLE THRUST BEARING
SPACER
THRUST BEARING RACE WASHER
DIRT AND WATER SEAL
SEAL ADAPTER
SEAL
LEATHER WASHER
SEAL
SNAP RING
SECTOR SHAFT BEARING

CAP SCREW
VALVE COVER SEAL
VALVE COVER ADAPTER-3E608
PORT SEAL
SEAL
INPUT SHAFT
SPIRAL LOCK RING-3D771
SEAL
WASHER

UNLOADER VALVE AND SEAT

CAP
SEAL
WASHER
PISTON RING
RETAINING RING
RETAINING RING WASHER
WASHER (BRONZE)
RETAINING RING

PISTON RACK
WORM FOLLOWER LOCKING SCREW

O-RING

UNLOADER VALVE ADJ. SCREW

HOUSING
SECTOR SHAFT
SECTOR SHAFT ADJ. SCREW
SCREW RETAINER
SEAL
LEATHER WASHER
STEEL BACK-UP WASHER
SECTOR SHAFT BEARING
SEAL
SIDE COVER
RELIEF PLUG
LOCK NUT

Ross model H-64 steering gear (© Ford Motor Co.)

9. Remove the unloader valve retainer, unloader valves, rod and the spring from the rack piston.
10. If all parts appear undamaged, do not disassemble the rack piston assembly. If there is evidence of damage, place the rack piston on a clean surface with the ball return guides facing upward. Remove the two ball return guide retainer attaching screws, lock washers, guide retainer, guide and balls. It may be necessary to tilt the rack piston over a clean pan and oscillate the

worm shaft to empty the rack of all the balls. Lift the worm shaft from the rack after all the balls have been removed.
11. Carefully hold the input shaft in a vise equipped with soft jaws. Remove the snap-ring, washer, bronze washer, cup, seal and washer. It may be necessary to cut the teflon cup off the shaft.
12. Remove the valve cover dirt and water seal.
13. Remove the four valve cover attaching screws. Lift the cover from the control valve.

14. Unstake the thrust bearing adjustment nut lock washer and remove the adjustment nut.
15. Remove the lock washer, internal tang washer, bearing race (small), thrust bearing and the large bearing race.
16. Lift the control valve and the control valve adapter from the input shaft.
17. Remove spiral lock ring, seal and washer from the counterbore of the valve cover adapter. Discard the washer and seal.
18. Do not disassemble the valve un-

CYLINDER FEED HOLES
(THIS SIDE OF VALVE FACES GEAR HOUSING)

VALVE BODY

OIL TRANSFER HOLES

INTERNAL IDENTIFICATION RING
(FACES GEAR HOUSING)

SOLID CENTERING PLUNGERS
(12-6 SETS OF 2 PLUNGERS)

REACTION SPRINGS
(1 PER SET OF PLUNGERS)

CHECK VALVE PLUNGERS
(ASSEMBLE AS SHOWN)

VALVE SPOOL

Hydraulic valve control assembly (© Ford Motor Co.)

less absolutely necessary. The valve is the control center of the hydraulic system. The major parts, which are the body and spool, are machined to very close tolerances and with precision machined edges. The spool and valve body are selectively fitted at the factory, and therefore these two parts are not separately replaceable. If either is damaged or excessively worn, the complete valve assembly should be replaced. Good performance of power steering is not assured if a mismatched valve spool and body are used. Care should be exercised in the handling of these parts to prevent damage. Sealing edges of the valve bore and the spool should not be broken. This will result in excessive leakage and reduced hydraulic power. If valve parts should drop out during gear disassembly, reassemble the valve as follows:

a. Clean all parts with a clean petroleum base solvent and blow dry with clean, dry air.

b. Insert the valve spool in the control valve making certain that the machined identification groove in the ID of one end of the spool is toward the gear housing.

c. There are 7 sets of plungers, each set having one reaction spring. Insert the 6 solid centering plunger sets first along with one spring per set. The remaining plunger set should be inserted in the valve body with the small hole on each plunger facing outboard.

Cleaning and Inspection

1. All parts should be cleaned in a clean petroleum base solvent and blown dry with clean dry air. Avoid wiping parts with a cloth, since lint may cause binding and sticking of closely fitted components.

2. Inspect the worm grooves in the rack piston and on the input shaft for wear scores. Inspect the OD of the rack piston and the ring or teeth for wear or scores. On the HF-64 gear, the ball nut and input shaft are serviced as a matched assembly. Therefore, both must be replaced if either are worn or damaged. The rack piston is not matched.

3. Inspect the inside ends of the ball return guides for wear or damage.

4. Inspect the housing bore for wear or scores or being cracked and replace as required.

5. Inspect the sector shaft teeth for wear or the bearing surfaces for wear or scores.

6. Replace the sector shaft bearings if worn or damaged. Note the sector shaft bearing in the side cover is replaced as part of the side cover assembly.

7. Replace all seals at time of disassembly.

Assembly

1. Lubricate all rubber parts prior to assembly.

2. If the sector shaft bearing was removed from the steering gear housing, install the snap-ring in the outboard side of the housing (HF-54 gear only).

3. Place the steering gear housing in a press with the side cover area on a wood block to prevent damage to the machined area.

4. Position the bearing on the housing with the numbered end facing up. Carefully press the bearing into the housing until the outer surface is flush. Use a tool that pilots in the ID of the bearing and contacts the bearing end surface.

5. Coat the unloader valve pressure adjusting screw O-ring liberally with clean grease or oil. Carefully slide it into the groove on the non-threaded end of the adjusting screw.

6. Thread the adjusting screw into the lower end of the housing leaving 7/8 inch of the screw exposed. Install the lock nut on the adjusting screw and tighten it securely.

7. Carefully secure the input shaft in a vise equipped with soft jaws to permit access to both ends of the shaft.

8. On HF-54 gears, slide the bearing race (large) thrust bearing, control valve (with cylinder ports toward the shoulder), bearing race (small), internal tang washer, lock washer and thrust bearing adjustment nut. On HF-64 gears, slide the thrust bearing race washer, spacer, control valve (with cylinder ports toward the shoulder), needle thrust bearing, thrust bearing race washer, tang washer, lock washer and thrust bearing adjustment nut.

9. Tighten the adjustment nut to 20 ft-lbs, then back it off 1/2-1 lock washer tangs. Bend one tang of the lock washer into the slot provided on the adjustment nut. When adjusted in this manner, the control valve should rotate freely on the shaft with a torque of 2-3½ in-lbs and have no perceptible end play.

10. Assemble a new washer seal and the spiral lock ring in the counterbore of the valve cover adapter. Make sure that the lip of seal is facing toward the spiral lock ring.

11. Coat a new valve cover seal and two new cylinder port seals with grease to retain them in place. Position the seals in the recesses provided in the control valve cover adapter on the surface adjacent to the control valve.

12. Reposition the input shaft in the vise securing the serrated end.

13. Slip the adapter over the worn groove end of the input shaft. Align the cylinder port seals with the ports in the control valve. Install one of the attach-

TO CYLINDER   FROM CYLINDER

SUPPLY
(FROM PUMP)   RETURN
(TO RESERVOIR)

SPOOL MOVED IN
DIRECTION SHOWN

FLUID FLOW FOR RIGHT TURN

HYDRAULIC PORTS
TO POWER CYLINDER
REACTION CHAMBER

VALVE BODY   VALVE SPOOL
SUPPLY   RETURN
(FROM PUMP)   (TO RESERVOIR)

**SPOOL CENTERED
STRAIGHT AHEAD**

FROM CYLINDER   TO CYLINDER

SUPPLY
(FROM PUMP)   RETURN
(TO RESERVOIR)

SPOOL MOVED IN
DIRECTION SHOWN

FLUID FLOW FOR LEFT TURN

FLUID FROM PUMP (SUPPLY PRESSURE)
FLUID FROM CYLINDER (RETURN PRESSURE)
EQUALIZED PRESSURE

Semi-Integral Power Steering Gear Valve Power Flow

ing bolts finger tight to facilitate assembly.

14. Assemble the washer (steel), a new rubber seal, new teflon cup with the lip toward the seal, bronze washer and retaining washer. Compress the washer and seal, then install the snap-ring on the end of the input shaft. Make sure that the snap-ring is fully seated in the groove and the recessed area of the retaining washer.

15. Secure the rack piston in a soft-jawed vise with the ball guide holes facing upward.

16. Carefully expand the piston ring and install it in the piston groove.

17. Place the two unloader valves, spring, and rod in the rack piston. Apply a drop of sealer to the threads of the retainer. Install and torque the retainer to 25 ft-lbs.

18. Coat the input shaft seal at the end of worm with grease and place it in the rack piston bore.

19. Assemble sixteen balls while rotating the input shaft counterclockwise. The black spacer balls and the polished steel balls must be installed alternately. Coat the ball return guides with grease to retain the balls, then install the six remaining balls in the guides making sure that the balls in the guide alternate with the last balls installed in the rack piston. If a ball is lost, no more than three black spacer balls may be used for replacement. Secure the guide retaining clip to the rack piston with two screws and washers. Torque the screws to 30-35 ft-lbs and bend the tab of the locking washer against the flat.

20. Grip the serrated end of the sector shaft in a soft-jawed vise.

21. Coat the head of the sector shaft adjusting screw with grease. Position the head of adjusting screw into the slot in the end of sector shaft.

22. Install a new sector shaft adjustment screw retainer in the end of shaft. Tighten the retainer to permit free rotation of screw without perceptible end play. Stake the retainer in the two slots provided and recheck the rotation effort.

23. If the pressure relief plug has been removed or ruptured, press a new one into the side cover until it is flush with the surface.

24. Assemble the snap-ring, steel washer (with taper toward the snap-ring), leather washer and the two piece seal into the side cover. The seal has Oil Side molded into one side and must be visible after installation.

25. Coat the end of sector shaft with lubricant. Rotate the sector shaft adjusting screw counterclockwise to thread it into the side cover. Rotate the screw until a firm stop is reached. Make sure that the shaft seal has not fallen out of position.

26. Place the outer seal in the seal adapter. Then install the leather washer and inner seal making sure that the side having the mold "Oil Side" is visible after installation.

27. If the input shaft needle bearing has been removed from the control valve cover it must be installed with a tool that will pilot in the bearing and have clearance in the cover bore. The bearing must be pressed from the part number end, and to a depth of $1\frac{1}{8}$ inches from the face of the valve cover. After installation of the bearing, make sure that all rollers rotate freely.

28. Install the seal on the control valve cover with the lip facing toward the needle bearing. Coat the washer with grease and install it on the cover. Install the snap-ring to secure the seal and washer.

29. Pack the new dirt and water seal with grease and install it on the control valve cover.

30. Secure the steering gear housing in a vise equipped with soft jaws.

31. Lubricate the steering gear housing bore. Start the rack piston into the bore, then compress the ring and move the piston into position so that the teeth are visible through the side cover opening. Install the four adapter-to-housing attaching bolts. Remove the one bolt that was previously installed.

32. Lubricate a new valve cover seal with grease and position it in the recess of the valve cover.

33. Slide the valve cover onto the input shaft and install the four cover-to-control valve attaching bolts.

34. Rotate the input shaft as required to align the center tooth of the rack piston (marked tooth) with the side cover opening.

35. Lubricate a new side cover O-ring and position it on the side cover.

36. Position the sector shaft and side cover to the steering gear housing making sure that the center tooth (marked tooth) engages the center space (marked space).

37. Install the four side cover attaching bolts and lock washers. Torque the bolts to 45-55 ft-lbs.

38. Adjust sector shaft adjustment screw as outlined in the Sector Shaft Adjustment.

39. Cover the sector shaft serrations with a layer of scotch tape to prevent damage to the seal in the adapter.

40. Position the adapter over the sector shaft and on the housing. Install and tighten the attaching bolts.

41. Pack the seal adapter outer seal with grease, then install it on the adapter to prevent water entry.

Final Checks

1. After rotating the input shaft through its full travel for a minimum of five cycles, recheck the sector shaft adjustment. No rotational lash or bind of the sector shaft in center position is permissible.
2. If the gear is properly assembled and adjusted, the input torque of the empty gear should not exceed 15 in-lbs over full travel of 95 degrees at the output shaft.
3. Reverse-torque applied to output shaft for full gear travel should not exceed 50 ft-lbs.

International—Semi Integral Power Steering Gear

This gear is a semi-integral hydraulic steering gear which incorporates a hydraulic control valve on a single stud cam and lever mechanical steering gear. When the steering wheel is turned it actuates the control valve. The valve then directs fluid from a pump to a power cylinder located in the linkage.

Adjustments

The following are the two principal adjustments on this type gear:

1. Adjustment of the needle thrust bearings on the cam shaft on each side of the centering washer assembly.
2. Adjustment of the tapered stud in the cam groove for backlash.

If adjustments are made with the steering gear mounted in the vehicle, free the steering gear of all load by disconnecting the drag link from the steering gear arm. Disconnect the coupling if the gear is the stub shaft type.

Thrust Bearing Adjustment

If the gear is mounted in the vehicle it may be necessary to remove any parts restricting the removal of the actuator housing.

1. Remove the four screws retaining the valve to the actuator housing and remove the valve.
2. Pull out the actuator lever.
3. Remove the four actuator housing mounting screws and remove the actuator housing.
4. Remove the adjusting nut, tongued washer, upper thrust washer and needle bearing. Wash all parts in solvent and coat with a light oil.
5. Reassemble the thrust bearing parts, tongued washer and adjusting nut.
6. Turn the steering gear off its center position to free the lever-shaft stud in the cam groove.
7. Torque the nut to 10 ft. lbs. Back the nut off 10°-20° and restake the lip of the adjusting nut in the slot of the cam shaft.
8. Position the actuator housing to the gear housing. Make sure that the pin engages in the hole of the actuator housing.
9. Position the actuator lever in the actuator housing making sure that the slotted end of the lever straddles the centering washer assembly and position on the slot in the other end of the lever so that the pin in the clevis of the valve fixture rod will fit freely into it when mounting the valve.
10. Mount the valve and gasket on the actuator housing making sure the valve spool clevis pin fits freely into the slot of the actuator lever. Install all four mounting screws and tighten lightly in rotation, then torque to 10-15 ft. lbs.

NOTE: Careless tightening may cause the valve spool to be pulled off center by actuator lever interference with the clevis pin.

Backlash adjustment (stud in cam groove)

1. Turn the adjusting screw clockwise in the side cover until a very slight drag is felt when turning the gear through the mid position.
2. Lock the adjusting screw with the locknut and turn the gear from the extreme left to the ex-

1 Housing, actuator
2 Nut, lock
3 Washer, tongued
4 Washer, thrust
5 Bearing, thrust asm.
6 Washer, centering
7 Spring, thrust bearing center
8 Pin (Not Serviced Separately)
9 Retainer, valve spring
10 Bearing, needle cam
11 Ring, snap
12 Gasket, actuator to housing
13 Housing
14 Gasket, side cover
15 Plug, housing vent
16 Nut, adjusting screw
17 Cover, side
18 Retainer, adjusting screw
19 Screw, adjusting
20 Levershaft
21 Stud, asm.
22 Bushing, housing
23 Tube, w/cam
24 Cover, housing upper
25 Sleeve, w/seal
26 Clamp, jacket tube

27 Lever, actuating
28 Gasket, control valve
29 Connector, hose to valve
30 Ring, valve end plate retaining
31 Plate, valve end
32 Seal, valve end plate, "O"-ring
33 Rod, valve
34 Housing (Not Serviced Separately)
35 Seal, valve upper cover, "O"-ring
36 Seal, valve spring lower "O"-ring
37 Washer, valve centering
38 Ball, steel
39 Spring, valve plug relief
40 Seal, valve plug "O"-ring
41 Plug, relief
42 Spring, valve
43 Seal (Not Serviced Separately)
44 Washer, valve centering
45 Retainer, "O"-ring seal
46 Nut, hex. lock 5/16 NF
47 Cover, valve end
48 Valve, control asm.
49 Seal, housing oil
50 Arm, steering
51 Washer, lock
52 Nut, hex.

International—semi integral power steering gear—solid column type
(© International Harvester Company) (Truck Division)

Power Steering Gears

1 Reinforcement, steering gear
2 Nut, adjusting screw
3 Cover, side
4 Gasket, side cover
5 Retainer, adjusting screw
6 Nut, levershaft stud
7 Washer, lock
8 Washer, roller
9 Screw, adjusting

10 Levershaft
11 Bearing, roller
12 Stud, cover to housing
13 Stud, levershaft
14 Plug, housing vent
15 Cover, lower housing
16 Gasket, lower housing cover
17 Bearing, needle cam
18 Ring, snap
19 Housing
20 Arm, steering
21 Seal, housing oil
22 Bushing, housing
23 Gasket, actuator to housing
24 Tube, w/cam
25 Retainer, valve spring
26 Bearing, thrust, assy.
27 Spring, thrust bearing center
28 Pin, (Not Serviced Separately)
29 Washer, centering
30 Washer, thrust
31 Washer, tongued
32 Nut, lock
33 Plug, sq-hd 1/8 pipe
34 Seal, oil
35 Housing, actuator
36 Lever, actuating
37 Gasket, control valve
38 Connector, hose to valve
39 Ring, valve end plate retaining
40 Plate, valve end
41 Seal, valve end plate, O-ring
42 Rod, valve
43 Housing, (Not Serviced Separately)
44 Seal, valve upper cover O-ring
45 Seal, valve spring lower O-ring
46 Washer, valve centering
47 Ball, steel
48 Spring, valve plug relief
49 Seal, valve plug O-ring
50 Plug, relief
51 Spring, valve
52 Seal, (Not Serviced Separately)
53 Retainer, O-ring seal
54 Nut, hex, lock 5/16 NF
55 Cover, valve end
56 Valve, control, assy.

International—semi integral power steering gear—jointed column type
(© International Harvester Company) (Truck Division)

treme right and back again to check adjustment.

Steering Gear Disassembly

1. Unscrew the locknut and adjusting screw.
2. Slide the sub-assembly of the side cover and the levershaft from the housing and remove the gasket.
3. Remove the four screws retaining the valve to the actuator housing and remove the valve.
4. Pull out the actuator lever.
5. Remove the four actuator housing mounting screws and remove the actuator housing.
6. Remove the cam and wheel tube and centering washer assembly as a unit from the housing.
7. Remove the adjusting nut then remove the tongued spacer washer and upper thrust washer and needle bearing.
8. Remove the centering washer assembly and bearing and without losing any springs remove the spring retainer.

Inspection

1. Clean all parts with solvent and blow dry with compressed air.
2. Examine all parts for chips, wear or pitting.

NOTE: The cam is copper plated. The operation of the stud in the cam groove will wear away the copper plating. This is a normal condition.

Control Valve Disassembly

1. Remove the retainer ring, cover plate and O-ring seal.
2. Remove the end cover from the valve body.
3. Remove the elastic stop nut and washer from the end of the fixture rod and pull the fixture rod out of the spool.
4. Push the spool out in the same direction to permit removal of the centering washers, O-ring and centering spring from the valve body.
5. Remove the O-ring from the spool.
6. Remove the by-pass valve parts, plug assembly and spring and ball.

NOTE: The spool and valve body are selectively fitted at the factory and should not be replaced separately. A "mis-matched" spool and body could result in a loss of good performance of the power steering.

Steering Gear Assembly

1. Use new gaskets and seals.
2. Replace any needle bearings in

the ends of the housing that were removed.
3. Install the valve spring retainer over the wheel tube and then assemble in the following order: Springs into retainer, bearing, centering washer assembly, bearing, thrust washer, tongued washer, adjusting nut.
4. Adjust the bearings (See "Thrust Bearing Adjustment").
5. Assemble the cam in the housing making sure it rotates freely.
6. Use a new gasket and install the actuator housing and pin to the gear housing. Make sure the pin engages in the hole of the actuator housing.
7. Assemble the retainer, screw and seal washer to the actuator housing. Screw the retainer in far enough to eliminate play between the adjusting screw and levershaft but the screw must be free to rotate.
8. Assemble the side cover to the adjusting screw. Position the gasket and install the side cover and levershaft in the housing.
9. Install the locknut to the adjusting screw and adjust the screw properly (see "Backlash Adjustment").

NOTE: On stub shaft type gears,

assemble the lubricated oil seal with the lip out, into the counterbore of the actuator housing.

Control Valve Assembly

1. Install the O-ring on the spool.
2. Apply a light coat of lubricating oil to the spool and O-rings and position the spool in the valve body with the O-ring toward the clevis end of the valve.
   NOTE: Easily twist the spool into place: do not force it.
3. Assemble the centering washer, spring, centering washer, O-ring, centering washer into the valve body.
4. Assemble the flexure rod into the spool.
5. Install the washer and nut to the flexure rod and torque to 125-150 in. lbs.
6. If the by-pass valve parts were removed replace the O-ring on the plug before reassembly in the body. Assemble the ball, spring and plug into the body.
7. Position the actuator lever in the actuator housing making sure that the slotted end of the lever straddles the centering washer assembly and position on the slot in the other end of the lever so that the pin in the clevis of the valve fixture rod will fit freely into it when mounting the valve.
8. Mount the valve and gasket on the actuator housing making sure the valve spool clevis pin fits freely into the slot of the ac-

tuator lever. Install all four mounting screws and tighten lightly in rotation then torque to 10-15 ft. lbs.
   NOTE: Careless tightening may cause the valve spool to be pulled off center by actuator lever interference with the clevis pin.
9. Make sure the valve spool actuaes before assembling the end covers.
   NOTE: Valve spool travel should be a minimum of .065 in. each direction for full flow.
10. Position the O-rings on the end of the valve body and install the end cover.
11. Install the O-ring, cover plate, and retaining ring to the clevis end of the valve.

Rotary Valve Power Steering Gear (Cross-Section View)
(©International Harvester Company) (Truck Division)

Steering Shaft-to-Gear Flexible Couplings
(©International Harvester Company) (Truck Division)

Truck Front End Trouble Diagnosis

Steering Wheel Spoke Position Not Centered
1. Start with steering gear set on high-spot.
2. Check for proper toe-in.
3. Check for proper relation between lengths of each tie rod.

Front End Rides Hard
1. Improper tires.
2. Improper air pressure.
3. Shock absorbers too severe or malfunctioning.

Rides Too Soft
1. Improper tire pressure.
2. Loss of spring load-rate, (weak springs).
3. Weak or leaking shock absorbers.

Truck Steers to One Side At All Times
1. Incorrect caster angle.
2. Incorrect camber angle.
3. Incorrect kingpin inclination or wheel support angle.
4. Unequal air pressure or unequal tread.
5. Unequal or one-side brake drag.
6. Unequal shock absorber control.
7. Bent or damaged steering suspension components.
8. Uneven or weak spring condition, front or rear, causing truck to sit unevenly.
9. Improper tracking.

Truck Steers to One Side Only When Brakes Are Applied
1. Improper brake adjustment, damaged or worn shoes or anchors.
2. Grease or foreign substance on brake lining.
3. Excessive wear or bent condition in suspension components.

Truck Steers Down Off Crowned Road But Normally on Flat Road
1. Excessive positive camber at one or both sides.

2. Weak or uneven shock absorber action.
3. Excessive or unequal wear in suspension components.

Truck Wanders—Steers Erratically
1. Incorrect caster.
2. Improper tire pressure or unequal treads.
3. Excessively worn or damaged suspension components.
4. Power steering gear damaged, causing power assist to function abnormally.

Truck Steers Hard
1. Binding steering or suspension parts.
2. Improper lubrication.
3. Improper (too large) tires.
4. Low tire pressure.

Tires Cup on Outside Edge With Ripple Wear Pattern
1. Generally incorrect camber or toe-in.

Tires Wear Unevenly in Center and Faster Than Outer Edges
1. Generally too much tire pressure.

Tires Wear and Scuff on Both Outer Edges, Not in Center
1. Generally low tire pressure.

Uneven Outer Wear—Center and Inner Edge Wear Normal
1. With adjustments normal this is usually caused by driving into turns at too high speed. Do not confuse with outer edge cupping.

Unequal Tire Wear Between Front Wheels
1. Unequal tire pressure.
2. Unequal tire quality or size.
3. Bent or worn steering suspension components.
4. Improper tracking.

Tire Squeal on Turns
1. Low tire pressure.
2. Driving into turn too fast.
3. Damaged or misaligned parts causing improper front wheel toe-out steering radius.
4. Improper camber adjustment.

Wheel Bounce
1. Unequal tire pressure.
2. Unbalanced wheels or tires.
3. Excessive wheel or tire run-out.
4. Weak or broken front springs.
5. Inoperative shock absorber.
6. Loose or damaged wheel bearings.

Noisy Front End
1. Lack of, or improper, lubrication.
2. Loose tie rod ends.
3. Worn spring shackle.
4. Inoperative shock absorber.
5. Loose U-bolts or clips.
6. Broken spring.
7. Worn universal (FWD).
8. Worn differential (FWD).

Lubricant Leaking Into Drums
1. Too much differential lubricant (FWD).
2. Clogged axle housing vent (FWD).
3. Damaged or worn universal driveshaft oil seal (FWD).
4. Loose steering knuckle flange bearings (FWD).
5. Defective outer oil seal.
6. Rough spindle bearing surface.
7. Wheel bearings over-packed or using wrong type lubricant.
8. Clogged wheel bearing oil slinger drain.
9. Cracked steering knuckle outer flange.

Wheel Alignment
For a truck to have safe steering control with a minimum of tire wear, certain established rules must be followed. These rules fix the values of

	RAPID WEAR AT SHOULDERS	RAPID WEAR AT CENTER	CRACKED TREADS	WEAR ON ONE SIDE	FEATHERED EDGE	BALD SPOTS
CONDITION						
CAUSE	UNDER INFLATION	OVER INFLATION	UNDER-INFLATION OR EXCESSIVE SPEED	IMPROPER CAMBER	INCORRECT TOE	WHEEL UNBALANCED
CORRECTION	ADJUST PRESSURE TO SPECIFICATIONS WHEN TIRES ARE COOL		ADJUST CAMBER TO SPECIFICATIONS	ADJUST FOR TOE-IN 1/8 INCH	DYNAMIC OR STATIC BALANCE WHEELS

CAMBER AND KING PIN INCLINATION   **TOE-IN**   **KING PIN INCLINATION**

FRONT AXLE CASTER

*A Camber (degrees positive)
*B King pin inclination (degrees)
*C Minus D Toe-in (inches)

*E Caster (degrees positive)
*Refer to "Specifications" for correct dimensions

Front end alignment chart (© G.M.C.)

planes, angles and radii relative to each other and to truck and tire dimensions. Some factors are built in, with no provision for adjustment; others are adjustable within limits. The entire system, being a relative one, depends upon all value factors, separately and combined. It is therefore difficult to change some of the established settings without influencing others.

This system is called steering geometry or wheel alignment and requires a complete check of all the factors involved. Definitions of these factors and the effect each one has on the truck are given in the following paragraphs.

For adjustment data relative to each separate truck and year, refer to the individual truck sections.

Toe-in, Relative to Steering Wheel Position

Toe-in, or straightaway alignment, is a value given the negative distance between the front extremes of the two front, or rear, wheels relative to a like measurement taken at the rear extremes of the same wheels. This factor of alignment is blamed for more steering and tire wear troubles than any other. The careless or inexperienced mechanic will attempt all sorts of corrective measures with a turn of the tie-rod adjustments.

Always check steering wheel alignment in conjunction with and at the same time as, toe-in. In fact, the steering wheel spoke position, with the truck on a straight section of highway, may be the first indication of front end misalignment. Check the spoke position relative to straight-ahead truck travel. If the wheel is

not in a normal straight position, the condition may be corrected during toe-in adjustment.

1. Loosen the tie-rod adjusting clamps.
2. If the steering wheel position is satisfactory, shorten or lengthen both tie-rods (the same amount) to the required toe-in specifications.

If, however, after correcting the toe-in value, the steering wheel position is wrong, shorten the left and lengthen the right tie-rod, or lengthen the left and shorten the right tie-rod (the same amount) to obtain the desired steering wheel position.

If the truck has been wrecked, or indicates any evidence of steering gear or linkage disturbance, the pitman arm should be disconnected from the sector shaft. The steering wheel (or gear) should be disconnected and turned from extreme right to extreme left to determine the halfway point in its turning scope. This will be the spot on the gear that is in action during straight ahead driving and in which position the steering gear should be adjusted. With the steering wheel in the straight-ahead position and the steering gear adjusted to zero lash status, reconnect the pitman arm.

Steering Geometry

Camber Angle

Camber is the amount that the front wheels are inclined outward at the top. Camber is spoken of, and measured, in degrees from the perpendicular.

The purpose of the camber angle is

to take some of the load off the spindle outboard bearing.

Caster Angle

Caster is the amount that the kingpin (or in the case of trucks without king-pins, the knuckle support pivots) is tilted towards the back of the truck. Caster is usually spoken of, and measured, in degrees. Positive caster means that the top of the kingpin is tilted toward the back of the truck. Positive caster is indicated by the sign +.

Negative caster is exactly the opposite; the top of the kingpin is tilted toward the front of the truck. This is generally indicated by the sign −.

Negative caster is sometimes referred to as reverse caster.

The effect of positive caster is to cause the truck to steer in the direction in which it tends to go. This is not necessarily a straight line, since trucks with independently sprung front wheels usually steer easily. Positive caster in the front wheels may cause the truck to steer down off a crowned road or steer in the direction of a cross wind. For this reason, many of our modern trucks are arranged with negative caster so that the opposite is true; the truck tends to steer up a crowned road and into a cross wind.

Angle of Kingpin Inclination

In addition to the caster angle, the kingpins (or knuckle support pivots) are also inclined toward each other at the top. This angle is known as kingpin inclination and is usually spoken of, and measured, in degrees.

The effect of kingpin inclination is to cause the wheels to steer in a

Front Axle and Suspension

Caster angle, note that if the pivot tilts forward, caster is negative, tilted back, caster is positive

Steering wheel position

Camber, king pin slant and included angle

straight line, regardless of outside forces such as crowned roads, cross winds, etc., which may tend to make it steer at a tangent. As the spindle is moved from extreme right to extreme left it apparently rises and falls. Notice that it reaches its highest position when the wheels are in the straight-ahead position. In actual operation, the spindle cannot rise and fall because the wheel is in constant contact with the ground.

Therefore, the truck itself will rise at the extreme right turn and come to its lowest point at the straight-ahead position, and again rise for an extreme left turn. The weight of the truck will tend to cause the wheels to come to the straight-ahead position, which is the lowest position of the truck itself.

Included Angle

Included angle is the name given to that angle which includes kingpin inclination and camber. It is the relationship between the centerline of the wheel and the centerline of the kingpin (or the knuckle support pivots). This angle is built into the knuckle (spindle) forging and will remain constant throughout the life of the truck, unless the spindle itself is damaged.

When checking a truck on the front end stand, always measure kingpin inclination as well as camber unless some provision is made on the stand for checking condition of the spindle. Where no such provision is made, add the kingpin inclination to the camber for each side of the truck. These totals should be exactly the

same, regardless of how far from the norm the readings may be.

For example, the left side of the truck checks $5\frac{1}{2}°$ kingpin inclination and $1°$ positive camber—total $6\frac{1}{2}°$. Since both sides check exactly the same for the included angle, it is unlikely that both spindles, in this instance, are bent. Adjusting to correct for camber will automatically set correct kingpin inclination.

A bent spindle would show up like this: left side of the truck has $\frac{3}{4}°$ positive camber, $5\frac{1}{4}°$ kingpin inclination—total $6°$ included angle. Right side of truck has $1\frac{1}{4}°$ positive camber, $6°$ kingpin inclination—total $7\frac{1}{4}°$ included angle. One of these spindles is bent and if adjustments are made to correct camber, the kingpin inclination will be incorrect due to the bent spindle.

Since the most common cause of a bent spindle is striking the curb when parking, which causes the spindle to bend upward, the side having the greater included angle usually has the bent spindle. It will be found impossible to achieve good alignment and minimum tire wear unless the bent spindle is replaced.

Toe-in

Toe-in is the amount that the front wheels are closer together at the front than they are at the back. This dimension is usually spoken of, and measured, in inches or fractions of inches.

Generally speaking, the wheels are toed-in because they are cambered. When a truck operates with $0°$ camber it will be found to operate with zero toe-in. As the required camber increases, so does the toe-in. The reason for this is that the cambered wheel tends to steer in the direction in which it is cambered. Therefore it is necessary to overcome this tendency of the wheel by compensating very slightly in the direction opposite to that in which it tends to roll. Caster and camber both have an effect on toe-in. Therefore toe-in is the last thing on the front end which

should be corrected. Always set caster, camber and kingpin inclination (included angle) before setting toe-in.

Toe-out Steering Radius

When a truck is steered into a turn, the outside wheel of the vehicle scribes a much larger circle than the inside wheel. Therefore, the outside wheel must be steered to a somewhat less angle than the inside wheel. This difference in angle is often called toe-out.

The change in angle from toe-in in the straight-ahead position to toe-out in the turn is caused by the relative position of the steering arms to the kingpin and to each other.

If a line were drawn from the center of the kingpin through the center of the steering arm-tie rod attaching hole at each wheel, these lines would be found to cross almost exactly in the center of the rear axle.

If the front end angles, including toe-in, are set correctly, and the toe-out is found to be incorrect, one or both of the steering arms are bent.

Tracking

While tracking is more a function of the rear axle and frame, it is difficult to align the front suspension when the truck does not track straight. Tracking means that the

Stop screw adjustment (© G.M. Corp.)

Steering geometry on turns (© Chrysler Corp.)

Twin-I-Beam caster increase tool installation (© Ford Motor Co.)

centerline of the rear axle follows exactly the path of the centerline of the front axle when the truck is moving in a straight line.

On trucks that have equal tread, front and rear, the rear tires will follow in exactly the tread of the front tires, when moving in a straight line. However, there are many trucks whose rear tread is wider than the front tread. On such trucks, the rear axle tread will straddle the front axle tread an equal amount on both sides, when moving in a straight line.

Perhaps the easiest way to check a truck for tracking is to stand directly in back of it and watch it move in a straight line down the street. If the observer will stand as near to the center of the truck as possible, he can readily observe, even with the difference in perspective between the front and rear wheels, whether or not they are tracking properly. If the truck is found to track incorrectly, the difficulty will be found in either the frame or in the rear axle alignment.

Another more accurate method to check tracking is to park the truck on a level floor and drop a plumb-line from the extreme outer edge of the front suspension lower A-frame. Use the same drop point on each side of the truck. Make a chalk line where the plumb-line strikes the floor. Do the same with the rear axle, selecting a point on the rear axle housing for the plumb-line.

Measure diagonally from the left rear mark to the right front mark and from the right rear mark to the left front mark. These two diagonal measurements should be exactly the same. A ¼″ variation is acceptable.

If the diagonal measurements taken are different, measure from the right rear mark to the right front mark and from the left rear to the left front. These two measurements should also be the same within ¼″.

If the diagonal measurements are different, but the longitudinal measurements are the same, the frame is swayed (diamond shaped).

However, in the event that the diagonal measurements are unequal and the longitudinal measurements are also unequal, and the truck is tracking incorrectly, the rear axle is misaligned.

If the diagonal and longitudinal measurements are both unequal, but the truck appears to track correctly on the street, a kneeback is indicated.

NOTE: A kneeback means that one complete side of the front suspension is bent back. This is often caused by crimping the front wheels against the curb when parking the vehicle, then starting up without straightening the wheels out.

Suspension and Ball Joint Checks

When checking the suspension and ball joints, it is advisable to fol-

Tool installation for camber increase
(© Ford Motor Co.)

Twin-I-Beam caster decrease tool installation (© Ford Motor Co.)

Tool installation for camber decrease
(© Ford Motor Co.)

Front Axle and Suspension

Rock tire top and bottom
Reject if movement at tire sidewall exceeds maximum tolerance, but do not confuse wheel bearing looseness with ball joint wear

Check ball joint radial (side) play

Reject if axial play in ball joint exceeds maximum tolerance

Check ball joint axial (up and down) play

Checking lower ball joint (typical)
(© G.M. Corp.)

low the manufacturer's recommendations. For all practical purposes, however, the following general procedures are applicable.

Suspension System Check

This check is made with the ball joints fully loaded, so that suspension elements other than the ball joints may be checked.

When the front spring or torsion bar is supported by the lower control arm, the jackstand should be located under the front crossmember or frame.

When the front spring is supported by the upper control arm, the jackstand should be located under the lower control arm.

Vertical or horizontal movement at the road wheel should not exceed the following:

Up to and including 16 inches .... 1/4"
16 to 18 inches .... 1/3"
More than 18 inches .... 1/2"

Ball Joint Check

When checking the ball joints for any wear, they must be free of any load.

When the front spring or torsion bar is supported by the lower control arm, the jackstand should be positioned under the lower control arm.

When the front spring is supported by the upper control arm, the jackstand should be located under the front crossmember or frame.

Replace the upper ball joint if any noticeable play is present in the joint when the spring is supported by the upper control arm.

Replace the load carrying ball joint if the sideplay (horizontal motion) of the wheel, when rocked, exceeds specifications; or if the up and down (vertical motion) exceeds specifications.

Wheel Bearing and Seal Replacement

Place jack under lower suspension arm. Remove hub cover and grease cap. Remove spindle nut, keyed washer and outer bearing. Slide off hub and drum.

NOTE: In some cases, drum removal may require loosening of brake adjustment.

At this point, brakes and drums should be inspected for their condition.

With hub and drum on bench, remove seal and inner bearing. Thoroughly clean all parts. Drive out inner and outer races of roller type. Use care not to mar the bearing surfaces.

Pack bearings with approved lubricant. When replacing cups, use a bearing race driver if possible. If a punch is used, make sure it is blunt and then drive parts in very carefully to avoid cocking the bearings.

Install new grease seal in hub. As-

semble hub and drum on spindle and replace the outer bearing, key washer and nut.

A common method of adjustment is to tighten to zero clearance and then back off to first cotter pin castellation. Some manufacturers recommend tightening to approximately 10 to 12 ft. lbs., then backing off nut 1/6 turn. If cotter pin hole does not line up, loosen slightly.

Readjust brake if necessary and install grease cap and hub cover. Remove jack.

Kingpin and Bushing Replacement

Kingpins and bushings can be placed in two general classes; (A) with bushings in knuckle, (B) with bushings in spindle.

Jack up the truck and remove the hub as described in the wheel bearing section.

1. Remove backing plate to knuckle bolts and lift assembly, with brakes, from the knuckle. Suspend it with a piece of wire to prevent damage to brake hose.
2. Drive out lock pin or bolt. With a sharp punch, remove top welch plug. Now drive pin and lower welch plug down through knuckle and support.
3. Drive bushings from the spindle and replace them. Be sure, when driving new bushing, that grease

Removing tie rod end from steering knuckle
(© Chrysler Corp.)

PLACE PROTRACTOR HAVING LEVEL INDICATOR ON TOP OR BOTTOM OF FRAME

TYPICAL NEGATIVE FRAME ANGLE "FA"

LEVEL

T-2887

Method of checking frame angle
(© G.M.C.)

holes line up with those in knuckle.

4. Align and ream bushings to a snug running fit for the new kingpin.

5. Insert the kingpin through the top of the spindle, support, thrust bearing (with shims to control vertical play) and into the spindle bottom. Keep the kingpin in proper rotation so that the lockpin can be inserted. Install lockpin or bolt. Install upper and lower welch plugs.

6. Install backing plate with steering arms and lubricate properly.

7. Install hubs, drums and wheels, then remove jack.

Ball Joint Replacement

Upper Ball Joint R & R
Riveted Type

On some trucks, the upper ball joint is riveted to the control arm. Place jack under lower arm and raise wheel clear of the floor. Remove wheel. Remove nut from ball joint. If joint is being replaced, it may be driven out with a heavy hammer. If threads are to be saved, a spreader tool should be used.

After removing joint from knuckle support, cut off rivets at upper arm. Drilling rivets eases this job.

To replace the ball joint: install in upper arm, using special bolts supplied with new joint. Do not use ordinary bolts.

Next, set the taper into the upper end of the knuckle support and install nut and cotter pin. Check alignment.

Threaded Type

On some trucks, the upper ball joint is threaded into the control arm.

Place jack under lower control arm and relieve load on torsion bar. Raise wheel clear of floor. Remove wheel. Remove nut from ball joint. If ball joint is being replaced, it may be driven out with a heavy hammer. If threads are to be saved, use a spreader tool.

After removing from knuckle support, the ball joint can be unscrewed from the support arm. Special tools are recommended for this operation.

When replacing the ball joint, be sure to engage the threads into the control arm squarely. Torque to 125 ft. lbs. If this torque cannot be obtained, check for bad threads in arm or on joint. Install new balloon seal.

Place joint in knuckle and install nut. Reload torsion bar (if so equipped) and reset height.

When the spring is supported on the lower control arm, vehicle must be jacked from the frame or cross member

When the spring is supported by the upper control arm, the vehicle must be jacked at the lower control arm

Steering and suspension jacking procedure

When the spring is supported at the upper control arm, the truck must be hoisted at the frame

When the spring is supported at the lower control arm, truck must be hoisted at the arm Reject if upper joint is perceptibly loose

Ball joint inspection jacking procedure

MAXIMUM TOLERANCE

Rock tire top and bottom
Reject if movement at tire sidewall exceeds maximum tolerance, but do not confuse wheel bearing looseness with ball joint wear

Check ball joint radial (side) play

MAXIMUM TOLERANCE

Reject if axial play in ball joint exceeds maximum tolerance

Check ball joint axial (up and down) play

Lower Ball Joint R & R
Pressed Type

These ball joints are pressed into support arms. To replace pressed-in units, it is necessary to remove the front spring and support arm.

After removing wheel and drum, loosen nut slightly at ball joint taper and hammer lightly around area to loosen. If new ball joints are being installed, it is not necessary to protect the threads.

Place support arm in an arbor press with a suitable tool and press ball joint from the arm.

Install ball joint by reversing the pressing procedure.

NOTE: Special tools of the C-clamp type are available and can be used on some trucks to avoid re-

Front Axle and Suspension

moval of front spring and support arm.

Integral Type

On some trucks, the lower ball joint is integral with the steering arm and is not serviced separately. To service this unit: Remove the upper arm bumper. Raise truck so that front suspension is under no load. If jacks are used, a support must be placed between the jack and K-member.

1. Remove the wheel and drum assembly. Remove the two lower bolts holding the steering arm to the backing plate.
2. Disconnect tie-rod end from the steering arm. Do not damage seal.
3. Remove the ball joint stud from the lower control arm. A spreading tool will aid in this operation.
4. Install new seal on ball joint. Bolt the steering arm to the backing plate. Insert the ball joint into control arm and torque nut.
5. Connect the tie-rod end. Install drum and wheel.

Reverse Elliott type front axle (© Chrysler Corp.)

King pin bushings installed (Reverse Elliott type axle) (© Chrysler Corp.)

Removing king pin bushings (reverse Elliott type axle) (© Chrysler Corp.)

Index

DRIVE AXLE SERVICE DIAGNOSIS

Condition	Possible Cause	Correction
Rear Wheel Noise	(1) Wheel loose.	(1) Tighten loose nuts.
	(2) Faulty, brinelled wheel bearing.	(2) Faulty or brinelled bearings must be replaced. Check rear axle shaft end play.
	(3) Excessive axle shaft end play.	(3) Readjust axle shaft end play.
Rear Axle Drive Shaft Noise	(1) Misaligned axle housing.	(1) Inspect rear axle housing, alignment. Correct as necessary.
	(2) Bent or sprung axle shaft.	(2) Replace bent or sprung axle shaft.
	(3) End play in drive pinion bearings.	(3) Refer to Pinion Bearing Pre-load.
	(4) Excessive gear lash between ring gear and pinion.	(4) Check adjustment of ring gear and pinion. Correct as necessary.
	(5) Improper adjustment of drive pinion shaft bearings.	(5) Adjust pinion bearings.
	(6) Loose drive pinion companion flange nut.	(6) Tighten drive pinion flange nut to torque specified.
	(7) Improper wheel bearing adjustment.	(7) Check axle shaft end play. Readjust as necessary.
	(8) Scuffed gear tooth contact surfaces.	(8) If necessary, replace scuffed gears.
Rear Axle Drive Shaft Breakage	(1) Improperly adjusted wheel bearings.	(1) Replace broken shaft and readjust end play.
	(2) Misaligned axle housing.	(2) Replace broken shaft after correcting rear axle housing alignment.
	(3) Vehicle overloaded.	(3) Replace broken shaft. Avoid excessive weight on vehicle.
	(4) Abnormal clutch operation.	(4) Replace broken shaft, after checking for other possible causes. Avoid erratic use of clutch.
	(5) Grabbing clutch.	(5) Replace broken shaft. Inspect clutch and make necessary repairs or adjustments.
	(6) Normal fatigue.	(6) Replace broken shaft. Inspect to determine causes or damage.
Differential Case Breakage	(1) Improper adjustment of differential bearings.	(1) Replace broken case; examine gears and bearings for possible damage. At reassembly, adjust differential bearings.
	(2) Excessive ring gear clearance.	(2) Replace broken case; examine gears and bearings for possible damage. At reassembly, adjust ring gear and pinion backlash.
	(3) Vehicle overloaded.	(3) Replace broken case; examine gears and bearings for possible damage. Avoid excessive weight on vehicle.
	(4) Erratic clutch operation.	(4) Replace broken case. After checking for other possible causes, examine gears and bearings for possible damage. Avoid erratic use of clutch.
Differential Side Gear Broken at Hub	(1) Excessive axle housing deflection.	(1) Replace damaged gears. Examine other gears and bearings for possible damage. Check rear axle housing alignment.
	(2) Misaligned or bent axle shaft.	(2) Replace damaged gears. Check axle shafts or alignment. Examine other gears and bearings for possible damage.
	(3) Worn thrust washers.	(3) Replace damaged gears. Examine other gears and bearings for possible damage. Replace thrust washers that are badly worn.
Scoring of Differential Gears	(1) Insufficient lubrication.	(1) Replace scored gears. Scoring marks on the pressure face of gear teeth or in the bore are caused by instantaneous fusing of the mating surfaces. Scored gears should be replaced. Fill rear axle to required capacity with proper lubricant.
	(2) Improper grade of lubricant.	(2) Replace scored gears. Inspect all gears and bearings for possible damage. Clean out and refill axle to required capacity with proper lubricant.
	(3) Excessive spinning of one wheel.	(3) Replace scored gears. Inspect all gears, pinion bores and shaft for scoring, or bearings for possible damage. Service as necessary.
Tooth Breakage (Ring Gear and Pinion)	(1) Overloading.	(1) Replace gears. Examine other gears and bearings for possible damage. Replace parts as needed. Avoid overloading of vehicle.
	(2) Erratic clutch operation.	(2) Replace gears, and examine remaining parts for possible damage. Avoid erratic clutch operation.
	(3) Ice-spotted pavements.	(3) Replace gears. Examine remaining parts for possible damage. Replace parts as required.
	(4) Normal fatigue.	(4) Replace gears. Examine broken parts to determine cause of normal fatigue.
	(5) Improper adjustment.	(5) Replace gears. Examine other parts for possible damage. Make sure ring gear and pinion backlash is correct.

DRIVE AXLE SERVICE DIAGNOSIS

Condition	Possible Cause	Correction
Rear Axle Noise	(1) Insufficient lubricant.	(1) Refill rear axle with correct amount of the proper lubricant. Also check for leaks and correct as necessary.
	(2) Improper ring gear and pinion adjustment.	(2) Check ring gear and pinion tooth contact.
	(3) Unmatched ring gear and pinion.	(3) Remove unmatched ring gear and pinion. Replace with a new matched gear and pinion set.
	(4) Worn teeth on ring gear or pinion.	(4) Check teeth on ring gear and pinion for contact. If necessary, replace with new matched set.
	(5) Loose drive pinion bearings.	(5) Adjust drive pinion bearings.
	(6) Loose differential gear bearings.	(6) Adjust differential gear bearings.
	(7) Misaligned or sprung ring gear.	(7) Check ring gear for runout.
	(8) Loose carrier housing bolts.	(8) Tighten carrier housing nuts to Specifications. Also, check for oil leaks and correct as necessary.
Loss of Lubricant	(1) Lubricant level too high.	(1) Drain excess lubricant by removing filler plug and allow lubricant to level at lower edge of filler plug hole.
	(2) Worn axle shaft oil seals.	(2) Replace worn oil seals with new ones. Prepare new seals before replacement.
	(3) Cracked rear axle housing.	(3) Repair or replace housing as required.
	(4) Worn drive pinion oil seal.	(4) Replace worn drive pinion oil seal with a new one.
	(5) Scored and worn companion flange.	(5) Replace worn or scored companion flange and oil seal.
Overheating of Unit	(1) Lubricant level too low.	(1) Refill rear axle.
	(2) Incorrect grade of lubricant.	(2) Drain, flush and refill rear axle with correct amount of the proper lubricant.
	(3) Bearings adjusted too tightly.	(3) Readjust bearings.
	(4) Excessive wear in gears.	(4) Check gears for excessive wear or scoring. Replace as necessary.
	(5) Insufficient ring gear to pinion clearance.	(5) Readjust ring gear and pinion backlash and check gears for possible scoring.

Differential Component Failure Diagnosis

Scoring and seizure of spider and pinion gears

The spider arms and pinion gears were badly discolored by heat, caused by the unit operating for a long time after the initial scoring took place. The most probable cause of this type of failure is excessive wheelspin, particularly in off-road or icy road conditions. Other possible causes are inadequate lubrication or overstress. Friction causes the hardened areas to overheat, score, and eventually to seize. The best way to prevent this problem is to avoid wheelspin and overloading under rough terrain or poor traction conditions.

Shock fracture

These differential pinion and side gears show a grainy structure which indicates a shock fracture. This type of damage occurs instantaneously. The usual cause is a sudden excessive load, as might be caused by sudden clutch engagement at high engine speed. Another cause is a rapidly spinning wheel suddenly reaching a good traction area. This failure can be prevented by proper clutch operation, and by avoiding wheelspin and overloading under rough terrain or poor traction conditions.

Fatigue fracture of the differential side gears

This damage occurs in stages. An initial stress caused a crack, and repeated stresses caused complete failure. Some of the gear teeth were broken off in the later stages. The failures can be seen best at points A and B. All differential gears should be checked when this type of failure is found, very often the other gears will be in the initial stages of failure and must be replaced. This is most often caused by abuse such as sudden clutch engagement or incorrect two-speed axle operation, combined with overloading.

Differential Component Failure Diagnosis

Scored and Scuffed Gear Teeth
This wear pattern is a result of the gears running without enough lubrication between the tooth surfaces. Either poor quality gear lube or low lubricant level can cause this condition. Excessive torque input to the rear can also cause this wear since it will break down even the best of gear lubes. Changing gear lube at regular recommended intervals and keeping excessive torque input to a minimum will usually prevent this problem.

Overheated Gear Set
This problem can be caused by one of three, or any combination of the following circumstances. The causes are low gear lubricant level; improper gear lubricant; or infrequent lubricant change. When one or more of these conditions is present in the rear, it causes the lubricant to break down and allows the gear surface to build up heat because of increased friction. In the failure shown, the gears became so hot the pinion bearing fused to the pinion gear and the pinion gear teeth became distorted. To prevent this problem a good quality gear lubricant must be used in the rear to prevent the breakdown of lubricant under a heavy load.

Fatigue Fractured Pinion Gear
This type of fracture develops over a period of time. The fracture works through the gear tooth until the tooth is not strong enough to support the load applied. Failure happens and a section of the tooth breaks away. Continued use of pitted gears is the usual cause of this type of gear failure. As the gear pits, the support area is reduced and must carry the entire load of the gear tooth. As this continues the gear tooth fatigues and the final result is failure of the gear. To prevent this problem the ring and pinion must be replaced if there is any pitting on the gears.

Fractured Gear Teeth
This problem is caused by improper gear adjustment. The picture on the left shows the result of excessive backlash between the ring and pinion gear. Such backlash allows overloading of the heel section of the gear; gear fracture will follow. The picture on the right shows the result of too little backlash thus allowing the toe section of the gear to overload and become fractured. The best way to eliminate this problem is to correctly adjust the ring and pinion gears, when necessary, according to specifications.

Misalignment Fatigue Fracture
This problem comes from misalignment in the axle shafts. This kind of failure can also happen when the axle shaft breaks. If twisted, bent or sprung axle shafts are not replaced after they are damaged, this kind of failure to the side gears can occur. Bent axle housing can also cause this to happen. In most cases, this type of failure is not instantaneous. It tends to happen over a period of time. The usual cause of this type of failure is abusive operation of the vehicle and severe overloading.

Twisted Axle Shaft
This problem with the axle comes from abusive and/or extremely severe operation of the vehicle. This is only the first stage of failure where the axle shaft has only twisted, but has not yet started to crack. At this stage the shaft should be replaced. If it is not, the shaft will continue to twist and eventually will break. When this happens it will almost certainly damage other axle parts. To eliminate this problem, the shaft should be replaced if found to be twisted. The driver of the vehicle should be informed to adopt better driving procedures.

Differential Component Failure Diagnosis

Pitted Pinion Teeth
This problem is the result of extremely high pressure on the gear teeth due to severe use. The pitting located at the heel end of the pinion gear teeth happens when overloading of the pinion moves the pinion out of its proper position relative to the ring gear. The result is a concentrated area of contact on the heel part of the gear teeth which will break down the oil film, and thus allow the pinion teeth to pit. Sometimes the ring gear will appear to be undamaged. This is because ring gear damage might not be visible to the naked eye; but the contour of the gear teeth will have changed. The ring and pinion gears must be replaced as a pair, or early failure will occur. The best way to eliminate this problem is to use good quality gear lube. The more severely the vehicle is used the better quality the gear lube should be.

Scuffed Gear Teeth on the Coast Side Only
This wear can be caused by two different things. The first is worn pinion bearings which allow excessive end play in the pinion gear. The result is incorrect contact between the ring and pinion gear teeth on the coast side. This allows excessive pressure to build up on the gear teeth and will break down the oil film, resulting in scoring of the teeth. The second cause is hard, abusive driving in vehicles equipped with a manual transmission. This usually happens when going down a steep grade at high speed and slowing the vehicle by using the clutch to brake the speed. The best way to eliminate this problem is to replace the pinion bearing if worn and recommend good driving procedures.

General Axle Service Section

Cleaning Bearings

Proper bearing cleaning is important. Bearings should always be cleaned separately from other rear axle parts.
1. Soak all bearings in clean kerosene or Diesel fuel oil. CAUTION: Ordinary gasoline should not be used. Bearings should not be cleaned in a hot solution tank.
2. Slush bearings in cleaning solution until all oil lubricant is loosened. Brush bearings with soft bristled brush until ALL dirt has been removed. Remove loose particles of dirt by striking flat against a wood block.
3. Rinse bearings in clean fluid. While holding races to prevent rotation, blow dry with compressed air. Caution: *Do not spin bearings while drying*.
4. After bearings have been inspected, lubricate thoroughly with regular axle lubricant; then wrap each bearing in clean cloth until ready to use.

Cleaning Parts

Immerse all parts in suitable cleaning fluid and clean thoroughly. Use a stiff bristle brush as required to remove foreign deposits. Clean all lubricant passages or channels in pinion cage, carrier, caps and retainers. Make certain that interior of housing is thoroughly cleaned. Clean vent plugs and breathers.

Small parts such as cap screws, bolts, studs, nuts etc., should be cleaned thoroughly.

Inspection

Magna Flux all steel parts, except ball and roller bearings, to detect presence of wear and cracks.

Bearings

Rotate each bearing and check to see if the rollers are worn, chipped, rough or in any other way damaged. Check the cage to see if it is in any way damaged. If either the bearing rollers or the cage are damaged the bearing must be replaced.

Gears

Examine drive gear and drive pinion, differential pinions and differential side gears carefully, for damaged teeth, worn spots in surface hardening, distortion and where drive gear is attached to differential case with rivets, inspect rivets for looseness, replace loose rivets. Check radial clearances between differential side gears and differential case. Check fit of differential pinions on spider.

Differential Case

Inspect case for cracks, distortion or damage, if in good condition, thoroughly clean case and cover; then assemble case with bolts and mount in lathe centers of "V" block stand. If lathe is not available, install differential side bearings and mount case in differential carrier. Install dial indicator and check differential case run out.

Differential case with drive gear installed is checked in the same manner, except that dial indicator reading must be taken at rear instead of at case flange.

Whenever run-out exceeds limits, it may be corrected as later described under "Repair" in this section. However, the support case used in the 2-speed axle cannot be repaired and should be replaced with new case.

Axle Shafts

Examine splined end of axle shaft for twisted or cracked splines, twisted shaft, and worn dowel holes in flange. Install new shafts if necessary.

Install axle shaft assembly in lathe centers and check shaft run-out with dial indicator, if run-out exceeds limits, replace shaft. Place dial indicator so that indicator shaft end contacts inner surface of flange near outer edge of flange and check flange run-out.

Checking drive gear run-out
(© G.M.C.)

Shims

Carefully inspect shims for uniform thickness. Where various thickness of shims are used in a pack, it is recommended that the thickest shims be used between the thin shims.

Thrust Washers

Replace all thrust washers.

Spider

Carefully inspect spider arms for wear or defects.

Differential Pinion Bushings

Examine bushings (when used) for excessive wear, looseness, or damage. Check fit of gears on spider for excessive clearance. See "repair" paragraph for directions on bushing replacement.

Axle Housing Sleeves

Sleeves showing damaged threads, wear, or other damage should be replaced if hydraulic press is available, otherwise replace housing.

Housing Check

Before Removal

A check for bent axle housing can be made with unit in vehicle; however, conventional alignment instruments can be used if available.

1. Raise rear axle with a jack until wheels clear floor. Block up axle under each spring seat.
2. Check wheel bearing adjustment and adjust if necessary, then check wheels for looseness and tighten wheel nuts if necessary.
3. Place a chalk mark on outer side wall of tires at bottom. Measure across tires at chalk marks with a toe-in gauge.
4. Turn wheels half-way around so that chalk marks are positioned at top of wheel. Measure across tires again. If measurement at top is 1/8" or more, smaller than measurement at bottom of wheels, axle housing has sagged and is bent. If measurement at top exceeds bottom dimension by 1/8" or more, axle housing is bent at ends.
5. Turn chalk marks on both wheels so that marks are level with axle and at rear of vehicle. Take measurement with toe-in gauge at chalk marks; then turn both chalk marks to front and level with axle and take another measurement. If measurement at front exceeds rear dimension by 1/8" or more, axle is bent to the rear. If the measurement condition is the reverse, the axle is bent forward.

After Removal

After axle assembly has been completely disassembled, housings may be checked for bent condition in following manner:

1. Temporarily install wheel hubs, and adjust wheel bearings so that hubs will just turn. Do not lock adjustment.
2. After axle shafts have been inspected as previously described, install shafts and draw stud nuts up tight.
3. Indicators can be made locally from 3/16" drill rod to dimensions shown. Remove any burrs from splines; then use hose clamps to hold indicators to shafts.
4. Each indicator must be positioned at right angle to its shaft. Both indicators must be in alignment with one another. There should be a slight gap between the points. Measure and note dimensions of this gap.
5. Rotate shafts simultaneously and measure gap at four points, 90 degrees apart. If gap at any point exceeds original gap by more than 1/16", axle housing is bent.

General Repair

Oil Seal Contact Surfaces

Surface of parts, contacted by oil seals must be free of corrosion, pits and grooves. When abrasive cleaning fails to clean up the seal contact surface and restore smooth finish, a new part must be installed.

Oil Seal Removal

Oil seals can be removed with a drift pin. When removing a seal, be careful that it does not become cocked and result in damage to the retainer. Clean surface of retainer carefully, so that seal will seat properly in retainer.

Installation

Coat outer surface of seal retainer with a light coat of sealer, to prevent lubricant leaks. Carefully start seal in retainer. Cutting, scratching, or curling of lip of seal seriously impairs its efficiency and usually results in premature replacement. Lip of seal should be coated with a high temperature grease containing zinc oxide to help prevent scoring and damage to

parts during installation.

Seals must always be installed so that seal lip is toward the lubricant.

Pinion Bearing Adjustments (Pre-Load)

Pinion bearing must be adjusted for pre-load before assembly is installed in carrier.

Do not install oil seal until after adjustment is made—installation of seal would produce false rotating torque.

Cage Type

1. With pinion bearings, and adjusting spacers (or shims) installed in cage, check bearing contact by rotating cage.
2. Using a press, apply pressure (approx. 20,000 lbs.) to outer bearing.
3. Wrap soft wire around cage and pull on horizontal line with spring scale. Rotating (not starting) torque should be within limits recommended by manufacturer. NOTE: Method of determining inch-pounds torque with scale is to determine radius of cage. Multiply radius in inches by pounds pull required to rotate cage to determine inch-pounds torque. Example: An 8-inch diameter divided by 2 equals 4-inch radius. Multiply 4-inch (radius) by 5 pounds (pull) equals 20 inch pounds torque.
4. If press is not available, check preload torque by installing propeller shaft yoke, washer, and nut and torque to specifications; then check as previously explained. Remove yoke after correct adjustment is obtained.

Bevel Gear Shaft Bearing Adjustment

Bevel gear shaft bearings must be adjusted for pre-load before pinion and cage assembly and differential assembly are installed in carrier.

1. Wrap several turns of soft wire around gear teeth on cross shaft, then pull on a horizontal line with spring scale. Rotating (not starting) torque should be used. NOTE: Method of determining

Checking pinion bearing pre-load
(© G.M.C.)

Checking pre-load on bevel gear cross shaft
(© G.M.C.)

inch-pounds torque with scale is to determine radius. Multiply radius in inches by pounds pull required to rotate shaft to determine inch-pounds torque. Example: An 8-inch diameter divided by 2 equals 4-inch radius times 5 pounds (pull) equals 20 inch-pounds torque.

2. Remove or add shims from under cage or cap opposite bevel gear to obtain specified bearing pre-load.

3. When making bevel gear and pinion tooth contact or backlash adjustments it is sometimes necessary to remove or add shims from one side. *Always remove or add an equal thickness to the opposite side so to maintain correct pre-load.*

Gear Tooth Contact and Backlash

Method of adjusting pinion and bevel gear to obtain proper gear tooth contact and backlash varies with the axle type. Therefore, the following instructions cover all types of axles, except as noted. Proper gear tooth contact can be determined by using marking dye on gear teeth, or by using a pinion setting gauge.

When using the gauge method, backlash is established after the pinion has been properly set. With dye method, backlash is obtained first, then proper tooth contact is established.

Pinion Setting Gauge Method

The pinion setting gauge is a direct reading micrometer mounted in arbor. Adapter discs, which fit in differential bores are mounted in sleeves that fit over the arbor. The "Nominal Assembly Dimension" chart lists the proper adapter discs to be used for the various axle models. The proper discs hold the gauge assembly so that center line of arbor coincides with centerline of carrier bores.

Terms Used

Certain dimensions must be determined when using the pinion setting gauge:

1. *Nominal Assembly Dimension.* This dimension (varying with axle model) is the distance between the center line of the drive gear (or differential carrier bore) and the end of the drive pinion. This dimension may be marked on the pinion or listed on the "Nominal Assembly Dimension and Adapter Disc" chart.

2. *Individual Variation Distance,* This dimension is a plus or minus variation of the *Nominal*

A Backlash
B Nominal assembly dimension
C Individual variation distance
D Gear and pinion matching number

Pinion and bevel gear markings (typical)
(© G.M.C.)

Assembly Dimension on each individual pinion which may be caused by manufacturing variations.

3. *Corrected Nominal Dimension.* This dimension is the *Nominal Assembly Dimension* plus or minus the *Individual Variation Distance.*

4. *Corrected Micrometer Distance* is the *Corrected Nominal Dimension* less the thickness of the gauge set step plate (0.400″) mounted on end of pinion.

5. *Initial Micrometer Reading* is the dimension taken by micrometer to the gauge step plate.

6. *Shim Pack Correction* is determined by the difference between the *Corrected Micrometer Distance* and the *Initial Micrometer Reading,* and represents the amount of shim pack to be added or removed as later explained.

Markings on Pinion and Drive Gear

Nominal Assembly Dimension

The Nominal Assembly Dimension, is etched on the end of pinion on Timken axles and shown is "*Nominal Assembly Dimension and Adapter Disc*" chart. On Eaton axles, this dimension must be obtained from the chart.

Individual Variation Distance

The *Individual Variation Distance* is a plus (+) or minus (−) dimension representing thousandths of an inch, and is etched on end of pinion on Timken axles.

Nominal assembly dimension
(© G.M.C.)

On some Eaton axles, the dimension is etched on end of pinion or may be found on the outside diameter of pinion splines.

Other Markings

All other markings on pinion or drive gear should not be confused with *Nominal Assembly Dimension* or *Individual Variation Distance* markings.

Pinion Setting Procedures

1. Determine the *Nominal Assembly Dimension* from the pinion marking or from chart. Also note *Individual Variation Distance* from marking on pinion.

2. When the nominal assembly dimension is greater than the micrometer span, add the 1″ or 2″

Installing clamp and step plate
(© G.M.C.)

extension as required to micrometer. Be sure parts are clean and securely attached.

3. Locate the assembled micrometer in master gauge using the proper checking block. The micrometer should be accurate within 0.0005″.

4. Remove any nicks or burrs from carrier bores with crocus cloth.

5. Install pinion and cage assembly in carrier. *Using the original shim pack,* be sure that shims are clean and properly aligned with oil passages in cage and carrier. Install cap screws or stud nuts and *tighten to recommended torque.*

6. Install gauge set step plate clamp assembly tightly to carrier with clamp screw at center of pinion. On some axles clamp can be secured to carrier by using bracket.

7. With step plate clamp assembly securely attached to carrier, install gauge set step plate.

8. After determining the *Nominal Assembly Dimension*, select the proper adapter disc from the chart. In some instances, two identical discs are used, and in other instances two different slightly tapered discs are used. When tapered discs are used, assemble the discs and sleeves to the arbor with smaller outside diameter of discs toward outside. Tighten the sleeve nuts.

9. Retract micrometer and install the assembled gauge in carrier.

10. Subtract from or add to the *Nominal Assembly Dimension*, the *Individual Variation Dimension* to arrive at the *Corrected Nominal Dimension*.

11. Subtract the thickness (0.400") of the step plate (mounted on pinion end), from *Corrected Nominal Dimension* to get the *Corrected Micrometer Distance*.

12. Run Micrometer thimble down to measure distance from center of carrier bores (drive gear center) to step plate on pinion. This is the *Initial Micrometer Reading*.

13. The difference between the *Corrected Micrometer Distance* and the *Initial Micrometer Reading* determines the thickness of shim pack to be removed or added.

NOTE: When adjusting shims are located at pinion bearings instead of between pinion cage and carrier it will be necessary to remove instead of adding shims (paragraph a) or add, instead of remove (paragraph b), shims.

a. When the "corrected micrometer distance" is more than the "initial micrometer reading," shim pack thickness equal the difference must

Position of pinion setting gauge
(© G.M.C.)

Installation of pinion gauge (Timken 2-speed)
(© G.M.C.)

be added. As an example:

	In.
Nominal assembly dimension	3.551
Individual variation distance	+0.008
Corrected nominal dimension	3.559
Deduct step plate thickness	0.400
Corrected micrometer distance	3.159
Subtract initial micrometer reading	3.139
Shim pack to be added	0.020

b. When the "corrected micrometer distance" is less than the "initial micrometer reading," shim pack thickness equal the difference must be removed. As an example:

	In.
Nominal assembly dimension	2.656
Individual variation distance	−0.002
Corrected nominal dimension	2.654

Deduct step plate thickness	0.400
Corrected micrometer distance	2.254
Initial micrometer reading	2.274

Subtract 2.254" from 2.274 = the amount of shim pack to be removed 0.020

14. Remove gauge and discs and step plate.

15. Remove pinion and cage assembly as instructed in respective axle assembly.

16. Add to or remove from original pinion cage to carrier adjusting shim pack as determined by calculations in paragraph 13.

17. Install shim pack pinion and cage assembly as described in separate axle sections. Recheck in manner described above. The "Corrected Micrometer Reading" must be within plus or minus 0.002" of the "Corrected Nominal Distance." This will insure properly adjusted tooth contact.

18. Check gear tooth contact by using dye and adjust gear backlash. Both procedures described later.

Setting New Pinion (Without Gauge)

Whenever a pinion setting gauge is not available, the approximate thickness of the pinion shim pack at the rear pinion bearing cup, change the sign of the marking (individual variation distance) on the *new* pinion (plus to minus or minus to plus), then add the variation of the old pinion (sign unchanged) which will determine the amount the original shim pack must be changed when installing a new pinion.

On those types of axles where the shims are located between the pinion cage and differential carrier, change the sign of the marking (individual variation distance) on the *old* pinion

Pinion Markings		Difference
Old Pinion	New Pinion	Between Markings
+5	+8	−3 Remove .003" Shim
+8	+5	+3 Add .003" Shim
−3	−5	+2 Add .002" Shim
−5	−3	−2 Remove .002" Shim
−3	+4	−7 Remove .007" Shim
+2	−4	+6 Add .006" Shim

The sign of the new pinion is changed and then added algebraically to the old pinion sign.

Determining pinion shim pack thickness (if shim pack is located at rear pinion bearing cup)
(© G.M.C.)

Pinion Markings		Difference
Old Pinion	New Pinion	Between Markings
+8	+6	−2 Remove .002" Shims
+6	−2	−8 Remove .008" Shims
−4	+4	+8 Add .008" Shims
+2	+6	+4 Add .004" Shims
−7	−4	+3 Add .003" Shims
−2	−6	−4 Remove .004" Shims

The sign of the old pinion is changed and then added algebraically to the new pinion sign.

Determining pinion shim pack thickness (if shims are located between pinion cage and differential carrier)
(© G.M.C.)

PAINTING GEAR TEETH

CORRECT TYPE TOOTH CONTACT

A
CONTACT
ADJUSTMENT
B
BACKLASH
CORRECTION

A HIGH NARROW CONTACT is not desirable. If gears are permitted to operate with an adjustment of this kind, noise, galling and rolling over of top edge of teeth will result. To obtain correct contact, move pinion toward bevel gear. This lowers contact area to proper location. This adjustment will decrease the backlash which may be corrected by moving bevel gear away from pinion.

A
CONTACT
ADJUSTMENT
B
BACKLASH
CORRECTION

A LOW NARROW CONTACT is not desirable. If gears are permitted to operate with an adjustment of this type, galling, noise and grooving of teeth will result. To obtain correct contact, move pinion away from drive gear. This will raise contact area to proper location. A correct backlash is obtained by moving bevel gear toward pinion.

A
CONTACT
ADJUSTMENT
B
BACKLASH
CORRECTION

A SHORT TOE CONTACT is not desirable. If gears are permitted to operate with an adjustment of this type, chipping at tooth edges and excessive wear due to small contact area will result. To obtain correct contact, move drive gear from pinion. This will increase the lengthwise contact and move contact toward heel of tooth. Correct backlash is obtained by moving pinion toward bevel gear.

A
CONTACT
ADJUSTMENT
B
BACKLASH
CORRECTION

A SHORT HEEL CONTACT is not desirable. If gears are permitted to operate with an adjustment of this type, chipping, excessive wear and noise will result. To obtain correct contact, move drive gear toward pinion to increase lengthwise contact and move contact toward toe. A correct backlash is obtained by moving pinion away from drive gear.

Gear tooth contact chart (© G.M.C.)

(plus to minus or minus to plus), then add variation of the new pinion (sign unchanged) which will determine how much the original shim pack must be altered when installing a new pinion.

When the approximate thickness of shim pack has been determined, final check of gear tooth contact must be made using dye method.

Gear Tooth Contact (dye)

Gear tooth contact cannot be successfully accomplished until pinion and bevel gear bearings are in proper adjustment and gear backlash is within specified limits.

Check for proper tooth contact by painting a few teeth of bevel gear with marking dye. Turn pinion in direction of normal rotation, then

Checking gear backlash (bevel gear)
(© G.M.C.)

check tooth impression on bevel gear.

Gear Backlash

Gears that have been in extended service, form running contacts due to wear of teeth; therefore the original shim pack (between pinion cage and carrier) should be maintained when checking backlash. If backlash exceeds maximum tolerance, reduce backlash only in the amount that will avoid overlap of worn tooth section. Smoothness and roughness can be noted by rotating bevel gear.

If a slight overlap is present at worn tooth section, rotation will be rough.

If new gears are installed, check

backlash with dial indicator.

Backlash is increased by moving bevel gear away from pinion, and may be decreased by moving bevel gear toward pinion.

When the drive gear is attached to the differential, backlash is accomplished at differential bearing adjusting rings. It should be remembered that when one ring is tightened, the opposite ring must be loosened an equal amount to maintain previously established bearing adjustment.

On axles where the bevel gear is supported by cross shaft, backlash is accomplished by adding or removing shims under bearing cages.

Chevrolet Full Floating Single Speed

This is a full floating axle design using special hypoid type drive and pinion gears. The pinion gear is supported by three bearings, two in front of the pinion gears and one behind. The differential assembly has either two or four pinions depending upon the application.

Differential Carrier Removal

1. With vehicle raised and supported securely, drain the lubricant.
2. Remove the axle shafts from the axle.
3. Remove the two drive shaft "U" bolts from the rear yoke and separate the rear universal joint from the yoke.
   NOTE: The bearing can be left in place in the trunnion and can be secured with tape.
4. Push the drive shaft to one side and secure it in place to the frame side rail.
5. Place a jack under the carrier assembly and remove the bolts and lock washers that hold the carrier to the axle housing and supporting the carrier with the jack roll it from under the truck.

Differential Carrier Disassembly

1. Mount the carrier assembly in a bench vise or holding fixture.
2. On axles so equipped, loosen the ring gear thrust pad lock nut and remove the thrust pad.
3. Remove the differential adjusting nut locks and bearing cap bolts and lockwashers.
4. Mark the bearing caps and carrier for reassembly in the same position. Remove the bearing caps and adjusting nuts by tapping on the bosses of the caps until free from the dowels.

5. Remove the differential and ring gear assembly from the carrier.
6. Remove the bolts which attach the pinion bearing retainer to the carrier.
7. Remove the pinion and bearing assembly from the carrier. NOTE: It may be necessary to drive this unit from the carrier. Use a brass drift against the pilot end of the pinion.
8. On all axles except the 11,000 lb. from 1967, remove shims from inside the carrier housing making note of the number and total thickness of shims removed.
9. On all axles except the 11,000 lb., the pinion rear bearing outer race and roller assembly is pressed into the carrier. Remove the assembly by driving it from its seat using a soft drift or punch.

Pinion and/or Bearing Replacement

1. Clamp the pinion drive flange in a bench vise.
2. Remove the cotter pin, nut and washer from the end of the pinion.
3. Remove the drive flange and bearing retainer assembly.
4. Drive the oil seal, and packing if present, from the retainer.
5. On the 11,000 lb. axle, remove the pinion rear bearing snap ring and press the bearing from the pinion.
6. On the 13,500, 15,000 and 17,000 lb. axles press the inner race of the rear bearing from the pinion.
7. On the 5200 and 7200 lb. axles press the pinion from the bearing.

1 Universal joint yoke
2 Pinion bearing retainer and oil seal
3 Oil seal packing
4 Oil seal
5 Front pinion bearing
6 Drive pinion
7 Pinion bearing shim
8 Rear pinion bearing
9 Ring gear
10 Differential spider

PINION   REAR PINION BEARING   PRESS PLATE

Pinion rear bearing removal (11,000 lb. axle)
(© Chevrolet Div., G.M. Corp.)

11 Differential pinion (spider) gear
12 Differential side gear
13 Differential case—left half
14 Axle shaft
15 Differential bearing
16 Differential bearing
adjusting nut
17 Adjusting nut lock
18 Differential case—right half

5200 and 7200 lb. axle—cross section (© Chevrolet Div., G.M. Corp.)

8. On the 11,000 lb. axle, press the front bearing from the pinion.
9. On the 13,500, 15,000 and 17,000 lb. axles press the front bearing from the pinion. Wash all the parts in solvent and inspect the pinion gear for signs of wear, chipping, pitting or scoring. Check the splines on the pinion shaft for signs of wear or distortion. Check the bearings for signs of wear, roughness or defects.
10. Soak the new oil seal (and packing) in engine oil. Install the felt packing, if so equipped, in the bottom of the retainer. Press the oil seal into the retainer.
11. On the 5200, 7200, 13,500, 15,000 and 17,000 lb. axles, lubricate the pinion rear bearing and press it into the carrier. Then install the inner race on the 13,500, 15,000 and 17,000 lb. axle pinion shaft.
12. On the 11,000 lb. axle, install the pinion rear bearing on the pinion shaft making sure that the chamfered side of the inner race seats against the shoulder on the pinion shaft. Then install the pinon bearing lock ring.
13. On the 11,000 lb. axle, position the one piece double row ball bearing on the pinion shaft so that the extended portion of the inner race is toward the pinion head. Press the bearing onto the shaft until it seats against the pinion head.
14. On the 5200, 7200, 13,500, 15,000 and 17,000 lb. axles, place one cone and roller assembly on the pinion shaft so that the large end of bearing is toward the pinion. Then position the outer race, spacer and cone and roller assembly on the pinion shaft. Press the bearing until it seats against the pinion head.
15. Slide the oil seal retainer on the pinion shaft, then tap the flange onto the splines.
16. Clamp the drive flange in a bench vise and install the flange

washer and nut. Torque the nut to 220 ft. lbs. and install the cotter pin without backing off on the nut.

Differential Disassembly

1. Check the differential case to make sure that the two halves are marked so they may be reassembled in the same relation.
2. Remove the bolts holding the case and cover together.
3. Separate the cover from the case and remove the differential side gears and thrust washers, pinion gears with thrust washers and differential spider.
4. Remove the ring gear from the case by tapping the back of the gear with a soft faced hammer.

Differential Reassembly

1. Install two guide pins (made from cap screws with the heads cut off and ends slotted) to the new gear opposite each other.
2. Start the guide pins through the case flange and tap the ring gear on the case.

1 Universal joint yoke
2 Pinion bearing and oil seal retainer
3 Oil seal
4 Gasket
5 Front pinion bearing
6 Drive pinion
7 Pinion Bearing shim
8 Rear pinion bearing
9 Ring gear thrust pad
10 Ring gear
11 Differential spider
12 Differential pinion (spider) gear

3. Lubricate the differential side gears, pinions and thrust washers.
4. Place the differential pinions and thrust washers on the spider.
5. Assemble the side gears and pinions and thrust washers to the left half of the case.
6. Assemble the case halves being sure to line up the marks on the two halves.
7. Install the differential to ring gear bolts and lock washers and tighten evenly until the ring gear is flush with the case flange.
8. Remove the two guide pins and install the remaining two bolts.
9. Torque all bolts to specifications:
   Except below—110 ft. lbs.
   15,000 lb. and 17,000 lb. axles—160 ft. lbs.

Differential Bearing Replacement

1. Using a bearing puller, remove the bearings from the case.

Pinion rear bearing removal—exc. 11,000 lb. axle (© Chevrolet Div., G.M. Corp.)

13 Differential side gear
14 Differential case—left half
15 Axle shaft
16 Differential bearing
17 Differential bearing
adjusting nut
18 Adjusting nut lock
19 Differential case—right half

5200 and 7200 lb. axle—with adjusting screw (© Chevrolet Div., G.M. Corp.)

2. Place the new bearing on the hub of the case, thick side of inner race toward case. Using a bearing driver, drive the bearing into place.

Differential Carrier Reassembly

To facilitate adjusting the pinion depth in the ring gear, there are five shims available for service use. They are .012″, .015″, .018″, .021″ and .024″.

NOTE: Pinion depth adjustment shims are not required for the 11,000 lb. axle.

If the original ring gear and pinion are to be used it is advisable to replace the same thickness of shims in the carrier counter bore that were removed.

If a new ring gear and pinion are used, one .021″ shim should be used as a standard starting set up.

1. Place the shim in the bore in the carrier.
2. Place a new pinion bearing retainer gasket on the retainer and install the pinion assembly in the carrier.

3. Install and tighten the pinion bearing retainer bolts and lock washers.
4. Lubricate the differential bearing rollers with engine oil and place the outer races over them.
5. Install the differential assembly in the carrier and install the adjusting nuts.
6. Install the differential bearing caps making sure the marks on the caps line up with the marks on the carrier.
7. Install the bearing cap bolts and lock washers and tighten until the lock washers just flatten out.

Ring Gear and Pinion Adjustment

1. With the differential bearing cap bolts loosened just enough to permit turning the bearing adjusting nuts, remove all lash between the ring gear and pinion.
2. Back off the left hand adjusting nut one or two notches to a locking position.
3. Tighten the right hand adjusting nut firmly to force the differential in solid contact with the left hand adjusting nut.

Drive pinion front bearing removal—typical
(© Chevrolet Div., G.M. Corp.)

4. Back off the right hand adjusting nut and again tighten snugly against the bearing.
5. Tighten the right hand adjusting nut from one to two additional notches to a locking position. NOTE: This method of adjustment provides for proper preload of the bearings.
6. Mount a dial indicator on the carrier and check the backlash between the ring gear and pinion Backlash should be .003″ to .012″ (.005″ to .008″ preferred). If the backlash is more than .012″ loosen the right hand adjusting nut one notch and tighten the left hand adjusting nut one notch. If the backlash is less than .003″ loosen the left hand adjusting nut one notch and tighten the right hand adjusting nut one notch.
7. Tighten the bearing cap bolts to specifications.
   Except below—205 ft. lbs.
   5200 and 7200 lb. axles—
      100 ft. lbs.
8. Install the side bearing adjusting nut locks and torque to 15 ft. lbs.

Checking Pinion Depth

1. Coat the ring gear teeth lightly and evenly with a mixture of red lead and oil to produce a contact pattern. Then turn the pinion shaft several revolutions in both directions.

1 Universal joint yoke
2 Pinion bearing retainer
3 Oil seal
4 Shims
5 Pinion bearing assembly
6 Drive pinion
7 Rear pinion bearing
8 Ring gear thrust pad
9 Ring gear
10 Differential spider
11 Differential pinion (spider) gear
12 Differential side gear
13 Differential case (left half)
14 Axle shaft
15 Differential bearing
16 Differential bearing adjusting nut
17 Adjusting nut lock
18 Differential case (right half)

13,500, 15,000 and 17,000 lb. axle—cross section (© Chevrolet Div., G.M. Corp.)

Pinion inner bearing inner race removal
(13,500-15,000 and 17,000 lb. axles)
(© Chevrolet Div., G.M. Corp.)

Ring gear and pinion adjustment
(© Chevrolet Div., G.M. Corp.)

Pinion rear bearing inner race installation
(13,500 15,000 and 17,000 lb. axles)
(© Chevrolet Div., G.M. Corp.)

LINE UP

Differential case line up marks
(© Chevrolet Div., G.M. Corp.)

2. Examine the pattern on the ring gear teeth. If the pinion depth is correct, the tooth pattern will be centered on the pitch line and toward the toe of the ring gear. (See Illustration in this section).
3. If the pattern is below the pitch line on the ring gear teeth, the pinion is too deep and it will be necessary to remove the pinion assembly and increase the shim thickness between the pinion bearing and the carrier.
4. If the pattern is above the pitch line on the ring gear teeth, the pinion is too shallow and it will be necessary to decrease the shim thickness.

5. Changing the pinion depth will make some change in the backlash; therefore, it will be necessary to readjust the backlash.

Ring Gear Thrust Pad Adjustment

On axles equipped with a thrust pad, inspect the bronze tip of the thrust pad and if worn install a new one.
1. Install the thrust pad and tighten the screw until the bronze tip engages the back face of the ring gear while rotating the gear.
2. Back off the screw one-twelfth (1/12) turn and tighten the locknut.

Differential Assembly Installation

1. Clean out any dirt or sludge that may be in the axle housing or on the cover.

2. Install a new gasket on the axle housing and install the differential carrier to the housing securing it in place with the lockwashers and nuts. Torque the nuts to 70 ft. lbs.
3. Install the housing cover, if it was removed, using a new gasket.
4. Reconnect the drive shaft to the yoke on the differential and torque the "U" bolts to 20 ft. lbs.
5. Install the axle shafts in the axle.
6. Fill the axle with gear lubricant until the level is even with the bottom of the filler hole.
7. Road test the vehicle to check for noise and proper operation.

Chevrolet-Full Floating Single Speed 5200 Through 17,000 lb. Axle, Non-Removable Carrier Type

This axle is a full floating type that uses special Hypoid type drive and pinion gears. The pinion gear is supported by three bearings, two in front of the pinion gear and one behind. The differential assembly has either two or four pinions depending on the application of the axle. This axle assembly must be removed from the vehicle to remove and service the differential.

Differential Removal

1. With the axle assembly removed from the vehicle, place the axle assembly in a vise or holding fixture.
2. Remove the bolts that retain the cover assembly and remove the cover, allowing the gear lubricant to drain into a pan.
3. Remove the axle shafts from the axle assembly.
NOTE: Before going any further, check the pinion backlash and record

the measurement so that if the same gears are reused they may be installed at the same backlash to avoid changing the gear tooth pattern.
4. From the bearing caps, remove the adjusting nut lock retainers.
5. Mark the bearing caps so they may be reinstalled in the same position and remove the bearing caps.
6. Loosen the side bearing adjusting nut and remove the differential carrier from the axle housing.

Pinion Assembly Removal

1. Remove the differential assembly from the axle.
2. Check the pinion bearing for the proper preload. The force required to turn the pinion should be 25-35 in. lbs. for new bearings and 5-15 in. lbs. for used bearings. If there is no reading, shake the companion flange to check for

any looseness in the bearing. If there is any looseness present the bearing should be replaced.
3. Remove the retaining bolts for the pinion bearing from the axle housing.
4. Remove the bearing retainer and pinion assembly from the axle housing. It may be necessary to tap the pilot end of the pinion shaft to help remove the pinion assembly from the carrier.
5. Record the thickness of the shims that are removed from between the carrier assembly and the bearing retainer assembly.

Drive Pinion Disassembly

1. With the pinion assembly clamped in a vise, install a holder assembly on the flange.
2. Using the proper size socket, remove the pinion nut and washer from the pinion. When reassem-

Drive Axles

bling the pinion use a new nut and washer assembly.

3. With the holder assembly still in place, use a puller to remove the flange from the pinion.

4. With the bearing retainer supported in a press, press the pinion out of the retainer assembly. Be careful not to allow the pinion gear to fall onto the floor because this can damage the gear.

5. Separate the pinion flange, oil seal, front bearing and the bearing retainer. If the oil seal needs to be replaced it may have to be driven from the retainer.

6. Using a drift, drive the front and rear bearing cups from the bearing retainer.

7. Support the pinion assembly in a press, with the bearing supported, Press the bearing from the pinion gear.

8. Using a drift, drive the straddle bearing from the carrier assembly.

Cleaning and Inspection

1. Clean off all the parts in solvent and blow dry.

2. Check the pinion gear for signs of wear, chips, cracks or any other imperfections. Check the splines for signs of wear or distortion.

3. Check the bearings for signs of wear or pitting on the rollers and races and check the bearing cage for dents and bends. Check the bearing retainer for any cracks, pits, grooves or corrosion.

4. Check the pinion flange splines for any signs of wear or distortion.

5. Replace parts that show any of the signs mentioned above.

Differential Case Disassembly

1. Scribe a line across the two halves of the differential case so they may be reassembled in the same position, and with the ring gear removed, separate the two halves. To remove the ring gear, remove the ring gear bolts and washers, and using a soft hammer tap the ring gear from the case.

2. Remove the internal parts from the inside of the case and set them aside in order that they may be reassembled in the same position.

Cleaning and Inspection

1. Check the differential gears, pinions, thrust washers and spider for any signs of unusual wear, chips, cracks or pitting.

2. Check all mating surfaces for signs of wear.

3. Replace parts that show any of

the signs mentioned above.

Differential Case Assembly

1. Using a good quality gear lubricant coat all of the parts.

2. Assemble the differential pinions and thrust washers onto the spider and install the assembly into the differential case.

3. Line up the scribe marks on the two halves of the differential case and install the ring gear. Install the ring gear washers and bolts and torque the bolts to approx. 110 ft. lbs.

Side Bearing Replacement

1. Install a bearing puller on the bearing and remove the bearing assembly from the differential case.

2. Check the bearings for any signs of wear on distortion.

3. Install the new bearing by setting it in place on the differential case and, using a bearing driver, drive the bearing onto the case assembly until it seats against the shoulder on the case.

Drive Pinion Assembly and Adjustment

1. Coat all of the parts with a good quality gear lubricant.

2. With the pinion gear in a press, press the rear bearings onto the pinion assembly.

3. In the bearing retainer, install the front and rear bearing cups using a driver of the proper size.

4. In the axle housing, install the straddle bearing assembly using the proper size driver.

5. Install the bearing retainer with the bearing cups in place on the pinion gear and install a new collapsible spacer.

6. Press the front bearing onto the pinion gear.

7. Lubricate the oil seal with a good quality high pressure grease and install the seal into the retainer bore. Be sure to press the seal down until it rests against the internal shoulder.

8. Install the pinion flange and oil deflector onto the splines of the pinion gear and install a new lock washer and pinion nut.

9. With the pinion flange clamped in a vise and a holder assembly installed on the flange, tighten the nut to obtain the proper preload. Measure the amount of torque required to turn the pinion gear. For a new bearing the torque required is 25-35 in. lbs. and for an old bearing it is 5-15 in.

1. Companion Flange	10. Straddle Bearing	19. Retainer Screw
2. Oil Deflector	11. Ring Gear	20. Bearing Cap
3. Oil Seal	12. Differential Spider	21. Case-to-Ring Gear Bolt
4. Bearing Retainer	13. Differential Case	22. Differential Cover
5. Shim	14. Differential Pinion	23. Bearing Cap Bolt
6. Pinion Front Bearing	15. Differential Side Gear	24. Cover Screw
7. Collapsible Spacer	16. Side Bearing	25. Axle Shaft
8. Pinion Rear Bearing	17. Side Bearing Adjusting Nut	
9. Drive Pinion	18. Adjusting Nut Retainer	

Chevrolet 5,200-17,000 lb. axle cross-section (© Chevrolet Div., G.M. Corp.)

lbs. To preload the bearing, tighten the pinion nut to approx. 350 ft. lbs. and take a reading of the torque required to turn the pinion. Continue tightening the nut until the proper preload is obtained.

CAUTION: Do not tighten the nut too tightly because it will collapse the spacer too much. This will make replacement necessary.

Drive Pinion Assembly Installation

1. If installing a new pinion gear, check the top of the new gear for the depth code number.
2. Compare the new number with the old number on top of the old pinion and check the pinion depth chart for preliminary setting of the pinion depth.

		CODE NUMBER ON ORIGINAL PINION			
		+2	+1	0	-1	-2
	+2	–	ADD .001	ADD .002	ADD .003	ADD .004
CODE NUMBER ON SERVICE PINION	+1	SUBT. .001	–	ADD .001	ADD .002	ADD .003
	0	SUBT. .002	SUBT. .001	–	ADD .001	ADD .002
	-1	SUBT. .003	SUBT. .002	SUBT. .001	–	ADD .001
	-2	SUBT. .004	SUBT. .003	SUBT. .002	SUBT. .001	–

3. Check the thickness of the original shims removed from the pinion and either add or subtract from the shims according to the chart.
4. Place the shim on the carrier assembly and line the holes up with those in the axle housing. Make sure the surfaces are clean of all dirt and grease.

5. Install the retainer and pinion assembly in the housing making sure the holes line up and install the retaining bolts. Torque the bolts to approx. 45 ft. lbs.

Differential Case Installation and Adjustments

1. Place the bearing cups over the side bearings on the differential assembly and place the unit into the carrier in the axle housing.
2. Install the bearing caps making sure the marks are lined up and install the bolts. Tighten the bearing retaining bolts.
3. Loosen the right side nut and tighten the left side nut until the ring gear comes in contact with the pinion gear. Do not force the gears together. This brings the gears to zero lash.
4. Back off the left side adjusting nut about two slots and install the lock fingers into the nut.
5. In this order tighten the right side adjusting nut firmly to force the case assembly into tight contact with the left side adjusting nut and then loosen the right side nut until it is free from the bearing.
6. Again retighten the right side adjusting nut until it comes in contact with the bearing. Tighten the right adjusting nut about two slots if it is an old bearing or three slots if it is a new bearing.
7. Install the lock retainers into the slots and torque the bearing cap bolts to 100 ft.-lbs. This procedure now insures that the bearings are preloaded properly. If more adjustments are made, make sure the preload stays the same. To do this, one adjusting nut must be loosened the same amount the other nut is tightened.
8. Install a dial indicator on the housing and measure the amount of backlash between the ring and pinion gear. The backlash should measure between .003 to .012 of an inch with the best figure being between .005 to .008 of an inch.
9. If the backlash is more than .012 of an inch, loosen the right side adjusting nut one slot and tighten the left side one slot. If the backlash is less than .003 of an inch, loosen the left side nut one slot and tighten the right side one slot. These adjustments should bring the backlash measurement into an acceptable range.

Pattern Check

1. Clean all the oil off the ring gear and using a gear marking compound, coat all of the teeth of the ring gear.
2. Make sure the bearing caps are torqued to 110 ft. lbs. and apply load to the gears while rotating the pinion. Rotate the ring gear one full turn in both directions.

NOTE: Load must be applied to the assembly while rotating or the pattern will not show completely.

3. Check the pattern on the ring gear and following the chart, adjust the assembly to get the contact pattern located centrally on the face of the ring gear teeth.

Chevrolet-Semifloating Single Speed, Non-Removable Carrier Type 2400 to 3500 lb. Axle

Description

This axle assembly is the semifloating type with Hypoid type drive pinion and ring gears. The drive pinion gear is supported by two bearings. The differential case contains two pinion gears. The carrier assembly is not removable since it is part of the axle assembly but the design allows for the differential assembly to be serviced while the axle is still in the vehicle. The ring gear is bolted to a one piece differential case that is supported by two preloaded roller bearings.

Differential Case Removal

1. Remove the inspection cover from the axle housing and drain the gear lubricant into a pan.
2. Remove the screw or pin that holds the pinion shaft in place and remove the shaft.
3. Push the axle shafts in a little and remove the "C" locks from the ends of the shafts. Remove the axle shafts from the housing.
4. Before going any further, the backlash should be measured and recorded. This will allow the old gears to be reassembled at the same amount of lash to avoid changing the gear tooth pattern. It also helps to indicate if there is gear or bearing wear, and if there is any error in the original backlash setting.
5. Roll the differential pinions and thrust washers out of the case and also remove the side gears and thrust washers. Make sure to mark the pinions and side gears so they can be reassembled in their original position.
6. Mark the bearing caps and housing and loosen the retaining bolts. Tap the caps lightly to loosen them. When the caps are loose, take the bolts all the way out and then reinstall the bolts just a few turns. This will keep the case from falling out of the housing when it is pried loose.
7. With a pry bar, very carefully pry the case assembly loose. Be careful not to damage the gasket surface on the housing when prying. The case assembly may suddenly come free if the bearings were preloaded, so pry very slowly.
8. When the case assembly is loose, remove the bolts for the bearing caps and remove the caps. Place the caps so they may be

Chevrolet 2,400-3,600 lb. axle cross section (© Chevrolet Div., G.M. Corp.)

1. Companion Flange	7. Differential Case	13. Cover	19. Thrust Washer
2. Deflector	8. Shim (A) with Service Shim	14. Pinion Shaft	20. Differential Pinion
3. Pinion Oil Seal	9. Gasket	15. Ring Gear	21. Shim
4. Pinion Front Bearing	10. Differential Bearing	16. Side Gear	22. Pinion Rear Bearing
5. Pinion Bearing Spacer	11. "C" Lock	17. Bearing Cap	23. Drive Pinion
6. Differential Carrier	12. Pinion Shaft Lock Bolt	18. Axle Shaft	

reinstalled in the same position. Place any shims that are removed with the cap they were removed from.

Drive Pinion Removal

1. With the differential removed, check the pinion preload. Do this by checking the amount of torque needed to turn the pinion gear. For a new bearing, it should be 20-25 in. lbs., and for a used bearing it should be 10-15 in. lbs. If there is no preload reading check the pinion for looseness. If there is any looseness the bearing should be replaced.
2. With a holder assembly installed on the flange, use a socket of the proper size and remove the flange nut and washer.
3. Remove the flange by using a puller assembly and drawing the flange off the pinion splines.
4. Thread the pinion nut a few turns onto the pinion shaft. Using a brass drift and hammer, lightly tap the end of the pinion shaft to remove the pinion from the carrier. Be careful not to allow the pinion to fall out of the carrier after it breaks loose.
5. With the pinion removed from the carrier, discard the old seal, pinion nut and collapsible spacer

and install new ones when reassembling.

Cleaning and Inspection

1. Clean all parts in solvent and blow dry.
2. Check all of the parts for any signs of wear, chips, cracks or distortion. Replace any parts that are defective.
3. Check the fit of the differential side gears in the case and the fit of the side gear and axle shaft splines.

Differential Bearing Replacement

1. With a bearing puller attached to the bearing, pull the bearing from the case.
2. Place the new bearing on the case hub with the thick side of the inner race toward the case. Using a bearing driver, drive the bearing onto the case until it seats against the shoulder on the case.

Drive Pinion Bearing Replacement and Adjustment

1. Depending on the bearing that is being replaced, remove the front or rear bearing cup from the carrier assembly.
2. With the pinion gear mounted in

a press, press the rear bearing from the pinion shaft. Be sure to record the thickness of the shims that are removed from between the bearing and the gear.

3. Using a bearing driver of the proper size, install a new bearing cup for each one that was removed. Make sure the cups are seated fully against the shoulder in the housing.
4. The pinion depth must now be checked to determine the nominal setting. This allows for machining variations in the housing and enables you to select the proper shim so that the pinion depth can be set for the best gear tooth contact.
5. Clean the housing and carrier assemblies to insure accurate measurement of the pinion depth.
6. Lubricate the front and rear pinion bearings with gear lubricant and install them in their races in the carrier assembly.
7. Using a Pinion Setting Gauge, select the proper clover leaf plate, and install it on the preload stud.
8. Insert the stud through the rear bearing, with the proper size pilot on the stud, and through the front bearing using the proper pilot. Install the hex nut and tighten it until it is just snug.
9. Holding the preload stud with a wrench, tighten the hex nut until 20 in. lbs. of torque are required to rotate the bearings.
10. Install the side bearing discs on the ends of the arbor assembly, using the step of the disc that fits the bore of the carrier.
11. Install the arbor and plunger assembly into the carrier. Make sure the side bearing discs fit properly.
12. Install the bearing caps in the carrier assembly finger tight to make sure the discs do not move.
13. Mount a dial indicator on the mounting post of the arbor. Have the contact button resting on the top surface of the plunger.

Gauge plate installed

(© Chevrolet Div., G.M. Corp.)

Gauge tools installed in carrier
(© Chevrolet Div., G.M. Corp.)

14. Preload the dial indicator by turning it one-half revolution and tightening it in this position.
15. Use the button on the gauge plate that corresponds to the ring gear size and turn the plate so the plunger rests on top of it.
16. Rock the plunger rod back and forth across the top of the button until the dial indicator reads the greatest amount of variation. Set the dial indicator to zero at the point of most variation. Repeat the rocking of the plunger several times to check the setting.
17. Turn the plunger until it is removed from the gauging plate button. The dial indicator will now read the pinion shim thickness required to set the "nominal pinion depth." Make a note of the reading.
18. Check for the pinion code number on the rear face of the pinion gear being used. This number will indicate the necessary change to the pinion shim thickness. If the pinion is marked with a plus (+) and a number, add that much to the reading you got from the dial indicator. If the pinion has no mark, use the reading from the dial indicator as the correct shim thickness. If the pinion is marked with a minus (−) and a number, subtract that much from the reading on the dial indicator.
19. Remove the depth gauging tools from the carrier assembly and install the proper size shim on the pinion gear.
20. Lubricate the bearing with gear lubricant and using a press, press the bearing into place on the pinion shaft.

Pinion Gear Installation and Adjustment

1. Lubricate the front bearing with gear lubricant and install it in the front cup.
2. Install the pinion seal in the bore. Using a seal driver and the proper size gauge plate, drive the seal in until the gauge plate is flush with the shoulder of the carrier.
3. Coat the seal lips with gear lubricant and install a new bearing spacer on the pinion gear.
4. Install the pinion gear in the carrier assembly and using a large washer and nut, draw the pinion gear in through the front bearing far enough to get companion flange in place.
5. With the companion flange installed on the pinion shaft, use a holder assembly and tighten the pinion nut until all of the end play is removed from the drive pinion.
6. When there is no more end play the preload should be checked. The preload of the bearing is the amount of torque required to turn the pinion gear. The preload should be 20-25 inch. lbs. on new bearings and 10-15 inch. lbs. on reused bearings. Tighten the pinion nut until these figures are reached. *Do Not* over tighten the pinion. This will collapse the spacer too much and make it necessary to replace it.
7. Turn the pinion gear several times to make sure the bearings are seated and recheck the preload.

Ring Gear Replacement

1. Remove all of the bolts that hold the ring gear to the differential case and with a soft hammer, tap the ring gear off the case.

NOTE: Do not try to pry the ring gear off the case. This will damage the machined surfaces.

2. Clean all dirt from the case assembly and lubricate the case with gear lube. Align the ring gear bolt holes with the holes in the carrier and lightly press the ring gear onto the case assembly. Install all of the bolts and tighten them all evenly, using a criss-cross pattern to avoid cocking the ring gear.
3. When the ring gear is firmly seated against the case, tighten the bolts to 60 ft. lbs.

Differential Case Assembly, Installation, and Adjustment

1. Install the thrust washers and side gears into the case assembly. If the original parts are being used, be sure to place them in their original position.
2. Place the pinions in the case so they are 180 degrees apart as they engage the side gears.
3. Turn the pinion gears so the hole in the case lines up with the holes in the gears. When the holes are aligned, install the pinion shaft and lock screw. Do not tighten the lock screw too tightly at this time.
4. Check the bearings, bearing cups, cup seat and carrier caps to make sure they are in good condition.
5. Lubricate the bearings with gear lube. Install the cups on the proper bearings and install the differential assembly in the carrier. Support the carrier assembly to keep it from falling.
6. Install a support strap on the left side bearing and tighten the bearing bolts to an even, snug fit.
7. With the ring gear tight against the pinion gear, insert a gauging tool between the left side bearing cup and the carrier housing.
8. While lightly shaking the tool back and forth, turn the adjusting wheel until a slight drag is felt. Tighten the lock nut.
9. Between the right side bearing and carrier, install a service spacer, .170 of an inch thick, a service shim and a feeler gauge. The feeler gauge must be thick enough so a light drag is felt when it is moved between the carrier and the shim.
10. Add the total of the service spacer, service shim and the feeler gauge. Remove the gauging tool from the left side of the carrier and using a micrometer, measure the thickness in at least three places. Average the readings and record the result.
11. Refer to the chart to determine the proper thickness of the shim packs.
12. Install the left side shim first, then install the right side shim between the bearing cup and spacer. Position the shim so the chamfered side is outward or next to the spacer. If there is not enough chamfer around the outside of the shim, file or grind the chamfer a little to allow for easy installation.
13. If there is difficulty in installing the shim, partially remove the case from the carrier and slide both the shim and case back into place.
14. Install the bearing caps and torque them to 60 ft. lbs. Tighten the pinion shaft lock screw.

NOTE: The differential side bearings are now preloaded. If any adjustments are made in later procedures, make sure not to change the preload. Do Not change the total thickness of the shim packs.

15. Mount a dial indicator on the carrier assembly with the indicator button perpendicular to the tooth angle and in line with the gear rotation.
16. Measure the amount of backlash between the ring and pinion gears. The backlash should be

Shim pack selection chart (© Chevrolet Div., G.M. Corp.)

EXAMPLE

RING GEAR SIDE		OPPOSITE SIDE	
.250″	Thickness of Tool J-22779 required to force ring gear into contact with pinion	Combined total of: Service Spacer (A) Service Shim (B) Feeler Gauge (C)	.265″
$\dfrac{-.010″}{.240″}$	TO MAINTAIN PROPER BACKLASH (.005″ – .008″), ring gear is moved away from pinion by subtracting .010″ shims from ring gear side and adding .010″ shims to other side		$\dfrac{+.010″}{.275″}$
+ .004″	TO OBTAIN PROPER PRELOAD on side bearings, add .004″ shims to each side.		+ .004″
.244″	Shim dimension required for ring gear side	Shim dimension required for opposite side	.279″

between .005-.008 of an inch. Take readings at four different spots on the gear. There should not be variations greater than .002 of an inch.

17. If there are variations greater than .002 of an inch between the readings, check the runout between the case and ring gear. The gear runout should not be greater than .003 in. If the runout does exceed .003 in. check the case and ring gear for deformation or dirt between the case and gear.

18. If the gear backlash exceeds .008 in., increase the thickness of the shims on the ring gear side and decrease the thickness of the shims on the opposite side, an equal amount.

19. If the backlash is less than .005 in., decrease the shim thickness on the ring gear side and increase the shim thickness on the opposite side an equal amount.

Gear Pattern Check

Before final assembly of the differential, a pattern check of the gear teeth must be made. This determines if the teeth of the ring and pinion gears are meshing properly, for low noise level and long life of the gear teeth. The most important thing to note is if the pattern is located centrally up and down on the face of the ring gear.

1. Wipe any oil out of the carrier and wipe all dirt and oil from the teeth of the ring gear.
2. Coat the teeth of the ring gear with a gear marking compound.
3. With the bearing caps torqued to 55 ft.-lbs., expand the brake shoes until it takes 20-30 ft. lbs. of torque to turn the pinion gear.
4. Turn the companion flange so the ring gear makes one full rotation in one direction, then turn it one full rotation in the opposite direction.
5. Check the pattern on the teeth and refer to the chart for any adjustments necessary.
6. With the gear tooth pattern checked and properly adjusted, install the axle housing cover gasket and cover and tighten securely. Fill the axle with gear lube to the correct level.
7. Road test the vehicle to check for any noise and proper operation of the rear.

Gear tooth contact check (© Chevrolet Div., G.M. Corp.)

Dodge/Plymouth 8¾ in. Removeable Carrier Axle

See the Dodge/Plymouth truck section for external identification and axle shaft service.

Differential Removal

1. Raise and support vehicle under rear axle housing.
2. Remove wheels, drums and rear axle shafts, as described in truck section. Drain lubricant.
3. Disconnect rear universal joint and place out of way.
4. Remove attaching bolts and remove carrier assembly to bench.

Differential Reconditioning

NOTE: Before disassembling the differential, check and record the side bearing play and ring gear run-out. Also, make a gear tooth contact pattern test, and measure pinion bearing preload.

1. Mount carrier in holding tool, with pinion flange up.
2. Remove pinion shaft nut and washer. Remove flange with puller.
3. With puller screwed into oil seal, pull seal from housing.
4. Rotate assembly with holding tool to allow oil slinger, shim pack and spacer (where used), to drop from the carrier.
5. Matchmark the differential pedestals, adjusting nuts, and bearing caps for reassembly identification.
6. Remove the bearing lockscrews and locks.
7. Remove the cap bolts, caps and back off bearing adjusting nuts slightly.

8. Remove the differential assembly, being sure to keep each bearing cup with the proper bearing.
9. Remove the pinion and rear bearing cone from the carrier.
10. The bearing cone and pinion locating washer may now be removed from the shaft.
11. Remove the bearing cups from the carrier housing.

Differential Case Disassembly

1. Mount the differential case and ring gear in vise with soft jaws. Remove and discard the ring gear bolts.

NOTE: the ring gear bolts have left-hand threads.

2. Tap the ring gear loose, using a non-metallic hammer.
3. If the ring gear runout exceeds .005 in., when previously measured, recheck the case as follows:
   a. Install the cap bolts, bearing caps and bearing adjusters.
   b. Tighten the cap bolts and adjusters sufficiently to prevent any sideplay in the bearings.
   c. Mount a dial indicator so that the pointer contacts the ring gear surface of the differential case flange. Measure the runout, which should not exceed .003 in. If the runout exceeds .003 in., the case must be replaced.
4. With a hammer and drift, remove the differential pinion shaft lockpin from the rear side of the ring gear flange. The hole is reamed only part way

through, making it necessary to remove the pin from the proper side.
5. Remove the pinion shaft and axle shaft thrust block.
6. Rotate differential side gears until the pinions and thrust washers can be removed.
7. Remove both differential side gears and thrust washers.

Differential Case Assembly

1. Lubricate all parts before assembly, with rear axle lubricant.
2. Install the thrust washers on the differential side gears and install the side gears into the case.
3. Place thrust washers on both differential pinions and, working through the large access window, mesh the pinion gears with the side gears. The pinions should be exactly 180° apart.
4. Rotate the side gears 90° to align the pinions and thrust washers with the pinion shaft holes.
5. From the pinion shaft lockpin hole side of the case, insert the slotted end of the pinion shaft through the case, conical thrust washer and just through one of the pinion gears.
6. Install the thrust block through the side gear hub, so that the slot is centered between the side gears.
7. Hold all these parts in alignment, and align the lockpin holes in the pinion shaft and case. Install the lockpin from the pinion

8¾ in. Dodge/Plymouth rear axle assembly (© Chrysler Corp.)

8¾ in. Dodge/Plymouth differential carrier assembly (© Chrysler Corp.)

shaft side of the ring gear flange.

8. With a stone, relieve the edge of the chamfer on the inside diameter of the ring gear.

9. Heat the ring gear (fluid bath or heat lamp) to a temperature not exceeding 300° F.

NOTE: do not heat ring gear with a torch.

10. Align the ring gear with the case. Insert new ring gear screws through the case flange and into the ring gear.

11. Alternately tighten each cap screw to 55 ft lbs.

12. Position each differential bearing cone on the hub of the differential case (taper away from ring gear) and install the bearing cones with an arbor press.

13. Install the pinion bearing cups squarely in the bores of the carrier.

Differential Assembly, Pinion Bearing Preload and Depth of Mesh

This type axle uses two types of pinions. Pinion depth of mesh and bearing preload are determined in the same manner for small and large stem pinions; only the sequence of adjustments varies. Small stem pinions require bearing preload adjustment first, while large stem pinions require pinion depth of mesh adjustment first. The position of the drive pinion, relative to the position of the ring gear (depth of mesh) is determined by the location of the bearing cup shoulders in the carrier and by the portion of the pinion behind the rear bearing.

NOTE: factory service procedures recommend the use of very specialized tools to assure proper adjustment of the rear axle without duplicating labor. However, the special tools are not readily available. The

following procedures are substituted in place of special factory tools.

Differential Assembly

1. Assembly procedures, excluding adjustments and selection of shims, are the reverse of disassembly.

NOTE: some rear axles of this type use a collapsible spacer. Once this spacer has been collapsed or the pinion bearing preload exceeded, the collapsible spacer must be replaced with a new one. Before assembly, gather together shims of several sizes and several spacers in case the assembly is not properly adjusted the first time.

If the differential assembly was satisfactory when disassembled, the drive pinion may be assembled with the original components, excepting the pinion front bearing and collapsible spacer (if used). If any replacement parts are installed, a complete adjustment will be necessary. Ring gears and pinions are available in matched sets only, and the adjustment position for best tooth contact is marked on the end of the pinion head.

Proper pinion setting, relative to the ring gear is determined by a shim, selected before the pinion is installed in the carrier. Pinion bearing shims are available in .002 in. increments (small stem) and in .001 in. increments (large stem with collapsible spacer).

Depth of Mesh

The head of the pinion is marked with a (+) or (−) followed by a number ranging from 0 to 4. If the old and new pinion have the same marking and the old bearing is being installed, use a shim of the original thickness. But, if the old pinion is marked (0), for example, and the new pinion is marked +2, try a .002 in. thinner shim. If the new pinion is

marked −2, try a .002 in. thicker shim. The exact size of the pinion shim cannot be determined exactly without special equipment. This method provides a starting point. When the unit is assembled, check the ring gear teeth contact pattern and adjust the shim size accordingly. The entire unit must be disassembled to change the shim size.

Pinion Bearing Preload (Small Stem)

1. If the bearings are being replaced, place the bearings in the carrier and drive into place with a drift.

2. Assemble the pinion shim (chamfered side toward the gear) onto the pinion stem. Install the tubular spacer if equipped, and the preload shims on the pinion stem.

3. Insert the pinion assembly into the carrier.

4. Install the front pinion bearing cone, U joint flange, Belleville washer (convex side up) and nut. Do not install the oil seal.

5. Tighten the flange nut to 240 ft lbs. (210 ft.lbs. in 1973 and later).
   Rotate the pinion to properly seat the bearing rollers. The preload torque required to turn the pinion with the bearings oiled, should be 20-30 in. lbs. with new bearings and 0-15 in. lbs. for used bearings. Use a thinner shim pack to increase preload and a thicker shim pack to decrease preload.

6. After the correct pinion depth has been established and the preload obtained, remove the drive pinion flange.

7. Lubricate and install the drive pinion oil seal.

8. Install the pinion flange, washer and nut. Torque the nut to 240

ft.lbs. (210 ft.lbs. in 1973 and later).

Pinion Bearing Preload (Large Stem)

1. Place the rear pinion bearing cone on the pinion stem (small side away from pinion head).
2. Lubricate front and rear bearing cones and install the rear pinion bearing cone onto the pinion stem with an arbor press.
3. Insert the pinion bearing and collapsible spacer assembly through the carrier and install the front bearing cone. Install the companion flange.

NOTE: during installation of pinion bearing, do not collapse the spacer.

4. Install the drive pinion oil seal into the carrier. Use tool C-3890 to insure proper seal depth.
5. Support the pinion in the carrier and install the anti-rattle washer.
6. Install the Belleville washer (convex side up) and pinion nut.
7. Hold the companion flange and tighten the pinion nut to remove all end-play, while rotating the pinion to insure proper bearing seating. Remove the tools and rotate the pinion several revolutions.
8. Torque the pinion nut to 170 ft. lbs. (210 ft.lbs. in 1973 and later). With an in. lb. torque wrench, measure the pinion bearing preload, which should be 20-30 in.lbs. for new bearings or 10 in.lbs. over the original figure if the old pinion bearing is used.

NOTE: the correct preload reading can only be obtained with the carrier nose upright. The final assembly is incorrect if the final pinion nut torque is below 170 ft.lbs. (210 ft.lbs. in 1973 and later) or if the pinion bearing preload is not within specifications. Under no circumstances should the pinion nut be backed off to reduce the pinion bearing preload. If this is done, a new collapsible spacer will have to be installed and the unit adjusted again until proper preload is obtained.

9. Check the ring gear teeth contact pattern.

Carrier Assembly

1. Install the differential bearing cups onto their respective bearings and position assembly in the carrier.
2. Install the caps and bolts and tighten bolts finger tight. Be sure all identification markings are properly aligned and positioned.
3. Tighten the adjusters enough to square the bearing cups with the bearings and eliminate end-play. Allow some backlash to remain.
4. Tighten one corresponding bolt on each cap to 85-90 ft lbs.
5. Set dial gauge to contact outer end of ring gear tooth and take readings at 90° intervals to find the spot with the least clearance. Do not rotate ring gear after this position is found.
6. Turn both adjusters equally until backlash is between .005 and .0015 in.
7. Install adjuster lock into adjuster at rear face of ring gear. If holes do not align, tighten to next hole. Never back off to meet hole.
8. Turn the adjuster, on tooth side of ring gear, a notch at a time until the backlash is a minimum of .006 in. and a maximum of .008 in. This will establish proper bearing preload and correct backlash. Tighten the bearing cap bolts to 85-90 ft. lbs.
9. Install the remaining adjuster lock and tighten cap screws to 15-20 ft.lbs.

Final Installation

1. Thoroughly clean the gasket surfaces of the carrier and housing.
2. Install the carrier on the housing using a new gasket. Tighten the nuts to 45 ft.lbs.
3. Install the axle shafts and adjust the axle shaft end-play if necessary.
4. Install the driveshaft and torque the screws to 15 ft.lbs.
5. Install the backing plates, hubs and drums and bleed and adjust the brakes (if necessary).
6. Fill the differential with SAE 90 lubricant to the bottom of the filler plug opening. Lower and road-test the vehicle.

Dodge/Plymouth 8⅜ and 9¼ in. Integral Carrier Axle

See the Dodge/Plymouth truck section for external identification and axle shaft service.

Differential Removal

1. Keep a pencil and paper handy to record data.
2. Jack up the rear of the vehicle and remove the wheels, drums, and axle shafts.
3. Loosen the housing cover screws and drain the lubricant from the rear axle.
4. Remove the cover.
5. Clean the inside of the differential case with solvent and blow dry with compressed air.
6. Check for differential side-play by inserting a large screwdriver between the left side of the axle housing and the differential case flange. Using a prying motion, determine whether side-play exists. There should be no side-play.
7. Paint the ring gear teeth and make a gear tooth contact pattern. Determine if proper depth of mesh can be obtained.
8. If side-play was found in step six, proceed to step nine. If no side-play was found in step six, check the drive gear run-out. Mount a dial indicator and index the indicator stem at right angles to the rear face of the ring gear. Rotate the ring gear and mark the ring gear and case at the point of greatest run-out. Total indicator reading should not exceed 0.005 in. If it does, the possibility exists that the case must be replaced.
9. Measure and record the pinion bearing preload. Use an in. lb. torque wrench to measure the preload.
10. Remove the pinion nut, washer and pinion flange.
11. Remove and discard the pinion oil seal.
12. Match-mark the axle housing and the differential bearing caps.
13. Remove the threaded adjusters and the differential bearing caps. There is a special wrench to do this through the axle tube on late models.
14. Remove the differential case from the housing. The differential bearing cups and threaded adjusters must be kept together so they can be installed in their original position.

Differential Disassembly

1. To remove the drive pinion or front bearing cone, drive the pinion rearward out of the bearing. This will result in damage to the bearing and cup. The bearing cone and cup must be replaced with new parts. Discard the collapsible spacer.
2. Drive the front and rear bearing cups from the housing with a brass drift. Remove the shim from behind the rear bearing cup and record the thickness. Discard the shim.
3. Remove the rear bearing cone from the pinion stem with a puller.
4. Clamp the differential case and ring gear in a vise with soft jaws.

9¼ in. integral carrier Dodge/Plymouth axle (© Chrysler Corp.)

5. Remove the ring gear bolts (left-hand thread). Tap the ring gear loose with a soft-faced mallet.

6. If the ring gear run-out exceeded 0.005 in., recheck the case as follows. Install the differential case, cups, caps, and adjusters in the housing. Turn the adjusters to eliminate all side-play and tighten the differential cap bolts snugly. Measure the run-out at the ring gear flange face. Total indicator reading should not exceed 0.003 in. It is often possible to reduce run-out by removing the ring gear and remounting 180° from its original position. Remove the differential case from the housing.

7. Remove the pinion shaft lockscrew and remove the pinion shaft.

8. Rotate the differential side gears until the differential pinion shafts can be removed through the opening in the case.

9. Remove the differential side gears and thrust washers.

10. Using a puller or a press and press plates, remove the differential side bearings.

Differential Assembly

1. Lubricate all parts, before assembly, with rear axle lubricant.

2. Install the thrust washers on the differential side gears and install the side gears into the case.

3. Place thrust washers on both differential pinions and, working through the large access window mesh the pinion gears with the side gears. The pinions should be exactly 180° apart.

4. Rotate the side gears 90° to align the pinions and thrust washers with the pinion shaft holes.

5. From the pinion shaft lockpin hole side of the case, insert the slotted end of the pinion shaft through the case, conical thrust washer and just through one of the pinion gears.

6. Install a thrust block through the side gear hub, so that the slot is centered between the side gears.

7. Hold all these parts in align-

ment, and align the lockpin holes in the pinion shaft and case. Install the lockpin from the pinion shaft side of the ring gear flange.

8. With a stone, relieve the edge of the chamfer on the inside diameter of the ring gear.

9. Heat the ring gear (fluid bath or heat lamp) to a temperature not exceeding 300° F.

NOTE: do not heat ring gear with a torch.

10. Align the ring gear with the case. Insert the ring gear screws through the case flange and into the ring gear.

11. Alternately tighten each cap screw to 55 ft. lbs.

12. Position each differential bearing cone on the hub of the differential case (taper away from ring gear) and install the bearing cones. An arbor press may be helpful.

Pinion Depth of Mesh

1. The proper pinion setting (relative to the ring gear) is determined by a shim which has been selected before the pinion is to be installed in the carrier. Pinion bearing shims are available in 0.001 in. increments.

2. The head of the pinion is marked with a "plus" (+) or a "minus" (−) mark that is followed by a number ranging from zero to four. If the old and new pinions have the same marking and the old bearing is being installed, use a shim of the original thickness. If the old pinion is marked zero (0), however, and the new pinion is marked plus two (+2), try a shim that is 0.002 in. thinner. If the new pinion is marked axle housing cup bore and install minus two (−2), try a shim that is 0.002 in. thicker.

3. Position the selected shim in the the rear bearing cup.

4. Place the rear pinion bearing cone on the pinion stem (small side away from pinion head).

5. Lubricate the front and rear bearing cones and install the rear pinion bearing cone onto the pinion stem with an arbor press.

6. Insert the pinion bearing and collapsible spacer assembly through the carrier and install the front bearing cone. Install the companion flange.

NOTE: during installation of the pinion bearing do not collapse the spacer.

7. Install the drive pinion oil seal into the carrier. Be sure to properly seat the seal.

8. Support the pinion in the carrier and install the anti-clang washer.

9. Install the Belleville washer (convex side up) and pinion nut.

10. Hold the companion flange and tighten the pinion nut to remove all end-play, while rotating the pinion to ensure proper bearing seating. Remove the tools and rotate the pinion several revolutions.
11. Torque the pinion nut to 170 ft. lbs. (210 from 1972 on). With an in. lbs torque wrench, measure the pinion bearing preload, which should be 20-30 in. lbs. for new bearings or 10 in. lbs. over the original figure if the old pinion bearing is used.

NOTE: The correct preload reading can only be obtained with the carrier nose upright. The final assembly is incorrect if the final pinion nut torque is below 170 ft.lbs. (210 from 1972 on) or if the pinion bearing preload is not within specifications. Under no circumstances should the pinion nut be backed off to reduce the pinion bearing preload; if this is done, a new collapsible spacer will have to be installed and the unit adjusted again until proper preload is obtained.

Differential Bearing Preload and Ring Gear-to-Pinion Backlash— Before 1972

NOTE: for later axles see Side Bearing Preload Adjustment following.

1. With the pinion bearings installed and preload set, install the differential case and ring gear in the housing with the respective bearing caps and adjusters. The adjusters should be flush with the caps. Tighten the bolts on each cap to 10 in. lbs.
2. Turn the right adjuster until the assembly has approximately 0.005 in. spread, measured with a dial indicator.
3. Tighten all four cap bolts to 60 ft.lbs.
4. Turn the adjuster on the right until all spread is removed.
5. Turn the adjusters in until all bearing free-play is eliminated and there is some backlash between the ring and pinion gear. Turn the ring gear and pinion several times to seat the bearings.
6. Install a dial indicator to register on the rear face of any ring gear tooth. Measure the backlash at four points equally spaced around the ring gear. Turn the ring gear to position it at the point of least backlash.

7. Turn both adjusters in, the same amount and in the same direction until backlash is 0.001-0.002 in.
8. Turn the bearing adjuster on the right side in until 0.006-0.008 in. minimum backlash is obtained. Setting the required backlash will also obtain the proper preload.
9. Make a ring gear contact pattern test and evaluate the results. If the unit must be disassembled to put in a new shim behind the pinion, the entire assembly operation must be repeated.
10. Install the axle shafts, drums, and wheels.
11. Install a new cover gasket and the differential cover. Refill the unit with the specified lubricant.
12. Lower and road-test the car.

Side Bearing Preload— 1972

A number of changes have been incorporated into these axles. The new type of axles still use threaded adjusters to control side bearing preload. The threaded adjuster uses a hex drive hole, and requires special tool C-4164 to adjust the side bearing preload through the axle tube. An adjuster lock with two pointed teeth which embed in the exposed adjuster thread when the lock is tightened is provided. Previously, spacers were used from 0.084-0.100 in. The new shims will range from 0.020-0.038 in. and will be equipped with internal centering tabs. The new shims, marked with a number which represents its thickness in thousandths of an inch, can be installed with either side against the pinion head. To accommodate the new adjuster locks, a new axle cover is used.

The axle pinion has been redesigned to use a short collapsible spacer The short collapsible gear sets are interchangeable with the previous gearsets the only precaution being to ensure that the proper spacer is used.

1. Index the gears so that the same gear teeth are in contact throughout the adjustment.
2. The differential bearing cups will not always move with the adjusters. It is important to seat the bearings by rotating them 5-10 times in each direction, each time the adjusters are moved.
3. With the pinion bearings installed and the preload set, install the differential with adjust-

ers, caps and bearings. Lubricate the bearings and adjuster threads. Check to be sure that there are no crossed threads. Tighten the cap screws on the right and left to 10 ft. lbs. Tighten the bottom cap screws finger-tight until the head is just seated on the bearing cap.
4. Using the tool, check to be sure that the adjuster rotates freely. Turn both adjusters in until bearing play is eliminated with some drive gear backlash (0.010 in.). Seat the bearing rollers.
5. Install and register a dial indicator against the drive side of a gear tooth. Check the backlash at four positions to find the point of minimum backlash. Rotate the gear to the position of least backlash and mark the tooth so that all readings will be taken at the same point.
6. Loosen the right adjuster and turn the right adjuster until the backlash is 0.003-0.004 in. with each adjuster tightened to 10 ft. lbs. Seat the bearings rollers.
7. Tighten the differential bearing cap screws to 100 ft. lbs.
8. Tighten the right adjuster to 70 ft. lbs. and seat the rollers, until the torque remains constant at 70 ft. lbs. Measure the backlash. If the backlash is not 0.006-0.008 in. increase the torque on the right adjusters and seat the rollers until the correct backlash is obtained. Tighten the left adjuster to 70 ft. lbs. and seat the bearings until the torque remains constant.
9. If the assembly is properly done, the initial reading on the left adjuster will be approximately 70 ft. lbs. If it is substantially less, the entire procedure should be repeated.
10. After adjustments are complete, install the adjuster locks. Be sure the teeth are engaged in the adjuster threads. Torque the lockscrews to 90 in. lbs.

Final Assembly

1. Install the axle shafts.
2. Install the cover on the differential housing, using a new gasket.
3. Refill the rear axle housing with SAE 90 lubricant. On 8⅜ in. axles, fill to ¼ below the plug opening through 1971, and ½ in. below from 1972 on. Fill 9¼ in. axles to the bottom of the plug opening.

Dodge RA115 12½ in. Axle

The RA115 is a full-floating rear axle with hypoid drive gear and pinion and uses a two-pinion differential assembly. The drive pinion shaft is supported by three tapered roller bearings (two front and one rear).

IMPORTANT: Before proceeding with disassembly, consult the "General Axle Service" section for instructions on important pre-assembly inspections and checks. After removing differential assembly from the car-

RA115 Dodge differential assembly (© Chrysler Corp.)

1. Differential side gear thrust washer
2. Differential pinion thrust washer
3. Differential pinion
4. Rear axle drive gear bolt nut
5. Rear axle drive gear bolt nut lock
6. Differential pinion shaft
7. Differential case
8. Rear axle drive gear
9. Differential bearing adjuster
10. Differential bearing cup
11. Differential bearing cone and rollers
12. Differential bearing cup
13. Differential carrier
14. Rear axle drive pinion front bearing retainer nut lock screw
15. Rear axle drive pinion front bearing assembly
16. Rear axle drive pinion front bearing washer
17. Rear axle drive companion yoke
18. Rear axle drive pinion companion yoke nut
19. Rear axle drive pinion companion yoke nut washer
20. Rear axle drive pinion bearing oil seal
21. Rear axle drive pinion front bearing retainer nut

22. Differential bearing adjuster
23. Differential bearing cup
24. Differential bearing cone and rollers
25. Differential bearing cap
26. Differential bearing cap screw and lock washer
27. Rear axle drive pinion rear bearing cup
28. Rear axle drive pinion rear bearing cone and rollers
29. Rear axle drive pinion
30. Rear axle gear bolts
31. Rear axle drive gear thrust pad
32. Rear axle gear thrust screw
33. Rear axle drive gear thrust screw nut and lock washer
34. Differential pinion shaft lock pin
35. Differential side gear thrust washer
36. Differential side gear
37. Differential pinion thrust washer
38. Differential pinion
39. Differential side gear
40. Differential bearing adjuster lock pin
41. Differential bearing adjuster lock pin cotter pin
42. Rear axle drive pinion bearing spacer

rier, remove the drive gear thrust block from the drive gear side of carrier housing. Break weld and remove thrust block adjusting screw.

Disassembly

1. Unscrew nut from drive pinion shaft and remove companion yoke.
2. Remove drive pinion oil seal.
3. Loosen drive pinion front bearing retainer lock screw and remove bearing.
4. Remove drive pinion shaft assembly and front bearing forward cone from carrier.
5. Remove front bearing rear cone and pre-load spacer from pinion shaft, then pull rear bearing from shaft.
6. Complete disassembly by driving cups·out of carrier.

Assembly

1. Install pinion bearing cups in carrier, making sure they are seated evenly. The front bearing cup is designed so that front bearing cones are seated in taper of cup from opposite sides. The cup is marked with the letter "Y", which must face toward the front (engine side). The front bearing cone that operates in this cup is also marked "Y". The cone must be assembled with corresponding marks mated together.
2. Press rear bearing on pinion shaft. Install front bearing rear cone on shaft.
3. Lubricate bearing cones and cups with axle lubricant and insert shaft assembly into carrier. Adjustment of pinion bearing pre-load is required whenever a change is made in pinion or bearings. Adjustment is made with spacers available in .020 inch graduations from .1790 to .1930 inch.
4. Select and install a spacer between the two front bearings. This spacer will separate front bearing rear cone from cup.
5. Install and tighten bearing retainer nut. Rotate pinion shaft to seat bearings.
6. Rotate pinion shaft with an inch-pound torque wrench. Torque should be from 35 to 70 inch-pounds while shaft is turning (40 inch-pounds preferred). It may be necessary to change spacer to arrive at specified torque.
7. Remove spacer from between two front bearings and install it in its proper location. After tightening bearing retainer nut, recheck bearing pre-load. Torque should be from 60 to 95 inch-pounds while rotating pinion (70 to 80 inch-pounds preferred). Tighten front bearing retainer nut lock screw.
8. Place front bearing washer on pinion shaft and install new oil seal.
9. Install companion yoke, washer and nut and tighten nut to 325-foot-pounds. Install cotter key.

Install drive gear thrust block before installing differential assembly in carrier. Thread thrust block adjusting screw through carrier with one thread inside carrier. Hold thrust block on screw with heavy grease.

Drive Gear Thrust Block Adjustment

Turn in thrust block screw approximately four turns to force block against back face of drive gear. Install lock nut on screw, back out screw 1/8 turn to provide .006-.008 inch clearance, then tighten lock nut securely. Spot-weld lock nut to carrier and screw.

Torque Chart

Axle drive shaft nut (cotter key type)	175-250
Axle drive shaft flange nut	30-35
Axle drive shaft bearing retainer bolt	30-35
Carrier to housing screw	40
Differential bearing cap bolt	85-90
Differential bearing adjuster lock bolt	20
Differential case bolt	45
Drive gear bolts to differential case (anti-spin)	40-45
Drive pinion yoke nut (two bearing pinion)	180-200
Drive pinion yoke nut (three bearing pinion)	325

GMC Single Speed Axle Service
H052, H072, H110, H130, H135, H150

Disassembly of Subassemblies

Differential Disassembly

1. Remove lock nut, adjusting screw, and thrust block.
2. Remove two adjuster lock cap screws and locks.
3. Punch-mark bearing caps and carrier to help in locating caps for assembly. Remove bearing adjusters and bearing caps. NOTE: Do not pry caps free with a screwdriver or distort locating dowels.
4. Carefully remove differential assembly from carrier.
5. Use differential side bearing remover to pull bearing cones off each side of case.
6. Make sure that differential case halves are punch-marked so that they can be reassembled in same position.
7. Remove drive gear, and separate case halves.
8. Remove two side gears; differential spider, and four differential pinions.
9. On H110, H135, and H150 models remove pinion and side gear thrust washers to complete differential disassembly.

Drive Pinion Disassembly

1. Remove seal retainer and gasket from carrier.
2. Use brass drift against inner end of pinion to drive out pinion and bearings assembly.
3. Remove shim pack from carrier from those models having tapered roller outer bearings.
4. According to the model, it may be necessary to use a drift to remove the pinion rear bearing.
5. Clamp yoke in soft-jawed vise. Remove yoke nut and washer and separate drive pinion from yoke.
6. Separate yoke from oil seal retainer.
7. Place retainer in a soft-jawed vise and, using a hammer and chisel, remove oil seal and then the felt oil seal.
8. On models with tapered roller outer bearing, remove bearing cup, outer tapered bearing cone, and bearing spacer from drive pinion.
9. Using bearing remover press plate with press, separate bearing cone (some models) or roller bearing (on all other models) from drive pinion.
10. On H110 and H135 models remove bearing lock ring, and use press plates with arbor press to remove roller bearing from inner end of drive pinion. This completes drive pinion diassembly.

Assembly of Subassemblies

NOTE: Thoroughly clean and lubricate all components with axle lubricant before reassembling.

Drive Pinion Assembly

1. Clean counterbore of oil seal retainer. Saturate felt seal in oil and install evenly in retainer. Soak oil seal in light engine oil for about one hour before installing. Coat outer surface of seal lightly with sealing compound to prevent oil leaks between seal and retainer.
2. Install oil seal into retainer with lip of seal toward inner side of retainer. Using a seal installer, press oil seal into retainer with face of seal flush with retainer face.
3. Retainer surface must be clean and smooth to prevent oil leaks between retainer and carrier.
4. On H052, H072, and H150 models, press bearing into place into carrier bore.
5. On H110 and H135 models, press roller bearing into position on drive pinion with chamfered side of inner race facing toward pinion shoulder. Position bearing lock ring to secure bearing on drive pinion. NOTE: Opposed tapered roller bearing cones, two bearing cups, and spacer used on some models are serviced and replaced as a unit. The spacer is a preselected one to provide proper bearing adjustment.
6. Models with tapered roller bearings:
   a. Press inner bearing cone into place with largest side of cone facing pinion gear end.
   b. Thoroughly grease and install original shim pack in carrier. If original ring gear and pinion are reinstalled, use shims that were removed. Shims are available in five thicknesses -0.012, 0.015, 0.018, 0.021, and 0.024 inch. When using new gears, start with one 0.021 inch shim and refer to "General Axle Service" section for details on checking pinion depth.
   c. Insert pinion assembly into carrier (on H150 model), align roller bearing with carrier boss. Install bearing spacer, bearing cup and bearing cone with wide side facing pinion splines.
7. Models with double-row ball bearing: Using a 2-inch pipe or tubing, drive bearing unit into proper seating position.
8. With pinion assembly properly positioned in carrier, install new gasket. Install seal retainer onto yoke, and assemble yoke and retainer assembly onto splined end of drive pinion.
9. Secure retainer to carrier with lock washers and cap screws and torque to specifications.
10. Secure pinion assembly with yoke washer and nut and torque to 220 ft. lf. This completes drive pinion assembly.

Differential Assembly

1. To facilitate installation of drive gear, install two guide pins (cut ½"-20x2" bolts) in gear. Start guide pins through case flange holes and tap drive gear onto case. If one differential gear is bad, the complete set should be replaced.
2. Lubricate differential case inner walls and all component parts with axle lubricant. Place differential pinions and thrust washers (thrust washers are used only on H110, H135, and H150 axles) on spider.
3. Assemble side gears, pinions and side gear and pinion thrust washers to left half of differential.

4. Assemble drive gear half (right half of differential, being sure to line up marks on the two halves.

5. Install differential-to-drive gear cap screw and lock washers and tighten evenly until drive gear is flush with case flange. Remove guide pins and install cap screws and torque to specifications.

6. Differential side bearing cones can be installed with special installer tool.

Installation and Subassemblies

Differential Installation

1. Install bearing cap locating dowels in caps. Lubricate side bearings and place bearing cups on bearings.

2. Install differential assembly into carrier. Carefully install bearing adjusters into carrier.

3. Install bearing caps, aligning punch marks previously made. Be sure that bearing adjuster threads are engaged with carrier and caps. Tighten adjusters alternately and evenly. Tighten bearing cap screws until lock washers are flat.

Drive Gear and Pinion Adjustment

1. Loosen bearing cap screws just enough to loosen right-hand bearing adjuster (pinion side) and tighten left-hand bearing adjuster (opposite pinion side.) Using adjuster, remove all backlash between drive gear and pinion.

2. Back off left-hand bearing adjuster about two notches to point where notch in adjuster is aligned with lock. Tighten right-hand bearing adjuster solidly to seat bearing. Again loosen right-hand adjuster enough to free bearing; then retighten snugly against bearing. Draw up right-hand adjuster one or two more notches until adjuster notch aligns with lock.

3. With dial indicator on carrier adjuster, slowly oscillate drive gear and take backlash reading. Backlash should be 0.005 to 0.008-inch.

4. If backlash exceeds 0.008-inch, loosen right-hand adjuster one notch; then tighten left-hand adjuster one notch. If less than 0.005 inch, loosen left-hand adjuster one notch and tighten right-hand adjuster one notch.

5. After backlash has been adjusted, again tighten bearing cap screws until their respective lock washers flatten out.

6. Check drive gear run-out.

7. Install side bearing adjusting nut lock and secure with cap screws and lock washers.

Checking Pinion Depth (Models with Tapered Roller Bearings Only)

NOTE: Refer to tooth contact chart in the "General Axle Service" section.

1. Coat drive gear with red lead. Turn pinion shaft several revolutions in both directions while applying considerable drag on drive gear.

2. Pinion depth is determined by shim pack selection. Shim packs are available in thicknesses of: 0.012, 0.015, 0.018, 0.021, and 0.024- inch.

3. Changing pinion depth will again require adjusting backlash. After pinion depth and backlash have been adjusted, torque bearing caps to specifications.

Thrust Block Installation

1. Install thrust block and lock nut to adjusting screw. Thread screw and block into carrier until block contacts drive gear. Rotate gear and note change of drag. Adjust these parts until point of greatest drag is reached. Back screw off about a 30 degree turn to provide 0.005 to 0.007-inch clearance between block and gear. Make certain screw does not turn at all when tightening lock nut to 135 foot-pounds torque.

Specifications GMC H-052, H-072, H-110, H-135, H-150

Make	GMC
Type	Hypoid
Adjustment and Clearances	
Backlash—gear to pinion	0.005"-0.008"
Adjustment method	See text
Pinion backlash adjustment	
Models with tapered bearings	Shims
Models with ball bearing	None
Shim pack thickness	0.021" Initial
Shims available	0.012"-0.015"-0.018"-0.021"-0.024"
Differential bearing adjustment method	Threaded rings
Drive Gear	
Backlast—gear to pinion	0.005"-0.008"
Adjustment method	See text
Runout (mounted to case)	0.006"
Drive Pinion	
Backlash—pinion to drive gear	0.005"-0.008"
Adjustment method	See text
Differential Case	
Runout at flange (max.)	0.002"
Diameter at side gear	
H-052, H-072	1.927"-1.929"
H-110, H-135	2.193"-2.195"
H-150	2.409"-2.411"
Side Gear	
Backlash—side gear to pinion gear	0.004"-0.007"
Hub diameter—H-052, H-072	1.923"-1.925"
Hub diameter—H-110, H-135	2.189"-2.191"
Hub diameter—H-150	2.405"-2.407"
Pinion Gear	
Inside diameter—H-052 H-072	0.814"-0.815"
Inside diameter—H-110, H-135	0.880"-0.881"
Inside diameter—H-150	0.9435"-0.9445"
Thrust Washer Thickness (H-110, H-135, H-150)	
Side gear	0.058"-0.062"
Pinion gear	0.058"-0.062"
Spider	
Diameter of arms—H-052, H-072	0.808".0.809"
Diameter of arms—H-110, H-135	0.874"-0.875"
Diameter of arms—H-150	0.9365"-0.9375"
Thrust Block	
Thickness	0.1845"-0.1885"
Clearance—block to gear	0.005"-0.007"
Axle Shafts	
Diameter of splines—H-052, H-072	1.5275"-1.5325"
Number of splines—H-052, H-072	17
Diameter of splines—H-110, H-135	1.724"-1.732"
Number of splines—H-110, H-135	27
Diameter of Splines—H-150	1.848"-1.856"
Number of Splines—H-150	29
Torque Specifications (Ft. Lbs.)	
Drive gear bolts	
H-052, H-072	85-95
H-110, H-135	100-110
H-150	150-170
Differential side bearing cap bolts	
H-052, H-072	95-105
H-110, H-135, H-150	190-220
Pinion bearing retainer bolts	
H-052, H-072	90-100
H-110, H-135, H-150	160-170
Pinion flange nut	160-280
Diff. bearing adj. nut lock	10-20
Axle shaft flange to hub	
H-052, H-072	85-95
H-110, H-135, H-150	10-20
Carrier to housing	
H-052, H-072	40-50
H-110, H-1.5, H-150	75-90
Axle shaft nuts	
All models	80-100

Model T150

Description and Operation

The Corporation T150 is a 2-speed axle (planetary type) which can be shifted by the driver when desired. Operating the shift control button activates an electric or vacuum shift unit (attached to differential carrier) which, in turn, changes axle speed from low to high or vice-versa.

CAUTION: There is no "Neutral" position. There are just "High" and "Low" ratios. To attempt to coast with axle in a supposedly "Neutral" position could cause serious axle damage.

Differential Carrier Removal

1. Remove all but two cap screws holding carrier to axle housing. Loosen the two remaining cap screws and, with a soft hammer, break carrier loose from housing. CAUTION: Do not use pinch bar. This might cause damage to carrier or housing.
2. Place a roller jack under carrier, remove the two cap screws and remove carrier and differential assembly from housing.
3. Place carrier and differential assembly in a suitable repair stand.
4. Remove shift unit.

Differential and Planetary Removal

1. Remove anchor from end of sun gear.
2. Drive shift lever out of carrier.
3. Remove shift yoke and sleeve assembly. Separate yoke from sleeve.
4. Remove adjusting nut lock.
5. Remove oil trough.
6. Tap bearing caps from carrier.
7. Remove differential and planetary assembly from carrier assembly.
CAUTION: DO NOT drop bearing cones and cups.

Drive Pinion and Retainer Removal

1. With carrier still in repair stand, use holding bar to hold propeller shaft yoke while removing nut and washer.
2. Using a soft faced hammer or a blunt chisel, work retainer cap and pinion assembly from carrier.
3. Remove pinion adjusting shim pack and record or tag thickness for reassembly information.
4. If necessary, use hammer and drift to remove drive pinion rear bearing from carrier.

Drive Pinion and Retainer Disassembly

1. Carefully pry pinion oil seal from pinion and bearing retainer.
2. Using a press, press downward on end of pinion shaft to separate pinion assembly from retainer. Remove yoke and deflector.
3. Remove pinion front bearing cone from retainer. Pull bearing preload spacer off drive pinion shaft.
4. When necessary, use bearing cup remover to force bearing cups out of retainer cap.
5. Slide pinion bearing remover up over pinion head, and press drive pinion out of intermediate bearing cone.

Differential and Planetary Disassembly

1. Punch-mark drive gear, differential support case, and differential case cover to facilitate proper alignment during reassembly.
2. Remove drive gear and case cover.
3. Tag sun gear and four planetary gears so they may be correctly reassembled. Remove planet gears.
4. Lift differential and planet support assembly away from support case.
5. Punch-mark planet support cover and support and separate.
6. Again mark or tag all pinion and side gears for reassembly to same positions, and remove them along with their respective thrust washers. Slide four pinion gears off differential spider.
7. Remove differential side bearing cups. Insert brass drift through holes in case and cover and drive left and right side bearing cones off hubs.
NOTE: Alternately tap drift from hole on one side to hole on other side to prevent race from binding on hub.

Axle Assembly

Before axle is assembled, make sure that all parts have been thoroughly cleaned, especially oil passages. Lightly lubricate all parts while assembling.

When assembling axle unit, it is recommended that new lock washers and gaskets be installed wherever possible. See "General Axle Service" section for details on cleaning and inspection.

Drive Pinion and Retainer Assembly

Drive pinion and drive gear must be replaced as a matching set.
1. If it was necessary to remove pinion rear bearing, use a driver handle with bearing installer to bottom bearing into position in carrier.
2. Position pinion intermediate bearing cone and cup in pinion bearing retainer with thicker end of cup facing inward. Use driver handle with bearing cup installer to firmly seat cup in place.
3. Follow step 1 procedure to install pinion front bearing and cup to pinion bearing retainer. Seat cup with handle and cup installer.
4. Use arbor press with a 2 inch inner diameter pipe of suitable length to position pinion intermediate bearing cone with thicker end up against shoulder of drive pinion.
5. Place new pinion bearing spacer on pinion up against bearing cone.
6. Position dive pinion assembly in retainer cap assembly, and install pinion front bearing cone in place. Thicker end of cone should face outward.
7. Again use arbor press with a 2 inch inner diameter pipe of suitable length to press inner race of cone up tightly against spacer.
8. Install pinion oil seal in retainer. See "oil seal replacement" in the "General Axle Service" section.

Differential and Planetary Assembly

1. Lubricate thrust washers, pinion gears, spider, and side gears. Assemble pinion gears to arms of differential spider and install all above components into planetary support (match up punch-marks made earlier).
2. Align and secure support cover with new lock washers and cap screws. Tighten cap screws to specifications.
3. Install left and right differential bearing cones to support case and support case cover hubs. Use bearing installer for left and right bearings.
4. Install planet gears on journal arms of support. Position sun gear in the planet gears.
5. Align punch-marks and install drive gear to support case cover. Improvised guide pins can be made from drive gear retaining cap screws.
6. Turn differential assembly over so drive gear teeth face downward. Position assembled planet and differential assembly in cover, making sure thrust washer at case bottom is properly positioned.
7. Using lock washers and cap screws, join support case, case cover and drive gear together.

Specifications

Make	G. M. Corp.
Type	2-Speed planetary
Ratios	5.83:1-7.95:1
Adjustments and Clearances	
Backlash—gear to pinion	0.005"-0.008"
Backlash adjustment method	See text
Pinion backlash adjustment	Shims
Shim pack thickness (starting)	0.021"
Shims Available	0.006"-0.009"-0.012"-0.015"-0.018"-
	0.021"-0.024"
Pinion bearing adjustment method	Pre-selected spacer
Differential bearing adjustment method	Threaded adjusters
Drive Gear	
Backlash—gear to pinion	0.005"-0.008"
Adjustment method	See text
Gear teeth	
5.83:1-7.95:1	35
Run out-max.	0.005"
Drive Pinion	
Backlash—gear to pinion	0.005"-0.008"
Adjustment method	See text
Bearing pre-load (max. in. lbs.)	
New bearing	15-25
Used bearing	5-15
Gear teeth	
5.83:1-7.95:1	6
Differential Spider	
Diameter of arms	0.9365"-0.9375"
Differential Side Gear	
Backlash	0.007"-0.009"
Hub diameter	2.405"-2.407"
Differential Pinion	
Backlash	0.007"-0.009"
Inside diameter	0.9435"-0.9445"

Differential Case	
Diameter of planet gear studs	1.3122"-1.3132"
Distance across studs	6.583"-6.593"
Run-out at flange (max.)	0.002"
Thrust Washer Thickness	
Side gear	0.058"-0.062"
Pinion gear	0.058"-0.062"
Differential case to case cover	0.058"-0.062"
Planet Gear	
Bushing inside diameter	1.3158"-1.3164"
Sun Gear	
Diameter over retainer	3.339"-3.400"
Backlash	0.004"-0.008"
Shifter Yoke	
Yoke width	0.395"-0.400"
Shifter sleeve	
Backlash	0.004"-0.008"
Width at yoke groove	0.445"-0.457"
Axle Shaft	
Diameter at splines	1.848"-1.856"
Number of splines	29
Torque Specifications (Ft. Lbs.)	
Differential case cap screws	100-110
Planetary support case & cover to bevel gear cap screws	100-110
Differential bearing cap screws	190-220
Differential carrier to housing cap screws	75-90
Universal joint yoke nut	160-280
Anchor plate to differential bearing cap screws	40-45
Differential bearing lock cap screws	10-15
Shift housing to carrier cap screws	25-30
Axle shaft cover cap screws	10-20

Remove guide pins and install rest of lock washers and cap screws. Tighten all cap screws in a cross-wise pattern to specified torque.

Differential and Planetary Installation

1. Position left and right side bearing cups over their respective cones. Position differential and planetary assembly into carrier.
2. Install differential adjusting nuts at both sides.
3. Position bearing caps on carrier making certain adjusting nuts properly engage threads in caps. If bearing caps seat flush in place while adjusting nuts turn freely, caps are properly installed. Use soft hammer to seat caps properly. Tap lightly. CAUTION: Do not force bearing caps on nuts.
4. Tighten cap screws evenly until adjusting nuts turn freely in threads.

Drive Pinion and Retainer Installation

1. Install original shim pack to carrier, making sure shim holes are aligned with carrier cap screw holes.
2. Properly install pinion and retainer assembly to carrier bore. Make sure pilot end of pinion

properly seats in pinion rear bearing.

3. Assemble retainer to carrier with new lock washers and cap screws and torque to specifications.
4. Tap yoke onto pinion shaft splined end, making sure proper spline engagement is made.
5. Install and torque pinion washer and nut to end of drive pinion.
6. Continue tightening nut in small degrees until torque required to rotate drive pinion in carrier is from 25 to 35 inch-pounds (when new pinion bearings are installed). Only 5 to 15 in. lbs. torque is required if same bearings are reinstalled.

Drive Gear and Pinion Adjustment

1. Loosen right differential adjusting nut. Tighten left adjusting nut. Use differential nut wrench on right side nut and a drift hammer to the left side nut.
2. Tighten left adjusting nut until drive gear contacts pinion and zero lash is obtained; however, do not force gears into contact so as to bind them.
3. Back off left adjusting nut about two notches to a point where nut lock and nut are aligned. Install nut lock and torque to specifications.

4. Tighten right adjusting nut firmly to force the differential and planet assembly into solid contact with left adjusting nut. Loosen right adjusting nut until it no longer contacts its bearing, then retighten until nut contacts bearing. Tighten right adjusting nut from one to two notches more if old bearings are used, and two to three notches if new bearings are used, to a position where nut and nut lock are aligned. Install nut lock and torque to specifications. NOTE: At this point the differential bearings are properly preloaded. If any additional adjustments are required, make sure that this proper preload remains. If one adjusting nut is loosened, the other nut must be tightened an equal amount to maintain this preload.
5. Mount a dial indicator on the housing and measure the backlash between the drive gear and pinion. Backlash should be from 0.003 to 0.012 inch with 0.005 to 0.008 inch preferred.

NOTE: If backlash is more than 0.012 inch, loosen the right adjusting nut one notch and tighten left adjusting nut one notch. If backlash is less than 0.003 inch, loosen the left adjusting nut one notch and tighten the right adjusting nut one notch.

Checking Pinion Depth

1. Thoroughly clean drive and pinion gear teeth.
2. Paint drive gear teeth lightly and evenly with a mixture of powdered red lead and oil.
3. Rotate pinion through several revolutions in both directions until a definite contact pattern is developed on drive gear. Apply pressure to drive gear while turning pinion. This will create load on gears to simulate a driving pattern.
4. Examine the pattern on drive gear teeth. If the pinion depth is correct, the tooth pattern will be centered on the pitch line and toward the toe of drive gear.
5. If the pattern is below the pitch line on drive gear teeth, the pinion is too deep and it will be necessary to remove the pinion assembly and increase the shim thickness between the pinion bearing retainer and the carrier.
6. If the pattern is above the pitch line on drive gear teeth, the pinion is too shallow and it will be necessary to remove the pinion assembly and decrease the shim thickness between the pinion bearing retainer and the carrier.
7. Changing the pinion depth will cause some change in backlash. Therefore adjust backlash to maintain correct specifications.
8. Torque bearing cap screws to specifications and recheck drive gear to pinion backlash. Install adjusting nut locks and torque to specifications.
9. Install oil trough to differential carrier, adjust trough to drive gear so that clearance is 0.03 to 0.09-inch. Torque retaining cap screws.

Shifter Components Installation

1. Position shift yoke in shift sleeve groove.
2. Slide yoke and sleeve assembly over sun gear. Splines of sleeve and sun gear should properly mesh.
3. Install shift lever through carrier housing into yoke mating splines together. Tap end of lever lightly to seat it in yoke.
4. Position the shifter unit and gasket over mounting pad, aligning lever in carrier with shift rod in shift unit. NOTE: On axles equipped with electrical shift units, shift electrical leads must be connected to shift unit before installing unit to carrier See section on "electric shift system".
5. Install and torque bolts.
6. Install differential assembly into axle housing.

GMC Single Reduction, Integral Housing Axles

Models H024, H029, H033, H035, H036

IMPORTANT: Before disassembling unit, perform the following:
1. Inspect axle housing for lubricant leaks before cleaning; then clean thoroughly.
2. Check and record drive gear and pinion backlash.

Differential Case and Drive Pinion Removal

Differential Case Removal

1. Remove wheels and brake drums.
2. Drain lubricant and remove cover.
3. Remove pinion shaft from differential.
4. Remove "C" locks from axle shafts and pull shafts from housing.
5. Extract the differential pinions, side gears and thrust washers and tag them for reassembly.
6. Punch-mark differential bearing caps and housing for proper reassembly and remove caps.
NOTE: Do not attempt to pry caps free as this may damage machined face of caps.
CAUTION: When prying out differential case do not damage gasket surface on carrier housing.
7. Using a pry bar, pry differential case and ring gear assembly out of carrier. If the differential bearings are under preload, the case will fall free at a certain point; therefore, prevent case from falling.
8. Place both the left and right bearing cups and shims with their respective bearing caps so they will be re-installed in their original positions.

Drive Pinion Removal

1. Using a suitable tool, remove and discard flange nut and washer and pull off flange.
2. Using a soft hammer, remove drive pinion. Remove pinion front bearing cone and pinion bearing spacer. Replace spacer when assembling.

Pinion Oil Seal Replacement

1. Pry oil seal out of carrier.
2. Pack the cavity between lips of new oil seal with lithium base lubricant. Place seal in carrier bore and place gauge plate over seal between seal flange and carrier.
3. On H024 axle, use installers and press seal into carrier. On all others, drive seal into carrier.
4. Press or drive seal into carrier bore until gauge plate is snug between seal flange and carrier. Rotate gauge plate 180 degrees from original position; seal must be square in carrier bore.
5. Using gauge plates will create ⅛" gap between the carrier and seal flange. Applying unnecessary pressure after seal installation may distort the seal.
6. If necessary to replace oil deflector on companion flange, clean up stake points on flange, then install the deflector. Stake in place at three new equally spaced positions.

Pinion and/or Bearing Replacement

1. Tap out front and rear pinion bearing cups from carrier. Remove carefully to avoid cocking the cups in carrier.
2. Use installers to install front and rear bearing cups against carrier shoulders. Do not cock the cups.
3. Remove pinion rear bearing cone and roller assembly, using suitable tools:
   H024 Axle - use press plate holder with remover plates.
   All Other Axles - use a discarded ring gear as a press plate holder for remover plates. Remove shim and record thickness.
4. If the original ring gear and drive pinion and the rear bearing assembly are re-used, then the original shim can also be used.
5. If any one of the three components; the ring gear, pinion, or rear bearing assembly require replacement, attain correct shim thickness by the following methods:
   a. Lubricate pinion bearing cone and roller assemblies and place them in proper cups.
   b. Position pinion depth setting gauge plate in pinion rear bearing.
   (1) H024 Axle - position gauge plate with lower surface of

gauge (X stamped near low side) toward top of carrier.

(2) All Other Axles - position gauge plate with higher surface toward top of carrier.

c. Insert clamp screw through gauge plate and both of the pinion bearings.

d. Position plug on threaded end of clamp screw and index it in front bearing. Install hex nut and rotate bearings several times to seat them.

e. Tighten hex nut until 20 inch-pounds of torque is required to rotate bearings.

f. After establishing torque, check position of gauge plate in carrier (see step b).

g. Position dial indicator on gauge post of barrel adapter so that indicator button rests on top of tool plunger.

h. Position tool in carrier. Swing tool body so that plunger does not touch gauge plate, and set indicator dial at zero. NOTE: Pinion setting gauge sleeves must be used when gauging all except H024 axles. Adapter must be seated in bearing bores of carrier before measuring depth.

i. Slowly swing inner end of tool plunger across gauge plate until highest indicator reading is obtained. Record and recheck this measurement.

j. All service pinion gears are stamped with a code number on the threaded end of the pinion. The numerical difference between the code number and the gauge reading obtained in step i determines the required thickness of the pinion locating shim.

Example:
Pinion code number	45
Dial indicator reading	16
Difference	29
Proper shim thickness	0.029-in.

NOTE: Shims are available in thicknesses from 0.021 to 0.037-inch. Each shim is etched with its thickness.

6. Remove pinion setting gauge and pinion bearing cone and roller assemblies from carrier.

7. Position the selected shim against pinion head on shaft.

8. Install new cone and roller assembly, using a suitable installer. Press cone tight against shim.

Differential Bearing Replacement

1. Install the differential bearing remover making sure puller legs are fitted securely in notches of case and against bearing cone.

2. Tighten puller screw to remove bearing.

3. Place new bearing on one hub with thick side of inner race against case and drive into place using suitable tool.

4. Before installing bearing on opposite hub, support differential case on adapter plug to allow case to rest on adapter instead of bearing cage. Install remaining bearing as instructed in step 3.

Ring Gear or Differential Case Replacement

1. Remove ring gear. NOTE: Do not attempt to pry ring gear from case; to do so may cause damage.

2. Install guide pins, made from ⅜"-24 x 1½" long cap screws to ring gear.

3. Position ring gear over pilot diameter of the case. Install every other ring gear bolt and lock washer and tighten so that gear face is flush with face of case.

4. Remove guide pins and install remaining bolts and torque to 40-60 ft.lbs.

5. Install thrust washers and side gears in case; if same parts are used, replace in original sides. Position pinions and thrust washers through loading holes in case 180 degrees apart so that they engage side gears. Rotate gears until pinion shaft holes are aligned and install shaft and lock screw.

Axle Assembly

Drive Pinion and Bearing

1. Position pinion and rear bearing cone and roller assembly in carrier, install a new pinion bearing spacer on shaft, and install pinion front bearing cone and roller assembly.

2. Install flange on pinion shaft using companion flange installer and tool.

3. Pack the cavity between end of pinion splines and pinion flange with a non-hardening sealer before installing washer and nut on pinion.

4. Install washer and a new self-locking nut on pinion shaft. Tighten nut to remove end play. Continue tightening, in small increments, and checking preload with torque wrench and adapter until torque required to rotate pinion is 20 to 30 inch-pounds for new bearings and seal or 5 to 15 inch-pounds when used parts are reinstalled.

Differential Bearing Preload and Ring Gear Adjustment

1. Check bearing cups and cup seat for nicks and burrs and replace if necessary.

2. Lubricate bearings, position cups to proper bearings then install differential assembly in carrier. Install right bearing cap and torque to 55 foot-pounds. Check to be sure cup is seated in carrier bore.

3. Service spacers are available in one thickness only for each axle: 0.170 ± .001-inch for model H024 and 0.160 ± .001-inch for all other axles. Steel service shims are used with the spacer. See shim chart below for shim availability and identification.

Differential Bearing Shim Identification

Thick-ness*	Identification Notches			
	I.D.		O.D.	
	H024	All Others	H024	All Others
.064	0	0	0	2
.066	0	0	1	3
.068	0	0	2	4
.070	0	1	3	0
.072	1	1	0	1
.074	1	1	1	2
.076	1	1	2	3
.078	1	1	3	4
.080	2	2	0	0
.082	2	2	1	1
.084	2	2	2	2
.086	2	2	3	3
.088	3	2	0	4
.090	3	3	1	0
.092	3	3	2	1
.094	3	3	3	2
.096		3		3
.098		3		4
.100		4		0

*Additional shims are available for the H-024 axle.

These shims, with a thickness of 0.052-inch through 0.062-inch, have the shim thickness stamped on the shim. NOTE: Do not re-use original bearing preload shims. They are made of cast iron and may be broken easily.

4. With ring gear tight against the pinion gear (0.000 to 0.001-inch backlash) and with gauging tool inserted between left bearing cup and carrier housing, turn tool adjusting nut clockwise until a noticeable drag is produced. NOTE: Do not apply pressure on bearing so as to cause preload.

5. Tighten locking bolt on the side of the gauge and remove gauge. Using a micrometer, measure the thickness of the two gauging plates. By subtracting the thickness of the service spacer to be used from the thickness of the plates, the thickness of the service shim may be determined.

Example:
Gauge thickness	0.254"
Service spacer to be used	0.070"
Service shim size	0.084"

6. Install the selected shim between the service spacer and bearing. Install the left bearing cap and check backlash for a 0.000 to 0.001-inch reading.

7. Remove right bearing cap and insert tool between right bearing cap and carrier housing. Turn tool adjusting nut clockwise until a noticeable drag is produced. Tighten locking bolt on the side of the tool and remove gauge.

8. Using a micrometer, measure the thickness of the gauge plate. Subtract the service spacer thickness from the total thickness and add 0.008-inch to this figure. This total will be the size of the service shim to be used on the right side.

Example:

Gauge thickness	0.224″
Service spacer	0.170″
	0.054″
Preload	0.008″
Total shim thickness (right side)	0.062″

NOTE: Service shims are available in 0.002-inch graduations. If the shim measurement falls between the available shims, select the shim that is 0.001 inch thinner.

9. Using a soft hammer, tap the selected shim between the service spacer and bearing.

10. Install right bearing cap and torque both caps to 55 foot-pounds.

11. Mount a dial indicator on the carrier and check backlash between ring gear and pinion.

Specifications

Make	GMC
Type	Hypoid
Models	H-024, H-029, H-033, H-035, and H-036
Adjustment & Clearances	
Backlash—gear to pinion	0.005″-0.008″
Adjustment method	See text
Pinion bearing pre-load (in.-lbs.)	20-35
Pinion backlash adjustment shims	
Available (0.001″ increments)	0.021″ to 0.037″
Differential bearing and backlash adjustment method	Selective spacer
Thrust Washer Thickness	
Pinion gear	0.028″-0.032″
Side gear	0.029″-0.031″
Differential pinion shaft Diameter	0.808″-0.809″
Differential pinion gear Inside diameter	0.813″-0.816″
Torque Specifications (Ft. Lbs.)	

Torque Specifications Foot-Pounds

Carrier cover bolts	
H-024, H-029	15-25
H-033, H-035, H-036	20-25
Differential bearing cap bolts	55
Differential pinion lock bolt	15-25
Filler plug	20
Ring gear to case bolts	50

Backlash should range within 0.003 to 0.010-inch with a reading of 0.005 to 0.008-inch preferred. Check reading at four equally spaced positions around the ring gear. Variation in reading should not exceed 0.002-inch.

NOTE: The dial indicator button should be perpendicular to tooth angle and in line with gear rotation.

12. If variation in backlash exceeds 0.002-inch, measure ring gear and case runout. Gear runout should be a maximum of 0.002-inch; should it be more, check ring gear and case for deformation and/or foreign matter between case and gear.

13. If gear lash is not within limits, correct by decreasing shim thickness on one side and increasing thickness of the other shim the same amount. Total shim thickness must be maintained to maintain the proper preload. (By decreasing shim on right side 0.002-inch and increasing shim thickness on left side by 0.002-inch backlash will decrease by 0.001-inch.)

Single-Speed, Single Reduction Eaton

This is a full-floating axle having spiral bevel drive gear and pinion, and using a four-pinion differential assembly. The pinion has three roller bearings—two in front of the pinion teeth and one behind.

Disassembly

1. Remove thrust block screw.
2. Punch mark carrier leg, bearing cap and bearing adjusting nut to aid in reassembly.
3. Remove bearing caps and adjusting nuts.
4. Lift assembly out of carrier housing.
5. Punch mark differential case halves for correct alignment. Separate case halves.
6. Remove pinion shaft pinions, side gears, thrust washers and bearing cones.
7. Separate drive gear from cage.
8. Remove pinion shaft yoke.
9. Using a drift, drive pinion and cage assembly from carrier. CAUTION: Support bearing cage when driving assembly from carrier.
10. Wire bearing cage shim pack together to facilitate reassembly.
11. Lift bearing cage from pinion and remove cork seal. Remove pinion drive yoke washer and front bearing cone from cage.
12. Remove pinion bearing spacer washer, spacer, inner bearing cone and pilot bearing from pinion shaft.
13. Remove pinion cage bearing cups.
14. Clean all parts thoroughly in a suitable solvent and blow dry with compressed air. The bearings should be immersed in clean solvent and rotated by hand until clean. After cleaning, blow dry with compressed air. Do not spin bearings with air pressure, as they might score due to absence of any lubrication. Inspect all parts for wear or imperfections. The thrust shoulders must be flat, so that bearing cups will seat properly. Install a new case if cracked or distorted. (For further details, see "cleaning" and "inspection" in the "General Axle Service" section).

Assembly

1. Press drive pinion inner bearing cone and rear pilot bearing firmly against pinion shoulder.
2. Stake pilot bearing in at least four places. Install pinion cage bearing cups.
3. Place bearing spacer and washer on pinion shaft. Lubricate bearing cone with SAE 90 oil and position bearing cage on bearing. Lubricate and press outer bearing on pinion shaft. Rotate cage to assure normal bearing contact. If a press is not available,

1 Lockwire
2 Cap screw
3 Cotter pin
4 Adjuster lock
5 Differential carrier and
   bearing caps (matched
   parts) (conical type)
6 Differential bearing
   adjust (RH)
7 Differential bearing cup (RH)
8 Differential bearing cone (RH)
9 Lockwire
10 Cap screw
11 Nut

12 Differential case (Plain Half)
13 Side gear thrust washer (RH)
14 Side gear (RH)
15 Side pinion thrust washer
16 Side pinion
17 Spider
18 Side gear (LH)
19 Side gear thrust washer (LH)
20 Bolt and nut

21 Ring gear and drive pinion
   (Matched Set)
22 Differential case
   (Flanged Half)
23 Bolt
24 Differential bearing cone (LH)
25 Differential bearing cup (LH)
26 Differential bearing
   Adjuster (LH)
27 Carrier gasket
28 Pinion pilot bearing
29 Pinion bearing cone (Inner)
30 Pinion bearing spacer
31 Pinion bearing spacer washer
32 Pinion bearing cup (Inner)

33 Pinion bearing cage shims
34 Pinion bearing cage
35 Lock washer
36 Cap screw
37 Pinion bearing cup (Outer)
38 Pinion bearing cone (Outer)
39 Companion flange flat washer
40 Strip sealer (Seal Retainer)
41 Oil seal
42 Oil seal retainer
   (Pressed-in-Type)
43 Companion flange
44 Cotter pin
45 Pinion nut
46 Flat washer

Eaton single-speed, single reduction rear axle (© Eaton Yale & Towne Inc.)

install pinion yoke washer and nut and torque to specifications.

4. While the assembly is in the press under pressure or pinion nut torqued to specifications, check pinion bearing pre-load. The correct pressures and torques for preload are:

Pinion Shaft Thread Size and Number of Threads Per Inch	Required Pressure to Obtain Correct Pre-Load lbs.	Required Torque to Obtain Correct Pre-Load ft. lbs.
7/8 in. x 16	10,000	200-325
1 1/8 in. x 18	12,000	325-450
1 1/4 in. x 12	15,000	400-600

5. Wrap a soft wire around cage and pull on horizontal line with pound scale. Measure diameter of pinion cage. Assuming cage diameter is 6 inches, pulling radius would be 3 inches; therefore, 6 pounds pull on scale would equal 18 inch-pounds preload.

6. Use rotating torque, not starting torque. If rotating torque is not within 15 to 35 inch-pounds, use thinner spacer to increase preload or thicker spacer to decrease pre-load. Torque must be

near low limit inch-pounds with original pinion bearings and near high limit when using new bearings.

7. Upon obtaining correct preload, install a new pinion oil seal assembly. Install pinion yoke spacer, yoke and nut, and torque nut to specifications. Install a new cork seal on pinion cage.

Pinion and cage assembly components (© Eaton Yale & Towne Inc.)

Staking pinion shaft with bearing ball
(© Eaton Yale & Towne Inc.)

Differential assembly components (© Eaton Yale & Towne Inc.)

Eaton Axle Drive Pinion Adjustment Specifications

Axle Models	Specifications for Drive Pinion Bearing Preload Adjustment				Drive Pinion Position Adjustment	
	Pinion Bearing Spacer Thickness	Drive Pinion Nut Torque Setting (ft.-lbs.)	Arbor Press Preload Pressure Setting (tons)	Spring Scale Reading (pounds) To obtain 15 to 35 in.-lbs. Torque	Pinion Bearing Cage Shim Pack	Depth Gauge Setting
Single 17101, 17121	0.639	400-600	7-8	6-14	0.030 + 0.125 Spacer	4.2187
Reduction 18101, 18121	0.639	400-600	7-8	6-14	0.030 + 0.125 Spacer	4.2187
Axles 19121	0.185	550-850	10-11	5-11	0.024	4.600

8. Place original shim pack on carrier, tap pinion and cage assembly into place with a soft mallet. Make sure oil passages in cage and carrier align. Install lock washers and bolts at 100-125 foot-pounds. See the "General Axle Service" section if a new pinion is being installed and follow the "Pinion Setting Procedures" (Depth Gauge Method) for adjusting pinion location.

9. Position drive gear on differential case, install and torque bolts.

10. Lubricate differential case inner walls and all parts with rear axle gear lubricant during assembly.

11. Install thrust washer and side gear in drive gear half of case. Assemble pinions and thrust washers on pinion shaft, and place in case. Place other side and thrust washer on four pinions.

12. Align mating marks and install other case half. Draw case down evenly with four bolts. Check for free rotation of differential gears and correct if necessary. Install remaining bolts at 80-100 foot-pounds and install lock wire.

13. Press differential bearings squarely and firmly on differential case halves.

14. Thread drive gear thrust block screw in carrier far enough to install thrust block. Coat thrust block with heavy grease and place it on end of screw.

15. Lubricate differential bearings and cups with rear axle lubricant. Place cups over bearing and position assembly in carrier housing. Hand-tighten adjusting nuts against bearing cups.

16. Install bearing caps in correct location and tap lightly into position, making sure they are not cross-threaded. Make certain that some backlash is present between drive gear and pinion. Install bearing cap bolts snugly with allowance for turning adjusting nuts.

17. Attach a dial indicator to the carrier with the pointer resting against back face of drive gear. Eliminate all end play by turning right adjusting nut clockwise.

18. Tighten adjusting nuts, one notch each, to pre-load differential bearings. Align notches for installation of adjusting nut locks.

19. Position dial indicator so that the pointer rests against face of one of the drive gear teeth. Check backlash between drive gear and pinion at 90 degree intervals of rotation.

20. Adjust backlash to .008-.015 inch (.008 preferred, especially on new gears.) When adjusting backlash, back off one adjusting nut and advance opposite nut the same amount to maintain bearing pre-load.

21. If the Depth Gauge Method for adjusting the pinion depth was not used as mentioned in paragraph 8, then use the Tooth Contact Method. Then proceed to step 22. See "General Axle Service" section. If pinion was adjusted by the Depth Gauge Method go directly to step 22.

22. Tighten bearing cap bolts, to 175-200 foot-pounds. Install the adjusting nut locks and lock wires.

23. Tighten thrust block adjusting screw sufficiently to locate thrust block firmly against back face of gear. Back off adjusting screw ¼ turn to provide .010-.015 inch clearance and lock securely with nut.

24. Place oil distributor in carrier with taper side of scoop down, install spring and retaining plug.

Torque Chart

Carrier to housing bolt
or stud nut   7/16-14   50-70
      1/2-13   80-100
      5/8-11   150-175

Differential case bolt	7/16-14	50-70				Pinion cage bolt	9/16-12	100-125
	1 2-13	80-100		13/16-10	225-250	Pinion shaft yoke nut	7/8-16	200-325
			Differential bearing				1-1/8-18	325-450
Differential bearing cap bolt			adjuster lock bolt	9/16-12	100-125		1-1/4-12	400-600
	5/8-11	150-175		5/8-11	150-175			
	11/16-11	175-200	Electric shift unit (mounting)					
				7/16-20	50-70			

Eaton Two-Speed and Planetary Double Reduction Axles

Description

The two-speed axle is a full-floating type with bevel drive gear and pinion, and uses a four-pinion differential assembly. The pinion has three roller bearings—two tapered bearings in front of the pinion teeth and one straight roller bearing be-

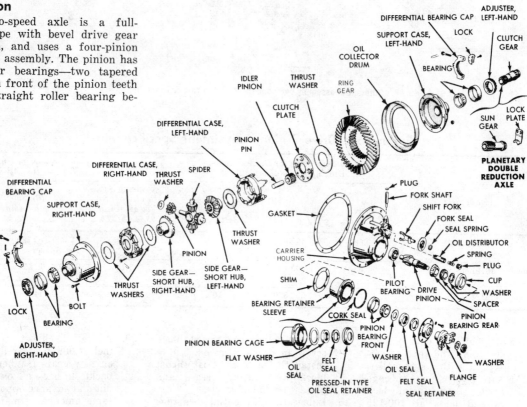

Eaton planetary two-speed or double reduction axle (© Eaton Yale & Towne Inc.)

hind the teeth. An oiling system provides lubrication to the pinion bearings, differential bearings and planetary unit. The planetary double reduction axle combines the ring and pinion and the planetary unit in one axle housing. Procedures for disassembly are the same as the two-speed except the double reduction axle has no shift mechanism and, instead of a sliding clutch gear, it uses a sun gear.

Differential Carrier

Disassembly

1. Inspect the carrier before disassembly. (See "cleaning" and "inspection" paragraph in the "General Axle Service" section).
2. After removing the oil distributor plug, pull the oil distributor and spring out of the differential carrier.
3. Remove the shift fork shaft

plugs, and shaft.
4. Remove the shift fork seal and the shift fork from the housing. Pull the sliding clutch gear out of the differential carrier.
5. Punch the right and left bearing adjusters to aid in relocating the adjustment when reassembling.

Removing Pinion Pilot Bearing

Removal or installation of pinion bearing cup (© Eaton Yale & Towne Inc.)

Removing or Installing Differential Bearing

Removing Pinion Rear Bearing Cone

Remove the differential bearing cap bolts. Back off one bearing adjusting nut to relieve the bearing preload.

6. Remove the right and left bearing caps, bearing adjusters, and locks.

7. Lift the differential and planetary assembly out of the differential side bearing cups.

8. Mark the right and left support cases so that they can be reassembled in the same relative position. Remove the bolts which hold the ring gear to the gear support cases.

9. Clamp the differential assembly (ring gear end up) in a soft-jawed vise.

10. Tap the ring gear with a soft hammer on the gear tooth side until the gear is free of the flange on the right support case.

11. Lift the left support case, thrust washer, oil collector drum, and ring gear from the right support case.

12. Using a soft hammer, remove the high-speed clutch plate from the differential case.

13. Remove the planetary gears and gear pins.

14. Lift the differential assembly and the thrust washer out of the right support case. Mark the two pieces of the differential case for proper assembly.

15. Separate the right and left differential cases. Remove the differential side gears and thrust washers.

16. Remove the differential spider gears, thrust washers, and the differential spider.

17. If the differential support case bearings are to be replaced, they may be removed with a drift. Press on the new bearing so that the ram pressure is against the bearing inner race and not against the roller cage.

18. Hold the pinion shaft flange and remove the pinion shaft nut.

19. Remove the bolts that attach the pinion bearing sleeve to the carrier housing. With a drift, drive the pinion assembly out of the front of the carrier housing.

20. Press the pinion shaft out of the shaft flange and pinion shaft front bearing cone. Remove the bearing preload spacer from the pinion shaft.

21. If the pinion rear bearing cone is to be replaced, remove the pilot bearing, then remove the pinion rear bearing cone with a bearing remover tool.

22. If the pinion bearing cups are to be replaced they may be removed with a small steel bar.

Assembly

1. Press the pilot bearing on the pinion shaft and stake the pinion shaft end at 4 points.

2. Press the pinion rear bearing onto the shaft until seated.

3. To install a new bearing cup, place the pinion bearing retainer sleeve in a press and, using a steel bar, press the cup in the sleeve until it is seated against the recess in the sleeve. Repeat this operation for the other cup.

4. Install the pinion in the bearing retainer sleeve. Place the old spacer on the pinion shaft and install the spacer washer and the pinion front bearing.

5. Check and adjust the pinion bearing preload (see "General Axle Service" section).

6. Install a new oil seal in the seal retainer or bearing sleeve.

7. Press the universal joint flange on the pinion shaft. Install the flat washer and nut and torque to specifications.

8. If the pinion and ring gear are being replaced, adjust the shim pack between the pinion bearing sleeve and carrier housing as explained in the "General Axle Service" section.

9. Install a new gasket in the pin-

ion bearing sleeve, if so equipped.

10. Place the shim pack on the bearing sleeve and install the pinion and sleeve assembly in the carrier housing. Install the sleeve to housing bolts and lock washers and torque to specifications.

11. Place the left half of the differential support case in a vise with the planetary side facing downward. Place one of the differential side gear thrust washers in position in the case. Place the differential left-hand side gear (with the short hub) in position in the case.

12. Install the four differential pinions and thrust washers on the differential spider, then place the spider in the differential case. Place the right side gear and thrust washer on the differential pinions.

13. Place the right half of the differential case in position over the differential spider, then install and torque the case bolts.

14. Insert the four planetary gear pins in the holes in the differential case.

15. Place the four planetary gears on the planetary gear pins. Position the high speed clutch plate on the planetary gear pins with the chamfered teeth facing the planetary gears. Tap the plate in place with a brass hammer.

16. Position the gear support thrust washer in the right gear support case.

17. Place the differential assembly in the gear support case with the planetary end facing upward. Place the ring gear (teeth facing down) over the differential assembly, and engage the planetary gears with the internal teeth on the ring gear.

18. Align the ring gear bolt holes with those in the gear support case. Place the oil collector drum on the ring gear (open side facing gear) with the notches be-

Drive Axles

DIFFERENTIAL CASE BOLTS (8 LONG)
DIFFERENTIAL CASE (RIGHT HAND)
SPIDER
DIFFERENTIAL SPIDER GEARS
DIFFERENTIAL CASE (LEFT HAND)
PLANETARY GEAR PINS
HIGH SPEED CLUTCH PLATE
THRUST WASHER
DIFFERENTIAL CASE BOLTS (4 SHORT)
THRUST WASHER
PLANETARY GEARS
SLIDING CLUTCH GEAR
DIFFERENTIAL SIDE GEAR
THRUST WASHERS
DIFFERENTIAL SIDE GEAR

Planetary and differential assembly (© Eaton Yale & Towne Inc.)

tween the bolt holes in the ring gear.

19. Apply oil to each side of the high-speed clutch plate thrust washer and position on the high-speed clutch plate. Place the left gear support case on the ring gear, and line up the bolt holes in the ring gear and both gear support cases.

20. Install the 6 bolts through the gear support cases with the bolt heads against the flange of the right gear support case. Install and torque the nuts and secure with lock wire.

21. Install the differential assembly in the carrier housing and adjust backlash and preload (see "General Axle Service" section).

22. Check and adjust the gear tooth contact pattern.

23. Install the sliding clutch gear and attach the shift fork to it. Install the shift fork shaft through the hole in the differential carrier and into the shift fork. Install the shift fork shaft plugs. Place the shift fork seal and retainer on the shift fork. Shift the axle into the low range.

24. Place the oil distributor and spring in the carrier. Install the oil distributor plug and gasket.

Drive Pinion Adjustment Specifications

Axle Models		Specifications for Drive Pinion Bearing Preload Adjustment				Drive Pinion Position Adjustment	
		Pinion Bearing Spacer Thickness	Drive Pinion Nut Torque Setting (ft.-lbs.)	Arbor Press Preload Pressure Setting (tons)	Spring Scale Reading (pounds) To obtain 15 to 35 in.-lbs. Torque	Pinion Bearing Cage Shim Pack	Depth Gauge Setting
2-speed Axles	13802, 15201	0.530	225-350	4-5	7-16	0.040 + 0.250	3.6244
	16802, 16244	0.528	325-450	5-6	7-16	0.043	4.125
	17201, 17221	0.638	400-600	7-8	6-14	0.037	4.062
	18201, 18221	0.638	400-600	7-8	6-14	0.037	4.4062
	19221	0.188	600-800	10-11	5-11	0.025	4.7812
Planetary Double Reduction Axles	18301	0.638	400-600	7-8	6-14	0.037	4.4062

Torque Chart

Description		Ft.-Lbs.
Differential bearing adjuster lock	Cap screw 9/16-12 (Grade 5)	115-125
	Cap screw 5/8-11 (Grade 5)	160-175
	Cap screw 3/4-10 (Grade 5)	275-300
Differential bearing cap to carrier	Cap screw 5/8-11 (Grade 7)	150-170
	Cap screw 11/16-11 (Grade 7)	210-250
	Cap screw 13/16-10 (Grade 7)	350-425
	Cap screw 7/8-9 (Grade 7)	425-500
Differential carrier to axle housing	Cap screw 7/16-14 (Grade 5)	45-55
	Cap screw 1/2-13 (Grade 5)	75-85
	Cap screw 5/8-11 (Grade 5)	160-175
	Stud nut 1/2-20 (Grade 8)	110-130
	Stud nut 5/8-18 (Grade 8)	220-240
Differential case (axle)	Cap screw 7/16-14 (Grade 7)	55-65
	Cap screw 1/2-13 (Grade 7)	90-105
	Cap screw 9/16-12 (Grade 7)	135-155
Ring gear support case	Bolt/nut 7/16-20 (Grade 7)	60-80
	Bolt/nut 1/2-20 (Grade 7)	90-100
	Bolt/nut 9/16-18 (Grade 7)	130-150
	Bolt/nut 5/8-18 (Grade 7)	190-210
	Locknut 5/8-18	165-190

Description		Ft.-Lbs.
Drive pinion	Nut 1-20	225-350
	Nut 1-1/8-18	325-450
	Nut 1-1/4-12	400-600
	Nut 1-1/2-18	500-700
	Nut 1-3/4-12	600-800
Drive pinion bearing cage to carrier	Cap screw 9/16-12 (Grade 5)	115-125
	Cap screw 9/16-12 (Grade 7)	135-155
	Cap screw 5/8-11 (Grade 5)	160-175
	Cap screw 5/8-11 (Grade 7)	170-190
Inspection cover to axle housing	Cap screw 7/16-14 (Grade 3)	35-50
	Cap screw 7/16-14 (Grade 5)	45-55
Shift units to carrier (2-speed)	Stud nut 7/16-20 (Grade 5)	35-45
	Stud nut 1/2-20 (Grade 5)	85-95
Cover plate to carrier (pdr) (At shift unit opening)	Cap screw 7/16-14 (Grade 5)	45-55
	Cap screw 1/2-13 (Grade 5)	75-85
Oil pickup through to carrier	Nylock screw 1/4-20 (Grade 5)	35-50 in.-lbs.

Ford Semi-Floating Single Speed Axle, Removable Carrier Type

This is a conventional type axle used on light duty Ford trucks. The axle design uses a removable carrier with the assembly bolted to the axle housing. The axle uses hypoid type gears and has the pinion gear mounted below the center line on the ring gear. The pinion gear is supported by two bearings in front of the gear and one behind. It is important to refer to the tag showing the axle and model number which is secured to the housing to obtain proper replacement parts.

Carrier Assembly Removal

1. With the vehicle raised on a lift, remove the axle shafts from the housing.
2. Remove the drive shaft from the carrier assembly.
3. With a drain pan under the axle, remove the retaining bolts from the carrier and drain the gear lube.
4. Remove the carrier assembly from the axle.

Installation

1. Clean the surfaces of the carrier and the axle housing. Install a new gasket.
2. Position the carrier assembly on the studs in the housing and install the retaining nuts. Torque the nuts to 30-40 ft. lbs.
3. Install the drive shaft and torque the bolts to 13-17 ft. lbs.
4. Install the axles in the housing and secure.
5. Fill the axle housing to the proper level with gear lube and road test for proper operation.

Differential Case Removal and Disassembly

1. Remove the carrier assembly from the axle housing and mount the carrier in a holding fixture.
2. Mark the bearing caps and adjusting nuts so they may be installed in their original positions when assembling.
3. Remove the adjusting nut locks, bearing caps and adjusting nuts.
4. Lift the differential assembly out of the carrier. Using a bearing puller, remove the side bearings from the differential case.
5. Mark the side of the case, the ring gear and the cover so they can be installed in their original positions.
6. Remove the bolts that retain the ring gear to the case and using a soft hammer, tap the ring gear from the case.
7. Using a drift, drive the lock pin from the pinion shaft and seperate the halves of the differential case.
8. Drive the pinion shaft out of the case using a brass drift and remove the thrust washers and gears.

Drive Pinion and Bearing Retainer Removal and Disassembly

1. With a holding fixture installed on the flange, remove the pinion nut and washer. Leave the holding fixture on the flange and using a puller, remove the flange from the pinion shaft.
2. Using a seal puller, remove the pinion seal from the retainer assembly.
3. Remove the bolts from the retainer assembly and lift the retainer from the carrier. Measure the thickness of the shim that was between the retainer and the carrier assembly. Record the result.
4. Install a piece of hose on the pinion pilot bearing surface in front of the pinion gear. Mount the retainer assembly in a press and press the pinion gear out of the retainer.
5. Mount the pinion shaft in a press and press the rear bearing from the pinion shaft.

Pinion Bearing Cup Replacement

1. With the retainer assembly mounted in a press, using the proper tool, press the front and rear bearing cups from the assembly.
2. Check the inside surfaces of the retainer for any nicks, dirt or distortion.
3. Install the new cups by pressing them into place with the proper tool. When the cups are installed, make sure they are seated in the retainer by trying to fit a .0015 in. feeler gauge, between the cup and the bottom of the bore.

Pilot Bearing Replacement

1. Using a bearing driver, drive the bearing and retainer out of the carrier assembly.
2. Using the same tool, drive the new bearing into place until the

OLD PINION MARKING

New Pinion Marking	+15	+14	+13	+12	+11	+10	+9	+8	+7	+6	+5	+4	+3	+2	+1	0	-1	-2	-3	-4	-5	-6	-7	-8	-9	-10	-11	-12	-13	-14	-15
+15	0	-001	-002	-003	-004	-005	-006	-007	-008	-009	-010	-011	-012	-013	-014	-015	-016	-017	-018	-019	-020	-021	-022	-023	-024	-025	-026	-027	-028	-029	-030
+14	+001	0	-001	-002	-003	-004	-005	-006	-007	-008	-009	-010	-011	-012	-013	-014	-015	-016	-017	-018	-019	-020	-021	-022	-023	-024	-025	-026	-027	-028	-029
+13	+002	+001	0	-001	-002	-003	-004	-005	-006	-007	-008	-009	-010	-011	-012	-013	-014	-015	-016	-017	-018	-019	-020	-021	-022	-023	-024	-025	-026	-027	-028
+12	+003	+002	+001	0	-001	-002	-003	-004	-005	-006	-007	-008	-009	-010	-011	-012	-013	-014	-015	-016	-017	-018	-019	-020	-021	-022	-023	-024	-025	-026	-027
+11	+004	+003	+002	+001	0	-001	-002	-003	-004	-005	-006	-007	-008	-009	-010	-011	-012	-013	-014	-015	-016	-017	-018	-019	-020	-021	-022	-023	-024	-025	-026
+10	+005	+004	+003	+002	+001	0	-001	-002	-003	-004	-005	-006	-007	-008	-009	-010	-011	-012	-013	-014	-015	-016	-017	-018	-019	-020	-021	-022	-023	-024	-025
+9	+006	+005	+004	+003	+002	+001	0	-001	-002	-003	-004	-005	-006	-007	-008	-009	-010	-011	-012	-013	-014	-015	-016	-017	-018	-019	-020	-021	-022	-023	-024
+8	+007	+006	+005	+004	+003	+002	+001	0	-001	-002	-003	-004	-005	-006	-007	-008	-009	-010	-011	-012	-013	-014	-015	-016	-017	-018	-019	-020	-021	-022	-023
+7	+008	+007	+006	+005	+004	+003	+002	+001	0	-001	-002	-003	-004	-005	-006	-007	-008	-009	-010	-011	-012	-013	-014	-015	-016	-017	-018	-019	-020	-021	-022
+6	+009	+008	+007	+006	+005	+004	+003	+002	+001	0	-001	-002	-003	-004	-005	-006	-007	-008	-009	-010	-011	-012	-013	-014	-015	-016	-017	-018	-019	-020	-021
+5	+010	+009	+008	+007	+006	+005	+004	+003	+002	+001	0	-001	-002	-003	-004	-005	-006	-007	-008	-009	-010	-011	-012	-013	-014	-015	-016	-017	-018	-019	-020
+4	+011	+010	+009	+008	+007	+006	+005	+004	+003	+002	+001	0	-001	-002	-003	-004	-005	-006	-007	-008	-009	-010	-011	-012	-013	-014	-015	-016	-017	-018	-019
+3	+012	+011	+010	+009	+008	+007	+006	+005	+004	+003	+002	+001	0	-001	-002	-003	-004	-005	-006	-007	-008	-009	-010	-011	-012	-013	-014	-015	-016	-017	-018
+2	+013	+012	+011	+010	+009	+008	+007	+006	+005	+004	+003	+002	+001	0	-001	-002	-003	-004	-005	-006	-007	-008	-009	-010	-011	-012	-013	-014	-015	-016	-017
+1	+014	+013	+012	+011	+010	+009	+008	+007	+006	+005	+004	+003	+002	+001	0	-001	-002	-003	-004	-005	-006	-007	-008	-009	-010	-011	-012	-013	-014	-015	-016
0	+015	+014	+013	+012	+011	+010	+009	+008	+007	+006	+005	+004	+003	+002	+001	0	-001	-002	-003	-004	-005	-006	-007	-008	-009	-010	-011	-012	-013	-014	-015
-1	+016	+015	+014	+013	+012	+011	+010	+009	+008	+007	+006	+005	+004	+003	+002	+001	0	-001	-002	-003	-004	-005	-006	-007	-008	-009	-010	-011	-012	-013	-014
-2	+017	+016	+015	+014	+013	+012	+011	+010	+009	+008	+007	+006	+005	+004	+003	+002	+001	0	-001	-002	-003	-004	-005	-006	-007	-008	-009	-010	-011	-012	-013
-3	+018	+017	+016	+015	+014	+013	+012	+011	+010	+009	+008	+007	+006	+005	+004	+003	+002	+001	0	-001	-002	-003	-004	-005	-006	-007	-008	-009	-010	-011	-012
-4	+019	+018	+017	+016	+015	+014	+013	+012	+011	+010	+009	+008	+007	+006	+005	+004	+003	+002	+001	0	-001	-002	-003	-004	-005	-006	-007	-008	-009	-010	-011
-5	+020	+019	+018	+017	+016	+015	+014	+013	+012	+011	+010	+009	+008	+007	+006	+005	+004	+003	+002	+001	0	-001	-002	-003	-004	-005	-006	-007	-008	-009	-010
-6	+021	+020	+019	+018	+017	+016	+015	+014	+013	+012	+011	+010	+009	+008	+007	+006	+005	+004	+003	+002	+001	0	-001	-002	-003	-004	-005	-006	-007	-008	-009
-7	+022	+021	+020	+019	+018	+017	+016	+015	+014	+013	+012	+011	+010	+009	+008	+007	+006	+005	+004	+003	+002	+001	0	-001	-002	-003	-004	-005	-006	-007	-008
-8	+023	+022	+021	+020	+019	+018	+017	+016	+015	+014	+013	+012	+011	+010	+009	+008	+007	+006	+005	+004	+003	+002	+001	0	-001	-002	-003	-004	-005	-006	-007
-9	+024	+023	+022	+021	+020	+019	+018	+017	+016	+015	+014	+013	+012	+011	+010	+009	+008	+007	+006	+005	+004	+003	+002	+001	0	-001	-002	-003	-004	-005	-006
-10	+025	+024	+023	+022	+021	+020	+019	+018	+017	+016	+015	+014	+013	+012	+011	+010	+009	+008	+007	+006	+005	+004	+003	+002	+001	0	-001	-002	-003	-004	-005
-11	+026	+025	+024	+023	+022	+021	+020	+019	+018	+017	+016	+015	+014	+013	+012	+011	+010	+009	+008	+007	+006	+005	+004	+003	+002	+001	0	-001	-002	-003	-004
-12	+027	+026	+025	+024	+023	+022	+021	+020	+019	+018	+017	+016	+015	+014	+013	+012	+011	+010	+009	+008	+007	+006	+005	+004	+003	+002	+001	0	-001	-002	-003
-13	+028	+027	+026	+025	+024	+023	+022	+021	+020	+019	+018	+017	+016	+015	+014	+013	+012	+011	+010	+009	+008	+007	+006	+005	+004	+003	+002	+001	0	-001	-002
-14	+029	+028	+027	+026	+025	+024	+023	+022	+021	+020	+019	+018	+017	+016	+015	+014	+013	+012	+011	+010	+009	+008	+007	+006	+005	+004	+003	+002	+001	0	-001
-15	+030	+029	+028	+027	+026	+025	+024	+023	+022	+021	+020	+019	+018	+017	+016	+015	+014	+013	+012	+011	+010	+009	+008	+007	+006	+005	+004	+003	+002	+001	0

driver bottoms against the case.

3. Drive a new retainer into place with the concave side up.

Drive Pinion and Bearing Retainer Assembly and Installation

1. Mount the pinion gear in a press and press the rear bearing into place.

2. Install the bearing spacer, bearing retainer and front bearing on the pinion shaft and press them into place. Be careful not to crush the bearing spacer.

3. Install a new O-ring in the groove in the retainer assembly. Do not twist the O-ring when fitting it into place.

4. Lubricate both pinion bearings.

5. Check the thickness of the original shim that was recorded earlier. Located on the head of the pinion gear is the shim adjustment number. Compare the number on the old pinion with the one on the new pinion. Refer to the table which indicates the amount of change to the original shim thickness for proper operation.

6. Install the new shim on the hous-

THRUST WASHER — PINION SHAFT

THRUST WASHER

PINION SHAFT LOCK PIN

Differential case assembly

ing and install the pinion and retainer assembly, being careful not to damage the O-ring.

7. Install the bearing retainer bolts and torque them to 30-40 ft.lbs.

8. Using a seal driver, install a new pinion seal in the retainer assembly.

9. Position a holding tool on the flange and install the flange on the pinion shaft. With the holding tool still in place, install the washer and nut on the pinion shaft and torque the nut to 175 ft.lbs. Check the pinion bearing preload. The preload should be 8-14 in.lbs. for used bearings and 22-32 in.lbs. for new bearings. *Do Not* overtighten the nut. *Do Not* back off the nut to obtain the proper preload. If the 175 ft.lbs. initial torque was too much, the collapsible spacer must be replaced. Tighten the pinion only enough to obtain the right preload torque.

Differential Case Assembly and Installation

1. Lubricate all of the differential parts with gear lube before assembling.

2. Install a side gear and thrust washer in the case bore. Using a soft hammer, drive the pinion shaft into the case far enough to hold a pinion thrust washer and gear. Place the second pinion thrust washer and gear in position and carefully tap the pinion shaft into place. Be sure to line

up the holes for the lock pin in the pinion shaft.

3. With the second side gear and thrust washer in place, install the cover on the differential case. Drive the pinion lock pin into place. Insert an axle shaft spline into the side gear and check for free rotation of the gears.

4. Install two, two inch long 7/16 (N.F.) bolts through the differential case and thread them a little way into the ring gear. These will act as a guide when installing the ring gear on the case. Tap the ring gear into place.

5. Remove the guide pins and install the ring gear bolts. Tighten the bolts evenly to 65-85 ft.lbs.

6. If the differential bearings were removed, install the assembly in a press and press the new bearings into place.

7. Coat the bearing bores in the carrier with gear lube and install the bearing cups on the bearings. Place the differential assembly in the carrier.

8. Slide the differential case in the carrier bore until there is a slight amount of backlash between the gears.

9. Install the adjusting nuts in the carrier so that they just contact the bearing cups. The nuts should be engaged about the same number of threads on each side.

10. Position the bearing caps in the carrier. Be careful to line up the marks. Install the cap bolts and torque them to 70-80 ft.lbs. Make sure the adjusting nuts

turn freely as the bolts are being tightened.

11. Adjust the backlash and bearing preload as follows:

   a. Loosen the bearing cap bolts then retighten them to 35 ft.-lbs.

   b. Loosen the adjusting nut on the pinion side so that it is away from the bearing cup. Tighten the nut on the opposite side so that the ring gear is forced into the pinion with no backlash.

   c. Recheck the nut on the pinion side to make sure it is still loose. Now tighten this nut until it contacts the bearing cup. After is contacts the cup, turn it two more notches.

   d. Rotate the ring gear several times in each direction. This helps to seat the bearings in the cups.

   e. Again loosen the nut on the pinion side. If there is any backlash between the gears, tighten the nut on the ring gear side until the backlash is removed.

   f. Install a dial indicator on the carrier assembly. Tighten the nut on the pinion side until it just contacts the cup. With the dial indicator set at zero, tighten the pinion side nut until the case is spread .008-.012 in. with new bearings and .005-.008 in. with old bearings. As this preload is applied the ring gear is forced away from the pinion and usually results in the correct backlash.

   g. Mount the dial indicator on the ring gear and check the gear for backlash. Make sure the bearing caps are torqued to 75-85 ft.lbs.

   h. The backlash should be between .008-.012 in. If the backlash is not correct, loosen one nut and tighten the other an equal amount to move the ring gear in or out to correct the measurement. When making final adjustments, always move the adjusting nuts in a tightening direction. To do this, if a nut had to be loosened one notch, loosen it two notches and tighten it one. This makes certain the nut is in contact with the cup and will not shift when the vehicle is in operation.

   i. Coat the ring gear teeth with a marking compound and check the tooth pattern. If the pattern is not correct make the necessary changes to bring it into adjustment.

12. Install the carrier assembly in the vehicle and road test for proper operation.

Single-Speed, Single Reduction Rockwell-Standard

HOUSING
THRUST WASHER
SPIDER
VENT
ADJUSTER NUT
THRUST WASHER
LOCK NUT
DIFFERENTIAL CASE
SIDE GEAR
PINION
AXLE SHAFT
GASKET
LOCKWASHER
DRAIN PLUG
BEARING
GASKET
ADJUSTER
LOCK
CAP AND CARRIER HOUSING
DOWEL
SNAP RING
PINION BEARING
RING GEAR AND PINION ASSEMBLY
FILLER PLUG
PINION LOCATING SHIM
REAR BEARING
SPACER
PINION BEARING RETAINER
FRONT BEARING
GASKET
SEAL
WASHER
SEAL RETAINER
FLANGE

single-speed, single reduction rear axle (© Ford Motor Co.)

Description

This rear axle is a full-floating type with a hypoid drive gear and pinion, and uses a four-pinion differential assembly. The straddle mounted pinion has two tapered roller bearings in front of the pinion teeth and a straight roller bearing behind the pinion teeth. The differential carrier assembly can be removed while the axle remains in the truck.

Differential Carrier Assembly

Removal

1. Remove axle shafts.
2. Drain lubricant. Disconnect propeller shaft at pinion shaft yoke.
3. Remove carrier from axle housing and clean thoroughly.

Disassembly

1. Punch mark carrier leg, bearing cap, and bearing adjusting nut to assist in reassembly.
2. Remove screws, adjusting nut locks, bearing caps and adjusting nuts.
3. Loosen lock nut and back off drive gear thrust block adjusting screw.
4. Lift differential out of carrier and remove thrust block from end of adjusting screw inside of carrier.
5. Punch mark differential case halves for correct reassembly alignment and separate case halves.
6. Remove pinion shaft, pinions, side gears, thrust washers and differential bearing cones.
7. To remove drive gear, carefully center punch each rivet in center of rivet head. Use a drill 1/32 inch smaller than the body of rivet to drill through the rivet head. Press out rivets.
8. Remove pinion shaft nut, washer and yoke. Driving yoke off will cause runout.
9. Remove pinion bearing cover and oil seal assembly and, using puller screws, remove bearing cage. Using a pinch bar to remove cage will damage shims. Driving pinion from inner end with a drift will damage bearing lock ring groove.
10. Wire bearing cage shim pack together to facilitate adjustment when reassembling.
11. Tap pinion shaft out of cage with soft mallet or press shaft from cage. Remove bearing from cage.
12. Remove spacers and inner bearing from shaft.
13. Remove pinion shaft rear pilot bearing lock ring; and then bearing.
14. Remove oil seal assembly from bearing cover.
15. Clean all parts thoroughly in a suitable solvent and blow dry with compressed air. Do not spin bearings with air pressure as they might score due to absence of any lubrication.

Exploded view of side gear and pinion assembly
(© Chrysler Corp.)

Inspect all parts for wear or roughness and replace if necessary. (For details, see "cleaning" and "inspection" in "General Axle Service" section).

Inspect all machined surfaces for nicks, burrs or scratches.

Assembly

1. Press drive pinion inner bearing cone firmly against pinion shoulder.
2. Press rear pilot bearings firmly against pinion shoulder and install lock ring into pinion shaft groove.
3. Press bearing cups firmly against bearing cage shoulders.
4. Lubricate pinion bearings with SAE 90 oil and insert pinion and bearing assembly into pinion cage.
5. Place original spacers on pinion shaft, and install front bearing and press firmly against spacers. Rotate cage several revolutions to assure normal bearing contact. If a press is not available, install pinion yoke and nut and torque to specifications.
6. While the assembly is in the press under pressure or pinion nut torqued to specifications, check pinion bearing pre-load. The correct pressures and torque for checking pre-load are:

Pinion Shaft Thread Size and Number of Threads Per Inch	Required Pressure to Obtain Correct Pre-Load lbs.	Required Torque to Obtain Correct Pre-Load ft. lbs.
1 in. x 20	12,000	300- 400
1¼ in. x 18	22,000	700- 900
1½ in. x 12	28,000	800-1100
1½ in. x 18	28,000	800-1100
1¾ in. x 12	28,000	800-1100

7. Wrap a soft wire around cage and pull on horizontal line with pound scale when determining pinion bearing pre-load, first measure diameter of the pinion cage. Assuming cage diameter is 6 inches, the pulling radius would be 3 inches; therefore, 5 pounds pull on the scale would equal 15 inch-pounds pre-load.
8. Use rotating torque, not starting torque. If rotating torque is not within 5 to 15 inch-pounds, use thinner spacer to increase pre-load or thicker spacer to decrease pre-load. Torque must be near low limit inch-pounds with original pinion bearings and near high limit when using new bearings. Remove yoke and install new oil seal.
9. Lubricate pinion shaft oil seal and lightly coat outer edge of seal body with non-hardening sealing compound. Press seal against cover shoulder. Install new gasket and bearing cover.
10. Install pinion yoke, washer and nut. Place pinion and cage as-

Checking pinion bearing pre-load (© G.M.C.)

sembly over carrier studs, hold yoke and tighten nut to specified torque. Install cotter key without backing off nut to align cotter key holes.

11. Place original shim pack on carrier studs with thin shims on both sides to create maximum sealing. Position pinion and cage assembly over studs and tap into position with soft mallet. Install lock washers and nuts. Tighten nuts to specified torque. If a new pinion is being installed, consult the "General Axle Service" section for correct procedure.
12. Rivet drive gear to differential case using new rivets. Rivets should not be heated, but always upset cold. When correct rivet is used, head being formed will be at least ⅛ inch larger in diameter than rivet hole and approximately the same height as performed head. Avoid excessive pressure as it might distort case holes and cause gear eccentricity. Unless shops are equipped to do cold upsetting of rivets properly, replacement bolts should be used.
13. Lubricate differential case inner walls and all component parts with rear axle gear lubricant during assembly.
14. Install thrust washer and side gear in drive gear half of case. Assemble pinions and thrust washers on pinion shaft and position this assembly in the case. Place other side gear and thrust washer in position on the four pinions.
15. Install other case half with mating marks aligned. Draw case down evenly with four bolts. Check for free rotation of differential gears and correct if necessary. Install and torque remaining bolts and then lock wire.
16. Press differential bearings squarely and firmly on differential case halves. Differential bearing cup fit in the pedestal bores should be checked before installing assembly in carrier.
17. Temporarily install bearing cups, threaded adjusting nuts or split ring and bearing caps. Tighten cap bolts to specified

torque. Bearing cups must be of a hand push fit in the bores; if not, the bores must be enlarged with a scraper or emery cloth. Use a blued bearing cup as a gauge to check each fit.

18. Lubricate differential bearings and cups with axle lubricant. Place cups over bearings and position assembly in carrier housing. Turn adjusting nuts hand tight against bearing cups.
19. Install bearing caps in correct location as marked, and tap lightly into position. Be sure caps fit over adjusting nuts properly and are not cross-threaded. Some backlash must be present between drive gear and pinion. Install and torque bearing cap bolts.
20. Attach a dial indicator to the carrier with the pointer resting against back face of drive gear. Eliminate all end play by turning right adjusting nut clockwise. Rotate drive gear and check runout. If runout exceeds .008 inch, remove differential and check the cause.
21. Tighten adjusting nuts, one notch each, to pre-load differential bearings.
22. Position dial indicator so the pointer rests against face of one of the drive gear teeth. Check backlash between drive gear and pinion at 90 degree intervals of rotation.
23. Adjust backlash to .006-.012 inch (.006 preferred, especially on new gears). When adjusting backlash, back off one adjusting nut and advance opposite nut the same amount to maintain bearing pre-load.
24. If the "Pinion Setting Procedures" (Depth Gauge Method) for adjusting pinion depth (see "General Axle Service" section) was not used, adjust gears using the Tooth Contact Method. Then proceed to step 25. If Depth Gauge Method was used, go directly to step 25.
25. Torque bearing cap bolts and install and torque adjusting nut locks and cap screws and lock wire.
26. Hold drive gear thrust block on rear face of gear with heavy grease, rotate gear until hole in thrust block aligns with adjusting screw hole in carrier. Install adjusting screw and lock nut, tighten screw enough to locate thrust block firmly against back face of gear. Back off adjusting screw ¼ turn to create .010-.015 inch clearance and lock securely with nut. Recheck to assure minimum clearance of .010 inch during full rotation of drive gear.

Drive Axles

Installation

1. Install a new gasket on axle housing flange. Start carrier into clean housing and hold in place with four equally spaced washers and nuts. Tighten nuts alternately to draw carrier evenly into housing. Install and torque carrier flange lock washers and nuts.
2. Install axle drive shafts and connect universal joint at pinion flange.
3. Fill axle housing to proper level and road test vehicle.

Torque Chart

Carrier to housing screw or stud nut		
	1/2-20	94-102
	5/8-18	186-205
	3/4-16	325-360

Differential case alignment marks (© G.M.C.)

Differential case bolt	1/2-20	94-102
	9/16-18	132-145
	5/8-18	186-205
	3/4-16	325-360
Differential bearing cap bolt	5/8-11-18	127-140
	3/4-10-16	230-250
	7/8-9	345-370
	7/8-14	375-415
	1-12	555-615
Differential bearing adjuster lock bolt	5/16-18	15-17
	1/2-13	85-91
	9/16-12	120-129
	5/8-11	168-180
Pinion shaft yoke nut	1-20	300-400
	1-1/4-18	700-900
	1-1/2-18	800-1100
	1-1/2-12	800-1100
	1-3/4-12	800-1100
Shaft flange stud	7/16-20	52-58

Rockwell-Standard Bearing Preload

Axle Model	Pinion Shaft Nut-Thread Size and Torque Limits (Foot-Pounds)		Press Ram Pressure for Preload Check (Tons)	Pinion and Cross Shaft Bearing Preload (Inch-Pounds)	Backlash Limits (Inches)	Differential Bearing Preload Adjusting Nut Notches Tighten from Zero End Play (each Adjusting Nut)
	1-20	300-400	6	5-15	0.005-0.015	1
Single-speed	1¼ x 18	700-900	11	5-15	0.005-0.015	1
Single reduction	1¼ x 18	800-1100	14	5-15	0.005-0.015	1
	1½ x 12	800-1100	14	5-15	0.005-0.015	1
	1½ x 18	800-1100	14	5-15	0.005-0.015	1

Rockwell-Standard Single-Speed Double Reduction Axles

Description

This axle includes a hypoid helical drive and a two-step gear reduction. The first reduction is through the hypoid pinion and ring gears with the second reduction through the helical gears. The helical pinion gear engages with the helical drive gear. The axle housings are one-piece with full-floating axle shafts.

Disassembly of Rear Axle

Differential Carrier

1. Before disassembling, inspect the unit as described in the "cleaning" and "inspection" paragraph of the "General Axle Service" section.
2. Punch-mark one differential bearing cap and the corresponding carrier leg. This will be an aid to proper reassembly.
3. Remove the locking wires and bolts from both bearing caps and remove both bearing adjuster nuts.
4. Back off both bearing adjusters one full turn to reduce bearing pre-load. Remove both bearing caps and adjusters and wire together.

5. Lift the differential out of the carrier.
6. Remove the U-joint flange nut and then remove flange with a rawhide mallet. If this is unsuccessful, the flange can be pressed off when the hypoid pinion cage is being disassembled.
7. Using two 3 inch 38—16 puller screws, remove the cage and pinion gear from the carrier.
8. Remove the pinion adjusting shims from the carrier and re-use if the same hypoid gear set is to be used again when the carrier is assembled.
9. Place a wooden block under the helical pinion gear to support the cross shaft. Then remove the bolts from the cross shaft bearing cap mounted on the differential carrier—opposite the hypoid ring gear.
10. Force the bearing cap out of the carrier about ¼ inch by prying the hypoid ring gear away from the side of the carrier.
11. Place metal strips under both puller screw holes in the bearing cap and, using puller screws, hold them in place against the adjusting shims. Do not tighten

the screws directly onto the adjusting shims.
12. Tighten the puller screws evenly against the metal strips, and remove the bearing cap and the adjusting shims from the carrier.
13. Carefully remove the hypoid ring gear and cross shaft from the carrier.
14. Replace either cross shaft bearing cup if necessary. Remove the damaged or worn cup from the bearing cap with a suitable puller. To operate the cup in the bearing cap, tap the cap out of the carrier about ¼ inch with a soft drift and remove from the carrier.

Cross Shaft

1. Remove the locking wire, two screws, and the bearing retaining plate from the hypoid ring gear end of the cross shaft.
2. Press the cross shaft out of the ring gear and the bearing next to the gear. Remove the Woodruff key that holds the gear on the shaft.
3. Press the remaining bearing from the cross shaft.

Single-speed, double reduction power flow
(© Rockwell Stand. Div.)

Differential Gear and Case

1. Mount the differential in a soft-jawed vise. Then, if necessary, remove both differential side bearings.
2. Punch-mark each case half to aid proper assembly.
3. Separate the helical drive gear and the two case halves. If rivets are binding these parts, center—punch the head of each rivet followed by a 1/8 inch pilot hole at each punch-mark, and then a 1/2 inch hole drilled 1/2 inch deep and complete by pressing out all the rivets with a 1/2 inch punch. *Do not attempt to remove the rivets with a hammer and chisel.*
4. Remove the spider, pinion gears, thrust washers, and side gears.

Pinion Cage

1. Press the hypoid pinion gear shaft out of the pinion cage, and then remove the bearing preload spacer from the shaft.
2. Press the rear bearing from the shaft and pull the rear bearing cup from the pinion cage.
3. Press the front bearing cup and the oil seal from the pinion cage and clean and inspect all parts as explained in the "General Axle Service" section.

Assembly of Rear Axle

Pinion Cage

1. Install the rear bearing on the hypoid pinion gear shaft against the gear shoulder. Use a 3 inch sleeve about one inch long under the bearing race so that the press ram won't damage roller cage.
2. Press the rear bearing cup *firmly against the shoulder in the pinion cage.*
3. Install the front bearing cup in the pinion cage making sure that the cup seats firmly against the shoulder in the cage.
4. Coat the pinion rear bearing with axle lubricant, and position the pinion gear in the cage.
5. Position the original bearing preload spacer on the pinion gear shaft and press the pinion front bearing onto the shaft against the spacer. Use a 3 inch sleeve about 5 inches long over the bearing race so that the press ram doesn't damage the bearing roller cage.
6. Rotate the pinion cage several times to be sure that the bearings are properly seated. Then check the pinion bearing preload as explained in the "General Axle Service" section. If the preload is too low, install a thinner spacer under the front bearing. To decrease the preload, install a

Removing cross shaft bearing cap
and positioning metal strips
(© Rockwell Stand. Div.)

thicker spacer under the bearing.
7. When the preload is correct, install the oil seal in the pinion cage.

Differential Gear and Case

1. Check the mating surfaces of the differential case halves and the helical drive gear to be sure they are clean and free of burrs. Then coat all differential parts and the inner walls of the case, with axle lubricant.
2. Install the differential side bearings, making sure they are properly seated. Use a 3 1/4 inch sleeve about one inch long over the bearing race so that the force of the press ram doesn't damage the bearing roller cage.
3. Position a thrust washer and a side gear in one of the differential case halves. Then place the spider, the pinion gears, and their thrust washers in position. Install the remaining side gear and thrust washer in the case.

Differential gear and case components
(© Rockwell Stand. Div.)

HYPOID PINION GEAR — REAR BEARING — SPACER — FRONT BEARING — BEARING CUP — OIL SEAL — BEARING CUP — PINION CAGE

Hypoid pinion gear and cage (exploded view)
(© Rockwell Stand. Div.)

4. Position the helical drive gear and install the other case half, aligning the marks on both halves.
5. Install 6 bolts in alternate holes around the case on the side of the gear having the smaller offset. Tighten the bolts and nuts enough to draw the gear and both case halves together. Then check the rotation of the side gears and pinion gears.
6. Install the remaining 6 bolts and nuts, and torque them evenly to specifications and lock wire.

Cross Shaft

1. Place the Woodruff key (tapered end toward pinion gear) in the cross shaft. Then press the hypoid ring gear on the shaft—seating it against the shaft shoulder.
2. Carefully press the shaft into the bearing, seating the bearing against the shoulder.
3. Install the remaining bearing on the other end of the shaft. Use a 3 inch sleeve about one inch long over the bearing race so that the press ram won't damage the bearing roller cage.
4. Install the bearing retaining plate and torque and wire the screws.
5. Press the cross shaft bearing cups into the bearing caps. Be sure that the cups are properly seated against the shoulders in the cap bores.

Differential Carrier

1. Coat all parts with axle lubri-

cant before assembly.
2. Position the original shim pack on the right cross shaft bearing cap and install and torque the cap on the differential carrier.
3. Install the cross shaft in the carrier so that the end of the shaft opposite the hypoid ring gear enters the bore of the left bearing cap. The right bearing should enter and seat in its bearing cap. Place a wooden block under the helical pinion gear to support the cross shaft.
4. Position the original shim pack on the left cross shaft bearing cap and install and torque the cap on the differential carrier.
5. Rotate the cross shaft to test for normal bearing contact. Then check the cross shaft bearing preload. *Do not read the pull required to start the cross shaft rotating. Read only the steady rotating pull on the scale.* To change the scale reading into in-lbs. torque, multiply the scale reading by one-half the diameter of the helical pinion gear at the point where the cord is wound around the gear.
6. If the bearing preload torque is not within 5-15 in-lbs., add shims to decrease the preload, or remove shims to increase the preload. *To prevent changing the hypoid ring gear backlash setting, change shims only at the bearing cap opposite the ring gear.*

7. Install the pinion cage-filler hole at top. Install and torque the bolts and lock washers. Use the original shim pack between the pinion cage and the differential carrier if the original hypoid gears (ring gear and pinion set) are used. If new hypoid gears are installed, follow the shim selection procedure in the "General Axle Service" section.
8. Install the U-joint flange, torque the nut and install cotter pin.
9. The backlash can be adjusted by transferring shims from one cross shaft bearing cap to the other. To move the hypoid ring gear away from the hypoid pinion gear, transfer shims from the right cap to the left cap. To move the ring gear closer to the pinion gear, transfer shims from left to right. For each 0.010 inch movement of the ring gear, the backlash changes about 0.008 inch. Adjust backlash to 0.010 inch and check the gear tooth contact pattern. After obtaining a good pattern at 0.010 backlash, increase backlash to 0.020-0.026 inch regardless of the backlash marking on the ring gear.
10. Check and adjust the tooth contact pattern (see the "General Axle Service" section).
11. Check the fit of the differential side bearing cups and the bearing adjusters in the bearing caps. The adjusters should thread freely into the caps, and they should move the bearing cups into the bores with the cap bolts tightened to normal torque. If the cups do not move when the adjusters are hand tightened, remove the caps and clean the bearing surfaces.
12. Position a bearing cup on each differential side bearing. Then place the differential on the carrier so that the bearing cups rest in the carrier legs centering the drive gear on the helical pinion gear.
13. Place the bearing adjusters on

BEARING CAP — BEARING ADJUSTER — BEARING ADJUSTER LOCK — CAP BOLTS — Adapter — LOCATING MARKS

Installation of bearing caps
(© Rockwell Stand. Div.)

Spring Scale — HELICAL PINION GEAR

Checking cross shaft bearing preload
(© Rockwell Stand. Div.)

HELICAL DRIVE GEAR — Dial Indicator — Pinch Bar

Determining differential end play
(© Rockwell Stand. Div.)

Bearing Preload

Axle Model	Pinion Shaft Nut-Thread Size and Torque Limits (Foot-Pounds)		Press Ram Pressure for Preload Check (Tons)	Pinion and Cross Shaft Bearing Preload (Inch-Pounds)	Backlash Limits (Inches)	Differential Bearing Preload Adjusting Nut Notches Tighten from Zero End Play (each Adjusting Nut)
Single-Speed	1¼ x 18	700-900	11	5-15	0.020-0.026	1
Double Reduction	1½ x 12	800-1100	14	5-15	0.020-0.026	1
	1½ x 18	800-1100	14	5-15	0.020-0.026	1

the threads in the carrier legs, and position the bearing caps on the carrier leg with the matching marks aligned. Check to see that the threads in the caps and legs are matched—if so, install and torque the cap bolts.

14. Hand tighten the bearing adjusters until they just touch the bearing cups. Then install a dial indicator and check the differential end play using a pinch bar to move the differential away from indicator. Then tighten the bearing adjuster opposite the dial indicator until there is no side-to-side movement of the differential, and the dial indicator shows no end play.

15. After obtaining the correct end play, adjust the differential bearing preload by tightening the bearing adjusters an additional ¾-2½ notches (total for both adjusters).

16. Install the bearing adjuster locks and cap screws.

17. Install locking wires on the lock cap screws and bearing cap bolts.

Torque Chart

Location	Cap Screws or Stud Nuts		
	Diameter	Threads per. in.	Torque-Lb. Ft. Min.-Max.
These torques are	3/8	24	38-49
given according	3/8	16	33-43
to diameter and	7/16	14	53-77
threads per inch.	7/16	20	53-67
The torque will	1/2	13	81-104
be the same for	1/2	20	81-104
a specific size	9/16	12	116-149
no matter where	9/16	18	116-149
the bolt or cap	5/8	11	160-205
screw is used	5/8	18	160-205
on the axle	3/4	10	290-370
except for those	3/4	16	290-370
listed below.	7/8	9	470-595
	7/8	14	510-655
	1	14	580-745
Adjusting nut lock	5/16	18	16-20
	1/2	13	75-96
Inspection cover	3/8	16	.27-35
Shift unit (mounting)	3/8	16	27-35
Shift unit lock nut, set	3/8	16	30-33
screw and clamp screw	7/16	14	30-33
Shift unit travel limiting	1/2	13	40-45
screws	5/8	11	30-33

Torques given apply to parts coated with machine oil; for dry (as received) parts increase torques 10%; for parts coated with multi-purpose gear oil decrease torques 10%. Nuts on studs to use same torque as for driving the stud.

Rockwell-Standard Two-Speed Double Reduction Axles

Description

This is a full-floating rear axle having a hypoid drive gear and pinion and using a four-pinion differential assembly. The pinion and cross shaft are each mounted on two tapered roller bearings.

Disassembly

1. Punch-mark one carrier leg and bearing cap for reassembly reference.
2. Remove differential and gear assembly.
3. Punch-mark case halves for correct alignment when assembling.
4. Separate differential case halves. Remove side gears, thrust wash-

Differential carrier on stand
(© Rockwell Stand. Div.)

Cross shaft components
(© Rockwell Stand. Div.)

ers, pinions and pinion shaft.

5. Remove differential side bearing.

6. Separate gears from case. Center-punch rivets in center of head. Use drill 1/32 inch smaller than body of rivet to drill through head, and then press out rivets.

7. Remove pinion shaft yoke.

8. Remove pinion bearing cage assembly. If cage is not free, tap loose, or use puller screws in holes provided.

9. Wire bearing cage shim pack together to facilitate adjustment when reassembling.

10. Press pinion shaft out of cage and remove adjusting spacers from shaft. Remove rear bearing from pinion shaft.

11. Press front bearing and pinion shaft oil seal from pinion cage.

12. Remove two bearing cups from pinion cage.

13. Remove shift fork shaft and shift fork.

14. Tap sleeve from carrier *with a soft mallet.* Wire shim pack together to facilitate reassembly.

15. Remove screws and force out bearing cage by using a small pinch bar between back of hypoid gear and carrier housing. Wire shim pack together to facilitate reassembly.

16. Remove cross shaft and hypoid gear assembly.

17. Remove cap screws and press cross shaft from bearing and hy-

poid gear (ring gear). Slide off high speed pinion and remove shift collar, plungers and springs. Precautions should be taken when removing shift collar as the plungers and springs will fly out. Reinstall shift collar and press shaft through low speed pinion and bearing.

18. Remove cross shaft bearing cups. If cross shaft bearing cover is removed (hypoid gear side), be sure to wire shim pack together.

19. Clean all parts thoroughly in a suitable solvent and blow dry with compressed air. Remove any foreign material from carrier housing. The bearings should be submerged in clean solvent and rotated by hand until clean. After cleaning, blow dry with compressed air. *Do not spin bearings with air pressure, as they might score due to absence of any lubrication.* See the "General Axle Service" section for details on cleaning and inspection.

Assembly

1. Press drive pinion rear bearing cone firmly against pinion shoulder.

2. Press pinion cage bearing cups squarely and firmly against cage shoulder.

3. Place bearing spacer on pinion shaft with bevel side toward front bearing. Lubricate bearing

cone with axle lubricant and position bearing cage on shaft. Lubricate and press front bearing on pinion shaft. Rotate cage to assure normal bearing contact. If a press is not available, install pinion yoke and nut and torque to specifications.

4. While assembly is in the press under pressure or pinion nut torqued to specifications, check pinion bearing pre-load. The correct pressures and torques for checking pre-load are:

Pinion Shaft Thread Size and Number of Threads Per Inch	Required Pressure to Obtain Correct Pre-Load lbs.	Required Torque to Obtain Correct Pre-Load ft. lbs.
1 in. x 20	12,000	300- 400
1¼ in. x 18	22,000	700- 900
1½ in. x 12	28,000	800-1100

5. Wrap a soft wire around cage and pull on horizontal line with pound scale. When determining pinion bearing pre-load, first measure diameter of pinion cage. Assuming cage diameter is 6 inches, pulling radius would be 3 inches; therefore, 4 pounds pull on scale would equal 12 inch-pounds pre-load.

6. Use rotating torque, not starting torque. If rotating torque is not within 5 to 15 inch-pounds, use thinner spacer to increase preload or thicker spacer to decrease pre-load. Torque must be near low limit inch-pounds with original pinion bearings and near high limit when using new bearings.

Differential gears and case (exploded view)
(© Rockwell Stand. Div.)

7. Lubricate a new pinion oil seal and install in pinion cage. Install pinion yoke, washer and nut, tighten to specified torque. Pinion and cage assembly is not installed until after cross shaft and hypoid gear installation. However, if pinion depth gauge tool is being used, install pinion assembly with original shims, then refer to "Pinion Setting Procedures" ("General Axle Service" section). After pinion depth is established, remove pinion and cage assembly.

8. Lubricate inner bearing surfaces on low and high speed pinions with axle lubricant. On some axles (H341, L345), the low speed (small) pinion is located next to the hypoid gear. On the others (Q345, RT340) the high speed (large) pinion is next to the hypoid gear.

9. Position correct pinion on hypoid gear end of cross shaft, with splined row of teeth toward center of cross shaft. Install key in shaft and start cross shaft into hypoid gear in line with keyway, then press shaft into hypoid gear. Insert feeler gauge between end of helical pinion and thrust surface on cross shaft must be .010-.025 inch.

10. Coat the three plungers and springs with axle lubricant, and install in cross shaft. Align the three tapered splines in shift collar with the three plungers, slide collar over plungers with side of collar marked LOW SIDE toward low speed (small) pinion.

11. Install remaining pinion on cross shaft with splined row of teeth toward center of shaft. Press cross shaft bearing firmly against cross shaft shoulder. Pinion end play must be .010 to .026 inch.

12. Install bearing retaining washers and torque cap screws to 42-45 foot-pounds and install lock wire.

13. Press bearing cups firmly against shoulder in the bearing covers.

Shift unit adjustment
(© Rockwell Stand. Div.)

14. Install cross shaft bearing cover (hypoid gear side) in carrier housing with original shim pack. Torque cap screws.

15. Lubricate bearing cones with axle lubricant, then position cross shaft assembly in bearing cup in carrier. If a front mounted shift unit is used, position shift fork and install shift shaft through its bearings in the carrier and fork. Align hole in fork with detent in shaft. Torque lock screw and install lockwire. Start the other bearing cover and original shim pack in carrier housing (side opposite hypoid gear). Tap cover into position and torque down cap screws. Rotate cross shaft and gear assembly several times to assure normal bearing contact.

16. Lock low speed pinion and cross shaft with shift collar. Wrap a soft wire around the pinion and pull horizontally with a pound scale. To calculate cross shaft bearing pre-load, first measure diameter of pinion gear. Assuming pinion diameter is 4 inches, pulling radius would be 2 inches; therefore, 7 pounds pull on scale would equal 14 inch-pound pre-load.

17. Use rotating torque, not starting torque. If rotating torque is not

within 5 to 15 inch-pounds, use thinner shim under bearing cover (side opposite hypoid gear) to increase pre-load or thicker shim to decrease pre-load.

18. Install drive pinion and cage assembly using corrected shim pack if pinion setting gauge was used, or original shim pack if gauge was not used. Install lock washers and torque cap screws.

19. Attach a dial indicator to the carrier with the pointer resting against face of one of the drive gear teeth and adjust backlash temporarily to .010 inch.

To increase backlash, remove sufficient shims from under cross shaft bearing cover (opposite hypoid gear), and insert shims of equal thickness under opposite bearing cover. To decrease backlash, reverse procedure. Following this method, cross shaft bearing pre-load will be retained.

With backlash temporarily set at .010 inch, check gear tooth pattern. Refer to "Gear Tooth Contact" in the "General Axle Service" section. After correct tooth contacts have been made, readjust backlash to measure .020 to .026 inch.

20. If axle has a side mounted shift unit, tap shaft unit sleeve into carrier housing with original shim pack. Install lock washers and tighten nuts to 26-29 foot-pounds.

If electric shift unit is used, hold shift fork in the collar, lubricate and slide shift shaft through sleeve and into collar. Install and tighten lock screw. Tighten lock nut to 30-35 foot-pounds and install lock wire. Install shift unit.

Check clearance of shift fork pads in shift collar. The clearance should be .010 minimum on each side of fork in both high and low speed positions. Add or remove shims to achieve correct adjustment.

Check Operation of Shift Unit

If air shift control is used, hold shift fork in position in the collar, lubricate and slide air shift unit

Determining cross shaft preload
(© Rockwell Stand. Div.)

Split ring installation
(© Rockwell Stand. Div.)

Determining shift fork clearance
(© Rockwell Stand. Div.)

shaft through the sleeve and into the fork. Install lock screw. Tighten lock nut to 30-35 foot-pounds and install lockwire.

21. On those axles with a front mounted air shift unit, shift both shift unit and shift fork in HI position using no gaskets. Position the shaft unit and bellcrank assembly in slot of shift shaft. Install lock washers and nut and torque to specifications.

With collar and fork shifted to engage helical pinion next to hypoid gear, adjust Allen screw and nut in top of carrier to center the fork in the collar within .005".

With collar and fork shifted to engage the helical pinion away from hypoid gear, adjust hex head bolt and lock nut in cross shaft cage to center the fork in the collar within .005". (When checking shift fork clearance, make certain collar is flush with end face of pinion being engaged.)

Check Shift Unit Operation

22. Install high and low speed helical gears on their respective differential case halves. If rivets are used, install them cold. Instead of rivets, bolts can be used but must be tightened to specified torque.
23. Lubricate case inner walls and all parts with axle lubricant.
24. Install thrust washer and side gear in one of case halves. Assemble pinions and thrust washers on pinion shaft (spider) and install assembly. Engage the other side gear and thrust washer with pinions.
25. Aligning mating marks, unite case halves with four of the long bolts equally spaced. Check assembly for free rotation of gears and correct if necessary. Torque remaining bolts and install lock wire.
26. Press differential side bearings squarely and firmly on case halves.
27. Temporarily install bearing

Adjusting differential bearing preload
(© Rockwell Stand. Div.)

cups, threaded adjusting nuts or split ring and bearing caps. Torque cap bolts. Bearing cups must be hand pushed into the bores; or enlarged with a scraper or emery cloth until a hand push fit is obtained. Use a blued bearing cup as a gauge to check fit. If split rings cannot be turned by hand, reduce their O.D. slightly with a fine mill file.

28. Lubricate side bearings with axle lubricant. Place bearing cups in the cones, then position differential assembly between grooves in carrier legs.
29. Insert thin split rings in carrier leg grooves, making certain there is clearance betwen bearing cup faces and the rings.
30. Attach a dial indicator to the carrier housing with its pointer resting against side surface of one of the drive gears. With a pair of small pinch bars, manipulate assembly back and forth between the split rings and measure the end play.
31. Remove and measure split ring thickness. To the total thickness of the two thin rings, add the end play figure, plus another .017 to .022 inch to obtain total thickness of two thicker rings required to obtain proper bear-

ing pre-load. For example: If necessary thin rings were .290 inch each for a total of .580 inch, and the end play is .005 inch, then .580 inch plus .005 inch equals .585 inch. Adding an additional .020 inch for a total of .605 inch thickness for the two split rings would provide .020 inch pre-load on the bearings. The .605 inch may be divided between the two rings such as .300 and .305 inch.

32. Insert one split ring in carrier leg groove and move differential assembly tightly against ring. Install opposite split ring (with gap upward) by tapping it into the groove with a blunt drift.
33. Tap bearing caps into correct location. Torque cap bolts and install lock wire.

Torque Chart

Carrier to housing bolt or stud nut	7/16-14-20	54-58
	1/2-13-20	85-91
	5/8-11-18	168-180
Cross shaft bearing cage and cover screw	1/2-13-20	85-91
	9/16-12-18	120-129
	5/8-11	168-180
Cross shaft bearing lock screw	7/6-14	42-45
	9/16-12	92-101
Differential case bolts	3/8-16	34-37
	7/16-14	54-58
	1/2-20	94-102
	9/16-18	132-145
	5/8-18	186-205
	3/4-16	325-360
Differential bearing cap bolt	5/8-11-18	127-140
	3/4-10-16	230-250
	7/8-9-14	345-370
	7/8-14	375-415
	1-14	375-415
Pinion cage bolt	3/8-16	34-37
	7/16-14-20	54-58
	1/2-13-20	85-91
	9/16-12-18	120-129
	5/8-11	168-180
Pinion shaft yoke nut	7/8-20	175-250
	1-20	300-400
	1-1/4-18	700-900
	1-1/2-12-18	800-1100
	1-3/4-12	800-1100

Dana-Spicer Single Reduction Models 27, 30, 44, 44-1, 53, 60, 60-35, 70

Differential Removal

1. Drain lubricant.
2. Remove cover and gasket. *NOTE: Attached to a cover bolt is a metal tag which shows the number of teeth on pinion and ring (drive) gear.*
3. Remove bearing cap screws. Note the matching marks on cap and carrier and make sure caps are reassembled to correct markings.
4. Using a spreader tool, spread carrier a maximum of 0.020 inch and meausre amount of spread

with a dial indicator. IMPORTANT: Carrier may be permanently damaged if spread more than 0.020 inch. Do not attempt differential removal without using a spreader.

5. Carefully lift differential assembly out of carrier.
6. Remove the spreader assembly after removing the differential assembly from the housing.

Differential Disassembly

1. Remove and label the two bearing cups.

Installation of spreader and dial indicator
(© Dana Corp., Spicer Div.)

Mark locations on carrier and caps
(© Dana Corp., Spicer Div.)

2. Use a suitable type puller to remove the bearing cones. Remove and label adjusting shims.
3. Drive out pinion shaft lock pin.

NOTE: On the Spicer Model 70 rear axle, punch-mark the differential case halves (for reassembly reference) and separate. Remove the differential spider, pinion gears, side gears and thrust washers.

4. Separate ring gear from case.
5. Remove pinion shaft, two pinions, two side gears, and four thrust washers from case.

Drive Pinion Disassembly

1. Pull flange (yoke) from shaft splines of drive pinion.
2. Using a press or soft hammer, drive pinion and inner bearing cone assembly out of carrier.
3. Remove and tag shim pack from splined end of pinion. NOTE: If either ring (drive) gear or pinion are to be replaced, write down markings (+), (−), or (0) located at face end of pinion for reassembly reference.
4. Remove oil seal assembly from carrier bore. This frees oil seal gasket, oil slinger, and bearing cone.
5. If replacement of the pinion tapered bearings is necessary, the bearing cups should be removed from carrier as follows:
   a. Use remover with a driver or slide hammer to remove inner bearing cup from carrier. This frees shim pack. Remove and tag shims for reassembly.
   b. Remove outer bearing cup.
6. Use remover set to separate bearing cone from drive pinion.
7. Separate oil slinger from pinion.

NOTE: This oil slinger is only found on some axle models.

Differential Assembly

1. Place side gears with new thrust washers in position inside case.
2. Place pinions and thrust washers in position in case.
3. Install the differential pinion shaft in position in case between two pinions. Align shaft lock pin hole with lock pin hole in case and install pinion shaft lock pin. Peen hole to prevent pin from falling out. NOTE: On the Spicer Model 70 rear axle, install the differential spider along with its pinion gears, side gears and thrust washers into the differential case halves. Bolt the two halves together making sure the punch-marks line up.
4. Place ring (drive) gear in proper position against flange of case and bolt ring gear to case. Alternately tighten these bolts until all bolts are tightened to proper torque.

NOTE: Do not install differential cones or shim packs until pinion depth and bearing preload have been checked out. Differential bearing adjustment is a part of axle assembly procedure.

Differential Bearing Adjustment

1. Press fit bearing cones tightly against shoulders on case.
   IMPORTANT: Do not install shims at this time.
2. Install bearing cups.
3. Install spreader tool and dial indicator, and spread carrier as described in "Differential Removal."
4. Place differential assembly into carrier.
5. Install bearing caps using their respective cap screws. Make sure caps are assembled to their correct markings. Hand tighten bearing cap screws.
6. Install dial indicator at carrier with indicator button contacting back of ring (drive) gear. Rotate ring gear and check run-out.
7. If run-out exceeds 0.002-inch, remove the differential assembly and remove ring gear from the case.
8. Reinstall differential assembly without ring gear and check run-out of differential case flange. If run-out still exceeds 0.002-inch, the defect is probably due to bearings or case, and should be corrected before proceeding.
9. Remove differential from carrier.

NOTE: Do not install shims behind the bearings until final installation.

Drive Pinion Installation

1. If either drive pinion or ring (drive) gear must be replaced, they must be installed as a set. (These parts are matched and lapped at time of manufacture to obtain the correct gear tooth contact.)
2. Whenever it is necessary to install a new drive pinion, the plus (+) or minus (−) marking on face of rear end of pinion must be considered. Select a new pinion and ring gear set with markings as near as possible to those on old pinion. If marking on both old and new pinion is the same, do not change thickness of shim pack.
3. The approximate difference between markings on old and new drive pinion is the adjustment that will have to be made in the shim packs.
4. In the first listing below note that the new pinion is a plus eight (+8) while the old pinion is a plus five (+5). Making a difference of plus three (+3). This means that the thickness of each shim pack must be decreased by 0.003-inch. Other examples are:

Pinions New Pinion	Old Pinion	Difference Between Markings	Amount To Change Each Shim Pack (in.)
+8	+5	+3	Dec. 0.003
+5	+8	−3	Inc. 0.003
−5	−3	−2	Inc. 0.002
−3	−5	+2	Dec. 0.002
+5	−3	+8	Dec. 0.008
−4	+2	−6	Inc. 0.006

Bearing Preload

Axle Model	Pinion Shaft Nut-Thread Size and Torque Limits (Foot-Pounds)		Press Ram Pressure for Preload Check (Tons)	Pinion and Cross Shaft Bearing Preload (Inch-Pounds)	Backlash Limits (Inches)	Differential Bearing Preload Adjusting Nut Notches Tighten from Zero End Play (each Adjusting Nut)
2-Speed	1¾ x 12	800-1100	14	5-15	0.020-0.026	1
Double Reduction	1 x 20	300-400	6	5-15	0.020-0.026	1
	1¼ x 18	700-900	11	5-15	0.020-0.026	1
	1½ x 12	800-1100	14	5-15	0.020-0.026	1

5. Once proper adjustment in shim packs has been made, place oil slinger, if so equipped, over pinion shaft. Install pinion inner bearing cone over shaft, and use bearing installer and an arbor press to press bearing onto pinion shaft. Bearing must be seated tightly against shoulder or oil slinger.

6. Use pinion front bearing cup installer to install outer bearing cup into carrier bore.

7. Install the selected inner shim pack in carrier. Then use pinion rear bearing cup installer to install inner bearing cup.

8. Insert pinion, oil slinger (when used) and inner bearing cone assembly into carrier and place the selected shim pack into position on outer end of pinion shaft.

9. Place outer bearing cone over pinion shaft, then use installer to seat bearing tight against shim pack.

10. Install pinion flange (yoke), washer and nut. Hold flange while tightening nut to proper torque.
    NOTE: Install oil slinger and oil seal only after pinion depth and pinion bearing preload have been checked out.

Checking Pinion Depth Adjustment

1. A pinion depth gauge and correct adapter, which gives a micrometer reading, should be used to determine pinion depth. The actual pinion depth setting can be determined by adding gauge reading to thickness of step plate and comparing result with the nominal dimension of 2.625-inch (models 44/60-35) or 3.125-inch (model 60).

2. If the pinion setting is within minus (−) 0.001-inch to plus (+) 0.003-inch of this nominal dimension, the pinion position can be considered satisfactory.

3. If pinion setting exceeds these limits, it must be corrected by adjusting thickness of shim pack behind the pinion inner bearing cup.

Pinion Bearing Preload Adjustment

1. Use a torque wrench to check pinion bearing preload.

2. Rotating torque of pinion should be from 15 to 30 inch-pounds.

3. Add or remove shims from pack just behind outer bearing cone to bring preload within these torque limits.

Differential Installation

1. Use dial indicator and spreader tool as described in "Differential Removal," to spread carrier a maximum of 0.020-inch.

2. Install bearing cups and place differential assembly in carrier. Rotate differential and, with a soft hammer, tap ring (drive) gear to assure a proper bearing seating.

3. Reinstall bearing caps in their proper locations as indicated by marks made during the removal procedure. Finger tighten cap screws. Relieve the spreader tool pressure, and tighten cap screws to 70-90 foot-pounds.

4. Move differential assembly tightly against drive pinion.

5. Install dial indicator securely to carrier, then set button at zero and against back of drive gear.

6. Move the differential toward the dial indicator and note the reading. For accuracy, repeat this operation several times.

7. Remove the differential assembly from carrier. Install a shim pack behind differential bearing cone at drive gear side, equal to the dimension indicated by dial indicator.

8. Subtract the indicator reading from the reading previously obtained in paragraph "Differential Bearing Adjustment."

9. To the above result should be added 0.015 to 0.020-inch in shims to provide bearing preload.

10. Install the above shim pack behind differential bearing cone at side opposite to drive gear.

11. Spread differential carrier, using spreader tool.

12. Install differential bearing cups then locate differential assembly in carrier.

13. Rotate differential assembly, tapping gear to seat bearings.

14. Install differential bearing caps in their correct location as indicated by marks made upon disassembly. Finger tighten cap screws.

15. Remove differential carrier spreader tool. Tighten differential bearing cap screws to proper torque.

16. Install dial indicator and check drive gear to drive pinion backlash at four equally spaced points around the drive gear. Backlash must be held to 0.003 to 0.006-inch and must not vary more than 0.002-inch between positions checked.

17. Whenever backlash is not within limits, differential bearing shim pack should be corrected.

Axle Shaft Installation

Procedures for installation of axle shafts remain the same with axle assembly removed or installed on the vehicle.

Nominal Assembly Dimension and Adapter Disc Chart

Axle Model	Nominal Assembly Dimension	Adapter Disc Tool Number						
44	2.625"	SE-1065-9-SS	1618-9	4.125"	SE-1065-9-G	17800-1	4.4062"	SE-1065-9-I
60	3.125"	SE-1065-9-Y			SE-1065-9-I			SE-1065-9-M
			1790A-1A	4.2190"	SE-1065-9-CC			SE-1065-9-G
					SE-1065-9-E	G361	2.625"	SE-1065-9-PP
			G161	3.551"	SE-1065-9-E			SE-1065-9-O
			H140	3.551"	SE-1065-9-E	H340	2.625"	SE-1065-9-PP
			H162	3.719"	SE-1065-9-F			SE-1065-9-O
			13800	3.6244"	SE-1065-9-G	H362	2.937"	SE-1065-9-R
					SE-1065-9-E			SE-1065-9-PP
			16802-3	4.125"	SE-1065-9-G	28M	3.4725"	SE-1065-9-D

Dana-Spicer Power-Lok Differential

Description

Unlike the standard differential, the locking differential equally divides the torque load between the driving wheels. The vehicle equipped with the locking differential can be operated on any surface (sand, snow, etc.) with a minimum of slippage through one wheel and provides the greatest power to the wheel getting traction. The vehicle with the standard differential provides power to the

1 Differential case bolt
2 Differential case—plain half
3 Differential case—flanged half
4 Friction plate—tabbed (Belleville)
*5 Friction plate—toothed (Belleville)
6 Friction plate—tabbed (Flat)

7 Friction disc—toothed (Flat)
8 Side gear ring
9 Side gear
10 Pinion gears
11 Cross shafts

Powr-Lok differential (exploded view) (© G.M.C.)

wheel that's easiest to turn—that is, the one experiencing the poorest traction while the other wheel may be gripping well.

When negotiating a turn, the locking differential allows the outer wheel to turn faster than the inner. When traveling in a straight direction, and the vehicle loses traction over a rough or slippery road, the clutches will lock up and neither wheel will spin. A specified lubricant must be used for locking differentials.

Disassembly

1. Remove and tag differential bearing cups and cones.
2. Tag each bearing cone and shims and punch-mark differential halves for re-location reference.
3. Separate differential case halves.
4. Remove five plates and discs from side gear ring. IMPORTANT: Carefully observe the

order in which the plates are used, since they must be replaced in the same order.
5. Remove side gear ring and side gear.
6. Remove two cross shafts and pinion gears.
7. Remove side gear, side gear ring, and five plates and discs from the opposite side and tag them for reassembly.

Cleaning and Inspection

1. Check cross shafts and pinions for scoring, wear, pitting, etc. If the center lands of either cross shaft are worn, inspect axle shaft ends to determine if the axle shaft is rubbing against cross shaft. This rubbing condition may cause a whine or howl that is similar to a pinion bearing noise, at 40 to 50 mph. This can be corrected by grinding 1/32" off the end of the axle shaft.

2. Inspect clutch discs and plates for wear, cracked, or distorted condition.
3. Inspect side gear rings, side gears, and differential cases for worn, cracked, or distorted condition. For further information on cleaning and inspection, see "General Axle Service" section.

Assembly

During assembly operations, lightly coat all parts with the correct lubricant.

1. Place tabbed Belleville friction plate in flanged differential case, being extremely careful that convex (bulged) side is toward the case.
2. Assemble remaining plates and discs to splines of side gear ring, being sure they are assembled in the same order of removal. The convex (bulged) side of the Belleville friction disc should be toward the case and it should nest into the Belleville friction plate. CAUTION: Do not attempt to operate the Powr-Lok with only one wheel on a jack. This might cause the vehicle to jump off the jack. Both wheels must be elevated from the ground.
3. Place assembled side gear ring with plates and discs in flanged half of differential case.
4. Install side gear and cross shafts with pinions.
5. In the order listed install the following: side gear, side gear ring, flat plate with tabs, flat disc with teeth, flat plate with tabs, Belleville disc with convex (bulged) side up, or toward case, Belleville plate, with con-

BOTH PINS MOVE UP RAMPS UNDER LOAD

CLUTCH RINGS ENGAGED (BOTH SIDES)

Location of cross pins with vehicle making a left hand turn (Powr-Lok)
(© International Harvester Co.)

ONE CROSS PIN MOVES DOWN RAMP

ENGAGING FORCE RELEASED

Location of cross pins with vehicle moving in a straight forward direction (Powr-Lok)
(© International Harvester Co.)

vex (bulged) side up, or toward case.

6. Position plain half of differential case over previously assembled parts with punch marks on both halves aligned.

7. Install but do not tighten, differential case bolts.

8. Before tightening bolts, use axle shafts and align splines of the side gear and side gear ring, on each side. Tighter bolts evenly and alternately. Remove axle shafts.

9. Re-check components for proper assembly. Each pinion cross shaft can be tight on its ramp or if there is clearance it should be only a few thousands, and it should be equal at all four cross shaft ends.

Testing Procedure

The Powr-Lok can be effectively tested for correct operation by placing one rear wheel on good dry pavement and the other on ice, snow, mud, gravel, grease, etc.

It can easily be determined whether or not the non-slipping wheel is providing pulling power. This procedure should be repeated with the opposite wheels on the dry and slippery surfaces.

If suspected that the unit is not operating properly, it can be checked by the following procedure.

Place transmission in neutral. Raise one wheel off the floor and place a block in the front and rear of the opposite wheel. Install a special tool across two wheels studs and a torque wrench to special tool. Disregard breakaway torque and observe only the torque required to continuously turn the wheel smoothly.

If the torque reading is less than 40 foot-pounds, the unit should be disassembled and repairs made.

Ford Traction-Lok Limited Slip Differential

Ford Traction-Lok differential (exploded view) (© Ford Motor Co.)

Disassembly

1. Remove the ring gear and separate the case halves.
2. Press the ring gear from the case.
3. Place the differential case in a press to load the case at the bearing journals so that the pre-load of the springs is overcome (approx. 1,500 lbs.). If a press is not available, use two 7/16 inch bolts and nuts in the ring gear mounting holes (one on each side) to compress the case halves together and overcome pre-load spring tension. With case under pressure, loosen the two Allen or Phillips head screws which hold the case halves together until one or two threads of the screws remain engaged. Remove case from press, tap on the cover to loosen it; then, remove both screws.
4. With the cover facing down, lift off the case. Remove the pre-load spring plate and four pre-load springs.
5. Remove the side gear, four clutch plate ear guides, clutch hub, friction and steel clutch plates and shim(s).
6. Drive out the pinion shaft lock pins and long pinion shaft from the case.
7. Remove the two short pinion shafts. Lift out the center block, then remove the pinion gears, thrust washers and side gear and thrust washer.
8. If removed, the differential bearings can be installed in one of the following ways:

a. With the differential case and cover completely assembled.
b. On the case or cover when disassembled. However, when pressing the bearing on the cover, a block of wood must be used to prevent cover damage.

Assembly

1. Lubricate all parts with recommended lubricant during assembly.
2. Mount the differential case in a soft jaw vise and place a side gear thrust washer and side gear in the counterbore.
3. Install the pinion thrust washers and place the pinion gears on the side gear aligning the holes in

Center block and pre-load springs installation (Traction-Lok)
(© Ford Motor Co.)

Installation of clutch pack (Traction-Lok)
(© Ford Motor Co.)

the washers and gears with those in the case.

4. Install the center block. The center block has two machined sides and two rough sides.

5. Drive in the long pinion shaft aligning the lock pin holes in the shaft with the case holes. The center block should be positioned so the long shaft is driven through the rough side and short shafts driven through the machined side.

6. Install shaft lock pins. Make sure the pinion and side gears move freely.

7. Place the four pre-load springs in the center block.

8. Position the pre-load plate over the seated springs, making sure the springs are properly seated.

9. Mount the differential cover in a soft-jawed vise.

10. Insert shim(s) of 0.050 total thickness in the cover cavity.

11. Install the composite plate on the back side of the clutch hub with the friction side against the hub; next, install a friction plate, then steel, friction, steel, friction, steel, friction, and lastly a steel plate. When using new clutch plates, soak the plates in hypoid lubricant for 30 minutes before installation.

12. Place the clutch hub with the clutch plates into the clutch ear cavities in the differential cover. Make sure that the splines on the last friction plate are engaged on the hub.

13. Obtain a 5/8 inch x 2½ inch or 9/16 inch x 2½ inch bolt, nut and two 1½ inch outside diameter flat washers approx. ⅛ inch in thickness. These parts are necessary to compress the clutch pack in order to obtain the proper shim selection. Insert a bolt and washer through the clutch hub and place a flat washer on the bolt and then install the nut and torque to 10 or 15 ft. lbs.

14. Place the shim template tool in the clutch hub. Some clearance should be present between the shim tool and the cover-to-case mating surface and measured with a feeler gauge. A shim pack thickness chart (see manufacturer's specifications) will indicate the correct amount of shim(s) to subtract from the

0.050 shim originally installed.

15. After determining shim size, remove the bolt, nut and flat washers. If necessary to change the shim thickness, remove the clutch hub and clutch plates.

16. Install the selected shim(s) in the cover cavity, re-install the components as outlined in Steps 11 and 12.

17. Install the four steel clutch ear guides and side gear.

18. Press the two halves together; then, insert the two Allen head or Phillips head screws, and tighten evenly. If a press is not available, any two stock bolts and nuts may be used opposite each other in the ring gear retaining holes to compress both halves.

19. Install the ring gear and bolts

Shim template tool application (Traction-Lok) (© Ford Motor Co.)

and washers. Tighten evenly and alternately across the diameter of the ring gear at 65-80 ft. lbs.

20. Before installing the differential into a vehicle, a bench torque check must be made. Check the torque required to rotate one side gear while the other is held stationary. The initial breakaway torque may exceed 250 ft.

lbs. The rotating torque required to keep the side gear turning with new clutch plates is 100 to 250 ft. lbs. (The torque may fluctuate 10-40 ft. lbs.).

D.A.P. No-Spin Differntial

Description

The No-Spin differential is a locking differential operating through a system of dog clutches and cams. In the No-Spin unit the rear wheels are locked together at the axle shafts by dog clutches. The limited slip differential has conventional gearing with a system of clutches serving to slow down the normal differential action. When the vehicle is turning, differentiation results when a series of cams disengages the dog clutch on the side turning in the largest circle. When the vehicle returns to straight line travel, the dog clutches engage and lock the axle shafts together at the differential case. In the No-Spin

No-Spin operation when making a left hand turn (© Ford Motor Co.)

No-Spin differential action when making a right hand turn in a rearward direction (© International Harvester Co.)

Holdout ring removal (No-Spin) (© G.M. Corp.)

Aligning spider key and holdout ring (No-Spin) (© G.M. Corp.)

No-Spin differential action when moving in a straight forward direction (© International Harvester Co.)

No-Spin differential action when making a forward right hand turn (© International Harvester Co.)

differential, the inside wheel turns at the same speed as the ring gear because it is locked up to the differential case. On the other hand, a geared differential system averages the power to the rear wheels, so that the inside wheel may turn slower than the ring gear.

The main difference between the silent type and the standard type is that the silent type contains a hold out ring placed between the driven clutch and the spider. When the vehicle is turning (outside wheel unlocked) the driven clutch on that side walks around the spider creating a clicking noise in the standard type. The in-and-out motion of the driven clutch creates this noise. The silent type limits this in-and-out motion until the moment the wheels return to straight-ahead movement.

Disassembly

1. Punch-mark differential case halves. *CAUTION:* The No-Spin differential is assembled under spring tension and held together with a retaining bolt and washers. If this bolt is not available, use a ½-13x6″ bolt with nut and washers. If a retainer bolt is not used, hold differential case halves firmly to prevent sudden spring release.

2. Remove differential case and No-Spin.

No-Spin differential-silent type (no case) (© Ford Motor Co.)

Inserting assembly retaining bolt (No-Spin)
(© International Harvester Co.)

Releasing spring pressure (No-Spin)
(© International Harvester Co.)

Position of No-Spin differential when installed
(© Ford Motor Co.)

Measuring spring free height (No-Spin)
(© G.M. Corp.)

No-Spin differential—silent type (splined drive member with case) (© Ford Motor Co.)

3. Remove side gears, springs and retainers and driven clutches.
4. Remove split holdout rings.

NOTE: Do not disassemble spider, center cam and snap-ring assembly as they are not serviced separately.

Cleaning and Inspection

1. Using a solvent, thoroughly clean all parts.
2. Check side gear and driven clutch splines for excessive wear or fracture.
3. Check spider, center cam, holdout ring and driven clutch teeth for excessive chipping or burring. Minor chips or burrs may be dressed down with a fine stone.

NOTE: Replace holdout rings or cams in pairs only.

4. Check spring retainer seat and splines for fractures.
5. Measure spring height. Free height should be 2⅛"-2¼".

Assembly

1. Lubricate all clutch teeth and cams before assembly.
2. Assemble split holdout rings to center cam and spider assembly. Align spider key with slot in holdout ring.
3. Assemble driven clutches, spring retainers, springs and side gears to spider and center cam assembly.

NOTE: Carefully position spring seats inside retainer cups.

4. Compress assembly with retainer bolt if available. If not available, install No-Spin in differential case, rotate to engage splines, and hold tightly until case and cover bolts are torqued to specifications.
5. Install No-Spin unit in carrier and adjust bearings and backlash as outlined previously for the standard differential unit.

6. Test operation of unit as follows:
   A. Raise both rear wheels off the floor.
   b. Shift transmission into gear.
   c. Rotate both rear wheels as far forward as possible.
   d. With assistant holding left wheel forward, rotate the right wheel to the rear, checking for free rotation.
   e. Rotate both wheels as far to the rear as possible.
   f. While holding the left wheel to the rear, rotate the right wheel forward and check for free rotation.
   g. Repeat Steps c-f, holding the right wheel and rotating the left wheel for left side forward and rearward operation check.
   h. If wheels cannot be rotated freely in this manner, remove and inspect the unit.

Standard No-Spin differential (exploded view) (© Ford Motor Co.)

No-Spin differential-standard type (© Ford Motor Co.)

Traction Equalizer Differential

Description

When driving straight ahead or straight to the rear, drive torque is sent to the wheels in the same way as on a standard rear axle.

When making a turn, the differential acts to turn the outside wheel faster and further than the inside wheel. While differentiation takes place, the outer wheel ground traction overpowers the clutch pack friction and the clutch plates rotate. This action takes place constantly in both units mounted on the axle shafts as the vehicle deviates minutely from a straight forward or straight rearward drive.

The Traction Equalizer consists of an internally splined cartridge which mates with the externally splined differential case extension. The shell contains a series of clutch plates which are splined alternately on the inside and outside diameters to match the internal splines of the cartridge and the external axle shaft splines. A constant pressure is maintained on the clutch plates by several Belleville spring washers. Oil scoops automatically pick up the standard axle lubricant.

Disassembly

Place cartridge assembly under press with oil scoop end down. Apply light pressure to the retainer assembly to compress the spring and permit removal of outer snap-ring. Remove the snap-ring, retainer spring and axle shaft collar.

Replace cartridge under press, oil scoop end down. Insert mandrel with flange end up. Compress Belleville springs with a light pressure (2-3 tons) and remove washer retaining snap-ring.

Release press pressure and remove mandrel. Place cartridge assembly over a post or bar (this will keep internal parts in original order). Hold internal parts down with a sleeve and lift off cartridge shell. Clean and inspect shell and snap-ring at oil scoop end.

Wire internal parts together in their original order, clean in a suitable solvent such as kerosene or diesel fuel oil. *Do Not Use Gasoline*. Dry immediately after cleaning with soft, clean, lintless wiping rags.

Clean housing thoroughly and blow dry with compressed air.

Inspect housing for cracks, nicks,

Traction Equalizer differential (cross section) (© International Harvester Co.)

1 Hypoid gear
2 Differential
3 Case bolt
4 Case bolt nut
5 Differential bearing
6 Adjusting ring
7 Oil Scoop
8 Snap ring
9 Washer
10 External and internal splined discs
11 Belleville springs
12 Cartridge
13 Axle shaft equalizer splines
14 Spring
15 Axle shaft collar
16 Spring retainer
17 Axle shaft
18 Housing sleeve
19 Cartridge retaining screw
20 Cartridge retaining screw jam nut

Traction Equalizer differential (© International Harvester Co.)

and burrs at machined surfaces and if present, remove with small file or stone. Make all necessary repairs before reassembling.

Reassembly

Install snap-ring at oil scoop end.

Place cartridge shell with oil scoop end down over mandrel.

Starting with a thick washer followed by discs and Belleville springs, remove and oil (axle lubricant) internal parts from post, one at a time. Install parts in shell over mandrel.

NOTE: Install discs alternately, starting with an externally splined disc. Belleville springs are to be installed in alternating groups of four, starting with concave side down (toward last disc which is to be an externally splined disc). If discs bind in

the cartridge, tap (do not force) into position.

Carefully remove mandrel and insert at top of cartridge, with flange end up. Position a sleeve against the washer at bottom of assembly.

Using a press, compress (2-3 tons pressure) Belleville springs and install the retaining snap-ring.

Release the press pressure and mount a dial indicator with its stem against the top of the mandrel flange.

Apply a 2 to 3 ton press pressure and read dial indicator for movement required to compress discs and springs. Compression should be between .120" to .160", if more, add one or more splined discs (discs are approximately .040" thick).

NOTE: Last disc must be an externally splined disc.

Release press pressure and remove mandrel. Install axle shaft collar (chamfered edge up) and retainer.

Compress spring with a slight amount of press pressure and install snap-ring.

CAUTION: When working on a truck equipped with a differential locking device, raise BOTH rear wheels off the ground. If only one

Lubrication

The Traction Equalizer assembly is lubricated with the same lubricant that is used in conventional differentials.

Check level at each chassis lubrication or 1,000-mile interval.

Drain and flush differential carrier every 10,000 miles or twice a year, preferably in the spring and fall.

Sure-Grip Differential

CAUTION: When working on vehicles equipped with sure-grip axles, raise BOTH rear wheels while engine is running. These axles can exert significant driving force with one wheel. If truck is supported so only one wheel is raised, power will be transferred to the other wheel and the truck will force itself off its supports.

Using Proper Lubricant

If an axle assembly produces a chatter or moan, change the lubricant before attempting to disassemble it. The wrong lubricant can pro-

duce these noises and result in scoring of clutch plates and discs. Operate vehicle to increase lubricant temperature and, with a suction pump, withdraw old lubricant. Refill axle with special sure-grip lubricant and road-test for 100 miles to determine if noise condition has been corrected—if not, disassemble unit and repair.

Removal and Disassembly of Differential

NOTE: For details on removing and installing differential, refer to

the Spicer single reduction axle section and "General Axle Service" section.

1. Place carrier and tube assembly in a vise.
2. Remove carrier cover and drain lubricant.
3. Clean components and dry with compressed air.
4. In preparing to measure drive gear back face runout (provided no side play was found) mount a dial indicator on pilot stud, and load the indicator stem slightly

Spicer 60 Sure-Grip rear axle assembly (© Chrysler Corp.)

when plunger is at right angles to back face of drive gear.

5. Measure drive gear back face runout by making several rotations of drive gear and reading dial indicator. Mark drive gear and differential case at point of maximum runout, this will be very helpful later in checking differential case runout. Total indicator readings in excess of .006 inch might indicate possible loose drive gear or damaged differential case.

6. Check the clearance between the

differential bearing cap and bearing cup by trying to insert a .003 inch feeler gauge between them. If gauge enters, then there is excessive clearance possibly caused by bearing cup having turned in carrier.

7. Note identifying letters stamped on bearing caps and face of carrier housing seal surface. Letters stamped on left side are in horizontal position while right side are in vertical position. Always match identifying letters for proper reassembly.

8. Remove the differential bearing caps and locate spreader tool in locating holes of axle housing and turn tight at this time.

9. Install pilot stud on left side of axle housing. Attach dial indicator and load indicator stem slightly against opposite side of axle housing.

10. Tighten spreader tool nut enough to create .015 inch movement of dial indicator so that differential case and ring gear assembly can be removed. *Do not spread over .020 inch as it will result in per-*

Sure-Grip differential
(© Chrysler Corp.)

Identifying bearing caps (Sure-Grip)
(© Chrysler Corp.)

manent damage to carrier casting.

11. Remove dial indicator and differential case and ring gear assembly from housing. Using a screwdriver, carefully lift out differential case and ring gear. Keep respective bearing cups with bearing cones unless they need replacement.

12. Place the differential case in a soft-jawed vise and remove and discard the drive gear screws. Using a fiber mallet, tap the drive gear loose from the differential case pilot.

13. If the drive gear runout exceeded .006 inch in step 5, differential case flange runout should be remeasured. Install differential case with respective bearing cups into axle housing. Remove spreader tool. Install bearing caps and tighten snugly. Mount dial indicator in contact with flange face of differential case, and measure runout as described in Step 5. Total maximum runout should be .003 inch. It is often possible to reduce excessive runout by positioning drive gear 180 degrees from point of maximum runout when reassembling ring gear on differential case.

14. Position carrier and tube assembly in vise. Remove drive pinion nut and washer and drive pinion flange.

15. Remove drive pinion oil seal, slinger, gasket, front pinion bearing cone and preload shim pack. Record the thickness of the shims in case they should be lost.

16. Press out the drive pinion stem and rear bearing cone assembly.

17. Drive out the front and rear pinion bearing cups from housing. Remove the shim from behind the rear bearing cup and record the thickness of shim pack.

18. Remove rear bearing cone from drive pinion stem.

19. Remove differential bearing cones from differential case hubs. Be careful that bearing remover adapters are located so as not to pull on bearing cage.

20. Remove the shims located behind each bearing and record thickness to aid in reassembly.

Determining runout on drive gear mounting flange face (Sure-Grip)
(© Chrysler Corp.)

Removing or installing differential case cap (Sure-Grip)
(© Chrysler Corp.)

Installing pinion shafts and gears (Sure-Grip)
(© Chrysler Corp.)

Side gear installation (Sure-Grip)
(© Chrysler Corp.)

Removing or installing side gear (Sure-Grip)
(© Chrysler Corp.)

Installing clutch plates and discs (Sure-Grip)
(© Chrysler Corp.)

Proper sequence of plates and discs on the
Sure-Grip
(© Chrysler Corp.)

Disassembling the Differential Case

1. Remove the axle drive gear. Measure runout of the drive gear mounting flange and replace both case halves if more than .003 inch.
2. Punch-mark case halves for realignment reference. Remove case cap and clutch plates.
3. Remove side gear retainer and side gear.
4. Remove pinion shafts with pinion gears.
5. Remove remaining side gear, side gear retainer and clutch plates.

Cleaning and Inspection

1. Clean all parts in cleaning solvent and, with the exception of bearing cones, dry with compressed air.
2. All machined contact surfaces should be smooth and free of any burrs. Raised metal on shoulders of bores caused by cup removal should be flattened with a flat nosed punch.
3. Check differential bearings and pinion bearing cone and cup assemblies for any defects. When replacing bearings, always replace the cup and cone in a set only.
4. Clean and inspect all differential parts for wear, nicks and burrs. The inner and outer flat clutch plates and outer flat clutch disc should be replaced if worn or distorted. Replace both case halves if one is worn. See "Cleaning and Inspection" in "General Axle Service" section for further details.

Assembling the Differential Case

1. Position clutch plates and discs in each case half.
2. Place side gears in their retainers and insert retainer splines through the splines of clutch discs.
3. Place aligning pin through one axle shaft thrust spacer. Assemble pinion shafts on aligning pin.
4. Place pinion gears on shafts and install assembly in drive gear half of case.
5. Place the cap half of case on drive-gear half and align the punch-marks.
6. Install the differential case bolts and turn in a few threads.
7. With shafts installed, center the cross shafts between the two ramp surfaces in differential case. Tighten differential case bolts evenly by alternately turning opposite bolts to 45 ft. lbs. To keep side gear and clutch plate splines in exact alignment during the tightening procedure, move axle shafts back and forth as bolts are being tightened. After assembly, slight misalignments of the splines can be corrected by moving axle shafts back and forth until free. Remove axle shafts.

Installation of Case and Drive Gear

The contacting surfaces of the drive gear and differential case flange must be clean and free of all burrs.

1. Position drive gear on differential case pilot, aligning threaded holes in drive gear and differential case flange.
2. Insert drive gear screws through case flange and into drive gear. After all cap screws are properly started, tap drive gear against differential case flange with a leather or rubber mallet.
3. Clamp unit in a brass jaw vise and alternately tighten each cap screw to 100-200 foot-pounds.
4. Position each differential bearing cone on hub of differential case (without shims), small end away from drive gear. CAUTION: Never exert pressure against the bearing cage, since this would damage the bearing and make it unfit for further use.
5. Position differential bearing cups on their respective cones and insert differential case in carrier. Install bearing caps and finger tighten bolts.
6. Install dial indicator fixture with pointer contacting back face of drive gear.
7. Insert a screwdriver blade between bearing cup and housing and pry case assembly as far as possible to one side of housing. Set dial indicator at zero. Using screwdriver, pry case to opposite side of housing and record the reading. This reading indicates the amount of shims needed to take up the clearance between the differential bearing cups and the case.
8. Remove dial indicator, and remove bearing caps. Remove differential assembly from housing.

Dana Positraction Differential

Disassembly

1. Remove ring gear and install spring compresser tool.
2. Compress and remove springs and spring cups.
3. Rotate differential side gear

Drive Axles

1 Differential case
2 Cage
3 Lock pin
4 Clutch disc
5 Clutch plate
6 Spring seat
7 Side gear
8 Spring and spring cups
9 Pinion
10 Thrust washer
11 Pinion shaft
12 Shim

Dana positraction (exploded view) (© G.M. Corp.)

with axle shaft until pinions align with case opening. Remove pinions and thrust washers by prying clutch pack away from pinion.

4. Remove clutch packs and side gears. NOTE: The clutch pack is assembled to a predetermined height of .552″ ± .002″, therefore make sure that clutch pack components are removed and kept together as a unit. Do not mix plates, discs or shims from one pack with those of another pack.

5. Pry clutch pack cage out of differential case.

Inspection

1. Clean and inspect components for excessive wear and replace where necessary.
2. Inspect clutch pack for excessive wear or overheating and replace as a unit if necessary.
3. If plates and discs are suitable for reinstallation, measure the clutch pack thickness (including shim). Total thickness should be .552″ ± .002″, replace shims as required to maintain this height.

Shims are available in thickness of .016″, .020″, .024″, .026″ and .028″.

Reassembly

1. Place clutch pack cages into case with side tabs up and flat sides parallel with flat sides in case.
2. Place aluminum spring seat plate over side gear.
3. Alternately place clutch plate and clutch disc on side gear until pack is complete. Make sure clutch discs align with side gear teeth, then place shim over last clutch disc.
4. Install clutch pack and side gear assemblies in case.
5. Place pinion gear between differential side gears through large opening in case. Rotate side gears and install second pinion and thrust washers directly opposite first.
6. Place spring cup in bore and, using the spring compressor, install spring, and spring cup into spring seats. Repeat for remaining springs.
7. Install ring gear on case.
8. Place differential in carrier and

adjust bearings and backlash (see "General Axle Service" section).

9. Test unit as follows:
   a. Raise rear of vehicle until both rear wheels are off the ground, and remove one wheel and tire assembly.
   b. Attach an adapter to axle shaft flange and install a ½-13 bolt into adapter.
   c. With wheel and tire assembly still on vehicle held firmly to prevent turning, measure torque required to rotate opposite axle shaft with a 0-150 lb. torque wrench attached to an adapter. Torque required to rotate axle shaft should be no less than 40 ft. lbs.

Clutch pack installation
(Dana) (© G.M. Corp.)

Determining positraction rotating torque
(Dana) (© G.M. Corp.)

Removing positraction spring
(Dana) (© G.M. Corp.)

Eaton Positraction Differential

Disassembly

1. Remove ring gear and side bearings.
2. Remove pinion shaft from the case.
3. Remove the preload spring re-

tainer and springs by tapping on the spring retainer. Drive the spring retainer from the case

1 Ring gear-to-case bolt
2 Differential case
3 Side bearing
4 Pinion lock screw
  and washer
5 Ring gear
6 Shim
7 Clutch pack guide
8 Clutch disc
9 Clutch plates
10 Side gear
11 Spring retainer
12 Pinion thrust washer
13 Pinion gear
14 Pinion shaft
15 Preload spring

Eaton positraction (© G.M. Corp.)

sufficiently to allow insertion of a ¼ inch bolt and nut in each of the two front springs.

4. Continue to drive out spring retainer until enough is exposed to permit installation of bar stock and "C" clamp. Center the bar stock over the axle shaft hole in the spring retainer, then compress "C" clamp and withdraw spring pack.

5. Place spring pack in vise and remove bolts and relieve pressure.

6. Remove the pinion thrust washers from behind the pinion.

7. Remove pinion gears from case by rotating them in one direction only. Rotate differential case clockwise to remove the first gear, then rotate case counter-clockwise to remove the second gear. To remove second gear, it may be necessary to assist pinion gear upon its seat by prying on gear through observation hole in case.

8. Remove side gear, clutch pack, shims and guides from case and tap assembly from case. Repeat removal on opposite gear.

9. Separate clutch pack assembly

from side gear. Retain clutch pack assembly with original side gear.

Inspection

1. Replace worn or scored clutch plates and discs. NOTE: Clutch plates and discs are not serviced separately, if replacement is necessary, entire clutch pack must be replaced.

2. Inspect preload springs for defects.

3. Replace any weak springs.

4. Examine spring retainer for alignment between the retainer

Removing pre-load spring pack
(Eaton) (© G.M. Corp.)

Position of "C" clamp and bar stock for spring removal
(Eaton) (© G.M. Corp.)

Drive Axles

halves and for excessive wear at spring seats.

Reassembly

1. Lubricate clutch plates and discs with special positraction lubricant.
2. Alternately position clutch plate and disc on side gear, beginning and ending with clutch plate, until clutch pack is complete.
3. Install clutch pack guides on the clutch plate lugs. Make sure that the clutch disc lugs engage with side gear teeth.
4. Select shims of equal thickness as those removed from the case, or if old shims are suitable, reinstall them over the side gear hub.
5. Lubricate and assemble opposite side gear as above.
6. Install one side gear, clutch pack assemby and shim(s) in the differential case.
7. Position pinion gears and thrust washers on side gears. Install pinion shaft through case and gears.
8. Install dial indicator with button against pinion gear.
9. Compress clutch pack and move the pinion gear to obtain a tooth clearance.
10. Remove side gear assembly and repeat tooth clearance procedure

for opposite side gear.
11. Remove pinion shaft, gears and thrust washers.
12. Install remaining side gear, clutch pack assembly and shims in case.
13. Install pinion gears and thrust washers (installation is reversal of removal).
14. Assemble springs in spring retainer and clamp assembly in vise. Install "C" clamp and bar stock on spring retainer then install a ¼ inch bolt and nut in each front spring.
15. Position spring pack between side gears and remove bar stock and "C" clamp.
16. Drive spring pack into side gears sufficiently to retain front springs, then remove bolts from springs. Drive spring pack into position.
17. Install the pinion shaft and torque lock screw.
18. Check alignment of spring retainer with side gears and change if necessary.
19. Install side bearings and ring gear to case (same procedure as conventional differential).
20. Place differential in carrier and adjust bearings and backlash as outlined for the conventional differential.

21. Check operation of unit as follows:
    a. Raise rear of vehicle with *Both* rear wheels off ground, and remove one wheel and tire assembly.
    b. Attach Adapter to axle shaft flange and install a ½-13 bolt into adapter.
    c. With wheel and tire assembly still on vehicle held firmly to prevent turning, measure torque required to rotate opposite axle shaft with a 0-150 lb. torque wrench attached to adapter. Torque required to rotate axle shaft should be minimum of 40 ft. lbs.

Determining clearance of pinion gear tooth
(Eaton) (© G.M. Corp.)

Spring pack installation
(Eaton) (© G.M. Corp.)

Measuring positraction rotating torque
(Eaton) (© G.M. Corp.)

Index

Diagnosis

Jumping out of High Gear

1. Misalignment of transmission case or clutch housing.
2. Worn pilot bearing in crankshaft.
3. Bent transmission shaft.
4. Worn high speed sliding gear.
5. Worn teeth in clutch shaft.
6. Insufficient spring tension on shifter rail plunger.
7. Bent or loose shifter fork.
8. End-play in clutch shaft.
9. Gears not engaging completely.
10. Loose or worn bearings on clutch shaft or mainshaft.

Sticking in High Gear

1. Clutch not releasing fully.
2. Burred or battered teeth on clutch shaft.
3. Burred or battered transmission main-shaft.
4. Frozen synchronizing clutch.
5. Stuck shifter rail plunger.
6. Gearshift lever twisting and binding shifter rail.
7. Battered teeth on high speed sliding gear or on sleeve.
8. Lack of lubrication.
9. Improper lubrication.
10. Corroded transmission parts.
11. Defective mainshaft pilot bearing.

Jumping out of Second Gear

1. Insufficient spring tension on shifter rail plunger.
2. Bent or loose shifter fork.
3. Gears not engaging completely.
4. End-play in transmission main-shaft.
5. Loose transmission gear bearing.
6. Defective mainshaft pilot bearing.
7. Bent transmission shaft.
8. Worn teeth on second speed sliding gear or sleeve.
9. Loose or worn bearings on transmission mainshaft.
10. End-play in countershaft.

Sticking in Second Gear

1. Clutch not releasing fully.
2. Burred or battered teeth on sliding sleeve.
3. Burred or battered transmission main-shaft.
4. Frozen synchronizing clutch.
5. Stuck shifter rail plunger.
6. Gearshift lever twisting and binding shifter rail.
7. Lack of lubrication.
8. Second speed transmission gear bearings locked will give same effect as gears stuck in second.
9. Improper lubrication.
10. Corroded transmission parts.

Jumping out of Low Gear

1. Gears not engaging completely.

2. Bent or loose shifter fork.
3. End-play in transmission main-shaft.
4. End-play in countershaft.
5. Loose or worn bearings on transmission mainshaft.
6. Loose or worn bearings in countershaft.
7. Defective mainshaft pilot bearing.

Sticking in Low Gear

1. Clutch not releasing fully.
2. Burred or battered transmission main-shaft.
3. Stuck shifter rail plunger.
4. Gearshift lever twisting and binding shifter rail.
5. Lack of lubrication.
6. Improper lubrication.
7. Corroded transmission parts.

Jumping out of Reverse Gear

1. Insufficient spring tension on shifter rail plunger.
2. Bent or loose shifter fork.
3. Badly worn gear teeth.
4. Gears not engaging completely.
5. End-play in transmission main-shaft.
6. Idler gear bushings loose or worn.
7. Loose or worn bearings on transmission mainshaft.
8. Defective mainshaft pilot bearing.

Sticking in Reverse Gear

1. Clutch not releasing fully.
2. Burred or battered transmission main-shaft.
3. Stuck shifter rail plunger.
4. Gearshift lever twisting and binding shifter rail.
5. Lack of lubrication.
6. Improper lubrication.
7. Corroded transmission parts.

Failure of Gears to Synchronize

1. Binding pilot bearing on mainshaft, will synchronize in high gear only.
2. Clutch not releasing fully.
3. Detent springs weak or broken.
4. Weak or broken springs under balls in sliding gear sleeve.
5. Binding bearing on clutch shaft.
6. Binding countershaft.
7. Binding pilot bearing in crankshaft.
8. Badly worn gear teeth.
9. Scored or worn cones.
10. Improper lubrication.
11. Constant mesh gear not turning freely on transmission mainshaft. Will synchronize in that gear only.

Gears Spinning When Shifting into Gear from Neutral

1. Clutch not releasing fully.
2. In some cases an extremely light lubricant in transmission will cause gears to continue to spin for a short time after clutch is released.
3. Binding pilot bearing in crankshaft.

Cleaning of Transmission Components

Cleanliness of parts, tools, and work area is of the utmost importance. All transmission components (except bearing assemblies) should be cleaned in cleaning solvent and dried with compressed air before any inspection or work is begun. Great care should be taken when cleaning bearings. Bearings should always be cleaned separately from other parts in clean cleaning solvent and not gasoline. They must never be cleaned in a hot solution tank. It is advisable that they be soaked in cleaning fluid and then tapped against a block of wood in order to free any solidified lubricant that may be trapped inside. Rinse bearings thoroughly in clean solvent and then dry them with moisture-free compressed air being careful not to spin the bearings with the air stream. Rotate each bearing slowly and inspect rollers or balls for any signs of excessive wear, roughness, or damage. Those bearings not in excellent condition must be replaced. If they pass this inspection, they should be dipped in clean oil and wrapped in clean lintless cloth to protect them until installation.

Inspection of Transmission Components

All parts must be completely and carefully inspected and replaced for any signs of wear, stress, discoloration or warpage due to excessive heat. Whenever available, the magna flux process should be used on all parts except roller and ball bearings, to detect small cracks unseen by the eye. Inspect the breather assembly to see that it is not clogged or damaged and check all threaded parts for stripped or cross threads. Oil passages must be cleared of obstructions by the use of air pressure or brass rods and all gaskets, oil seals, lock wires, cotter pins, and snap rings are to be replaced. Small nicks or burrs in gears or splines can be removed with a fine abrasive stone. It is important that any housings or covers having cracks or other damage should be replaced and not welded.

Synchronizers, not in excellent condition, must be replaced. The bronze synchronizer cone should be checked for wear or for any steel chips that may have become imbedded in it. Springs must be inspected for free length, compressed length, distortion, or collapsed coils.

IMPORTANT: The splines on many clutch gears, mainshafts, etc., are equipped with a machined relief called a "hopping guard". With the clutch gear engaged, the mating gear is free to slip into this notch, preventing the two gears from separating or "walking out of gear" under various load conditions. This is *not* a worn or chipped gear. Do not grind or discard the gear.

Check all shafts for spline wear or damage. If the mainshaft 1st and reverse sliding gear or clutch hub have worn into the sides of the splines, the shaft should be replaced. Shift forks, shift rods, interlock balls and pins must be replaced if scored, worn, distorted or damaged.

Clark 280V Series-Five Speed Transmissions

Disassembly of Transmission

1. Remove the remote control or shift tower from the control cover. Remove the control cover capscrews and lock washers. Remove the control cover assembly from the transmission. Remove the back-up light switch.
2. Remove the universal joint assembly and the drive shaft from the parking brake drum.
3. Remove the parking brake drum. Disconnect the parking brake actuating lever from the linkage.
4. Remove the transmission spline flange. Remove the bolts holding the carrier plate to the transmission housing. Slide the plate with the brake shoes and retaining springs off the transmission.
5. Lock the transmission in two gears and remove the brake drum retaining nut. Remove the brake drum.
6. Remove the output shaft rear bearing retainer and the speedometer drive gear.
7. Remove the countershaft rear bearing retainer. Remove the bearing snap ring.
8. Remove the input shaft bearing retainer and pull the input shaft out of the case. *Be careful not to drop the output shaft pilot bearing rollers into the transmission case.*
9. Move the output shaft rearward until the rear bearing is exposed. bearing is exposed. Remove the rear bearing with a suitable bearing puller.
10. Lift the output shaft out of the transmission case.
11. Remove the reverse idler shaft using the special tool. Lift the reverse idler gear, bearing and thrust washer out of the case.
12. Move the countershaft rearward until the rear bearing is exposed. Remove the bearing and the oil slinger with a suitable puller.
13. Lift the countershaft out of the case.
14. If the countershaft front bearing or the pilot bearing is to be replaced, remove the clutch housing from the transmission.
15. Press the pilot bearing out of the transmission case. *Do not ham-*

Transmission parking brake—Clark 280V (© Ford Motor Co.)

mer or drive the bearing out of the as damage to the bearing bore may result.

Sub-Assemblies
Output Shaft

Disassembly

1. Remove the first reverse gear from the output shaft.
2. Clamp the output shaft, front end facing up, in a soft-jawed vise. Remove the fourth-fifth speed synchronizer assembly from the shaft. Remove the snap ring retaining the fourth gear and remove the shift hub sleeve and the fourth gear.
3. Remove the third gear snap ring and lift the locating washer and the gear off the shaft.
4. Lift the second-third speed synchronizer off the shaft.
5. Remove the snap ring retaining the second-third speed gear shift hub sleeve and lift the sleeve off the shaft.
6. Remove the second gear snap ring and remove the locating washer and the gear.

Assembly

1. Install the output shaft, forward end up, in a soft-jawed vise.
2. Install the second gear lower snap ring and the locating washer on the output shaft. Install the second gear on the output shaft with the clutching teeth facing upward. Install the upper snap ring.
3. Install the second-third shift hub sleeve and snap ring. *While*

pressing downward on the second gear to compress the lower helical snap ring, check the gap between the second gear and the upper snap ring. This gap must be minimum of 0.006 inch.

4. Install the second-third speed synchronizer assembly on the shaft.
5. Install the third gear on the shaft with clutching teeth facing downward. Install the third gear locating washer and snap ring.
6. Install the fourth gear with the clutching teeth facing upward.
7. Install the bottom cone of the fourth-fifth synchronizer over the clutching teeth of the fourth gear.
8. Install the fourth-fifth shift sleeve hub. *Be sure the chamfered side is facing down.* Install the snap ring.
9. Install the fourth-fifth synchronizer on the shift hub sleeve.
10. Reverse the output shaft and install the first-reverse gear with the shift fork facing downward. *A minimum of 0.006 inch end play must be maintained on all mainshaft gears. Synchronizer end play on both synchronizers must be maintained at 0.060 inch minimum and 0.160 inch maximum.*

Input Shaft

Disassembly

1. Remove the bearing retaining snap ring from the input shaft. Remove the bearing, using the special tool illustrated.

Assembly

1. Install the oil slinger and press the bearing on the input shaft. Be sure the snap ring groove is facing the forward end of the shaft. *To prevent damage to the bearing, apply pressure on the inner race of the bearing only.*
2. Install the bearing snap ring.

Countershaft

Disassembly

1. Remove the snap ring at the forward end of the countershaft.
2. Place the countershaft assembly in a hydraulic press, and press the drive gear off the shaft.
3. Remove the key from the shaft and press the fourth gear off the shaft. Remove the remaining key.

Assembly

1. Install the fourth speed gear key in the slot on the shaft. Position the fourth gear on the shaft with the long hub facing toward the front.
2. Install the countershaft main drive gear key in the keyway in the shaft. Install the countershaft drive gear on the shaft with the long hub facing toward the rear. Install the snap ring on the countershaft.

Gear Shift Housing

Disassembly

NOTE: It is not necessary to disassemble the gear shift housing assembly to determine if the parts are worn. Note the condition of the shifter fork shafts and forks by visual inspection. If the forks are excessively worn or if they bind when shifted, disassemble the gear shift housing assembly to make repairs. Check the interlocking system.

1. With the control cover in neutral, pry the fourth-fifth shift fork to the fourth speed position (toward the rear of the cover). Remove the front rail support capscrews and remove the front rail support.
2. Remove the interlock tapered

Tool—T53T-7065-A

INPUT SHAFT

Removing the input shaft bearing—Clark 280V
(© Ford Motor Co.)

Clark 280V Series transmission—exploded view (© Ford Motor Co.)

pin supports. Note the position of the interlock tapered pins for reassembly.
3. Remove the rear rail support capscrews and remove the rear rail support.
4. Remove the first-reverse shift fork and rail assembly. Remove the fourth, fifth, second, and third shift fork and rail assembly. Use caution so as not to lose the interlock cross pin, interlock tapered pins, or the mesh lock poppet balls.
5. Remove the first-reverse shift rail. Remove the four mesh lock poppet balls. Remove the four poppet springs.
6. Remove the first-reverse rocker arm. Remove the reverse latch plunger spring retaining plug and the reverse latch plunger spring and plunger.
7. If the fork bushings are worn, secure the fork in a soft-jawed vise and remove the worn bushings with a drift. Install new bushings in the fork. Turn the

fork over on the anvil of the vise and secure the bushings in the fork, using a prick punch and upsetting the bushing metal on the outside of the fork.

Assembly

1. Position the first-reverse rocker arm on the pivot pin. Install the reverse latch plunger, spring and retaining plug. Tighten the plug securely.
2. Install the four poppet springs and the four mesh lock poppet balls. Note the first-reverse shift fork rail poppet ball in the pocket.
3. Align one tapered interlock cross pin with the hole in the first-reverse shift rail. Position the rail on the poppet ball, in neutral position with the interlock pin aligned with the first interlock tapered pin. Install the second interlock tapered pin. Align the pin with the interlock cross pin hole.
5. Position the fourth-fifth shift

fork and rail assembly on the poppet ball in neutral position. Slightly raise the rear of the rail and align the second interlock tapered pin with the cross hole in the rail. Note the positions of the tapered interlock pins and the shift rails.

6. Install the first-reverse shift fork and rail assembly on the poppet ball in a neutral position. Align the first-reverse rocker arm in the notch at the rear of the rail. Position the rear rail support.

7. Install the rail support capscrews and washers. Tighten the capscrews slightly. Install the interlock tapered pin supports. Tap the fourth-fifth shift fork to the rear (fourth speed position).

8. Position the front rail support and install the capsecrews and washers. Tighten the front and rear support capscrews to 20-25 ft-lbs.

9. Tap the fourth-fifth shift fork and rail assembly forward to a neutral position.

Assembly of Transmission

1. Coat the countershaft needle bearings with grease and install them in the front countershaft bore.

2. Tip the rear of the countershaft down and lower it into the case. Push the countershaft forward and insert the shaft through the bearing.

3. Position the countershaft rear bearing oil slinger and bearing on the shaft. Drive the bearing in to the bearing bore in the case. The countershaft drive gear should be supported while driving the shaft to prevent damage to the front bearing. Install the rear bearing retainer.

4. Coat the reverse idler thrust washers with grease and position them in the case.

5. Insert the two roller bearings in the reverse idler bear bore. Place the gear assembly in position in the transmission case, with the small gear toward the rear of the case.

6. Insert the reverse idler shaft through the hole in the case, through the reverse idler gear, and into the forward support boss. Drive the reverse idler shaft into the case until the slot in the shaft is lined up with the lock bolt hole. Install the retainer in the slot and secure the retainer with the lock bolt. Tighten the bolt to specifications.

7. Tilt the rear of the output shaft assembly downward and insert the end of the shaft through the output shaft bore in the case.

Gear shift housing—exploded view—Clark 280V (© Ford Motor Co.)

Lower the front end of the output shaft until it is in line with the pilot bearing opening. Move the assembly forward into position.

8. Insert the pilot bearing in the input shaft bore.

9. Position the input shaft and bearing assembly in the forward end of the transmission case. Tap the front end of the shaft with a soft faced hammer until the snap ring is seated against the case. Be sure the clutching teeth of the input shaft gear mesh with the fifth speed synchronizer without binding.

10. Position a new gasket on the input shaft bearing retainer. *Be sure that the oil return holes in the retainer and gasket are aligned with the holes in the transmission case.*

11. Install the lock washers and bolts on the input shaft bearing retainer and tighten the bolts to specifications.

12. Position the output shaft rear bearing on the shaft and drive the bearing into the bore until the snap ring is seated against the case.

13. Position the countershaft rear bearing cap and gasket on the case and install the lock washers and bolts. Tighten the bolts to specification.

14. Install the speedometer drive gear on the output shaft and position a new oil seal in the output shaft bearing retainer. Be sure the seal is correctly installed. Position a new gasket and the bearing retainer on the case and install the cock washers and bolts. Tighten the bolts to specification.

15. Install the parking brake drum and companion flange assembly. Tighten the yoke retaining nut to specification.

16. With the transmission in neutral, position the control cover over the gears, aligning the shift

forks in the shift cover with the gear shift hubs. If the control cover is in neutral and the transmission is in neutral, the transmission drive gear should turn without the brake drum or output shaft turning. Install the capscrews and washers. Tighten to 20-25 ft lbs. Install the remote control or shift tower in the control cover. Tighten the capscrews to 20-25 ft-lbs.

Torque Specifications

	Foot-Pounds
Companion flange nut	350-420
Countershaft rear bearing cap	20-25
Input shaft bearing retainer	20-25
Output shaft bearing retainer	20-25
Reverse idler shaft lock bolt	20-25
Shift control to case	20-25
Shift cover to case	20-25
Shift tower to shift cover	20-25
Transmission to clutch housing	60-80

Lubricant Capacity

	Pints
Clark 280V Series	8

Clark 320V & 380V Series-Five Speed Transmissions

Disassembly of Transmission

1. Remove the gearshift housing assembly.
2. Shifting by hand, engage the transmission into two speeds at the same time.
3. Remove the output flange nut cotter pin. Remove the nut.
4. Remove the parking brake band assembly. Remove the brake drum and flange assembly.
5. Remove the output shaft and countershaft rear bearing caps and gaskets.
6. With the transmission still locked in two gears, remove the countershaft rear bearing attaching nut.
7. Remove the input shaft bearing cap and gasket.
8. Remove the input shaft and bearing assembly from the front of the case.

CAUTION: Do not drop the pilot bearing from the pocket of the drive gear if it remains with the gear. If the bearing is not in the pocket of the gear, remove it from the end of the output shaft pilot.

9. Remove the speedometer drive gear and spacer from the output shaft. Move the output shaft assembly toward the rear of the case so that the rear bearing clears the case. Working with a suitable puller, remove the bearing from the end of the shaft.
10. Tilt the forward end of the output shaft upward to clear the front of the case and remove the entire assembly.
11. Remove the screw and lock washer holding the reverse idler shift lock plate at the rear of the case and remove the lock.
12. Working with a suitable puller in the slot in the end of the reverse idler shaft, pull the shaft from the case.

Clark 320V or 380 V Series Transmission—exploded view (© Ford Motor Co.)

13. Lift the reverse idler gear and two thrust washers from the case.
14. Push the countershaft toward the rear of the transmission case, far enough that the rear countershaft bearing can be removed from the countershaft.
15. Tilt the forward end of the countershaft upward to clear the front of the case and remove the entire assembly.
16. If the countershaft front bearing or pilot bearing is to be replaced, remove the clutch housing from the transmission.

17. Press the pilot bearing out of the case. *Do not hammer or drive out the bearing as damage to the bearing bore in the case will result.*

Sub-Assemblies
Output Shaft

Disassembly

1. Remove the first-reverse sliding gear and the fourth-fifth synchronizer from the output shaft.
2. Place the remainder of the output shaft assembly in a soft-jawed vise, with the front end facing upward.
3. Remove the snap ring holding the fourth gear. Remove the gear and washer from the shaft.
4. Remove the assembly from the vise and with the front end facing downward, tap the assembly lightly on a block of wood, allowing the weight of the third gear to force the fourth gear bushing off the output shaft. Once the bushing has loosened, remove it from the shaft along with the fourth gear locating washer. When the bushing is removed, the locating pin will come off with it. Be sure that this pin is not lost.
5. Remove the third gear from the front end of the output shaft.
6. Remove the second-third synchronizer assembly.
7. Remove the second gear retaining ring and washer. Remove the second gear.
8. Remove the second gear bushing and locating washer from the output shaft.

Assembly

1. Clamp the output shaft in a soft-jawed vise with the front end facing upward.
2. Install the second gear locating washer on the output shaft.
3. Position the lock pin in the second gear bushing. Install the bushing on the output shaft with the lock pin toward the upper end.
4. *To be sure that the second gear locating washer, bushing sleeve, retaining washer, and snap ring are properly tight, use the following procedure.* Before the second gear is installed on the bushing sleeve, place the retaining washer on the shaft and hold it down tightly against the bushing sleeve. Hold the snap ring next to the retaining washer, and slip the snap ring in the groove in the shaft. Select a washer that will give a 0.004 inch maximum snap ring clearance. Remove the washer and install the gear over the bushing sleeve. Place the washer in position and install the snap ring on the shaft so that it is locked

Installing the bushing sleeve—Clark 320V & 380V (© Ford Motor Co.)

Setting the second or fourth gear end play—Clark 320V & 380V (© Ford Motor Co.)

securely in the groove. End play of the second gear must be a minimum of 0.006 inch.
5. Install the second-third synchronizer assembly on the splines of the shaft and drop it into position.
6. Install the third gear thrust washer.
7. Install the third gear on the shaft with the toothed hub facing downward.
8. Install the fourth gear locating washer.
9. Position the lock pin in the fourth gear bushing. Install the bushing on the shaft with the lock pin toward the upper end.
10. *To be sure that the fourth gear locating washer, bushing sleeve, retaining washer, and snap ring are properly tight, use the following procedure. Before the fourth gear is installed on the bushing sleeve, place the retaining washer on the shaft and hold it down tightly against the bushing sleeve. Hold the snap ring next to the retaining washer, and slip the snap ring in the groove on the shaft. Select a washer that will give a 0.004 inch maximum clearance. Remove the washer and install the gear over the bushing sleeve. Place the washer in position and install the snap ring on the shaft so that it is locked securely in the groove. Output shaft gears must maintain a minimum gear end play as follows; Fourth-0.006 inch, Third-0.009 inch, Second-0.006 inch.
11. Remove the assembly from the vise and install the sliding gears on the shaft as follows; fourth-fifth synchronizer hub with the large end facing toward the rear, and the first-reverse gear with the fork slot toward the front.

Countershaft

Disassembly

1. Remove the snap ring from the front end of the countershaft.

2. Remove the countershaft drive gear, spacer, fourth gear and third gear with an arbor press or suitable gear puller.
3. Remove the gear keys from the shaft.

Assembly

1. Install a key in each keyway on the countershaft except at the drive at the drive gear.
2. Press the third gear onto the shaft with the long hub toward the rear.
3. Press the fourth gear onto the shaft with the long hub toward the rear.
4. Install the drive gear spacer and the drive gear key.
5. Press the countershaft drive gear onto the shaft with the long hub toward the rear.
6. Install the remaining key in the slot at the drive gear.

Input Shaft and Bearing

Disassembly

1. Place the input shaft gear in a soft-jawed vise.
2. Remove the snap ring holding the bearing on the input shaft.
3. Working with a suitable puller or arbor press, remove the bearing from the input shaft.

Assembly

1. Assemble the bearing on the input shaft with the snap ring toward the pilot end of the gear.
2. Install the bearing snap ring.

Output Shaft Rear Bearing Cap

Disassembly

Press or drive the oil seal out. *This should only be done if the seal is in need of replacement.*

Assembly

Press a new oil seal in the bearing cap with the lip of the seal toward the transmission.

Gearshift Housing

Disassembly

1. Place the cover on a bench in an inverted position with the extension plug opening facing upward.
2. Remove the expansion plugs from the forward openings in the cover.
3. Remove the lock wires from the shifter lugs and forks.
4. Shift all rails to their neutral position.
5. Remove the lock screws from the second-third shift fork and move the rail toward the rear of the cover so that the lock screw can be removed.
6. Holding a thumb over the detent ball hole in the center rail

support (to prevent losing the ball), remove the rail, lug and fork from the cover.
7. Remove the lock screw from the fourth-fifth shift fork and move the rail toward the rear of the cover so the lock screw can be removed from the lug.
8. Holding a thumb over the detent ball hole (to prevent loss of the ball), remove the fourth-fifth shift rail, fork and lug from the cover.
9. Remove the lock screw from the first-reverse shift fork.
10. Holding a thumb over the detent ball in the center rail support (to prevent loss of the ball), remove the shift fork and rail from the cover.
11. Remove the mesh lock springs and the interlock balls located in the crossbore holes between the first-reverse, fourth-fifth and second-third detent ball holes of the center rail support.
12. Remove the lock screw from the first-reverse rocker lug, move the rail toward the rear of the cover so that the lock screw can be removed from the first-reverse lug.
13. Lift the rocker arm from the pivot pin.

Assembly

1. Push the fourth-fifth shift rail through the forward opening in the cover.
2. Install the two interlock balls between the first-reverse and fourth-fifth rails.
3. Place the detent ball spring in position in the well of the forward rail support.
4. Place the detent ball in position on the spring.
5. Working with a suitable tool, compress the spring and ball so they will pass between the guide fingers of the first-reverse rocker lug if the fingers are aligned.
6. Slide the fourth-fifth shift fork on the rail with the offset for the lock screw toward the rear of the cover.
7. Install the lock screw in the fork, and wire it securely.
8. Shift the assembly into neutral.
9. Push the second-third rail through the forward opening in the cover.
10. Install the two interlock balls between the second-third and fourth-fifth detent ball holes on the forward rail support.
11. Place the detent ball spring in position in the well of the rail support.
12. Using a suitable tool, compress the spring and ball to allow the rail to pass through the support.
13. Slide the second-third shift fork onto the rail with the offset for

the lock screw toward the front of the cover.
14. Install the lock screw in the fork and wire securely.
15. Shift the cover into neutral position.
16. Install the expansion plugs in the forward opening.
17. Install the detent ball lock spring and ball in the well of the first-reverse shift fork.
18. Using a suitable tool, compress the ball and spring so that the rail will pass through the fork.
19. Push the first-reverse rail in the rear opening of the cover.
20. Holding the fork in position on the rocker arm, and with the offset to the rear of the cover, push the rail through the fork and into the rail support.
21. Install the lock screw in the rail support and rail and wire it securely.
22. Check the assembly of the cover by shifting in out of all speed ranges. Shift into the fifth gear position and attempt to shift into first, reverse, second, or third at the same time. This provides a check for the proper assembly of the interlock balls and pin. The shift lever should not shift into more than one speed at a time.
23. Return the shift rail to neutral.

Gear Shift Lever and Tower

Disassembly

1. Remove the gearshift knob and dust cover.
2. Remove the shift lever, support spring, and washer.
3. Remove the shift lever from the shift tower.

Assembly

1. Position the shift lever in the shift tower.
2. Place the shift lever on the transmission case. Replace the washer and spring support.
3. Replace the dust cover and the gearshift knob.

Reverse Lug Assembly

Disassembly

1. Remove the cotter key from the end of the plunger.
2. Remove the nut from the end of the plunger.
3. Remove the spring and plunger from the well in the lug.

ZERO TO 1/32"

Reverse lug plunger adjustment tolerance —Clark 320V & 380V (© Ford Motor Co.)

Gear shift housing—exploded view—Clark 320V & 380V (© Ford Motor Co.)

Assembly

1. Install the plunger and spring in the well in the lug.
2. Install the nut on the end of the plunger. Adjust the plunger flush to 1/32 inch above the face of the lug.
3. Install the cotter key.

Assembly of Transmission

1. If the countershaft front bearing is to be replaced, coat the outer diameter of the pilot bearing with a suitable sealer.
2. From the clutch housing end of the case with the open end of the bearing toward the rear of the transmission, press the bearing 0.007 inch below the front face of the case.
3. Tip the rear of the countershaft down and lower it into the case, running it through the countershaft opening, in the rear of the case, far enough so that the front of the countershaft may be lowered into position. Push the countershaft into position.
4. Position the countershaft rear bearing oil slinger and bearing on the shaft. Drive the bearing into the bore. The countershaft drive gear should be supported while driving the shaft to prevent damage to the front bear-

ing. Install the rear bearing retainer ring.
5. Coat the reverse idler thrust washers with grease and position them in the case.
6. Insert the two roller bearings in the reverse idler gear bore. Place the gear assembly in position in the case, with the small gear toward the rear of the case.
7. Insert the reverse idler shaft through the hole in the case, through the reverse idler gear, and into the forward support boss. Drive the reverse idler shaft into the case until the slot in the shaft is lined up with the lock bolt hole. Install the retainer in the slot and secure the retainer with the lock bolt.

Installing the rear countershaft Bearing— Clark 320V & 380V (© Ford Motor Co.)

Tighten the bolt to specification.
8. Tilt the rear end of the output shaft down and lower it into, and through, the opening in the rear of the transmission case. Lower the front end, in line with the pilot bearing opening, and move the output shaft assembly forward into position. Let the shaft rest in this position until assembly is completed.
9. Assemble the output shaft rear bearing over the end of the output shaft with the snap ring in the outer race facing toward the rear.
10. Install the pilot bearing on the output shaft.
11. Install the input shaft and bearing assembly in the case. Be sure the input shaft gear engages and meshes with the countershaft gear, and the output shaft and pilot bearing are seated in the input shaft bore. If a new pilot bearing is being used, it will be in a plastic sleeve, stand the drive gear on end. Set the bearing and sleeve over the bearing pocket in the drive gear. Slide the bearing rollers and cage from the plastic sleeve into the bearing pocket.

NOTE: When a new bearing is used, always install a new bearing race on the output shaft. If the old pilot bearing is used, set the rollers in the bearing cage and hole them in place with a rubber band. Slide the bearing rollers and the cage from the rubber band into the bearing pocket.

12. Install the output shaft bearing cap with a new gasket. Be sure that the oil hole in the cap is lined up with the oil return hole in the case. This passage must be open and clear.
13. Lock the gears in two gears at one time, and install the countershaft rear bearing attaching nut. Tighten the nut to specifications and stake it in position.
14. Install the countershaft rear bearing cap and gasket.
15. Install the speedometer drive gear spacer and the speedometer drive gear on the output shaft.
16. Install the output shaft rear bearing cap assembly and gasket.
17. Install the parking brake drum and the companion flange assembly.
18. Install the companion flange nut. Tighten the nut to specification.
19. Move the gears to neutral and assemble the gearshift housing and gasket to the transmission case. Make sure the shift forks engage the slots on the gears.
20. Assemble the gasket, gearshaft lever, and tower assembly to the shift bar housing.

Nomenclature	Torque Limits	Nomenclature	Torque Limits
Bolt-Reverse Lockout Plunger Retainer	11/16—16 90-100	Bolt-Parking Brake to Trans. Bearing Retainer	1/2—20C 45-55
Bolt-Clutch Housing to Engine Block	7/16—14 24-32 33-45		5/8—18 180-220 7/16—20 50-70
Bolt-Output Shaft Bearing Retainer to Trans. Case	3/8—16 20-25 7/16—14 30-38 1/2—13 50-62 5/8—11 96-120	Nut-Bellcrank to Trans.	9/16—18 70-90 3/8—16C 20-25
		Bolt-Countershaft & Reverse Idler Shaft Retainer	1/2—13 60-70 5/16—18 25-30 3/8—16 25-37 3/8—16 18-25 7/16—14 40-45 1/2—13 8C-85
Bolt-Gear Shift Lever Tower to Gearshift Housing	3/8—16 20-25 5/16—18 11-16 7/16—14 30-45		
Nut-Drum Parking Brake to Companion Flange	3/8—24 37-50 7/16—20 40-55 1/2—20 74-86	Nut-Countershaft Bearing Lock (5-Speed Extra Heavy Duty & 5-Speed Exclusive)	1 1/4—18 350-450
Bolt—Lever Assy. to Trans.	3/8—16 20-25	Bolt-Gear Shaft Housing Trans. Case	5/16—18 20-25 3/8—16 35-40
Nut-Handbrake Anchor Bar to Trans. Case (except 5-Speed Extra-Heavy Duty)	9/16—18 100-110	Bolt-Clutch Housing to Trans. Case	7/16—14 30-38 5/8—11 96-120 9/16—12 70-90 5/8—18C 115-140 9/16—18C 81-102
Nut Handbrake Anchor Bar to Trans. Case (5-Speed Extra-Heavy Duty only) Nut-U-Joint Flange to Trans. Output Shaft	9/16—18 120-130 1.00—20 90-125 1 1/4—18 225-275 1 1/2—18 275-350	Bolt—Gear Shift Housing Trans. Case	7/16—14 45-50
Nut-Input Shaft Yoke to Aux. Trans.	1 1/4—18 275-350		
Bolt-Countershaft Rear Bearing Retainer	5/16—18 25-30 3/8—16 35-40 7/16—14 45-55 1/2—13 60-70	Nut-Countershaft Bearing Lock (5-Speed Exclusive Heavy Duty) Bolt-Countershaft Front Bearing Retainer	1 1/2—18 350-450 5/16—18 25-30 3/8—16 25-35 7/16—14 50-55
Jam Nut—Adjusting Height Main Trans.	150-200		

Lubricant Capacity	
	Pints
Clark 320V & 380V (SAE 50 Engine Oil)	13

Clark 390V Series-Five Speed Transmission

Disassembly of Transmission

1. Remove the remote-control or shift tower from the control cover. Remove the control cover capscrews and lockwashers. Remove the control cover assembly from the transmission. Remove the back-up light switch.
2. Remove the universal joint assembly and the drive shaft from the parking brake drum.
3. Remove the parking brake drum.

Disconnect the parking brake actuating lever from the linkage.

4. Remove the transmission spline flange. Remove the bolts holding the carrier plate to the transmission housing. Slide the plate with the brake shoes and retaining springs off the transmission.
5. Lock the transmission in two gears and remove the brake drum retaining nut. Remove the brake drum from the output shaft.

6. Remove the output shaft rear bearing retainer and the speedometer drive gear.
7. Remove the countershaft rear bearing retainer, then remove the bearing snap ring.
8. Remove the input shaft bearing retainer and pull the input shaft out of the case. Be careful not to drop the output shaft pilot bearing rollers into the transmission case.
9. Force the output shaft rearwar

until the rear bearing is exposed. Working with a bearing puller, remove the rear bearing from the bore.

10. Lift the output shaft out of the case.
11. Remove the reverse idler shaft using special tool. Lift the reverse idler gear, bearing and thrust washer out of the transmission case.
12. Move the countershaft rearward until the rear bearing is exposed. Remove the bearing and oil slinger with a suitable gear puller.
13. Lift the countershaft from the case.
14. If the countershaft front bearing or pilot bearing is to be replaced, remove the clutch housing from the transmission.
15. Press the pilot bearing out of the case. *Do not hammer or drive the bearing out as damage or distortion to the bearing bore will result.*

Sub-Assemblies
Output Shaft

Disassembly

1. Clamp the output shaft, front end facing upward, in a soft-jawed vise. Remove the fifth gear synchroninizer and the fourth and fifth gear synchronizer assembly.
2. Remove the shift hub thrust bearing and race.

Clark 390V Series transmission—exploded view (© Ford Motor Co.)

Transmission parking brake—Clark 390V (© Ford Motor Co.)

First gear retention—Clark 390V (© Ford Motor Co.)

3. Remove the fourth and fifth shift hub sleeve and the fourth speed synchronizer ring. Remove the fourth gear.
4. Remove the third gear snap ring, locating washer. Lift the third gear off the shaft.
5. Remove the third gear synchronizer ring and the synchronizer assembly.

NOTE: There is a variation in the mainshaft first gear retention. One version has a split washer and a split washer retainer ring. Working with a three-legged puller, pull against the split washer retainer ring to remove the rear bearing.

The other version of the mainshaft first gear retention is a thrust washer between the first gear and the rear bearing. In this version there is not enough room to get a puller behind the thrust washer and it will be necessary to pull on the first gear.

6. Remove the rear bearing and the first gear. Be sure not to lose the needle bearings under the first gear.
7. Remove the first and reverse shift hub sleeve retainer and remove the shift hub and sleeve.
8. Remove the reverse gear. Be sure not to lose the needle bearings under the reverse gear.
9. Remove the second gear retainer and the second gear.

Assembly

1. Install the output shaft, forward end up, in a soft-jawed vise.
2. Position the third gear on the output shaft with the clutching teeth down. Install the locating washer and snap ring.
3. Turn the output shaft over and install the third gear synchronizer ring and the second and third synchronizer assembly.
4. With the clutching teeth of the second gear down, coat the inside diameter of the gear with a high quality heavy grease. This will hold the needle rollers in place during assembly. Install the first row of needle rollers.
5. Position the bearing spacer and install the second row of bearings. Position the outer bearing spacer.
6. Install the second gear on the output shaft, using caution so as not to catch the needle rollers on the edge of a spline or snap ring groove.
7. Install the second gear split washer locating ball and split washer on the output shaft. Install the retaining ring over the split washer.
8. Coat the inside of the reverse gear with grease and install the bearing spacers and the bearings.
9. Install the reverse gear on the

output shaft, position the shift hub sleeve and the shift hub, and install the shift hub sleeve snap ring.
10. Install the spacers and bearings in the first gear and install the gear on the output shaft.
11. Install the first gear retaining washer. Install the output shaft bearing. Be sure that the bearing is tight against the washer.
12. Turn the output shaft over and install the fourth gear with the clutching teeth facing upward.
13. Position the fourth gear synchronizer ring on the clutching teeth of the fourth gear. Install the fourth and fifth shift hub sleeve on the output shaft.
14. Install the fourth and fifth synchronizer and the fifth speed synchronizer ring on the output shaft.
15. Install the thrust bearing and race.

Input Shaft

Disassembly

1. Remove the bearing snap ring from the input shaft. Remove the bearing with the special tool shown in the illustration.
2. Remove the needle bearing retainer and the washer. Remove the needle bearings.

Assembly

1. Press the bearing on the input shaft.
2. Install the needle bearings, the washer and snap ring.

Tool—T53T-7065-A

INPUT SHAFT

Removing the input shaft bearing—Clark 390V
(© Ford Motor Co.)

Counter Shaft

Disassembly

1. Remove the snap ring at the forward end of the counter shaft.
2. Place the countershaft assembly in a hydraulic press, and press the drive gear off the shaft.
3. Remove the key from the shaft and press the fourth-speed gear off the shaft. Remove the remaining key.

Assembly

1. Install the fourth-speed gear key in the slot on the shaft. Position

the fourth-speed gear on the shaft with the long hub facing toward the front.
2. Install the countershaft main drive gear key in the keyway on the shaft. Install the countershaft drive gear on the shaft with the long hub facing toward the rear. Install the snap ring on the countershaft.

Gear Shift Housing

Disassembly

NOTE: It is not necessary to disassemble the gear shift housing assembly to determine if the parts are worn. Note the condition of the shifter fork shafts and the forks by visual inspection. If the forks are excessively worn, or if they bind when shifted into the various positions, disassemble the gear shift housing. Check the interlocking system.

1. With the control cover in neutral, pry the fourth-fifth speed shift fork to the fourth speed position (toward the rear of the cover). Remove the front rail support capscrews and remove the front rail support.
2. Remove the interlock tapered pin supports. Note the position on the interlock tapered pins for reassembly.
3. Remove the rear rail support capscrews and remove the rear rail support.
4. Remove the first-and-reverse shift fork and rail assembly, remove the fourth, fifth, second and third shift fork and rail assembly. Use caution so that the interlock cross pin, interlock tapered pins, or the mesh lock poppet balls are not lost.
5. Remove the first-reverse shift rail. Remove the four mesh lock poppet balls, and then remove the four poppet springs.
6. Remove the first-reverse rocker arm. Remove the reverse latch plunger spring retaining plug and the reverse latch plunger spring and plunger.
7. If the fork bushings are worn, secure the fork in a soft-jawed vise and remove the worn bushings with a suitable drift. Install the new bushings in the fork. Turn the fork over on the anvil of the vise and secure the bushing in the fork, using a pick punch and upsetting the bushing metal on the outside of the fork.

Assembly

1. Position the first-reverse rocker arm on the pivot pin. Install the reverse latch plunger, spring and the retaining plug. Tighten the plug securely.
2. Install the four poppet springs and the four mesh lock poppet balls.

NOTE: the first-reverse poppet ball in the pocket.

3. Align one tapered interlock cross pin with the hole in the first-reverse shift rail. Position the rail on the poppet ball, with the rail in the neutral position. Note the position of the tapered interlock pin in relation to the rail.
4. Install the interlock cross pin in the second-third shift rail. Position the rail on the poppet ball, in neutral position with the interlock pin aligned with the first interlock pin aligned with the first tapered pin. Install the second interlock tapered pin. Align the pin with the interlock cross pin hole.
5. Position the fourth-fifth shift fork rail assembly on the poppet ball in the neutral position. Slightly raise the rear of the rail and align the second interlock tapered pin with the cross hole in the rail. Note the positions of the tapered interlock pins in the shift rails.
6. Install the first-reverse shift fork and rail assembly on the poppet ball in a neutral position. Align the first-reverse rocker arm in the rear of the rail.
7. Install the rail support capscrews and washers. Tighten the capscrews slightly. Install the interlock tapered pin supports. Tap the fourth-fifth shift fork to the rear (fourth-speed position).
8. Position the front rail support and install the capscrews and washers. Tighten the front and rear support capscrews to 20-25 ft-lbs.
9. Tap the fourth-fifth shift fork and rail assembly forward to a neutral position.

Assembly of Transmission

1. Coat the front counter shaft needle bearings with grease and install them in the front countershaft bore.
2. Tap the rear of the countershaft down and lower into the case. Push the countershaft forward and insert the shaft into the front bearing.
3. Position the countershaft rear bearing oil slinger and bearing on the shaft. Drive the bearing into the bore. The countershaft drive gear should be supported while driving the shaft to prevent damage to the front bearing. Install the rear bearing retainer.
4. Coat the reverse idler thrust washer with grease and position them in the transmission case.
5. Insert the bearings in the reverse idler bore. Place the gear assembly in position in the case,

Gear shift housing—exploded view—Clark 390V (© Ford Motor Co.)

Installing the rear countershaft bearing—Clark 390V (© Ford Motor Co.)

with the small gear toward the rear of the case.
6. Insert the reverse idler shaft through the hole in the case, through the reverse idler gear, and into the forward support boss. Drive the reverse idler shaft into the case until the slot in the shaft is lined up with the

lock bolt hole. Install the retainer in the slot and secure the retainer with the lock bolt. Tighten the bolt to specification.
7. Tilt the rear of the output shaft assembly downward and insert the end of the shaft through the output shaft in the bore in the case. Lower the front end of the output shaft until it is in line with the pilot bearing opening. Move the assembly forward into position.
8. Insert the pilot bearing in the input shaft bore.
9. Position the input shaft and bearings in the forward end of the transmission case. Tap the front end of the shaft with a soft faced hammer until the snap ring is seated against the case. Be sure the clutching teeth of the input shaft gear mesh with the fifth-speed synchronizer without binding.
10. Position a new gasket on the input shaft bearing retainer. *Be*

sure that the oil return holes in the retainer and gasket are aligned with the holes in the transmission case.

11. Install the lock washers and bolts on the input shaft bearing retainer and tighten the bolts to specification.

12. Position the output shaft rear bearing on the shaft and drive the bearing into the bore until the snap ring is seated against the case.

13. Position the countershaft rear bearing cap and gasket on the case and install the lock washers and bolts. Tighten to specification.

14. Install the speedometer drive gear on the output shaft, and position a new oil seal in the output shaft bearing retainer. Be sure the seal is correctly installed. Position a new gasket and the bearing retainer on the case and install the lock washers and bolts. Tighten to specification.

15. Install the parking brake drum and companion flange assembly. Tighten the yoke retaining nut to specification.

16. With the transmission in neutral, position the control cover over the gears, aligning the shift forks in the shift cover with the gear shift hubs. If the control cover is in neutral and the transmission is in neutral, the transmission drive gear should turn without the brake drum or output shaft turning. Install the capscrews and washers, and tighten to 20-25 ft-lbs. Install the remote control or shift tower in the control cover. Tighten the capscrews to 20-25 ft-lbs.

TIGHTEN 15-20 FT. LBS. TORQUE (2,1-2,7 m.kg)

APPLY APPROVED SEALER TO THE FOUR SCREW THREADS

TIGHTEN .5625 THD. NUT AND STUDS 85-105 FT. LBS. TORQUE (11,8-14,5 m.kg)

THESE GASKETS INSTALLED DRY

TIGHTEN FLANGE NUT 400-450 FT. LBS. TORQUE (55,4-62,2 m.kg)

TIGHTEN BOLTS 55-65 FT. LBS. TORQUE (7,7-8,9 m.kg) APPLY APPROVED SEALER TO THE FOUR SCREW THREADS

SHELLAC GASKETS TO BEARING CAPS

TIGHTEN BOLTS MAXIMUM TORQUE 5 FT. LBS. (0,6 m.kg)

SHIM HERE TO OBTAIN .002-.008 (0,051-0,203) ENDPLAY ON MAIN DRIVE GEAR WHEN MAINSHAFT REAR BEARING CUP ASSEMBLY IS TIGHTLY CLAMPED TO REAR FACE OF CASE.

TIGHTEN BOLTS 10-15 FT. LBS. TORQUE BOTH SIDES (1,4-2,0 m.kg)

APPLY APPROVED SEALER TO SCREW THREADS

TIGHTEN DRAIN AND FILLER PLUG 35-45 FT. LBS. TORQUE (4,9-6,2 m.kg)

TIGHTEN .6250-18 THD. NUTS AND STUDS 125-145 FT. LBS. TORQUE (17,3-20,0 m.kg)

UNLESS OTHERWISE SPECIFIED TIGHTEN ALL CAPSCREWS 20-25 FT. LBS. TORQUE (2,8-3,4 m.kg)

Torque specifications—Clark 390V (© Ford Motor Co.)

Dodge/Plymouth A-230 3 Speed

Description

The Dodge A-230 is a three-speed transmission equipped with two synchonizer units to assist in the engagement of all forward gears. Lubricant capacity is 5 pints.

Disassembly of Transmission
Shift Housing and Mechanism
1. Shift to second gear.
2. Remove side cover. If shaft O-ring seals need replacement:
a. Pull shift-forks out of shafts.
b. Remove nuts and operating levers from shafts.
c. Deburr shafts. Remove shafts.

Drive Pinion Retainer and Extension Housing
1. Remove pinion bearing retainer from front of transmission case.

Pry off retainer oil seal. For clearance:
a. With a brass drift, tap drive pinion as far forward as possible. Rotate cut away part of second gear next to countershaft gear. Shift second-third synchronizer sleeve forward.
b. Remove speedometer pinion adapter retainer. Work adapter and pinion out of extension housing.
c. Unbolt extension housing. Break housing loose with plastic hammer and carefully remove.

Idler Gear and Mainshaft
1. Insert dummy shaft in case to push reverse idler shaft and key out of case.

2. Remove dummy shaft and idler rollers.
3. Remove both tanged idler gear thrust washers.
4. Remove mainshaft assembly through rear of case.

Countershaft Gear and Drive Pinion
1. Using a mallet and dummy shaft, tap the countershaft rearward enough to remove key. Drive countershaft out of case, being careful not to drop the washers.
2. Lower countershaft gear to bottom of case.
3. Remove snap-ring from pinion bearing outer race (outside front of case).

1 Gear first	20 ring	39 Retainer	59 Lever, interlock
2 Ring	21 Spring	40 Gasket	60 Lever
3 Spring	22 Sleeve	41 Seal	61 Fork
4 Sleeve	23 Struts (3)	42 Snap ring	62 Spring
5 Struts (3)	24 Spring	43 Snap Ring	63 Snap ring
6 Spring	25 Ring	44 Bearing	64 Washer
7 Snap ring	26 Gear, second	45 Pinion, drive	65 Gear, countershaft
8 Bushing	27 Shaft, output	46 Roller	66 Washer
9 Gear, reverse	28 Washer	47 Snap ring	67 Roller
10 Bearing	29 Roller	48 Case	68 Gear, idler
11 Snap ring	30 Washer	49 Plug, Drain	69 Washer
12 Snap ring	31 Roller	50 Fork	70 Shaft
13 Retainer	32 Washer	51 Lever	71 Key
14 Gasket	33 Countershaft	52 Housing	72 Washer
15 Extension	34 Washer	53 Lever	73 Plug, filler
16 Bushing	35 Roller	54 Nut, locking	74 Gear, Clutch
17 Seal	36 Washer	55 Switch	75 Gear, clutch
18 Yoke	37 Roller	56 Lever	76 Key
19 Snap ring	38 Washer	57 Bolt	77 Gasket
		58 Gasket	

A-230 3 speed transmission (© Chrysler Corp.)

Mainshaft assembly (© Chrysler Corp.)

1st-reverse synchronizer (© Chrysler Corp.)

2nd-3rd synchronizer (© Chrysler Corp)

4. Drive pinion shaft into case with plastic hammer. Remove assembly through rear of case.
5. If bearing is to be replaced, remove snap-ring and press off bearing.
6. Lift counter shaft gear and dummy shaft out through rear of case.

Mainshaft

1. Remove snap-ring from front end of mainshaft along with second gear stop ring and second gear.
2. Spread snap-ring in mainshaft bearing retainer. Slide retainer back off the bearing race.
3. Remove snap-ring at rear of mainshaft. Support front side of reverse gear. Press bearing off mainshaft.
4. Remove from press. Remove mainshaft bearing and reverse gear from shaft.
5. Remove snap-ring and first-reverse synchronizer assembly from shaft. Remove stop ring and first gear rearward.

Cleaning and Inspection

See "Cleaning and Inspection" instructions at front of transmission section.

Assembly of Transmission
Countershaft Gear

1. Slide dummy shaft into countershaft gear.
2. Slide one roller thrust washer over dummy shaft and into gear, followed by 22 greased rollers.
3. Repeat Step 2, adding one roller thrust washer on end.
4. Repeat steps 2 and 3 at other end of countershaft gear. There is a total of 88 rollers and 6 thrust washers.
5. Place greased front thrust washer on dummy shaft against gear with tangs forward.
6. Grease rear thrust washer and stick it in place in the case, with tangs rearward. Place countershaft gear assembly in bottom of

transmission case until drive pinion is installed.

Pinion Gear

1. Press new bearing on pinion shaft with snap-ring groove forward. Install new snap-ring.
2. Install 15 rollers and retaining ring in drive pinion gear.
3. Install drive pinion and bearing assembly into case.
4. Position countershaft gear assembly by positioning it and thrust washers so countershaft can be tapped into position. Be careful to keep the countershaft against the dummy shaft to keep parts from falling between them. Install key in countershaft.
5. Tap drive pinion forward for clearance.

Mainshaft

1. Place a stop ring flat on the bench. Place a clutch gear and a sleeve on top. Drop the struts in their slots and insert a strut spring with the tang inside on strut. Turn the assembly over and install second strut spring, tang in a different strut.
2. Slide first gear and stop ring over rear of mainshaft and against thrust flange between assembly over rear of mainshaft, first and second gears on shaft.
3. Slide first-reverse synchronizer

indexing hub slots to first gear stop ring lugs.
4. Install first-reverse synchronizer clutch gear snap-ring on mainshaft.
5. Slide reverse gear and mainshaft bearing in place. Press bearing on shaft, supporting inner race of bearing. Be sure snap-ring groove on outer race is forward.
6. Install bearing retaining snap-ring on mainshaft. Slide snap-ring over the bearing and seat it in groove.
7. Place second gear over front of mainshaft with thrust surface against flange.
8. Install stop ring and second-third synchronizer assembly against second gear. Install second-third synchronizer clutch gear snap-ring on shaft.
9. Move second-third synchronizer sleeve forward as far as possible. Install front stop ring inside sleeve with lugs indexed to struts.
10. Rotate cut out on second gear toward countershaft gear for clearance.
11. Insert mainshaft assembly into case. Tilt assembly to clear cluster gears and insert pilot rollers in drive pinion gear. If assembly is correct, the bearing retainer will bottom to the case without force. If not, check for a misplaced strut, pinion roller, or stop ring.

Reverse Idler Gear

1. Place dummy shaft into idler gear. Insert 22 greased rollers.
2. Position reverse idler thrust washers in case with grease.
3. Position idler gear and dummy shaft in case. Install idler shaft and key.

Extension Housing

1. Remove extension housing yoke seal. Drive bushing out from inside housing.
2. Align oil hole in bushing with oil slot in housing. Drive bushing into place. Drive new seal into housing.
3. Install extension housing and gasket to hold mainshaft and bearing retainer in place.

Drive Pinion Bearing Retainer

1. Install outer snap-ring on drive pinion bearing. Tap assembly back until snap-ring contacts case.
2. Using seal installer tool or equivalent, install a new seal in retainer bore.
3. Position main drive pinion bearing retainer and gasket on front of case. Coat threads with sealing compound, install bolts, torque to 30 ft. lbs.

Gearshift Mechanism and Housing

1. If removed, place two interlock levers in pivot pin with spring hangers offset toward each other, so that spring installs in a straight line. Place E-clip on pivot pin.

Gearshift mechanism and housing
(© Chrysler Corp.)

2. Grease and install new O-ring seals on both shift shafts. Grease housing bores and insert shafts.
3. Install spring on interlock lever hangers.
4. Rotate each shift shaft fork bore to straight up position. Install shift forks through bores and under both interlock levers.
5. Position second-third synchronizer sleeve to rear, in second gear position. Position first-reverse synchronizer sleeve to middle of travel, in neutral position. Place shift forks in the same positions.
6. Install gasket and gearshift mechanism. The bolt with the extra long shoulder must be installed at the center rear of the case. Torque bolts to 15 ft. lbs.

7. Install speedometer drive pinion gear and adapter. Range number on adapter, which represents the number of teeth on the gear, should be in 6 o'clock position.

Torque Chart

Manual A-203 3-Speed

	Foot-Pounds
Back up light switch	15
Extension housing bolts	50
Drive pinion bearing retainer bolts	30
Gearshift operating lever nuts	18
Transmission to clutch housing bolts	50
Transmission cover retaining bolts	12
Transmission drain plug	25

Dodge/Plymouth A-250 3 Speed

Description

The Dodge A-250 is a three speed transmission equipped with a synchronizer between second and third gears. Lubricant capacity is 4½ pints.

Disassembly of Transmission

1. Remove case cover and gasket.
2. Measure the synchronizer "float" with a pair of feeler gauges. Measurement is made between the synchronizer outer ring pin and the opposite synchronizer outer ring. This measurement must be made on two pins 180 degrees apart with equal gap on both ends for "float" determination. The measurement should be between 0.060-0.117 inch. A snug fit should be maintained between feeler gauge and pins.
3. Remove the bolt and retainer holding the speedometer pinion adapter in the extension housing. Carefully work the adapter

'Cover removal—Dodge A-250

and pinion out of the extension housing.
4. Remove extension housing bolts and extension housing.
5. Remove the bolts that attach the drive pinion bearing retainer to case, then slide the retainer off the pinion. Pry the seal out of

retainer using a screwdriver. Be cautious not to nick or scratch the bore.
6. Rotate the drive pinion so that the blank clutch tooth area is opposite the countershaft for removal clearance.
7. Slide drive pinion assembly

GEAR
SPRING
GEAR
RING
RING
SLEEVE
RING
COVER
SCREW
GEAR
FORK
SHAFT
BEARING
SNAP RING
EXTENSION
BUSHING
SEAL
SPACER
ROLLERS
WASHER
RING
RING
WASHER
ROLLERS
GEAR
WASHER
GEAR
ROLLERS
LEVER
WASHER
FORK
LEVER
SPRING
SLEEVE
GASKET
BALL
PIN
GASKET
PLUG
KEY
SHAFT
KEY
SHAFT
BEARING
WASHER
SCREW
PLUG
PIN
SCREW
WASHER
GASKET
RING
CASE
PIN
PLUG
SEALS
LEVER
NUT
PIVOT PIN
SPRING WASHER
RING
ROLLERS
PINION
OIL SLINGER
WASHER
WASHER
NUT
CLIP
WASHER
SEAL
GASKET
RETAINER
LOCKWASHER
LOCKWASHER
PAWL

Dodge A-250 transmission—exploded view

slightly out of case. Move the synchronizer front inner stop ring from the short splines on the pinion shaft. Slowly remove drive pinion assembly.

8. Remove snap ring that holds bearing on pinion shaft. Remove pinion bearing washer. Using an arbor press, press pinion shaft out of bearing. Remove oil slinger.
9. Remove snap ring and bearing rollers from the end of the drive pinion.
10. Remove clutch gear retaining snap ring from the mainshaft.
11. Remove the mainshaft bearing securing snap ring from case.
12. Slide mainshaft and bearing rearward out of case while holding the gears as they drop free.
13. Remove the snap ring from mainshaft and press the bearing off of mainshaft.

14. Remove the synchronizer components, second gear, first-reverse gear and shift forks from case.

NOTE: Steps 15 thru 18 need only be performed if gear shift lever seals are leaking.

15. Remove the shift levers from the shift shafts.
16. Drive out the tapered retaining pin from the first-reverse shift shaft. Remove the shift shaft from inside the case.
   As the detent balls are spring loaded, when the shafts are removed the balls will drop to the bottom of the transmission case.
17. Remove the interlock sleeve, spring and both detent balls from case. Drive tapered retaining pin out of second-third shaft and remove shaft from case.
18. Drive shift shaft seals out of case with a suitable drift.

19. Check end play of countershaft gear with a feeler gauge. The end play should be between 0.005-0.022 inch. This measurement is used to determine if a new thrust washer is necessary during reassembly.
20. Using a countershaft bearing arbor, drive the countershaft towards the rear of the case until the small key can be removed from the countershaft.
21. Drive the countershaft the rest of the way out of the case, keeping the arbor tight against the end of the countershaft. This will prevent loss of roller bearings.
22. Remove the countershaft gear, front thrust washer and rear thrust washer from the case.
23. Remove the bearing rollers, spacer ring and center spacer from the countershaft gear.

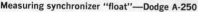

PIN
FEELER GAUGE
RING
RING
PIN
FEELER GAUGE

Measuring synchronizer "float"—Dodge A-250

3 TEETH OMITTED TO CLEAR CLUSTER GEAR DURING ASSEMBLY
BEARING AND SNAP RING
WASHER
SNAP RING (SELECT THICKNESS FOR MINIMUM END PLAY)
SLINGER
OIL SEAL SURFACE

Drive pinion assembly—Dodge A-250

SYNCHRONIZER-OUTER STOP RINGS

PILOT END OF MAINSHAFT

DRIVE PINION AND BEARING

CLUTCH GEAR SLEEVE

MAINSHAFT PILOT BEARING ROLLERS

SNAP RING

Removing of Installing drive pinion—Dodge A-250

Mainshaft pilot bearings in the end of the drive pinion—Dodge A-250

CLUTCH GEAR SNAP RING ON MAINSHAFT

SPRING-SYNCHRONIZER STOP RING

Removing of installing clutch gear snap ring—Dodge A-250

BACK UP LIGHT SWITCH

MAINSHAFT BEARING TO CASE SNAP RING (SELECT THICKNESS FOR MINIMUM END PLAY)

SPEEDOMETER DRIVE WORM ON MAINSHAFT

Removing mainshaft-to-case snap ring

SYNCHRONIZER INNER STOP RING

SYNCHRONIZER CLUTCH GEAR

MAINSHAFT BEARING

Removing mainshaft from case and gear—Dodge A-250

PROP SHAFT SLIDING YOKE SPLINES

1ST-REVERSE SLIDING GEAR SPLINES

2ND-GEAR BEARING SURFACE

CLUTCH GEAR SPLINES

PILOT BEARING SURFACE

MAINSHAFT BEARING SNAP RING (SELECT THICKNESS FOR MINIMUM END PLAY)

Mainshaft and bearing assembly—Dodge A-250

24. Drive the reverse idler gear shaft out of the transmission case using a suitable drift. Remove the woodruff key from the end of the reverse idler shaft.

25. Remove the reverse idler gear and thrust washers out of the case. Remove the bearing rollers from the gear.

Cleaning and Inspection

See "Cleaning and Inspection" instructions at the front of the transmission section.

Assembly of Transmission

1. Slide the countershaft gear bearing roller spacer over arbor tool. Coat the bore of gear with lubricant and slide tool and spacer into gear bore.

2. Lubricate the bearing rollers with heavy grease and install two rows of 22 rollers each in

LOW AND REVERSE CAM

R N L

BALL
SPRING
PIN
SLEEVE
CASE

2ND AND DIRECT CAM

D N S

2ND AND DIRECT FORK

2ND AND DIRECT LEVER

LOW AND REVERSE FORK

BALL PIN

SLEEVE SPRING

BALL

LOW AND REVERSE LEVER

Shift forks and levers—Dodge A-250

both ends of gear in area around arbor. Cover with heavy grease and install bearing spacer rings in each end of gear and between roller rows.

3. If countershaft gear end play was found to be excessive during disassembly, install new thrust washers. Cover with heavy grease and install thrust washer and thrust needle bearing and cap at each end of countershaft gear and over arbor. Install gear and arbor in the case, and make sure that tabs on rear thrust washer slide into grooves in the case.

4. Drive the arbor forward out of the countershaft gear and through the bore in the front of the case using the countershaft and a soft faced hammer. When the countershaft is almost

Synchronizer—exploded view—Dodge A-250

SNAP RING
CLUTCH GEAR
CLUTCH GEAR SLEEVE
SPRING
OUTER STOP RINGS
INNER STOP RINGS

Checking countershaft gear end play—Dodge A-250

BACK-UP LIGHT SWITCH
REVERSE IDLER GEAR
FEELER GAUGE
COUNTERSHAFT GEAR

in place, make certain the keyway in the countershaft is aligned with the key slot in the rear of the case. Insert the shaft key and continue to drive the countershaft into the case until the key is bottomed in the slot.

5. Position special arbor tool in the reverse idler gear and install the 22 roller bearings using a heavy grease.

6. Place the front and rear thrust washers at each end of the reverse idler gear. Position the assembly in the transmission case with the chamfered end of the gear teeth towards the front. Make sure that the thrust washer tabs engage the slots in case.

7. Insert reverse idler shaft into the bore at rear of case with keyway to the rear, pushing the arbor towards the front of the case.

8. When the keyway is aligned with the slot in the case, insert the key in the keyway. Drive the shaft forward until the key is seated in the recess.

NOTE: Steps 9 thru 14 need only be performed if the shift levers have been disassembled.

9. Place new shift shaft seals in the case and drive it into position with suitable drift.

10. Carefully slide the first-reverse shift shaft into the case and lock into place with a tapered retaining pin. Position the lever so that the center detent is aligned with the interlock bore.

11. Install the interlock sleeve into the bore followed by a detent ball, spring and pin.

12. Install remaining detent ball and hold in place with detent ball holding tool.

13. Depress the detent ball and carefully install the second-third shift shaft. Align center detent with detent ball and secure lever with tapered retaining pin.

14. Install shift levers and tighten retaining nuts to 18 foot-pounds.

15. Press the bearing on the mainshaft and select and install snap ring that gives minimum end play.

16. Move shift lever to reverse position, and then place the first-reverse gear and shift fork in the case.

NOTE: Both shift forks are offset toward the rear of the transmission case.

17. Assemble the synchronizer parts with shift fork and second gear.

18. Place the second gear assembly in the transmission case and insert the shift fork into its lever.

19. Install the mainshaft carefully through the gear assembly until it bottoms in rear of case.

20. Install synchronizer clutch gear snap ring on mainshaft.

21. Select and install mainshaft bearing snap ring in case.

22. If "float" measurement was found to be outside specifications, install or remove shims to place "float" within range.

23. Install oil slinger on drive pinion shaft and slide against the gear.

24. Slide the bearing over the pinion shaft with snap ring groove away from gear, then seat bearing on shaft using an arbor press.

25. Install keyed washer between bearing and retaining snap ring groove.

26. Secure bearing and washer with selected thickness snap ring. If large snap ring around bearing was removed, install it at this time.

27. Place drive pinion shaft in a vise with soft faced jaws and install the 14 roller bearings in the shaft cavity. Coat the roller bearings with a heavy grease and install retaining ring in groove.

28. Rotate the drive pinion so that the blank clutch tooth area is next to the countershaft. Guide the drive pinion through the front of case and engage the inner stop ring with the clutch teeth. Then seat pinion bearing.

1ST-REVERSE LEVER
2ND-3RD LEVER
DETENT BALL-HOLDING TOOL

Installing shift levers and detent—Dodge A-250

SUPPORTING GEARSET FOR MAINSHAFT INSTALLATION

Installing mainshaft into the gears and case—Dodge A-250

DRIVE PINION BEARING RETAINER

SEAL INSTALLING TOOL

Drive pinion seal replacement—Dodge A-250

SPREADER SPRING

2ND SPEED GEAR

INSERT SHIM AGAINST THIS FACE

Synchronizer shim location—Dodge A-250

The pinion shaft is fully seated when the snap ring is in full contact with the case.

29. Install a new seal in the pinion bearing retainer.

30. Position retainer assembly and new gasket on the case. Use sealing compound on bolts and tighten to 30 foot-pounds.

31. Slide the extension housing and a new gasket over mainshaft. Guide shaft through bushing and oil seal. Use sealing compound on the bolt used in the hole tapped through the transmission case. Install remaining bolts and tighten all to 50 foot-pounds.

32. Install the transmission cover and gasket and tighten cover bolts to 12 foot-pounds.

33. Rotate the speedometer pinion gear and adapter assembly so that the number on the adapter corresponding to the number of teeth on the gear is in the 6 o'clock position as the assembly is installed.

34. Fill the transmission with the proper lubricant and install the drain plug and tighten to 25 ft.-lbs. Install the back-up light switch and tighten to 15 ft.-lbs.

35. Rotate the drive pinion shaft and check operation of transmission by running the transmission through all gear ranges.

Dodge/Plymouth A-390 Three Speed

Description

The A-390 is a three speed synchromesh transmission. Lubricant capacity is 4½ pints.

Disassembly of Transmission

1. Remove the bolts that attach the cover to the case. Remove the cover and gasket.

2. Remove the long spring that retains the detent plug in the case. Remove the detent plug with a small magnet.

3. Remove the bolt and retainer securing the speedometer pinion adapter to the transmission case. Carefully work the adapter and pinion out of the extension housing.

4. Remove the bolts that attach the extension housing to the transmission case. Slide the extension housing off the output shaft.

5. Remove the bolts that attach the input shaft bearing retainer to the case. Slide the retainer off the shaft. Using a suitable tool, pry the seal out of the retainer. Be careful not to nick or scratch the bore in which the seal is pressed of the surface on which the seal is bottomed.

6. Remove the lubricant fill plug from the right side of the case. Working through the fill plug opening, drive the roll pin out of the countershaft with a ¼ inch punch.

7. Working with the countershaft bearing arbor and a soft faced hammer, tap the countershaft toward the front of the case with the arbor tool to remove the expansion plug from the countershaft bore at the front of the case. The countershaft is a loose fit in the case and will slide easily.

8. Insert the arbor tool through the front of the case and push the countershaft out of the rear of the case so the roll pin hole in the countershaft does not travel through the roller bearings. The countershaft gear will drop to the bottom of the case. Remove the countershaft from the rear of the case.

9. Place both shift levers in neutral (center) position.

10. Remove the input shaft assembly and stop ring from the front of the case.

11. Remove the set screw that secures the first-reverse shift fork to the shift rail. Slide the

¼ INCH PUNCH

ROLL PIN

COUNTERSHAFT GEAR

Removing the roll pin from the countershaft—A-390 (© Chrysler Corp.)

COUNTERSHAFT GEAR

C-4337 ARBOR

COUNTERSHAFT

Removing the countershaft—A-390 (© Chrysler Corp.)

1003

Manual Transmissions

1 Transmission case cover
2 Transmission case cover screw
3 Transmission case cover gasket
4 Countershaft roller bearing
5 Countershaft bearing washer
6 Countershaft thrust washer
7 Reverse idler thrust washer
8 Reverse idler bushing
9 Countershaft
10 Countershaft roll pin
11 Reverse idler gear
12 Output shaft bearing
13 Reverse idler shaft
14 Reverse idler stop pin
15 Output shaft bearing outer snap ring
16 Output shaft inner snap ring
17 Extension
18 Extension seal
19 Back-up light switch
20 Back-up lamp switch gasket
21 Extension screw and lockwasher
22 Output shaft bearing retainer
23 Extension gasket
24 First-reverse shift rail
25 Shift fork set screw
26 First-reverse shift fork
27 Shift lever oil seal
28 Gearshift lever
29 Transmission case
30 Plug
31 Second-third shift rail
32 Shift detent spring pin
33 Second-third shift fork
34 Shift detent pin
35 Shift detent pin spring
36 Plug
37 Transmission case filler plug
38 Countershaft gear
39 Second-third synchronizer assembly
40 Second-third synchronizer stop ring
41 Second gear
42 Low speed gear thrust washer snap ring
43 Low speed gear thrust washer
44 Low speed gear
45 First-reverse synchronizer stop ring
46 First-reverse synchronizer clutch gear snap ring
47 First-reverse synchronizer assembly
48 Output shaft
49 Output shaft pilot roller bearing
50 Input shaft
51 Input shaft bearing
52 Bearing outer snap ring
53 Bearing inner snap ring
54 Bearing retainer oil seal
55 Bearing retainer snap ring
56 Bearing retainer
57 Bearing retainer screw

Dodge/Plymouth A-390 Transmission—exploded view (© Chrysler Corp.)

first-reverse shift rail out through the rear of the case.

12. Move the second-third shift fork rearward for access to the set screw. Remove the setscrew from the fork. Using a suitable tool, rotate the shift rail one quarter (¼) turn.
13. Lift the interlock plug from the case with a magnet.
14. Tap on the inner end of the second-third shift rail to remove the expansion plug from the front of the case. Remove the shift rail through the front of the case.
15. Remove the second-third shift rail detent plug and spring from the detent bore with a magnet.
16. Tap the output shaft assembly rearward until the output shaft bearing clears the case. Remove both shift forks. Remove the snap ring that retains the output shaft bearing to the output shaft.

17. Assemble the output shaft bearing removal tool over the output shaft and bearing. Remove the output shaft bearing.
18. Remove the output shaft assembly through top of the case.
19. Using a suitable drift, drive the reverse idler gear shaft toward the rear, and out of the transmission case.
20. Lift the reverse idler gear and thrust washer out of the case.
21. Remove the countershaft gear, arbor assembly, and thrust washers from the bottom of the case.
22. Remove the countershaft roll pin from the bottom of the case.
23. Remove the snap ring that retains the second-third synchronizer clutch gear and sleeve assembly on the output shaft. Slide the second-third synchronizer assembly off the end of the output shaft.

NOTE: Do not separate the second-third synchronizer clutch gear, sleeve,

struts, or spring unless inspection reveals that a replacement is necssary.
24. Slide the second gear and stop ring off the output shaft.
25. Remove the snap ring and thrust washer retaining the first gear. Slide the first gear and stop ring off the output shaft.
26. Remove the snap ring that retains the first-reverse synchronizer hub on the output shaft. The first-reverse synchronizer hub is a press fit on the output shaft. To avoid damage to the synchronizer, remove the synchronizer hub using an arbor press. Do not attempt to remove or install the hub by hammering or prying.

Sub-Assembly Overhaul
Shift Levers and Seals

1. Remove the operating levers from their respective shafts. Remove any burrs from the shafts to avoid damage to the case.
2. Push the shift levers out of the

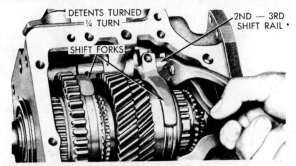

Rotating the second-third shift rail ¼ turn—A-390 (© Chrysler Corp.)

Shift rails and forks—exploded view—A-390 (© Chrysler Corp.)

transmission case. Remove and discard the "O" ring seal from each shaft.

3. Lubricate the new seals with transmission oil and install them on the shafts.
4. Install the shift levers in the case.
5. Install the operating levers and tighten the retaining nuts to 18 ft-lbs.

Input Shaft Bearing and Rollers

1. Remove the snap ring securing the bearing on the input shaft. Carefully press the input shaft out of the bearing with an arbor press.
2. Remove the fifteen bearing rollers from the cavity in the end of the input shaft.
3. Install the 15 bearing rollers in the cavity of the input shaft. Coat the rollers with a thin film of grease to retain them during installation.
4. Slide the input shaft bearing over the input shaft, snap ring groove away from the gear end. Seat the bearing assembly on the input shaft with an arbor press.
5. Secure the bearing with the snap ring. Be sure the snap ring is properly seated. If a large snap ring around the bearing was removed, be sure to install it at this time.

Synchronizers

NOTE: If either synchronizer is to be disassembled, mark all parts so that they will be reassembled in the same position. Do not mix parts from the two synchronizers.

1. Push the synchronizer hub off each synchronizer sleeve.
2. Separate the struts and springs from the hubs.
3. Install the spring on the front side of the first-reverse synchronizer hub, making sure that all three strut slots are fully covered. Hang the three struts on the spring and in the slots with the wide end of the strut inside the hub.
4. With the alignment marks on the hub and sleeve aligned, push the

Removing the output shaft bearing—A-390 (© Chrysler Corp.)

Removing and installing the first-reverse synchronizer hub—A-390 (© Chrysler Corp.)

sleeve down on the hub until the struts are in the neutral detent. Place the stop ring on top of the synchronizer assembly.

5. With the alignment marks on the second-third synchronizer sleeve and hub aligned, slide the sleeve on the hub. Drop in the three struts in the strut slots. Install the spring with the hump in the center, into the hollow of the strut. Turn the assembly over and install the other spring so

that the hump in the center of the spring is inserted in the same strut. Place the stop ring on each end of the synchronizer assembly.

Countershaft Gear and Bearing

1. Remove the countershaft bearing arbor, the roller bearings and the two bearing retainers from the countershaft gear.
2. Coat the bore in each end of the countershaft gear with grease.
3. Insert the countershaft arbor and install twenty five roller bearings and the retainer washer in each end of the countershaft gear.
4. Position the countershaft gear and arbor assembly in the transmission case. Align the gear bore and the thrust washers with the bores in the case and install the countershaft.
5. Using a feeler gauge, check the countershaft gear end play. The end play should be within 0.004-0.018 inch. If the clearance is not within limits, replace the thrust washers.
6. After establishing the correct end play, install the arbor tool in the countershaft gear and lower the gear and tool out of the bottom of the transmission case.

Assembly of Transmission

1. Coat the countershaft gear thrust surfaces in the case with a thin film of grease and position the two thrust washers in place. Place the countershaft gear and arbor assembly in the proper position in the bottom of the transmission case. The countershaft gear will remain in the bottom of the case until the output and input shafts are installed.
2. Coat the reverse idler gear thrust surfaces in the case with a thin film of grease and position the two thrust washers in place. Install the reverse idler gear in the case and align the gear bore with

Assembling the first-reverse synchronizer—A-390 (© Chrysler Corp.)

Assembling the second-third synchronizer—A-390 (© Chrysler Corp.)

Countershaft and gear—exploded view—A-390 (© Chrysler Corp.)

the thrust washers in the case bore. Install the reverse idler shaft.

3. Measure the reverse idler gear end play with a feeler gauge. End play should be 0.004-0.018 inch. If the clearance is not within limits, replace the thrust washers. If the end play is correct, leave the reverse idler gear in place.

4. Lubricate the output shaft splines and the machined surfaces with transmission oil.

5. Slide the first reverse synchronizer onto the output shaft with the fork groove toward the front. The first-reverse synchronizer hub is a press fit on the output shaft. To eliminate the possibility of damage to the hub, install the hub using an arbor press. *Do not attempt to install the hub by hammering or driving.* Secure the hub on the output shaft with the snap ring.

6. Slide the first gear and stop ring onto the output shaft, aligning the slots in the stop ring with the struts. Install the thrust washer and snap ring.

7. Slide the second gear and stop ring on the output shaft.

8. Install the second-third synchronizer assembly on the output shaft. Rotate the second gear to index the struts with the slots in the stop ring. Secure the synchronizer with a snap ring.

9. Position the output shaft assembly in the transmission case. Place the transmission in a vertical position with the front of the case flat on the work bench.

Place a 1¼ inch block of wood under the end of the output shaft. The block of wood will hold the output shaft assembly up during installation of the output shaft bearing.

10. Install the large snap ring on the output shaft bearing. Place the bearing on the output shaft with the large snap ring up. Drive the bearing on the shaft until it

Output shaft assembly—exploded view—A-390 (© Chrysler Corp.)

is seated on the shaft. Secure the bearing on the output shaft with the snap ring. Return the transmission to a horizontal position.

11. Insert both shift forks in the case and in their proper sleeves. Push the output shaft assembly into position and tap it forward until the output shaft bearing is seated in the transmission case.
12. Install the *shortest* detent spring followed by a detent plug into the case. Place the second-third synchronizer assembly in the second gear position.
13. Align the second-third shift fork and install the second-third shift rail. The second-third shift rail is the shortest of the two shift rails. It will be necessary to depress the detent plug to enter the shift rail in the bore. Move the rail inward until the detent plug engages the forward notch (second gear position).
14. Secure the fork to the rail with the set screw. Move the synchronizer to the neutral position.
15. Install a new expansion plug in the transmission case.
16. Install the interlock plug in the transmission case with a magnet. If the second-third shift rail is in the neutral position, the top of the interlock plug will be slightly lower than the surface of the first-reverse shift rail bore.
17. Align the first reverse fork and install the first-reverse shift rail. Move the rail inward until the center notch (neutral) is aligned with the detent bore. Secure the fork to the rail with the set screw.
18. Using a suitable tool, install a new oil seal in the input shaft bearing retainer bore.
19. Coat the bore of the input shaft

gear with a thin film of grease. *A thick, heavy grease will plug the lubricant holes and prevent lubrication of the roller bearings.* Install the fifteen roller bearings in the bore.
20. Place the stop ring, slots aligned with the struts, into the second-third synchronizer. Tap the input shaft assembly into place in the case while holding the output shaft to prevent the roller bearings from dropping.
21. Roll the transmission over so that it rests on both the top edge and the shift levers. The countershaft gear will drop into place. Using a screw driver, align the countershaft gear and thrust washers with the bore in the transmission case.
22. Working from the rear of the case, slide the countershaft into position being careful to keep the countershaft in contact with the arbor to avoid dropping parts out of position. Be sure that the roll pin hole in the countershaft aligns with the roll pin hole in the case.
23. Install the roll pin. Install a new expansion plug in the counter-

shaft bore at the front of the case. Install the plug flush of below the face of the case to prevent interference with the clutch housing.
24. Slide the extension housing, with a new gasket, over the output shaft and against the case. Coat the attaching bolt threads with a sealing compound. Install and tighten the attaching bolts to 50 ft-lbs.
25. Install the input shaft bearing retainer and a new gasket. Make sure that the oil return slot is at the bottom. Coat the threads with a sealing compound, install the attaching bolts and tighten to 30 ft-lbs.
26. Install the remaining detent plug into the case followed by the detent spring.
27. Install the filler plug and the back-up light switch. Pour lubricant over the entire gear train while rotating the input shaft and the output shaft.
28. Place the cover and a new gasket on the transmission. Coat the attaching screw threads with a sealing compound. Install and tighten the attaching screws to 22 ft-lbs.

Torque Specifications

	Foot-Pounds
Cover to case screws	22
Back-up light switch	15
Extension housing to case bolts	50
Extension housing to cross member bolts	50
Gearshift lever nuts	18
Input shaft bearing retainer bolts	30
Shift fork to shift rail set screw	10
Transmission to clutch housing bolts	50
Transmission drain plug	25
Transmission filler plug	15

Dodge/Plymouth A-745 3 Speed

Description

The Dodge A-745 is a three-speed synchromesh transmission having helical type gears. Lubricant capacity is 3¼ pints.

Disassembly of Transmission

1. Remove output flange nut, then the drum and flange assembly, if so equipped. Remove parking brake assembly, if so equipped.
2. Remove case cover. Measure synchronizer float with a feeler gauge between the end of a synchronizer pin and the opposite synchronizer outer ring. A measurement from .050-.090 in. is acceptable for 1964-67 models. The measurement should be .060-.117 in. for 1968 and up models.

3. Remove the extension housing from the case.
4. Remove the mainshaft rear bearing, if it did not come off with the extension housing.
5. Remove transmission case cover and gasket.
6. Remove the drive pinion bearing retainer.
7. When removing the drive pinion and bearing assembly from the transmission case, slide the front inner stop ring from the short splines on the pinion as the assembly is being removed from the case.
8. Remove the main drive pinion bearing snap-ring.
9. Press bearing off pinion shaft and remove oil slinger.

10. Remove mainshaft pilot bearing snap-ring from the cavity of the pinion gear.
11. Remove the 15 pilot roller bearings.
12. Remove seal from pinion retainer.
13. Remove mainshaft rear bearing snap-ring from groove in mainshaft rear bearing bore in the case.
14. Remove the rear bearing snap-ring from groove in mainshaft rear bearing bore in the case.
14. Remove the rear bearing from the case by moving the mainshaft and rear bearing assembly to the rear.
15. Remove synchronizer assembly from case.

Synchronizer components (© Chrysler Corp.)

Drive pinion assembly (© Chrysler Corp.)

16. Remove second and third-speed shift fork.
17. Remove synchronizer clutch gear, snap-ring, clutch gear, second-speed gear, and first and reverse sliding gear from the mainshaft.
18. Withdraw mainshaft and bearing out through the rear of the case.
19. Remove the synchronizer clutch gear, second-speed gear, low and reverse sliding gear, and low and reverse shift fork from the case.
20. With a dummy shaft, drive the countershaft toward the rear of the case until the small key can be removed from the countershaft.
21. Remove the countershaft from the case.

22. Lift the cluster gear, the thrust washers and the dummy shaft assembly out of the case.
23. Dismantle the cluster gear, (88 rollers, four spacer rings and the center spacer from the cluster).
24. With a blunt drift, drive the reverse idler shaft toward the rear of the case far enough to remove the key from the shaft.
25. Completely remove the shaft from the case, then remove the idler gear.
26. Remove the thrust washers and 22 rollers.
27. Wtih a small punch, remove low and reverse gear lever shaft tapered lock pin by driving it toward the top of the transmission case.

28. Remove the second and third gear lever shaft in the same manner.
29. Remove the lever shafts from the transmission case being careful not to lose the spring-loaded detent balls.
30. Remove the interlock sleeve, spring pin and detent balls.
31. Remove both lever shaft seals and discard same.

Assembly of Transmission

1. Place oil slinger on the main drive pinion with the offset outer portion next to the drive pinion teeth.
2. Place the main drive pinion bearing on the pinion shaft with

The A-745 transmission (© Chrysler Corp.)

the outer snap-ring away from the pinion gear.

3. Press the bearing into position so it is seated firmly against the oil slinger and pinion gear.

4. Install the bearing retaining snap-ring in its groove on the pinion shaft.

5. Heavily grease the 15 pilot bearing rollers and install them in the cavity at the rear of the main drive pinion.

6. Install the snap-ring.

7. Place the bearing spacer in the center of the bore in the cluster gear and use the dummy shaft to assist in assembling the roller bearings.

8. Install a row of 22 rollers next to one end of the spacer, using heavy grease to hold them.

9. Place one of the four bearing spacer rings next to the row of rollers, and install another row of 22 rollers next to the spacer ring.

10. Install another spacer ring at the outside end of the second row of bearing rollers.

11. At the opposite end of the cluster gear bore, install the remaining spacer rings and bearing rollers in the same sequence as listed in Steps 8, 9, and 10.

12. With a small amount of grease, install the front thrust washer on the dummy shaft at the front end of the cluster gear, with the tabs outward.

13. Install the tabbed rear thrust washer onto the dummy shaft against the rear of the cluster gear with the tabs inserted in the cluster gear grooves.

14. Install the remaining rear thrust washer plate onto the rear of the gear and dummy shaft with the step in the washer facing upward, as viewed from the rear.

15. Align tabs of the front thrust washer vertically to index with notches in the transmission case and with the step in the rear thrust washer positioned upward. Insert the cluster gear and dummy shaft in the transmission case.

16. Using the countershaft, drive the dummy shaft forward, out of the case. Countershaft end play should be .0045-.028 in.

17. Position a dummy shaft in the reverse idler gear and, using heavy grease, install the 22 roller bearings into the gear.

18. Place the thrust washers at each end of the reverse idler gear, then place the assembly in the case with the chamfered end of the gear teeth toward the front.

19. Insert the reverse idler shaft into the rear case bore with the keyway to the rear, pushing the dummy shaft toward and out of the front of the transmission.

20. With the keyway in proper alignment, insert the key and continue driving the shaft forward until the key seats in the recess.

21. Install two new lever shaft seals in the transmission case.

22. Lubricate and install second and third-speed lever shaft in the bores of the case.

23. Install the second and third speed lever shaft lock pin in the hole in the case.

24. Place interlock parts in the case in the following order: ball, sleeve, spring, pin and ball.

25. Enter low and reverse lever shaft in the case bore, depress the detent ball against spring tension and push the lever shaft firmly into position, in order to prevent the ball from escaping.

26. Install low and reverse lever shaft lock pin in the case.

27. Place low and reverse fork in the lever shaft, with the offset facing the rear.

28. While holding the low and reverse sliding gear in position in the fork, with the hub extension to the rear, insert the mainshaft with the rear bearing through the rear of the case and into the sliding gear.

29. Place synchronizer stop ring spring, then the rear stop ring, on the synchronizer splines of the second-speed gear. Install the second-speed gear onto the mainshaft. Synchronizer shims must be added if synchronizer float is more than the maximum in Step 2, disassembly. If float was less than minimum, the six pins must be shortened. gear on the mainshaft with the

30. Install the synchronizer clutch shoulder to the front.

31. Select the thickest synchronizer clutch gear snap-ring that can be used, and install it in the mainshaft groove.

32. Check to see that clearance between clutch gear and second-speed gear is .004-.014 in.

33. Hold the synchronizer clutch gear sleeve and two outer rings together with pins properly entered into the holes in the clutch gear sleeve and with the clutch gear sleeve engaged in the groove of the second- and third-speed shift fork, position the fork in the second- and third-speed lever shaft.

34. While holding the synchronizer parts and fork in position, slide the mainshaft forward, entering the synchronizer clutch gear into the clutch gear sleeve and simultaneously entering the mainshaft rear bearing in the case bore.

SECOND AND DIRECT LEVER
SECOND AND DIRECT FORK
LOW AND REVERSE FORK
BALL
PIN
SLEEVE
SPRING
BALL
LOW AND REVERSE LEVER

Shift fork assembly (© Chrysler Corp.)

SECOND-HIGH LEVER
SPRING WASHER
WASHER
CROSS OVER PIN RETAINER
CROSS OVER PIN
LOW-REVERSE LEVER
FITTING
WASHER
BUSHING
BRACKET
CLAMP

Gearshift controls (© Chrysler Corp.)

35. While still holding the synchronizer parts in position, tap the mainshaft forward until the rear bearing bottoms in the case bore.
36. Install the mainshaft rear bearing snap-ring into place in the case bore.
37. Install a new drive pinion retainer seal.
38. Place the synchronizer front inner ring in position in the front outer ring, and enter the main drive pinion through the case bore.
39. Engage the splines on the rear of the pinion with the inner stop ring, and tap the drive pinion into the case until the outer snap-ring on the pinion bearing is against the transmission case.
40. Place the drive pinion bearing retainer over the pinion shaft and against the transmission case. While holding the retainer against the transmission case, measure the clearance between the retainer and case and choose a gasket .003-.005 in. thicker than this reading.
41. Torque the front bearing retainer bolts to 30 ft. lbs.
42. Install a new extension housing seal.
43. Install extension housing and torque the bolts to 50 ft. lbs.
44. Install the parking brake assembly, on vehicles so equipped.
45. Install the parking brake drum (if so equipped) and flange assembly and torque to 175 ft. lbs.
46. Install the drain plug in the transmission case.
47. Install the gearshift operating levers, and torque to 12 ft. lbs.
48. Install the back-up light switch.
49. Install the speedometer cable and drive gear. Bring transmission to lubricant level.

Torque Chart

Gearshift rod and swivel assembly nuts	5/16-24	70 (in.-lbs.)
Backup light switch hole plug	9/16-18	15
Case drain plug	3/8	20
Case filler plug	1/2	30
Cast to clutch housing bolt	7/16-18	50
Drive pinion bearing retainer bolt	5/16-18	15
Extension bolt	3/8-16	30
Gearshift fork lock bolt	3/8-24	30
Gearshift housing lower bolt	5/16-18	15
Gearshift housing upper bolt	5/16-18	20
Gearshift operating lever nut	3/8-24	35
Gearshift selector ball spring bolt	1/2-20	25
Gearshift selector lever washer nut	5/16-24	20
Manual remote gearshift lever shaft bolt	1/4-20	10
Shaft flange nut	3/4-16	175

Ford 3.03 3 Speed

Transmission case and exterior parts—Ford 3.03 (© Ford Motor Co.)

Description

The Ford 3.03 is a fully synchronized three speed transmission. All gears except reverse are in constant mesh. Forward speed gear changes are accomplished with synchronizer sleeves.

Disassembly of Transmission

1. Drain the lubricant by removing the lower extension housing bolt.
2. Remove the case cover and gasket.
3. Remove the long spring that holds the detent plug in the case and remove the detent plug with a small magnet.
4. Remove the extension housing and gasket.
5. Remove the front bearing retainer and gasket.
6. Remove the filler plug on the right side of the transmission case. Working through the plug opening, drive the roll pin out of the case and countershaft with a ¼ inch punch.

Removing countershaft roll pin—Ford 3.03
(© Ford Motor Co.)

Removing countershaft—Ford 3.03
(© Ford Motor Co.)

7. Hold the countershaft gear with a hook. Install dummy shaft and push the countershaft out of the rear of the case. As the countershaft comes out, lower the gear cluster to the bottom of the case. Remove the countershaft.
8. Remove the snap ring that holds the speedometer drive gear on the output shaft. Slip the gear off the shaft and remove the gear lock ball.
9. Remove the snap ring that holds the output shaft bearing. Using a special bearing puller, remove the output shaft bearing.
10. Place both shift levers in the neutral (center) position.
11. Remove the set screw that holds the first-reverse shift fork to the shift rail. Slip the first-reverse shift rail out through the rear of the case.
12. Move the first-reverse synchronizer forward as far as possible. Rotate the first-reverse shift fork upwards and lift it out of the case.
13. Place the second-third shift fork in the second position. Remove the set screw. Rotate the shift rail 90 degrees.
14. Lift the interlock plug out of the case with a magnet.
15. Remove the expansion plug from the second-third shift rail by

Removing output shaft bearing—Ford 3.03 (© Ford Motor Co.)

lightly tapping the end of the rail. Remove the second-third shift rail.

16. Remove the second-third shift rail detent plug and spring from detent bore.
17. Remove the input gear and shaft from the case.
18. Rotate the second-third shift fork upwards and remove from case.
19. Using caution, lift the output shaft assembly out through top of case.

Reverse idler shaft—exploded view—Ford 3.03 (© Ford Motor Co.)

20. Lift the reverse idler gear and thrust washers out of case. Remove the countershaft gear, thrust washer and dummy shaft from case.
21. Remove the snap ring from the front of the output shaft. Slip the synchronizer and second gear off shaft.
22. Remove the second snap ring from output shaft and remove the thrust washer, first gear and blocking ring.
23. Remove the third snap ring from the output shaft. The first reverse synchronizer hub is a press fit on the output shaft. Remove the synchronizer hub with an arbor press.
CAUTION: Do not attempt to remove or install the synchronizer hub by prying or hammering.

Disassembly and Assembly of Sub-Assemblies, Shift Levers and Seals

1. Remove shift levers from the shafts. Slip the levers out of case. Discard shaft sealing O-rings.
2. Lubricate and install new O-rings on shift shafts.
3. Install the shift shafts in the case and secure shift levers.

Input Shaft Bearings

1. Remove the snap ring securing the input shaft bearing. Using an arbor press, remove the bearing.
2. Press the input shaft bearing onto shaft using correct tool.

Output shaft—exploded view—Ford 3.03 (© Ford Motor Co.)

Rotating second-third shift rail—Ford 3.03 (© Ford Motor Co.)

Shift rails and forks—exploded view—Ford 3.03 (© Ford Motor Co.)

Synchronizers

1. Scribe alignment marks on synchronizer hubs before disassembly. Remove each synchronizer hub from the synchronizer sleeves.
2. Separate the inserts and insert springs from the hubs.
CAUTION: Do not mix parts from the seperate synchronizer assemblies.
3. Install the insert spring in the hub of the first-reverse synchronizer. Be sure that the spring covers all the insert grooves. Start the hub on the sleeve making certain that the scribed marks are properly aligned. Place the three inserts in the hub, small ends on the inside. Slide the sleeve and reverse gear onto hub.
4. Install one insert spring into a groove on the second-third syn-

Removing and installing first-reverse synchronizer—Ford 3.03 (© Ford Motor Co.)

Input shaft gear—exploded view—Ford 3.03 (© Ford Motor Co.)

First-reverse synchronizer—exploded view—Ford 3.03 (© Ford Motor Co.)

Second-third synchronizer—exploded view—Ford 3.03 (© Ford Motor Co.)

First-reverse synchronizer insert spring installation—Ford 3.03 (© Ford Motor Co.)

Shift lever and shaft—exploded view—Ford 3.03 (© Ford Motor Co.)

Replacing input shaft bearing—Ford 3.03 (© Ford Motor Co.)

chronizer hub. Be sure that all three insert slots are covered. Align the scribed marks on the hub and sleeve and start the hub into the sleeve. Position the three inserts on the top of the retaining spring and push the assembly together. Install the remaining retainer spring so that the spring ends cover the same slots as the first spring. Do not stagger the springs. Place a synchronizer blocking ring on the ends of the synchronizer sleeve.

Countershaft Gear Bearings

1. Remove the dummy shaft, needle bearings and bearing retainers from the countershaft gear.
2. Coat the bore in each end of the countershaft gear with grease.
3. Hold the dummy shaft in the gear and install the needle bearings in the case.
4. Place the countershaft gear, dummy shaft, and needle bearings in the case.
5. Place the case in a vertical position. Align the gear bore and the thrust washers with the bores in the case and install the countershaft.
6. Place the case in a horizontal position. Check the countershaft gear end play with a feeler gauge. Clearance should be between 0.004-0.018 inch. If clearance does not come within specifications, replace the thrust washers.
7. Install the dummy shaft in the countershaft gear and leave the

NEEDLE BEARINGS (25 EACH END)

COUNTERSHAFT

BEARING RETAINER   REVERSE IDLER GEAR

ROLL PIN

BEARING RETAINER

Countershaft gear—exploded view—Ford 3.03 (© Ford Motor Co.)

gear at the bottom of the transmission case.

Assembly of Transmission

1. Cover the reverse idler gear thrust surfaces in the case with a thin film of lubricant, and install the two thrust washers in the case.
2. Install the reverse idler gear and shaft in the case. Align the case bore and thrust washers with gear bore and install the reverse idler shaft.
3. Measure the reverse idler gear end play with a feeler gauge; clearance should be between 0.004-0.018 inch. If end play is not within specifications, replace the thrust washers. If clearance is correct, leave the reverse idler gear in case.
4. Lubricate the output shaft splines and machined surfaces with transmission oil.
5. The first-reverse synchronizer hub is a press fit on the output shaft. Hub must be installed in an arbor press. Install the synchronizer hub with the teeth-end of the gear facing towards the rear of the shaft.
CAUTION: Do not attempt to install the first-reverse synchronizer with a hammer.
6. Place the blocking ring on the tapered surface of the first gear.
7. Slide the first gear on the output shaft with the blocking ring toward the rear of the shaft. Rotate the gear as necessary to engage the three notches in the blocking ring with the synchronizer inserts. Install the thrust washer and snap ring.
8. Slide the blocking ring onto the tapered surface of the second gear. Slide the second gear with blocking ring and the second-third synchronizer on the mainshaft. Be sure that the tapered surface of second gear is facing the front of the shaft and that the notches in the blocking ring engage the synchronizer inserts. Install the snap ring and secure assembly.
9. Cover the core of the input shaft with a thin coat of grease.
CAUTION: A thick film of grease will plug lubricant holes and cause damage to bearings.
Install bearings.

10. Install the input shaft through the front of the case and insert snap ring in the bearing groove.
11. Install the output shaft assembly in the case. Position the second-third shift fork on the second-third synchronizer.
12. Place a detent plug spring and a plug in the case. Place the second-third synchronizer in the second gear position (toward the rear of the case). Align the fork and install the second-third shift rail. It will be necessary to depress the detent plug to install the shift rail in the bore. Move the rail forward until the detent plug enters the forward notch (second gear).
13. Secure the fork to the shift rail with a set screw and place the synchronizer in neutral.
14. Install the interlock plug in the case.
15. Place the first-reverse synchronizer in the first gear position (towards the front of the case). Place the shift fork in the groove of the synchronizer. Rotate the fork into position and install the shift rail. Move the shift rail inward until the center notch (neutral) is aligned with the detent bore. Secure shift fork with set screw.
16. Install a new shift rail expansion plug in the front of the case.
17. Hold the input shaft and blocking ring in position and move the

output shaft forward to seat the pilot in the roller bearings on the input gear.
18. Tap the input gear bearing into place while holding the output shaft. Install the front bearing retainer and gasket. Torque attaching bolts to specifications.
19. Install the large snap ring on the rear bearing. Place the bearing on the output shaft with the snap ring end toward the rear of the shaft. Press the bearing into place using a special tool. Secure the bearing to the shaft with the snap ring.
20. Hold the speedometer drive gear lock ball in the detent and slide the speedometer drive gear into position. Secure with snap ring.
21. Place the transmission in the vertical position. Working with a screwdriver through the drain hole in the bottom of the case, align the bore of the countershaft gear and the thrust washer with the bore in the case.
22. Working from the rear of the case, push the dummy shaft out of the countershaft gear with the countershaft. Align the roll pin hole in the countershaft with the matching hole in the case. Drive the shaft into place and install the roll pin.
23. Position the new extension housing gasket on the case with sealer. Install the extension housing and torque to specification.
24. Place the transmission in gear and pour gear oil over entire gear train while rotating the input shaft.
25. Install the remaining detent plug and long spring in case.
26. Position cover gasket on case with sealer and install cover. Torque cover bolts to specifications.
27. Check operation of transmission in all gear positions.

Torque Specifications	*Foot-Lb.*
Input shaft gear bearing retainer to transmission case	30-36
Transmission to flywheel housing	37-42
Transmission cover to transmission case	14-19
Speedometer cable retainer to transmission extension	3-4.5
Transmission extension to transmission case	42-50
Flywheel housing to engine	40-50
Gear shift lever to cam and shaft assembly lock nuts	18-23
U-Joint flange to output shaft	60-80
Filler plug	10-20
Shifter fork set screws	10-18
T.R.S. switch to case	15-20

Lubricant Refill Capacity (Pints)	U.S.	Imp.
Ford Type 3.03	3.5	3.0

Muncie Model SM330 3 Speed

Description

The G.M. Corporation Model SM 330 (Muncie) is a three-speed transmission using helical constant mesh gears. The engagement of all gears except reverse is assisted by synchronizers.

General Data

Type	3-Speed
Synchromesh gears	
	1st, 2nd, and 3rd
Model	SM330

Gear Ratios

1st Speed	3.03:1
2nd Speed	1.75:1
3rd Speed	1.00:1
Reverse	3.02:1

Transmission Disassembly

1. Remove side cover and shift forks.
2. Unbolt extension and rotate to line up groove in extension flange with reverse idler shaft. Drive reverse idler shaft and key out of case with a brass drift.
3. Move second-third synchronizer sleeve forward. Remove extension housing and mainshaft assembly.
4. Remove reverse idler gear from case.
5. Remove third speed blocker ring from clutch gear.
6. Expand snap-ring which holds mainshaft rear bearing. Tap gently on end of mainshaft to remove extension.
7. Remove clutch gear bearing retainer and gasket.
8. Remove snap-ring. Remove clutch gear from inside case by gently tapping on end of clutch gear.

9. Remove oil slinger and 16 mainshaft pilot bearings from clutch gear cavity.
10. Slip clutch gear bearing out front of case. Aid removal with a screwdriver between case and bearing outer snap-ring.
11. Drive countershaft and key out to rear.
12. Remove countergear and two tanged thrust washers.

Mainshaft Disassembly

1. Remove speedometer drive gear. Some speedometer drive gears, made of metal, must be pulled off.
2. Remove rear bearing snap-ring.
3. Support reverse gear. Press on rear of mainshaft to remove reverse gear, thrust washer, and rear bearing. Be careful not to cock the bearing on the shaft.
4. Remove first and reverse sliding clutch hub snap-ring.
5. Support first gear. Press on rear of mainshaft to remove clutch assembly, blocker ring, and first gear.

Side cover assembly
(© G.M.C.)

6. Remove second and third speed sliding clutch hub snap-ring.
7. Support second gear. Press on front of mainshaft to remove clutch assembly, second speed blocker ring, and second gear from shaft.

Cleaning and Inspection

For more detailed information, see the "Cleaning and Inspection" instructions at front of transmission section.

1. Wash all parts in solvent.
2. Air dry.

Clutch Keys and Springs

Keys and sprnigs may be replaced if worn or broken, but the hubs and sleeves must be kept together as originally assembled.

1. Mark hub and sleeve for reassembly.
2. Push hub from sleeve. Remove keys and springs.
3. Place three keys and two springs, one on each side of hub, so all three keys are engaged by both springs. The tanged end of the springs should not be installed into the same key.
4. Slide the sleeve onto the hub, aligning the marks.

Extension Oil Seal and Bushing

1. Remove seal.
2. Using bushing remover and installer, or other suitable tool, drive bushing into extension housing.
3. Drive new bushing in from rear. Lubricate inside of bushing and seal. Install new oil seal with extension seal installer or suitable tool.

1	Main drive gear
2	Snap ring
3	Main drive gear bearings
4	Oil slinger
5	3rd speed blocker ring
6	Mainshaft pilot bearings
7	Speedometer retainer clip
8	Mainshaft
9	Speedometer drive gear
10	Snap ring
11	Rear bearing
12	Reverse gear thrust washer
13	Reverse gear
14	Snap ring
15	1st & reverse synchronizer assembly
16	First speed blocker ring
17	First speed gear
18	Shoulder (part of mainshaft)
19	Second speed gear
20	Second speed blocker ring
21	2nd and 3rd synchronizer assembly
22	Snap ring

Main drive gear and mainshaft assembly (© G.M.C.)

Clutch Bearing Retainer Oil Seal

1. Pry old seal out.
2. Install new seal using seal installer or suitable tool. Seat seal in bore.

Mainshaft Assembly

1. Lift front of mainshaft.
2. Install second gear with clutching teeth up; the rear face of the gear butts against the mainshaft flange.
3. Install a blocking ring with clutching teeth downward. All three blocking rings are the same.
4. Install second and third synchronizer assembly with fork slot down. Press it onto mainshaft splines. Both synchronizer assemblies are identical but are assembled differently. The sec-

ond-third speed hub and sleeve is assembled with the sleeve fork slot toward the thrust face of the hub; the first-reverse hub and sleeve, with the fork slot opposite the thrust face. Be sure that the blocker ring notches align with the synchronizer assembly keys.
5. Install synchronizer snap-ring. Both synchronizer snap-rings are the same.
6. Turn rear of shaft up.
7. Install first gear with clutching teeth upward; the front face of the gear butts against the flange on the mainshaft.
8. Install a blocker ring with clutching teeth down.
9. Install first and reverse synchronizer assembly with fork slot down. Press it onto main-

shaft splines. Be sure blocker ring notches align with synchronizer assembly keys and synchronizer sleeves face front of mainshaft.
10. Install snap-ring.
11. Install reverse gear with clutching teeth down.
12. Install steel reverse gear thrust washer with flats aligned.
13. Press rear ball bearing onto shaft with snap-ring slot down.
14. Install snap-ring.
15. Install speedometer drive gear and retaining clip.

Transmission Assembly

1. Place a row of 29 roller bearings, a bearing washer, a second row of 29 bearings, and a second bearing washer at each end of

1 Bearing retainer	16 Bearing washer	33 1st speed blocker ring
2 Bolt and lock washer	17 Needle bearings	34 Synchronizer key spring
3 Gasket	18 Countergear	35 Synchronizer keys
4 Oil seal	19 Countershaft	36 1st and reverse synchronizer hub assembly
5 Snap ring (bearing-to-main drive gear)	20 Woodruff key	37 Snap ring
6 Main drive gear bearing	21 Bolt (extension-to-case)	38 1st and reverse synchronizer collar
7 Snap ring bearing	22 Reverse gear	39 Main drive gear
8 Oil slinger	23 Thrust washer	40 Pilot bearings
9 Case	24 Rear bearing	41 3rd speed blocker ring
10 Gasket	25 Snap ring	42 2nd and 3rd synchronizer collar
11 Snap ring (rear bearing-to-extension)	26 Speedometer drive gear	43 Snap ring
12 Extension	27 Retainer clip	44 Synchronizer key spring
13 Extension bushing	28 Reverse idler gear	45 Synchronizer keys
14 Oil seal	29 Reverse idler bushing	
15 Thrust washer	30 Reverse idler shaft	
	31 Woodruff key	
	32 1st speed gear	

46 2nd and 3rd synchronizer hub	
47 2nd speed blocker ring	
48 2nd speed gear	
49 Mainshaft	
50 Gasket	
51 2nd and 3rd shifter fork	
52 1st and reverse shifter fork	
53 2-3 shifter shaft assembly	
54 1st and reverse shifter shaft assembly	
55 Spring	
56 O-ring seal	
57 1st and reverse detent cam	
58 2nd and 3rd detent cam	
59 Side cover	
60 Bolt and lock washer	

SM330 transmission components (© G.M.C.)

the countergear. Hold in place with grease.

2. Place countergear assembly through rear case opening with a tanged thrust washer, tang away from gear, at each end. Install countershaft and key from rear of case. Be sure that thrust washer tangs are aligned with notches in case.

3. Place reverse idler gear in case. Do not install reverse idler shaft yet. NOTE: The reverse idler gear bushing may not be replaced separately—only as a unit.

4. Expand snap-ring in extension. Assemble extension over mainshaft and onto rear bearing. Seat snap-ring.

5. Load 16 mainshaft pilot bearings into clutch gear cavity. Assemble third speed blocker ring onto clutch gear clutching surface with teeth toward gear.

6. Place clutch gear assembly, without front bearing, over front of mainshaft. Make sure that blocker ring notches align with keys in second-third synchronizer assembly.

7. Stick gasket onto extension housing with grease. Assemble clutch gear, mainshaft, and extension to case together. Make sure that clutch gear teeth engage teeth of countergear antilash plate.

8. Rotate extension housing. Install reverse idler shaft and key.

9. Torque extension bolts to 45 ft. lbs.

10. Install oil slinger with inner lip facing forward. Install front bearing outer snap-ring and slide bearing into case bore.

11. Install snap-ring to clutch gear stem. Install bearing retainer and gasket and torque to 20 ft. lbs. Retainer oil return hole must be at 6 o'clock.

12. Shift both synchronizer sleeves to neutral positions. Install side cover, inserting shifter forks in synchronizer sleeve grooves.

13. Torque side cover bolts to 20 ft. lbs.

Torque Specifications

Foot-Pounds

Extension to case attaching	45
Drain plug	30
Filler plug	15
Side cover attaching bolts	22
Main drive gear retainer bolts	22
Transmission case to clutch Housing bolts	45

Muncie Model SM465 4 Speed

Description

Muncie model CH 465-SM465 transmission is a four speed transmission using helical gears. The action of all gears except reverse is aided by synchronizers.

Disassembly of Transmission

1. Remove transmission cover assembly. NOTE: Move reverse shifter fork so that reverse idler gear is partially engaged before attempting to remove cover. Forks must be positioned so rear edge of the slot in the reverse fork is in line with the front edge of the slot in the forward forks as viewed through tower opening.

2. Lock transmission into two gears. Remove the universal joint flange nut, universal joint front flange and brake drum assembly. NOTE: On 4-wheel drive models, use a special tool to remove mainshaft rear lock nut.

3. Remove parking brake and brake flange plate assembly on those vehicles having a driveshaft parking brake.

4. Remove rear bearing retainer and gasket.

5. Slide speedometer drive gear off mainshaft.

6. Remove clutch gear bearing retainers and gasket.

7. Remove countergear front bearing cap and gasket.

8. Using a screwdriver, pry off countershaft front bearing.

9. Remove countergear rear bearing snap-rings from shaft and bearing. Using special tool, remove countergear rear bearings.

10. Remove clutch gear bearing outer race to case retaining ring.

11. Remove clutch gear and bearing by tapping gently on bottom side of clutch gear shaft and prying directly opposite against the case and bearing snap-ring groove at the same time. Remove 4th gear synchronizer ring. CAUTION: Index cut out section of clutch gear in down position with countergear to obtain clearance for removing clutch gear.

12. Remove rear mainshaft bearing snap-ring and, using special tools, remove bearing from case. Slide 1st speed gear thrust washer off mainshaft.

13. Lift mainshaft assembly from case. Remove synchronizer cone from shaft.

14. Slide reverse idler gear rearward and move countergear rearward, then lift to remove from case.

15. To remove reverse idler gear, drive reverse idler gear shaft out of case from front to rear using a drift. Remove reverse idler gear from case.

Disassembly of Subassemblies

Transmission Cover Disassembly

1. Remove shifter fork retaining pins and drive out expansion plugs. NOTE: The third and fourth shifter fork must be removed before the reverse shifter head pin can be removed.

2. With shifter shafts in neutral position, remove shafts. CAUTION: Care should be taken when removing the detent balls and springs since removal of the shifter shafts will cause these parts to be forcibly ejected.

3. Remove retaining pin and drive out reverse shifter shaft.

Assembly

1. In reassembling the cover, care should be taken to install the shifter shafts in order—reverse, 3rd.-4th, and 1st.-2nd.

2. Place fork detent ball springs and balls in cover.

3. Start shifter shafts into cover and, while depressing the detent balls, push the shafts over the balls. Push reverse shaft through the yoke.

4. With the 3rd.-4th. shaft in neutral, line up the retaining holes in the fork and shaft. NOTE: Detent balls should line up with detents in shaft.

5. After 1st and 2nd fork is installed, place two inner-lock balls between the low speed shifter shaft and the high speed shifter shaft in the crossbore of the front support boss. Grease the interlock pin and insert it in the 3rd-4th shifter shaft hole. Continue pushing this shaft through cover bore and fork until retainer hole in fork lines up with hole in shaft.

6. Place two interlock balls in crossbore in front support boss between reverse, and 3rd and 4th shifter shaft. Then push remaining shaft through fork and cover bore, keeping both balls in position between shafts until retaining holes line up in fork and shaft. Install retaining pin.

7. Install 1st/2nd fork and reverse fork retaining pins. Install new shifter shaft hole expansion plugs.

Clutch Gear and Shaft Disassembly

1. Remove mainshaft pilot bearing rollers from clutch gear if not already removed, and remove

roller retainer. Do not remove snap-ring on inside of clutch gear.

2. Remove snap-ring securing bearing on stem of clutch gear.

3. To remove bearing, position a special tool to the bearing and, with an arbor press, press gear and shaft out of bearing.

Assembly

1. Press bearing and new oil slinger onto clutch gear shaft using a special tool. Slinger should be located flush with bearing shoulder on clutch gear. CAUTION: Be careful not to distort oil slinger.

2. Install bearing snap-ring on clutch gear shaft.

3. Install bearing retainer ring in groove on O.D. of bearing. CAUTION: The bearing must turn freely on the shaft.

4. Install snap-ring on I.D. of mainshaft pilot bearing bore in clutch gear.

5. Lightly grease bearing surface in shaft recess, install transmis-

1 Transmission cover
2 Interlock balls
3 3rd-4th shifter shaft
4 Reverse shifter shaft
5 Fork retaining pin
6 Detent ball
7 Detent spring
8 3rd-4th shifter fork
9 "C" ring lock clip
10 Reverse shifter fork
11 Shifter shaft hole plugs
12 1st-2nd shifter fork
13 Interlock plunger spring
14 Reverse interlock plunger
15 1st-2nd shifter shaft
16 Interlock pin
17 Cover gasket

Shift cover assembly components (© G.M.C.)

1 Clutch gear bearing retainer
2 Retainer gasket
3 Lip seal
4 Snap ring
5 Clutch gear bearing
6 Oil slinger
7 Clutch gear and pilot bearings
8 Power take-off cover gasket
9 Power take-off cover
10 Retaining screws
11 1st-2nd speed blocker ring
12 Synchronizer spring
13 1st-2nd speed synchronizer hub
14 Synchronizer keys
15 Synchronizer spring
16 Reverse driven gear
17 1st gear bushing
18 1st gear
19 Thrust washer
20 Rear main bearing
21 Bearing snap ring
22 Speedometer gear
23 Rear mainshaft lock nut
24 2nd speed bushing (on shaft)
25 Mainshaft
26 2nd speed gear
27 3rd gear bushing
28 Thrust washer
29 3rd speed gear
30 3rd speed blocker ring
31 Synchronizer spring
32 Synchronizer keys
33 3rd-4th synchronizer hub
34 Synchronizer spring
35 3rd-4th speed blocker ring
36 3rd-4th speed synchronizer sleeve
37 Snap ring
38 Snap ring
39 Thrust washer
40 Clutch countergear
41 Snap ring
42 Snap ring
43 3rd speed countergear
44 Countergear shaft
45 Countergear rear bearing
46 Snap ring
47 Bearing outer snap ring
48 Rear retainer gasket
49 Rear retainer
50 Retainer bolts
51 Retainer lip seal
52 Reverse idler shaft
53 Drain plug
54 Reverse idler gear
55 Case
56 Fill plug
57 Countergear front bearing
58 Gasket
59 Front cover
60 Cover screws

Transmission components (© G.M.C.)

OIL SLINGER

RETAINER RING

SNAP RING

Clutch gear assembly (© G.M.C.)

sion mainshaft pilot roller bearings and install roller bearing retainer.

NOTE: This roller bearing retainer holds bearings in position, and, in final transmission assembly, is pushed forward into recess by mainshaft pilot. Clutch Gear Bearing Retainer Oil Seal.

Bearing Retainer Oil Seal Replacement

1. Remove retainer and oil seal assembly and gasket.
2. Pry out oil seal.
3. Install new seal with lip of seal toward flange of tool.
4. Support front surface of retainer in press and drive seal into retainer.
5. Install retainer and gasket on case.

Mainshaft Disassembly

1. Remove first speed gear.
2. Remove reverse driven gear.
3. Press behind second speed gear to remove 3rd-4th synchronizer assembly, 3rd speed gear and 2nd speed gear along with 3rd speed gear bushing and thrust washer.
4. Remove 2nd speed synchronizer ring and keys.
5. Using a press, remove 1st speed gear bushing and 2nd speed synchronizer hub.
6. Without damaging the mainshaft, chisel out the 2nd speed gear bushing.

Inspection

Wash all parts in cleaning solvent and inspect them for excessive wear or scoring.

NOTE: Third and fourth speed clutch sleeve should slide freely on clutch hub but clutch hub should fit snugly on shaft splines.

Third speed gear must be running fit on mainshaft bushing and mainshaft bushing should be press fit on shaft.

First and reverse sliding gear must be sliding fit on synchronizer hub and must not have excessive radial or circumferential play. If sliding gear is not free on hub, inspect for burrs which may have rolled up on front end of half-tooth internal splines and remove by honing as necessary.

Mainshaft Assembly

1. Lubricate with E.P. oil and press onto mainshaft. CAUTION: 1st, 2nd and 3rd speed gear bushings are sintered iron, exercise care when installing.
2. Press 1st and 2nd speed synchronizer hub onto mainshaft with annulus toward rear of shaft.
3. Install 1st and 2nd synchronizer keys and springs.
4. Press 1st speed gear bushing onto mainshaft until it bottoms against hub. NOTE: Lubricate all bushings with E.P. oil before installation of gears.
5. Install synchronizer blocker ring and 2nd speed gear onto mainshaft and against synchronize hub. Align synchronizer key slots with keys in synchronizer hub.
6. Install 3rd speed gear thrust washer onto mainshaft inserting washer tang in slotted shaft. Then press 3rd speed gear bushing onto mainshaft against thrust washer.
7. Install 3rd speed gear and synchronizer blocker ring against 3rd speed gear thrust washer.
8. Align synchronizer key ring slots with synchronizer assembly keys and drive 3rd and 4th synchronizer assembly onto mainshaft. Secure assembly with snap-ring.
9. Install reverse driven gear with fork groove toward rear.
10. Install 1st speed gear against 1st and 2nd synchronizer hub. In-

stall 1st speed gear thrust washer.

Countershaft Disassembly

1. Remove front countergear retaining ring and thrust washer. Do not re-use this snap-ring or any others.
2. Press countershaft out of clutch countergear assembly.
3. Remove clutch countergear and 3rd speed countergear retaining rings.
4. Press shaft from 3rd speed countergear.

Countershaft Assembly

1. Press the 3rd speed countergear onto the shaft. NOTE: Install gear with marked surface toward front of shaft.
2. Using snap-ring pliers, install new 3rd speed countergear retaining ring.
3. Install new clutch countergear rear retaining ring. CAUTION: Do not over stress snap-ring. Ring should fit tightly in groove with no side play.
4. Press countergear onto shaft against snap-ring.
5. Install clutch countergear thrust washer and front retaining ring.

Transmission Assembly

1. Lower the countergear into the case.
2. Place reverse idler gear in transmission case with gear teeth toward the front. Install idler gear shaft from rear to front, being careful to have slot in end of shaft facing down and flush with case.
3. Install mainshaft assembly into case with rear of shaft protruding out rear bearing hole in case. Rotate case onto front end. NOTE: Install 1st speed gear thrust washer on shaft, if not previously installed.
4. Install snap-ring on bearing

1 1st speed gear
2 Reverse driven gear
3 1st gear bushing
4 1st-2nd gear synchronizer hub assembly

5 2nd speed blocker ring
6 2nd speed gear
7 Thrust washer
8 3rd speed bushing
9 3rd speed gear

10 3rd speed blocker ring
11 3rd-4th speed synchronizer hub assembly
12 3rd-4th speed synchronizer sleeve

13 4th speed blocker ring
14 Snap ring
15 Mainshaft
16 2nd speed gear bushing

Mainshaft assembly (© G.M.C.)

O.D. and place rear mainshaft bearing on shaft. Drive bearing onto shaft and into case.

5. Install synchronizer cone on mainshaft and slide rearward to clutch hub. CAUTION: Make sure three cut-out sections of 4th speed synchronizer cone align with three clutch keys in clutch assembly.

6. Install snap-ring on clutch gear bearing O.D. Index cut out portion of clutch gear teeth to obtain clearance over countershaft drive gear teeth, and install into case.

7. Install clutch gear bearing retainer and gasket and torque to 15-18 ft. lbs.

8. Rotate case onto front end.

9. Install snap-ring on countergear rear bearing O.D., and drive bearing into place. Install snap-ring on countershaft at rear bearing.

10. Tap countergear front bearing assembly into case.

11. Install countergear front bear-

ing cap and new gasket and torque to 20-30 in. lbs.

12. Slide speedometer drive gear over mainshaft to bearing.

13. Install rear bearing retainer with new gasket. Be sure snap-ring ends are in lube slot and cut out in bearing retainer. Install bolts and tighten to 15-18 ft. lbs. Install brake backing plate assembly on those models having driveshaft brake. NOTE: On models equipped with 4-wheel drive, install rear lock nut and washer and torque to 120 ft. lbs. and bend washer tangs to fit slots in nut.

14. Install parking brake drum and/or universal joint flange. NOTE: Lightly oil seal surface.

15. Lock transmission in two gears at once. Install universal joint flange locknut and tighten to 90-120 ft. lbs.

16. Move all transmission gears to neutral except the reverse idler gear which should be engaged approximately ³⁄₈ of an inch

(leading edge of reverse idler gear taper lines up with the front edge of the 1st speed gear). Install cover assembly and gasket. Shifting forks must slide into their proper positions on clutch sleeves and reverse idler gear. Forks must be positioned as in removal.

17. Install cover attaching bolts and gearshift lever and check operation of transmission.

Torque Chart

Foot-Pounds

Rear bearing retainer	18
Cover bolts	25
Filler plug	35
Drain plug	35
Clutch gear bearing retainer bolts	18
Universal joint front flange nut	95
Power take off cover bolts	18
Parking brake	22
Countergear front cover screws	25
Rear mainshaft lock nut (4 wheel drive models)	95

New Process 435 Four Speed Transmission

Disassembly of Transmission

1. Mount the transmission in a holding fixture. Remove the parking brake assembly, if one is installed.

2. Shift the gears into neutral by replacing the gear shift lever temporarily, or by using a bar or screw driver.

3. Remove the cover screws, the second screw from the front on each side is shouldered with a split washer for installation alignment.

4. While lifting the cover, rotate slightly counterclockwise to provide clearance for the shift levers. Remove the cover.

5. Lock the transmission in two gears and remove the output flange nut, the yoke, and the parking brake drum as a unit assembly. *The drum and yoke are balanced and unless replacement of parts are required, it is recommended that the drum and yoke be removed as a assembly.*

6. Remove the speedometer drive gear pinion and the mainshaft rear bearing retainer.

7. Before removal and disassembly of the drive pinion and mainshaft, measure the end play between the synchronizer stop ring and the third gear. *Record this reading for reference during assembly.* Clearance should be within 0.050-0.070 inch. If necessary, add corrective shims during assembly.

8. Remove the drive pinion bearing retainer.

9. Rotate the drive pinion gear to align the space in the pinion gear clutch teeth with the countershaft drive gear teeth. Remove the drive pinion gear and the tapered roller bearing from the transmission by pulling on the pinion shaft, and rapping the face of the case lightly with a brass hammer.

10. Remove the snap ring, washer, and the pilot roller bearings from the recess in the drive pinion gear.

11. Place a brass drift in the front center of the mainshaft and drive the shaft rearward.

12. When the mainshaft rear bearing has cleared the case, remove the rear bearing and the speedometer drive gear with a suitable gear puller.

13. Move the mainshaft assembly to the rear of the case and tilt the front of the mainshaft upward.

14. Remove the roller type thrust washer.

15. Remove the synchronizer and stop rings separately.

16. Remove the mainshaft assembly.

New Process 435 Transmission—exploded view (© Chrysler Corp.)

Measuring the synchronizer end-play—New Process 435 (© Chrysler Corp.)

Drive pinion gear showing the teeth removed—New Process 435 (© Chrysler Corp.)

17. Remove the reverse idler lock screw and lock plate.
18. Using a brass drift held at an angle, drive the idler shaft to the rear while pulling.
19. Lift the reverse idler gear out of the case.

NOTE: If the countershaft gear does not show signs of excessive side play or end play and the teeth are not badly worn or chipped, it may not be necessary to replace the countershaft gear.

20. Remove the bearing retainer at the rear end of the countershaft. The bearing assembly will remain with the retainer.
21. Tilt the cluster gear assembly and work it out of the transmission case.
22. Remove the front bearings from the case with a suitable driver.

Overhaul of Sub-Assemblies

Mainshaft
Disassembly

1. Remove the clutch gear snap ring.
2. Remove the clutch gear, the synchronizer outer stop ring to third gear shim, and the third gear.
3. Remove the special split lock ring with two screw drivers. Remove the second gear and synchronizer.

Cover and shift fork assembly—New Process 435 (© Chrysler Corp.)

4. Remove the first-reverse sliding gear.
5. Drive the old seal out of the bearing retainer.

Assembly

1. Place the mainshaft in a soft-jawed vise with the rear end up.
2. Install the first-reverse gear. Be sure the two spline springs, if used, are in place inside the gear as the gear is installed on the shaft.
3. Place the mainshaft in a soft-jawed vise with the front end up.

4. Assemble the second speed synchronizer spring and synchronizer brake on the second gear. Secure the brake with a snap ring making sure that the snap ring tangs are away from the gear.
5. Slide the second gear on the front of the mainshaft. Make sure that the synchronizer brake is toward the rear. Secure the gear to the shaft with the two piece lock ring. Install the third gear.
6. Install the shim between the third gear and the third-fourth synchronizer stop ring. Refer to the measurements of end play made during disassembly to determine if additional shims are needed.

NOTE: The exact determination of end-play must be made after the complete assembly of the mainshaft and the main drive pinion is installed in the transmission case.

Reverse Idler Gear

DO NOT disassemble the reverse idler gear. If it is no longer serviceable, replace the assembly complete with the integral bearings.

Cover and Shift Fork Assembly

NOTE: The cover and shift fork assembly should be disassembled ONLY if inspection shows worn or damaged parts, or if the assembly is not working properly.

Disassembly

1. Remove the roll pin from the first-second shift fork and the shift gate with an "easy out".

NOTE: A square type or a closely wound spiral "easy out" mounted in a tap is preferable for this operation.

2. Move the first-second shift rail forward and force the expansion plug out of the cover. Cover the detent ball access hole in the cover with a cloth to prevent it from flying out. Remove the rail, fork, and gate from the cover.
3. Remove the third-fourth shift rail, then the reverse rail in the manner outlined in steps 1 and 2 above.

Cover and shift fork assembly—exploded view—New Process 435 (© Chrysler Corp.)

4. Compress the reverse gear plunger and remove the retaining clip. Remove the plunger and spring from the gate.

Assembly

1. Install the spring on the reverse gear plunger and hold it in the reverse shift gate. Compress the spring in the shift gate and install the retaining clip.
2. Insert the reverse shift rail in the cover and place the detent ball and spring in position. Depress the ball and slide the shift rail over it.
3. Install the shift gate and fork on the reverse shift rail. Install a new roll pin in the gate and the fork.
4. Place the reverse fork in the neutral position.
5. Install the two interlock plungers in their bores.
6. Insert the interlock pin in the third-fourth shift rail. Install the shift rail in the same manner as the reverse shift rail.
7. Install the first-second shift rail in the same manner as outlined above. Make sure the interlock plunger is in place.
8. Check the interlocks by shifting the reverse shift rail into the "Reverse" position. It should be impossible to shift the other rails with the reverse rail in this position.
9. If the shift lever is to be installed at this point, lubricate the spherical ball seat and place the cap in place.
10. Install the back-up light switch.
11. Install new expansion plugs in the bores of the shift rail holes in the cover. Install the rail interlock hole plug.

Drive Pinion and Bearing Retainer Disassembly

1. Remove the tapered roller bearing from the pinion shaft with a suitable tool.
2. Remove the snap ring, washer, and the pilot rollers from the gear bore, if they have not been previously removed.
3. Pull the bearing race from the front bearing retainer with a suitable puller.
4. Remove the pinion shaft seal with a suitable tool.

Assembly

1. Position the drive pinion in an arbor press.
2. Place a wood block on the pinion gear and press it into the bearing until it contacts the bearing inner race.
3. Coat the roller bearings with a light film of grease to hold the bearings in place, and insert them in the pocket of the drive pinion gear.

Installing the pinion bearing—
New Process 435 (© Chrysler Corp.)

4. Install the washer and snap ring.
5. Press a new seal into the bearing retainer. Make sure that the lip of the seal is toward the mounting surface.
6. Press the bearing race into the retainer.

Assembly of Transmission

1. Press the front countershaft roller bearings into the case until the cage is flush with the front of the transmission case. Coat the bearings with a light film of grease.
2. Place the transmission with the front of the case facing down. If uncaged bearings are used, hold the loose rollers in place in the cap with a light film of grease.
3. Lower the countershaft assembly into the case placing the thrust washer tangs in the slots in the case, and inserting the front end of the shaft into the bearing.
4. Place the roller thrust bearing and race on the rear end of the countershaft. Hold the bearing in place with a light film of grease.
5. While holding the gear assembly in alignment, install the rear bearing retainer gasket, retainer, and bearing assembly. Install and tighten the cap screws.
6. Position the reverse idler gear and bearing assembly in the case.
7. Align the idler shaft so that the

Installing the seal in the bearing retainer—
New Process 435 (© Chrysler Corp.)

lock plate groove in the shaft is in position to install the lock plate.
8. Install the lock plate, washer, and cap screw.
9. Make sure the reverse idler gear turns freely.
10. Lower the rear end of the mainshaft assembly into the case, holding the first gear on the shaft. Maneuver the shaft through the rear bearing opening.

NOTE: With the mainshaft assembly moved to the rear of the case, be sure the third-fourth synchronizer and shims remain in position.

11. Install the roller type thrust bearing.
12. Place a wood block in-between the front of the case and the front of the mainshaft.
13. Install the rear bearing on the mainshaft by carefully driving the bearing onto the shaft and into the case, snap ring flush against the case.
14. Install the drive pinion shaft and bearing assembly. Make sure that the pilot rollers remain in place.
15. Install the spacer and speedometer drive gear.
16. Install the rear bearing retainer and gasket.
17. Place the drive pinion bearing retainer over the pinion shaft, without the gasket.
18. Hold the retainer tight aginst the bearing and measure the clearance between the retainer and the case with a feeler gauge.

NOTE: End play in steps 19 and 20 below allows for normal expansion of parts during operation, preventing seizure and damage to bearings, gears, synchronizers, and shafts.

19. Install a gasket shim pack 0.010-0.015 inch thicker than measured clearance between the retainer and case to obtain the required 0.007-0.017 inch pinion shaft end play. Tighten the front retainer bolts and recheck the end play.
20. Check the synchronizer end play clearance (0.050-0.070 inch) after all mainshaft components are in position and properly tightened. Two sets of feeler gauges are used to measure the clearance. Care should be used to keep both gauges as close as possible to both sides of the mainshaft for best results.

NOTE: In some cases, it may be necessary to disassemble the mainshaft and change the thickness of the shims to keep the end play clearance within the specified limits, 0.050-0.070 inch. Shims are available in two thicknesses.

21. Install the speedometer drive pinion.
22. Install the yoke flange, drum, and drum assembly.
23. Place the transmission in two

gears at once, and tighten the yoke flange nut.

24. Shift the gears and/or synchronizers into all gear positions and and check for free rotation.

25. Cover all transmissions components with a film of transmission oil to prevent damage during start up after initial lubricant fill-up.

26. Move the gears to the neutral position.

27. Place a new cover gasket on the transmission case, and lower the cover over the transmission.

28. Carefully, engage the shift forks into their poper gears. Align the cover.

29. Install a shouldered alignment screw with split washer in the screw hole second from the front of the cover. Try out gear operation by shifting through all ranges. Make sure everything moves freely.

30. Install the remaining cover screws.

Lubricant Capacity

New Process 435	7 pt.

Torque Specifications

	Foot-Pounds
Cover screws	20-40
Drive gear retaining screw	15-25
Front countershaft retainer screw	15-25
Front countershaft bearing washer screw	12-22
Flange nut	125
Mainshaft rear retainer screw	15-25
Rear countershaft retainer screw	15-25
PTO cover screws	8-12
Filler and drain plugs	25-45
Reverse idler shaft lock screw	20-40
Brake link shoulder screw	20-40

New Process Model 445 Four Speed Transmission

Disassembly of Transmission

1. Place the transmission in a holding fixture and drain the lubricant.

2. Shift the transmission gears into neutral. Remove the gearshift cover attaching bolts. Note that the two bolts opposite the tower are shouldered to properly position the cover. Lift the cover straight up and remove.

3. Lock the transmission in two gears at once and remove the mainshaft nut and yoke.

4. Loosen and remove the extension housing bolts. Remove the mainshaft extension housing and the speedometer drive pinion.

5. Remove the bolts from the drive pinion front bearing retainer and pull the bearing retainer and gasket off.

6. Rotate the drive pinion gear to align the pinion gear flat with the countershaft drive gear teeth. Remove the drive pinion gear and the tapered roller bearing from the transmission.

7. Remove the mainshaft thrust bearing.

8. Push the mainshaft assembly to the rear of the transmission and tilt the front of the mainshaft up.

9. Remove the mainshaft assembly from the transmission case.

10. Remove the reverse idler lock screw and lock plate.

11. Using a suitable size brass drift, carefully drive the reverse idler shaft out the REAR of the case.

NOTE: DO NOT ATTEMPT TO DRIVE THE REVERSE IDLER

New Process 445 transmission—exploded view (© Chrysler Corp.)

Drive pinion gear—New Process 445 (© Chrysler Corp.)

Cover and shift fork assembly—New Process 445 (© Chrysler Corp.)

SHAFT FORWARD! This will damage the transmission case and the reverse idler shaft.

12. Remove the countershaft rear bearing retainer.
13. Slide the countershaft to the rear, then up and out of the case.
14. Drive the countershaft forward, out of the bearing and the case.

Overhaul of Sub-Assemblies

Mainshaft
Disassembly

1. Place the mainshaft in a soft-jawed vise with the front end up.
2. Lift the third-fourth synchronizer and high speed clutch off the mainshaft.
3. Remove the third gear.
4. Remove the second gear snap ring. Lift off the thrust washer.
5. Remove the second gear.
6. Remove the first-reverse synchronizer and clutch gear.
7. Install the mainshaft in the vise rear end up.
8. Remove the tapered bearing from the shaft with a suitable gear puller.
9. Remove the first gear snap ring and thrust washer.
10. Remove the first gear.

Assembly

1. Lubricate all parts with transmission lubricant prior to assembly.
2. Place the mainshaft in a soft-jawed vise with the rear end up.
3. Slide the first gear over the mainshaft, with the clutch gear facing down. Install the thrust washer and snap ring.
4. Install the reverse gear over the end of the mainshaft with the fork groove facing down.
5. Install the mainshaft rear bearing on the mainshaft with a sleeve of suitable size. Press the bearing on its inner race.
6. Install the mainshaft in the vise with the front end facing up.
7. Install the first-reverse synchronizer.
8. Install the second gear on the mainshaft.
9. Install the keyed thrust washer, ground side toward the second gear and secure with the snap ring.
10. Install the third gear and one shim on the mainshaft.
11. Install the third fourth synchronizer over the mainshaft. Make sure that the slotted end of the clutch gear is positioned toward the third gear.

Cover and Shift Fork Assembly
Disassembly

NOTE: The cover and shift fork assembly should be disassembled ONLY if inspection shows worn or damaged parts, or if the assembly is not working properly.

1. Remove the roll pin from the first-second shift fork and the shift gate. Use a square-type or spiral wound "easy-out" mounted in a tap handle for these operations.
2. Move the first-second shift rail rearward and force the expansion plug out of the cover. Cover the detent ball access hole in the cover with a cloth to prevent it from flying out. Remove the rail, fork, and gate from the cover.
3. Remove the third-fourth shift rail, then the reverse rail in the manner outlined in steps 1 and 2 above.
4. Compress the reverse gear plunger and remove the retaining clip. Remove the plunger and spring from the gate.

Assembly

1. Apply a thin film of grease on the interlock slugs and slide them into the openings in the shift rail supports.
2. Install the reverse shift rail through the reverse shift fork plate and the reverse shift fork.
3. Secure the reverse shift plate and the shift fork with the roll pins. Install the interlock pin in the third-fourth shift rail. Hold in place with a thin film of grease.
4. Slide the third-fourth shift rail into the rail support from the rear of the cover. Slide the rail through the third-fourth shift fork and poppet ball and spring. Secure the third-fourth shift fork with the roll pin.
5. Install the interlock pin in the first-second shift rail and secure with a light coat of grease. Slide the first-second shift rail into the case, through the shift fork and shift gate. Hold the poppet ball and spring down until the shaft rail passes.
6. Secure the first-second shift rail and gate with the roll pins.

Assembly of Transmission

1. Install the countershaft front bearing in the case using a 1⅜ inch socket as a driver. Grease the needle bearings prior to installation. Hold the bearings in place with a socket of suitable size while seating the bearing retainer. Drive the retainer in until it is flush with the case.
2. Install the tanged thrust washer on the countershaft with the tangs facing out. Install the countershaft in the transmission case.
3. Install the countershaft rear bearing retainer over the rear bearing. Use a new washer and position the retainer with the curved segment toward the bottom of the case.
4. Install the reverse idler gear into the case with the chamfered section facing the rear. Hold the thrust washer and needle bearings in position.
5. Slide the reverse idler shaft into the case, from the rear, and through the reverse idler gear. Make sure that the lock notch is down and at the rear of the case.
6. Install the reverse idler shaft lock and bolt.
7. Place the mainshaft in a soft-jawed vise with the front end facing up.
8. Install the drive gear on top of the mainshaft.

9. Measure the clearance between the high-speed synchronizer and the drive gear with two feeler gauges.
   If the clearance is greater than 0.043-0.053 inch, install synchronizer shims between the third gear and the synchronizer brake drum. After the required shims have been installed, remove the drive gear from the mainshaft.

10. Install the mainshaft into the transmission case. Place the thrust washer over the pilot end of the mainshaft.

11. Position the drive gear so that the cutaway portion of the gear is facing down. Slide the drive gear into the front of the case and engage the mainshaft pilot in the pocket of the drive gear.

12. Slip the drive gear front bearing retainer over the shaft on gasket, and do not secure with bolts.

13. Install the mainshaft rear bearing retainer. Tighten the screws to specifications.

14. Hold the retainer against the front of the transmission case and measure the clearance between the front bearing retainer and the front of the case with a feeler gauge. Record the measurement and remove the bearing retainer.

15. Install a gasket pack on the front bearing retainer which is 0.010-0.015 inch thicker than the clearance measured in step 14. Install the front bearing retainer and torque attaching screws to specification.

16. The end play float of the front synchronizer must be checked before installation of the transmission cover assembly. Measure the end play "float" by inserting two feeler gauges opposite one another between the third gear and the synchronizer stop ring. Accurate measurement can be made only after all mainshaft parts are in place and torqued to specification.

17. If the front synchronizer end play "float" does not fall between 0.050-0.070 inch, shims should be added or removed as required, from between the third gear and the synchronizer stop ring.

18. Install the yoke retaining nut on the rear of the mainshaft. Shift the transmission into two gears at the same time and torque the yoke nut to 125 ft.-lbs.

19. Shift the transmission into neutral.

20. Install the cover gasket.

21. Shift the transmission into second gear. Shift the cover into second.

22. Carefully lower the cover into position. It may be necessary to position the reverse gear to permit the fork to engage its groove.

23. Install the cover aligning screws (shouldered) and tighten with fingers only.

24. Install the remaining cover screws and tighten to specifications.

Torque Specifications

	Foot-Pounds
Cover screws	20-40
Drive gear retaining screw	15-25
Front countershaft retaining screw	15-25
Front countershaft bearing washer screw	12-22
Flange nut	125
Mainshaft rear retainer screw	15-25
Rear countershaft retainer screw	15-25
PTO cover screws	8-12
Filler and drain plugs	25-45
Reverse idler shaft lock screw	20-40
Brake link shoulder screw	20-40

Lubricant Capacity

New Process 445	7½ pts.

New Process 540 & 542 Series Five Speed

Disassembly of Transmission

1. Shift gears into neutral.
2. Remove cover by rotating it slightly counter-clockwise to provide clearance to shifting forks. Check and record the amount of synchronizer end play for assembly reference.
3. Remove yoke and parking brake drum as an assembly. The drum and yoke are balanced and unless replacement of parts is required it is recommended that drum and yoke be removed as a unit assembly.
4. Remove speedometer drive pinion, and rear mainshaft bearing support.

Drive Pinion

Remove drive pinion bearing retainer and rotate the gear to align the notch in pinion gear clutch teeth with countershaft drive gear teeth. Remove drive pinion gear and tapered roller bearing from transmission.

Mainshaft

1. Using a brass drift, drive mainshaft to rear, making certain the synchronizer assembly remains free on shaft.
2. Using a puller, remove rear bearing and speedometer gear (with spacer).

Removing synchronizer assembly
(© New Process Gear Div.)

3. Move mainshaft assembly to rear and tilt front of mainshaft up.
4. Remove roller type thrust bearing.
5. Remove sliding components of synchronizer separately.
6. Remove mainshaft assembly.

Reverse Idler Gear

Using a special tool, remove the reverse idler shaft and gear.

Countershaft Cluster Gear

1. Remove bearing retainer at rear end of countershaft. The roller bearing assembly at rear end of shaft remains with retainer.
2. Work cluster gear assembly out of case.
3. Using a suitable driver, remove front bearings.

Overhaul of Sub-Assemblies

In performing assembly operations, use new expansion plugs, gaskets and seals. Lubricate all parts with transmission lubricant before assembly.

Mainshaft
Disassembly

1. Remove clutch gear snap-ring.
2. Remove clutch gear, synchronizer outer stop ring to 3rd speed gear shim (or shims) and 3rd speed gear.
3. Remove special split lock ring with two screwdrivers and remove 2nd speed gear, and synchronizer.
4. Remove low 2nd sliding gear.
5. Drive old seal from rear bearing support housing.

Assembly

1. Place mainshaft in a soft jawed vise with forward end up.

2. Install the low and reverse speed gear.
3. Install the 2nd speed gear and synchronizer and lock in position with split lock ring.
4. Install 3rd speed gear shim (or shims) and oil slots down.
5. Install clutch gear and a snap-ring that will eliminate all clutch gear end play. Snap rings are available in four thicknesses marked A, B, C and D.

When installing the synchronizer assembly on main shaft, the selection of shims on the 2rd speed gear, will be determined by the original number of shims and the amount of end play clearance recorded at this point during disassembly. The correct thickness of shims necessary to obtain proper end play clearance when unit is completely reassembled (.050 to .070), cannot be accurately measured until all the mainshaft components are in position and properly tightened.

Reverse Idler Disassembly

1. Remove snap-ring and needle bearing retaining washer.
2. Remove bearings race.
3. Remove needle bearings (34 per row) and center washer.

Assembly

1. Using a suitable grease, install needle bearings in reverse idler gear (34 per row) and center washer.
2. Install bearing race, retaining washer and snap-ring.

Cover and Shift Fork Assembly Disassembly

1. Remove roll pin from 3rd and 4th speed fork (center rail) with an "easy out." A square type or a closely wound spiral "easy out" mounted in a tap handle is preferable for this operation.
2. After removing pin, drive rail to rear and remove fork.
3. Continue driving rail to rear to remove rear expansion plug; being careful to catch poppet

New Process transmission (typical)
(© New Process Gear Div.)

ON-BENCH SYNCHRONIZER CLEARANCE CHECK

INPUT SHAFT

FEELER GAUGE

FEELER GAUGE

SYNCHRONIZER ASSEMBLY

THIRD-SPEED GEAR

SYNCHRONIZER SHIM

THIRD-SPEED GEAR

SYNCHRONIZER SHIM LOCATION

SECOND-SPEED GEAR

IN-CASE SYNCHRONIZER CLEARANCE CHECK

INPUT GEAR

FEELER GAUGE

FEELER GAUGE

THIRD-SPEED GEAR

Measuring input shaft to synchronizer clearance
(© New Process Gear Div.)

Removing or installing cover
(© New Process Gear Div.)

Drive Pinion and Bearing Retainer
Disassembly

1. Remove tapered roller bearing from pinion shaft with special tool.
2. Remove lock ring washer and pilot rollers from gear bore.
3. Pull bearing race from front bearing retainer.
4. Remove pinion shaft seal, with seal remover tool.

ball and spring as rail clears rail support in housing. Also, note interlock pin and rail.
4. Remove remaining rails, lugs and shift forks in same manner as center rail. To replace interlocks, remove plug from interlock passage in cover, remove interlocks.

Assembly

1. Sight along reverse rail bore in cover to be certain the interlock pin is clear of the hole. Start reverse rail through hole at rear of cover and position fork on rail. Continue to push rail into cover until rail enters rail support containing cavity for poppet ball and spring.
2. Install spring and ball in support and push rail over ball.
3. Install lug on rail and expansion plug in cover.
4. Drive roll pins through lug, shift fork and rail.
5. Install 1st and 2nd speed rail assembly in same manner followed by 3rd and 4th speed rail assembly; being certain that interlock pin is in position in 3rd and 4th speed rail.

BOOT
CAP
SPRING SEAT
SPRING
GEAR SHIFT LEVER
BACK-UP LIGHT SWITCH
CAP RETAINER
COVER
FIRST AND SECOND SPEED SHIFT FORK
DETENT BALL AND SPRING
GATE
GASKET
FIRST AND SECOND SPEED SHIFTER SHAFT
FORK SHOES
THIRD AND FOURTH SPEED SHIFTER SHAFT
REVERSE GEAR PLUNGER AND SPRING
INTERLOCK PLUNGER
INTERLOCK PIN
REVERSE FORK
GATE
THIRD AND FOURTH SPEED SHIFT FORK
INTERLOCK PLUNGER
FORK SHOES
DETENT BALLS AND SPRINGS
REVERSE SHIFTER SHAFT

Gearshift cover components
(© New Process Gear Div.)

Installing input shaft bearing
(© New Process Gear Div.)

Assembly

1. Position drive pinion in arbor press.
2. Place a wood block on pinion gear and press into bearing until it contacts bearing inner race.
3. Insert lubricated roller bearings in pocket of drive gear.
4. Install washer and snap-ring.
5. Press in new bearing retainer seal with lip of seal toward mounting surface.
6. Press bearing race into retainer.

Installing front bearing race
(© New Process Gear Div.)

Assembly of Transmision

Countershaft

Lower countershaft assembly into case. Install rear bearing support gasket support and bearing assembly. Install end cover and gasket.

Reverse Idler Assembly

1. Position reverse gear in case.
2. Install lock plate on idler shaft.
3. Tap shaft through case and re-cap screw.
4. Install lock plate, washer and reverse gear.
5. Make sure gear turns freely on shaft.

Mainshaft and Drive Pinion

1. Lower rear end of mainshaft into case holding 1st speed gear on shaft and maneuver shaft through rear bearing opening.
2. Install synchronizer components one at a time.
3. Install roller type thrust bearing.
4. Carefully drive rear bearing onto shaft and into case (snap-ring flush against case) using a suitable sleeve against inner race of bearing.
5. Install drive pinion shaft and bearing assembly.
6. Install spacer and speedometer gear.
7. Install rear support and gasket.
8. Place drive pinion bearing retainer over pinion shaft without gasket.
9. Hold retainer tight against bearing and measure clearance between retainer and case with a feeler gauge.
10. Install a gasket shim pack .010-.015 inch thicker than this measured clearance to obtain the required 0.007 to 0.017 inch pinion shaft end play. Tighten front retainer bolts and recheck end play.
11. Check the synchronizer end play clearance (.050 to .070) after all

Measuring synchronizer end play
(© New Process Gear Div.)

mainshaft components are in position and properly tightened. Using two sets of feeler gauges, keep gauges as close as possible to both sides of the mainshaft for best results. In some cases, it may be necessary to change the shim thickness (A, B, C or D thickness) to keep the end play clearance within the specified (.050 to .070).

12. Install speedometer drive pinion.
13. Install yoke flange, drum and brake assembly.
14. Final tightening of nut may be performed on truck if transmission is locked into two gears.
15. Shift gears and/or synchronizer into all speed positions and check for free rotation. Be sure synchronizer pins are properly aligned.

Cover

1. Move gears into neutral position and lower cover and new gasket into place.
2. Install one screw on each side of case and try gears for free rotation by shifting gears through cover tower with a long screwdriver.
3. Install remaining cover screws.

INPUT SHAFT BEARING END PLAY CHECK

INPUT SHAFT BEARING END PLAY ADJUSTMENT

Checking input shaft end play
(© New Process Gear Div.)

Torque Chart

Nomenclature	Nuts and/or Bolts and Torque Limits		Nomenclature	Nuts and/or Bolts and Torque Limits		Nomenclature	Nuts and/or Bolts and Torque Limits	
Bolt—gear shift lever tower to gearshift housing	3/8-16 20-25	7/16-14 30-35	Bolt—bellcrank to trans.	3/8-16 20-25		Nut—countershaft bearing lock (5-speed extra H.D. & 5-speed exclusive)	1¼-18 350-450	
Bolt—clutch housing to trans. case	7/16-14 30-38 5/8-11 96-120	9/16-12 70-90	Bolt—reverse lockout plunger retainer	11/16-16 80-100		Nut—countershaft bearing lock (5-speed exclusive H.D.)	1½-18 350-450	
Nut—U-joint flange to trans. output shaft	1.00-20 1½-18 90-125 275-350	1¼-18 225-275	Bolt—countershaft rear bearing retainer	5/16-18 25-30 3/8-16 35-40	7/16-14 45-55 1/2-13 60-70	Bolt—Input shaft bearing retainer to trans. case	5/16-18 25-30 3/8-16 25-30	7/16-14 50-55
Nut—drum parking brake to companion flange	3/8-24 35-45	7/16-20 50-70	Bolt—countershaft & reverse idler shaft retainer	5/16-18 25-30 3/8-16 25-37 3/8-16† 18-25†	7/16-14 40-45 1/2-13 80-85	Bolt—countershaft front bearing retainer	5/16-18 25-30 3/8-16 25-35	7/16-14 40-45
Nut—bellcrank to trans.	9/16-18 70-90							
Bolt—lever assy. to trans.	3/8-16 20-25		Bolt—gear shift housing to trans. case	5/16-18 20-25 3/8-16 35-40	3/8-16†† 30-35†† 7/16-14 45-50	### Lubricant Capacity		
Nut—handbrake anchor bar to trans. case (5-speed extra-heavy duty only)	9/16-18 120-130		Bolt—power take off cover to trans. case	3/8-16 20-30				

Model	Pints
540	9.5
542	9

New Process 7550 & 7590 Five Speed Transmissions

Disassembly of Transmission

1. Mount the transmission in a housing fixture and remove the parking brake assembly.
2. Shift the gears into neutral.
3. Remove the shift cover screws, the second screw from the front on each side is shouldered with split washers for installation alignment.
4. Lift the cover and turn slightly either way to clear the shift forks, remove the cover.
5. Lock the transmission in two gears at once and remove the out-put flange nut.
6. Remove the brake drum and yoke assembly by tapping with a brass hammer. *The drum and yoke assembly are balanced and unless replacement of parts is required, it is recommended that the drum and yoke be removed as a single unit.*
7. Remove the brake band assembly bracket and support bolts and lock washers. Remove the brake band assembly as a complete unit.
8. Before removal and disassembly of the drive pinion and mainshaft, measure the end-play between the synchronizer stop ring and the fourth gear. *Record this measurement for reference during assembly.* The correct end-play is 0.050-0.070 inch. Note any difference from the limits so that corrective shims can be added or removed as required.
9. Remove the drive pinion bearing retainer.
10. Remove the drive pinion gear and ball bearing from the trans-

mission by pulling on the shaft and rapping the face of the case with a brass hammer.
11. Remove the speedometer drive pinion and the mainshaft rear bearing retainer.
12. Place a brass drift in the front center of the mainshaft and drive the mainshaft to the rear.
13. Pull the rear bearing from the mainshaft with a suitable gear puller.
14. Once the mainshaft rear bearing has cleared the case, remove the rear bearing and the speedometer gear with a suitable puller.
15. Move the mainshaft assembly to the rear and tilt the front of the mainshaft up.
16. Hold the first-reverse gear and the fourth-fifth synchronizer to keep them from sliding off the shaft, remove the mainshaft from the transmission case.
17. Remove the reverse idler lock screw and lock plate.
18. Using a brass drift, held at an angle, drive the idler shaft to the rear while pulling.

19. Lift the reverse idler gear and thrust washers out of the case. *NOTE: Loose needle bearings are usually replaced. Never mix old and new bearings.*
20. Remove the countershaft rear bearing retainer, gasket and bearing.
21. Tip the countershaft upward and remove it from the case. Remove the thrust washer from the front end of the countershaft.
22. Remove the countershaft front needle bearing from the case bore by tapping on the bearing cage from inside the case, with a suitable driver.

Overhaul of Sub-Assemblies

Drive Pinion
Disassembly

1. Remove the snap ring and washer holding the pilot needle bearings in place and remove the bearings.
2. Relieve the staked area, remove the drive pinion ball bearing retainer nut and remove the ball

SNAP RING

NUT (LH THREAD)

DRIVE PINION

STAKE

BEARING ASSEMBLY

PILOT NEEDLE BEARINGS (LOOSE)

Drive pinion shaft assembly—New Process 7550-7590 (© Chrysler Corp.)

FOURTH AND FIFTH SPEED SYNCHRONIZER (FRONT)

CLUTCH GEAR

FOURTH SPEED GEAR

THIRD SPEED GEAR

MAIN SHAFT

SPLIT (2 PIECE) THRUST WASHER

FIRST SPEED GEAR

SNAP RING

PIN

SECOND AND THIRD SPEED SYNCHRONIZER GROUP (BACK)

SECOND SPEED GEAR

RETAINER

REVERSE GEAR

SNAP RING (A, B, C, D)

SNAP RING (A, B, C, D)

KEY

TANGED THRUST WASHER

COUNTERSHAFT

NEEDLE BEARINGS

SPACER

ENERGIZER SPRINGS

REVERSE AND FIRST SLIDING CLUTCH ASSEMBLY

DRIVE GEAR

4TH SPEED GEAR

OIL SEAL

THRUST WASHER

PILOT BEARING ROLLERS

POWER TAKE-OFF COVER AND GASKET

THRUST WASHER

SPACER WASHER

REAR BEARING, GASKET AND RETAINER

DRIVE PINION RETAINER ASSEMBLY

DRIVE PINION

SNAP RING

SEAL

BEARING

THRUST WASHER

BEARING ASSEMBLY

SPEEDOMETER DRIVE GEAR

FLANGE

COVER AND GASKET

POWER TAKE-OFF COVER AND GASKET

CASE

REVERSE IDLER SHAFT

LOCK SCREW

LOCK PLATE

New Process 7550 & 7590 transmission—exploded view (© Chrysler Corp.)

bearing. *The ball bearing retainer nut has left hand threads.*
3. Remove the snap ring from the drive pinion ball bearing.
4. Remove the seal from the drive pinion bearing retainer.

Assembly
1. Grease the loose pilot bearings to hold them in place and insert them into the pocket of the drive gear. Install the washer and snap ring.
2. Press the large bearing on the pinion shaft. Make sure the bearing is properly seated.
3. Install the bearing retainer nut and tighten securely. Stake in place.
4. Install the snap ring on the large bearing. Make sure the snap ring is properly seated. *The bearing retainer nut has left hand threads.*

Mainshaft Disassembly
1. Remove the spacer washer and the first gear from the mainshaft.
2. Remove the retaining ring and the first-reverse clutch and clutch gear assembly.

MAIN SHAFT (BACK END)

RETAINER (PIN AND THRUST WASHER)

PIN (ANTI ROTATION)

THRUST WASHER (TWO-PIECE)

SECOND SPEED GEAR

Installing or removing the second gear— New Process 7550-7590   (© Chrysler Corp.)

3. Remove the reverse gear.
4. Remove the second gear retaining thrust washer. This two-piece split washer consists of two halves held in position on the mainshaft by a pin in a hole on the mainshaft together with a retaining ring.
5. Remove the second gear.
6. Remove the second-third synchronizer assembly. The second-

third clutch gear is integral with the mainshaft.
7. Remove the snap ring and the four-fifth synchronizer assembly and clutch gear.
8. Remove the fourth gear, retain the shims for assembly.
9. Remove the retaining snap ring, tanged thrust washer and the third gear.

Assembly
1. Place the mainshaft, front end up, in a soft-jawed vise.
2. Place the third gear on the shaft with the clutching teeth facing down. Install the tanged thrust washer and the one piece snap ring.
3. Place the fourth gear on the shaft with the clutching teeth up.
4. Check the end-play measurements recorded during disassembly and select shims to provide 0.050-0.070 inch end play between the fourth gear and the fourth-fifth synchronizer.
5. Place the fourth-fifth synchronizer clutch gear, with the oil slots down, on the mainshaft. Select a snap ring of the greatest possible thickness to eliminate all end-play of the clutch gear.

6. Remove the mainshaft from the vise and install the second-third synchronizer group. The synchronizer sleeve is marked "Front" for proper installation.
7. Place the second speed gear on the mainshaft.
8. Place the thrust washer retaining pin in the hole in the mainshaft and position the two thrust washer halves. Install the thrust washer retaining ring with the large diameter contacting the second gear.
9. Install the reverse gear.
10. Position the reverse-first clutch gear on the shaft. Install the retaining snap ring. Select a snap ring with the greatest possible thickness to eliminate all end-play of the clutch gear.
11. Position the sliding clutch on the clutch gear. Install the first gear on the mainshaft.
12. Place the spacer washer on the mainshaft.

Countershaft

Note: It is only necessary to disassemble the countershaft if inspection shows signs of damage or malfunction.

Disassembly

1. Remove the snap ring.
2. Place the assembly in an arbor press with a block supporting the drive gear. Carefully press the shaft out.
3. Support the fourth gear with wood blocks and carefully drive the shaft out.
4. Remove the key.

CHECK END-PLAY FRONT SYNCHRONIZER (FLOAT .050-.070 INCH)   THIRD SPEED GEAR   CHECK END-PLAY REAR SYNCHRONIZER (FLOAT .070-.090 INCH)

FRONT

FOURTH SPEED GEAR   SECOND SPEED GEAR   REVERSE GEAR   FIRST SPEED GEAR

Synchronizer end-play "float" check points—New Process 7550-7590 (© Chrysler Corp.)

Assembly

1. Place the key in position on the countershaft.
2. Press the gears on the countershaft until properly seated.
   Note: Make sure that the key does not move out of position as the gears are being pressed on the shaft.
3. Install the snap ring on the countershaft. Select a snap ring with the greatest possible thickness to eliminate all possible end-play.
4. Install the washer on the countershaft drive gear.

Cover and Shift Fork Assembly

Note: The cover and shift fork assembly should be disassembled ONLY if inspection shows worn or damaged parts, or if the assembly is not working properly.

Disassembly

1. Mount the cover assembly in a soft-jawed vise. Mark each fork and rail for location during assembly.
2. Place the shift forks in neutral. Remove the spiral roll pins from the shift forks and lugs. The roll pins may be removed by working with a "easy-out" mounted in a tap handle.
3. Drive the short first-reverse shift rail toward the rear and out of the shift cover. Remove the fork.
4. Remove the first-reverse shift rail pivot bolt and nut. Remove the crossover level.
5. Drive the fourth-fifth and the second-third shift rail forward and out of the shift cover. Remove the long first-reverse shift rail in the same manner.

Note: Place a cloth over the shift rails while driving the shift rails out of the cover to prevent the poppet balls and springs from flying out.

6. Remove the four interlock balls

FIRST AND SECOND SPEED SHIFT RAIL   SECOND AND THIRD SPEED SHIFT RAIL   COVER   SHORT FIRST — REVERSE SHIFT RAIL

SPRINGS   PLUG

PLUGS   NUT   LOCKWASHER   CROSSOVER LEVER   PIVOT SCREW

INTERLOCK BALLS AND PINS   GUIDE   CLIP

POPPET BALLS   PIN   GATE

FOURTH AND FIFTH SPEED SHIFT RAIL   SPRING   PIN   LUG

FIRST SPEED AND REVERSE SHIFTER FORK

FOURTH AND FIFTH SPEED SHIFT FORK   INSERT   SECOND AND THIRD SPEED SHIFT FORK

Cover and shift fork assembly—exploded view—New Process 7550-7590 (© Chrysler Corp.)

Manual Transmissions

and pin from the bore through the width of the cover. To make sure that the pin and balls are out, shake the cover or tap lightly on a wood block.

Assembly

1. Push the long first-reverse shift rail into the cover bore far enough to permit the installation of the gates, poppet ball and springs and the roll pins. Move the shift rail into neutral position.
2. Place a small quantity of grease on the four interlock balls and pin.
3. Place two balls in the interlock bore. Move both of the balls toward the shift rail to seat the ball in the neutral notch.
4. Grease the interlock pin and place it in the hole located in the second-third shift rail. Install the second-third shift rail, gate, and fork as outlined in step 1. Move the rail into neutral.
5. Install the remaining balls into the interlock bore.
6. Push the fourth-fifth shift rail into the cover bore and install the shift fork as outlined in step 1. Move the shift rail into neutral.
7. Place the crossover lever in position in the cover in such a way that the short first-reverse shift rail, fork, and roll pin can be installed. Install the short first-reverse shift rail and parts.
8. Reposition the crossover level to mate in the notches in both the long and short first-reverse shift rails.
9. Install the pivot bolt through the crossover level and the cover. Install the retaining nut and washer.
10. Install new expansion plugs in the shift cover.

Assembly of Transmission

1. Coat all parts and assemblies with transmission fluid prior to assembly. This will insure that there is no damage during initial start-up.
2. Install the front bearing assembly into the countershaft bearing bore in the case.
3. Grease the thrust washer and place in position in the transmission case.
4. Install the countershaft front bearing journal into the front bearing and seat it against the thrust washer. Be sure to keep the centerline of the countershaft aligned with the rear bearing bore during installation to prevent damage to the countershaft front bearing.
4a. Install the countershaft rear bearing assembly, gasket, and

cover. Tighten the screws to specification.
5. Check the counter shaft end clearance, it should be 0.008-0.020 inch. Clearance can be adjusted by changing the countershaft rear bearing cover gasket.
6. With the reverse idler needle bearings held in place on each side of the spacer with grease, place the reverse idler gear and thrust washer in position in the case.
7. Drive the shaft through the case and gear using a hammer and a brass drift. Be sure that the needles stay in place and that the lock strap slot in the shaft will line up so that the lock strap, cap, and cap screw can be installed.
8. Install the lock strap on the shaft and tighten the cap screw securely.
9. Carefully lower the rear end of the mainshaft into the case while holding the first gear and washer on the shaft.
10. Place a hardwood block at the front of the mainshaft and drive the mainshaft bearing onto the shaft and into the case.
11. Install the drive pinion by carefully driving on the bearing outer race, forcing it into the case while guiding the front end of the mainshaft into the pilot bearing pocket. Make sure the bearing is fully seated.
12. Replace the retainer oil seal, pressing the seal into the retainer until the seal makes contact with its seat. Do not press beyond this point.
13. Install the bearing retainer and gasket and torque the screws to specification.
14. Install the speedometer drive gear on the output shaft.
15. Install the oil seal on the mainshaft flange, pressing the seal on until it makes contact with its seat. Do not press beyond this point.
16. Place the gasket on the output shaft bearing retainer, and install the retainer on the case. Tighten the screws to specifications.
17. Position the universal joint flange and brake drum on the output shaft.
18. Shift the transmission into two gears at the same time, and install the flange nut. Tighten to specifications.
19. Check the fourth-fifth synchronizer end-play "float" as follows:
  a. With all transmission parts in place, with the exception of the cover, place two feeler gauges between the fourth-fifth synchronizer and the stop ring. End-play should

be 0.050-0.070 inch.
  b. If end-play is not within limits, shims should be added or removed, as required, from between the fourth-fifth synchronizer and the stop ring.
  c. Reassemble and recheck the end-play.
20. Check the second-third synchronizer end-play "float" as follows:
  a. With all transmission parts in place, with the exception of the cover, place two feeler gauges between the second-third synchronizer and the outer stop ring. End-play should be 0.070-0.090 inch.
  b. If the end-play is not within limits, install new parts as required. *Shims cannot be used at this point.*
  c. Reassemble and recheck the end-play.
21. Place the transmission gears and the shift cover in neutral.
22. Position the cover gasket on the transmission.
23. Carefully lower the cover into position on the transmission. Make sure that all shift forks engage their grooves correctly.
24. Install the shouldered aligning screws and split washers, in the second hole from the front, and tighten finger tight.
25. Install the remaining screws and tighten all screws to specification.
26. Shift the transmission through all gear ranges to be sure that the transmission is working properly.

Torque Specifications

	Foot-Pounds
Cover screws	20-40
Drive gear retaining screw	15-25
Front countershaft retaining screw	15-25
Front countershaft bearing washer screw	12-22
Flange nut	125-175
Mainshaft rear retainer screw	20-40
Rear countershaft retainer screw	20-40
PTO cover screws	8-12
Filler and drain plugs	25-45
Reverse idler shaft lock screw	20-40
Bar brake screw	70-110
Bell housing screw	70-110
Brake link shoulder screw	25-45

Lubricant Capacity

New Process 7550 & 7590	18¼ pts.

Saginaw Three Speed (GM-SM326)

Description

The G.M. Corporation Model SM326 (Saginaw) is a synchromesh three-speed transmission using helical constant mesh gears. The engagement of all gears except reverse is assisted by synchronizers.

General data
Type   3-Speed
Synchromesh Gears 1st, 2nd, and 3rd
Model   SM326   and   SM326 w/Overdrive

Gear Ratios
1st Speed   2.85:1
2nd Speed   1.68:1
3rd Speed   1.00:1
Reverse   2.95:1

Transmission Disassembly

1. Remove side cover assembly and shift forks.
2. Remove clutch gear bearing retainer.
3. Remove clutch gear bearing to gear stem snap-ring. Pull clutch gear outward until a screwdriver can be inserted between bearing and case. Remove clutch gear bearing.
4. Remove speedometer driven gear and extension bolts.
5. Remove reverse idler shaft snap-ring. Slide reverse idler gear forward on shaft.
6. Remove mainshaft and extension assembly.
7. Remove clutch gear and third-speed blocker ring from inside case. Remove 14 roller bearings from clutch gear.
8. Expand the snap-ring which retains the mainshaft rear bearing. Remove the extension.
9. Usnig a dummy shaft, drive the countershaft and key out the rear of the case. Remove the gear, two tanged thrust washers, and dummy shaft. Remove bearing washer and 27 roller bearings from each end of countergear.
10. Use a long drift to drive the reverse idler shaft and key through the rear of the case.
11. Remove reverse idler gear and tanged steel thrust washer.

Mainshaft Disassembly

1. Remove second and third speed sliding clutch hug snap-ring from mainshaft. Remove clutch assembly, second speed blocker ring, and second speed gear from front of mainshaft.
2. Depress speedometer drive gear retaining clip. Remove gear. Some units have a metal speedometer drive gear which must be pulled off.
3. Remove rear bearing snap-ring.
4. Support reverse gear. Press on rear of mainshaft. Remove reverse gear, thrust washer, spring washer, rear bearing, and snap-ring. When pressing off the rear bearing, be careful not to cock the bearing on the shaft.
5. Remove first and reverse sliding clutch hub snap-ring. Remove clutch assembly, first speed blocker ring, and first gear.

Cleaning and Inspection

See "Cleaning and Inspection" instructions at front of transmission section.

Clutch Keys and Springs

Keys and springs may be replaced if worn or broken, but the hubs and sleeves are matched pairs and must be kept together.
1. Mark hub and sleeve for reassembly.
2. Push hub from sleeve. Remove keys and springs.
3. Place three keys and two springs, one on each side of hub, in position, so all three keys are engaged by both springs. The tanged end of the springs should not be installed into the same key.
4. Slide the sleeve onto the hub, aligning the marks.
NOTE: A groove around the outside of the synchronizer hub marks the end that must be opposite the fork slot in the sleeve when assembled.

Extension Oil Seal and Bushing

1. Remove seal.
2. Using bushing remover and installer tool, or other suitable tool, drive bushing into extension housing.
3. Drive new bushing in from the rear. Lubricate inside of bushing and seal. Install new oil seal with extension seal installer tool or other suitable tool.

Clutch Bearing Retainer Oil Seal

1. Pry old seal out.
2. Install new seal using seal installer or suitable tool. Seat seal in bore.

Mainshaft Assembly

1. Turn front of mainshaft up.
2. Install second gear with clutching teeth up; the rear face of the gear butts against the flange on the mainshaft.
3. Install a blocker ring with clutching teeth down. All three blocker rings are the same.
4. Install second and third speed synchronizer assembly with fork slot down. Press it onto mainshaft splines. Both synchronizer assemblies are the same. Be sure that blocker ring notches align with synchronizer assembly keys.
5. Install synchronizer snap-ring. Both synchronizer snap-rings are the same.
6. Turn rear of shaft up.
7. Install first gear with clutching teeth up; the front face of the gear butts against the flange on the mainshaft.
8. Install a blocker ring with clutching teeth down.
9. Install first and reverse synchronizer assembly with fork slot down. Press it onto mainshaft splines. Be sure blocker ring notches align with synchronizer assembly keys.
10. Install snap-ring.
11. Install reverse gear with clutching teeth down.
12. Install steel reverse gear thrust washer and spring washer.
13. Press rear ball bearing onto shaft with snap-ring slot down.
14. Install snap-ring.
15. Install speedometer drive gear and retaining clip. Press on metal speedometer drive gear.

Transmission Assembly

1. Using dummy shaft load a row of 27 roller bearings and a thrust washer at each end of countergear. Hold in place with grease.
2. Place countergear assembly into case through rear. Place a tanged thrust washer, tang away from gear at each end. Install countershaft and key, making sure that tangs align with notches in case.
3. Install reverse idler gear thrust washer, gear, and shaft with key from rear of case. Be sure thrust washer is between gear and rear of case with tang toward notch in case. NOTE: The reverse idler gear bushing may not be replaced separately—only as a unit with the gear.
4. Expand snap-ring in extension. Assemble extension over rear of mainshaft and onto rear bearing. Seat snap-ring in rear bearing groove.
5. Install 14 mainshaft pilot bearings into clutch gear cavity. Assemble third speed blocker ring onto clutch gear clutching surface with teeth toward gear.
6. Place clutch gear, pilot bearings, and third speed blocker ring assembly over front of mainshaft assembly. Be sure blocker rings

1 Thrust washer—front
2 Bearing washer
3 Needle bearings
4 Countergear
5 Needle bearings
6 Bearing washer
7 Thrust washer—rear
8 Countershaft
9 Woodruff key
10 Bearing retainer
11 Gasket
12 Oil seal
13 Snap ring—bearing to case
14 Snap ring—bearing to gear
15 Clutch gear bearing
16 Case
17 Clutch gear
18 Pilot bearings
19 3rd speed blocker ring
20 Retainer E-Ring
21 Reverse idler gear
22 Reverse idler gear bushing
   (not serviced separately)
23 Reverse idler shaft
24 Woodruff key
25 Snap ring—hub to shaft
26 2-3 synchronizer sleeve
27 Synchronizer key spring
28 2-3 Synchronizer hub assy.
29 2nd speed blocker ring
30 2nd speed gear
31 Mainshaft
32 1st speed gear
33 1st speed blocker ring
34 1st and reverse synchronizer
   hub assembly
35 1st and reverse synchronizer
   sleeve
36 Snap ring—hub to shaft
37 Reverse gear assy.
38 Thrust washer
39 Thrust washer
40 Rear bearing
41 Snap ring—bearing to shaft
42 Speedometer drive gear
43 Gasket
44 Snap ring—rear bearing to
   extension
45 Extension

46 Oil seal
47 Gasket
48 2-3 shift fork
49 1st and reverse shift fork
50 2-3 shifter shaft assembly
51 1st and reverse shifter shaft
   assembly

52 O-ring seal
53 Detent cam retainer ring
54 Spring
55 2nd and 3rd detent cam
56 1st and reverse detent cam
57 Side cover

SM326 transmission components (© G.M.C.)

align with keys in second-third synchronizer assembly.
7. Stick extension gasket to case with grease. Install clutch gear, mainshaft, and extension together. Be sure clutch gear engages teeth of countergear anti-lash plate. Torque extension bolts to 45 ft. lbs.
8. Place bearing over stem of clutch gear and into front case bore. Install front bearing to

clutch gear snap-ring.
9. Install clutch gear bearing retainer and gasket. The retainer oil return hole must be at the bottom. Torque to 10 ft. lbs.
10. Install reverse idler gear shaft E-ring.
11. Shift synchronizer sleeves to neutral positions. Install cover, gasket, and forks, aligning forks with synchronizer sleeve grooves. Torque side cover bolts

to 10 ft. lbs.
12. Install speedometer driven gear.

Torque Specifications
Foot-Pounds

Extension to case attaching bolts	35-55
Drain and filler plugs	10-15
Side cover attaching bolts	18-24
Clutch gear retainer bolts	18-24

Saginaw Four Speed

Disassembly of Transmission
1. Remove the side cover bolts and the side cover assembly.
2. Remove the drive gear bearing retainer.
3. Remove the drive gear to gear stem snap ring. Remove the drive gear bearing by pulling outward on the gear until a screwdriver can be inserted between the bearing and the large snap ring. The drive gear bearing is a slip fit on the gear and into the case bore. This provides clearance between

the case bore and the shaft for removal of the drive gear and the mainshaft assembly.
4. Remove the extension housing bolts.
5. Remove the drive gear, mainshaft and the extension housing assembly through the rear case opening. Remove the drive gear and bearing from the mainshaft.
6. Using snap ring pliers, expand the snap ring in the extension housing which holds the mainshaft rear bearing and remove

the housing.
7. Using a suitable size drift at the front of the countershaft, drive the countershaft and the woodruff key out the rear of the case. The drift will hold the countergear bearings in place. Remove the gear and thrust washers.
8. Remove the reverse idler gear stop ring. Use a long drift or punch through the front bearing case bore and drive the reverse idler shaft and woodruff key out of the rear of the case.

1. Bearing Retainer
2. Gasket-Retainer to Case
3. Oil Seal
4. Snap Ring-Bearing to Shaft
5. Snap Ring-Bearing to Case
6. Drive Gear Bearing
7. Drive Gear
8. Mainshaft Pilot Bearings
9. 4th Speed Blocker Ring
10. Case
11. Filler Plug
12. Reverse Idler Gear
13. Reverse Idler Shaft
14. Woodruff Key
15. Thrust Washer-Front Gear
16. Needle Retainer Washer
17. Needle Bearings
18. Countergear
19. Needle Retainer Washer
20. Thrust Washer-Rear Gear
21. Countershaft
22. Woodruff Key
23. Synchronizer Sleeve
24. Snap Ring-Hub to Shaft
25. Key Retainer
26. 3-4 Synchronizer Hub
27. Clutch Keys
28. Key Retainer
29. 3rd Speed Blocker Ring
30. 3rd Speed Gear
31. Needle Bearings
32. Second Speed Gear
33. 2nd Speed Blocker Ring
34. Mainshaft
35. 1st Speed Blocker Ring
36. First Speed Gear
37. Thrust Washer
38. Wave Washer
39. Rear Bearing
40. Snap Ring-Bearing to Shaft
41. Speedo Drive Gear and Clip
42. Gasket-Extension to Case
43. Snap Ring-Extension to Rear Bearing
44. Extension
45. Vent
46. Bushing
47. Oil Seal
48. 1-2 Synchronizer Sleeve and Reverse Gear
49. Key Retainer
50. 1-2 Synchronizer Hub
51. Clutch Keys
52. Key Retainer
53. Snap Ring-Hub to Shaft
54. 3-4 Shift Fork
55. Detent Spring
56. 3-4 Detent Cam
57. 1-2 Detent Cam
58. 3-4 Shifter Shaft
59. Gasket-Cover to Case
60. Cover
61. TCS Switch and Gasket
62. Lipseal
63. Detent Cam Retainer
64. 1-2 Shift Fork
65. "O" Ring
66. 1-2 Shift Shaft
67. Spring
68. Ball
69. "O" Ring
70. Reverse Shifter Shaft and Fork

Saginaw Four Speed Transmission—exploded view (© GM Corp.)

Overhaul of Sub-Assemblies
Cleaning and Inspection
Transmission Case

1. Wash the transmission case thoroughly with clean solvent. Inspect the case for cracks.
2. Check the front and rear faces for burrs. If burrs are present, dress them off with a mill file.

Front and Rear Bearings

1. Wash the front and rear bearings with clean solvent.
2. Blow the bearings out with compressed air.

NOTE: Do not allow the bearings to spin. Turn them slowly by hand. Spinning bearings will damage the race and balls.

3. Make sure that the bearings are clean. Lubricate the bearings with light engine oil and check them for roughness by turning the race slowly by hand.

Bearing Rollers

All clutch gear and countergear bearing rollers should be closely inspected and replaced if they show signs of wear. Inspect the countershaft and the reverse idler shaft, re-

Removing the drive gear bearing—Saginaw Four Speed (© GM Corp.)

place if damaged. Replace all worn washers.

Gears

1. Inspect all gears for excessive wear, chips, or cracks. Replace as necessary.
2. Check both clutch sleeves to see that they slide freely on their hubs.

Mainshaft Disassembly

1. Using snap ring pliers, remove the third-fourth sliding clutch hub snap ring from the mainshaft. Remove the clutch assembly, third gear blocking ring, and the third gear from the mainshaft.

1. Clutch Gear Bearing
2. Clutch Gear
3. Mainshaft Pilot Bearings
4. 3-4 Synchronizer Assembly
5. Third Speed Gear
6. Second Speed Gear
7. 1-2 Synchronizer and Reverse Gear Assembly
8. First Speed Gear
9. Thrust Washer
10. Spring Washer
11. Rear Bearing
12. Speedo Drive Gear
13. Mainshaft
14. Snap Ring
15. Synchronizing "Blocker" Ring

Mainshaft and clutch gear—exploded view—Saginaw Four Speed (© GM Corp.)

Synchronizer assembly (third-fourth)—Saginaw Four Speed (© GM Corp.)

2. Depress the speedometer retaining clip and slide the gear from the shaft.
3. Remove the rear bearing snap ring from the shaft groove.
4. Support the first gear with press plates and press on the shaft to remove the first gear, thrust washer, and rear bearing.
5. Remove the first-second sliding clutch hub snap ring from the shaft and remove the clutch assembly, the second gear blocking ring, and the second gear.

Assembly

1. Position the mainshaft with the front end facing upward.
2. Install the third gear with the clutching teeth upward, the rear face of the gear will butt against the flange of the mainshaft.
3. Install the blocking ring with the clutching teeth downward over the synchronizing surface of the third gear.

NOTE: All four blocking rings used in the transmission are identical.

4. Install the third-fourth synchronizer assembly with the fork slot facing downward. Push the assembly onto the splines on the mainshaft until it bottoms against the flange.

CAUTION: Be sure that the notches of the blocking ring align with the keys on the synchronizer assembly.

5. Install the synchronizer hub retaining snap ring on the mainshaft.
6. Position the mainshaft with the rear end facing uward.
7. Install the second gear with the clutching teeth facing upward. The front face of the gear will butt against the flange of the mainshaft.
8. Install the blocking ring with the clutching teeth downward over

the synchronizing surface of the second speed gear.
9. Install the first-second synchronizer assembly with the fork slot facing downward.

NOTE: Be sure the notches of the blocking ring align with the keys of the synchronizer assembly.

10. Install the synchronizer retaining snap ring on the mainshaft.
11. Install a blocker ring with the notches downward so that they align with the keys on the first-second synchronizer assembly.
12. Install the first gear with the clutching teeth facing downward.
13. Install the first gear steel thrust washer.
14. Install the first gear spring washer.
15. Install the rear ball bearing with the snap ring slot facing downward. Press the bearing onto the shaft.
16. Install the rear bearing snap ring.
17. Install the speedometer drive gear and clip.

Synchronizer Assemblies

1. Mark the hub and sleeve so they can be matched during assembly.
2. Push the hub from the sliding sleeve, the keys and springs may be easily removed.
3. Place the three keys and the two springs in position, one on each side of the hub, so all three keys are engaged with both springs. The tanged end of each synchronizer spring should be installed into different key cavities on either side. Slide the sleeve onto the hub, aligning the marks made before disassembly.

Note: A groove around the outside of the synchronizer hub identifies the end that must be opposite the fork slot in the sleeve when assembled. This groove indicates the end of the hub with the greatest recess depth.

Assembly of Transmission

1. Using a suitable size drift, load a row of roller bearings (27) and a bearing washer at each end of the countergear. Use heavy grease to hold the bearings in place.
2. Install the countergear ssembly through the rear opening in the case, along with a tanged thrust washer, tang away from the gear, at each end of the gear. Install the countershaft and woodruff key from the rear of the case.

CAUTION: Be sure that the countershaft picks up both thrust washers and that the tangs are aligned with the notches in the case.

3. Install the reverse idler gear and shaft with its woodruff key from the rear of the case.
4. Using snap ring pliers, expand the snap ring in the extension housing and install the housing over the rear of the mainshaft and onto the rear bearing. Seat the snap ring in the rear bearing groove.
5. Load the mainshaft pilot bearings (14) into the drive gear cavity and assemble the fourth gear blocker ring onto the drive gear clutching surface, with the clutching teeth toward the drive gear.
6. Install the drive gear, pilot bearings and fourth gear blocker ring assembly over the front of the mainshaft.

NOTE: Be sure that the notches in the blocker ring align with the keys in the third-fourth synchronizer assembly.

7. Place the extension housing gasket on the rear of the case, hold in place with grease. From the rear of the case, install the mainshaft and extension housing assembly.

8. Install the extension housing retaining bolts. Use a sealing compound on the bottom bolt only. Tighten to specification.

9. Install the front bearing outer snap ring and position the bearing over the stem of the drive gear and into the front of the case.

10. Install the snap ring on the drive gear stem. Install the bearing retainer and gasket on the case. *Make sure that the bearing retainer oil hole is at the bottom.*

11. Shift the synchronizer sleeves to the neutral position and install the cover, gasket and fork assembly on the transmission. Make sure that the forks align with the synchronizer sleeve grooves.

12. Tighten all bolts to specification.

Torque Specifications

	Foot-Pounds
Clutch gear retainer to case	15
Side cover to case	15
Extension to case	45
Shift lever to shaft bolts	25
Filler plug	18
Case to clutch housing	75
Crossmember to frame	25
Crossmember to mount— mount to extension	40
Mount to transmission	32

5000 Series 5 Speed

Description

The extra heavy-duty five-speed transmission (Spicer,) is a manually shifted, synchromesh, helical gear type. Fifth forward speed is direct drive. A power take-off is located on the right and left side of the transmission case.

Disassembly of Transmission

1. Remove the gear shift housing from the transmission case. Remove the detent balls from the housing and shift the transmission into two gears.

2. Remove the brake drum and spline flange.

3. Remove the brake shoe assembly, the output shaft bearing retainer, speedometer driving gear, and spacer.

4. Remove the countershaft rear bearing retainer, gasket, and countershaft nut.

5. Remove the left-side power take-off cover.

6. Remove the input shaft bearing retainer and gasket from the case. Using a soft drift, drive the input shaft and front bearing from the case. Remove the pilot rollers from the drive gear.

7. With a hardwood or fiber block placed against the front side of the second-speed gear, drive the input shaft assembly rearward until the output shaft bearing clears the case. Be careful not to hit the second-speed gear against the countershaft reverse gear. Remove the bearing from the output shaft.

8. When removing the output shaft from the case, slide off the first-speed gear.

9. Using a puller, remove the countershaft rear bearing.

10. Lift the countershaft assembly out of the case.

11. Remove the countershaft front bearing retainer, gasket and bearing from the front of the case.

12. Remove the reverse idler gear, and bearings from the gear bores.

13. Remove any of the 14 output shaft pilot rollers which may have dropped into the case.

Disassembly of Sub-Assemblies

Output Shaft

1. Remove the fourth and fifth speed synchronizer assembly snapping and thrust washer at the front of the fourth-speed gear. Remove the gear.

2. Remove the snap-ring at the front of the third-speed gear sleeve. The second and third-speed synchronizer can then be removed by bouncing the front of the output shaft on a block of wood.

3. Press the output shaft out of the second and third-speed syn-

Tool—T53T-4242-F

Removing output shaft bearing using special puller
(© Dana Corp., Spicer Div.)

chronizer clutch gear and second-speed gear.

Countershaft

When replacing the countershaft or countershaft gear, press off one gear at a time. To remove the second-speed gear use special tool.

Spicer 5 speed transmission (© Dana Corp., Spicer Div.)

Manual Transmissions

Gearshift housing components (© Dana Corp., Spicer Div.)

Replacing countershaft second speed gear
(© Dana Corp., Spicer Div.)

Input Shaft

Remove the input shaft bearing only for replacement. Remove the retaining snap-ring, and press the bearing off the shaft.

Gearshift Housing

1. Attach the gear shift housing to the transmission case. Cut the lock wire from the retaining screws in the shifter forks and gates.
2. Mark the shifter forks, shafts, and gates for correct assembly. Shift the shafts into neutral. Drive out the housing plugs at the front of the shafts.
3. Remove the fourth and fifth speed-shaft from the front of the housing.
4. Remove the second and third-speed fork and shaft and interlocking pin.
5. Remove the low and reverse shifter shaft, fork, and gate. Remove the interlocking pin and plungers from the housing.

Assembly of Sub-Assemblies
Gearshift Housing

1. Place the low and reverse shifter

1038

Gearshift housing
(© Dana Corp., Spicer Div.)

gate and fork in the housing, and slide the shaft into the housing and through the gate and fork. Install the retaining screws in the gate and fork and hold with lock wire.
2. Install two plungers in the housing interlocking bore between the low and reverse and second and third shifter shaft bores. Install the interlock pin in the shaft and the second and third-speed fork in the housing. Slide the shaft into the housing and through the fork. Install the retaining screw, and lock wire.
3. Install the interlocking pin and plunger in the housing interlocking bore between the second and third-speed and fourth and fifth-speed shifter shaft guides. Install the fourth and fifth-speed shaft and fork. Install the retaining screw and lock wire.
4. Check the interlocking system

for correct operation and, using sealer, install the housing plugs. Remove the housing from the transmission case.

Output Shaft

1. Place the second-speed gear onto the output shaft, with the clutch teeth facing forward.
2. Insert the two Woodruff keys in the output shaft and install the second and third-speed synchronizer clutch gear.
3. Place the second and third-speed synchronizer, and third speed gear and sleeve on the output shaft. Press the sleeve onto the shaft until it bottoms on the synchronizer clutch gear. The third-speed gear sleeve slots must line up with the Woodruff keys in the output shaft.
4. Remove the assembly from the press and install the snap-ring at the front of the third-speed gear sleeve.
5. Install the fourth-speed gear, thrust washer, and snap-ring on the output shaft. Install the fourth and fifth-speed synchronizer on the output shaft.

Countershaft

Install gears and spacer onto shaft and hold with the snap-rings. Each gear takes a specific Woodruff key, so install them one at a time.

Input Shaft

Press the input shaft bearing onto the shaft using special tool.

Assembly of Transmission

As a protection against scoring, coat all parts with transmission lubricant.

1. Tap the countershaft front bearing into the case and install retainer and new gasket. Line up the oil return holes in the retainer, gasket and case and torque the 7/16" retainer bolts at 50-55 ft. lbs. (30 ft. lbs. for smaller bolts).
2. Place the assembled countershaft in the transmission case into the front bearing.
3. Drive the countershaft rear bearing onto the countershaft and into the case.
4. Install the idler gear bearings, and gear in the case. Drive the idler gear shaft into position, and install the power takeoff cover.
5. Tap the input shaft and bearing into the case. Place the pilot bearing rollers in the input shaft.
6. Install the input shaft bearing retainer without a gasket and tighten the bolts. With a feeler gauge, check the clearance between the bearing retainer and

the case to determine gasket size.

7. Install the bearing retainer and gasket, making certain that the oil drain-hole is in line with the gasket and case holes. Torque retainer bolts to 30 ft. lbs., 40 ft. lbs. for 7/16" bolt.
8. Install the low and reverse gear on the output shaft and place the assembly in the case. Drive the output shaft bearing into position.
9. Shift the transmission into two gears. Install the countershaft nut and torque at 350-450 ft. lbs. Install the countershaft rear bearing retainer and torque the 7/16" bolts to 45 ft. lbs.
10. Install a new oil seal in the output shaft bearing retainer. Place the spacer and speedometer driving gear on the output shaft, and install the bearing retainer. Torque the bolts to specification.
11. Install the parking brake shoe assembly.
12. Install the brake drum and the spline flange. Torque the output shaft nut to specification.
13. Shift the transmission and gear shift housing into neutral, and install the gear shift housing and, using 7/16" bolts, torque to 45 ft. lbs.

Torque Chart

Nomenclature	Nuts and/or Bolts and Torque Limits		Nomenclature	Nuts and/or Bolts and Torque Limits	
Bolt-gear shift lever tower to gearshift housing	3/8-16 20-25	7/16-14 30-35	Bolt—countershaft & reverse idler shaft retainer	5/16-18 25-30 3/8-16 25-37 3/8-16† 18-25†	7/16-14 40-45 1/2-13 80-85
Bolt-clutch housing to trans. case	7/16-14 30-38 5/8-11 96-120	9/16-12 70-90	Bolt—gear shift housing to trans. case	5/16-18 20-25 3/8-16 35-40	3/8-16†† 30-35†† 7/16-14 45-50
Nut-U-joint flange to trans. output shaft	1.00-20 90-125	1 1/2-18 275-350 1 1/4-18 225-275	Bolt—power take off cover to trans. case	3/8-16 20-30	
Nut—drum parking brake to companion flange	3/8-24 35-45	7/16-20 50-70	Nut—countershaft bearing lock (5-speed extra h.d. & 5-speed exclusive)	1 1/4-18 350-450	
Nut—bellcrank to trans.	9/16-18 70-90				
Bolt—lever assy. to trans.	3/8-16 20-25		Nut—countershaft bearing lock (5-speed exclusive h.d.)		
Nut—handbrake anchor bar to trans. case (5-speed extra-heavy duty only)					
Bolt—bellcrank to trans.			Bolt—input shaft bearing retainer to trans. case	5/16-18 25-30 3/8-16 25-30	7/16-14 40-45
Bolt—reverse lock-out plunger retainer	11/16-16 80-100				
Bolt—countershaft rear bearing retainer	5/16-18 25-30 3/8-16 35-40	7/16-14 45-55 1/2-13 67-70	Bolt—countershaft front bearing retainer	5/16-18 25-30 3/8-16 25-35	7/16-14 50-55

Spicer 6000 Series 5 Speed

Description

This transmission is a 5-speed synchromesh helical gear design with direct drive in 5th speed on all models, except the 6853C, which has overdrive in 5th speed.

Engagement of all gears, except first and reverse, is aided by sleeve type synchronizers. All gears are of helical design, with the exception of

Using puller to remove mainshaft rear bearing
(© Dana Corp., Spicer Div.)

first and reverse gears. Lubricant capacity is 17 pints.

General data

Make		Spicer
Type		5-Speed Synchromesh
Models		6852S, 6852K, 6852G, and 6853C
Clutch housing		S.A.E. #2

Gear ratios—all ratios are (to 1)

Transmission Model	6852G	6852K
1st	6.70	6.70
2nd	3.52	4.02
3rd	1.97	2.49
4th	1.17	1.57
5th	1.00	1.00
Reverse	6.72	6.72
Transmission Model	6852S	6853C
1st	5.71	5.71
2nd	3.20	3.00
3rd	1.89	1.78
4th	1.15	1.00
5th	1.00	0.85
Reverse	5.73	5.73

Disassembly of Transmission
Removal of Mainshaft

1. Remove clutch housing and clutch release mechanism as a unit.
2. Engage 2nd and 3rd synchronizer with mainshaft 2nd speed gear, and engage 4th and 5th synchronizer with mainshaft 4th speed or overdrive gear to lock transmission in two gears.
3. Remove companion flange or yoke retaining nut. Use puller to remove flange or yoke.
4. Remove speedometer driven gear and adapter (if used) from mainshaft rear bearing cap.
5. Remove mainshaft and countershaft rear bearing caps and gaskets.
6. Remove cotter pin and countershaft rear bearing nut.
7. Remove speedometer drive gear or spacer from rear end of mainshaft.
8. Remove mainshaft rear bearing snap-ring.
9. Using bearing puller, remove mainshaft rear bearing.
10. Remove mainshaft and gear assembly from the transmission case by clearing it from main drive gear and sliding assembly up and forward out of rear bearing bore.

Disassembly of Mainshaft

1. Remove the 1st and reverse sliding gear from mainshaft.
2. Remove 4th and 5th synchronizer.
3. Remove snap-ring and thrust washer.
4. Slide mainshaft 4th speed or ov-

1039

Mainshaft components (© Dana Corp., Spicer Div.)

Main drive gear components
(© Dana Corp., Spicer Div.)

1 4th and 5th speed
  synchronizer
2 Snap ring
3 Thrust washer
4 4th speed or
  overdrive gear
5 Sleeve pin
6 4th speed or
  over-drive gear
  sleeve
7 3rd speed gear

8 2nd and 3rd
  speed synchro-
  nizer
9 Snap ring
10 2nd and 3rd
  clutch gear
11 2nd speed gear
12 Mainshaft
13 1st and reverse
  sliding gear

1 Main drive gear
  bearing retainer
  ring
2 Main drive gear
  bearing
3 Main drive gear
4 Pilot bearing rollers

erdrive gear from end of main-shaft.

5. Remove mainshaft 3rd speed gear and mainshaft 4th speed or overdrive gear sleeve. NOTE: If necessary to press off gear and sleeve, shift 2nd and 3rd synchronizer into engagement with mainshaft 2nd speed gear and support under 3rd speed gear. Be sure to remove sleeve pin from the inside of 4th speed or overdrive gear sleeve.

6. Slide 2nd and 3rd synchronizer from mainshaft.

7. Remove snap-ring from 2nd and 3rd speed clutch gear.

8. Support mainshaft 2nd speed gear under arbor press and press mainshaft out of 2nd and 3rd speed clutch gear and 2nd speed gear.

Removal of Maindrive Gear

1. Remove 14 mainshaft pilot bearing rollers which may have remained in cavity of main drive gear.

2. Remove main bearing cap and gasket.

3. Remove snap-ring from main drive gear bearing.

4. Remove main drive gear and bearing assembly from transmission case.

Disassembly of Main Drive Gear

1. Remove main drive gear bearing retaining snap-ring.

2. Using bearing remover plates with an arbor press, remove bearing from main drive gear.

Reverse Idler Gear Removal

IMPORTANT: When removing the reverse idler gear shaft, support the gear to prevent it from being damaged.

1. Using remover tool, remove reverse idler gear shaft, gear and bearings.

Removal of Countershaft

1. Using puller, remove countershaft rear bearing.

1 Main drive gear
2 Main drive gear bearing cap
3 Mainshaft pilot bearing rollers
4 Snap ring
5 Clutch housing
6 4th and 5th shift rod
7 4th and 5th shift fork
8 4th and 5th synchronizer
9 Poppet ball
10 Poppet spring
11 Snap ring
12 Thrust washer
13 Mainshaft 4th speed or
  overdrive gear
14 Mainshaft 4th speed or
  overdrive gear sleeve
15 Mainshaft 3rd speed gear
15 Mainshaft 3rd speed gear
16 2nd and 3rd shift fork
17 Snap ring
18 Mainshaft 2nd and 3rd speed
  clutch gear
19 2nd and 3rd synchronizer
20 Mainshaft 2nd speed gear
21 1st and reverse shift rod
22 1st and reverse shift fork
23 Mainshaft 1st and reverse
  sliding gear
24 Mainshaft
25 Shifter housing
26 Mainshaft rear bearing
27 Snap ring
28 Speedometer driven gear
29 Mainshaft rear bearing cap
  oil seal
30 Companion flange
31 Companion flange nut
32 Mainshaft rear bearing cap
33 Speedometer drive gear
34 Countershaft rear bearing
35 Countershaft rear bearing cap
36 Countershaft rear bearing nut

NOTE
Reverse Idler Gear Shaft
(Item 38) Is Intentionally
Shown Out Of Normal Position

37 Snap ring
38 Reverse idler gear shaft
39 Reverse idler gear bearings
40 Reverse idler gear
41 Countershaft 1st gear teeth
42 Countershaft reverse gear

teeth
43 Countershaft 2nd speed gear
44 Countershaft 3rd speed gear
45 Countershaft 4th speed or
  overdrive gear
46 Countershaft
47 Countershaft drive gear

48 Transmission case
49 Countershaft front bearing
50 Main drive gear bearing
51 Snap ring
52 Main drive gear bearing cap
  oil seal

Spicer 6000 Series 5 speed transmission (© Dana Corp., Spicer Div.)

1 Snap ring
2 Countershaft drive gear
3 Snap ring
4 4th speed or overdrive gear
5 3rd speed gear
6 2nd and 3rd gear spacer
7 2nd speed gear
8 Countershaft
9 Countershaft gear keys

Countershaft components (© Dana Corp., Spicer Div.)

2. Lift the countershaft assembly out of transmission case.
3. Press or drive countershaft front bearing from bore of transmission case.

Disassembly of Countershaft

1. Support countershaft drive gear with parallel bars under hub and press countershaft free of gear.
2. Remove exposed countershaft gear key and snap-ring. Support 4th speed or overdrive gear and press countershaft free of gear.
3. Follow the same procedure and remove 2nd and 3rd speed gear.
4. Remove the remaining countershaft gear key.

Assembly of Subassemblies

Cleanliness is of the utmost importance. The transmission should be rebuilt in a clean working area. All parts, except those actually being worked on should be covered with clean lint-free paper. Avoid nicking, marring, or burring all surfaces.

IMPORTANT: Coat all thrust washers, splines of shafts, and bores of all gears with lubricant to provide initial lubrication thus preventing scoring or galling.

Assembly of Mainshaft

1. Position mainshaft in a soft-jawed vise, front end up. NOTE: Fit of new parts may require the use of an arbor press. If so, set up vertically and follow same procedure.
2. Position 2nd speed gear on mainshaft with clutch teeth and synchronizer cone facing up.
3. Using a suitable sleeve, press or drive 2nd and 3rd speed clutch gear on mainshaft. Install snap-ring in mainshaft groove. NOTE: Minimum end clearance between 2nd and 3rd speed clutch gear and 2nd speed gear should be 0.004". Correct accordingly.
4. Slide 2nd and 3rd speed synchronizer on mainshaft until engaged with 2nd and 3rd speed clutch gear. IMPORTANT: The 2nd and 3rd speed synchronizer is often assembled backward on the mainshaft. Make sure that the long hub on synchronizer clutch gear faces the 2nd speed gear.

5. Place 3rd speed gear on mainshaft with clutch teeth and synchronizer cone facing downward.
6. Assemble sleeve pin to 4th speed or overdrive gear sleeve with head of pin inside sleeve, with flanged end of sleeve facing the 3rd speed gear, align sleeve pin with splines and press on the mainshaft.
7. Place 4th speed or overdrive gear on sleeve with clutch hub facing up and secure with thrust washer and snap-ring.

Assembly of Main Drive Gear

1. Press or drive main drive gear bearing onto main drive gear shaft and install snap-ring.

Assembly of Countershaft

1. Position first countershaft gear key in slot of countershaft. Press 2nd speed gear and, 2nd and 3rd gear spacer onto countershaft.
2. Install the remaining countershaft gear keys. It may be necessary to dress the keys with a file.
3. Press 3rd speed gear on the countershaft, followed by 4th speed gear, a snap-ring and drive gear secured by a snap-ring.

Assembly of Transmission

Installation of Mainshaft

1. Place mainshaft 1st and reverse sliding gear at an angle in the rear of the transmission case with shift fork collar facing toward front of case.
2. Place 4th and 5th synchronizer on mainshaft. Shift synchronizer clutch collar into engagement with mainshaft 4th speed or overdrive gear to help lock synchronizer in place during installation in case.
3. Lower rear of mainshaft into case, through 1st and reverse sliding gear and out mainshaft rear bearing bore. NOTE: There must be fourteen pilot bearing rollers in the main drive gear pocket.
4. Lower front of mainshaft to mesh with countershaft gears. Slide rear of mainshaft into pocket of main drive gear.

5. Slide rear bearing onto mainshaft with snap-ring facing the rear.
6. Tap bearing into case bore with its snap-ring flush with rear of case.
7. Press speedometer drive gear or spacer onto the mainshaft against bearing. NOTE: Install new oil seal in mainshaft rear bearing cap.
8. Install gasket with sealing cement and mainshaft rear bearing cap and torque cap screws to 35 to 40 foot-pounds. NOTE: Install speedometer driven gear (when used) through opening in mainshaft rear bearing cap.
9. Engage 2nd and 3rd synchronizer with mainshaft 2nd speed gear, and 4th and 5th synchronizer with mainshaft 4th speed or overdrive gear to lock transmission in two gears.
10. Install companion flange or yoke on mainshaft and secure with a washer and nut at a torque of 320 to 350 foot-pounds.
11. Remove rear bearing cap from countershaft and torque bearing nut to 320 to 350 foot-pounds and secure with cotter pin.
12. Install gasket and countershaft rear bearing (with sealing cement) and torque cap screws to 35 to 40 foot-pounds. NOTE: The projection on the countershaft rear bearing cap locks the reverse idler gear shaft into proper position.
13. Rotate main drive gear to check for free rotation of all gears and shafts.
14. Use pressure type oil can, filled with transmission lubricant (S.A.E. 50 engine oil of good quality) to force oil through holes and end slots of all mainshaft gears to open oil passageways. NOTE: Using the pressure type oil can, spray gear teeth with transmission lubricant to provide initial lubrication and to prevent corrosion.

Installation of Main Drive Gear

1. Install main drive gear and bearing from inside the transmission case, by tapping bearing through case bore.
2. Install snap-ring on outer race

of bearing. Tap bearing rear-ward, so snap-ring is flush with case. NOTE: Install new oil seal in main drive gear bearing cap.

3. Install gasket (with sealing cement) and main drive gear bearing cap to transmission case and torque to 60 to 80 foot-pounds. IMPORTANT: Be sure the oil passages in the bearing cap, gasket and transmission case are all aligned.

4. Coat the pocket of main drive gear with Light Weight Ball and Roller Bearing Grease.

5. Place the fourteen pilot bearing rollers in main drive gear pocket.

Installation of Reverse Idler Gear

1. Install reverse idler gear bearings into gear and install in transmission case, with large gear on idler gear toward front of case. Mesh idler gear with countershaft and align bore of bearings with hole in transmission case.

2. Insert reverse idler gear shaft in rear of case, noting that "flat" on shaft is squared toward countershaft so that it can be locked by rear bearing cap.

3. Set countershaft rear bearing cap in place to check lock of reverse idler shaft. Finger-tighten bearing cap screws to prevent countershaft from moving during installation of mainshaft.

Installation of Countershaft

1. Press countershaft front bearing on front of countershaft.

2. Lower countershaft assembly into case, guiding rear end of shaft out through rear of case.

3. Guide countershaft front bearing into countershaft front bearing bore.

4. Place two strips of flat steel stock, approximately ⅜-inch thick, between countershaft drive gear and wall of case.

5. Seat bearing on shaft (should be

tight fit) then remove the two steel strips and tap bearing into bore seating snap-ring against case.

6. Hand-tighten countershaft rear bearing nut.

Removal of Remote Control Assembly

NOTE: The Spicer 6000 transmission uses two different remote control assemblies: Prop shaft type and rod type.

1. Remove retainer, plunger pin spring, and plunger.

2. Remove remote control assembly from transmission as described below: IMPORTANT: Tilt the remote control assembly slightly to the left during removal to prevent the plunger from falling into the transmission.

3. Remove the plunger from the 1st and reverse shift finger.

Installation of Remote Control Assemblies

NOTE: The 6000 transmission is available with one of two different remote control assemblies but the installation procedures are the same for both.

1. Coat remote control assembly position on shifter housing.

2. Position plunger in 1st and reverse shift finger; then carefully install remote control assembly as shown, keeping the assembly slightly tilted to the left to prevent the plunger from falling into transmission.

3. Install plunger pin, plunger pin spring, and retainer.

4. Install remote control assembly-to-shifter housing attaching parts. Tighten cap screws firmly.

Installation of Control Tower

Install control tower as described below only when the transmission is going into storage.

1. Coat gasket with sealing cement and position on shifter housing.

Rod type remote control adjustment
(© Dana Corp., Spicer Div.)

2. Position plunger in 1st and reverse shift finger, then place the assembly and new gasket (with cement) on the shifter housing.

3. Install plunger, plunger spring, and plunger retainer and tighten down the tower with washers and capscrews.

Removal of Shifter Housing

NOTE: The Spicer 6000 transmission uses a forward control shifter housing and a center control shifter housing.

1. Remove shifter housing-to-transmission case attaching

Replacing remote control assembly
(© Dana Corp., Spicer Div.)

1 1st and reverse shift rod bracket
2 Poppet ball
3 Poppet spring
4 1st and reverse shift rod
5 1st and reverse shift fork
6 Breather
7 Forward control shifter housing
8 Expansion plug
9 2nd and 3rd shift fork
10 Setscrew
11 4th and 5th shift rod
12 4th and 5th shift fork
13 Interlock
14 Interlock pin
15 2nd and 3rd shift rod
16 Setscrew
17 Expansion plug
18 2nd and 3rd shift rod bracket
19 Setscrew
20 Shift rod thimble

Shifter housing components (© Dana Corp., Spicer Div.)

parts. NOTE: Carefully remove forward control shifter housing to prevent loss of the three poppet balls and springs.

2. Carefully remove shifter housing from the case.

Installation of Shifter Housing

NOTE: Make certain that shift forks and transmission clutch collars are in neutral position.

1. Carefully position shifter housing and gasket (use cement) on

transmission case and make sure all three shift forks are in their corresponding shift collar and tighten down.

2. Use large screwdriver or small pry bar and check movement of each shift rod for proper shift action. Return shift rods to neutral position.

IMPORTANT: On transmissions using the forward control shifter housing, place the three poppet balls and springs in the shifter housing.

Torque Specifications

Location	Foot-Pounds
Shift fork set screws	45-50
Main drive gear bearing cap retaining cap screws	60-80
Mainshaft rear bearing cap retaining cap screws	35-40
Mainshaft flange or yoke retaining nut	320-350
Countershaft rear bearing retaining nut	320-350
Countershaft rear bearing cap retaining cap screws	35-40
Clutch housing retaining cap screws	90-95

Warner T-10 4 Speed

Description

The Warner T-10 is a fully synchronized four-speed transmission having a floor mounted shift lever. Lubricant capacity is 2½ pints.

Disassembly of Transmission

1. Drain transmission, mount in stand and remove side cover and shift controls.
2. Remove front bearing retainer and gasket.
3. Remove output shaft companion flange.
4. Drive out lock pin and pull reverse shift shaft out about ⅛ in. to disengage shifter fork from reverse gear.
5. Remove bolts and tap the case extension (with soft hammer) rearward. When idler gear shaft is out as far as it will go, move extension to the left so the reverse fork clears the reverse gear. Remove extension and gasket.
6. Remove rear bearing snap-ring from mainshaft.
7. Remove case extension oil seal.
8. Using a puller, remove speedometer drive gear.
9. Remove the reverse gear, reverse idler gear and tanged thrust washer.
10. Remove self-locking bolt holding the rear bearing retainer to transmission case.
11. Remove the entire mainshaft assembly.
12. Unload bearing rollers from main drive gear and remove fourth-speed synchronizer blocking ring.
13. Lift the front half of reverse idler gear and its thrust washer from the case.
14. Remove the main drive gear snap-ring and spacer washer.
15. With soft hammer, tap main drive gear out of front bearing.
16. From inside the case, tap out front bearing and snap-ring.
17. From the front of the case, tap out the countershaft with a dummy shaft.

18. Then lift out the countergear assembly with both tanged washers.
19. Dismantle the countergear, consisting of 80 rollers, six .050 in. spacers and a roller tubular spacer.
20. Remove mainshaft front snap-ring and slide third and fourth-speed clutch assembly, third-speed gear and synchronizer ring, second and third-speed gear thrust bearing, second-speed gear and second-speed synchronizer ring from front of mainshaft.
21. Press mainshaft out of retainer.
22. Remove the mainshaft rear snap-ring.
23. Support first and second-speed clutch assembly and press on rear of mainshaft to remove shaft from rear bearing, first-speed gear, and synchromesh ring, first and second-speed clutch sliding sleeve and first-speed gear bushing.

Assembly

Mainshaft

1. From the rear of the mainshaft, assemble first and second-speed clutch assembly to mainshaft (sliding clutch sleeve taper toward the rear, hub to the front) and press the first-speed gear bushing onto the shaft.
2. Install first speed gear synchronizing ring aligning notches in ring with keys in hub.
3. Install first-speed gear (hub toward front) and thrust washer with the washer grooves facing first-speed gear.
4. Press on the rear bearing, with the snap-ring groove toward the front of the transmission. Be sure the bearing is firmly seated against the shoulder on the mainshaft.
5. Install the selective fit snap-ring onto the mainshaft behind the rear bearing. Use the thickest ring that will fit between the

rear face of the bearing and the front face of the snap-ring.
6. From the front of the mainshaft, install the second-speed gear synchronizing ring so that the ring notches correspond with the hub keys.
7. Install the second-speed gear (hub toward the back) and the second and third-speed gear thrust bearing.
8. Install third-speed gear (hub to front) and third-speed gear synchronizing ring (notches front).
9. Install third and fourth-speed gear clutch assembly (hub and sliding sleeve) with taper front, being sure keys in the hub correspond with notches in third-speed gear synchronizing ring.
10. Install snap-ring (.086-.088 in. thickness) into mainshaft groove in front of the third and fourth-speed clutch assembly.
11. Install rear bearing retainer plate. Spread the snap-ring on the plate to allow the snap-ring to drop around the rear bearing and press on the end of the mainshaft until the snap-ring engages the groove in the rear bearing.
12. Install reverse gear (shift collar to the rear).
13. Press speedometer drive gear onto the mainshaft so that there is a measurement of 4½ in. from the center of the gear to the flat surface of the rear bearing retainer.
14. Install special snap-ring into the groove at the rear of the mainshaft.

Countergear

1. Install countergear dummy and tubular roller bearing spacer into the countergear.
2. Using heavy grease to hold the rollers, install 20 bearing rollers in either end of the countergear, two spacers, 20 more rollers, then one spacer. Install the same combination of rollers and spac-

ers in the other end of the countergear.

3. Set the countergear assembly in the bottom of the transmission case making sure the tanged thrust washers are in their proper position.

Main Drive Gear

1. Press bearing (snap-ring groove front) onto main drive gear until the bearing fully seats against the shoulder on the gear.
2. Install spacer washer and selective fit snap-ring in the groove in the main drive gear shaft.

NOTE: Variable thickness snap-rings are available to obtain a prescribed clearance of .000-.005 in. between the rear face of the snap-ring and the front face of the spacer washer.

Assembly of Transmission

1. Install main drive gear and bearing assembly through the side cover opening and into position in the transmission front bore. After assembly is in place, install front bearing snap-ring.
2. Lift countergear and thrust washers into place. Install

Woodruff key into end of countershaft, then from the rear of the case, press the countershaft in until flush with rear of case and the dummy shaft is displaced. Maximum countergear end play is .025 in.

3. Install the 14 bearing rollers into the grease-coated end of the main drive gear.
4. Using heavy grease, position gasket on front face of rear bearing retainer. Install the fourth-speed synchronizing ring onto main drive gear with clutch key notches toward rear of transmission.

1 Bearing retainer
2 Gasket
3 Selective fit snap ring
4 Spacer washer
5 Bearing snap ring
6 Main drive gear bearing
7 Transmission case
8 Rear bearing retainer gasket
9 Main drive gear
10 Bearing rollers (14)
11 Snap ring (.086" to .088")
12 Fourth speed gear synchronizing ring
13 Third and fourth speed clutch sliding sleeve
14 Third speed synchronizing ring
15 Third speed gear
16 Second and third speed gear thrust washer (needle roller bearing)
17 Second speed gear
18 Second speed gear synchronizing ring
19 Mainshaft
20 First and second speed clutch assembly
21 Clutch key spring
22 Clutch keys
23 Clutch hub
24 Clutch key spring
25 First and second speed clutch sliding sleeve
26 First speed gear synchronizing ring
27 First speed gear
28 First speed gear bushing
29 First speed gear thrust washer
30 Rear bearing snap ring
31 Rear bearing
32 Rear bearing retainer
33 Selective fit snap ring
34 Reverse gear
35 Speedometer drive gear
36 Rear bearing retainer to case extension gasket
37 Case extension
38 Rear oil seal
39 Reverse idler shaft
40 Reverse shifter shaft lock pin
41 Reverse shift fork
42 Reverse shifter shaft and detent plate
43 Reverse shifter shaft ball detent spring
44 Reverse shifter shaft detent ball
45 Reverse shifter shaft "O" ring seal
46 Reverse shifter lever
47 Speedometer driven gear and fitting
48 Retainer and bolt
49 "O" ring seal
50 Tanged washer
51 Spacer (.050")
52 Bearing rollers (20)
53 Spacer (2—.050")
54 Bearing rollers (20)
55 Countergear
56 Countergear roller spacer
57 Bearing rollers (20)
58 Spacers (2—.050")
59 Bearing rollers (20)
60 Spacer (.050")
61 Tanged washer
62 Countershaft
63 Countershaft woodruff key
64 Reverse idler front thrust washer (flat)
65 Reverse idler gear (front)
66 Reverse idler gear (rear)
67 Tanged thrust washer
68 Forward speed shift forks
69 First and second speed gear shifter shaft
70 Third and fourth speed gear shifter shaft and detent plate
71 "O" ring seals
72 Gasket
73 Interlock pin
74 Poppet spring
75 Detent balls
76 Interlock sleeve
77 Transmission side cover
78 Third and fourth speed shifter lever
79 First and second speed shifter lever

The Warner T-10 4-speed transmission—typical (© Borg Warner Corp.)

5. Position the reverse idler gear thrust washer on the machined face of the ear cast in the case for the reverse idler shaft. Position the front reverse idler gear on top of the thrust washer, hub facing toward rear of case.

6. Lower the mainshaft assembly into the case, with the fourth-speed synchronizing ring notches aligning with the keys in the clutch assembly.

7. Install self-locking bolt, attach the rear bearing retainer to the transmission case and torque the bolt to 20-30 ft. lbs.

8. From the rear of the case, insert the rear reverse idler gear, engaging the splines with the portion of the gear within the case.

9. Place a greased gasket on the rear face of the rear bearing retainer.

10. Install remaining tanged thrust washer into place on reverse idler shaft, being sure the tang on the thrust washer is in the notch in the idler thrust face of the extension.

11. Place the two clutches in neutral position.

12. Pull reverse shifter shaft to left side of extension and rotate shaft to bring reverse fork to extreme forward position in the extension. Align forward and reverse idler gears.

13. Position the extension onto the transmission case by uniting the reverse idler shaft with the idler gears and engaging the shift fork with the reverse shift collar by turning the shifter shaft, the reverse gear will move rearward thus enabling installation of the extension.

14. Install three extension and retainer to case attaching bolts at 35-45 ft. lbs. and two extension to retainer attaching bolts (20-30 ft. lbs.). Use sealer on the lower, right bolt.

15. Align groove in reverse shift shaft with hole in boss and drive in lock pin.

16. Install the main drive gear bearing retainer and gasket aligning the oil well with the oil outlet hole and torque the sealer-coated bolts to 15-20 ft. lbs.

17. Install a shift fork into each clutch sleeve.

18. With both clutches in neutral, install side cover and gasket and torque to 10-20 ft. lbs. Use sealer on the lower right bolt.

19. Install first and second, and third and fourth shift levers.

Torque Chart

Part	Location	Thread Size	Torque Ft. Lbs.
Bolt	Front bearing retainer to transmission case	5/16-18	15-20
Bolt	Side cover bolts	5/16-18	15-20
Nut	Shift lever to shaft	5/16-18	12-18
Bolt	Transmission to flywheel housing	1/2-13	45-60
Bolt	Flywheel housing to engine	3/8-16	30-35

Warner T-14A, T-15A 3 Speed

Description

The Warner T-14A, T-15A are fully synchronized three-speed transmissions having helical drive gears throughout. Lubricant capacity is 2½ pints.

Disassembly of Transmission

1. Separate transfer case from transmission by removing five capscrews.
2. Remove gearshift housing and disassembly by removing shift rails, poppet balls, springs, and shift forks.
3. Remove nut, flat washer, transfer case drive gear, adapter, and spacer.
4. Remove main drive gear bearing retainer gasket.
5. Remove main drive gear and mainshaft bearing snap-rings and bearings.
6. Remove main drive gear and mainshaft assembly. NOTE: The T-15A transmission must be shifted into second gear to allow removal of the mainshaft and gear assembly.
7. On remote shift models, remove roll pins from lever shafts and housing. From inside case, slide levers and interlock assembly out. Remove forks and lever assemblies.
8. Remove lock plate from reverse idler shaft and countershaft.
9. Drive countershaft out to rear with dummy shaft. Remove countergear and two thrust washers. Remove spacer washers, rollers, and spacer from gear.
10. Drive reverse idler shaft out to rear. Remove gear, washers, and roller bearings.
11. Remove clutch hub snap-ring and second-third synchronizer assembly.
12. Remove second and reverse gears.
13. Remove clutch hub snap-ring and low synchronizer assembly.
14. Remove low gear.

Synchronizer Disassembly and Assembly

1. Remove springs. Low synchronizer has only one spring; second-third, two.
2. Mark sleeve and hub before separating.
3. Remove hub.
4. Remove three shifter plates from hub.
5. Inspect all parts for wear.
6. Assembly in reverse order of disassembly. On second-third unit, make sure that spring openings are 120 degrees from each other, with spring tension opposed.

NOTE: If a synchronized assembly is replaced on a floor shift unit, the shift fork operating the synchronizer being replaced must have the letter A just under the shaft hole on the side opposite the pin.

Inspection

1. Wash all parts in solvent.
2. Air dry but do not spin bearings with air pressure.
3. Check case bearing and shaft bores for cracks or burrs.
4. Check all gears and bronze blocking rings for cracks, and chipped, worn, or cracked teeth. If any gears are replaced, also replace the meshing gears.
5. Check all bearings and bushings for wear or damage.
6. Check that synchronizer sleeves slide freely on clutch hubs.

1 Clutch hub
2 Shifter plate
3 Synchronizer spring (1)
4 Clutch sleeve

Low synchronizer assembly (© Borg Warner Corp.)

15 Bearing adapter
16 Snap ring
17 Mainshaft bearing
18 Reverse gear
19 Snap ring
20 Low synchronizer
   assembly
21 Synchronizer
   blocking ring
22 Low gear
23 Mainshaft
24 Second gear
25 Synchronizer
   blocking ring
26 Second-third
   synchronizer
   assembly
27 Synchronizer
   blocking ring
28 Snap ring
29 Countershaft
   front thrust
   washer (large)
30 Countershaft gear
31 Reverse idler gear
   bearing washer
32 Reverse idler gear
   roller bearings
33 Reverse idler gear
34 Countershaft rear
   thrust washer
   (small)
35 Countershaft
   bearing spacer
   washer
36 Countershaft
   roller bearings
37 Reverse idler
   shaft
38 Spacer
39 Countershaft
40 Lockplate

6 Snap ring (large)
7 Main drive gear
   bearing
8 Oil retaining
   washer (slinger)
9 Main drive gear
10 Mainshaft pilot
   bearing rollers
11 Case
12 Nut
13 Flatwasher
14 Spacer

1 Retainer screws
2 Main drive gear
   bearing retainer
3 Retainer gasket
4 Oil seal
5 Snap ring (small)

T-14A, T-15A three-speed transmission (© Borg Warner Corp.)

1 Reverse gear
2 Low synchronizer
   assembly
3 Low gear
4 Second gear
5 Second-Third synchro-
   nizer assembly
6 Main drive gear

Mainshaft assembly
(© Borg Warner Corp.)

1 Synchronizer spring (2)
2 Clutch hub
3 Clutch sleeve
4 Shifter plate

Second—third synchronizer assembly (© Borg Warner Corp.)

Assembly of Transmission

1. Place reverse idler gear with dummy shaft, roller bearing, and thrust washers in case. Install reverse idler shaft.
2. Assembly countershaft center spacer, four bearing spacers, and bearing rollers in countershaft gear.
3. Install large countergear thrust washer in front of case. Position small thrust washer on countergear hub with lip facing groove in case. Holding countergear in position, push in countershaft from rear.
4. Install lock plate in slots of reverse idler shaft and countershaft.
5. Install to mainshaft:
   a. Low gear.
   b. Bronze blocking ring.
   c. Low synchronizer assembly.
   d. Largest snap-ring that fits in groove.
   e. Second gear.
   f. Bronze blocking ring.
   g. Second-third synchronizer assembly.
   h. Largest snap-ring that fits in groove.
   i. Reverse gear.
6. Install mainshaft assembly through top of case.
7. Install bronze blocking ring to second-third synchronizer assembly.
8. On remote shift units, install shifter shafts, with new O-rings, into case. NOTE: T-15 interlock levers are marked as to location.

1 Low-Reverse shift fork
2 Screwdriver
3 Second-Third interlock lever
4 Second-Third shift fork

Installing shifter forks
(© Borg Warner Corp.)

1 Control lever housing pin
2 Control housing
3 Interlock plunger and plug
4 Second-third shift fork
5 Shift fork pin
6 Poppet spring
7 Poppet ball
8 Second-third shift rail
9 Shift rail caps
10 Low-Reverse shift fork
11 Low-reverse shift rail
12 Shift lever
13 Shift lever support spring

Shift control assembly components
(© Borg Warner Corp.)

T-14 levers have no marks and are interchangeable.

9. Depress interlock lever while installing shift fork into shift lever and synchronizer clutch sleeve. Install poppet spring. Install tapered pins securing shafts in case.
10. Install main drive gear roller bearings.
11. Install main drive gear and oil slinger into case with cutaway portion of gear toward countergear. Install main drive gear to mainshaft.
12. Using bearing installer and thrust yoke tool, install main drive gear and mainshaft bearings and drive into position. The thrust yoke is needed to prevent damage to the synchronizer clutch.
13. Install main drive gear and mainshaft bearing snap-rings. The mainshaft bearing snapring is .010 thicker than main drive gear bearing snap-ring.
14. Install mainshaft rear bearing adapter, spacer, transfer case drive gear, flat washer, and nut. Torque nut to 130-170 ft. lbs.
15. Install main drive gear bearing retainer (with new oil seal) and gasket. Align oil drain holes in retainer and gasket.

1 Case
2 Low-Reverse shift fork
3 Low-Reverse shift lever shaft
4 Tapered pin
5 O-ring
6 Poppet spring
7 Second-Third interlock lever
8 Second-Third shift lever shaft
9 Second-Third shift fork
10 Low-Reverse interlock lever

Shift bar housing components—remote control (© Borg Warner Corp.)

16. Install case cover gasket. On remote shift units, install cover gasket with vent holes to left side.
17. Position gear train and floor-shift assembly in neutral. Insert shifter forks into clutch sleeves and torque to 8-15 ft. lbs.

General Information

Model	T14A
Make	Warner
Ratios:	
Low	3.100:1
Second	1.612:1
High	1.000:1
Reverse	3.100:1

Warner T-18, T-19 Series 4 Speed

Description

The Warner T-18, T-19 are four-speed fully synchronized transmissions having a floor-mounted shift lever and a power take-off opening on the right side of the case. The T-18 first and reverse gears are spur gears while the others are helical. The T-19 has all helical gears.

Disassembly of Transmission

1. After draining the transmission and removing the parking break drum (or shoe assembly), lock the transmission in two gears and remove the U-joint flange, oil seal, speedometer driven gear and bearing assembly. Lubricant capacity is 6½ pints.
2. Remove the output shaft bearing retainer and the speedometer drive gear and spacer.
3. Remove the output shaft bearing snap-ring, and remove the bearing.
4. Remove the countershaft and idler shaft retainer and the power take-off cover.
5. After removing the input shaft bearing retainer, remove the snap-rings from the bearing and the shaft.
6. Remove the input shaft bearing and oil baffle.
7. Drive out the countershaft (from the front). Keep the dummy shaft in contact with the countershaft to avoid dropping

4-speed Warner T-18 transmission (© Borg Warner Corp.)

any rollers.

8. After removing the input shaft and the synchronizer blocking ring, pull the idler shaft.

9. Remove the reverse gear shifter arm, the output shaft assembly, the idler gear, and the cluster gear. When removing the cluster, do not lose any of the rollers.

Disassembly of Sub-Assemblies

Output Shaft

1. Remove the third- and high-speed synchronizer hub snap-ring from the output shaft, and slide the third- and high-speed synchronizer assembly and the third-speed gear off the shaft. Remove the synchronizer sleeve and the inserts from the hub. Before removing the two snap-rings from the ends of the hub, check the end play of the second-speed gear (0.005-0.024 inch).

2. Remove the second-speed synchronizer snap-ring. Slide the

Removing countershaft (© Borg Warner Corp.)

second-speed synchronizer hub gear off the hub. Do not lose any of the balls, springs, or plates. Pull the hub off the shaft, and remove the second-speed synchronizer from the second-speed gear. Remove the snap-ring from the rear of the second-speed gear, and remove the gear, spacer, roller bearings, and thrust washer from the output shaft. Remove the remaining snap-ring from the shaft.

Cluster Gear

Remove the dummy shaft, pilot bearing rollers, bearing spacers, and center spacer from the cluster gear.

Reverse Idler Gear

Rotate the reverse idler gear on the shaft, and if it turns freely and smoothly, disassembly of the unit is not necessary. If any roughness is noticed, disassemble the unit.

Gear Shift Housing

1. Remove the housing cap and lever. Be sure all shafts are in neutral before disassembly.

2. Tap the shifter shafts out of the housing while holding one hand over the holes in the housing to prevent loss of the springs and balls. Remove the two shaft lock plungers from the housing.

Assembly of Sub-Assemblies

Cluster Gear Assembly

Slide the long bearing spacer into the cluster gear bore, and insert the dummy shaft in the spacer. Hold the

cluster gear in a vertical position, and install one of the bearing spacers. Position the 22 pilot bearing rollers in the cluster gear bore. Place a spacer on the rollers, and install 22 more rollers and another spacer. Hold a large thrust washer against the end of cluster gear and turn the assembly over. Install the rollers and spacers in the other end of the gear.

Reverse Idler Gear Assembly

1. Install a snap-ring in one end of the idler gear, and set the gear on end, wtih the snap-ring at the bottom.

2. Position a thrust washer in the gear on top of the snap-ring. Install the bushing on top of the washer, insert the 37 bearing rollers, and then a spacer followed by 37 more rollers. Place the remaining thrust washer on the rollers, and install the other snap-ring.

Output Shaft Assembly

1. Install the second speed gear thrust washer and snap-ring on the output shaft. Hold the shaft vertically, and slide on the second-speed gear. Insert the bearing rollers in the second-speed gear, and slide the spacer into the gear. (The T-18 model does not contain second speed gear rollers or spacer). Install the snap-ring on the output shaft at the rear of the second-speed gear. Position the blocking ring on the second-speed gear. Do not invert the shaft because the bearing rollers will slide out of the gear.

2. Press the second-speed synchronizer hub onto the shaft, and install the snap-ring. Position the shaft vertically in a soft-jawed vise. Position the springs and plates in the second-speed synchronizer hub, and place the hub gear on the hub.

3. With the T-19 model, press the first and second speed synchronizer onto the shaft and install the snap-ring. Install the first speed gear and snap-ring on the shaft and press on the reverse gear. For the T-19, ignore steps 2 and 4.

4. Hold the gear above the hub spring and ball holes, and position one ball at a time in the hub, and slide the hub gear downward to hold the ball in place. Push the plate upward, and insert a small block to hold the plate in position, thereby holding the ball in the hub. Follow these procedures for the remaining balls.

5. Install the third speed gear and synchronizer blocking ring on the shaft.

6. Install the snap-rings at both ends of the third and high-speed synchronizer hub. Stagger the openings of the snap-rings so that they are not aligned. Place the inserts in the synchronizer sleeve, and position the sleeve on the hub.

7. Slide the synchronizer assembly onto the output shaft. The slots in the blocking ring must be in line with the synchronizer in-

Conventional cab shift linkage (© Borg Warner Corp.)

4-speed Warner T-19 transmission (© Borg Warner Corp.)

serts. Install the snap-ring at the front of the synchronizer assembly.

Gear Shift Housing

1. Place the spring on the reverse gear shifter shaft gate plunger, and install the spring and plunger in the reverse gate. Press the plunger through the gate, and fasten it with the clip. Place the spring and ball in the reverse gate poppet hole. Compress the spring and install the cotter pin.

2. Place the spring and ball in the reverse shifter shaft hole in the gear shift housing. Press down on the ball, and position the reverse shifter shaft so that the reverse shifter arm notch does not slide over the ball. Insert the shaft part way into the housing.

3. Slide the reverse gate onto the shaft, and drive the shaft into the housing until the ball snaps into the groove of the shaft. Install the lock screw lock wire to the gate.

4. Insert the two interlocking plungers in the pockets between the shifter shaft holes. Place the spring and ball in the low and second shifter shaft hole. Press down on the ball, and insert the shifter shaft part way into the housing.

5. Slide the low and second shifter shaft gate onto the shaft, and install the corresponding shifter fork on the shaft so that the offset of the fork is toward the rear of the housing. Push the shaft all the way into the housing until the ball engages the shaft groove. Install the lock screw and wire that fastens the fork to the shaft. Install the third and high shifter shaft in the same manner. Check the interlocking system. Install new expansion plugs in the shaft bores.

Assembly of Transmission

1. Coat all parts, especially the bearings, with transmission lubricant to prevent scoring during initial operation.

2. Position the cluster gear assembly in the case. Do not lose any rollers.

3. Place the idler gear assembly in the case, and install the idler shaft. Position the slot in the rear of the shaft so that it can

Stop yoke tool
(© Borg Warner Corp.)

engage the retainer. Install the reverse shifter arm.

4. Drive out the cluster gear dummy shaft by installing the countershaft from the rear. Position the slot in the rear of the shaft so that it can engage the retainer. Use thrust washers as required to get 0.006 to 0.020 inch cluster gear end play. Install the countershaft and idler shaft retainer.

5. Position the input shaft pilot rollers and the oil baffle, so that the baffle will not rub the bearing race. Install the input shaft and the blocking ring in the case.

6. Install the output shaft assembly in the case, and use a special tool to prevent jamming the blocking ring when the input shaft bearing is installed.

7. Drive the input shaft bearing onto the shaft. Install the thickest select-fit snap-ring that will fit on the bearing. Install the input shaft snap-ring.

8. Install the output shaft bearing.

9. Install the input shaft bearing without a gasket, and tighten the bolts only enough to bottom the retainer on the bearing snap-ring. Measure the clearance between the retainer and the case, and select a gasket (or gaskets) that will seal in the oil and prevent end play between the retainer and the snap-ring. Torque the bolts to specification.

10. Position the speedometer drive gear and spacer, and install a new output shaft bearing retainer seal.

11. Install the output shaft bearing retainer. Torque the bolts to specification, and install safety wire.

12. Install the brake shoe (or drum), and torque the bolts to specification. Install the U-joint flange. Lock the transmission in

two gears and torque the nut to specification.

13. Install the power take-off cover plates with new gaskets. Fill the transmission according to specifications.

Torque Chart

Nomenclature	Nuts and/or Bolts and Torque Limits		
Bolt—gear shift lever tower to gearshift housing	3/8-16 20-25	7/16-14 30-35	
Bolt—clutch housing to trans. case	7/16-14 30-38 5/8-11 96-120	9/16-12 70-90	
Nut—U-joint flange to trans. output shaft	1.00-20 90-125	1 1/2-18 275-350	1 1/4-18 225-275
Nut—drum parking brake to companion flange	3/8-24 35-45	7/16-20 50-70	
Nut—bellcrank to trans.	9/16-18 70-90		
Bolt—lever assy. to trans.	3/8-16 20-25		
Nut—handbrake anchor bar to trans. case (5-speed extra-heavy duty only)	9/16-18 120-130		
Bolt—belcrank to trans.	3/8-16 20-25		
Bolt—reverse lock-out plunger retainer	11/16-16 80-100		
Bolt—countershaft rear bearing retainer	5/16-18 25-30 3/8-16 35-40	7/16-14 45-55 1/2-13 60-70	
Bolt—countershaft & reverse idler shaft retainer	5/16-18 25-30 3/8-16 25-37 3/8-16† 18-25†	7/16-14 40-45 1/2-13 80-85	
Bolt—gear shift housing to trans. case	5/16-18 20-25 3/8-16 35-40	3/8-16†† 30-35†† 7/16-14 45-50	
Bolt—power take off cover to trans. case	3/8-16 20-30		
Nut—countershaft bearing lock (5-speed extra h.d. & 5-speed exclusive)	1 1/4-18 350-450		
Nut—countershaft bearing lock (5-speed exclusive h.d.)	1 1/2-18 350-450		
Bolt—input shaft bearing retainer to trans. case	5/16-18 25-30 3/8-16 25-30	7/16-14 40-45	
Bolt—countershaft front bearing retainer	5/16-18 25-30 3/8-16 25-35	7/16-14 50-55	

Warner T-85N 3 Speed W/O.D.

Description

The Warner T-85N overdrive is a synchronized 3 speed transmission with a 2 speed planetary gear transmission attached to the rear of the housing. An electrical control system automatically controls the overdrive shifts. Lubricant capacity is 4 pints.

Disassembly of Transmission

1. Mount the transmission in a vise.
2. Remove the gearshift housing assembly and gasket from the transmission.
3. Remove the shaft levers from the camshafts. Pull the shifter forks and cams out of the gearshift housing. With the cams removed, the interlock balls, sleeve, and spring will fall out of the housing.
4. Pull the shifter forks out of the cam and shaft assembly. Remove the oil seals from the camshafts.
5. Pull the solenoid body about ¼ turn, and remove it. Remove the governor.
6. With a sharp punch, pierce the snap-ring hole cover and remove the cover.
7. Remove the overdrive housing bolts, and the overdrive control shaft and lever pin.

Mainshaft bearing removal or installation
(© Borg Warner Corp.)

8. Pull out the manual control shaft and lever as far as possible. Spread the snap-ring that retains the overdrive main shaft front bearing, and then remove the overdrive housing. It may be necessary to tap the overdrive main shaft to free the main shaft bearing from the housing.
9. Remove the overdrive main shaft from the assembly and the free-wheel unit rollers.
10. Remove the speedometer gear and drive ball. To install the main shaft bearing, press on the new bearing, and then install the thickest snap-ring that will fit. Snap-rings are available in the following sizes: 0.086-0.088,

Removing free wheel unit retainer
(© Borg Warner Corp.)

0.0890-0.091, 0.092-0.094, and 0.095-0.097 inch.

11. Remove the free-wheel unit retainers. The free-wheel unit, planetary gear, sun gear, and shaft rail can now be removed.
12. Remove the snap-ring from the adapter, and then remove the plate and trough, balk ring and gear, and pawl.
13. Remove the input shaft bearing retainer and gasket and replace seal if necessary.
14. Rotate the overdrive adapter to expose the countershaft lock, and remove the lock.
15. With a drift, drive the countershaft toward the rear until it just clears the front case bore, and then push the countershaft out the rear with the tool shown.
16. Tap the input shaft and bearing out of the front of the case.
17. If the input shaft bearing is to

Removing countershaft—typical
(© Borg Warner Corp.)

be replaced, press off the bearing. The bearing baffle acts as a slinger, and must be installed so that it does not rub the bearing outer race as the shaft turns.

18. Remove the overdrive adapter and transmission output shaft as an assembly.
19. Remove the snap-ring at the front of the transmission output shaft, and then slide the synchronizer assembly, intermediate gear, and the sliding low and reverse gear off the shaft.
20. Disassemble the synchronizer unit by sliding the intermediate and high sleeve off the hub. Remove the three inserts and two springs from the hub.
21. Remove the snap-ring that holds the output shaft in the adapter and tap the bearing and shaft out of the adapter. Remove the baffle from the adapter.

Warner 3-speed transmission
(© Borg Warner Corp.)

KEEP SHIFT FORK IN GROOVE

SHIFT RAIL   SUN GEAR

Synchronizer assembly
(© Borg Warner Corp.)

ADAPTER   SNAP RING   BEARING

TRANSMISSION OUTPUT SHAFT

Removing output shaft bearing snap-ring
(© Borg Warner Corp.)

Special tool

Special tool

REMOVAL   INSTALLATION

Input shaft bearing replacement
(© Borg Warner Corp.)

22. If the output shaft or bearing is to be replaced, press the old bearing off and the new bearing on and install the thickest snap-ring that will fit. Snap-rings are available in the following thicknesses: 0.0890-0.091, 0.092-0.094, 0.095-0.097, and 0.100-0.0102 inch.

23. While holding the washers and bearing retainer tool at the small end of the cluster gear to prevent the roller bearings and bearing retainer tool from falling out, lift the cluster gear assembly from the case.

24. Drive the reverse idler gear shaft out of the rear of the case.

Assembly of Transmission

Always use new gaskets and gasket cement during assembly. Put a thin coating of lubricant on all parts before installation.

1. Install new oil seals in the camshaft grooves. Place one cam and shaft assembly in position in the gearshift housing, and install the flat washer, lockwasher, and nut. Tighten the nut to specifications.

2. Assemble the interlock pin and balls in the interlock sleeve, and install the interlock assembly in the gearshift housing.

3. Place the other cam and shaft assembly in position and install the flat washer, lockwasher, and nut. Tighten the nut to specifications. Install the gearshift levers on the camshafts and the shifter forks to the cams.

4. Insert the bearing retainer tool in the cluster gear, and install the cluster gear bushings and spacer in the gear. Use cup grease to hold the bearings and bearing retainers in the cluster gear bore. After applying a thin coating of grease to the gear side of the thrust washers, properly position the washers at each end of the bearing retainer tool.

5. Position the cluster gear assembly in the transmission case. Install the countershaft, and check the clearance between the cluster gear front thrust washer and the case (0.004-0.018 inch).

Special tool

Special tool

REMOVAL   INSTALLATION

Removing adapter and output shaft
(© Borg Warner Corp.)

Remove the countershaft by installing the bearing retaining tool.

6. Position the reverse idler gear in the case, with the chamfered gear teeth ends toward the front.

7. Drive the reverse idler shaft into the case, with the locking notch aligned with the countershaft hole.

8. Place the output shaft bearing baffle in the overdrive adapter with the convex side toward the overdrive unit.

9. Install the output shaft bearing in the adapter, and install the snap-ring. Install the thickest snap-ring that will fit. Snap-rings are available in the following thicknesses: 0.086-0.088, 0.089-0.091, 0.092-0.094 and 0.095-0.097 inch.

10. Install the low and reverse slid-

INSERT   SPRING

ETCHED MARK

Installing sun gear and shift rail
(© Borg Warner Corp.)

ing gear on the output shaft, with the shifter fork groove toward the front.

11. Install the intermediate gear on the output shaft, with the clutch teeth toward the front.

12. Assemble the synchronizer unit by installing the two springs on the hub, and placing the three inserts in the hub. Hook one spring end in an insert.

13. After lining up the etched marks on the sleeve and hub splines, slide the sleeve onto the hub.

14. Place a blocking ring on the intermediate gear, and install the synchronizer assembly on the transmission output shaft, with the hub thrust surface toward the rear.

15. Install the snap-ring that holds the synchronizer in place.

16. Position a new front gasket with gasket sealer on the overdrive adapter.

17. Position the overdrive adapter and transmission output shaft assembly in the transmission.

18. Seat the overdrive adapter squarely against the transmission case, and secure with a cap screw.

19. Insert the pilot roller bearings in the input shaft and hold with grease.

20. Place the blocking ring on the input shaft gear.

21. Tap the input shaft and bearing into the case while lining up the slots in the blocking ring with the synchronizer inserts.

22. Position the input shaft bearing retainer without a gasket, and tighten the bolts to bottom the retainer on the bearing outer race snap-ring. Check the clearance between the retainer gasket surfaces and the case.

23. Select a gasket (or gaskets) which will seal the oil, and at the same time prevent end play between the bearing outer race snap-ring and the retainer. Gaskets are available in 0.010, 0.015, 0.020 and 0.025 inch thicknesses.

24. Install the input shaft bearing retainer on the transmission

Overdrive unit
(© Borg Warner Corp.)

case. Torque the bolts to specification.

25. Pull out the adapter about ¼ inch, and rotate it to expose the countershaft hole.
26. Work the cluster gear into normal position by rotating the input and output shafts.
27. Push the countershaft into the case from the rear.
28. Align the slot in the countershaft with the slot in the reverse idler shaft, and install the lock plate.
29. Rotate the adapter to its normal position and seat it squarely against the transmission case. Check the block rings to make sure the slots are aligned with the synchronizer inserts.

30. Move the transmission so that the input shaft is pointing down.
31. Install the stud in the transmission case.

PAWL   BALK RING GEAR

INSTALL WITH MACHINED RECESS IN THIS POSITION

Installing plate and trough
(© Borg Warner Corp.)

32. Place the balk ring gear assembly and pawl in the adapter.
33. Place the plate and trough assembly in the adapter and install its snap-ring.
34. Install the sun gear and shift rail.
35. Install the planet carrier and the clutch cam. Install the retainers.

Installing Mainshaft assembly
(© Borg Warner Corp.)

Overdrive electrical system (© Borg Warner Corp.)

Kickdown switch adjustment
(© Borg Warner Corp.)

36. Install the 12 free-wheel unit rollers and hold them in position with a strong rubber band.

37. Rotate the roller cage counterclockwise (from the rear) until the rollers are off the cam surfaces. The rubber band will hold them there.

38. Slide the overdrive main shaft carefully over the free-wheel unit rollers. The rubber band will not affect operation of the overdrive.

39. Align the shift rail spring with the holes in the overdrive housing.

40. Position a new rear gasket with gasket sealer on the overdrive adapter.

41. Position the overdrive housing over the overdrive main shaft and shift rail.

42. If the overdrive main shaft bearing snap-ring does not drop into its groove when the housing is seated squarely on the adapter, pry the overdrive main shaft bearing toward the rear, working through the snap-ring hole. Install the three bolts and one stud nut.

43. Engage the overdrive shaft lever by pushing it inward. The lever is correctly engaged when a spring load is apparent as the lever is pushed.

44. Install the retaining pin in the overdrive housing to hold the control shaft in place.

45. If necessary, replace the overdrive housing bushing.

46. Thread the governor into the overdrive housing.

47. With the cap drain hole at the bottom, rotate the solenoid ¼ turn from normal position, so that the half ball on the solenoid stem can engage the pawl. Install the two solenoid cap screws.

48. If the solenoid stem is properly engaged, the solenoid cannot be removed from the overdrive in its normal position. Any attempt to pull it out will merely com-

press the engaging spring in the solenoid.

49. Install a new gasket and the gearshift housing on the transmission. Be sure the shifter forks enter the grooves in the synchronizer and low and reverse sliding gear. Torque gearshift housing to transmission bolts to specifications.

50. Install the drain plugs in the transmission case and the overdrive housing.

51. Fill the transmission with the specified lubricant. This transmission should not be filled through the speedometer cable attachment opening like all other manual transmissions. Instead, pour ½ pint of lubricant in the speedometer cable attachment opening, one pint into the fill plug opening of the overdrive unit and, finally, 3 pints into the fill plug opening of the transmission case.

Torque Chart

Nomenclature	Torque Limits	Nomenclature	Torque Limits
Bolt-input shaft bearing retainer to trans. case	5/16-18 25-30 3/8-16 25-30 7/16-14 40-45	Nut-U-joint flange to trans. output shaft	1.00-20 90-125 1 1/4-18 225-275 1 1/2-18 275-350
Bolt-countershaft front bearing retainer	5/16-18 25-30 3/8-16 25-35 7/16-14 50-55	Bolt-bellcrank to trans.	3/8-16 20-25
		Bolt-countershaft rear bearing retainer	5/16-18 25-30 3/8-16 35-40 7/16-14 45-55 1/2-13 60-70
Bolt-reverse lockout plunger retainer	11/16-16 90-100		
Bolt-clutch housing to engine block	7/16-14 24-32 33-45	Nut-bellcrank to trans.	9/16-18 70-90 3/8-16C 20-25
Nut-drum parking brake to companion flange	3/8-24 37-50 7/16-20 40-55 1/2-20 74-86	Bolt-countershaft & reverse idler shaft retainer	1/2-13 60-70 5/16-18 25-30 3/8-16 25-37 3/8-16 18-25 7/16-14 40-45 1/2-13 80-85
Bolt-lever assy. to trans.	3/8-16 20-25		
Bolt-clutch housing to trans. case	7/16-14 30-38 5/8-11 96-120 9/16-12 70-90 5/8-18C 115-140 9/16-18C 81-102	Bolt-gear shaft housing trans. case	5/16-18 20-25 3/8-16 35-40

Warner T86 Three Speed

1 Bearing retainer screws	15 Control housing	31 Low and reverse shift fork
2 Main drive gear bearing retainer	16 Interlock plunger	32 Low and reverse shift rail
3 Bearing retainer oil seal	17 Shift lever spring	33 Bearing spacer
4 Bearing snap ring	18 Shift tower gasket	34 Rear bearing adapter
5 Main drive gear snap ring	19 Blocking ring	35 Rear bearing
6 Main drive gear bearing	20 Clutch hub snap ring	36 Rear bearing snap ring
7 Front bearing oil retaining washer	21 Synchronizer spring	37 Nut
8 Main drive gear	22 Synchronizer plate	38 Washer
9 Pilot roller bearing	23 Clutch hub	39 Transfer case drive gear
10 Shift rail cap	24 Clutch sleeve	40 Lock plate
11 Poppet ball	25 High and intermediate clutch fork	41 Countershaft
12 Poppet spring	26 Shift fork pin	42 Rear Countershaft thrust washer (steel)
13 Lock washer	27 High and intermediate shift rail	43 Rear countershaft
14 Shift housing bolt	28 Second speed gear	
	29 Main shaft	
	30 Low and reverse sliding gear	

	thrust washer (bronze)
44	Countershaft bearing washer
45	Countershaft bearing
46	Countershaft center bearing spacer
47	Reverse idler gear shaft
48	Reverse idler gear bearing washer
49	Reverse idler gear roller bearings
50	Reverse idler gear
51	Countershaft gear
52	Countershaft front thrust washer
53	Plug
54	Shift lever
55	Transmission case
56	Retainer gasket

T-86 three-speed transmission—floor shift (© Borg Warner Corp.)

Description

The Warner T-86 is a synchronized three-speed transmission having either a floor-mounted or a column shift lever.

Disassembly of Transmission

Except Jeep Models

1. Remove cover.
2. Remove front bearing cap, clutch shaft snap-ring and bearing lock-ring.
3. Remove the front bearing, using a bearing puller and a thrust yoke to prevent damaging synchronizer clutches.
4. Remove extension housing. Drive out seal from inside housing with oil seal remover and installer tool. Use bushing remover and installer tool to replace bushing.
5. Move mainshaft assembly back about ¾ in. Lower front end of clutch shaft, move mainshaft assembly over countergear and out of shift forks. Remove clutch shaft from front of case.
6. Check clutch shaft roller bearings for wear or damage.
7. Remove snap-ring speedometer drive gear, and key.
8. Remove snap-ring, synchro-clutch assembly, second gear, friction ring, and low-reverse sliding gear. Press off rear bearing.
9. Remove shifter forks.
10. Remove shaft lock plate from rear of case.
11. Drive countershaft out to rear, using dummy shaft. Lower countergear to bottom of case.
12. Drive out reverse idler shaft. Remove reverse idler gear and countergear.
13. Remove outer shift levers and shifter shaft lock pins. Remove shifter shafts, two interlock ball bearings, sleeve and spring. Remove shaft oil seals from case.

Assembly of Transmission

1. Install new shift shaft oil seals.
2. Install low-reverse shift shaft, interlock sleeve, ball bearing, pin, and spring. Install second-high shift shaft and second ball bearing.
3. Shift mechanism into any gear position with one end of interlock sleeve against shift shaft quadrant, clearance between opposite end of sleeve and quadrant on other shaft should be .001-.007 in. Interlock sleeves are available in several sizes for adjustment.
4. Install lock pins and shift levers.
5. Install dummy shaft and bearings in countergear. Install thrust washers; the bronze front washer must index with the case.
6. Place countergear and dummy shaft in bottom of case.
7. Install reverse idler gear with chamfered side of teeth to front of case. Drive in shaft from rear.
8. Align slots in countershaft and reverse idler shaft. Position countergear and drive in countershaft. Install lock plate.
9. Install shifter forks.
10. Press rear bearing onto mainshaft. Install key, speedometer drive gear, and snap-ring.
11. Install low-reverse sliding gear on mainshaft with sliding collar to front. Gear should slide easily. Install second gear with tapered cone to front.
12. Install rear bearing snap-ring—the thickest possible.
13. Install synchro-clutch assembly and front snap-ring.
14. When synchro-clutch hub is

pressed against snap-ring, there should be .003-.010 in. clearance between second gear and shoulder on mainshaft.

15. Install 14 greased rollers in clutch shaft.
16. Install front friction ring on clutch shaft and insert through top of case. Install mainshaft assembly through rear of case, moving to right to engage shifter forks in synchro-clutch collar and low-reverse sliding gear. Guide clutch shaft onto main shaft.
17. Install extension housing oil seal.
18. Install extension housing.
19. Install oil slinger, concave side to rear. Drive in front bearing using thrust yoke to prevent synchronizer damage.
20. Install thickest clutch shaft snap-ring that will fit in groove.
21. Install front bearing cap with new gasket. Choose thickness of gasket to give zero clutch shaft end play.
22. Clearance of friction rings should be .056-145 in.
23. Install cover end gasket.

Disassembly of Transmission

Jeep Models

1. Drain lubricant and flush out the case.
2. If a transfer case is involved, remove its rear cover.

3. If a power take-off is involved, remove the shift unit which replaces the cover.
4. Remove cotter pin, nut and washer and remove the transfer case main drive gear.
5. Remove the transmission shift cover.
6. Loop a piece of wire around the mainshaft just back of second-speed gear. Twist the wire and attach one end to the right front cover screw, the other end to the left cover screw. Tighten the wire to prevent the mainshaft from pulling out of the case when the transfer case is removed. Should the mainshaft come out, the synchronizer parts will drop into the bottom of the case.
7. Remove transfer case screws then tap lightly on the end of the transmission mainshaft to sep-

Transfer case driving gear
(© Borg Warner Corp.)

arate the two units. The transmission mainshaft bearing should slide out of the transfer case and stay with the transmission.
8. Remove front main drive gear bearing retainer and gasket.
9. Remove the oil collector hollowhead screws.
10. Remove lock plate from the reverse idler shaft and countershaft, at the rear of the case.
11. Drive the countershaft out the rear of the case with a dummy shaft and a brass drift.
12. Remove the mainshaft assembly through the case rear opening. Remove main drive gear.
13. Remove the countershaft gear set and three thrust washers from the bottom of the case, then dismantle the countershaft gear assembly.
14. Remove the reverse idler shaft and gear using a brass drift.
15. On column shift models, check clearance between ends of interlock sleeve and notched surface of each shift lever. The correct clearance is .001-.007 in. Several sizes of interlock sleeves are available for adjustment.

Assembly of Transmission

To assemble, reverse the disassembly procedures, giving the following points particular attention:
1. The countershaft gear set, when assembled in the case, should

1 Retainer screws	12 Case cover gasket	27 Bearing
2 Main drive gear retainer	13 Case	28 Snap ring
3 Oil seal	14 Blocking ring	29 Transfer case drive gear
4 Snap ring (large)	15 Synchronizer spring	30 Washer
5 Snap ring (small)	16 Shifting plate	31 Nut
6 Main drive gear bearing	17 Snap ring	32 Locking plate
7 Main drive gear	18 Clutch hub	33 Countershaft
8 Main shaft bearing rollers	19 Clutch sleeve	34 Washer (steel)
9 Retainer gasket	20 Shift fork	35 Washer (bronze)
10 Cover bolt and lock washer	21 Second speed gear	36 Spacer
11 Case cover	22 Main shaft	37 Needle bearings
	23 Shifting shoe	38 Spacer washer
	24 Sliding gear	39 Reverse idler gear shaft
	25 Seal	
	26 Bearing adapter	

40 Spacer washer	49 Intermediate and high control lever (outer)
41 Reverse idler gear roller bearings	50 Control lever (inner)
42 Reverse idler gear	51 Low and reverse shift lever
43 Countershaft gear	52 Spacer
44 Countershaft front thrust washer	53 Spring
45 Nut	54 Ball
46 Lock washer	55 Intermediate and high shift lever
47 Control lever washer	56 Plug
48 Low and Reverse control lever (outer)	57 Oil seal
	58 Taper pin

T-86 three-speed transmission—remote control (© Borg Warner Corp.)

have from .012-.018 in. end-play controlled by the thickness of the rear steel thrust washer.

2. Assemble the large bronze with the lip entered in the slot in the case.

3. The bronze-faced steel washer is placed next to the gear at the rear end, and the steel washer next to the case.

4. To assemble the countershaft bearing rollers, use a dummy shaft. Use grease and a loading sleeve to facilitate reassembly of the countershaft gear components.

5. In assembling the mainshaft gears, low and reverse gear is installed with the shift shoe groove toward the front.

6. In assembling the synchronizer unit, install the two springs in the high and intermediate clutch hub with spring tension opposed.

Place the right lipped end of a spring in the hub slot and place the spring in the hub. Turn the hub around and make the same installation with the other spring, starting with the same slot. Install the three synchronizer shifting plates into the three slots in the hub, wih the smooth sides of the plates out. Hold the plate in position and slip the second and direct clutch sleeve over the hub, with the long beveled edge toward the long part of the clutch hub. Install the completed assembly onto the mainshaft with the beveled edge of the clutch sleeve toward the front end of the shaft.

7. When installing the mainshaft, be sure the bearing rollers are in place in the pilot bore of the clutch gear.

8. Be sure that the countershaft

and reverse idler shaft lock plate are in position and completely recessed into the indents of the transfer case.

Interlock sleeve clearance
(© Borg Warner Corp.)

Warner T-89 Series 3 Speed

Description

The Warner T-89 is a fully synchronized three-speed transmission controlled by a column mounted shift lever.

Disassembly of Transmission

1. Install the transmission in a work stand.

2. Remove the gear shift housing.

3. Shift the transmission into two gears. Remove the output shaft nut and remove the parking brake assembly.

4. Remove the input shaft bearing retainer. Tap the input shaft and bearing toward the front as far as it will go.

5. Remove the output shaft bearing retainer bolts. Turn the retainer to expose the end of the countershaft.

6. Drive the countershaft toward the rear until it just clears the hole at the front of the case. Push the counter shaft out of the rear of the case. Remove the Woodruff key from the countershaft.

7. Remove the output shaft assembly. Remove the pilot rollers from the rear of the input shaft.

8. Remove the bearing snap-ring

and spacer washer from the input shaft. Drive the input shaft through the bearing. Remove the input shaft and bearing from the case.

9. Drive the reverse idler shaft out of the rear of the case.

10. Remove the cluster gear roller bearings and washers.

11. Remove the snap-ring at the front of the output shaft, and slide the synchronizer, intermediate gear, and low and reverse sliding gear off the shaft.

12. Remove the snap-ring that holds the outer race, and tap the output shaft bearing and shaft out of the bearing retainer casting and replace the bearing if worn.

Parts Repair or Replacement

Synchronizer

1. Slide the clutch sleeve off the hub and remove the three inserts and springs.

2. To assemble the synchronizer, align the index mark on the hub with the one on the sleeve.

3. Position the insert on the hub and slide the sleeve into place.

4. Install the insert springs. cover.

Shift Cover

Check the condition of the shift levers and forks. If there is any binding or clashing of gears when the lever is operated, disassemble the cover.

Assembly

1. Install new seal rings in the shifter cam grooves.

2. Position one cam assembly in the gear shift cover.

3. Assemble the interlock spring and balls in the interlock, install the interlock assembly in the gear shift cover, and position the other cam assembly.

4. Install the gear shift levers and forks on the cams.

Assembly of Transmission

1. Position the cluster gear bearings and washers.

2. Position the cluster gear assembly in the case. The tang on the front thrust washer must be fitted into the slot in the case thrust surface. The tab on the rear steel washer must be up. Install the countershaft, and check the cluster gear end play (0.006-0.020 inch).

3. Place the reverse idler gear in the case with the chamfered teeth ends toward the front. Drive the reverse idler shaft through the gear from the rear of the case. When the end of the shaft is nearly flush with the case install the Woodruff key.

4. Tap the input shaft bearing into the case until the snap-ring bottoms on the case. Install the input shaft bearing retainer without a gasket. Install the retainer and barely tighten the cap screws.

5. Position the baffle on the input shaft and hold it there with a light coat of grease. It must be installed at the rear of the bearing with the dished side away from the bearing so that the baffle does not rub the bearing outer race.

6. Place the input shaft (with baffle) in the case and drive the

Tool—T57L-7111-A

Removing countershaft
(© Borg Warner Corp.)

DRIVEN GEAR BEARING
SPEEDOMETER DRIVEN GEAR
COUPLING SHAFT GREASE RETAINER
BEARING RETAINER
CASE
GASKET
GASKET
BEARING RETAINER
P-350
BLOCKING RING INSERTS
ROLLER
SLEEVE
HUB
SNAP RING
SNAP RING
WASHER
BEARING
WASHER
SNAP RING
BLOCKING RING
WASHER
BEARING
SNAP RING
SPEEDOMETER DRIVE GEAR
SNAP RING
INPUT SHAFT
OIL BAFFLE
SNAP RING
OUTPUT SHAFT
BEARING
SPACER
SNAP RING
U-JOINT SPLINE FLANGE
SNAP RING
ROLLERS
THRUST WASHERS
COUNTERSHAFT
WOODRUFF KEY
INTERMEDIATE GEAR AND BUSHING
LOW AND REVERSE SLIDING GEAR
ROLLERS
SPACERS
REVERSE IDLER GEAR AND BUSHING
WOODRUFF KEY
THRUST WASHER
SPACERS
SPACER
CLUSTER GEAR
IDLER SHAFT

Warner T-89 series transmission—typical (© Borg Warner Corp.)

shaft into the bearing with a hardwood block.

7. Remove the input shaft bearing retainer, and install the spacer washer and snap-ring on the shaft. Install the thickest snap-ring that will fit. Snap-rings vary from 0.086-0.103 inch. Tap the input shaft and bearing as far to the front as they will go. Place the pilot bearing rollers in the input shaft and hold them with grease.

8. Install the output shaft and bearing in the bearing retainer casting. Install the thickest snap-ring that will fit. Assemble the low and reverse gear, intermediate gear and synchronizer assembly on the output

Removing or installing output shaft
(© Borg Warner Corp.)

shaft. Install the snap-ring at the front of the output shaft, and place the pilot bearing flat washer on the shaft.

9. Place a new gasket on the output shaft bearing retainer casting and install assembly in the case. Position the bearing retainer casting so that the countershaft hole is exposed.

10. Tap the input shaft bearing toward the rear until the bearing outer race snap-ring hits the case.

11. Raise the cluster gear assembly and install the countershaft. When the end of the countershaft is nearly flush with the case, install the Woodruff key.

12. Turn the output shaft bearing retainer to a normal position, and torque the retainer bolts to specification.

13. Install a new grease retainer, if necessary, and apply lubricant to the seal lips and cavity.

14. Install the input shaft bearing retainer and gasket. Torque the bolts to specification. Select a gasket that will seal and prevent end play. Gaskets are available

in the following thicknesses: 0.010, 0.015, 0.020, 0.025 inch.

15. Install the spacer and speedometer driving gear on the output shaft. Install the parking brake assembly.

16. Shift the transmission into two gears and install the output shaft nut.

17. Pour the specified lubricant over the entire gear train to prevent scoring when the transmission is initially operated.

18. Shift the transmission into neutral. Install the shift cover and gasket and torque the bolts to specification.

19. Fill the transmission with the proper lubricant through the speedometer cable opening.

CLUSTER GEAR
BRONZE THRUST WASHER
THRUST WASHER
STEEL THRUST WASHER
FLAT WASHERS
SPACER
ROLLER BEARINGS

Cluster gear and components
(© Borg Warner Corp.)

Torque Chart

Nomenclature	Nuts and/or Bolts and Torque Limits		Nomenclature	Nuts and/or Bolts and Torque Limits		Nomenclature	Nuts and/or Bolts and Torque Limits	
Bolt—gear shift lever tower to gearshift housing	3/8-16 20-25	7/16-14 30-35	Nut—handbrake anchor bar to trans. case (5-speed extra-heavy duty only)	9/16-18 120-130		Bolt—gear shift housing to trans. case	5/16-18 20-25 3/8-16 35-40	3/8-16†† 30-35†† 7/16-14 45-50
Bolt—clutch housing to trans. case	7/16-14 30-38 5/8-11 96-120	9/16-12 70-90	Bolt—bellcrank to trans.	3/8-16 20-25		Bolt—power take off cover to trans. case	3/8-16 20-30	
Nut—U-joint flange to trans. output shaft	1.00-20 90-125	1 1/2-18 275-350 1 1/4-18 225-275	Bolt—reverse lockout plunger retainer	11/16-16 80-100		Nut—countershaft bearing lock (5-speed extra H.D. & 5-speed exclusive)	1 1/4-18 350-450	
Nut—drum parking brake to companion flange	3/8 24 35-45	7/16-20 50-70	Bolt—countershaft rear bearing retainer	5/16-18 25-30 3/8-16 35-40	7/16-14 45-55 1/2-13 60-70	Nut—countershaft bearing lock (5-speed exclusive H.D.)	1 1/2-18 350-450	
Nut—bellcrank to trans.	9/16-18 70-90		Bolt—countershaft & reverse idler shaft retainer	5/16-18 25-30 3/8-16 25-37 3/8-16† 18-25†	7/16-14 40-45 1/2-13 80-85	Bolt—input shaft bearing retainer to trans. case	5/16-18 25-30 3/8-16 25-30	7/16-14 40-45
Bolt—lever assy. to trans.	3/8-16 20-25					Bolt—countershaft front bearing retainer	5/16-18 25-30 3/8-16 25-35	7/16-14 50-55

Warner T-150 Three Speed Transmission

Disassembly of Transmission

1. Remove the bolts securing the transfer case to the transmission. Remove the transfer case.
2. Remove the transfer case drive gear locknut, flat washer, and drive gear. Remove the large fiber washer from the rear bearing adapter. Move the second-third clutch sleeve forward and the first-reverse sleeve to the rear before removing the locknut.
3. Remove the transmission oil plug and drive the countershaft out of the case with a suitable size drift. *Do not lose the countershaft access plug when removing the countershaft.* With the countershaft removed the countershaft gear will lie at the bottom of the case, leave it there until the mainshaft is removed.
4. Punch alignment marks in the front bearing cap and the transmission case for assembly reference.
5. Remove the front bearing cap and gasket.
6. Remove the large lock ring from the front bearing.
7. Remove the clutch shaft, front bearing, and the second-third synchronizer assembly. *A special tool is required for this operation, see illustration.*
8. Remove the rear bearing and adapter assembly with a brass drift and hammer. Drive the adapter out the rear of the case with light blows from the hammer.
9. Remove the mainshaft assembly. Tilt the spline end of the shaft downward and lift the front end

1. MAINSHAFT RETAINING SNAP RING
2. SYNCHRONIZER BLOCKING RINGS (3)
3. SECOND-THIRD SYNCHRONIZER SLEEVE
4. SECOND-THIRD SYNCHRONIZER INSERT SPRING (2)
5. SECOND-THIRD HUB
6. SECOND-THIRD SYNCHRONIZER INSERT (3)
7. SECOND GEAR
8. FIRST GEAR RETAINING SNAP RING
9. FIRST GEAR TABBED THRUST WASHER
10. FIRST GEAR
11. FIRST-REVERSE SYNCHRONIZER INSERT SPRING
12. FIRST-REVERSE SLEEVE AND GEAR
13. FIRST-REVERSE HUB RETAINING SNAP RING
14. FIRST-REVERSE SYNCHRONIZER INSERT (3)
15. FIRST-REVERSE HUB
16. COUNTERSHAFT ACCESS PLUG
17. MAINSHAFT
18. MAINSHAFT SPACER
19. REAR BEARING ADAPTER LOCK RING
20. REAR BEARING AND ADAPTER ASSEMBLY
21. FIBER WASHER
22. FLAT WASHER
23. LOCKNUT
24. ROLL PIN
25. REVERSE IDLER GEAR SHAFT
26. THRUST WASHER
27. BUSHING (PART OF IDLER GEAR)
28. REVERSE IDLER GEAR
29. TRANSMISSIONCASE
30. THRUST WASHER (2)
31. BEARING RETAINER (2)
32. COUNTERSHAFT NEEDLE BEARINGS (50)
33. COUNTERSHAFT GEAR
34. FRONT BEARING CAP
35. BOLT (4)
36. FRONT BEARING CAP OIL SEAL
37. GASKET
38. FRONT BEARING RETAINER SNAP RING
39. FRONT BEARING LOCKRING
40. FRONT BEARING
41. CLUTCH SHAFT
42. MAINSHAFT PILOT ROLLER BEARINGS
43. ROLL PIN
44. COUNTERSHAFT

Warner T-150 Transmission—exploded view (© American Motors)

Removing the clutch shaft—Warner T-150
(© American Motors)

up and out of the case.

10. Remove the countershaft tool and arbor as an assembly. Remove the countershaft thrust washers, countershaft roll pin, and any pilot roller bearings that may have fallen into the case.

11. Remove the reverse idler shaft. Insert a brass drift through the clutch shaft bore in the front of the case and tap the shaft until the end with the roll pin clears the counter bore in the rear of the case. Remove the shaft.

12. Remove the reverse idler gear and thrust washers from the case.

13. Remove the retaining snap ring from the front of the mainshaft. Remove the second-third synchronizer assembly and second gear. Mark the hub and sleeve for reference during assembly.

NOTE: Observe the position of the insert springs and the inserts during removal for correct assembly.

14. Remove the insert springs from the second-third synchronizer, remove the three inserts, and separate the sleeve from the synchronizer hub retaining snap ring.

15. Remove the snap ring and the tabbed thrust washer from the mainshaft and remove the first gear blocking ring.

16. Remove the first-reverse synchronizer hub snap ring.

NOTE: Observe the position of the insert springs and the inserts during removal for correct assembly.

17. Remove the first-reverse sleeve, insert spring and the three insert from the hub. Remove the spacer from the rear of the mainshaft.

CAUTION: Do not attempt to remove the press fit hub by hammering. Hammer blows will damage the hub and mainshaft.

18. Remove the front bearing retaining snap ring and any remaining roller bearings from the clutch shaft.

19. Press the front bearing off the clutch shaft with an arbor press.

CAUTION: Do not attempt to remove the bearing by hammering. Hammer blows will damage the bearing and the clutch shaft.

20. Clamp the rear bearing adapter in a soft-jawed vise. *Do not overtighten.*

21. Remove the rear bearing retaining snap ring. Remove the bearing adapter from the vise.

22. Press the rear bearing out of the adapter with an arbor press. clean solvent and dry with compressed air.

Cleaning and Inspection

1. Thoroughly wash all parts in clean solvent and dry with compressed air.

NOTE: Do not dry the bearings with compressed air, use a clean shop cloth.

2. Clean the needle and clutch shaft bearings by placing them in a shallow parts cleaning tray and covering them with solvent. Allow the bearings to air dry on a clean shop cloth.

3. Check the case for the following:
   a. Cracks in the bores, bosses, or bolt holes.
   b. Stripped threads in bolt holes.
   c. Nicks, burrs, rough surfaces in the shaft bores or on the gasket surfaces.

4. Check the gear and synchronizer assemblies for the following:
   a. Broken, chipped, or worn gear teeth.
   b. Damaged splines on the synchronizer hubs or sleeves.
   c. Bent or damaged inserts.
   d. Damaged needle bearings or bearing bores in the countershaft gear.
   e. Broken or worn teeth or excessive wear of the blocking rings.
   f. Wear of galling of the countershaft, clutch shaft, or reverse idler shaft.
   g. Worn thrust washers.
   h. Nicked, broken, or worn mainshaft or clutch shaft splines.
   i. Bent, distorted, or weak snap rings.
   j. Worn bushings in the reverse idler gear. Replace the gear if the bushings are worn.
   k. Rough, galled, or broken front or rear bearings.

Assembly of Transmission

1. Lubricate the reverse idler shaft bore and bushings with transmission oil.

2. Coat the transmission case reverse idler gear thrust washer surfaces with petroleum jelly and install the thrust washers in the case.

NOTE: Make sure the locating tangs on the thrust washers are aligned in the slots in the case.

3. Install the reverse idler gear. Align the gear bore, thrust washers, and case bore. Install the reverse idler shaft from the rear of the transmission case. Be sure to align and seat the roll pin in the shaft into the counter bore in the rear of the case.

4. Measure the reverse idler gear end-play by inserting a feeler gauge between the thrust washer and the gear. End-play should be 0.004-0.018 inch. If end play exceeds 0.018 inch, remove the reverse idler gear and replace the thrust washers.

5. Coat the needle bearing bores in the countershaft gear with petroleum jelly. Insert the arbor tool in the bore of the gear and install the twenty-five (25) needle bearings and the retainer washers at each end of the countershaft gear.

6. Coat the countershaft gear thrust washer surface with petroleum jelly and position the thrust washers in the case.

Removing or installing the reverse idler shaft—Warner T-150 (© American Motors)

NOTE: Make sure the locating tangs on the thrust washers are aligned in the slots in the case.

7. Insert the countershaft into the bore at the rear of the case just far enough to hold the thrust washer in place.
8. Install the countershaft gear in the case. *Do not install the roll pin at this time.* Align the gear bore, thrust washers, the bores in the case, and install the countershaft.

NOTE: Do not remove the arbor tool completely.

9. Measure the countershaft gear end-play by inserting a feeler gauge between the washer and the countershaft gear. End-play should be 0.004-0.018 inch. If the end-play exceeds 0.018 inch, remove the gear and replace the thrust washer.
10. When the correct countershaft gear end-play has been obtained, install the countershaft arbor and remove the countershaft. Allow the countershaft gear to remain at the bottom of the case, leave the countershaft in the case enough to hold the thrust washer in place.
11. Coat the splines and machined surfaces on the mainshaft with transmission oil. Install the first-reverse synchronizer on the output shaft spines by hand. The end of the hub with the slots should face the front of the shaft. Use an arbor press to complete the hub installation. Install the retaining snap ring in the groove farthest to the rear.

CAUTION: Do not attempt to drive the hub on the shaft with a hammer.

12. Coat the splines of the first-reverse hub with transmission oil and install the first reverse sleeve and gear halfway onto the hub, with the gear end of the sleeve facing the rear of the shaft. Align the marks made during disassembly.
13. Install the insert spring in the first-reverse hub. Make sure the spring bottoms in the hub and covers all three insert slots. Position the three "T" shaped inserts in the hub with the small ends in the hub slots and the large ends inside the hub. Push the inserts fully into the hub so they seat on the insert spring, slide the first-reverse sleeve and gear over the inserts until the inserts engage in the sleeve.
14. Coat the bore and the blocking ring surface of first gear with transmission oil and place blocking ring on the tapered surface of the gear.
15. Install the first gear on the output shaft. Rotate the gear until the notches in the blocking ring

Installing the inserts in the first-reverse synchronizer hub—Warner T-150 (© American Motors)

Installing the first gear thrust washer on the mainshaft—Warner T-150 (© American Motors)

Installing the second gear on the mainshaft— Warner T-150 (© American Motors)

Measuring the mainshaft end-play— Warner T-150 (© American Motors)

engage the inserts in the first-reverse synchronizer assembly. Install the tanged thrust washer, sharp end facing out, and retaining snap ring on the mainshaft.

16. Coat the bore and blocking ring surface of the second gear with transmission oil. Place the second gear blocking ring on the tapered surface of second gear.
17. Install the second gear on the output shaft with the tapered surface of the gear facing the front of the mainshaft.
18. Install one insert spring into the second-third synchronizer hub. Be sure that the spring covers all three insert slots in the hub. Align the second-third sleeve with the hub using the marks made during disassembly. Start the sleeve onto the hub.
19. Place the three inserts into the hub slots and on top of the insert spring. Push the sleeve fully onto the hub to engage the inserts in the sleeve. Install the remaining insert spring in the exact position as the first spring. The ends of both springs must cover the same slot in the hub and not be staggered.

NOTE: The inserts have a small lip on each end. When they are correctly installed, this lip will fit over the insert spring.

20. Install the second-third synchronizer assembly on the mainshaft. Rotate the second gear until the notches in the blocking ring engage the inserts in the second-third synchronizer assembly.
21. Install the retaining snap ring on the mainshaft and measure the end-play between the snap ring and the second-third synchronizer hub. The end-play should be 0.040-0.014 inch. If the end-play exceeds the limit, replace the thrust washer and all the snap rings on the mainshaft assembly. Install the spacer on the rear of the mainshaft.
22. Install the mainshaft assembly in the case. Be sure that the first-reverse sleeve and gear is in the neutral (centered) position.
23. Press the rear bearing into the rear bearing adapter with an arbor press. Install the rear bearing retaining ring and the bearing adapter lockring.
24. Support the mainshaft assembly and install the rear bearing and adapter assembly in the case. Use a soft faced hammer to seat the adapter in the case.
25. Install the large fiber washer in the rear bearing adapter. Install the transfer drive gear, flat washer, and locknut. Tighten the locknut to 150 ft-lbs. torque.
26. Press the front bearing onto the clutch shaft. Install the bearing

retaining snap ring on the clutch shaft and the lockring into its groove.

27. Coat the bore of the clutch shaft assembly with petroleum jelly and install the fifteen (15) roller bearings in the clutch shaft bore.
    CAUTION: Do not use chassis grease or a similar heavy grease in the clutch shaft bore. Heavy grease will plug the lubricant holes in the shaft and prevent proper lubrication of the roller bearings.
28. Coat the blocking ring surface of the clutch shaft with transmission oil. Position the blocking ring on the clutch shaft.
29. Support the mainshaft assembly and insert the clutch shaft through the front bearing bore in the case. Seat the mainshaft pilot in the clutch shaft roller bearings. Tap the bearings into place with a shoft faced hammer.
30. Apply a thin film of sealer to the front bearing cap gasket and position the gasket on the case. Be sure the cutout in the gasket is aligned with the oil return hole in the case.
31. Remove the front bearing cap oil seal with a suitable tool. Install a new seal with a suitable driver.
32. Install the front bearing cap and tighten the bolts to 33 ft-lbs. Be sure that the marks on the cap and the transmission case are aligned and the oil return slot in the cap lines up with the oil return hole in the case.
33. Make a wire loop about 18-20 inches long and pass the wire under the countershaft gear assembly. The wire loop should raise and support the countershaft gear assembly when it is pulled upward.
34. Raise the countershaft gear with the wire. Align the bore in the countershaft gear with the front thrust washer and the countershaft. Start the countershaft into the gear with a soft faced hammer.
35. Align the roll pin hole in the countershaft with the roll pin holes in the case and complete the installation of the countershaft. Install the countershaft access plug in the rear of the case and seat with a soft faced hammer.
36. Install the countershaft roll pin in the case. Use a magnet or needle nose pliers to insert and start the pin in the case. Use a ½ inch punch to seat the pin. Install the transmission filler plug.
37. Shift the synchronizer sleeves through all gear ranges and check their operation. If the clutch shaft and mainshaft ap-

pear to bind in the neutral position, check for blocking rings sticking on the first or second gear tapers.
38. Install the transfer case on the transmission. Tighten the attaching bolts to 30 ft-lbs.

Shift Control Housing

Disassembly

1. Remove the back-up light switch and the transmission controlled spark switch (TCS) if so equipped.
2. Remove the shift control housing cap, gasket, spring retainer, and the shift lever spring as an assembly.
3. Invert the housing and mount in a soft-jawed vise.
4. Move the second-third shift rail to the rear of the housing, rotate the shift fork toward the first-reverse rail until the roll pin is accessible. Drive the roll pin out of the fork and rail with a pin punch. Remove the shift fork and the roll pin.
   NOTE: The roll pin hole in the shift fork is offset. Mark the position of the shift fork for assembly reference.
5. Remove the second-third shift rail using a brass drift or hammer. Catch the shift rail plug as the rail drives it out of the housing. Cover the shift and poppet ball holes in the cover to prevent the poppet ball from flying out. Mark the location of the shift rail for assembly reference.
6. Rotate the first-reverse shift fork away from the notch in the housing until the roll pin is accessible. Drive the role pin out of the fork and rail using a pin punch. Remove the shift fork and roll pin.
   NOTE: The roll pin hole in the shift fork is offset. Mark the position of the shift fork for assembly reference.

SHIFT CONTROL CAP

GASKET
SPRING RETAINER
SHIFT LEVER SPRING
INTERLOCK PLUNGER
SHIFT RAIL (LOW-REVERSE)
POPPET SPRING
POPPET BALL
SHIFT RAIL (SECOND-THIRD)
SHIFT RAIL CAP
SHIFT FORK

Shift control housing—Warner T-150
(© American Motors)

7. Remove the first-reverse shift rail using a brass drift or hammer. Catch the shift rail plug as the rail drives it out of the housing. Cover the shift and poppet ball holes in the cover to prevent the poppet ball from flying out. Mark the location of the shift rail for assembly reference.
8. Remove the poppet balls, springs, and the interlock plunger from the housing.

Assembly

1. Install the poppet springs and the detent plug in the housing.
2. Insert the first-reverse shift rail into the housing, and install the shift fork on the shift rail.
3. Install the poppet ball on the top of the spring in the first-reverse rail.
4. Using a punch or wooden dowel, push the poppet ball and spring downward into the housing bore and install the first-reverse shift rail.
5. Align the roll pin holes in the first-reverse shift fork and install the roll pin. Move the shift rail to the neutral (center) detent.
6. Insert the second-third shift rail into the housing and install the poppet ball on top of the spring in the shift rail bore.
7. Using a punch or wooden dowel, push the poppet ball and spring downward into the housing bore and install the second-third shift rail.
8. Align the roll pin holes in the second-third shift rail and the shift fork and install the roll pin. Move the shift rail to the neutral (center) position.
9. Install the shift rail plugs in the housing, and remove the shift control cover from the vise.
10. Install the shift lever, shift lever spring, spring retainer, gasket, and the shift control housing cap as an assembly. Tighten the cap securely.
11. Install the back-up light switch and the TCS switch if so equipped.

Torque Specifications

	Foot-Pounds
Back-up light switch	15-20
Fill and drain plugs	10-20
Front bearing cap bolt	30-36
Shift control housing bolts	20-25
Transfer case drive gear locknut	150
Transfer case to transmission bolts	30
TCS switch	18

Lubricant Capacity

SAE 80-90 Gear Lube	3 pts.

Index

Transfer Case Trouble Analysis

Slips Out of Gear (High-Low)
1. Shifting poppet spring weak.
2. Bearing broken or worn.
3. Shifting fork bent.
4. Improper control rod adjustment.

Slips Out of Front Wheel Drive
1. Shifting poppet spring weak or broken.
2. Bearing worn or broken.
3. Excessive shaft end-play.
4. Shifting fork bent.

Hard Shifting
1. Lack of lubricant.
2. Shift lever binding on shaft.
3. Shifting poppet ball scored.
4. Shifting fork bent.
5. Low tire pressure.

Backlash
1. Companion yoke loose.
2. Transfer case loose on mounts.
3. Internal parts excessively worn.

Noisy
1. Low lubricant level.
2. Bearings improperly adjusted or excessively worn.
3. Gears worn or damaged.
4. Improper alignment of driveshafts or U-joints.

Oil Leakage
1. Excessive amount of lubricant in case.
2. Vent clogged.
3. Gaskets or seals leaking.
4. Bearings loose or damaged.
5. Driveshaft yoke mating surfaces scored.

Overheating
1. Excessive or insufficient amount of lubricant.
2. Bearing adjustment too tight.

Transfer Case Application Chart

	Chevrolet	Dodge	Ford	GMC	International Harvester	Jeep	Plymouth
Dana 20	X		①	X			
Dana 21			②				
Dana 24			③				
International Harvester TC-143					④		
New Process 201		X					
New Process 202					X		
New Process 203 Full Time	X	X	X	X			X
New Process 205	X		X	X	X		
Rockwell T223		X	X		X		
Spicer 20					X	X	
Warner Quadra-Trac						X	

① Bronco only
② F-100 only
③ F-250 only through 1973
④ Scout only

Cleaning and Inspection

Cleaning
During overhaul, all components of the transfer case (except bearing assemblies) should be thoroughly cleaned with solvent and dried with air pressure prior to inspection and reassembly.

1. Clean the bearing assemblies as follows.

NOTE: Proper cleaning of bearings is of utmost importance. Bearings should always be cleaned separately from other parts.

   a. Soak all bearing assemblies in CLEAN solvent, gasoline, or fuel oil. Bearings should never be cleaned in a hot solution tank.
   b. Slush bearings in solvent until all old lubricant is loosened. Hold races so that bearings will not rotate; then clean bearings with a soft bristled brush until all dirt has been removed. Remove loose particles of dirt by tapping bearing flat against a block of wood.
   c. Rinse bearings in clean solvent; then blow bearings dry with air pressure.

CAUTION: Do not spin bearings while drying.

   d. After drying, rotate each bearing slowly while examining balls or rollers for roughness, damage, or excessive wear. Replace all bearings that are not in first class condition.

NOTE: After cleaning and inspecting bearings, lubricate generously with recommended lubricant, then wrap each bearing in clean paper until ready for reassembly.

2. Remove all portions of old gaskets from parts, using a stiff brush or

Inspection
1. Inspect all parts for discoloration or warpage.
2. Examine all gears and splines for chipped, worn, broken or nicked teeth. Small nicks or burrs may be removed with a fine abrasive stone.
3. Inspect the breather assembly to make sure that it is open and not damaged.
4. Check all threaded parts for damaged, stripped, or crossed threads.
5. Replace all gaskets, oil seals and snap-rings.
6. Inspect housings, retainers and covers for cracks or other damage. Replace the damaged parts.
7. Inspect keys and keyways for condition and fit.
8. Inspect shift forks for wear, distortion or any other damage.
9. Check detent ball springs for free length, compressed length, distortion or collapsed coils.
10. Check bearing fit on their respective shafts and in their bores or cups. Inspect bearings, shafts and cups for wear.

NOTE: If either bearings or cups are worn or damaged, it is advisable to replace both parts.

11. Inspect all bearing rollers or balls for pitting or galling.
12. Examine detent balls for corrosion or brinneling. If shift bar detents show wear, replace them.
13. Replace all worn or damaged parts. When assembling the transfer case, coat all moving parts with recommended lubricant.

Dana Model 20

Description

The Dana Model 20 is a two-speed gearbox that controls the power from the transmission to the front and rear driving axles. Positions of the transfer case are: four-wheel-drive low (4L), neutral (N), two-wheel-drive high (2H) and four-wheel-drive high (4H).

Disassembly

Transfer Case

1. Clean any dirt from the transfer case and remove the bottom cover plate.
2. Remove the retaining plug, flat washer, detent spring and ball which engages the front drive shift rail detent rod. Then, remove plug from front drive detent rod access hole.
3. Remove the retaining plug, detent spring and ball which engages the rear drive shift rail detent rod.
4. Remove the idler shaft lockplate.
5. Using a hammer and soft drift, drive the idler shaft rearward and out of the case; then lift out the thrust washers and idler gear.

NOTE: When removing the idler gear, do not lose any of the rollers.

6. Remove the flange retaining nuts from the front and rear output shafts.
7. Remove the flange from the front and rear output shafts. Discard the O-ring.
8. Remove the bolts securing the adapter housing to the case; then remove the adapter as an assembly.
9. Remove the bolts which attach the rear output shaft bearing retainer to the case; then remove the retainer and output shaft as an assembly.

NOTE: Be sure not to lose any of the rollers.

10. Disconnect the shift rail link from the two shift rails.
11. Lift out the rear output shaft sliding gear.
12. Remove the setscrew securing the rear fork to the shift rail; then remove the rear drive shift rail and fork.
13. Remove the front output shaft rear cover and shims. Fasten the shims together.

1 Input shaft
2 Transfer case
3 Input gear
4 Snap ring
5 Sliding clutch gear
6 Rear input shaft needle bearing
7 Rear output shaft front bearing
8 Rear Output shaft front bearing cup
9 Rear output shaft housing gasket
10 Rear output shaft housing breather
11 Speedometer driven gear
12 Rear output shaft housing
13 Rear output shaft rear bearing cup
14 Rear output shaft rear bearing
15 Rear output shaft yoke
16 Rear output shaft locknut
17 Washer
18 Rear output shaft
19 Rear output shaft seal
20 Shims
21 Speedometer drive gear
22 Intermediate shaft lock plate bolt
23 Intermediate shaft lock plate
24 Intermediate shaft bearing spacer
25 Intermediate shaft
26 Intermediate shaft needle bearings

27 Intermediate shaft tanged thrust washer
28 Intermediate gear
29 Front output shaft rear cover
30 Front output shaft rear bearing
31 Front output shaft rear cover shim pack
32 Front output shaft rear bearing cup
33 Front output shaft sliding clutch gear
34 Drain Plug
35 Front output shaft drive gear
36 Spacer
37 Front output shaft front bearing
38 Front output shaft front bearing cup
39 Spacer
40 Front output shaft seal
41 Front output shaft bearing
42 Front output shaft yoke
43 Rubber "O" ring
44 Washer
45 Front Output shaft locknut

FRONT

Cutaway view of the Dana 20 transfer case (© G.M.C.)

14. Remove the front output shaft bearing retainer and gasket.
15. Tap the threaded end of the front output shaft; then remove the rear cup.
16. Angle the front output shaft front bearing away from the main drive gear to allow removal of the snap-ring; then tap the shaft and rear bearing out of the case.
17. Lift out the sliding gear, main drive gear, front bearing, spacer and snap-ring.
18. Remove the front cup.
19. Remove the setscrew securing the front shift fork to the shift rail; then remove the rail and fork.
20. Remove the detent rods.
21. Remove shift rail oil seal.

Input Shaft

1. Remove the snap-ring from the front of the shaft.
2. Place the adapter housing and input shaft on a press and force the shaft out of the main drive gear and housing.
3. Remove the bearing retaining snap-ring; then remove bearing.
4. Remove the seal in the adapter housing.

Rear Output Shaft

1. Remove needle bearings from bore of shaft.
2. Remove speedometer driven gear.
3. Place bearing retainer and shaft assembly in a press; then force shaft out of retainer.
4. Lift off speedometer drive gear and shims. Tag shims for reassembly.
5. Press out the outer cup, bearing and seal.
6. Remove the inner cup.
7. Remove the inner bearing.

Front Output Shaft

Using the sliding gear as a base, press rear bearing off shaft.

Assembly

Input Shaft

1. Install a new seal in the adapter housing.
2. Install bearing in the housing and secure with snap-ring.
3. Using the main drive gear as a base, force the input shaft through the housing, seal, bearings and main drive gear. Secure with snap-ring on front of shaft.

Rear Output Shaft

1. Press the shaft into the inner bearing.
2. Install outer cup in the bearing retainer.
3. Install the inner cup.

Exploded view of the input shaft on a Dana 20 transfer case
(© Ford Motor Company)

Exploded view of the rear output shaft on a Dana 20 transfer case
(© Ford Motor Company)

Exploded view of the front output shaft on a Dana 20 transfer case
(© Ford Motor Company)

4. Position the outer bearing in the retainer; then place the shims and speedometer drive gear on the shaft. Install shaft in the bearing retainer housing.
5. Place the bearing retainer and shaft in a vise. Install the output shaft flange and torque the retaining nut to specifications.
6. With a dial indicator on the flange end of the shaft, measure end-play. Adjust shim pack between the speedometer drive gear and outer bearing to achieve correct clearance.
7. After setting correct end-play, remove flange and press bearing retainer seal into housing.
8. Install the flange, washer and nut. Tighten the nut to specifications.

Front Output Shaft

Using a press, force front output rear bearing on shaft.

Shift Rail Oil Seals

Using the tool shown in illustration, install the two shift rail oil seals.

Transfer Case

1. Install the front detent rod in the case.
2. Slide the front drive shift rail all the way into the case and place the shift fork on the rail as it enters the case. Secure the fork to the rail with the setscrew.
3. Position the front output shaft sliding gear in the shift fork.
4. Install the rear detent rod.
5. Slide the rear drive shift rail into the case and position the shift fork on the rail as the rail enters the case. Secure the fork to the rail with the setscrew.

NOTE: The shift rails should be inserted so that the detents are positioned as shown in illustration.

6. While holding the sliding gear and main drive gear in position, install the front output shaft and rear bearing assembly through the two gears.
7. Install the main drive gear spacer and secure with the snapring.
8. Install the front output shaft rear bearing cup.
9. Place the front output shaft rear cover and shims on the case and install the attaching bolts.
10. Install the front output shaft front bearing on the shaft. Install the front bearing cup.

11. If the front bearing retainer oil seal was removed, install a new seal. Position the bearing retainer and gasket to the case and install the attaching bolts.
12. Place the rear output shaft rear bearing retainer on a work bench and install 13 needle bearings in the splined hub of the output shaft, using vaseline or grease.
13. Position the rear output shaft rear bearing retainer assembly to the case and install the attaching bolts.
14. Install the rear output shaft sliding gear in the shifting fork and on the splines of the output shaft.
15. Position the adapter housing assembly on the rear output shaft and case. Install the attaching bolts.
16. Install the roller bearings in the bore of the idler shaft gear with vaseline or grease.
17. Position the idler gear and thrust washers in the case; then drive the idler shaft into the rear of the case through the idler gear and thrust washers.

NOTE: After installing the idler shaft, tap the sides of the case to relieve any possible binding.

18. Install the idler shaft lock plate.
19. Secure the shift rail link to the two shift rails.

20. Install the front and rear drive shift rail detent balls, springs and retaining plugs.

NOTE: Be sure that the heavier loaded spring and flat washer are installed in the front drive shift rail.

21. Install the rod access hole plug.
22. Install the flange, washer and retaining nut on each of the output shafts. Be sure to install a new O-ring in the front output shaft flange. Torque the attaching nuts to specifications.
23. With a dial indicator on the front drive output shaft, check the end-play. If not within specifications, adjust the shim pack at the front output shaft rear cover.
24. Place the cover plate on the case and install the attaching bolts.

Specifications

END PLAY (IN.)

Front Output Shaft	0.001-0.005
Rear Output Shaft	0.001-0.005

TORQUE LIMITS (FT. LBS.)

Transfer Case to Transmission Extension Bolts	20-30
Transfer Case to Transmission Output Shaft Nut	60-80
Front Output Shaft Rear Cover Bolts	25-32
Front Output Shaft Bearing Retainer Bolts	25-32
Idler Shaft Cover Bolts	25-32
Front and Rear Output Flanges	80-85

Dana Model 21

Description

The Dana Model 21 is a single-speed gearbox that transmits power to the front driving axle. There are two positions of the transfer case; front drive axle engaged and front drive axle disengaged.

Disassembly

Transfer Case

1. Clean all dirt from transfer case and drain lubricant.
2. Remove bolts that attach the cover to the top of the case; then remove the cover.
3. Remove the setscrew securing the shift fork to the rail. Tap the shift rail rearward; then remove the rail cap from the rear of the case.
4. Remove the shift rail and fork.
5. Remove the detent spring and ball which engages the front drive shift rail.
6. Remove the flange attaching nuts, flat washer and O-ring from the front and rear output shafts. Discard the O-rings.
7. Remove the flange from the front and rear output shafts.

8. Remove the bolts that attach the rear output shaft bearing retainer to the case; then remove the retainer and output shaft as an assembly.
9. Remove the front and rear idler shaft covers.

10. Using a hammer and soft drift, drive the idler shaft and rear idler bearing rearward out of the case; then lift out the front bearing and idler gear.
11. Remove the front output shaft bearing retainer and gasket. Re-

Exploded view of the transfer case housing and shift mechanism on a Dana 21 (© Ford Motor Company)

Exploded view of the rear output shaft on a Dana 21 (© Ford Motor Company)

move the retainer seal if it is worn or damaged.

12. Remove the front output shaft rear cover and shims. Tie the shims together for reassembly.

13. Tap the end of the front output shaft toward the front of the case; then remove the front bearing cup. Remove the rear bearing cup by tapping the shaft rearward.

14. Angle the front output shaft front bearing away from the main drive gear to remove the snap-ring from its groove in the shaft. Drive the output shaft and rear bearing out of the case.

15. Remove the sliding gear, main drive gear, front bearing, thrust washer and snap-ring from the case.

16. Remove the shift rail seal.

Front Output Shaft Bearing

To remove the front output shaft rear bearing, use the sliding gear as a base and press off the bearing.

Idler Shaft

1. Remove the snap-ring from the idler shaft.

2. Using the idler gear as a base, press the idler shaft out of the rear bearing.

Rear Output Shaft

1. To remove the output shaft from the bearing retainer tap shaft rearward. Remove the shims and spacer.

2. Remove the inner bearing from the output shaft.

3. Place the bearing retainer on a press and force out the outer cup, outer bearing and oil seal.

4. Using a soft drift, drive out the inner bearing cup.

Assembly

Front Output Shaft

Using an arbor press, force rear bearing on front output shaft.

Idler Shaft

1. Using a press, install rear idler bearing on the shaft.

2. Install snap-ring.

Rear Output Shaft

1. Press the inner bearing on the output shaft.

2. Using a soft-faced hammer, tap the inner bearing cup into the retainer.

3. Install the outer cup.

4. Place spacer and shims on the output shaft; then install the shaft in the bearing retainer housing.

5. Install the outer bearing on the shaft.

6. Place the bearing retainer and output shaft in a vise. Measure end-play with a dial indicator on end of the shaft. If not within specifications, adjust shim pack between the spacer and the front and rear bearing cones.

7. After setting correct end-play, install the bearing retainer seal.

Transfer Case

1. While holding the drive gear, sliding gear and thrust washer in the case, install the front output shaft, from the rear, through the gears and washer. Install the snap-ring.

2. Install the front output shaft rear bearing cup.

3. Place the front output shaft rear cover and shims on the case. After removing old sealant from all mating surfaces with thinner, apply gasket sealer to the attaching bolts and torque to specifications. With the cover installed, apply sealer to the outside edge of the adjusting shims, case and cover joints.

4. Install the front output shaft rear bearing on the shaft. Install the front bearing.

5. If the front bearing retainer oil seal was removed, install a new seal. Position the bearing retainer and gasket to the case and install attaching bolts.

6. Install the flange, new O-ring, washer and attaching nut on the front output shaft.

7. With a dial indicator on the front drive output shaft, check the end-play. If not within specified limits, increase or decrease the shim pack thickness at the front output shaft rear cover.

8. Place the idler gear in the case; then install the idler shaft through the gear. Install the front bearing.

Exploded view of the front output shaft on a Dana 21 (© Ford Motor Company)

Exploded view of the idler shaft on a Dana 21 (© Ford Motor Company)

9. Place the front and rear idler covers and gaskets on the case; then install attaching bolts.
10. Install a new shift rail seal.
11. Install the shift rail detent ball and spring in the top of the case.
12. Slide the shift rail into the case and position the fork on the rail as the rail enters the case. Depressing the detent ball and spring will allow the rail to pass. Secure the fork to the rail with the setscrew. Install the shift rail cap.

13. Position the rear output shaft and bearing retainer assembly to the case, then install the attaching bolts.
14. Install the flange, new O-ring, washer and attaching nut on the rear output shaft.
15. Place the top cover and gasket on the case, then install attaching bolts.
16. Fill the transfer case to the proper level with the recommended lubricant.

Specifications

END PLAY (IN.)
Front Output Shaft 0.001-0.005
Rear Output Shaft 0.001-0.005

TORQUE LIMITS (FT. LBS.)
Transfer Case to Transmission
  Extension Bolts 20-30
Transfer Case to Transmission
  Output Shaft Nut 125-150
Front Output Shaft Rear
  Cover Bolts 25-32
Front Output Shaft Bearing
  Retainer Bolts 25-32
Idler Shaft Cover Bolts 25-32

Dana Model 24

Description

The Dana Model 24 is a two-speed gearbox that is manually controlled by a shift lever in the cab. The transfer case positions are: four-wheel-drive low (4L), neutral (N), two-wheel-drive high (2H) and four-wheel-drive high (4H).

Disassembly

1. Clean any dirt from the transfer case and remove the power take-off cover plate.
2. Remove both idler shaft bearing retainers.
3. Using a soft-faced hammer, tap the idler shaft and bearing to the rear until the bearing is free of the case.
4. Remove the idler shaft, two gears and spacer.
5. Remove the idler shaft front bearing.
6. Remove the flange retaining nuts from the front output shaft, the input shaft and the rear output shaft.
7. Remove the flanges and washers.
8. Remove the front output shaft front and rear bearing retainers.
9. Tap the front output shaft and rear bearing through the gears and case. Remove the high speed gear.

10. Remove the front output shaft front bearing and washer.
11. Remove the setscrew that retains the front drive shaft fork to the shift rail.
12. Remove the front output shaft sliding gear.
13. If the input shaft oil seal is to be replaced, remove it with a four-jaw puller and slide hammer.
14. Remove the input shaft bearing retainer.
15. If the output shaft bearing retainer oil seal is to be replaced, remove it with a puller and slide hammer.
16. Remove the rear output shaft bearing retainer; then remove the speedometer drive assembly.
17. Loosen the rear output shaft assembly from the case by driving on the front end of the input shaft with a soft-faced hammer.
18. Remove the rear output shaft and bearing retainer as an assembly.

Removing/installing the front output shaft on a Dana 24 transfer case
(© Ford Motor Company)

19. Tap the input shaft through the front bearing, through the main drive gear, through the sliding gear and out of the case.
20. Lift the main drive gear out of the case and then drive out the input shaft front bearing.
21. Remove the setscrew that retains the rear drive shift fork to the shift rail.
22. Remove the rear output shaft sliding gear.

Removing/installing the input shaft on a Dana 24 transfer case
(© Ford Motor Company)

The rear drive shift fork and sliding gear on a Dana 24 transfer case
(© Ford Motor Company)

The shift mechanism on a Dana 24
(© Ford Motor Company)

23. Remove the shift rail link from the two shift rails.
24. Remove the retaining plug, detent spring and ball which en-

gage the front drive shift rail detent rod.

25. Remove the retaining plug detent spring and ball which engages the rear drive shift rail detent rod. Remove the front drive detent rod access hole plug.
26. Pull the front drive shift rail to the furthest outward position.
27. Pull the rear drive shift rail far enough to allow the two detent rods to slide out.
28. Remove the rear drive shift rail and fork.
29. Remove the shift rail seals.

Assembly

1. Slide the front drive shift rail all the way into the case and position the shift fork on the rail as the rail enters the case.
2. Install the two detent rods in the case.
3. Install the rear drive shift fork and hold the detent rods and the fork in place as the rear drive shift rail is pushed in as far as possible.

NOTE: In steps 2 and 3, the shift rails should be inserted so that the detents are positioned as shown in illustration.

4. Pull the front drive shift rail out to its next detent. This will permit the rear drive shift rail to be pushed in to the full extent of its travel. After pushing the rear drive shift rail all the way in, push the front drive shift rail back to its extreme inward position.
5. Install the rear drive shift detent ball, spring and retaining plug; then install the access hole plug.
6. Install the front drive shift rail detent ball, spring and retaining plug.
7. Secure the shift rail link in the two shift rails.
8. Place the rear output sliding gear in the shift fork and secure the fork to the rear drive shift rail with the setscrew.
9. Install input shaft front bearing and retainer assembly. Coat retainer and bolts with sealer.
10. Place the main drive gear in the case; then slide the input shaft into the rear of the case through the main drive gear and through the front bearing and retainer.
11. Install the roller bearings in the splined hub of the rear output shaft assembly with petrolatum or grease. Then install the shaft and bearing retainer assembly, making sure that the output shaft is aligned correctly with the input shaft. Coat the case, bearing retainer and bolts with sealer.
12. Position the front output sliding gear in the shift fork and secure the folk to the front drive shift rail with the setscrew.
13. While holding the sliding gear and high speed gear in position, install the front output shaft and rear bearing assembly through the two gears from the rear of the case.
14. After coating with sealer, install the front output shaft rear bearing retainer and gasket.
15. Install the washer and bearing over the front output shaft at the front of the case and then install the front bearing retainer and gasket. Coat retainer with sealer.
16. Install the flange, washer, flange retaining nut and cotter key on each of the three shafts. Torque to specifications.
17. Place the idler shaft gears in the case and install the shaft and rear bearing assembly from the rear. After applying sealer to the plate and bolts, install the rear bearing retainer.
18. Position the spacer on the front end of the idler shaft and install the front bearing. Tap the bearing lightly with a mallet or soft-faced hammer.
19. Install the washer, retaining nut and cotter pin on the front end of the idler shaft.
20. After applying sealer to the plates and bolts, install the idler shaft front bearing retainer and the power take-off cover plate.

Specifications

END PLAY (IN.)
Front Output Shaft 0.003-0.007
Rear Output Shaft 0.003-0.007

TORQUE LIMITS (FT. LBS.)
Transfer Case to Transmission
Extension Bolts 20-30
Transfer Case to Transmission
Output Shaft Nut 60-80
Front Output Shaft Rear
Cover Bolts 25-32
Front Output Shaft Bearing
Retainer Bolts 25-32
Idler Shaft Cover Bolts 25-32

International Harvester   Model TC-143

The IH Model TC-143 "Silent Drive" transfer case is a chain driven single speed unit. Unlike conventional gear driven transfer cases, this unit has a high-strength link-belt type loop of chain driving two broad-faced sprockets. There is no neutral position. There are two variations of this transfer case; one is frame mounted with a short intermediate drive shaft between the input shaft of the transfer case and the transmission output shaft and the other type is mounted directly to the rear of the transmission.

Disassembly

1. After removing the transfer case from the vehicle and draining all of the lubricant out, clean the outside of the case.
2. Remove the shift cover.
3. Unscrew and remove the indicator light switch from the case.
4. With the rear output shaft flange clamped in a soft jawed

1. Input shaft end nut
2. Washer
3. Seal
4. Flange bolt
5. Frame-mounted type case
6. Gasket
7. Shift cover
8. Bearing snap ring
9. Ball bearing
10. Long spacer
11. Upper sprocket (Old style)

12. Chain
13. Input shaft
14. Short spacer
15. Dowel ring
16. Cover
17. Flange nut

18. Roller bearing
19. Drain plug
20. Thrust washer
21. Output shaft
22. Lower sprocket
23. Thrust washer

24. Sliding clutch
25. Ball bearing
26. Seal
27. Washer
28. Output shaft end nut
29. Shift shoe

30. Assembly shifter
31. Spring stud
32. Shift spring
33. Shift clevis
34. Clevis pin
35. Shift cover gasket
36. Upper sprocket (new style)

Exploded view of a frame-mounted type International Harvester TC-143 transfer case (© International Harvester Company)

vise, remove the flange retaining nut. Remove the flange from the vise and remove the flange from the rear output shaft. Use a puller, if necessary.

5. Turn the case so it rests on the flanges and remove the bolts securing the two halves of the case. Lift the top (rear) half of the case from the assembly and discard the gasket.

6. If present, remove the short spacer from the rear side of the input shaft. Also, if the thrust washer did not stay with the cover when removed, remove it now from the front output shaft.

7. With the case again secured in a soft jawed vise, place your thumbs on the ends of the shafts with your fingers under the sprockets. Pull the sprockets together with the chain off the shafts and out of the case as an assembly.

8. Unhook and remove the shift spring.

9. Remove the shift assembly mounting bolt and spring stud from the case.

10. Pull the shift cranks from the bosses inside the case.

11. If present, remove the long spacer from the input shaft and the washer from the front output shaft.

12. Lift the sliding clutch and its shift shoe from the front output shaft.

13. The two shafts are removed from the case with a press or by tapping them out with a soft hammer.

NOTE: If the transfer case is a transmission mounted unit, a snap ring on the input shaft must be removed before the shaft can be removed from the case.

14. After the shafts are removed, remove the oil seals and the bearing snap rings, and press or tap out the two ball bearings.

1. Transmission shaft coupling
2. Washer
3. Transmission shaft end nut
4. Input shaft coupling
5. Speedometer gear
6. Gasket
7. Transmission mounted type case
8. Flange bolt
9. Gasket
10. Snap input shaft ring
11. Bearing snap ring
12. Ball bearing

Exploded view of a transmission-mounted type International Harvester TC-143 transfer case (© International Harvester Company)

13. Long spacer	23. End nut	33. Washer
14. Upper sprocket (Old style)	24. Roller bearing	34. Output shaft end nut
15. Chain	25. Drain plug	35. Shift shoe
16. Input shaft	26. Thrust washer	36. Assembly shifter
17. Short spacer	27. Output shaft	37. Spring stud
18. Dowel ring	28. Lower sprocket	38. Shift spring
19. Cover	29. Thrust washer	39. Shift clevis
20. Flange nut	30. Sliding clutch	40. Clevis pin
21. Seal	31. Ball bearing	41. Shift cover gasket
22. Washer	32. Seal	42. Shift cover
		43. Upper sprocket (new style)

Removing the shifter mechanism from an I.H. TC-143 transfer case (© International Harvester Company)

Removing the shifter cover on an I.H. TC-143 transfer case (© International Harvester Company)

Removing the rear half of the case (cover) from an I.H. TC-143 transfer case (© International Harvester Company)

15. Pry and remove the thrust washer from the boss for the front output shaft roller bearing in the other half of the case.
16. Press the roller bearing cage from the inside and out of the cover.
17. Press the ball bearing on the outer race from the outside and out of the cover.

Cleaning and Inspection

1. Clean all parts in solvent, removing all traces of old gaskets, sealants and lubricants, and dry the parts with compressed air.
2. Examine all the ball and roller bearings for wear or damage and replace as necessary.
3. Inspect the sprocket teeth and bores for damage and wear. Check the internal splines and clutch teeth for chipped surfaces. Small nicks or burrs can be removed with a file.
4. Check the smooth and splined surfaces of the shafts for wear or damage. The sliding clutch must move freely on the output shaft, but excessive clearance is remedied by replacement of parts.
5. Examine the chain for bent or broken links. If either condition exists, replace the chain.

Assembly

1. Install the two snap rings in the outer grooves of both bearing bores in the front half of the case.
2. Coat both bearing bores with lubricant and press or tap with a soft hammer both ball bearing assemblies into the case.
3. Install the two snap rings in the inner grooves of the two bearing bores in the front case half.
4. Install the shaft oil seals from the outside of the front case half. They are best installed with a press.
5. On a frame mounted transfer case, position the lightly lubricated shafts in the bearings, then, pull the shafts into the bearings by tightening the flange attaching nuts with the flanges installed. The input shaft is installed with the identification groove toward the rear of the transfer case. Tighten the flange attaching nut on the front output shaft to 200-250 ft. lbs., and the flange attaching nut on the input shaft until it bottoms, then back off two turns and retighten to 140-150 ft. lbs.
6. The output shaft in transmission mounted transfer cases is installed in the same manner as outlined for frame mounted units in step 5.

Installation of the thrust washer and long spacer, if so equipped, on an I.H. TC-143 transfer case (© International Harvester Company)

7. The input shaft in transmission mounted transfer cases has a snap ring to be installed on the front end of the shaft prior to installation in the bearing. The shaft is then pressed or tapped into the bearing with a soft hammer until the snap ring is bottomed against the bearing.
8. Assemble the shift shoe to the sliding clutch and install sliding clutch to the front output shaft.
9. Insert the shifter assembly into the transfer case so the shift cranks of the shifter pass through the shift shoe before being guided into the shift bosses. Make sure the shifter operates the sliding clutch and then secure the assembly with the bolt and spring stud.

NOTE: The flange bolt must be installed before the spring stud because the position of the spring stud when installed prevents the installation of the flange bolt.

10. Install the thrust washer to the front output shaft and the long spacer to the input shaft, if so equipped with a long spacer.

NOTE: Be sure the thrust washer tangs fit down into the splines on the shaft.

11. Lightly lubricate the bores of both sprockets and secure the case in a soft jawed vise by the end of the input shaft.
12. Install the upper sprocket to the outer end of the input shaft. Do not slide the sprocket completely into the case.
13. Position the chain over the sprocket and place the lower sprocket inside the chain.
14. Pull down on the lower sprocket enough to slide the lower sprocket onto the output shaft.
15. Slide both sprockets and chain onto the sprockets as far as they will go.
16. Install the short spacer on the input shaft (not required on later models).

17. Install the shift spring between the spring post and the shifter assembly.
18. Press the ball bearing into the input shaft bore of the rear cover from the inside surface.
19. Press the roller bearing into the output shaft bore of the rear cover from the outside surface until it is flush with the bearing bore.
20. Press the seal for the rear of the input shaft (rear output) into the cover until it is flush.
21. Place the cover on a bench, inside facing up. Coat the back side of the thrust washer with a thin coat of sealant and position it on the roller bearing boss with the tang on the washer mated with the oil passage in the boss.

NOTE: Use the sealant sparingly and make sure none of it enters the bearing or blocks the two oil passages.

22. Position a new gasket and two dowel rings on the mating surface of the case.
23. Position the cover onto the case, guiding the two shafts into their respective bearings. Secure the cover to the case with the attaching nuts and bolts, tightening them to 29-38 ft. lbs.
24. Install the indicator light switch to the case and check its operation with a test light.
25. Install the shift cover gasket and cover on the case and secure it with bolts and lockwashers tightened to 4-6 ft. lbs. *Do not overtighten.*
26. Install the rear output flange on the rear of the input shaft so both the input flange and the output flange are on the same plane. The flanges must be assembled in this manner to prevent vibration.
27. Install the washer and a nylon insert locknut on the shaft tightened to 140-150 ft. lbs. to secure the flange.

New Process Model
T201

Description

The New Process Model 201 transfer case is a 2-speed gearbox which provides speed reduction and couples power to the front and rear driving axles.

CAUTION: Do not engage front driving axle when operating truck on hard surfaced roads at high speeds.

De-Clutch and Shift Rod Adjustment

NOTE: All adjustments must be made with the front axle engaged and the transfer case in low range.

1. Disconnect de-clutch and shift rods at shift levers.
2. Adjust de-clutch rod length until lever clears rear end of slot in cab underbody by ⅝ in. Secure adjusting yoke with locknut.
3. Adjust shift rod length until distance between protusions on shift and de-clutch levers is ¼ in. Secure adjusting yoke with locknut.
4. Connect de-clutch and shift rods at shift levers and then road test vehicle.

Disassembly

Rear Output Shaft

1. Remove cotter pin and flange nut at rear output shaft.
2. Remove attaching bolts and nuts, then remove bearing retainer and gasket. Discard gasket.
3. Remove output shaft assembly from case.
4. Remove nut and washer at rear of shaft.
5. Remove brake drum by tapping on it lightly (if necessary).

1 Ball, shift bar poppet
2 Spring, shift bar poppet ball
3 Bar, front output shaft
4 Fork, shift
5 Screw, set
6 Clutch, front output sliding
7 Fork, shift
8 Gear, front output drive
9 Bearing, roller (70 req'd)
10 Spacer, bearing
11 Shaft, front output front gear
12 Washer, thrust
13 Bearing, ball
14 Retainer, lock
15 Nut, bearing retaining
16 Shaft, idler gear
17 Cone, idler gear bearing
18 Cup, idler gear bearing
19 Shim, set
20 Spacer, bearing
21 Shaft input
22 Ring, snap
23 Bearing, roller (15 req'd)
24 Gear, rear output drive w/shaft
25 Gear, speedometer drive
26 Spacer, speedometer drive gear
27 Clutch, two-speed sliding
28 Plug, pipe
29 Gasket, set
30 Bolt, hex head, w/lock washer
31 Retainer, front output shaft rear bearing
32 Bolt, hex head, w/lock washer
33 Washer, lock
34 Nut, hex
35 Breather
36 Cup, rear output shaft outer bearing
37 Cone, rear output shaft outer bearing
38 Support, hand brake
39 Seal, rear output shaft outer bearing oil
40 Stud
41 Retainer, rear output drive gear bearing
42 Plate, idler shaft cover
43 Cup, rear output shaft inner bearing
44 Cone, rear output shaft inner bearing
45 Case, transfer
46 Bolt w/washer
47 Bolt, hex head
48 Washer, lock
49 Cover, power take-off opening

50 Gasket, power take-off cover
51 Stud
52 Bearing, input and front output ball
53 retainer, input and front output bearing
54 Washer, lock
55 Nut, hex
56 Seal, input and front output bearing retainer oil
57 Gasket
58 Seal, front and rear output shift bar oil
59 Screw, poppet ball retainer
60 Washer, thrust
61 Bearing, roller (70 req'd)
62 Spacer, bearing
63 Gear, input drive
64 Gear, power take-off
65 Bar, two-speed shift
66 Washer
67 Nut, hex
68 Pin, cotter
69 Gear, idler

Exploded view of the New Process T-201 transfer case
(© Chrysler Corporation)

Removing/installing the rear output shaft on a New Process
T-201 transfer case   (© Chrysler Corporation)

FRONT OUTPUT SHAFT ASSEMBLY

Removing/installing the front output shaft on a New Process
T-201 transfer case   (© Chrysler Corporation)

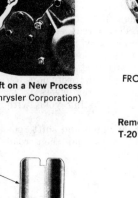

REMOVING AND INSTALLING ARBOR

Removing/installing the idler gear shaft on a New Process
T-201 transfer case   (© Chrysler Corporation)

INPUT SHAFT ASSEMBLY

Removing/installing the input shaft assembly on a New Process
T-201 transfer case   (© Chrysler Corporation)

6. Remove shaft and gear from bearing retainer.
7. Remove shims, spacer and speedometer drive gear. Tie shims together for reassembly.
8. Remove inner bearing cone, using a suitable puller.
9. Remove snap-ring and roller bearings from shaft gear bore.

NOTE: The rear output shaft and gear is serviced as an assembly. *Do not remove gear from shaft.*

10. Remove attaching nuts, brake support, bearing and oil seal. Discard seal.

Front Output Shaft

1. Remove attaching bolts and nuts, then remove rear bearing retainer and gasket. Discard gasket.
2. Remove cotter pin and nut at front output shaft.
3. Remove attaching nut, washer and companion flange.
4. Remove the front output shaft assembly through the rear of the case.
5. Remove sliding clutch gear.
6. Position front output shaft assembly in a soft-jawed vise.
7. Remove lock retainer and bearing nut.
8. Using a suitable puller, remove bearing.
9. Remove front output shaft drive gear by lifting upward and holding the thrust washers against the hub to retain bearing rollers.

10. Carefully set aside thrust washers, then remove the two rows of bearing rollers (70 rollers) and the spacer separating them.
11. Remove attaching nuts and bearing retainer with gaskets. Note number of gaskets used.

Idler Gear, Shift Bar and Fork

1. Remove safety wire and setscrews securing shift forks to shift bars.
2. Remove poppet ball retaining plugs, gaskets and poppet ball springs.
3. Pull shift bars out of the case, then remove shift forks and poppet balls.
4. Remove cotter pin, nut and washer from front end of idler shaft.
5. Remove attaching bolts, gasket and idler gear shaft cover plate.
6. Remove idler gear assembly.

NOTE: When removing the idler gear assembly, use an arbor as shown in illustration and perform the following:

a. Install arbor on threaded end of shaft so that it seats against the shaft shoulder.
b. Drive arbor until shaft is free at rear of case.
c. Separate shaft and arbor.
d. Remove gear with arbor through front output shaft opening.
e. Remove arbor, shims, spacer and bearing cones. Tie shims together for reassembly.

Input Shaft

1. Remove cotter pin and input shaft flange nut.
2. Remove nut, flat washer and companion flange.
3. Remove input shaft assembly through rear output shaft opening in case.

NOTE: Make certain to retain power take-off and drive gear on the shaft.

4. Mount input shaft in a soft-jawed vise.
5. Remove power take-off gear.
6. Remove input drive gear while holding thrust washers tightly against hub.
7. Carefully remove the two rows of bearing rollers (70 rollers) and the separating spacer.
8. Remove attaching nuts, bearing retainer, gaskets and oil seal. Note the number of gaskets used and discard the oil seal.

Assembly

The transfer case is assembled in the reverse order of disassembly. The following procedures concerning preloading bearings and bearing adjustment however, must all be completed before (or in some cases, during) installation of shaft and gear assemblies.

Input Shaft

1. The input shaft drive gear bearing consists of 70 rollers divided into two rows by a spacer.

2. Coat gear bore with grease, then position rollers and spacer.
3. Hold thrust washers against hub to retain rollers, then install gear on shaft.
4. Input shaft end-play is controlled by gasket thickness between case and bearing retainer.
5. Position retainer on case, then measure clearance with a feeler gauge.
6. Select gasket(s) with a thickness .005 in. more than measured clearance.
7. Remove retainer and install selected gasket(s), then reinstall retainer.

Rear Output Shaft

1. Rear output shaft bearing preload is set by shim set size selection.
2. Using an arbor press and suitable sleeve, install inner bearing cone on shaft. The cone should be firmly seated against gear.
3. Install speedometer drive gear, spacer and original bearing shim set.
4. Install rear output shaft in bearing retainer, then position outer bearing cone on shaft.
5. Install parking brake drum, flat washer and slotted nut. Torque nut to 125 ft. lbs.
6. Mount shaft and retainer assembly in a vise so that shaft is free to rotate.
7. Turn shaft until bearing rolls smoothly. Then, using an inch-pound torque wrench, measure bearing preload with the wrench in motion. Subtract or add shims as necessary to meet specifications.

NOTE: Shims for adjusting bearing preload are available in four thicknesses.

8. After the final adjustment, remove slotted nut, washer and brake drum.
9. Install parking brake support and new support oil seal.
10. Reinstall brake drum, washer and slotted nut. Torque nut to specfications.

Idler Gear

1. Idler gear bearing end-play is controlled by shim set size selection.
2. Clamp the idler gear shaft (large end) in a soft-jawed vise.
3. Install bearing cone against shoulder on shaft.
4. Install bearing spacer and original shim set.
5. Install idler gear (small end down) on shaft, then install other bearing cone.
6. Position spacer tool as shown in illustration, then install flat washer and nut. Torque nut to specifications.
7. Rotate gear until bearing rolls smoothly. Then using a dial indicator, measure idler gear bearing end-play. Add or subtract shims as necessary to meet specifications.
8. Disassemble idler gear shaft assembly. Tie newly selected shims together.
9. To install gear assembly in the case, position bearing cone in in the large end of the gear, then place gear (small end up) on a bench.
10. Install the same arbor used to remove idler gear shaft, a spacer, new shims and other bearing cone in the idler gear.
11. Hold the idler gear assembly in the case with the small diameter gear facing rearward, then insert the shaft through the case (from rear) and thread it into the previously installed arbor.
12. Tap on the shaft until arbor extends through opposite side of case.
13. Remove arbor.

Two-Speed Clutch

When installing the two-speed clutch on the input shaft, make certain that the recessed side of the gear is toward the front of the case.

Front Output Shaft

1. The front output shaft drive gear bearing consists of 70

bearing rollers divided into two rows by a spacer.
2. Coat gear bore with grease, then position rollers and spacer.
3. Hold thrust washers against each hub to retain rollers, then install gear on shaft.
4. Shaft end-play is controlled by gasket thickness between case and bearing retainer.
5. Position retainer on case, then measure clearance with a feeler gauge.
6. Select gasket(s) with a thickness .005 in. more than measured clearance.
7. Remove retainer and install selected gasket(s), then reinstall retainer.
8. When installing the front output shaft assembly in the case, locate front output shift bar as far toward rear of case as possible. This will make it possible to position shift fork in clutch gear collar and to align clutch gear splines on front output shaft.

Specifications

END PLAY (IN.)
Input Shaft .... Approx. 0.005
Front Output Shaft ...... Approx. 0.005
Idler Gear 0.000-0.002

BEARING PRELOAD (IN. LBS.)
Rear Output Shaft Bearings 15-30

TORQUE LIMITS (FT. LBS.)
Front Retainer Nut 35-55
Poppet Screw 15-25
Idler Cover Screw 15-25
Drain and Filler Plugs 25-45
Top Cover 38-42
All Bearing Caps 38-42
Flange and Idler Shaft Nut 125
Input Shaft 300-400
Front Output Shaft 300-400
Rear Output Shaft 300-400
Idler Shaft Nut 140-160
Front Output Shaft Flange Nut .. 140-160
Input Shaft Flange Nut 140-160
Driveshaft Mating Flange Nuts 35
Breather 8-12
Brake Support Nut 25-45
Brake Retaining Screw 20-40
Brake Retainer Nut 25-45
Brake Drum 60-66
Brake Mounting 60-66
Brake Drum Nut 140-160
P.T.O. Screw 8-12
P.T.O. to Case 38-42
P.T.O. Bearing Cap 38-42
P.T.O. Top Cover 38-42
P.T.O. Shaft 300-400

New Process Model 202

Description

The New Process Model 202 transfer case is a two-speed gear box which is used to transmit power from the main transmission to a front driving axle, as well as to a conventional rear axle. Sliding clutch gears in the transfer case are controlled by a single lever to select various driving ranges. A separate control lever is provided for operating the power take-off assembly on units so equipped.

The transfer case should not be operated in four-wheel high range on dry, hard surface roads, as rapid tire wear will result.

CAUTION: Do not operate transfer case in neutral range for extended periods of time when power take-off assembly is disengaged.

Disassembly

NOTE: The following procedure covers a disassembly of the transfer case removed from the chassis and mounted in a suitable stand.

Rear (Upper) Output Shaft

1. Remove cotter pin from flange nut located at end of rear output shaft. Apply hand brake to

Exploded view of the New Process T-202 transfer case
(© International Harvester Company)

1 Link, shift lever
2 Lever, shift
3 Pin, rod
4 Spring, shift bar poppet
5 Ball, shift bar poppet
6 Bar, shift, two-speed
7 Pin, rod
8 Plunger, shift bar interlock
9 Bar, shift idler
10 Fork, shift, two-speed
11 Fork, shift, idler
12 Pin, idler shaft
13 Bearing, thrust, race
14 Bearing, thrust, needle
15 Ring, snap, idler
16 Gear, idler drive
17 Gear, sliding, idler
18 Bearing, roller, idler, shaft
19 Gear, lower shaft (front output)
20 Spacer, rotating shaft
21 Shaft, idler gear, rotating
22 Shaft, idler gear, stationary
23 Gear, PTO, input shaft, upper
24 Spring, friction washer, input shaft

25 Washer, friction, input shaft
26 Gear, drive, input shaft, upper
27 Bearing, roller, input shaft, front
28 Spacer, input shaft drive gear bearing
29 Washer, input shaft sliding clutch
30 Gear, clutch, input shaft, upper
31 Shaft, input
32 Ring, snap
33 Bearing, roller, drive gear
34 Gear, shaft, output drive
35 Seal, oil, input and output shaft, front
36 Retainer, bearing, input and output shaft, front
37 Gasket, bearing retainer
38 Bearing, input and output shaft, front
39 Seal, oil, shift bar
40 Gasket, shift bar poppet screw
41 Screw, shift bar poppet
42 Gasket, PTO cover
43 Cover, PTO opening

44 Plug, pipe
45 Case, transfer
46 Bearing, gear, output shaft, inner
47 Gasket, rear bearing retainer, upper
48 Plug, pipe
49 Gasket, rear bearing retainer, lower
50 Retainer, lower rear bearing (front output shaft)
51 Bearing, lower shaft, rear
52 Retainer, upper rear (output shaft) bearing
53 Gear, speedometer drive gear
54 Spacer, speedometer drive gear
55 Bearing, output shaft drive gear, outer
56 Spacer, brake drum flange
57 Gasket, brake drum support
58 Support, hand brake
59 Seal, oil, output shaft bearing, rear

prevent shaft from rotating; then break the torque on nut.
2. Remove hex head bolts and two nuts securing bearing retainer to case. Remove the rear output shaft assembly. Remove and discard gasket.
3. Place the output shaft assembly on a bench.
4. Remove the nut and flat washer at rear of shaft. Tap brake drum lightly and remove drum from shaft. Slide off brake drum flange spacer.
5. Remove output shaft with drive gear from upper rear bearing retainer. Slide off speedometer drive gear, spacer and drive gear inner bearing. Remove snap-ring and fifteen roller bearings.
6. Remove hex nuts and lock washers securing hand brake support to upper rear bearing retainer. Remove brake support and drive gear outer bearing. Remove oil seal and discard.

Input Shaft
1. Remove ten capscrews and lock washers attaching power take-off cover or assembly (if so equipped). Remove and discard gasket.
2. Remove shift bar poppet screw, spring and ball. Through the rear output shaft opening in case, remove roll pin securing two-speed shift fork on bar. Use a 5/32 in. diameter steel rod to drive out roll pin.

Removing/installing the rear output shaft from a New Process T-202 transfer case
(© International Harvester Company)

NOTE: Where case interference prevents complete removal of roll pin, drive the pin until shift bar can be removed. Shift fork can then be moved toward input shaft clutch gear to provide clearance for removal of roll pin.
3. Position idler shift bar in four-wheel high drive position (shift bar to extreme rear in case). Simultaneously remove input shaft clutch gear and two-speed shift fork.
4. Remove cotter pin from nut at outer end of input shaft. Use a suitable flange holder to prevent shaft from turning; then break torque on nut. Remove the nut, flat washer and companion flange.
5. Move the input shaft and gear assembly toward rear of case

by lightly tapping on the outer end of shaft. This will free shaft from bearing and permit shaft and power take-off gear to be removed.
CAUTION: Hold input drive gear firmly against shoulder on shaft to retain roller bearings in bore of gear.
6. Place input shaft on a bench and remove drive gear, roller bearings, spacer and sliding clutch gear washer. Remove friction washer and washer spring from hub of power take-off gear.
7. Remove input shaft bearing retainer, gasket and bearing. If necessary, remove and discard oil seal from bearing retainer.

Front (Lower) Output Shaft
1. Remove cotter pin from nut at outer end of front output shaft. Use a suitable flange holder to prevent shaft from turning; then break torque on nut. Remove nut, flat washer and flange.
2. Remove hex head bolts and nuts attaching input shaft rear bearing retainer to case. Lightly tap on end of shaft, moving it toward rear of case to displace shoulder on rear bearing retainer. Remove drive gear and shaft.
3. Press drive gear rear bearing from retainer. Remove front bearing retainer and bearing. If

Removing the input shaft and P.T.O. gear from a New Process T-202 transfer case (© International Harvester Company)

Removing the front output shaft assembly from a New Process T-202 transfer case (© International Harvester Company)

Checking the side clearance between the idler drive gear and retaining snap ring; New Process T-202 transfer case (© International Harvester Company)

lubricant leakage is evident at the retainer, remove oil seal and discard.

Idler Shift Bar and Gear

1. Remove roll pin securing fork to idler shift bar. Use a 5/32" diameter steel rod to drive out pin. Withdraw shift bar and fork.

NOTE: Spring tension on poppet ball will displace ball from case upon removing shift bar.

2. Remove shift bar interlock plunger and spring.
3. Remove roll pin from outer end of idler gear stationary shaft. Using a brass drift, drive the idler shaft toward rear of case. Remove shaft.
4. Remove idler gear rotating shaft assembly through the opening from which the rear output shaft assembly was removed. Place the gear assembly on a bench.
5. Remove thrust bearing and thrust bearing race at each end of rotating shaft. Remove individual roller bearing and spacer.
6. Remove snap-ring; then separate idler drive gear and shaft. Remove sliding clutch gear.

Assembly

Lubricate all bearings, bushings, spline shafts and shift bar forks at their contact surfaces during assembly. This will provide initial lubrication and avoid possible damage when the transfer case is first operated.

Idler Shift Bar and Gear

1. Place the idler gear rotating shaft in a vertical position with the large splined gear end resting on bench.

2. Position sliding clutch gear on shaft with the groove which receives idler shift fork, facing upward.
3. Position drive gear on shaft so that gear internal splines engage splines on shaft.

CAUTION: The long shoulder side of drive gear must face sliding clutch gear to provide clearance with the inside face of case.

4. Install snap-ring and check for proper side clearance with drive gear. This is accomplished by inserting a feeler gauge between the ring and gear. Three different thicknesses of snap-rings are available for obtaining proper clearance. Select and install proper size. Refer to Specifications for recommended snapping side clearance.

NOTE: Snap-ring side clearance must be maintained to prevent possible ring breakage.

5. Coat the bore of idler gear rotating shaft with Lubriplate No. 110; then assemble roller bearings and spacer. Apply Lubriplate to thrust bearing and bearing race; then assemble at each end of idler rotating shaft.

Carefully place rotating shaft assembly in case. Align shaft with opening in front and rear of case for installing the stationary shaft. Install stationary shaft, making certain not to disturb roller bearing arrangement in bore of rotating shaft. Tap the shaft lightly until seated. Install roll pin in shaft at front of case.

6. Position poppet spring and ball in case. Hold the spring and ball in a compressed position and insert idler shift bar at front side of case. Place idler shift fork in position on sliding gear (shoulder on fork toward front of case) and install on shift bar. Secure fork to shift bar with roll pin.

NOTE: Side of shift bar employing only one detent must be facing upward.

Input Shaft

1. Place the input drive gear on a bench and assemble roller bearings and spacer. Coat the gear bore with Lubriplate No. 110 to retain bearing rollers.

2. Install sliding clutch washer; then carefully position drive gear with bearings on shaft. Place friction washer on shaft next to drive gear, with the tang opposite gear.
3. Assemble friction washer spring on hub of power take-off gear.
   NOTE: Install spring on recess side of gear
4. Assemble input shaft with drive gear and power take-off gear in case. Hold the drive gear firmly to clutch gear washer to keep roller bearings in place.
   NOTE: Rotate friction washer until tang engages blind hole in power take-off gear.
5. With the idler shift bar in four-wheel high drive position (shift bar to extreme rear of case), insert interlock plunger in case.
6. Install two-speed shift bar in case so that side of bar with the single detent is facing the idler shift bar. Install sliding clutch gear and two-speed shift bar fork. Install roll pin to secure fork to shift bar.
7. Install input shaft bearing.
   CAUTION: Movement of input shaft toward rear of case while installing bearing will permit rollers to become displaced from bore of drive gear.
8. Position bearing retainer to case and install hex head bolts finger

tight. Do not torque bolts at this time since gasket thickness must be determined following installation of rear output shaft assembly.

Front (Lower) Output Shaft

1. Install front output shaft bearing in face of case.
2. Install front output shaft and drive gear.
3. Press drive gear rear bearing in retainer. Install bearing with stamped end of bearing resting on press. Position gasket and retainer at rear face of case. Install hex head bolts with lock washers and tighten securely.
4. Install new oil seal in bearing retainer. Assemble retainer to front face of case and install hex head bolts finger tight. Do not torque bolts at this time.

Rear (Upper) Output Shaft

1. Support rear output shaft bearing retainer in a press; then install shaft inner bearing flush with outer surface of retainer.
2. Place bearing retainer on a bench and assemble drive gear and shaft. Position speedometer drive gear and spacer on shaft. Assemble outer bearing on shaft and install in upper rear bearing retainer. Install hand brake drum spacer.

3. Install new oil seal in hand brake support. Install gasket and brake support to upper rear bearing retainer.
4. Position gasket to bearing retainer and install the rear output assembly on case.

Input and Front Output Shaft Bearing Adjustment

The fit of the input and front output shaft bearing retainer to their respective bearings is controlled by gasket thickness. To determine the correct thickness or number of gaskets required, measure the clearance between retainer and case with a feeler gauge. Select gasket(s) which will give a bearing retainer fit within specified limits. See Specifications. Remove the retainer; then install selected gasket(s) and retainer.

Specifications

BEARING CLEARANCE
Input and Front Output
Shaft Bearings ...... 0.003-0.006 in.
Gasket Thickness Available 0.009-0.011 in.
0.0135-0.0165 in.

SNAP RING
Side Clearance .... 0.007-0.013 in.
Thickness Available .... 0.092-0.094 in.
0.095-0.097 in.
0.098-0.100 in.

POPPET BALL SPRING
Free Length .... 1.0 in.
Pressure @ 21/32" .... 30 Lbs.

TORQUE LIMITS
Flange Nut ....Minimum 125 ft lbs.

New Process Model 205

Description

The New Process Model 205 transfer case is a two-speed gearbox mounted between the main transmission and the rear axle. The gearbox transmits power from the transmission and engine to the front and rear driving axles.

Disassembly

Transfer Case

1. Clean the exterior of the case.
2. Remove the nuts from the universal joint flanges.
3. Remove the front output shaft rear bearing retainer, front bearing retainer and drive flange.
4. Tap the front output shaft assembly from the case with a soft hammer. Remove the sliding clutch, front output high gear, washer and bearing from the case.
5. Remove the rear output shaft housing attaching bolts and remove the housing, output shaft, bearing retainer and speedometer gear.
6. Slide the rear output shaft from the housing.

Front view of a New Pocess 205 transfer case. This unit would have a short driveshaft connected to the input shaft. Others are bolted directly to the transmission (© International Harvester Company)

Rear view of a New Process 205 transfer case (© G.M.C.)

1. Shift lever link
2. Bar
3. Bar
4. Plunger
5. Seal
6. Screw
7. Gasket
8. Spring
9. Ball
10. Plug
11. Nut
12. Washer
13. Seal
14. Retainer
15. Gasket
16. Bearing
17. Washer
18. Gear
19. Shaft
20. Pin
21. Clutch
22. Fork
23. Pin
24. Bearing
25. Spacer
26. Gear
27. Washer
28. Ring
29. Bearing
30. Gasket
31. Retainer
32. Cone
33. Cup
34. Shim set
35. Gear
36. Spacer
37. Shaft
38. Gasket
39. Cover
40. Bearing
41. Shaft
42. Ring
43. Washer
44. Bearing
45. Gear
46. Washer
47. Bearing
48. Gear
49. Spacer
50. Retainer
51. Breather
52. Gasket
53. Retainer
54. Seal
55. Case
56. Gasket
57. Cover

Exploded view of a New Process 205 transfer case
(© International Harvester Company)

NOTE: Be careful not to lose the 15 needle bearings that will be loose when the rear output shaft is removed.

7. Drive the two ¼ in. shift rail pin acess hole plugs into the transfer case with a punch and hammer.
8. Remove the two shift rail detent nuts and springs from the case. Use a magnet to remove the two detent balls.
9. Position both shift rails in neutral and remove the shift fork retaining roll pins with a long punch.
10. Remove the clevis pin from one shift rail and rail link.
11. Remove the range shift rail first, then the 4WD shift rail.
12. Remove the shift forks and and sliding clutch from the case. Remove the input shaft bearing retainer, bearing and shaft.
13. Remove the cup plugs and rail pins, if they were driven out, from the case.
14. Remove the locknut from the idler gear shaft.
15. Remove the idler gear shaft rear cover.
16. Remove the idler gear shaft, using a soft hammer and a drift.
17. Roll the idler gear assembly to the front output shaft hole and remove the assembly from the case.

Rear Output Shaft and Yoke

1. Loosen rear output shaft yoke nut.
2. Remove shaft housing bolts, then remove the housing and retainer assembly.
3. Remove retaining nut and yoke from the shaft, then remove the shaft assembly.
4. Remove and discard snap ring.

Removal of thrust washer, retainer pin and tanged bronze washer from the rear output shaft assembly on a New Process 205 (© International Harvester Company)

Rear output shaft assembly removed; removal of the bearing, spacer, and speedometer gear—New Process 205 (© International Harvester Company)

5. Remove thrust washer and pin.
6. Remove tanged bronze washer. Remove gear needle bearings, spacer and second row of needle bearings.

7. Remove tanged bronze thrust washer.
8. Remove pilot rollers, retainer ring and washer.
9. Remove oil seal retainer, ball bearing, speedometer gear and spacer. Discard gaskets.
10. Press out bearing.
11. Remove oil seal from the retainer.

Front Output Shaft

1. Remove lock nut, washer and yoke.
2. Remove attaching bolts and front bearing retainer.
3. Remove rear bearing retainer attaching bolts.
4. Tap output shaft with a soft-faced hammer and remove shaft, gear assembly and rear bearing retainer.
5. Remove sliding clutch, gear, washer and bearing from output high gear.

6. Remove sliding clutch from the high output gear; then remove gear, washer and bearing.
7. Remove gear retaining snapring from the shaft, using large snap-ring picks. Discard ring.
8. Remove thrust washer and pin.
9. Remove gear, needle bearings and spacer.
10. Replace rear bearing, if necessary.

CAUTION: Always replace the bearing and retainer as an assembly. Do not try to press a new bearing into an old retainer.

Shift Rails and Forks

1. Remove the two poppet nuts, springs, and using a magnet, the poppet balls.
2. Remove cup plugs on top of case, using a 1/4" punch.
3. Position both shift rails in neutral, then remove fork pins with a long handled screw extractor.
4. Remove clevis pins and shift rail link.
5. Lower shift rails; upper rail first and then lower.
6. Remove shift forks and sliding clutch.
7. Remove the front output high gear, washer and bearing. Remove the shift rail cup plugs.

Input Shaft

1. Remove snap-ring in front of bearing. Tap shaft out rear of case and bearing out front of case, using a soft-faced hammer or mallet.
2. Tilt case up on power take-off and remove the two interlock pins from inside.

Idler Gear

1. Remove idler gear shaft nut.
2. Remove rear cover.
3. Tap out idler gear shaft, using a soft-faced hammer and a drift approximately the same diameter as the shaft.
4. Remove idler gear through the front output shaft hole.
5. Remove two bearing cups from the idler gear.

Assembly

Transfer Case

1. Assemble the idler shaft gears, bearings, spacer and shims, and bearings on a dummy shaft tool and install the assembly into the case through the front output shaft bore, large end first.
2. Install the idler shaft from the large bore side, using a soft hammer to drive it through the bearings, spacer, gears, and shims.
3. Install a washer and new locknut on the end of the idler shaft. Check to make sure the idler

Removing the sliding clutch, front output high gear, washer and bearing— New Process 205 (© International Harvester Company)

gear rotates freely. Tighten the locknut to specification.
4. Install the idler shaft cover with a new gasket so the flat side faces the rear bearing retainer of the front output shaft. Install and tighten the two retaining screws to the proper torque.
5. Install the interlock pins into the interlock bore through the front of the output shaft opening.
6. Start the 4WD shift rail into the front of the case, solid end of the rail first, with the detent notches facing up.
7. Position the shift fork onto the shift rail with the long end facing inward. Push the rail through the fork and into the Neutral position.
8. Position the input shaft and bearing in the case.
9. Start the range shift rail into the case from the front, with the detent notches facing up.
10. Position the sliding clutch to the shift fork. Place the sliding clutch on the input shaft and align the fork with the shift rail. Push the rail through the fork into the Neutral position.
11. Install the roll pins that lock the shift forks to the shift rails with a long punch.
12. Position the front wheel drive high gear and its thrust washer in the case. Position the sliding clutch in the shift fork. Shift the rail and fork into the front wheel drive (4WD-Hi) position ,while at the same time, meshing the clutch with the mating teeth on the front wheel drive high gear.
13. Align the thrust washer, high gear and sliding clutch with the bearing bore in the case and insert the front output shaft and low gear into the high gear assembly.
14. Install a new seal in the front bearing retainer of the front output shaft, and install the bearing and retainer and new gasket in the case. Tighten the bearing retainer cap screws to the proper torque.

15. Lubricate the roller bearing in the front output shaft rear bearing retainer, which is the aluminum cover, and install it over the front output shaft and to the case. Install and tighten the retaining screws to the proper torque.
16. Move the range shift rail to the High position and install the rear output shaft and retainer assembly to the housing and input shaft. Use one or two new gaskets, as required, to adjust the clearance on the input shaft pilot. Install the rear output shaft housing retaining bolts and tighten them to specification.
17. Using a punch and sealing compound, install the shift rail pin access plugs.
18. Install the fill and drain plugs and the cross-link clevis pin.

Idler Gear

1. Press the two bearing cups in the idler gear.
2. Assemble the two bearing cones, spacer, shims and idler gear on a dummy shaft, with bore facing up. Check end-play.
3. Install idler gear assembly (with dummy shaft) into the case, large end first, through the front output shaft bore.
4. Install idler shaft from large bore side, driving it through with a soft-faced hammer or mallet.
5. Install washer and new locknut. Check for free rotation and measure end-play. Torque locknut to specifications.
6. Install idler shaft cover and new gasket. Torque cover bolts to specifications.

NOTE: Flat side of cover must be positioned towards front output shaft rear cover.

Shift Rails and Forks

1. Press the two rail seals into the case.

NOTE: Install seals with metal lip outward.
2. Install interlock pins from inside case.

3. Insert slotted end of front output drive shift rail (with poppet notches up) into back of case.
4. While pushing rail through to neutral position, install shift fork (long end inward).
5. Install input shaft and bearing into case.
6. Install end of range rail (with poppet notches up) into front of case.
7. Install sliding clutch on fork, then place over input shaft in case.
8. Push range rail, while engaging sliding clutch and fork, through to neutral position.
9. Drive new lockpins into forks through holes at top of case.
   NOTE: Tilt case on power take-off opening to install range rail lock-pin.

Front Output Shaft and Gear

1. Install two rows of needle bearings in the front low output gear and retain with grease.
   NOTE: Each row consists of 32 needle bearings and the two rows are separated by a spacer.
2. Position front output shaft in a soft-jaw vise, with spline end down. Place front low gear over shaft with clutch gear facing down; then install thrust washer pin, thrust washer and new snap-ring.
   NOTE: Position snap ring gap opposite the thrust washer pin.
3. Place front drive high gear and washer in case. Install sliding clutch in the shift fork, then put fork and rail into 4-High position, meshing front drive high gear and clutch teeth.
4. Align washer, high gear and sliding clutch and bearing bore. Insert front output shaft and

low gear assembly through the high gear assembly.
5. Install front output bearing and retainer with a new seal in the case.
6. Clean and grease rollers in front output rear bearing retainer. Install on case with one gasket and bolts coated with sealant. Torque bolts to specifications.
7. Install front output yoke, washer and locknut. Torque locknut to specifications.

Rear Output Shaft

1. Install two rows of needle bearings into the output low gear, retaining them with grease.
   NOTE: Each row consists of 32 needle bearings and the two rows are separated by a spacer.
2. Install thrust washer (with tang down in clutch gear groove) onto the rear output shaft.
3. Install output low gear onto shaft with clutch teeth facing downward.
4. Install thrust washer over gear with tab pointing up and away. Install washer pin.
5. Install large thrust washer over shaft and pin. Turn washer until tab fits into slot located approximately 90° away from pin.
6. Install snap-ring and measure shaft end-play.
7. Grease pilot bore and install needle bearings.
   NOTE: There are 15 pilot needle bearings.
8. Install thrust washer and new snap-ring in pilot bore.
9. Press new bearing into retainer housing.
10. Install housing on output shaft assembly.
11. Install spacer and speedometer gear. Install rear bearing.

12. Install rear bearing retainer seal.
13. Install bearing retainer assembly on housing, using one or two gaskets to achieve specified clearance. Torque attaching bolts to specifications.
14. Install yoke, washer and locknut on output shaft.
15. Position range rail in high, then install output shaft and retainer assembly on case. Torque housing bolts to specifications.

Case

1. Install power take-off cover and gasket. Torque attaching bolts to specifications.
2. Install cup plugs at rail pin holes.
   NOTE: After installing, seal the cup plugs.
3. Install drain and filler plugs. Torque to specifications.
4. Install shift rail cross link, clevis pins and lock pins.

Specifications

END PLAY

Idler Gear	0.000-0.002 in.
Rear Output Shaft	0.002-0.027 in.

TORQUE LIMITS (FT. LBS.)

Idler Shaft Locknut	150
Idler Shaft Cover	20
Front Output Shaft Front Bearing Retainer	30-35
Front Output Shaft Yoke Locknut	130-150
Rear Output Shaft Bearing Retainer and Housing	30-35
Rear Output Shaft Yoke Locknut	130-150
P.T.O. Cover	15
Front Output Shaft Rear Bearing Retainer	30-35
Filler and Drain Plugs	30
Case to Frame	130
Case to Adapter	25
Adapter Mount	75
Case Bracket to Frame Upper	30
Lower	65
Adapter to Transmission Manual Transmission	30-35
Automatic Transmission	30-35

Spicer Model 20

Description

The Spicer Model 20 transfer case is essentially a two-speed gear box located at the rear of the standard transmission, which provides low and direct gear ranges. It also provides a means of connecting the power to the front axle.

Disassembly

1. Remove cover and gasket from bottom of transfer case.
2. Remove the front drive shift bar poppet spring access hole plugs from front output shaft bearing retainer. If necessary to remove shift bar lock plungers, remove the two expansion plugs from the housing.

3. Remove the idler gear shaft lock plate bolt and lock plate from rear of transfer case.
4. Using a hammer and brass drift, remove idler gear shaft, driving from the front end of the transfer case (opposite slotted end of shaft). As shaft passes thrust washers, remove washers. Remove idler gear with bearings and spacers as a sub-assembly. Remove bearings and spacer from bore of idler gear.
5. Remove end yoke retaining lock nuts from the front and rear output shafts. Using a suitable puller, remove the end yokes from both shafts.
6. Remove steady springs from shift levers. Remove setscrew

securing shift lever pivot pin. Remove pin and lift out each lever as it is freed.
7. Remove socket-head setscrew from underdrive shift fork.
8. Move underdrive shift fork and rear output shaft sliding gear forward far enough for gear to clear splines on rear output shaft. Swing fork and gear toward cover opening and lift out gear.
9. Remove rear output shaft bearing retainer and output shaft as an assembly.
10. Remove front output shaft rear cover and shims. Tag shims for reassembly.
11. Remove socket-head setscrew from front wheel drive shift fork.

1. Output shaft oil seal (felt)
2. Control link
3. ⅝ in. hose
4. Transfer case control guide
5. Lever end ball
6. Shift bar oil seal

24. Front output shaft cone bearing
25. Front output shaft cup bearing
26. Bearing adjusting shim
27. Front output shaft bearing cover
28. Transfer case breather
29. Companion flange nut
30. Companion flange nut washer

7. Transfer case control lever
8. Shift lever handle
9. Pivot pin lubricator
10. Shift lever pivot pin
11. Front output shaft bearing retainer
12. Shift bar poppet ball spring
13. Poppet spring plug
14. Shift bar poppet ⅜ in. ball
15. Front output shaft bearing retainer gasket
16. End rod pin
17. Shift bar lock plunger
18. Front drive shift bar
19. Underdrive shift bar
20. Transfer case (filler) plug
21. Transfer case
22. Shift fork bar dust cup
23. Front output shaft

31. Rear output shaft rear cone bearing
32. Rear output shaft rear cup bearing
33. Bearing adjust shim
34. Speedometer drive gear
35. Rear output shaft bearing retainer
36. Rear output shaft bearing gasket
37. Rear output shaft front cup bearing
38. Rear output shaft front cone bearing

39. Rear output shaft
40. Idle gear shift lock
41. Idler gear thrust washer
42. Idler gear shaft
43. Transfer case-to-transmission gasket
44. Idler gear bearing spacer
45. Low speed shift fork
46. Shift fork set screw
47. Front wheel drive shift fork
48. Front sliding gear
49. Front output driven gear
50. Front output driven gear thrust washer
51. Front output shaft bearing snap ring
52. Idler gear
53. Idler gear bearing
54. Main drive gear
55. Rear sliding gear
56. Bottom cover gasket
57. Bottom case cover
58. Drain plug

Exploded view of a Spicer 20 transfer case. This model has single lever control. Some models in I.H. trucks have dual lever control. Spicer 20 models installed in Jeep vehicles have a slightly different single lever control mechanism. (© International Harvester Company)

12. Remove front output shaft bearing retainer with shift bars and gasket.
13. Pull forward on front output shaft as far as possible to permit removal of bearing cup. Remove bearing cone from front output shaft, using suitable puller.
14. Remove front output shaft bearing snap-ring. Using a soft-faced hammer, tap on front end of output shaft and remove it from the rear side of housing. Take out driven gear and sliding gear with shift fork as shaft is withdrawn.
15. Remove shift bars from retainer.

CAUTION: Be sure the poppet balls and springs are secured when withdrawing shift bars. This will prevent possible personal injury.

16. Remove shift bar oil seals.
17. Remove speedometer driven gear.
18. Support inner face of bearing retainer on an arbor press and press output shaft from retainer.
19. Remove oil seal from retainer bore.

20. Remove tapered bearing cone and cup from rear bore of retainer. Remove tapered bearing cup from front bore. Remove O-ring seal.
21. Using a suitable puller, remove bearing cone from output shaft. Remove shims from shaft and tie together before laying aside. Remove speedometer drive gear.
22. Using a puller, remove bearing cone from front output shaft.

Assembly

1. Press bearing cone on rear end of front output shaft.
2. Install speedometer drive gear, shims and bearing cone on output shaft.
3. Position new O-ring seal in bore of rear output shaft bearing retainer. Install tapered bearing cup in front bore of retainer. Install other tapered bearing cup in rear bore of bearing retainer.
4. Place rear output shaft into bearing retainer and support shaft in an arbor press. Position bearing cone over end of shaft

and using an adapter slightly larger in diameter than the shaft, press bearing cone on shaft. Locate rear output shaft bearing retainer assembly in a fixed position. Set up a dial indicator and check shaft end-play. Add or remove shims between speedometer drive gear and rear bearing cone to bring end-play within specifications.

NOTE: It is very important to set end-play correctly, since it controls the seating of the tapered bearings. Incorrect endplay will shorten the life of bearings.

5. Install new oil seal in rear bore of bearing retainer, using proper adapter.
6. Install speedometer driven gear.
7. Using an adapter of correct size, install shift bar oil seals in front output shaft bearing retainer.
8. Install poppet springs and balls into bearing retainer.

NOTE: make certain that the heavier loaded spring is installed for the front drive shift bar.

9. Depress poppet balls and insert shift bars into front output shaft bearing retainer.

NOTE: Be sure when installing shift bars that the seal lips are not damaged.

10. Start front output shaft into transfer case from rear. As shaft emerges inside of case, sliding gear with shift fork and front output driven gear can be installed. Hold shaft in position and install bearing cup in rear bore of case. Install front output shaft bearing snap-ring.

11. Support rear end of front output shaft and using an adapter of correct diameter, tap bearing cone onto front end of shaft. With shaft held in position, install bearing cup in front bore of case.

12. Using a new gasket, install front output shaft bearing retainer with shift bars on front of transfer case.

13. Install socket-head setscrew in front wheel drive shift fork.

14. Install shims and front output shaft rear cover on case. Secure with bolts and torque to specifications. Set up a dial indicator at front end of front output

shaft and check end-play. Add or remove shims under rear cover to meet specifications.

NOTE: It is essential to set end-play within specifications, since it controls seating of the tapered bearings. Improper end-play can shorten life of bearings.

15. Install rear output shaft bearing retainer and output shaft as an assembly. Secure with bolts and tighten to specifications.

16. Place rear output shaft sliding gear in underdrive shift fork. Swing fork and gear into case until gear can be positioned on rear output shaft.

17. Install socket-head setscrew in underdrive shift fork.

18. Position shift levers in front output shaft bearing retainer and install shift lever pivot pin. Install pivot pin retaining bolt. Install steady springs on shift levers.

19. Install end yokes on front and rear output shafts and secure with retaining lock nuts.

20. Install spacers and bearings in bore of idler gear. Position idler gear and thrust washers in transfer case. Insert idler shaft into rear of case until slot is

flush with case face. Install lock plate and secure with retaining bolt. Tighten to specifications.

21. Install shift bar lock plungers and expansion plugs. Install shift bar poppet spring access hole plugs.

22. Position new gasket on bottom of transfer case and install cover. Secure with bolts and tighten to specifications.

Specifications
END PLAY
Rear Output Shaft ....0.003-0.005 in.
Front Output Shaft ....0.000-0.001 in.

BALL POPPET SPRING
Free Length
  Red ....1.028 in.
  Yellow ....1.078 in.
Pressure @ Test Length
  Red @ 59/64 in. ....26 Lbs.
  Yellow @ 49/64 in. ....12 Lbs.

TORQUE LIMITS (FT. LBS.)
Rear Output Shaft Bearing
  Retainer 25-32
Front Output Shaft Rear Bearing
  Cover 25-32
Front Output Shaft Front
  Bearing Retainer 25-32
Bottom Cover 10-15
Idler Shaft Lock Bolt 12-17
Companion Flange Nut 225-300

New Process Model 203 (Full Time Four Wheel Drive)

Description
The New Process Model 203 transfer case is a full-time 4WD unit that operates in 4WD at all times. The unit incorporates a differential similar to axle differentials; compensating for different speeds of the front and rear axles resulting from varying speeds while turning and operating over different surfaces.

There are five shift positions with this transfer case; Neutral, High and High Lock, and Low and Low Lock. The Lock positions are used under low traction conditions. In the Lock position, the differential action of the transfer case is eliminated, by locking the front and rear output shafts together. In this mode, neither the front or rear axle can rotate independently of the other.

Disassembly
1. Loosen rear output shaft flange retaining nut and remove front output shaft flange and washer.
2. Tap the front output shaft dust seal away from case assembly. Remove front output shaft bearing retainer and gasket.
3. Position transfer case assembly on blocks with input shaft facing downward.

Removing the rear output shaft. The differential carrier assembly is removed next— New Process 203 (© Ford Motor Company)

4. Remove rear output shaft assembly from transfer case. Slide the differential carrier off the shaft.
5. Place a 1½ in. to 2 in. band type hose clamp on input shaft to retain bearings.
6. Lift shift rail and driveout pin retaining shift fork.
7. Remove shift rail poppet ball plug, gasket and ball from case. Use a magnet to remove poppet ball.

8. Push shift rail down, lift up on lockout clutch and remove shift fork from clutch assembly.
9. Remove front output shaft rear bearing retainer. It may be necessary to gently tap front of shaft or cautiously pry retainer from case. Make certain that no roller bearings are lost from rear cover.
10. When necessary, remove rear bearing by pressing.
11. Pry front output shaft front bearing from lower side of case.
12. Remove front otuput shaft assembly from case.
13. Lift intermediate housing from range box, after removing bolts.
14. Remove chain from intermediate housing.

Driving the pin retaining the shift fork to the shift rail in a New Process 203 (© Ford Motor Company)

Place a hose clamp around the end of the input shaft to prevent losing the 123 roller bearings out of the clutch assembly—New Process 203 (© Ford Motor Company)

15. Remove lockout clutch, drive gear and input shaft from range box.
16. Install a 1½" to 2" band type hose clamp on end of input shaft to retain roller bearings.
17. Pull up on shift rail and remove rail from link.
18. Lift input shaft assembly from range box.

Assembly

1. Position range box with input gear side down, on wood blocks.

Disengaging the shift rail from the lockout connecting link in a New Process 203 (© Ford Motor Company)

2. Place gasket on input housing.
3. Install lockout clutch and drive sprocket on input shaft assembly. Install a 2" band type hose clamp on end of input shaft to prevent loss of bearings during installation.
4. Place input shaft, lockout clutch and drive sprocket in range box. Align tab on bearing retainer with notch in gasket.
5. Engage lockout clutch shift rail to the connector link. Position rail in housing bore and turn shifter shaft lowering rail into the housing. This will prevent the link and rail from becoming disconnected.
6. Place the drive chain in housing with the chain around the outer wall.

7. Secure the chain housing to the range box. Be sure that the shift rail engages the channel of the housing. Place the chain on the input drive sprocket.
8. Place the front output sprocket in transfer case. Turn the clutch drive gear to assist in positioning chain on sprocket.
9. Position the shift fork and rail on the clutch assembly. Install the clutch assembly completely into the drive sprocket. Insert retaining pin in shift fork and rail.
10. Install front output bearing, gasket, retainer, bolts, flange, gasket, seal, washer and retaining nut.
11. If rear bearing was removed from front output shaft, press a new bearing into the outside face of cover until bearing is flush with opening.
12. Install front output shaft, rear bearing retainer, gasket and bolts.
13. Slip differential carrier assembly on the input shaft. Bolts on carrier must face rear of shaft.
14. Load bearings in pinion shaft, install rear output housing assembly, gasket and bolts.
15. Install a dial indicator on the rear housing. The indicator must contact the end of the output shaft. While holding the rear flange, rotate the front output

Exploded view of the New Process 203 full-time 4WD transfer case (© Ford Motor Company)

shaft and find the highest point of gear hop. Reset indicator and with rear output shaft at high point, pull up on the end of the shaft to determine end play. Remove indicator and install shim pack to control end play to between 0 and .005″. The shim pack is positioned on the shaft in front of the rear bearing. Check for binding of rear output shaft.

16. Insert lockout clutch shift rail poppet ball, spring and screw plug in transfer case.
17. Install poppet plate spring, gasket and plug, if they were not previously installed.
18. Install shift levers on the range box, if these were not left on vehicle.
19. Torque all bolts, locknuts and plugs to specifications.
20. Fill transfer case with specified lubricant until the proper level is reached. Secure filler plug.

Transfer Case Subassemblies Overhaul

Lockout Clutch Assembly

Disassembly

1. Remove front side gear from input shaft assembly.
2. Remove thrust washer, roller bearings and spacers from front side gear bore. The position of the spacers must be noted.
3. Remove the snap ring which holds the drive sprocket to clutch assembly. Slip the drive sprocket from the front side gear.
4. Remove the lower snap ring.
5. Remove sliding gear, spring and spring cup washer from the front side gear.
6. Throughly clean and inspect all component parts. Replace any component that is worn or defective.

Assembly

1. Place spring cup washer, spring and sliding clutch gear on front side gear.
2. Secure sliding clutch to front side gear with a snap ring.
3. Spread petroleum jelly on front side gear and install roller bearings and spacers.
4. Place thrust washer in gear end of front side gear.
5. Slide drive sprocket on clutch splines and secure with snap ring.

Differential Carrier Assembly

Disassembly

1. Separate differential carrier sections and lift out pinion gear and spider assembly.
2. Note that undercut side of pinion gear spider faces toward front of side gear.

3. Remove pinion thrust washers, pinion roller washer gears and roller bearings from spider unit.
4. Throughly clean and inspect all component parts. Replace any component that is worn or damaged.

Assembly

1. Spread petroleum jelly on pinion gears and install roller bearings.
2. Position on the leg of each spider, pinion roller washer, pinion gear and thrust washer.
3. Position the spider assembly in front half of the carrier. The undercut surface of the spider thrust surface face downward or toward teeth.
4. Secure carrier halves together. Make certain the marks are aligned. Torque all bolts to specifications.

Input Shaft Assembly

Disassembly

1. Remove thrust washer and spacer from shaft.
2. Remove bearing retainer assembly from input shaft.
3. Hold low speed gear and lightly tap shaft from gear. Note the position of the thrust washer pins in input shaft.
4. Remove snap ring holding input bearing in retainer using a screw driver. Lightly tap rear bearing out of retainer.
5. Remove pilot roller bearing and 'O' ring from end of input shaft.
6. Throughly clean and inspect all component parts. Replace any component that is worn or damaged.

Assembly

1. Tap or press input bearing into retainer. Be sure that ball loading slots are toward concave side of retainer. Install securing snap ring. Make certain that selective snap ring of proper thickness is used to provide tightest fit.
2. Position low speed gear on shaft, clutch end facing gear end of input shaft.
3. Place thrust washers on input shaft, align slot in washer with pin in shaft. Slide or tap washers into position.
4. Place input bearing retainer on shaft and secure with snap ring. Snap rings are selective. Use snap ring that provides tightest fit.
5. Slip spacer and thrust washer on shaft and align with locating pin.
6. Spread heavy grease on end of shaft and install roller bearings.
7. Install rubber 'O' ring at end of shaft.

Range Box

Disassembly

1. Remove poppet plate spring, plug and gasket.
2. Remove clutch fork and sliding gear by disengaging sliding clutch gear from input gear.
3. Remove upper shift lever from shifter shaft.
4. Remove snap ring and lower shift lever.
5. Push shifter shaft assembly down and remove lockout clutch connector link. The long end of connector link engages poppet plate.
6. Remove shifter shaft assembly and separate shafts. Remove 'O' rings.
7. When necessary to remove poppet plate, drive pivot shaft out and remove plate and spring from bottom of case.
8. Remove input gear bearing retainer and seal assembly. Release snap ring from retainer and tap bearing out of assembly.
9. Release snap ring holding input shaft bearing to shaft and remove bearing.
10. Remove countershaft from cluster gear and case assembly from intermediate case side. Remove cluster gear assembly from range box.
11. Remove cluster gear thrust washers from case.
12. Thoroughly clean and inspect all component parts. Replace any component that is worn or damaged.

Assembly

1. Spread heavy grease in cluster bore and using proper tool install roller bearings and spacers.
2. Spread heavy grease on case and install thrust washers. Engage tab on thrust washers with slot in case.
3. Place cluster gear assembly in case and install countershaft through front of range box and into gear assembly. Flat face of countershaft must be aligned with case gasket.
4. Place bearing on input gear shaft with snap ring groove facing out, install a new retaining ring. Insert input gear and bearing in housing. The retaining ring used in this operation is a select fit. Use ring that provides the tightest fit.
5. Secure input gear and bearing with a snap ring.
6. Match up oil slot in retainer with drain hole in case and insert input gear bearing retainer and gaskets. Install bolts and torque to specifications.
7. Spread sealant on pin and install poppet pin and pivot pin in housing.

Transfer Cases

8. Lubricate and install new 'O' rings on inner and outer shifter shafts.
9. Insert shifter shafts in housing and engage long end of lockout clutch connector link with outer shifter shaft. Complete this operation before assembly bottoms out.
10. Install lower shift lever and retaining ring.
11. Install upper shift lever and shaft retaining nut.
12. Install shift fork and sliding clutch gear. Push fork up into shifter shaft and engage poppet plate. Move sliding clutch gear onto input shaft gear.
13. Insert poppet plate spring, gasket and plug in housing top. Make certain that spring engages poppet plate.

Input Gear Bearing

Replacement

1. Remove bearing retainer and gasket from housing.
2. Remove and discard snap ring holding bearing in retainer.
3. Pry bearing from case and remove from shaft.
4. Inspect input gear and bearing retainer for damage or wear. Replace if necessary.
5. Place new bearing and snap ring on input gear. Using a soft hammer, tap bearing into position. Secure snap ring.
6. Insert bearing retainer into housing and secure with attaching bolts. Tighten bolts to specifications.

Input Gear Retainer Seal

Replacement

1. Remove bearing retainer from housing.
2. Remove seal from retainer by prying.
3. Place new seal on retainer and install with proper seal driver.
4. Install bearing retainer in housing and secure with attaching bolts. Tighten bolts to specifications.

Rear Output Shaft Housing Assembly

Disassembly

1. Remove speedometer driven gear from housing.
2. Remove rear output flange and washer, if they have not been removed previously.
3. Using a soft hammer tap on flange end of pinion and remove the pinion. If speedometer drive gear does not come off with pinion reach into case and remove.
4. Remove old seal from bore with suitable prying tool.
5. Remove snap ring retaining rear output rear bearing.
6. Tap bearing out of housing.
7. Install a long drift into rear opening of housing and drive out front output bearing. Remove seal and discard.

Assembly

1. Spread grease on front bearing seal and place in bore. Place bearing in bore and press until it bottoms in housing.
2. Using a soft hammer tap rear bearing into place. Secure with proper snap ring. Snap rings are selective, use the one that provides the tightest fit.
3. Place rear seal in bore and drive into position with suitable tool. When seal is in position it should be approximately 1/8" to 3/16" below housing face.
4. Place speedometer drive gear on output shaft with shims of approximately .050" thickness. Insert output shaft into carrier through housing front opening.
5. Install flange and washer on output shaft. Leave retaining nut loose until shim requirements are known.
6. Install speedometer driven gear.

Front Output Shaft Bearing Retainer Seal

Replacement

1. Remove old seal from retainer bore.

Warner Quadra-Trac

Description

The Quadra-Trac transfer case provides full-time, four-wheel drive under all driving conditions. The front and rear driveshafts are driven by a limited slip differential in the transfer case. The limited slip differential is connected to the input shaft by a link-belt type chain. In operation, if the rear axle loses traction, then the engine torque will be transfered through the transfer case differential to the front axle.

The transfer case contains a manually actuated lockout system that locks the front and rear driveshafts together, cancelling the differential action. This feature is used under extreme marginal traction situations.

NOTE: In order to spare the transfer case differential side gears and brake cones from excessive, and possibly, damaging wear, do not spin the wheels excessively when the vehicle is stuck or bogged down.

An optional gear reduction unit mounted at the rear of the input shaft is available for the Quadra-Trac unit, making it a two-speed transfer case.

2. Inspect and clean retainer.
3. Spread sealer on outer edge of new seal.
4. Place new seal in retainer bore and drive into position with proper tool.

Front Output Bearing

Replacement

1. Remove rear cover from case assembly and discard gasket.
2. Press old bearing from cover.
3. Place new bearing on outside face of cover. Cover bearing with a wood block and press into cover until bearing is flush with opening.
4. Place gasket on transfer case and tap cover into position using a soft hammer. Secure cover with attaching bolts and tighten to specifications.

Torque Specifications (Ft Lbs)

Adapter to Transfer Case Bolts	38
Adapter to Transmission Bolts	40
Transfer Case to Frame Nuts (Upper)	50
Transfer Case to Frame Nuts (Lower)	65
Shift Lever Attaching Nuts	25
Shift Lever Rod Swivel Locknuts	50
Shift Lever Locking Arm Nut	150 in. lbs.
Skid Plate Bolt Retaining Nuts	45
Crossmember Bolt Retaining Nuts	45
Adapter Mount Bolts	25
Intermediate Case to Range Box Bolts	30
Front Output Bearing Retainer Bolts	30
Output Shaft Yoke Nuts	150
Front Output Rear Bearing Retainer Bolts	30
Differential Assembly Screws	45
Rear Output Shaft Housing	30
Poppet Ball Retainer Nut	15
PTO Cover Bolts	15
Front Input Bearing Retainer Bolts	20
Filler Plug	25

Performance Checks
Transfer Case Differential Torque Bias Check

1. With the lock-out feature *not* engaged and the transmission in Park, raise the vehicle until the front wheels are free of the ground.
2. Disconnect the rear driveshaft from the transfer case.
3. Turn the rear yoke retaining nut with a torque wrench and socket, taking note of how much torque

1086

Exploded view of the Warner Quadra-Trac without the optional reduction unit
(© Jeep Corporation)

Exploded view of the optional reduction unit for a Warner Quadra-Trac transfer case (© Jeep Corporation)

is required to force the cone clutches to slip. They should slip when 110 to 270 ft. lbs. are applied.

Slippage below 110 ft. lbs. indicates replacement of the differential is needed. If no slippage occurs at 270 ft. lbs., improper lubrication is indicated. Drain and refill the transfer case and reduction unit, if so equipped, with the proper lubricant mixture.

Drive Chain Tension Check

1. Drain the lubricant from the transfer case.
2. Remove the chain inspection plug and insert a steel rule into the hole.
3. A new chain will be 1.575 in. from the outer edge of the plug hole. When the slack in the chain reaches 1/2-3/4 in., the chain should be replaced. No adjustment is possible.
4. Reinstall the drain and chain inspection plugs, and refill the unit with the proper lubricant mixture.

Rear Case Cover

Removal

Most Quadra-Trac components can be serviced without removing the complete unit from the vehicle. To gain access to the rear output shaft, drive sprocket and thrust washer, chain, differential and needle bearing, or the diaphragm control system, just the rear cover has to be removed.

1. Lift and support the vehicle.
2. If the vehicle is equipped with a reduction unit, continue on to the next step for the reduction unit removal procedure. If the vehicle is not equipped with a reduction unit, proceed to Step 7.
3. Loosen all the bolts that attach the reduction unit to the transfer case cover.
4. Move the reduction unit backward just enough to allow the oil to drain from the unit.
5. Loosen the cable retaining bolt at the shift control lever. Loosen the cable clamp bolt and remove the control cable from the clamp bracket and control lever.
6. When the oil has drained, remove the bolts which hold the reduction unit to the transfer case cover. Move the reduction unit rearward to clear the transmission output shaft and pinion cage which is attached to the transfer case drive sprocket. The pinion cage will remain with the transfer case assembly.

NOTE: The pinion cage should not be removed if the transfer case cover assembly is to be removed, but may be removed for inspection or replacement if the transfer case cover assembly is to remain in the vehicle. Removal of the pinion cage involves only removing the snap-ring which holds the cage to the sprocket and sliding the cage backward.

7. Remove the transfer case drain plug and allow the unit to drain.
8. Mark the rear output shaft yoke and universal joint to provide an alignment reference during reassembly. Disconnect the rear drive shaft front universal joint from the transfer case rear yoke.
9. Mark the diaphragm control vacuum hoses for identification during reassembly, then disconnect them. Also remove the lock-up indicator switch wire and the speedometer cable. Remove the indicator switch.
10. Disconnect the parking brake cable guide from the pivot on the right frame side.
11. Remove the bolts which attach the case cover assembly to the case (front housing). Carefully slide the cover assembly backward off the front output shaft and the transmission output shaft.

Disassembly

1. To disassemble the unit, remove the rear output shaft yoke.
2. If the unit is *not* equipped with a reduction unit, remove the power take-off cover from the rear of the transfer case cover. Remove the sealing ring from the transfer case cover.
3. Using a piece of wood 2 in. × 4 in. and 6 in. long, support the cover and drive sprocket.
4. If *not* equipped with a reduction unit, remove the drive hub and sleeve from the drive sprocket rear splines by expanding the internal snap-ring. The ring expanding tabs are accessible through a slot in the outside edge of the drive sleeve.
5. If equipped with a reduction unit, remove the pinion cage snap ring and carrier.
6. Lift the case cover from the drive sprocket and differential. The cover, rear output shaft, bearings and seal, drive sprocket rear needle bearing, and lock-up hub can now be serviced without any further disassembly of other components.
7. Slide the drive sprocket toward the differential unit and remove the chain. The differential unit may now be serviced without any further disassembly of other components.

Assembly

1. Position the drive sprocket on a block of wood 2 in. × 4 in. and 6 in. long.
2. Place the differential assembly about 2 in. from the drive sprocket and with the front end of the differential on the bench.
3. Position the drive chain around the drive sprocket and the differential assembly. Be sure that the chain is properly engaged with the sprocket and differential teeth and that the slack is removed from the chain.
4. Insert the rear output shaft into the differential.
5. Shift the lock-up hub rearward in the case cover. Lubricate the drive sprocket thrust washer and insert it in position on the case cover.
6. Carefully align the case cover and position it onto the drive sprocket and differential. The output shaft may have to be slightly rotated to align it with the lock-up hub. Be sure that the drive sprocket thrust washer stays positioned correctly.
7. If equipped with a reduction unit, install the pinion cage onto the drive sprocket rear splines. Install the snap-ring. Be sure that the snap-ring seats properly in the groove.
8. If the vehicle is *not* equipped

The differential and drive sprocket positioned for installation of the drive chain —Warner Quadra-Trac (© Jeep Corporation)

The Quadra-Trac transfer case positioned for disassembly (© Jeep Corporation)

with a reduction unit, assemble the drive hub, drive sleeve, and snap-ring, then install them onto the drive sprocket rear splines. Be sure the snap-ring seats properly.

9. Turn the drive sleeve or pinion cage to make sure the drive sprocket thrust washer did not come out of position. No binding should be present.

10. If *not* equipped with a reduction unit, install the power take-off sealing ring and cover and tighten the attaching screws.

11. Install the speedometer gear on the rear output shaft.

12. Install the rear output shaft oil seal and the rear yoke and nut. Tighten the nut to specification.

Installation

13. Clean the groove which the front oil seal gasket fits into and install the seal.

14. Install two ⅜ in. 16 × 2 in. long pilot studs into the transfer case front cover housing.

15. On 1973-74 models only, insert the oil tube into the case bore at the front output shaft bearing boss. Insert a 6 in. length of 5/16 in. rod into the tube. The rod will be used as a pilot to align the tube with the case cover. Lift the cover assembly and align the tube pilot with the hole in the cover. Move the assembly forward over the pilot studs.

16. Move the cover assembly forward to mesh with the front output shaft and transmission output shaft. It may be necessary to rotate the rear output shaft slightly to allow the two sets of splines to engage.

17. After the cover assembly has been moved forward and is evenly touching the front half of the case, remove the pilot studs and install the rear cover attaching bolts. Tighten the bolts alternately and evenly to specifications.

18. Install the lock out indicator switch and connect the lock out switch wire, diaphragm control vacuum hoses, and the speedometer cable.

19. Install the rear drive shaft.

20. Install the parking brake cable guide to the pivot on the right frame side.

21. Install the reduction unit, if so equipped as follows:

22. Position the reduction unit to the transfer case and mesh the caged pinions with the sun gear and ring gear, and align the sun gear inner splines with the transmission output shaft splines.

23. Move the reduction unit forward until it touches the sealing ring.

24. Install the attaching screws loosely, then tighten them alternately to specification.

25. Connect the shift control cable and adjust it by first removing the swivel block from the control lever. Move the control lever to the most forward position. Thread the swivel block in or out on the cable end to obtain the correct length to fit the swivel block in the control lever.

26. Install the proper type and amount of lubricant and lower the vehicle.

NOTE: Use 8 oz. of Jeep Lubricant Concentrate Part No. 8123004 or 5356068 or Lubrizol® 762 (there is no substitute) mixed with SAE 30 non-detergent motor oil (Valvoline preferred). 3.5 pints of the mixture is required to fill the transfer case without a reduction unit, 4.5 pints with a reduction unit.

Differential Assembly

Disassembly

1. Mark end caps and case sprocket with paint. Marks must be used to identify front end cap, rear end cap and proper orientation of caps to case sprocket.

2. Remove front end cap. If necessary, tap gently with a soft hammer.

3. Remove thrust washer, preload springs, brake cone and side gears from case sprocket. Care must be taken to keep the various pieces together as they must be installed as a unit.

4. Invert the case sprocket and remove rear cap. If necessary, tap gently with a soft hammer.

5. Remove the thrust washers, preload springs, brake cone and side gears. Care must be taken to keep the various pieces together as they must be installed as a unit.

6. Raise the case sprocket. The pinion shaft lock pin should fall out. If the pin does not fall, drive the pin out with a ¼ in. pin punch.

7. Drive the pinion mate shaft out of case sprocket, using a brass drift and hammer. Care must be taken to avoid damaging the pinion mate thrust washers.

8. Thoroughly clean and inspect all component parts. Replace any damaged or worn parts with a complete matched set.

Assembly

Prelubricate all bearings and thrust surfaces with Jeep Lubricant Concentrate Part No. 8123004 or 5356068 or Lubrizol 762 (there is no substitute) prior to installation.

1. Slide the pinion mate shaft in the case sprocket three inches.

2. Install the pinion mate thrust washers and gears on shaft in the proper order.

3. Align the pinion mate shaft lockpin hole with hole in case sprocket. Lightly drive the pinion mate shaft into case sprocket until lockpin holes are exactly aligned.

4. Move the pinion mate gears apart until the gears are press-

Mark the end caps and case sprocket of the differential assembly before disassembling the differential—Warner Quadra-Trac
(© Jeep Corporation)

Matched Front Set   Matched Rear Set

Front End Cap | Small Thrust Washer | Preload Springs | Large Thrust Washer | Brake Cone | Side Gear | Case Sprocket | Side Gear | Brake Cone | Large Thrust Washer | Preload Springs | Small Thrust Washer | Rear End Cap

Exploded view of the differential assembly—Warner Quadra-Trac
(© Jeep Corporation)

Transfer Cases

ing the washers against the case sprocket.

5. Engage the pinion mate gear with the front side gears. Insert the brake cone over the gear and in case sprocket. Install the large thrust washer and preload springs, concave side of springs facing toward brake cone.
6. Lubricate the small thrust washer and place it on the front end cap. Install the front end cap, secure with attaching screws and alternately tighten to proper torque. Make certain that alignment marks are in order.
7. Invert the case sprocket and end cap and install the pinion shaft lock pin.
8. Mesh remaining side gear with pinion mate gears.
9. Insert the remaining brake cone over the side gear. Install the large thrust washer and preload spring, concave side of springs facing toward brake cone.
10. Lubricate the small thrust washer and place it on the rear end cap. Install the rear cap, tighten attaching screws finger tight.
11. Insert the front and rear output shafts in the differential and rotate until both shafts have aligned with the splines on the brake cones and side gears. Alternately tighten the retaining screws to proper torque.

Torque Specifications (Ft Lbs)

Transfer Case
Breather 6-10
Chain Measuring Access
  Hole Plug 6-14
Drain Plug 15-25
Fill Plug 15-25
Lock-Up Cover to
  Transfer Case 8-10
Lock-Out Indicator Switch . . .10-15
Output Shaft Nut 90-150
PTO Cover to Transfer Case
  bolts: 3/8 in.-16 15-25
  5/16 in.-18 10-20
Speedometer Adapter 20-30
Transfer Case Cover to
  Transfer Case 15-25
Transfer Case to Transmission
  Extension Bolt 30-50
Reduction Unit
Cable Housing Clamp Nut 7-12
Fill Plug 15-25

Shift Lever Cable
  Clamp Nut 10-20
Shift Lever to Shift Nut 15-25
Reduction PTO Cover
  to Case 15-25
Reduction Unit to Transfer
  Case Bolts: 3/8 in.-16 15-25
              5/16 in.-18 8-10

Diaphragm Control, Shift Fork and Lock-Up Hub

Disassembly

1. Remove the vent cover and seal ring.
2. Remove the retaining rings positioning the shift fork on diaphragm. Carefully pry the shift fork forward to gain access to the retaining rings. Remove the spring with a magnet.
3. Caution must be exercised in removal of the diaphragm control rod as it is retained by a spring loaded detent ball. Insert a magnet into the hole to hold the detent ball. Slip the diaphragm control rod out of case. Remove detent ball and spring.
4. Remove shifting fork, plastic shifting shoes and lock-up hub.

Assembly

1. Lubricate the shifting shoes and place them in the shift fork.
2. Install the shift fork and lock-up hub assembly in the case cover, long end of shift fork first (toward rear). Make certain that the shift fork does not separate from the lock-up hub by reaching through the needle bearings.
3. Insert the diaphragm control rod in the case and shifting fork, stopping before the detent ball hole is reached.
4. Install the detent ball and spring. Depress the detent ball with a 1/4 in. pin punch and slide the diaphragm control rod into place.
5. Install the shift fork retaining pin, (clips) and the diaphragm retaining spring, the spring should be below the surface of the bore.
6. Install the vent cover and seal ring.

Reduction Unit

Disassembly

1. Remove PTO cover and gasket.
2. Remove snap ring from reduction main shaft rear end, slide the reduction main shaft and sun gear assembly forward and out. Remove needle bearings.
3. Remove as an assembly, the ring gear, reduction collar plate, pinion cage lock plate, shift collar hub and reduction collar hub. Using a soft hammer, remove the shift collar hub from the pinion cage lock plate.
4. Remove the pinion cage lock plate, needle bearing, ring gear, reduction collar plate and shift collar hub. Separate the reduction collar hub and needle bearing from shift collar hub.
5. When necessary, separate the reduction collar plate and ring gear by removing retaining snap ring.
6. Remove needle bearing and direct drive sleeve from the reduction shift collar.
7. Shift the reduction shift collar to the neutral (center) detent with the control lever. Disengage the shift fork. Place the shift in the direct drive detent position (rear), align the collar outer teeth with the inner teeth in the reduction holding plate. Place the fork and collar in the reduction position (front) detent, and remove the reduction shift collar.
8. Remove the annular bearing rear snap ring and bearing.
9. Remove the shift fork locating spring pin, large expansion plug, shift rail taper plug, and control lever.
10. Drive the spring pin out of the shift fork and rail with a 3/16 in. pin punch. Slide the shift rail forward out of the shift fork, and remove the shift fork. Remove the spring shift fork poppet ball. Drive the poppet taper plug into the shift rail bore and remove the plug and spring.
11. Remove the shift lever retaining pin and the shift lever assembly.
12. Remove the reduction holding

Removing the diaphragm control rod—Warner Quadra-Trac (© Jeep Corporation)

Install the lock-up hub assembly shift fork with the long side of the fork facing toward the rear—Warner Quadra-Trac (© Jeep Corporation)

plate snap ring and reduction holding plate.

Assembly

1. Align the shift fork locating spring holes in the reduction holding plate and housing. Install the reduction holding plate. Locating pins should index the plate in the case. Secure the plate with a snap ring, tabs facing forward.
2. Install the shift lever assembly into the housing, lever towards the rear. Position seal ring on groove in shift lever shaft.
3. Move the shift lever assembly inward and install taper pin.
4. Install the shift rail in the shift rail rear bore, grooved end first. Position the shift rail with flat side towards the poppet spring. Engage the shift rail with the shift lever assembly and position the rail so it is flush with the edge of the poppet bore. Place the poppet ball on the end of spring and insert the assembly in the poppet bore, using a spring pin as an installation tool. Depress the poppet ball and slide the shift rail over the poppet ball as far as the spring pin will allow. Remove the spring pin and place the shift rail in the first detent position.

5. Position the shift rail so the flat side is facing the shift lever assembly and the spring pin bore is aligned with the spring pin bore in the shift fork. Once the spring pin holes are aligned, install the spring pin so that it is flush with the outside surface of the shift fork.
6. Install the shift rail taper plug, poppet bore taper plug, shift rail cover expansion plug, shift fork spring locating pin and the control lever.
7. Place the shift fork in the neutral position (center) detent. Install the reduction shift collar so that the outer teeth engage with the reduction holding plate inner teeth, and the shift collar fork groove forward of the shift fork. Place the shift fork in the direct drive (rear) detent. Move the shift collar away and to the rear of the shift fork until the groove aligns with the shift fork. Engage the collar groove with the shift fork.
8. Place the direct drive sleeve in the reduction shift collar, needle bearing surface facing toward the front. Lubricate and install the needle bearing, against the direct drive sleeve.
9. Assemble the reduction collar

plate hub and ring gear. Make certain that snap rings are seated in their grooves.
10. Install the needle bearing and reduction collar hub on the shift collar hub.
11. Install the ring gear, reduction collar plate and hub on the shift collar hub.
12. Place a needle bearing on the shift collar hub and the reduction collar hub.
13. Tap the pinion cage lock into place on the shift collar hub with a soft hammer and install assembly in housing. Place needle bearings on the shift collar hub and the pinion cage lock plate.
14. Install the reduction main shaft and sun gear into shift collar hub and through the direct drive sleeve and annular bearing. With a brass drift gently tap the assembly as far to the rear as possible. Place the rear spacer on the main shaft and secure with the selective snap ring which gives the tightest fit, between .004 in. and .009 in. clearance. Snap rings are available in thicknesses ranging from 0.089 in. to 0.105 in.
15. Install PTO cover and gasket, tighten attaching bolts to proper torque.

Rockwell T-223

Disassembly

Transfer Case

1. Clean the exterior of the case and remove the three driving yokes from the input and output shafts, using a slide hammer.
2. Remove the retaining screws and lift the top cover and gasket. Discard the gasket and clean the mating surfaces.

Shift Components

1. Remove the detent springs and remove the detent balls with a magnet.
2. Pull both of the shift shafts out through the front of the case. If the shafts cannot be removed this way, drive the shafts and expansion plugs out through the rear of the case.
3. Remove the shift shaft oil seals from the front of the case.
4. Lift the range and declutch shift forks from the case.

Front Output Shaft

1. Remove the front output shaft bearing cap and gasket and pull the shaft and declutch collar from the case.
2. Slide a long bar through the front output shaft gear and tap

out the small and large expansion plugs in the brake hub.

Parking Brake

1. Cut the wire lock and remove the retaining screws from the brake drum, and remove the brake drum from the hub.
2. Remove the brake hub retaining snap ring and remove the brake hub from the front output shaft, using a large gear puller.
3. Disconnect the brake shoe return springs and remove the brake shoes and lever.
4. Remove the brake backing plate mounting bolts and remove the backing plate, washer, deflector plate and washer.

NOTE: Do not try to remove the front output shaft at this time. The idler shaft must be removed first, due to the interference of the gears.

Idler Shaft

1. Remove the idler shaft front and

rear bearing caps. Wire the forward bearing cap shims together for reassembly.
2. Remove the screws and retainer plate from the front end of the idler shaft and press the idler shaft out through the rear of the case.
3. Lift the Low gear, spacer and front bearing from the case.
4. Remove the High gear and tap the idler shaft front bearing cup from the case.
5. Remove the retaining snap ring and press the bearing from the idler shaft.

Front Output Gear

1. After removing the idler shaft assembly, remove the front output shaft rear bearing cap and gasket.
2. Remove the bearing retaining snap ring and tap the front output gear and bearing into the

Font output shaft assembly—Rockwell T-223 (© Ford Motor Company)

1. Cotter key
2. Nut
3. Washer
4. Oil seal
5. Rear output shaft rear bearing cap
6. Cap screw
7. Lock washer
8. Cap screw
9. Lock washer
10. Speedometer driven gear bushing
11. Speedometer driven gear and shaft
12. Gasket
13. Speedometer drive gear
14. Spacer
15. Rear output shaft rear bearing cup
16. Rear output shaft rear bearing
17. Brake backing plate
18. Cap screw
19. Lock washer
20. Input shaft rear bearing cage
21. Gasket
22. Idler shaft rear bearing
23. Input shaft rear bearing
24. Gasket
25. Spacer

26. Shift shaft hole plug
27. Cap screw
28. Lock washer
29. Snap ring
30. Idler shaft rear bearing cup
31. Idler shaft rear bearing
32. Front output shaft
33. Idler shaft hi gear
34. Gear spacer
35. Direct drive gear
36. Direct drive gear bushing
37. Low speed sliding gear

38. Range shift fork
39. Detent ball
40. Detent spring
41. Beather
42. Cap screw
43. Washer
44. Housing cover
45. Detent spring
46. Detent ball
47. Shift fork set screw
48. Shift fork set screw
49. Front axle declutch shift fork
50. Idler shaft lo gear

51. Rear output shaft gear
52. Shift shaft oil seal
53. Direct drive gear spacing washer
54. Range shift shaft
55. Input shaft
56. Input shaft front bearing
57. Shims
58. Input shaft front bearing cap
59. Lock washer
60. Screw
61. Oil seal
62. Washer
63. Nut
64. Idler shaft
65. Idler shaft front bearing

66. Idler shaft front bearing cup
67. Bearing retainer plate
68. Cap screw
69. Idler shaft front bearing cap
70. Lock washer
71. Cap screw
72. Cotter key
73. Declutch shift shaft
74. Rear output shaft
75. Rear output shaft front bearing
76. Rear output shaft front bearing cup
77. Shims
78. Rear output shaft front bearing cap
79. Cap screw
80. Locker washer
81. Nut
82. Cotter key
83. Washer
84. Oil seal
85. Cap screw
86. Lock washer

87. Front output shaft front bearing cap
88. Gasket
89. Shims
90. Front output shaft front bearing (with snap ring)
91. Front output shaft
92. Declutch collar
93. Shift shaft oil seal
94. Oil filler plug (some units employ elbow arrangement)
95. Drain plug
96. Cover to housing gasket
97. Transfer case housing
98. Front output shaft rear bearing (with snap ring)
99. Shift shaft hole plug
100. Oil seal
101. Gasket
102. Front output shaft rear bearing cap
103. Washer
104. Cap screw
105. Brake shoe return spring
106. Brake shoe
107. Gasket
108. Oil deflector
109. Washer
110. Brake lever
111. Oil baffle
112. Brake hub
113. Snap ring
114. Small expansion plug
115. Brake drum
116. Lock washer
117. Large expansion plug
118. Cap screw
119. Lock wire

Exploded view of the Rockwell T-223 transfer case (© Chrysler Corporation)

case. Reach through the cover opening and lift the gear and bearing out of the case.

3. The bearing has to be pressed off the front output shaft.

Rear Output Shaft

1. Remove the retaining screws and lift the rear output shaft front and rear bearing caps off the case. Wire the shims together for reassembly.
2. Remove the speedometer drive gear and spacer.
3. Block the rear output gear with a piece of wood and press the rear output shaft and front bearing out of the case. The rear output gear and rear bearing can be lifted out through the cover opening.

Input Shaft

1. Remove the input shaft front and rear bearing covers and wire the shims together for reassembly.
2. Place a block of wood between the sliding gear and the case and press out the input shaft and front bearing.

NOTE: If the gear should cock and

become bound on the shaft, try to block it evenly with an additional piece of wood. Do not pound on the shaft.

3. Lift the sliding gear, drive gear, and spacer from the case.
4. Remove the front bearing from the input shaft.

Assembly

Input Shaft

1. Slide the input shaft front bearing onto the input shaft with the shielded side against the shaft shoulder.
2. Start the input shaft into the case. Mount the sliding gear, spacer and drive gear with its bushing onto the input shaft, working through the cover opening.

3. Tap the input shaft into position using a suitable sleeve placed against the inner race of the front bearing and a soft hammer.
4. Position the input shaft front cover and the original shim pack plus an adidtional 0.010 in. shim on the case. Tighten the retaining screws to the proper torque.
5. Install the rear thrust washer on the shaft and install the rear bearing with the shielded side toward the inside of the case.
6. Position a new gasket on the rear bearing cover and install the cover. Tighten the retaining screws to the proper torque.
7. Mount a dial indicator to the transfer case with the stem against the front end of the input

Idler shaft assembly—Rockwell T-223 (© Ford Motor Company)

shaft and check the amount of end play present. Remove enough shims from under the front bearing cover to provide 0.003 to 0.005 in. end play. Tighten the front bearing cover retaining screws to specification.

Rear output shaft assembly—Rockwell T-223 (© Ford Motor Company)

Input shaft assembly—Rockwell T-223 (© Ford Motor Company)

Rear Output Shaft

1. Press the front bearing onto the rear output shaft.
2. Hold the rear output gear in position inside the case and slide the shaft through it.
3. Install the front bearing cup and the original shim pack plus an additional 0.010 in. shim, together with the front bearing cover. Install the retaining screws and tighten them to specifications.
4. Press the rear bearing onto the rear output shaft and tap the bearing cup into place.
5. Install the speedometer drive gear and spacer on the shaft.
6. Position a new gasket and the bearing cap and oil seal over the shaft. Install the retaining screws and tighten them to the proper torque.
7. Rotate the shaft to seat the bearings, then install a dial indicator against the rear end of the shaft to check the end play. Remove enough shims from under the front bearing cap to provide zero end play and zero preload.

Front Output Gear

NOTE: The front output gear must be installed in the case before the idler shaft assembly is installed.

1. Install the ball bearing on the front output gear hub.
2. Position the gear and bearing in the case and install the retaining snap ring on the bearing.
3. Install the rear bearing cap over a new gasket and tighten the retaining screws to the proper torque.

Idler Shaft

1. Press the rear bearing onto the idler shaft and install the retaining snap ring.
2. Hold the high gear in position inside the case and tap the idler shaft through it with a soft hammer. The short hub side of the gear faces toward the rear of the case.
3. Install the gear spacer on the idler shaft, then install the low gear with the long hub toward the front of the case.
4. Install the rear bearing cup in the case and install the rear bearing cap with a new gasket, tightening the retaining screws to the proper torque.

5. Drive the front bearing onto the idler shaft while holding the shaft rigid to avoid damaging the rear bearing and cup. Install the bearing retainer plate, torque the retaining screws and lock wire them.
6. Tap the front bearing cup into place in the case.
7. Install the front bearing cap with the original shim pack and some extras in order to set up the shaft end play. Torque the front bearing cap retaining screw to specification.
8. Mount a dial indicator on the case with the stem set against the inside face of the lower gear. Check the amount of end play by working the assembly back and forth with a pry bar. Remove enough shims to arrive at 0.003 to 0.005 in. end play.

Front Output Shaft

1. Install the ball bearing onto the front output shaft with the retaining snap ring toward the front.
2. Install the sliding declutch collar onto the shaft and install the shaft into the case.
3. With the shaft in position, install the bearing cap with a new gasket and torque the retaining screws to specification.

Parking Brake

1. Mount the brake backing plate to the case, together with the deflector and stamped washer, with a new gasket between the backing plate and the case. Tighten the retaining screws with star washers to the proper torque.
2. Position the brake lever on the backing plate.
3. Position the brake shoes on the backing plate with the actuating pawl in the web slot.
4. Install the brake shoe return springs.

5. Slide the brake hub onto the splines of the front output shaft and install the retaining snap ring.
6. Install the brake drum with the attaching lockwashers and screws. Tighten the screws to specification and insert lock wires.
7. Install the expansion plugs. The smaller plug goes in the bore of the front output gear.

Shift Components

1. Install the new shift shaft oil seals in the case.
2. Position the declutch fork in the shift collar.
3. Lubricate the declutch shift shaft and slide it into the case and through the shift fork bore.
4. With the shift shaft in position, insert the set screw. Tighten the screw and lock wire it to the fork.
5. Position the range shift fork in the sliding gear.
6. Slide the range shift shaft through the bore of the fork and install the set screw. Tighten the set screw and lock wire it to the shift fork.
7. Install the expansion plugs at the rear of the case and flatten them to expand them.
8. Place the detent balls and springs in position in the case bores and install the case cover with a new gasket, tightening them to the specified torque.
9. Install the driving yokes on the shafts with their lockwashers and retaining nuts and tighten them to the proper torque.

Torque Specifications (Ft. Lbs.)

Top cover-to-case bolts	38-49
Bearing cap retaining bolts	38-49
Brake drum-to-hub bolts	60-77
Brake mounting plate bolts	60-77
Input shaft yoke nut	300-400
Output shaft yoke nuts	300-400

LEVER ASSY. (REF)

VIEW FOR CLARK 285 TRANSMISSION

BRAKE ROD
2A672

PARKING BRAKE
ROD
2A656

FLAT WASHER
44730

BELLCRANK
2A663

SPRING WASHER
356383

44730

VIEW IN DIRECTION OF ARROW **W**

LOCATE BRAKE LEVER ASSY 2780 IN OFF POSITION WITH BRAKE ROD
ASSY ATTACHED - REMOVE FREE PLAY IN PARKING BRAKE MOVE
BELLCRANK TO ADJUST CLEVIS AND INSTALL PIN, WASHERS AND
COTTER PIN.
TIGHTEN JAM NUT.

LEVER
7A400

LEVER
7E067

LEVER
2780

SPRING WASHER
377755

CLEVIS PIN
73963

VIEW IN DIRECTION
OF ARROW **V**

HIGH-NEUTRAL-LOW

TRANSFER CASE

ENGAGED & DISENGAGED

COAT CLEVIS PIN &
ATTACHING PARTS
WITH ESA-MIC75-B

3/4"

2 1/4"

INSTALLATION OF TRANSFER CASE
CONTROL LEVER ROD & SHIFT LEVER ROD
(TRANSFER CASE END)

VIEW IN DIRECTION OF ARROW **X**
FOR T-19 & 285 LEVER ASSY.

VIEW FOR WARNER T-19 TRANSMISSION

RODS ARE TO BE SET TO THESE DIMENSIONS PRIOR TO INSTALLATION	A
ENGAGED & DISENGAGED ROD	41.52
HIGH-NEUTRAL-LOW ROD	40.18

A

RUN JAM NUT ON EACH CLEVIS FULL THREAD.
THEN INSTALL CLEVISES IN TRANSFER CASE SO
THEY BOTTOM IN SHIFT RAILS. BACK OFF CLEVISES
(NOT OVER 90°) SO CLEVIS PINS ARE HORIZONTAL
TO GROUND AND TIGHTEN JAM NUTS.
WHEN ADJUSTING CONTROL & SHIFT LEVER RODS
THE LEVERS SHOULD BE 3/4" FROM SEAT CUSHION
FRAME WITH SEAT IN FULL FORWARD POSITION-THE
SHIFT RAILS IN TRANSFER CASE SHOULD BE LOCATED
IN DETENT DISENGAGE & LOW POSITION AS SHOWN ABOVE

COAT BUSHING SURFACES
WITH ESA-MIC75-B

7A133

SPRING WASHER
356373

INSTALLATION OF TRANSFER
CASE CONTROL ROD AS SHOWN
INSTALLATION OF SHIFT ROD IS
TYPICAL EXCEPT CLEVIS
PIN & SPRING WASHER ARE
INSTALLED IN OPPOSITE DIRECTIONS

WASHER
356508

BUSHING
7A133

RING
97522

VIEW IN DIRECTION OF ARROW **Z**

COAT CLEVIS PIN &
ATTACHING PARTS
WITH ESA-MIC75-B

VIEW IN DIRECTION OF ARROW **Y**

Rockwell Transfer Case Controls
(© Ford Motor Company)

Index

Automatic Transmissions

TROUBLE SHOOTING CHART

Trouble Symptoms	Items to Check		
	In Truck		Out of Truck
Shifts At Too High a Speed	KL		
Shifts At Too Low a Speed With Full Throttle	L		
Low Main Pressure In All Ranges	BEFG		a
Low Main Pressure In First Gear	F		c
Intermittent Buzzing Noise	ABEG		
Excessive Creep In First And Reverse Gears	H		
Low Lubrication Pressure I	BDFI		
Oil Leaking From Converter Housing			abc
Transmission Overheating In All Ranges	BJI		b
No Response To Movement Of Shift Lever	CF		
High Stall Speed	BF		cde
Low Stall Speed	M		b
Rough Shifting	CFHKL		
Engine Over Speeds On Full Throttle Upshift	L		c
Excessive Slippage And Clutch Chatter In One Range	F		defgh
Dirty Oil	AEI		defgh
Slippage In All Forward Ranges	BDFG		ad
Slippage In Fourth And Reverse Only			ch
Slippage In First and Reverse Only			ce
Vehicle Moves Forward In Neutral	C		d
Vehicle Moves Backwards In Neutral			h
Throws Oil From Filler Tube	BN		

Key to Checks

A. Oil	F. Valve Body	K. Modulator	a. Oil Pump	f. Second Clutch
B. Oil Level	G. Oil Intake Pipe	L. Governor	b. Converter	g. Third Clutch
C. Linkage	H. Idle Speed (engine)	M. Engine	c. Seals	h. Fourth Clutch
D. Oil Pressure Check	I. Cooler Lines	N. Breather	d. Forward Clutch	
E. Oil Filter	J. Cooling System (engine)		e. First-Reverse Clutch	

General Information

This transmission is a hydraulically operated automatic transmission with four forward speeds and one reverse.

The transmission consists basically of a torque converter, a planetary gear train and a hydraulic control system for shifting gears.

Power is transmitted from engine to transmission gearing through a three element torque converter. The torque converter operates as a torque multiplier and a fluid coupling.

The forward and reverse speeds are controlled by the planetary gear ratios. The planetary gear train is operated by hydraulic clutches. All gearing is in constant mesh.

Adjustments

Range Selector Lever Linkage Adjustment

Chevrolet and GMC

1. Place selector in N (neutral) position.
2. Adjust cable so .38 inch dimension is attained (end of cable to

TORQUE CONVERTER · OIL PUMP · PTO DRIVE GEAR · FOURTH CLUTCH · FRONT SUPPORT · FORWARD CLUTCH · THIRD CLUTCH · SECOND CLUTCH · MAIN SHAFT · FIRST AND REVERSE CLUTCH · GOVERNOR DRIVE GEAR · SPEEDOMETER DRIVE GEAR · OUTPUT SHAFT · REAR PLANETARY GEAR SET · CENTER PLANETARY GEAR SET · FRONT PLANETARY GEAR SET · STATOR SHAFT · TURBINE SHAFT · OIL FILTER · CONTROL VALVE BODY

Allison AT 540 Automatic Transmission (© Detroit Diesel Allison)

center of fitting on lever assembly). Secure cable to base of selector bracket.

3. Disconnect clevis from transmission manual shift lever. Secure cable to transmission with existing clamp.

4. Place transmission manual shift lever in N (neutral) position. Neutral position is found by moving lever completely forward, then back one notch.

5. Align clevis and lever for free-entry of pin. Next, shorten cable by moving clevis two turns clockwise. Tighten jam nut against clevis, install clevis pin and secure with cotter pin.

Ford

1. Place selector lever in R (reverse) position.
2. Disconnect cable at transmission manual shift lever and move lever all the way forward.
3. Adjust sleeve so it enters manual shift lever freely. Install flat washers, spring washer and secure with cotter pin.
4. Check operation of shift linkage.

Neutral Safety and Back Up Light Switch Adjustment
Chevrolet and GMC

NOTE: Selector lever adjustment should be made prior to this operation.
1. Remove secondary wire from distributor cap. Block front wheels and set parking brake.
2. Place selector lever in N (neutral) position. Loosen jam nuts and adjust push rod to .79 inch. Tighten jam nut.
3. Check each range to insure that starter only operates in N (neutral) position. Place selector in R (reverse) and check back up lamps).

4. Reconnect secondary wire.

Ford

1. Loosen neutral switch retaining screws.
2. Position switch so it will only function in N (neutral) position on selector.
3. Check operation of switch.

Maintenance

Checking Oil Level

The oil level should be checked at least every 1000 miles, if necessary add oil to attain proper level on dipstick. Avoid overfilling as this causes transmission overheating.

1. Run transmission until normal operating temperature is reached (150° to 200°F)
2. Position vehicle on level ground. Set parking and service brakes.
3. Move transmission through all drive ranges so that all clutch cavities and oil passages are filled.
4. Place selector in N (neutral) and operate engine at idle.
5. Check oil level on dipstick.

Chevrolet and GMC control linkage (ⓒ Chevrolet)

Hydraulic control system (ⓒ Detroit Diesel Allison)

Automatic Transmissions

Changing Oil and Filter

Transmission oil should be changed every 25,000 miles or 12 months. A new filter is also required at this interval. Use only Dexron® type automatic transmission fluid.

1. Run transmission to normal operating temperature.
2. Remove filler tube and drain oil.
3. Remove transmission oil pan. Discard the pan gasket and clean pan with proper solvent.
4. Remove filter and oil intake pipe.
5. Install new seal ring on intake pipe. Lubricate seal with transmission oil.
6. Replace oil intake pipe in transmission and place new filter assembly on oil intake pipe. Tighten retaining bolt to 10 to 13 foot pounds torque. Caution: No gasket sealing compounds should be used on oil pan gasket.
7. Install oil pan with new gasket. Tighten screws to 10 to 13 foot pounds torque.
8. Install filler tube. Add 10 quarts of oil and refer to "Checking Oil Level"

Service Operations in Truck

Some sub assemblies can be removed for repair without removing the transmission from the truck. Detailed reconditioning is covered further in the text.

Vacuum Modulator

Removal

1. Disconnect the vacuum line from modulator.
2. Remove retaining bolt and retainer.
3. Remove modulator and valve actuating rod from transmission case. Remove the seal ring from the modulator.

Installation

1. Install the valve actuating rod in case. Larger diameter end inserted first.
2. Place a new seal ring on modulator. Lubricate the seal ring with oil-soluble grease and install modulator in case.
3. Position the modulator so that vacuum connector pipe faces directly forward. Place retainer on modulator with the bent tabs against transmission and secure with bolt. Reconnect vacuum line.

Control Valve Body

Removal

1. Drain transmission. Remove oil pan, transmission oil filter and oil intake pipe.
2. Remove detent spring retaining bolt and spring.
3. Remove valve body attaching bolts, valve body and the three attached tubes from transmission case.

CAUTION: *Do not drop selector valve out of valve body.*

Removing vacuum modulator
(© Detroit Diesel Allison)

Installation

1. Place the governor feed tube, first-reverse tube and pressure tube in valve body.
2. Align tubes with holes in case and install valve body. Install attaching bolts, make certain that long bolt is placed near center of valve body. Torque bolts to 8-12 foot pounds.

Ford control linkage (© Ford)

Ford neutral start switch (© Ford)

3. Place the detent spring on valve body with spring roller in center of selector lever. Install attaching bolt.
4. Install new seal ring on intake pipe and place pipe in transmission. Install filter and oil pan with new gasket.

Governor
Removal
1. Remove governor cover and gasket from case. Rotate the governor clockwise to disengage drive gears. Remove governor.

Installation
1. Install governor in case, replace gasket and cover.

Extension Housing Rear Oil Seal
Removal
1. Disconnect drive shaft. Remove parking brake linkage.
2. Remove parking brake drum.
3. Remove seal with proper tool.

Installation
1. Lubricate the oil seal lip with a high temperature grease. Coat the outer edge of oil seal with a non-hardening sealer.
2. Place the oil seal, lip first, squarely into rear of transmission case. Using a seal installer, drive the oil seal into case until driver contacts against case. Note: The oil seal should be .51 to .55 inch forward of brake mounting surface on case.
3. Install output flange components, tighten retaining bolts to 83 to 100 foot pounds torque. Stake the tab washer into the flange washer and bend the tab washer against a flat of the bolt head.
4. Install the parking brake drum, parking brake linkage and drive shaft.

Installing governor assembly (© Detroit Diesel Allison)

1 Governor Drive Gear
2 Speedometer Drive Gear
3 Spacer
4 Snap Ring
5 Ball Bearing
6 Snap Ring
7 Oil Seal
8 First-Reverse Tube
9 Governor Tube
10 Governor Oil Screen
11 Bolt
12 Bolt
13 Detent Roller and Spring Assembly
14 Detent Roller
15 Retainer Pin
16 Detent Spring
17 Bolt
18 Seal Ring
19 Intake Pipe
20 Oil Filter
21 Washer-head screw
22 Oil pan gasket
23 Washer-head screw
24 Oil pan
25 Bolt
26 Plain washer
27 Steel Ball
28 Locknut
29 Selector shaft retainer pin
30 Selector lever
31 Selector shaft
32 Seal

1 Breather
2 Gasket
3 PTO Cover
4 Lockwasher
5 Bolt
6 Pipe Plug
7 Drive Screw
8 Name Plate
9 Case and Pin Assembly
10 Transmission Case
11 Governor Drive Pin
12 Governor Assembly
13 Gasket
14 Governor Cover
15 Bolt
16 Vacuum Modulator
17 Bolt
18 Modulator Retainer
19 Modulator Seal Ring
20 Modulator Valve Actuating Rod
21 Pipe Plug
22 Neutral Start Plug
23 Gasket

Transmission external components (© Detroit Diesel Allison)

OIL SEAL INSTALLER

Installing output shaft oil seal
(© Detroit Diesel Allison)

BOLT, 2 1/4 LONG (17)   BOLT, 2 3/4 LONG

FIRST-REVERSE CLUTCH TUBE   VALVE BODY   INTAKE PIPE

GOVERNOR FEED TUBE

GOVERNOR FEED TUBE BORE

GOVERNOR PRESSURE TUBE   BOLT, 1 3/4 LONG   SELECTOR VALVE   SEALRING

DETENT SPRING

GOVERNOR OIL SCREEN LOCATION (SOME MODELS)

Removing oil intake pipe (© Detroit Diesel Allison)

1   Output shaft seal installer
2   Oil pump seal installer
3   Stator shaft rear bearing installer
4   Stator shaft front bushing installer
     (also sun gear shaft bushings)
5   Shift valve adjusting ring tool
6   Selector shaft seal installer
7   Output shaft bushing installer
8   Forward and fourth-clutch spring compressor
9   Center support lifting bracket
10 Sun gear shaft retainer
10A Thumb screw for item 10
11 Thrust washer selection gauge bar
12 Converter end play checking fixture
13 Spacer selection gauge
14 Forward clutch clearance gauge
15 Fourth-clutch clearance gauge
16 First-and-reverse clutch clearance gauge
17 Third clutch clearance gauge

18 Converter leak test fixture
19 Transmission holding fixture base
     (used with holding fixture 20)
20 Transmission holding fixture
     (used with base 19)
21 First-and-reverse clutch spring compressor
21A First-and-reverse clutch spring compressor base
22 Output shaft positioning sleeve
23 Front support slide hammer (2)
24 Center support compressor assembly
25 Snapring gauge
26 Forward clutch inner seal protector
27 First-and-reverse clutch inner seal protector
28 Forward and fourth clutch outer seal protector

Special tools (© Detroit Diesel Allison)

Transmission Disassembly and Assembly

Disassembly

1. Remove converter.
2. Remove vacuum modulator, governor, oil pan, oil filter and intake pipe.
3. Remove detent spring and valve body with attached oil tubes.

Removing fourth-clutch assembly
(© Detroit Diesel Allison)

Removing governor check valve ball
(© Detroit Diesel Allison)

Removing center support assembly
(© Detroit Diesel Allison)

CAUTION: *Do not drop selector valve out of valve body.*

4. Remove the three oil tubes from the valve body and the oil screen at the governor feed tube bore.
5. Remove governor check valve spring ball from channel in case with magnet. Remove center support anchor bolt and flat washer.
6. Remove bolts and lockwashers from front support.
7. Remove two bolts and washers from opposite holes in the oil pump body. Install slide hammers in holes.
8. Hammer upward with slide hammers to free oil pump assembly. Remove oil pump assembly from case.
9. Remove slide hammers and replace bolts, do not tighten.
10. Remove hook type seal rings and thrust washers from oil pump assembly.
11. Remove front support gasket. Lift the turbine shaft and forward clutch assembly out of case. Remove nylon thrust washer from rear of clutch assembly.
12. Remove the fourth clutch assembly by holding the spring retainer and lifting out of case.
13. Remove sun gear shaft.
14. Remove snap ring from third clutch back plate and back plate.
15. Remove third clutch plates.
16. Remove the snap ring that holds the center support assembly.
17. Install center support lifting tool into recess between the hook type seal rings on center support hub.
18. Remove center support carefully, lifting straight upward on tool.

CAUTION: *The center support is fitted to the case with very little clearance. If the case is cold the assembly may bind. Heat the case slightly with a sun lamp or warm air. DO NOT use a torch. Once assembly is moved upward and binds, tap lightly down to straighten and lift again.*

19. Remove thrust washers from planetary sun gear.
20. Remove rear output flange.
21. Hold the main shaft and lift the planetary gears and shaft as a unit. NOTE: If assembly binds, tap lightly upward on output shaft with a soft faced mallet while lifting.
22. Remove governor and speedometer drive gears if they did not come out with planetary gear pack.
23. Remove snap ring that holds the second clutch. Remove second clutch plates and backs.
24. Remove snap ring that holds the first-reverse clutch. Remove first-reverse clutch plates and backs.
25. Remove ring gear and remaining clutch plates.
26. Install the first-reverse spring compressor and tighten until snap ring is cleared.
27. Remove snap ring, spring compressor tool, spring retainer, piston return spring and piston.

Removing first-and-reverse clutch spring retainer spring
(© Detroit Diesel Allison)

Installing oil pump assembly
(© Detroit Diesel Allison)

Removing second-clutch snapring
(© Detroit Diesel Allison)

Installing first-and-reverse clutch plates onto rear ring gear (© Detroit Diesel Allison)

INTERNAL-SPLINED PLATE

RING GEAR

INTERNAL-SPLINED PLATE

EXTERNAL-TANGED PLATE

Installing first-and-reverse clutch piston (© Detroit Diesel Allison)

INNER SEAL PROTECTOR

PISTON

28. Remove the two lip type seal rings from piston.
29. Remove output shaft seal. Remove the rear bearing snap ring and bearing.

Assembly

1. Place the first-reverse inner seal protector tool over hub in transmission case.
2. Lubricate with transmission oil and install new lip type seal rings into grooves in first-reverse clutch piston. The lips of both seal rings must face the rear of the transmission.
3. Place the piston and seal rings into transmission, making sure that piston tang engages slot in transmission case. Check and make certain that seal ring on the outside of piston is not distorted. Remove protective tool.
4. Place piston return spring in piston recesses, align springs and position spring retainer on springs. Place snap ring on spring retainer.
5. Install spring compressor tool. Compress springs until retainer clears snap ring groove. Engage snap ring and remove tool.
6. Place the first-reverse ring gear

on a flat surface, front side down. Starting with a internal splined plate, alternately install six internal splined plates and six external tanged plates onto the rear of the ring gear.
7. Align the external tangs on the clutch plates. Install the ring gear and clutch plates as a unit. Extended teeth on the ring gear must remain at top of gear after installation. Install the two remaining plates, steel plate first. Install back plate and secure with snap ring.
8. Check clearance between the snap ring and back plate. The clearance range for first-reverse clutch is .0405 to .1005 inch. If clearance is excessive new plates should be installed. If clearance is insufficient a thinner back plate is required. Back plates are stamped with numbers to identify thickness.
   - #1 .... .683 to .693 inch
   - #2 .... .647 to .657 inch
   - #3 .... .611 to .621 inch
9. Holding the main shaft, lower the unit into the transmission. Mesh the internal teeth with the previously installed ring gear with the rear planetary carrier

Installing first-and-reverse clutch back plate (© Detroit Diesel Allison)

BACK PLATE

REAR RING GEAR

PRESS (2000 LB)

INTERNAL-SPLINED PLATES (3)

EXTERNAL-TANGED PLATES (3)

STEEL PLATE

STEEL PLATE

SECOND-CLUTCH PISTON

MEASURE PLATES AND PISTON AT X
Checking second-clutch plate running clearance (© Detroit Diesel Allison)

SNAP RING

BACK PLATE

RING GEAR

CLEARANCE GAGE

Checking first-and-reverse clutch running clearance (© Detroit Diesel Allison)

Compressing center support for snapring measurement
(© Detroit Diesel Allison)

Measuring for selection of rear bearing spacer
(© Detroit Diesel Allison)

Checking end play of output shaft
(© Detroit Diesel Allison)

Sun gear shaft clearance
(© Detroit Diesel Allison)

Positioning components for front thrust washer measurements
(© Detroit Diesel Allison)

pinion teeth. Be sure that assembly bottoms.

10. Install sun gear shaft and front sun gear thrust washer.

11. Place the second clutch back plate in case. Install the clutch plates alternately starting with the internal splined plate. The single tangs of the clutch plate must align with the single tang on the back plate. Install snap ring, marked green (.155 to .157 inch), with gap located towards the top of case.

12. Remove the third clutch piston and its attaching parts from center support.

13. Install the center support assembly with the lifting tool. Make certain that tapped hole in support is aligned with the bolt hole in the bottom of case.

14. Remove the lifting tool. Install the plain washer and new center support anchor bolt. Caution: Do not tighten bolt at this time.

15. Install center support compressor tool. Use two oil pump retaining bolts to secure tool. Tighten the compressor bolt to 8-10 foot pounds.

16. Measure snap ring groove clearance and select proper size from chart below.

.148 to .150 inch . . . . Blue
.152 to .154 inch . . . . Yellow
.155 to .157 inch . . . . Green
.158 to .160 inch . . . . Red

17. Remove center support compressor and install lifting tool. Remove center support assembly. Clean assembly and remove any foreign matter from piston bore.

18. Inspect the third clutch piston seal rings for damage. Lubricate and install seal rings. Install third clutch piston and its attaching parts. Engage the small lug on the third clutch spring retainer with the slot in the center support. Make certain that the lips of the seal ring face the bottom of the piston cavity. Caution: Both the second and third

clutch pistons must bottom in their bores. Failure to do this will result in poor transmission performance.

19. Install center support lifting tool and carefully lower assembly into transmission. Alignment of anchor bolt hole is important and should be checked prior to installation. Install the anchor bolt with plain washer. DO NOT tighten.

20. Install previously selected snap ring. Make certain that snap ring gap is located towards top of case. It may be necessary to use center support compressor to install snap ring.

21. Install sun gear shaft retainer on main shaft, retainer sleeve

must be seated on shaft while tightening thumb screw.

22. Place the transmission with its rear end upward. Install the governor drive gear, engaging slot on governor with pin on output shaft. Install speedometer drive gear and tap with a soft drift to seat all internal components.

23. Place the spacer selector gauge against the output shaft and push the straight section against the speedometer drive gear. Position the lipped section against the rear bearing front snap ring. Tighten thumbscrew and remove gauge. Measure the distance between the straight section and lip section with a depth micrometer. Use this measurement to select proper spacer from following chart.

Mirometer Dimension	Identification
1.0003 to 1.0138	1 Groove
1.0138 to 1.0273	2 Grooves
1.0273 to 1.0408	3 Grooves
1.0408 to 1.0543	4 Grooves
1.0543 to 1.0678	5 Grooves
1.0678 to 1.0813	6 Grooves

24. Install the selected spacer, rear bearing and snap ring. Snap ring should be installed flat side down.

25. Position the first-reverse clutch spring compressor base, flange down, on output shaft. Secure

Measuring turbine shaft end play (© Detroit Diesel Allison)

1/2-13 BOLT (2)

SPRING COMPRESSOR BASE

Measuring for selection of front thrust washer (© Detroit Diesel Allison)

the tool to the shaft. Lifting the output shaft with a screwdriver measure the distance from top of flange to rear of transmission. Release output shaft and repeat the operation. A measurement of .003 ot .042 inch is acceptable.

26. Remove spring compressor, invert and secure to transmission case at parking brake flange. Tighten securing bolts to 5 to 8 foot pounds torque and center bolt to 5 pounds torque. All components are now properly aligned for selection of thrust washer.

27. Place the transmission with front upward. Cautiously remove sun gear shaft retainer without movement of shaft.
CAUTION: *Do not remove the sun gear shaft assembly before measuring clearances.*

28. There should be a ⅛ inch clearance from the end of the sun gear shaft to the shoulder of the main shaft. If this clearance is not present the sun gear shaft is not properly seated. To seat shaft, first, slowly rotate shaft with slight up and down motion. If this is not successful, note sun gear shaft position relative to main shaft, remove shaft and center the front sun gear thrust washer so sun gear shaft will pass. The sun gear shaft assembly must be seated properly so accurate clearance between forward clutch housing, front support and bearing assembly is maintained.

29. Starting with external tanged clutch plate, alternately install three external tanged and three internal splined plates. The single tang on the plates must engage the single slot in the transmission case.

30. Align tangs on third clutch back

plate with clutch plates and install. DO NOT use plate marked 1. Install snap ring with gap towards top of transmission case. This snap ring is identified by a green mark and has a thickness of .155 to .157 inch.

31. Check running clearance of clutch, clearance should be between .029 to .119 inch. If clearance is excessive new plates should be installed. When clearance is achieved remove clutch pack until needed.

32. Make certain that the two hook type seal rings are in place on the hub of the center support. Lubricate the seal rings with oil-soluble grease.

33. Install fourth clutch assembly on splines of sun gear. Install third clutch pack (previously removed, refer to step 29 for procedure).

34. Lubricate with oil-soluble grease and install thrust washer on hub of forward clutch assembly.

35. Place the forward clutch and turbine shaft assembly in case.

TAB

THRUST WASHER
HOOK-TYPE SEAL RINGS

Removing or installing front support seal rings and thrust washer
(© Detroit Diesel Allison)

The hub splines engage the main shaft and the splines of forth clutch drive hub engage internal splined plates of forth clutch pack. Pushing forward, rotate the forward clutch assembly one or two times.

36. Place the thrust washer selection gauge bar in transmission. Position a micrometer so that the stem passes through hole in center of gauge bar. Align the gauge bar so that micrometer stem is above the thrust washer surface of forward clutch housing. Measure distance from top of bar to thrust washer surface. Subtract the thickness of the bar and note the difference. Select the proper washer from the following chart.

Dimension	Identification
.7329 to .7493	0
.7493 to .7656	1
.7656 to .7820	2
.7820 to .7983	3
.7983 to .8714	4
.8147 to .8311	5

37. Lubricate selected thrust washer and install on oil pump assembly. Tab on washer must engage recess in front support. Install two hook type seal rings on hub of front support.

38. Position front support gasket in transmission so that holes in gasket are aligned with bolt holes in case.

39. Install slide hammers in two opposite holes on front support. Install two headless guide bolts in two opposite holes on transmission case.

Allison AT series automatic transmission valve body (© Detroit Diesel Allison)

40. Install front support and oil pump assembly in case. Make certain that assembly bottoms. Remove slide hammers and guide bolts. Install self locking bolts with new rubber coated washers, into front support and transmission case. Torque bolts to 15 to 20 foot pounds.

41. Place a Vernier dial caliper on turbine shaft. Raise the shaft and bring the gauge to bear on sector shaft, note the dial reading. Release the shaft and note dial reading. If the dial reading does not drop within the end play range (.0053 minimum to .0337 maximum), the thrust washer selected in step 36 must be recalculated.

42. Remove the spring compressor

Adjusting Vacuum modulator valve ring
(© Detroit Diesel Allison)

base from output shaft and flange. Tighten center support anchor bolt to 39 to 46 foot pounds torque.

43. Install governor, vacuum modulator, extension housing oil seal, control valve body, oil intake pipe, oil filter and oil pan, as outlined in previous section.

44. Install torque converter, engaging turbine shaft with converter turbine, sector shaft with sector and hub with oil pump drive gear. Secure torque converter for handling by attaching strap between drive lug and transmission case.

Transmission Subassemblies Overhaul

Control Valve Body Disassembly

1. Remove manual selector valve, vacuum modulator body and spacer plate.
2. Remove priority valve, spring and valve stop. NOTE: Prior to removing retainer pin from modulator valve body, note slot in adjusting ring where pin is engaged.
3. Keeping pressure on adjusting ring, remove retainer pin from modulator valve body.
4. From the vacuum modulator valve body, remove adjusting ring, stop, spring washer, valve spring and vacuum modulator valve. NOTE: Hold trimmer cover while removing, as it is spring loaded.

5. Remove trimmer cover, trimmer springs, valve stops, trimmer plugs, trimmer valves from valve body. NOTE: Relay valve spring spacers are spring loaded and must be held during removal.
6. Remove retainer pins, spring spacers, valve stops, relay valve springs and relay valves. NOTE: Valve plug on hold regulator valve is spring loaded and must be held during removal.
7. Remove retainer pin, valve plug, valve stop, valve spring and hold regulator valve. NOTE: Prior to removing retainer pins from shift signal valves, note slot in adjusting rings and pins are engaged. The adjusting rings are spring loaded and must be held during removal.
8. Remove retaining pins, adjusting rings, valve stop springs, modulator valves and signal valves. NOTE: Trimmer regulator valve and 3-4 relay valve spacers and stops are spring loaded and must be held during removal.
9. Remove retainer pins, spring spacers, valve stops, valve springs, 3-4 relay valve and trimmer valve.

Cleaning and Inspection

1. Carefully clean all parts with volatile mineral spirits. Clean oil passages by running a pipe cleaner through and flushing with mineral spirits. Dry all parts with compressed air. Make

1 Torque Converter
2 Oil Pump
3 Oil Seal
4 Pump Body & Gear
5 Pump Body Assembly
6 Bushing
7 Pump Body
8 Pump Driven Gear
9 Pump Drive Gear
10 Seal Ring
11 Pin
12 Front Support & Bearing

13 Front Support Assembly
14 Stator Shaft Bushing
15 Stator Shaft
16 Plug
17 Front Support
18 Roller Bearing
19 Self-Locking Bolt
20 Self-Locking Bolt
21 Self-Locking Bolt
22 Valve Plug
23 Main Pressure Regulator & Plug Assembly
24 Orifice Plug

25 Main Pressure Valve
26 Valve Spring
27 Spring Stop
28 Retainer Ring
29 Seal Ring
30 Rubber Coat Washer
31 Self-Locking Bolt
32 Self-Locking Bolt
33 Rubber Coat Washer
34 Gasket
35 Thrust Washer
36 Hook Type Seal Ring (2)

Torque converter and oil pump assemblies—exploded view (© Detroit Diesel Allison)

certain that all passages are free of foreign matter and obstructions.

CAUTION: *Never use abrasives or scraping tools in cleaning valve body components.*

2. Thoroughly check all parts for dirt, cracks, wear, breaks and burrs. Burrs may be removed with a soft abrasive stone. Do not damage the sharp edges of valves. Replace all parts that are in question.
3. Check all springs free length and condition.
4. Prior to assembly check all parts for free movement in bores, never force.
5. Cover all parts until assembly to exclude dirt.

Assembly

CAUTION: *Proper assembly of control valve body is critical! Before making any installation be certain that the position of all parts, the identity of all springs and the configuration of all valves are thoroughly checked.*

1. Insert the trimmer regulator valve, 3-4 relay valve, springs and stops in valve body. Align

valve stop pin hole with hole in body, place pressure on stop or spacer and insert pin.

2. Insert 1-2, 2-3 relay valves, springs, valve stops and spring spacers in valve body. Secure with retaining pin.
3. Insert 1-2, 2-3, 3-4 shift signal and modulator valves, springs and valve stops in there proper valve body bores. If original

springs are used, align adjusting rings in previously noted position and install retaining pins. When springs have been replaced, align adjusting rings with intermediate height slot with retaining pins. Use proper tool for adjustment. Engage retaining pins.

4. Insert hold regulator valve, valve spring, valve stop and plug in valve body. Secure with retaining pin.
5. Insert trimmer valves, trimmer plugs, springs and valve stops in valve body. Secure cover.
6. Insert vacuum modulator valve, spring, spring washer and valve stop in modulator valve body. Place adjusting ring in modulator body, if original springs are used, align adjusting rings in previously noted position and install retaining pins. When springs have been replaced, align adjusting ring with intermediate height slot with retaining pins. Use proper tool for adjustment. Engage retaining pin.
7. Insert the priority valve stop, spring and valve in valve body. Depress the priority valve and install the spacer plate.
8. Install the vacuum modulator valve body.
9. Install the manual selector valve.

Oil Pump

Disassembly

1. Remove large seal ring from outer edge of forward support.
2. Remove bolts and seals from oil pump body and front support. Separate front support and oil pump.
3. Remove drive and driven gears from pump body.
4. Remove seal ring from outer edge of pump body. Drive oil seal out of pump body.
5. If parts are being replaced, remove bushing from sector shaft.

Installing stator shaft front bushing
(© Detroit Diesel Allison)

Installing stator shaft rear bearing
(© Detroit Diesel Allison)

Removing PTO gear from forward clutch housing
(© Detroit Diesel Allison)

CHECK CLEARANCE HERE

Forward clutch clearance point (© Detroit Diesel Allison)

1	Hook Type Seal Ring	15	Forward Clutch Piston
2	Snapring (Early)	16	Clutch Spring (16)
3	PTO Gear (Early)	17	Spring Retainer
4	Wave Type Snap Ring (Early)	18	Snap Ring
5	Forward Clutch and Turbine Shaft Assembly (w/PTO)	19	Thrust Bearing Race
6	Forward Clutch Assembly	20	Thrust Needle Bearing
7	Housing & Shaft Assy.	21	Thrust Bearing Race
8	Turbine Shaft	22	Forward Clutch Hub
9	Forward Clutch Housing Assy.	23	External Tanged Clutch (5)
10	Forward Clutch Housing	24	Internal Splined Clutch (5)
11	Ball	25	Fourth Clutch Driving Hub
12	Clutch Housing Seal Ring	26	Snap Ring
13	Piston Inner Seal Ring	27	Snap Ring (Late)
14	Piston Outer Seal Ring	28	PTO Gear (Late)
		29	Thrust Washer

Forward clutch and turbine shaft assembly (© Detroit Diesel Allison)

Be cautious not to damage bore. Remove roller bearing from sector shaft.

CAUTION: *Do not remove sector shaft or bushing from oil pump body. If bushing is defective replace oil pump body.*

6. Remove main pressure regulator valve assembly by depressing spring stop and removing retaining ring.
7. Invert front support and remove retaining pin from small end of main pressure regulator bore, remove plug.

Assembly

1. Insert valve plug in oil pump side of front support and secure with retaining pin.
2. Invert front support, insert main pressure regulator valve (stem first), valve spring and spring stop. Depress spring stop and install retainer ring.
3. Press a new bearing (lettered end first) on sector shaft until it is .595 to .615 inch from end of shaft. Press new bushing on opposite end of shaft until it is .005 inch from end of shaft.
4. Coat oil seal bore in pump body with a non-hardening sealer. Drive oil seal, lip first, into oil pump body.
5. Position a new seal ring on outer edge of pump body.
6. Place oil pump body and front support together, aligning bolt holes. Install all bolts, with new rubber coated washers where required. Torque bolts to 15 to 20 foot pounds.
7. Install new seal ring on outer edge of front support assembly.

Forward Clutch and Turbine Shaft

Disassembly

NOTE: On transmissions not equipped with PTO gear proceed to step 5. Early models with PTO gear use step 4.

1. Place forward clutch housing on flat surface, shaft side up. Using 5/32 drill rod, prepair eight, five inch sections with pointed ends.
2. Locate snap ring gap. Place one pin, point end first, in flat area opposite snap ring gap. Push pin between snap ring and PTO gear, insert remaining pins in same manner alternately from first.
3. Tap PTO gear downward and remove.
4. On early models, place forward clutch assembly shaft up. Using a screwdriver remove snap ring and PTO gear.
5. Remove hook type seal rings from turbine shaft and invert assembly.

Installing forward clutch piston, using seal ring protector tool
(© Detroit Diesel Allison)

6. Remove snap ring from forward clutch housing with a screwdriver. Remove fourth clutch driving hub, clutch plates and forward clutch hub from housing.
7. Remove thrust bearing race, needle bearing and clutch pack from housing.
8. Position forward clutch spring compressor tool on spring retainer. Using press, depress springs until snap ring can be removed. Release pressure.
9. Remove spring retainer, clutch springs, piston and seal rings from housing.
10. Remove outer and inner seal rings from piston.
11. Inspect the ball in forward clutch housing to insure that it moves freely.

Assembly

1. Place the forward clutch housing on flat surface with turbine shaft down. Install seal ring, be sure that lip of seal ring is facing down and that it is centered in groove, lubricate.

2. Place the clutch piston return spring side up. Install inner and outer seal rings. Position the inner seal protector, insert piston back first into outer seal protector. Install piston and protectors into housing as a unit. Remove seal protectors when piston is seated in housing. Make certain that lips of seal rings are facing down, lubricate. Do not install springs at this time.
3. Starting with external tanged plate, alternately install clutch plates.
4. Install fourth clutch hub and secure with snap ring.
5. Hold clutch driving hub and measure clutch running clearance. The measurement is taken between clutch pack and driving hub, clearance should be between .0765 to .1125. If clearance is excessive new clutch plates must be installed. When a new clutch housing or drive hub has been installed, it may be necessary to use a piston of different dimension.
6. Once specified clearance has been achieved remove snap ring, driving hub and clutch plates as a unit.
7. Place clutch springs on piston with spring retainer on top. Place assembly in press and position spring compressor tool on spring retainer. Apply pressure until snap ring groove is clear. Install snap ring. Release pressure and remove from press.
8. Install thrust bearing race and thrust needle bearing on hub of forward clutch housing. Make certain that lips on race cover bearing. Hold the bearing assembly in position with oil-soluble grease.
9. Install forward clutch hub, clutch package and fourth clutch

drive hub and secure with snap ring. NOTE: The following step is for transmissions with PTO gear only.
10. Place snap ring in outer edge of clutch housing snap ring groove. Install PTO gear, chamfered inner edge down, and secure with snap ring. Make certain that gear is properly seated.
11. Install hook type seal ring on turbine shaft.

Fourth Clutch

Disassembly

1. Remove snap ring, back plate and clutch plates.
2. Place fourth clutch housing in press and compress piston return springs until snap ring can be removed. Remove snap ring, release pressure and remove assembly from press. Remove spring retainer, springs and fourth clutch piston.
3. Remove seal ring from outer edge and inner diameter of piston. Inspect seal ring grooves for burrs and rough spots.

Assembly

1. Install clutch housing seal ring, lip facing down, in inner hub. Center seal ring in groove and lubricate.
2. Install seal ring on outer edge of piston, lip facing down, lubricate. No seal ring is used on inner diameter of this piston. Place seal ring protector on outside of piston and install as a unit, be certain that piston bottoms. Remove seal protector.
3. Starting with external tanged clutch plate, install alternately clutch plates. Position clutch back plate, flat side first, and secure with snap ring.

1 Snap Ring	10 Third Clutch Piston	19 Second Clutch Piston
2 Third Clutch Back Plate	11 Piston Inner Seal Ring	20 Piston Return Spring
3 Internal Splined Clutch (3)	12 Piston Outer Seal Ring	21 Spring Retainer
4 External Tanged Clutch (3)	13 Hook Type Seal Ring	22 Self-Locking Washer (4)
5 Snap Ring	14 Support & Bushing Assy.	23 Snap Ring
6 Center Support Assembly	15 Bushing	24 External Tanged Clutch (3)
7 Self Locking Retainer Washer (4)	16 Center Support	25 Internal Splined Clutch (3)
8 Spring Retainer	17 Piston Inner Seal Ring	26 Second Clutch Back Plate
9 Piston Return Spring (12)	18 Piston Outer Seal Ring	

Second clutch, third clutch and center support assembly

Checking fourth clutch clearance
(© Detroit Diesel Allison)

1 Fourth Clutch Assembly
2 Snapring
3 Clutch Back Plate
4 Internal Splined Clutch (5)
5 External Tanged Clutch (5)
6 Snap Ring
7 Spring Retainer
8 Clutch Return Spring
9 Fourth Clutch Piston
10 Piston Outer Seal Ring
11 Clutch Housing Seal Ring
12 Fourth Clutch Housing Assy.
13 Ball
14 Fourth Clutch Housing

Fourth clutch (© Detroit Diesel Allison)

Fourth clutch clearance check point
(© Detroit Diesel Allison)

4. Hold back plate firmly and measure clutch running clearance. Measurement is made between clutch pack and back plate and should range from .0625 to .1125 inch. If clearance is not within range install new clutch plates. NOTE: If clutch housing or back plate has been replaced it may be necessary to change piston to bring running clearance into proper range.
5. Place springs on piston with retainer on top. Position assembly on press. Depress spring retainer until snap ring groove is cleared, install snap ring and release pressure. Remove clutch assembly from press.

Center Support Assembly

Disassembly

1. Remove from support assembly, spring retainers and attached parts.
2. Remove retainer washers, separate parts which are freed.
3. Remove inner and outer seal rings from pistons.
4. Remove two hook type seal rings from support assembly.
5. When parts replacement is necessary, place support assembly in press, seal ring side up, and

press out bushing. Be careful not to damage bore.

Assembly

1. Place center support assembly in a press, seal ring side up, and install flush with surface of bore. It is important that notch on bushing is in its specified place, refer to illustration for location.
2. Place return springs on pistons with spring retainers on top. Align holes in retainers with ejector pins. Depress return springs and start self-locking washers on ejector pin bosses. Insert piston assembly in support. Pistons should bottom before washers touch side of support. Check alignment of tangs in slots of support assembly. Remove assembly. Secure washers to seat springs.
3. Lubricate and install inner and outer seal rings on pistons. Seal ring lips must face down. Carefully insert pistons in to center support assembly, engaging tangs of spring retainers with slots.
4. Install two hook type seal rings on center support hub.

Planetary Gears and Shafts

Disassembly

1. Remove sun gear shaft, thrust washer, front planetary sun gear, front planetary carrier assembly.
2. Remove thrust washers from front planetary carrier assembly and center planetary carrier assembly.
3. Remove snap ring retaining front planetary ring gear and ring gear and center planetary carrier assembly.
4. Remove center planetary sun gear and thrust washer.
5. Remove snap ring retaining rear planetary carrier assembly and output shaft with attaching parts.
6. Remove needle bearing and race between output shaft and rear sun gear.

Center support assembly
(© Detroit Diesel Allison)

Output shaft assembly
(© Detroit Diesel Allison)

Front planetary carrier bushing
(© Detroit Diesel Allison)

Sun gear and shaft bushings
(© Detroit Diesel Allison)

Automatic Transmissions

1 Planetary Assembly
2 Sun Gear Shaft Assy.
3 Bushing (2)
4 Sun Gear Shaft
5 Trans. Main Shaft
6 Thrust Washer
7 Front Planetary Sun Gear
8 Thrust Washer
9 Front Planetary Carrier Assy.
10 Pinion Pin
11 Front Planetary Carrier & Flange Assy.
12 Carrier Flange
13 Carrier & Bushing Assy.
14 Planetary Carrier
15 Bushing
16 Carrier Rivet Pin
17 Pinion Thrust Washer
18 Pinion
19 Needle Roller Bearing
20 Thrust Washer
21 Snap Ring
22 Front Planetary Ring Gear
23 Center Sun Gear
24 Center Planetary Carrier Assy.
25 Center Planetary Carrier
26 Pinion Thrust Washer (16)
27 Pinion
28 Needle Roller Bearing
29 Pinion Pin
30 Thrust Washer
31 Planetary Connecting Drum
32 Snap Ring
33 Center Planetary Ring Gear
34 Rear Planetary Sun Gear
35 Needle Thrust Bearing
36 Thrust Bearing Race
37 Spiral Snap Ring
38 Snap Ring
39 Rear Planetary Carrier Assembly
40 Rear Planetary Carrier
41 Thrust Washer (16)
42 Pinion (4)
43 Needle Roller Bearing
44 Pinion Pin (4)
45 Snap Ring
46 Ball Bearing
47 Outer Shaft Assembly
48 Shaft and Bushing Assy.
49 Bushing
50 Output Shaft
51 Plug
52 Governor Drive Spring Pin
53 Spiral Retainer Ring (Early)
54 Spacer Washer (Early)
55 Rear Planetary Ring Gear (Early)
56 Spacer Washer (Early)

Planetary gears and shafts assembly (© Detroit Diesel Allison)

7. Position output shaft with rear planetary carrier up. Remove snap ring and bearing by moving planetary carrier down until snap ring is clear, remove carrier.
8. On early models, remove spiral snap ring, thrust washers and ring gear.
9. Remove spiral snap ring, rear sun gear, snap ring, center ring gear and main shaft.
10. When replacing parts, remove roll pin, bushings, orifice plug from output shaft and bushings from sun gear shaft.

Measuring depth of front planetary carrier (© Detroit Diesel Allison)

Selection of thrust washer for planetary gears assembly (© Detroit Diesel Allison)

1110

Assembly

1. Install new bushings on output shaft and sun gear shaft, if they were removed.
2. Install orifice plug and roll pin on output shaft.
3. Install rear planetary sun gear, small end first, spiral snap ring, center ring gear and snap ring.
4. Install bearing assembly over snap ring groove on output shaft, output shaft with snap ring groove first and snap ring.
5. On early models, install rear ring gear.
6. Install spacer washer on hub of rear planetary carrier, rear planet ring gear on carrier hub, spacer washer and spiral snap ring.
7. Place positioning tool over output shaft and tighten bolt to 30 foot pounds. Install rear planetary carrier assembly in carrier connecting drum and secure with snap ring. Broad groove in carrier connecting drum is positioned away from rear carrier.
8. Lubricate and install bearing assembly over output shaft next to rear sun gear.
9. Insert small end of main shaft, with attached parts, in output shaft.
10. Install thrust washer on front of rear sun gear.

11. Install center planetary carrier small end first, in planetary connecting drum. Engage carrier splines with splines in drum.

12. Install center sun gear, large end first against thrust washer.

13. Install front planetary ring gear, large end first in planetary connecting drum, attach snap ring.

13. Lubricate and install thrust washer on front planetary carrier hub. Install front carrier assembly on center sun gear.

14. With a depth micrometer, measure the depth of the center planetary sun gear and front planetary carrier. Difference in measurements determines thrust washer thickness. Select washer from following chart.

Thickness	Identification
.071 to .090	#1
.090 to .109	#2
.109 to .128	#3

Remove positioning tool from output shaft. Lubricate and install selected thrust washer. Reinstall.

15. Install front planetary sun gear, spline chamfer first, in planetary carrier.

NOTE: Thrust washer and sun gear shaft after planetary gears and shafts are positioned in transmission.

Transmission Case

Disassembly

1. Remove retainer pin and lock nut from manual shift lever.
2. Pull the selector shaft carefully through oil seal out of case. Remove seal.
3. Do not remove snap ring from rear of output flange bearing unless replacement is necessary.
4. Remove governor support pin if damaged.
5. Remove and inspect test plugs, replace if necessary.

Assembly

1. Install output bearing rear snap ring if it was removed. Inspect for damage to bore.
2. Install test plugs.
3. Lubricate and install selector shaft oil seal, lip first. Slide selector shaft through seal and into case. Attach locknut and retainer pin to shaft. Tighten locknut to 15 to 20 foot pounds.
4. Install governor support pin if it was removed. Press to dimensions shown in illustration. Alignment of pin must be correct or damage to governor will occur.

AUTOMATIC TRANSMISSION SPECIFICATIONS

General Specifications

Dry Weight	275 Lbs.
Oil Capacity	15 Qts.
Maximum Oil Temperature	
Sump	250°F
Converter Out	300°F
PTO Drive Gear	55 Teeth, 6/8 Pitch
PTO Mounting	6 Bolt, SAE Regular Duty

Main Pressure Checks

Forward and Neutral	150 psi
Reverse	250 psi

Torque Limits	Foot Pounds
Oil Pump to Support Bolts	15 to 20
Output Flange Bolts	83 to 100
Front Support to Case Bolts	15 to 20
PTO Cover Bolts	15 to 20
Pressure Tap Plugs	10 to 15
Governor Cover Bolts	15 to 20
Vacuum Modulator Retaining Bolts	15 to 20
Modulator Valve Body to Control Valve Body	8 to 12
Trimmer Cover to Valve Body Bolts	8 to 12
Detent Spring to Valve Body Bolt	8 to 12
Control Valve Body to Case Bolts	8 to 12
Oil Filter Bolt	10 to 15
Oil Pan Bolts	10 to 13
Center Support Anchor Bolt	39 to 46
Selector Shaft Nut	15 to 20
Converter to Flywheel Bolts	34 to 40

Selector shaft components (© Detroit Diesel Allison)

Governor support pin location (© Detroit Diesel Allison)

Diagnosis

This guide covers the most common symptoms and is an aid to careful diagnosis. The items to check are listed in sequence to be followed for quickest results. Follow the checks in the order given for the particular transmission type.

Trouble Symptoms	Items to Check	
	In Truck	Out of Truck
Harsh N to D or N to R shift	CDEFGIJ	ab
Delayed shift—N to D	ACIHKJ	ca
Runaway on upshift and 3-2 kickdown	ABCDLIHK	b
Harsh upshift and 3-2 kickdown	BCDLIHJ	b
No upshift	ABCDLIHKM	b
No kickdown on normal downshift	ABNCDLIHKM	d
Erratic shifts	ABNCFOPQIKMJ	c
Slips in forward drive positions	ACIHK	abd
Slips in reverse only	CEGIK	
Slips in all positions	ACOIK	e
No drive in any position	ACOQIKJ	ca
No drive in forward positions	CDOLIHK	abd
No drive in reverse	CEGKMI	b
Drives in neutral	NIJ	a
Drags or locks	DELG	abfd
Noises	AORPMIJ	a
Hard to fill or blows out	AORSTQI	
Transmission overheats	ADEORTMI	abe
Unable to push-start truck	ACEGI	g

Key to Checks

A. Oil Level
B. Control Linkage
C. Oil Pressure Check
D. Kickdown Band
E. Low-Reverse Band
F. Improper Engine Idle
G. Servo Linkage
H. Accumulator
I. Valve Body Assembly
J. Manual Valve Lever
K. Air Pressure Check
L. K-D Servo Link
M. Governor
N. Gear Shift Cable
O. Regulator Valve and/or Spring
P. Output Shaft Bushing
Q. Strainer
R. Converter Control Valve
S. Breather Clogged
T. Cooler or Lines
a. Front-Kickdown Clutch
b. Rear Clutch
c. Front Pump and/or Sleeve
d. Overrunning Clutch
e. Converter
f. Planetary
g. Rear Pump (Not after 1965)

General Information

This transmission is a hydraulically operated automatic transmission with six forward gear ratios and one reverse.

The transmission consists basically of a torque converter, a planetary gear train and a hydraulic control system for shifting gears.

The torque converter operates as a hydraulic torque multiplier and a fluid coupling between the engine and the gear train. The torque multiplying phase of the converter operates when the vehicle starts moving from a standstill and when a heavy load slows down the vehicle.

At certain speeds (when the action of the torque converter is no longer needed) an automatic lockup clutch in the converter locks the engine directly to the gear train for greater efficiency. The lockup clutch automatically disengages momentarily while shifts are being made.

A pedal operated hydraulic retarder assists the service brakes in controlling vehicle speed during long down hill braking and when slowing down in stop and go traffic.

Two separate fluid velocity type governors provide the fluid pressures needed to operate the hydraulic control system and make the shifts.

When the range selector lever is at D3-6 position the transmission can be operated in 3rd, 4th, 5th and 6th gears. The D3-4 position permits the use of only 3rd and 4th gears. When the lever is in the D3-5 position the vehicle can be operated in 3rd, 4th and 5th gears only. When the lever is at L1-2 (low range) the transmission will operate only in first and second gears. The reverse gear ratio is effective when the range selector is at R.

The gear ratios within the selected range are upshifted or downshifted automatically to meet changing road and load conditions. When the accelerator pedal is depressed to full throttle, each gear ratio shift point should occur at the highest speed for the shift. When the throttle is partly open, the shift points should occur at lower speeds.

A detent at the full throttle position of the accelerator pedal permits the driver to control certain shifts. When the pedal is pushed through the full throttle detent, the transmission will remain in the same gear ratio during acceleration or will immediately downshift to a lower gear to provide the best engine performance for the driving.

Adjustments

Range Selector Lever Linkage Adjustment

1. Place range selector lever in R (reverse) position.
2. Remove cotter pin from connection at transmission range selector lever. Move connector out of the way. Shift transmission lever all the way forward.
3. With the range selector lever in

Neutral safety switch circuit diagram
(© Chrysler Corp.)

Range selector lever control adjustment
(© Chrysler Corp.)

cab and transmission selector lever in R (reverse) position, the pin in cable connector should be aligned with hole in transmission range selector lever.

4. If alignment is not correct, loosen jam nut at connector and turn connector in or out until alignment is obtained and connector pin can be installed easily.

5. Secure connector pin with cotter pin and tighten jam nut. Check operation of selector lever in all positions.

Neutral Safety Switch Adjustment

1. Check starter circuit at all range selector lever positions, by positioning lever and turning ignition switch to extreme clockwise position.

2. The engine should start only when the lever is in the N (neutral) position. If necessary to make an adjustment, first loosen neutral safety switch to bracket screws, and rotate switch clockwise so the starter circuit is closed when starter lever is set in N (neutral). Tighten switch mounting screws.

3. If engine fails to start with the range selector lever in N (neutral) position check switch lead wires and switch, by making a circuit check with a test lamp.

Throttle Linkage Adjustment

1. Remove throttle control spring and governor arm spring (if equipped).

2. At transmission, remove throttle control shift rod swivel cotter pin and remove swivel from TV lever.

3. Remove carburetor air cleaner.

4. Place carburetor throttle lever in idle position.

5. Adjust throttle control rod so that accelerator control bell crank stop is against bracket. Tighten nuts on throttle rod.

6. Move carburetor throttle lever to wide open position.

7. Wide open throttle stop bolt must be adjusted so that the bolt head contacts the bell crank when the throttle is in wide open position.

8. With throttle control shaft pushed upwards until travel of rod is stopped, at the transmission rotate the throttle control lever forward until the TV lever is firm against the internal stop. At this position the swivel pin should freely enter the lower hole in the transmission throttle valve control lever. Finger tighten front and rear adjusting nuts against swivel.

9. Back off the swivel three turns to back off valve, connect linkage tighten all nuts.

10. On all models the through detent pedal stop (located on throttle control bell crank) must be adjusted so that pedal forced cannot be applied to TV linkage. To do this adjust stop so that it contacts the bracket bolted to the engine at the same time the TV lever contacts the stop in the transmission. Then turn bolt 1/16" turn further to eliminate any force being applied through the linkage from the stop in the transmission.

Retarder Linkage Adjustment

1. Adjust master cylinder push rod so there is a .010 inch free play (measured at pedal pad approxi-

mately 1/16 inch between push rod and master cylinder piston, when piston is in its fully returned position. The system must be free of air and master cylinder filled to ½" of top.

2. Push rod on slave cylinder should travel ½ inch for full retarder action.

Maintenance

Checking Oil Level

1. The oil level should be checked every 1,000 miles and oil added when necessary.

2. The transmission oil should be at normal operating temperature 180° to 260° F.

3. The vehicle should be on level ground.

4. The parking brake and service brakes should be applied. CAUTION: Do not apply the hydraulic retarder while checking oil level. Applying the hydraulic retarder while in a stalled position will aerate the oil, making an accurate oil level check impossible.

5. Place range selector lever in N position and run engine at fast idle.

6. The oil should be at the "Full" mark on the dipstick. If not add oil till the proper level is obtained.

Changing Oil

1. Drain oil immediately while oil is still warm.

2. Loosen filter cover and allow oil to drain thoroughly.

3. Remove filter and install new one.

4. Pour eight quarts of transmission fluid into transmission.

5. Apply parking brake and position range selector lever in N and start engine.

6. Run engine at normal idle speed and add sufficient oil to bring level to "Full" mark on dipstick.

Oil Cooler

When clutch failure or other internal trouble has occured in the transmission any metal particles or clutch plate material that may have been carried into the oil cooler should be removed from the system by flushing

Transmission (cross section) typical (© Detroit Diesel Allison)

the cooler before the transmission is put back into service. Foreign matter in the oil cooler system could block off the front pilot feed hole, get into various gears and clutches, or block off the output shaft bushing lubrication orifice in the splitter shaft.

1. Disconnect both oil cooler lines at hydraulic retarding valve body.
2. Back-flush oil cooler and lines with clean solvent and compressed air.
3. Remove all remaining solvent from the system and flush system with automatic transmission fluid. If after the final flushing there is no flow through the cooler or if it is restricted, replace oil filter.

Air Pressure Checks

Compressed air may be used to check operation of various clutches in the transmission and to find leaks that may be caused by broken, damaged or omitted seals. Be sure that air from source of supply is clean and dry.

1. To make air pressure checks, remove oil pan, valve body and oil transfer plate from transmission. Apply 85-100 psl (do not exceed 150 psl) air pressure at the appropriate holes in the mounting pad at bottom of transmission housing.
2. When air is applied as directed, listen for the noise that occurs when clutch is applied. If no clutch application noise is heard,

a leak may exist in the hydraulic system.

Fluid Pressure Checks

Four 1/8" pipe plugs are provided in the transmission to check lockup, and governor pressures.

All four pressures can be checked without driving the truck on the road.

All gauge readings should be taken with the transmission fluid at normal operating temperature, and with the throttle and range selector linkages properly adjusted.

The test point for main pressure is pump outlet and the main pressure regulator valve. Since there is no check valve between the front pump and the main regulator valve a gauge

Fluid passages in transmission housing
(© Chrysler Corp.)

Retarder linkage adjustment
(© Chrysler Corp.)

Allison MT Series

installed at this point will read main pressure under all operating conditions. In normal operation, main pressure varies from 75 to 255 psl. Pressure vary with the converter and converter lockup operations, throttle positions and range selector valve positions. Refer to chart.

Main Pressure Check (Engine Idle)

1. With engine stopped connect pressure gauge at plug hole in converter housing.
2. Apply parking brake and start engine. The engine idle speed should be 475-500 rpm with range selector lever in neutral. With engine idling, read gauge in all selector lever positions.

Maximum Main Pressure Check

Converter Operation

1. Stop engine, remove transmission throttle control rod. Make certain swivel adjustment is not disturbed.
2. Move transmission throttle control lever to rear to insure throttle valve is fully closed.
3. Start engine and apply service brakes. With hand throttle, set engine speed at 1,200 rpm, use a tachometer.
4. Read pressure gauge at all selector lever positions.
5. Return engine to idle speed before each shift. The readings represent the maximum pressure in convertor operation at closed transmission throttle valve.
6. Rotate transmission throttle control lever forward to its stop and fix lever in this position. Transmission throttle valve is now fully open.
7. With engine running at 1,200 rpm read pressure in all range selector positions.

Lockup Pressure Check (Closed Throttle)

To check converter lockup pressure in 2nd, 4th and 6th gears proceed as follows:

1. Remove propeller shaft and transmission throttle control rod, and move transmission lever rearward to fully close throttle valve. Release parking brake.
2. Start engine and move selector lever to L1-2, increase engine speed to 2,000 rpm and transmission will shift to second gear, then to lockup.
3. Read pressure gauge; it represents second gear converter lockup pressure at closed transmission throttle valve.
4. Move selector lever to D3-4, set

Clutches Air Pressure Check Chart

Check Passage	Leak Location	Cause of Leak
Low-splitter clutch	Between diaphragm and case	Bottom two anchor bolts loose, or not drawing diaphragm to case
	At piston ID	Hook-type oil seal for id broken, or omitted
	At piston OD	Seal at piston od broken, nicked or expander omitted
High-splitter clutch	Between diaphragm and case	Bottom two anchor bolts loose, or not drawing diaphragm to case
	At piston ID	Hook-type oil seal for id broken, or omitted
	At piston OD	Seal at piston od broken, nicked or expander omitted
	Lube hole in retarder valve body pad	Diaphragm front hub hook-type seal ring broken or omitted
	Retarder feed	Diaphragm rear hub hook-type seal ring broken or omitted
High-range clutch	Between diaphragm and case	Bottom two anchor bolts loose, or not drawing diaphragm to case
	At front-pilot hole or at lube in retarder valve body pad	Inner hook-type seal ring on rear hub broken or omitted
	At lube hole in retarder valve body pad	Rear hook-type seal ring on rear hub broken or omitted
	Around clutch piston spring	Hook-type seal ring for clutch piston id broken or omitted
	Around high-range clutch hub	Seal at piston od broken, nicked or expander omitted
Intermediate-range clutch	Between case and intermediate clutch piston housing	Anchor bolts loose, intermediate clutch housing not tight against hole in case
	At piston ID	Hook-type ring broken or omitted
	Around low-range clutch plate	Same as above
	At piston return spring and piston OD	Seal at piston od broken, nicked or expander omitted
Low-range clutch	Between case and low-reverse piston housing	Anchor bolt loose; low-reverse clutch housing not tight against case
	At piston ID	Hook-type seal broken or omitted
	Around clutch ID	Same as above
	At piston OD	Seal at piston od broken, nicked or expander omitted
Reverse clutch	Between case and low-reverse piston housing	Anchor bolt loose; low-reverse clutch housing not tight against case
	At piston ID	Hook-type seal broken or omitted
	Around clutch ID	Same as above
	At piston OD	Seal at piston od broken, nicked or expander omitted
Lockup clutch	At piston OD	Seal broken, nicked, or omitted
	At od of converter cover	Seal between reaction plate and cover, or between plate and converter pump flange, damaged or omitted
	At turbine shaft	Broken or omitted hook-type rings at front end of turbine shaft, front end of splitter shaft, or center of splitter shaft

Fluid pressure test point locations
(© Chrysler Corp.)

Oil filter assembly
(© Chrysler Corp.)

engine speed at 2,000 rpm and read pressure gauge. This reading represents fourth gear converter lockup pressure at closed transmission throttle valve.

5. Move selector lever to D3-6, set engine speed at 2,000 rpm. Read the pressure gauge. This reading represents sixth gear converter lockup pressure at closed throttle.

Governor Pressure Check

1. Remove propeller shaft and transmission control rod; move lever rearward to fully close throttle valve. Release parking brake. Attach pressure gauge. At G-1 check point.
2. Start engine and increase speed to 2,800 rpm with selector lever at D3-6. Transmission will shift to sixth gear. Read gauge after pressure has stabilized.

3. To check G-2, stop engine and connect pressure gauge to G-2 checkpoint. Follow the same procedure as for G-1 pressure check.

Oil Pan and Filter (Removal)

1. Remove oil filter cover and gasket, then remove retainer and filter element from transmission oil pan.
2. Remove oil pan and gasket, then remove seal rings from front pump pickup tubes.

Valve Bodies (Removal)

1. Remove the range selector valve body from oil transfer plate. *The shift valve steel detent ball and spring are free to fall out of the valve body when it is removed from the transfer plate.*
2. Remove downshift timing valve body from transfer plate.

1 Lock washer	12 Filter cover
2 Bolt, ¼-20 x 3	assembly
3 Bolt, ¼-20 x 3	13 Cover strap
4 Oil pan gasket	14 Bolt, 5/16-24 x 1
5 Oil pan	15 Nut, 5/16-24
6 Bolt, 5/16-18 x 1/2	16 Bolt, ¼-20 x 1-⅛
7 Oil filter element	17 Lockwasher
8 Seal ring	18 Oil filter can
9 Oil filter element	assembly
retainer	19 Oil suction tube
10 Spring	seal ring
11 Seal ring	

3. Remove transfer plate and gasket from transmission housing. *Nylon ball in plate is free to fall when plate is removed.*
4. Remove retarder linkage and oil lines from retarder valve body.
5. Remove hydraulic retarder valve body and gasket. Remove nylon ball from housing.

Oil Transfer Plate

Disassembly

1. Remove converter lubrication supply cover. Do not remove valve seat unless it is bad.

Throttle linkage assembly (© Chrysler Corp.)

2. Remove retainer, spring, seat and steel ball. *The low range clutch exhaust regulator valve is pressed into the oil transfer plate and should not be removed unless it is to be replaced. An orifice cup is situated under this regulator valve. The cup serves to slow the exhaust of the low-range clutch when shifts occur between second and third gears.*

3. Clean transfer plate and check valve operation. The valve should retain the cleaning solvent on side opposite spring for at least 15 seconds.

Assembly

1. Install lube supply valve seat (if removed) in lubrication supply cover and install cover.

2. Tighten screws from 24 to 36-inch-pounds. *The nylon ball is installed from the other side of oil transfer plate when plate is assembled to transmission housing.*

3. Assemble steel ball, seat, spring, and converter pressure regulator valve retainer to oil transfer plate. Torque screws at 24 to 36 inch-pounds.

Downshift Timing Valve

Disassembly

1. Remove downshift timing valve body from transfer plate.
2. Remove downshift timing valve cover.
3. Remove spring and downshift timing valve.

The oil passage orifice in valve body is .01875 to 0.1400 inch. In addition, the inside diameter at rear (closed end) of valve bore is approximately 0.04 inch. The diameter of the rear valve land is approximately 0.04 inch. Two coils at one end are painted blue.

Assembly

1. Insert valve in body and place spring on the stem of valve.

Exhaust regulator valve body (rear view) (© Detroit Diesel Allison)

2. Install valve cover over spring and tighten screws from 24 to 36 inch-pounds.

Control Valve Body

Disassembly

Do not mix the various valve body springs.

1. Place the control valve body assembly with mating surface (oil transfer plate side) facing down.

2. Remove oil transfer tubes by pulling upward.

3. Remove exhaust regulator valve body.

4. Remove selector valve detent spring and lift valve body separator plate off the control valve body. Remove ⅜ inch steel detent ball from valve body.

Maximum Main Pressure Check—Converter Operation

Selector Lever Position	Engine rpm	Gauge Reading (psi)	
		Closed Throttle	Full Throttle
N, R, D3-4, D3-5, D3-6 and L1-2	1200	155 (Minimum)	200 (Minimum)

Main Pressure Check—Hydraulic Retarder Operation

Selector Lever Position	Throttle Position at Transmission and Engine	Retarder Pedal Position	Minimum Main Pressure (psi)
N	Closed	At Stop	125

Governor Pressure Check G-1 and G-2

Selector Lever Position (Drive Shaft Disconnected)	Gear	Engine rpm	Throttle Position at Transmission	Gauge G-1 Limits	Reading (psi) G-2 Limits
D3-6	Sixth	2800	Closed	60-70	67-70

Pressure Check Chart

Main Pressure Check—Engine Idle

Selector Lever Position	Gear	Clutches Applied	Engine rpm	Throttle Position at Transmission	Gauge Readings (psi) Minimum Main Pressure
N (Neutral)		Low Splitter	475-500	Closed	100
R (Reverse)	Third	Low Splitter, Reverse	Idle	Closed	50
D3-4, D3-5 or D3-6		Low Splitter, Intermediate Range	Idle	Closed	50
L1-2	First	Low Splitter, Low Range	Idle	Closed	50

Lockup Pressure Check—Operation (Maximum Throttle)

Selector Lever Position (Drive Shaft Disconnected)	Gear	Clutches Applied	Engine rpm	Throttle Position at Transmission	Gauge Readings (psi)
D3-5, D3-6	Third	Lockup, Low Splitter, Intermediate Range	2700	Maximum	107-125

Lockup Pressure Check (Closed Throttle)

Selector Lever Position (Drive Shaft Disconnected)	Gear	Clutches Applied	Engine rpm	Throttle Position at Transmission	Gauge Readings (psi)
L1-2	Second	Lockup, High Splitter, Low Range	2000	Closed	65-75
D3-4	Fourth	Lockup, High Splitter, Intermediate Range	2000	Closed	65-75
D3-5 D3-6	Sixth	Lockup, High Splitter, High Range	2000	Closed	65-75

5. Remove accelerator plug cover and plug.

6. Remove the regulator cover and lockup-knock-down plug, accumulator valve spring and accumulator valve.

7. Remove two screws and throttle valve retainer from valve body. Do not remove screw from retainer.

8. Remove valve body rear cover (spring loaded), then remove the low-to-intermediate shift valve spring, and regulator plug.

9. Remove the throttle valve and throttle valve spring, manual selector valve, hydraulic retarder regulator plugs, lock-up plug, rear pitot plug, front pitot spiltter plug, low-to-intermediate shift valve, and intermediate-to-high shift plug from the control valve body.

10. Position control valve body on rear cover mounting surface.

11. Remove splitter over-control valve body.

12. Remove the splitter overcontrol valve.

13. Remove splitter shift plug spring and plug.

14. Remove the three screws attaching the intermediate-to-high shift valve cover to control valve body front cover. Remove cover, intermediate-to-high shift valve spring and blocker plug.

15. Remove three screws holding the valve body front cover to the control valve body. *Don't exert pressure on the cover because it is spring loaded.*

16. Remove valve body front cover assembly.

17. Remove ¼-inch ball which is freed when front cover is removed. Remove inhibitor valve and spring from cover. Remove main-pressure regulator spring, secondary spring, splitter relay valve spring and lockup shift valve spring which are exposed by removing front cover.

18. Remove throttle valve plug from valve body front cover. Remove retainer spring and withdraw pump overage valve assembly from front cover.

19. Remove the two overage valve spring retainers and spring from front cover. Remove throttle regulator valve, main-pressure regulator valve, lockup shift valve, splitter shift valve, splitter relay valve, and intermediate-to-high shift valve from front of control valve body.

20. Replace reverse-range clutch exhaust pressure regulator valve only if necessary. Check valve operation while cleaning valve body. The valve should retain solvent on side opposite spring for 15 seconds. If solvent leaks through sooner, valve is defective.

21. Do not remove reverse lockup inhibitor check valve retainer and 7/32-inch ball. If retainer, ball or valve body is defective, all three items must be replaced.

← VALVE BODY ATTACHING BOLTS
DOWNSHIFT TIMING VALVE BODY
RANGE SELECTOR AND EXHAUST REGULATOR VALVE BODIES
OIL TRANSFER PLATE
SPLITTER OVER CONTROL VALVE BODY
OIL TRANSFER TUBES

Valve bodies installed in transmission
(© Chrysler Corp.)

OIL TRANSFER PLATE
CONVERTER PRESSURE REGULATOR
LUBRICATION SUPPLY COVER
REAR PUMP NYLON BALL
RANGE SELECTOR VALVE DETENT BALL AND SPRING
DOWNSHIFT TIMING VALVE BODY

Removing control valve body from transfer plate (typical)
(© Chrysler Corp.)

Oil transfer plate (© Chrysler Corp.)

TRANSFER PLATE

VALVE SEAT

LUBE SUPPLY COVER

CONVERTER PRESSURE REGULATOR VALVE BALL

WASHER

SPRING

SPRING RETAINER

LOW RANGE VALVE

LOCKWASHER

SCREW

Cleaning and Inspection

Wash all parts in cleaning solvent and dry thoroughly with air. Check all parts and castings for cracks, nicks and burrs. Replace any cracked or damaged covers. Remove any nicks or burrs with a fine stone. *Do not sand or polish any radius on the valves or plugs. The valves and plugs are manufactured with a sharp edge to prevent dirt from sticking in the valve bore.*

Control Valve Body

1. *All valves and plugs should be installed dry and must move in* the valve body bore by their own weight. Do not attempt to force any valves into the valve body bore, as it will damage the casting. If any valves or plugs stick, recheck for nicks or burrs. Remove the nicks or burrs with a fine stone.

2. Position the range selector valve body with valve body front cover surface facing up and install the following parts in main valve body.

3. Throttle regulator valve, main pressure regulator valve, lockup shift valve, splitter shift valve, splitter relay valve, and in-

DOWNSHIFT TIMING VALVE

DOWNSHIFT TIMING VALVE SPRING

DOWNSHIFT TIMING VALVE COVER

DOWNSHIFT TIMING VALVE BODY

SCREW AND WASHER

Downshift timing valve

CONVERTER "OUT"

"FEED"

"IN" FROM VALVE BODY

LUBRICATION

"OUT"

SUMP

Oil passages in retard valve
(© Detroit Diesel Allison)

BODY

VALVE

VALVE

REAR

FRONT

VALVE

VALVE

VALVE

VALVE

SPRING

Control valve body component parts (front) (© Detroit Diesel Allison)

CONTROL VALVE BODY FRONT COVER

CONTROL VALVE BODY

INTERMEDIATE-TO-HIGH SHIFT PLUG

LOW-TO-INTERMEDIATE SHIFT VALVE

REAR (G2) SPLITTER PLUG

FRONT (G1) SPLITTER PLUG

LOCKUP PLUG

MANUAL SELECTOR VALVE

TOP

REAR

RETARDER REGULATOR PLUG

SPRING

THROTTLE VALVE

Rear of control valve body (© Detroit Diesel Allison)

BACK PLATE

CONVERTER PUMP

PISTON

STATOR

RETURN SPRING

CLUTCH PLATE

STATOR

CONVERTER TURBINE

GROUND SLEEVE

CONVERTER OUTPUT SHAFT

Torque converter and lock-up clutch (cross section) (© Detroit Diesel Allison)

termediate-to-high shift valve. *The splitter relay valve should be installed with the widest land into control valve body first.*

Install the following parts in valve body front cover:

4. TV plug (hold in place with oil soluble grease), the main pressure regulator primary spring, and main pressure regulator secondary spring, 1/4 inch nylon ball (hold in place with oil soluble grease), inhibitor valve and inhibitor valve spring and splitter relay spring.

5. Position the range selector valve body on its side, place valve body front cover against range selector valve body, front cover surface and push it into position, compressing the splitter relay valve and main pressure regulator springs. *Be careful to keep*

the 1/4 inch nylon ball in position. Install three screws, do not tighten at this time.

6. Install the intermediate-to-high shift plug, spring and shift valve cover.

7. Install three screws to hold the cover but do not tighten the screws at this time.

8. Check the mating surface between front cover assembly and range selector body assembly. Be sure there is a tight seal and that none of the springs are caught between the housings. The front cover should not protrude above main valve body face since it assembles against the oil transfer plate.

9. Install splitter shaft plug into valve body front cover. Install overcontrol valve into overcontrol valve body. Install overcontrol valve body cover and hold with one screw (short). Install spring into recessed end of valve previously installed. Install complete overcontrol valve assembly on control valve body front cover, install the remaining two screws but do not tighten at this time.

10. Install the following parts in valve body rear cover side of the control valve body:

Throttle valve spring and throttle valve, manual selector valve, one hydraulic retarder regulator plug, lockup plug, front splitter plug and the rear splitter plug, low-to-intermediate shift valve, and intermediate-to-high shift plug. *All valves and plugs should be installed dry and must move in the valve body bore by their own weight. Do not*

force any valves or plugs, as the casting will be damaged.

11. Install the regulator plug and the intermediate-to-low shift valve spring in valve body rear cover.

12. Install the three rear cover retaining screws. Install throttle valve retainer and screw, do not tighten screws at this time.

13. If throttle valve adjusting screw was removed from retainer, install at this time but do not lock. Refer to section on adjustments.

14. Install the lockup knockdown plug (small end first). Install accumulator valve. Install accumulator valve spring and regulator cover secure with four screws, tighten 24 to 36 inch-pounds.

15. Install accelerator plug and cover. On models which include the ball spring and bracket, install these parts at this time and secure with two screws but do not tighten. On models without ball, spring and bracket, install the three cover retaining screws, do not tighten at this time.

Exhaust Regulator Valve Body

Disassembly

1. On models using the valve guide bracket, remove two screws, bracket, trimmer ball regulator spring and ball. Remove the six remaining screws securing exhaust regulator valve body cover to exhaust regulator valve body on models which do not use the bracket assembly, remove eleven screws securing cover to valve body. *This cover is spring loaded and must be held while screws are being removed.* Remove cover.

2. Removal of exhaust regulator cover will expose the intermediate exhaust regulator valve spring, low-splitter valve spring and lockup cutoff valve spring. Remove these springs.

FRONT

REAR

PLUG

SCREW

COVER

BALL

SPRING

BRACKET

SCREW

Accelerator plug and cover (© Detroit Diesel Allison)

SCREW — NUT — RETAINER

BODY

VALVE

SPRING

VALVE

VALVE

PLUG

SPRING

SPRING

SPRING

BODY

SPRING

SPRING

PIN

BALL

VALVE

VALVE

SPRING

COVER

SCREW

SCREW

SPRING

BALL

BRACKET

SCREW

SCREW

Exhaust regulator valve body (© Chrysler Corp.)

SEAL

RETURN SPRING

VALVE

ATTACHING BOLT AND LOCKWASHER (LONG)

ATTACHING BOLT (SHORT)

VALVE BODY

PIN

LUBE REGULATOR VALVE BALL

SPRING

LOCKWASHER

RETAINER

Hydraulic retarder valve body
(© Chrysler Corp.)

MANUAL SELECTOR VALVE

THROTTLE VALVE RETAINER

CONTROL VALVE BODY ASSY.

SELECTOR VALVE LEVER

THROTTLE VALVE LEVER

Control valve body (installed)

3. Remove intermediate exhaust regulator valve, lockup cutoff valve and low-splitter exhaust regulator valve.

4. Remove extender valve, extender valve spring and valve ball spring. Do not remove extender valve body and roll pin unless replacement is necessary. If replacement is necessary, remove roll pin and tap out extender valve body toward nearest opening (front) of exhaust regulator valve body.

5. Remove trimmer cover from fear of exhaust regulator valve body, remove cover. *This cover is spring loaded and must be held while screws are being removed.*

6. Remove trimmer valve, trimmer valve inner and outer springs, trimmer plug, trimmer primary spring, trimmer stop and trimmer secondary spring from exhaust regulator valve body.

7. Remove screw and retainer. Remove low-splitter exhaust regulator stop plug and low-splitter exhaust regulator plug. Remove intermediate exhaust stop plug from exhaust regulator valve body. *Models using the set screw on bottom of valve body do not use regulator plug.*

Assembly

1. Install intermediate exhaust reg-

1121

Oil Control valve body

1 Nylon ball, 1/2
2 Shift valve detent spring
3 Shift valve detent ball
4 Bolt, 1/4-20 x 2-3/4
5 Bolt, 1/4-20 x 3-1/4
6 Bolt, 1/4-20 x 3-3/4
7 Lock washer, 1/4
8 Valve body bolt sleeve
9 Control valve body assembly
10 Drive transfer tube clip
11 Drive transfer tube
12 High transfer tube
13 High transfer tube clip
14 Pump overage regulator spring
15 Screw and washer
16 Regulator spring retainer
17 Retainer spring
18 Pump overage regulator valve assembly
19 Overcontrol valve body
20 Overcontrol valve
21 Overcontrol valve cover
22 Screw and washer, 10-24 x 7/16
23 Screw and washer, 10-24 x 2-3/8
24 Screw and washer, 10-24 x 7/16
25 Screw and washer, 10-24 x 2-⅜
26 Intermediate-to-high shift valve cover
27 Intermediate-to-high shift valve spring
28 Splitter shift plug spring
29 Splitter shift plug
30 Intermediate-to-high blocker plug
31 Oval point setscrew, 10-24
31A Oval point setscrew, 10-24
32 Valve body front cover
33 Throttle valve plug
34 Nylon ball, 1/4
35 Main-pressure regulator valve spring (primary)
35A Main-pressure regulator valve spring (secondary)
36 Front splitter shift (G1) plug
37 Intermediate-to-high shift plug
38 Low-to-intermediate shift valve
39 Rear-splitter shift (G2) plug
40 Lockup plug
41 Regulator plug
42 Hydraulic retarder regulator plug
43 Manual selector valve
44 Intermediate-to-low shift valve spring
45 Oval point setscrew, 10-24
46 Valve body rear cover
47 Accelerator plug
48 Accelerator plug cover
49 Ball
50 Trimmer ball regulator spring
51 Valve guide bracket assembly
52 Screw and washer, 10-24 x 1-5/8
53 Screw and washer, 10-24 x 3/4
54 Accumulator valve
55 Lockup knockdown plug
56 Accumulator valve spring
57 Regulator cover
58 Screw and washer, 10-24 x 7/16
59 Screw and washer, 10-24 x 3/4
60 Throttle valve adjusting screw
61 Throttle valve retainer
62 Screw and washer, 10-24 x 3/8
63 Exhaust regulator valave body
64 Low-splitter exhaust regulator plug

65 Low-splitter exhaust regulator stop plug
66 Intermediate-exhaust regulator stop plug
67 Plug retainer
68 Screw and washer, 10-24 x 7/16
69 Trimmer secondary spring
70 Trimmer stop
71 Trimmer primary spring
72 Screw and washer, 10-24 x 7/16
73 Trimmer cover
74 Trimmer valve
75 Trimmer return inner spring
76 Pipe plug, 1/4
77 Screw and washer, 10-24 x 3/4
78 Trimmer return outer spring
79 Trimmer plug
80 Exhaust regulator valve cover
81 Lockup cutoff valve spring
82 Lockup cutoff valve
83 Extender valve body
84 Extender valve ball
85 Extender tralve ball spring
86 Extender valve return spring

87 Extender valve
88 Screw and washer, 10-24 x 7/16
89 Valve guide bracket assembly
90 Trimmer ball regulator spring
91 Ball
92 Extender valve body roll pin
93 Low-splitter exhaust regulator valve spring
94 Inermediate exhaust regulator valve spring
95 Low-splitter exhaust regulator valve
96 Intermediate exhaust regulator valve
97 Valve body separator plate
98 Throttle valve
99 Throttle valve (TV) spring
100 Selector valve detent spring
101 Selector valve detent ball
102 Control valve body
103 Reverse lockup inhibitor check valve retainer
104 Nylon ball, 7/32
105 Reverse-range clutch exhaust regulator valve assembly

106 Throttle regulator valve
107 Main-pressure regulator valve
108 Lockup shift valve spring
109 Lockup shift valve
110 Splitter shift valve
111 Splitter relay valve spring
112 Intermediate-to-high shift valve
113 Splitter relay valve
114 6-5 inhibitor valve
116 Low inhibitor plug
117 Low inhibitor valve
118 3-2 inhibitor spring
119 Inhibitor spring retainer
120 Tee nut
121 Inhibitor spring adjusting screw
122 5-4 inhibitor valve
123 5-4 inhibitor spring
124 Spring retainer washer
125 Cotter pin
126 Signal tube
127 Signal tube clip

ulator stop plug (small diameter first) into exhaust regulator valve body.

2. Install low-splitter exhaust regulator plug. *Some models do not use a plug in this location.*
3. Install low-splitter regulator stop plug, small diameter first.
4. Install signal tube, retainer, clip and screw. Tighten screw to 24-36 inch-pounds. *Tube must not protrude through body to interfere with separator plate to be installed later.*
5. Install trimmer secondary spring, trimmer stop, trimmer primary spring and trimmer plug.
6. Install trimmer inner and outer spring and trimmer valve. Install cover and four screws. Tighten screws to 24-36 inch-pounds.
7. Install the 5-4 inhibitor valve, inhibitor spring, flat washer and a new cotter pin into bottom of valve body.
8. Install extender valve body if removed previously, secure with roll pin. Press roll pin into valve body until slightly below flat surface of the body.
9. Install low-splitter exhaust regulator valve, intermediate exhaust regulator valve, low-splitter exhaust regulator spring and intermediate exhaust regulator valve spring.
10. Install extender valve ball, extender valve ball spring, extender valve return spring and extender valve, recessed end first.
11. Install lockup cutoff valve and spring.
12. Install inhibitor spring, inhibitor valve and inhibitor plug.
13. Install exhaust regulator cover, secure with nine screws. On models using bracket, spring and ball, install these parts and secure with two screws.
14. Tighten cover screws to 24 to 36 inch-pounds. Screw which secures drive transfer tube clip is not installed at this time.

Installation on Control Valve Body

1. Install range selector valve detent ball and spring in control valve body.
2. Install valve body separator plate on valve body assembly.
3. Install assembled exhaust regulator valve body and tighten screws 24-36 inch-pounds.
4. Place control valve body, flat (top) side down on a flat surface. Check to determine if the end covers project below the valve body. Tap valve body downward to correct any such projection. Tighten all screws at front and rear of valve body

24-36 inch-pounds. *This check is important. The valve body must seat tightly against the oil transfer plate.*

5. Assemble pump overage spring retainer to each end of pump valve spring. Compress spring and install between ribs on valve body front cover.
6. Install pump overage valve assembly and fasten with retainer spring. *Seat of valve assembly must protrude at least 0.005 inch beyond valve body mounting plane to assure seating of the valve against oil transfer plate.*
7. Install high transfer tube with clip. Install drive transfer tube with clip. Tighten screws 24 to 36 inch-pounds. *Signal tube installed previously is not to be depressed further at any time after separator plate is installed.*

Hydraulic Retarder Control Valve Body

Disassembly

1. Place hydraulic retarder control valve body assembly on wood blocks or vise equipped with soft jaws (mounting surface downward).
2. Drive valve retaining pin out of valve body.
3. Place valve body on a wood surface (or vise equipped with soft jaws) with valve pointing upward. Using a soft hammer drive valve against spring in the body. The spring pressure will bounce valve back out and loosen the oil seal. *Remove any paint, dirt or burrs around seal to make seal removal operation easier.*
4. Remove seal, valve and spring from valve body. Loosen lubrication regulator valve retainer by tapping lightly around edge of retainer, then remove retainer, spring, and steel ball.

Assembly

1. Insert lubrication regulator valve steel ball in valve body and install lubrication regulator valve spring and retainer, starting the retainer straight in valve body.
2. Press retainer in until the large diameter is flush with mounting surface to .030 inch maximum below surface of valve body.
3. Insert the hydraulic retarder valve return spring in valve body bore, and insert valve against spring. The valve must move into the bore by its own weight.
4. Start valve retainer pin straight in body from mounting surface side of the body. Place valve

body in a press so mounting surface is level and body is evenly supported. Hold valve in body against return spring and far enough to clear retaining pin holes, press pin into body.

5. Remove body from press and drive pin further to be sure it does not protrude above mounting surface of valve body.
6. Coat outer shell of a new valve oil seal with a suitable sealer and start seal straight into valve body. Press seal in until it is flush with valve body. *After assembly, valve must return to its normal position against retaining pin after actuation.*
7. Install hydraulic retarder valve body on transmission case and transfer plate and range selector valve bodies in transmission case. Make all necessary adjustments as outlined in adjustment section.

Servicing Torque Converter and Transmission out of Vehicle

Torque Converter Components

Removal

1. Drain oil from transmission.
2. Position transmission in a repair stand.
3. Remove pump cover assembly using a lifting strap and eye if necessary.
4. Remove lockup-clutch plate, seal ring and clutch back plate.
5. Remove hook-type seal ring, snap ring and seal ring.
6. Remove converter turbine assembly. Twist converter stator counterclockwise to lock it to the freewheel roller race and lift up while sliding fingers under the race end before it comes all the way off the shaft. Insert stator before releasing fingers.
7. Remove snap ring and converter pump spacer. Remove converter pump assembly. Remove converter housing.
8. Remove needle bearing assembly and needle bearing race, remove converter housing gasket.
9. Remove hydraulic retarder shaft and rotor assembly. Remove hook-type seal ring and thrust washer.

Oil Pan and Valve Body

Removal

1. Position transmission, bottom up and remove filter cover and seal ring.
2. Remove retainer, seal ring and filter element.

30 Bushing
31 Gasket
32 Self-locking bolt,
   5/16-18 x 3/4
33 Bolt, 5/16-18 x1
34 Lock washer, 5/16
35 Plain washer, 5/16
36 Pipe plug, 1/8-27
37 Plain washer, 7/16
38 Lock washer, 7/16
39 Bolt, 7/16-14 x 2
40 Converter housing
41 Seal ring
42 Front oil pump assembly
43 Oil pump cover
44 Oil pump drive gear

1 Converter pump cover
   assembly
2 Bushing
3 Oil seal retainer
4 Oil seal
5 Lockup clutch piston
   assembly
6 Seal ring
7 Lockup clutch plate
8 Seal ring
9 Snap ring
10 Snap ring
11 Lockup clutch back plate
12 Turbine assembly
13 Stator and cam assembly
14 Thrust bearing assembly

15 Freewheel roller race
16 Freewheel roller spring
17 Freewheel roller
18 Snap ring
19 Spacer
20 Bolt, 1/4-20 x 5/8
21 Lock strip
22 Bearing retainer
23 Ball bearing
24 Converter pump hub
25 Converter pump hub gasket

26 Thrust bearing assembly
27 Needle thrust bearing race
28 Needle thrust bearing
   assembly
29 Converter ground sleever
   assembly

45 Oil pump driven gear
46 Oil pump body
47 Seal
48 Converter pump assembly
49 Bolt, 5/16-24 x 1.30
50 Hook-type seal ring
51 Seal ring
52 Lock nut, 5/16-24
53 Spacer (AR)—
      0.027 thk (gold)
      0.045 thk (silver)
      0.063 thk (copper)
      0.081 thk (black)
      0.099 thk (plain)
54 Retainer—0.015 thk

Torque converter, lock up clutch and front pump assemblies (© Chrysler Corp.)

3. Remove oil pan.

4. Remove oil filter can assembly, remove seal ring from pipe.

5. Remove retarder valve body, 5/8 teflon ball and gasket.

6. Remove control valve body assembly, being very careful not to drop the two balls into the trans-

mission case. Remove balls and spring.

7. Remove the downshift timing valve body assembly. Remove oil transfer plate assembly from case, being careful not to drop ball under plate into transmission case. Remove ball after plate is removed.

Rear Bearing Retainer

Removal

1. Position transmission with rear bearing retainer up. Remove speedometer drive (or plug).

2. Remove reverse, low and intermediate-range clutch reaction housing anchor bolt nuts, low

1 Reverse planetary carrier
  assembly
2 Reverse planetary carrier
3 Planetary carrier pinion pin
4 Thrust washer
5 Planetary carrier pinion
6 Roller
7 Rear pilot collector ring
8 Rear pilot collector ring
8 External lock washer
9 Rivet, 1/4 x 2-1/2
10 Rear pitot tube
11 Bolt, 5/16-18 x 1-3/8
12 Washer, 5/16 lock
13 Rear pitot adapter
14 Bearing retainer gasket
   (AR)—0.012 thk
        —0.016 thk
        —0.021 thk
15 Rear bearing retainer
16 Washer, 7/16 lock
17 Bolt, 7/16-14 x 2-1/2
18 Bolt, 7/16-14 x 1-3/8
19 Pipe plug, 1/8-27

20 Speedo bushing
22 Speedo drive gear
22A Washer
23 Ball bearing assembly
24 Rear pitot bolt
25 Internal snap ring
26 Output flange seal
27 Output flange
28 Flange retainer washer
29 Seal ring
30 Tab lock washer
31 Bolt, 1/2-20 x 1-1/2
36 Serrated shank bolt
37 Brake drum
38 Brake band assembly
39 Brake cam shoe
40 Brake adjusting bolt
41 Brake cam link
42 Cotter pin, 1/8 x 7/8
43 Clevis pin, 1/2 x 1-27/64
44 Lock washer, 1/4

45 Hexagon nut, 1/4-20
46 Brake cam
47 Brake release spring
48 Bolt
49 Brake bracket
52 Hexagon nut
53 Lock washer
55 Brake band anchor bolt
   spring
56 Clip screw
57 Lock wire

Rear bearing retainer and output flange (typical)

and reverse-range piston housing anchor bolt and intermediate-range piston housing anchor bolt.

3. Remove rear bearing retainer from transmission housing.

Reverse Planetary Gearing and Clutch

Removal

1. Remove reverse-range planetary carrier assembly and thrust washer.

2. Lift out reverse-range clutch reaction housing with clutch plates and ring gear, place on a bench with plate up. Lift plates out of housing. *These parts have red markings and should not be intermixed with other clutches*

3. Lift out reverse-range clutch spring. Remove round wire snap ring, remove reverse-range reaction housing anchor bolt.

4. Using hoist and sling to release pressure from snap ring, remove snap ring from reverse-range sun gear shaft; disconnect slinge.

5. Remove reverse-range sun gear and internal splined reverse-range sun gear thrust washer.

Low and Intermediate-Range Gearing and Clutches

Removal

1. Working through openings in transmission housing, remove low and reverse-range piston

housing assembly. *Keep fingers out of transmission housing.*

2. Lift out low-range clutch spring and low-range clutch apply plate. *Low-range clutch parts have green markings.*

3. Remove low-range clutch plates from transmission housing.

4. Remove internal snap ring from low-range ring gear and lift out reverse-range sun gear shaft.

5. Lift out transmsision output shaft assembly and the low-range ring gears and intermediate-range planetary assembly.

6. Remove low-range clutch reaction housing and anchor bolt.

7. Remove intermediate-range piston housing assembly from transmission.

ROLLER   SPRING   ROLLER THRUST BEARING ASSY.

THRUST WASHER

STATOR ASSY.

Converter stator

Automatic Transmissions

1 Oil collector
2 Intermediate-range clutch reaction housing
3 Internal-splined clutch plate
4 External-splined clutch plate
5 Intermediate-range ring gear assembly
6 Intermediate-range clutch apply plate
7 Intermediate-range clutch spring
8 Seal ring
8A Seal ring expander
9 Intermediate-range clutch piston
10 Hook-type seal ring
11 Intermediate-range piston housing
12 Low-range clutch reaction housing
13 Internal-splined clutch plate
14 External-splined clutch plate
15 Low-range clutch apply plate
16 Intermediate-range planetary carrier assembly
17 Thrust washer
18 Intermediate-range planetary pinion
19 Roller
20 Intermediate-range planetary pinion pin
21 Intermediate-range planetary carrier
22 Internal-snap ring
23 Low-range ring gear
24 Low-range planetary carrier and transmission output shaft assembly
25 Thrust washer
26 Roller
27 Planetary pinion
28 Planetary pinion pin
29 Bushing
30 Low-range planetary carrier and transmission output shaft
31 Internal-snap ring
32 Reverse-range sun gear shaft
33 Clutch spring
34 Seal ring
34A Seal ring expander
35 Low-range piston
36 Hook-type seal ring
37 Low and reverse-range piston housing
38 Hook-type seal ring
39 Reverse-range piston
40 Seal ring
40A Seal ring expander

41 Thrust washer
42 Reverse-range sun gear
43 Snap ring
44 Thrust washer
45 Snap ring
46 Clutch spring
47 Reverse-range clutch apply plate
48 Internal-splined clutch plate
49 External-splined clutch plate
50 Reverse-range ring gear assembly
51 Reverse-range clutch reaction housing
52 Clutch plate retaining ring
53 Clutch reaction housing (2, 12, 51)

ANCHOR BOLT SLOT

AFTER S/N 5-2069

Intermediate, low and reverse range clutches and intermediate planetary carrier
(© Chrysler Corp.)

8. Remove intermediate-range clutch spring and intermediate-range clutch apply plate from transmission housing. *Intermediate range clutch parts have yellow markings.*
9. Remove intermediate-range ring gear and clutch plates from intermediate-range clutch reaction housing. Remove intermediate range clutch reaction housing, anchor bolt and oil collector ring from transmission housing.

Splitter Mechanism, High-Range Clutch and Power Take-off Gear
Removal
1. Position transmission, converter end up. Remove low-splitter clutch reaction plate anchor bolt and the two high-range clutch diaphragm anchor bolts.
2. Remove low-splitter reaction plate from transmission housing. Remove high-range clutch diaphragm anchor bolt.
3. Install lifting eye into threaded hole in splitter output shaft. Hoist the entire splitter and high-range clutch section carefully from transmission housing.

CONVERTER HOUSING   WOOD BLOCK

GROUND SLEEVE

Removing converter ground sleeve

Transmission and Component Parts Overhaul

Converter Pump Cover and Lockup Clutch
Disassembly
1. Remove lockup clutch back plate from converter pump cover, then lift out clutch plate. If necessary, tap edge of cover against a wooden block to remove back plate.
2. Remove seal ring from front flange of the back plate.
3. Remove snap ring from the lock-up clutch piston in pump cover, using compressor tool.
4. Remove piston from pump cover

Positioning torque converter ground sleeve in housing

Anchor bolt locations

by tapping edge of cover against a wooden block.

5. Remove seal ring from outer groove in the piston.

Inspection

Clean all of the converter cover and lockup clutch parts and inspect for wear or damage. Replace all parts that are worn beyond the specified limits or that are damaged. (Consult Specifications).

Assembly

1. Install seal ring in outer groove in lockup clutch piston, then lightly oil the seal.
2. Install piston in converter pump cover so the dowel holes in piston engage dowels in the cover. *Be sure the balance marks on both parts are also aligned.* To align the parts correctly, place a heavy pencil mark in line with a dowel on bolt circle of the cover, then match this mark with another part on piston in line with a dowel hole on reverse side. *If dowels do not enter dowel holes, the lockup clutch will not disengage and the converter will not function.*
3. Install snap ring. If piston does not push far enough into pump cover to install the snap ring, use compressor tool to compress the piston.

Low Range Ring Gear and Intermediate Range Planetary Carrier

Disassembly

1. Remove the snap ring that locks reverse range sun gear shaft to low range ring gear (if not previously done).
2. Remove internal snap ring from low range ring gear.
3. Remove intermediate range planetary carrier.

Assembly

1. Mesh external teeth of planetary carrier wtih internal teeth of ring gear and push carrier into ring gear.
2. Install internal snap ring to hold assembly together. *Refer to Paragraph "Procedure for Checking Range Clutch Clearances Before Installation."*

Splitter Mechanism, High Range Clutch and Power Take-off Gear

Shaft and Rotor
Disassembly

1. Remove hook-type seal ring from groove in gear outside diameter of hydraulic retarder shaft and rotor assembly.
2. If bushing needs replacement, remove from large end of shaft.

Assembly

To assemble, reverse disassembly procedures.

Clutch Package Disassembly

Splitter Planetary Carrier

1. Remove splitter output shaft snap ring.
2. Remove splitter planetary carrier assembly and bronze splitter washer.

SEAL DRIVER (TOOL)

FRONT PUMP HOUSING

Installing front pump oil seal

3. Do not disassemble carrier assembly. If there is evidence of excessive wear or damage, replace carrier assembly as a unit.

Splitter Clutches

1. Lift off splitter clutch assembly and place it flat side down. Lift off bronze thrust washer. (On models having an 8 tanged, low-splitter clutch plate, remove plate at this time.)
2. Remove high-splitter clutch reaction plate.
3. Remove one high-splitter clutch, internal splined plate, one external splined plate and the other internal splined plate.
4. Place splitter clutch housing assembly in a press and using a remover and installing sleeve, depress the high-splitter clutch piston return spring to remove pressure against snap ring. Remove snap ring and piston return spring.
5. Remove high-splitter clutch piston, seal ring and expander if used from piston outside diameter.
6. Remove hook-type seal ring from high-splitter clutch housing.
7. Replace splitter sun gear bushing if necessary.

High-Range Clutch Diaphragm

1. Remove the two hook-type seal rings from hub of high-range clutch diaphragm assembly.
2. Turn the diaphragm and high-range clutch assembly over so the rear end of splitter output shaft is up. *When turning assembly over, grip all components together to prevent damage to the pitot tube.*
3. Remove snap ring from rear end of splitter output shaft. Remove the low and intermediate-range sun gears.
4. Turn diaphragm and high-range clutch over, placing low-splitter clutch piston up. *When turning*

1 Hook-type seal ring
2 Turbine shaft and hydraulic retarder rotor assembly
3 Bushing
4 Hook-type seal ring
5 Thrust washer
6 Snap ring
7 Low-splitter clutch reaction plate
8 Splitter planetary carrier assembly
9 Splitter planetary carrier
10 Splitter planetary pin
11 Thrust washer
12 Splitter planetary pinion
13 Roller
14 Thrust washer
15 Internal-snap ring
16 High-splitter clutch reaction plate

17 Internal-splined clutch plate
18 External-splined clutch plate
19 Snap ring
20 Low-splitter clutch plate
21 Piston return spring
22 High-splitter piston
23 Seal ring
23A Seal ring expander
24 Hook-type seal ring
25 Bushing
26 High-splitter housing and gear assembly
27 Hook-type seal ring
28 Thrust washer
29 Snap ring
30 Piston return spring
31 Low-splitter clutch piston
32 Seal ring
32A Seal ring expander
33 Hook-type seal ring

34 Screw and washer, 10-32 x 5/8
35 Diaphragm assembly
36 Sleeve
37 Front pitot tube
38 Hook-type seal ring
39 Bushing
40 High-range clutch housing assembly
41 Hook-type seal ring
42 Seal ring
42A Seal ring expander
43 High-range clutch piston assembly
44 Ball, 1/4 Dia.
45 High-clutch piston
46 Inner spring
47 Outer spring
48 High-range clutch spring retainer

49 Snap ring
50 Internal-splined clutch plate
51 External-splined clutch plate
52 Power take off gear
53 High-range clutch reaction plate
54 Snap ring
55 Hook-type seal ring
56 Wire-type snap ring
57 Hook-type seal ring
58 Splitter output shaft assembly
59 Splitter output shaft
60 Lube orifice plug
61 Intermediate-range sun gear
62 Low-range sun gear
63 Snap ring

Splitter mechanism, hydraulic retarder and high range clutch (© Chrysler Corp.)

assembly over, grip all components together to prevent damage to the pitot tube.

5. Remove splitter output shaft assembly, the two hook-type seal rings and two wire type snap rings. *Do not remove orifice plug in end of shaft.*

6. Place assembly in a press and using remover and installer sleeve, depress the low-splitter piston return spring to reline pressure on snap ring. Remove snap ring.

7. Remove low-splitter clutch piston, seal ring and seal expander if used from piston outside diameter.

8. Remove hook-type seal ring from hub of diaphragm.

9. Lift off high-range clutch dia-

phragm and remove the two hook-type seal rings from hub. Remove pitot tube.

High-Range Clutch and Piston

1. Turn high-range clutch over and remove internal snap ring from clutch housing.

2. Remove high-range clutch reaction plate.

3. On 5-plate clutch assemblies, remove three internal-splined and two external-splined high-range clutch plates. The **7-plate** clutch assemblies have four internal-splined and three external-splined clutch plates. Remove power take-off gear (on those models which use a separate gear).

4. Block up the assembly so that no

weight will be on the governor oil collector ring and use a press and a remover and installer sleeve to compress high-range clutch piston return springs. Remove snap ring. *Do not attempt to remove snap ring without a press.*

5. Remove the high-range clutch piston return spring retainer and two springs.

6. Tap rear of high-range clutch housing assembly on wood blocks to loosen piston. Remove high-range clutch piston seal ring (and expander, if used) from piston outside diameter. Remove hook-type seal ring from hub of high-range clutch housing.

7. Replace high-range clutch hous-

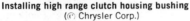

Installing high range clutch housing bushing
(© Chrysler Corp.)

Installing high range clutch diaphram assembly
(© Chrysler Corp.)

ing bushing (or needle bearing) if necessary.

Clutch Package Assembly

Splitter Clutches

1. If splitter sun gear bushing was removed from a high-splitter clutch housing, use a press and bushing installer to replace it.
2. Install hook-type seal ring on hub of high-splitter clutch housing assembly.
3. Install seal ring expander (if used) and seal ring in groove in high-splitter piston outside diameter and install piston in high-splitter clutch housing. On models which have external tangs on high-splitter piston, align the tangs with any opposite pair of slots in high-splitter housing. On models having dowels in high-splitter housing, be sure they are inserted in high-splitter piston recesses.
4. Using a press and installer sleeve, install the high-splitter piston return spring, concave side down, install snap ring. *Depress spring only enough to install snap ring.*

5. On models using a 6-tanged plate, install the low-splitter, internal tanged clutch plate, making sure that tangs are not in the same slots as piston tangs. *Low-splitter clutch failure will result if piston tangs and clutch tangs are in the same slot.*
6. In 3-plate clutch assemblies, install an internal-splined plate, the external-splined and the other internal-splined plate. In 5-plate assemblies, install another external-splined plate and another internal-splined plate.
7. Install high-splitter clutch reaction plate with smooth side facing clutch plates. Install snap ring.

High-Range Clutch and Piston

1. If the high-range clutch housing bushing was removed from the housing, install a new bushing. Press bushing flush to 0.010 below surface. On models using a needle bearing at this location, install new needle bearing numbered end out. Using a suitable tool, press against bearing shell and square with bore, press

bearing flush to 0.010 below surface.
2. Install hook-type seal ring on hub of high-range clutch housing.
3. Install seal ring expander (if used) and seal ring in groove in outside diameter of high-range clutch piston and install high-range clutch piston in housing, smooth side first. *On models using pistons with external tangs, tangs must be engaged in slots in housing. On models using dowels in housing, dowels must engage recesses in piston.*
4. Install the two high-range clutch piston return springs and place cup of retainer over spring.
5. Place the assembly in a press keeping governor oil collector ring off the bench. Compress springs and install snap ring.
6. On the 5-clutch plate model, install an internal-splined, high-range clutch plate first, then install an external-splined plate, another internal-splined plate, another external-splined plate and a third internal-splined plate. For the 7-plate model, install a third external-splined plate and a fourth internal-splined plate.
7. Install power take-off gear with end slots up (on models using a separate gear).
8. Install high-range clutch reaction plate so the two longer tangs engage slots in power take-off gear. Install internal snap ring. See paragraph on "checking range clutch clearances" using clearance tolerance of 0.040-0.050.

Splitter and High-Range Clutch Package

1. Install a wire type snap ring in groove around spline on ends of splitter output shaft. Install two hook-type seal rings in seal ring grooves near center of shaft. In-

Installing high range clutch spring retainer snap ring
(© Chrysler Corp.)

stall shaft into high-range clutch housing orifice end first.

2. Install intermediate and low-range sun gears (chamfered end out) on output shaft, orifice end.

3. Install snap ring on orifice end of splitter output shaft.

4. Install two hook-type seal rings on long hub end of high-range clutch diaphragm assembly. Install two 10-32 guide bolts in front pitot tube with tube center oil hole facing bolts. Position guide bolts through the high-range clutch diaphragm with pitot tube tip toward outside diameter. Guide the pitot tube into oil slinger trough and carefully slide sleeve over the two hook-type seal rings on splitter shaft and the two hook seal rings on diaphragm hub into high-range clutch hub. Diaphragm sleeve end enters a bushing (or needle bearing) in clutch hub. Replace the guide bolts with screws and washers and torque to 30-48 inch-pounds.

5. Install hook-type seal ring on hub diaphragm. Install seal ring expander (if used) with ends down toward piston, and seal ring in groove in outside diameter of low-splitter clutch piston.

6. Install low-splitter clutch piston into diaphragm assembly. Install piston return spring with inside cone up. Seat snap ring against spring with hammer and drift.

7. Install two hook-type rings on hub of diaphragm assembly. Grease and install bronze thrust washer in bore of splitter clutch housing.

8. On models using the 8-tanged the plate on the assembled low-splitter clutch plate, install high-splitter clutch engaging the 8 slots on outside of housing. (Six tang plate is installed at time of high splitter plate installation). Install the assembled splitter clutch on diaphragm hub using care as hook-type seals enter housing.

9. Install a greased bronze thrust washer in hub of splitter planetary carrier.

10. Install splitter planetary carrier assembly into clutch housing. Install snap ring.

Range Selector and Throttle Control Levers

1. Install a new "O" type seal ring on range selector lever shaft and insert shaft (from inside transmission) through transmission housing.

2. Install range selector valve lever (external) on shaft so that both lever and shaft arms point approximately toward bottom of transmission.

3. Install range selector lever washer and nut and tighten nut from 14 to 17 foot-pounds. *Bend washer against a flat on nut.*

4. Install a new "O" type seal ring on throttle control lever shaft and insert shaft through range selector shaft from inside transmission.

5. Install throttle external lever on shaft so that both lever and shaft arms point approximately toward bottom of transmission.

6. *Bend washer against a flat on nut and tighten from 14 to 17 foot-pounds.*

Procedure for Checking Range Clutch Clearances Before Installation

If any pistons, piston housings, apply plates, reaction housings, cushion springs or clutch plates have been replaced in the low-intermediate or reverse range clutches, clutch clearances must be checked. This can be done prior to assembly in transmission housing, by using a fixture tool.

1. Place intermediate range clutch reaction housing (coded yellow) in fixture tool with four of the housing lots adjacent to the four posts of the tool. Various clutch parts are color coded. These parts should be assembled in the same location when transmission is serviced to insure

proper fitting. Parts coded with yellow are for intermediate range clutch, those coded green are for low range clutch, and red marking identifies reverse range clutch parts.

2. Place intermediate range clutch plate and ring gear in intermediate range reaction housing, long part of ring gear down.

3. Install intermediate range clutch plate. Install intermediate range clutch cushion spring with convex side up.

4. Install intermediate range clutch piston and piston housing (piston down).

5. Install low range clutch reaction housing (slots up).

6. Install low range clutch plate (flat side down). Install low range cushion spring with convex side up.

7. Install low and reverse range piston and housing assembly with red marking up. Install reverse range cushion spring with convex side down.

8. Install the reverse range clutch plate (flat side up). Install reverse range clutch reaction housing (slots down). Place top plate of fixture tool on clutch stack.

9. Install top to tool and tighten nut to 30 foot-pounds. *Make certain cushion springs and other components are all concentric as pressure is applied.*

10. Using a feeler gauge, measure clearances between clutch friction plates and clutch plates of reverse range clutch. Repeat this procedure for low range clutch.

11. Clearance should be .010 to .015 inches for reverse range and low range clutch. The intermediate range clutch should show a clearance of .020 to .030 inches.

12. If clutches do not meet specified clearances, it will be necessary to change the apply plates. Apply plates are available for reverse, low, and intermediate ranges in three thicknesses for each clutch. The thicknesses are: .458 inch to .462, .465 inch to .469

Internal control lever identification
(© Chrysler Corp.)

Checking range clutch clearance using fixture
(© Chrysler Corp.)

Installing low splitter clutch reaction plate (© Chrysler Corp.)

Installing oil connector ring

inch, and .472 inch to .476 inch.

13. By measuring the maximum thickness of the apply plate from clutch stack, and by considering the clearance measurement taken while stack is assembled, the correct plate (required to bring the clearance to specifications) may be chosen.

14. When the correct clutch clearances for three ranges have been made, remove clutch pack from fixture and place on a bench in reverse order. In this way, each part may be selected in correct order for assembly in transmission.

Installation of Subassemblies in Transmission Housing

All clutch plates must be soaked in specified transmission oil for 2 minutes before being installed. All thrust surfaces, gears, bushings and bearings must be oiled as they are installed.

Splitter Mechanism, High Range Clutch and Power Take-off Gear

Installation

1. Using a lifting eye, install the splitter section and high range clutch assembly. The three anchor bolt holes in the high range clutch diaphragm assembly must align with three holes in transmission housing (two holes in the bottom and one hole in the top of housing).

2. Install the three anchor bolts (the shorter bolt is installed at top of transmission). Tighten the two bottom bolts to 17-20 foot-pounds. *Do not tighten the top bolt at this time. Failure to tighten the bolts in the correct sequence may result in internal oil leakage.*

Hydraulic Retarder Section

Installation

1. Install low splitter clutch reaction plate with *vanes toward front of housing* and the anchor *bolt hole in line with hole in bottom of housing.*

2. Install reaction plate anchor bolt and tighten to 17-20 foot-pounds. Tighten the support anchor bolt (at the top of the transmission) to 17-20 foot-pounds.

3. Install the hook type seal ring around splitter ring gear of turbine shaft and hydraulic retarder rotor.

4. Make sure thrust washer is in front of the splitter planetary carrier assembly and the hook type seal ring is in the groove at front of splitter output shaft assembly. Oil the thrust washer and hook type seal ring, then install turbine shaft and hydraulic retarder rotor assembly. *Be careful to avoid damaging the hook type seal ring at the front of the splitter output shaft.*

Torque Converter Components

Installation

1. Place converter housing gasket on transmission housing. Tape rotor shaft for protection, remove tape after stator is installed.

2. Check needle roller thrust bearing assembly to be sure that it is being held in place at rear of reaction shaft by oil soluble grease.

3. Install converter housing on transmission housing assembly and tighten the 10 mounting bolts and lock washers from 42 to 50 foot-pounds.

4. Install the hook type seal ring on converter pump hub.

5. Install converter pump in converter housing. Make sure the slots in the hub mate with the front pump drive lugs and the hook type seal ring on hub passes through front pump seal without damage to seal ring or seal.

6. Install seal in groove just inside the bolt circle.

7. Install the overrun race spacer on reaction shaft with concave side up.

8. Install a new snap ring to hold the spacer.

9. Carefully install the assembled stator and roller race. *The stator when installed, should overrun in the direction of the arrow on the converter pump and should lock when turned in the opposite direction.*

10. Install torque converter turbine on turbine shaft.

11. Install snap ring and hook type seal ring on turbine shaft. Install the polyacrylate seal ring in groove just inside the bolt circle on front of the lockup clutch back plate. *Be sure the seal is in place inside the bolt circle of converter pump.*

12. Install back plate. *If inked balance marks are found on back plate, converter pump lockup piston and pump cover, assemble the parts with marks aligned.*

13. Install lockup clutch plate on back plate with integral teeth engaging the turbine splined ring.

14. Install converter pump cover assembly on converter pump stud. If balance marks are on cover and pump align balance marks.

15. Install four nuts at 90 degree intervals and tighten alternately to 10 foot-pounds to prevent the polyacrylate seal from being forced out of its groove. Install the remaining nuts and tighten all nuts from 19 to 23 foot-pounds.

16. If any of the parts listed below are replaced in the course of transmission assembly, the dimension indicated by "A" must be checked. The required dimension is 1.572-1.592 inches. Parts replacement which may affect dimension "A" are: the converter pump cover assembly, lockup clutch reaction plate, converter pump, converter pump hub, converter reaction shaft assembly or the converter housing.

17. Dimension "A" may be checked by fastening a sling or strap to two opposite converter pump cover studs and applying a pull of 100 pounds or more to remove

all end play. While the pull is applied, measure distance "A". If the dimension is not within 1.572-1.592 inch, install or remove converter stack control spacers at the pump cover studs as needed.

18. The correct dimension should be established at each of the six stud positions. The spacers are furnished as follows:

Thickness	Color Code
.027-inch	Gold
.045-inch	Silver
.063-inch	Copper
.081-inch	Black
.099-inch	Plain

When the correct dimension is established, stake the spacers to the studs.

Low-Intermediate Range Clutches, Gearing and Low Range and Reverse Clutch Piston Housing

Installation

1. Position transmission rear end up. Install oil collector with the conical portion facing toward front of the housing.
2. Install the intermediate range clutch reaction housing so threaded anchor bolt hole is aligned with anchor hole in the bottom of the transmission housing.
3. Install anchor bolt (do not tighten) *Refer to disassembly procedure for the color coding of the clutch components.*
4. Install the intermediate range ring gear .296 inch to .300 inch thick with the longer section of gear toward front of transmission and toward reaction plate.
5. Install the intermediate range

clutch apply plate. Install the intermediate range clutch spring *with convex side toward rear of transmission. Make sure the spring is centered perfectly on the clutch apply plate on which it seats so the intermediate range piston housing will seat properly around it.*

6. Install the intermediate range piston housing, and with taped hole in piston housing in line with the corresponding anchor bolt hole in bottom of transmission housing.
7. Install (but do not tighten) the intermediate range clutch piston housing anchor bolt.
8. Install the low range clutch reaction housing, aligning taped hole in the plate with its corresponding anchor bolt hole in bottom of transmission housing.
9. Install the low range ring gear and intermediate range planetary carrier. Rotate assembly until planetary pinion teeth engage internal teeth of the intermediate range ring gear.
10. Install (but do not tighten) the reaction housing anchor bolt.
11. Install clutch plate and clutch apply plate.
12. Install transmission output shaft assembly, engaging the planetary pinion teeth with the internal teeth of the low range ring gear.
13. Install the reverse sun gear shaft over the output shaft. Mesh teeth on flange with internal teeth of the low range ring gear.
14. Install a new snap ring in the internal groove of low range ring gear, then install low range clutch spring *with convex side toward rear of transmission.* Make sure the spring is centered on the clutch apply plate so low

range reverse clutch piston housing will seat around it.

15. Install assembled low range and reverse clutch piston housing, aligning tapped hole in piston housing with corresponding anchor bolt hole in bottom of transmission housing. *Refer to disassembly procedure for correct color code. Do not install the anchor bolt at this time.*

Reverse Range Planetary Gearing and Clutch

Installation

1. Install splined thrust washer and sun gear on reverse range sun gear shaft.
2. Place snap ring on transmission output shaft, using a hoist, raise the output shaft and sun gear shaft until snap ring groove in sun gear shaft clears sun gear. Install snap ring.
3. Lift transmission output shaft and install snap ring.
4. Press low and reverse range piston housing into transmission housing and finger tighten anchor bolt. Install reverse range clutch spring with concave side up, center spring carefully. Depress spring edge and install anchor bolt through hole from inside transmission.
5. Place clutch apply plate on a bench with flat surface up. Position the reverse ring gear and clutch plate assembly on the apply plate with longer section of ring gear (external teeth up). Over these two parts, position reverse reaction housing with slots down so slots engage clutch apply plate tangs.
6. Install this assembly in transmission housing aligning anchor bolt slot in reaction housing with anchor bolt head previously in-

Converter pump cover shim selector

Using hoist to install snap ring

Pilot tube alignment and extension housing installation

stalled in transmission housing. Anchor bolt nut, finger tighten.

7. Install reverse planetary carrier and rear pitot collector ring on the output shaft. *Make sure the planetary pinions mesh with the sun gear and internal teeth of reverse ring gear.*

Rear Bearing Extension and Output Flange

Installation

1. Install the rear bearing retainer (without a gasket) on rear of transmission housing. Install four retainer mounting bolts at 90° intervals and tighten the bolts to 7 foot-pounds. Draw bearing retainer down evenly.

2. Check clearance between bearing retainer and rear surface of transmission housing near the points bolts. This clearance will determine which gaskets to use.

3. Gaskets are available in .012, .016 and .021 inch thicknesses. If the gaskets are not clearly marked, measure each with a micrometer. If clearance is .005-.015 inch, use the .012 gasket. If clearance is .015-.021 inch use the .016 gasket. If clearance is .022-.027 inch use the .021 gasket. For clearance of .028-.029 inch, use one .012 and one .016 gasket.

4. Install but do not tighten the low range reverse clutch piston housing and reverse clutch reacton housing anchor bolts.

5. Remove the bearing retainer. Tighten the five anchor bolts to 10-foot-pounds at this time.

6. Install the previously selected rear bearing retainer gasket.

7. Install two guide bolts in the rear pitot tube. Make sure the open (drilled port) side of the pitot tube is toward the bolts. *To make a guide bolt, thread one end of a 6 inch by ¼ inch diameter brazing rod. Use a ¼ inch—28 die and thread for a distance of ⅜ inch. Round off the unthreaded end.*

8. Swing the pitot tube toward the center of bearing retainer so that it will clear the pitot collector ring when the retainer is installed, install retainer.

9. Turn pitot tube to its normal position and start the other mounting bolt. Leave 1/16 inch or more of the mounting bolts protruding at rear of retainer.

10. Place the pitot tube in the rear pitot collector ring with tube portion toward the vanes and guide bolts toward rear of transmission. Carefully lower the rear bearing retainer over the output shaft while guiding the ends of the guide bolts through the pitot tube mounting bolt holes in the retainer. *Do not remove the pitot tube guide bolts at this time. Do not turn the output shaft until the output flange retaining bolt is installed. Otherwise, damage to the pitot tube or governor vanes may result.*

11. Install the rear bearing retainer bolts and lock washers. Tighten from 42-50 foot-pounds. Tighten the two anchor bolts to 17 to 20 foot pounds. Tighten the three self locking anchor bolt nuts to 35 to 40 foot-pounds.

12. Replace the two guide bolts with pitot tube bolts and tighten to 8-10 foot-pounds.

13. Install the output flange. *Do not turn the output shaft while installing flange. If shaft is turned, damage to the pitot tube or governor may result.*

14. Install the "O" type seal ring, tab lock washer and output flange bolt. Tighten bolt from 83 to 100 foot-pounds.

15. Install the speedometer fitting in rear bearing extension housing.

Diagnosis

This guide covers the most common symptoms and is an aid to careful diagnosis. The items to check are listed in sequence to be followed for quickest results. Follow the checks in the order given for the particular transmission type.

TROUBLE SYMPTOMS	Items to Check	
	In Truck	Out of Truck
Harsh N to D or N to R shift	CDEFGIJ	ab
Delayed Shift—N to D	ACIHKJ	ca
Runaway on upshift and 3-2 kickdown	ABCDLIHK	b
Harsh upshift and 3-2 kickdown	BCDLIHJ	b
No upshift	ABCDLIHKM	b
No kickdown on normal downshift	ABNCDLIHKM	d
Erratic shifts	ABNCFOPQ IKMJ	c
Slips in forward drive positions	ACIHK	abd
Slips in reverse only	CEGIK	
Slips in all positions	ACOIK	e
No drive in any position	ACOQIKJ	ca
No drive in forward positions	CDOLIHK	abd
No drive in reverse	CEGKMI	b
Drives in neutral	NIJ	a
Drags or locks	DELG	abfd
Noises	AORPMIJ	a
Hard to fill or blows out	AORSTQI	
Transmission overheats	ADEORTMI	abe

Key to Checks

A. Oil level
B. Control linkage
C. Oil pressure check
D. Kickdown band
E. Low-reverse band
F. Improper engine idle
G. Servo linkage

H. Accumulator
I. Valve body assembly
J. Manual valve lever
K. Air pressure check
L. K-D servo link
M. Governor
N. Gear shift cable

O. Regulator valve and/or spring
P. Output shaft bushing
Q. Strainer
R. Converter control valve
S. Breather clogged
T. Cooler or lines

a. Front-kickdown clutch
b. Rear clutch
c. Front pump and/or sleeve
d. Overrunning clutch
e. Converter
f. Planetary

Tests

Air Pressure Tests

The front clutch, rear clutch, kickdown servo and low and reverse servo may be checked with air pressure, after the valve body assembly has been removed.

To make air pressure tests, proceed as follows:

CAUTION: Compressed air must be free of dirt and moisture. Use pressure of 30-100 psi.

Front Clutch

Apply air pressure to the front clutch apply passage and listen for a dull thud. This will indicate operation of the front clutch. Hold the air pressure at this point for a few seconds and check for excessive oil leaks.

NOTE: If a dull thud cannot be heard in the clutch, place finger tips on clutch housing and again apply air pressure. Movement of piston can be felt as clutch is applied.

Rear Clutch

Apply air pressure to the rear clutch apply passage and proceed in an identical manner as that described in the previous paragraph.

Kickdown Servo

Air pressure applied to the kickdown servo apply passage should tighten the front band. Spring tension should be sufficient to release the band.

Low and Reverse Servo

Direct air pressure into the low and reverse servo apply passage. Response of the servo will result in a tightening of the rear band. Spring tension should be enough to release the band.

If clutches and servos operate properly, no upshift or erratic shift conditions existing, trouble exists in the control valve body assembly.

Governor

Governor troubles can usually be found during a road or pressure test.

Hydraulic Control Pressure Checks

Line Pressure and Front Servo Release Pressure

NOTE: These pressure checks must be made in the D position with the rear wheels free to turn. The transmission fluid must be at operating temperature (150°-200°F).

1. Install an engine tachometer, then, raise the truck on a hoist and locate the tachometer so it can be read from under the truck.
2. Connect two 0-100 psi pressure gauges to pressure takeoff points at the top of the accumulator and at the front servo release.
3. With the selector in D position, increase engine speed gradually until the transmission shifts into High. Reduce engine speed slowly to 100 rpm. The line pressure must be 54-60 psi with front servo release having no more than a 3 psi drop.

Bottom view of transmission (pan removed)
(© Chrysler Corp.)

4. Disconnect throttle linkage from transmission throttle lever and more throttle lever gradually to full throttle position. Line pressure must rise to maximum of 90-96 psi just before or at kickdown into low gear. Front servo repressure must follow line pressure up to kickdown point and should not be more than 3 psi below line pressure. If pressure is not 54-60 psi at 1000 rpm, adjust line pressure.

If line pressure is not as above, adjust the pressure as outlined under the heading: Hydraulic Control Pressure Adjustments—"Line Pressure."

If front servo release pressures are less than specified, and line pressures are within limits, there is excessive leakage in the front clutch and/or front servo circuits.

Lubrication Pressures

A lubrication pressure check should be made when line pressure and front servo release pressures are checked.

1. Install a T fitting between the cooler return line fitting and the

Dodge loadflite transmission (© Chrysler Corp.)

fitting hole in the transmission case at the rear left side of the transmission. Connect a 0-100 psi pressure gauge to the T-fitting.

2. At 1000 engine rpm, with throttle closed and transmission in High, lubrication pressure should be 5-15 psi. Lubrication pressure will approximately double as throttle is opened to maximum line pressure.

Rear Servo Apply Pressure

1. Connect a 0-300 psi pressure gauge, to the apply pressure take off point at the rear servo.
2. With the control in the R position, and the engine running at 1600 rpm, the reverse servo apply pressure should be 230-300 psi.

Governor Pressure

1. Connect a 0-100 psi gauge (same as the one used for line pressure and front servo release pressure) to the governor pressure takeoff point. This location is at

Pressure test locations (right side of case)
(© Chrysler Corp.)

the lower left rear corner of the extension mounting flange.
2. Governor pressure should fall within limits in chart.

Pressure should change smoothly with truck speeds.

If governor pressures are incorrect at the prescribed speeds, the governor valve and/or weights are probably sticking.

Hydraulic Control Pressure Adjustments

Line Pressure

An incorrect throttle pressure setting will cause incorrect line pressure even though line pressure adjustment is correct. Always inspect and correct throttle pressure adjustment before adjusting line pressure.

NOTE: Before adjusting line pressure, measure distance between manual valve (valve in 1-low position and line pressure adjusting screw. This measurement must be 1⅞ in. Correct by loosening spring retainer screws and repositioning spring retainer. The regulator valve may cock and hang up in its bore if spring retainer is out of position.

If line pressure is not correct remove valve body assembly to adjust. The correct adjustment is 1-5/16 in. measured from valve body to inner edge of adjusting nut. Vary adjustment slightly to obtain specified line pressure.

One complete turn of the adjusting screw (Allen head) changes closed

Pressure test locations (right side of case)
(© Chrysler Corp.)

Speedometer drive (© Chrysler Corp.)

Line pressure adjustments (© Chrysler Corp.)

Air pressure test points (© Chrysler Corp.)

Throttle pressure adjustment (© Chrysler Corp.)

Measuring spring retainer location (© Chrysler Corp.)

ADAPTER

6 O'CLOCK POSITION

Speedometer pinion and adapter installed
(© Chrysler Corp.)

throttle line pressure about 1.66 psi. Turning the screw counterclockwise increases pressure, clockwise decreases pressure.

Throttle Pressure

Because throttle pressures cannot be checked, exact adjustments should be checked and made correct whenever the valve body is disturbed.

1. Remove the valve body assembly, as outlined in a succeeding coverage entitled, Valve Body Assembly and Accumulator Piston.
2. Loosen throttle lever stop screw locknut and back off the screw about five turns.
3. Insert gauge pin between the throttle lever cam and the kickdown valve.
4. Push on the tool and compress the kickdown valve against its spring, so that the throttle valve is completely bottomed inside the valve body.
5. As the spring is being compressed, finger tighten the throttle lever stop screw against the throttle lever tang, with the lever cam touching the tool and the throttle valve bottomed. (Be sure the adjustment is made with the spring fully compressed and the valve bottomed in the valve body.)
6. Remove the tool and secure the stop screw locknut.

Service Operations in Truck

Some sub-assemblies can be removed for repairs without removing the transmission from the truck. Detailed reconditioning of sub-assemblies is covered further in the text.

Speedometer Pinion

Removal and Installation

Rear axle gear ratio and tire size determine pinion gear size.
1. Remove bolt and retainer securing speedometer pinion adapter in extension housing.

2. With cable housing connected, carefully work adapter and pinion out of extension housing.
3. If transmission fluid is found in cable housing, replace seal in adapter. Start seal and retainer ring in adapter, then push them into adapter until tool bottoms. CAUTION: Before installing pinion and adapted assembly make sure adapter flange and mating area on extension housing are perfectly clean. Dirt or sand will cause misalignment and speedometer pinion gear noise.
4. Note number of gear teeth and install pinion gear into adapter.
5. Rotate pinion gear and adapter assembly so that number on adapter corresponding to number of teeth on gear is in six o'clock position as assembly is installed.
6. Install retainer and bolt with retainer tangs in adapter positioning slots. Tap adapter firmly into extension housing and tighten retainer bolt to 100 in. lbs.

Output Shaft Oil Seal

Replacement

1. Mark parts for reassembly. Disconnect driveshaft at rear universal joint. Carefully pull shaft yoke out of transmission extension housing. Be careful not to scratch or nick ground surface of sliding spline yoke.
2. Remove extension housing yoke seal by gently tapping out around circumference of seal with slide hammer.
3. To install new seal, place seal in opening of extension housing and drive it into housing with suitable drift.
4. Carefully guide front universal joint yoke into extension housing and onto the mainshaft splines. Align marks made at removal and connect driveshaft to pinion shaft yoke.

Short Extension Housing
Removal

1. Mark parts for reassembly. Dis-

connect driveshaft at rear universal joint. Carefully pull shaft out of extension housing.
2. Remove speedometer pinion and adapted asembly. Drain approximately two quarts of fluid from transmission.
3. Remove bolts securing extension housing to crossmember. Raise transmission slightly with service jack and remove center crossmember and support assembly.
4. Remove extension housing to transmission bolts. On console shifts, remove two bolts securing gearshift torque shaft lower bracket to extension housing. Swing bracket out of way. NOTE: Gearshift lever must be in 1-low position so that parking lock control rod can be engaged or disengaged with parking lock sprag.
5. Remove two screws, plate, and gasket from bottom of extension housing mounting pad.
6. Spread large snap ring from output shaft bearing.
7. With snap ring spread as far as possible tap extension housing gently off output shaft bearing.
8. Carefully pull extension housing rearward to bring parking lock control rod knob past parking sprag and remove housing.

Long Extension Housing Bushing and Output Shaft Bearing

Removal

1. Mark drive shaft components for reassembly then disconnect drive shaft at rear universal joint. Carefully, pull the drive shaft assembly out of the extension housing.
2. Remove the speedometer pinion and adapter assembly. Drain two quarts of fluid from the transmission.
3. Remove the bolts securing the extension housing to the crossmember. Raise the transmission slightly with a service jack, then remove the crossmember and support assembly.

4. Remove the extension housing to transmission bolts.

NOTE: When removing or installing the extension housing the gearshift lever must be in the 'l' (low) position. This positions the parking lock control rod rearward so it can be disengaged or engaged with the parking lock sprag.

5. Remove the access plate gasket from the extension housing. Spread the large snap ring from the output shaft bearing. When the snap ring is spread as far as possible, carefully tap the extension housing off the output shaft bearing. Carefully pull the extension housing rearward to remove parking lock rod control rod knob past the parking sprag, then remove the extension housing.

Bushing Replacement

1. Remove the oil seal with special Chrysler tool.
2. Press or drive out the bushing.
3. Slide a new bushing on installation tool. Align the oil hole in the bushing with the oil slot in the housing, then press or drive the bushing into place.
4. Position a new seal in the opening of the extension housing and drive it into the housing.

Bearing Replacement

1. Using a heavy duty snap ring pliers, remove the output shaft bearing rear snap ring and remove the bearing from the shaft.
2. Install a new bearing on the shaft with the outer race ring groove toward the front. Install the rear snap ring.

Installation

1. Place a new extension housing gasket on the transmission case. Position output shaft bearing retaining snap ring in the extension housing. Slide the extension housing on the output shaft, guiding the parking lock control rod knob past the parking sprag. While spreading the large snapring in the housing, carefully tap

the housing into place. Release the snap ring. Make sure that the snap ring is fully seated in the bearing outer race ring groove.

2. Install and tighten the extension housing bolts to 24 foot-pounds.
3. Install the gasket and access plate on the extension housing.
4. Install the center crossmember and the rear mount assembly. Tighten the retaining bolts. Lower the transmission, install the extension housing and torque bolts to 40 foot-pounds.
5. Install the speedometer pinion and adapter.
6. Carefully guide the front universal joint yoke into the extension housing and on the output shaft splines. Align the marks made during removal and connect the drive shaft to the rear axle pinion shaft yoke.
7. Add fluid to the transmission to bring it up to proper operating level.

Governor

Removal

1. Remove extension housing. NOTE. Remove output shaft support bearing if so equipped.
2. With a screwdriver, carefully pry the snapring from the weight end of governor valve shaft. Slide the valve and shaft assembly out of the governor housing.
3. Remove the large snap-ring from the weight end of the governor housing and lift out the governor weight assembly.
4. Remove snap-ring from inside governor weight, remove inner weight and spring from the outer weight.
5. Remove the snap-ring from behind the governor housing, then slide the governor housing and support assembly from the output shaft. If necessary, remove

the four screws and separate the governor housing from the support.

Cleaning and Inspection

The primary cause of governor operating trouble is sticking of the valve or weights. This is brought about by dirt or rough surfaces. Thoroughly clean and blow dry all of the governor parts, crocus cloth any burrs or rough bearing surfaces and clean again. If all moving parts are clean and operating freely, the governor may be reassembled.

Installation

1. Assemble governor body and screen to the support, if disassembled, and tighten the bolts finger tight. Make sure the oil passages of the governor body aligns with the passage in the support.
2. Position the support and the governor on the output shaft. Align the assembly so that the valve shaft hole in the governor body alighs with the hole in the output shaft, then slide the assembly in place. Torque the body support bolts to 100 inch-pounds. Bend the ends of the lock straps over the bolt heads.
3. Assemble the governor weights and spring, and secure with the snap ring inside of the large governor weight. Place the weight assembly in the governor body and install the snap ring.
4. Place the governor valve on the valve shaft, insert the assembly into the body and through the governor weights. Install the valve shaft retaining snap ring. Inspect the valve and weight assembly for free-movement after installation.
5. Install the output shaft bearing and the extension housing.

SPRING

BODY

VALVE SHAFT

VALVE

SNAP RINGS

OUTER WEIGHT

INNER WEIGHT

SNAP RING

Governor assembly (© Chrysler Corp.)

GOVERNOR SUPPORT AND PARKING GEAR

SNAP RINGS

SNAP RING

GOVERNOR BODY

BOLTS (4)

LOCK STRAPS

Governor shaft and weight snap-rings
(© Chrysler Corp.)

Parking lock components (© Chrysler Corp.)

Valve body and control assembly
(© Chrysler Corp.)

Parking Lock Components

Removal

1. Remove the extension housing.
2. Slide the shaft out of the extension housing to remove the parking sprag and spring. Remove the snap ring and slide the reaction plug and pin assembly out of the housing.
3. To replace the parking lock rod, refer to "Valve Body-Removal and Installation".

Assembly

1. Install the reaction plug and pin assembly in the housing and secure with a snap ring.
2. Position the sprag and spring in the housing and insert the shaft. Make sure that the square lug on the sprag is toward the parking gear, and the spring is positioned so it moves the sprag away from the gear.
3. Install the extension housing.

Removal

1. Raise vehicle on hoist and loosen oil pan bolts, tap pan to break it loose, allowing fluid to drain.
2. Remove pan and gasket.
3. Disconnect throttle and gear shift linkage from levers on transmission. Loosen clamp bolts and remove levers.
4. Remove E clip securing parking lock rod to valve body manual lever.
5. Remove backup light and neutral start switch.
6. Place drain pan under transmission, remove ten hex head valve body to transmission case bolts. Hold valve body in position while removing bolts.
7. While lowering valve body down out of transmission case, disconnect parking lock rod from lever. To remove rod pull if forward out of case. If necessary rotate

driveshaft to align parking gear and sprag to permit knob on end of control rod to pass sprag.
8. Withdraw accumulator piston from transmission case. Inspect piston for scoring, and rings for wear or breakage.
9. If valve body manual lever shaft seal requires replacement, drive it out of case with punch.
10. Drive new seal into case with 15/16 in. socket and hammer.

Installation

1. If parking lock rod was removed, insert it through opening in rear of case with knob positioned against plug and sprag. Move front end of rod toward center of transmission while exerting rearward pressure on rod to force it past sprag. Rotate driveshaft if necessary.
2. Install accumulator piston in transmission case.
3. Place accumulator spring on valve body.
4. Place valve body manual lever in low position. Lift valve body into its approximate position, connect parking lock rod to manual lever and secure with E clip. Place valve body in case, install retaining bolts finger tight.
5. With neutral start switch installed, place manual lever in neutral position. Shift valve body if necessary to center neutral finger over neutral switch plunger. Snug bolts down evenly. Torque to 100 in. lbs.
6. Install gearshift lever and tighten clamp bolt. Check lever shaft for binding by moving lever through all detends. If lever binds, loosen valve body bolts and re-align.
7. Make sure throttle shaft seal is in place, install flat washer and lever and tighten clamp bolt.

Connect throttle and gearshift linkage and adjust as required.
8. Install oil pan using new gasket. Add transmission fluid to proper level.

Detailed Unit Reconditioning

The following reconditioning data covers the removal, disassembly, inspection, repair, assembly and installation procedures for each subassembly ni detail.

NOTE: In the event that any part has failed in the transmission, the converter should be thoroughly flushed to insure the removal of fine particles that may cause damage to the reconditioned transmission.

Oil Pan Removal

1. Secure transmission in a repair stand.
2. Unscrew attaching bolts and remove oil pan and gasket.

Valve Body Removal

1. Loosen clamp bolts and remove throttle and gearshift levers from transmission.
2. Remove backup light and neutral start switch.
3. Remove ten hex head valve body to transmission bolts. Remove E clip securing parking lock rod to valve body manual lever.
4. Whie lifting valve body upward out of transmission case, disconnect parking lock rod from lever.

Accumulator Piston and Spring

Removal

Lift the spring from the accumulator piston and withdraw the piston from the case.

Checking Drive Train End-Play

1. Attach a dial indicator to the extension housing and seat the plunger on the end of the output shaft.
2. Pry the output shaft out and tap it in to register the extreme shaft end-play.

Transfer and separator plate (© Chrysler Corp.)

Valve body controls (© Chrysler Corp)

Steel ball locations (© Chrysler Corp.)

3. Record this reading for possible future use. Correct end play is found at front of section.

Governor and Support Removal

1. Remove the snap-ring from the weight end of the governor valve shaft. Slide the valve and shaft assembly from the governor housing.
2. Remove the snap-ring from behind the governor housing, then slide the governor housing and support from the output shaft.

Oil Pump and Reaction Shaft Support

Shaft Support Removal

1. Tighten the front band on the front clutch retainer.
2. Remove front pump housing retaining bolts.
3. Attach slide hammers to the pump housing flange, using the

eleven and four o'clock hole locations.
4. Bump outward, evenly, with tool to withdraw oil pump and reaction shaft support assembly from the case.

Front Band and Front Clutch

Removal

1. Loosen the front band adjuster, remove the head strut and slide the band from the case.
2. Slide the front clutch assembly from the case.

Input Shaft and Rear Clutch

Removal

Grasp the input shaft and slide the shaft and rear clutch assembly out of the case.
NOTE: Don't lose the thrust washer located between the rear end of the input shaft and the front end of the output shaft.

Planetary Gear Assemblies, Sun Gear, Driving Shell, Low and Reverse Drum Removal

While hand-supporting the output shaft and driving shell, carefully slide the assembly forward and out of the case.

Rear Band and Low-Reverse Drum Removal

Remove low-reverse drum, loosen rear band adjuster, remove band strut and link, and remove band from case.

Overrunning Clutch Removal

1. Notice the established position of the overrunning clutch rollers and springs before disassembly.
2. Slide out the clutch hub and remove rollers and springs.

Kickdown Servo Removal

1. Compress kickdown servo spring

OIL SEAL

GASKET

VENT BAFFLE

SEAL RINGS

REACTION SHAFT SUPPORT

"O" RING

INNER ROTOR

OUTER ROTOR

OIL PUMP BODY

THRUST WASHER (SELECTIVE)

BOLTS (6)

Oil pump and reaction shaft support (© Chrysler Corp.)

using engine valve spring compressor. Then remove snap ring.
2. Remove the rod guide, spring and piston rod from the case. Don't damage the piston rod or guide during removal.
3. Withdraw piston from the transmission case.
4. If so equipped, disassemble the "controlled load" servo piston assembly by removing small snapring from servo piston then remove the washer, spring and piston rod from servo piston.

Low and Reverse Servo Removal

1. Using a suitable tool, depress the piston spring retainer and remove the snap ring.

2. Remove the spring retainer, spring, servo piston and plug assembly from the case.

Flushing the Torque Converter

1. The torque converter must be removed in order to flush it.
2. Place the converter in a horizontal position and pour two quarts of new clean solvent into the converter through the impeller hub.
3. Turn and shake the converter, swirling the solvent through the internal parts. Turn the turbine and stator with the input and reaction shafts to dislodge foriegn material.

4. Position the converter in its normal position with the drain plug at its lowest point. Drain the solvent. At the same time, rotate the turbine and stator and shake the converter, to prevent dirt particles from settling.
5. Repeat the flushing operation at least once, until the solvent or kerosene is clear.
6. After flushing, shake and rotate the converter several times, with the drain plug removed, to drain out any residual solvent or dirt.
7. Flush any remaining solvent or dirt with two quarts of new transmission fluid. Tighten the drain plug to 110 in. lbs.
8. Flush and blow out the oil cooler and lines.

SHUTTLE VALVE E-CLIP

TORQUE CONVERTER CONTROL VALVE

THROTTLE VALVE

REGULATOR VALVE

SPRING RETAINER

LINE PRESSURE ADJUSTING SCREW ASSY.

1-2 SHIFT VALVE GOVERNOR PLUG

MANUAL VALVE

KICKDOWN VALVE

2-3 SHIFT VALVE GOVERNOR PLUG

SHUTTLE VALVE

SHUTTLE VALVE THROTTLE PLUG

KICKDOWN DETENT

THROTTLE LEVER STOP SCREW ASSY.

GOVERNOR PLUG END PLATE

Valve body—lever side (© Chrysler Corp.)

REGULATOR VALVE THROTTLE PRESSURE PLUG

SLEEVE

REGULATOR VALVE LINE PRESSURE PLUG

REGULATOR VALVE END PLATE

SHIFT VALVE END PLATE

2-3 SHIFT VALVE

1-2 SHIFT VALVE

Valve body—shift valve side
(© Chrysler Corp.)

Before removing any of the transmission sub-assemblies, thoroughly clean the exterior of the unit, preferably by steam. When disassembling, each part should be washed in a suitable solvent, and either set aside to drain or dried with compressed air. Do not wipe with shop towels. All of the transmission parts require extremely careful handling to avoid nicks and other damage to the accurately machined surfaces.

Sub-Assembly Reconditioning

The following procedures cover the disassembly, inspection, repair and assembly of each sub-assembly as removed from the transmission.

The use of crocus cloth is permissible but not encouraged as extreme care must be used to avoid rounding off sharp edges of valves. The edge portion of valve body and valves is very important to proper functioning.

NOTE: Use all new seals and gaskets, and coat each part with automatic transmission fluid, type A, suffix A, during assembly.

Valve Body

Disassembly

NOTE: This area is extremely critical, and sensitive to distortion. Never champ any portion of the valve body or transfer plate in a vise. Clean with new solvent and dry with compressed air. Start all valves into their respective chambers with a twisting motion, seeing that they are well lubricated with automatic transmission fluid.

1. With the valve body in a clean repair stand, remove three attaching screws and the oil screen.
2. Hold the spring retainer bracket against spring tension, remove the three bracket retaining screws.

3. Remove spring bracket, torque converter valve spring, and the regulator valve spring with line pressure adjusting screw assembly.

NOTE: do not alter the setting of the line pressure adjusting screw and nut. The nut has an interference thread and does not turn easily on the screw.

4. Slide the regulator valve and spring retainer ring from the valve body. Slide torque converter control valve from the valve body.
5. Remove the transfer plate retaining screws. Lift the transfer plate and steel plate assembly off the valve body.
6. Invert the transfer plate assembly and remove the stiffener plate. Remove the remaining screws securing the steel plate to the transfer plate, and lift off the steel plate.
7. Note the location of seven steel balls and one spring. Two of these balls are larger than the others so care should be taken not to mix them up. One ball is 3/8 in. in diameter and goes on the spring in the corner. The other ball is 5/16 in. in diameter and is located in the large chamber; this is the front clutch ball check. Remove the steel balls and the spring.
8. Invert the valve body and lay it on clean paper. Remove the E-clip and washer from the throttle lever shaft. While holding manual lever detent ball and spring in their bore, slide manual lever from the throttle shaft. Remove detent ball and spring.
9. Remove manual valve from valve body.
10. Remove throttle lever and shaft from body.
11. Remove shuttle valve cover plate. Remove E-clip from the exposed end of shuttle valve.
12. Remove throttle lever stop

screw, being careful not to disturb the setting.
13. Remove kickdown detent, kickdown valve, throttle valve spring and throttle valve.
14. Remove governor plug and end plate. Tip up the valve body to allow the shuttle valve throttle plug, spring, shuttle valve and the shift valve governor plugs to slide out.

NOTE: the first-second valve plug has a longer stem.

15. Remove the shift valve end plate and slide out the two springs and valves. On six cylinder truck, remove the downshift plug cover and plug, and pull out the two springs and valves.
16. Remove the regulator valve end plate. Slide the regulator valve line pressure plug, sleeve, and the regulator valve throttle pressure plug from the body.

Disassembly 1971-74

1. Place the valve body on a clean repair stand. Never place any part of the valve body or transfer plate in a vise, since distortion can cause sticking valves and excessive leakage.
2. Remove the three screws from the fluid filter and remove the filter.
3. Remove the transfer plate retaining screws and 2 of the spring retainer mounting screws.
4. Lift off the transfer plate assembly. Separate the stiffener and separator plate for cleaning.
5. Remove the seven balls and spring from the valve body. Tag all springs as they are removed, for identification.
6. Turn the valve body over and remove the shuttle valve cover plate.
7. Remove the governor plug end plate and slide out the shuttle valve, throttle valve and spring, 1-2 shift valve governor plug and the 2-3 shift valve governor plug.
8. Remove the shuttle valve E-clip and remove the shuttle valve. If equipped, also remove the secondary spring and guides which are held by the clip.
9. Hold the spring retainer firmly against the spring and remove the last screw from the valve body.
10. Remove the spring retainer, line pressure adjusting screw (do not disturb the setting), and the line pressure and torque converter regulator springs.
11. Slide the torque converter and line pressure valves out of their bores.
12. Remove the E-clip and washer from the throttle lever shaft. Remove any burrs from the shaft,

and, while holding the manual lever detent ball and spring in their bore, slide the manual lever from the throttle shaft. Remove detent ball and spring.

13. Slide the manual valve from its bore.
14. Remove the throttle lever stop screw assembly from the valve body and slide out the kickdown detent, kickdown valve, throttle valve spring and throttle valve.
15. Remove the line pressure regulator valve end plate and slide out the regulator valve sleeve, line pressure plug and throttle pressure plug. If equipped, remove end plate and downshift housing assembly.
16. Remove the throttle plug housing and slide the throttle plug out. If equipped, remove retainer. limit valve, and spring.
17. Remove the shift valve springs and slide both shift valves from their bores.

Disassembly 1975-76

1. Place the valve body on a repair stand. Remove the three screws from the fluid filter and lift off the filter.
2. Remove the top and bottom screws from the spring retainer and adjustment screw basket.
3. Hold the spring retainer firmly against the spring force while removing the last screw from the side of the valve body.
4. Remove the spring retainer, with the line and throttle pressure adjusting screws (do not disturb the setting). Remove the line pressure and torque converter regulator springs.
5. Slide the torque converter and line pressure valves out of their bores.
6. Remove the transfer plate retaining screws and lift off the transfer plate and separator plate assembly.
7. Remove the screws from the stiffener and separate parts for cleaning.
8. Remove the rear clutch ball check valve from the transfer plate and regulator valve screen from the separator plate for cleaning.
9. Remove the seven balls and spring from valve body.

NOTE: Tag all springs as they removed for reassembly identification.

10. Turn the valve body over and remove the shuttle valve and cover plate.
11. Remove the governor plug end plate and slide out the shuttle valve throttle plug and spring, the 1-2 shift valve governor plug and the 2-3 shift valve governor plug.
12. Remove the shuttle valve "E"

clip and slide the shuttle valve out of its bore. Also remove the secondary spring and guides which were retained by the "E" clip.

13. Remove the "E" clip and the park control rod from the manual lever.
14. Remove the "E" clip and washer from the throttle lever shaft. Remove any burrs from the shaft, then while holding the manual lever off the throttle shaft. Remove the detent ball and spring.
15. Slide the manual valve out of its bore.
16. Slide out the kickdown detent, kickdown valve, throttle valve spring and throttle valve.
17. Remove the line pressure regulator valve end plate and slide out the regulator valve sleeve, line pressure plug, and the throttle pressure plug.
18. Remove the end plate and the downshift housing assembly.
19. Remove the throttle plug from the housing.
20. Slide the retainer plug from the housing and remove the limit valve and spring.
21. Remove the three springs and shift valves from the valve body.

Cleaning and Inspection

Inspect all components for scores, loose or bent levers, burrs and warping. Don't straighten bent levers; renew them. Loose levers may be silver soldered at the shaft. Burrs and minor nicks may be carefully removed with crocus cloth. Check for valve body warpage or distortion with a surface plate (plate glass will do) and a feeler gauge. Do not attempt to service a distorted plate or valve body, since this is a very critical area. Check all springs for distortion or fatigue. Check valves for scores and freedom of movement in the bores, they should fall of their own weight, in and out of the bore.

Assembly 1970

1. Place separator plate on transfer plate.
2. Install stiffener plate and retaining screws exactly as shown. Make sure all bolt holes are aligned. Tighten stiffener plate screws to 28 in lbs.
3. Insert the first-second and second-third shift valve governor plugs into their respective bores. Install shuttle valve, valve spring and shuttle valve throttle plug. Install governor plug end plate and torque the four retaining screws to 28 in. lbs.
4. Install E-clip onto end of shuttle valve. Install shuttle valve cover plate and torque the four retaining screws to 28 in. lbs.

5. Install the first-second and second-third shift valves and springs. Install shift valve end plate and torque the three retaining screws to 28 in. lbs. On six-cylinder trucks, install the 3-2 downshift plug and cover, and tighten screws to 28 in. lbs.
6. Insert regulator valve throttle pressure plug, sleeve (with the undercut on the sleeve toward the end plate), and the line pressure plug. Install regulator valve end plate and torque the two retaining screws to 28 in. lbs.
7. Insert throttle valve and spring. Slide the kickdown detent onto kickdown valve (with counterbore side of detent toward valve), then insert the assembly in the valve body.
8. Install throttle lever stop screw and tighten locknut finger tight.
9. Insert manual valve into the valve body.
10. Install throttle lever and shaft on the valve body. Insert detent spring and ball into its bore in the valve body. Depress ball and spring and slide manual lever over throttle shaft so that it engages manual valve and detent ball. Install seal, washer and the retaining E-clip onto the throttle shaft.
11. Position the valve body assembly on the bench or holding stand.
12. Place six steel balls in the valve body chambers (with large ball in the large chamber). Install the five smaller balls, the 5/16 in. ball in the large chamber and the spring and 3/8 in. high-pressure relief valve ball in the corner.
13. Position transfer plate assembly on the valve body. Install the retaining screws, starting at the center and working outward. Torque screws, 35 in. lbs.
14. Install the torque converter valve, regulator valve.
15. Place the torque converter valve spring and the regulator valve spring over the ends of their respective valves. Place line pressure adjusting screw assembly on the end of the regulator valve spring, with the long dimension of the nut at right angles to the valve body.
16. Install spring retainer bracket (make sure the converter valve spring is engaged on the tang in the bracket). Torque the three bracket retaining screws to 28 in. lbs.
17. Install oil strainer and torque the three retaining screws to 35 in. lbs.

NOTE: after reconditioning the valve body, adjust the throttle and line pressure. However, if line pressure was satisfactory before disas-

sembly, do not change this adjustment.

Assembly 1971-74

1. Slide the shift valves and springs into the proper valve body bores.
2. If so equipped, assemble the downshifts housing. Insert the limit valve and spring into the housing. Slide the spring retainer into the groove.
3. Insert the throttle plug into the housing bore and install the housing on the valve body. Torque the screws to 28 in. lbs.
4. Install the throttle pressure plug, line pressure plug and sleeve, fastening the end plate. Torque to 28 in. lbs.
5. Install the throttle valve, throttle valve spring, kickdown valve, kickdown detent and throttle lever stop screw with the locknut (do not adjust yet).
6. Slide the manual valve into its bore.
7. Install the throttle lever and shaft on the valve body. Insert the detent ball and spring into its bore in the valve body. Depress the ball and spring and slide the manual lever over the throttle shaft. Be sure that it engages the manual valve and detent ball. Install the seal, retaining washer and E-clip on the throttle shaft.
8. Insert the torque converter control valve and spring into the valve body.
9. Insert the line pressure regulator and spring into the valve body.
10. Install the line pressure adjusting screw assembly and spring retainer on the springs temporarily with one screw.
11. Place the 1-2 and 2-3 shift valve governor plugs in their proper bores.
12. Install the shuttle valve, spring, and shuttle valve throttle plug. If so equipped, install the secondary spring with two guides and clip on the other end.
13. Install the governor plug end plate and torque the screws to 28 in. lbs.
14. On those valve bodies not having a secondary spring, install the E-clip on the end of the shuttle valve.
15. Install the shuttle valve cover plate and torque screws to 28 in. lbs.
16. Install the spring and seven balls in the valve body. The seven include: five 1/4 in. balls, one 3/8 in. diameter ball in the corner and one 11/32 in. diameter ball in the large chamber.
17. Place the separator plate on the transfer plate. Make sure all bolt holes are aligned and torque the two transfer plate screws and two stiffener plate screws to 28 in. lbs.
18. Place the transfer plate assembly on the valve body. Align the spring loaded ball as the 17 shorter screws are installed. Start at the center and work outward, tightening the screws to 35 in. lbs.
19. Install the oil filter and torque to 35 in. lbs.
20. Check spring engagement with the tang and adjusting nut. Install the remaining spring retainer screws. Check alignment and torque to 28 in. lbs.
21. After valve body has been serviced and completely assembled, adjust throttle and line pressures. If pressures were satisfactory prior to disassembly, use the original settings.

Assembly 1975-76

1. Slide the shift valves and springs into their proper valve body bores.
2. Assemble the downshift housing as follows:
   a. Insert the limit valve and spring into the housing.
   b. Slide the spring retainer into the groove in the housing.
   c. Insert the throttle plug in the housing bore. Position the assembly against the shift valve springs.
3. Install the end plate and tighten the screws to 28 inch-pounds.
4. Install the throttle pressure plug, line pressure plug and sleeve, then fasten the end plate to the valve body. Tighten to 28-inch pounds torque.
5. Install the throttle valve, throttle valve spring, kickdown valve, and the kickdown detent.
6. Slide the manual valve into its bore.
7. Install the throttle lever and shaft on the valve body. Insert the detent spring and ball in its bore in the valve body. Depress the ball and spring and slide the manual lever over the throttle shaft so that it engages the manual valve and detent ball. Install the seal, retaining washer, and "E" clip on the throttle shaft.
8. Install the torque converter control valve and spring into the valve body.
9. Insert the line pressure regulator valve and spring into the valve body.
10. Install the pressure adjusting screw and bracket assembly on the springs and fasten it with the screw which goes into the side of the valve body. Start the screws on the top and bottom, do not tighten, and then tighten the

screw on the side of the valve body.
11. Place the 1-2 and 2-3 shift valve governor plugs in their respective bores.
12. Install the shuttle valve and hold it in the bore with your index finger, while installing on the other end of it the secondary spring with the guides and retaining "E" clip.
13. Install the primary shuttle valve spring and the throttle plug.
14. Install the governor plug end plate and tighten the five retaining screws to 28 inch-pounds.
15. Install the shuttle valve cover plate and tighten the six retaining screws to 28 inch-pounds.
16. Install the spring and seven balls in the valve body in their respective locations.
17. Place the separator plate on the transfer plate. Install the stiffener plate and retaining screws in their original positions.
18. Make sure that all the bolt holes are aligned, then tighten two transfer plate screws and two stiffener plate screws to 28 inch pounds.
19. Place the transfer plate assembly on the valve body. Be careful to align the spring loaded ball as the 17 shorter scerws are installed, the three longer srcews are for the oil filter.
20. Starting in the center and working outward tighten the screws to 35 inch-pounds.
21. Check the spring engagement and install the remaining top and bottom screws in the adjusting screw bracket. Tighten the side screw first to 28 inch pounds, then tighten the top and bottom screws.
22. Install the oil filter and tighten to 35 inch-pounds.
23. After the valve body has been serviced and completely assembled, adjust the throttle and line pressures. If pressures were satisfactory prior to disassembly, use oirginal settings.

Accumulator Piston and Spring

Insepct both seal rings for wear and freedom in the piston grooves. Check the piston for scores, burrs, nicks and wear. Check the piston bore for corresponding damage and check piston spring for distortion and fatigue. Replace parts as required.

Governor

Disassembly

1. Carefully remove the snap-ring from weight end of governor valve shaft and pull out valve and shaft. Remove the large snap-ring from the weight end

of governor housing and lift out the governor weight assembly.

2. Remove the snap-ring from inside the governor weight, remove the inner weight and spring from the outer weight.

NOTE: throughly clean all parts in a suitable and clean solvent. Check for damage and free movement before assembly.

3. If lugs on support gear are damaged, remove four bolts and separate support from governor body.

Assembly

1. If support was separated from governor body, assemble and tighten bolts finger-tight. Make sure the oil passage of the body aligns with passage in the support. Position support and governor on output shaft so that the valve shaft hole in the governor aligns with the hole in the output shaft. Install a snap-ring behind the governor body and tighten the bolts to 100 in. lbs.

2. Assemble the governor weights and spring, then secure with snap-ring inside large governor weight.

3. Place the weight assembly in the governor housing and install snap-ring.

Oil Pump and Reaction Shaft Support

Disassembly

1. Remove the bolts from the rear side of the reaction shaft support and lift the support off the pump.

2. Remove the rubber seal ring from the pump body flange.

3. Drive the oil seal out with a blunt punch.

Inspection

1. Inspect the interlocking steel rings on the reaction shaft for wear or broken locks, make sure they turn freely in the grooves.

2. Inspect the machined surfaces on the pump body and the reaction shaft support for nicks and burrs.

3. Inspect the pump body and reaction shaft support bushings for wear or scores.

4. Inspect the pump rotors for scoring or pitting.

5. With the rotors cleaned and installed in the pump body, place a straight edge across the face of the rotors and pump body. Use a feeler gauge to measure the clearance between the straight edge and the face of the rotors. Clearance limits are 0.0015-0.003 inch. Also measure the rotor tip clearance between the inner and outer teeth. Clearance limits are

0.005-0.010 inch. Clearance between outer rotor and its bore in the oil pump body should be from 0.004-0.008 inch.

Oil Pump Bushing Replacement

1. Place the pump housing on a clean smooth surface with the rotor cavity down.

2. Place the removing head of the special bushing tool in the bushing, and install the tool handle.

3. Drive the bushing straight down and out of the bore. Be careful not to cock the tool in the bore.

4. Place a new bushing on the installation tool.

5. With the pump housing on a smooth clean surface, hub end down, start the bushing and installation head in the bushing bore. Install the tool handle in the installation head.

6. Drive the bushing into the housing until the tool bottoms in the pump cavity. Be careful not to cock the tool during installation.

7. Stake the bushing in place using a blunt punch or similar tool. A gentle tap at each stake slot location will suffice.

8. Using a narrow bladed knife, remove high points of burrs around the staked area. Do not use a file that will remove more metal than is necessary.

9. Thoroughly clean the pump housing before installation.

Reaction Shaft Bushing Replacement

CAUTION: Do not clamp any part of the reaction shaft or support in a vise.

1. Assemble the special bushing removal tool which consists of: cup, hex nut and removal tool.

2. With the cup held firmly against the reaction shaft, thread the remover into the bushing as far as possible by hand.

3. Using a wrench to screw remover into the bushing 3 to 4 additional turns to firmly engage the threads in the bushing.

4. Turn the hex nut down against the cup to pull the bushing out of the reaction shaft. Throughly clean the reaction shaft to remove chips made by the remover threads.

5. Lightly grip the bushing in a vise or with pliers and back the tool out of the bushing. Be careful not to damage the threads on the bushing remover.

6. Slide a new bushing (chamfered end first) on the installing head of the special tool and start them in the bore of the reaction shaft.

7. Support the reaction shaft upright on a clean smooth surface

and install the installation tool handle. Drive the bushing into the shaft until the tool bottoms.

8. Thoroughly clean the reaction shaft support assembly before installation.

Assembly

1. Assemble the pup rotors and 'O' ring in the pump housing.

2. Install the reaction shaft support. Install the retaining bolts and torque to 160 inch-pounds.

3. Place a new oil seal in the opening of the pump housing, lip of the seal facing inward, and drive the seal into the housing until it bottoms.

Front Clutch

Disassembly

Exploded view of front clutch assembly is illustrated.

1. With screwdriver or pick, remove large snap-ring, which holds the pressure plate in the clutch piston retainer. Lift pressure plate and clutch plates out of the retainer.

2. Install spring compresison tool or similar tool, over piston spring retainer. Compress spring and remove snap-ring, then, slowly release tool until the spring retainer is free of the hub. Remove the compressor, retainer and spring.

3. Turn the clutch retainer upside down and bump on a wooden block to remove the piston. Remove seal rings from the piston and clutch retainer hub.

Inspection

Inspect clutch discs for evidence of burning, glazing and flaking. A general method of determining clutch plate breakdown is to scratch the lined surface of the plate with a finger nail. If material collects under the nail, replace all driving discs. Check driving splines for wear or burrs. Inspect steel plates and pressure plate surfaces for discoloration, scuffing or damaged driving lugs. Replace if necessary.

Check steel plate lug grooves in clutch retainer for smooth surfaces. Plate travel must be free. Inspect band contacting surface of clutch retainer, being sure the ball moves freely. Check seal ring surfaces in clutch retainer for scratches or nicks, light annular scratches will not interfere with the sealing of neoprene rings.

Inspect inside bore of piston for score marks. If light marks exist, polish with crocus cloth. Check seal ring grooves for nicks and burrs. Inspect neoprene seal rings for deterioration, wear and hardness. Check piston spring, retainer, and snapring for distortion and fatigue.

PISTON SEAL RING (INNER)

PISTON

SPRING RETAINER

CLUTCH PLATES

SNAP RING (SELECTIVE)

PISTON RETAINER ASSEMBLY

PISTON SEAL RING (OUTER)

SPRINGS(10)

SNAP RING

DRIVING DISCS

PRESSURE PLATE

Front clutch assembly (© Chrysler Corp.)

Front Clutch Retainer Bushing Replacement

1. Lay clutch retainer (open end down) on a clean smooth surface and place removing head in the bushing. Install the bushing removal tool handle.
2. Drive the bushing straight down and out of clutch retainer bore. Be careful not to cock the tool in the bore.
3. Lay the clutch retainer (open end up) on a clean smooth surface. Slide a new bushing on the intsallation head tool, and start them in the clutch retainer bore.
4. Install the bushing installation tool handle and drive the bushing into the clutch retainer until the tool bottoms.
5. Thoroughly clean the clutch retainer before assembly and installation.

Assembly

1. Lubricate and install inner seal ring onto hub of clutch retainer. Be sure that lip of seal faces down and is properly seated in the groove.
2. Lubricate and install outer seal ring onto clutch piston, with lip of seal toward the bottom of the

clutch retainer. Place piston assembly in retainer and, with a twisting motion, seat the piston in the bottom of the retainer.
3. Place spring on the piston hub and position spring retainer and snap-ring on spring. Compress spring with tool, or suitable ring compressor, and seat snap-ring in the hub groove. Remove compressor.
4. Lubricate all clutch plates, then, install a steel plate, followed by a lined plate, until all plates are installed. Install the pressure plate and snap-ring. Be sure the snap-ring is correctly seated.
5. With front clutch assembled, insert a feeler gauge between the pressure plate and snap-ring. The clearance should be to specification. If not, install a snapring of proper thickness.

Rear Clutch

Disassembly

1. With a small screwdriver or

pick, remove the large snap-ring that secures the pressure plate in the clutch piston retainer. Lift the pressure plate, clutch plates, and inner pressure plate from the retainer.
2. Carefully pry one end of wave spring out of its groove in clutch retainer and remove wave spring, spacer ring and clutch piston spring.
3. Turn clutch retainer assembly upside down and bump on a wood block to remove the piston. Remove seal rings from the piston.
4. If necessary, remove snap-ring and press the input shaft from the clutch piston retainer.

Inspection

Inspect driving discs for indication of damage; handle as previously outlined under front clutch inspection.

Input Shaft Bushing Replacement

1. Clamp the input shaft in a vise

Front clutch piston return springs
(© Chrysler Corp.)

TOOL

SNAP RING

Removing front clutch retainer snap-ring
(© Chrysler Corp.)

Rear clutch assembly (©Chrysler Corp.)

with soft faced jaws, being careful not to clamp on the seal ring lands or bearing journals.

2. Assemble the remover tool, cup tool and hex nut

3. With the cup held firmly against the clutch piston retainer, thread the remover into the bushing as far as possible by hand.

4. Using a wrench, screw the remover into the bushing as far as possible by hand.

5. Turn the hex nut down against the cup to pull the bushing from the input shaft.

6. Thoroughly clean the input shaft to remove the chips made by the remover threads. Make sure that the small lubrication hole next to the ball in the end of the shaft is not plugged. Make certain that no chips have lodged next to the steel ball.

7. Slide a new bushing on the installation head of the bushing tool and start them in the bore of the input shaft.

8. Stand the input shaft upright on a clean surface and position the handle on the installation tool.

Drive the bushing into the shaft until the tool bottoms.

9. Thoroughly clean the input shaft and clutch piston retainer before assembly and installation.

Assembly

1. If removed, press input shaft into the piston retainer and install snap ring

2. Lubricate, then install inner and outer seal rings onto the clutch piston. Be sure the seal lips face toward the head of the clutch retainer and seals are properly seated in the piston grooves.

3. Place piston assembly in retainer and, with a twisting motion, seat piston in bottom of retainer.

4. Place spring over piston with outer edge of spring positioned below snap ring groove. Start one end of snap ring in groove. Make sure spring is exactly centered on piston. Progressively tap snap ring into groove. Be sure snap ring is fully seated in groove.

5. Install inner pressure plate into clutch retainer, with raised por-

tion of plate resting on the spring.

6. Lubricate all clutch plates, then install one lined plate, followed by a steel plate, until all plates are installed. Install outer pressure plate and snap-ring.

7. With rear clutch completely assembled, insert a feeler gauge between the pressure plate and snap-ring. The clearance should be to specification. If not, install snap-ring of proper thickness to obtain the required clearance.

NOTE: Rear clutch plate clearance is very important to obtaining satisfactory clutch performance. Clearance is influenced by the use of various thickness outer snap-rings.

Planetary Gear Train End Play

NOTE: Before removal of the planetary gear assemblies, sun gear and drive shell parts from the output shaft, measure the end play as follows:

1. With the assembly in an upright position, push the rear annulus

Planetary gear train and output shaft assembly (© Chrysler Corp.)

Automatic Transmissions

Kickdown servo (© Chrysler Corp.)

Low and reverse servo (© Chrysler Corp.)

Overrunning clutch, low and reverse band link
(© Chrysler Corp.)

Low and reverse band and linkage
(© Chrysler Corp.)

gear support downward on the output shaft.
2. Insert a feeler gauge between the rear annulus gear support hub and sholder on the output shaft.
3. The clearance should be 0.01-0.025 inch. If the clearance is not within limits, replace thrust washer and/or necessary parts.

Disassembly

Refer to illustrations for assembly and disassembly of these units.
1. Remove thrust washer from forward end of output shaft.
2. Remove snap-ring from forward end of output shaft, then, slide front planetary assembly from the shaft.
3. Slide front annulus gear off planetary gear set. Remove thrust washer from rear side of planetary gear set.
4. Slide the sun gear, driving shell, and rear planetary assembly, from the output shaft.
5. Remove sun gear and driving shell from the rear planetary assembly, remove thrust washer from inside driving shell, remove snap-ring and steel washer from sun gear (rear side of driving shell). Slide sun gear out of driv-

ing shell, then remove snap-ring and steel washer from opposite end of sun gear, if necessary.
6. Remove thrust washer from forward side of rear planetary assembly. Remove the planetary gear set and thrust plate from the rear annulus gear.

Inspection

Inspect output shaft bearing surfaces for burrs or other damage. Light scratches or burrs may be polished out with crocus cloth or a fine stone. Check speedometer drive gear for damage, and make sure all oil passages are clear.

Check bushings in the sun gear for wear or scores. Replace sun gear assembly if bushings show wear or other damage. Inspect all thrust washers for wear and scores. Replace if necessary. Check lockrings for distortion and fatigue. Inspect annulus gear and driving gear teeth for damage. Inspect planetary gear carrier for cracks and the pinions for broken or worn gear teeth.

Assembly

1. Install rear annulus gear on output shaft. Apply thin coat of grease on thrut plate, place it on shaft, and in annulus gear

making sure teeth are over shaft splines.
2. Position rear planetary gear assembly in rear annulus gear. Place thrust washer on front side of planetary gear assembly.
3. Install snap-ring in front groove of sun gear (long end of gear). Insert sun gear through front side of driving shell. Install rear steel washer and snap-ring.
4. Carefully slide driving shell and sun gear assembly on output shaft, engaging sun gear teeth with rear planetary pinion teeth. Place thrust washer inside front driving shell.
5. Place thrust washer on rear hub of front planetary gear set. Slide assembly into front annulus gear.
6. Carefully work front planetary and annulus gear assembly on output shaft, meashing planetary pinions with sun gear teeth.
7. With all components properly positioned, install selective snap ring on front end of output shaft. Measure end-play of assembly. Adjust end-play with selective snap rings.

Overrunning Clutch Inspection
Inspect clutch rollers for smooth

1148

round surfaces, they must be free of flat spots, chipped edges and flaking. Inspect roller contacting surfaces on both cam and race for pock marks and roller wear-marks. Check springs for distortion and fatigue and inspect low and reverse drum thrust. Inspect cam set screw for tightness. If loose, tighten and restake the case.

Overrunning Clutch Cam Replacement

If the overrunning clutch cam or roller spring retainer are found to be defective, replace the cam and spring in the following manner:

1. Remove the set screw from the case below the clutch cam.
2. Remove the four bolts securing the output shaft support to the rear transmission case. Insert a punch through the bolt holes an drive the cam from the case. Alternately, punch from one bolt hole to another so the cam will be driven evenly from the case.

NOTE: The output shaft support must be in the case to install the overrunning clutch cam. If the support requires replacement, drive it rearward out of the case with a wood block and hammer. To install, screw two pilot studs into the case. Chill the support with dry ice. Quickly position the support over the pilot studs, and drive it firmly into the case with a wood block and hammer.

3. Clean all burrs and chips from the cam area in the case.
4. Place the spring retainer on the cam, making sure the retainer lugs snap firmly into the notches on the cam.
5. Position the cam in the case with the cam serrations aligned with those in the case. Tap the cam evenly into the case as far as possible with a soft faced mallet.

6. Position the cam installation tool on the cam and tighten the hex nut on the tool to seat the cam in the case. Make sure that the cam is firmly seated. Install the cam retaining set screw and stake the case around the set screw to prevent it coming loose.
7. Remove the cam installation tool. Install the support retaining screws and tighten to 140 inch-pounds torque. Stake the case around the cam in twelve places with a blunt chisel.

Kickdown Servo and Band

Disassembly

Disassemble the controlled load servo piston by removing the small snap ring from the servo piston. Remove the washer, spring and piston rod from the servo piston.

Inspection

Inspect piston and guide seal rings for wear, and be sure of their freedom in grooves. It is not necessary to remove seal rings, unless circumstances warrant. Inspect piston for scores, burrs or other damage. Check fit of guide on piston rod. Check piston for distortion and fatigue. Inspect band lining for wear and fit of lining material to the metal band. This lining is grooved; if grooves are not still visible at the ends or any part of the band, replace the band. Inspect band for distortion or cracked ends.

Assembly

Assemble the controlled load servo piston as follows:
1. Grease the "O" ring and install on the piston rod.
2. Install the piston rod into the servo piston.

3. Install the spring, flat washer and snap ring to complete the assembly.

Low and Reverse Servo and Band

Disassembly

Remove snap-ring from piston and remove the piston plug and spring.

Inspection

Inspect neoprene seal ring for damage, rot, or hardness. Check piston and piston plug for nicks, burrs, scores and wear. The piston plug must operate freely in the piston. Check the piston bore in the case for scores or other damage. Examine springs for distortion and fatigue.

Check band lining for wear and the fit of the lining to the metal band. This lining has a grooved surface; if the grooves are worn away at the ends or at any part of the band, replace the band. Inspect the band for distortion or cracked ends.

Assembly

Lubricate and insert the piston plug and spring into the piston, and secure with the snap-ring.

Sub-Assemblies Installation

The following assembly procedures include the installation of sub-assemblies into the transmission case and adjustment of the drive train endplay. Do not use force to assemble any of the mating parts. Always use new gaskets during the assembly operations.

NOTE: use only automatic transmission fluid, type A, suffix A, or fluid of equivalent chemical structure, to lubricate automatic transmission parts during, or after, assembly.

Measuring front clutch plate clearance

Measuring rear clutch plate clearance

Kickdown band and linkage (© Chrysler Corp.)

Measuring end play of planetary gear assembly

Overrunning Clutch

With transmission case in upright position, insert clutch race inside cam. Install overrunning clutch rollers and springs as shown in figure.

Low and Reverse Servo and Band

1. Carefully work servo piston assembly into the case with a twisting motion. Place spring, retainer and snap-ring over the piston.
2. Using a valve spring compressor, compress the spring and install the snap-ring.
3. Position rear band in the case, install the short strut, then connect the long lever and strut to the band. Screw in band adjuster just enough to hold struts in place. Install low-reverse drum. Be sure long link and anchor assembly is installed to provide running clearance for low-reverse drum.

Kickdown Servo

1. If equipped with a controlled load servo piston, sub-assemble the unit as follows: grease the O ring and install on the piston rod; install the piston rod into the servo piston; install the spring, flat washer and snapring.
2. Carefully insert servo piston into case bore. Install piston rod, two springs and guide.
3. Compress the kickdown servo springs by using a engine valve spring compressor. Install the snapring.

Planetary Gear Assemblies, Sun Gear, Driving Shell, Low and Reverse Drum

1. While supporting the assembly in the case, insert the output shaft through the rear support. Carefully work the assembly rearward, engaging the carrier lugs with low-reverse drum slots.
   CAUTION: Be careful not to damage the ground surfaces of the output shaft during installation.

Front and Rear Clutch

1. The following method may be used to support the transmission; cut a 3½″ hole in a bench, small drum or box, strong enough to support the transmission; file notches at the edge so the output shaft support will lie flat; insert the output shaft into the hole and support the transmission upright.
2. Apply a coat of grease to the input shaft to output shaft thrust washer and install the thrust washer on the front end of the output shaft.
3. Align the front clutch plate inner splines, and place the assembly in position on the rear clutch. Be sure the clutch plate splines are fully engaged.
4. Align the rear clutch plate inner splines and lower the two clutch assemblies in to the case.
5. Carefully, work the clutch assemblies in a circular motion to engage the rear clutch splines over the front annulus gear splines. Make sure the front clutch drive lugs are fully engaged in the driving shell.

Front Band

1. Slide the band over the front clutch assembly.
2. Install band strut, screw in the adjuster just enough to hold the band in place.

Oil Pump and Reaction Shaft Support

1. If drive train end-play was not within specifications, replace the thrust washer on the reaction shaft support hub, with one of proper thickness (see specifications).
2. Screw (two) pilot studs into front pump opening in the case.
3. Place a new rubber seal ring in groove on outer flange of pump. Be sure the seal ring is not twisted.
4. Install the assembly into the case, tap lightly with a soft mallet if necessary. Install four bolts, remove pilot studs, install remaining bolts and pull down evenly.
5. Rotate the input and output shafts to see if any binding exists. Tighten bolts to 175 inch-pounds. Check shafts again for free rotation. Adjust both bands.

Governor and Support

1. Place the governor and support on the output shaft. Position it so that the governor valve shaft hole aligns with the hole in the output shaft, then slide the assembly into place. Install snapring behind the governor housing. Torque housing-to-support screws to specification.
2. Place the governor valve on the valve shaft, insert the assembly into the housing and through the governor weights. Install the valve shaft retaining snap-ring.

Extension Housing-Short

1. Position a new gasket on the extension housing. Carefully slide the extension housing into place. Install the remaining bolts and washers and tighten to 24 foot-pounds torque.
2. Install the transmission yoke. Install the nut with its three projections toward the washer. Hold the yoke and tighten to 175 foot-pounds.
3. Install the speedometer pinion and adapter assembly.

Extension Housing-Long

1. Install the snap ring in the front groove on the output shaft. Install the bearing on the shaft with its outer race ring groove toward the front. Press or tap the bearing tight against the front snap ring. Install the rear snap ring.
2. Position a new gasket on the transmission case. Place the output shaft bearing retaining snap ring in the extension housing. Spread the snap ring as far as possible. Carefully, tap the ex-

tension housing into place. Make sure that the snap ring is fully seated in the bearing groove.

3. Install and tighten the extension housing bolts to 24 foot-pounds.
4. Install the access plate and gasket on the side of bottom of the extension housing mounting pad.
5. Install the speedometer pinion and adapter assembly.
6. Measure the input shaft end play, correct if necessary.

Valve Body Assembly and Accumulator Piston

1. Clean the mating surfaces and inspect for burrs on both the transmission case and the valve body steel plate.
2. Install the accumulator piston in the transmission case and place the piston spring on the accumulator piston.

NOTE: There is no spring used with the 440 cu. in. engine.

3. Make sure that the back-up light and neutral start switches have been removed.
4. Insert the parking lock rod through the opening in the rear of the case with the knob positioned against the reaction plug and sprag. Move the front end of the rod toward the center of the transmission while exerting rearward pressure on the rod, to force it past the sprag, rotate the output shaft if necessary.
5. Place the valve body manual lever in the low position. Place the valve body in its approximate position in the case. Connect the parking lock rod to the manual lever and secure with an "E" clip. Align the valve body in the case, install the retaining bolts finger tight.
6. With the neutral start switch installed, place the manual valve in the neutral position. Shift the valve body if necessary to the center neutral finger over the neutral switch plunger. Snug the bolts down evenly, and torque to 100 inch-pounds.

7. Install the gearshift lever and tighten the clamp bolt. Check the lever shaft for binding in the case by moving the lever through all detent positions. If binding exists, loosen the valve body bolts and realign.
8. Install the flat washer and throttle lever, then tighten the lever clamp bolt.
9. Adjust the kickdown and low-reverse bands.
10. Install the oil pan, using a new gasket. Tighten the pan bolts to 150 inch-pounds.

Torque Reference

	Foot-Pounds	Inch-Pounds
Kickdown band adjusting screw locknut (eight cylinder cars)	29	
Kickdown lever shaft plug	25	150
Reverse band adjusting screw locknut (eight cylinder cars)	35	
Reverse band adjusting locknut (six cylinder cars)	20	
Cooler line fitting		110
Converter drive plate to crankshaft bolt	55	
Converter drive plate to torque converter bolt		270
Extension housing to transmission case bolt		
Extension housing to insulator mounting bolt	40	
Extension housing—crossmember to frame bolt	75	—
Oil pump housing to transmission case bolt		175
Governor body to parking sprag bolt		100
Neutral starter switch	25-30	
Oil pan bolt		150
Overrunning clutch cam set screw		40
Reaction shaft support to front oil pump bolt		160
Transmission to engine bolt	25-30	
Valve body screw		35
Valve body to transmission case bolt		100

Specifications—Dodge Loadflite

Torque Converter Diameter	11¾ in	10¾ in
Oil Capacity	19 pt	16¼ pt
Oil Type	Dexron	Dexron
Cooling	Water	
Lubrication	Pump (Rotor Type)	
Pump Clearances		
Outer Rotor to Case Bore	0.004-0.008 in	
Outer to Inner Tip	0.005-0.010 in	
End Clearance-Rotors	0.0015-0.003 in	
Gear Train End Play	0.010-0.025 in	
Input Shaft End Play	0.036-0.082 in	

Clutch Plate Data	No. of Discs	Clearance (in)	No. of Springs
Front			
Six	3	0.076-0.123	13
V-8	4	0.088-0.145	9
Rear			
All engines	4	0.025-0.045	1

Band Adjustments	
Kickdown Band-Turns*	2½ 1
Low-Reverse-Turns*	2

* Backed off from 72 in-lbs.
1 440 engine 2 (two) turns.

Diagnosis

This guide covers the most common symptoms and is an aid to careful diagnosis. The items to check are listed in sequence to be followed for quickest results. Follow the checks in the order given for the particular transmission type.

TROUBLE SYMPTOMS	Items to Check	
	In Truck	Out of Truck
Harsh N to D or N to R shift	CDEFGIJ	ab
Delayed Shift—N to D	ACIHKJ	ca
Runaway on upshift and 3-2 kickdown	ABCDLIHK	b
Harsh upshift and 3-2 kickdown	BCDLIHJ	b
No upshift	ABCDLIHKM	b
No kickdown on normal downshift	ABNCDLIHKM	d
Erratic shifts	ABNCFOPQ IKMJ	c
Slips in forward drive positions	ACIHK	abd
Slips in reverse only	CEGIK	
Slips in all positions	ACOIK	e
No drive in any position	ACOQIKJ	ca
No drive in forward positions	CDOLIHK	abd
No drive in reverse	CEGKMI	b
Drives in neutral	NIJ	a
Drags or locks	DELG	abfd
Noises	AORPMIJ	a
Hard to fill or blows out	AORSTQI	
Transmission overheats	ADEORTMI	abe

Key to Checks

A. Oil level
B. Control linkage
C. Oil pressure check
D. Kickdown band
E. Low-reverse band
F. Improper engine idle
G. Servo linkage

H. Accumulator
I. Valve body assembly
J. Manual valve lever
K. Air pressure check
L. K-D servo link
M. Governor
N. Gear shift cable

O. Regulator valve and/or spring
P. Output shaft bushing
Q. Strainer
R. Converter control valve
S. Breather clogged
T. Cooler or lines

a. Front-kickdown clutch
b. Rear clutch
c. Front pump and/or sleeve
d. Overrunning clutch
e. Converter
f. Planetary

New Process A-345

General Specifications and Fluid Capacity

Type ......4 speed fully automatic
Oil Capacity (Dry) .....28½ pints
Cooling ....Water
Oil Filter Type
..........Bottom suction screen
Clutches 4
Overrunning Clutches 2
Bands & Servos 2
Planetary Gear Sets 3

Sub-Assembly Removal

NOTE: Before removing any transmission sub-assemblies, plug all openings and thoroughly clean the exterior of the unit with steam. Cleanliness during the entire disassembly and assembly cannot be over-emphasized. When disassembling, each part should be washed in a suitable solvent, then dried by compressed air. Do not wipe parts with shop towels. All mating surfaces in the transmission are accurately machined; therefore, careful handling of parts must be exercised to avoid damage.

Input Shaft End Play

Measurement of the input shaft end play before disassembly will usually indicate when a thrust washer should be changed. The thrust washer is located between the reaction shaft support and the front clutch retainer.

1. Attach a dial indicator to the transmission bell housing with

its plunger seated against the end of the input shaft. Move the input shaft in and out to obtain the end play reading. End play should be 0.018-0.062 inch.
2. Record the indicator reading for reference during reassembly.

Oil Pan
1. Place the transmission assembly in repair stand.
2. Remove the oil pan bolts and remove the oil pan. Discard the gasket.

Valve Body
1. Loosen the clamp bolts and remove the throttle and gearshift levers.
2. Remove the back-up light and neutral safety switches.

New Process Model A-345 Automatic Transmission (© Chrysler Corp.)

3. Remove the bolts securing the valve body to the transmission case, remove the valve body.

Accumulator Piston and Spring
1. Remove the accumulator piston from the case and lift the spring from the case.

Transmission Compounder Disassembly
NOTE: Before removing the compounder, reduce the input shaft end play to zero by inserting and wedging a flat screw driver between the low-reverse drum and the transmission case. When the low-reverse drum is as far forward as possible, tighten the rear band until the band is tight on the low-reverse drum. Remove the screw driver. This prevents the #2 thrust washer or one of the clutches from coming out of position.

1. Remove the propeller shaft companion flange and yoke retaining nut and washer from the output shaft and remove the drum and yoke. Carefully pull the shaft yoke out of the transmission extension housing. Remove the parking brake assembly.
2. Remove the speedometer pinion and governor cover and gasket.
3. Remove the governor assembly from the extension housing.
4. Remove the compounder extension to compounder adapter screws and remove the compoun-

der extension for further disassembly on work bench.
5. Remove the snap ring retaining the compounder annulus gear to intermediate shaft and remove the annulus gear and fiber washer and direct clutch.
6. Remove the two seal rings from the adapter. Unlock the seal ring hooks by compressing the rings.
7. Spring the seal rings just enough so that they can be removed without scratching the adapter hub.
NOTE: The two seal rings for the direct clutch are different metal than the two seal rings for the reaction clutch. Do not mix these seal rings.
8. Remove the snap ring retaining the reaction clutch to the adapter clutch hub using snap ring tool.

1153

Measuring input shaft end play—A-345 (© Chrysler Corp.)

Removing or installing direct clutch seal rings—A-345 (© Chrysler Corp.)

Removing or installing the reaction clutch snap ring (© Chrysler Corp.)

Removing or installing the rear driving shell—A-345 (© Chrysler Corp.)

9. Remove the reaction clutch assembly.
10. *DO NOT remove the reaction clutch seal rings unless they are worn or damaged.*
11. Remove the snap ring retaining the compounder planetary gear assembly to the output shaft.
12. Remove the planetary gear assembly.
13. Remove the driving shell and the sun gear assembly.
14. Remove the overrunning clutch hub rollers and springs. Note the position of the overrunning clutch rollers and springs before disassembly to assist during assembly.
15. Remove the output shaft oil seal with a suitable hook type slide hammer. *Place the puller hooks between the output shaft and*

under the side of the seal so that the hooks do not damage the housing bore.
16. Remove the output shaft bearing snap ring with special tool.
17. Remove the output shaft from the rear of the compounder extension.

NOTE: The output shaft bearing is a sliding fit in the housing bore and an interference fit on the output shaft. The overrunning clutch cam and spring retainer cannot be removed from the extension housing. If the clutch cam or roller spring retainer is damaged, it will be necessary to replace the extension housing with the cam and retainer as an assembly.

18. Remove the output shaft bearing by tapping the threaded end of the output shaft on a hard wood

block or press. Note the position, then remove the snap ring, governor drive gear, the drive ball, and the speedometer drive gear from the output shaft.
19. Remove the line pressure plug and remove the governor screen retainer clip and the screen.
20. Thoroughly clean the inside of the compounder extension housing with a suitable solvent. Blow out all passages and blow dry with compressed air. Reinstall or replace the governor screen, retainer and line pressure plug.

Direct Clutch Disassembly

1. Remove the large waved snap ring which secures the pressure plate in the clutch piston retainer. Lift the pressure plate and clutch plates out of the retainer.

Compounder pinion carrier snap ring—A-345 (© Chrysler Corp.)

Rear overrunning clutch and output shaft—A-345 (© Chrysler Corp.)

GOVERNOR COVER · SNAP RING · GOVERNOR COVER · FLUID FILTER

Removing or installing the governor fluid filter—A-345 (© Chrysler Corp.)

2. Install the compressor over the spring retainer. Compress the springs and remove the snap ring. Slowly release the pressure on the springs until the spring retainer is free of the hub. Remove the compressor tool, retainer, and springs.
3. Invert the clutch retainer assembly and bump it on a wood block to remove the piston. Remove the seals from the piston and the clutch retainer hub.

Inspection

1. Inspect the clutch plates and discs for flatness. They must not be warped or cone shaped.
2. Inspect the facing mateial on driving discs. Replace the discs that are charred, glazed or heavily pitted. Discs should also be replaced if they show evidence of material flaking off or if the facing material can be scraped off easily. Inspect the driving disc splines for wear or damage. Inspect the steel plate and pressure plate surfaces for burning, scoring of damaged driving lugs. Replace if necessary.
3. Inspect the steel plate lug grooves in the clutch retainer for smooth surfaecs, the plates must travel freely in the grooves. Note the ball check in the retainer, make sure the ball moves freely.
4. Inspect the seal surfaces in the clutch retainer for nicks of deep scratches, light scratches will not interfere with the neopreme seals.
5. Inspect the neopreme seals for deterioration, wear, and hardness.
6. Inspect the piston springs, wave spring, and spacer for distortion or breakage.

Assembly

1. Lubricate and install the inner seal on the clutch retainer hub. Make sure the lip of the seal faces down and is properly seated in the groove.

2. Install the outer seal in the clutch piston and with the lip of the seal toward the bottom of the clutch retainer, apply a coating of wax type lubricant (Door Ease) to the outer edge of the seals. Place the piston assembly in the retainer and carefully seat the piston in the retainer.
3. Install the eight springs on the piston. Position the spring retainer and snap ring over the springs. Compress the springs with special tool and seat the snap ring in the hub groove. Remove the compressor tool.
4. Lubricate all the clutch plates. Install one steel plate by a friction plate (wa e type) until the four discs are installed. Install the pressure plate and snap ring. Make sure that the snap ring is completely seated in the groove.
5. Push downward on the pressure plate and insert a feeler gauge between the pressure plate and the waved snap ring to measure the maximum clearance where the snap ring is waved way from the pressure plate. Clearance should be 0.088-0.145 inch.

Reaction Clutch
Disassembly

1. Remove the large waved snap ring that secures the pressure palte in the clutch retainer. Lift the pressure plate and the clutch plates out of the retainer.
2. Install the spring compressor tool over the piston spring retainer. Compress the springs and remove the snap ring. Slowly release the tool until the spring retainer is free of the hub. Remove the tool, the retainer, and springs.
3. Invert the clutch retainer assembly and bump it on a wood block to remove the piston. Remove the seals from the piston and the clutch retainer hub.

Inspection

1. Inspect the plates and discs for

flatness. They must not be warped or cone shaped.
2. Inspect the facing material on all driving discs. Replace any discs that are charred, glazed, or show heavy pitting. Discs should also be replaced if they show evidence of material flaking off or if the facing material can be scraped off easily. Inspect the driving disc splines for wear or damage. Inspect the steel plate and pressure plate for burning, scoring, or damaged driving lugs.
3. Inspect the steel plate lug grooves in the clutch retainer for smooth surfaces, plates must travel freely in the grooves. Inspect the seal surfaces in the clutch retainer for nicks or deep scratches. Light scratches will not interfere with the neoprene seals. Inspect the neoprene seals for deterioration, wear and hardness.
4. Inspect the pitson spring, wave spring and spacer for distortion or breakage.

Assembly

1. Lubricate and install the inner seal on the hub of the cultch retainer. Make sure that the lip faces down and is properly seated in the groove.
2. Install the outer seal on the clutch piston with the lip of the seal toward the bottom of the clutch retainer. Apply a coat of a wax type lubricant (Door Ease) to the outer edge of the seals. Place the piston assembly in the retainer and carefully seat the piston.
3. Install the eight springs on the piston. Position the spring retainer and snap ring over the springs. Install the spring compressor tool and compress the piston spring until the snap ring is seated in the groove on the hub. Remove the compressor tool.
4. Lubricate all the cultch plates. Install one steel plate by a friction plate (plain gray) until four discs are installed. Install the pressure plate and snap ring. Make sure that the snap ring is properly seated.
5. Push downward on the pressure plate and insert a feeler gauge between the pressure plate and the waved snap ring. Clearance should be 0.088-0.145 inch.

Installation of Governor Bushing

1. Loosely bolt the reamer fixture to the compounder extension.
2. Place the alignment arbor into the reamer fixture and down into the governor bore.
3. Righten the screws on the rea-

Automatic Transmissions

mer fixture to 8-12 foot pounds.

CAUTION: Do not over-torque and strip the threads.

NOTE: Be sure the alignment arbor rotates freely after the screws are properly tightened.

4. Remove the alignment arbor.
5. Working with the proper reamer and drive ratchet, hand ream the governor bore in the following manner:
   a. Oil the reamer, reamer fixture, and governor bore.
   b. Using a 5-10 pound feeding force on the reamer, ream until the reamer bottoms in the extension and then continue to rotate the reamer 10 (ten) complete revolutions.
   c. Remove the reamer using a *clockwise rotation* and 5-10 pounds force upward.

CAUTION: Pulling the reamer out without using a rotating motion may score the governor bore and cause a leak between the extension and the bushing.

6. Remove the reamer fixture from the extension.
7. Thoroughly clean the chips from the extension. Visually check the governor feed holes to insure that they are free of chips.
8. Install the bushing using the following operation:
   a. Note the position of the two (2) notches at one end of the bushing.
   b. Position the notches so that one notch is at the 11 o'clock position and the other is at the 2 o'clock position, viewing the extension in its normal installed, parallel position.
   c. Use the alignment arbor and the bushing installation tool to drive the bushing into the extension. A brass hammer should be used to strike the hardened steel bushing installation tool.
   d. Drive the bushing until it is flush with the top of the bore.

Selecting the proper thrust washer thickness with special tool and feeler gauge—A-345 (© Chrysler Corp.)

9. Oil a new governor and insert it into the installed bushing. The governor should spin freely. If slight honing on the bushing is required, use crocus cloth around your finger and rotate the cloth within the new bushing.

Transmission Compounder Assembly

NOTE: Be sure the #2 thrust washer, front clutch discs, and rear clutch discs are in their proper position.

1. Push the intermediate shaft forward to reduce the input shaft end play to zero.
2. Insert and wedge a flat screw driver between the low-reverse drum and the transmission case, moving the low-reverse drum as far forward as possible.
3. Tighten the rear (low-reverse) band adjusting screw until the band is tight on the low-reverse drum. Remove the screw driver.
4. Install the two seal rings on the forward grooves on the adapter hub.
5. Inspect the seal rings for wear or broken locks. Be sure that the rings move freely in the grooves.
6. Install the reaction clutch assembly on the adapter hub.
7. Install the fiber thrust washer. Install the snap ring.
8. Install the two seal rings on the

rear grooves of the adapter hub. Inspect for wear or broken hock locks. Be sure that the rings turn freely in the groves.
9. Install the direct clutch assembly on the adapter with the direct clutch drum gear teeth engaging all the clutch discs in the reaction clutch.
10. Use the thrust washer selection tool and a feeler gauge to select the proper thrust washer thickness.
11. Assemble the compounder annulus gear to the annulus gear support and retain with a snap ring.
12. Install the selective fiber thrus washer on the compounder annulus gear support.
13. Install the annulus gear assembly into the direct clutch, engaging all the clutch discs in the direct clutch. Install the snap ring in the groove on the intermediate shaft.
14. Install the speedometer drive gear, drive ball, governor drive gear, and snap ring on the output shaft.
15. Assemble the bearing to the output shaft. Install the output shaft and bearing into the extension housing.
16. Install the bearing retainer snap ring. Avoid scoring the housing bore.
17. Install a new output shaft oil seal.

Selecting snap ring with special tool and feeler gauge—A-345 (© Chrysler Corp.)

Aligning the direct clutch with the driving shell, and the annulus gear with the compounder planetary pinions—A-345 (© Chrysler Corp.)

1156

18. Place the extension housing in an upright position, insert the overrunning clutch hub (race) inside the clutch cam.
19. Install the overrnning clutch rollers and spring.
20. Install the governor pressure and line pressure tubes in the extension.
21. Assemble the sun gear and the overrunning clutch roller retainer to the driving shell. Install the snap ring.
22. Install the driving shell and sun gear assembly on the output shaft.
23. Install the bronze thrust washer in the driving shell. Install the planetary carrier assembly and install the selective snap ring.

NOTE: Use the snap ring selector tool and a feeler gauge to measure the clearance between the pinion carrier and selector tool hub. Position the feeler gauge in the output shaft snap ring groove. Do not rest the extension housing assembly on the output shaft.

24. Install the speedometer gear and the governor assembly in the extension housing. Install the governor cover with a new gasket. Tighten the cover screws to 12 foot-pounds torque.
25. Install the gasket and position the extension housing assembly on the compounder adapter using pilot studs. Carefully align the pressure tubes with the matching holes in the adapter. With light pressure against the extension housing, use a 3/16 inch diameter phillips head screw driver in the hole in the direct clutch drum, rotate the drum to align the tangs of the drum with the slots in the driving shell and the compounder annulus gear with the compounder planetarp gear pinions.

Compressing the kickdown servo spring —A-345 (© Chrysler Corp.)

26. Install the compounder extension housing to the compounder adapter. Tighten the retaining bolts to 30 foot-pounds.
27. Install the parking brake assembly, drum and yoke on the compounder extension housing. Tighten the output shaft nut to 175 foot-pounds.

Transmission Disassembly Oil Pump and Reaction Shaft Support

1. Tighten the front band adjusting screw until the band is tight on the front clutch retainer. This prevents the clutch retainer from coming out with the oil pump which might cause damage to the clutches.
2. Remove the oil pump housing retaining bolts.
3. Install the two slide hammers on the pump housing flange.
4. Move the slide hammer weights

outward evenly to reove the pump and reaction shaft from the case.

Front Band and Front Clutch

1. Loosen the front band adjuster remove the band strut and slide the band out of the transmission case.
2. Slide the front clutch assembly out of the transmission case.

Input Shaft and Rear Clutch

1. Grasp the input shaft and slide the input shaft and rear clutch assembly out of the transmission acse. *Be careful not to lose the thrust washer located between and the forward end of the intermediage shaft.*

Planetary Gear Assemblies, Sun Gear and Driving Shell

1. While supporting the intermediate shaft and drive shell, carefully slide the assembly forward and out through the case.

Rear Band and Low-Reverse Drum

1. Loosen the rear band adjuster, remove the low-reverse drum, remove the band strut and link. Remove the band from the case.

Front Overrunning Clutch

1. Note the position of the overrunning clutch rollers and springs before disassembly to assist during reassembly.
2. Carefully slide the clutch hub out of the case and remove the rollers and springs. *If the overrunning clutch cam and roller*

Oil pump and the reaction shaft support—A-345 (© Chrysler Corp.)

spring retainer are found to be damaged or worn, refer to replacement procedures later in this section.

Kickdown Servo (Front)

1. Compress the kickdown servo spring with an engine valve spring compressor and remove the snap ring.
2. Remove the rod guide, springs and piston rod from the case. Be careful not to damage the piston rod or guide during removal.
3. Withdraw the piston from the transmission case.

Low and Reverse Servo (Rear)

1. Compress the low and reverse servo piston spring with an engine valve spring compressor and remove the snap ring.
2. Remove the spring retainer, spring, and servo piston and plug asesmbly from the transmission case.

Compounder Adapter

1. Remove the ten compounder to transmission case bolts. Remove the adapter and discard the gasket.,
2. Inspect the intermediate shaft bushings and replace if necessary.

Sub-Assemblies Reconditioning Accumulator Piston and Springs Inspection

1. Inspect the seal rings for wear and make sure they turn freely in the piston grooves. It is not necessary to remove the rings unless conditions warrant.
2. Inspect the piston for nicks, burrs, scores, and wear.
3. Inspect the piston bore in the case for scores or other damage.
4. Inspect the piston spring for distortion.
5. Replace parts as required.

Replacing the oil pump bushing—A-345 (© Chrysler Corp.)

Oil Pump and Reaction Shaft Support Disassembly

1. Remove the bolts from the rear side of the reaction shaft support, and lift the support off the pump.
2. Remove the rubber seal ring from the pump body flange.
3. Drive the oil seal out with a blunt punch.

Inspection

1. Inspect the interlocking steel rings on the reaction shaft support for wear or broken locks Make sure the rings turn freely in the grooves.
2. Inspect the machined surfaces on the pump body and reaction shaft support for nicks and burrs.
3. Inspect the pump body and reaction shaft support bushings for wear or scoring.
4. Inspect the pump rotors for scoring or pitting.
5. Clean the rotors and install them in the pump body. Place a straight edge across the face of the rotors and pup body. Use a

feeler gauge to measure the clearance between the straight edge and the face of the rotors. Clearance limits are 0.0015 0.003 inch.
6. Measure the rotor tip clearance between the inner and outer teeth. Clearance limits are 0.005-0.010 inch.
7. Measure the clearance between the outer rotor and its bore in the oil pump body. Clearance limits are 0.004-0.008 inch.

Oil Pump Bushing Replacement

1. Place the oil pump housing on a clean smooth surface with the rotor cavity down.
2. Place the bushing removal tool head in the bushing and install the handle on the tool.
3. Drive the bushing straight down and out of the bore. Be careful not to cock the tool in the bore.
4. Place a new bushing on the installation tool head.
5. With the pump housing on a clean smooth surface, hub end down, start the bushing and installation head in the bushing bore. Install the tool handle.
6. Drive the bushing into the housing until the tool bottoms in the pump cavity. Be careful not to cock the tool during installation. Remove the installation tool.
7. Stake the bushing in place by using a blunt punch. A gentle tap at each stake slot should be sufficient.
8. Working with a narrow-bladed knife, remove the high points or burrs around the staked area. Do not use a file that will remove more metal than necessary.
9. Thoroughly clean the pump housing before installation.

Reaction Shaft Bushing Replacement

1. Assemble the removal tool complete with the cup and hex nuts.

Staking the oil pump bushing—A-345 (© Chrysler Corp.)

Replacing the reaction shaft bushing—A-345 (© Chrysler Corp.)

Front clutch assembly (© Chrysler Corp.)

Do not clamp any part of the re-action shaft or support in a vise.
2. With the cup held firmly against the reaction shaft, thread the remover into the bushing as far as possible by hand.
3. Screw the remover three or four additional turns into the bushing with a wrench to firmly engage the threads in the bushing.
4. Turn the hex nut down against the cup to pull the bushing from the reaction shaft. Thoroughly clean the reaction shaft to reove any chips made by the remover threads.
5. Lightly grip the bushing in a vise or pair of pliers and back the removal tool out of the old bushing. Be careful not to damage the threads on the bushing remover.
6. Slide a new bushing (chamfered end first) on the installation head of bushing tool and start the bushing and tool into the reaction shaft bore.
7. Support the reaction shaft in an upright position on a clean smooth surface and install the installation tool handle. Drive the bushing into the shaft until the installation head bottoms. Remove the bushing installation tool.
8. Thoroughly clean the reaction shaft support assembly before installation.

Assembly
1. Assemble the pump rotor and "O" ring in the pump housing.
2. Install the reaction shaft spuport. Install the retaining bolts and tighten to 160 inch-pounds.
3. Place a new oil seal in the opening of the pump housing (lip of the seal facing inward) using a suitable drift.

Front Clutch
1. Remove the large waved snap ring that secures the pressure plate in the clutch piston retainer. Lift the clutch plates out of the retainer.
2. Install the piston spring compressor over the piston spring retainer. Compress the springs and remove the snap ring. Slowly release the tool until the spring retainer is free of the hub. Remove the tool, the spring retainer and the springs.
3. Invert the clutch retainer assembly and tap it on a wood block to remove the piston. Remove the seals from the piston and the clutch retainer hub.

Inspection
1. Inspect the facing material on all the driving plates. Replace any plates that are charred, glazed or heavily pitted. Plates should also be replaced if they show evidence of material flaking off or if the facing material can be scraped off easily.
2. Inspect the driving plate splines for wear or other damage.
3. Inspect the steel plate and pressure plate surfaces for burring, scoring or damaged driving lugs.
4. Inspect the steel plate lug grooves in the clutch retainer for smooth surfaces, plates must travel freely in the grooves.
5. Inspect the band contacting surface on the clutch retainer for scores.
6. Note the ball check in the clutch retainer, make sure that the ball moves freely.
7. Inspect the seal surfaces in the clutch retainer for nicks or deep scratches, light scratches will not interfere with the neoprene seals.
8. Inspect the clutch retainer bushing for wear or scoring.
9. Inspect the inside bore of the piston for score marks, if light remove with crocus cloth.

Replacing the front clutch retainer bushing—A-345 (© Chrysler Corp.)

Automatic Transmissions

Front spring location—9 springs—A-345 (© Chrysler Corp.)

10. Inspect the neoprene seals for deterioration, wear, and hardness.
11. Inspect the piston springs, retainer and snap ring for distortion.

Front Clutch Retainer Bushing Replacement

1. Place the clutch retainer (open end down) on a clean smooth surface. Install the removing head of bushing tool in the bushing. Install the bushing tool handle.
2. Drive the bushing straight down and out of the clutch retainer bore. Be careful not to cock the tool in the bore.
3. Lay the clutch retainer (open end up) on a clean smooth surface. Slide a new bushing on the installation head of the bushing tool. Start the tool and bushing in the clutch retainer bore.
4. Install the bushing tool handle. Drive the bushing into the clutch retainer until the tool bottoms.
5. Thoroughly clean the clutch retainer before assembly and installation.

Assembly

1. Lubricate and install the inner seal on the clutch retainer hub. Make sure that the lip of the seal

faces down and is properly seated in the groove.
2. Install the outer seal on the clutch piston, with the lip toward the bottom of the clutch retainer. Apply a coating of wax type lubricant (Door Ease) to outer edges of the seals. Place the piston assembly in the retainer and carefully seat the piston in the bottom of the retainer.
3. Install the clutch piston springs on the piston exactly as they were removed.
4. Place the spring retainer and snap ring over the springs. Install the spring compressor tool. Compress the springs and seat the snap ring in its groove. Remove the compressor tool.
5. Lubricate all clutch plates. Install one steel plate followed by a lined (driving) plate until all the plates are installed. Install the pressure plate and snap ring. Make sure that the snap ring is correctly seated in the groove.
6. When the front clutch is completely assembled, push down-

Measuring the front clutch plate clearance—A-345 (© Chrysler Corp.)

ward on the pressure plate and insert a feeler gauge between the pressure plate and the snap ring. Clearance should be 0.088-0.145 inch.

Rear Clutch Disassembly

1. Remove the large selective snap ring that secures the pressure plate in the clutch retainer. Lift the pressure plate, clutch plates and the inner pressure plate out of the clutch retainer.
2. Carefully pry one end of the wave spring out of its groove in the clutch retainer. Remove the wave spring, spacer ring, and the clutch piston spring.
3. Invert the clutch piston retainer assembly and tap it on a wood block to remove the piston. Remove the seals from the piston.
4. If necessary, remove the snap ring and press the input shaft from the clutch retainer.

Rear clutch—exploded view—A-345 (© Chrysler Corp.)

Inspection

1. Inspect the facing material on all the driving plates. Replace any plates that are charred, glazed or heavily pitted. Plates should also be replaced if they show evidence of material flaking off or if the facing material can be scraped off easily.
2. Inspect the driving plate splines for wear or other damage.
3. Inspect the steel plate and the pressure plates surfaces for burring, scoring or damaged driving lugs.
4. Inspect the steel plate lug grooves in the clutch retainer for smooth surfaces, plates must travel freely in the grooves.
5. Inspect the band contacting surface on the clutch retainer for scores.
6. Note the ball check in the clutch retainer, make sure that the ball moves freely.
7. Inspect the seal surfaces in the clutch retainer for nicks or deep scratches, light scratches will not interfere with the neoprene seals.
8. Inspect the neoprene seals for deterioration, wear, and hardness.
9. Inspect the piston springs, wave spring, and spacer for distortion or breakage.
10. Inspect the interlocking seal rings on the input shaft for wear or broken locks. Make sure that they turn freely in the grooves. Do not remove the seal rings unless necessary.
11. Inspect the bushing in the input shaft for wear or scores.
12. Inspect the rear clutch to front clutch thrust washer for wear. Washes thickness should be 0.061-0.063 inch, replace if necessary.

Input Shaft Bushing Replacement

NOTE: Perform this operation only if necessary.

1. Clamp the input shaft in a vise

Measuring the rear clutch plate clearance—A-345 (© Chrysler Corp.)

with soft faced jaws. Be careful not to clamp on the seal ring lands or the bearing journals.
2. Assemble the removal tool, cup and hex nut.
3. Hold the cup firmly against the clutch piston retainer and thread the remover into the bushing as far as possible by hand.
4. Working with a wrench, screw the remover into the bushing three or four additional turns to firmly engage the threads in the bushing.
5. Turn the hex nut down against the cup to pull the bushing out of the input shaft.
6. Thoroughly clean the input shaft to remove any chips made by the remover threads. Make sure that the smapp lubrication hole next to the ball in the end of the shaft is not plugged. Be sure no chips have lodged next to the steel ball.
7. Place a new bushing on the installation head of the bushing tool and start them into the input shaft bore.
8. Stand the input shaft on a clean smooth surface and install the installation tool handle. Drive

the bushing into the shaft until the tool bottoms.
9. Thoroughly clean the input shaft and the clutch piston retainer before installation.

Assembly

1. If removed, press the input shaft into the clutch piston retainer, and install the snap ring.
2. Lubricate and install the inner and outer seal rings on the clutch piston. Be sure that the lip of the seals face toward the head of the clutch retainer, and that they are properly seated in the piston grooves.
3. Place the piston assembly in the retainer and with a twisting action, seat the piston in the bottom of the retainer.
4. Place the clutch retainer over the piston retainer splines and support the assembly so that the clutch retainer remains in position.
5. Place the clutch piston spring and the spacer ring on the top of the piston in the clutch retainer. Make sure that the spring and the spacer ring are positioned in

Replacing the input shaft bushing—A-345 (© Chrysler Corp.)

Installing the rear clutch springs, spacer ring, and wave spring—A-345 (© Chrysler Corp)

the retainer recess. Start one end of the waved spring in the retainer groove, then progressively push or tap the spring into place. Make sure that the waved spring is fully seated in its groove.

6. Install the inner pressure plate in the clutch retainer with the raised position of the plate resting on the spring.

7. Lubricate all the clutch plates, install one lined plate followed by a steel plate until all the plates are installed. Install the outer pressure plate and secure with the selective snap ring.

8. Measure the rear clutch plate clearance by having an assistant press downward firmly on the outer pressure plate, then insert a feeler gauge between the plate and the snap ring. Clearance should be 0.025-0.045 inch. If clearance is not within limits, install a snap ring of the proper thickness to obtain the proper clearance. Low limit clearance is desirable. *Rear clutch plate clearance is very important in obtaining the proper clutch operation. The clearance can be adjusted by the use of various thickness outer snap rings. Snap rings are available in .060, .074, .088, and .106 inch thickness.*

Planetary Gear Train End Play

1. Place the planetary gear assembly in an upright position, push the rear annulus gear support downward on the intermediate shaft.

2. Insert a feeler gauge between the rear annulus gear support hub and the shoulder on the intermediate shaft.

3. The clearance should be 0.010 to 0.025 inch. If the clearance is excessive, replace the thrust washers and/or necessary parts.

Disassembly

1. Remove the thrust washer from the forward end of the intermediate shaft.

2. Remove the selective snap ring from the forward end of the intermediate shaft, then slide the front planetary assembly off the shaft.

3. Slide the front annulus gear off the planetary gear set. Remove the thrust washer from the rear side of the planetary gear set.

4. Slide the sun gear, driving shell and the rear planetary assembly off the intermdiate shaft.

5. Lift the sun gear and the driving shell off the rear planetary gear assembly. Remove the thrust washer from the inside of the driving shell. Remove the snap ring and the steel washer from the sun gear (rear side of the driving shell) and slide the sun gear out of the shell. Remove the front snap ring from the sun gear if necessary. Note that the front end of the sun gear is longer than the rear.

6. Remove the thrust washer from the forward side of the rear planetary gear assembly. Remove the planetary gear set and the thrust plate from the rear annulus gear.

Inspection

1. Inspect the bearing surface on the output shaft for nicks, burrs, scores or other damage. Light srcatches can be removed with crocus cloth or a fine stone. Be sure that all oil passages in the shaft are open and clean.

2. Inspect the bushings in the sun gear for wear or scores. Replace the sun gear assembly if the bushings are damaged.

3. Inspect all the thrust washers for wear and scores. Replace any washer that is in questionable condition.

4. Inspect the thrust faces of the planetary gear carriers for wear, scoring or other damage. Replace as necessary.

5. Inspect the planetary gear carriers for cracks and pinions with broken teeth or ware. Check the pinion shaft for broken lock pins.

6. Inspect the annulus gear and the driving gear teeth for damage. Replace distorted lock rings.

Assembly

1. Install the rear annulus gear on the intermediate shaft. Apply a thin coat of petroleum jelly on the thrust plate, place it on the shaft and in the annulus gear making sure that the teeth are over the shaft splines.

2. Position the rear planetary gear assembly in the rear annulus gear. Place the thrust washer on the front side of the planetary gear assembly.

3. Install the snap ring in the front groove of the sun gear (long end of the gear). Insert the sun gear through the front side of the driving shell, install the rear steel washer and snap ring.

4. Carefully slide the driving shell and the sun gear assembly on the intermediate shaft, engaging the sun gear teeth with the rear planetary pinion teeth. Place the

Front planetary gear train and the intermediate shaft-exploded view—A-345 (© Chrysler Corp.)

Measuring the end play of the planetary gear train—A-345 (© Chrysler Corp.)

Overrunning clutch and the low-reverse band link—A-345 (© Chrysler Corp.)

Removing the front overrunning clutch cam—A-345 (© Chrysler Corp.)

Installing the front overrunning clutch cam—A-345 (© Chrysler Corp.)

thrust washer inside the front driving shell.

5. Place the thrust washer on the rear hub on the front planetary gear set and slide the assembly into the front annulus gear.

6. Carefully work the front planetary and annulus gear assembly on the output shaft, meshing the planetary pinions with the sun gear teeth.

7. With all components properly positioned, install the selective snap ring on the front end of the intermediate shaft. Remeasure the end play of the assembly. *The clearance can be adjusted by use of various thickness snap rings. Snap rings are available in .048, .055, and .062 inch thickness.*

Front Overrunning Clutch Inspection

1. Inspect the clutch rollers for smooth round surfaces, they must be free of flat spots and chipped edges.

2. Inspect the roller contacting surfaces in the cam and race for brinnelling.

3. Inspect the roller springs for distortion, wear or other damage.

4. Inspect the cam set screw for tightness. If loose, tighten and restake the case around the screw.

Front Overrunning Clutch Cam Replacement

NOTE: If the overrunning clutch cam or the roller spring retainer are damaged, replace the cam and spring retainer in the following manner:

1. Remove the set screw from the case below the clutch cam.

2. Insert a blunt punch through the bolt holes and drive the cam from the case. Alternate the punch from one hole to another so that the cam will be driven evenly from the case.

3. Clean all burrs and chips from the cam area in the case.

4. Place the spring retainer on the cam, making sure that the retainer lugs snap firmly into the notches on the cam.

5. Position the cam in the case with the cam serrations aligned with those in the case. Tap the cam *evenly* into the case as far as possible, use a soft faced mallet.

6. Install the cam replacement tool and adapter, tighten the nut on the tool to seat the cam in the case. Make sure that the cam is firmly bottomed, then install the cam retaining set screw. Stake the case around the sets crew to prevent it from coming loose.

7. Remove the cam installation tool. Stake the case around the cam in twelve places with a blunt chisel.

Kickdown Servo and Band Inspection

1. Inspect the piston and the guide seal rings for wear, and make sure that they turn freely in the grooves. It is not necessary to remove the seal rings unless they are worn or damaged.

2. Inspect the piston for nicks, burrs, scores, and wear.

3. Inspect the piston bore in the case for scores or other damage.

4. Inspect the fit of the guide on the piston rod.

5. Inspect the piston spring for distortion.

6. Inspect the band lining for wear and the bond of the lining to the band. Check the lining for burn marks, glazing, non-uniform wear patterns and flaking. If the lining is worn so that the grooves are not visible at the ends or any portion of the bands, replace the band.

7. Inspect the band for distortion or cracked ends.

Low-Reverse Servo and Band Disassembly

Remove the snap ring from the piston and remove the piston plug.

Inspection

1. Inspect the seal for deterioration, wear and hardness.

Kickdown servo-exploded view—A-345 (© Chrysler Corp.)

Low-reverse servo-exploded view—A-345 (© Chrysler Corp.)

Valve body assembly mounted in the repair stand—A-345 (© Chrysler Corp.)

Valve body controls—A-345 (© Chrysler Corp.)

2. Inspect the piston and the piston plug for nicks, burrs, scores and wear; the piston plug must operate freely in the piston.
3. Inspect the piston bore in the case for scores or other damage.
4. Inspect the spring for distortion.
5. Inspect the band lining for wear and the bond of the lining to the band. If the lining is worn so that the grooves are not visible at the ends or any portion of the bands, replace the band.
6. Inspect the band for distortion or cracked ends.

Assembly

Lubricate and insert the piston plug in the piston and secure with the snap ring.

Valve Body

NOTE: Do not clamp any portion of the valve body or transfer plate in a vise. Any distortion on the aluminum body or transfer plate will result in sticking valves excessive leakage

or both. When removing or installing the valves or plugs, slide them in or out carefully. Do not use force.

Disassembly

1. Place the valve body assembly on the special repair stand. Remove the three screws from the fluid filter and lift off the filter.
2. Remove the lower valve body and the steel plate from the transfer plate. Observe the two steel balls in the transfer plate for proper location.
NOTE: Tag all springs as they are removed for assembly identification.
3. Remove the flat end plate, 3-4 shaft valve governor plug, 1-2 governor modulator valve spring.
4. Remove the end cover from the opposite side of the lower valve body.
5. Remove the part throttle downshift plug, the 3-4 shift valve.
6. Remove the remaining transfer

plate screws and the top and bottom spring retainer mounting screws.
7. Lift off the transfer plate and the separator plate assembly. Remove the four screws from the stiffener and separator plates and separate the parts for cleaning.
8. Observe the location of the seven balls and springs in the valve body. Remove the balls and springs.
9. Turn the valve body over and remove the shuttle valve cover plate.
10. Remove the governor plug end plate and slide the shuttle valve throttle plug and spring, the 1-2 shift valve throttle plug and spring, the 1-2 shift valve governor plug, and the 2-3 shift valve governor, out of the valve body.
11. Remove the shuttle valve "E" clip and slide the shuttle valve out of its bore. Remove the secondary guides and spring which

Governor modulator and the 3-4 governor plug—A-345 (© Chrysler Corp.)

Transfer and separator plates—A-345 (© Chrysler Corp.)

1/4'' DIAMETER BALLS (2)

Stell ball locations (two)—A-345 (© Chrysler Corp.)

3/8'' DIAMETER BALL AND SPRING

11/32'' DIAMETER BALL

1/4'' DIAMETER BALLS (5)

Steel ball locations (seven)—A-345 (© Chrysler Corp.)

are retained by an "E" clip.

12. Hold the spring retainer firmly against the spring force while removing the last retaining screw from the side of the valve body.

13. Remove the spring retainer, with the line and the throttle pressure adjusting screws (do not disturb the settings) and the line pressure and torque converter regulator springs.

14. Slide the torque converter and line pressure valves out of their bores.

15. Remove the "E" clip and washer from the throttle lever shaft. Remove any burrs from the shaft. While holding the manual lever detent ball and spring in their bore with a suitable tool, slide the manual lever off of the throttle shaft. Remove the detent ball and spring.

LOWER VALVE BODY

3-4 SHIFT VALVE SPRING

4-3 PART THROTTLE DOWNSHIFT PLUG END COVER

3-4 SHIFT VALVE

4-3 PART THROTTLE DOWNSHIFT PLUG

The 3-4 shift valve and the downshift plug—A-345 (© Chrysler Corp.)

UPPER VALVE BODY

2-3 SHIFT VALVE GOVERNOR PLUG

SHUTTLE VALVE PRIMARY SPRING

SHUTTLE VALVE THROTTLE PLUG

GOVERNOR PLUG END PLATE

1-2 SHIFT VALVE GOVERNOR PLUG

THROTTLE VALVE AND SPRING

KICKDOWN VALVE

KICKDOWN DETENT

TORQUE CONVERTER CONTROL VALVE

TORQUE CONVERTER PRESSURE REGULATOR SPRING

LINE PRESSURE REGULATOR VALVE

LINE PRESSURE REGULATOR VALVE SPRING

SPRING RETAINER AND ADJUSTING SCREW BRACKET

Pressure regulators and governor plug—A-345 (© Chrysler Corp.)

16. Slide the manual valve out of its bore.
17. Slide the kickdown detent, kickdown valve, throttle valve spring and the thorttle valve out of their bores in the valve body.
18. Remove the line pressure regulator valve end plate. Slide the pressure regulator valve sleeve, line perssure plug, and the throttle pressure plug out of the valve body.
19. Remove the shift valve end plate.
20. Remove the three springs, two shift valves and the 1-2 shift control valve from the valve body.

Cleaning and Inspection

1. Soak all parts in a suitable solvent for a few minutes. Wash thoroughly and blow dry with filtered compressed air. Make sure that all passages are clean and free of obstructions.
2. Inspect the manual valve operating levers and shafts for distortion or wear. If a lever is loose on its shaft, it may be *silver soldered* only, or replace the shaft assembly. *Do not attempt to straighten a bent lever.*
3. Inspect all mating surfaces for burrs, nicks and scratches. Minor defects can be removed with crocus colth, *use very light pressure.*
4. Inspect all mating surfaces for warpage or distortion with a straight edge. Slight distortion can be corrected with a surface plane.
5. Inspect all metering holes in the

steel plate and the valve body to make sure that they are open.
6. Inspect the bores in the valve body for scores, scratches, pits and irregularities with a pen light.
7. Inspect all valve springs for distortion and collapsed coils.
8. Inspect all valves and plugs for burrs, nicks or scoring. Small nicks and scores may be removed with crocus cloth using *extreme* care not to round off sharp edges. The sharpness of these edges is vitally important because it prevents foreign matter from lodging between the valve and the valve body.
9. Inspect all valves and plugs for freedom of operation in the valve body bores.

NOTE: The valve body bores do not change dimensionally with use. Therefore, a valve body that was functioning properly when the truck was new, will operate correctly if it is properly and thoroughly cleaned. There is no need to replace the valve body unless it is damaged in handling.

Assembly

1. Slide the shift valves, 1-2 shift control valve and springs into their bores in the vaive body.
2. Install the end plate and tighten the screws to 28-inch-pounds.
3. Install the throttle pressure plug, the line pressure plug and sleeve. Attach the end plate for the valve body and tighten the screws to 28 inch-pounds.
4. Install the throttle valve, throttle

valve spring, kickdown valve, and the kickdown detent.
5. Slide the manual valve into the bore in the valve body.
6. Install the throttle lever and shaft on the vavle body. Insert the detent spring and ball in the bore of the valve body. Depress the ball and spring with a suitable tool and slide the manual lever over the throttle shaft so that it engages the manual valve and the detent ball. Install the seal, retaining washer and the "E" clip on the throttle shaft.
7. Install the torque converter control valve and spring in the valve body.
8. Install the line pressure regulator valve and spring in the valve body.
8. Install the line pressure regulator valve and spring in the valve body.
9. Install the pressure adjusting screw and bracket assembly on the springs and fasten, finger tight, with the screw which goes on the side of the valve body.
10. Install the 1-2 and the 2-3 shift valve governor plugs into their bores in the valve body.
11. Install the shuttle valve and hold it in the bore with your index finger while instalilng the secondary spring, with guides, on the other end. Retain the shuttle valve components with an "E" clip.
12. Install the primary shuttle valve spring and throttle plug in the valve body.

Shift valves and pressure regulator valve plugs—A-345 (© Chrysler Corp.)

LOWER STEEL PLATE

1/4" DIAMETER BALLS (2)

LOWER VALVE BODY ASSEMBLY

SPACING TOOL

THROTTLE PRESSURE ADJUSTING SCREW

WRENCH

Lower valve body and steel plate—A-345 (© Chrysler Corp.)

Adjusting the throttle pressure—A-345 (© Chrysler Corp.)

13. Install the governor plug end plate and tighten the retaining screws to 28 inch-pounds.
14. Install the shuttle valve cover plate and tighten the retaining screws to 28 inch-pounds.
15. Install the 3-4 shift valve and the downshift valve and spring in the lower valve body.
16. Install the part throttle downshift plug into the end cover. Install the end cover and tighten the screws to 28 inch-pounds.
17. Install the 1-2 governor modulator valve spring, 1-2 governor modulator valve, and the 3-4 shift valve governor plug. Install the end plate and tighten the screws to 28 inch-pounds.
18. Install the spring and the seven balls in the valve body.
19. Place the separator plate on the transfer plate. Install the stiffener plate. Make sure that all the bolt holes are aligned, then tighten the two transfer plate screws and the two stiffener plate screws to 28 inch-pounds.
20. Place the transfer plate assembly on the valve body. Be sure that you carefully align the spring loaded ball as the shorter screws are installed.
21. Install the two steel balls in the transfer plate. Place the steel plate and the lower valve body on the transfer plate.
22. Install the screws attaching the lower valve body to the transfer plate. Tighten the screws, from the center outward, to 35 inch-pounds.
23. Install the oil filter with the three long screws and tighten to 35 inch-pounds.
24. Insert the throttle pressure adjusting tool between the stamped bracket and the throttle cam, adjust the throttle pressure. However, if the pressures were satisfactory prior to disassembly, use the original settings.

Governor Disassembly

1. Cut off one end of each of the governor weight pins and remove. Remove the governor thrust cap, governor weights, and springs.
NOTE: The governor weights are interchangeable from side to side and there is no need for identification.
2. Remove the governor valve from the governor sleeve. Be careful not to damage the valve.

Inspection

1. Wash all parts in a clean suitable solvent. Air dry and blow out all passages.
2. Inspect the governor sleeve for nicks, burrs, scoring or galling.
3. Check the governor sleeve for free operation in the bore of the transmission case.
4. Inspect the governor valve for nicks, burrs, scoring, or galling.
5. Inspect the governor weights for free operation in the bore of the governor sleeve.
6. Inspect the governor weights for free operation in their retainers.
7. Check the governor weight springs for distortion or damage.
8. Check the governor driven gear for looseness on the governor sleeve, nicks, burrs or damage. If replacement of the governor driven gear is necessary, follow the next procedure.

Governor Driven Gear Replacement

1. Drive the governor driven gear retaining roll pin with a small punch.
2. Support the governor on 3/16 inch plates installed in the exhaust slots of the governor sleeve. Place the assembly in an arbor press, and working with a long punch, press the gear out of the sleeve.
3. Carefully clean the governor sleeve of chips that remain from the original gear installation.
4. Support the governor on 3/16 inch plates installed in the exhaust ports of the sleeve, position a new gear in the sleeve and, with a suitable socket, press the gear into the sleeve until it is nearly seated. Carefully remove

any chips that may have shaved off the gear hub. Press the gear in until it bottoms on the shoulder.
5. A new roll pin must be drilled through the sleeve and gear. Locate the hole 90 degrees away from the existing hole, center punch, and while supporting the governor, drill a new hole through the sleeve and gear with a 1/8 inch bit.
6. Install a new retaining roll pin.
7. Clean the governor thoroughly of any chips that may have collected.

Assembly

1. Install the governor valve in the bore of the governor sleeve, large end first.
2. Install the governor weights, springs and thrust cap on the governor.
NOTE: The lip of the secondary weights must be over the end of the valve.
3. Align the pin holes in the thrust cap, governor weights, governor sleeve, and install the new retaining pin. Crimp both ends of the pins to prevent them from falling out.
4. Check the governor weights for free movement on the pins.
5. Check the governor valve for free movement in the governor sleeve.
6. Suspending the governor assembly by its driven gear (weights out), check the valve opening at the feed port. Opening must be 0.020 inch, minimum.
7. Check the governor valve opening at the exhaust port while holding the weights completely inward. The opening must be 0.020 inch minimum. If the opening is found to be smaller than allowed, the governor assembly must be replaced.

Transmission Assembly-Sub-Assembly Installation

NOTE: Do not force any parts into their assembled position. If the parts do not assemble freely, investigate the cause, and correct the problem before proceeding with the assembly procedures. Use all new gaskets during installation of components. Use only "Dexron" type transmission fluid to lubricate parts during installtion.

Overrunning Clutch Installation

1. Insert the clutch hub inside the cam.
2. Install the overrunning clutch rollers and springs in the exact way as removed.

Low Reverse Servo and Band Installation

1. Carefully work the servo piston assembly into the case with a twisting motion. Place the spring, retainer, and snap ring over the piston.
2. Compress the low and reverse servo piston spring with an engine valve spring compressor. Install the snap ring.
3. Position the rear band in the case. Install the short strut, and connect the long link and anchor to the band. Screw the band adjuster in far enough to secure the sturt in place.
4. Install the low reverse drum. Be sure that the long link and anchor assembly are installed correctly to provide proper running clearance for the low-reverse drum.

Kickdown Servo Installation

1. Carefully, push the servo piston into the transmission case bore. Install the piston rod, springs, and guide.
2. Compress the kickdown servo springs with an engine valve compressor and install the retaining snap ring.

Planetary Gear Assemblies, Sun Gear, and Driving Shell Installation

1. Support the assembly in the case and carefully work the assembly rearward. Engage the rear planetary carrier lugs in the low-reverse drum slots.
   CAUTION: Be very careful not to damage the machined surfaces on the intermediate shaft during installation.

Front and Rear Clutch Assemblies Installation

1. Apply a coat of grease on the input to intermediate shaft thrust washer. Install the thrust washer on the rear of the input shaft. The three tabs must seat properly in the rear clutch piston retainer.

Kickdown band and linkage—A-345 (© Chrysler Corp.)

2. Align the front clutch plate inner splines, and place the assembly in position on the rear clutch. Make sure the front clutch plate splines are fully engaged on the rear clutch splines.
3. Align the rear clutch plate inner splines, grasp the input shaft and install the two clutch assemblies in the transmission case.
4. Carefully, work the clutch assemblies in a circular motion to engage the rear clutch splines over the splines on the front annulus gear. Make sure that the front clutch drive lugs are fully engaged in the driving shell.

Front Band Installation

1. Slide the band over the front clutch assembly.
2. Install the band strut and screw in adjuster just enough to hold the strut and anchor in place.

Oil Pump and Reaction Shaft Support

NOTE: If difficulty was encountered in removing the pump assembly from the case, due to an overly tight fit, it may be necessary to expand the case with heat during pump installation. Working with a suitable heat lamp, heat the case in the area of the pump for a few minutes before installation of the pump.

1. Screw two piolt studs in the pump opening in the transmission case. Install a new gasket over the pilot studs.
2. Position a new rubber seal ring in the groove on the outer flange of the pump houisng. Make sure the seal ring is not twisted. Coat the seal ring with ptroleum jelly prior to installation.
3. Install the pump assembly in the case, if necessary, tap the assembly with a soft faced mallet. Install the four pump body bolts, remove the pilot studs and install the remaining bolts and snub down evenly. Tighten the bolts to 175 inch-pounds.
   CAUTION: *Be sure that the #2 thrust washer, front clutch discs,*

and rear clutch discs are in their proper location.

4. Push the intermediate shaft forward to reduce the input shaft end play to zero.
5. Carefully, wedge a flat screw driver between the low-reverse drum and the transmission case, while moving the low-reverse drum as far forward as possible.
6. Tighten the rear (low-reverse) band adjusting screw until the band is tight on the low-revesre drum. Remove the screw driver.
7. Proceed to "Compounder-Assembly" earlier in this section.

Valve Body, Accumulator Piston, and Oil Pan Installation

1. Make sure that the back-up light and the neutral start switches have been removed.
2. Install the accumulator spring and piston in the transmission case.
3. Place the valve body manual lever in the *low* position. Lift the valve body into its approximate position, install the retaining bolts finger tight.
4. Install the neutral start switch. Place the manual lever in the neutral position. Shift the valve body if necessary to center the neutral finger over the neutral switch plunger. Snug the bolts down evenly and tighten to 100 inch-pounds.
5. Install the gearshift lever and tighten the clamp bolt. Check the lever shaft for binding in the case by moving the lever through all detent positions. If binding exists, loosen the valve body and re-align.
6. Install the throttle shaft seal, flat washer, and lever. Tighten the lever clamp bolt. Connect the throttle and gearshift linkage and adjust as required.
7. Install the oil pan with a new gasket. Add transmission fluid to bring the transmission up to proper level.

Diagnosis

This diagnosis guide covers the most common symptoms and is an aid to careful diagnosis. The items to check are listed in the sequence to be followed for quickest results. Thus, follow the checks in the order given for the particular transmission **type**

TROUBLE SYMPTOMS	Items to Check	
	In Truck	Out of Truck
Rough initial engagement in D1 or D2	KBUFEG	a
1-2 or 2-3 shift points incorrect or erratic	ABLCDUER	
Rough 1-2 shifts	BJGUEF	
Rough 2-3 shifts	BJUFGER	bl
Dragged out 1-2 shift	ABJUGEFR	c
Engine overspeeds on 2-3 shift	CABJUEFG	bl
No 1-2 or 2-3 upshift	CLBDUEGJ	bc
No 3-1 shift in D1 or 3-2 shift in D2	DE	
No forced downshift	LEB	
Runaway engine on forced downshift	UJGFEB	c
Rough 3-2 or 3-1 shift at closed throttle	KBJEF	
Shifts 1-3 in D1 and D2	GJBEDR	
No engine braking in first gear—manual low	CHIEDR	
Creeps excessively	KW	
Slips or chatters in first gear, D1	ABUFE	acg
Slips or chatters in second gear	ABJGUFER	ac
Slips or chatters in R	ABHUIFER	bcl
No drive in D1	ACUER	g
No drive in D2	ACUJER	cg
No drive in L	ACUEIR	cg
No drive in R	ACHUIER	bcl
No drive in any selector position	ACUFER	cd
Lockup in D1		bec
Lockup in D2	HI	becg
Lockup in L	GJ	bec
Lockup in R	GJ	aec
Parking lock binds or does not hold	C	e
Transmission overheats	OFBU	i
Maximum speed too low, poor acceleration	VW	i
Transmission noisy in N and P	AF	df
Transmission noisy in any drive position	AF	fadg
Fluid leaks	AMNOPQSTBIJX	hik
Car moves forward in N	C	a

Key to Checks

A. Fluid level
B. Vacuum diaphragm unit or tube
C. Manual linkage
D. Governor
E. Valve body
F. Pressure regulator
G. Intermediate band
H. Reverse band
I. Reverse servo
J. Intermediate servo
K. Engine idle speed
L. Downshift linkage—inner lever position
M. Converter drain plug

N. Oil pan and/or filler tube gaskets/seals
O. Oil cooler and/or connections
P. Manual or downshift lever shaft seal
Q. Pipe plug, side of case
R. Perform air pressure checks
S. Extension housing-to-case gasket or washers
T. Extension housing rear oil seal
U. Make control pressure test
V. Engine performance
W. Vehicle brakes
X. Speedometer driven gear adaptor seal

a. Forward clutch
b. Reverse—high clutch
c. Hydraulic system leakage
d. Front pump
e. Parking brake linkage
f. Planetary assembly
g. Planetary one-way clutch
h. Engine rear oil seal
i. Front oil pump seal
j. Converter oneway clutch
k. Front pump-to-case seal or gasket
l. Reverse—high clutch piston air bleed valve

Transmission Checks

Transmission Fluid Leakage Checks

Make the following checks if a leakage is suspected from the transmission case:

1. Clean all dirt and grease from the transmission case.
2. Inspect the speedometer cable connection at the extension housing of the transmission. If fluid is leaking here, disconnect the cable and replace the rubber seal.
3. Inspect the oil pan gasket and attaching bolts for leaks. Tighten any bolts that appear loose to the proper torque (10-13 ft-lbs) Recheck for signs of leakage. If necessary, remove the pan attaching bolts and old pan gasket and install new gasket and reinstall the pan and its attaching bolts.
4. Check filler tube connection at the transmission for signs of leakage. If tube is leaking, tighten the connection to stop the leak. If necessary, disconnect the filler tube, replace the O-ring, and reinstall the filler tube.
5. Inspect all fluid lines between the transmission and the cooler core in the lower radiator tank. Replace any lines or fittings that appear to be worn or damaged. Tighten all fittings to the proper torque.
6. Inspect the engine coolant for signs of transmission fluid in the radiator. If there is transmission fluid in the engine coolant,

the oil cooler core is probably leaking. The oil cooler core may be tested further by disconnecting all lines to it and applying 50-75 psi air pressure through the fittings. Remove the radiator cap to relieve any pressure buildup outside the cooler core. If air bubbles appear in the coolant or if the cooler core will not hold pressure, the oil cooler core is leaking and must be replaced. Oil cooler core repair and replacement is discussed in the section on Cooling Systems in this manual.

7. Inspect the openings in the case where the downshift control lever shaft and the manual lever shaft are located for leaks. If necessary, replace the defective seal.
8. Inspect all plugs or cable connections in the transmission for signs of leakage. Tighten any loose plugs or connectors to the proper torque according to the specifications.
9. Remove the lower cover from the front of the bellhousing and inspect the converter drainplugs for signs of leakage. If there is a leak around the drainplugs, loosen the plug and coat the threads with a sealing compound and tighten the plug to the proper torque.

NOTE: fluid leaks from around the converter drainplug may be cause of the leak before beginning rear main bearing or from the oil gallery plugs. To determine the exact cause of the leak before beginning repair procedures, an oil-soluble aniline

or fluorescent dye may be added to the transmission fluid to find the source of the leak and whether the transmission is leaking. If a fluorescent dye is used, a black light must be used to detect the dye.

If further converter checks are necessary, remove the transmission from the truck and the converter from the transmission. The converter cannot be disassembled for cleaning or repair. If the converter is leaking, it must be replaced with a new unit. To further check the converter for leaks, assemble and install the converter leak checking tool shown and fill the converter with 20 psi air pressure. Then, place the converter in a tank of water and watch for air bubbles. If no air bubbles are seen, the converter is not leaking.

Control Pressure Check for Automatic Transmissions (C4)

When the vacuum diaphragm unit operates properly and the downshift linkage is adjusted correctly, all transmission shifts (automatic and kickdown) should occur within the specified road speed limits. If these shifts do not occur within the limits or if the transmission slips during a shift point, perform the following procedure to locate the problem:

1. Connect the Automatic Transmission Tester (see illustration) as follows:
   a. Tachometer cable to engine
   b. Vacuum gauge hose to the transmission vacuum diaphragm unit (see illustration)
2. Apply the parking brake and start the engine. On a truck equipped with a vacuum brake release, discon-

C-4 automatic transmission (© Ford Motor Co.)

Automatic transmission tester
(© Ford Motor Co.)

Converter leak checking tool (© Ford Motor Co.)

nect the vacuum line or use the service brake since the parking brake will release automatically when the transmission is put in any Drive position.

3. Check engine idle speed and throttle and downshift linkage for correct operation. Check the transmission diaphragm unit for leaks.

Vacuum Diaphragm Unit Check —Non-Altitude Compensating Type

1. Remove the vacuum diaphragm unit from the transmission after disconnecting the vacuum hose.
2. Connect the vacuum hose to the vacuum diaphragm unit and note the reading on the vacuum gauge. If the reading is 18 inches of vacuum, the vacuum diaphragm unit is good. While removing the vacuum hose from the vacuum diaphragm unit, hold a finger over the end of the control rod. As the vacuum is released, the internal spring of the vacuum diaphragm unit will push the control rod out.

Vacuum Diaphragm Unit Check —Altitude-Compensating Type

The vacuum diaphragm unit may be checked for damaged or ruptured bellows by doing the procedure below:

1. Remove the diaphragm and the throttle valve rod from the transmission.
2. Insert a rod into the diaphragm unit until it is seated in the hole.

Converter leak checking tool installed
(© Ford Motor Co.)

Make a reference mark on the rod where it enters the diaphragm (see illustration).

3. Place the diaphragm unit on a weighing scale with the end of the rod resting on the weighing pan and gradually press down on the diaphragm unit.
4. Note the force (in pounds) at which the reference mark on the rod moves into the diaphragm. If the reference mark is still visible at 12 pounds of pressure on the scale, the diaphragm bellows is good. But if the reference mark on the rod disappears before four pounds of force, the diaphragm bellows are damaged and the diaphragm unit must be replaced.

Air Pressure Checks

If the truck will not move in one or more ranges, or, if it shifts erratically, the items at fault can be determined by using air pressure at the indicated passages.

Drain the transmission and remove the oil pan and the control valve assembly.

NOTE: oil will spray profusely during this operation.

Front Clutch

Apply sufficient air pressure to the front clutch input passage. (See illustration.) A dull thud can be heard when the clutch piston moves. Check also, for leaks.

Governor

Remove the governor inspection cover from the extension housing. Apply air to the front clutch input passage. (See illustration). Listen for a sharp click and watch to see if the governor valve snaps inward as it should.

Rear Clutch

Apply air to the rear clutch passage (See illustration) and listen for the dull thud that will indicate that the rear clutch piston has moved. Listen also for leaks.

Front Servo

Apply air pressure to the front servo apply tube (See illustration.) and note if front band tightens. Shift the air to the front servo release tube, which is next to the apply tube, and watch band release.

Rear Servo

Apply air pressure to the rear servo apply passage. The rear band should tighten around the drum.

Conclusions

If the operation of the servos and clutches is normal with air pressure, the no-drive condition is due to the control valve and pressure regulator valve assemblies, which should be disassembled, cleaned and inspected.

Typical vacuum test line connections
(© Ford Motor Co.)

If operation of the clutches is not normal; that is, if both clutches apply from one passage or if one fails to move, the aluminum sleeve (bushing) in the output shaft is out of position or badly worn. (See illustration.)

Use air pressure to check the passages in the sleeve and shaft, and also check the passages in the primary sun gear shaft.

If the passages in the two shafts and the sleeve are clean, remove the clutch assemblies, clean and inspect the parts.

Erratic operation can also be caused by loose valve body screws. When reinstalling the valve body be careful to tighten the control valve body screws as specified in the Torque Limits table.

In-Vehicle Adjustments and Repairs

The adjustments and repairs presented in this part of the section on transmissions may be done without removing the entire transmission from the truck. Some of these procedures will require the use of special tools and instruments.

Band Adjustments

Intermediate Band

1. Clean all the dirt from the adjusting screw and remove and discard the locknut.
2. Install a new locknut on the adjusting screw. Using the tool shown in the illustration, tighten the adjusting screw until the wrench clicks and breaks at 10 ft-lbs. torque.
3. Back off the adjusting screw *Exactly 1¾ turns*.
4. Hold the adjusting screw steady and tighten the locknut to the proper torque.

Low-Reverse Band

1. Clean all dirt from around the band adjusting screw, and remove and discard the locknut.
2. Install a new locknut on the ad-

justing screw. Using the tool shown in the illustration, tighten the adjusting screw until the wrench clicks and breaks at 10 ft-lbs torque.
3. Back off the adjusting screw *Exactly 3 full turns*.
4. Hold the adjusting screw steady and tighten the locknut to the proper torque.

Testing transmission vacuum for leakage
(© Ford Motor Co.)

Typical vacuum diaphragm
and control pressure connecting point
(© Ford Motor Co.)

Transmission Component Removal and Installation

The components that may be removed from and installed in the transmission while it is in the truck are discussed in this part of the C4 transmission section. Only procedures for removing and installing these components are given here. Disassembly and repair of the units is given in a later part.

To avoid repetition, the following tasks should be done before proceeding with the removal and installation of components.

1. Raise the truck so the transmission is accessible from under the truck.
2. Drain the fluid from the transmission. Some models are drained by removing the filler tube from the transmission oil pan. Others are drained by removing the oil pan attaching bolts gradually from the rear of the pan. If the same fluid is to be reused, filter it through a 100 mesh screen. Reuse the fluid only if it is in good condition.
3. Remove the oil pan attaching bolts, the oil pan, and the old gasket. Discard gasket.
4. Be sure to have a good transmission jack available and a holding device for the transmission if it is removed from the truck later.

Oil Pan and Control Valve Removal

1. Do all the preliminary operations given at the beginning of this section.
2. Shift the transmission to Park position and remove the two bolts holding the manual detent spring to the control valve body and case.
3. Remove all the valve body-to-case attaching bolts. Hold the manual valve in place and remove the valve body from the case.
CAUTION: If the manual valve is not held in place, it could be bent or damaged.
4. Refer to the Component Disas-

BELLOWS INTACT   BELLOWS FAILED

Checking vacuum unit bellows (© Ford Motor Co.)

Control valve body detent spring installed (© Ford Motor Co.)

Case fluid passage hole identification (© Ford Motor Co.)

sembly and repair section for control valve body repair procedures.

5. Thoroughly clean the old gasket material from the case and remove the nylon shipping plug from the oil filler tube hold. This nylon plug is installed before shipment and should be discarded when the transmission oil pan is removed.

Installation

1. Be sure the transmission is in the Park position (manual detent lever is in P detent position). Install the valve body in the case. Position the inner downshift lever between the

Adjusting intermediate band
(© Ford Motor Co.)

Adjusting low-reverse band
(© Ford Motor Co.)

downshift lever stop and the downshift valve. Be sure the two lands on the end of the manual valve engage the actuating pin on the manual detent lever.

2. Install seven valve body attaching bolts but do not tighten them.

3. Place the detent spring on the lower valve body and install the spring-to-case bolt finger tight.

4. While holding the detent spring roller in the center of the manual detent lever, install the detent spring-to-lower valve body bolt and tighten it to 80-120 in-lbs. torque.

5. Tighten the remainder of the control valve body attaching bolts to 80-120 in-lbs. torque.

6. Put a new gasket on the oil pan, install pan in place, and install and tighten all the pan attaching bolts to the proper torque.

7. If the filler tube was removed, reinstall it and tighten securely. If necessary, replace the oil seal around the filler tube to prevent leakage.

8. Lower the car and fill the transmission with enough fluid to bring the level up to the FULL mark on the dipstick. Check for fluid leaks at this time.

Intermediate Servo Removal and Installation

1. Raise the truck and remove the four servo cover attaching bolts (right-hand side of case). Remove the cover and identification tag (*do not lose tag*).

2. Remove the gasket, piston, and piston return spring.

3. Install the piston return spring

in the case. Place a new gasket on the cover. Install the piston and cover in the transmission case, using two 51/6-18 x 1¼ bolts 180 degrees apart to align the cover against the case.

4. Install the transmission identification tag and two attaching bolts. Remove the two 1¼ bolts and install the other two cover attaching bolts. Tighten all cover attaching bolts to the proper torque.

5. Adjust the intermediate band. Lower the truck and fill the transmission with enough fluid to raise the fluid level to the FULL mark on the dipstick.

6. If the intermediate band cannot be adjusted correctly, remove

Control valve body attaching bolts
(© Ford Motor Co.)

the oil pan and control valve body and see if the struts are installed correctly. Adjust the struts and reinstall the control valve body and oil pan with a new gasket. Refill the transmission with fluid.

Low-Reverse Servo Piston Removal and Installation

1. Raise the truck on a hoist.
2. Loosen the reverse band adjusting screw locknut and tighten the adjusting screw to 10 ft-lbs torque. This operation will hold the band strut against the case and prevent it from falling when the reverse servo piston is removed.
3. Remove the four servo cover attaching bolts and remove the servo cover and seal from the case.
4. Remove the servo piston from the case. *The piston and piston seal are bonded together and must be replaced together.*
5. Install the servo piston assembly into the case. Place a new cover seal on the cover and position them by installing two 51/6-18 bolts, 1¼ in. long, at 180 degrees apart on the case. Install two cover attaching bolts with the identification tag.
6. Remove the two positioning bolts and install the other two cover bolts. Tighten all the cover attaching bolts to the proper torque.
7. Adjust the low-reverse band. Lower the truck and fill the transmission with enough fluid to raise the fluid level to the FULL mark on the dipstick.
8. If the low-reverse band cannot

be adjusted properly, the transmission must be drained and the oil pan and valve body removed. Check the alignment of the band struts. Reinstall the valve body and the oil pan with a new gasket, and refill the transmission with fluid.

Extension Housing Bushing and Rear Seal Removal and Installation

1. Disconnect the drive shaft from the transmission.
2. If only the rear seal needs replacing, carefully remove it with a tapered chisel or use the tools shown in the illustration. Remove the bushing as shown. Be careful not to damage the spline seal with the bushing remover.
3. Install the new bushing, using the special tool shown.
4. Before installing a new rear seal, inspect the sealing surface of the universal joint yoke for scores. If the universal joint yoke is scored, replace the yoke.
5. Inspect the housing counterbore for burrs and remove them with crocus cloth if necessary.
6. Install the new rear seal into the housing, using the tool shown in the illustration. The seal should be firmly seated in the housing. Coat the inside diameter of the fiber portion of the seal with lubricant.
7. Coat the front universal joint spline with lubricant and install the drive shaft.

Extension Housing Removal and Installation

1. Raise the truck on a hoist.
2. Remove the drive shaft. Place a

Removing extension housing bushing
(© Ford Motor Co.)

Installing extension housing bushing
(© Ford Motor Co.)

transmission jack under the transmission for support.
3. Remove the speedometer cable from the extension housing.
4. Remove the extension housing-to-crossmember mount attaching bolts. Raise the transmission and remove the mounting pad between the extension housing and the crossmember.
5. Loosen the extension housing attaching bolts to drain the transmission fluid.
6. Remove the six extension housing attaching bolts and remove the extension housing.
7. To install the extension housing, reverse the above removal instructions. Install a new extension housing gasket. When the extension housing has been installed and all parts have been secured, lower the truck and fill the transmission with the correct amount of fluid. Check for fluid leaks around the extension housing area.

Governor Removal and Installation

1. After removing the extension housing according to the instructions above, remove the governor housing-to-governor distributor attaching bolts. Remove the governor housing from the distributor.
82. Refer to the Component Disassembly and Repair section for instructions on repairing the governor assembly.
3. Install the governor housing on the governor distributor and tighten the attaching bolts to the proper torque.
4. Install the extension housing with a new gasket according to the instructions above.
5. When the extension housing has been installed and all bolts have been tightened to the proper torque, lower the truck and fill the

Removing extension housing seal (© Ford Motor Co.)

Installing extension housing seal (© Ford Motor Co.)

transmission with fluid to the proper level. Check around the extension housing area for leaks.

Transmission Overhaul Procedures

The transmission overhaul procedures presented here are the checks and repairs that must be done with the transmission out of the truck. Disassembly of each transmission subassembly is illustrated by exploded views of the subassembly showing how the individual parts fit together. Reassembly of the subassembly is often the reverse of the disassembly procedure except for alignment, special tolerances, etc.

Procedures for removing the transmission from the truck and reinstalling it back in the truck are given in the Truck Section.

During the transmission disassembly and reassembly operations, ten thrust washers that are installed between the subassemblies of the gear train must be removed and reinstalled correctly. Since it is very important that these thrust washers be installed correctly, they are shown in their positions and they are numbered for further identification. The No. 1 thrust washer is located at the front pump, and the No. 10 thrust washer is located at the packing pawl ring gear.

During all repairs to the transmission subassemblies, the following instructions must be followed:

1. Be sure that no dirt or grease gets in the transmission. All parts must be clean. *Remember—a little dirt can disable a transmission completely if it gets in a fluid passage.*
2. Handle all transmission parts carefully to avoid burring or nicking bearing or mating surfaces.
3. Lubricate all internal parts of the transmission with clean transmission fluid before assembling. *Do not use any other lu-*

bricants except on gaskets or thrust washers which may be coated lightly with vaseline to ease assembly.
4. Always use new gaskets when assembling the parts of the transmission.
5. Tighten all bolts and screws to the recommended torque limits using a torque wrench.

Transmission Disassembly

Disassemble the transmission by following the procedures below:

1. Thoroughly clean the outside of the transmission to prevent dirt or grease from getting inside the mechanism. *Do this before removing any subassembly.*
2. Place the transmission in the transmission holder. See illustration.
3. Remove the converter from the transmission front pump and converter housing.
4. On a C4 automatic transmission, remove the transmission vacuum unit with the tool shown in the illustration. Remove the vacuum unit gasket and the control rod.
5. On a C4 automatic transmission, remove the primary throttle valve from the opening at the rear of the case.
6. Remove the transmission pan attaching bolts, oil pan, and gasket.
7. Remove the control valve body attaching bolts and then lift the control valve body from the case.
8. Loosen the intermediate band adjusting screw and remove the intermediate band struts from the case. Loosen the low-reverse band adjusting screw and remove the low-reverse band struts.

Transmission End-Play Check

1. Remove one of the converter housing attaching bolts and mount the dial indicator support tool in the hole. Mount a dial indicator on the support so that a contact rests on the end of the input shaft. See illustration.
2. Install the extension housing seal replacer tool on the output shaft to provide support and alignment for the shaft.
3. Using a screwdriver, move the input shaft and the gear train to the rear of the case as far as possible. Set the dial indicator at zero while holding a slight pressure on the screwdriver.
4. Remove the screwdriver and insert it behind the input shell. Move the input shell and the front part of the gear train forward.
5. Record the dial reading for later reference during transmission reassembly. The end play read-

ing should be from 0.008 to 0.042 in. If the end play reading is not within this range, selective thrust washers must be used to obtain the proper reading. The selective thrust washers to be used are listed in the table shown.
6. Remove the dial indicator, its support bar, and the extension housing seal replacer tool.

Removal of Case and Extension Parts

1. Rotate the transmission in the holding fixture until it is in a vertical position with the converter housing up.
2. Remove the five converter housing attaching bolts and remove the converter housing from the transmission case.
3. Remove the seven front pump attaching bolts. Remove the front pump by inserting a screwdriver behind the input shell and pushing it forward until the front pump seal is above the edge of the case. Remove the front pump and gasket from the case. If the selective thrust washer No. 1 did not come out with the front pump, lift it from the top of the reverse-high clutch.
4. Remove the intermediate and low-reverse adjusting screws from the case. Rotate the intermediate band to align the band ends with the clearance hole in the case. Remove the intermediate band from the case.
5. Using a screwdriver between the input shell and the rear planet carrier (see illustration), lift the input shell upward and remove the forward part of the gear train as an assembly.
6. Place the forward part of the gear train in the holding fixture shown.
7. With the gear train in the holding fixture, remove the

GOVERNOR BOLTS (4) GOVERNOR DISTRIBUTOR GOVERNOR DISTRIBUTOR SLEEVE

Governor location
(© Ford Motor Co.)

Tool—T57L-500-A or 6005-M or 6005-MS

Transmission mounted in holding fixture
(© Ford Motor Co.)

SNAP-ON
Tool S-8696-A

Removing or installing vacuum unit
(© Ford Motor Co.)

reverse-high clutch and drum from the forward clutch. If thrust washer No. 2 did not come out with the front pump, remove the thrust washer from the forward clutch cylinder. If a selective spacer was used, remove the spacer. Remove the forward clutch from the forward clutch hub and ring gear.

8. If the thrust washer No. 3 did not come out with the forward clutch, remove the thrust washer from the forward clutch hub and lift the forward clutch hub and ring gear from the front planet carrier.

9. Remove thrust washer No. 4 and the front planet carrier from the input shell.

10. Remove the input shell, sun gear and thrust washer No. 5 from the holding fixture.

11. From inside the transmission case, remove thrust washer No. 6 from the top of the reverse planet carrier. Remove the reverse planet carrier and thrust washer No. 7 from the reverse ring gear and hub.

12. Move the output shaft forward and, with the tool shown in the illustration, remove the reverse ring gear and hub from the output shaft. Remove the thrust washer No. 8 from the low and reverse drum.

13. Remove the low-reverse band from the case. Remove the one-way clutch inner race by rotating the race clockwise as it is removed.

14. Remove the 12 one-way clutch rollers, springs and the spring retainer from the outer race. *Do not lose or damage any of the 12*

BACK
OF CASE

PRIMARY
THROTTLE
VALVE

Removing or installing primary throttle valve
(© Ford Motor Co.)

INTERMEDIATE
BAND STRUTS

INTERMEDIATE BAND
ADJUSTING SCREW

LOW-REVERSE BAND
ADJUSTING SCREW

LOW REVERSE
BAND STRUTS

Layout of band struts
(© Ford Motor Co.)

springs or rollers. The outer race of the one-way clutch cannot be removed from the case until the extension housing, output shaft and governor distributor sleeve are removed.

15. Remove the transmission from the holding fixture. Place the transmission on the bench in a vertical position with the extension housing up. Remove the four extension housing attaching bolts, the extension housing, and the gasket from the case.

16. Pull outward on the output shaft and remove the output shaft and governor distributor assembly (if so equipped) from the governor distributor sleeve.

17. Remove the governor distributor lock ring from the output shaft. Remove the governor distributor from the output shaft.

18. Remove the four distributor sleeve attaching bolts and the distributor sleeve from the case. *Do not bend or distort the fluid tubes as the tubes are removed from the case with the distributor sleeve.*

19. Remove the parking pawl return spring, pawl, and pawl retaining pin from the case.

20. Remove the parking gear and

GEAR TRAIN
END PLAY
LIMITS
0.008-0.042
INCH

Tool—4201-C

Checking gear train end play
(© Ford Motor Co.)

CONVERTER HOUSING

INPUT
SHAFT

FRONT PUMP

Removing or installing input shaft
(© Ford Motor Co.)

thrust washer No. 10 from the case.

21. Remove the six one-way clutch outer race attaching bolts with the tool shown. As the bolts are removed, hold the outer race that is located inside the case in position. Then, remove the outer race and thrust washer No. 9 from the case.

Component Disassembly and Assembly

Downshift and Manual Linkage

1. Loosen the outer downshift lever nut with penetrating oil. Remove the nut and the inner and outer downshift levers.
   From inside the case, remove the upper retaining ring and the flat washer from the manual lever link. Remove the upper end of the lever link from the case retaining pin.

2. From the back of the transmission case, remove the upper retaining clip and flat washer from the parking pawl link. Remove the pawl link and spacer from the case retaining pin, and remove the parking pawl link, toggle rod, and the manual lever link as an assembly.

3. Remove the inner manual lever retaining nut and lever. Remove the outer manual lever from the case. Remove manul lever seal, and drive a new seal into the case with an appropriate driver. Install outer manual lever into

PRY
INPUT SHELL
FORWARD

Removing front pump
(© Ford Motor Co.)

Forward part of gear train disassembled (© Ford Motor Co.)

Lower part of gear train disassembled (© Ford Motor Co.)

the case. Install inner manual lever and retaining nut. Torque nut to specifications.

4. From back of the transmission case, install parking toggle rod and link into the case. Install parking pawl link spacer onto the case retaining pin. Dimpled side of the spacer should be facing the link.

5. Install the parking pawl link onto the case retaining pin. Install flat washer and retaining ring.

6. Position inner manual lever behind the manual lever link, with the cam on the lever contacting the lower link pin.

7. Install the upper end of the manual lever link onto the case retaining pin. Install flat washer and retaining ring.

8. Operate the manual lever and check for correct linkage operation.

Position of intermediate band for removal or installation
(© Ford Motor Co.)

Control Valve Body Removal

1. Remove the screws attaching the oil screen to the valve body and remove the oil screen. Be careful not to lose the throttle pressure limit valve and spring when separating the oil screen from the valve body.

2. Remove the attaching screws from the lower valve body and separate the upper and lower valve bodies, the gasket, separator plate and the hold-down plate. Be careful not to lose the upper valve body shuttle valve and check valve when separating the upper and lower valve bodies.

Lifting input shell and gear train
(© Ford Motor Co.)

Removing or installing forward part of gear train
(© Ford Motor Co.)

Holding Fixture Tool—77530-A
Forward part of gear train in holding fixture
(© Ford Motor Co.)

Reverse ring gear retaining ring-removal
(© Ford Motor Co.)

3. Slide the manual valve out of the body.

Control Valve Body Disassembly

1. Remove the screws attaching the oil screen to the valve body and remove the oil screen. Be carefu not to lose the throttle pressure limit valve and spring when separating the oil screen from the valve body.

LOW-REVERSE BAND

Removing low-reverse band
(© Ford Motor Co.)

Tool— T65P-7B456-B

Removing one way clutch outer race retaining bolts
(© Ford Motor Co.)

LOW-REVERSE PISTON

Low-reverse servo piston-removal
(© Ford Motor Co.)

PARKING PAWL

PAWL RETAINING PIN

SPRING

THRUST WASHER NO. 10

PARKING GEAR

Parking pawl, disassembled (© Ford Motor Co.)

2. Remove the attaching screws from the lower valve body and separate the upper and lower valve bodies, the gasket, separator plate and the hold-down plate. Be careful not to lose the upper valve body shuttle valve and check valve when separating the upper and lower valve bodies.
3. Slide the manual valve out of the body.
4. Pry the low servo modulator valve retainer from the body and remove the retainer plug, spring, and valve from the valve body. While working in the same bore, pry the retainer, spring, and the downshift valve from the valve body (see illustration).
5. Depress the throttle booster plug and remove the retaining pin. Then, remove the plug, valve, and spring from the valve body.
6. Remove the cover over the cut-back valve and the transition valve from the valve body.
7. Remove the cut-back valve and the transition valve spring, transition valve, 2-3 back-out valve, and spring from the valve body.
8. Remove the cover from over the 1-2 shift valve and the 2-3 shift valve. Remove the 2-3 shift valve, spring, and the throttle modulator valve from the valve body. Remove the 1-2 shift valve, D-2 valve, and spring from the valve body.
9. Remove the retaining pin from the retainer after depressing the intermediate servo accumulator valve. Remove the retainer, intermediate servo accumulator valve, and spring from the valve body.
10. Depress the main oil pressure booster valve and remove the retaining pin. Remove the main oil pressure booster valve, sleeve, springs, retainer, and main oil

pressure regulator valve from the valve body.
11. Remove the line coasting boost valve retaining clip, the spring, and line coasting boost valve from the valve body.

GOVERNOR DISTRIBUTOR

LOCK RING

Removing governor snap-ring
(© Ford Motor Co.)

OUTPUT SHAFT

GOVERNOR DISTRIBUTOR

GOVERNOR DISTRIBUTOR SLEEVE

OIL TUBES

Removing or installing output shaft and governor distributor
(© Ford Motor Co.)

Upper & lower valve bodies C-4 (© Ford Motor Co.)

Transmission case internal linkage (© Ford Motor Co.)

Front Pump Disassembly

1. Remove the four seal rings from the stator support and, on 1967 models, the O-ring seal from the pump housing.
2. Remove the five bolts that secure the stator support to the front pump housing. Remove stator support from pump housing.
3. Replace the stator bushings if they are worn or damaged. Use a cape chisel to cut the bushing through. Then, pry up the loose ends of the bushing with an awl and remove the bushing. Press a new bushing into the stator support.
   NOTE: ensure that the oil hole in the bushing lines up with the hole in the stator support.
4. Remove drive and driven gears from the front pump housing.
5. Replace the bushing in the pump housing with the tools shown, making sure the slot and groove are toward the rear of the body and 60° below the horizontal centerline of the pump.
6. Install the drive and driven gears in the pump housing. The chamfered side of each gear has an identification mark that must be positioned downward, against the face of the pump housing.
7. Place stator support in pump housing. Install and torque the five retaining bolts.
8. Install four seal rings onto the stator support. The two large oil rings are assembled first, in the oil ring grooves toward the front of the stator support. Install the O-ring seal onto the pump housing.
9. Check pump gears for free rotation by placing pump on the converter drive hub and turning pump housing.
10. If the front pump seal must be replaced, mount the pump in the transmission case and remove the seal with a seal removing tool.

Reverse-High Clutch Disassembly and Assembly

1. Remove pressure plate retaining snap-ring.
2. Remove the pressure plate, and the drive and driven clutch plates.
   CAUTION: Use no detergent or other cleaning solution on the lined clutch plates. Wipe the plates with a line-free cloth.
3. Remove piston spring retainer by applying pressure to the clutch hub. Compress piston return springs, and remove the retainer.

4. Remove the ten piston return springs.
5. Remove the piston by applying air pressure to the piston apply hole of the clutch hub.
6. Remove piston outer seal from the piston and the piston inner seal from the clutch drum.
7. Remove the drum bushing if it is worn or damaged. Use a cape chisel to cut the bushing seam until it is broken. Pry up the loose ends of the bushing with an awl and remove the bushing. *To prevent leakage at the stator support O-rings, do not nick or damage the hub surface with the chisel.*
8. Position the drum and a new bushing in a press and install the bushing with the tool shown.
9. Install a new inner seal into the clutch drum and a new outer seal onto the clutch piston. Lubricate and install the piston into the clutch drum.
10. Locate the ten piston return springs on the piston. Place retainer on top of the springs. Compress the assembly with a press, and install the retainer snap-ring.
11. Soak new composition plates in transmission fluid before installation. Install clutch plates, alternately, starting with a steel plate. The last plate installed is the pressure plate with the internally-chamfered side up.
12. Install the pressure plate retaining snap-ring.
13. Using feeler gauges, check the clearance between the pressure plate and the snap-ring while applying pressure to the plate. If clearance is not within specifications, selective thickness snap-rings are available.

Forward Clutch Disassembly and Assembly

1. Remove the clutch pressure plate retaining snap ring.
2. Remove the pressure plate, drive and driven plates from the hub.
3. Remove the disc spring retaining snap-ring.
4. Apply air pressure to the clutch piston pressure hole to remove the piston from the hub.
5. Remove piston outer seal and the inner seal from the clutch hub.
6. Install new piston seals onto the clutch piston and drum.

Removing manual lever seal
(© Ford Motor Co.)

Low-reverse servo disassembled (© Ford Motor Co.)

V-8 ENGINE

Intermediate servo-disassembled (© Ford Motor Co.)

Parking lever pawl link and spacer
(© Ford Motor Co.)

Parking pawl toggle rod
(© Ford Motor Co.)

Upper valve body check ball and spring location
(© Ford Motor Co.)

Hold down plate location
(© Ford Motor Co.)

7. Lubricate and insert the piston into the clutch hub. Install the disc spring and retaining snap-ring.
8. Install the lower pressure plate, with the flat side up and the radiused side downward. Install one composition clutch plate and alternately install the drive and driven plates. Install the pressure plate with the internally chamfered side up.
9. Install pressure plate retaining snap-ring.
10. With a feeler gauge, check clearance between the snap ring and the pressure plate. Downward pressure on the plate should be used when making this check. If clearance is not within specifications, selective snap-rings are available.

Forward Clutch Hub and Ring Gear Disassembly and Assembly

1. Remove forward clutch hub retaining snap-ring.
2. Separate clutch hub from ring gear.
3. Press the bushing from the clutch hub.
4. Install a new bushing into the clutch hub as shown.
5. Install clutch hub into ring gear.
6. Install hub retaining snap-ring.

Input Shell and Sun Gear Disassembly and Assembly

1. Remove external snap-ring from sun gear.
2. Remove thrust washer No. 5 from input shell and sun gear.
2. From inside the shell, remove the sun gear. Remove internal snap-ring from sun gear.
4. If the sun gear bushings are to be replaced use the tool shown in the illustration and press both bushings through the gear.
5. Press a new bushing into each end of the sun gear.

Removing reverse-high clutch bushing
(© Ford Motor Co.)

Removing stator support bushings
(© Ford Motor Co.)

Typical front pump and stator support (© Ford Motor Co.)

Removing forward clutch piston
(© Ford Motor Co.)

Removing reverse-high clutch piston
(© Ford Motor Co.)

6. Install internal snap-ring onto sun gear. Install sun gear into the input shell.
7. Install thrust washer No. 5 onto sun gear and input shell.
8. Install external snap-ring onto sun gear.

Governor and Oil Distributor Disassembly

1. Remove the oil rings from the governor oil distributor.
2. Remove the governor housing attaching bolts and remove the governor assembly from the distributor. Remove the governor oil screen.
3. Remove the primary governor valve retaining ring. Remove the washer, spring, and primary governor valve from the housing.
4. Remove the secondary governor valve retaining clip, spring, and governor valve from the housing.
5. After cleaning and inspecting all governor parts, install the secondary governor valve in its housing. Install the spring and spring retaining clip with its small concave area facing downward.
6. Install the primary governor valve in the housing. Install the spring, washer, and retaining clip. Be sure the washer is centered in the housing on the spring and the retaining ring is fully seated in the ring groove in the housing.
7. Install the oil rings on the governor distributor. Install the governor oil screen and mount the governor assembly on the distributor, tightening the attaching bolts to the proper torque.

Transmission Assembly

1. Install thrust washer No. 9 in-

Front pump seal removal
(© Ford Motor Co.)

Installing front pump seal
(© Ford Motor Co.)

Replacing sun gear bushing
(© Ford Motor Co.)

Forward clutch-disassembled (© Ford Motor Co.)

Automatic Transmissions

side the transmission case.

2. Place the one-way clutch outer race inside the case. From the rear of the case, install the six outer race-to-case retaining bolts. Torque to specifications.
3. Stand the transmission case on end (rear end up). Install parking pawl retaining pin.
4. Install parking pawl on the case retaining pin. Install pawl return spring.
5. Install thrust washer No. 10 onto the parking pawl gear. Place gear and thrust washer on back face of case.
6. Place two oil distributor tubes in the governor distributor sleeve. Install the sleeve onto the case.

Removing or installing clutch piston retainer snap-ring (© Ford Motor Co.)

Removing front pump housing bushing (© Ford Motor Co.)

Reverse-high clutch 1970 C-4 (© Ford Motor Co.)

Reverse-high clutch 1970 C-4 (© Ford Motor Co.)

Ford C-4 (Dual Range)

Forward planet carrier-disassembled (© Ford Motor Co.)

Governor and oil distributor (© Ford Motor Co.)

Input shell and sun gear disassembly (© Ford Motor Co)

As the distributor sleeve is installed, the oil tubes have to be inserted into the two holes in the case and the parking pawl retaining pin has to be inserted in the alignment hole in the distributor.

7. Install the four governor distributor sleeve-to-case retaining bolts and torque to specifications.
8. Install governor distributor assembly onto the output shaft. Install the distributor retaining snap-ring.
9. Check oil rings in the governor distributor for free rotation. Install the output shaft and governor distributor into the distributor sleeve.
10. With a new gasket in place on the extension housing, install the extension housing, vacuum tube clip and the extension housing to case retaining bolts. Torque bolts to specifications.
11. Rotate transmission case so that front end is up, making sure that thrust washer No. 9 is in position at the bottom of the case.
12. Install the 12 one-way clutch springs onto the spring retainer.
13. Place the one-way clutch spring retainer, with springs installed, into the outer race, located inside the transmission.
14. Install the inner race inside the spring retainer and 12 springs.
15. Starting at the back of the one-way clutch outer race, install the 12 clutch rollers.
16. After the clutch has been assembled, rotate the inner race clockwise to center the rollers and springs. Install low and reverse drum. The splines of the drum must engage the splines of the one-way clutch inner race. Check the clutch operation by rotating

RETAINS REVERSE RING GEAR AND HUB TO OUTPUT SHAFT

RETAINS GOVERNOR DISTRIBUTOR TO OUTPUT SHAFT

Governor and reverse ring gear and hub identification
(© Ford Motor Co.)

1183

the low and reverse drum. The drum should rotate clockwise but not counterclockwise.

17. Install thrust washer No. 8 on top of the low and reverse drum. Install the low and reverse band into the case, with the small strut end facing the low-reverse servo.

18. Install the reverse ring gear and hub onto the output shaft.

19. Move the output shaft forward and install the reverse ring gear hub-to-output shaft retaining ring.

20. Place thrust washers Nos. 6 and 7 on the reverse planet carrier. Install planet carrier into the reverse ring gear and engage the tabs of the carrier with the slots in the low-reverse drum.

21. From inside the transmission case, install the inner downshift lever.

22. Install the forward clutch into the reverse-high clutch by meshing the reverse-high clutch plates with the splines of the forward clutch. Using the end-play check reading obtained during the transmission disassembly, determine which No. 2 thrust washer is necessary to get the proper end-play reading and proceed as follows:

a. Place the stator support vertically on the bench and install the correct No. 2 thrust washer or washer and spacer as required to bring the end-play within the correct range.

b. Install the reverse-high clutch and the forward clutch on the stator support.

c. Invert the complete assembly making sure the intermediate brake drum bushing is seated on the forward clutch mating surface. Select the thickest fiber washer (No. 1) that can be inserted between the stator support and the intermediate brake drum thrust surfaces and still maintain a slight clearance. Do not select a washer that must be forced between the stator support and the intermediate brake drum.

d. Remove the intermediate brake drum and forward clutch unit from the stator support.

e. Install the selected No. 1 and No. 2 thrust washers on the front pump stator support using vaseline to hold the thrust washers in place while installing the front pump.

23. Install thrust washer No. 3 onto the forward clutch.

24. Install forward clutch hub and ring in the forward clutch by ro-

tating the units to mesh the forward clutch plates with the splines on the forward clutch hub.

25. Install thrust washer No. 4 on the front planet carrier, and install the planet carrier into the forward clutch hub and ring gear.

26. Install input shell and sun gear onto the gear train. Rotate the input shell to engage the drive lugs of the reverse-high clutch.

Extension housing and output shaft related parts (© Ford Motor Co)

If the drive lugs will not engage, the outer race inside the forward planet carrier is not centered in the end of the sun gear inside the input shell. Center the thrust bearing race and install the input shell.

27. Hold the gear train together and install the forward part of the gear train assembly into the case. The input shell sun gear must mesh with the reverse pinion gears. The front planet car-

Control Pressure at Zero Governor RPM-Ford C4

Year	Engine Speed	Trottle	Manifold Vac. Ins. Hg.	Range	P.S.I.
1970	Idle	Closed	Above 18	P, N, D	52-69
				2, 1	80-110
				R	100-180
	As Required	As Required	10	D, 2, 1	96-110
	As Required	As Required	3.0	D, 2, 1	135-155
				R	220-250
1971-72	As Required	As Required	15 and Above	P, N, D	52-85
				2, 1	52-115
				R	52-180

rier internal splines must mesh with the splines of the output shaft.

28. Install intermediate band through front of case. The side of the band with the anchor tabs faces the back of the transmission. If using a new band, soak it in transmission fluid prior to installation.

29. Install a new front pump gasket onto the case. Install selective thrust washers No. 1 and 2 onto the front pump stator support. Use vaseline to hold the washers in place.

30. Lubricate the front pump O-ring with transmission fluid, and install the front pump stator support into the reverse-high clutch. Align the pump to the case and install the front pump to case retaining bolts.

31. Install the converter housing onto the front pump and case. Install the six converter housing to case retaining bolts. Torque bolts to specifications.

32. Install input shaft. Place transmission in horizontal position, then check transmission end play. If end-play is not within limits, either the wrong selective thrust washers were used, or one of the 10 thrust washers is improperly positioned.

33. Remove the dial indicator used for checking end play and install the one converter housing to case retaining bolt. Torque the bolt to specifications.

34. Install the intermediate and low-reverse band adjusting screws into the case. Install the struts for each band.

35. Adjust intermediate and low-reverse band.

36. Install a universal joint yoke onto the output shaft. Rotate the input and output shafts in both directions to check for free rotation of the gear train.

37. Install control valve body. As the valve body is installed, engage the manual and down-shift valves with the inner control levers. Torque the eight control valve body-to-case bolts to specifications.

38. With a new oil pan gasket in place, install the oil pan and torque the bolts to specifications.

39. Install primary throttle valve into the transmission case.

40. Install vacuum unit, gasket and control rod into the case.

41. Make sure the input shaft is properly installed in the front pump, stator support and gear train. Install the converter into the front pump and the converter housing.

	As Required	As Required	10	P, N, D	96-110
	Stall	Thur Detent	Below 1.0	D, 2, 1 R	143-160 230-260
1973	As Required	As Required	12 and Above	P, N, D 2, 1 R	55-86 55-122 55-197
	As Required	As Required	10	P, N, D	98-110
	Stall	Thru Detent	Below 1.0	D, 2, 1 R	143-164 239-272
1974-75	Idle	As Required	15 and Above	P, N, D 2, 1 R	55-86 55-122 55-197
	As Required	As Required	10	D 2, 1	98-110 90-115
	Stall	Thru Detent	Below 1.0	D, 2, 1 R	143-164 239-272

Ford C4 Torque Specifications

	Foot Pounds
Converter to flywheel	20-30
Converter housing to transmission case	28-40
Front pump to transmission case	28-40
Overrunning clutch face to case	13-20
Oil pan to case	12-16
Rear servo cover to case	12-20
Stator support to pump	12-20
Converter cover to converter housing	12-16
Intermediate servo cover to case	16-22
Diaphragm assembly to case	15-23
Extension assembly to transmission case	28-40
Engine to transmission	23-33
Starter attaching bolts	20-30
Engine support-to-crossmember	40-60
Pressure gauge tap	6-12
Band adjusting screw locknut to case	35-45
Yoke to output shaft	60-120
Reverse servo piston to rod	12-20
Converter drain plug	20-30
Manual valve inner lever to shaft	30-40
Downshift lever to shaft	12-16
Filler tube to engine	23-33
Filler tube to pan	32-42
Transmission to engine	40-50
Distributor sleeve to case	12-20
T.R.S. switch to case	4-8
Transfer case to transmission	21-30
Crossmember attaching bolts	14-24

	Inch Pounds
Lower to upper valve body	40-55
Reinforcement plate to body	40-55
Screen and lower to upper valve body	40-55
Neutral switch to case (Econoline)	55-75
Neutral Switch to column	20
Seperator plate to lower valve body	40-55
Control Assembly to case	80-120
Governor assembly to collector body	80-120
Cooler line fittings	80-120
Detent spring to lower valve body	80-120
Upper valve body to lower valve body	80-120
Oil tube connector	80-120
End plates to body	20-35

Checks and Adjustments C4—1970-76

Operation	Specification
Transmission end play	0.008-0.042 inch (selective thrust washers available)
Turbine and stator end play	Model PEE, PEA, PEF—New or rebuilt 0.023 max. Used 0.040 max.
Intermediate band adjustment	Remove and discard lock nut. Adjust screw to 10 ft-lbs torque, then back off 1¾ turns. Install new lock nut and torque to specification.
Low-reverse band adjustment	Remove and discard lock nut. Adjust screw to 10 ft-lbs torque, then back off 3 turns. Install new lock nut and torque to specification.
Forward clutch pressure plate to snap ring clearance	0.025-0.050 Selective snap ring thicknesses 0.082-0.078, 0.068-0.064, 0.054-0.050
Reverse-high clutch pressure plate to snap ring clearance	0.050-0.071 Selective snap ring thicknesses 0.096-0.092, 0.082-0.078, 0.068-0.064, 0.054-0.050

Selective Thrust Washers

Thrust washer No. 1		Thrust Washer No. 2	
Nylon Thrust Washer W/Tangs	Color of Washer	No. Stamped On Washer	Metal Thrust Washer
.053-.0575	Red	1	.041-.043
.070-.074	Green	2	.056-.058
.087-.091	Natural (White)	3	.073-.075
.104-.108	Black	Spacer	.032-.036①
.121-.125	Yellow		

① This is a selective spacer. The spacer must be installed next to the stator support to obtain correct end play.

Diagnosis

This diagnosis guide covers the most common symptoms and is an aid to careful diagnosis. The items to check are listed in the sequence to be followed for quickest results. Thus, follow the checks in the order given for the particular transmission type.

TROUBLE SYMPTOMS	Items to Check In Truck	Out of Truck
No drive in D, 2 and 1	CWER	ac
Rough initial engagement in D or 2	KBWFE	a
1-2 or 2-3 shift points incorrect or erratic	ABLCDWER	
Rough 1-2 upshifts	BJGWEF	
Rough 2-3 shifts	BJWFGER	br
Dragged out 1-2 shift	ABJWGEFR	c
Engine overspeeds on 2-3 shift	CABJWEFG	br
No 1-2 or 2-3 shift	CLBDWEGJ	bc
No 3-1 shift in D	DE	
No forced downshifts	LEB	
Runaway engine on forced 3-2 downshift	WJGFEB	c
Rough 3-2 or 3-1 shift at closed throttle	KBJEF	
Shifts 1-3 in D	GJBEDR	
No engine braking in first gear—1 range	CHEDR	
Creeps excessively	K	
Slips or chatters in first gear, D	ABWFE	aci
Slips or chatters in second gear	ABJGWFER	ac
Slips or chatters in R	ABHWFER	bcr
No drive in D only	CWE	i
No drive in 2 only	ACWJER	c
No drive in 1 only	ACWER	c
No drive in R only	ACHWER	bcr
No drive in any selector lever position	ACWFER	cd
Lockup in D only		gc
Lockup in 2 only	H	bgci
Lockup in 1 only		gc
Lockup in R only		agc
Parking lock binds or does not hold	C	g
Transmission overheats	OFBW	ns
Maximum speed too low, poor acceleration	YZ	n
Transmission noisy in N and P	AF	d
Transmission noisy in first, second, third or reverse gear	AF	hadi
Fluid leak	AMNOPQS UXBJ	jmp
Car moves forward in N	C	a

Key to Checks

Fluid level	N.	Oil pan gasket, filler tube or seal	b.	Reverse-high clutch	F.
Vacuum diaphragm unit or tubes restricted—leaking—adjustment	O.	Oil cooler and connections	ç.	Leakage in hydraulic system	L.
		Manual or downshift lever shaft seal	d.	Front pump	B.
Manual linkage	P.		g.	Parking linkage	G.
Governor	Q.	⅛ inch pipe plugs in case	h.	Planetary assembly	K.
Valve body	R.	Perform air pressure check	i.	Planetary one-way clutch	C.
Pressure regulator	S.	Extension housing-to-case gasket	j.	Engine rear oil seal	H.
Intermediate band	U.	Extension housing rear oil seal	m.	Front pump oil seal	E.
Low-reverse clutch	W.	Perform control pressure check	n.	Converter one-way clutch	A.
Intermediate servo	X.	Speedometer driven gear adapter seal	p.	Front pump to case gasket or seal	J.
Engine idle speed	Y.	Engine performance	r.	Reverse-high clutch piston air bleed valve	D.
Downshift linkage—including inner level position	Z.	Vehicle brakes	s.	Converter pressure check valves	
Converter drain plugs	a.	Forward clutch			

General Information

The C6 automatic transmission is very similar to the C4 automatic transmission, and most of the maintenance and overhaul procedures given for the C4 transmission will apply to the C6 transmission. One important difference between the C6 and the C4 transmissions is that the C6 transmission uses a low-reverse clutch in place of the low-reverse band. Otherwise, the gear trains are the same as are the clutch combinations. The hydraulic control systems are very similar, except for minor differences in design. All components which are different from the C4 components are illustrated and the procedures to repair them are given.

Transmission Checks

Vacuum Diaphragm Unit Check—Altitude-Compensating Type

The vacuum diaphragm unit may be checked for damaged or ruptured bellows as follows:

1. Remove the diaphragm and the throttle valve rod from the transmission.

2. Insert a rod into the diaphragm unit until it is seated in the hole. Make a reference mark on the rod where it enters the diaphragm.

3. Place the diaphragm unit on a scale with the end of the rod resting on the weighing pan and gradually press down on the diaphragm unit.

4. Note the force (in pounds) at which the reference mark on the rod moves into the diaphragm. If the reference mark is still visible at 12 pounds of pressure on the scale, the diaphragm bellows are good. If the reference mark on the rod disappears before four pounds of force, the diaphragm bellows are damaged and the diaphragm unit must be replaced.

Vacuum Diaphragm

A screw is provided in the inlet tube of the vacuum diaphragm assembly, to permit small adjustments in control pressure. If control pressure is uniformly high or low, in all ranges, it may be brought within specifications by turning this screw. Control pressure may also be varied to alter shift feel, but in no case should it go beyond the specified minimum or maximum.

Control pressure is increased by turning the adjusting screw clockwise, and reduced by turning counterclockwise. One full turn will change control pressure approximately 2-3 psi.

Adjustments

Intermediate Band

1. Raise the truck on a hoist or place on jack stands.
2. Clean threads of the intermediate band adjusting screw.

1 Front pump seal ring
2 Front pump
3 Gasket
4 Seal
5 Number 1 thrust washer (selective)
6 Reverse—high clutch assembly
7 Number 2 thrust washer
8 Forward clutch assembly
9 Number 3 thrust washer
10 Number 4 thrust washer
11 Forward clutch hub assembly
12 Number 5 thrust washer
13 Forward planet assembly
14 Input shell and sun gear assembly
15 Number 6 thrust washer
16 Snap ring
17 Number 7 thrust washer
18 Reverse planet assembly
19 Number 8 thrust washer
20 Reverse ring gear and hub retaining ring.
21 Reverse ring gear and hub
22 Number 9 thrust washer
23 Low—reverse clutch hub
24 One-way clutch
25 One-way clutch inner race
26 Snap ring
27 Low—reverse clutch
28 Snap ring
29 Low—reverse piston return spring retainer
30 Return spring
31 Low—reverse piston
32 Case
33 Number 10 thrust washer
34 Parking gear
35 Governor distributor sleeve
36 Snap ring
37 Governor distributor
38 Governor
39 Output shaft

Drive train disassembled (© Ford Motor Co.)

onto the output shaft and slide it off of the shaft.

3. Remove the seal rings from the distributor.
4. Carefully install new seal rings onto the distributor.
5. Slide the governor distributor into place on the shaft, and install the snap-ring to secure it. Make sure the snap-ring is seated in the groove.

6. Position the governor on the distributor and secure with attaching screws.

Parking Pawl Linkage

1. Unbolt and remove the parking pawl guide plate from the case.
2. Remove the spring, parking pawl, and shaft from the case.
3. Drill a ⅛ in. hole in the park

plate shaft retainer plug, and pull the plug out with a wire hook. Unhook the spring from the park plate.

4. Thread a bolt into the park plate shaft, and pull the shaft from the case. Remove the park plate and spring.
5. Position the spring and park plate in the case and install the

Front pump disassembled (© Ford Motor Co.)

Removing reverse clutch piston
(© Ford Motor Co.)

Removing park plate shaft
(© Ford Motor Co.)

Output shaft hub and ring gear
(© Ford Motor Co.)

Parking pawl mechanism (© Ford Motor Co.)

One way clutch—disassembled (© Ford Motor Co.)

Forward clutch disassembled (© Ford Motor Co.)

shaft. Hook the spring on the park plate.

6. Install a new retainer plug.
7. Install the parking pawl shaft in the case, and slip the parking pawls and spring onto the shaft.
8. Bolt the guide plate to the case, making sure that the actuating rod is seated in the slot of the plate.

Transmission Assembly

1. Place transmission case in a holding fixture.
2. Tap the reverse clutch piston into place with a rubber hammer.
3. Hold the one-way clutch inner race in position, install and torque attaching bolts.
4. Install a low-reverse clutch return spring into each pocket of the reverse clutch piston. Press the springs firmly into the piston to prevent their falling out.
5. Position the spring retainer over the springs and position the retainer snap-ring in place on the one-way inner race.
6. Install the compressing tool and compress the springs just enough to install the low-reverse clutch piston retainer snap-ring.
7. Place the transmission case on the bench, bellhousing facing downward.
8. Position the parking gear thrust washer and gear on the case.

Servo—disassembled (© Ford Motor Co.)

SPRING LOAD ON ROLLERS MUST BE IN A COUNTERCLOCKWISE DIRECTION FOR INSTALLATION

Installing one-way clutch (© Ford Motor Co.)

9. Position the oil distributor sleeve and tubes in place on the rear of the case. Install and torque the attaching bolts.
10. Install the output shaft and as an assembly.
11. Place a new gasket on the rear of the transmission case. Position the extension housing on the case and install attaching bolts. Return the case to the holding fixture.
12. Align the low-reverse clutch hub and one-way clutch with the inner race at the rear of the case. Rotate the low-reverse clutch hub clockwise, while applying pressure to seat it.

Reverse high clutch disassembled (© Ford Motor Co.)

Upper control valve body —disassembled (© Ford Motor Co.)

13. Install the low-reverse clutch plates. Start with a steel plate and follow with friction and steel plates, alternately. If new composition (friction) plates are being used, soak them in transmission fluid for 15 minutes before installation. Install the pressure plate and snap-ring. Test the operation of the low-reverse clutch by applying air pressure at the clutch pressure apply hole in the case.

14. Install the reverse planet ring gear thrust washer, ring gear and hub assembly. Insert the snap-ring onto its groove in the output shaft.

15. Assemble the front and rear thrust washers onto the reverse planet assembly. Retain them with vaseline, then insert the assembly into the ring gear. Install the snap-ring into the ring gear.

16. Install the thrust washer onto the rear end of the reverse-high clutch assembly. Retain the thrust washer with vaseline and insert the splined end of the forward clutch into the open end of the reverse-high clutch so that the splines engage the reverse-high clutch friction plates.

17. Install the thrust washer onto the front end of the planet ring gear and hub. Insert the ring gear into the forward clutch.

18. Install the thrust washer onto the front end of the forward planet assembly. Retain the washer with vaseline and insert the assembly into the ring gear. Install the input shell and sun gear assembly.

Converter pressure relief valve, throttle pressure relief valve and 2-3 shift check valve locations
(© Ford Motor Co.)

Output shaft disassembled (© Ford Motor Co.)

Upper and lower valve bodies—disassembled (© Ford Motor Co.)

19. Install the reverse-high clutch, forward clutch, forward planet assembly and input shell and sun gear, as an assembly, into the transmission case.

20. Insert the intermediate band into the case around the reverse and high clutch cylinder, with the narrow band end facing the servo apply lever. Install the struts and tighten the band adjusting screw just enough to retain the band.

21. Place a selective thickness bronze thrust washer on the rear shoulder of the stator support and retain it with vaseline. Lay a new gasket on the rear mounting face of the pump and position it on the case, being careful not to damage the O-ring. Install six of the seven mounting bolts. Adjust the intermediate band as previously described. Then, install the input shaft.

22. Install a dial indicator stand in place of the seventh mounting bolt, and check the transmission end-play. Remove the tool, and install the remaining bolt.

23. Install the control valve into the case, making sure that the levers engage the valves properly.

24. Install the primary throttle valve, rod, and the vacuum diaphragm into the case.

25. Install a new oil pan gasket, and the oil pan.

26. Install the converter assembly.

Control Pressure at Zero Governor RPM

Year	Engine Speed	Throttle	Manifold Vac. In. Hg.	Range	Psi
1970	Idle	Closed	Above 18①	P, N, D, 2, 1 R	56-62 71-86
	As Required	As Required	10	D, 2, 1	100-115
	As Required	As Required	Below 10	D, 2, 1 R	160-190 250-300
1971	Idle	As Required	Above 15	P, N, D, 2, 1 R	56-62 71-86
	As Required	As Required	10	D, 2, 1	100-115
	Stall	Thru Detent	Below 1.0	D, 2, 1	160-190
1972	Idle	As Required	Above 15	D, 2, 1 R	56-94 78-132
	As Required	As Required	10	D, 2, 1	100-125
	Stall	Thru Detent	Below 1.0	D, 2, 1 R	160-190 240-300
1973-75	Idle			D, 2, 1, P, N R	56-112 78-161
	As Required	As Required	10	D, 2, 1	100-125
	Stall	Thru Detent	Below 1.0	D, 2, 1 R	160-190 240-300

① It may not be possible to obtain 18 inches of engine vacuum at idle. For idle vacuum of less than 18 inches, the following chart provides idle speed pressure specifications in the "D" range:

Vac.	Psi	Vac.	Psi
17	56-69	13	56-98
16	56-75	12	56-105
15	56-84	11	56-111
14	56-92		

Checks and Adjustments—1970-75

Operation	Specification
Transmission end play	0.008-0.044 (selective thrust washers available)
Turbine and stator end play	New or rebuilt 0.021 in .max. Used 0.030 in. max. ①
Intermediate band adjustment	Remove and discard locknut. Adjust screw to 10 ft-lbs torque, then back off 1 turn ,install new lock nut and tighten locknut to specification. ②
Forward clutch pressure plate-to-snap ring clearance	0.031-0.044
Selective snap ring thicknesses	0.056-0.060 in., 0.065-0.069 in., 0.074-0.078 in., 0.083-0.87 in., 0.092-0.096 in.
Reverse-high clutch pressure plate-to-snap ring clearance	*Transmission Models* PGA, PJA, PJB (1973-74) 0.022-0.036 in. PGB-AF2, F3, G3, PJB, PJC-A, B, E, F, PJD ③ 0.027-0.043 in.
Selective snap ring thicknesses	0.065-0.069 in., 0.074-0.078 in, 0.083-0.087 in. ④

① To check end play, exert force on checking tool to compress turbine to cover thrust washer wear plate. Set indicator at zero.
② 1971-74 models: back off adjusting screw 1½ turns.
③ PJB only to 1972.
④ For 1973-4 add 0.056-0.060; 0.092-0.096.

Selective Thrust Washers—1970-75

Identification No.	Thrust Washer Thickness—Inch	Identification No.	Thrust Washer Thickness—Inch
1	0.056-0.058	4	0.103-0.105
2	0.073-0.075	5	0.118-0.120
3	0.088-0.090		

Torque Limits—1970-75

	Ft-Lbs
Converter to flywheel	20-30
Front pump to trans. case	12-20
Overrunning clutch race to case	18-25
Oil pan to case	12-16
Stator support to pump	12-16
Converter cover to converter hsg.	12-16
Guide plate to case	12-16
Intermediate servo cover to case	10-14
Diaphragm assy to case	15-23
Distributor sleeve to case	12-16
Extension assy. to trans. case	25-30
Pressure gauge tap	9-15
Band adj. screw locknut to case	35-45
Cooler tube connector lock	25-35②
Converter drain plug	14-28
Manual valve inner lever to shaft	30-40
Downshift lever to shaft	12-16
Filler tube to engine	20-25
Transmission to engine	40-50
Steering col. lock rod adj. nut	10-20
Neutral start switch actuator lever bolt	6-10
T.R.S. switch-to-case	4-8

	In-Lbs
End plates to body	20-30
Inner downshift lever stop	20-30
Reinforcement plate to body	20-30
Screen and lower to upper valve body	50-60
Neutral switch to case	55-75
Neutral switch-to column	20
Control assy. to case	90-125
Gov. body to collector body	80-120
Oil tube connector	80-145①

① 1972 torque limits—80-120 in. lbs.;
1973-75 torque limits—60-120 in. lbs.
② 1972-75 torque limits—20-35 in. lbs.

C6 automatic transmission (© Ford Motor Co)

Diagnosis

This diagnosis guide covers the most common symptoms and is an aid to careful diagnosis. The items to check are listed in the sequence to be followed for quickest results. Thus, follow the checks in the order given for the particular transmission type.

TROUBLE SYMPTOMS	Items to Check	
	In Truck	Out of Truck
Rough initial engagement in D1 or D2	KBWFEG	
1-2 or 2-3 shift points incorrect or erratic	ABCDWEL	
Rough 2-3 shifts	BGFEJ	
Engine overspeeds on 2-3 shift	BGEF	m
No 12 or 2-3 upshift	DECJG	bcf
No 3-1 shift	KBE	
No forced downshift	LWE	
Runaway engine on forced downshift	GFEJB	c
Rough 3-2 or 3-1 shift at closed throttle	KBE	
Creeps excessively	KZ	
Slips or chatters in first gear, D1	ABWFE	acfi
Slips or chatters in second gear	ABGWFEJ	ac
Slips or chatters in R	AHWFEIB	bcf
No drive in D1	CE	i
No drive in D2	ERC	acf
No drive in L	CER	acf
No drive in R	HIERC	bef
No drive in any selector position	ACWFER	cd
Lockup in D1	CIJ	bgc
Lockup in D2	CHI	bgci
Lockup in L	GJE	bjc
Lockup in R	GJ	agc
Parking lock binds or does not hold	C	g
Transmission overheats	OFG	l
Engine will not push-start	ACFE	ec
Maximum speed to low, poor acceleration	Y	l
Transmisison noisy in N and P	F	ad
Noisy transmission during coast 30-20 mph with engine stopped		e
Transmission noisy in any drive position	F	hbad
Fluid leaks	MNOPQSTUX	jkl

Key to Checks

A. Fluid level
B. Vacuum diaphragm unit or tubes
C. Manual linkage
D. Governor
E. Valve body
F. Pressure regulator
G. Front band
H. Rear band
I. Rear servo
J. Front servo
K. Engine idle speed
L. Downshift linkage
M. Converter drain plug
N. Oil pan, filler tube and/or seals

O. Oil cooler and/or connections
P. Manual or throttle shaft seals
Q. Pipe plug, side of case
R. Perform air pressure checks
S. Extension housing-to-case gasket or washer
T. Center support bolt lock washer
U. Extension housing rear oil seal
W. Make control pressure check
X. Speedometer drive gear adaptor seal
Y. Engine performance
Z. Vehicle brakes

a. Front clutch
b. Rear clutch
c. Hydraulic system leakage
d. Front pump
e. Rear pump
f. Fluid distributor sleeve—output shaft
g. Parking linkage
h. Planetary assembly
i. Planetary oneway clutch
j. Engine rear oil seal
k. Front oil pump seal
l. Front pump-to-case seal or gasket
m. Rear clutch piston air bleed valve

General Information

This section provides procedures for testing, inspection, adjustment, and repair of the FMX 3-speed automatic transmission. Where there are differences in procedures or specifications for various model changes, these differences will be outlined.

The Ford FMX 3-speed automatic transmission is a three-speed unit that provides automatic upshifts and downshifts through three forward gear ratios and also provides manual selection of first and second gears. The transmission consists of a torque converter, planetary gear assembly, two multiple disc clutches, and a hydraulic control system.

The FMX transmission cools its transmission fluid through a cooler core in the radiator lower tank when a steel converter is used. If an aluminum converter is used, the transmission fluid is air-cooled.

Towing

If the disabled truck is to be towed a short distance, it may be towed safely by placing the selector lever in the Neutral position and releasing the parking brake. The driver of the towed truck should be careful to maintain a safe distance behind the towing vehicle. The towing speed should not exceed 30 mph.

If the disabled truck is to be towed a long distance, the transmission cannot be put in the Neutral gear, or if there is no driver for the towed truck, raise the truck so the rear wheels clear the ground and tow the truck backwards.

Starting the Engine without the Starter

The transmission may be used to start an engine when the starter cannot be used by moving the disabled truck at a road speed of about 25 mph while in Neutral and then placing the transmission in Low gear while the ignition is on. The resultant turning over of the engine will start the engine and the truck may move under its own power. The disabled truck may be towed or pushed but extreme care must be taken not to lose control of the truck's motion and cause a collision. When the engine starts, the truck will move forward quickly and must be slowed enough to avoid a collision. If the disabled truck is being pushed, the rear truck must drop back before the transmission is engaged to avoid hitting the front truck.

Transmission Checks

Prior to performing any of the tests or adjustments described below, engine idle speed, manual linkage adjustment, and transmission fluid level must be checked.

If fluid level is excessively low, check for leakage as follows.

Transmission Fluid Leakage Checks

Make the following checks if leakage is suspected from the transmission:

1. Clean all dirt and grease from the transmission case.
2. Inspect the speedometer cable connection at the extension housing of the transmission. If fluid is leaking here, disconnect the cable and replace the rubber seal.

Tire Inflating Chuck
Tire Pressure Gauge

Typical converter leak checking tool
(© Ford Motor Co.)

3. Inspect the oil pan gasket and attaching bolts for leaks. Tighten any bolts that appear loose to the proper torque (10-13 ft. lbs.). Recheck for signs of leakage. If necessary, remove the pan attaching bolts and old pan gasket and install new gasket. Reinstall the pan and its attaching bolts.
4. Check filler tube connection at the transmission for signs of leakage. If tube is leaking, tighten the connection to stop the leak. If necessary, disconnect the filler tube, replace the O-ring, and reinstall the filler tube.
5. Inspect all fluid lines between the transmission and the cooler core in the lower radiator tank. Replace any lines or fittings that appear to be worn or damaged. Tighten all fittings to the proper torque.
6. Inspect the engine coolant for signs of transmission fluid in the radiator. If there is transmission fluid in the engine coolant, the oil cooler core is probably leaking.
   NOTE: The oil cooler core may be tested further by disconnecting all lines to it and applying 50-75 psi air pressure through the fittings. Remove the radiator cap to relieve any pressure build-up outside the cooler core. If air bubbles appear in the coolant or if the cooler core will not hold pressure, the oil cooler core is leaking and must be replaced.
7. Inspect the openings in the case

Typical MX—H.D. transmission (© Ford Motor Co.)

Typical control pressure connecting points
(© Ford Motor Co.)

Rotunda are—
29-05 automatic transmission tester
(© Ford Motor Co.)

Converter leak checking tool (© Ford Motor Co.)

where the downshift control lever shaft and the manual lever shaft are located. If necessary, replace the defective seal.

8. Inspect all plugs or cable connections in the transmission for signs of leakage. Tighten any loose plugs or connectors to the proper torque (see torque chart at end of this section).

9. Remove the lower cover from the front of the bellhousing and inspect the converter drainplugs for signs of leakage. If there is a leak around the drainplugs, loosen the plug and coat the threads with sealing compound. Tighten the plug to the proper torque.

NOTE: Fluid leaks from around the converter drainplug may be caused by engine oil leaking past the rear main bearing or from the oil gallery plugs. To determine the exact cause of the leak before beginning repair procedures, an oil-soluble aniline or fluorescent dye may be added to the transmission fluid to find the source of the leak and whether the transmission is leaking. If a fluorescent dye is used, a black light must be used to detect the dye.

If further converter checks are necessary, remove the transmission from the truck and the converter from the transmission. The converter cannot be disassembled for cleaning or repair. If the converter is leaking, it must be replaced with a new unit. To check the converter for leaks, assemble and install the converter leak checking tool and fill the converter with 20 psi air pressure. Then, place the converter in a tank of water and watch for air bubbles. If no air bubbles are seen, the converter is not leaking.

Control Pressure Check

When the vacuum diaphragm unit operates properly and the downshift linkage is adjusted correctly, all transmission shifts (automatic and kickdown) should occur within the specified road speed limits. If these shifts do not occur within the limits or if the transmission slips during a shift point, perform the following procedure to locate the problem:

1. Connect the Automatic Transmission Tester (see illustration) as follows:
   a. Tachometer cable to engine.
   b. Vacuum gauge hose with a T-fitting between the vacuum hose and vacuum diaphragm (see illustration).
   NOTE: On vehicles equipped with a dual area diaphragm (DAD), check the control pressure at 10 in. of vacuum by removing the exhaust gas recirculation (EGR) control hose from the diaphragm and plugging the hose. Do not plug the EGR port in the diaphragm; this port must be left open to atmospheric pressure. When checking the control pressure at stall and idle, keep the hose connected.
   c. Pressure gauge to the control pressure outlet on the transmission (see illustration).

2. Apply the parking brake and start the engine. On a truck equipped with a vacuum brake release, use the service brakes since the parking brake will release automatically when the transmission is put in any Drive position.

3. Check the transmission diaphragm unit for leaks (see below).

4. Check control pressure in all selector lever positions at specified manifold vacuum (see specifications). Record readings and compare to specifications.

Testing transmission vacuum unit for leakage
(© Ford Motor Co.)

Vacuum Diaphragm Unit Check

1. Remove the vacuum diaphragm unit from the transmission using crowfoot wrench, after disconnecting the vacuum hose (see illustration).

2. Adjust a vacuum pump until the vacuum gauge shows 18 in/Hg. with the vacuum hose blocked.

3. Connect the vacuum hose to the vacuum diaphragm unit and note the reading on the vacuum gauge. If the reading is 18 inches of vacuum, the vacuum diaphragm unit is good. While removing the vacuum hose from the vacuum diaphragm unit, hold a finger over the end of the control rod. As the vacuum is released, the internal spring of the vacuum diaphragm unit will push the control rod out.

Removing or installing vacuum diaphragm
(© Ford Motor Co.)

Typical vacuum test line connections
(© Ford Motor Co.)

Case fluid hole identification
(© Ford Motor Co.)

Air Pressure Checks

If the truck will not move in one or more ranges, or, if it shifts erratically, the items at fault can be determined by using air pressure at the indicated passages.

Drain the transmission and remove the oil pan and the control valve assembly.

NOTE: Oil will spray profusely during this operation.

Front Clutch

Apply sufficient air pressure to the front clutch input passage. A dull thud can be heard when the clutch piston moves. Check also, for leaks.

Governor

Remove the governor inspection cover from the extension housing. Apply air to the front clutch input passage. (See illustration). Listen for a sharp click and watch to see if the governor valve snaps inward as it should.

Rear Clutch

Apply air to the rear clutch passage (See illustration) and listen for the dull thud that will indicate that the rear clutch piston has moved. Listen also for leaks.

Front Servo

Apply air pressure to the front servo apply tube and note if front band tightens. Shift the air to the front servo release tube, which is next to the apply tube, and watch band release.

Rear Servo

Apply air pressure to the rear servo apply passage. The rear band should tighten around the drum.

Conclusions

If the operation of the servos and clutch is normal with air pressure, the no-drive condition is due to the control valve and pressure regulator valve assemblies, which should be disassembled, cleaned and inspected.

If operation of the clutches is not normal; that is, if both clutches apply from one passage or if one fails to move, the aluminum sleeve (bushing) in the output shaft is out of position or badly worn. (See illustration.)

Use air pressure to check the passages in the sleeve and shaft, and also check the passages in the primary sun gear shaft.

If the passages in the two shafts and the sleeve are clean, remove the clutch assemblies, clean and inspect the parts.

Erratic operation can also be caused by loose valve body screws. When reinstalling the valve body be careful to tighten: the pressure regulator valve to case bolts to 17-22 ft. lbs., the pressure regulator valve cover screws to 20-30 in. lbs., the control valve body screws to 20-30 in. lbs., the 1/4-20 capscrew (lower to upper valve body) to 4-6 ft. lbs., and the control valve body to case bolts to 8-10 ft. lbs.

Shift Point Checks for Automatic Transmissions

To determine if the transmission is shifting at the proper road speeds, use the following procedure:

1. Check the minimum throttle upshifts by placing the transmission selector lever in the Drive position and noting the road speeds at which the transmission shifts from first gear to second gear to third gear. All shifts should occur within the specified limits.

2. While driving in third gear, depress the accelerator pedal past the detent (to the floor). Depending on vehicle speed, the transmission should downshift from third gear to second gear or from second gear to first gear.

Front servo disassembled (© Ford Motor Co.)

Rear servo disassembled (© Ford Motor Co.)

Automatic Transmissions

3. Check the closed-throttle down-shift from third gear to first gear by coasting down from about 30 mph in third gear. This downshift should occur at the specified road speed.
4. With the transmission in third gear and the truck moving at a road speed of 35 mph, the transmission should downshift to second gear when the selector lever is moved from D to 2 to 1. This check will determine if the governor pressure and shift control valves are operating properly. If the transmission does not shift within the specified limits or certain gears cannot be obtained, refer to the Trouble Diagnosis chart at the beginning of this section.

Front band adjustment—typical
(© Ford Motor Co.)

Front and rear band adjusting tools
(© Ford Motor Co.)

In-Vehicle Adjustments and Repairs

The following adjustments and repairs may be performed without removing the transmission.

Band Adjustments

Front Band Adjustment

When it is necessary to adjust the front band of the transmission, perform the following procedure:
1. Drain the transmission fluid and remove the oil pan, fluid filter screen, and clip. The same transmission fluid may be reused if it is filtered before being installed. Only transmission fluid in good condition should be used.

2. Clean the pan and filter screen and remove the old gasket.
3. Loosen the front servo adjusting screw locknut.
   NOTE: Special band adjusting wrenches are recommended to do this operation correctly and quickly.
4. Pull back the actuating rod and insert a ¼ in. spacer bar between the adjusting screw and the servo piston stem. Tighten the adjusting screw to 10 in. lbs. torque. Remove the spacer bar and tighten the adjusting screw an additional ¾ turn. Hold the adjusting scew and tighten the locknut securely (20-25 ft. lbs.).
5. Install the transmission fluid filter screen and clip. Install the pan with a new pan gasket.
6. Refill the transmission to the FULL mark on the Dipstick. Start the engine, run for a few minutes, shift the selector lever through all positions, and place it in Park. Recheck the fluid level again and add fluid to proper level is necessary.

Rear Band Adjustments

The rear band of the FMX transmission may be adjusted by any of the methods given below. On most trucks the basic external band adjustment is satisfactory. The internal adjustment may be performed in cases where the adjustment required is outside the range of the external adjustment.

Rear band adjustment
(© Ford Motor Co.)

Adjusting rear band
(© Ford Motor Co.)

Rear Band External Adjustment

The procedure for adjusting the rear band externally is as follows:
1. Locate the external rear band adjusting screw on the transmission case, clean all dirt from the

threads, and coat the threads with light oil.
   NOTE: The adjusting screw is located on the upper right side of the transmission case. Access is often through a hole in the front floor to the right of center under the carpet.
2. Loosen the locknut on the rear band external adjusting screw.
3. Using the special preset torque wrench shown, tighten the adjusting screw until the handle clicks at 10 ft. lbs. torque. If the adjusting screw is tighter than 10 ft. lbs. torque, loosen the adjusting screw and retighten to the proper torque.
4. Back off the adjusting screw 1½ turns. Hold the adjusting screw steady while tightening the locknut to the proper torque (35-40 ft. lbs.).
   CAUTION: Severe damage may result if adjusting screw is not backed off exactly 1½ turns.

Rear Band Internal Adjustment

The rear band is adjusted internally as follows:
1. Drain the transmission fluid. If it is to be resued, filter it as it drains from the transmission. Reuse the transmission fluid only if it is in good condition.
2. Remove and clean the pan, fluid filter, and clip.
3. Loosen the rear servo adjusting locknut.
4. Pull the adjusting screw end of the actuating lever away from the servo body and insert the spacer tool (see illustration) between the servo accumulator piston and the adjusting screw. Be sure the flat surfaces of the tool are placed squarely between the adjusting screw and the accumulator piston. Tool must not touch servo piston and the handle must not touch the servo piston spring retainer.
5. Using a torque wrench with an allen head socket adapter tighten the adjusting screw to 24 in. lbs.
6. Back off the adjusting screw exactly 1½ turns. Hold adjusting screw steady and tighten the locknut securely. Remove the spacer tool.
7. Install the fluid filter, clip, and pan with a new gasket.
8. Fill the transmission with the correct amount of fluid.

Transmission Component Removal and Installation

Various components of the FMX transmission may be removed while the transmission is in the truck. Installation is often the reverse of the removal instructions except for adjustment and alignment. Repair of the individual components is given in the overhaul section.

Governor Assembly

Removal

1. Raise the truck so that the transmission extension housing is accessible.
2. Remove the governor inspection cover from the extension housing.
3. Rotate the drive shaft until the governor is in line with the inspection hole.
4. Remove the governor valve body from the counterweight.
   CAUTION: Do not drop the attaching bolts of the valve parts into the extension housing.

Installation

1. Lubricate the new governor valve parts with clean transmission fluid.
   NOTE: The valve must move freely in the valve body bore.
2. Install the governor body on the counterweight so that the valve body cover is facing the rear. Tighten the attaching bolts.
3. Install the governor inspection cover with a new gasket on the extenison housing. Tighten the attaching bolts to proper torque specifications. (Torque specifications are at the end of this section).

Extension Housing Bushing and Rear Seal

Removal

1. Raise the truck and remove the drive shaft. Remove the parking brake drum if so equipped. Remove the transmission output shaft and attaching nut with special tool.
2. Working with a sharp chisel, remove the seal from the extension housing.

Installing extension housing seal (© Ford Motor Co.)

CAUTION: Do not allow any metal chips to enter the output shaft bearing.
3. To remove the output shaft bearing, remove the snap ring securing the bearing to the extension housing.
4. Remove the bearing from the extension housing.

Installation

1. Position a new bearing in the extension housing and secure with a snap ring.
2. Install a new extension housing seal with the proper seal replacement tool. Install the output shaft yoke and retaining nut. Torque the attaching nut to specifications. Install the parking brake drum, if so equipped.
3. Install the drive shaft and torque bolts to specifications.
4. Lower the truck and check the transmission fluid level.

Control Valve Body and Oil Pan

Removal

1. Raise the truck on a hoist or jackstands and place a drain pan under the transmission.

FRONT SERVO FLUID TUBES

PRESSURE REGULATOR

COMPENSATOR PRESSURE TUBE

MAIN CONTROL VALVE TUBE

VACUUM DIAPHRAGM

REAR SCREEN RETAINING CLIP

FRONT SERVO   REAR SERVO

Typical hydraulic control system (© Ford Motor Co.)

2. Drain the transmission.
3. Remove the oil pan, fluid filter screen, and clip and clean them thoroughly. Discard the old pan gasket.
4. Remove the vacuum diaphragm assembly using a crowfoot wrench. *Do not use pliers, pipe wrenches, etc. to remove the vacuum diaphragm unit. Do not let any solvents enter the vacuum diaphragm unit.* Remove the push rod, the fluid screen and its retaining clip.
5. Remove the small compensator pressure tube.
6. Disconnect the main pressure oil tube by carefully loosening the end connected to the control valve body first and then removing the tube from the pressure regulator unit.
   CAUTION: Be sure to remove the tube in this manner. Otherwise, the tube could be kinked or bent causing improper fluid pressures and possible damage to the transmission.
7. Loosen the front servo attaching bolts about three turns.
8. Remove the three control valve body attaching bolts and carefully lower the valve body, sliding it off the front servo tubes. *Do not damage the valve body or the tubes.*

Installation

1. When installing the control valve body, align the front servo tubes with the holes in the valve body. Shift the manual lever to the 1 detent and place the inner downshift lever between the downshift lever stop and the downshift valve. Be sure the manual lever engages the actuating pin in the manual detent lever.
2. Loosely install the control valve body attaching bolts and move the control valve body toward the center of the transmission case until there is a clearance of 0.050 in. between the manual valve and the actuating pin on the manual detent lever.
3. Tighten the attaching bolts to 8-10 ft. lbs. torque. Ensure that the rear fluid filter retaining clip

is installed under the valve body.

4. Install the main pressure oil tube, connecting the end to the pressure regulator unit first and then connecting the other end to the main control valve assembly by gently tapping it with a soft-faced hammer.
5. Install the compensator pressure tube on the pressure regulator and control valve body.
6. Check the manual lever for free motion in each detent position by rotating it one full turn. If the manual lever binds in any detent position, loosen the valve body attaching bolts and move the valve body away from the center of the transmission case until the binding is relieved. Retighten the attaching bolts according to step 3.
7. Place the pushrod in the bore of the vacuum diaphragm unit and install the vacuum diaphragm unit.
8. Tighten the front servo attaching bolts.
9. Adjust the front band.
10. Install the fluid filter and its retaining clip.
11. Adjust the rear band.
12. Install the oil pan with a new, pan gasket.
13. Fill transmission with fluid. Start and run engine for a few minutes and check the fluid level after shifting the transmission through all positions. *Do not overfill the transmission.*
14. Check the adjustment of the transmission control linkage.

Pressure Regulator
Removal

1. Drain the transmission of fluid and remove the pan, fluid filter screen, and its retaining clip. Discard the used pan gasket.
2. Remove the compensator pressure tube from between the control valve body and the pressure regulator.
3. Remove the main pressure oil tube by gently prying off the end connected to the control valve first and then disconnect the other end from the pressure regulator. *Be sure to remove the tube in this order to prevent kinking or bending it.*
4. Loosen the spring retainer clip and carefully release the spring tension on the pressure springs. Remove the valve springs, retainer and valve stop, and the valves from the pressure regulator body.
5. Remove the pressure regulator attaching bolts and washers and take the regulator body out of the transmission case.

Installation

1. Place the replacement regulator

body on the transmission case and install the two securing bolts, tighten the bolts to specifications.
2. Check the converter pressure and the control pressure valves to be sure that the valves are operating freely in the bores.
3. Install the valve springs, spacer and retainer.
4. Install the main pressure oil tube.
   NOTE: Be sure to install the end of the tube that connects to the pressure regulator assembly first. Then, install the other end of the tube into the main control assembly by tapping it gently with a soft faced hammer.
5. Install the small compensator pressure tube.
6. Install the fluid screen and the oil pan. Fill the transmission to the correct level with the specified fluid.

Front Servo
Removal

1. Drain the transmission fluid from the transmission and remove the pan, fluid filter screen, and its retaining clip.
2. Remove the vacuum diaphragm unit.
3. Loosen the three control valve body attaching bolts.
4. Remove the front servo attaching bolts, hold the band strut steady, and remove the front servo unit.

Installation

1. After repairing the front servo unit, install it by first positioning the front band forward in the transmission case with the end of the band facing downward. Be sure the front servo anchor pin is placed in the case web. Align the large end of the servo strut with the servo actuating lever, and align the small end with the band end.
2. Rotate the band, strut, and servo to align the anchor end of the band with the anchor in the case.

Push the servo unit onto the control valve body tubes.
3. Install the attaching bolts and tighten them to 30-35 ft. lbs. torque.
4. Tighten the control valve body attaching bolts to 8-10 ft. lbs. torque. Check the clearance (0.050 in.) between the manual valve and the manual lever actuating pin.
5. Adjust the front band.
6. Install the vacuum diaphragm unit and its pushrod.
7. Install the fluid filter screen, its retaining clip, and the pan with a new pan gasket.
8. Fill the transmission with fluid.
9. Adjust the downshift and manual shift linkage.

Rear Servo
Removal

1. Drain the transmission fluid from the transmission, and remove the pan, fluid filter screen, and its retaining clip.
2. Remove the vacuum diaphragm unit.
3. Remove the control valve body and the two front servo tubes.
4. Remove the rear servo attaching bolts, hold the actuating and anchor struts, and remove the rear servo unit.

Installation

1. Before installing the rear servo unit, position the servo anchor strut on the servo band and rotate the band to engage the strut.
2. While holding the servo anchor strut in place, position the actuating lever strut and install the rear servo unit in place.
3. Loosely install the rear servo attaching bolts, with the longer bolt in the inner bolt hole.
4. Move the rear servo unit toward the center of the transmission case against the attaching bolts. While holding the servo in this position, tighten the attaching bolts.
5. Install the two front servo tubes and the control valve body.

Tool—7000-CJ

Transmission mounted in holding fixture (© Ford Motor Co.)

Check for proper clearance (0.050 in.) between the manual valve and the manual actuating pin.

6. Adjust the rear band.
7. Install the fluid filter screen, its retaining clip, and the oil pan with a new gasket. Fill the transmission with fluid.

Transmission Overhaul Procedures

The transmission overhaul procedures presented here are the checks and repairs that must be done with the transmission out of the truck. Each transmission subassembly is illustrated by exploded views of the subassembly showing how the individual parts fit together. Assembly is often the reverse of the disassembly procedure except for alignment, special tolerances, etc.

During all repairs to the transmission subassemblies, the following instructions must be followed:

1. Be sure that no dirt or grease gets in the transmission. All parts must be clean. *Remember —a little dirt can disable a transmission completely if it gets in a fluid passage.*
2. Handle all transmission parts carefully to avoid burring or nicking bearing or mating surfaces.
3. Lubricate all internal parts of the transmission with clean transmission fluid before assembling. *Do not use any other lubricants except on gaskets or thrust washers which may be coated lightly with vaseline to ease assembly.*
4. Always use new gaskets when assembling the transmission.
5. Tighten all bolts and screws to the recommended torque limits using a torque wrench.

Transmission Disassembly

1. Thoroughly clean the outside of the transmission to prevent dirt or grease from getting inside. *Do this before removing any subassembly.*
2. Place the transmission in the transmission holder or stand.
3. Remove the transmission oil pan, gasket, and fluid filter retaining clip.
4. Lift the fluid filter screen off the forward tube, and then off the rear tube.
5. Remove the spring seat from the pressure regulator. *Maintain constant pressure on the spring seat and release slowly to prevent spring distortion and personal injury.*
6. Remove the pressure regulator springs and pilots, but do not remove the valves yet.

7. Loosen but do not remove the pressure regulator attaching bolts.
8. Remove the small compensator pressure tube from the pressure regulator and the control valve body.
9. Remove the main pressure oil tube from the pressure regulator and the main control valve body assembly. Gently pry off the end connected to the main control valve body first and then remove the tube from the pressure regulator. *Failure to do this may kink or bend the tube causing damage to the transmission.*
10. Loosen the front and rear band adjusting screws five turns. Loosen the front servo attaching bolts three turns.
11. Remove the vacuum diaphragm unit and pushrod.
12. Remove the control valve body attaching bolts and align the levers to allow removal of the valve body. Lift the valve body up and pull it off the servo tubes. Place the valve body on a clean surface.
13. Remove the pressure regulator from the case. Keep the control pressure valve and the converter pressure valve in the regulator body to avoid damaging the valves.
14. Remove the front servo supply and release tubes by twisting and pulling at the same time. Remove the front servo attaching bolts. While holding the front servo strut, lift the front servo from the case.
15. Remove the rear servo attaching bolts. While holding the actuating and anchor struts, lift the rear servo from the case.

Transmission End-Play Check

The transmission end-play is checked as follows:

1. Remove one of the front pump attaching bolts and mount the dial indicator support tool in the hole. Mount a dial indicator on the support so that the stem rests on the end of the turbine shaft.

2. Install the extension housing seal replacer on the output shaft to provide support for the shaft.
3. Using a screwdriver, move the front clutch cylinder to the rear of the transmission case as far as possible. Set the dial indicator to zero while holding a slight pressure on the screwdriver.
4. Remove the screwdriver. Insert it between the large internal gear and the case and move the front clutch cylinder to the front of the case.
5. Record the indicator reading for later use during transmission reassembly. The end-play reading should be between 0.010-0.029 in. If the reading is not within these limits, a new selective thrust washer must be used when reassembling the transmission.

Extension Housing Parts and Case

Removal

1. Remove the front pump attaching bolts. Remove the front pump and gasket. It may be necessary to tap the screw bosses with a soft faced hammer to loosen the pump from the case.
NOTE: If the parking brake drum is mounted on the transmission, remove the drum and yoke from the output shaft.

Output shaft and rear pump installed
(© Ford Motor Co.)

Parking brake drum and extension housing components—Ford FMX (© Ford Motor Co.)

2. Remove the extension housing seal. Remove the lubrication tube from the case. Remove the transmission-to-extension housing bolts and the extension housing. These bolts also secure the rear support to the case.

3. Remove the output shaft assembly. Be sure not to bend the pressure tubes between the distributor sleeve and case, as the tubes are being removed from the case.

4. Place the output shaft assembly on the bench and remove the oil distributor tubes from the sleeve.

5. Slide the speedometer drive gear ball off the shaft.

6. If the drive gear ball does not fall out as the speedometer gear is removed, remove the ball from the seat in the output shaft.

7. Remove the distributor sleeve. Remove the four seal rings from the output, be careful not to break the rings.

8. Remove the governor snap ring from the output shaft. Slide the governor assembly off the output shaft. Remove the governor drive ball. Remove the extension housing and pump gaskets.

9. Remove the rear pump drive key from the output shaft. Remove the bronze thrust washer from the output shaft.

10. Remove the selective thrust washer from the rear pinion carrier.

11. Remove the two seal rings from the primary gear shaft. Remove the pinion carrier.

12. Remove the primary sun gear rear thrust bearing and race from the pinion carrier.
    NOTE: Record the rear ban position for reference during assembly.

13. The end of the band next to the adjusting screw has a depression in the center of the boss. Squeeze the ends of the rear band together, tilt the band to the rear, and remove the rear band from the case.

14. Remove the two center support outer bolts from the transmission case.

15. Hold the clutch units together on the input shaft. Remove the center support and the front and rear clutches as a unit.

16. Place the clutch assemblies in a holding fixture.

17. Remove the thrust washers from the front of the input shaft.

18. Position the front band ends between the case webbing and tilt the bottom of the band rearward. Squeeze the ends of the band together and remove the front band from the rear of the case.

19. Lift the front clutch assembly from the primary sun gear shaft.

Input shaft and clutch mounted in holding fixture
(© Ford Motor Co.)

Removing input shaft and clutch
(© Ford Motor Co.)

20. Remove the bronze and the steel thrust washers from the rear clutch assembly, wire the thrust washers together to be sure of correct assembly.

21. Remove the front clutch seal rings from the primary sun gear shaft. Lift the rear clutch assembly from the primary sun gear shaft and remove the rear clutch seal rings from the primary sun gear shaft.
    CAUTION: Do not break the rear clutch seal rings.
    Remove the primary sun gear front thrust washer.
    NOTE: If the transmission case bushing is worn or damaged, replace the bushing.

22. If the rear brake drum support bushing is worn or damaged, replace it.

23. Remove the output shaft bushing if it is worn or damaged. Use a chisel and cut along the bushing seam until the chisel breaks through the bushing wall. Pry the loose ends of the bushing up with an awl and remove the bushing.

Removing rear clutch sun gear bushing
(© Ford Motor Co.)

24. Install a new bushing with its proper installation tool. The bushing must be pressed into position.

Installing output shaft bushing
(© Ford Motor Co.)

Assembly

NOTE: Do not use force to assemble mating parts. If the parts do not go together easily, examine them for

REMOVAL   INSTALLATION

Replacing rear brake drum support bushing (© Ford Motor Co.)

Planetary clutch, planet carrier and center support—Ford FMX (© Ford Motor Co.)

Installation of planetary clutch in carrier-Ford FMX (© Ford Motor Co.)

the cause of the problem. Always use new gaskets and seals during assembly operations.

1. Install the front band in the transmission case with the anchor end aligned with the anchor in the case.
2. Make sure the thrust washer is in place on the input shaft. Lift the clutch assemblies out of the holding fixture.
   CAUTION: Do not allow the clutches to separate.
3. Install the clutch sub-assemblies in the transmission case while positioning the servo band on the drum. Hold the units together while installing them.
4. Assemble and install the center support assembly as follows:
   a. Install the center support and the rear band in the case.
   b. Install the one piece needle bearing and race assembly in the planet carrier, be sure that the black oxide coated race is facing the front of the transmission.
   c. Lubricate the bearing surface on the center support, the rollers of the planetary clutch, and the cam race in the carrier with petroleum jelly.
   d. Install the planetary clutch in the carrier.
   e. Carefully, position the planet carrier on the center support.

Move the carrier forward until the clutch rollers are felt to contact the bearing surface on the center support.
   f. While applying forward pressure on the planet carrier, rotate it counterclockwise, as viewed from the rear. The clutch rollers will roll towards the large opening end of the cams in the race, compressing the spring slightly and the rollers will ride up the chamber on the planetary support onto the inner race.
   g. Push the planet carrier all the way forward.
   h. Check the operation of the planetary clutch by rotating the carrier counterclockwise, viewed from the rear, with a slight drag, and should lock up when attempting to rotate in the clockwise direction.
   i. Install the selective thrust washer on the pinion carrier rear pilot. If the end play was not within specifications when checked prior to disassembly, replace the washer with one of proper thickness. Refer to the specifications at the end of this section.
   j. Install the output shaft, carefully meshing the internal gear with the pinions.
5. With the center support properly

assembled, position the rear pump drive key in the keyway on the output shaft.
6. Position the new front and rear gaskets on the pump body. Retain the gaskets with clean transmission fluid. Then install the rear pump. Be sure that the key is aligned with the keyway in the pump drive gear.
7. Position the governor drive ball in the pocket in the output shaft. Retain the ball with clean transmission fluid.
8. Install the governor assembly aligning the groove with the ball in the output shaft.
9. Install the governor with the governor body plate facing towards the rear of the transmission. Install the governor snap ring.
10. Place the four seal rings in the distributor seleves, and check the ring gap.
11. Check the fit of the grooves in the output shaft. The rings should rotate freely. Install the rings in the grooves of the output shaft.
12. Install the three tubes in the distributor sleeve.
13. Install the distributor sleeve on the output shaft, with the chamfer facing forward. Lubricate the parts with clean transmission fluid to facilitate assembly. Slide the sleeve over the four rings and at the same time start the tubes into the case. The distributor sleeve is located between the governor snap ring and the speedometer drive gear.
14. Make sure that the speedometer drive gear lock ball is in place, then install the speedometer drive gear.
15. Install the output shaft ball bearing front spacer and the ball bearing with the snap ring toward the rear.
16. Install the output shaft rear spacer and the speedometer drive gear.
17. Install the rear bearing retainer gasket and the retainer. Torque the bolts to specification.
18. Install the parking brake drum, if so equipped, and/or the u-joint yoke. Torque the nut to specification. Tighten the nut to the nearest cotter pin hole, and install a new cotter pin.
19. Install the front pump gasket in the counter bore of the transmission case.
20. Install the front pump, aligning the pump bolt holes with the holes in the case. Install the front pump attaching bolts and torque to specifications.
21. Mount a dial indicator support in a front pump bolt hole. Mount a dial indicator on the support so

that the contact rests on the end of the turbine shaft.

22. Pry the output shaft all the way forward by using a screw driver between the large internal gear and the case.

23. Lightly block the output shaft in the forward position to eliminate all output shaft end play.

24. Inserting a screwdriver between the planet carrier and the large internal gear move the pinion carrier all the way forward. Maintain slight forward pressure, and set the dial indicator at zero.

25. Measure and record the end play between the front of the case and the large internal gear by prying between the front clutch cylinder and the case. This end play should be 0.010-0.029 inch. Total end play including the output shaft must not exceed 0.044 inch. If the end play is not within limits, a new selective thrust washer must be used.

26. Remove the dial indicator and install the remaining pump retaining bolt, tighten to specifications.

27. Position the front band forward in the case with the band end up.

28. Position the servo strut with the slotted end aligned with the servo actuating lever, and the small end aligned with the band end. Rotate the band, strut and servo into position, engaging the anchor end of the band with the anchor pin in the case.

29. Locate the servo on the case, and install the attaching bolts. Tighten the attaching bolts only 2 or 3 threads.

30. Install the servo tubes.

31. Position the servo anchor strut, and rotate the rear band to engage the strut.

32. Position the servo actuating lever strut with a finger, and then install the servo and attaching bolts. Move the servo toward the centerline of the case, against the attaching bolts. While holding the servo in this position, torque the attaching bolts to specification.

33. Install the pressure regulator body and attaching bolts. Torque the bolts to specifications.

34. Install the control and converter valve guides and springs. Install the spring retainer.

35. Install the control valve assembly, carefully alining the servo tubes with the control valve. Align the inner downshaft lever between the stop and the downshift valve. Shift the manual lever to the #1 position. Align the manual valve with the actuating pin in the manual detent lever. Do not tighten the attach-

Control valve—disassembled (© Ford Motor Co.)

ing bolts.

36. Install the main pressure oil tube. Be sure to install the end of the tube that connects to the pressure regulator assembly first. Then, install the other end of the tube into the main control assembly, by tapping gently with a soft faced hammer.

37. Install the small control pressure compensator tube in the valve body and regulator.

38. Move the control valve body toward the center of the case, until the clearance is less than 0.050 inch between the manual valve and the actuating pin on the manual detent lever.

39. Torque the attaching bolts to specifications. Be sure that the rear fluid screen retaining clip is installed under the valve body bolt.

40. Turn the manual valve one full turn in each manual lever detent position. If the manual valve binds against the actuating pin in any detent position, loosen the valve body attaching bolts and move the body away from the center of the case. Move the body

only enough to relieve the binding. Torque the attaching bolts to specifications. Recheck the manual valve for binding.

41. Torque the front servo attaching bolts to specifications.

42. Adjust the front and rear bands as outlined in the "Adjustment" section.

43. Position the control rod in the bore of the vacuum diaphragm unit and install the diaphragm unit. Make sure that the control rod enters the throttle valve as the vacuum unit is installed, torque the retaining bolts to specifications.

44. Position the fluid screen under the rear clip and over the front pump inlet tube. Press the screen down firmly. Install the screen retaining clip.

45. Place a new gasket on the transmission case and install the pan.

Install the attaching bolts and lock washers. Tighten the bolts to specifications.

46. If the converter and converter housing were removed from the transmission, install these components. Position the transmission assembly on a transmission jack and install in the vehicle.

Control Valve Body

NOTE: During disassembly of the control valve assembly, avoid damage to the valve parts and keep the valve parts clean. Place the valve assembly on a clean shop towel while performing the disassembly operations. Do not separate the upper and lower valve bodies and cover until after the valves have been removed.

1. Remove the manual valve.
2. Remove the throttle valve body and the separator plate. Be careful not to lose the check valve when removing the separator plate from the valve body. Remove the throttle valve and plug.
3. Remove one screw attaching the separator plate to the lower valve body. Remove the upper body front plate. The plate is spring-loaded. Apply pressure to the plate while removing the attaching screws.
4. Remove the compensator sleeve and plug, remove the compensator valve springs. Remove the compensator valve.
5. Remove the throttle boost short valve and sleeve. Remove the throttle boost spring and valve.
6. Remove the downshift valve and spring.
7. Remove the upper valve body rear plate.
8. Remove the compensator cut back valve.
9. Remove the lower body side plate. The plate is spring-loaded. Apply pressure to the plate while removing the attaching screws.
10. Remove the 1-2 shift valve and spring. Remove the inhibitor valve and spring.
11. Remove the two screws attaching the separator plate to the cover. Remove the lower valve body end plate. The end plate is spring-loaded. Apply pressure to the plate while removing the attaching screws.
12. Remove the low servo lockout valve, low servo modulator valve and spring.
13. Remove the 2-3 delay and throttle reducing valve sleeve, the throttle reducing valve, spring, and the 2-3 shift delay valve. The reducing valve sleeve is lightly staked in the valve body bore. To remove the sleeve, use a blunt instrument against the end of the 2-3 shift valve and push the sleeve from its bore. Remove the

2-3 shift valve spring, spring retainer and the valve.
14. Remove the transition valve spring and valve.
15. Remove the plate from the valve body cover.
16. Remove the check ball spring and the check ball.
17. Remove the 1-2 shift accumulator valve spring from the cover. Remove the spring, the 1-2 accumulator valve and the 1-2 shift accumulator lockout valve.
18. Remove the through bolts and screws. Then separate the upper and lower control valve bodies and cover. Be careful not to lose the check valves.

Assembly

1. Arrange all the parts in their correct positions. Rotate the valves and plugs when inserting them in their bores, to avoid shearing off the soft body castings.
2. Place the check valve in the upper body, then position the separator plate on the body.
3. Position the lower body on the upper body, and start, but do not tighten the attaching bolts.
4. Position the cover and separator plate on the lower body. Start the four through bolts.
5. Align the separator with the upper and lower valve body attaching bolt holes. Install and torque the four valve body bolts to specifications.
   CAUTION: Excessive tightening of these bolts will distort the valve bodies and cause the valves and plugs to bind.
6. Install the check ball and spring in the cover. Install the plate.
7. Insert the 1-2 shift accumulator lockout valve, 1-2 shift accumulator valve, and the spring in the cover. Install the valve spring retainer.
8. Install the transition valve and spring in the lower valve body.
9. Install the 2-3 shift valve, spring retainer and spring. Install the 2-3 shift delay valve, spring and throttle reducing valve in the sleeve. Slide the assembly into position in the lower body. Do not restake the sleeve.

10. Install the low servo lockout valve and spring. Install the low servo modulator and the low servo lockout valves. Install the lower body end plate.
11. Install the inhibitor valve spring and valve in the lower body.
12. Install the 1-2 shift valve spring and valve. Install the lower body side plate.
13. Install the compensator cutback valve in the upper body. Install the upper body rear plate.
14. Install the downshift valve and spring in the body.
15. Install the throttle boost valve and spring. Install the throttle boost short valve and spring.
16. Install the compensator valve, inner and outer compensator springs, and the compensator sleeve and plug.
17. Position the front plate. Apply pressure to the plate while installing the two attaching screws.
18. Install the throttle valve, plug, and check valve in the throttle valve body. Position the separator on the upper body and install the throttle valve body. Install the three attaching screws.
19. Install the four screws attaching the cover to the lower body, two screws attaching the separator plate to the lower body. Torque the cover and body screws to specifications.
20. Install the manual valve.

Front Servo

Disassembly

1. Remove the servo piston retainer snap ring. The servo piston is spring loaded. Apply pressure to the piston when removing the snap ring.
2. Remove the servo piston retainer, and the servo piston from the servo body. If necessary, tap the piston stem lightly with a soft-faced hammer to separate the piston retainer from the servo body.
3. Remove all the seal rings, and remove the spring from the servo body.
4. Inspect the servo body for cracks, and the piston bore and

Check valve locations—Ford FMX (© Ford Motor Co.)

Front servo disassembled—Ford FMX (© Ford Motor Co.)

Governor disassembled—Ford FMX (© Ford Motor Co.)

the servo piston stem for scores. Check the fluid passages for obstructions.

5. Check the actuating lever for free movement and inspect it for wear. To replace the actuating lever shaft, it will be necessary to press the shaft out of the bracket. The shaft is retained in the body by serrations on one end of the shaft. These serrations cause a press fit at the end. To remove the shaft, press on the end opposite the serrations. Inspect the adjusting screw threads and the threads in the lever.
6. Check the servo spring and the servo band strut for distortion.
7. Inspect the servo band lining for excessive wear and bonding of the metal. The band should be replaced if worn to a point where the grooves are not clearly evident.
8. Inspect the band ends for cracks and check for band distortion.

Assembly

1. Lubricate all parts of the front servo with clean transmission fluid before starting assembly.
2. Install the inner and outer 'O' rings on the piston retainer. Install a new 'O' ring on the return piston and on the servo piston.
3. Position the servo piston release spring in the servo body. Install the servo piston, retainer, and return piston in the servo body. Compress the assembly into the body and secure it with the snap ring. Make sure that the snap ring is fully seated in the groove.
4. Install the adjusting screw and lock nut in the actuating lever if they were removed.

Rear Servo

Disassembly

1. Remove the servo actuating lever shaft retaining pin with a ⅛ inch punch.
2. Press down on the servo spring retainer, and remove the snap ring. Release the pressure on the retainer slowly to prevent the spring from flying out.
3. Remove the retainer and servo spring.
4. Force the piston out of the servo body with air pressure. Hold one hand over the piston to prevent damage.
5. Remove the piston seal ring.

Assembly

1. Install a new piston seal ring on the servo piston.
2. Install the piston in the servo body. Lubrication of the parts with clean transmission fluid will facilitate assembly. Install the servo spring with the small coiled end against the servo piston.
3. Install the spring retainer. Compress the spring with a C-clamp. Then, install the snap ring. The snap ring must be fully seated in the groove.
4. Install the actuating lever with the socket in the lever bearing on the piston stem. Install the actuating lever shaft, aligning the retaining pin holes, and install the pin.
5. Check the actuating lever for free movement.

Governor

Disassembly

1. Remove the governor valve body cover.
2. Remove the valve body from the counterweight.
3. Remove the plug, sleeve, and the valve and spring from the governor body.
4. Remove the screen from its bore in the valve body.

Assembly

1. Install the governor valve and spring assembly in the bore of the valve body. Install the sleeve and plug.
2. Install the screen.
3. Install the body counterweight. Make sure that the fluid passages in the body and counterweight are aligned.
4. Position the valve body cover on the body, and install the screws.

Pressure Regulator

Disassembly

1. Remove the valves from the regulator body.
2. Remove the regulator body cover attaching screws, and remove the cover.
3. Remove the separator plate.
4. Wash all parts thoroughly in a clean solvent and blow dry with moisture-free compressed air.
5. Inspect the regulator body and cover mating surfaces for burrs.
6. Check all fluid passages for obstructions.
7. Inspect the control pressure converter pressure valves and bores for burrs and scoring. Remove all burrs with crocus cloth.
8. Check the free movement of the valve in their bores. Each valve should fall freely into its bore when both the valve and bore are dry.
9. Inspect the valve springs for distortion.

Assembly

1. Position the separator plate on the regulator cover.

Rear servo disassembled—Ford FMX (© Ford Motor Co.)

Pressure regulator assembly (© Ford Motor Co.)

2. Position the regulator cover and separator plate on the regulator body and install the attaching screws. Tighten to specifications.
3. Insert the valves in the pressure regulator body.

Downshift and Manual Linkage

Disassembly

1. Remove the inner downshift lever shaft nut. Then remove the inner downshift lever.
2. Remove the outer downshift lever and shaft. Remove the downshift seal from the counterbore in the manual lever shaft.
3. Remove the cotter pin from the parking pawl toggle operating rod and remove the clip from the parking pawl operating lever. Remove the parking pawl operating rod.

4. Rotate the manual shaft until the detent lever clears the detent plunger. Then, remove the detent plunger and spring. Do not allow the detent plunger to fly out of the case.
5. Remove the manual lever shaft nut and remove the detent lever. Remove the outer manual lever and shaft from the transmission case.
6. Tap the toggle lever sharply toward the rear of the case to remove the plug and pin.
7. Remove the pawl pin by working the pawl back and forth. Remove the pawl and toggle lever assembly and then disassemble.
8. Remove the manual shaft seal and the case vent tube.

Assembly

1. Coat the outer diameter of a new manual shaft seal with sealer

and install the seal in the transmission case with a driver.
2. Install the vent tube in the transmission case.
3. Assemble the link to the pawl with the pawl link pin, washer, and pawl return spring. Assemble the toggle lever to the link with the toggle link pin. Position the pawl return spring over the toggle link pin and secure in place with the washer and small retainer clip. Position the pawl assembly in the transmission case and install the pawl pin, and the toggle lever pin. Press the retaining plug tightly against the toggle lever pin. Install the torsion lever assembly. Position the spring on the torsion lever with a screwdriver. Make sure that the short side of the toggle lift lever does not extend beyond the largest diameter of the ball on the toggle link. Tap the toggle lift lever in or out as necessary to center the lever on the ball.
4. Install the manual lever and shaft in the transmission case. Position the detent lever on the shaft, and secure with the nut. Tighten the nut to 20-30 ft-lbs of torque. Rotate the manual lever to the rear of the case. Position the detent spring in the case. Hold the detent plug on the spring with a 3/16 inch socket wrench, then depress the spring until the plug is flush with the case. Carefully rotate the manual lever to the front of the case to secure the plug. A piece of thin walled tubing may be used to depress the plug if a small socket wrench is not available.
5. Position the ends of the parking pawl operating rod in the detent lever and toggle lift lever, secure with the two small retaining pins.
6. Install a new seal on the downshift lever shaft, then install the lever and shaft in the transmission case. Position the inner end of the shaft with the mark "O" racing toward the center of the case. Install the lock washer and nut, then tighten the nut to 17-20 ft-lbs torque.
7. Check the operation of the linkage. The linkage should operate freely without binding.

Front Pump

Disassembly

1. Remove the stator support attaching screws and remove the stator support. Mark the top surface of the pump driven gear with Prussian blue to assure correct assembly. Do not scratch the pump gears.
2. Remove the drive and driven gears from the pump body.

REMOVAL   INSTALLATION

Replacing front pump housing bushing (© Ford Motor Co.)

Transmission case control linkage—Ford FMX (© Ford Motor Co.)

Front pump disassembled
(© Ford Motor Co.)

3. Inspect the pump body housing, gear pockets and crescent for signs of wear or damage.
4. If the pump housing bushing is worn or damaged, replace the bushing with the proper tool.
5. If any parts other than the stator support, bushings of oil seal are found to be defective, replace the pump as a unit. Minor burrs and scores may be removed with crocus cloth. The stator support is serviced separately.
6. If the oil seal requires replacement, bolt the front pump to the transmission case. Install the seal removing tool and pull the seal from the body.
7. Clean the pump body counterbore. Inspect the bore for rough spots. Smooth up the counterbore with crocus cloth.
8. Remove the pump body from the transmission case.

Assembly

1. If the oil seal was removed, coat the outer diameter with sealing compound. Position the seal in the pump body and drive the new seal into the pump body with the proper tool. Be sure that the seal is firmly seated.
2. Place the pump driven gear in the pump body with the mark on the gear or tooth gear chamfer facing down. Install the drive gear in the pump body with the chamfered side of the flats facing down.
3. Install the stator support and the attaching screws. Check the pump gears for free rotation.

Replacing rear support housing bushing (© Ford Motor Co.)

Rear Pump

Disassembly

1. Remove the screws and lock washers securing the pump cover to the pump body and remove the cover.
2. Remove the drive gear from the pump body.
3. If the pump housing bushing is worn or damaged, replace the bushing with the proper installation and removal tool.

Assembly

1. Install the drive gear in the pump body.
2. Install the pump cover, attaching screws, and lock washers. Torque the screws to specifications.

Rear Clutch

Disassembly

1. Remove the clutch pressure plate snap ring and remove the plate from the drum. Remove the waved cushion spring. Remove the composition and steel plates.
2. Compress the spring with the special spring compression tool, and remove the snap ring.
3. Guide the spring retainer while

releasing the pressure, this will prevent retainer from locking in the snap ring grooves.
4. Position the primary sun gear shaft in the rear clutch. Place an air hose nozzle in one of the holes in the shaft, and place one finger over the other hole. Force the clutch piston out of the clutch drum with air pressure. Hold one hand over the piston to prevent damage to the piston during removal.
5. Remove the inner and outer seal rings from the clutch piston.
6. Remove the rear clutch sun gear bushing if it is worn or damaged. Use a cape chisel and cut along the bushing seam until the chisel breaks through the bushing wall. Pry the loose ends of the bushing up with an awl and remove the bushing.

Assembly

1. If the rear sun gear bushing was removed, press a new bushing into the rear clutch sun gear.
2. Install a new inner and outer seal ring on the piston.
3. Lubricate the piston seals and tools with clean transmission fluid. Push the small fixture over the cylinder hub. Insert the piston into the large fixture with

Installing front pump seal
(© Ford Motor Co.)

Removing rear clutch spring snap-ring (© Ford Motor Co.)

Installing rear clutch sun gear bushing
(© Ford Motor Co.)

Installing rear clutch piston
(© Ford Motor Co.)

the seal toward the thin walled end. Hold the piston and large fixture and insert as unit into the cylinder. Push down over the small fixture until the large tool stops against the shoulder in the cylinder; then push the piston down, out of the tool until it bottoms in the cylinder. Remove the tool.

4. Install the clutch release spring, and position the retainer on the spring.

5. Install the tool on the spring retainer. Compress the clutch spring and install the snap ring. While compressing the spring, guide the retainer to avoid interference of the retainer with the snap ring grooves. Make sure that the snap ring is fully seated in the groove. When a new composition clutch plate is used, soak the plates in clean transmission fluid for 15 minutes before assembly.

6. Install the external tabbed waved cushion spring. Install the composition and the steel clutch plates alternately, starting with a steel plate.

7. Install the clutch pressure plate with the bearing surface down. Install the clutch pressure plate snap ring. Make sure that the snap ring is fully seated in the groove.

8. Check the free pack clearance between the pressure plate and the first internal plate with a feeler gauge. The clearance

should be 0.030-0.055 inch. If the clearance is not within limits, selective snap rings are available in the following thicknesses; 0.060-0.064, 0.074-0.078, 0.088-0.092 and 0.102-0.106 inch. Insert the correct size snap ring and recheck the clearance.

9. Install the thrust washer on the primary sun gear shaft. Be sure the thrust washer is installed with the tabs of the washer away from the sun gear thrust face. Lubricate all parts with clean transmission fluid or with petroleum jelly. Install the two center seal rings.

10. Install the rear clutch on the primary sun gear shaft. Be sure all of the needles are in the hub if the unit is equipped with loose needles. Install the two seal rings in the front grooves.

11. Install the steel and the bronze thrust washers on the front of the secondary sun gear assembly. If the steel washer is chamfered, place the chamfered side down.

Front Clutch

Disassembly

1. Remove the clutch cover snap rings with a screwdriver, and remove the input shaft from the front clutch drum.

2. Remove the thrust washer from the thrust surface on the clutch hub. Place one finger in the clutch hub and lift the hub straight up to remove the hub from the clutch drum.

3. Remove the composition and the steel pressure plates, and then remove the pressure plate from the clutch drum.

4. Place the front clutch spring compressor on the release spring, position the clutch drum on the bed of an arbor press, and compress the release spring with the arbor press until the release spring snap ring can be removed.

5. Remove the clutch release spring from the clutch drum.

6. Install the special air nozzle on an air line. Place the nozzle

Removing front clutch snap-ring
(© Ford Motor Co.)

Removing front clutch piston
(© Ford Motor Co.)

against the clutch apply hole in the front clutch housing and force the piston out of the housing.

7. Remove the piston inner seal from the clutch housing. Remove the piston outer seal from the groove in the piston.

8. Remove the input shaft bushing if it is worn or damaged. Use a cape chisel and cut along the bushing seam until the chisel breaks through the bushing wall. Pry the loose ends of the bushing up with an awl and remove the bushing.

Assembly

1. If the input shaft bushing was removed, slip a new bushing over the end of the bushing installation tool and place the tool and bushing on the bushing hole. Press the bushing into the input shaft.

2. Lubricate all parts with clean transmission fluid. Install a new piston inner seal ring in the clutch cylinder. Install a new piston outer seal in the groove in the piston.

3. Install the piston in the clutch housing. Make sure that the steel bearing ring is in place on the piston.

4. Position the release spring in the clutch cylinder with the concave side up. Place the release spring compressor on the spring and

Installing input shaft bushing
(© Ford Motor Co.)

compress the spring with an arbor press. Install the snap ring. Make sure that the snap ring is firmly seated in the groove.

5. Install the front clutch housing on the primary sun gear shaft. Rotate the clutch units to mesh the rear clutch plates with the serrations on the clutch hub. Do not break the seal rings.
6. Install the clutch hub in the clutch cylinder with the deep counterbore down. Install the thrust washer on the clutch hub.
7. Install the pressure plate in the

Installing front clutch hub
(© Ford Motor Co.)

clutch cylinder with the bearing surface up. Install the composition and steel clutch plates alternately, starting with a composition plate. When new composition clutch plates are used, soak them in clean transmission fluid for 15 minutes before assembly.

8. The finial friction plate to be installed is selective. Install the thickest plate what will be a minimum of 0.010 inch below the input shaft shoulder in the cylinder. For all other plates, use the thinnest available (see specifications at end of section).
9. Install the turbine shaft in the clutch cylinder, and secure with the snap ring. Make sure that the snap ring is firmly seated in the groove.
10. Install the thrust washer on the turbine shaft.

Primary Sun Gear Shaft
1. Position the primary sun gear shaft in the clutch bench fixture.

Installing pressure plate
(© Ford Motor Co.)

Installing clutch plates
(© Ford Motor Co.)

2. Check the fit of the seal rings in their bores. A clearance of 0.002-0.009 inch should exist between the ends of the rings.
3. Replace the seal rings, and check for free movement in the grooves.

Specifications

Checks and Adjustments Operation	Specification
Transmission end play	0.010-0.029 plus end play between output shaft ball bearing and retainer. Not to exceed a total of .044 inch.
Turbine and stator end play check	New or rebuilt 0.023 maximum. Used 0.040 maximum.
Front band adjustment (Use ¼ inch spacer between adjustment screw and servo stop piston stem)	Adjust screw to 10 in-lbs torque. Remove spacer, then tighten screw an additional ¾ turn. Hold screw and tighten lock nut.
Rear band adjustment	Adjust screw to 10 ft-lbs torque, and back off 1½ turns. Hold screw and tighten lock nut.
Primary sun gear shaft ring end gap check	0.002-0.009

Front Clutch Selective Clutch Plate-FMX

Thickness (in.)	Identification
0.0565-0.0605	No Stripe
0.0705-0.0745	One Stripe
0.0845-0.0885	Two Stripes
0.0985-0.1025	Three Stripes

Selective Thrust Washers-FMX

Thickness (in.)	Identification
0.061-0.063	by thickness
0.067-0.069	by thickness
0.074-0.076	by thickness
0.081-0.083	by thickness
0.092-0.094	by thickness
0.105-0.107	by thickness

Control Pressure at Zero Governor RPM

Year	Range	Control Pressure (psi) Manifold Vacuum (in. Hg)		
		① 18 and Above	10	Below 1.0
1970	P, N, D, 2, 1	56-79	—	
	R	61-108		185-221
	D, 2, 1	—	70-124	134-187
	P, N, D, 2, 1	56-80	—	—
	R	59-110		184-221
	D, 2, 1	—	69-125	133-188
	P, N, D, 2, 1	56-82	—	—
	R	59-111		184-221
	D, 2, 1		69-126	133-189
		15 and Above		
1971-1972	P, N, D, 2, 1	56-81	82-112	—
	R	60-110	—	185-221
	D, 2, 1			146-175
		12 and Above		
1973	P, N, D, 2, 1	61-107	75-120	—
	R	90-156	—	185-225
	D, 2, 1	—		154-188
1974-76	D, 2, 1	58-80	75-120	143-188
	R	64-124		185-225
	P, N	56-80	—	—

① 15 and above-1971-72 and 1974-76; 12 and above 1973

Capacity

Model	Refill (qt.)
All ①	11

① F-100 with 302 engine-9¼ qts.

Diagnosis

This diagnosis guide covers the most common symptoms and is an aid to careful diagnosis. The items to check are listed in the sequence to be followed for quickest results. Thus, follow the checks in the order given for the particular transmission type.

TROUBLE SYMPTOMS	Items to Check	
	In Truck	Out of Truck
Car will not move in any selector position	ABC	cab
Engine speed flares, as slipping clutch	ABDFE	def
Engine speed flares on upshift	ADBG	ghi
Transmission will not upshift	HIJ	klm
Harsh upshift	JDGK	
Harsh deceleration downshift	DLMNG	
No downshift	MHI	
Clutch failure, burnt plates	DAHO	hi
Excessive creep in drive	JL	
Car creeps in neutral	J	hd
No drive in reverse	J	jng
Improper shift points	JIH	l
Unable to push-start car		m
Oil leaks	PQG	oa
Oil forced out at filler tube	AQ	p

Key to Checks

A. Oil level
B. Oil screen
C. Pressure regulator valve
D. Band adjustment
E. Servo seal
F. Servo blocked
G. Vacuum modulator or line
H. Governor
I. Throttle valve

J. Throttle linkage
K. Hydraulic modulator valve
L. Too high idle speed
M. Valves malfunctioning
N. Make pressure tests
O. Driving too fast in low
P. Oil leaks at external points
Q. Oil cooler or lines

a. Front pump
b. Input shaft
c. Front pump priming valve
d. Low band
e. Low band linkage
f. Converter stator
g. Clutch feed blocked
h. High clutch

i. Front clutch relief valve
j. Reverse clutch relief valve
k. Low clutch valve stuck
l. Rear pump priming valve
m. Rear pump or drive
n. Low clutch
o. Front pump attaching bolts
p. Pump circuit leakage

General Description

The Powerglide transmission is a two speed unit with a one piece aluminum case and an aluminum case extension.

Driving ranges are low, high and reverse, with a throttle controlled downshift to low range available for sudden acceleration.

The oil pump is the gear type; the pump housing is used as the front bulkhead of the transmission. The torque converter is a three element welded unit bolted to the engine flywheel; it drives through a two speed planetary gearset. Low range uses a band clutch; drive and reverse ranges use disc clutches. The valve body assembly is bolted to the bottom of the transmission case; the modulator valve bore is in the upper part of the valve body assembly. The governor is mounted to the output shaft, inside the case extension.

Transmission removal and installation, shift linkage adjustment, low band adjustment in the truck, neutral safety switches, and transmission downshift linkages are covered in the truck section.

Fluid Change Schedule

The manufacturer recommends draining the transmission sump every 24,000 miles; 2 quarts to all models. The fluid level should then be rechecked. This should be done with the engine idling, the selector lever in Nutral, and the transmission at operating temperature.

Transmission Disassembly

Extension, Governor and Rear Oil Pump

1. Place transmission in a holding fixture, if possible.
2. Remove converter holding tool, then lift off the converter.
3. If replacement is necessary, remove speedometer driven gear. Loosen cap screw and retainer clip and remove gear from extension.
4. Remove transmission extension by removing five attaching bolts. Note seal ring on rear pump body.
5. Remove speedometer drive gear from output shaft.
6. Remove C-clip from governor shaft of the weight side of governor, then remove the shaft and governor valve from the opposite side of the governor assembly and the two belleville springs.
7. Loosen the governor drive screw and slide the governor over the end of the output shaft.
8. Remove four bolts holding the rear oil pump to the transmission case and remove the pump body, drain back baffle, extension seal ring, drive and driven gears.
9. Remove oil pump drive pin. (This is of extreme importance.)
10. Remove the rear pump wear plate.

Transmission Internal Components

11. Rotate holding fixture, or turn the transmission, until the front end is pointing up. Then remove the seven front oil pump bolts. (The bolt holes are of unequal spacing to prevent incorrect location upon installation.)
12. Remove the front oil pump and stator shaft assembly and the selective fit thrust washer using an inertia puller or substitute.

1 Reverse ring gear
2 Reverse clutch pack snap ring
3 Reverse clutch
     pressure plate
4 Reverse clutch
     reaction plates
5 Reverse clutch drive plates
6 Reverse clutch cushion spring
7 Reverse clutch piston return
     spring retainer snap ring
8 Reverse clutch piston return
     spring retainer
9 Reverse clutch piston return
     springs
10 Reverse clutch piston inner
      seal
11 Reverse clutch piston
12 Reverse clutch piston outer
      seal

Transmission case   (© G.M. Corp.)

13 Transmission case	20 Servo piston rod spring	31 Governor support
13A Transmission case screen	retainer	32 Governor support to case
14 Servo piston return spring	21 Servo cover seal	attaching bolts
15 Servo piston rod	22 Servo cover gasket	33 Governor assembly
16 Servo piston apply	23 Servo cover	34 Speedometer drive gear
spring seat	24 Servo cover plug	and clip
17 Servo piston apply spring	25 Servo cover bolts	35 Seal
18 Servo piston seal ring	26 Transmission case bushing	36 Speedometer shaft fitting
19 Servo piston	27 Gasket	37 Speedometer shaft fitting
	30 Governor support bushing	

oil seal
38 Lock plate attaching screw
39 Lock plate
40 Speedometer driven gear
41 Transmission extension
42 Extension bushing
43 Extension oil seal
44 Extension to case
      attaching screws

13. Release tension on the low band adjustment, then with transmission horizontal, grasp the transmission input shaft and carefully work it and the clutch drum out of the case. Be careful not to lose the low sun gear bushing from the input shaft. The low sun gear thrust washer will probably remain in the planet carrier.

14. The low brake band and struts may now be removed.

15. Remove the planet carrier and the output shaft thrust caged bearing from the front of the transmission.

16. Remove reverse ring gear if it did not come out with the planet carrier.

17. With a large screwdriver, remove the reverse clutch pack retainer ring and lift out the reverse clutch plates and the cushion spring.

18. Install reverse piston spring compressor through rear bore of the case, with the flat plate on the rear face of the case, and turn down wing nut to compress the rear piston spring retainer and springs. Then remove the snap ring. A spring compressor may be made up from a suitable length bolt and large flat washers.

19. Remove the compression tool, the reverse pistol spring retainer, and the 17 piston return springs.

20. Remove the rear piston by applying air pressure to the reverse port in the rear of the transmission case. Remove inner and outer seals.

21. Remove the three servo cover bolts, servo cover, piston and spring.

Oil Pan and Valve Body

NOTE: the oil pan and valve body may be serviced without removing the extension, and internal components, covered in the preceding steps.

22. Rotate the transmission until the unit is upside down (oil pan on top). Remove oil pan attaching bolts, oil pan, and gasket.

23. Remove vacuum modulator and gasket, and vacuum modulator plunger, dampening spring, and valve.

24. Remove two bolts holding the detent guide plate to the valve body and the transmission case. Remove the guide plate and the range selector detent roller spring.

25. Remove the remaining valve body-to-transmission case attaching bolts and lift out the valve body and gasket. Disengage the servo apply tube from the transmission case as the valve body is removed.

26. If necessary, the throttle valve, shift and parking actuator levers and the parking pawl and bracket may be removed.

Unit Assembly Overhaul

Converter and Stator

The converter is a welded assembly and no internal repairs are possible. Check the seams for stress or breaks and replace the converter if necessary.

REAR PUMP DRIVE PIN

Removing rear oil pump drive pin (© G.M. Corp.)

Front Pump

Seal Replacement

If the front pump seal requires replacement, remove the pump from the transmission, pry out and replace the seal. Drive new seal into place. Then, if no further work is needed on the front pump, reinstall it into the case. (The outer edge of the seal should be coated with non-hardening sealer before installation.)

Disassembly

1. Remove pump cover-to-body attaching bolts and the cover.
2. Remove pump gears from body.
3. Remove rubber seal from pump body.

Inspection

1. Wash all parts in solvent. Blow out all oil passages.
2. Inspect pump gears for nicks or damage.
3. Inspect body and cover faces for nicks or scoring. Inspect cover hub outside diameter for nicks or burrs.

4. Check for free operation of priming valve. Replace if necessary.
5. Inspect body bushing for galling or scoring. Check clearance between body bushing and converter pump hub. Maximum clearance is .005 in. If the bushing is damaged, replace the pump body.
6. Inspect converter housing hub outside diameter for nicks or burrs. Repair or replace.
7. If oil seal is damaged or leaking, pry out and drive in a new seal.
8. Check condition of oil cooler by-pass valve. Replace if leaking. An "Easy-Out" type remover may be used to remove the valve. Tap new valve seat into place with a soft hammer or brass drift so that it is flush or up to .010 in. below the surface.
9. With all parts clean and dry, install pump gears and check:
   a. clearance between outside diameter of driven gear and body should be .0035-.0065 in.
   b. clearance between inside diameter of driven gear and crescent should be .003-.009 in.

c. gear end clearance should be .0005-.0015 in.

Assembly

1. Remove the input shaft, clutch drum, low band and struts as outlined under "Transmission Disassembly."
2. Install downship timing valve, conical end out, into place in the pump cover to a height of 17/32 in. measured from shoulder of valve assembly to face of pump cover.
3. Oil the drive and driven gears and install them into the pump body.
4. Set pump cover in place over the body and loosely install two attaching bolts.
5. Place pump assembly, less the rubber seal ring, upside down into the pump bore of the case. Install remaining attaching bolts and torque to 20 ft. lbs.
6. Remove pump assembly from case bore. Replace the clutch drum and input shaft, low band and struts as described under "Transmission Assembly."
7. Renew rubber seal ring in its groove in the pump body and install the pump assembly in place in the case bore, using a new gasket. Be sure that the selective fit thrust washer is in place.

1 Converter assembly
2 Input shaft
3 Input shaft oil seals
4 Oil pump to case attaching bolts and sealing washers
5 Low sun gear bushing
6 Pump oil seal
7 Oil pump body
8 Pump to case oil seal
9 Oil pump drive gear
10 Oil pump driven gear
11 Downshift timing valve
12 Oil pump cover to pump body attaching screws
13 Oil pump cover and converter stator shaft
14 Oil pump gasket
15 Clutch drum thrust washer (selective fit)
16 High clutch seal rings
17 Pump priming valve
18 Pump priming valve spring
20 Pump priming valve spring retaining pin
*21 Oil cooler by-pass valve spring
*22 Oil cooler by-pass valve
*23 Oil cooler by-pass valve seat
27 Band apply strut
28 Band anchor strut

29 Band anchor adjusting screw
30 Band anchor adjusting screw nut
31 Low brake band
32 Clutch drum bushing
33 Clutch drum bushing
34 Clutch piston outer and inner seals
35 Clutch piston
36 Clutch return springs
37 Clutch spring retainer
38 Clutch spring retainer snap ring
39 Clutch hub front thrust washer
40 Clutch hub
41 Clutch driven plates (flat)
42 Clutch cushion spring (waved)

Internal Mechanism (© G.M. Corp.)

43 Clutch drive plates (waved)
44 Clutch hub rear thrust washer
45 Low sun gear and clutch flange assembly
46 Clutch flange retainer ring
47 Planet carrier and output shaft assembly
49 Output shaft thrust bearing

*Except air cooled and 11" converter models

Removing rear piston spring retainer snap-ring
(© G.M. Corp.)

Applying air pressure to remove rear piston
(© G.M. Corp.)

8. Install attaching bolts. (Use new bolt sealing washers if necessary.)

Clutch Drum

Disassembly

CAUTION: When working with the clutch drum, use extreme care that the machined face on the front of the drum not be scratched, scored, nicked, or otherwise damaged. This machined face must be protected whenever it is brought to bear on a press or tool of any sort.

1. Remove retainer ring, low sun gear and clutch flange assembly from the clutch drum.
2. Remove the hub rear thrust washer.
3. Lift out clutch hub, then remove clutch pack and hub front thrust washer. Note the number and sequence of plates.
4. Remove spring retainer. Compress the springs with a spring compressor or an arbor press enough to permit removal of the retainer snap-ring. Then, releasing pressure on the springs, remove retainer and the 24 springs.
5. Lift up on the piston with a twisting motion to remove it from the drum, then remove inner and outer seals.

Inspection

1. Wash all parts in solvent, blow out all passages, and air dry. Do not use rags to dry parts.
2. Check drum bushing for scoring or excessive wear.
3. Check steel ball relief valve in clutch drum. Be sure that it is free to move and that orifice in front face of drum is open. If

ball is loose enough to come out, or not loose enough to rattle, replace drum. Do not attempt replacement or restaking of ball.
4. Check fit of low sun gear and clutch flange assembly in clutch drum slots. There should be no appreciable radial play.
5. Check low sun gear for nicks or burrs. Check gear bore for wear.
6. Check clutch plates for burring, wear, pitting, or metal pick-up. Faced plates should be a free fit over clutch hub; steel plates should be a free fit in clutch drum slots.
7. Check condition of clutch hub splines and mating splines of clutch faced plates.
8. Check clutch pistons for cracks or distortion.

Clutch Drum Bushing Replacement

If replacing drum bushing, carefully press out the old bushing. Then press (don't hammer) the new bushing into place from the machined face side of the drum. Press only far enough to bring the bushing flush with the clutch drum. Do not force the tool against the clutch drum machined face.

Assembly

1. Install new piston inner seal into hub of clutch drum with seal lip toward front of transmission.
2. Install new piston seal into clutch piston. Seal lips must be pointed toward the clutch drum, (front of transmission). Lubricate the seals and install piston into clutch drum with a twisting motion.
3. Place 24 springs in position on the piston, then place the retainer on the springs.

4. Depress the retainer plate and springs far enough to permit installation of the spring retainer snap-ring into its groove on the clutch drum hub.
5. Install the hub front washer with its lip toward the clutch drum, then install the clutch hub.
6. Install cushion spring if used. Install the steel reaction plates and drive (faced) plates alternately, beginning with a steel reaction plate.

NOTE: the number and sequence of plates varies with the power and torque requirements of the truck model involved. On some models, the first driven plate is a selective fit. See the clutch assemblies chart for details.

Clutch Assemblies

Models 1969-70	307 V8; 230 L6 250-L-6 292 L-6	350 V-8
Drive plate	4	5
Driven plate	5	6
Cushion Spring	1	None

350 V-8 Selective Driven Plate Chart

Plate Stack Height (Less Selective Plate)	Plate Part Number	Color Code	Plate Thickness
.903-.872	3883903	Orange	.060±.0025
.872-.798	3883904	Blue	.090±.0025

7. Install the rear hub thrust washer with its flange toward the low sun gear, then install the low sun gear and flange assembly and secure with retaining ring. When installed, the openings in the retainer ring should be adjacent to one of the lands of the clutch drum.

8. Check assembly by turning the clutch hub. If free, assembly is OK.

Low Band

Due to band design and transmission characteristics, this band should require very little attention. However, while the transmission is disassembled, the bands hould be thoughly cleaned, then replaced if any trace of scoring, burning, cracks, or excessive wear or damage is found.

Planet Assembly and Input Shaft

Inspection

1. Wash planet carrier and input shaft in cleaning solvent, blow out all passaes, and air dry. Do not use rags to dry parts.
2. Inspect planet pinions for nicks or other tooth damage.
3. Check end clearance of planet gears. The clearance should be .006-.030 in. of the clutch drum.
4. Check input sun gear for tooth damage. Check thrust washer for damage.
5. Inspect output shaft bearing surface and input pilot bushing for nicks or scoring.
6. Inspect input shaft splines for nicks or damage. Check fit in clutch hub, input sun gear, and turbine hub.
7. Check oil seal rings for damage; rings must be free in input shaft ring grooves. Remove rings and

Inner control levers, parking pawl and bracket
(© G.M. Corp.)

insert in stator support bore. Check to see that hooked ring ends have clearance. Replace rings on shaft.

Repairs

NOTE: some large planet carrier assemblies have the pinion shafts flared at each end for retention in the carrier. No overhaul of this type of carrier assembly should be attempted. If inspection shows excessive wear or damage, replace the entire carrier assembly.

1. Place the planet carrier assembly in a padded vise so that the front (parking lock gear end) of the assembly is up.
2. Using a prick punch, mark each pinion shaft and the carrier assembly so that, when reassembling, each shaft will be returned to its original location.
3. Remove pinion shaft lock plate screws and rotate plate counterclockwise far enough to remove it.
4. Starting with a short planet pinion, drive the lower end of the pinion shaft up until the shaft is above the press fit area of the output shaft flange. Feed a dummy shaft into the short planet pinion from the lower end, pushing the planet pinion shaft ahead of it until the tool is centered in the pinion and the pinion shaft is removed.
5. Remove short planet pinion.
6. Remove dummy shaft, needle and bearing spacers from short pinion. NOTE: twenty needle bearings are used in each end of each gear and are separated by a bearing spacer in the center.
7. By following Steps 4, 5, and 6, remove the adjacent long planet pinion that was paired, by thrust washers, to the short pinion now removed.
8. Remove upper and lower thrust washers.

1 Park lock and range selector outer lever and shaft
2 Throttle valve control shaft oil seal
3 Throttle valve control shaft washer
4 Throttle valve control lever and shaft
5 Throttle valve control inner lever to control shaft attaching screw and nut
6 Throttle valve control inner lever
7 Park lock and range selector inner lever
8 Park lock and range selector inner lever attaching screw and nut
9 Park lock pawl disengaging spring
10 Range selector detent roller spring
11 Park lock actuator assembly
12 Range selector detent roller spring retainer
13 Park lock pawl shaft
14 Park lock pawl
15 Park lock pawl shaft retaining ring
16 Park lock pawl reaction bracket
17 Park lock pawl reaction bracket attaching bolts
18 Park lock actuator to park lock and range selector inner lever retaining clip

Checking planet gear end clearance
(© G.M. Corp.)

9. Remove and disassemble remaining planet pinions, in pairs, as above.
10. Remove low sun gear needle thrust bearing, input sun gear, and thrust washer.
11. Wash all parts in solvent and blow dry, then inspect.
12. Inspect input shaft bushing in base of output shaft. If damaged, it may be removed by using a slide hammer. New bearing can be installed by using pilot end of input shaft as press tool.
13. Using dummy shaft, assemble needle bearings and spacer (20 rollers in each end) in one of the long planet pinions. Use petroleum jelly to aid in holding the rollers in position.
14. Position long planet gear, with dummy shaft centered in the pinion and with thrust washers at each end, in the planet carrier. Oil grooves on thrust washers must be toward the gears. NOTE: long pinions are located opposite the closed portions of the carrier and short pinions are located in the openings.
15. Feed a second dummy shaft in from the top, picking up the upper thrust washer and the pinion and pushing the already installed dummy shaft out the lower end. As the first dummy is pushed down, be sure that it picks up the lower thrust washer.
16. Select the correct pinion shaft, as marked in Step 2, lubricate the shaft and install it from the top, pushing the assembling tools (dummy) ahead of it.
17. Turn the pinion shaft so that the slot or groove at the upper end faces the center of the assembly.
18. With a brass drift, drive the shaft in until the lower end is flush with the lower face of the planet carrier.
19. Following the same procedure as outlined in Steps 13 through 18, assemble and install a short planet pinion into the planet carrier adjacent to the long pinion now installed. NOTE: the thrust washers, already installed with the long planet pinion, also serve for this short planet pinion, because the two pinions are paired together on one set of thrust washers.
20. Install the input sun gear thrust washer, input sun gear, and low sun gear needle thrust bearing.
21. Assemble and install the remaining planet pinions, in pairs, as previously explained.
22. Check end clearance of planet gears. This clearance should be .006-.030 in.
23. Place the shaft lock plate in position. Then, with the extended portions of the lock plate aligned with slots in the planet pinion

Checking gear end play (© G.M. Corp.)

shafts, rotate the lock plate clockwise until the three attaching screw holes are accessible.
24. Install lock plate attaching screws and torque to 2½ ft. lbs.

Governor

The governor assembly is a factory balanced unit. If body replacement is needed, the two sections must be replaced as a unit.

Disassembly

NOTE: the governor valve and shaft were removed in Step 6 of "Transmission Disassembly" procedures.
1. Remove the outer weight by sliding toward center of body.
2. Remove smaller inner weight retaining snap-ring and remove inner weight and spring.
3. Remove the four body assembly bolts and separate the body, hub and gasket. Remove the two seal rings.

Inspection
1. Clean all parts in solvent and air dry.
2. Check all parts. Replace all bent, scored, or otherwise damaged parts. Body and hub must be replaced as a unit.

Assembly
1. Reassemble governor weights and install into body bore. Replace seal ring on hub.
2. Slide hub into place on output shaft and lock into place with drive screw. Install gasket and governor body over output shaft, install governor shaft, line up properly with output shaft and install body attaching bolts. Torque bolts to 6-8 ft. lbs.
3. Check governor weight for free fit in body after the four attaching bolts are torqued. If the weight sticks or binds, loosen the bolts and retorque.

Valve Body

Removal

Remove valve body, as described under "Transmission Disassembly". If performing the operation on the

truck, the vacuum modulator valve, oil pan and gasket, guide detent plate and range selector detent roller spring must be removed in order to remove the valve from the transmission.

Disassembly
1. Remove manual valve, suction screen and gasket.
2. Remove cover bolts, then remove lower valve body and transfer plate from upper valve body. Discard gaskets.
3. Remove the front and rear pump check valves and springs from 1964-66 models.
4. From the upper valve body, remove the throttle valve and detent valve and the downshift timing valve as follows:
A. Throttle Valve and Detent Valve—Remove the retaining pin by wedging a thin screw-driver between its head and the valve body, then removing the detent valve assembly and throttle spring. Tilt valve body to allow the throttle valve to fall out. If necessary, remove the C clip and disassemble the detent valve assembly. NOTE: do not change adjustment of hex nut on the detent valve assembly. This is a factory setting and should not normally be changed. However, some adjustment is possible if desired. See "Throttle Valve Adjustment," in later text.
B. Downshift Timing Valve — Drive out the roll pin, remove valve spring and downshift timing valve.
5. From the lower valve body, remove the low-drive shift valve and the pressure regulator valve as follows:
A. Low-Drive Shift Valve—Remove the snap-ring and tilt valve body to remove low-drive regulator valve sleeve and valve assembly, valve spring seat, valve springs and the shifter valve.
B. Pressure Regulator Valve—Remove the snap-ring, then tilt valve body to remove the hydraulic modulator valve sleeve and valve, pressure regulator valve spring seat, spring, damper valve, spring seat and valve.

1 Valve to shaft
   retaining snap
   ring
2 Valve
3 Shaft
4 Urethane washer
5 Body
6 Outer weight
7 Spring
8 Inner weight
9 Inner weight to
   outer weight
   retaining snap

   ring
10 Outer weight to
   body retaining
   snap ring
11 Body to hub
   screws and
   lock washers
12 Gasket
13 Hub drive screw
14 Hub
15 Hub oil seal rings
16 Inner weight to
   shaft retaining
   snap ring

Governor assembly (© G.M. Corp.)

Inspection

1. Clean all parts in solvent; air dry. Use no rags.
2. Check all valves and valve bores for burrs or other deformities which could cause valve hang-up.

Assembly

1. Replace valve components in proper bores, reversing the steps of disassembly outlined above.
2. Install the gasket and transfer plate.
3. Install lower valve body and gasket and install attaching bolts. Torque to 15 ft. lbs.
4. Install valve body onto transmission, as outlined under "Transmission, Assembly" in later text.

Vacuum Modulator

The vacuum modulator is mounted on the left rear of the transmission and can be serviced from beneath the truck.

Removal

1. Remove vacuum line at the modulator.
2. Unscrew the modulator from the transmission with a thin 1 in. tappet-type wrench.
3. Remove vacuum modulator valve.

Inspection

1. Check the vacuum modulator plunger and valve for nicks and burrs. If such damage cannot be repaired with a stone, replace the part.
2. Check the vacuum modulator for

leakage with a vacuum source. If the modulator leaks, replace the assembly.

Installation

Reverse removal procedure.

Transmission Assembly

NOTE: if removed, assemble manual linkage to case, as described in Steps 1-7.

1. Install parking lock pawl and shaft and insert a new E-ring retainer.
2. Install parking lock pawl pullback spring over its boss at rear of pawl. The short leg of the spring should locate in the hole in the pawl.
3. Install parking pawl reaction bracket with its two bolts.
4. Fit the actuator assembly between the parking pawl and the bracket.
5. Insert outer shift lever into the case. Pick up inner shift lever and parking lock assembly. Tighten Allen-head lock.
6. Insert outer throttle valve lever and shaft, special washer, and O-ring into case and pick up inner throttle valve lever. Tighten Allen-head lock.
7. Thread low band adjusting screw into case.

NOTE: to prevent possible binding between throttle lever and range selector controls, allow .010-.020 clearance between inner throttle valve lever and inner shift lever.

Transmission Internal Components

8. Install inner and outer rear piston

seals onto reverse piston and, (with lubrication) install piston into the case.
9. With transmission case facing up, install the 17 reverse piston springs and their retainer ring.
10. Install spring compressing tool. Compress the return springs, allowing the retaining ring snapring to be installed. Remove the ring to be installed. Remove the compressor.
11. Install the cushion spring.
12. Lubricate and install reverse clutch pack, beginning with a reaction spacer plate and alternating with the faced plates until all plates are installed.

NOTE: the number and sequence of plates varies with the power and torque requirements of the truck model involved.

The notched lug on each reaction plate is installed in the groove at the seven o'clock position in the case. Then, install the thick pressure plate which has a dimple in one lug to align with the same slot in the case as the notched lugs on the other reaction plates.

13. Install clutch plate retainer ring.
14. Turn rear of transmission case down.
15. Align the internal lands and grooves of the reverse clutch pack faced plates, then engage the reverse ring gear with these plates. This engagement must be made by feel while turning the ring gear.
16. Place output shaft thrust bear-

Small planet carrier assembly (© G.M. Corp.)

ing over the output shaft and install the planetary carrier and output shaft into the transmission case.

17. Move transmission to horizontal position.

18. The two input shaft seal rings should be in place on the shaft. Install clutch drum (machined face first) onto the input shaft and install the low sun gear bushing against shoulder.

19. Install clutch drum and input shaft assembly into case, align-

ing thrust washer on input shaft and indexing low sun gear with the short pinions on the planet carrier.

20. Remove rubber seal ring from the front pump body and install front pump, gasket and selective fit thrust washer into case. Install pump-to-case bolts.

21. To check for correct thickness of the selective fit thrust washer, move transmission so that output shaft points down and proceed as follows:

A. Mount a dial indicator so that the indicator plunger is resting on the end of the input shaft. Zero the indicator.

B. Push up on the output shaft and watch the total dial movement.

C. The indicator should read .028-.059 in. If reading is not within specifications, remove front pump change to a thicker or thinner selective thrust washer. Repeat above checking procedure. NOTE: washers are available in thicknesses of .061, .078, .092 in. and .106 in.

22. Install servo piston, piston ring, and spring into the servo bore. Then, using a new gasket and O-ring, install the servo cover.

23. Remove front pump and selective fit washer from the case, and install the low brake band, anchor

1 Snap ring
2 Hydraulic modulator valve sleeve
3 Hydraulic modulator valve
4 Pressure regulator spring retainer
5 Pressure regulator spring

23 High speed down shift timing valve
24 Upper valve body
25 Manual control valve
26 Vacuum modulator valve, plunger and spring
27 Throttle valve
28 Throttle valve spring

6 Pressure regulator spring seat
7 Pressure regulator valve
8 Lower valve body
9 Suction screen, gasket and attaching screws
10 Low and drive valve
11 Low and drive valve inner spring
12 Low and drive valve outer spring
13 Low and drive regulator valve
14 Low and drive regulator valve sleeve and cap
15 Snap ring
16 Transfer plate to lower valve body gasket
17 Transfer plate
18 Transfer plate to upper valve body gasket
21 High speed down shift timing valve stop pin
22 High speed down shift timing valve spring

29 Throttle valve spring seat
30 Throttle valve spring regulator guide washer
31 Detent valve spring
32 Detent valve
33 Throttle valve spring regulator
34 Throttle valve spring regulator nut
35 Upper valve body plate gasket
36 Upper valve body plate
37 Detent valve and spring retaining stud
38 Range selector detent lever
39 Snap ring
40 Upper valve body plate to upper valve body attachings bolts and washers

Valve body assembly sequence (© G.M. Corp.)

Removing Oil Pump

DAMPENING SPRING
(EXC. L-153)

MODULATOR
VALVE

MODULATOR
PLUNGER

GASKET

A

B

Vacuum Modulator, Dampening Spring,
Plunger and Valve

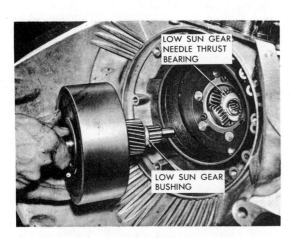

LOW SUN GEAR
NEEDLE THRUST
BEARING

LOW SUN GEAR
BUSHING

Removing Clutch Drum and Input Shaft

Checking Pump Body Bushing to
Converter Pump Hub Clearance

Checking Driven Gear to Pump Body Clearance

Driven Gear to Crescent Clearance

Automatic Transmissions

Installing clutch plates—typical
(© G.M. Corp.)

Installing detent guide plate
(© G.M. Corp.)

and apply struts into the case. Tighten the low band adjusting screw enough to prevent struts from falling out of case.

24. Place the seal ring in the groove around front pump body and the two seal rings on the pump cover extension. Install the pump, gasket and thrust washer into the case. Install all pump bolts. Torque bolts to 15 ft. lbs.
25. Turn transmission so that output shaft points upward.
26. Install governor support and gasket, drain back baffle, and support to case attaching bolts.
27. Install governor over output shaft. Install governor shaft and valve, urethane washer, and retaining C clips. Center shaft in output shaft bore and tighten governor hub drive screw.
28. Install speedometer gear to output shaft.
29. Place extension seal ring over governor support. Install transmission extension and five retaining bolts.
30. Replace speedometer driven gear.

Oil Pan and Valve Body

31. With transmission upside down, the manual linkage and the selector lever detent roller installed, install the valve body with a new gasket. (Carefully guide the servo apply line into its boss in the case as the valve body is set in place.) Position the manual valve actuating lever fully forward to more easily pick up the manual valve. Install six mounting bolts and the range selector detent roller spring. Install new gasket and suction screen to valve body.
32. Install the guide plate. Install attaching bolts.
33. Install vacuum modulator valve, the vacuum modulator and the gasket.
34. Install oil pan, using a new gasket, then the pan attaching bolts.
35. Install the converter and safety holding strap.

Throttle Valve TV Adjustment

No provision is made for checking TV pressures. However, if operation of the transmission is such that some adjustment of the TV is indicated, pressures may be raised or lowered by adjusting the position of the jam nut on the throttle valve assembly. To raise TV pressure 3 psi, back off the jam nut one full turn.

Conversely, tightening the jam nut one full turn, lowers TV pressure 3 psi. A difference of 3 psi in TV pressure will cause a change of about 2-3 mph in the wide open throttle upshift point. The end of the TV adjusting screw has an Allen head so the screw may be held stationary while the jam nut is locked.

NOTE: use care in changing this adjustment, as no pressure tap is provided to check TV pressure.

Low Band Adjustment

Tighten the low servo adjusting screw to 70 in. lbs. The input and output shaft must be rotated simultaneously to properly center the low band on the clutch drum. Then, back off four complete turns for a band which has been in use for 6,000 miles or more, or three turns for one in use less than 6,000 miles, and tighten the locknut.

CAUTION: The amount of back-off is very critical. Back off exactly three or four turns.

Torque References

	Foot-Pounds
Transmission case to engine	35
Oil pan to case	7-10
Extension to case	20-30
Servo cover to case	20
Front pump to case	13-17
Front pump cover to body attaching bolts	20
Pinion shaft lock plate attaching screws	2-3
Governor body to hub	6-8
Governor hub drive screw	6-8
Rear pump or governor support to case	8-11
Valve body to case	15
Suction screen attaching screws	2-3
Upper valve body plate	5
Lower to upper valve body	15
Inner control lever allen head locks	2½
Low band adjusting locknut	13-17
Converter to engine	35

TV ADJUSTMENT NUT   ALLEN WRENCH

Diagnosis

This diagnosis guide is a list of the most common troubles and their causes. The items to check are listed in the sequence to be followed.

TROUBLE SYMPTOMS	Items to Check	
	In Truck	Out of Truck
Slips in all ranges	ACDFGMO	N
Drive slips—no 1st gear	ACDFGMO	NQV
No 1-2 upshift	BEFGH	SU
1-2 upshift, early or late	BEFH	
Slips, 1-2 upshift	ACFGHL	NSU
Harsh 1-2 upshift	BCG	
No 2-3 upshift	FI	R
2-3 upshift, early/late	BCEFIK	
Slips, 2-3 upshift	ACFGI	NR
Harsh 2-3 upshift	BCGIL	
No full throttle downshift	K	
2-3 upshift, wide open throttle only	BK	
L₁ gear—no engine braking	GHJM	PQU
Car drives in neutral	K	Q
Slips in reverse	ACDFGHMO	RT
1-2, 2-3 shift noisy	A	RSY
Noisy in all ranges	ADFO	NXYW
Spews oil out of breather	AD	

Key to Checks

A. Low oil level/water in oil
B. Vacuum leak
C. Modulator and/or valve
D. Strainer and/or gasket leak
E. Governor valve/screen
F. Valve body gasket/plate
G. Pressure regulator and/or boost valve
H. 1-2 shift valve

I. 2-3 shift valve
J. Manual low control valve
K. Detent valve and linkage
L. 2-3 accumulator
M. Manual valve linkage
N. Pump gears
O. Gasket screen-pressure
P. Band—intermediate overrun roller clutch

Q. Forward clutch assembly
R. Direct clutch assembly
S. Intermediate clutch assembly
T. Low & reverse clutch assembly
U. Intermediate roller clutch
V. Low & reverse roller clutch
W. Parking pawl/linkage
X. Converter assembly
Y. Gear set and bearings

Sectional view of the General Motors Turbo Hydra-Matic 350 (© General Motors)

Capacity and General Specifications

Oil Capacity (dry) ....20 Pints
Cooling ....Water
Oil Filter Type
.........Bottom Suction Screen
Clutches 4
Roller Clutches 2
Band (non-adjustable) 1

Transmission Disassembly

Clean outside of transmission thoroughly to prevent dirt from entering the unit.

1. With transmission in a holding fixture, lift off torque converter assembly.
2. Remove vacuum modulator assembly attaching bolt and retainer.
3. Remove vacuum modulator assembly, O-ring seal and modulator valve from the case.
4. Remove four extension housing-to-case attaching bolts.
5. Remove extension housing and the square cut O-ring seal.
6. Remove extension housing lip seal from output end of housing, using a screwdriver.
7. Remove extension housing bushing, using chisel to collapse bushing.
8. Drive in new extension housing bushing.
9. Install extension housing lip seal.
10. Depress speedometer drive gear retaining clip, then slide speedometer drive gear off output shaft.
11. Remove governor cover retainer wire with a screwdriver.
12. Remove governor cover and O-ring seal from case, then remove O-ring seal from governor cover.

Check ball locations—Turbo Hydra-Matic 350 (© General Motors)

13. Remove governor assembly from case.
    NOTE: Check governor bore and sleeve for scoring.
14. Remove oil pan attaching screws, pan, and gasket.
15. Remove two oil pump suction screen (strainer) to valve body attaching screws.
16. Remove oil pump screen (strainer) and gasket from valve body.
17. Remove detent roller and spring assembly from valve body. Remove valve body-to-case attaching bolts.
18. Remove manual control valve link from range selector inner lever. Remove valve body. Remove detent control valve link from detent actuating lever.
    NOTE: Refer to later text for valve body disassembly and passage identification.
    NOTE: At this time, when han-

dling valve body assembly, do not touch sleeves, because retaining pins may fall into the transmission.
19. Remove valve body-to-spacer plate gasket.
20. Remove spacer support plate gasket. Remove spacer support plate.
21. Remove valve body spacer plate and plate-to-case gasket.
22. Remove four check balls from passages in case face.
    NOTE: If, during assembly, any of the balls are omitted or installed in the wrong locations, transmission failure will result.
23. Remove oil pump pressure screen from oil pump pressure hole in the case.
24. Remove governor feed screen from governor feed passage in case. Remove the manual control valve link from the range selector inner lever.
25. Remove manual shaft to case retainer with a screwdriver.

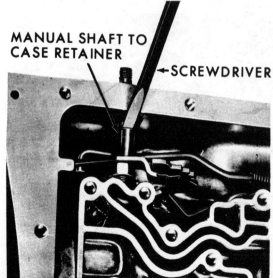

Removing the manual shift to case retainer—Turbo Hydra-Matic 350 (© General Motors)

Removing the oil pump pressure screen-Turbo Hydra-Matic 350 (© General Motors)

General Motors Turbo Hydra-Matic 350—exploded view—transmission case, extension housing and planet carrier parts (© General Motors)

1 Input ring gear thrust washer
2 Output planet carrier assembly
3 Sun gear assembly
4 Sun gear bushings
5 Sun gear drive shell retaining ring
6 Sun gear drive shell
7 Sun gear thrust washer
8 Sun gear rear thrust washer
9. Low and reverse clutch race
10 Low and reverse clutch assembly
11 Low and recerse clutch ring
12 Low and reverse clutch cam (part of support assembly)
13 Low and reverse clutch support spring
14 Low and reverse clutch support spring retainer
15 Low and reverse clutch support assembly
16 Low and reverse reaction plate
17 Low and reverse clutch drive plate assy
18 Reaction planet carrier assembly
19 Output ring gear front thrust washer
20 Output ring gear
21 Output ring
22 Output ring gear rear thrust bearing
23 Output ring gear support to output shaft ring
24 Low and reverse clutch seat assembly with springs
25 Low and reverse clutch piston
26 Low and reverse clutch piston seal unit
27 Low and reverse clutch piston return spring seat retainer
28 Reaction planet carrier bushing
29 Output shaft bushing
30 Output shaft assembly
31 Drive gear retaining clip
32 Speedometer drive gear
33 Intermediate clutch accumulator piston retainer
34 Intermediate clutch accumulator piston cover
35 Intermediate clutch piston accumulator cover seal
36 Intermediate clutch accumulator piston spring
37 Intermediate clutch accumulator piston assembly with seals
38 Case vent assembly
39 Vacuum modulator valve assembly
40 Vacuum modulator to transmission case seal
41 Vacuum modulator retainer
42 Vacuum modulator to transmission bolt
43 Vacuum modulator
44 Transmission case bushing
45 Extension housing to case seal
46 Extension housing to transmission case bolt
47 Extension housing assembly
48 Extension housing bushing
49 Extension housing oil seal assembly
50 Speedometer driven gear
51 Speedometer drive fitting assy with seal
52 Speedometer drive fitting retainer
53 Speedometer drive fitting retainer to case bolt
54 Speedometer drive fitting seal
55 Governor cover retainer
56 Governor cover
57 Governor cover seal
58 Governor assembly
59 Shaft assembly with parking pawl plug
60 Parking lock pawl
61 Parking lock spring
62 Parking lock reaction bracket
63 Parking lock bracket bolt
64 Parking lock and range selector shaft retaining ring
65 Parking lock and range selector shaft (outer)
66 Manual shift seal assembly
67 Manual valve control link
68 Detent spring assembly
69 Parking lock actuator assembly
70 Parking lock and range selector lever (inner)
71 Selector shaft to lever nut
72- Transmission case assembly

26. Remove jam nut holding range selector inner lever to manual shaft. Remove manual shaft.

27. Disconnect parking pawl actuating rod from range selector inner lever. Remove both from case.

28. Remove manual shaft to case lip oil seal, using a screwdriver.

29. Remove parking lock bracket.

30. Disconnect and remove parking pawl disengaging spring.

31. Remove parking pawl shaft retaining plug with a bolt extractor. Cock parking pawl on shaft. Using drift and hammer, tap on drift to force the parking pawl shaft from the case. Remove the parking pawl.

32. Remove intermediate servo pis-ton and metal oil seal ring. Remove washer, spring seat, and apply pin.

GOVERNOR SCREEN

GOVERNOR FEED HOLE

Removing the governor feed screen—Turbo Hydra-Matic 350
(© General Motors)

SLIDE HAMMERS

TIGHTEN JAM NUTS

Removing the oil pump from the transmission case—
Turbo Hydra-Matic 350 (© General Motors)

33. Remove eight pump attaching bolts with washer-type seals. Discard seals.
34. Install two threaded slide hammers into threaded holes in pump body. Tighten jam nuts and remove pump assembly from the case.
35. Remove pump assembly to case gasket and discard.
36. Remove intermediate clutch cushion spring.
37. Remove intermediate clutch faced plates and steel separator plates. Inspect lined plates for pitting, flaking, wear, glazing, cracking and chips or metal particles imbedded in lining. Replace any lined plates showing any of these conditions. Inspect steel plates for heat spot discoloration or surface scuffing. If the surface is smooth and has an even color smear, the steel plates may be re-used.
38. Remove intermediate clutch pressure plate.

39. Remove intermediate overrun brake band.
40. Remove direct and forward clutch assemblies.
41. Remove forward clutch housing-to-input ring gear front thrust washer.
    NOTE: Washer has three tangs.
42. Remove output carrier-to-output shaft snap-ring.
43. Remove input ring gear.
44. Remove input ring gear to output carrier thrust washer.
45. Remove output carrier assembly.
46. Remove sun gear drive shell assembly.
47. Remove low and reverse roller clutch support to case retaining ring.
48. Remove low and reverse roller clutch, support assembly, and retaining spring.
49. Remove low and reverse clutch faced plates and steel separator plates.
50. Remove reaction carrier assembly from output ring gear and shaft assembly.

51. Remove output ring gear and shaft assembly from case.
52. Remove reaction carrier to output ring gear tanged thrust washer.
53. Remove output ring gear-to-case needle bearing assembly.
54. Compress low and reverse clutch piston spring retainer and remove piston retaining ring and spring retainer.
55. Remove 17 piston return coil springs from piston.
56. Remove low and reverse clutch piston by application of air pressure.
57. Remove low and reverse clutch piston outer seal.
58. Remove low and reverse clutch piston center and inner seal.
59. Install suitable tool to compress intermediate clutch accumulator cover and remove retaining ring.
60. Remove intermediate clutch ac-

J-23327

Compressing the low and reverse clutch piston spring retainer
—Turbo Hydra-Matic 350 (© General Motors)

APPLY AIR PRESSURE HERE TO REMOVE LOW & REVERSE CLUTCH PISTON

Removing low and reverse clutch piston—Turbo Hydra-Matic 350
(© General Motors)

General Motors Turbo Hydra-Matic 350—exploded view—pump, central support, forward, direct and intermediate clutchs (© General Motors)

1 Torque converter assembly
2 Front oil pump seal
3 Oil pump to case screw
4 Oil pump body assembly
5 Oil cooler bypass valve
6 Oil pump drive gear
7 Oil pump driven gear
8 Oil pump to case seal
9 Startor shaft front bushing
10 Oil pump cover assembly
11 Direct clutch drum oil seal
12 Forward clutch housing oil seal
13 Stator shaft rear bushing
14 Oil pump to case gasket
15 Intermediate clutch piston seal
16 Intermediate clutch piston
17 Intermediate clutch piston return spring
18 Intermediate clutch piston return spring seat
19 Direct clutch drum front thrust washer
20 Oil pump to cover bolt
21 Intermediate clutch piston cushion spring
22 Intermediate clutch reaction plate
23 Intermediate clutch drive plate assembly
24 Intermediate clutch pressure plate assembly
25 Intermediate overrunning clutch retainer
26 Intermediate overrunning clutch outer race
27 Intermediate overrunning clutch inner race
28 Intermediate overrunning clutch assembly

29 Intermediate overrunning brake band assembly
30 Intermediate overrunning brake and band assembly
31 Direct clutch drum assembly
32 Direct clutch piston seal
33 Direct clutch piston
34 Direct clutch piston return spring and seat assembly
35 Direct clutch piston return spring seat retainer ring
36 Direct clutch drive plate
37 Direct clutch drive plate assembly
38 Direct clutch pressure plate assembly
39 Direct clutch pressure plate retaining ring
40 Direct clutch drum rear thrust bearing
41 Imput shaft
42 Forward clutch housing assembly
43 Forward clutch piston seal unit (inner and outer)
44 Forward clutch piston
45 Forward clutch piston return spring
46 Forward clutch piston return spring seat
47 Forward clutch piston return spring seat retaining ring
48 Input ring gear front thrust washer
49 Input ring gear assembly with support
50 Input ring gear bushing
51 Forward clutch piston cushion spring
52 Forward clutch driven plate
53 Forward clutch drive plate assembly
54 Forward clutch pressure plate
55 Forward clutch pressure plate retaining ring

Removing the accumulator piston cover retaining ring —Turbo Hydra-Matic 350 (© General Motors)

Checking the oil pump body to gear face clearance —Turbo Hydra-Matic 350 (© General Motors)

cumulator piston cover. Remove cover O-ring seal from case.
61. Remove intermediate clutch accumulator piston spring.
62. Remove intermediate clutch accumulator piston assembly. Remove inner and outer hook-type oil seal rings if required.

Component Disassembly

Valve Body

Disassembly

1. Position valve body assembly with cored face up and direct clutch accumulator piston pocket located as illustrated in valve body assembly illustration.
2. Remove manual valve from lower left-hand bore, A.
3. From lower right-hand bore, B, remove the pressure regulator valve train retaining pin, boost valve sleeve, intermediate boost valve, reverse and modulator boost valve, pressure regulator valve spring, and the pressure regulator valve.
4. From the next bore, C, remove the second-third shift valve train retaining pin, sleeve, control valve spring, second-third shift control valve, shift valve spring, and the second-third shift valve.
5. From the next bore, D, remove the first-second shift valve train retaining pin, sleeve, shift control valve spring, first-second shift control valve, and the first-second shift valve.
6. From the next bore, E, remove retaining pin, plug, manual low control valve spring, and the manual low control valve.
7. From the next bore, F, remove retaining pin, spring seat and the detent regulator valve.
8. Install spring compressor onto direct clutch accumulator piston and remove retaining E-ring at H.
9. At location H, remove direct clutch accumulator piston, then metal oil seal ring and spring.
10. From the upper left hand bore, G, remove the detent actuating lever bracket bolt, bracket, actuating lever and retaining pin, stop, spring retainer, seat, outer spring, and the detent valve.

Valve Body Springs

Valve	Free Length of Spring (in.)	Diameter (in.)
Detent regulator	1 7/8	9/16
Manual low control valve	1 1/2	7/16
1-2 shift control valve	1 15/16	1/4
2-3 shift valve	2 1/16	7/8
2-3 shift control valve	11/16	3/16
Pressure regulator valve	1 11/16	17/32
Direct clutch accumulator	1 3/4	1 1/2
Detent valve	1 7/8	3/4

Inspection

1. Wash all parts in solvent. Air dry. Blow out all passages.
2. Inspect all valves for scoring, cracks, and free movement in their bores.
3. Inspect sleeves for cracks, scratches, or distortion.
4. Inspect valve body for cracks, scored bores, interconnected oil passages, and flatness of mounting face.

J—1	MANUAL VALVE
2	PRESSURE REGULATOR VALVE
3	PRESSURE REGULATOR VALVE SPRING
A 4	REVERSE AND MODULATOR BOOST VALVE
5	INTERMEDIATE BOOST VALVE
6	BOOST VALVE SLEEVE
7	RETAINING PIN
8	2-3 SHIFT VALVE
9	2-3 SHIFT VALVE SPRING
10	2-3 SHIFT CONTROL VALVE
B 11	2-3 SHIFT CONTROL VALVE SPRING
12	2-3 SHIFT CONTROL VALVE SLEEVE
13	RETAINING PIN
14	1-2 SHIFT VALVE
15	1-2 SHIFT CONTROL VALVE
C 16	1-2 SHIFT CONTROL VALVE SPRING
17	1-2 SHIFT CONTROL VALVE SLEEVE
18	RETAINING PIN
19	MANUAL LOW CONTROL VALVE
20	MANUAL LOW CONTROL VALVE SPRING
E 21	PLUG
22	RETAINING PIN
23	DETENT REGULATOR VALVE
F 24	DETENT REGULATOR VALVE SPRING SEAT
25	DETENT REGULATOR VALVE SPRING
26	RETAINING PIN
27	DETENT VALVE
28	WASHER
29	DETENT VALVE INNER SPRING
30	DETENT VALVE OUTER SPRING
31	DETENT VALVE OUTER SPRING SEAT
D 32	DETENT VALVE SPRING RETAINER
33	DETENT VALVE STOP
34	DETENT VALVE ACTUATING LEVER BRACKET
35	DETENT VALVE ACTUATING LEVER
36	RETAINING BOLT
37	RETAINING PIN
38	DIRECT CLUTCH ACCUMULATOR SPRING
39	OIL SEAL RING
G 40	DIRECT CLUTCH ACCUMULATOR PISTON
41	RETAINER RING

Exploded view of the valve body—Turbo Hydra-Matic 350 (© General Motors)

1 Transmission case assembly
2 Governor pressure screen assembly
3 Oil check valve ball
4 Oil pump pressure screen assembly
5 Intermediate servo apply rod
6 Intermediate servo piston spring
7 Intermediate servo piston return spring
8 Intermediate servo piston washer
9 Intermediate servo piston
10 Intermediate servo piston seal
11 Direct clutch accumulator piston ring
12 Direct clutch accumulator piston
13 Direct clutch accumulator piston seal
14 Direct clutch accumulator piston spring
15 Valve body spacer plate gasket (upper)
16 Valve body spacer plate gasket (lower)
17 Valve body spacer plate support
18 Valve body spacer plate assembly with gasket
19 Detent regulator valve
20 Detent regulator valve spring seat
21 Detent regulator valve spring
22 Valve retaining pin
23 Manual control valve
24 Manual control valve spring
25 Manual control valve plug
26 1-2 shift valve
27 1-2 shift control valve
28 1-2 shift control valve spring
29 1-2 shift control valve sleeve
30 2-3 shift valve
31 2-3 shift valve spring
32 2-3 shift control valve
33 2-3 shift control valve spring
34 2-3 shift control valve sleeve
35 Pressure regulator valve
36 Pressure regulator valve spring
37 Modulator and reverse boost valve
38 Intermediate boost valve
39 Modulator and reverse boost valve sleeve
40 Valve body assembly
41 Valve body bolt
42 Oil pump screen gasket
43 Oil pump screen unit
44 Oil pump screen to valve body bolt
45 Oil pan gasket
46 Transmission oil pan
47 Oil pan bolt
48 Manual valve unit
49 Detent valve
50 Detent valve washer
51 Detent valve spring
52 Detent valve spring seat
53 Detent valve retainer
54 Detent valve stop
55 Detent valve actuator lever
   bracket
56 Detent valve actuator lever
   bracket to valve body bolt
57 Detent valve actuator lever
58 Detent valve control wire
59 Detent valve actuator lever pin

General Motors Turbo Hydra-Matic 350—exploded view—front and rear servos, and control valve body (© General Motors)

5. Check all springs for distortion or collapsed coils.

Assembly

1. Reverse disassembly procedures for assembly. Refer to Valve Body Springs chart for identification of springs.

Oil Pump

Disassembly

1. Remove five pump cover-to-body attaching bolts. Remove spring seat retainer.
2. Remove the intermediate clutch spring seat retainer, intermediate clutch return springs, and the intermediate clutch piston assembly.

3. Remove intermediate clutch piston inner and outer seals.
4. Remove two forward clutch-to-pump hub hook-type oil seal rings. Remove three direct clutch-to-pump hub hook type oil rings.
5. Remove pump cover-to-direct clutch drum selective thrust washer.
6. Remove pump cover and stator shaft assembly from pump body.
7. Remove pump drive gear and driven gear from pump body.
8. Remove pump outside diameter-to-case square cut O-ring seal.
9. Pry out pump body to converter hub lip seal, using a screwdriver. Place pump on wood blocks to

prevent damage to surface finish.
10. Install pump-to-converter hub lip seal, using seal driver. Examine after installation to be sure the sealing surface is not damaged.
11. Remove oil pump priming valve and spring.
    NOTE: The valve and spring have been deleted from all transmissions built after Feb. 1971.
12. Remove cooler by-pass valve seat. Pack cooler by-pass passage with grease. Insert 5/16 in. dia. rod and tap with hammer to lift seat. Remove check ball and spring.

Inspection

1. Wash all parts in solvent. Air dry. Blow out all passages.

J-21359

PUMP TO
CONVERTER
HUB LIP SEAL

PUMP BODY

WOOD BLOCKS

Installing the hub lip seal—Turbo Hydra-Matic 350
(© General Motors)

Installing the oil pump drive and driven gears—
Turbo Hydra-Matic 350 (© General Motors)

2. Inspect drive and driven gears, gear pocket, and crescent for nicks, galling or other damage.
3. Inspect pump body and cover for nicks or scoring.
4. Check pump cover outer diameter for nicks or burrs.
5. Inspect pump body bushing for galling or scoring. Check clearance between pump body bushing and converter hub. It must be no more than .005 in. If bushing is damaged, replace pump body.
6. Install pump gears in body and check pump body face to gear face clearance. It should be from .0005-.0015 in.
7. Inspect pump body to converter hub lip oil seal. Inspect converter hub for nicks or burrs which might have damaged pump lip oil seal or pump body bushing.
8. Check priming valve for free operation. Replace if necessary.
9. Check condition of cooler bypass valve. Replace valve if it leaks excessively.
10. Check all springs for distortion or collapsed coils.
11. Check oil passages in pump body and in pump cover.
12. Inspect three pump cover stator shaft bushings for galling or

scoring. If they are damaged, remove using a slide hammer. Drive the new bushings into place. The front stator shaft bushing must be .250 in. below the front face of the pump body. The center bushing should be 11/32 in. below the face of the pump cover hub. The rear bushing should be flush or up to .010 in. below the face of the pump cover hub.
13. Check three pump cover and hub lubrication holes to make certain they are not restricted.

Assembly

1. Install cooler by-pass valve spring, check ball and seat. Press seat into bore until top of seat is flush to .010 in. with face of pump body.
2. Install oil pump priming valve and spring. The priming valve is used on all pump bodies having a reamed hole in the priming valve area and on all replacement pump assemblies.
3. Install new pump outside diameter to case square cut O-ring seal.
4. Install pump drive and driven gears. If drive gear has offset

tangs, assemble with tangs face up to prevent damage by converter.
5. Install selective thrust washer and five oil seal rings on pump cover hub.
6. Install intermediate clutch piston inner and outer seals.
7. Install pump cover on pump body.
8. Install intermediate clutch piston and clutch return springs.
9. Install spring retainer and pump cover bolts. Position aligning strap over pump body and cover. Tighten strap. Torque pump bolts to 18 ft. lbs.

Direct Clutch and Intermediate Overrun Roller Clutch

Disassembly

1. Remove intermediate overrun clutch front retainer ring and retainer.
2. Remove intermediate overrun clutch outer race.
NOTE: Before removal, check for correct assembly. The outer race should free wheel counterclockwise only.
3. Remove intermediate overrun roller clutch assembly.

PUMP BODY

Oil pump oil passages—Turbo Hydra-Matic 350 (© General Motors)

PUMP COVER AND STATOR SHAFT ASSEMBLY

Oil pump cover oil passages—Turbo Hydra-Matic 350 (© General Motors)

Compressing the direct clutch spring seat—Turbo Hydra-Matic 350
(© General Motors)

.020″ PIANO WIRE CRIMPED INTO COPPER TUBING

PISTON

DIRECT CLUTCH HOUSING

Install the direct clutch piston—Turbo Hydra-Matic 350
(© General Motors)

4. Remove intermediate overrun roller clutch cam.
5. Remove direct clutch drum to forward clutch housing special needle bearing.
6. Remove direct clutch pressure plate to clutch drum retaining ring and pressure plate.
7. Remove direct clutch lined and steel plates.
8. Remove direct clutch piston return spring seat retaining ring and spring seat.
9. Remove 17 clutch return coil springs and piston.
10. Remove direct clutch piston inner and outer seals.
11. Remove direct clutch piston center seal.

Inspection

1. Wash all parts in solvent. Blow out all passages. Air dry.
2. Inspect clutch plates for burning, scoring, or wear.
3. Check all springs for collapsed coils or distortion.
4. Inspect piston for cracks and free operation of ball check. Ball should be loose enough to rattle but not to fall out.
5. Check overrun clutch inner cam and outer race for scratches, wear, or indentations.
6. Inspect overrun roller clutch assembly rollers for wear. Check springs for distortion.
7. Inspect clutch drum for wear, scoring, cracks, proper opening of oil passages, wear on clutch plate drive lugs, and free operation of ball check.
8. Check direct clutch drum bushing for galling or scoring. When replacing bushing, drive the new bushing 9/32 in. below clutch plate side of hub face and .010 in. below slot in hub face.

Assembly

1. Install direct clutch drum center seal.
2. Install direct clutch piston inner and outer seals.

3. Install direct clutch piston into housing with a loop of .020 in. wire crimped into a length of copper tubing.
4. Install 17 clutch return springs on piston.
5. Install direct clutch piston return spring seat and retaining ring using snap-ring pliers and spring compressor.
6. Install direct clutch housing. Install steel and faced plates alternately, beginning with a steel plate.
7. Install direct clutch pressure plate in clutch drum. Install retaining ring.
8. Install intermediate overrun roller clutch inner cam on hub of direct clutch drum.
9. Replace intermediate overrun roller clutch assembly.
10. Install intermediate overrun clutch outer race. The outer race must free-wheel in the counterclockwise direction only.
11. Replace intermediate overrun clutch retainer and retainer ring. If the retainer ring is dished, install the ring so that it compresses the retainer.
12. Install direct clutch drum to forward clutch housing needle thrust washer on hub of roller clutch inner race.

Forward Clutch

Disassembly

1. Remove forward clutch drum to pressure plate retaining ring.
2. Remove forward clutch pressure plate.
3. Remove forward clutch housing faced plates, steel plates and cushion spring.
4. Compress springs. Remove forward clutch piston return spring seat retaining ring and spring seat.
5. Remove 21 clutch return springs.
6. Remove forward clutch piston assembly.

7. Remove forward clutch piston inner and outer seals.
8. Be sure the ball check exhaust in the drum is operable and free of dirt.

Inspection

1. Wash all parts in solvent. Blow out all passages. Air dry.
2. Inspect clutch plates for burning, scoring, or wear.
3. Check all springs for distortion or collapsed coils.
4. Inspect piston for cracks.
5. Inspect clutch drum for wear, scoring, cracks, proper opening of oil passages, and free operation of ball check.
6. Check input shaft for:
   a. Open lubrication passages at each end.
   b. Damage to splines or shaft.
   c. Damage to ground bushing journals.
   d. Cracks or distortion of shaft.

Assembly

1. Install forward clutch piston inner and outer seals.
2. Install forward clutch piston with a loop of .020 in. wire crimped into a length of copper tubing.
3. Install the 21 forward clutch return springs. These springs are identical to those used in the direct clutch. Install spring seat.
4. Compress springs and replace spring seat retaining ring.
5. Replace forward clutch housing cushion spring. Replace steel and faced plates alternately, starting with a steel plate.
6. Install forward clutch pressure plate and retaining ring.
7. Use a feeler gauge to check the clearance between the top of the clutch pack to the top of the clutch; dimension A, (use the chart that follows to select the correct pressure plate). Measure the distance between the lower edge of the notch on the inner surface of the drum and the end

WHEN DIM. C IS	USE (OR EQUIVALENT)
.0160— .0520	6261072
.0520— .0830	6261349
.0830— .1218	6261350

Determining the selective fit for the forward clutch pressure plate—Turbo Hydra-Matic 350 (© General Motors)

of the drum; dimension B. Subtract dimension B from dimension A to get dimension C.

*Subtract dim. B from C
to obtain dim. A*

When dim. A is:	use plate number
.016-.052 in.	6261072
.052-.083 in.	6261349
.083-.122 in.	6261350

8. Install direct clutch drum on input shaft and align faced plates with splines on forward clutch housing.

Sun Gear and Sun Gear Drive Shell

Disassembly

1. Remove sun gear to sun gear drive shell rear retaining ring.
2. Remove sun gear to drive shell flat rear thrust washer.
3. Remove sun gear and front retaining ring from drive shell.
4. Remove front retaining ring from sun gear.

Inspection

1. Wash all parts in solvent. Air dry.
2. Inspect sun gear and sun gear drive shell for wear or damage.
3. Inspect sun gear bushings for galling or scoring. Drive out damaged bushings. Install new bushings flush to .010 in. below surface of counterbore.

Assembly

1. Install new front retaining ring on sun gear. Be careful not to over-stress this ring.
2. Install sun gear and retaining ring in drive shell.
3. Install sun gear to drive shell flat rear thrust washer.
4. Install new sun gear to sun gear drive shell retaining ring.

Clutch Plates

Year	Model	Intermediate Clutch		Direct Clutch		Forward Clutch		Low-Reverse Clutch	
		Driven Plates	Drive Plates	Driven Plates	Drive Plates	Driven Plates	Drive Plates	Driven Plates	Drive Plates
1970-76	All	3	3	4	4	5	5	5	5

Low and Reverse Roller Clutch Support

Disassembly

1. Remove low and reverse clutch to sun gear shell thrust washer.
2. Remove low and reverse overrun clutch inner race.
3. Remove low and reverse roller clutch retaining ring.
4. Remove low and reverse roller clutch assembly.

Inspection

1. Wash all parts in solvent. Air dry.
2. Inspect roller clutch inner and outer races for scratches, wear, or indentations.
3. Inspect roller clutch assembly rollers for wear and roller springs for distortion. If rollers are removed from assembly, install rollers from outside in to avoid bending springs.

Assembly

1. Install low and reverse roller clutch assembly.
2. Install low and reverse roller clutch retaining ring.
3. Install low and reverse overrun clutch inner race. Inner race must free-wheel in the clockwise direction only.

Governor

NOTE: All components of the governor, with the exception of the driven gear, are a select fit and each assembly is calibrated. The governor, including the driven gear, is serviced as a complete assembly. It is necessary to disassemble the governor to replace the driven gear. Disassembly, may also be necessary due to improper operation of the governor.

Disassembly & Inspection

1. Cut off one end of each governor weight pin and remove pins, governor thrust cap, governor weights and springs. Governor weights are interchangeable from side to side and need not be identified.
2. Remove the governor valve from the governor sleeve. Be careful not to damage the valve.
3. Wash all parts in clean solvent, air dry and blow out all passages with filtered compressed air.
4. Inspect the governor sleeve for nicks, burrs, scoring or galling.
5. Check the governor sleeve for free operation in the bore of the transmission case.
6. Inspect the governor valve for nicks, burrs or galling.
7. Check governor valve for free operation in the bore of the governor sleeve.
8. Inspect the governor driven gear for nicks, burrs or damage.
9. Check the driven gear for excessive play on the governor sleeve.
10. Inspect the governor weight springs for distortion or damage.
11. Check governor weights for free operation in their retainers.
12. Check the valve opening at the entry and exhaust, 0.020 inch minimum.

Governor Driven Gear Replacement

1. Using a small punch, drive out the governor gear retaining split pin.
2. Support the governor on 3/16 inch plates installed in the exhaust slots of the governor sleeve, place in an arbor press,

Typical governor assembly, exploded view—Turbo Hydra-Matic 350 (© General Motors)

and with a long punch, press the driven gear out of the sleeve.

3. Carefully, clean the governor sleeve of chips that remain from original rear installation.

4. Support the governor on 3/16 inch plates installed in the exhaust slots of the sleeve, position the new gear in the sleeve 'and, with a suitable socket, press the gear into the sleeve until nearly seated. Carefully, remove any chips that may have shaved off the gear hub, and press the gear in until it bottoms on the shoulder.

5. A new pin must be drilled through the sleeve and gear. Locate the hole position 90 degrees away from the existing hole, center punch and while supporting the governor in press, drill the new hole through the sleeve and gear using a standard ⅛ inch drill.

6. Install new split retaining pin.

7. Wash governor assembly thoroughly to remove any chips that may have collected.

Assembly

1. Install the governor valve in bore of sleeve, large land first.

2. Install the governor weights and springs, and the thrust cap on the governor sleeve.

3. Align the holes in the thrust cap, governor weight assemblies and governor sleeve, install new pins. Crimp both ends of the pins to prevent them from falling out.

4. Check the operation of the governor weight assemblies. Pins should operate freely.

5. Check the governor valve for free movement in the governor sleeve.

Transmission Assembly

NOTE: During assembly of transmission, use only clean transmission fluid or petroleum jelly to lubricate or retain parts. Lubricate all bearings, seals rings, and clutch plates before assembly.

Internal Components

1. Install the low and reverse clutch piston assembly with the piston installed next to the parking pawl.

2. Install the piston return springs, there are seventeen.

3. Install the spring retainer and retaining ring. Use the special spring compressing tool. Compress the return seat so the spring retainer retaining ring can be installed. Install the output ring gear thrust bearing in the transmission case.

4. Install the output ring gear on the output shaft.

5. Position the reaction carrier on the output ring gear front tanged

Checking the end play for proper thrust washer selection—
Turbo Hydra-Matic 350 (© General Motors)

washer, and install in the output ring gear support.

6. Install the output shaft assembly in the transmission case.

7. Place the reaction carrier in the output ring gear and shaft assembly.

8. Lubricate (with clean transmission fluid) and install the low and reverse clutch steel reaction and face plates. Starting with a steel plate and alternating with a face plate, assemble the clutch. Install the low and reverse clutch support retainer spring, the notch in the steel separator plate must be placed toward the bottom of the transmission case.

9. Install the low and reverse clutch support assembly. The notch must be aligned so that the retainer spring is in proper contact.

10. Install the low and reverse roller clutch inner race to the sun gear shell thrust washer.

11. Install the low and reverse clutch support to case snap ring with retainer spring between gap.

12. Install thrust rear thrust washer and sun gear drive shell assembly.

13. Install output carrier assembly.

14. Install the input ring gear rear thrust washer.

15. Install the ring gear.

16. Install the new input ring gear

CAUTION: Do not over stress the snap ring.

17. Install the input gear front thrust washer.

18. Install the direct clutch assembly, and the special thrust washer to the forward clutch assembly.

19. Install the clutch assemblies in the transmission case.

CAUTION: Be sure the forward clutch face plates are positioned over the input ring gear. Make certain that the tangs on the direct clutch housing are installed in the slots on the sun gear drive shell.

20. Install the intermediate clutch overrun brake band.

21. Install the intermediate clutch pressure plate.

22. Lubricate (with clean transmission fluid) and install the steel and face plates of the intermediate clutch.

Starting with a face plate and alternating with a steel plate, assemble the clutch pack. The steel reaction plates are installed toward the selector lever inner bracket.

23. Install the intermediate clutch cushion spring.

24. Use the following procedure to check for the proper thickness of the selective thrust washer used between the oil pump cover and the direct clutch assembly.

   a. Install the selective fit thrust washer, oil pump gasket. Install the oil pump with two slide hammer bolts and two pump to case bolts.

   b. Move the transmission so that the output shaft points down. Mount a dial indicator on one of the slide hammer bolts so that the indicator plunger is resting on the end of the input shaft. Zero the indicator.

   c. Push the transmission output shaft upward and observe the total indicator movement.

   d. The indicator should read .032-.064 inch. If the reading is within these limits, the proper washer is being used. If the reading is not within the limits, it will be necessary to remove the pump and change the selective fit thrust washer to obtain the proper clearance. Selective fit thrust washers are available in thickness of; 0.066, 0.083, and 0.100 inch.

25. Install a new pump to case gasket.

26. Install a new pump to case square cut oil seal ring.

27. Install the guide pins in the case

28. Install the pump assembly in the transmission case. Install attaching bolts and new washer type seals.

NOTE: If the input shaft can not be rotated as the pump is being pulled into place, the direct and forward clutch housings have not been properly installed to index the faced plates with their respective parts.

1231

Automatic Transmissions

J-5154

**Installing the extension housing seal—
Turbo Hydra-Matic 350** (© General Motors)

This condition must be corrected before the pump is pulled into place.

Extension and Speedometer Drive Gear

1. Place the speedometer drive gear retaining clip in the hole on the output shaft.
2. Heat a new speedometer drive gear using a suitable heat source.
3. Align the slot in the speedometer drive gear with the retaining clip and install the gear.
4. Install the extension housing to case square cut 'O' ring.
5. Install the extension housing on the transmission case with the attaching bolts and tighten to 25 foot pounds torque.
6. Install a new extension housing rear seal, if necessary, with the proper size drift.

Manual Linkage Assembly

1. Install a new manual shift shaft seal using ¾ inch rod, be sure the seal seats in the transmission case.
2. Install the parking pawl, tooth toward the inside, in the transmission case.
3. Install the parking pawl shaft in the case through the parking pawl.
4. Install the parking pawl shaft retaining plug. Drive the retaining plug into the transmission case with a ⅜ inch rod, until the retaining plug is 0.1330-0.170 inch below the face of the transmission case. Stake the retaining plug in three places.
5. Install the parking pawl disengaging spring, with the square end hocked on the parking pawl.
6. Install the park lock bracket and tighten the bolts to 29 foot pounds torque.
CAUTION: These bolts are type 290 M and have six marks on their heads.

7. Install the actuating rods between the range selector inner lever and parking pawl.
8. Install the actuating rod under the park lock bracket and parking pawl.
9. Install the manual shift shaft through the transmission case and the range selector inner lever.
10. Install the retaining nut on the manual shift shaft and tighten to 30 foot pounds of torque.
11. Install the manual shift shaft to transmission case spacer clip.

Intermediate Servo Piston, Valve Body, Oil Pan, and Gasket Installation

1. Install the intermediate servo piston, apply pin, spring, and spring seat.
2. Install the intermediate servo piston and the metal oil seal ring.
3. Install the four check balls into the proper transmission case pockets.
4. Install the oil pump pressure screen and governor feed screen.
5. Install the valve body transfer plate and the gasket.
6. Install the valve body to the transfer plate.
7. Install the valve body. Connect the manual control valve link to the range selector inner lever. Torque the retaining bolts in a random sequence to 130 inch pounds.
8. Install the spacer support plate, tighten the bolts to 130 inch pounds torque.
9. Connect the detent control valve wire to the detent valve actuating lever, attach the lever to the valve body.
10. Attach the roller and spring assembly to the valve body.
11. Align the lube holes in the strainer with the holes in the valve body and install the strainer assembly gasket and strainer.
12. Install the oil pan with a new gasket. Tighten the bolts to 130 inch pounds torque.

Governor and Vacuum Modulator Installation

1. Install the governor assembly, cover and retainer wire.
2. Install the vacuum modulator valve.
3. Install the vacuum modulator retaining clip and tighten the retaining bolts to 130 inch pounds.
NOTE: Position the retainer with the tangs pointing toward the modulator.

Intermediate Clutch Accumulator Installation

1. Install the intermediate clutch accumulator piston assembly.
2. Install the intermediate clutch accumulator spring.
3. Install a new 'O' ring in the groove of the transmission case before installing cover.
4. Install the intermediate clutch accumulator cover and retaining ring.

Torque Specifications

	Foot pounds	Inch Pounds
Pump cover to pump body	17	—
Pump assembly to case	18½	—
Valve body and support plate	—	130
Parking lock bracket	29	—
Oil suction screen	—	40
Oil pan to case	—	130
Extension to case	25	—
Modulator retainer to case	—	130
Inner selector lever to shaft	25	—
Detent valve actuating bracket	—	52
Converter to flywheel bolts	32	—
Upper pan to transmission case	—	110
Transmission case to engine	35	—
Oil cooler pipe connection to transmission case or radiator	—	125
Oil cooler pipe to connections	10	—
Detent cable to transmission	—	75
Detent cable to carburetor	—	112

Oil Pressure Check

Year	Engine	Oil Pressure (psi) @ Altitude (± 5 psi) ①								
		Sea Level			2,000 ft.			8,000 ft.		
		D, P, N	L1, L2	R	D, P, N	L1, L2	R	D, P, N	L1, L2	R
1970	L6 & V8	139	139	250	139	139	235	125	129	195
1971	L6 & V8	168	166	254	158	159	240	133	141	202
1972-73	L6 & V8	150	150	244	150	150	233	126	150	194
1974-76	L6	173	166	262	163	159	248	138	141	210
	V8	167	166	254	158	159	240	133	140	202

① Pressures are at 0 (zero) output speed, 1,200 engine rpm and vacuum line disconnected and plugged.

Diagnosis

This diagnosis guide covers the most common symptoms and is an aid to careful diagnosis. The items to check are listed in the sequence to be followed for quickest results. Thus, follow the checks in the order given for the particular transmission type.

TROUBLE SYMPTOMS	Items to Check	
	In Truck	Out of Truck
No drive in D range	ABCD	abc
No drive in R or slips in reverse	ABCEGHIJL	efa
Drive in neutral	B	a
First speed only—no 1-2 shift	KG	g
1-2 shift at full throttle only	MNG	
First and second speeds only—no 2-3 shift	MNG	f
Slips in all ranges	ACEFG	dfahc
Slips—1-2 shift	ACELGO	gh
Rough 1-2 shift	CELGJOGJ	hi
Slips 2-3 shift	ACELG	fh
Rough 2-3 shift	CELO	
Shifts occur—too high or too low car speed	CKEMGL	
No detent downshifts	NMG	
No part throttle downshift (heavy-duty model "OE" only)	CEG	
No engine braking—super range—second speed	O	i
No engine braking—low range—first speed	GJ	ik
Park will not hold	BPQ	
Poor performance or rough idle—stator not functioning	RS	lo
Noisy transmission	TF	dafgn

Key to Checks

A. Oil level
B. Manual linkage (external)
C. Check oil pressure
D. Manual control disconnected inside
E. Modulator and/or lines
F. Clogged strainer or intake leaks
G. Valves, body and/or leaks
H. Reverse feed passages
I. Valve check balls
J. Rear servo and accumulator
K. Governor and/or feed line seals
L. Pump regulator and boost valve
M. Detent solenoid
N. Detent switch
O. Front servo and accumulator
P. Internal linkage
Q. Parking pawl and/or link
R. Stator switch
S. Valve body-stator section
T. Cooler or lines
a. Front clutch
b. Clutch feed seals and gaskets
c. Low sprags
d. Front pump
e. Rear band
f. Direct clutch
g. Intermediate clutch
h. Pump-to-case gasket
i. Intermediate check valve ball in case
j. Front band
k. Rear band
l. Turbine shaft
m. Converter assembly
n. Planetary assembly

General Information

The illustration is typical. While design and repair procedures are similar, components vary with truck application and should not be considered interchangeable.

Fluid Specifications

Oil capacity, transmission
and converter
    Approx. 22 pints
Capacity between marks
on dip stick
    1 pint
Type of oil
    Automatic transmission fluid
    Type A
Drain and refill
    24,000

Draining and Refilling

The transmission fluid should be drained and refilled at 24,000 mile intervals. To do this:

1. Drain transmission oil.
2. Remove oil pan attaching screws.
3. Remove oil pan and gasket.
4. Remove strainer or filter.
5. Thoroughly clean oil strainer or filter and oil pan in solvent. Blow dry with air.
6. Renew oil strainer gasket and oil pan gasket.
7. Install oil strainer or filter.
8. Install oil pan. Torque attaching screws to 10-12 ft. lbs.
9. Add about five pints of transmission fluid.
10. Start engine. Do not race engine. Move selector lever slowly through each range. Check fluid level.
11. With transmission cold, add enough fluid to bring level to ¼ in. below the Add mark. With the transmission at normal temperature, add enough fluid to bring the level to the Full mark. About fifteen miles of highway driving is required to bring the transmission to normal temperature.
12. In case of transmission overhaul, proceed as in Steps 9-11. Start with five pints of fluid if converter has not been replaced; eight pints if it has been replaced. Total capacity is about 22 pints, but correct level is determined by the mark on the dipstick rather than by amount of fluid added.

Transmission Disassembly

Clean outside of the unit thor-

General Motors type turbo hydra matic transmission (© G.M. Corp.)

oughly to prevent dirt from entering the unit.

1. With transmission in a work cradle or on a clean bench, lift the converter straight off the transmission input shaft.
2. With transmission bottom-up, remove modulator assembly attaching screw and retainer, then remove the modulator assembly and O-ring seal.

Governor, Speedometer Driven Gear, Oil Pan, Strainer and Intake Pipe Removal

1. Remove attaching screws, governor cover and gasket, then withdraw governor from the case.
2. Remove speedometer driven gear attaching screw and retainer, then withdraw the driven gear assembly.
3. Remove oil pan attaching

MODULATOR VALVE

O - RING SEAL

VACUUM MODULATOR

Removing vacuum modulator and valve
(© G.M. Corp.)

1234

screws, then the oil pan. Discard gasket.
4. Remove pump intake pipe and strainer assembly, then the pipe-to-case O-ring seal.

Control Valve Assembly, Governor Pipes and Detent Spring Assembly Removal

1. Disconnect the lead wire from the pressure switch assembly. Remove the switch assembly from the valve body, if necessary. This switch is installed on 1970 models only.
2. Remove control valve body attaching screws and detent roller and spring assembly. NOTE: do not remove solenoid attaching screws. Remove control valve body and governor pipes.
3. Remove the governor pipes from valve body. Then remove valve body-to-spacer gasket.

Rear Servo, Solenoid, Valve Body Spacer, Front Servo, Manual Detent and Parking Linkage Removal

1. Remove rear servo cover attaching screws, the cover and gasket, then the rear servo assembly from the case.
2. Remove servo accumulator springs.
3. Disconnect the solenoid leads from connector terminal. Withdraw connector and O-ring seal.
4. Make the band apply pin selection check to determine the possible cause of malfunction, proceed as follows:
   a. Attach the band apply pin selection gauge to the transmission case with attaching

screws. Make sure that the gauge pin does not bind in the servo pin hole.
   b. Apply 25 foot pounds torque and select the proper pin to be used during reassembly of the transmission.

Selection of the proper length pin is equivalent to adjusting the band. The band lug end of each selection apply pin bears an identification in the form of one, two or three rings.
   c. If both steps of the gauge lever are below the gauge surface, the long pin, identified by three rings must be used.
   d. If the gauge surface is between the steps, the medium pin, identified by 2 rings, should be used.
   e. If both steps are above the gauge surface, the short pin identified by 1 ring, should be used.

J 8763-01

Transmission in holding fixture
(© G.M. Corp.)

Removing speedometer drive gear and sleeve
(© G.M. Corp.)

Removing rear servo
(© G.M. Corp.)

NOTE: If the transmission is in the vehicle, be careful when the detent solenoid is removed as it prevents the spacer plate, gasket, and check balls from dropping down.

5. Remove the detent solenoid attaching screws, detent solenoid and gasket.
6. Remove the electrical connector and 'O' ring seal.
7. Remove valve body spacer plate and gasket.
8. Remove six check balls from cored passages in transmission case.
9. Remove the front servo assembly.
10. Loosen the jam nut which holds the detent lever to the manual shaft. Then remove detent lever from manual shaft and remove manual shaft.
11. Remove the parking actuator rod and detent lever assembly. Then remove detent lever E-ring and the detent lever.
12. Remove attaching screws and park bracket; then the parking pawl return spring.
13. Remove parking pawl shaft retainer, then the parking pawl shaft, O-ring and pawl.

Rear Oil Seal and Extension Housing Removal

1. Pry rear oil seal from extension housing.
2. Remove housing attaching bolts, then remove extension housing and housing-to-case oil seal.
3. Check the front unit end play as follows:
   a. Remove one front pump bolt and install a 3/8"-16 threaded slide hammer bolt.
   b. Mount a dial indicator on the slide hammer bolt and index the indicator to register with the end of the turbine shaft.
   c. Push the turbine shaft rearward and the output shaft forward.
   d. Set the dial indicator to Zero.
   e. Pull the turbine shaft forward and read the resulting travel or end play. Indicator readings should be .003-.024 inch.
   The selective thrust washer that controls the end play is located between the pump cover and the forward clutch housing. If end play is not within specifications, select a washer thickness from the

following chart for use during reassembly.

Thickness (inch)	Color
0.060-0.064	Yellow
0.071-0.075	Blue
0.082-0.086	Red
0.093-0.097	Brown
0.104-0.108	Green
0.115-0.119	Black
0.126-0.130	Purple

NOTE: An oil soaked washer may tend to discolor, so it may be necessary to measure the washer for its actual thickness.

Oil Pump, Forward Clutch and Gear Unit Removal

1. Pry front seal from the pump. Then remove pump attaching bolts.
2. With slide hammers attached, remove pump from transmission case. Discard pump-to-case seal ring. Discard pump-to-case gasket.
3. Remove turbine shaft from transmission.
4. Remove forward clutch assembly. Be sure that the bronze thrust washer came out with the clutch housing assembly.

Removing control valve assembly and governor pipes from case
(© G.M. Corp.)

Removing governor
(© G.M. Corp.)

5. Remove the direct clutch assembly. Remove front band and sun gear shaft.

6. Check the rear end play as follows:

   a. Install a ⅜" threaded bolt into one of the extension housing bolt holes. Mount a dial indicator on the bolt end and index with the end of the shaft.

   b. Move the output shaft in and out to read the end play. End play should be between 0.007-0.019 inch. The selective thrust washer controlling this end play is composed of steel having three lugs and is located between the output shaft thrust washer and the rear face of the transmission case.

   If the end play readings are not within limits, select one from the following chart and install during reassembly.

Thickness (inch)	Identification Notches	Numeral
0.074-0.078	None	1
0.082-0.086	1-tab side	2
0.090-0.094	2-tab side	3
0.098-0.102	1-tab O.D.	4
0.106-0.110	2 tabs O.D.	5
0.114-0.118	3-tabs O.D.	6

7. Remove the case center support-to-case bolt using a ⅜" 12-point thin wall deep socket.

8. Remove intermediate clutch backing plate-to-case snap-ring. Then remove the backing plate, three composition, and three steel clutch plates.

9. Remove the center support-to-case retaining snap-ring.

10. Remove the entire gear unit assembly.

11. Remove the output shaft-to-case thrust washer from the rear of the case, or from inside the case.

12. Remove rear unit selective washer from transmission case.

13. Remove rear band assembly.

14. Remove support to case spacer from inside case.

15. Remove rear band assembly.

Component Disassembly, Inspection, and Assembly

Governor

All components of the governor, except the driven gear, are a select fit and so calibrated. Therefore, service this unit as an assembly.

Clean and inspect all parts for wear or other damage. Check valve opening at feed port with a feeler

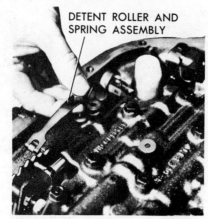

DETENT ROLLER AND SPRING ASSEMBLY

Removing detent roller and spring assembly
(© G.M. Corp.)

GASKET

Removing detent solenoid and gasket
(© G.M. Corp.)

J-6125-1 SLIDE HAMMERS

J-6125-2 ADAPTERS

Removing front pump using slide hammers
(© G.M. Corp.)

gauge, holding the governor with the weights extended completely outward. Check valve opening at exhaust port, holding governor with weights completely inward. If either opening is less than .020 in., replace governor assembly.

If a new governor drive gear is installed, a new pin hole must be

drilled 90 degrees from the original hole.

Front Servo Inspection

1. Inspect servo pin for admage.

2. Inspect servo piston for damaged oil ring groove, cracks, or porosity. Check freedom of oil seal ring in groove.

3. Check fit of servo pin in piston.

Rear Servo Disassembly

1. Remove E-ring which holds the servo piston to band apply pin.

2. Remove servo piston and seal from band apply pin. Remove second washer from band apply pin.

3. Remove washer, spring, and retainer.

Rear Servo Inspection

1. Check freedom of accumulator rings in piston.

2. Check fit of band apply pin in servo piston. Inspect pin for scores or cracks.

3. Inspect accumulator and servo pistons for cracks or porosity.

Rear Servo Assembly

1. Install spring retainer, spring, and washer on band apply pin.

2. Install band apply pin, retainer, spring, and washer into bore of servo piston and secure with E-ring.

3. Install oil seal on servo piston. Install outer and inner oil seal rings on accumulator piston and assembly into bore of servo piston.

Control Valve Body Disassembly

When disassembling control valve body, be careful to identify springs so that they can be replaced in their proper locations.

1. Position valve assembly with cored face up and accumulator pocket on bottom.

2. Remove manual valve from upper bore.

3. Compress accumulator piston spring and remove E-ring retainer. Remove accumulator piston and spring.

4. Press out retaining pin from upper right bore. Remove 1-2 modulator bushing, 1-2 regulator valve and spring, 1-2 detent valve, and 1-2 shift valve. 1-2 regulator valve and spring may be inside of 1-2 modulator bushing.

5. Press out retaining pin from center right bore. Remove 2-3 modulator bushing, 2-3 shift valve spring, 2-3 modulator valve, 3-2 intermediate spring, and 2-3 shift valve. 2-3 modulator valve will be inside of 2-3 modulator bushing.

Removing forward clutch
(© G.M. Corp.)

Removing front servo piston, washer and pin
(© G.M. Corp.)

1 Manual valve
2 Retaining pin
3 Bore plug
4 Detent valve
5 Detent regulator valve
6 Spacer pin
7 Detent regulator spring
8 1-2 shift valve
9 1-2 Dentent valve

9a 1-2 modulator valve
10 1-2 regulator spring
10a 1-2 modulator spring
11 1-2 regulator valve
12 1-2 modulator bushing
13 Retaining pin
14 Grooved retaining pin
15 Bore plug
16 1-2 accumulator valve

17 1-2 accumulator spring
18 2-3 shift valve
19 3-2 intermediate spring
20 2-3 modulator valve
21 2-3 valve spring
22 2-3 modulator bushing

23 Retaining pin
24 3-2 valve

25 Spacer pin
26 3-2 valve spring
27 Bore plug
28 Retaining pin
29 1-2 accumulator bushing
30 1-2 accumulator secondary spring
31 1-2 accumulator valve
32 1-2 primary accumulator valve

Control valve body layout (© G.M. Corp.)

Governor assembly
(© G.M. Corp.)

Exploded view of rear servo and accumulator (© G.M. Corp.)

RETAINING "E" RING
OIL SEAL RING
ACCUMULATOR SPRING
ACCUMULATOR PISTON

Removing front accumulator piston and spring
(© G.M..Corp.)

6 CHECK BALLS

Location of check bills
(© G.M. Corp.)

6. Press out retaining pin from lower right bore. Hold hand over bore, as plug may pop out. Remove plug, 3-2 valve spring, spacer, and 3-2 valve.
7. Holding hand over bore, press out retainer pin from upper left bore. Remove bore plug, detent valve, detent regulator valve, spacer, and detent regulator valve spring.
8. Pry out grooved retainer ring from lower left bore with long nose pliers. Remove bore plug, 1-2 accumulator bushing, 1-2 accumulator valve, secondary spring, primary 1-2 accumulator valve, and spring.
9. Remove governor oil feed screen from oil feed hole in valve body.

Control Valve Body Inspection

1. Wash control valve body, valves and other parts in solvent. Do not allow valves to bump together. Air dry parts and blow out all passages.
2. Inspect all valves and bushings carefully. Burrs may be removed with a fine stone or fine crocus cloth and light oil. Be careful not to round off shoulders of valves.
3. Test all valves and bushings for free movement in their bores. All valves should fall freely of their own weight.
4. The manual valve is the only valve that can be serviced separately. If any of the other valves are defective or damaged, install a new control valve assembly.
5. Inspect body for cracks or scored bores. Check all springs for distortion or collapsed coils.

Control Valve Body Assembly

1. Replace front accumulator spring and piston into valve body. Compress spring and piston, assuring that piston pin is correctly aligned with hole in piston and that oil seal ring does not catch on lip of bore when installing piston. Secure piston and spring with E-ring retainer.
2. Install 1-2 accumulator primary spring, 1-2 primary valve, and 1-2 accumulator bushing into lower left bore. Place 1-2 accumulator secondary valve, stem end out, into the 1-2 accumulator bushing. Place 1-2 accumulator secondary spring over stem end of valve. Replace bore plug and retaining pin.
3. Install detent regulator valve spring and spacer into upper left bore, making certain that spring seats in bottom of bore. Com press spring and hold with a small screwdriver between end of spring and wall on cored side of valve body. Insert detent regulator valve, stem end out, and detent valve, small land first. Insert bore plug, press inward, remove screwdriver, and install retaining pin.
4. Insert 3-2 valve in bottom right bore. Place spacer inside 3-2 valve spring and insert spacer and spring in bore. Install bore plug and retaining pin.
5. Install 3-2 intermediate spring on stem end of 2-3 shift valve. Install valve and spring, valve first, into center right bore. Be sure that valve seats in bottom of bore. Place 2-3 modulator valve, hole end first, into 2-3 modulator bushing. Install valve and bushing in bore. Install 2-3 shift valve spring into hole in 2-3 modulator valve. Secure with retaining pin.
6. Seat 1-2 shift valve, stem end out, in bottom of upper right bore. Install 1-2 regulator valve, larger stem first, and spring and 1-2 detent valve, hole end first, into 1-2 modulator bushing. Align spring in bore of 1-2 detent valve. Install assembly into upper right bore of control valve body. Install retaining pin.
7. Replace governor oil feed screen assembly in governor oil feed hole.
8. Install manual valve with detent pin groove to the right.

Oil Pump Disassembly

1. Place the pump over a hole in the bench, shaft down, cover up.
2. Compress regulator boost valve bushing against the pressure regulator spring and remove the snap-ring.
   CAUTION: Pressure regulator spring is under extreme pressure.
3. Remove the boost valve bushing and valve, then the spring.
4. Remove valve spring retainer and spacer/s, if present, and regulator valve.
5. Remove pump cover to body attaching bolts, then remove the cover.
6. Remove the retaining pin and bore plug from the pressure regulator bore.
7. Remove the two hook-type oil rings from the pump cover.
8. Remove pump to forward clutch housing selective washer.
9. Mark drive and driven gears for reassembly, then remove the gears.

Oil Pump Inspection

1. Inspect drive gear, driven gear, gear pocket, and crescent for scoring, galling, or other damage.
2. Replace pump gears in pump and check pump body face to face gear clearance. The clearance should be .0008-.0035 in.
3. Check pump body face for scoring or nicks. Check oil passages in pump body for roughness or obstructions. Check condition of cover bolt attaching threads. Check for flatness of pump body face. Check pump body bushing, for scores or nicks. If a new bushing is installed, drive it in flush to .010 in. below the gear pocket face.
4. Replace pump attaching bolt seals if necessary.
5. Check pump cover face for flatness. Check for scoring or chips in pressure regulator bore.

Check that all passages are unobstructed. Check for scoring or damage at pump gear face. Check that breather hole in pump cover is open.

6. Check condition of stator shaft splines and bushings.
7. Check oil ring grooves for damage or wear. Check selective thrust washer for wear.
8. Make sure that pressure regulator valve and boost valve operate freely.

Oil Pump Assembly

1. Install drive and driven gears into the pump body, alignment marks up and in proper index, (drive gear with drive tangs up).
2. Install pressure regulator spring spacer/s if required, retainer and spring into the pressure regulator bore.
3. Install pressure regulator valve from the opposite end of the bore, stem end first.
4. Install boost valve into bushing, stem end out, and install both parts into the pump cover by compressing the bushing against the spring. Install the snap-ring.
5. Install the regulator valve bore

Exploded view of pump cover
(© G.M. Corp.)

Installing pump drive gear
(© G.M. Corp.)

Removing pressure regulator valve
(© G.M. Corp.)

Check pump body face to gear clearance
(© G.M. Corp.)

Installing pressure regulator regaining pin and bore, lug
(© G.M. Corp.)

Removing forward clutch hub and thrust washers
(© G.M. Corp.)

1239

plug and retaining pin into opposite end of bore.

6. Install the front unit selective thrust washer over the pump cover delivery sleeve.
7. Install two hook-type oil seal rings.
8. Assemble pump cover to pump body with attaching bolts. (Leave bolts one turn loose at this time.)
9. Place pump aligning strap over pump body and cover, then tighten tool.
10. Install pump cover bolts. pump-to-case O-ring seal and gasket.

Forward Clutch Disassembly

1. Remove forward clutch housing-to-direct clutch hub snapring.
2. Remove direct clutch hub. Remove clamp and install
3. Remove forward clutch hub and thrust washers.
4. Remove five composition and five steel clutch plates. Press out the turbine shaft.
5. Compress the spring retainer and remove the snap-ring.
6. Remove the compressor, snapring, spring retainer and 16 release springs, then lift out the piston.
7. Remove inner and outer piston seals.
8. Remove center piston seal from the forward clutch housing.

Forward Clutch Inspection

1. Inspect clutch plates for burning, scoring, or wear.
2. Inspect springs for collapsed

FORWARD CLUTCH ASSEMBLY

PUMP ASSEMBLY

Air checking forward clutch
(© G.M. Corp.)

coils or distortion.
3. Check clutch hubs for worn splines, thrust faces, and open lubrication holes.
4. Check piston for cracks.
5. Check clutch housing for wear, scoring, open oil passages, and free operation of ball check.
6. Inspect turbine shaft for:
a. Open lubrication passages at each end.
b. Spline damage.
journals.
c. Damage to ground bushing
d. Cracks or distortion of shaft.

Forward Clutch Assembly

1. Place new inner and outer oil seals on clutch piston, lips away from spring pockets.

2. Place a new center seal on the clutch housing, lip faces up.
3. Place a seal protector (thimble) tool into clutch drum and install the piston.
4. Install 16 clutch release springs into pockets in the piston.
5. Lay the spring retainer and the snap-ring on the springs.
6. Compress springs using compressor, and install snap-ring. Press in turbine shaft.
7. Install the direct clutch hub washers; retain with petroleum jelly.
8. Place forward clutch hub into forward clutch housing.
9. Lubricate with transmission oil and install the clutch pack, five composition, and five steel plates, starting with steel and alternating steel and composition.
10. Install clutch hub and retaining snap-ring.
11. Place forward clutch housing on pump delivery sleeve and air-check clutch operation.

Direct Clutch and Intermediate Sprag Disassembly

1. Remove intermediate clutch retainer snap-ring, then the retainer.
2. Remove clutch outer race, bushings and sprag assembly.
3. Invert the unit and remove backing plate to clutch housing snap-ring.
4. Remove direct clutch backing plate, five composition, and five steel plates.
5. Using clutch compressor tool compress the spring retainer and remove the snap-ring.
6. Remove retainer and 16 piston release springs.

FORWARD CLUTCH ASSEMBLY

FLAT STEEL PLATES (4)

FORWARD CLUTCH HUB

DIRECT CLUTCH HUB

SNAP RING

WAVED STEEL PLATE

COMPOSITION PLATES (5)

THRUST WASHERS

Exploded view of forward clutch (© G.M. Corp.)

FORWARD CLUTCH HOUSING

CLUTCH CENTER SEAL

Removing forward clutch center seal
(© G.M. Corp.)

J 21362

J 21409

FORWARD CLUTCH PISTON

Installing forward clutch piston
(© G.M. Corp.)

7. Remove direct clutch piston, then remove the outer and inner seals from the piston.
8. Remove center piston seal from the direct clutch housing.

Direct Clutch and Intermediate Sprag Inspection

1. Check for popped or loose sprags.
2. Check sprag bushings for distortion or wear.
3. Inspect inner and outer races for scratches or wear.
4. Check clutch housing for cracks, wear, proper opening of oil passages, and wear on clutch plate drive lugs.
5. Check clutch plates for wear or burning.
6. Check backing plate for scratches or damage.
7. Check clutch piston for cracks and free operation of ball check.

Direct Clutch and Intermediate Sprag Assembly

1. Install a new clutch piston seal onto the piston, lips facing away from spring pockets. Apply transmission fluid to oil seals.
2. Install a new outer piston seal, and a new center seal onto the clutch housing, lip of seal facing up.
3. Place seal protectors over hub and clutch housing, then install piston.
4. Install 16 springs into piston, place retainer and snap-ring on retainer.
5. With clutch compressor, compress the clutch and install snap-ring.
6. Install five composition and five steel clutch plates, starting with steel and alternating composition and steel.
7. Install clutch backing plate, then install the backing plate snapring.
8. Invert the unit and install one

sprag bushing, cup side up, over the inner race.
9. Install sprag assembly into outer race.
10. With ridge on inner cage facing down, start sprag and outer race over inner race with clockwise turning motion. NOTE: outer race should not turn counterclockwise.
11. Install sprag bushing over sprag cup side down.
12 Install clutch retainer and snap-ring.
13. Place direct clutch assembly over center support and air check operation of direct clutch.
NOTE: it is normal for air applied to reverse passage to escape from direct clutch passage. Air applied to direct clutch passage should move direct clutch.

Center Support Disassembly

1. Remove four hook-type oil rings from center support.
2. Using clutch fingers, compress the spring retainer and remove the snap-ring.

3. Remove spring retainer and 12 clutch release springs.
4. Remove intermediate clutch piston.
5. Remove inner piston seal. *NOTE: do not remove the three screws holding the roller clutch inner race to the center support.*
6. Remove outer piston seal.

Center Support Inspection

1. Inspect roller clutch inner race for scratches or identations. Check that lubrication hole is open.
2. Check bushing for scoring, wear, or galling. If bushing is replaced, drive new bushing into bore until it is flush to .010 in. below the top of the oil delivery sleeve.
3. Check oil seal rings and ring grooves in the center support tower for damage.
4. Make air pressure check of oil passages to be sure they are not interconnected.
5. Inspect piston sealing surfaces for scratches. Inspect piston seal

COMPOSITION PLATES

STEEL PLATES

FORWARD CLUTCH HOUSING

Installing forward clutch composition and steel plates
(© G.M. Corp.)

Clutch plate identification
(© G.M. Corp.)

NOTE: 5 FLAT STEEL PLATES— NO WAVED STEEL PLATE IN PQ & PS MODELS

Layout of direct clutch
(© G.M. Corp.)

Removing direct clutch assembly
(© G.M. Corp.)

FORWARD CLUTCH PISTON

CLUTCH OUTER SEAL

Removing or installing forward clutch piston outer seal
(© G.M. Corp.)

CLUTCH INNER SEAL

Installing direct clutch inner seal
(© G.M. Corp.)

DIRECT CLUTCH BACKING PLATE
FLAT STEEL PLATES (4)
COMPOSITION PLATES (5)
WAVED STEEL PLATE (1)

NOTE: 5 FLAT STEEL PLATES— NO WAVED STEEL PLATE IN PQ & PS MODELS

Installing direct clutch backing plate, and clutches
(© G.M. Corp.)

grooves for damage. Check piston for cracks or porosity.

6. Check release springs for distortion or collapsed coils.

7. Check support to case spacer for burrs or raised edges. Repair with a stone or fine sand paper.

Center Support Assembly

1. Install new inner and outer seals on the piston, lip on inner seal facing away from the spring pocket.

2. Install inner spring protector tool onto the center support hub; lubricate the seal and install the piston.

3. Install 12 release springs into the piston.

4. Place spring retainer and

snap-ring over the springs.

5. Using the clutch spring compressor, compress the springs and install the snap-ring.

6. Install four hook-type oil rings.

7. Air check the operation of intermediate clutch piston.

Torque Converter Inspection

The torque converter is a welded assembly and must be serviced as a unit. If converter output shaft has more than .050 in. end-play, renew the unit.

Check for leaks as follows:

A. Install converter leak test fix-

ture and tighten.

B. Fill converter with air, 80 psi.

C. Submerge in water and check for bubbles.

Planetary Gear Unit Disassembly

1. Remove center support assembly.

2. Remove center support to reaction carrier thrust washer.

3. Remove center support to sun gear races and thrust bearing. One race may already have been removed with the center support.

4. Remove reaction carrier and roller clutch assembly.
5. Remove front internal gear ring from output carrier assembly.
6. Remove sun gear.
7. Take off reaction carrier to output carrier thrust washer.
8. Turn carrier assembly over. Remove output shaft to output carrier snap ring.
9. Output shaft may now be removed.
10. Measure to determine speedometer drive gear location with relation to the end of the shaft for reassembly. Remove nylon speedometer drive gear by depressing retaining clip and sliding gear off output shaft. Remove steel speedometer drive gear with a suitable puller.
11. Remove output shaft to rear internal gear thrust bearing and two races.
12. Remove rear internal gear and mainshaft. Remove rear internal gear to sun gear thrust bearing and two races. Remove rear internal gear to mainshaft snap ring. Remove mainsahft.

Inspection of Reaction Carrier, Roller Clutch, and Output Carrier Assembly

1. Insert band surface reaction carrier for burring or scoring.
2. Check roller clutch outer race for scoring or wear. Check thrust washer for wear.
3. Check bushing for damage. If bushing is damaged, replace reaction carrier.
4. Check reaction carrier pinions for damage, rough bearings, or excessive tilt. Check pinion end play. It should be .009-.024 in.

Air checks direct clutch assembly
(© G.M. Corp.)

INNER CAGE RIDGE (DOWN)

400 THM

Correct sprag rotation
(© G.M. Corp.)

Pinions may be replaced if necessary.
5. Check roller clutch for damaged members. Check roller clutch cage for damage.
6. Inspect front internal gear (out-put carrier) for damaged teeth. Inspect output carrier pinions, for damage, rough bearings, and excessive tilt. Check pinion end play. It should be .009-.024 in.
7. Inspect parking pawl lugs for cracks or damage. Inspect output locating splines for damage.
8. Check front internal gear ring for flaking.

Planetary Gear Unit Assembly

1. Install rear internal gear onto end of mainshaft, then install the snap-ring.
2. Install sun gear to internal gear thrust races and bearings against inner face of rear internal gear as follows:
   a. Place large race against the internal gear, with flange facnig up.
   b. Place thrust bearing against race.
   c. Place small race against the bearing, with inner flange facing the bearing, or down.
3. Install the output carrier over the mainshaft so that the pinions mesh with the rear internal gear.
4. Place the above portion of the assembly through a hole in the bench so that the mainshaft hangs downward.

Center support assembly—layout (© G.M. Corp.)

5. Install the rear internal gear to output shaft thrust races and bearings as follows:
   a. Small diamete race against internal gear, center flange facing up.
   b. Bearing onto the race.
   c. Second race onto the bearing, outer flange cupped over the bearing.
6. Install output shaft into the output carrier assembly.
7. Install output shaft to output carrier snap-ring.
8. Turn assembly over and support it so that the output shaft hangs downward.
9. Install the reaction carrier to output carrier thrust washer, tabs facing down and in their pockets.
10. Install sun gear, splines, chamfer down. Install gear ring over output carrier.
11. Install sun gear shaft, then the reaction carrier.
12. Install the center support to sun gear thrust races and bearing as follows:
    A. Install the large race, center flange up over the sun gear shaft.
    B. Install thrust bearing.
    C. Install the second race, center flange up.
13. Install roller clutch to reaction carrier outer race. Install the center support to reaction carrier thrust washer into the recess in the support. Retain with petroleum jelly.
14. Install center support into reaction carrier and roller clutch assembly. With reaction carrier held, center support should only turn counterclockwise.
15. Install a gear unit assembly

Air checking converter
(© G.M. Corp.)

holding tool to hold units in place. Install output shaft to case thrust washer tabs in pockets and retain with petroleum jelly.

Transmission Assembly

Parking Mechanism, Rear Band and the Complete Gear Assembly Installation

1. Install O-ring seal onto parking pawl shaft, then install parking pawl, tooth toward inside of case.
2. Install the pawl shaft retaining clip and the return spring, square-end hooked on the pawl.
3. Install parking brake bracket guides over pawl, using two attaching bolts.
4. Install rear band assembly so that the two lugs index with the two anchor pins. Install support to case spacer with ring gap adjacent to band anchor pin.
5. Install rear selective washer into slots provided inside rear of transmission case. Dip washer in transmission fluid.
6. Install the complete gear unit assembly into the case.
7. Lubricate and install center sup-

Gear unit—layout (© G.M. Corp.)

port to case snap-ring. Install bevel side up. NOTE: the support to case spacer is .040 in. thick and is flat on both sides. The center support to case snap-ring has one side beveled. The intermediate clutch backing plate to case snap ring is .093 in. thick and is flat on both sides.

8. On 1964-1968 models, install the case to center support locating screw and torque to 5 ft. lbs. Lubricate and install case to center support bolt and torque to 22 ft. lbs. Remove the locating screw. On 1969-70 models, install the case to center support bolt by placing a center support locating tool or equivalent tool into case direct clutch passage with handle of tool pointing to right as viewed from front of transmission and parallel to bell housing mounting face. Apply pressure downward on tool handle to hold the center support firmly against the case splines. Torque the case to center support bolt to 22 ft. lbs.

9. Install three steel and three composition clutch plates. Alternate the plates, starting with steel.

10. Install the backing plate, ridge up, then the snap-ring. Locate snap-ring gap opposite band anchor pin.

11. Check rear end-play as follows:
A. Install a threaded rod or a long bolt into an extension hous-attaching bolt hole.
B. Mount dial indicator on the rod and index it with the end of the output shaft.
c. Move the output shaft in and out. Read the end-play. End-play should be .007-.019 in. The selective washer controlling the end-play is the steel washer,

GEAR RING

OUTPUT CARRIER

Installing front internal gear ring to output carrier
(© G.M. Corp.)

O.D. FLANGED RACE

THRUST BEARING

I.D. FLANGED RACE

Installing rear internal gear to output shaft bearing and races
(© G.M. Corp.)

Installing output shaft
(© G.M. Corp.)

Installing reaction carrier and roller assembly
(© G.M. Corp.)

Installing dent lever and jam nut to manual shaft
(© G.M. Corp.)

having three lugs, that is located between the thrust washer and the rear face of the transmission case.

If a different washer thickness is required to obtain proper end-play, it can be selected from the following chart.

Thickness	Notches and/or Numeral		
.074—.078 in.	None		1
.082—.086 in.	1 Tab	Side	2
.090—.094 in.	2 Tabs	Side	3
.098—.102 in.	1 Tab	O.D.	4
.106—.110 in.	2 Tabs	O.D.	5
.114—.118 in.	3 Tabs	O.D.	6

Front Band, Direct Clutch and Forward Clutch Installation

1. Install front band, with band anchor hole placed over the band anchor pin, and apply lug facing the servo hole.
2. Install the direct clutch and intermediate sprag assembly. (Removal of direct clutch plates may help.)

3. Install forward clutch hub to direct housing bronze thrust washer onto the forward clutch hub. Retain with petroleum jelly.
4. Install forward clutch assembly, indexing the direct clutch hub so the end of the mainshaft will be flush with the end of the forward clutch hub. Use turbine shaft as a tool.
5. Install turbine shaft; end with the short spline goes into the forward clutch housing.
6. Install pump-to-case gasket onto the case face and install the front pump assembly and all but one attaching bolt and seal. Torque to 18 ft. lbs. NOTE: if turbine shaft cannot be rotated as pump is being pulled into place, forward or direct clutch housing has not been properly installed to index with all clutch plates. This condition must be corrected before pump is fully pulled into place.
7. Drive in a new front seal.
8. Check front unit end-play as follows:
   A. Install one rod of slide hammer, with 5/16-18 in. thread, into the empty pump assembly attaching bolt hole.
   B. Mount dial indicator on the rod and adjust the indicator probe to contact end of turbine shaft.
   C. Hold output shaft forward while pushing turbine shaft rearward to its stop.
   D. Set dial indicator to zero.
   E. Pull turbine
   F. Read end-play, as registered on dial. The reading should be .003-.024 in.
   The selective washer controlling this end-play is located between the pump cover and the forward clutch

Installing direct clutch assembly
(© G.M. Corp.)

housing. If more, or less, washer thickness is required to bring end-play within specifications, make selection from the thickness-color chart.

Thickness	Color
.060-.064 in.	Yellow
.071-.075 in.	Blue
.082-.086 in.	Red
.093-.097 in.	Brown
.104-.108 in.	Green
.115-.119 in.	Black
.126-.130 in.	Purple

9. Remove dial indicator and install the remaining front pump attaching bolt and seal. Torque to 18 ft. lbs.

Rear Extension Housing Assembly Installation

1. Install extension housing-to-case O-ring seal onto extension housing.
2. Attach extension housing to

Installing front band
(© G.M. Corp.)

Installing pump assembly
(© G.M. Corp.)

transmission case. Torque to 22 ft. lbs.

3. Drive in a new extension housing rear seal.

Manual Linkage Installation

1. Install new manual shift shaft seal into the case.
2. Insert actuator rod into the manual detent lever from the side opposite the pin.
3. Install actuator rod plunger under the parking bracket and over the pawl.
4. Install manual lever and shaft through the case and detent lever, then lock with hex nut on the manual shift shaft. (Be sure detent retaining nut is tight.) Install retaining pin.

Check Balls, Front Servo Gaskets, Spacer and Solenoid Installation

1. Install front servo spring and retainer into transmission case.
2. Install flat washer on front servo pin, on end opposite taper. Install pin and washer into case so that tapered end of pin is contacting band.
3. Install oil seal ring on front servo piston, and install on apply pin so that identification numbers on shoulders are exposed. Check freeness of piston in bore.
4. Install six check balls into transmission case pockets.
5. Install valve body spacer to case gasket and spacer plate. Install detent solenoid and gasket, with connector facing outer edge of case. Do not tighten bolts at this time.
6. Install O-ring seal on electrical connector. Lubricate and install electrical connector with locator tab in notch on side of case. Connect detent wire and lead wire to electrical connector. Be sure to install electrical wire clip.

Checking front unit end play
(© G.M. Corp.)

Rear Servo Installation

1. Before installing the rear servo assembly, check the band apply pin, using rear band apply fixture as follows:
   A. Attach band apply pin selection gauge, to the transmission case with attaching screws.
   B. Apply 25 ft. lbs. torque and select proper servo pin to be used from scale on the tool.
   C. Remove tool and make note of proper pin to be used during assembly.
   There are three selective pins:
   The identification consists of a ring located on the band lug end of the pin. Selecting the proper pin is equivalent to adjusting the band.
2. Install rear accumulator spring.
3. Install servo assembly, then the gasket and cover. Torque bolts to 18 ft. lbs.

Control Valve and Governor Pipe Installation

1. Install control valve-to-spacer gasket, then install governor pipes into the control valve body assembly.
2. Install two guide pins, then install the control valve body and governor pipe assembly into the transmission. NOTE: be sure the manual valve is properly indexed with the pin on the man-

ual detent lever.
3. Remove guide pins and install valve assembly attaching bolts and manual detent and roller assembly.
4. Tighten detent solenoid and control valve attaching bolts to 8 ft. lbs. torque.
5. On 1970 models, install the pressure switch assembly and torque to 8 ft. lbs. Connect pressure switch assembly lead wire.

Strainer and Intake Pipe Installation

1. Install case-to-intake pipe O-ring onto strainer and intake pipe assembly.
2. Install strainer and pipe assembly. Install new filter on models so equipped.
3. Install new pan gasket, then install the pan. Torque to 12 ft. lbs.
4. Install modulator shield and all pan attaching screws. Torque pan attaching screws.

Modulator Assembly Installation

1. Install modulator valve into the case, stem end out.
2. Install O-ring seal onto the vacuum modulator, then install assembly into the case.
3. Install modulator retainer and attaching bolt. Torque to 18 ft. lbs.

Governor and Speedometer Driven Gear Installation

1. Install governor assembly.
2. Attach governor cover and gasket with four bolts. Torque to 18 ft. lbs.
3. Install speedometer driven gear assembly. Install retainer and attaching bolt.

Converter Installation

1. Place transmission in cradle or portable jack.

Installing forward clutch assembly
(© G.M. Corp.)

Installing front pump oil seal
(© G.M. Corp.)

Installing Vacuum Modulator and Valve

Checking Rear Band Pin

Installing Rear Servo Assembly

Installing Control Valve Assembly and Governor Pipes

Installing governor assembly
(© G.M. Corp.)

2. Install converter assembly to pump assembly, making certain that the converter hub drive slots are fully engaged with the pump drive gear tangs and that the converter is installed all the way toward the rear of the transmission.

Torque Specifications
Foot-Pounds

Pump cover bolts	18
Parking pawl bracket bolts	18
Center support bolt	22
Pump-to-case attaching bolts	18
Extension-to-case attaching bolts	22
Rear servo cover bolts	18
Detent solenoid bolts	8
Control valve body bolts	8
Bottom pan attaching screws	12
Modulator retainer bolt	18
Governor cover bolts	18
Manual lever-to-manual shaft nut	20
Linkage swivel clamp screw	20
Transmission-to-engine mounting bolts	40
Rear mount-to-transmission bolts	40
Oil cooler line	16
Filter retainer bolt	10
Pressure switch assembly	8

Chilton's REPAIR MANUALS

MOTORCYCLE REPAIR MANUAL

This new manual is a complete guide to the tune-up, maintenance, and general repair of all component systems of the most popular motorcycles now sold in the United States. The following makes are covered, from the date indicated in parentheses through 1973: BMW (1960); BSA singles, twins and triples (1963); Bultaco (1963); Harley-Davidson singles and twins (1947); Honda singles, twins and fours, including the XL 250 and the MT 250 (1963); Kawasaki singles, twins, triples, and the 900 Z1 (1966); Montesa (1966); Moto Guzzi (1966); Norton 750 and 850 (1966); Ossa (1968); Suzuki singles, twins and triples (1963); Triumph singles, twins and triples (1963); and all Yamaha street and dirt bikes, including the TX 500, TX 650, and TX 750 (1964). All the necessary maintenance information, as well as removal, repair and installation procedures, and specifications are given. Also included are wiring diagrams and bulb charts for all models. $22.95

CHILTON'S IMPORT AUTOMOTIVE REPAIR MANUAL, 3rd ed.

Formerly CHILTON'S IMPORT CAR REPAIR MANUAL, this edition has been enlarged to include popular import pick-up trucks. Coverage from 1970 (or the date of importation) through the years in parentheses for: Audi (1975), Capri (1976), Colt (1975), Courier (1975), Datsun (1975), Fiat (1974), Honda (1974), LUV (1975), Mazda (1975), Mercedes-Benz (1975), MG (1975), Opel (1975), Porsche (1975), Subaru (1975), Toyota (1975), Triumph (1975), Volvo (1975), VW—types 1, 2, 3, 4 (1975), VW Dasher/Scirocco/Rabbit (1975). A separate section for each import gives identification and tune-up procedures, specifications and information for repair and maintenance of the engine electrical, mechanical and cooling systems, emission controls, fuel systems, transmissions, clutch, transaxle, drive axle, front and rear suspension, steering, brakes and the chassis electrical system. Includes sections on engine tune-up, troubleshooting and rebuilding with English to metric conversion tables. Nearly 4000 photographs and drawings. $18.95

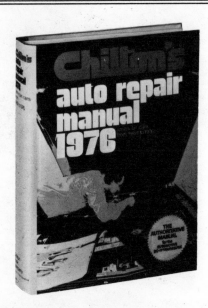

CHILTON'S AUTO REPAIR 1976

The 1976 edition of CHILTON'S AUTO REPAIR MANUAL contains do-it-yourself repair information for popular American cars including Jeep, 1969 to 1976, and Volkswagen from 1970 to 1975. The book has two major parts: 19 Car Sections which contain specifications and repair procedures for individual makes and models; and Unit Repair Sections covering Brakes, Carburetors, Charging and Starting Systems, Dash Gauges, Diagnostic Charts, Electronic Ignition Systems, Emission Controls, Engine Rebuilding, Engine Tune-up and Troubleshooting, Front End Alignment, Manual Steering, Manual Transmission, Power Brakes, and Power Steering. Particularly valuable to the do-it-yourselfer are the programmed sections on Engine Troubleshooting and Rebuilding, as well as the fault-finding Diagnostic Charts. Over 2700 illustrations complement the text. $12.95

Chilton's
EASY MECHANICAL AUTO CARE

Chilton's newest idea in do-it-yourself auto repair and maintenance is designed for use by the average car owner— you need no special technical or mechanical knowledge to perform simple automotive jobs and repairs. Each of Chilton's EASY MAC packages for a given car/model is presented on a 38″ x 25″ fold-out multi-colored chart. Each chart covers the eight basic areas of logical do-it-yourself car care, including Lubrication; Cooling System; Air Conditioning; Ignition and Tune-up; Fuel, Emission Controls and Carburetor; Tire and Suspension Systems; Electrical and Lighting Systems; and Safety Systems. Every chart provides comprehensive information on the tools, materials and precautions necessary to complete each job. Instructions are accompanied by clear and simple illustrations. CHILTON'S EASY MAC packages are available at $1.95 each for the following cars: Chevrolet 6; Chevrolet V-8; Comet 6; Comet V-8; Datsun 510 Series; Datsun 1200 Series; Ford 6; Ford V-8; Maverick 6; Maverick V-8; Pinto 1600, 2000, 2300; Toyota Corolla; Toyota Corona/Mark II; Vega; VW Type I; and VW Type II.